# Effective instructional approach builds students' confidence in their ability to do algebra . . .

- **Easy-to-follow instruction** with numerous step-by-step examples make content accessible for all.
- **Unique *Try This*** questions after each example, along with answers in the back of the text, build mastery and student confidence.
- **Lessons organized into parts** allow you to present material in manageable chunks for your students. Homework can be assigned accordingly for flexible lesson planning.

**PART 2 Using Multiplication to Solve Equations**

To solve an equation involving division, you can multiply each side by the same value.

**Multiplication Property of Equality**

You can multiply each side of an equation by the same value.

| Arithmetic | Algebra |
|---|---|
| $12 = 3(4)$ | If $a = b$, |
| $12 \cdot 2 = 3(4) \cdot 2$ | then $ac = bc$. |

**EXAMPLE 3**

**Solve $\frac{x}{-9} = -3$.**

$\frac{x}{-9} = -3$

$\frac{x}{-9}(-9) = -3(-9)$ Multiply each side by −9.

$x = 27$ Simplify.

8. Check the solution of Example 3.

**TRY THIS** Solve and check each equation.

9. $\frac{r}{-5} = 10$ 10. $s \div (-6) = 54$ 11. $-30 = \frac{t}{20}$

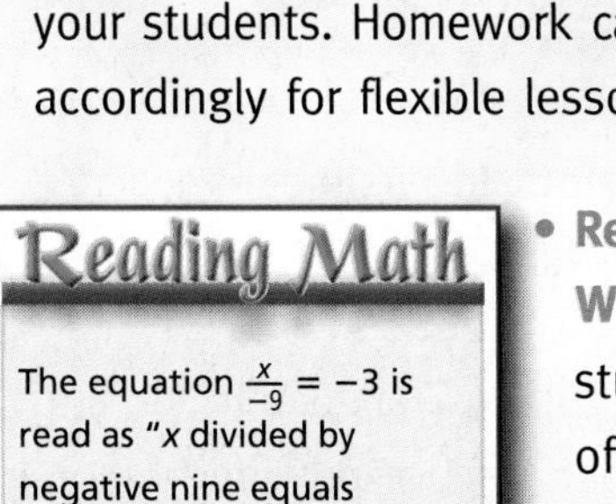

**Reading Math**

The equation $\frac{x}{-9} = -3$ is read as "x divided by negative nine equals negative thr

- **Reading** and **Writing Tips** build student confidence in using the language of mathematics.

**Writing Math**

When you go from words to an equation, the order of the math symbols may be different from the order of the words:

- ten fewer than $n \rightarrow n - 10$
- eight less than $r \rightarrow r - 8$
- $n$ times $5 \rightarrow 5n$

- **Different Ways to Solve a Problem** features/activities are presented to encourage creative thinking and to build better problem solvers.

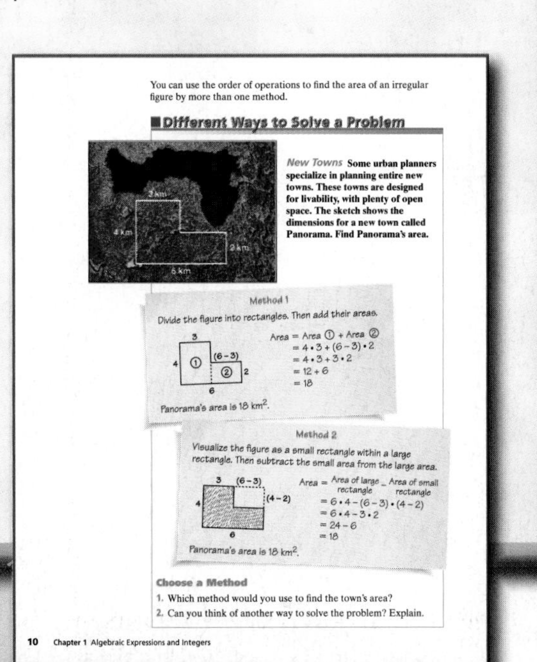

You can use the order of operations to find the area of an irregular figure by more than one method.

**Different Ways to Solve a Problem**

*New Towns* Some urban planners specialize in planning entire new towns. These towns are designed for livability, with plenty of open space. The sketch shows the dimensions for a new town called Panorama. Find Panorama's area.

Method 1

Divide the figure into rectangles. Then add their areas.

Area = Area ① + Area ②
= 4 • 3 + (6 − 3) • 2
= 4 • 3 + 3 • 2
= 12 + 6
= 18

Panorama's area is 18 km².

Method 2

Visualize the figure as a small rectangle within a large rectangle. Then subtract the small area from the large area.

Area = Area of large rectangle − Area of small rectangle
= 6 • 4 − (6 − 3) • (4 − 2)
= 6 • 4 − 3 • 2
= 24 − 6
= 18

Panorama's area is 18 km².

**Choose a Method**

1. Which method would you use to find the town's area?
2. Can you think of another way to solve the problem? Explain.

10 Chapter 1 Algebraic Expressions and Integers

"I can do this."

# . . . Innovative test prep validates this growing confidence and assures test-taking success.

TOOLS FOR A CHANGING WORLD

- **Test Prep questions in many exercise sets** mirror the types of questions found on today's standardized tests.
- **Test Prep tips right in the lesson** highlight key test-taking strategies.
- **Daily Mixed Review** questions—keyed to previously covered lessons—and **Daily Skills Warm-Up Transparencies** reinforce previously learned concepts and keep skills sharp.

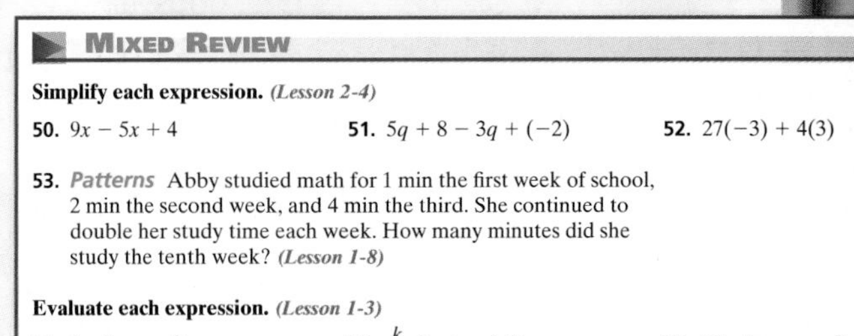

**MIXED REVIEW**

**Simplify each expression.** *(Lesson 2-4)*

**50.** $9x - 5x + 4$ **51.** $5q + 8 - 3q + (-2)$ **52.** $27(-3) + 4(3)$

**53.** *Patterns* Abby studied math for 1 min the first week of school, 2 min the second week, and 4 min the third. She continued to double her study time each week. How many minutes did she study the tenth week? *(Lesson 1-8)*

**Evaluate each expression.** *(Lesson 1-3)*

**54.** $6n$, for $n = 8$ **55.** $\frac{k}{20}$, for $k = 140$ **56.** $50x$, for $x = -8$

- **Standardized Test Prep** pages in every chapter provide abundant practice on multiple choice and free response question formats.
- **Unique Assessment Success Kits,** Test Taking Tips on Transparencies, and Computer Item Generator with Standardized Test Practice provide additional support to validate student performance and build confidence.

"We can do this."

# Complete coverage of all the skills students need to succeed in algebra.

Students learn to use variables, expressions, and integers early—so they are ready to solve equations beginning in Chapter 2.

Connections to Measurement, Geometry, and Data Analysis strands are woven throughout the program—emphasizing the relevance of algebraic concepts to a variety of math areas.



Students learn to solve equations with decimals in Chapter 3 and later on with fractions in Chapter 5. This foundation prepares students to solve two-step equations in Chapter 7.

Geometry coverage is integrated—effectively readying students for state and standardized tests.

*"We can do it. We're ready for algebra."*

# Comprehensive support package gets all students ready for algebra

- **Student Edition with Practice Workbook**
- **Teacher's Edition**
- **Teaching Resources**
  - Chapter Support Files
  - Teaching Aids and Teacher Letters
  - Lesson Planners Plus
  - Cumulative Assessment
  - Spanish Resources
  - Computational Practice Skills Review
  - Overhead Manipulatives Kit
- **Practice Workbook**
- **Teaching Transparencies**
- **Daily Skills Warm-Up Transparencies**
- **Student Edition Answers on Transparencies**
- **Solution Key**
- **Algebra Readiness Kit**
- **Assessment Success Kit**
- **Mathematics Standardized Test Prep, Student Edition**
- **Mathematics Standardized Test Prep, Teacher's Edition**
- **Test-taking Tips on Transparencies**
- **Daily Cumulative Review Masters**
- **Help at Home Copy Masters**
- **Graphing Calculator Handbook**
- **Student Manipulatives Kit**
- **Skills Intervention Kit** provides diagnostic tools for determining weak prerequisite skills for the course, along with follow-up testing, reteaching, and practice. Ideal for after-school programs, Saturday classes, and summer school. Practice Tutorial CD-ROM included.

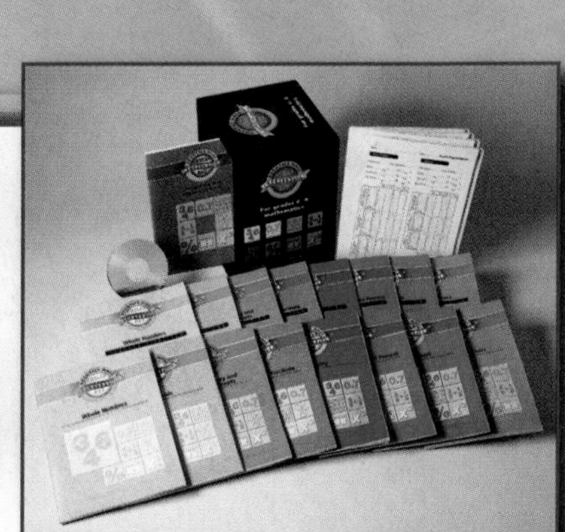

## Technology Resources

- **Interactive Math: Lessons & Tools CD-ROM (MAC/WIN)** features lessons and tools to make abstract concepts visual and accessible. Also contains challenge problems and journal activities to spark inquisitive minds.
- **Student Tutorial CD-ROM (MAC/WIN)**
- **Resource Pro® CD-ROM with Planning Express® (MAC/WIN)** contains electronic versions of all the teaching resources, along with Planning Express® software.
- **Computer Item Generator CD-ROM with Standardized Test Practice** allows you to custom develop quizzes, tests, and practice sheets. Choose from an unlimited supply of questions varying in level of difficulty.
- **Math Blaster® Pre-Algebra CD-ROM (MAC/WIN; School version)** As students make their way through Dr. Dabble's eerie mansion, they develop key pre-algebra skills such as logical thinking, estimation, ratios, order of operations, and more.
- **Video Fieldtrips, Volume I: Algebra Applications**
- **Video Fieldtrips, Volume II: Geometry Applications**
- **Wide World of Mathematics CD-ROM**
- **Wide World of Mathematics Video**

## Get them all ready for algebra

TEACHER'S EDITION

PRENTICE HALL

# PRE-ALGEBRA

## TOOLS FOR A CHANGING WORLD


AUTHORS

**David M. Davison**
Eastern Montana College
Billings, Montana

**Marsha S. Landau**
Formerly, National-Louis University
Evanston, Illinois

**Leah McCracken**
Lockwood Junior High School
Billings, Montana

**Linda Thompson**
Warrenton, Oregon


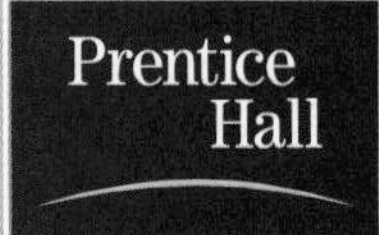



Needham, Massachusetts
Upper Saddle River, New Jersey
Glenview, Illinois

## REVIEWERS


**Chandler Cox**
White Knoll Middle School
West Columbia, South Carolina

**Joyce F. Henderson**
Robert A. Millikan High School
Long Beach, California

**Ellice P. Martin, Ed.D.**
Lanier County Middle School
Lakeland, Georgia

**Fred Ferguson**
Yough High School
Herminie, Pennsylvania

**Nancy Hughes**
Indian Hills Middle School
Shawnee Mission, Kansas

**Desireé Marcelin McNeal**
Susan Miller Dorsey High School
Los Angeles, California

**Dorothy (Dot) Johnson-Manning**
Siwell Road Middle School
Jackson, Mississippi


## CONSULTANTS

### Reading Consultant


**Bonnie B. Armbruster, Ph.D.**
Department of Curriculum and Instruction
University of Illinois at Champaign-Urbana
Champaign, Illinois


### Content Consultants


**Elizabeth Cunningham**
Mathematics
Prentice Hall National Consultant
Mansfield, Texas

**Shawyn Jackson**
Mathematics
Prentice Hall National Consultant
Bayshore, New York

**Bridget Hadley**
Mathematics
Director, Prentice Hall National Consultants
Hopkinton, Massachusetts

**Sandra Mosteller**
Mathematics
Prentice Hall National Consultant
Anderson, South Carolina

**Loretta Rector**
Mathematics
Prentice Hall National Consultant
Foresthill, California




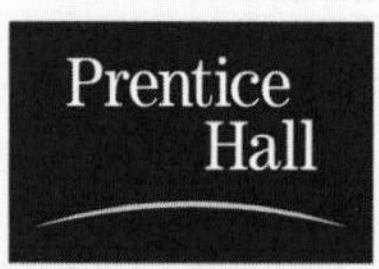



ISBN 0-13-050461-0
3 4 5 6 7 8 9 10 04 03 02 01 00

# AUTHORS

**David M. Davison, Ph.D.,** is a Professor of Mathematics Education at Montana State University in Billings, Montana. One of Dr. Davison's areas of special focus is the integration of mathematics with other disciplines, especially science. He is also the author of a book and several articles on teaching mathematics to Native Americans.

**Marsha Landau, Ph.D.,** formerly of National-Louis University in Evanston, Illinois, is an active workshop leader on preparing middle school students for success on standardized tests and related topics in city and suburban school districts. Dr. Landau also is a leader of programs for academically talented students at the Center for Talent Development at the School of Education and Social Policy at Northwestern University.

**Leah McCracken** is a teacher at Lockwood School in Billings, Montana, and an educational technologies instructor at Montana State University in Billings. Ms. McCracken is a very active member of the Montana Teachers of Mathematics and a recipient of numerous awards, including the Montana Teacher of the Year.

**Linda Thompson** is a mathematics consultant from Warrenton, Oregon. Ms.Thompson, who is listed in *Who's Who in American Education*, is a contributing author of books on elementary education, as well as numerous articles on math education and teacher-help books on the creative classroom.

PRENTICE HALL

# PRE-ALGEBRA

π

%

TOOLS FOR A CHANGING WORLD

2x =

**About the Cover:**

**The central image on the cover—the airborne hang glider—represents the integration of mathematics and science in a real-world application that is of high interest to students. The cover is a composite of four separate images, merged electronically.**

# TEACHER'S EDITION CONTENTS

# CONTENTS



The "Tools for Problem Solving" section, which appears before Chapter 1, helps students review their problem solving skills and can be used before or with Chapter 1. At the end of the book, there are several other useful resources. Extra Practice pages for each chapter contain additional exercises correlated to each lesson. The Skills Handbook provides an in-text tutorial of math skills that students may need to review. The Glossary/Study Guide provides not only definitions with page references, but also examples of most vocabulary terms.

CHAPTER 1

# Algebraic Expressions and Integers

## Problem Solving and Connections

Students begin the year reviewing variables, variable expressions, and integers. They extend their understanding of the Order of Operations by performing operations with integers. They also develop inductive reasoning skills using visual patterns and number patterns. The chapter ends with graphing integers in the coordinate plane.

CHAPTER 2

# Solving One-Step Equations and Inequalities

## Problem Solving and Connections

### REVIEW



### ASSESSMENT

CHAPTER PROJECT 2

### DON'T LOSE YOUR BALANCE!



Students review properties of numbers and how to use them to solve equations. They use their equation-solving skills to solve real-world problems and extend their skills to solving inequalities.

CHAPTER 3

# Decimals and Equations

## Problem Solving and Connections

### REVIEW



### ASSESSMENT



CHAPTER PROJECT 3

### CURRENCY EVENTS



Students use a variety of strategies to estimate decimal sums, differences, products, and quotients to evaluate when calculated answers are reasonable. They apply their decimal computation skills to real-life applications, such as finding measures of central tendency and using formulas. Students solve one-step equations that include decimals.

CHAPTER 4

# Factors, Fractions, and Exponents

## Problem Solving and Connections

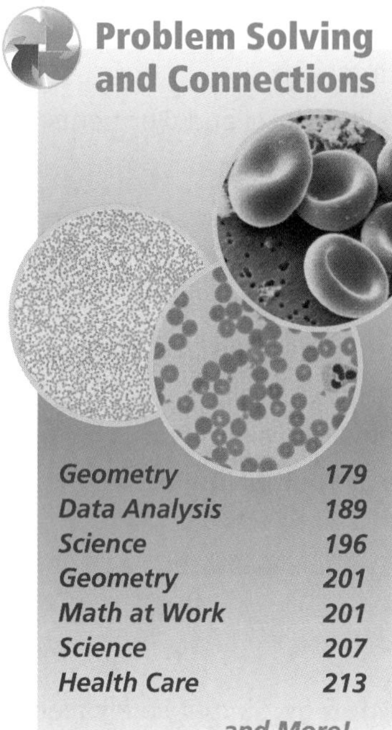



Students use number theory to understand and work with rational numbers. They also simplify expressions using properties of exponents. The chapter concludes with a connection to scientific notation, which pulls together many of the concepts of the chapter and shows their practical applications.

CHAPTER 5

# Operations with Fractions

In their study of fractions, students continue using estimates to determine when calculated answers are reasonable. Students further their understanding of algebra by solving equations containing fractions. They extend their study of numbers to include powers of products and quotients.

CHAPTER 6

# Ratios, Proportions, and Percents

Problem Solving and Connections

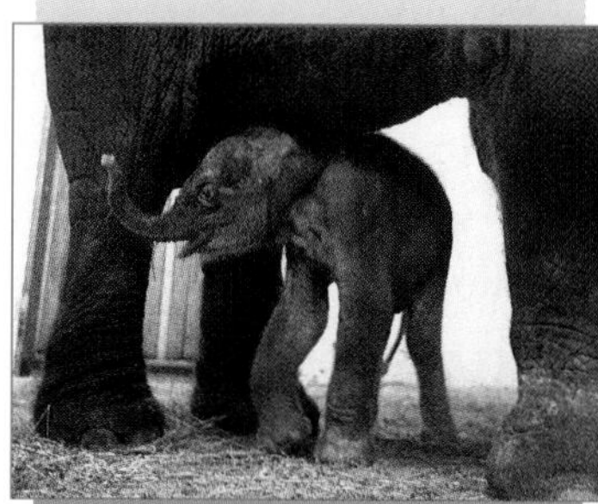



***REVIEW***



***ASSESSMENT***



CHAPTER PROJECT 6

**STRING BAND**



Students learn to use proportional reasoning to solve real-world problems, including ones involving indirect measurement and markup and discount. They use ratios to understand probability. Throughout the chapter, the interrelationship of fractions, decimals, and percents is emphasized.

CHAPTER 7

# Solving Equations and Inequalities

## Problem Solving and Connections

Students extend their equation-solving skills to two- and multi-step equations, including solving equations with variables on both sides. They apply their skills to two-step inequalities and transforming formulas. Students end the chapter applying their skills from Chapters 6 and 7 to find simple and compound interest.

CHAPTER 8

# Linear Functions and Graphing

Problem Solving and Connections

Students identify mathematical patterns and use their algebra skills to write rules for the patterns. Based on their understanding of patterns, they represent functions using tables, rules, and graphs. They graph linear equations and inequalities and extend their graphing skills to help solve systems of linear equations and inequalities.

CHAPTER

9

# Spatial Thinking

Problem Solving and Connections

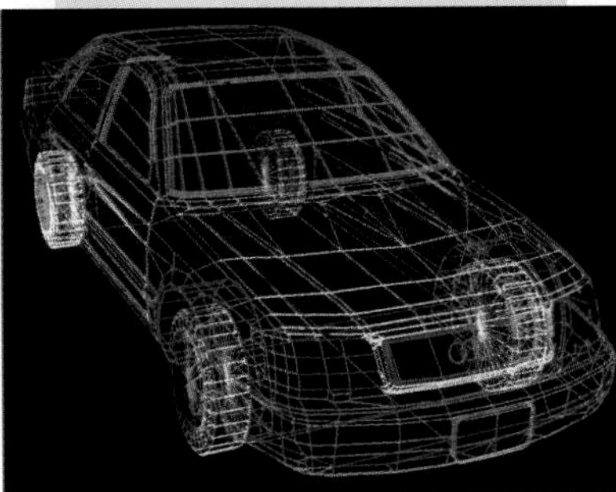



Students develop spatial thinking and apply their knowledge of geometry to the real world. Students use logical reasoning to explain the relationships among figures, including pairs of angles, congruent triangles, and types of polygons. In the final lessons of the chapter, students focus on the connection between congruence and transformations in the coordinate plane.

CHAPTER 10

# Area and Volume

***REVIEW***



***ASSESSMENT***



CHAPTER PROJECT 10

**MAKING A SPLASH**



Students begin the chapter with the study of area of two-dimensional figures. Then students apply this knowledge to find surface area of solid figures. They extend their use of formulas to include volume. Students apply algebraic reasoning and formulas to solve real-world problems involving solid figures, and they explore how changing the dimensions of a figure affects its surface area and volume.

CHAPTER 11

# Right Triangles in Algebra

## Problem Solving and Connections

Students extend their knowledge of real numbers to include irrational numbers. They use their knowledge in a variety of geometric contexts through a rich source of applications of the Pythagorean Theorem. The concluding lessons introduce students to trigonometry.

CHAPTER 12

# Data Analysis and Probability

## Problem Solving and Connections

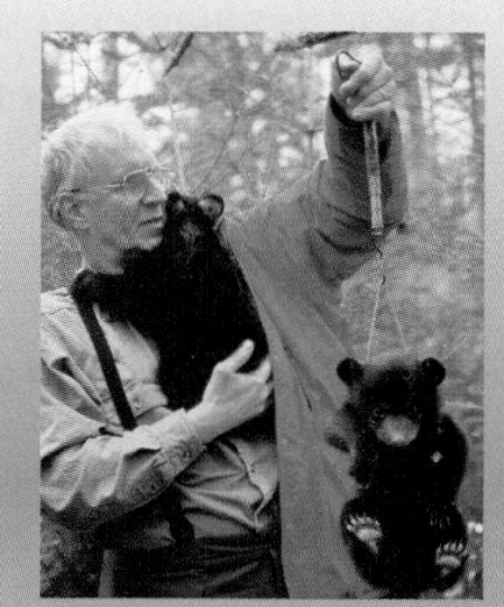



***REVIEW***



***ASSESSMENT***



CHAPTER PROJECT 12

**THE GOOD TIMES POLL**



Students learn about visual representations of relationships by interpreting and creating data displays. They further their understanding of data analysis by studying theoretical and experimental probability. They apply probability concepts to real-world situations using simulations.

CHAPTER 13

# Nonlinear Functions and Polynomials

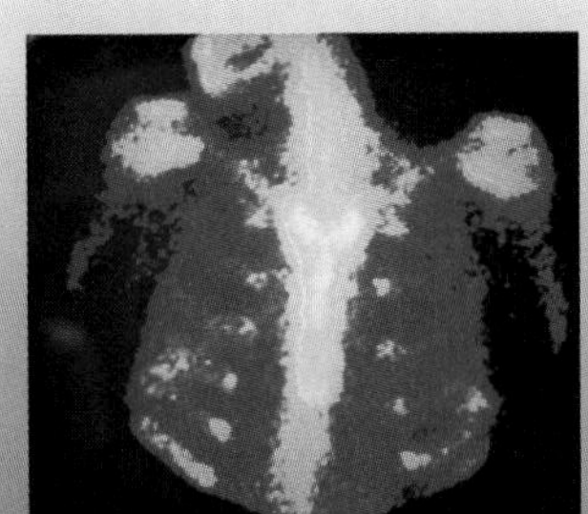



***REVIEW***



***ASSESSMENT***



CHAPTER PROJECT 13

**PRISM BUILDING**



Students build on their knowledge of the coordinate plane by graphing nonlinear functions. They extend their algebra skills to include adding and subtracting polynomials, multiplying polynomials by monomials, and multiplying binomials.

# Pacing Guide for *Prentice Hall Pre-Algebra*

**This chart is provided merely as a guide to help you customize your course. To accommodate flexible scheduling, most lessons are subdivided into parts. In your Teacher's Edition, these parts are indicated in red by the symbol ▼. The Assignment Guide in each lesson indicates which practice exercises in the Student Edition correspond to the parts of each lesson.**

**Detailed Chapter Pacing Options precede each chapter and give you lesson-by-lesson pacing suggestions for that specific chapter.**

| | Chapter 1 | Chapter 2 | Chapter 3 | Chapter 4 | Chapter 5 | Chapter |
|---|---|---|---|---|---|---|
| **Traditional** (40–45 min. class periods) | 15 days | 15 days | 11 days | 13 days | 14 days | 14 days |
| **Pre-Algebra Over 2 Years** (40–45 min. class periods) | 27 days | 26 days | 25 days | 26 days | 26 days | 26 days |
| **Block Scheduling** (90 min. class periods) | 7 days | 6 days | 5 days | 6 days | 7 days | 7 days |

## Management Tools to Help You Plan

There are a host of challenges facing you as a classroom teacher today. Among them are increased administrative responsibilities, lack of time, and heterogeneous groups. These management tools are designed to help you manage your time in a demanding environment.

## Lesson Planners Plus

This booklet serves as a guide to the many elements of the Prentice Hall Pre-Algebra program, including the Student Edition, Teacher's Edition, Teaching Resources, Transparencies, and Technology.

There are four parts in the Lesson Planners Plus booklet:

- **Pacing Options** is designed to assist you in effectively planning instruction time.
- **Chapter Organizers** give you a one-page summary of the most important resources for each chapter.
- **Lesson Planners** provide a detailed outline for each lesson of every chapter.
- **Teacher's Forms** are models designed to simplify planning, evaluation, and teacher-to teacher communication.

## Resource Pro® with Planning Express® on CD-ROM

This CD-ROM contains complete classroom planning tools and teaching resources for customizing and planning lessons. The Resource Pro® offers:

- **Electronic versions of the support material** for the entire Pre-Algebra program: practice, reteaching, enrichment, assessment, and transparencies. View them and print them out.
- **Planning Express®**
  Create your own lesson plans or choose from existing lesson plans—add your local curriculum objectives.
- **Computer Item Generator**
  Create customized practice worksheets, quizzes, and tests.
- **A Resource Pro® Tutorial**

| Chapter 7 | Chapter 8 | Chapter 9 | Chapter 10 | Chapter 11 | Chapter 12 | Chapter 13 | TOTAL |
|---|---|---|---|---|---|---|---|
| 13 days | 13 days | 14 days | 13 days | 10 days | 14 days | 11 days | **170 days** |
| 26 days | 26 days | 26 days | 26 days | 24 days | 26 days | 25 days | **335 days** |
| 6 days | 6 days | 7 days | 6 days | 5 days | 7 days | 5 days | **80 days** |

# Getting Off to the Right Start

## Reading and Writing Math

As you work through Prentice Hall's *Pre-Algebra,* you will notice places in the text that say "Reading Math" and "Writing Math." These tips and useful facts will help you understand the language of mathematics. The examples below show how to read an equation and how to go from words to math symbols.

**Reading Math**

The equation $\frac{x}{-9} = -3$ is read as "*x* divided by negative nine equals negative three."

**Writing Math**

When you go from words to an equation, the order of the math symbols may be different from the order of the words:

- ten fewer than $n \rightarrow n - 10$
- eight less than $r \rightarrow r - 8$
- $n$ times 5 $\rightarrow 5n$

Pay particular attention to vocabulary words. Some words may be familiar to you, and some you may not have seen before. Some words are used very differently in math than they are in everyday English. You need to be alert for these differences. The examples below explain *percent* and *bisect.*

**Reading Math**

Percent means "per hundred." The root *cent* shows up in many other words, such as centimeter, century, and centipede. In money, a cent is $\frac{1}{100}$ of a dollar, or \$.01.

**Reading Math**

To *bisect* means to divide into two equal parts. Therefore a segment bisector divides a segment into two congruent parts.

Remember, reading is not a spectator sport. When you are actively involved in thinking before, during, and after reading, you will find math easier to read, understand, and learn!



"Reading Math" and "Writing Math" are two of the types of tips that occur throughout the text. These tips are included to help students understand what they read, what they do, and how they can apply what they learn.

# Making Decisions: Using a Calculator

Touch this dot with your fingertip.

Now move your finger slowly from the dot to the end of your nose.

As you watch your finger approach your nose (slowly), think of the incredible amount of *information processing* and *decision making* that goes on in your brain to control the path of your fingertip.

Your brain is the finest computer you will ever use.

The computer inside your head has a data bank with a lifetime of information—enough to allow for continuous routine background (unconscious) processing. Nonroutine (conscious) problem solving, however, requires organized thinking by you, its user. Sometimes you may want to use an outside machine, like a calculator, for additional information. Your job is to manage the linked system of mind and machine as efficiently and productively as possible. Here are some guidelines.

***Use your brain***

1. to do a multi-step problem with manageable steps.
2. to compute when only estimates are needed.
3. to extend a simple pattern to the next two or three terms.
4. to find square roots of perfect squares.
5. to find one-digit factors.
6. to solve proportion problems using simple integers.

***Use a calculator***

1. to do a multi-step problem with complicated steps.
2. to compute to more than two decimal places of precision.
3. to extend a pattern to large numbers, or to many terms.
4. to find square roots of non-perfect squares.
5. to test for factors.
6. to find trigonometric ratios.

In general, the more you can extend both lists, the better equipped you will be for this course.



This short essay differentiates between problems that should be solved using brain power alone and problems for which technology is useful. You might wish to read and discuss this essay with students as you begin the school year.

# Tools for Problem Solving

## *An Overview*

CONTENTS

The "mini-lessons" in this Overview focus on the big picture of problem solving. They introduce students to the four-step problem solving plan, problem solving strategies, and standardized tests. The mini-lessons can be covered in any order and at any time throughout the year, but they're especially well-suited for use at the beginning of the course.

### *To the Student:*

*The key to your success in math is your ability to use math in the real world—both now and in the future. To succeed, you need math skills and some problem solving tools, too. In this Problem Solving Overview, you'll learn how to use a four-step plan for problem solving, how to choose strategies for solving problems, how to evaluate your solutions, and how to apply strategies to standardized tests.*

*As you work through the book, you'll find plenty of opportunities to improve your problem solving and reasoning skills. Some of the problems you'll work through are simple and routine, so you can practice and develop your skills. Other problems are more complex and require more time and thought to complete. No matter what, you'll find plenty of opportunities to use your skills in everyday life as well as in theoretical situations. Good luck!*

**Problem Solving Strategies**

- Account for All Possibilities
- Draw a Diagram
- Look for a Pattern
- Make a Model
- Make a Table
- Simplify a Problem
- Simulate a Problem
- Solve by Graphing
- Try, Test, Revise
- Use Multiple Strategies
- Work Backward
- Write an Equation
- Write a Proportion

# The Four-Step Approach

When *Apollo 13* was damaged in space, the three astronauts on board had to modify some of the equipment to get back to Earth safely. They could use only materials that were on the spacecraft, including plastic bags, cardboard, and tape. The solution required problem solving abilities and creativity.

You solve problems every day, both in and outside of school. Having an organized way to tackle problems can help you sort through information and find an effective solution strategy. Many successful problem solvers use a four-step method developed by the mathematician George Polya.

**Polya's Four-Step Approach**

1. Read and understand the problem.
2. Plan how to solve the problem.
3. Solve the problem.
4. Look back.

## Sample Problem

The Smiths' minivan averaged 24 mi/gal on a recent camping trip. They took the same route to and from the campsite, traveling a total of 480 mi. Because of heavy traffic, they averaged only 40 mi/h on the way to the campsite. The total driving time for the trip was 10 h. What was their average speed on the return trip?

### Read

Read the problem, and ask yourself questions.

*What information am I given?*

The van gets 24 mi/gal.
The distance was 480 mi round trip.
The van's speed on the way to the campsite was 40 mi/h.
The total driving time was 10 h.



The four-step approach gives students a simple yet effective path to problem solving success. Most students have used this approach (or a similar one) in earlier courses. By reviewing it at the beginning of the year, they can use problem solving tools as they approach word problems, which they will find in every lesson in this book.

*What am I being asked to find?*

I want to find the average speed traveled on the way home.

*Is any of the given information not needed?*

Since the problem does not ask about the amount of gas used, the fact that the van gets 24 mi/gal is not needed.

### Plan

Consider the strategies you know. Could you use one of them? Have you ever solved a similar problem? If so, try the same approach.

You have probably solved problems involving distance, speed, and time. In general, speed × time traveled = distance traveled. You can use the distance formula to solve the problem in three steps:

1. Determine the distance of the return trip.
2. Determine how long the return trip took.
3. Find the van's speed for the return trip.

### Solve

The total distance for the trip was 480 mi, so the return trip was 480 mi ÷ 2 = 240 mi.

Going to the campsite, the van traveled 240 mi at a speed of 40 mi/h. Since 240 ÷ 40 = 6, the trip took 6 h. Since the total driving time was 10 h, the return trip must have taken 10 h − 6 h = 4 h.

You now know that, on the way home, the van traveled 240 mi in 4 h. Its average speed was 240 mi ÷ 4 hr = 60 mi/h.

### Look Back

This is an important step in solving problems. Ask yourself

*Did I answer the question asked?* Reread the problem to be sure.

*Does my answer make sense?* Substitute your answer into the original problem.

*Could I have solved the problem another way?* Sometimes you can confirm your answer by using another method.

If the Smiths traveled 40 mi/h on the way to the campsite and 60 mi/h on the way back, then the total driving time in hours would be 240 ÷ 40 + 240 ÷ 60 = 6 + 4 = 10. So the answer is correct.



Students should remember the key words "Read," "Plan," "Solve," and "Look Back." You may want to discuss each step of the Sample Problem as a class or in small groups.

# Exercises

**Use George Polya's four-step method to solve each problem. Remember that there are many ways to solve problems.**

1. Nikki and Jing collect action figures. Together, they have 48 figures. Jing has six fewer figures than twice the number Nikki has. How many action figures does each girl have? Nikki 18; Jing 30
2. Yolanda's Yogurt Shoppe is having a special on sundaes. How many different sundaes are possible? 24 sundaes

Yolanda's Sundae Special
Only $1.69
Choose one item from each list.
Yogurt
Vanilla
Chocolate
Peach
Raspberry
Toppings
Strawberries
Bananas
Nuts 'n Stuff
Mixed Nuts
Granola
Sprinkles


3. *Number Sense* What is the ones digit of $3^{18}$? 9
4. Amelia, Brian, and Cody have three bicycles. One bike is blue, one is green, and one is red. Amelia's brother rides a red bike. Brian does not have a blue bike. Cody's bike is either red or green. Cody is not related to Amelia. Who owns the red bike? Brian
5. *Language* In another language, *desa tra* means "green pepper," *dro tra dam* means "big green house," and *tresti dam* means "big dog." What is the word for "house" in this language? C
   A. *dam* B. *desa* C. *dro* D. *tra*
6. *Number Sense* Mr. Lopez is packing the muffins he made for the school bake sale. He finds that whether he puts four, five, or six muffins in each bag, he has two muffins left over. What is the least number of muffins Mr. Lopez could have? 62
7. Jakob and Tom are the same age. Jakob is older than Clarisse. Clarisse is younger than Miko. Is Jakob older or younger than Miko, or can this not be determined from the information? cannot be determined
8. *Landscaping* A landscaper bought decorative fencing to enclose the flower bed at the right. The fencing cost $24.95/ft. How much did the landscaper spend on fencing? $1,397.20

Exercises can be worked on individually or in groups in class, or as homework. Encourage students to use the four-step approach to solve each Exercise.

PROBLEM SOLVING

# Using Strategies

When you need to solve a problem, it helps to be familiar with several solution strategies. Most problems can be solved in several different ways, and for some problems a combination of strategies works best.

Here are some strategies to consider when you are planning to solve a problem.

- Draw a Diagram
- Look for a Pattern
- Make a Table
- Simplify a Problem
- Try, Test, Revise
- Write an Equation

## Sample Problem

Ana is organizing a tennis tournament at her town's recreation center. Each participant will play each of the other participants exactly once. Six people have signed up for the tournament. How many games does Ana need to schedule?

### *Solution 1*

### STRATEGIES: *Simplify a Problem* and *Look for a Pattern*

You can start by using the strategy *Simplify a Problem*. Figure out the number of games needed for tournaments with two, three, and four players. Then use the strategy *Look for a Pattern* to find the number of games for a six-person tournament.



This section shows students that there is often more than one way to succeed at solving a problem and reviews familiar problem solving techniques. Not all the strategies are included here, but students will add to their repertoire of problem solving techniques as the year progresses.

What if only two players, A and B, sign up for the tournament? Then only one game would be played, A against B. You can use the notation AB to represent this game.

Now a third player, C, signs up. This adds two more games, since C must play both A and B. So a total of three games would be played: AB, AC, and BC.

If a fourth player, D, signed up for the tournament, then three more games would be needed, since D would need to play A, B, and C. A total of six games would be played: AB, AC, BC, AD, BD, and CD.

*Do you see a pattern?*

2 players: 1 game
3 players: 1 + 2 = 3 games
4 players: 1 + 2 + 3 = 6 games

*You can extend the pattern and find the number of games for a six-player tournament.*

6 players: 1 + 2 + 3 + 4 + 5 = 15 games

## *Solution 2*

### STRATEGIES: *Draw a Diagram*

You can also use the strategy *Draw a Diagram* to solve this problem. Use dots, labeled A to F, to represent the players. Use segments connecting the dots to represent the games.

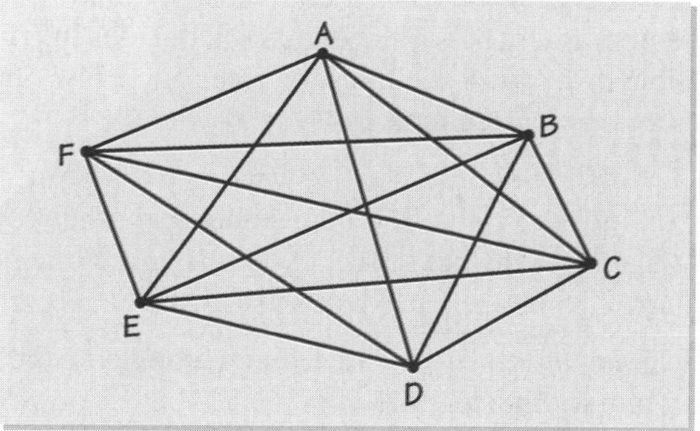


There are a total of 15 segments, so Ana needs to schedule 15 games.



Encourage students to solve the Sample Problem before looking at the strategies used in the book. Then they can compare their solutions to those presented. You could ask students to give solutions that differ from those in the book.

# Exercises

1. Roger has band practice every other day, meets with a math tutor every fourth day, and volunteers at a children's hospital once a week. Today, Roger had practice, met with his tutor, and worked at the hospital. In how many days will Roger have all three activities on the same day again? **28 days**

2. *Patterns* If the pattern below continues, how many squares will be in Stage 23? **67 squares**

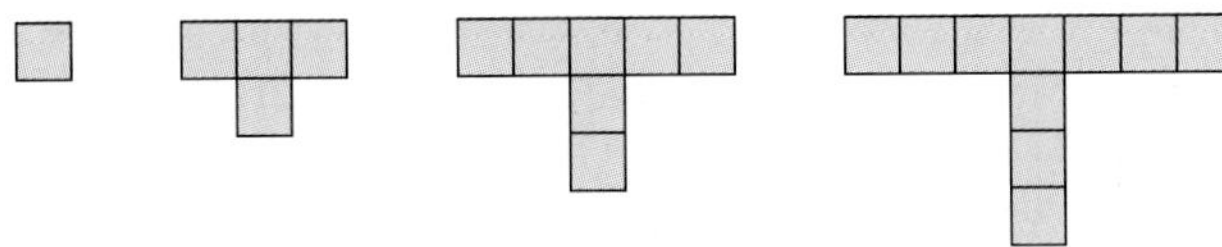

Stage 1 Stage 2 Stage 3 Stage 4

3. *Fund-raising* The basketball team is selling calendars to raise money for new uniforms. Wall calendars sell for \$7 each and desk calendars sell for \$5 each. On Saturday, Maya sold 11 calendars for a total of \$67 dollars. How many calendars of each type did she sell? **6 wall, 5 desk**

4. *Maps* Rama and Dan are using a trail map to plan a backpacking trip. On the first day, they plan to hike from the trail head to Miller's Pond—a map distance of about 4 in. The key on the map says that 1.25 in. represents 2.5 mi. About how many miles will Rama and Dan hike the first day? **8 mi**

5. *Geometry* How can you arrange 24 identical square tiles, without stacking, to create a shape with the least possible perimeter? **in a 6-by-4 array**

6. *Number Sense* Rose has forgotten the combination to her gym locker. She knows it has the digits 1, 3, 5, 7, and 9, but she doesn't remember the order of the digits. She decides to try every possible order until she finds the right one. How many five-digit numbers does Rose have to try? **120 numbers**

7. *Geography* Suppose you are walking west. You come to a corner and turn right. You then come to another corner and turn right again. At the next corner you turn left. Which direction are you now facing—north, south, east, or west? **north**

8. How many letters are in either the rectangle or the square at the right, but not in both? **6 letters**

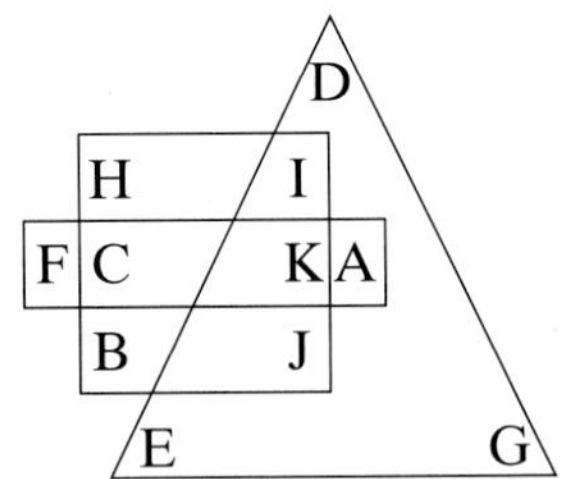




Encourage students to use any strategy to solve the problems in the Exercises, either at home or in class. You could ask some students or groups to solve one or more of the Exercises using as many different strategies as possible. Students should not be limited to the strategies used in the lesson.

# Using Rubrics

A *rubric* is a type of scoring guide. Rubrics are often used to grade projects or to score problems that require you to show your work or explain your thinking.

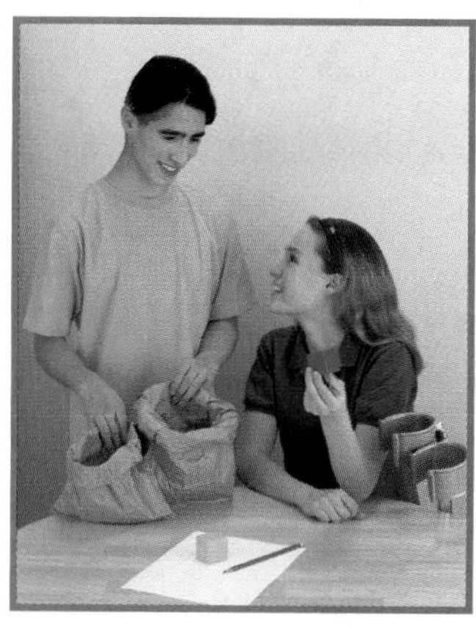

## Sample Problem

The Mixing Colors game involves two bags of colored blocks. Bag 1 contains one red block and two blue blocks. Bag 2 contains one yellow block and two red blocks. A player guesses a color—red, yellow, blue, orange, green, or purple—and then draws one block from each bag without looking. The colors of the blocks are "mixed" according the following rules:

| | |
|---|---|
| red + red = red | blue + blue = blue |
| yellow + yellow = yellow | red + blue = purple |
| red + yellow = orange | blue + yellow = green |

If the mixture color matches the guess, the player wins a prize.

What color should a player guess to have the best chance of winning the game? Show your work and explain how you found your answer.

Solutions to this problem are scored from a high of 3 points to a low of 0 points according to the rubric below.

**Rubric**

3 You correctly state that the player should choose purple and give a clear, logical explanation for your answer.

2 You correctly answer the question but provide a weak explanation, *or* you use correct reasoning but make a minor mistake that leads to an incorrect answer.

1 You give the correct answer but provide no explanation *or* give the correct answer or an incorrect answer with a flawed explanation.

0 You give an incorrect answer with no explanation *or* fail to attempt an answer.



Rubrics are a valuable tool for performance assessment, whether of others or of oneself. Familiarity with rubrics will help students understand the grading process and help increase their abilities to assess their school work.

*Sample Answer 1*

The table shows all the possible color combinations. Purple happens the most, so the player should choose purple to have the best chance of winning a prize.

| | | Bag 1 | | |
|---|---|---|---|---|
| | | R | B | B |
| | Y | O | G | G |
| Bag 2 | R | R | P | P |
| | R | R | P | P |

This response scores a 3. The student gives the correct answer with a clear, logical explanation.

*Sample Answer 2*

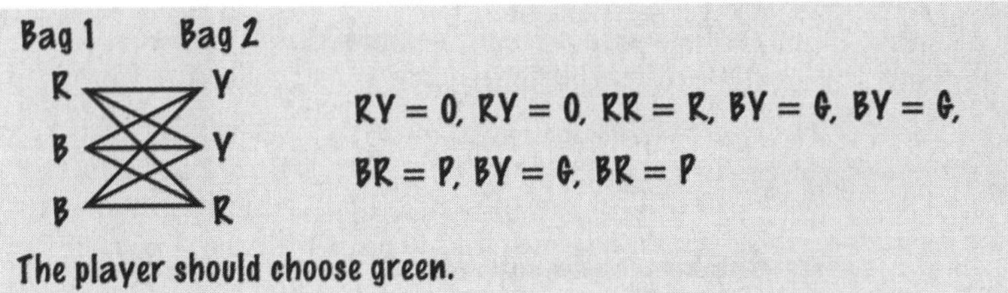
Bag 1 Bag 2
R Y
B Y
B R

RY = O, RY = O, RR = R, BY = G, BY = G,
BR = P, BY = G, BR = P

The player should choose green.

This response scores a 2. The strategy is a good one, but the student gets the incorrect answer because of listing the contents for Bag 2 incorrectly. The student also does not list one of the color combinations.

*Sample Answer 3*

Bag 1 + Bag 2 = Mixture
blue + red = purple
blue + red = purple
red + yellow = orange

Purple happens 2 out of 3 times. The player should choose purple.

This response scores a 1. The student gives the correct answer but uses faulty reasoning.



Students have an opportunity to view solutions to the sample problem and appraisals of the solutions before moving on to the Exercises.

## Exercises

**Use the given rubric to score each sample answer. Explain how you decided which score to give.**

One baseball and two bats cost \$51. Two baseballs and five bats cost \$125. Find the price of a baseball and the price of a bat. Explain how you found your answers.

**Rubric**

3 You correctly state that a baseball costs \$5 and a bat costs \$23, and you give a clear, logical explanation for your answer.

2 You correctly answer the question but provide a weak explanation, *or* you make a minor mistake that leads to the incorrect answer.

1 You give the correct answer but provide no explanation, *or* you give an incorrect answer with a flawed explanation.

0 You give the incorrect answer with no explanation *or* fail to attempt an answer.

**1.** Sample answer 1:

Ball \$5 Bat \$23

1 for correct answer, no explanation

**2.** Sample answer 2:

3 for correct answer with clear, logical explanation

1 ball + 2 bats cost \$51. Doubling everything, I get 2 balls + 4 bats cost \$102. Adding 1 more bat makes 2 balls + 5 bats, which cost \$125. So a bat costs \$23.

2 bats cost \$46 and 2 bats + 1 ball cost \$51. So a ball costs \$5.

**3.** Sample answer 3:

1 for incorrect answer and flawed explanation

1 ball and 2 bats cost \$51, and 2 balls and 5 bats cost \$125.

Combining everything: 3 balls and 7 bats cost \$176.
Guess: Bat costs \$20. Then, 7 bats cost \$140. So 3 balls cost \$36, or 1 ball costs \$12.
Test: 3(12) + 7(20) = 176 ✓



These Exercises provide students with problem solutions to appraise. You might prefer to assign these as class exercises for students to discuss in groups so that they have an opportunity to discuss the different levels of the rubric.

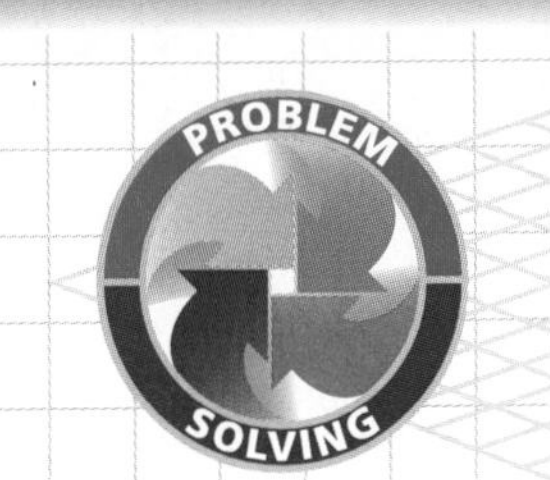


# Standardized Test Prep

You can use problem solving skills to answer multiple-choice questions. By thinking logically or using estimation, you can eliminate some of the answer choices.

**SAMPLE PROBLEM 1**

Sandra conducted a survey to find the type of movie that students in her school liked best. Of the students surveyed, one fourth preferred action movies and one third preferred dramas. The remaining 30 students said they like comedies best. How many students took part in Sandra's survey?

**A.** 28 **B.** 67 **C.** 72 **D.** 80 **E.** 84

## Read

Read the problem carefully. You need to find the total number of students Sandra surveyed.

The number of students Sandra surveyed must be greater than 30 and be divisible by 3 and by 4.

## Plan

You can think logically to eliminate some of the choices and then *Work Backward* to see which remaining answer choice fits the information given in the problem.

## Solve

Think about the choices you can eliminate easily.

Sandra surveyed more than 30 students, so you can eliminate choice A.

The number of students in each category must be a whole number. Since $67 \div 4 = 16.75$ and $80 \div 3 \approx 26.7$, you can eliminate choices B and D.



This section boosts students' preparation for standardized tests. Throughout the text—in Lessons, Mixed Reviews, Standardized Test Prep pages, and Cumulative Reviews—students will continue to practice standardized test-type problems.

Only choices C and E remain. *Work Backward* to see which answer fits the information in the problem.

Try choice C, 72:

$72 \div 4 = 18$ and $72 \div 3 = 24$
$72 - 18 - 24 = 30$ ✔

Choice C is correct.

Check your answer by making sure choice E is *not* correct.

$84 \div 4 = 21$ and $84 \div 3 = 28$
$84 - 21 - 28 = 35 \neq 30$ ✘

Choice E is not correct.

When *Not here* is a choice, you need to check each of the other choices before choosing *Not here*.

### Sample Problem 2

The mean of four numbers is 68. Three of the numbers are 74, 66, and 82. What is the fourth number?

**A.** 280 **B.** 73 **C.** 67 **D.** 50 **E.** Not here

***Think Logically*** Since the three given numbers are even and the mean is even, the fourth number must be even as well.

You can eliminate choices B and C because they are odd.

Since the mean of the four numbers is 68, the sum of the four numbers must be $4 \times 68 = 272$.

$280 > 272$, so you can eliminate choice A.

***Work Backward*** Only choices D and E remain. Check choice D.

$74 + 66 + 82 + 50 = 272$
$272 \div 4 = 68$ ✔

Choice D is the correct answer.

***Look Back*** Since one of the answer choices works in the original problem, choice E, *Not here,* is not correct.



Encourage students to discuss other helpful hints they can apply when taking standardized tests.

# Exercises

**Use problem solving strategies to choose the best answer.**

1. Desmond made a sketch of his dog Frankie. He used a photocopy machine to reduce his drawing to 75% of its original size. He then reduced the copy to 50% of its size. In the final copy, the distance from Frankie's nose to her tail was 10.5 cm. What was the distance from nose to tail in the original sketch? D
   **A.** 3.5 cm  **B.** 9 cm  **C.** 21 cm  **D.** 28 cm  **E.** 135.5 cm

2. Tracy's father is three times as old as Tracy. Six years ago, he was five times as old as Tracy. How old is Tracy? C
   **A.** 18  **B.** 15  **C.** 12  **D.** 10  **E.** 6

3. The square and the rectangle below have the same area. What is the value of $x$? C

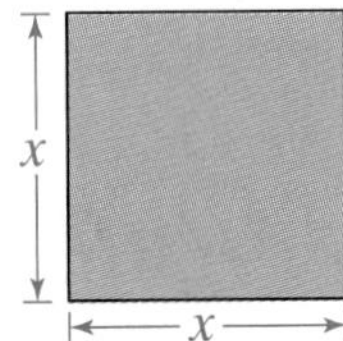


   **A.** 0  **B.** 2  **C.** 6  **D.** 8  **E.** 12

4. Five numbers have a mean of 25 and a median of 25. Three of the numbers are 20, 24, and 30. What are the other two numbers? C
   **A.** 21 and 26  **B.** 23 and 25  **C.** 25 and 26  **D.** 25 and 28  **E.** 28 and 32

5. In a pile of dimes and quarters, there are twice as many quarters as dimes. The total value of the coins is $7.80. How many dimes are in the pile? B
   **A.** 15  **B.** 13  **C.** 11  **D.** 9  **E.** Not here

6. One day last week, Suzanne ate lunch with Tommy, went to the library and borrowed two books, saw a photography exhibit at the museum, and had a cavity filled. Tommy was out of town on Monday. The library is closed on weekends. The museum is open only on Tuesdays, Wednesdays, and Fridays. The dentist has office hours on Mondays, Thursdays, and Fridays. On which day last week did Suzanne do all these things? E
   **A.** Monday  **B.** Tuesday  **C.** Wednesday  **D.** Thursday  **E.** Friday

7. ***Number Sense*** Given the numbers 1 and 4, it is *not* reasonable to conclude that D
   **A.** the difference is less than the sum.  **B.** the sum is greater than the product.
   **C.** the quotient is less than the sum.  **D.** the product is greater than the sum.



These Exercises can be assigned for homework or worked on in groups. Have students discuss which answers can be eliminated first and why, or any other helpful test-taking hints they wish to share with their classmates.

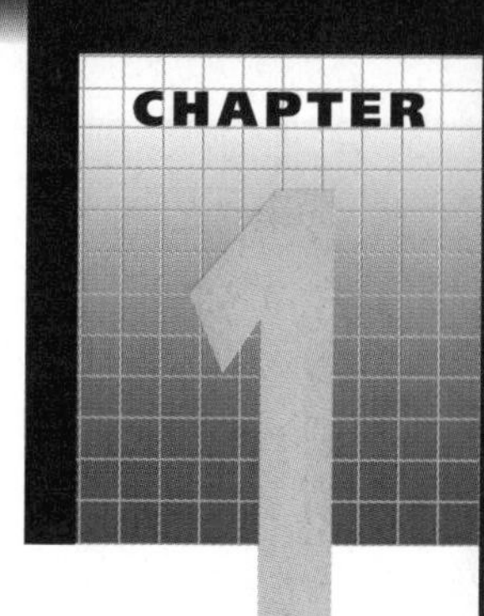


# Algebraic Expressions and Integers

## Content Overview for Chapter 1

Chapter 1 introduces the basic language and tools of algebra. You can represent an unknown number or quantity by using a letter variable, such as $x$ or $a$. Combining a variable with other numbers, for example, multiplying $x$ by the coefficient 2, leads to writing a variable expression such as $2x$ or $2x + 3$. You can substitute a value for the variable, such as $x = 5$, and evaluate the resulting expression: $2 \bullet 5 + 3$. The order of operations rule leads to a value of 13 for this expression.

The counting numbers 1, 2, 3, . . . , together with their opposites, −1, −2, −3, . . . , and 0 are called *integers.* You can model integers by graphing them on a number line or by using colored tiles, such as a yellow tile to model 1 and a red tile to model −1. You can model addition and subtraction of integers either on the number line or with tiles.

When you apply the rules for adding and subtracting integers to number patterns, you can derive the rules for multiplying and dividing integers. In the concluding lesson for this chapter, you extend modeling numbers on a number line to using ordered pairs of numbers, such as (3, −2) to name points on a coordinate plane.

## Making Connections

| Lesson | Interdisciplinary and Real-World Connections | Math Integration |
|---|---|---|
| 1-1 | Nutrition | Data Analysis |
| 1-2 | Consumer Issues | Geometry |
| 1-3 | Marine Biology | Data Analysis |
| 1-4 | Science | Measurement |
| 1-5 | Earth Science | Measurement |
| 1-6 | Meteorology | Measurement |
| 1-7 | Science | Geometry, Data Analysis |
| 1-8 | Reading | Problem Solving |
| 1-9 | Science | Data Analysis |
| 1-10 | Geography | Geometry |

**SCHOOL/HOME CONNECTION**
English and Spanish versions are available in the *Help at Home* book of copy masters.

**Helper's Page** You will find detailed instruction, more examples, and

**Student Page** **Review Exercises for Lessons 1-1 to 1-4**

**Write an expression for each quantity.** *(Lesson 1-1)*

1. the number of inches in 8 feet ______
2. the number of inches in $f$ feet ______
3. the number of weeks in 3 years ______
4. the number of weeks in $y$ years ______

**Simplify each expression.** *(Lesson 1-2)*

5. $3 + 18 \div 2$ ______
6. $14 - 2(9 - 5)$ ______
7. $28 \div (16 - 9)$ ______
8. $\frac{4 + 12}{5 - 1}$ ______

**Evaluate.** *(Lesson 1-3)*

9. $3(a + 5)$ for $a = 2$ ______
10. $\frac{x - y}{6}$ for $x = 26, y = 2$ ______
11. $6 - 4(7 - k)$ for $k = 6$ ______
12. $6m - n + \frac{n}{3}$ for $m = 7, n = 6$ ______

**Graph each set of numbers on a number line. Then order the numbers from least to greatest.** *(Lesson 1-4)*

13. −8, 2, −5 (number line −8 −7 −6 −5 −4 −3 −2 −1 0 1 2 3 4 5 6 7 8) ______
14. −3, −6, −2 (number line −8 −7 −6 −5 −4 −3 −2 −1 0 1 2 3 4 5 6 7 8) ______
15. **Test Prep** Which is equal to 3? *(Lesson 1-2)*
   **A.** $\frac{9 + 6}{5 - 2}$ **B.** $7 - 4(3 - 2)$ **C.** $5 - 2(2)$ **D.** $8 - 4 + 1$ ______

Helper: ______ Comments: ______

**Helper's Page** You will find detailed instruction, more examples, and

**Student Page** **Review Exercises for Lessons 1-5 to 1-9**

**Simplify each expression.** *(Lessons 1-5, 1-6, and 1-9)*

1. $4 + (-9)$ ______
2. $-7 + (-8)$ ______
3. $3 - 8$ ______
4. $-2 - (-10)$ ______
5. $-6 \cdot 7$ ______
6. $(-4)(-8)$ ______
7. $-28 \div (-4)$ ______
8. $-100 \div 10$ ______

**Write a numerical expression for each phrase. Then simplify.** *(Lessons 1-5 and 1-6)*

9. The temperature was 7° below zero and then increased by 4°. ______
10. You owe \$34 and borrow \$12 more. ______

**Write a rule for each pattern. Find the next three numbers in the pattern.** *(Lesson 1-7)*

11. 12, 7, 2, −3, ____, ____, ____
    Rule: ______
12. 3, −6, 12, −24, 48, −96, ____, ____, ____
    Rule: ______

**Look for a pattern to solve the problem.** *(Lesson 1-8)*

13. The Smith family has 5 children. They are 5, 7, 9, 11, and 13 years old. Marie, who is five, must set the table on October 1 to October 5. Nils, who is seven, must set the table for 7 days starting October 6. If the pattern continues through all 5 Smith children, on what day will Marie start the cycle again? ______
14. **Test Prep** Which is equal to −7? *(Lessons 1-5, 1-6, and 1-9)*
   **A.** $-21 \div (-3)$ **B.** $17 + (-10)$ **C.** $3 - (-4)$ **D.** $-2 - 5$ ______

Helper: ______ Comments: ______

CHAPTER 1

# Chapter 1 at a Glance

To accommodate flexible scheduling, most lessons are divided into parts. Assignment Options are given in the Teacher's Edition for each lesson.

### Lesson 1-1 — Variables and Expressions
Pages 4–7

NCTM 1, 2, 6, 10

- Part 1 Identifying Numerical and Variable Expressions
- Part 2 Writing Variable Expressions

### Lesson 1-2 — Geometry: The Order of Operations
Pages 8–12

NCTM 1, 2, 3, 6, 10

- Part 1 Using the Order of Operations
- Part 2 Using Grouping Symbols

### Lesson 1-3 — Evaluating Expressions
Pages 13–16

NCTM 1, 2, 5, 6, 10

- Part 1 Evaluating Variable Expressions
- Part 2 Solving Problems by Evaluating Expressions
- **Project Activity 1**

### Lesson 1-7 — Inductive Reasoning
Pages 35–39

NCTM 1, 2, 3, 6, 7, 9, 10

- Part 1 Writing Rules for Patterns
- Part 2 Predictions and Counterexamples

### Lesson 1-8 — Problem Solving Strategy
Pages 40–43

NCTM 1, 2, 3, 5, 6, 10

Look for a Pattern

### Lesson 1-9 — Data Analysis: Multiplying and Dividing Integers
Pages 44–49

NCTM 1, 2, 5, 6, 9, 10

- Part 1 Multiplying Integers
- Part 2 Dividing Integers
- **Checkpoint 2**

## Pacing Options

This chart suggests pacing for only the core lessons and their parts, and it is provided merely as a possible guide. It will help you determine how much time you have in your schedule to cover other features, such as the Chapter Project, Math Toolboxes, Standardized Test Prep, Wrap Up, and Assessment.

| | Day 1 | Day 2 | Day 3 | Day 4 | Day 5 | Day 6 | Day 7 | Day 8 | Day 9 | Day 10 | Day 11 |
|---|---|---|---|---|---|---|---|---|---|---|---|
| **Traditional** (40–45 min. class periods) | 1–1 ▽1, 1–1 ▽2 | 1–2 ▽1, 1–2 ▽2 | 1–3 ▽1, 1–3 ▽2 | 1–4 ▽1, 1–4 ▽2 | 1–5 ▽1 | 1–5 ▽2 | 1–6 ▽1, 1–6 ▽2 | 1–7 ▽1 | 1–7 ▽2 | 1–8 | 1–9 ▽1 |
| **Pre-Algebra Over 2 Years** (40–45 min. class periods) | 1–1 ▽1 | 1–1 ▽2 | 1–2 ▽1 | 1–2 ▽1 | 1–2 ▽2 | 1–3 ▽1 | 1–3 ▽2 | 1–3 ▽2 | 1–4 ▽1 | 1–4 ▽2 | 1–5 ▽1 |
| **Block Scheduling** (90 min. class periods) | 1–1 ▽1 ▽2, 1–2 ▽1 ▽2 | 1–3 ▽1 ▽2, 1–4 ▽1 ▽2 | 1–5 ▽1 ▽2, 1–6 ▽1 ▽2 | 1–7 ▽1 ▽2, 1–8 | 1–9 ▽1 ▽2, 1–10 ▽1 ▽2 | | | | | | |

| Pages 17–21 | Lesson 1-4 Measurement: Integers and Absolute Value |
|---|---|
| NCTM 1, 2, 4, 6, 8, 9, 10 | Part 1 Comparing Integers<br>Part 2 Finding Absolute Value<br>**Checkpoint 1** |

| Pages 23–28 | Lesson 1-5 Adding Integers |
|---|---|
| NCTM 1, 2, 4, 6, 8, 9, 10 | Part 1 Using Models to Add Integers<br>Part 2 Using Rules to Add Integers<br>**Math At Work** |

| Pages 29–33 | Lesson 1-6 Subtracting Integers |
|---|---|
| NCTM 1, 2, 4, 6, 8, 9, 10 | Part 1 Using Models to Subtract Integers<br>Part 2 Using a Rule to Subtract Integers<br>**Project Activity 2** |

| Pages 50–54 | Lesson 1-10 The Coordinate Plane |
|---|---|
| NCTM 2, 3, 6, 8, 9, 10 | Part 1 Naming Coordinates and Quadrants<br>Part 2 Graphing Points<br>**Project Activity 3** |

### NCTM STANDARDS 2000

1 Number and Operations
2 Algebra
3 Geometry
4 Measurement
5 Data Analysis and Probability
6 Problem Solving
7 Reasoning and Proof
8 Communication
9 Connections
10 Representation

| Day 12 | Day 13 | Day 14 | Day 15 | Day 16 | Day 17 | Day 18 | Day 19 | Day 20 | Day 21 | Day 22 | Day 23 | Day 24 |
|---|---|---|---|---|---|---|---|---|---|---|---|---|
| 1–9 2 | 1–10 1, 1–10 2 | | | | | | | | | | | |
| 1–5 2 | 1–5 2 | 1–6 1 | 1–6 2 | 1–7 1 | 1–7 1 | 1–7 2 | 1–8 | 1–8 | 1–9 1 | 1–9 1 | 1–9 2 | 1–10 1, 1–10 2 |

**Block Scheduling Notes**
Consider these suggestions:
- **Day 3** Before starting Lesson 1-5, teach Math Toolbox 1, p. 22.
- **Day 4** Before starting Lesson 1-7, teach the Standardized Test Prep, p. 34.
- **Day 4** After completing Lesson 1-7, begin presentations for Finish the Project.

# Math Background

## Lesson 1-1
### Variables and Expressions

Mathematics, in many ways, is a language. Students see that writing algebra involves the same operation symbols (+, −, ×, ÷) as arithmetic, but it also involves using one or more letters as "placeholders" in order to generalize a specific arithmetic statement. So $3 + 17$ becomes the more general $x + 17$.

In algebra, letters, called *variables,* act as placeholders. These placeholders were first introduced in previous grades as boxes, for example, ■ + 17 = 20. This becomes $x + 17 = 20$ in the language of algebra. The phrase $x + 17$ is called a *variable expression.*

An algebraic expression does not contain a verb, such as equals (=), is greater than (>), is less than (<), is less than or equal to (≤), or is greater than or equal to (≥). So $3b - 9$ is an algebraic expression. Because $3b \geq 9$ does contain a verb, it is an inequality, or algebraic sentence, rather than an expression.

## Lesson 1-2
### The Order of Operations

Algebra is a mathematical system with certain rules. One of these rules is consistency. For example, a variable cannot be equal to 7 and not equal to 7 at the same time. To ensure that everyone will find the same value for an expression such as $3 + 4 \bullet 2$, mathematicians have agreed on a rule called the *order of operations.* Without the order of operations, one person might choose to add first and another person might choose to multiply first.

$3 + 4 \bullet 2$

| | |
|---|---|
| $7 \bullet 2$ | $3 + 8$ |
| 14 | 11 |

The order of operations says that you multiply and divide first (in order from left to right), and only then do you add and subtract (in order from left to right). This means that the correct value of $3 + 4 \bullet 2$ is 11.

The order of operations also says that expressions in parentheses are simplified first. If there are several sets of grouping symbols, as in $2[3 + (2 - 1)]$, you work from the inside out, so $2[3 + (2 - 1)]$ simplifies to 8.

## Lesson 1-3
### Evaluating Expressions

In Example 3, the fraction $\frac{120}{24}$ simplifies to 5. You can simplify this fraction by dividing 120 by 24. Another method is to factor the numerator and denominator. Help students become aware of the underlying algebraic properties that make it possible to "reduce" a fraction.

$$\frac{120}{24} = \frac{2 \cdot 2 \cdot 2 \cdot 3 \cdot 5}{2 \cdot 2 \cdot 3}$$
$$= \frac{2}{2} \bullet \frac{2}{2} \bullet \frac{2}{2} \bullet \frac{3}{3} \bullet \frac{5}{1}$$

This renaming results from the fact that $\frac{ac}{bd} = \frac{a}{b} \bullet \frac{c}{d}$. Applying the identity properties ($\frac{a}{a} = 1$ and $\frac{a}{1} = a$) gives the following: $1 \bullet 1 \bullet 1 \bullet 1 \bullet 5$. Repeatedly applying the identity property of 1 ($a \bullet 1 = a$) leads to the statement that $\frac{120}{24} = 5$.

## Lesson 1-4
### Integers and Absolute Value

Students know that the counting numbers to the right of zero on a number line (1, 2, 3, 4, . . . ), together with 0, are called the *whole numbers.* In Lesson 1-4, they learn that the opposites of the counting numbers are to the left of zero on a number line (−1, −2, −3, −4, . . . ). Together, the whole numbers and their opposites form the set of integers. The number 0 is neither positive nor negative. 0 has no opposite.

Integers on the number line have two qualities; they have a distance from zero (such as 3 or 4), and they have a direction from zero indicated by the sign (+ or −).

Students learn that the distance from zero is called the *absolute value* of the integer. The absolute value of 0 is 0. On the number line, $-3$ and 3 are the same distance from zero, so $+3$ and $-3$ have the same absolute value, but they have opposite signs. In Chapter 4, students will further extend their knowledge of numbers on the number line by learning about rational numbers.

## Lessons 1-5 and 1-6

### Adding and Subtracting Integers

In the Math Toolbox before Lesson 1-5, students see how to model the addition and subtraction of integers with algebra tiles. Lesson 1-5 introduces additive inverses: $x + (-x) = 0$. Models help students develop the concept (in Lesson 1-6) that adding the opposite of an integer is the same as subtracting the integer.

Students use a number line as well as tiles to model the addition of integers. Modeling integer addition helps students understand and remember the abstract rules for combining integers.
For $a \geq 0$ and $b \geq 0$, $a + b = |a| + |b|$.
For $a < 0$ and $b < 0$, $a + b = -(|a| + |b|)$.
For $a < 0$ and $b > 0$, if $|a| > |b|$,
$a + b = -(|a| - |b|)$; if $|b| \geq |a|$,
$a + b = (|b| - |a|)$.

In Lesson 1-6, students model with algebra tiles the subtraction of integers and learn that
$a - b = a + (-b)$ and $a - (-b) = a + b$.

## Lessons 1-7 and 1-8

### Inductive Reasoning and Look for a Pattern

In Lessons 1-7 and 1-8, students study inductive reasoning and patterns so that they can use these tools to help them derive and understand the rules for multiplying and dividing integers in Lesson 1-9.

Recall that consistency is a basic rule in algebra, so consistent patterns can often explain why algebra works the way it does. Students are introduced to inductive reasoning as a way to make conjectures about the way an established pattern continues. In Lesson 1-8, students make conjectures about various patterns. In later courses, students will learn that a formal mathematical inductive proof contains two parts: (1) proving that the statement is true for the first integer and (2) proving that if the statement is true for $n$, it must be true for $(n + 1)$.

## Lesson 1-9

### Multiplying and Dividing Integers

The skills learned in the previous two lessons are used in Lesson 1-9 to see how to multiply and divide integers, thereby completing the process of combining integers that was begun in Lessons 1-5 and 1-6.

## Lesson 1-10

### The Coordinate Plane

This lesson of the chapter expands students' knowledge of integers on a number line to include graphing integers in the coordinate plane. Students apply their knowledge of integers as they graph ordered pairs on a coordinate grid formed by the perpendicular intersection of two number lines. In Chapter 8 they will use these skills to graph linear functions. Graphing points reinforces what students have learned in this chapter about integers and the language of algebra.

For professional development tips visit our Web site **www.phschool.com**.

# Monitoring Progress

## Universal Access

### ▶ Preventing a Student from Falling Behind

These resources are particularly helpful in preventing a student from falling behind his or her appropriate math level. For a complete list of resources for this chapter, see page 1H.

#### Skills You Need for Chapter 1

Student Edition, p. 1
Teacher's Edition, p. 1

- Adding and subtracting whole numbers
- Comparing whole numbers
- Multiplying and dividing whole numbers
- Reading numbers on a number line

#### Skills Handbook

Student Edition, pp. 723–741
Teacher's Edition, pp. 723–741

- Multiplying Whole Numbers, p. 725

#### Reteaching Worksheets

There is a Reteaching worksheet for every lesson in this chapter.

- Chapter 1 Support File, Teaching Resources box
- See TE p. 1H for a complete list of resources.

#### Skills Intervention Kit with CD-ROM

| For | Use |
|---|---|
| Lessons 1-3, 1-9 | Whole Numbers |
| Lesson 1-10 | Pre-Algebra Basics |

#### Daily Cumulative Review Blackline Masters

There is a Daily Cumulative Review worksheet for every lesson in this chapter.

- See TE p. 1H for a complete list of resources.

### ▶ Accommodating Diverse Learning Styles

#### Tactile Learning

Use a number line made with masking tape on the floor. (Lesson 1-4)

Use algebra tiles to work problems. (Lesson 1-6)

#### Advanced Learner

Every lesson has at least one challenge problem.

Find the result of adding the absolute value of an integer other than zero to the absolute value of its opposite. (Lesson 1-6)

#### ELL (English Language Learner)

Compare *rank,* in reference to order of operations, to *taking a number* while waiting to be served. (Lesson 1-2)

Share knowledge of patterns present in computer codes or DNA. (Lesson 1-8)

#### Auditory Learning

Work with a partner to read aloud and discuss writing and evaluating variable expressions. (Lesson 1-3)

Say a pattern to oneself while working through a problem. (Lesson 1-7)

#### Visual Learning

Simplify expressions by drawing a circle around the first pair of numbers to be combined. (Lesson 1-2)

Sketch moves in problems involving plays, dives, or climbing. (Lesson 1-5)

# Aligning Assessment with Instruction

## Assessment Options

| | Chapter Opener | 1-1 | 1-2 | 1-3 | 1-4 | 1-5 | 1-6 | 1-7 | 1-8 | 1-9 | 1-10 | End |
|---|---|---|---|---|---|---|---|---|---|---|---|---|
| Chapter Project | ■ | | | ■ | | | ■ | | | | | ■ |
| Try This Exercises | | ■ | ■ | ■ | ■ | ■ | ■ | ■ | ■ | ■ | ■ | |
| Mixed Reviews | | ■ | ■ | ■ | ■ | ■ | ■ | ■ | ■ | ■ | ■ | |
| Checkpoints | | | | | ■ | | | | | ■ | | |
| Writing | | ■ | ■ | ■ | ■ | ■ | ■ | ■ | | ■ | ■ | ■ |
| Chapter Assessment | | | | | | | | | | | | ■ |
| Cumulative Review | | | | | | | | | | | | ■ |
| Standardized Test Prep | | ■ | ■ | | ■ | ■ | ■ | ■ | | ■ | ■ | |
| | Standardized Test Prep, p. 34 | | | | | | | | | | | |
| Computer Item Generator | Can be used to create custom-made practice or assessment at any time. | | | | | | | | | | | |

### Test-Taking Tips on Transparencies

- Get plenty of sleep the night before your test.
- Eat a good breakfast the morning of your test.
- Bring a watch. Plan to spend 1–2 minutes per question.
- If you are nervous, stop and take three deep breaths.
- Underline important words or phrases.
- Keep your scratch work neat and organized.
- Do easy computations with pencil and paper. Use a calculator for the rest, if permitted.
- Cross out answer choices you know are wrong.
- Do the easy questions first.
- Do not stop to work on difficult questions. Skip them and return to them later if you have time remaining.
- Change an answer only when you are sure your first choice is wrong.
- Unless you are told not to guess, mark an answer for every question.
- Be careful to mark each answer in the right place, and fill in the mark completely.
- Think positively by telling yourself, "I have studied and I know this. I will do well."

*Use with Standardized Test Prep and Chapter Assessments.*

## Correlation to Standardized Tests

| Lesson | | CAT5 | CTBS/5 TerraNova™ | ITBS | MAT7 | SAT9 | LOCAL OBJECTIVES |
|---|---|---|---|---|---|---|---|
| 1-1 | Variables and Expressions | | ■ | ■ | ■ | ■ | |
| 1-2 | The Order of Operations | | ■ | ■ | ■ | ■ | |
| 1-3 | Evaluating Expressions | | ■ | ■ | | ■ | |
| 1-4 | Integers and Absolute Value | ■ | ■ | ■ | ■ | ■ | |
| 1-5 | Adding Integers | ■ | ■ | ■ | ■ | ■ | |
| 1-6 | Subtracting Integers | ■ | ■ | ■ | ■ | ■ | |
| 1-7 | Inductive Reasoning | | | | | ■ | |
| 1-8 | Problem Solving Strategy: Look for a Pattern | ■ | ■ | | ■ | ■ | |
| 1-9 | Multiplying and Dividing Integers | ■ | ■ | ■ | ■ | ■ | |
| 1-10 | The Coordinate Plane | ■ | ■ | ■ | ■ | ■ | |

**CAT5** California Achievement Test, 5th edition
**CTBS TerraNova** Comprehensive Test of Basic Skills, 5th edition
**ITBS** Iowa Test of Basic Skills, Form M
**MAT7** Metropolitan Achievement Test, 7th edition
**SAT** Stanford Achievement Test, Advanced 1

For other standardized test correlations, follow the link to your state at **www.phschool.com**.

# Resources for Chapter 1

| | TEACHING RESOURCES BOX | | | | | | | | | | | | | | |
|---|---|---|---|---|---|---|---|---|---|---|---|---|---|---|---|
| | CHAPTER 1 SUPPORT FILE | | | | | | | | | | | | | | |
| | Practice | Reteach | Enrichment | Project Manager | Checkpoints | Cumulative Review | Chapter Assessment | Alternative Assessment | Cumulative Assessment | Lesson Planners Plus | Daily Cum Review | Teaching Transparencies | Warm-Up Transparencies | Help at Home | SE Answers on Transparencies |
| Begin Chapter | | | | ■ | | | | | | ■ | | | | | |
| 1-1 | ■ | ■ | ■ | | | | | | | ■ | ■ | | ■ | | ■ |
| 1-2 | ■ | ■ | ■ | | | | | | | ■ | ■ | 22 | ■ | | ■ |
| 1-3 | ■ | ■ | ■ | | | | | | | ■ | ■ | 36 | ■ | | ■ |
| 1-4 | ■ | ■ | ■ | | ■ | | | | | ■ | ■ | 7, 37 | ■ | ■ | ■ |
| 1-5 | ■ | ■ | ■ | | | | | | | ■ | ■ | 16, 23 | ■ | | ■ |
| 1-6 | ■ | ■ | ■ | | | | | | | ■ | ■ | 23 | ■ | | ■ |
| 1-7 | ■ | ■ | ■ | | | | | | | ■ | ■ | | ■ | | ■ |
| 1-8 | ■ | ■ | ■ | | | | | | | ■ | ■ | | ■ | | ■ |
| 1-9 | ■ | ■ | ■ | | ■ | | | | | ■ | ■ | 24 | ■ | ■ | ■ |
| 1-10 | ■ | ■ | ■ | | | | | | | ■ | ■ | 2, 38 | ■ | | ■ |
| End Chapter | | | | | | ■ | ■ (2 forms) | ■ | After Ch. 3, 6, 9, 13 | | | | | | |

Also available for use with the chapter:

Solution Key
Computational Practice Skills Booklet
Mathematics Standardized Test Prep, Student Edition and Teacher's Edition
Overhead Manipulatives Kit
Practice Workbook
Algebra Readiness Kit
Student Manipulatives Kit
Test-Taking Tips on Transparencies
Assessment Success Kit
Teaching Aids and Letters
Graphing Calculator Handbook
Spanish Resources
Success-Building Puzzle and Problem Masters

## TECHNOLOGY

**Computer Item Generator with Standardized Test Prep**
CD-ROM with an unlimited supply of questions with varying degrees of difficulty for customized practice sheets, quizzes, and tests.

**Resource Pro® with Planning Express®**
CD-ROM with complete classroom planning tool and teaching resources for customizing and planning lessons.

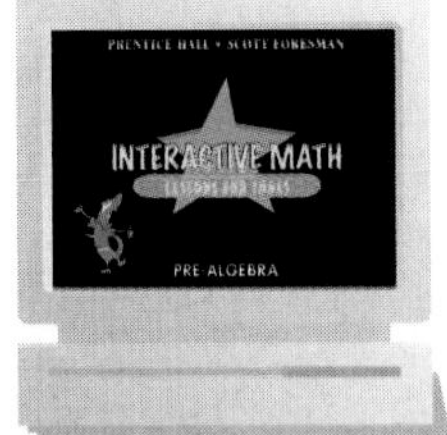


**Interactive Math Lessons and Tools**
CD-ROM with lessons and tools to make abstract concepts visual and accessible.

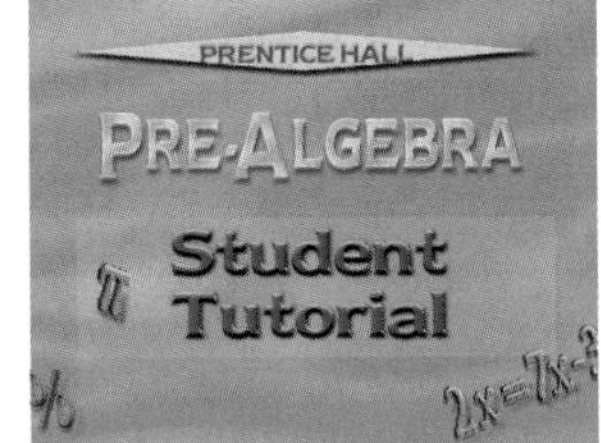


**Student Tutorial**
Test preparation software for students on CD-ROM with management system for teachers; includes Secondary Math Lab Toolkit™.

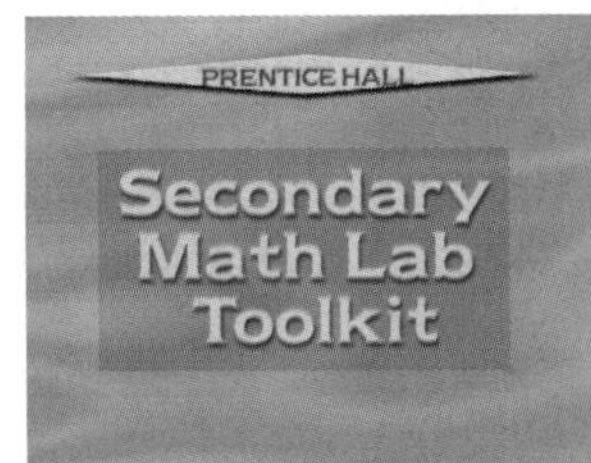


**Secondary Math Lab Toolkit™ with Integrated Math Labs**
Integrated software package with linkable math tools for exploring key concepts.

Also available for use with the chapter:

Math Blaster® Pre-Algebra CD-ROM
Video Fieldtrips, Vol. I: Algebra Applications
Video Fieldtrips, Vol. II: Geometry Applications
Wide World of Mathematics CD-ROM
Wide World of Mathematics Video

### *Web Extension*
**www.phschool.com**

**For Students**
- Chapter Support with Internet Links
- Internet Activities

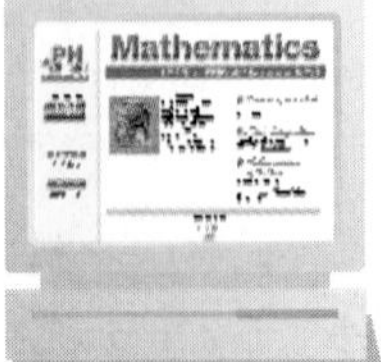


**For Teachers**
- Curriculum Support
- Professional Development
- Product Information
- Regional Support Information

# Skills You Need for Chapter 1

### ▶ *Adding and subtracting whole numbers*  Use before Lessons 1-2, 1-5, and 1-6.

**Find each sum or difference.**

1. 7 − 6  1
2. 9 + 2  11
3. 15 − 4  11
4. 11 + 8  19
5. 20 − 7  13
6. 32 + 8  40
7. 32 − 15  17
8. 26 + 17  43
9. 67 + 109  176
10. 82 − 54  28
11. 44 + 122  166
12. 91 − 16  75

### ▶ *Comparing whole numbers*  Use before Lessons 1-2 and 1-4.

**Compare. Use >, <, or = to complete each statement.**

13. 5 ■ 2  >
14. 1 ■ 0  >
15. 14 ■ 17  <
16. 6 + 12 ■ 7 + 13  <
17. 10 − 2 ■ 27 − 18  <
18. 4 × 7 ■ 2 × 14  =

### ▶ *Multiplying and dividing whole numbers*  Use before Lessons 1-2 and 1-9.

**Find each product or quotient.**

19. 36 ÷ 3  12
20. 10 × 3  30
21. 7(4)  28
22. 25 ÷ 5  5
23. 12 · 8  96
24. $7\overline{)35}$  5
25. 20 · 10  200
26. $9\overline{)720}$  80
27. 124 ÷ 4  31
28. $12\overline{)156}$  13
29. 4 · 12 · 10  480
30. 132 ÷ 11  12

### ▶ *Reading numbers on a number line*  Use before Lesson 1-4.

**What is the distance of each point from zero on the number line?**

31. *A*  1
32. *B*  4
33. *C*  7
34. *D*  10

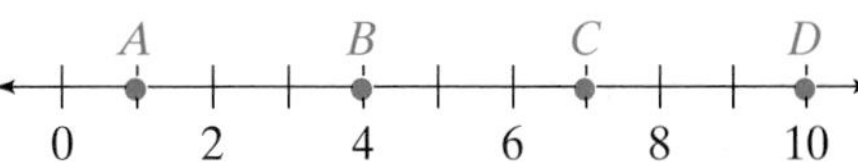




## Skills You Need

### Adding and subtracting whole numbers

**In Lesson 1-2** students will simplify expressions and use the order of operations.

**In Lesson 1-5** students will use models and rules to add integers.

**In Lesson 1-6** students will use models and rules to subtract integers.

### Comparing whole numbers

**In Lesson 1-2** students will simplify expressions and use the order of operations.

**In Lesson 1-4** students will graph integers and find opposites and absolute values.

### Multiplying and dividing whole numbers

**In Lesson 1-2** students will simplify expressions and use the order of operations.

**In Lesson 1-9** students will look for a pattern to solve a problem.

### Reading numbers

**In Lesson 1-4** students will graph integers and find opposites and absolute values.

## Skills Trace

| SKILL | INTRODUCED | DEVELOPED IN LESSON(S) | REVIEWED/REINFORCED |
|---|---|---|---|
| Variable expressions | 1-1 | 1-3, 2-3 | pp. 12, 21, 92 |
| Using the order of operations | 1-2 | 1-3 | pp. 16, 21, 28, 33, 68, 107, 201 |
| Representing, graphing, and ordering integers; opposites and absolute value | 1-4 | 1-10 | pp. 28, 33, 54, 68, 107, 130, 197, 268, 321 |
| Calculating with integers | 1-5 | 1-6, 1-9 | pp. 33, 39, 43, 54, 68, 73, 92, 97, 112, 126, 197 |
| Writing rules for patterns | 1-7 | 1-8, 1-9 | pp. 43, 88, 140, 149, 193, 197 |

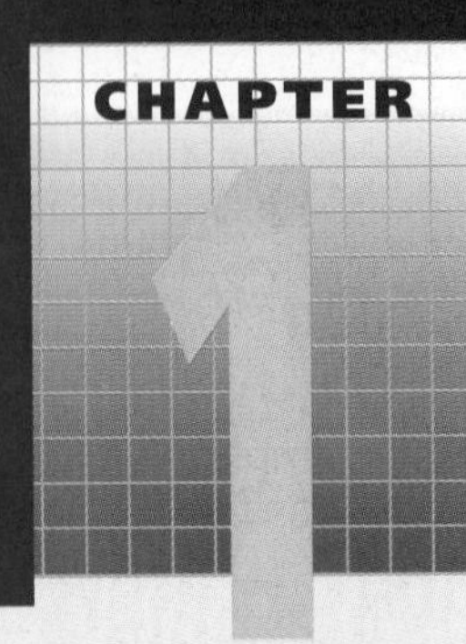

# Algebraic Expressions and Integers

## Connecting to Students' Lives

Ask students if they have ever read a story or seen a movie or television show that involved a code. Discuss the picture that opens this chapter and the information about it in the text. Invite them to conjecture about the process they might use to decode a message.

## Interdisciplinary Connections

The Chapter Project connects math, art, technology, and cryptography (the study of codes). You may want to have students find articles in periodicals or on the Web that discuss the pictured sculpture and give the complete text of the code as well as the parts that have been decoded to date.

## About the Project

The Chapter Project directs students to apply their analytic skills to writing and deciphering codes.

CHAPTER 1

# Algebraic Expressions and Integers

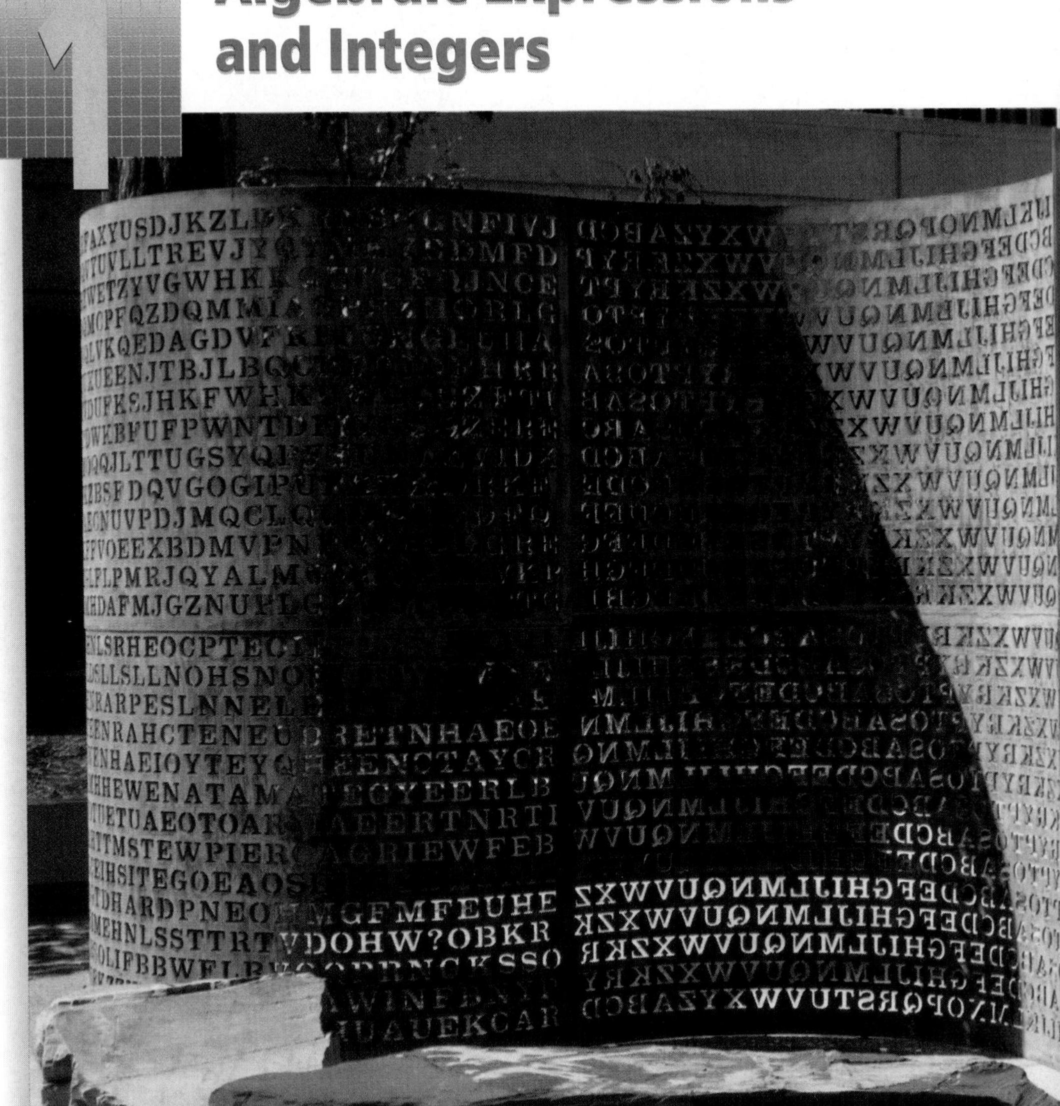

**What you'll learn in this chapter:**

- How to use variables and variable expressions
- How to perform operations with integers
- How to graph points in the coordinate plane

***Web Extension***
**www.phschool.com**

**For Students**
Chapter Support with Internet links
Interactive Activities

**For Teachers**
Curriculum Support
Professional Development
Product Information
Regional Support Information

# Cure for the Common Code

A special sculpture stands outside the headquarters of the United States Central Intelligence Agency (CIA) in Langley, Virginia. Carved in the copper sculpture is a message in secret code. The code is so complex that for many years even CIA agents could not figure it out. The sculptor, James Sanborn, provided the secret agents with a challenge they could appreciate.

***Invent a Secret Code*** For the chapter project, you will decode computer writing and write in a code used by Julius Caesar. Then you'll invent a code of your own.

*Steps to help you complete the project*


p. 16 ACTIVITY: READING

p. 33 ACTIVITY: WRITING

p. 54 ACTIVITY: CREATING

p. 55 FINISHING THE CHAPTER PROJECT

***Web Extension***
**www.phschool.com**

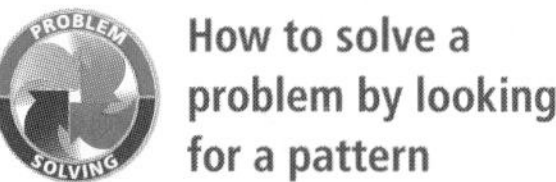

How to solve a problem by looking for a pattern

*The Chapter Project is optional and may be assigned at your discretion.*

Ask students:

- Have you ever made up or used a code to communicate in secret with your friends?
- Have you ever tried to figure out, or break, a code?
- How could the fact that the letter "e" is the most common letter in English help you to decode a message?
- What other facts do you know that might help you analyze a code?

Distribute a copy of the Project Manager and Scoring Rubric to help students get an overview of the project.

Review the scoring rubric with students.

## Project Notebook

Encourage students to keep all project-related materials in a separate folder or notebook. Call attention to the fact that they will find much useful information on the Web site **www.phschool.com**.

**Tracking the Project** Set benchmark deadlines for students to show you their work in progress.

*Available in the Chapter 1 Support File in the Teaching Resources box.*

### Project Manager and Scoring Rubric

**Getting Started** You will be creating a poster displaying a code you created. Read about the project in your textbook. As you work on the project, you will need materials to make your poster and materials to record your work.

**Checklist and Suggestions**

| | | |
|---|---|---|
| ❑ | Decode an ASCII message. | Replace each number with a letter. |
| ❑ | Write a letter to a friend in Caesar Cipher. | Write the letter in regular English first. |
| ❑ | Invent a cipher and make a key. | Be creative in choosing your symbols, but keep them easy to draw. |
| ❑ | Write a message in your cipher. | Use your key to translate your message. |
| ❑ | Make your poster. | Be sure to clearly explain how your cipher works and include a sample. |
| ❑ | Share your poster with a friend. | Make any necessary changes. |

**Scoring Rubric**

3 You translate the ASCII code accurately and use the Caesar Cipher correctly to write a letter. Your poster is complete, descriptive, well-organized, and easy to read. Your cipher is creative, accurate, and not overly complicated.

2 You make minor errors in translating the ASCII code, in using the Caesar Cipher, or in inventing your own code. Your poster is complete and descriptive, but could be better organized or easier to read.

1 You translate codes incorrectly. Your poster is incomplete and lacks organization.

0 Major elements of the project are incomplete or missing.

**Your Evaluation of the Project** Evaluate your work, based on the Scoring Rubric.

**Teacher's Evaluation of the Project**



## Scoring Rubric

3 You translate the ASCII code accurately and use the Caesar Cipher correctly to write a letter. Your poster is complete, descriptive, well-organized, and easy to read. Your cipher is creative, accurate, and not overly complicated.

2 You make minor errors in translating the ASCII code, in using the Caesar Cipher, or in inventing your own code. Your poster is complete and descriptive, but could be better organized or easier to read.

1 You translate codes incorrectly. Your poster is incomplete and lacks organization.

0 Major elements of the project are incomplete or missing.

# 1-1

## Getting Ready

**Key Terms and Symbols** variable, variable expression

**Resources** A complete list of resources for this lesson is on p. 1H.

### Daily Skills Warm-Up

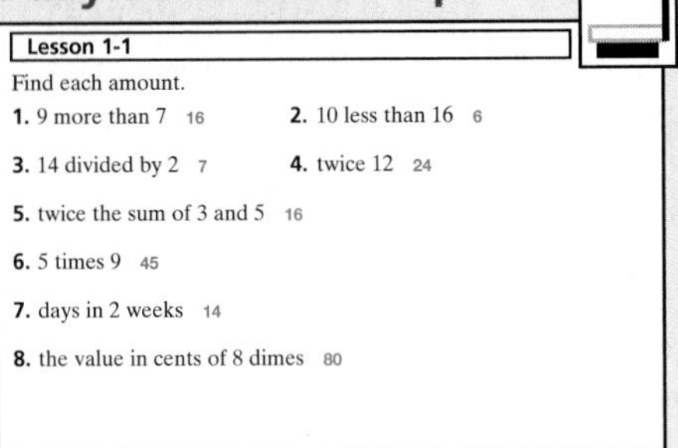

Lesson 1-1

Find each amount.

1. 9 more than 7 16
2. 10 less than 16 6
3. 14 divided by 2 7
4. twice 12 24
5. twice the sum of 3 and 5 16
6. 5 times 9 45
7. days in 2 weeks 14
8. the value in cents of 8 dimes 80

### Background for the Lesson

A given variable may occur more than once in a variable expression. The variable $h$ occurs twice in the expression $3h + 5 + 2h$. If a variable occurs more than once in an expression, its value is the same for each time it occurs. If you substitute a value of 6 for $h$ in the above expression, the value of each $h$ is 6.

## 1 Focus

### Connecting to Students' Lives

Explain that variables are useful to represent unknowns. Suppose that the last time your height was measured you were 61 inches tall. You know you have grown since that time, but you do not know how much. Your height can be represented by the expression $61 + x$, where $x$ is the unknown number of inches that you have grown.

### Connecting to Prior Knowledge

Ask students to give simple formulas they remember, such as those for finding distance ($d = rt$) or the area of a rectangle ($A = \ell w$). Ask them to name the variables in the formulas they recall.



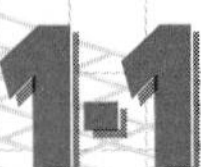

# Variables and Expressions

### What You'll Learn

1. To identify variables, numerical expressions, and variable expressions
2. To write variable expressions for word phrases

### . . . And Why

To use the language of algebra to model real-world problems

## PART 1 Identifying Numerical and Variable Expressions

*Gas Mileage* How many miles can you drive on ten gallons of gas? The answer depends on the type of vehicle you drive. The table shows some typical data.

| Vehicle Type | Miles | Gallons | Miles per Gallon |
|---|---|---|---|
| Subcompact | 330 | 10 | $330 \div 10$ |
| Compact | 300 | 10 | $300 \div 10$ |
| Mid-size sedan | 245 | 10 | $245 \div 10$ |
| Sport utility vehicle | 175 | 10 | $175 \div 10$ |
| Pickup truck | 160 | 10 | $160 \div 10$ |

The last column gives a *numerical expression* for each vehicle's miles per gallon.

If you don't know the number of miles, you can use a *variable* to stand for the number. Then you can write a *variable expression* for miles per gallon.

variable → $m$ ← miles on 10 gallons

variable expression → $m \div 10$ ← miles per gallon

A **variable** is a letter that stands for a number. A **variable expression** is a mathematical phrase that uses variables, numerals, and operation symbols.

#### EXAMPLE 1

**Identify each expression as a *numerical expression* or a *variable expression*. For a variable expression, name the variable.**

**a.** $50 - 5$

numerical expression

**b.** $c - 5$

Variable expression; $c$ is the variable.



# Tools to Monitor Progress

### BEFORE THE LESSON

**To check prerequisite skills:**

- Adding and subtracting whole numbers
- Multiplying and dividing whole numbers

**Skills Intervention Kit,** Whole Numbers

### DURING THE LESSON

**To check understanding:**

**Try This** exercises on student page

- **Additional Example 1**

Identify these expressions as numerical or variable expressions. Name any variables.

**a.** $7 \times 3$ **b.** $4t$

a. numerical expresssion
b. variable expression; $t$, variable

**■ Try This** Identify each expression as a *numerical expression* or a *variable expression*. For a variable expression, name the variable.

1. $8 \div x$ Variable expression; $x$ is the variable.
2. $100 \times 6$ numerical expression
3. $d + 43 - 9$ Variable expression; $d$ is the variable.

## Part 2 Writing Variable Expressions

You can translate word phrases into variable expressions.

| Word Phrase | Variable Expression |
|---|---|
| Nine more than a number $y$ | $y + 9$ |
| 4 less than a number $n$ | $n - 4$ |
| A number $z$ times three | $z \cdot 3$ or $3z$ or $3(z)$ |
| A number $a$ divided by 12 | $a \div 12$ or $\frac{a}{12}$ |
| 5 times the quantity 4 plus a number $c$ | $5 \cdot (4 + c)$ or $5(4 + c)$ |

### Writing Math

You can translate many words for operations into symbols.

| | |
|---|---|
| total | + |
| more than | + |
| increased by | + |
| difference | − |
| fewer than | − |
| less than | − |
| decreased by | − |
| product | × or · or ( ) |
| times | × or · or ( ) |
| quotient | ÷ or — |
| divided by | ÷ or — |

REAL-WORLD CONNECTION

### ■ Example 2

*Science* **The fastest dinosaur may have been *Ornithomimus*, which could run about 60 ft in a second. Write a variable expression for the distance *Ornithomimus* could run.**

**Words** 60 times number of seconds

Let $s$ = number of seconds.

**Expression** $60 \cdot s$

The variable expression $60 \cdot s$, or $60s$, describes the distance in feet *Ornithomimus* could run.

*Ornithomimus* was an ostrich-like oviraptor about 7 ft tall. Its long tail acted as a counterbalance and as a stabilizer during fast turns.

**■ Try This**

4. Bagels cost \$.50 each. Write a variable expression for the cost of $b$ bagels. $0.50b$
5. *Measurement* Write a variable expression for the number of hours in $m$ minutes. $\frac{m}{60}$



# 2 Teach

## Part 1 Teaching Notes

Verify that students understand the table by asking them to make a sentence from the information. Example: A compact car can go 300 mi on 10 gal of gas.

### ■ Example 1

**Build understanding.** Ask: How can you change a numerical expression to a variable expression? Change one of the numerals into a variable.

**Visual Learning** Suggest that students copy each expression on their papers and then circle any variables.

**ELL** Ask students what letter is left out when the word *number* is changed into *numerical*. b

## Part 2 Teaching Notes

Have students use the word phrases in **Writing Math** with counters or pencils to act out a variable expression. (Marie has 2 more than Jesse.) Then have students write the phrases with initials and variables ($M$ has $2 + J$).

**Extension** Challenge students to explain what symbols are used to represent the words *the quantity* in a variable expression. parentheses

**Error Prevention** A common error is to write the word phrase "4 less than $n$" as "$4 - n$." Point out that *less than* is not the same as *less*. Suggest that students think of a value for the variable as they read word phrases such as "4 less than 10." Then they can use that same value to check their variable expression.

**Connecting to Geometry** Ask students to write a variable expression for the perimeter of a square with side $s$. $4s$

### • Additional Example 2

Write a variable expression for the cost of $p$ pens priced at \$1.29 each. \$1.29$p$

### AFTER THE LESSON

**To assess knowledge:**

**Lesson Quiz**

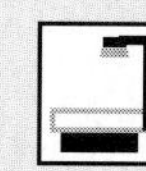

Write a variable expression for each word phrase.

1. the total of $h$ and 56 $h + 56$
2. three less than $d$ $d - 3$
3. $p$ decreased by three $p - 3$
4. $a$ divided by 7 $\frac{a}{7}$
5. the quotient of y and 24 $\frac{y}{24}$

• For enrichment and reteaching options see Resources on p. 1H.

# 3 Practice/Assess

## Assignment Guide

To provide flexible scheduling, this lesson can be divided into parts.

▼ Part 1

**Core** 1–3, 10–15

✪ **Extension** 40

▼ Part 2

**Core** 4–9, 16–39, 41–44

✪ **Extension** 45–49

Mixed Review can be assigned at any time for maintenance.

**ELL** Verify that students understand these key words: *product, quotient, value.*

## Exercises

**Exercises 30–35** Review days in a week, cents in a nickel, inches in a foot.

**Test Prep Exercise 42** Suggest that students use a value, such as 3 years ago, and then test that value in the answer choices.

## ✪ Challenge

What does the variable expression $a \bullet 365 \bullet 24 \bullet 60$ mean, where $a$ represents your age in years? about how old you are in minutes

## Closure

A variable is a letter that stands for a number. A variable expression is a mathematical phrase that uses variables numerals, and operation symbols.

### Daily Cumulative Review

**Mixed Review** *(From Last Year)*

**Find each sum or difference.**

1. $8 + 4$ 12
2. $7 - 3$ 4
3. $87 - 29$ 58
4. $56 + 139$ 195
5. $46 + 97$ 143
6. $175 - 78$ 97

**Find each product or quotient.**

7. $6 \times 8$ 48
8. $63 \div 9$ 7
9. $7 \cdot 6$ 42
10. $169 \div 13$ 13
11. $8\overline{)64}$ 8
12. $56 \div 8$ 7

**Compare. Use >, <, or = to complete each statement.**

13. $8 < 9$
14. $8 > 4$
15. $18 - 6 > 24 - 13$
16. $3 > 0$
17. $12 + 16 < 10 + 30$
18. $6 \times 4 = 3 \times 8$

**Complete each statement.**

19. 1 ft = 12 in.
20. 1 lb = 16 oz
21. 1 yd = 3 ft
22. 1 yr = 365 days
23. 1 kg = 1,000 g
24. 1 L = 1,000 mL

**Write a number sentence and use it to find each amount.**

25. twelve more than 3 $3 + 12 = 15$
26. eight less than 12 $12 - 8 = 4$
27. the sum of six and thirteen $6 + 13 = 19$
28. the difference of eleven and five $11 - 5 = 6$
29. nine subtracted from seventeen $17 - 9 = 8$



# Exercises

## Check Understanding

**Identify each expression as a *numerical expression* or a *variable expression*. For a variable expression, name the variable.**

1. $b + 6$ Variable expression; $b$ is the variable.
2. $80 \div 8$ numerical expression
3. $14 - n$ Variable expression; $n$ is the variable.

**Write an expression for each number of eggs.**

4. two dozen eggs $2 \cdot 12$
5. five dozen eggs $5 \cdot 12$
6. $d$ dozen eggs $d \cdot 12$

**Write an expression for each word phrase.**

7. 16 more than $m$ $m + 16$
8. 6 divided by $z$ $\frac{6}{z}$
9. the product of $c$ and 3 $3c$

## Practice and Problem Solving

**Identify each expression as a *numerical expression* or a *variable expression*. For a variable expression, name the variable.**

10. $14 \times 14$ numerical expression
11. $d + 53$ Variable expression; $d$ is the variable.
12. $\frac{g}{9}$ Variable expression; $g$ is the variable.
13. $100x$ Variable expression; $x$ is the variable.
14. $8 + 8 + 8 + 8$ numerical expression
15. $92 - 16 - p$ Variable expression; $p$ is the variable.

**Write a variable expression for each word phrase.**

16. $m$ more than nineteen $19 + m$
17. 8 less than $z$ $z - 8$
18. $n$ divided by 3 $\frac{n}{3}$
19. 3 divided by $n$ $\frac{3}{n}$
20. the sum of five and $a$ $5 + a$
21. thirty-two times $g$ $32g$
22. two less than a number $x$ $x - 2$
23. $x$ less than 2 $2 - x$
24. $s$ divided by fifty-four $\frac{s}{54}$
25. twelve times a number $v$ $12v$
26. the product of 10 and a number $p$ $10p$
27. a number $m$ increased by 250 $m + 250$
28. six subtracted from a number $k$ $k - 6$
29. the quotient of 100 divided by a number $z$ $\frac{100}{z}$

**Write an expression for each quantity.**

30. the number of days in 4 weeks $4 \cdot 7$
31. the number of days in $w$ weeks $7w$
32. the value in cents of 7 nickels $7 \cdot 5$
33. the value in cents of $n$ nickels $5n$
34. the number of feet in 100 inches $\frac{100}{12}$
35. the number of feet in $i$ inches $\frac{i}{12}$



## Alternative Assessment

Have students write in their journals an explanation of the difference between a *variable* and a *variable expression*.

*Mathematical Modeling* **In each model, the red line represents a variable expression. Match each expression with its model.**

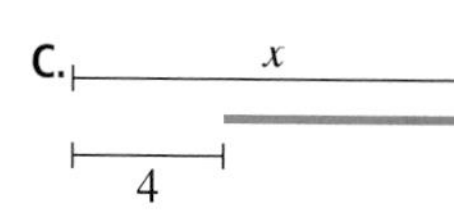

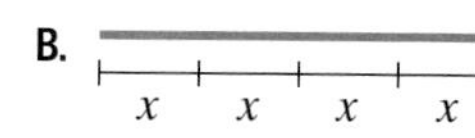

A. 4, $x$

B. $x$, $x$, $x$, $x$

C. $x$, 4

D. $x$

36. $4x$ B

37. $4 + x$ A

38. $\frac{x}{4}$ D

39. $x - 4$ C

40. *Writing* How are numerical expressions and variable expressions similar? How are they different? Both use numbers and operation symbols; only variable expressions use variables.

41. Mia has \$20 less than Brandi. Brandi has $d$ dollars. Write a variable expression for the amount of money Mia has. $d - 20$

42. **TEST PREP** Pam is 15 years old. Which expression gives Pam's age $p$ years ago? C

A. $p - 15$ B. $p + 15$ C. $15 - p$ D. $\frac{p}{15}$

**Use the calorie chart for Exercises 43 and 44.**

43. Write a variable expression for the number of calories in $e$ eggs and one slice of bread. $110e + 55$

44. Write a variable expression for the number of calories in a fruit salad made from $a$ apples and $b$ bananas. $70a + 100b$

**Calorie Chart**

| Food | Calories |
|---|---|
| Bread slice | 55 |
| Apple | 70 |
| Banana | 100 |
| Egg | 110 |

45. There are twice as many sophomores as freshmen.
   a. If there are $f$ freshmen, how many sophomores are there? $2f$
   b. If there are $s$ sophomores, how many freshmen are there? $\frac{s}{2}$

46. *Error Analysis* A student wrote the variable expression $n - 5$ for the word phrase *n less than fi e*. Explain the student's error. Answers may vary. Sample: The student confused the positions of $n$ and 5.

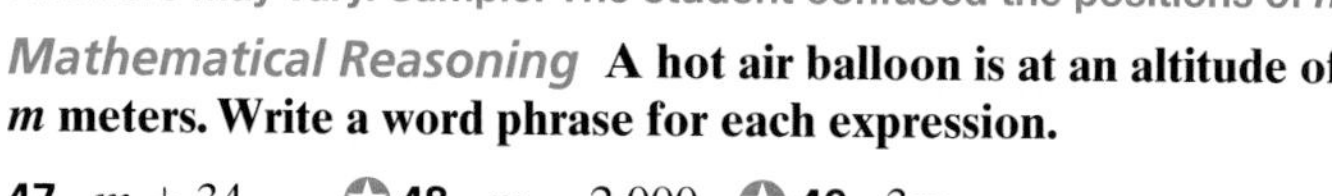

*Mathematical Reasoning* **A hot air balloon is at an altitude of *m* meters. Write a word phrase for each expression.**

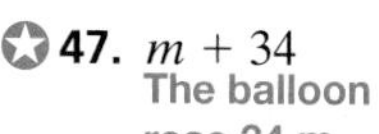

47. $m + 34$ The balloon rose 34 m.

48. $m - 2{,}000$ The balloon fell 2,000 m.

49. $3m$ The balloon tripled its altitude.

## Mixed Review

**Compute.** *(Previous Course)*

50. $105 + 25 + 95$ 225

51. $3 \times 6 \times 4$ 72

52. $8 + 1 - 1$ 8

53. $648 - 573$ 75

54. $169 \div 13$ 13

55. $22{,}534 - 12{,}971$ 9,563

56. *Choose a Strategy* A customer buys orange juice for \$.95 and two apples for \$.55 each. She gives the cashier a five-dollar bill. How much change should the cashier give the customer? \$2.95

See also Extra Practice section.



## Practice

**Write an expression for each quantity.**

1. the value in cents of 5 quarters 25(5)
2. the value in cents of $q$ quarters $25q$
3. the number of months in 7 years 12(7)
4. the number of months in $y$ years $12y$
5. the number of gallons in 21 quarts $\frac{21}{4}$
6. the number of gallons in $q$ quarts $\frac{q}{4}$

**Write a variable expression for each word phrase.**

7. 9 less than $k$ $k - 9$
8. $m$ divided by 6 $\frac{m}{6}$
9. twice $x$ $2x$
10. 4 more than twice $x$ $2x + 4$
11. the sum of eighteen and $b$ $18 + b$
12. three times the quantity 2 plus $a$ $3(2 + a)$

**Tell whether each expression is a numerical expression or a variable expression. For a variable expression, name the variable.**

13. $4d$ variable; $d$
14. $74 + 8$ numerical
15. $\frac{4(9)}{6}$ numerical
16. $14 - p$ variable; $p$
17. $5k - 9$ variable; $k$
18. $3 + 3 + 3 + 3$ numerical
19. $19 + 3(12)$ numerical
20. $25 - 9 + x$ variable; $x$

**The room temperature is *c* degrees centigrade. Write a word phrase for each expression.**

21. $c + 15$ 15°C warmer than the room temperature
22. $c - 7$ 7°C cooler than the room temperature



## Reteaching

A *variable* is a letter that stands for a number.

Thomas needs \$2 to ride the bus to Videoland. How much can he spend on video games for each amount in the table?

| Thomas has | Thomas can spend | |
|---|---|---|
| | Expression | Amount |
| \$5 | $5 - 2$ | \$3 |
| \$7 | $7 - 2$ | \$5 |
| \$10 | $10 - 2$ | \$8 |
| $d$ | $d - 2$ | $d - 2$ |

The letter $d$ is a variable that stands for the amount of money Thomas has. The expression $d - 2$ is a *variable expression*. It has a variable ($d$), a numeral (2), and an operation symbol (−).

Videoland tokens cost one dollar for 4. How many tokens can Jennifer buy for each amount of money in the table?

| | Jennifer has | Tokens Jennifer can buy | |
|---|---|---|---|
| | | Expression | Amount |
| 1. | \$5 | 4(5) | 20 |
| 2. | \$8 | 4(8) | 32 |
| 3. | \$6 | 4(6) | 24 |
| 4. | $d$ dollars | $4(d)$ | $4d$ |

**Write a variable expression for each word phrase.**

5. $h$ divided by 7 $\frac{h}{7}$
6. $j$ decreased by 9 $j - 9$
7. twice $x$ $2x$
8. two more than $y$ $y + 2$
9. the quotient of 42 and a number $s$ $\frac{42}{s}$
10. the product of a number $d$ and 16 $16d$



## Enrichment

To find your way through the maze, look for the word phrase that corresponds to each numbered junction. Move in the direction of the letter (A or B) beside the correct variable expression.

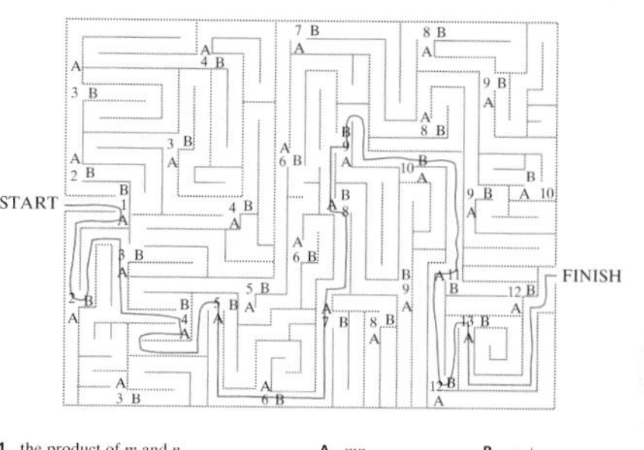


| | | A | B |
|---|---|---|---|
| 1. | the product of $m$ and $n$ | A. $mn$ | B. $m + n$ |
| 2. | two less than $k$ | A. $2 - k$ | B. $k - 2$ |
| 3. | the sum of $a$ and $b$ | A. $a + b$ | B. $ab$ |
| 4. | $h$ increased by 10 | A. $h + 10$ | B. $h(10)$ |
| 5. | the quotient of $x$ and 4 | A. $x \div 4$ | B. $x(4)$ |
| 6. | eight more than $p$ | A. $8(p)$ | B. $p + 8$ |
| 7. | the difference of $y$ and 3 | A. $y - 3$ | B. $y \div 3$ |
| 8. | twenty decreased by $c$ | A. $20 - c$ | B. $20 + c$ |
| 9. | twice the difference of $h$ and 5 | A. $2h - 5$ | B. $2(h - 5)$ |
| 10. | $t$ less than two | A. $t - 2$ | B. $2 - t$ |
| 11. | $k$ increased by twice $x$ | A. $k + 2x$ | B. $k + 2 + x$ |
| 12. | $s$ divided by $n$ | A. $n \div s$ | B. $s \div n$ |
| 13. | $y$ times the sum of 2 and $l$ | A. $y(2 + l)$ | B. $(y + 2)l$ |

# 1-2

## Getting Ready

**Resources** A complete list of resources for this lesson is on p. 1H.

### Daily Skills Warm-Up

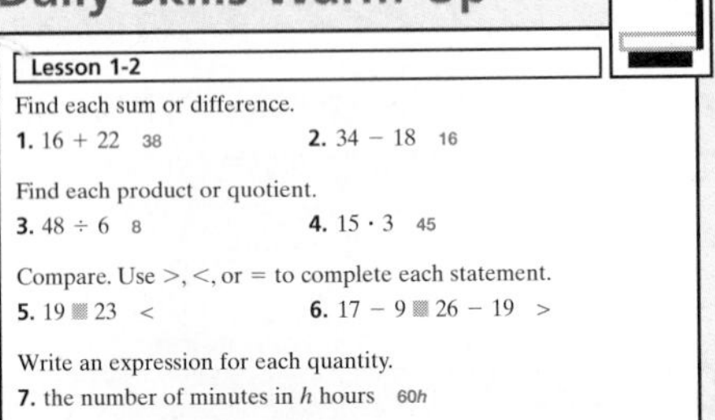

Lesson 1-2

Find each sum or difference.

1. 16 + 22 38
2. 34 − 18 16

Find each product or quotient.

3. 48 ÷ 6 8
4. 15 · 3 45

Compare. Use >, <, or = to complete each statement.

5. 19 ■ 23 <
6. 17 − 9 ■ 26 − 19 >

Write an expression for each quantity.

7. the number of minutes in $h$ hours 60$h$
8. the value in cents of $q$ quarters 25$q$

### Background for the Lesson

A popular mnemonic device for the order of operations is PMDAS (Please, My Dear Aunt Sally). The initials stand for Parentheses first, then Multiplication and Division (whichever comes first), and finally Addition and Subtraction (whichever comes first).

## 1 Focus

### Investigate

Discuss with students the importance of consistency in mathematics. For example, 2 + 12 ÷ 6 must always have the same value, 4. The order of operations ensures that the value of an expression is always the same, regardless of who calculates the value.

### Connecting to Students' Lives

Ask students if they can think of any rules similar to the order of operations that affect their lives. Driving rules are an example. Ask students to comment on what driving would be like if all drivers did not drive on the designated side of the road.

### Connecting to Prior Knowledge

Call attention to the fact that this lesson contains many numerical expressions, but no variable expressions (until the Mixed Review).





# 1-2 The Order of Operations

**What You'll Learn**

1. To use the order of operations
2. To use grouping symbols

**. . . And Why**

To find the value of an expression with more than one operation

## *Investigate*

EXPERIMENTING WITH ORDER

In most languages, the meaning of words depends on their order. For example, "sign the check" is not the same as "check the sign."

Similarly, order is important in the language of mathematics.

1. *Mental Math* Find the value of the expression $3 + 5 \times 2$. 13 or 16
2. *Analyze* What answer do you get to Question 1 if you multiply before adding? If you add before multiplying? 13; 16
3. *Critical Thinking* How does the order in which you do the operations affect your answer? Answers may vary. Sample: Different orders of operations can give different answers.

## PART 1 Using the Order of Operations

The order in which you perform operations can affect the value of an expression. To avoid confusion, mathematicians have agreed on an **order of operations.** Multiply and divide first. Then add and subtract.

To *simplify* an expression means to replace the expression with the simplest name for its value.

**EXAMPLE 1**

**Simplify 4 + 15 ÷ 3.**

$4 + 15 \div 3$

$4 + 5$ First divide.

$9$ Then add.

**TRY THIS** Simplify each expression.

4. $2 + 5 \times 3$ 17
5. $12 \div 3 - 1$ 3
6. $10 - 1 \cdot 7$ 3



# Tools to Monitor Progress

### BEFORE THE LESSON

**To check prerequisite skills:**

- Comparing whole numbers
- Adding and subtracting whole numbers
- Multiplying and dividing whole numbers

**Skills You Need,** p. 1

**Skills Handbook,** pp. 723, 725, 726

**Skills Intervention Kit,** Whole Numbers

### DURING THE LESSON

**To check understanding:**

**Try This** exercises on student page

- **Additional Example 1**

  Simplify 8 − 2 • 2. 4

When operations have the same rank in the order of operations, do them from left to right.

## Example 2

**Simplify $3 \cdot 5 - 8 \div 4 + 6$.**

$3 \cdot 5 - 8 \div 4 + 6$

$15 - 2 + 6$ Multiply and divide from left to right.

$13 + 6$ Add and subtract from left to right.

$19$ Add.

**Try This** Simplify each expression.

7. $4 - 1 \cdot 2 + 6 \div 3$ 4

8. $5 + 6 \cdot 4 \div 3 - 1$ 12

## Part 2 Using Grouping Symbols

Grouping symbols, such as parentheses, ( ), and brackets, [ ], indicate order. A fraction bar also is a grouping symbol, since $\frac{4+2}{3} = (4 + 2) \div 3$. Always work inside grouping symbols first.

### Order of Operations

1. Work inside grouping symbols.
2. Multiply and divide in order from left to right.
3. Add and subtract in order from left to right.

*Calculator HINT*

Many calculators use the order of operations. To test yours, enter 10 − 4 ÷ 2.

If the answer is 8, then your calculator uses the order of operations.

If the answer is 3, then your calculator does *not* use the order of operations.

## Example 3

**Simplify $10 \div [9 - (2 \cdot 2)]$.**

$10 \div [9 - (2 \cdot 2)]$

$10 \div [9 - 4]$ Multiply within parentheses.

$10 \div 5$ Subtract within brackets.

$2$ Divide.

**Try This** Simplify each expression.

9. $2[(13 - 4) \div 3]$ 6

10. $1 + \frac{10 - 2}{4}$ 3



# 2 Teach

## Part 1 Teaching Notes

Encourage students to take the time to write down intermediate steps when simplifying expressions. Writing down intermediate steps improves accuracy. Remind them that accuracy is more important than speed in mathematics.

### Example 1

**Build understanding.** Ask: In English, words are read from left to right. Are the math operations in this expression done from left to right? No; Multiplication and division must be done before addition and subtraction.

**ELL** Explain that *rank,* in reference to order of operations, means which comes first. Compare this to *taking a number* while waiting to be served.

### Example 2

**Build understanding.** Ask: Why do you divide eight by four before you subtract? Multiply and divide first. Then add and subtract.

## Part 2 Teaching Notes

Students who use the Calculator Hint and find that their calculators do not use order of operations may need to insert grouping symbols to evaluate expressions correctly.

### Example 3

**Build understanding.** Ask: Which part of the expression is simplified first? Why? 2 • 2; It is included in the innermost set of grouping symbols.

**Extension** Challenge students to write two expressions that have the same numbers in the same order, but use different grouping symbols. The results of the two expressions should be different when simplified.

- **Additional Example 2**
  Simplify 12 ÷ 3 − 1 • 2 + 1. 3
- **Additional Example 3**
  Simplify 20 − 3[(5 + 2) − 1]. 2

## AFTER THE LESSON

**To assess knowledge:**

**Lesson Quiz**

Simplify each expression.

1. 7(3) − 2 • 4 13
2. 6 ÷ 2 + 1 • 5 8

Insert grouping symbols to make the number sentence true.

3. 10 ÷ 4 + 1 = 2
   10 ÷ (4 + 1) = 2

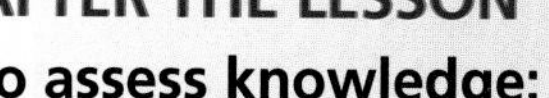

- For enrichment and reteaching options see Resources on p. 1H.

**Error Prevention** A common error is to multiply first in an expression with multiplication and division operations, such as 16 ÷ 2 • 4. Remind students that division and multiplication operations are done in order from left to right.

**Connecting to Geometry** To help students with Different Ways to Solve a Problem, review the formula $A = lw$ for finding the area of a rectangle.

**Visual Learning** When simplifying expressions, have students copy expressions on a sheet of paper and draw a red circle around the first pair of numbers to be combined.

**Connecting to Social Studies** Ask students to investigate which cultures read in an order different from left to right.

You can use the order of operations to find the area of an irregular figure by more than one method.

## Different Ways to Solve a Problem

*Urban Planning* **Some urban planners specialize in planning entire new towns. These towns are designed for livability, with plenty of open space. The sketch shows the dimensions for a new town called Panorama. Find Panorama's area.**

### Method 1

Divide the figure into rectangles. Then add their areas.

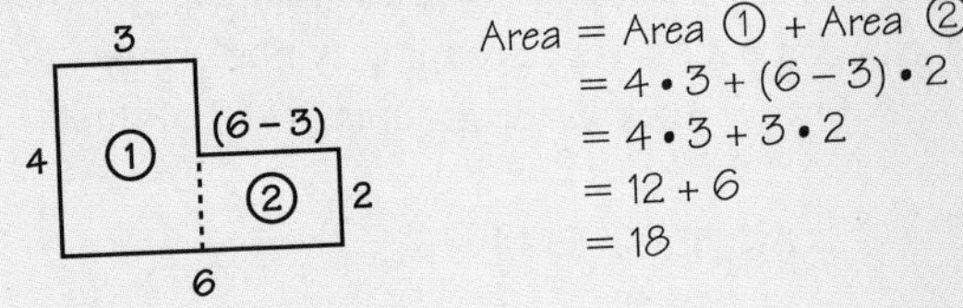

Area = Area ① + Area ②
$= 4 \cdot 3 + (6 - 3) \cdot 2$
$= 4 \cdot 3 + 3 \cdot 2$
$= 12 + 6$
$= 18$

Panorama's area is 18 $km^2$.

### Method 2

Visualize the figure as a small rectangle within a large rectangle. Then subtract the small area from the large area.

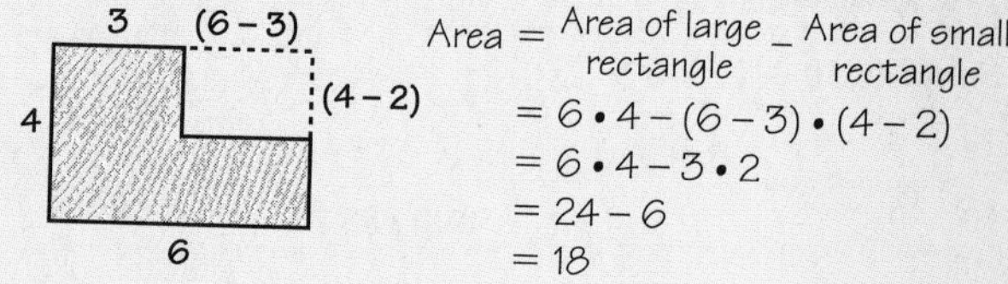

Area = Area of large rectangle − Area of small rectangle
$= 6 \cdot 4 - (6 - 3) \cdot (4 - 2)$
$= 6 \cdot 4 - 3 \cdot 2$
$= 24 - 6$
$= 18$

Panorama's area is 18 $km^2$.

**Choose a Method**

1. Which method would you use to find the town's area? Explain. Answers may vary.
2. Can you think of another way to solve the problem? Explain. Answers may vary. Sample: Put a grid on the figure and count squares.

# Exercises

## CHECK UNDERSTANDING

**Which operation would you perform first? Explain.**

1. 35 · 98 − 50 Multiplication; multiplication comes before subtraction in the order of operations.
2. 115 − 87 + 29 Subtraction; when operations have the same rank in the order of operations, do them from left to right.
3. 4(67 ÷ 6) Division; work within parentheses first.

**Simplify each expression.**

4. 6 − 6 ÷ 3 4
5. 21 − 13 + 8 16
6. 7 + 3 · (8 ÷ 4) 13
7. 2(15 − 9) · 9 108
8. [2 + (6 · 8)] − 1 49
9. $6 + \frac{6+2}{4}$ 8

## PRACTICE AND PROBLEM SOLVING

*Mental Math* **Simplify each expression.**

10. 12 − 8 ÷ 2 8
11. 21 ÷ 7 + 14 17
12. 6 · 2 + 4 16
13. 4(4) − 2 14
14. 3(7 + 4) 33
15. $2(6) + \frac{15}{3}$ 17

**Simplify each expression.**

16. 14 + 5 × 2 24
17. 60 ÷ 4 + 9 24
18. 16 ÷ 8 × 2 4
19. 12 ÷ 3 × 4 16
20. 2 + 3 · 24 74
21. 12 ÷ 3 − 2 + 1 3
22. 2 · 2 + 0 · 4 4
23. 36 − 27 ÷ 9 ÷ 1 33
24. 4 ÷ 4 · 4 + 4 − 4 4
25. (56 − 5) ÷ 17 3
26. 440 ÷ (2 + 18) 22
27. (21 + 3) ÷ 4 ÷ 2 3
28. [6(4 + 1) − 5] 25
29. $\frac{21+15}{3+6}$ 4
30. 2[8 + (5 − 3)] − 8 12

**Compare. Use >, <, or = to complete each statement.**

31. 15 · 3 − 2 ■ 15 · (3 − 2) >
32. 8 + 12 ÷ 4 ■ (8 + 12) ÷ 4 >
33. 12 ÷ 3 + 9 · 4 ■ 12 ÷ (3 + 9) · 4 >
34. (19 − 15) ÷ (3 + 1) ■ 19 − 15 ÷ 3 + 1 <

35. **TEST PREP** Which expression has a value of 18? D
    A. 3 · 2 + 4
    B. (18 − 10) ÷ 4 + 15
    C. 4 · 2 + 3 − 2
    D. 27 − 13 · 2 + 17(6 − 5)
    E. Not here

**Insert grouping symbols to make each number sentence true.**

✪ 36. 7 + 4 · 6 = 66 (7 + 4) · 6 = 66
✪ 37. 7 · 8 − 6 + 3 = 17 7 · (8 − 6) + 3 = 17
✪ 38. 3 + 8 − 2 · 5 = 45 (3 + 8 − 2) · 5 = 45
✪ 39. 2 · 3 − 8 − 5 · 2 = 0 2 · 3 − [(8 − 5) · 2] = 0, or 2 · [3 − (8 − 5)] · 2, or 2 · 3 − (8 − 5) · 2



# 3 Practice/Assess

## Assignment Guide

To provide flexible scheduling, this lesson can be divided into parts.

**Part 1**
**Core** 1–2, 4–5, 10–12, 16–24, 40–41
✪ **Extension** 42

**Part 2**
**Core** 3, 6–9, 13–15, 25–35, 43–49
✪ **Extension** 36–39, 50–51

Mixed Review can be assigned at any time for maintenance.

## Exercises

**Exercises 31–34** Review the meaning of the symbols < and >. Point out that the smaller end of the symbol points to the lesser number.

**Test Prep Exercise 35** Remind students to think, before evaluating, of "Please, My Dear Aunt Sally."

## ✪ Challenge

Simplify 9 ÷ (0 + 3). What would be the result if the parentheses were not there? 3; undefined since division by 0 is not defined

## Closure

To simplify a numerical expression, follow the order of operations: work inside grouping symbols first; then multiply and divide in order from left to right; finally add and subtract in order from left to right.

## Alternative Assessment

Have students work with a partner to write an expression involving order of operations on one side of an index card and the simplified expression on the other side.

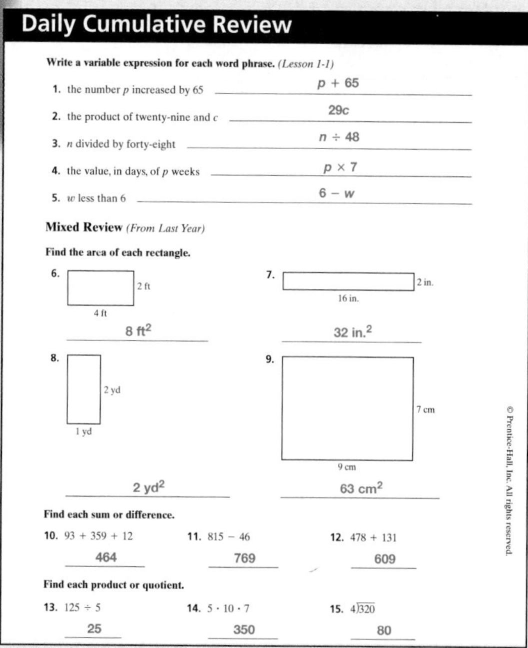

**Daily Cumulative Review**

**Write a variable expression for each word phrase.** *(Lesson 1-1)*

1. the number *p* increased by 65 — p + 65
2. the product of twenty-nine and *c* — 29c
3. *n* divided by forty-eight — n ÷ 48
4. the value, in days, of *p* weeks — p × 7
5. *w* less than 6 — 6 − w

**Mixed Review** *(From Last Year)*

**Find the area of each rectangle.**

6. 4 ft by 2 ft — 8 ft²
7. 16 in. by 2 in. — 32 in.²
8. 1 yd by 2 yd — 2 yd²
9. 9 cm by 7 cm — 63 cm²

**Find each sum or difference.**

10. 93 + 359 + 12 — 464
11. 815 − 46 — 769
12. 478 + 131 — 609

**Find each product or quotient.**

13. 125 ÷ 5 — 25
14. 5 · 10 · 7 — 350
15. 4)320 — 80

## Practice

**Simplify each expression.**

1. 3 + 15 − 5 · 2 8
2. 5 · 6 + 2 · 4 38
3. 48 ÷ 8 − 1 5
4. 68 − 12 ÷ 2 ÷ 3 66
5. 6(2 + 7) 54
6. 25 − (6 · 4) 1
7. 3[9 − (6 − 3)] − 10 8
8. 60 ÷ (3 + 12) 4
9. 4 − 2 + 6 · 2 14
10. 18 ÷ (5 − 2) 6
11. $\frac{16 + 24}{30 - 22}$ 5
12. 2[4(9 − 7) + 1] 18
13. (8 ÷ 8 + 2 + 11) ÷ 2 7
14. 9 + 3 · 4 21
15. 18 ÷ 3 · 5 − 4 26
16. 10 + 28 ÷ 14 − 5 7

**Insert grouping symbols to make each number sentence true.**

17. (3 + 5) · 8 = 64
18. 4 · (6 − 2) + 7 = 23
19. 10 ÷ (3 + 2) · 4 = 8
20. (3 + 6) · 2 = 18

A city park has two walkways with a grassy area in the center, as shown in the diagram.

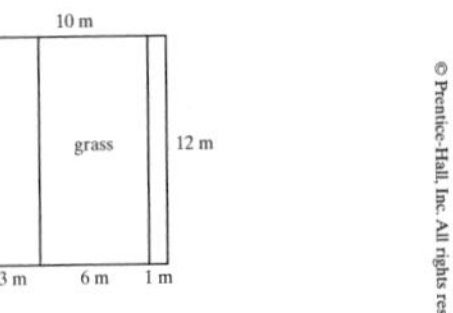


21. Write an expression for the area of the sidewalks, using subtraction. 12 · 10 − 12 · 6
22. Write an expression for the area of the sidewalks, using addition. 3 · 12 + 1 · 12

**Compare. Use >, <, or = to complete statement.**

23. (24 − 8) ÷ 4 [<] 24 − 8 ÷ 4
24. 3 · (4 − 2) · 5 [>] 3 · 4 − 2 · 5
25. (22 + 8) ÷ 2 [<] 22 + 8 ÷ 2
26. 20 ÷ 2 + 8 · 2 [>] 20 ÷ (2 + 8) · 2
27. 11 · 4 − 2 [>] 11 · (4 − 2)
28. (7 · 3) − (4 · 2) [=] 7 · 3 − 4 · 2



## Reteaching

Simplify $\frac{18 + 4}{2} - 3(10 \cdot 2 - 3 \cdot 6)$

| | |
|---|---|
| $\frac{18 + 4}{2} - 3(10 \cdot 2 - 3 \cdot 6)$ | Work inside grouping symbols first. |
| $= \frac{22}{2} - 3(10 \cdot 2 - 3 \cdot 6)$ | A fraction bar is a grouping symbol. |
| $= 11 - 3(10 \cdot 2 - 3 \cdot 6)$ | Divide the fraction. |
| $= 11 - 3(20 - 18)$ | Multiply within the parentheses. |
| $= 11 - 3(2)$ | Subtract within the parentheses. |
| $= 11 - 6$ | Multiply. |
| $= 5$ | Subtract. |

**Simplify each expression.**

1. 8 + 2 × 7 22
2. 16 ÷ 2 − 5 3
3. $\frac{8 + 12}{5}$ 4
4. 4 − 24 ÷ 8 1
5. 3 + 2 · 5 − 4 9
6. 15 − 2(5 − 2) 9
7. 9 · 3 + 2 · 5 37
8. 12 ÷ 4 − 6 ÷ 3 1
9. 5(2 + 4) + 15 ÷ (9 − 6) 35
10. 3 · 2 + 16 ÷ 4 − 3 7
11. (18 + 7) ÷ (3 + 2) 5
12. 3[8 − 3 · 2 + 4(5 − 2)] 42
13. 4 · 9 + 8 ÷ 2 − 6 · 5 10
14. [7 + 3 · 2 + 8] ÷ 7 3
15. 53 − [3(8 + 2) + 5(9 − 5)] 3
16. (20 + 22) ÷ 6 + 1 8
17. 2[9(6 − 5)] 18
18. 5 + 3 · 4 − 8 + 2 · 7 23



## Enrichment

A *binary operation* is an operation performed on two numbers. Addition, subtraction, multiplication, and division are all binary operations. Once you known how to use a binary operation, you can perform it on any two numbers.

Here is a new binary operation. # means "multiply the numbers, then add the second number to the product."

**Example** 5 # 4 = 5 × 4 + 4 = 24

**Use the operation # to solve.**

1. 3 # 2 8
2. 8 # 5 45
3. 1 # 7 14
4. 10 # 9 99
5. 4 # (2 # 7) 105
6. (3 # 4) # 5 85

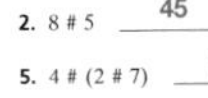
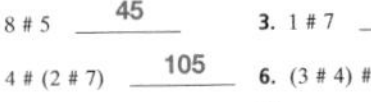

7. Evaluate 3 # 5 + 2 doing the operation # first. 22
8. Evaluate 3 # 5 + 2 doing the operation + first. 28
9. Complete the following order of operation rule, guaranteeing that the value of 3 # 5 + 2 will be 28: When evaluating an expression involving # and +, do the operation + first
10. Use your rule to evaluate 8 # 6 + 3. 81

**Discover how to use each binary operation by studying the examples. Then perform the operation on the given numbers.**

**Example** 2 * 5 = 20 4 * 3 = 24 7 * 5 = 70 10 * 10 = 200

11. 3 * 6 36
12. 5 * 5 50
13. 8 * 2 32
14. 12 * 12 288
15. (2 * 2) * 4 64
16. 2 *(2 * 4) 64

**Example** 4 $ 1 = 17 6 $ 3 = 39 9 $ 2 = 83 10 $ 1 = 101

17. 5 $ 3 28
18. 2 $ 7 11
19. 7 $ 13 62
20. 12 $ 10 154
21. (2 $ 3) $ 4 53
22. 2 $ (3 $ 4) 17





40. A part-time employee worked 4 hours on Monday and 7 hours each day for the next 3 days. Write and simplify an expression that shows the total number of hours worked. 4 + 7 · 3; 25

41. *Writing* Why do we need to agree on an order of operations? We must agree on an order of operations to ensure that everyone gets the same value for an expression.

42. *Error Analysis* A student found the value of the expression 30 ÷ 6 − 1 to be 6. Explain the student's error. The student subtracted 1 from 6 before dividing, instead of dividing and then subtracting.

**Write a numerical expression for each phrase. Then simplify.**

43. five added to the product of four and nine 4 · 9 + 5; 41

44. twenty-one minus the sum of fifteen and five 21 − (15 + 5); 1

45. seventeen minus the quotient of twenty-five and five 17 − (25 ÷ 5); 12

46. **TEST PREP** A music club member ordered three CDs at $14 each and four tapes at $8 each. The shipping charge for the entire order was $5. Which expression shows the total cost of the order? A
 A. 3 · 14 + 4 · 8 + 5
 B. 3(14 + 5) + 4(8 + 5)
 C. (3 + 4) · (14 + 8)
 D. 3 · 14 + 4 · 8

**Write two expressions you could use to find the area of each shaded figure. Find the area.**

47.

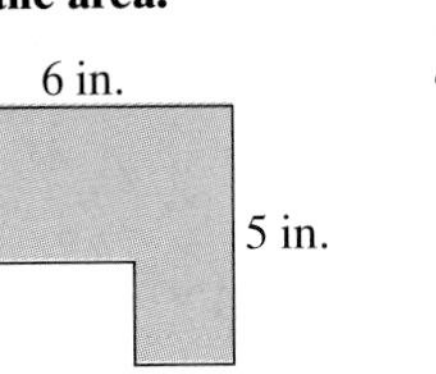


Sample: (6 × 5) − (4 × 2) and (6 × 3) + (2 × 2); 22 in.$^2$

48.

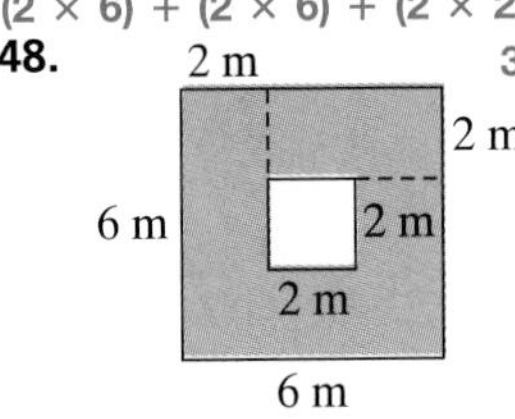


Sample: (6 × 6) − (2 × 2) and (2 × 6) + (2 × 6) + (2 × 2) + (2 × 2); 32 m$^2$

49.

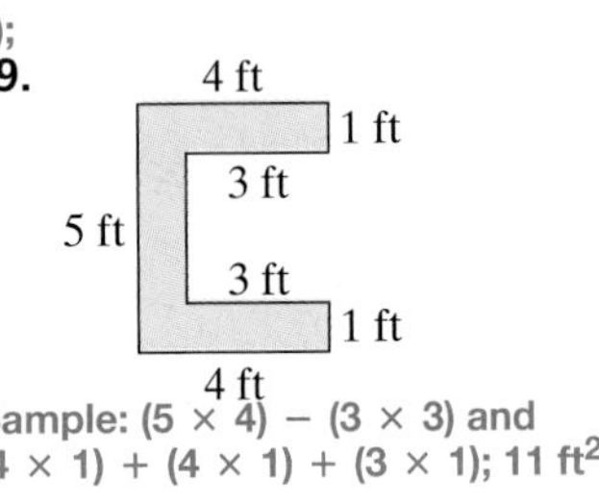


Sample: (5 × 4) − (3 × 3) and (4 × 1) + (4 × 1) + (3 × 1); 11 ft$^2$

50. *Open-ended* Write a word problem for the numerical expression 3(4 + 3) + 2. Then simplify the expression. Check students' work; 23.

51. *Number Sense* Use the digits 1–9 in order. Insert operation signs and grouping symbols to get a value of 100. Answers may vary. Sample: 1 + 2 + 3 + 4 + 5 + 6 + 7 + (8 · 9)

## Mixed Review

**Write a variable expression for each word phrase.** ***(Lesson 1-1)***

52. the product of a number $n$ and 8 $8n$

53. $k$ divided by 20 $\frac{k}{20}$

54. six less than a number $h$ $h - 6$

55. the value, in cents, of $d$ dimes $10d$

56. A telephone call costs $c$ cents per minute. Write a variable expression for the cost of a 15-minute call. ***(Lesson 1-1)*** 15c



See also Extra Practice section.

# Evaluating Expressions

1-3

## PART 1 Evaluating Variable Expressions

You can **evaluate** a variable expression by replacing each variable with a number. Then use the order of operations to simplify.

### EXAMPLE 1

**Evaluate $4y - 15$ for $y = 9$.**

| | |
|---|---|
| $4y - 15 = 4(9) - 15$ | Replace *y* with 9. |
| $= 36 - 15$ | Multiply. |
| $= 21$ | Subtract. |

**TRY THIS** Evaluate each expression.

**1.** $63 - 5x$, for $x = 7$ 28 **2.** $4(t + 3) + 1$, for $t = 8$ 45

Sometimes expressions have more than one variable.

### EXAMPLE 2

**Evaluate $3ab + \frac{c}{2}$ for $a = 2$, $b = 5$, and $c = 10$.**

| | |
|---|---|
| $3ab + \frac{c}{2} = 3 \cdot 2 \cdot 5 + \frac{10}{2}$ | Replace the variables. |
| $= 3 \cdot 2 \cdot 5 + 5$ | Work within grouping symbols. |
| $= 6 \cdot 5 + 5$ | Multiply from left to right. |
| $= 30 + 5$ | Multiply. |
| $= 35$ | Add. |

**TRY THIS** Evaluate each expression.

**3.** $6(g + h)$, for $g = 8$ and $h = 7$ 90

**4.** $2xy - z$, for $x = 4$, $y = 3$, and $z = 1$ 23

**5.** $\frac{r + s}{2}$, for $r = 13$ and $s = 11$ 12

**What You'll Learn**

1. To evaluate variable expressions
2. To solve word problems by evaluating expressions

**. . . And Why**

To solve real-world problems involving packaging and shopping

**Writing Math**

The × sign looks a lot like the variable *x*. To avoid confusion, use · or ( ) for multiplication.



# Tools to Monitor Progress

**BEFORE THE LESSON**

**To check prerequisite skills:**

- Combining whole numbers
- Adding and subtracting whole numbers
- Multiplying and dividing whole numbers

**Skills Intervention Kit,** Whole Numbers

**DURING THE LESSON**

**To check understanding:**

**Try This** exercises on student page

- **Additional Example 1**
  Evaluate $18 + 2g$ for $g = 3$. 24
- **Additional Example 2**
  The Omelet Café buys cartons of 36 eggs. Write a variable expression for the cartons needed for *x* eggs. How many cartons will they need for 180 eggs? $\frac{x}{36}$; 5

# 1-3

## Getting Ready

**Key Terms and Symbols** evaluate

**Resources** A complete list of resources for this lesson is on p. 1H.

### Daily Skills Warm-Up

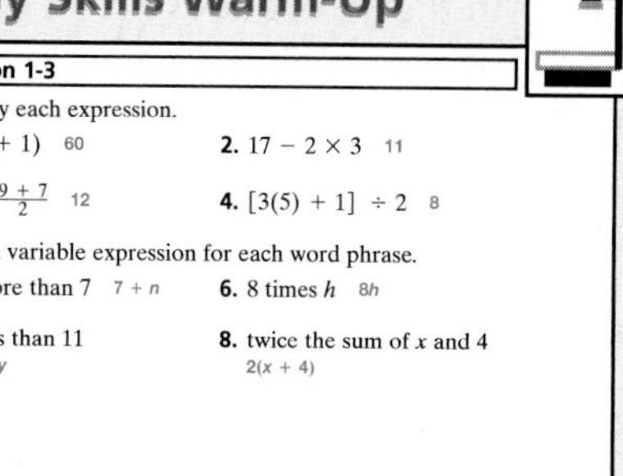

Lesson 1-3

Simplify each expression.

**1.** $6(9 + 1)$ 60 **2.** $17 - 2 \times 3$ 11

**3.** $4 + \frac{9 + 7}{2}$ 12 **4.** $[3(5) + 1] \div 2$ 8

Write a variable expression for each word phrase.

**5.** *n* more than 7 $7 + n$ **6.** 8 times *h* $8h$

**7.** *y* less than 11 $11 - y$ **8.** twice the sum of *x* and 4 $2(x + 4)$

### Background for the Lesson

In the expression 4*y*, 4 is the *coefficient* of *y*. Usually the word *coefficient* refers to a numerical factor. When a term such as *x* has no numerical factor, the coefficient is understood to be the number 1.

## 1 Focus

### Connecting to Students' Lives

Ask students if they have done a job that paid by the hour, such as babysitting. They might evaluate the expression \$2*h* (where the hourly pay is \$2 and *h* is the number of hours worked) to find their total pay.

### Connecting to Prior Knowledge

Students know Order of Operations from the previous lesson and should remember that division may be done before multiplication (and subtraction before addition) when the operations occur in that order from left to right.

# 2 Teach

## Part 1 Teaching Notes

Remind students to write down intermediate steps when they evaluate variable expressions.

### Example 1

**Build understanding.** Ask: Why are the parentheses added when 9 is substituted for *y*? Without them, the expression would read 49 instead of 4 *times* 9.

**ELL** Explain that *operations* in mathematics are the actions of adding, subtracting, multiplying, and dividing.

### Example 2

**Build understanding.** Ask: Does the order in which you multiply 3 • 2 • 5 make a difference in the value? No, multiplying in any order gives the same result.

## Part 2 Teaching Notes

Suggest that students write down key words and values as they read problems. They may then use these notes to write variable expressions for the problems.

### Example 3

**Build understanding.** Ask: How many cases are needed for 24 bottles? for 48 bottles? 1, 2

**Extension** Challenge students to write a problem, using boxes of 12 pencils each, that is similar to Example 3.

### Example 4

**Build understanding.** Ask: Does the amount charged for shipping increase if more CDs are ordered? no

**Error Prevention** A common error is to omit the dollar sign when giving the final answer. In addition to doing the math, students must also answer the question asked by including the dollar sign.

**Auditory Learning** Encourage students to read Examples 3 and 4 aloud with a partner, and then to discuss how to write and evaluate the variable expressions.

## Solving Problems by Evaluating Expressions

You can write and evaluate variable expressions to solve problems.

REAL-WORLD CONNECTION

### Example 3

*Purchasing* **Refer to the photo. (a) Write a variable expression for the number of cases a store should order to get *b* bottles of energy drinks. (b) Evaluate the expression for 120 bottles.**

**a.** ***b*** **bottles**

$\frac{b}{24}$

**b. 120 bottles**

$\frac{b}{24} = \frac{120}{24}$ Evaluate for $b = 120$.

$= 5$ Divide.

The store should order five cases to get 120 bottles.

These bottled energy drinks come in cases of 24.

### Try This

6. The store in Example 3 pays $29 for each case of energy drinks. Write a variable expression for the cost of *c* cases. Evaluate the expression to find the cost of five cases. 29c; $145

REAL-WORLD CONNECTION

### Example 4

*Online Shopping* **An online music store charges $14 for each CD. Shipping costs $6 per order. Write a variable expression for the cost of ordering CDs. Find the cost of ordering four CDs.**

| Words | $14 | for each | CD | plus | $6 shipping |
|---|---|---|---|---|---|
| | Let $n$ = number of CDs. | | | | |
| Expression | 14 | · | $n$ | + | 6 |

Evaluate the expression for $n = 4$.

$14 \cdot n + 6 = 14 \cdot 4 + 6$ Replace $n$ with 4.

$= 56 + 6$ Multiply.

$= 62$ Add.

It costs $62 to order four CDs.

**Writing Math**

The phrase *for each* implies multiplication. So *$14 for each CD* means "$14 times the number of CDs."

### Try This

7. Evaluate the expression in Example 4 to find the cost of ordering seven CDs. $104



• **Additional Example 3**

The One Pizza restaurant only makes one kind of pizza, which costs $16. Their delivery charge is $2. Write a variable expression for the cost of ordering pizzas. Evaluate the expression to find the cost of ordering two pizzas.

16 • *p* + 2; $34

## AFTER THE LESSON

**To assess knowledge:**

**Lesson Quiz**

Evaluate.

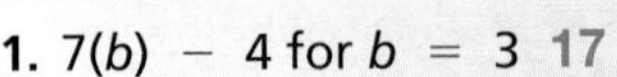

1. $7(b) - 4$ for $b = 3$ 17
2. $h \div 2 + 1$ for $h = 12$ 7

3. $3c + 4 \div d$ for $c = 8, d = 2$ 26

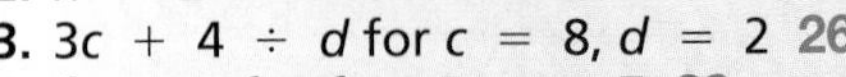

4. $fg - g$ for $f = 5, g = 7$ 28

• For enrichment and reteaching options see Resources on p. 1H.

# Exercises

## Check Understanding

**Evaluate each expression for $x = 2, y = 3$, and $z = 10$.**

**1.** $x + 5$ 7  **2.** $16 - z$ 6  **3.** $4y$ 12

**4.** $8 \div x$ 4  **5.** $2z - 4$ 16  **6.** $x + z$ 12

**7.** $y + 5y$ 18  **8.** $xyz$ 60  **9.** $8y \div x$ 12

**10.** An office assistant types 55 words per minute. How many words does the office assistant type in $m$ minutes? In 20 minutes? $55m$; 1,100 words

## Practice and Problem Solving

*Mental Math* **Evaluate each expression.**

**11.** $7b$, for $b = 5$ 35  **12.** $5 - c$, for $c = 3$ 2  **13.** $x \div 8$, for $x = 40$ 5

**14.** $3n + 2$, for $n = 7$ 23  **15.** $41 - 4h$, for $h = 10$ 1  **16.** $5a + 7$, for $a = 20$ 107

**Evaluate each expression.**

**17.** $12a$, for $a = 2$ 24  **18.** $x - 6$, for $x = 16$ 10

**19.** $2a + 5$, for $a = 5$ 15  **20.** $105z$, for $z = 7$ 735

**21.** $6 \div a + 8$, for $a = 2$ 11  **22.** $19 - (a - 4)$, for $a = 8$ 15

**23.** $13ab$, for $a = 1$ and $b = 7$ 91  **24.** $16 - 4mn$, for $m = 0$ and $n = 3$ 16

**25.** $3(a + b)$, for $a = 7$ and $b = 9$ 48  **26.** $rst$, for $r = 5, s = 5$ and $t = 5$ 125

**27.** $\frac{150}{z + y}$, for $y = 25$ and $z = 50$ 2  **28.** $\frac{x - y}{4}$, for $x = 52$ and $y = 12$ 10

✪ **29.** $4a - b + \frac{b}{2}$, for $a = 3$ and $b = 4$ 10  **30.** $j(5 + k)$, for $j = 11$ and $k = 4$ 99

**31.** *Data Analysis* Use the chart to find how many calories a 100-lb person uses in an hour of moderate walking.

**a.** Write an expression for the number of calories a 100-lb person uses in moderate walking for $h$ hours. $153h$

**b.** Evaluate the expression to find the number of calories a 100-lb person uses in moderate walking for 2 hours. 306 calories

**Calories Per Hour Used by a 100-lb Walker**

| Type of Walking | Calories |
|---|---|
| Slow | 110 |
| Moderate | 153 |
| Brisk | 175 |
| Racing | 295 |

SOURCE: www.nutristrategy.com

✪ **32.** *Error Analysis* Your friend evaluates $(10 - k) \div 5$ for $k = 5$, and gets 9 for an answer. Explain your friend's error.
Answers may vary. Sample: My friend did not work within the grouping symbols first.



# 3 Practice/Assess

## Assignment Guide

To provide flexible scheduling, this lesson can be divided into parts.

▼ **Part 1**
**Core** 1–9, 11–28, 30
✪ **Extension** 29, 32

▼ **Part 2**
**Core** 10, 31, 33–35
✪ **Extension** 36–37

Mixed Review can be assigned at any time for maintenance.

## Exercises

**Exercises 33–36** Suggest that students evaluate first for 1 hour, or month, or minute, then for 2 hours, or months, or minutes, and so on, to help them understand the problems.

## ✪ Challenge

For Exercise 36c, write an expression for how many rides you can afford if you have $d$ dollars to spend. sample answer: $(d - 5) \div 2$

## Closure

To evaluate a variable expression, substitute a value for each variable and use the order of operations to simplify.

## Alternative Assessment

Have students write and solve a problem similar to Exercises 33–36 by using a variable from their weekly activities, such as time spent eating lunch or miles traveled to and from school.

## Daily Cumulative Review

**Simplify each expression.** *(Lesson 1-2)*

**1.** $16 \div 4 \times 5$ 20  **2.** $78 - 15 \div 3$ 73  **3.** $24 + 3 \cdot 7$ 45

**4.** $(75 - 30) \div 9$ 5  **5.** $280 \div (6 + 34)$ 7  **6.** $[(7 + 2)8 - 13]$ 59

**Tell whether each expression is a numerical expression or a variable expression. For a variable expression, name the variable.** *(Lesson 1-1)*

**7.** $7b$ variable expression; $b$

**8.** $5 + 9 + 3 + 2$ numerical expression

**9.** $\frac{x}{5}$ variable expression; $x$

**10.** $y - 2$ variable expression; $y$

**11.** $13 \times 7$ numerical expression

**Mixed Review** *(From Last Year)*

**Order the following data from least to greatest.**

**12.** 34, 25, 18, 26, 20, 35, 6 6, 18, 20, 25, 26, 34, 35

**13.** 5, 7, 3, 10, 2, 0 0, 2, 3, 5, 7, 10

**14.** 18, 15, 21, 26, 9, 20, 29 9, 15, 18, 20, 21, 26, 29

**What is the distance of each point from zero on the number line?**

H J G K
0 4

**15.** $G$ 11  **16.** $H$ 2  **17.** $J$ 5  **18.** $K$ 16

**Compare. Use >, <, or = to complete each statement.**

**19.** 11 [>] 9  **20.** 9 [>] 7  **21.** 18 [>] 13

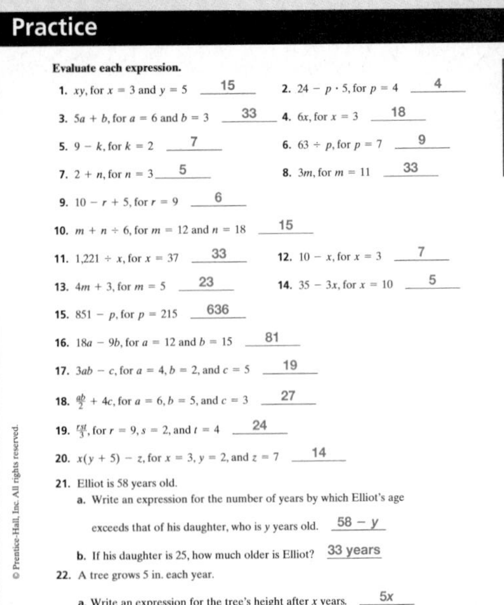

## Practice

**Evaluate each expression.**

1. $xy$, for $x = 3$ and $y = 5$ 15
2. $24 - p \cdot 5$, for $p = 4$ 4
3. $5a + b$, for $a = 6$ and $b = 3$ 33
4. $6x$, for $x = 3$ 18
5. $9 - k$, for $k = 2$ 7
6. $63 \div p$, for $p = 7$ 9
7. $2 + n$, for $n = 3$ 5
8. $3m$, for $m = 11$ 33
9. $10 - r + 5$, for $r = 9$ 6
10. $m + n \div 6$, for $m = 12$ and $n = 18$ 15
11. $1{,}221 \div x$, for $x = 37$ 33
12. $10 - x$, for $x = 3$ 7
13. $4m + 3$, for $m = 5$ 23
14. $35 - 3x$, for $x = 10$ 5
15. $851 - p$, for $p = 215$ 636
16. $18a - 9b$, for $a = 12$ and $b = 15$ 81
17. $3ab - c$, for $a = 4$, $b = 2$, and $c = 5$ 19
18. $\frac{ab}{2} + 4c$, for $a = 6$, $b = 5$, and $c = 3$ 27
19. $\frac{rst}{3}$, for $r = 9$, $s = 2$, and $t = 4$ 24
20. $x(y + 5) - z$, for $x = 3$, $y = 2$, and $z = 7$ 14
21. Elliot is 58 years old.
   a. Write an expression for the number of years by which Elliot's age exceeds that of his daughter, who is $y$ years old. $58 - y$
   b. If his daughter is 25, how much older is Elliot? 33 years
22. A tree grows 5 in. each year.
   a. Write an expression for the tree's height after $x$ years. $5x$
   b. When the tree is 36 years old, how tall will it be? 180 in.



## Reteaching

**Evaluate $a(b + 4) - c$, for $a = 2$, $b = 5$, and $c = 12$.**

| | |
|---|---|
| $a(b + 4) - c$ | |
| $= 2(5 + 4) - 12$ | Replace the variables. |
| $= 2(9) - 12$ | Work within grouping symbols. |
| $= 18 - 12$ | Multiply. |
| $= 6$ | Subtract. |

**Evaluate each expression.**

1. $2n - 7$, for $n = 8$ 9
2. $4ab$, for $a = 2$ and $b = 5$ 40
3. $\frac{x + y}{3}$, for $x = 7$ and $y = 8$ 5
4. $2(m + n)$, for $m = 3$ and $n = 2$ 10
5. $37 - 5h$, for $h = 7$ 2
6. $\frac{6}{a} + b$, for $a = 3$ and $b = 7$ 9
7. $4x + 5y - 3z$, for $x = 3$, $y = 4$, and $z = 2$ 26
8. $15a - 2(b + c)$, for $a = 2$, $b = 3$, and $c = 4$ 16
9. $7p + q(3 + r)$, for $p = 3$, $q = 2$, and $r = 1$ 29
10. $\frac{36}{j} - 4(k + l)$, for $j = 2$, $k = 1$, and $l = 3$ 2
11. $x + 3y - 4(z - 3)$, for $x = 4$, $y = 6$, and $z = 5$ 14
12. $(4 + d) - e(9 - f)$, for $d = 7$, $e = 4$, $f = 8$ 7
13. $3a - 2b + b(6 - 2)$, for $a = 4$, $b = 2$ 16
14. $r(p + 3) + q(p - 1)$, for $p = 7$, $q = 4$, $r = 3$ 54



## Enrichment

The value of a variable expression depends upon the value of the variable. By choosing the correct value, you can cause two expressions to be equal. The expressions $x - 6$ and $2x - 11$, for example, both have the same value when $x = 5$.

$$x - 6 = 5 - 6 = -1 \qquad 2x - 11 = 2(5) - 11 = 10 - 11 = -1$$

Complete the tables for the given values of the variables. Then in the space to the right, name the value of the variable for which the two expressions are equal.

1.

| $k$ | 10 | 11 | 12 | 13 | 14 | 15 | 16 | 17 |
|---|---|---|---|---|---|---|---|---|
| $5 + k$ | 15 | 16 | 17 | 18 | 19 | 20 | 21 | 22 |
| $2k - 9$ | 11 | 13 | 15 | 17 | 19 | 21 | 23 | 25 |

$k =$ 14

2.

| $x$ | 1 | 2 | 3 | 4 | 5 | 6 | 7 | 8 |
|---|---|---|---|---|---|---|---|---|
| $10 - x$ | 9 | 8 | 7 | 6 | 5 | 4 | 3 | 2 |
| $3x - 2$ | 1 | 4 | 7 | 10 | 13 | 16 | 19 | 22 |

$x =$ 3

3.

| $n$ | 2 | 3 | 4 | 5 | 6 | 7 | 8 | 9 |
|---|---|---|---|---|---|---|---|---|
| $2n - 3$ | 1 | 3 | 5 | 7 | 9 | 11 | 13 | 15 |
| $27 - 3n$ | 21 | 18 | 15 | 12 | 9 | 6 | 3 | 0 |

$n =$ 6

4.

| $h$ | 0 | 1 | 2 | 3 | 4 | 5 | 6 | 7 |
|---|---|---|---|---|---|---|---|---|
| $5h + 7$ | 7 | 12 | 17 | 22 | 27 | 32 | 37 | 42 |
| $6h + 1$ | 1 | 7 | 13 | 19 | 25 | 31 | 37 | 43 |

$h =$ 6

5.

| $a$ | 0 | 1 | 2 | 3 | 4 | 5 | 6 | 7 |
|---|---|---|---|---|---|---|---|---|
| $29 - 2a$ | 29 | 27 | 25 | 23 | 21 | 19 | 17 | 15 |
| $3a + 4$ | 4 | 7 | 10 | 13 | 16 | 19 | 22 | 25 |

$a =$ 5

6. Explain why there is no value of $x$ for which the expressions $x + 3$ and $x + 4$ are equal.
   For every value of $x$, $x + 3 < x + 4$.



33. ***Marine Biology*** Write an expression for the number of kilometers a dolphin travels in $h$ hours swimming at 8 km/h. Then find the number of kilometers the dolphin travels in 3 hours. $8h$; 24 km

34. A fitness club requires a \$100 initiation fee and dues of \$25 each month. Write an expression for the cost of membership for $n$ months. Then find the cost of membership for one year. $100 + 25n$; \$400

35. ***Vital Statistics*** Every minute about 145 babies are born in the world. About how many babies are born in $m$ minutes? In 6 minutes? In one day? $145m$; 870 babies; 208,800 babies

By *porpoising* (jumping clear of the water), dolphins can travel as fast as 26 km/h.

36. A carnival charges \$5 for admission plus \$2 per ride.
   a. Write an expression for the cost of admission plus $r$ rides. $5 + 2r$
   b. Find the cost of admission plus six rides. \$17
   c. How many rides can you afford if you have \$15 to spend? 5 rides

37. ***Writing*** Write a word problem that could be solved by evaluating the expression $3x - 5$ for $x = 5$. Check students' work.

## Mixed Review

**Simplify each expression.** ***(Lesson 1-2)***

38. $(60 - 6) \div 9$ 6
39. $80 \div 2 + 13$ 53
40. $5 \div 5 \cdot 5 - 5$ 0

**Write a variable expression for each word phrase.** ***(Lesson 1-1)***

41. $t$ fewer than 19 $19 - t$
42. the sum of 8 and $n$ $8 + n$
43. $d$ divided by 20 $\frac{d}{20}$

44. ***Error Analysis*** Valerie has test grades of 96, 82, 78, and 76. Using a calculator, she found her average grade to be 275. Is Valerie's answer reasonable? Explain how she got her answer. No; Valerie's average grade should be in the 80s. Valerie evaluated 96 + 82 + 78 + 76/4 on her calculator instead of (96 + 82 + 78 + 76)/4.

## Chapter Project 1 — Activity 1 Reading

American Standard Code for Information Interchange (ASCII) is a code used by computers. In ASCII, a number represents each English character. Use the tables below to decode the ASCII message at the right.

7765847269776584736783
3273833284726932766578
7185657169327970328472
6932857873866982836946

Mathematics is the language of the universe.

| ASCII Number | 32 | 46 | 65 | 66 | 67 | 68 | 69 | 70 | 71 | 72 | 73 | 74 | 75 | 76 |
|---|---|---|---|---|---|---|---|---|---|---|---|---|---|---|
| English Character | space | . | A | B | C | D | E | F | G | H | I | J | K | L |

| ASCII Number | 77 | 78 | 79 | 80 | 81 | 82 | 83 | 84 | 85 | 86 | 87 | 88 | 89 | 90 |
|---|---|---|---|---|---|---|---|---|---|---|---|---|---|---|
| English Character | M | N | O | P | Q | R | S | T | U | V | W | X | Y | Z |



See also Extra Practice section.

### Project Activity 1

**Reading** Suggest that students may want to separate the coded message into groups of two digits before they begin to substitute.

# Integers and Absolute Value

1-4

## PART 1 Comparing Integers

Antifreeze is mixed with the water in a car's radiator to prevent the water from freezing. Pure water freezes at about 32 degrees Fahrenheit (°F) *above* zero. A mixture of equal parts water and antifreeze freezes at about 32 degrees *below* zero.

**Freezing Points**

| Substance | Freezing Temperature (°F) |
|---|---|
| Water | 32 |
| Antifreeze and water | −32 |
| Seawater | 28 |
| Gasoline | −36 |

You can write 32 degrees above zero as +32°F or 32°F. You can write 32 degrees below zero as −32°F. Read the numbers 32 and −32 as "*positive* 32" and "*negative* 32."

**MEASUREMENT** CONNECTION

### Example 1

*Temperature* **Write a number to represent the temperature shown by the thermometer.**

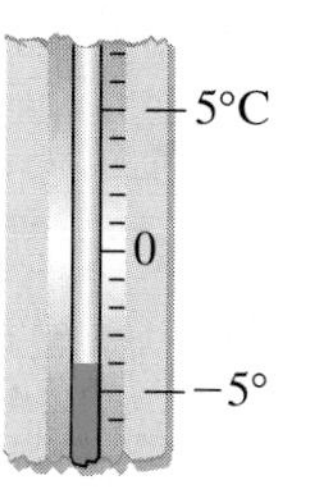


The temperature of the liquid in the thermometer is 4 degrees Celsius below zero, or −4°C.

### Try This

1. *Temperature* Seawater freezes at about 28°F, or about 2 degrees Celsius below zero. Write a number to represent the Celsius temperature. −2

You can graph positive and negative numbers on a number line. A number line helps you compare numbers and arrange them in order.

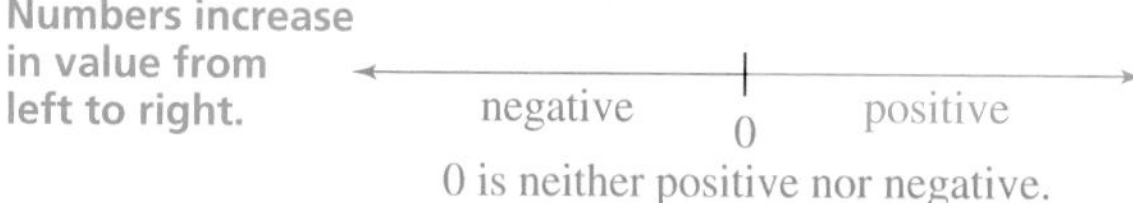




**What You'll Learn**

1. To represent, graph, and order integers
2. To find opposites and absolute values

**. . . And Why**

To represent real-world quantities that are less than zero, such as cold temperatures

# Tools to Monitor Progress

## BEFORE THE LESSON

**To check prerequisite skills:**

- Reading numbers on a number line

**Skills You Need,** p. 1

## DURING THE LESSON

**To check understanding:**

**Try This** exercises on student page

- **Additional Example 1**
  Write a number for 12 degrees Celsius below zero. −12°C
- **Additional Example 2**
  Graph 2, −2, and −3 on a number line.

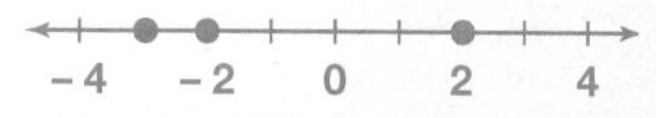


# 1-4

## Getting Ready

**Key Terms and Symbols** opposites, integers, absolute value

**Resources** A complete list of resources for this lesson is on p. 1H.

### Daily Skills Warm-Up

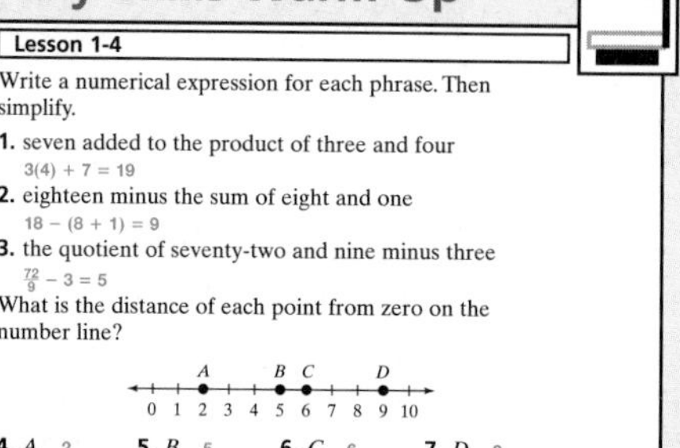

Lesson 1-4

Write a numerical expression for each phrase. Then simplify.

1. seven added to the product of three and four
   3(4) + 7 = 19
2. eighteen minus the sum of eight and one
   18 − (8 + 1) = 9
3. the quotient of seventy-two and nine minus three
   $\frac{72}{9} - 3 = 5$

What is the distance of each point from zero on the number line?

4. *A* 2 5. *B* 5 6. *C* 6 7. *D* 9

### Background for the Lesson

The integers are the whole numbers, including zero, and their opposites. Zero separates the positive and negative integers. Zero is neither positive nor negative, and zero has no opposite.

## 1 Focus

### Connecting to Students' Lives

Ask students to provide examples in their daily life for which they might use negative numbers. Examples could include games, sports, and financial matters.

### Connecting to Prior Knowledge

Students know how to use the symbols <, >, and = to compare the value of whole numbers. Write several pairs of integers on the board and ask students to supply the correct symbol to compare the values of the numbers. Include both positive and negative integers.

# 2 Teach

## Part 1 Teaching Notes

Draw a number line on the board, with zero in the middle. Ask students to place some positive and negative integers where they belong on the number line. Ask students to name a number that is not an integer (for example, 0.5).

### Example 1

**Build understanding.** Ask: Temperatures below zero and depths below sea level are usually written with what kind of numbers? **negative**

### Example 2

**Build understanding.** Ask: Is −2 greater than 1? Is −3 less than 2? **no; yes**

**ELL** Help students understand that the words *subtract, take away,* and *minus* all indicate a subtraction operation, such as 7 − 3. The word *negative* describes a number to the left of zero on the number line.

## Part 2 Teaching Notes

Show students that they can read the first vertical line in |4| as "the distance that," then read the number "four," and read the second vertical line as "is from zero." So |4| is the distance that four is from zero.

### Example 3

**Build understanding.** Ask: What is the same about −3 and 3? **their distance from zero on the number line** What is different about −3 and 3? **their direction from zero on the number line**

**Extension** Challenge students to determine how far zero is from zero on a number line, or to find the absolute value of zero. **zero; zero**

### EXAMPLE 2

**Graph −1, 4, and −5 on a number line. Order the numbers from least to greatest.**

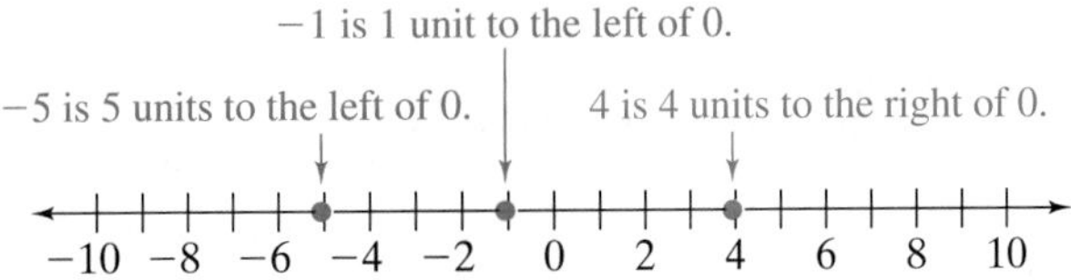


The numbers from least to greatest are −5, −1, and 4.

### TRY THIS

2. Graph 0, 2, and −6 on a number line. Order the numbers from least to greatest.
   −6 −1 0 1 2
   **−6, 0, 2**

## Part 2 Finding Absolute Value

Numbers that are the same distance from zero on a number line but in opposite directions are called **opposites.**

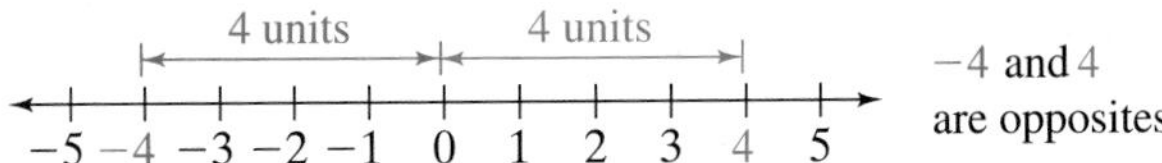


−4 and 4 are opposites.

**Integers** are the whole numbers and their opposites. A number's distance from zero on the number line is called its **absolute value.** You write *the absolute value of 3* as $|3|$.

### EXAMPLE 3

**Use a number line to find $|-3|$ and $|3|$.**

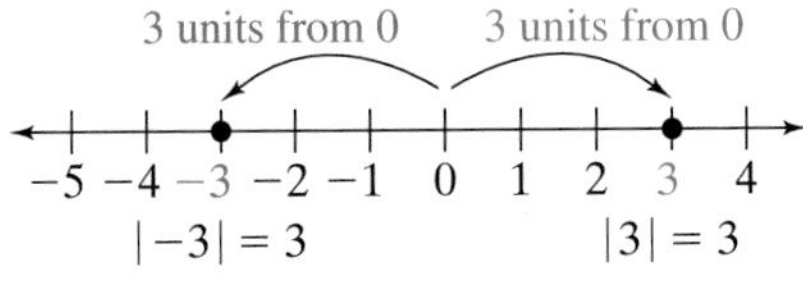


$|-3| = 3$ $|3| = 3$

### TRY THIS

3. Write $|-10|$ in words. Then find $|-10|$.
   **the absolute value of negative ten; 10**



- **Additional Example 3**
  Use a number line to find the value of |−5| and the value of |5|. **5, 5**

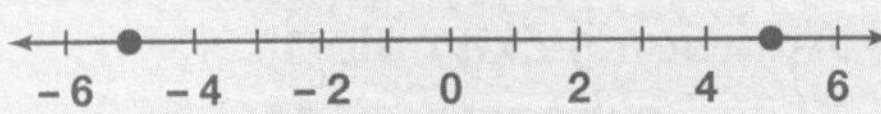


## AFTER THE LESSON

**To assess knowledge:**

**Lesson Quiz**

Write an integer to represent each situation.

1. a debt of $5 **−5**
2. a dive of 23 feet below the surface **−23**

Simplify.

3. |−12| **12**

- For enrichment and reteaching options see Resources on p. 1H.

# Exercises

## Check Understanding

**Write an integer to represent each quantity.**

**1.** a profit of $250 250 **2.** 18°C below zero −18 **3.** 45 s before launch −45

**Write the integer represented by each point on the number line.**

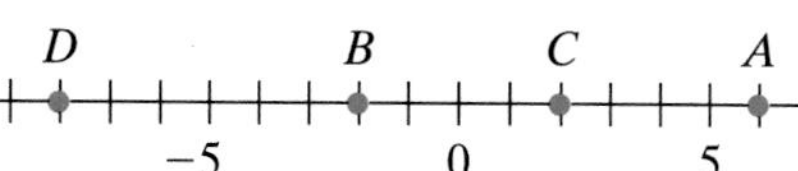


**4.** *A* 2 **5.** *B* 5 **6.** *C* −4

**Simplify each expression.**

**7.** $|18|$ 18 **8.** the opposite of −9 9 **9.** $|-3|$ 3

**10.** Suppose you use +1 to represent *saving* a dollar.
- **a.** What is the opposite of saving a dollar? spending a dollar
- **b.** What number would you use to represent the opposite of saving a dollar? −1

## Practice and Problem Solving

**Write an integer to represent each quantity.**

**11.** a deposit of $110 110 **12.** a debt of $50 −50 **13.** 300 ft below sea level −300

**14.** win by 7 points 7 **15.** a loss of 8 yd −8 **16.** an elevation of 3,400 ft 3,400

*Open-ended* **Describe a quantity each integer could represent.** Answers may vary. Samples are given.

**17.** −1,000 loss of 1,000 points in a board game **18.** 28 28 golf strokes over par **19.** −126 checkbook balance for checks totalling $126 more than is in the bank

**Graph each set of numbers on a number line. Then order the numbers from least to greatest.** 20–22. See margin for graphs.

**20.** −2, 8, −9 −9, −2, 8 **21.** −3, −12, −9 −12, −9, −3 **22.** 0, 6, −6 −6, 0, 6

**Write the integer represented by each point.**

D B C A
−5 0 5

**23.** *A* 6 **24.** *B* −2 **25.** *C* 2 **26.** *D* −8

**Simplify each expression.**

**27.** the opposite of 6 −6 **28.** $|-7|$ 7 **29.** $|0|$ 0

**30.** $|-1{,}000|$ 1,000 **31.** the opposite of −2 2 **32.** $-|-13|$ −13



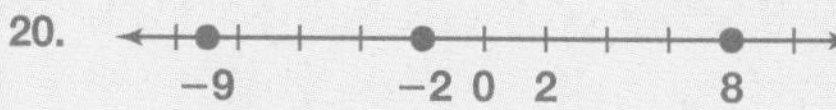


21. −12 −9 −3 0 2

22. −6 −2 0 2 6

**Error Prevention** A common error is to think that zero is positive and that its opposite is −0. Zero is neither positive nor negative, and it has no opposite. Zero is the dividing line between the positive and negative numbers.

**Tactile Learning** Make a number line on the floor with tape and have students walk the distance from −3 to zero. Then, have them compare this distance to the distance from 3 to zero.

# 3 Practice/Assess

## Assignment Guide

To provide flexible scheduling, this lesson can be divided into parts.

**Part 1**
**Core** 1–6, 11–26, 33, 54–55
**Extension** 51–53

**Part 2**
**Core** 7–10, 27–32, 34–37, 39–50
**Extension** 38, 56–62

Mixed Review can be assigned at any time for maintenance.

## Exercises

**Exercises 11–16** Verify that students understand the meaning of a *deposit*, a *debt*, and an *elevation*.

**Test Prep Exercise 33** Have students sketch a number line to check the truth of each statement.

**Exercises 51–53** Suggest that students begin by drawing a number line.

## Challenge

Evaluate $|-12| - |12|$. Will the answer be the same for any integer and its opposite? 0; yes

## Closure

Integers are the set of whole numbers and their opposites. The absolute value of an integer is its distance from zero on a number line. On a number line, the number farther to the right is the greater.

## Daily Cumulative Review

**Evaluate each expression.** *(Lesson 1-3)*

1. $z - 8$, for $z = 22$ — 14
2. $4d$, for $d = 6$ — 24
3. $9 \div w + 7$, for $w = 3$ — 10
4. $23 - (a + 11)$, for $a = 7$ — 5
5. $22fg$, for $f = 2, g = 1$ — 44
6. $3(s + t)$, for $s = 5, t = 2$ — 21

**Simplify each expression.** *(Lesson 1-2)*

7. $15 \div 3 + 2 - 5$ — 2
8. $6(5) + 11$ — 41
9. $3 \cdot 7 + 2 \cdot 7$ — 35
10. $3[2 + (8 \cdot 4)]$ — 102
11. $12 \div 3 \times 2 - 8$ — 0
12. $2[(15 - 7)3] + 5$ — 53

**Mixed Review**

**Write a variable expression for each word phrase.**

13. *p* divided by sixty-one (1-1) — $p \div 61$
14. the product of ten and a number *a* (1-1) — $10a$
15. fifty-eight less than *g* (1-1) — $g - 58$

**Find each sum or difference.** *(From Last Year)*

16. $14 + 29$ — 43
17. $397 + 264$ — 661
18. $783 - 295$ — 488
19. $78 - 39$ — 39
20. $442 - 75$ — 367
21. $837 + 98$ — 935



33. **TEST PREP** Which statement is *not* true? B
A. $-1$ is less than 3.
B. $-3$ is greater than $-1$.
C. 1 is greater than $-3$.
D. $-3$ is less than 1.

**Use numerals and absolute value symbols to represent each phrase. Then simplify.**

34. the absolute value of negative six $|-6|$; 6
35. the absolute value of the opposite of ninety $|-90|$; 90
36. the opposite of the absolute value of negative 9 $-|-9|$; $-9$
37. the opposite of the opposite of eight $-(-8)$; 8
38. the absolute value of the opposite of $|-1{,}000|$ $|-|-1{,}000||$; 1,000

**Graph each integer and its opposite on a number line.** 39–44. See margin.

39. 1
40. $-2$
41. $-8$
42. $-7$
43. 6
44. $-4$

**Compare. Use >, <, or = to complete each statement.**

45. $-8 \,\blacksquare\, 0$ <
46. $4 \,\blacksquare\, -25$ >
47. $-9 \,\blacksquare\, -2$ <
48. $|-1| \,\blacksquare\, |50|$ <
49. $|-6| \,\blacksquare\, |-12|$ <
50. $|10| \,\blacksquare\, |-10|$ =

*Open-ended* **Name two integers between the given integers.** 51–53. Answers may vary. Samples are given.

51. $-6, 2$ $-5, 0$
52. $0, -4$ $-3, -1$
53. $-8, -12$ $-11, -10$

### Finding Famous Ships

Scientist-explorer Robert D. Ballard led the expeditions that found two famous ships deep in the North Atlantic Ocean.

In 1912, the luxury passenger liner *Titanic* struck an iceberg. It came to rest 12,500 ft below sea level. *Titanic* was 882 ft long and 92 ft wide.

In 1941, the mighty warship *Bismarck* sank in battle. *Bismarck* was 823 ft long and 118 ft wide.

*Star Hercules*, only 269 ft long, towed the underwater camera sled that found *Bismarck* under 15,617 ft of water.

Star Hercules
−5,000 feet
−10,000 feet
Titanic
−15,000 feet
Bismarck

*Math in the Media* **Use the article above and the graph at the right for Exercises 54 and 55.**

54. Write integers that represent the positions of *Titanic, Bismarck,* and *Star Hercules.* $-12{,}500$; $-15{,}617$; 0
55. *Error Analysis* A friend says that *Bismarck's* resting place is higher than *Titanic's,* since 15,617 is higher than 12,500. Explain your friend's error. Answers may vary. Sample: My friend did not take into account the signs of the numbers.



## Alternative Assessment

Ask students to write a weather report in which the low temperature for the day is a negative integer and the high temperature for the day is a positive integer.

39.
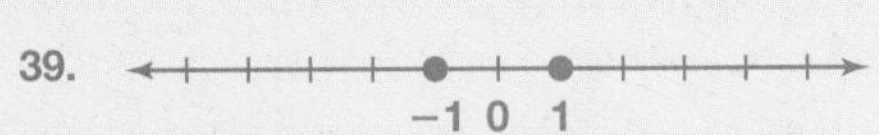


40.
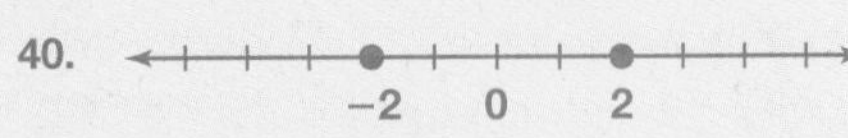


41. −8 −2 0 2 8

42. −7 −2 0 2 7

43. −6 −2 0 2 6

44. −4 −1 0 1 4

**Complete each sentence with a word that makes it true.**

56. An integer is negative, positive, or ___?___. zero

57. All ___?___ integers are less than zero. negative

58. The opposite of a ___?___ number is negative. positive

59. The absolute value of an integer is never ___?___. negative

60. a. *Data Analysis* Use a number line to graph the temperatures in the chart. Label each temperature with the name of the state where it was recorded. See margin.
b. Which state recorded the lowest temperature? b. Nevada

**Record Low Temperatures for Three States**

| State | Temperature (°C) |
|---|---|
| California | −43 |
| Nevada | −46 |
| Georgia | −27 |

SOURCE: *The World Almanac*

61. *Writing* How can you use integers to describe water levels at high tide and low tide? See margin.

62. *Critical Thinking* Is $|x + y|$ the same as $|x| + |y|$? Explain. no; in the first expression you add first and then find the absolute value, while in the second expression you find the absolute values and then add.

## MIXED REVIEW

**Evaluate each expression.** *(Lesson 1-3)*

63. $p - 5$, for $p = 19$ 14

64. $3d + 3$, for $d = 7$ 24

65. $55y$, for $y = 8$ 440

**Compare. Use >, <, or = to complete each statement.** *(Lesson 1-2)*

66. $5 + 10 \div 5$ ■ $(5 + 10) \div 5$ >

67. $(9 - 6) \div (2 + 1)$ ■ $9 - 6 \div 2 + 1$ <

68. Suppose you have *c* CDs. Your friend has 6 more CDs than you do. Write an expression for the number of CDs your friend has. *(Lesson 1-1)* $c + 6$

## CHECKPOINT 1 — Lessons 1-1 through 1-4

**Write a variable expression for each word phrase.**

1. 23 more than $f$ $f + 23$

2. $g$ divided by 34 $\frac{g}{34}$

3. the product of 9 and $p$ $9p$

**Simplify each expression.**

4. $17 + 16 - 13$ 20

5. $70 \div 5(3 + 4)$ 2

6. $9 \times 6 \div 3 + 1$ 19

**Evaluate each expression for $x = 4$, $y = 6$, and $z = 12$.**

7. $2x - 8$ 0

8. $3(z + y)$ 54

9. $4y - z + \frac{z}{x}$ 15

10. *Temperature* On Monday the average temperature was −10°F. On Tuesday it was −15°F. On Wednesday it was −13°F. On Thursday it was 0°F. Graph the temperatures on a number line. Write the days in order from coldest to warmest.
−15 −13 −10 −2 0
Tuesday, Wednesday, Monday, Thursday

See also Extra Practice section.



60a. −46 −43 −27 −10 0
Nevada California Georgia

## Practice

**Graph each set of numbers on a number line. Then order the numbers from least to greatest.**

1. −4, −8, 5 — −8, −4, 5
2. 3, −3, −2 — −3, −2, 3
3. 0, −9, −5 — −9, −5, 0
4. −7, −1, −6 — −7, −6, −1

**Write an integer to represent each quantity.**

5. 5 degrees below zero —5
6. 2,000 ft above sea level 2,000
7. a loss of 12 yd −12
8. 7 strokes under par −7

**Simplify each expression.**

9. the opposite of −15 15
10. |−9| 9
11. −|−25| −25
12. the opposite of |−8| −8
13. −|−31| −31
14. |847| 847

**Write the integer represented by each point on the number line.**

15. *A* −2
16. *B* 4
17. *C* 0
18. *D* −7
19. *E* 7

**Compare. Use >, <, or = to complete each statement.**

20. −3 < 4
21. 5 > 1
22. −2 > −6
23. 7 < |8|
24. |−2| = |2|
25. |−1| > −6
26. |4| < |−5|
27. 0 < |−7|



## Reteaching

**Compare. Use >, <, or = to complete each statement.**

a. −4 □ −2

Graph −4 and −2 on the number line.

A number on the left is less than a number on the right. Thus, −4 is less than −2. −4 < −2

b. |−4| □ |−2|

The *absolute value* of a number is its distance from zero on the number line.

Thus |−4| = 4 and |−2| = 2. Since 4 > 2, |−4| > |−2|

**Compare. Use >, <, or = to complete each statement.**

1. −3 < −2
2. −5 < 1
3. 0 > −2
4. 1 > 0
5. 1 > −1
6. −5 < −3
7. |−3| > 0
8. |−2| < |−5|
9. |−3| > 2
10. |−6| = 6
11. |3| > |−2|
12. |−7| > 0
13. −3 < |−3|
14. 4 > |−2|
15. |−2| < 3
16. |−5| > 3
17. |8| = |−8|
18. −6 < −4
19. 5 > |−4|
20. −3 > −5
21. |2| < |−3|
22. |−1| = |1|
23. |−3| > |−1|
24. −1 < 2



## Enrichment

The absolute value of an integer is its distance from zero on a number line. You can use that fact to solve absolute value equations.

**Example 1** Solve $|n| = 2$.
**Solution** Both −2 and 2 are at a distance of 2 units from 0 on the number line. Therefore, $n = -2$ or $n = 2$.

**Example 2** Solve $|n - 2| = 3$.
**Solution** Both −1 and 5 are at a distance of 3 units from 2 on the number line. Therefore, $n = -1$ or $n = 5$.

**Solve by naming the possible values of *n*. Use the number line.**

1. $|n| = 4$ $n =$ −4 or 4
2. $|n| = 1$ $n =$ −1 or 1
3. $|n| = 8$ $n =$ −8 or 8
4. $|n - 3| = 1$ $n =$ 2 or 4
5. $|n - 2| = 5$ $n =$ −3 or 7
6. $|n - (-4)| = 6$ $n =$ −10 or 2
7. $|5 - n| = 1$ $n =$ 4 or 6
8. $|2 - n| = 3$ $n =$ −1 or 5
9. $|-6 - n| = 2$ $n =$ −4 or −8
10. $|n| = 0$ $n =$ 0
11. $|n - 5| = 0$ $n =$ 5
12. $|-3 - n| = 0$ $n =$ −3
13. $|-n| = 10$ $n =$ −10 or 10
14. $|n - (-6)| = 3$ $n =$ −9 or −3
15. $|n - 7| = 3$ $n =$ 4 or 10
16. $|-4 - n| = 2$ $n =$ −6 or −2
17. $|n - 2| = 4$ $n =$ −2 or 6
18. $|1 - n| = 0$ $n =$ 1

19. How do you known that the equation $|n| = -3$ has no solution? Distance cannot be negative.



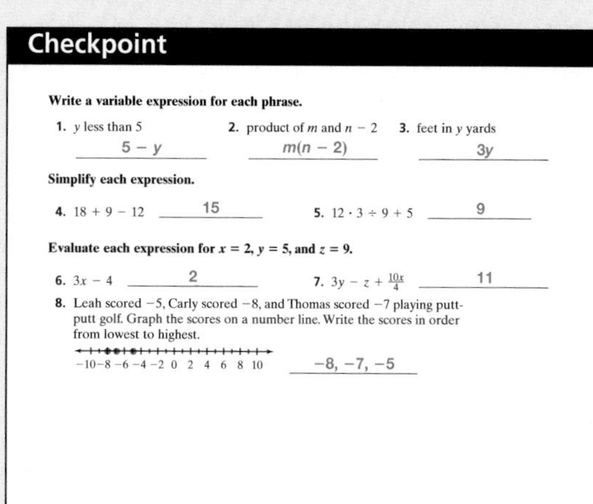

## Checkpoint

**Write a variable expression for each phrase.**

1. $y$ less than 5 — $5 - y$
2. product of $m$ and $n - 2$ — $m(n - 2)$
3. feet in $y$ yards — $3y$

**Simplify each expression.**

4. $18 + 9 - 12$ 15
5. $12 \cdot 3 \div 9 + 5$ 9

**Evaluate each expression for $x = 2$, $y = 5$, and $z = 9$.**

6. $3x - 4$ 2
7. $3y - z + \frac{10x}{4}$ 11

8. Leah scored −5, Carly scored −8, and Thomas scored −7 playing putt-putt golf. Graph the scores on a number line. Write the scores in order from lowest to highest. −8, −7, −5

# MATH TOOLBOX

## Modeling

In Lesson 1-4 students represented integers, opposites, and absolute values by graphing them on a number line. This Math Toolbox shows students how to use models, such as colored tiles, to represent integers.

## Math Background

You can use tiles or counters of two different colors to model integers. Each yellow tile represents 1 and each red tile represents −1. A yellow tile and a red tile together are called a zero pair since the sum of 1 and −1 is zero. When you use the tiles to model combining integers, you can always remove one or more zero pairs without changing the value of the combined integers.

## Teaching Notes

**Error Prevention** Some students may not understand how to model combining the integers. Demonstrate with transparent tiles on an overhead. Encourage students to work in pairs or groups to help each other.

**Monitoring Progress Example 1** Remind students that the model of 4 red tiles for −4 is a number which is less than the model of 3 yellow tiles for 3. The color of the tiles (and the sign of the integer) is a key piece of information for determining the size of the number.

**Monitoring Progress Example 2** Make sure that students remove tiles only in pairs of opposite colors.

**Block Scheduling** If you have block scheduling or extended periods, you may wish to insert this Math Toolbox lesson between the completion of Part 2 of Lesson 1-4 and the beginning of Part 1 of Lesson 1-5. Use the Pacing Options on page 1C to see the possibilities.



# MATH TOOLBOX

*Modeling*

*Before Lesson 1-5*

## *Modeling Integers*

You can use models, such as colored tiles, to represent integers. Use a yellow tile ▢ to represent a positive integer. Use a red tile ■ to represent a negative integer.

### Example 1

**Use models to represent the integers 3, −1, and −4.**

▢▢▢ 3 ■ −1 ■■■■ −4

An equal number of yellow tiles and red tiles combine to make zero.

These tiles make a *zero pair.*→ ▢■ represents zero, or ▢ + ■ = 0.

You can remove zero pairs in sets of mixed tiles.

### Example 2

**Write the integer that is represented by ■■■■■▢▢.**

Group the zero pairs. Then remove them.

Write the integer that the remaining tiles represent.

■■■ −3

**Use tiles to model each integer.** 1–8. Models may vary. Samples are shown.

1. −3
2. 5
3. −2
4. 7
5. 0
6. −6
7. 2
8. −8

**Write an integer for each model.**

9. 2
10. −5
11. −2
12. 6
13. 0
14. 1
15. 4
16. −1

# Adding Integers

## PART 1 Using Models to Add Integers

If a car goes forward 20 ft and then backs up 20 ft, it ends where it started. Using opposite integers, you can represent this situation as $20 + (-20) = 0$.

When you add two opposites, their sum is zero. So opposites are also called *additive inverses*.

**Addition of Opposites**

The sum of an integer and its opposite is zero.

| Arithmetic | Algebra |
|---|---|
| $1 + (-1) = 0$ | $x + (-x) = 0$ |
| $-1 + 1 = 0$ | $-x + x = 0$ |

You can use tiles to add integers. One positive tile and one negative tile combine to make a zero pair, since ▢ + ■ = 0.

To add integers with tiles, combine tiles and remove the zero pairs.

**EXAMPLE 1**

*Modeling* **Use tiles to find 2 + (−5).**

$2 + (-5)$ ▢▢ + ■■■■■ Model the sum.

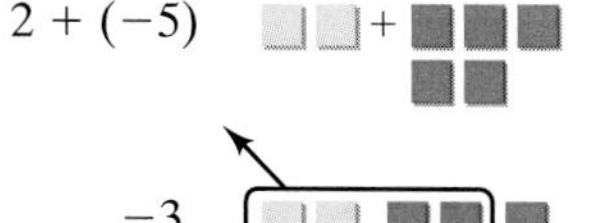

$-3$ Group and remove zero pairs. There are three negative tiles left.

$2 + (-5) = -3$

**TRY THIS** Use tiles to find each sum.

**1.** $-1 + 4$ 3 **2.** $7 + (-3)$ 4 **3.** $-2 + (-2)$ −4

## 1-5

### What You'll Learn

1. To use models to add integers
2. To use rules to add integers

### . . . And Why

To use integers to solve real-world problems in sports and Earth science



# Tools to Monitor Progress

### BEFORE THE LESSON

**To check prerequisite skills:**

- Adding and subtracting whole numbers

**Skills You Need,** p. 1

**Skills Handbook,** p. 723

**Skills Intervention Kit,** Whole Numbers

### DURING THE LESSON

**To check understanding:**

**Try This** exercises on student page

- **Additional Example 1**
  Use tiles to find $(-7) + 3$. −4
- **Additional Example 2**
  A diver goes down 20 feet and then comes back up 4 feet. Find $-20 + 4$ to find the position of the diver after these two dives. **−16 feet from the surface**

## 1-5

## Getting Ready

**Key Terms and Symbols** additive inverses, zero pair

**Materials** algebra tiles

**Resources** A complete list of resources for this lesson is on p. 1H.

### Daily Skills Warm-Up

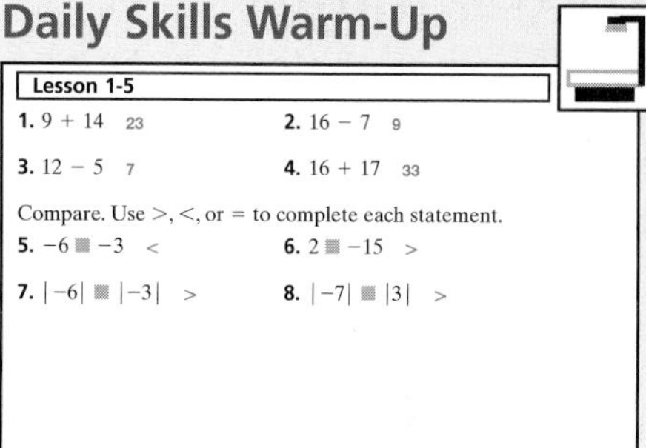

Lesson 1-5

1. 9 + 14 23
2. 16 − 7 9
3. 12 − 5 7
4. 16 + 17 33

Compare. Use >, <, or = to complete each statement.

5. −6 ■ −3 <
6. 2 ■ −15 >
7. |−6| ■ |−3| >
8. |−7| ■ |3| >

### Background for the Lesson

You can model the sum of two integers with tiles. Tiles of one color, such as yellow, represent positive integers, and tiles of a second color, such as red, represent negative integers. To combine integers, represent each integer in tiles and then put these tiles together. Then match a positive tile with a negative tile to form a zero pair. You then eliminate the zero pairs from the expression. The remaining tiles represent the sum of the integers.

## 1 Focus

### Connecting to Students' Lives

Ask students if they have ever played a guessing game such as this: Think of a number, add 5 to it, subtract 3, then subtract 5 and add 3; the result is your original number. Point out that games like this work because they use inverses, doing and undoing the same thing to the original number.

### Connecting to Prior Knowledge

Students should know that zero plus any integer equals the integer. This explains why zero pairs can be removed when adding with algebra tiles.

# 2 Teach

## Part 1 Teaching Notes

Review with students which numbers are the integers, and have them name the opposites of a few integers.

### Example 1

**Build understanding.** Ask: Why can you remove the zero pair tiles? because adding or subtracting zero leaves a number unchanged

### Example 2

**Build understanding.** Ask: What integer represents a loss of 8 yards? −8

**ELL** Saying that 3 and −3 are *opposites* is the same as saying that they are *additive inverses,* which is the same as saying that their sum is zero.

## Part 2 Teaching Notes

Point out to students that they may use tiles, rules, or the number line to help them understand how to add integers. Allow students to use the method with which they are most comfortable.

### Example 3

**Build understanding.** Ask: What is different about the sums in the two parts? The signs are alike in the first part, but different in the second part.

**Error Prevention** A common error is thinking that the absolute value of a number is its opposite. Explain that the absolute value of a number is its distance from zero, without regard to the direction from zero.

A number line is another model you can use to add integers.

### Example 2

**On two plays, a football team loses 8 yd and then gains 3 yd. Find $-8 + 3$ to find the result of the two plays.**

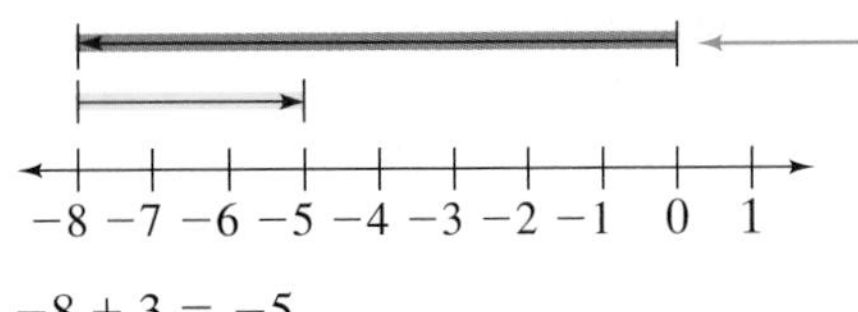


Start at 0. To represent −8, move left 8 units. To add positive 3, move right 3 units to −5.

$-8 + 3 = -5$

The result of the two plays is a loss of 5 yd.

**Try This** Use a number line to find each sum.

**4.** $2 + (-6)$ −4 **5.** $-4 + 9$ 5 **6.** $-5 + (-1)$ −6

## Part 2 Using Rules to Add Integers

You can also use rules to find the sum of two integers.

**Adding Integers**

**Same Sign** The sum of two positive integers is positive. The sum of two negative integers is negative.

**Different Signs** To add two integers with different signs, find the difference of their absolute values. The sum has the sign of the integer with the greater absolute value.

### Example 3

**Find each sum.**

**a.** $\mathbf{-12 + (-31)}$

$-12 + (-31) = -43$ Since both integers are negative, the sum is negative.

**b.** $\mathbf{7 + (-18)}$

$|-18| - |7| = 18 - 7$ Find the difference of the absolute values.

$= 11$ Simplify.

$7 + (-18) = -11$ Since −18 has the greater absolute value, the sum is negative.



- **Additional Example 3**
  Find the sum. $-20 + (-15)$ −35
- **Additional Example 4**
  A player scores 22 points and gets a penalty of 30 points. What is the player's score after the penalty? −8
- **Additional Example 5**
  Find $-7 + (-4) + 13 + (-5)$. −3

### AFTER THE LESSON

**To assess knowledge:**

**Lesson Quiz**

Find each sum.

1. $-37 + (-5)$ −42
2. $14 + (-4)$ 10
3. $-100 + 5 + (-3)$ −98

Evaluate for $t = -11$.

4. $33 + t$ 22

- For enrichment and reteaching options see Resources on p. 1H.

**Try This** Find each sum.

**7.** $-22 + (-16)$ $-38$ **8.** $60 + (-13)$ 47 **9.** $-125 + 35$ $-90$

REAL-WORLD CONNECTION

## Example 4

*Earth Science* **The earthquake monitor in Hockley, Texas, is located in a salt mine at an elevation of −416 m. The elevation of the monitor in Albuquerque, New Mexico, is 2,156 m higher than the one in Hockley. Find the elevation of the monitor in Albuquerque.**

| | |
|---|---|
| $-416 + 2{,}156$ | Write an expression. |
| $\lvert 2{,}156\rvert - \lvert -416\rvert = 2{,}156 - 416$ | Find the difference of the absolute values. |
| $= 1{,}740$ | Simplify. |
| $-416 + 2{,}156 = 1{,}740$ | Since 2,156 has the greater absolute value, the sum is positive. |

The elevation of the monitor in Albuquerque is 1,740 m.

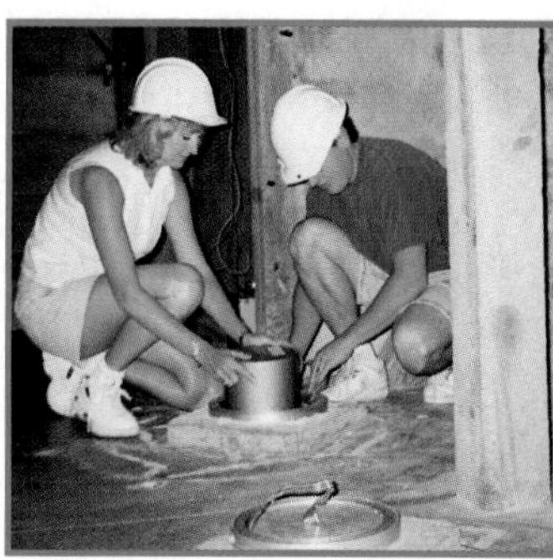
A worldwide network of monitors keeps track of earthquake activity. Here technicians check the monitor in Albuquerque.

**Try This**

**10.** The elevation of a monitor in Pinon Flat, California, is 1,696 m higher than the monitor in Hockley, Texas. Find the elevation of the monitor in Pinon Flat. 1,280 m

To add several integers, use the order of operations.

## Example 5

**Find $-12 + (-6) + 15 + (-2)$.**

| | |
|---|---|
| $-12 + (-6) + 15 + (-2)$ | Add from left to right. |
| $-18 + 15 + (-2)$ | The sum of two negative integers is negative. |
| $-3 + (-2)$ | $\lvert -18\rvert - \lvert 15\rvert = 3$. Since $-18$ has the greater absolute value, the sum is negative. |
| $-5$ | The sum of two negative integers is negative. |

$-12 + (-6) + 15 + (-2) = -5$

**Try This** Find each sum.

**11.** $1 + (-3) + 2 + (-10)$ $-10$ **12.** $-250 + 200 + (-100) + 220$ 70



### Example 4

**Build understanding.** Ask: What does an elevation of −416 meters mean? 416 m below sea level

### Example 5

**Build understanding.** Ask: In each step, what do you do with the numbers you do not combine in that step, such as 15 and −2 in the first step? You copy them unchanged into the next step.

**Extension** Challenge students to explain when the absolute value of a number would be equal to the opposite of the number. when the number is negative

**Connecting to Geography** Have students consult an atlas or other reference source to find the location and elevation of the highest point and lowest point in the United States.

# 3 Practice/Assess

## Assignment Guide

To provide flexible scheduling, this lesson can be divided into parts.

**Part 1**
**Core** 1–8, 13–16
✪ **Extension** 69–72

**Part 2**
**Core** 9–12, 17–50, 53–63, 68
✪ **Extension** 51–52, 64–67, 73

Mixed Review can be assigned at any time for maintenance.

### Exercises

**Exercises 17–20** Tell students that predicting the sign of the sum before doing the calculations can help them catch any careless errors.

**Visual Learning** Exercises 50, 60
Suggest that students sketch the moves in problems involving football plays, dives, or climbing.

**Test Prep** Exercise 62 Before doing the calculation, represent the problem by writing an expression with integers.

# Exercises

## Check Understanding

*Modeling* **Write an expression for each model. Find the sum.**

**1.** ■■■■ + □□□□□□□ −4 + 7; 3

**2.** □□□□□ + □■ 5 + 0; 5

**3.** 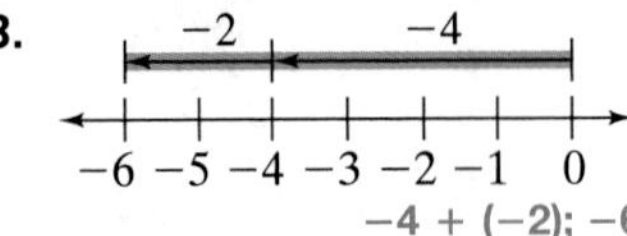

−4 + (−2); −6

**4.** 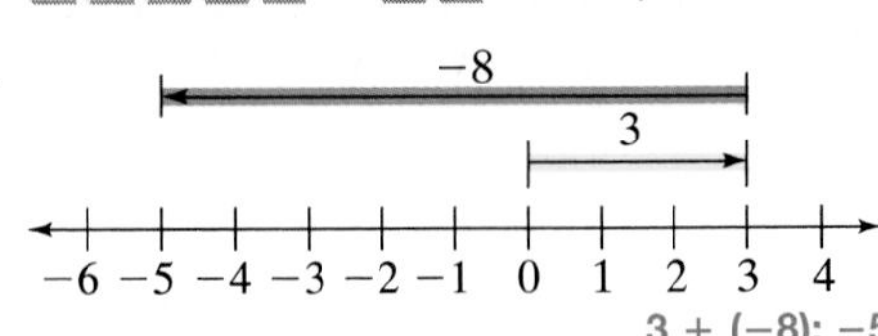

3 + (−8); −5

*Modeling* **Draw a model and find each sum.** 5–8. Models may vary. Samples are shown in margin.

**5.** $2 + (-5)$ −3 **6.** $-5 + 2$ −3 **7.** $5 + (-2)$ 3 **8.** $-5 + (-2)$ −7

**Find each sum.**

**9.** $-26 + (-39)$ −65 **10.** $-40 + 93$ 53 **11.** $235 + (-420)$ −185 **12.** $100 + (-100)$ 0

## Practice and Problem Solving

*Modeling* **Draw a model and find each sum.** 13–16. Models may vary. Samples are shown in margin.

**13.** $-6 + 1$ −5 **14.** $-3 + (-6)$ −9 **15.** $7 + (-4)$ 3 **16.** $-3 + 2$ −1

**Without adding, tell whether each sum is positive, negative, or zero. Explain your reasoning.**

**17.** $-4 + (-10)$ Negative; both numbers are negative.
**18.** $11 + (-3)$ Positive; the number with greater absolute value is positive.
**19.** $-8 + 5$ Negative; the number with greater absolute value is negative.
**20.** $6 + (-6)$ Zero; the numbers are opposites.

**Use rules to find each sum.**

**21.** $14 + (-11)$ 3 **22.** $0 + (-9)$ −9 **23.** $-6 + (-7)$ −13

**24.** $-18 + 4$ −14 **25.** $450 + (-350)$ 100 **26.** $-193 + 225$ 32

**27.** $-18 + 7 + 45$ 34 **28.** $30 + (-25) + (-15)$ −10 **29.** $19 + (-9) + 45$ 55

**30.** $-3 + 2 + (-7) + 7 + 13$ 12 **31.** $-94 + 68 + (-22)$ −48 **32.** $-20 + (-89) + 112 + 9$ 12

*Mental Math* **Find each sum.**

**33.** $-5 + 20$ 15 **34.** $6 + (-6)$ 0 **35.** $10 + (-3)$ 7 **36.** $-1 + (-8) + 2$ −7

**37.** $-5 + 5 + 16$ 16 **38.** $-4 + (-2) + (-2)$ −8 **39.** $-120 + 100 + (-20)$ −40



5.

6. 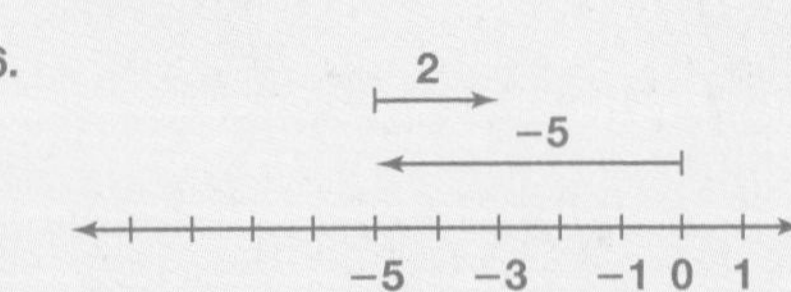


7. 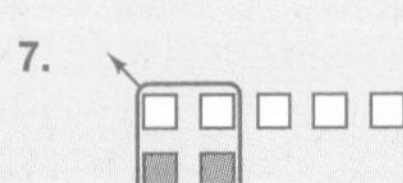

8. 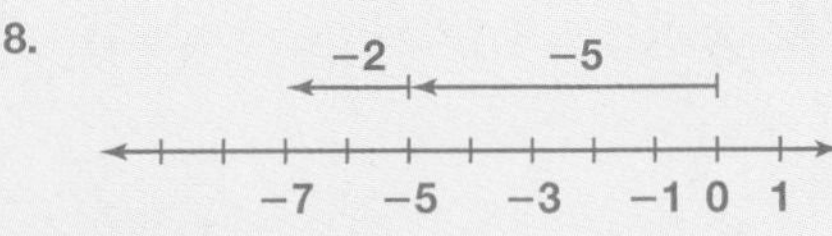


13–16. Models may vary. Samples are shown.

13. 

### Daily Cumulative Review

**Simplify each expression.** *(Lesson 1-4)*

1. $|-9|$ 9
2. the opposite of −18 18
3. $-|-32|$ −32
4. the opposite of 3 −3
5. $|0|$ 0
6. $|19|$ 19

**Evaluate each expression.** *(Lesson 1-3)*

7. $d - 19$, for $d = 21$ 2
8. $8w + 5$, for $w = 2$ 21
9. $j(9 + d)$, for $d = 3, j = 3$ 36
10. $abc$, for $a = 4, b = 0, c = 5$ 0

**Mixed Review**

**Compare. Use >, <, or = to complete each statement.**

11. *(1-2)* $6 + 14 \div 2$ [>] $(6 + 14) \div 2$
12. *(1-2)* $32 \div (8 - 4)$ [>] $32 \div 8 - 4$
13. *(1-2)* $(25 - 11) \cdot (2 + 3)$ [>] $25 - 11 \cdot 2 + 3$

**Write an expression for each number of bagels.**

14. *(1-1)* three dozen bagels $3 \times 12$
15. *(1-1)* $g$ dozen bagels $g \times 12$
16. *(1-1)* two dozen bagels $2 \times 12$
17. *(1-1)* one half dozen bagels $12 \div 2$

**Find each sum or difference.** *(From Last Year)*

18. $22 + 834 + 75$ 931
19. $326 - 87$ 239
20. $351 + 299$ 650

**Evaluate each expression for $n = -15$.**

40. $n + 7$ −8　41. $n + (-7)$ −22　42. $15 + n$ 0　43. $n + (-15)$ −30

**Compare. Use >, <, or = to complete each statement.**

44. $-6 + 1 \blacksquare 5 + 1$ <　45. $0 + 3 \blacksquare -2 + 0$ >　46. $10 + (-2) \blacksquare -4 + 12$ =

47. $-1 + 1 \blacksquare -2 + 0$ >　48. $49 + (-21) \blacksquare |-18|$ >　49. $|-20| + (-7) \blacksquare -11 + (-11)$ >

50. A football team gained 4 yd, lost 2 yd, gained 11 yd, lost 8 yd, and then lost 9 yd. Find the net gain or loss. lost 4 yd

51. *Error Analysis* A friend says that the value of $-17 + 5$ is $-22$. Explain how your friend may have made this error. Answers may vary. Sample: My friend subtracted 5 instead of adding 5.

52. *Open-ended* Write and solve a word problem that uses the integers −10, 3, 5, and −6. Check students' work.

**Write a numerical expression for each of the following. Then find the sum.**

53. negative two plus negative seven
$-2 + (-7)$; $-9$

54. twelve plus the absolute value of nine
$12 + |9|$; 21

55. positive three plus the opposite of eight
$3 + (-8)$; $-5$

56. one hundred added to negative nineteen
$-19 + 100$; 81

57. You borrow $20, and then pay back $18.
$-20 + 18$; $-2$

58. You save $200, and then spend $75.
$200 + (-75)$; 125

59. A man deposits $120, and then writes a check for $25.
$120 + (-25)$; 95

60. A submarine at 35 ft below sea level moves up 10 ft.
$-35 + 10$; $-25$

61. The temperature starts at −10°F, drops 2°, rises 8°, drops 5°, drops 13°, and rises 1°.
$-10 + (-2) + 8 + (-5) + (-13) + 1$; $-21$

62. **TEST PREP** Refer to the map at the right. The lowest temperature recorded in South America is 54 degrees higher than the lowest temperature recorded in North America. What is the lowest temperature recorded in South America? B

A. −135°F　B. −27°F　C. −17°F　D. −138°F

**Lowest Recorded Temperatures**

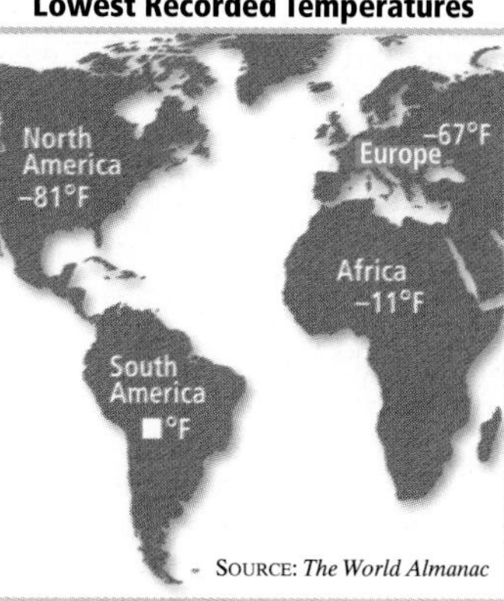


SOURCE: *The World Almanac*

63. Maria had $123. She spent $35, loaned $20 to a friend, and received her $90 paycheck. How much does she have now? $158

**Tell whether each sum is positive or negative. Then find each sum.**

64. $4.8 + (-6.2)$ negative; −1.4　65. $-0.6 + 1.0$ positive; 0.4　66. $-72.5 + 36.4$ negative; −36.1　67. $-9.35 + (-2.84)$ negative; −12.19

68. *Writing* A friend is having trouble finding the sum of −84 and 28. What explanation would you give to help your friend? Answers may vary. Sample: First find the difference of the absolute values of the two numbers. Then give the answer the sign of the number with the greater absolute value.



## Challenge

Is $|a + b|$ always equal to $|a| + |b|$? No; for example, when $a = -1$ and $b = 5$ then the expressions are ≠. It is true that $|a + b|$ is always ≤ to $|a| + |b|$.

## Closure

To add integers with the same sign, add their absolute values. The sum has the same sign as the integers. To add integers with different signs, find the difference of their absolute values. The sum has the sign of the integer with the greater absolute value.

14.



15.

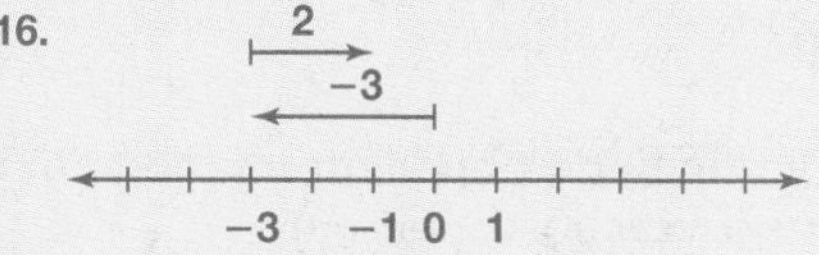

16.



## Alternative Assessment

Have students write in their journals a description of any two integers whose sum is zero.

## Practice

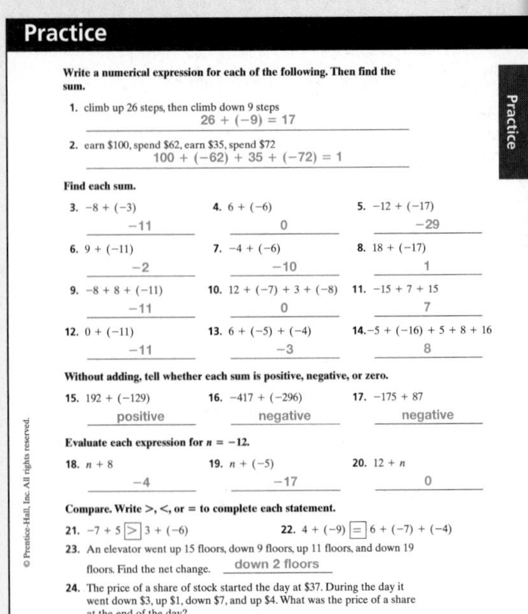

Write a numerical expression for each of the following. Then find the sum.

1. climb up 26 steps, then climb down 9 steps $26 + (-9) = 17$
2. earn \$100, spend \$62, earn \$35, spend \$72 $100 + (-62) + 35 + (-72) = 1$

Find each sum.

3. $-8 + (-3)$ $-11$
4. $6 + (-6)$ $0$
5. $-12 + (-17)$ $-29$
6. $9 + (-11)$ $-2$
7. $-4 + (-6)$ $-10$
8. $18 + (-17)$ $1$
9. $-8 + 8 + (-11)$ $-11$
10. $12 + (-7) + 3 + (-8)$ $0$
11. $-15 + 7 + 15$ $7$
12. $0 + (-11)$ $-11$
13. $6 + (-5) + (-4)$ $-3$
14. $-5 + (-16) + 5 + 8 + 16$ $8$

Without adding, tell whether each sum is positive, negative, or zero.

15. $192 + (-129)$ positive
16. $-417 + (-296)$ negative
17. $-175 + 87$ negative

Evaluate each expression for $n = -12$.

18. $n + 8$ $-4$
19. $n + (-5)$ $-17$
20. $12 + n$ $0$

Compare. Write >, <, or = to complete each statement.

21. $-7 + 5 \; \boxed{>} \; 3 + (-6)$
22. $4 + (-9) \; \boxed{=} \; 6 + (-7) + (-4)$
23. An elevator went up 15 floors, down 9 floors, up 11 floors, and down 19 floors. Find the net change. down 2 floors
24. The price of a share of stock started the day at \$37. During the day it went down \$3, up \$1, down \$7, and up \$4. What was the price of a share at the end of the day? \$32



Practice

## Reteaching

Use tiles and the rules for adding integers to find each sum.

a. $-4 + -3$

Four negative tiles plus 3 negative tiles gives 7 negative tiles.
$-4 + -3 = -7$
The sum of two negative integers is negative.

b. $-8 + 3$

Remove zero pairs

Since the signs of the integers are different, you must remove zero pairs. The number of tiles left is the number of negative tiles $|-8|$ minus the number of positive tiles $|3|$. Thus, you can always subtract the absolute values of the numbers to find how many tiles will be left.

$|-8| - |3| = 5$

Since there are more negative tiles than positive tiles, $|-8| > |3|$, there are negative tiles left after you subtract zero pairs. Thus, the sum is negative.

$-8 + 3 = -5$

Use rules or tiles to find each sum.

1. $9 + (-12)$ $-3$
2. $-4 + 10$ $6$
3. $-1 + (-8)$ $-9$
4. $-6 + (-11)$ $-17$
5. $-5 + 15$ $10$
6. $2 + (-14)$ $-12$
7. $(-3) - 6$ $-9$
8. $-(-2) + 9$ $11$
9. $(-2) - 4$ $-6$
10. $-5 - (-4)$ $-1$
11. $7 + (-2)$ $5$
12. $16 + (-6)$ $10$



Reteaching

## Enrichment

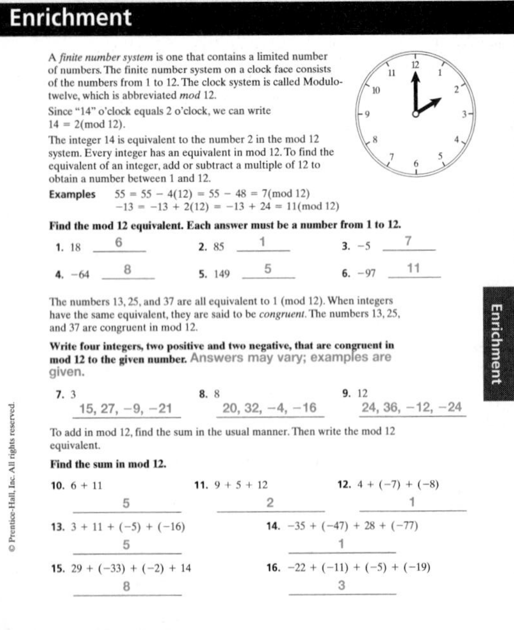

A *finite number system* is one that contains a limited number of numbers. The finite number system on a clock face consists of the numbers from 1 to 12. The clock system is called Modulo-twelve, which is abbreviated *mod* 12.

Since "14" o'clock equals 2 o'clock, we can write $14 = 2(\text{mod } 12)$.

The integer 14 is equivalent to the number 2 in the mod 12 system. Every integer has an equivalent in mod 12. To find the equivalent of an integer, add or subtract a multiple of 12 to obtain a number between 1 and 12.

**Examples** $55 = 55 - 4(12) = 55 - 48 = 7(\text{mod } 12)$
$-13 = -13 + 2(12) = -13 + 24 = 11(\text{mod } 12)$

Find the mod 12 equivalent. Each answer must be a number from 1 to 12.

1. 18 6
2. 85 1
3. −5 7
4. −64 8
5. 149 5
6. −97 11

The numbers 13, 25, and 37 are all equivalent to 1 (mod 12). When integers have the same equivalent, they are said to be *congruent*. The numbers 13, 25, and 37 are congruent in mod 12.

Write four integers, two positive and two negative, that are congruent in mod 12 to the given number. Answers may vary; examples are given.

7. 3 15, 27, −9, −21
8. 8 20, 32, −4, −16
9. 12 24, 36, −12, −24

To add in mod 12, find the sum in the usual manner. Then write the mod 12 equivalent.

Find the sum in mod 12.

10. $6 + 11$ 5
11. $9 + 5 + 12$ 2
12. $4 + (-7) + (-8)$ 1
13. $3 + 11 + (-5) + (-16)$ 5
14. $-35 + (-47) + 28 + (-77)$ 1
15. $29 + (-33) + (-2) + 14$ 8
16. $-22 + (-11) + (-5) + (-19)$ 3



Enrichment

*Mathematical Reasoning* **Refer to the number line. Is each sum positive or negative?**

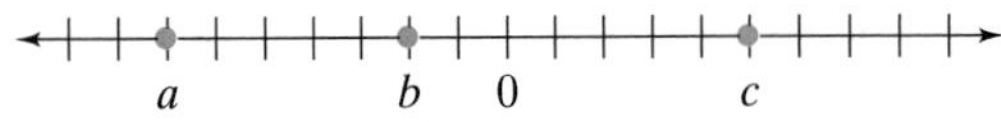


69. $a + b$ negative
70. $b + c$ positive
71. $a + a$ negative
72. $|a + b + c|$ positive
73. *Critical Thinking* Which statement is an example of additive inverses? B
    A. $xy = yx$
    B. $x[(y + (-y))] = x(0)$
    C. $x + y = y + x$
    D. $x\left(\frac{y}{y}\right) = x(1)$

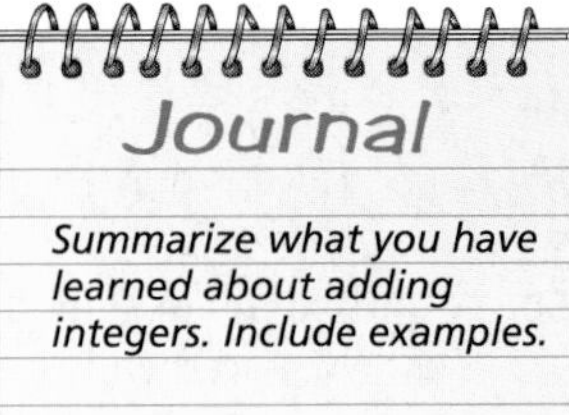

Journal
Summarize what you have learned about adding integers. Include examples.


## Mixed Review

**Compare. Use >, <, or = to complete each statement.** *(Lesson 1-4)*

74. $-9 \;\blacksquare\; -6$ <
75. $-2 \;\blacksquare\; -7$ >
76. $|-15| \;\blacksquare\; -15$ >
77. $0 \;\blacksquare\; -8$ >
78. $-45 \;\blacksquare\; -44$ <
79. $100 \;\blacksquare\; |-101|$ <

80. Write a numerical expression for the phrase *one hundred thirty added to the difference of one hundred sixteen and eight.* Then simplify the expression. *(Lesson 1-2)* $(116 - 8) + 130$; 238
81. A repair center charges a \$25 flat fee plus \$10 per hour for labor. Write an expression for the cost of a repair that takes $n$ hours. Then evaluate the expression to find the cost of an oven repair that takes 3 hours. *(Lesson 1-3)* $25 + 10n$; \$55

## Math at Work

### Weaver

A sturdy four-shaft floor loom, a 10-dent reed, a ski shuttle, two boat shuttles—these are some of the tools and terms of the ancient craft of weaving. Weavers use yarn, ribbon, and thread. They design and make colorful, unique items such as rugs, tapestries, and handbags. Like a pattern in algebra, each design has rules that must be followed for the desired result.

For more information about weaving, visit the Prentice Hall Web site.
**www.phschool.com**

See also Extra Practice section.

## Math at Work

If you have block scheduling or extended class periods, have small groups of students research the craft of weaving by using library books, talking to local weavers, and making simple weavings. Have them display weaving samples as well as information about the history, vocabulary, and mathematics of weaving.

Students can find additional information on the Web site **www.phschool.com**.

# Subtracting Integers

## PART 1 Using Models to Subtract Integers

You can use tiles to help you understand subraction of integers.

### EXAMPLE 1

**Find −6 − (−2).**

Start with 6 negative tiles.

Take away 2 negative tiles.
There are 4 negative tiles left.

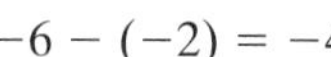

$-6 - (-2) = -4$

**TRY THIS** Use tiles to find each difference.

**1.** $-7 - (-2)$ −5 **2.** $-4 - (-3)$ −1 **3.** $-8 - (-5)$ −3

You can use zero pairs to subtract a larger integer from a smaller integer.

### EXAMPLE 2

**Find 3 − 5.**

Start with 3 positive tiles.

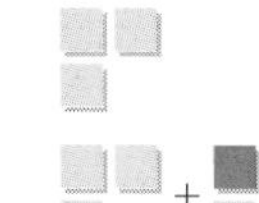

There are not enough positive tiles to take away 5. Add 2 zero pairs.

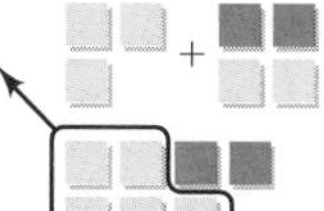

Take away 5 positive tiles.
There are 2 negative tiles left.

$3 - 5 = -2$

**TRY THIS** Use tiles to find each difference.

**4.** $4 - 8$ −4 **5.** $-1 - 5$ −6 **6.** $-2 - (-7)$ 5

## 1-6

### What You'll Learn

1. To use models to subtract integers
2. To use a rule to subtract integers

### . . . And Why

To use integers to solve real-world problems involving weather



# Tools to Monitor Progress

### BEFORE THE LESSON

**To check prerequisite skills:**

- Adding and subtracting whole numbers

**Skills You Need,** p. 1

**Skills Intervention Kit,** Whole Numbers

### DURING THE LESSON

**To check understanding:**

**Try This** exercises on student page

- **Additional Example 1**
  Find $-7 - (-5)$. **−2**
- **Additional Example 2**
  Find $8 - 2$. **6**

# 1-6

## Getting Ready

**Materials** algebra tiles

**Resources** A complete list of resources for this lesson is on p. 1H.

### Daily Skills Warm-Up

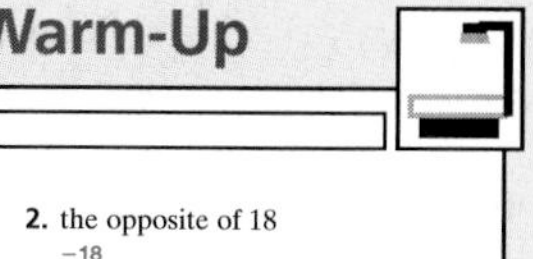

Lesson 1-6

Simplify.

1. the opposite of −9   9
2. the opposite of 18   −18
3. the opposite of |−4|   −4
4. the opposite of −|3|   3

Use rules to find each sum.

5. $-16 + (-12)$   −28
6. $-21 + 4$   −17
7. $-3 + 14$   11
8. $5 + 4 + -4$   5

### Background for the Lesson

You can read the expression $-(-3)$ as *the opposite of (the opposite of three).* It seems reasonable that taking the opposite of the opposite gets you back to where you started. Mathematically, this means that $-(-3)$ is the same as 3. So, you can rewrite $8 - (-3)$ as $8 + 3$, or 11.

## 1 Focus

### Connecting to Students' Lives

Ask students if they ever borrowed money to buy something. Maybe you borrowed \$50 to buy a skateboard. You agreed to pay back \$5 per week until the debt was paid. Your account balance is −\$50. When you make your first payment, that debt of \$5 is subtracted from your account: −\$50 − (−\$5). Your balance is then −\$45.

### Connecting to Prior Knowledge

Students know from previous lessons that −7 is greater than −9 because −9 is to the left of −7 on the number line. Point out that you are better off with a debt of \$7 than a debt of \$9, and 7 degrees below zero is warmer than 9 degrees below zero.

# 2 Teach

## Part 1 Teaching Notes

Encourage even those students who can do the math mentally to model expressions with tiles. Concrete examples such as tiles help students to understand reasons that underlie their answers.

### Example 1

**Build understanding.** Ask: Does taking away these two tiles leave a result that is greater or lesser than the set of tiles at the beginning of the problem? greater, because $-4 > -6$

**Tactile Learning** Students often learn the abstract mathematics more easily when they can handle concrete objects, such as algebra tiles, as they work the problems.

### Example 2

**Build understanding.** Ask: What is $3 + (-5)$? $-2$ Is this the same result as $3 - 5$? yes

## Part 2 Teaching Notes

To help students find the difference when subtracting integers, encourage them to add a middle step in which they change the subtraction sign to adding the opposite.

### Example 3

**Build understanding.** Ask: Was the temperature in Browning that January ever 100°F? No, that was the change in the temperature.

**Extension** Challenge students to explain whether the value of $-3 + |x|$ can ever be less than $-3$. no; $|x| \geq 0$

**Error Prevention** When subtracting integers, students may forget to change the integer to its opposite. Remind students that the rule involves two changes; change subtraction to addition, and use the opposite number.

**Technology Option** You may wish to have students use the Internet to find extreme temperatures in various cities and then subtract the integers to find the difference between the highest and lowest temperatures they find.

## Using a Rule to Subtract Integers

You can use models to show the relationship between adding and subtracting integers.

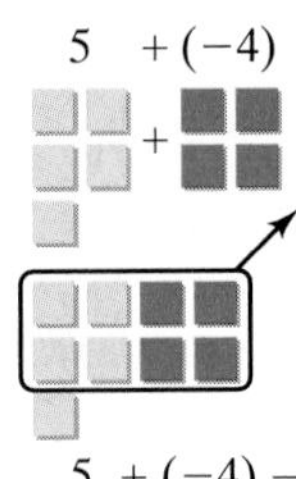


$5 + (-4) = 1$

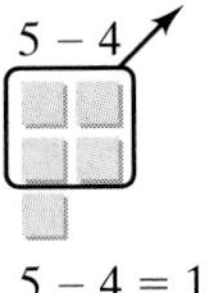


$5 - 4 = 1$

Both $5 + (-4)$ and $5 - 4$ equal 1. So, $5 + (-4) = 5 - 4$.

The models suggest the following rule for subtracting integers.

**Subtracting Integers**

To subtract an integer, add its opposite.

| Arithmetic | Algebra |
|---|---|
| $2 - 5 = 2 + (-5) = -3$ | $a - b = a + (-b)$ |
| $2 - (-5) = 2 + 5 = 7$ | $a - (-b) = a + b$ |

### EXAMPLE 3

*Weather* **In January 1916 the temperature in Browning, Montana, fell 100 degrees overnight. The initial temperature was 44°F. What was the final temperature?**

| | |
|---|---|
| $44 - 100$ | Write an expression. |
| $44 - 100 = 44 + (-100)$ | To subtract 100, add its opposite. |
| $= -56$ | Simplify. |

The final temperature was $-56$°F.

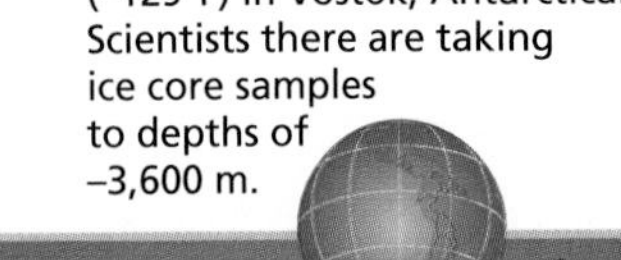

The lowest temperature ever recorded on Earth was –89°C (–129°F) in Vostok, Antarctica. Scientists there are taking ice core samples to depths of –3,600 m.

**TRY THIS** Find each difference.

**7.** $32 - (-3)$ 35 **8.** $-40 - 66$ $-106$ **9.** $2 - 48$ $-46$

**10.** The lowest temperature ever recorded in Antarctica was $-89$°C. The lowest temperature ever recorded on the moon was about $-170$°C. Estimate the difference in the temperatures. about 80°C



- **Additional Example 3**

  A plane left Houston where the temperature was 80°F. When the plane landed in Chicago, the temperature was 100 Fahrenheit degrees cooler. What was the temperature in Chicago? $-20$°F

## AFTER THE LESSON

**To assess knowledge:**

**Lesson Quiz**

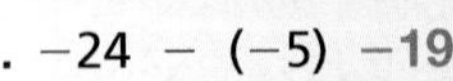
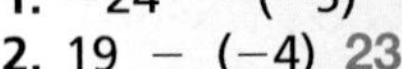

Find each difference.

1. $-24 - (-5)$ $-19$
2. $19 - (-4)$ 23
3. $-33 - 11$ $-44$
4. $-200 - 50 - (-10)$ $-240$
5. $14 - 46$ $-32$

- For enrichment and reteaching options see Resources on p. 1H.

# Exercises

## Check Understanding

**Model each situation. Then simplify.**

1\. You have \$3. You owe \$10.

1–2. Models may vary. Samples are shown.

2\. You are \$2 in debt. You borrow \$4 more.

1\. 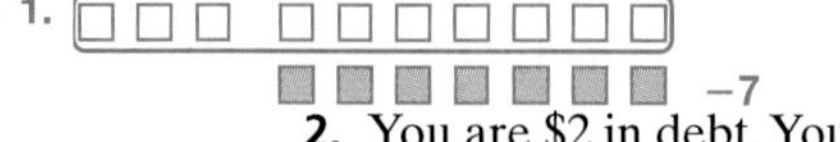 −7

2\. −6

**Write each difference as a sum. Then simplify.**

3\. $6 - 2$ $6 + (-2)$; 4
4\. $6 - (-2)$ $6 + 2$; 8
5\. $-6 - 2$ $-6 + (-2)$; −8
6\. $-6 - (-2)$ $-6 + 2$; −4
7\. $2 - 6$ $2 + (-6)$; −4
8\. $2 - (-6)$ $2 + 6$; 8
9\. $-2 - 6$ $-2 + (-6)$; −8
10\. $-2 - (-6)$ $-2 + 6$; 4

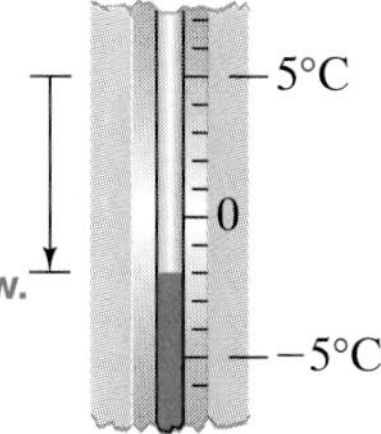


11\. a. *Writing* A thermometer is like a vertical number line. Explain how to use the one at the right to model a subtraction problem. See below.

b. Write and simplify a numerical expression for the model. $5 - 7$; −2

## Practice and Problem Solving

**Write a number sentence for each model.**

11a. Answers may vary. Sample: Use an arrow to represent subtraction. The point that you end at is the answer to the problem.

12\.

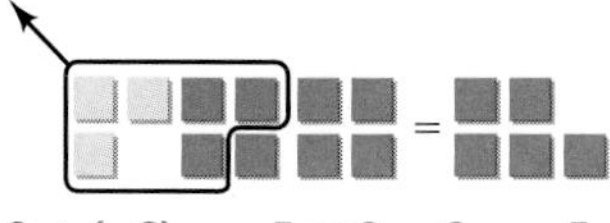

$3 + (-8) = -5$ or $3 - 8 = -5$

13\.

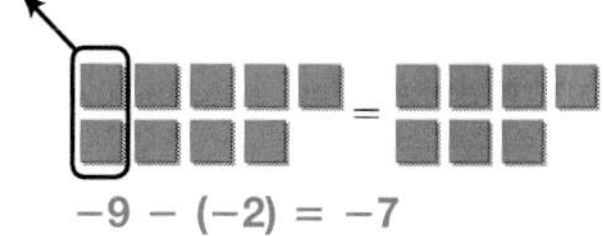

$-9 - (-2) = -7$

*Modeling* **Draw a model and find each difference.** 14–19. Models may vary. Samples are shown in margin.

14\. $2 - 3$ −1
15\. $-5 - (-6)$ 1
16\. $-9 - (-7)$ −2
17\. $-2 - 3$ −5
18\. $-7 - (-9)$ 2
19\. $-10 - 2$ −12

**Use a rule to find each difference.**

20\. $-16 - (-9)$ −7
21\. $5 - 11$ −6
22\. $-8 - (-3)$ −5
23\. $75 - (-25)$ 100
24\. $22 - (-7)$ 29
25\. $87 - (-9)$ 96
26\. $35 - (-15)$ 50
27\. $100 - (-91)$ 191
28\. $-49 - 75$ −124
29\. $-65 - 15$ −80
30\. $-92 - (-9)$ −83
31\. $16 - (-3)$ 19
32\. $120 - (-50)$ 170
33\. $-81 - (-13)$ −68
34\. $989 - 76$ 913
35\. $-59 - (-17)$ −42
36\. $-90 - (-80) - 20$ −30
37\. $810 - 30 - (-70)$ 850

*Mental Math* **Find each difference.**

38\. $-6 - (-8)$ 2
39\. $-45 - 15$ −60
40\. $-7 - (-7) + (-7)$ −7
41\. $100 - (-50)$ 150
42\. $20 - (-10) - 20$ 10
43\. $-11 + 22 - (-55)$ 66



# 3 Practice/Assess

## Assignment Guide

To provide flexible scheduling, this lesson can be divided into parts.

**Part 1**
**Core** 1–2, 11–19

**Part 2**
**Core** 3–10, 20–48, 51–53, 57–61
**Extension** 49–50, 54–56, 62–66

Mixed Review can be assigned at any time for maintenance.

## Exercises

**Test Prep Exercise 44** Explain to students that if they find two values that agree and one that is different, they can be sure that the different one is the correct answer without further work.

**Exercises 51–56** If students have difficulty rounding, suggest that they ask themselves questions such as, "Is 86 closer to 80 or to 90?"

## Challenge

What is the result if you add the absolute value of an integer (other than zero) to the absolute value of its opposite? twice the absolute value of the integer

## Closure

To subtract an integer, add its opposite.

14–19. Models may vary. Samples are shown.

14\.

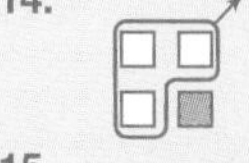

15\.

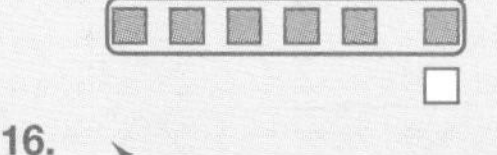

16\.

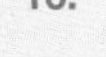

17\.

18\.

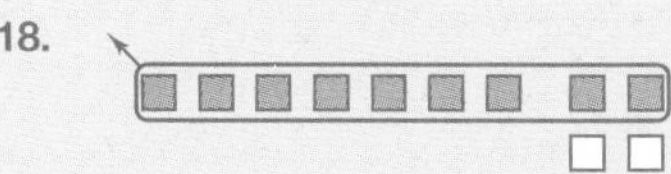

19\.

## Alternative Assessment

Have students model and explain the following expression using algebra tiles: $-7 - (-4)$.

## Daily Cumulative Review

**Use rules to find each sum.** *(Lesson 1-5)*

1\. $4 + (-6)$ −2
2\. $-3 + (-9)$ −12
3\. $24 + (-17)$ 7
4\. $-23 + 14 + (-7)$ −16
5\. $643 + (-521)$ 122
6\. $-7 + 4 + (-5) + 16$ 8

**Compare. Use >, <, or = to complete each statement.** *(Lesson 1-4)*

7\. $-3 < 2$
8\. $|23| = |-23|$
9\. $-87 < -86$
10\. $|-42| > 41$
11\. $-8 < -3$
12\. $|-65| = |65|$

**Mixed Review**

**Evaluate each expression.**

13\. (1-3) $12 \div b + 8$, for $b = 6$ 10
14\. (1-3) $3f - 7$, for $f = 9$ 20
15\. (1-3) $t(14 - s)$, for $s = 8, t = 12$ 72
16\. (1-3) $6ab + 23$, for $a = 2, b = 3$ 59

**Simplify each expression.**

17\. (1-2) $34 - 18 \div 2$ 25
18\. (1-2) $8 \cdot 6 + 7 \cdot 0$ 48
19\. (1-2) $12 \div 12 \cdot 1 + 6 - 2$ 5

**Write a numerical expression for each phrase. Then simplify.**

20\. (1-2) twenty-eight decreased by the sum of twelve and eleven $28 - (12 + 11) = 5$
21\. (1-2) thirty-eight decreased by the product of eight and four $38 - (8 \times 4) = 6$
22\. (1-2) six added to the quotient of forty-five and nine $(45 \div 9) + 6 = 11$

44. **TEST PREP** Which expression has a value different from the others? D

A. $6 + (-4)$ B. $6 - 4$ C. $|4 - 6|$

D. $-6 - 4$ E. They all have the same value.

***Open-ended*** **Use positive and negative integers to write two different subtraction number sentences for each difference.**

SAMPLE ■ − ■ = −5 ■ − ■ = −5

$-20 - (-15) = -5$ $17 - 22 = -5$

45–50. Answers may vary. Samples are given.

45. ■ − ■ = 0 $3 - 3 = 0$; $(-4) - (-4) = 0$

46. ■ − ■ = 10 $15 - 5 = 10$; $-5 - (-15) = 10$

47. ■ − ■ = −6 $1 - 7 = -6$; $-10 - (-4) = -6$

48. ■ − ■ = −15 $5 - 20 = -15$; $-10 - 5 = -15$

49. ■ − ■ = $|-3|$ $7 - 4 = |-3|$; $-2 - (-5) = |-3|$

50. ■ − ■ = $|11|$ $12 - 1 = |11|$; $5 - (-6) = |11|$

***Estimation*** **Round each number. Then estimate each sum or difference.**

SAMPLE $-216 - 88 \approx -220 - 90 = -310$

51. $-41 - (-86)$ 50

52. $-227 - 49$ −280

53. $-398 - 67$ −470

54. $-186 - 122$ −310

55. $88 - 592$ −500

56. $821 - (-924)$ 1,740

**Write a numerical expression for each phrase. Then simplify.**

57. A plane climbs 3,000 ft and then descends 600 ft. 3,000 − 600; 2,400

58. The temperature increases 15 degrees Fahrenheit and then drops 25 degrees. 15 − 25; −10

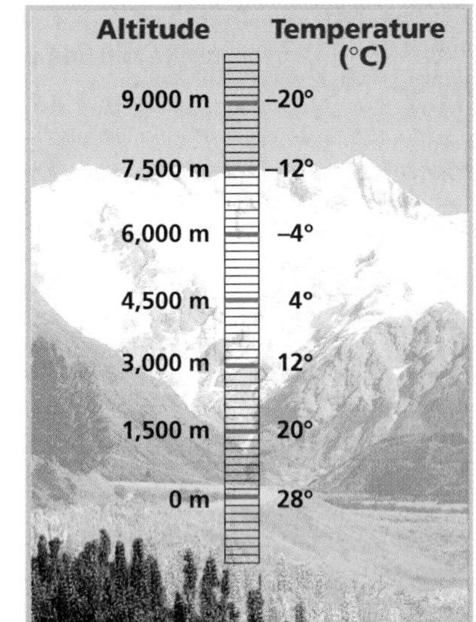


59. ***Meteorology*** The graph shows how temperature changes with altitude.
 a. As the altitude increases, what happens to the temperature? It decreases.
 b. By how much does the temperature change from 1,500 m to 6,000 m? −24°C
 c. What is the change in temperature for every 1,500-m increase in altitude? −8°C

60. Suppose you have a score of 35 in a game. You get a 50-point penalty. What is your new score? −15

61. ***Weather*** How much warmer is a temperature of 20°C than a temperature of −7°C? 27°C

62. a. ***Mathematical Reasoning*** When is $|a - b| = |a| - |b|$? Give an example.
 b. When is $|a - b| > |a| - |b|$? Give an example.
 c. When is $|a - b| < |a| - |b|$? never

 a. $a = b$, $a < b < 0$, or $0 < b < a$; $|5 - 5| = |5| - |5|$
 b. $a < 0 < b$, $0 < a < b$, $b < a < 0$, or $b < 0 < a$; $|-5 - 3| = 8 > |-5| - |3|$

**63. a.** *Patterns* Copy and complete. The first one is done for you.

$8 - (-4) = 12$ 8 − (−4) = 12
$12 - (-4) = ■$ 12 − (−4) = 16
$16 - (-4) = ■$ 16 − (−4) = 20
$20 - (-4) = ■$ 20 − (−4) = 24
$24 - (-4) = ■$ 24 − (−4) = 28

**b.** If you begin at 8 and subtract −4 five times, the result is ■. 28

**c.** Begin at 0 and subtract −4 six times. What is the result? 24

**In a magic square, each row, column, and diagonal has the same sum. Copy and complete each magic square.**

**64.**

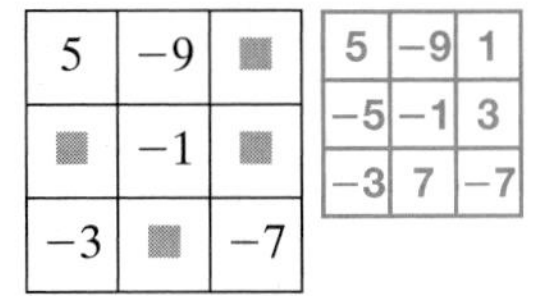

| 5 | −9 | ■ |
|---|---|---|
| ■ | −1 | ■ |
| −3 | ■ | −7 |

| 5 | −9 | 1 |
|---|---|---|
| −5 | −1 | 3 |
| −3 | 7 | −7 |

sum = ■ −3

**65.**

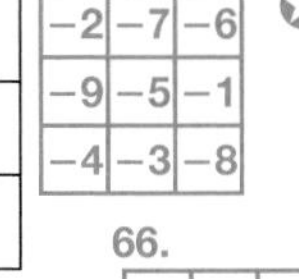

| −2 | ■ | ■ |
|---|---|---|
| −9 | −5 | ■ |
| −4 | ■ | ■ |

| −2 | −7 | −6 |
|---|---|---|
| −9 | −5 | −1 |
| −4 | −3 | −8 |

sum = ■ −15

**66.**

| ■ | −5 | ■ | 6 |
|---|---|---|---|
| ■ | 4 | 3 | ■ |
| 2 | 0 | ■ | 5 |
| −3 | ■ | ■ | −6 |

66.

| 9 | −5 | −4 | 6 |
|---|---|---|---|
| −2 | 4 | 3 | 1 |
| 2 | 0 | −1 | 5 |
| −3 | 7 | 8 | −6 |

sum = ■ 6

## Mixed Review

**Find each sum.** *(Lesson 1-5)*

**67.** $-17 + 12$ −5 **68.** $-8 + 15$ 7 **69.** $-9 + (-4) + 7$ −6

*Open-ended* **Complete with an integer.** *(Lesson 1-4)* Answers may vary. Samples are given.

**70.** $-5 > ■$ −7 **71.** $■ < 6$ 3 **72.** $|-1| > ■$ 0 **73.** $|■| < 8$ −6

**74.** Write an expression for the phrase *one hundred plus the product of six and nine.* Simplify the expression. *(Lesson 1-2)* 100 + 6 · 9; 154

CHAPTER PROJECT 1

## Activity 2 Writing

A cipher is a secret code. To decode it, you must know the key. Caesar Cipher, used by Julius Caesar, substitutes one letter for another by shifting each letter in the alphabet three places: *A* becomes *D*, *B* becomes *E*, and so on. In Caesar Cipher, *dog* is written *grj*. Write a letter to a friend in Caesar Cipher.

See also Extra Practice section.



## Project Activity 2

**Writing** You may want to have students write a report on this activity that contains their letter in "clear" as well as the encoded version. Ask students to check their work by exchanging with a partner to write a clear version of the partner's letter.

## Practice

**Use rules to find each difference.**

1. 8 − 12 —— −4
2. 13 − 6 —— 7
3. 9 − (−12) —— 21
4. 57 − 39 —— 18
5. −173 − 162 —— −335
6. 71 − (123) —— −52
7. 51 − 89 —— −38
8. −222 − (−117) —— −105
9. 843 − 677 —— 166
10. −98 − 183 —— −281
11. 366 − (−429) —— 795
12. −83 − (−48) − 65 —— −100

**Find each difference.**

13. 6 − 9 —— −3
14. 14 − 8 —— 6
15. −15 − 3 —— −18
16. −25 − 25 —— −50
17. −16 − (−16) —— 0
18. 32 − (−17) − 32 —— 17

**Round each number. Then estimate each sum or difference.**

19. −57 + (−98) —— −160
20. 448 − 52 —— 400
21. −191 + (−511) —— −700
22. −361 − (−58) —— −300
23. 888 + 1,177 —— 2,100
24. −484 − 1,695 —— −2,200

**Write a numerical expression for each phrase. Then simplify.**

25. A balloon goes up 2,300 ft, then goes down 600 ft. 2,300 − 600 = 1,700
26. You lose $50, then spend $35. −50 − 35 = −85
27. The Glasers had $317 in their checking account. They wrote checks for $74, $132, and $48. What is their checking account balance? 317 − 74 − 132 − 48 = 63



## Reteaching

a. Find −7 − (−3) and −7 + 3. Compare.

−7 − (−3) −7 + 3

Start with 7 negative tiles and take away 3 negative tiles. Remove zero pairs.

With both you start with 7 negative tiles. Taking away 3 negative tiles has the same effect as adding 3 positive tiles and removing zero pairs.
−7 − (−3) = −7 + 3 = −4

b. Find −4 − 2 and −4 + (−2). Compare.

−4 − 2 −4 + (−2)

With both you start with 4 negative tiles. Adding two zero pairs and taking away two positive tiles has the same effect as adding two negative tiles.
−4 − 2 = −4 + (−2) = −6

**Use rules for subtracting integers to find each difference. Use tiles to help.**

1. −5 − (−3) = −5 + 3 = −2
2. −8 − 6 = −8 + −6 = −14
3. 3 − (−9) = 3 + 9 = 12
4. −2 − (−7) = −2 + 7 = 5
5. 4 − 10 = 4 + −10 = −6
6. 1 − (−6) = 1 + 6 = 7
7. −9 − 5 = −9 + −5 = −14
8. −6 − (−2) = −6 + 2 = −4
9. 7 − 8 = 7 + −8 = −1



## Enrichment

A time line is a number line marked off in dates rather than in integers. On the History of Mathematics time line below, dates labeled B.C. fall where the negative integers normally lie. Dates labeled A.D. replace the positive integers. Years given are dates of birth.

B.C. A.D.
569 Pythagoras, 429 Plato, 330 Euclid, 287 Archimedes, 0, 98 Ptolemy, 250 Hero, 526 Aryabhata, 640 Brahmagupta

**Find the number of years between the given events. Write a subtraction expression. Then simplify.**

1. the births of Euclid and Hero 250 − (−330) = 580
2. the births of Pythagoras and Archimedes −287 − (−569) = 282
3. the births of Brahmagupta and Ptolemy 640 − 98 = 542
4. Legend has it that Rome was founded in 753 B.C. How many years after the founding of Rome was Plato born? −429 − (−753) = 324
5. One mathematician was born as many years before Ptolemy as Aryabhata was born after Ptolemy. Which one? Euclid
6. Which mathematician was born 1,069 years before Brahmagupta? Plato

Use the number line below to construct a time line. Write the letters of the given events below the appropriate tic mark. Above the line, write dates. Then, choose five other events relating to you, your family or friends, and include these on the time line. Also, include the year of your birth.

7.

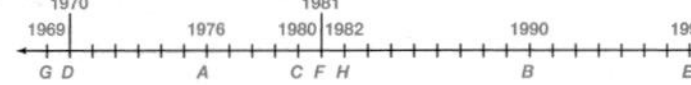


A. U.S. Bicentennial, 1976
B. East and West Germany reunite, 1990
C. Mount St. Helens erupts, 1980
D. First Earth Day, 1970
E. Cloned Sheep Dolly announced, 1997
F. First shuttle flight, 1981
G. First moon landing, 1969
H. Compact disks introduced, 1982

## Standardized Test Prep

Standardized tests, such as those administered for state assessment, SAT9, TerraNova™, ITBS, MAT7, or CAT5, may include multiple choice questions, free-response questions, and open-ended questions.

**Multiple Choice Questions** are followed usually by four choices, one of which is correct.

**Exercises 1–10** are multiple choice questions.

**Free-Response Questions** do not give answer choices. Student must provide the one correct answer on their own.

**Exercises 11–12** are free-response questions.

**Open-Ended Questions** allow for more than one solution. Students must construct their own responses instead of choosing from possible answers.

**Exercise 13** is an open-ended question.

### Resources

See p. 1G for a list of assessment options.

### Test-Taking Tip

After you read the problem once, making a quick sketch may sometimes help you understand the situation more clearly. Then read the problem a second time.

### Test-Taking Tips on Transparency

- Get plenty of sleep the night before your test.
- Eat a good breakfast the morning of your test.
- Bring a watch. Plan to spend 1–2 minutes per question.
- If you are nervous, stop and take three deep breaths.
- Underline important words or phrases.
- Keep your scratch work neat and organized.
- Do easy computations with pencil and paper. Use a calculator for the rest, if permitted.
- Cross out answer choices you know are wrong.
- Do the easy questions first.
- Do not stop to work on difficult questions. Skip them and return to them later if you have time remaining.
- Change an answer only when you are sure your first choice is wrong.
- Unless you are told not to guess, mark an answer for every question.
- Be careful to mark each answer in the right place, and fill in the mark completely.
- Think positively by telling yourself, "I have studied and I know this. I will do well."

## Standardized Test Prep

### Multiple Choice

**Choose the best answer.**

**1.** The temperature rose from $-6°C$ to $6°C$. Find the increase in temperature. C
A. 0°C B. –12°C C. 12°C D. 6°C

**2.** A stray dog ran back and forth down a straight street. First he ran 6 blocks west, then he ran 4 blocks east, and finally he ran 7 blocks west. Where did the dog finish in relation to his starting point? G
F. 17 blocks west G. 9 blocks west
H. 13 blocks west J. 17 blocks east

**3.** Simplify $5 + 10 \div 5 \cdot 4$. B
A. 12 B. 13 C. 24 D. 35

**4.** Evaluate $3(2d + 8)$ for $d = 7$. F
F. 66 G. 150 H. 51 J. 60

**5.** One inch is about 2.5 centimeters. Which expression would you use to find the length in centimeters of a 7-inch pencil? A
A. $7 \cdot 2.5$ B. $7 + 2.5$
C. $7 \div 2.5$ D. $7 - 2.5$

**6.** Sean borrowed $4 from his brother. He paid back $3. Then he borrowed two times the original amount. Which expression does *not* represent the amount Sean owes his brother? H
F. $3 - 12$ G. $-(4 + 8) + 3$
H. $4 - 3 - 2(4)$ J. $-4 + 3 + (-8)$

**7.** The stack consists of boxes that are all the same size. How many boxes are in the stack? C

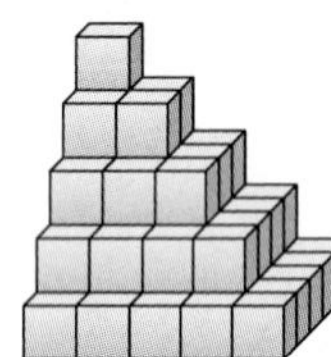

A. 25 B. 36 C. 55 D. 91

**8.** A mountain rises 7,000 ft from its base. The temperature at the base is 60°F. It decreases by 5°F every 1,000 ft. What is the temperature at the mountain's top? G
F. 30°F G. 25°F H. 95°F J. 40°F

**9.** The average 100-lb walker uses 175 calories for every hour of brisk walking. How many calories would an average 100-lb walker use for a 2-h brisk walk? B
A. 175 B. 350 C. 750 D. 1,750

**10.** Two enchiladas contain 732 calories. Suppose you use 175 cal/h by walking. How long would you need to walk to use the calories from two enchiladas? H
F. about 2 h G. about 3 h
H. about 4 h J. about 5 h

### Free Response

**For Exercises 11–13, show your work.**

**11.** A runner takes 8 min for each mile. Write a variable expression for the number of miles the runner completes in $m$ min. Evaluate the expression to find the distance completed in 40 min. $\frac{m}{8}$; 5 mi

**12.** A number machine uses a rule to change numbers into other numbers.

2 → 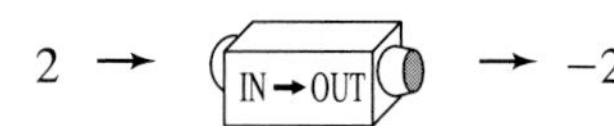 → −2



−5 → 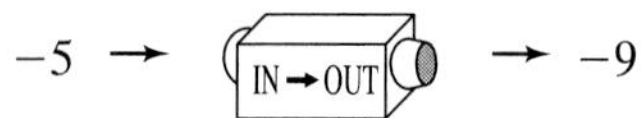 → −9



39 → IN → OUT → 35

This machine changed 2 into $-2$, $-5$ into $-9$, and 39 into 35. What number will 0 be changed into? $-4$

**13.** *Open-ended* The factors of $x$ include 4 and 5. Write three possible values for $x$.
Answers may vary. Sample: 20, 40, 60

# 1-7

# Inductive Reasoning

## PART 1 Writing Rules for Patterns

**Inductive reasoning** is making conclusions based on patterns you observe. A conclusion by inductive reasoning is a **conjecture.**

GEOMETRY CONNECTION

### EXAMPLE 1

*Visual Patterns* **Use inductive reasoning. Make a conjecture about the next figure in the pattern. Then draw the figure.**

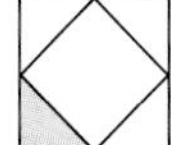 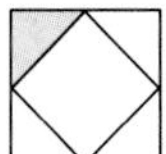 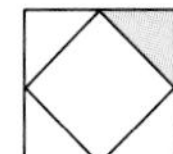

*Observation:* The shaded triangle is rotating clockwise around the square.

*Conjecture:* The next figure will have a shaded triangle in the bottom right corner.

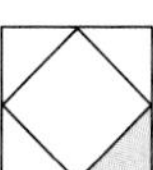

### TRY THIS

1. Make a conjecture about the next figure in the pattern at the right. Then draw the figure. Answers may vary. Sample: It is a six-sided figure with all corners on a circle.

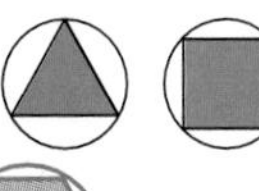 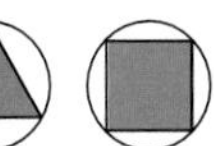 

For a number pattern, a conjecture can be a rule that explains how to make and continue the pattern.

### EXAMPLE 2

*Number Patterns* **Write a rule for the number pattern 640, 320, 160, 80, . . . Find the next two numbers in the pattern.**

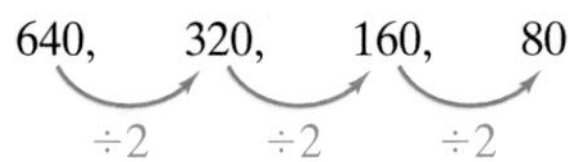


The first number is 640. The next numbers are found by dividing by 2.

The rule is *Start with 640 and divide by 2.* The next two numbers in the pattern are $80 \div 2 = 40$ and $40 \div 2 = 20$.

### What You'll Learn

1. To write rules for patterns
2. To make predictions and test conjectures

### . . . And Why

To use inductive reasoning in finding patterns and in making conjectures about economic data

### Reading Math

The three dots in a pattern tell you that the pattern continues.



# Tools to Monitor Progress

## BEFORE THE LESSON

**To check prerequisite skills:**

- Using whole number patterns

**Skills Intervention Kit,** Whole Numbers

## DURING THE LESSON

**To check understanding:**

**Try This** exercises on student page

- **Additional Examples 1–2**
  Write a rule for 110, 100, 90, 80, . . . Find the next two numbers in the pattern. Start with 100 and subtract 10 repeatedly. 70, 60
- **Additional Example 3**
  Write a rule for 0, –4, –8, –12, . . . From 0, subtract 4 repeatedly.

# 1-7

## Getting Ready

**Key Terms and Symbols** inductive reasoning, conjecture, counterexample

**Resources** A complete list of resources for this lesson is on p. 1H.

### Daily Skills Warm-Up

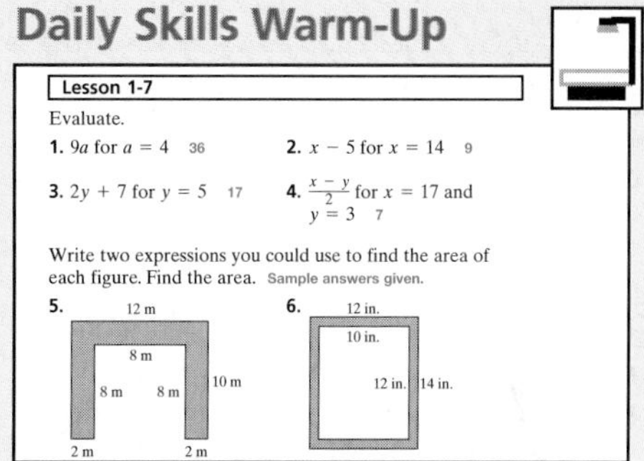
Lesson 1-7

Evaluate.

1. $9a$ for $a = 4$ 36
2. $x - 5$ for $x = 14$ 9
3. $2y + 7$ for $y = 5$ 17
4. $\frac{x - y}{2}$ for $x = 17$ and $y = 3$ 7

Write two expressions you could use to find the area of each figure. Find the area. Sample answers given.

5. 
6. 



### Background for the Lesson

Inductive reasoning assumes that an observed pattern will continue. Often this is true; sometimes it is not. Consider this statement: $x = x \bullet x$. It is true for $x = 0$ and $x = 1$, but then the pattern fails. Inductive reasoning can lead to conjectures that are likely but unproven. Proving some math statements may be complex, but a single counterexample is enough to disprove a statement.

## 1 Focus

### Connecting to Students' Lives

Ask students if they have ever tasted a pepper. Some may say that peppers are spicy. Others may say that they are not spicy. The conjecture depends on the kind of pepper tasted. Use this example to explain that a conjecture may be valid based on some observations, but it may not necessarily be true.

### Connecting to Prior Knowledge

Ask students to share the strategies they have used in the past, perhaps on standardized tests, that help them see and continue patterns, such as 2, 4, 6, 8, . . . One possible strategy is to describe the pattern in words. For example, this pattern starts with 2 and adds 2 every time.

# 2 Teach

## Part 1 Teaching Notes

Some students can see patterns quickly and easily; others have difficulty thinking in this way. Encourage them to ask a partner to describe the thinking process that leads to seeing the pattern.

### Example 1

**Build understanding.** Ask: What changes from the first figure to the second? **The position of the shaded area moves.**

### Example 2

**Build understanding.** Ask: How do you know that this math pattern is going to continue in the same way? **The three dots mean that the pattern continues.**

### Example 3

**Build understanding.** Ask: In pattern c., is 36 the next number? How do you know? **No; 39 is the next number because you multiply 13 times 3.**

## Part 2 Teaching Notes

Point out that people make predictions based on past experience all the time, particularly about the weather. Many of these are accurate; some are not. Ask students for examples of predictions that they make based on past experience.

### Example 4

**Build understanding.** Ask: What were the average hourly earnings in 1980? in 1990? **about $7; about $10**

### Example 5

**Build understanding.** Ask: What is true about a figure if it is a rectangle? **It has four sides; opposite sides are equal and parallel; and it has four right angles.**

**Auditory Learning** Students often find it helpful to say the pattern softly to themselves as they work through a problem.

### Try This

2. Write a rule for the pattern 1, 3, 5, 7, . . . Find the next two numbers in the pattern. **Start with 1 and add 2 repeatedly; 9, 11**

### Example 3

**Write a rule for each number pattern.**

| | |
|---|---|
| **a. 30, 25, 20, 15, . . .** | Start with 30 and subtract 5 repeatedly. |
| **b. 2, −2, 2, −2, . . .** | Alternate 2 and its opposite. |
| **c. 1, 3, 4, 12, 13, . . .** | Start with 1. Alternate multiplying by 3 and adding 1. |

### Try This
Write a rule for each pattern.

3. 4, 9, 14, 19, . . . **Start with 4 and add 5 repeatedly.**
4. 3, 9, 27, 81, . . . **Start with 3 and multiply by 3 repeatedly.**
5. 1, 1, 2, 3, 5, 8, . . . **Add the previous two numbers.**

## Predictions and Counterexamples

With sufficient information, you can make predictions based on reasonable conjectures. Such predictions will probably—but not necessarily—turn out to be accurate.

DATA ANALYSIS CONNECTION

### Example 4

*Statistics* **See the graph below. Is a conjecture that average hourly earnings in the year 2000 will be about $13 reasonable?**

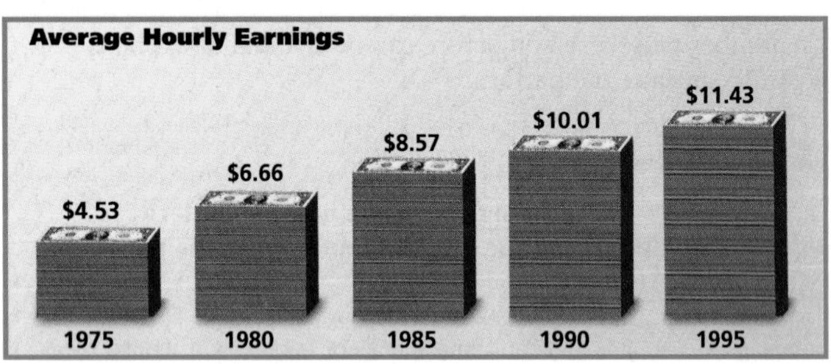


Average hourly earnings appear to increase by $1.50 to $2.00 every five years. The conjecture of $13 in 2000 is reasonable, since it is about $1.50 more than the earnings for 1995.



- **Additional Example 4**
  A child grows an inch a year for three years in a row. Is it a reasonable conjecture that this child will grow an inch in the year 2010? **No; children grow at an uneven rate, and eventually they stop growing when they mature.**
- **Additional Example 5**
  Is this conjecture correct or incorrect? If incorrect, give a counterexample. Every triangle has three equal sides. **Incorrect; examples will vary.**

## AFTER THE LESSON

**To assess knowledge: Lesson Quiz**

Find the next three numbers in the pattern.

1. 1, −1, 2, −2, 3, . . . **−3, 4, −4**
2. 1, 3, 7, 15, 31, . . . **63, 127, 255**
3. −11, −8, −5, −2, . . . **1, 4, 7**

- For enrichment and reteaching options see Resources on p. 1H.

■ **Try This**

6. You flip a coin four times, and it comes up heads each time. Is the conjecture *The coin will come up heads on every flip* reasonable? Explain. No; if the coin toss is fair, the coin can come up tails on any toss.

An example that proves a statement false is a **counterexample.** You need only one counterexample to prove that a conjecture is incorrect.

## Example 5

*Inductive Reasoning* **Is each conjecture correct or incorrect? If it is incorrect, give a counterexample.**

**a. Every four-sided figure is a rectangle.**
The conjecture is incorrect. The figure below has four sides, but it is not a rectangle.

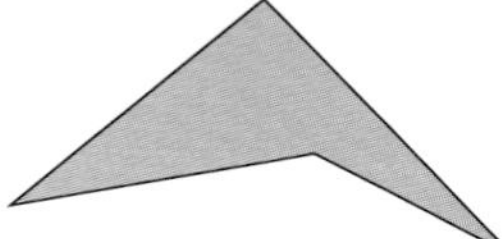

**b. The absolute value of any integer is positive.**
The conjecture is incorrect. The absolute value of zero is zero, which is neither positive nor negative.

**c. The next figure in the pattern below has 15 dots.**

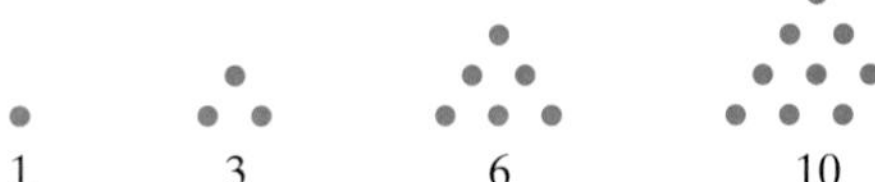


The conjecture is correct. The diagram at the right shows the next figure in the pattern.

■ **Try This** Is each conjecture correct or incorrect? If it is incorrect, give a counterexample.

7. The last digit of the product of 5 and a whole number is either 0 or 5. correct

8. A number and its absolute value are always opposites. Incorrect; 8 and $|8|$ are not opposites.



**Connecting to Science** Students can interview a scientist to find out more about the role of inductive reasoning in science and how conjectures are always changing as more knowledge is gained.

**Extension** Challenge students with the following question: Is the double of an integer always greater than the integer? No; $2(-3) = -6$ and $-6 < -3$.

**Error Prevention** Students may think that one, two, or three examples prove a statement is true. Remind them that seeing five black crows does not prove that all crows are black.

# 3 Practice/Assess

## Assignment Guide

To provide flexible scheduling, this lesson can be divided into parts.

**Part 1**
**Core** 1–5, 9–16

**Part 2**
**Core** 6–8, 18–22
**Extension** 17, 23

Mixed Review can be assigned at any time for maintenance.

## Exercises

**Exercises 3–5** Remind students that a rule must include the number at the start.

**Exercises 11–16** If students have difficulty seeing a pattern, encourage them to write down an operation that leads from the first number to the second. Then have them change that operation if it does not also lead from the second number to the third.

## Challenge

Is this conjecture correct or incorrect? If incorrect, give a counterexample. $2x$ is always greater than $x$. incorrect; $x = 0$ (or any negative integer)

## Closure

Inductive reasoning is making conclusions based on patterns you observe. A conclusion you reach by inductive reasoning is a conjecture.

# Exercises

## Check Understanding

*Geometry* **Describe the next figure in each pattern. Then draw the figure.**

1. a square with four corners shaded

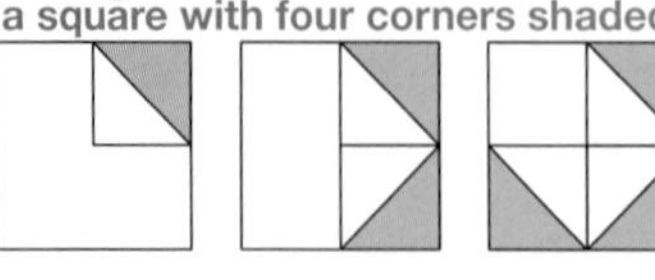
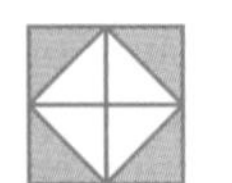

2. a six-sided figure with a six-sided figure inside it

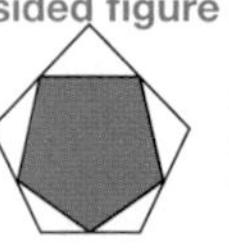

**Write a rule for each pattern. Find the next two numbers in each pattern.**

3. 100, 85, 70, 55, . . . Start with 100 and subtract 15 repeatedly; 40, 25
4. 5, 20, 80, 320, . . . Start with 5 and multiply by 4 repeatedly; 1,280, 5,120
5. 1, 2, 5, 6, 9, . . . Start with 1 and alternately add 1 and 3; 10, 13

**Is each statement correct or incorrect? If it is incorrect, give a counterexample.**

6. All birds can fly. Incorrect; an ostrich cannot fly.
7. Every square is a rectangle. correct
8. The product of two numbers is never less than either of the numbers. Incorrect; $0.2 \cdot 0.2 = 0.04$, which is less than 0.2.

## Practice and Problem Solving

*Geometry* **Describe the next figure in each pattern. Then draw the figure.**

9. an eight-sided figure with bottom right eighth shaded

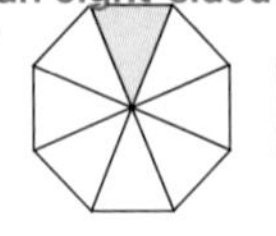

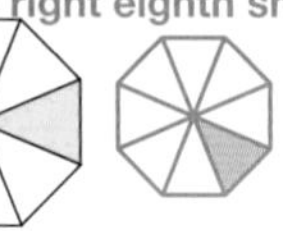

10.

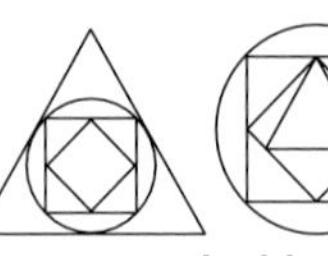

a square inside a circle inside a triangle inside a diamond

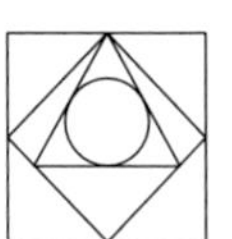

**Write a rule for each pattern. Find the next three numbers in the pattern.**

11. −10, −4, 2, 8, . . . Start with −10 and add 6 repeatedly. 14, 20, 26
12. 1, 4, 7, 10, . . . Start with 1 and 3 repeatedly. 13, 16, 19
13. 1, 1.5, 2, 2.5, 3, . . . Start with 1 and add 0.5 repeatedly. 3.5, 4, 4.5
14. −1, 1, −2, 2, −3, 3, . . . Start with −1 and alternate between finding the opposite and the next negative integer. −4, 4, −5
15. 1, 4, 10, 22, 46, 94, . . . Start with 1, add 3 initially, and then add the last added number multiplied by 2, repeatedly. 190, 382, 766
16. 1, −2, 4, −5, 7, −8, . . . Start with 1 and alternately subtract and add consecutive multiples of 3. 10, −11, 13



## Daily Cumulative Review

**Use a rule to find each difference.** *(Lesson 1-6)*

1. −4 − (−6) 2
2. 13 − 18 −5
3. −20 − (−4) − 32 −48
4. 24 − (−16) 40
5. −76 − (−20) − 84 −140
6. 543 − (−234) 777

**Use rules to find each sum.** *(Lesson 1-5)*

7. −7 + 19 12
8. −13 + 11 −2
9. 45 + (−65) −20
10. 23 + (−15) + (−24) −16
11. −4 + 5 + (−6) + 8 3
12. 532 + (−621) −89

**Mixed Review**

**Evaluate each expression for $a = 3$, $b = 4$, and $c = 20$.**

13. (1-3) $15 \div a$ 5
14. (1-3) $4a - b$ 8
15. (1-3) $c - ab$ 8

**Write an integer to represent each situation.**

16. (1-4) a debt of $267 −$267
17. (1-4) 800 ft below sea level −800 ft
18. (1-4) win by 12 points 12

**Write the variable expression for each word phrase.**

19. (1-1) the sum of thirteen and $b$ $13 + b$
20. (1-1) the product of a number 12 and $x$ $12x$

**Simplify each expression.**

21. (1-2) $\frac{15 + 17}{5 + 3}$ 4
22. (1-2) $3 + 1 \cdot 6$ 9
23. (1-2) $[5(2 + 1) + 7]$ 22



## Alternative Assessment

Have volunteers clap a pattern of beats or whistle a pattern of notes. Ask other students to see if they can repeat and continue the patterns.

Answers may vary. Sample: 4.4%; the unemployment rate stayed about the same for 1996 and 1997.

**17. a.** *Data Analysis* Use the graph at the right. Make a conjecture about the unemployment rate in 1998. Justify your reasoning.

**b.** How could you test your conjecture? Answers may vary. Sample: Look up unemployment records for 1998.

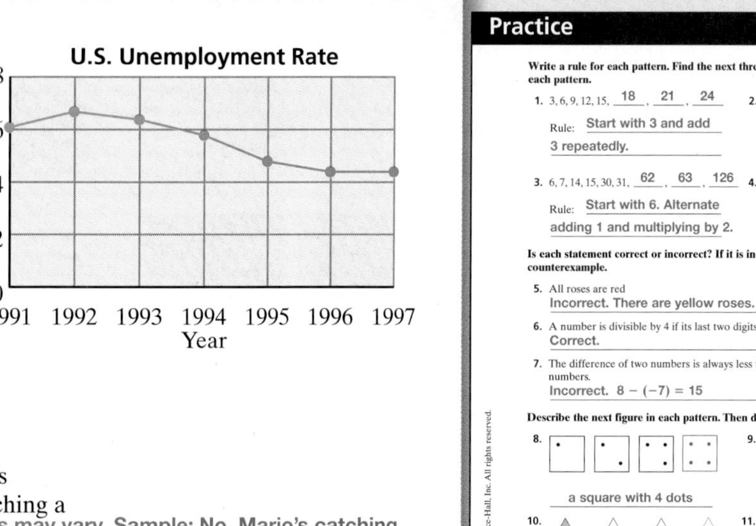


**Is each conjecture correct or incorrect? If it is incorrect, give a counterexample.**

**18.** A clover always has three leaves. Incorrect; some have 4.

**19.** The sum of two numbers is always greater than either of the two numbers. Incorrect; $8 + (-6)$ is 2, $2 < 8$.

**20.** A whole number is divisible by 3 if the sum of its digits is divisible by 3. correct

**21.** Mario caught a cold on each of his last three visits with his cousin. Is it reasonable for Mario to conclude that his catching a cold is the result of visiting his cousin? Explain. Answers may vary. Sample: No. Mario's catching a cold could be due to many different reasons.

**22.** **TEST PREP** Select the block that continues the given pattern. C

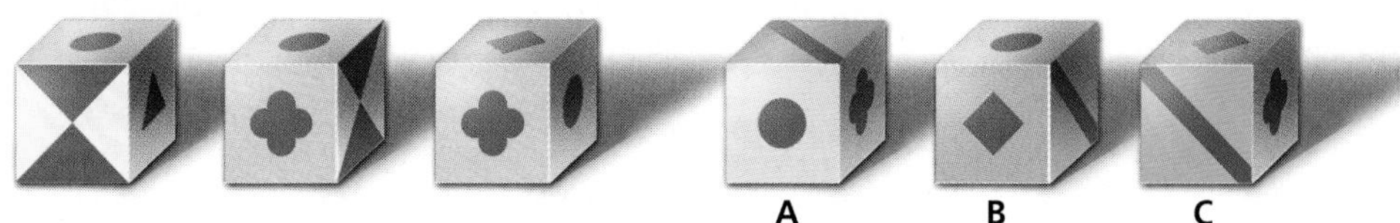


**23. a.** *Writing* Describe a pattern in the diagram at the right. See below.

**b.** Copy the pattern and show three more rows. See below right.

**c.** What is the sum of the numbers in each row? 1, 4, 9, 16, 25, 36, 49, 64

**d.** Predict the sum of the numbers in the ninth row. 81

1
1 2 1
1 2 3 2 1
1 2 3 4 3 2 1
1 2 3 4 5 4 3 2 1

23a. Answers may vary. Sample: Start at 1, count up until the middle of the row, and then count down.

## MIXED REVIEW

**Find each difference.** *(Lesson 1-6)*

**24.** $1 - 8$ $-7$ **25.** $3 - (-6)$ 9 **26.** $-4 - (-9)$ 5 **27.** $86 - (-17)$ 103

**Evaluate each expression for $x = -1$ and $y = -3$.** *(Lesson 1-5)*

**28.** $x + y$ $-4$ **29.** $y + x + 2$ $-2$ **30.** $-4 + x + y$ $-8$

**31.** *Science* The water in a stream flows at the rate of 1,500 gal/h.

**a.** Write a variable expression for the amount of water that flows in $n$ hours. $1{,}500n$

**b.** Evaluate your expression for $n = 24$. *(Lesson 1-3)* 36,000

23b.
1
1 2 1
1 2 3 2 1
1 2 3 4 3 2 1
1 2 3 4 5 4 3 2 1
1 2 3 4 5 6 5 4 3 2 1
1 2 3 4 5 6 7 6 5 4 3 2 1
1 2 3 4 6 5 7 8 7 6 5 4 3 2 1

See also Extra Practice section.



## Practice

**Write a rule for each pattern. Find the next three numbers in each pattern.**

1. 3, 6, 9, 12, 15, 18, 21, 24
Rule: Start with 3 and add 3 repeatedly.

2. 1, 2, 4, 8, 16, 32, 64, 128
Rule: Start with 1 and multiply by 2 repeatedly.

3. 6, 7, 14, 15, 30, 31, 62, 63, 126
Rule: Start with 6. Alternate adding 1 and multiplying by 2.

4. 34, 27, 20, 13, 6, $-1$, $-8$, $-15$
Rule: Start with 34 and subtract 7 repeatedly.

**Is each statement correct or incorrect? If it is incorrect, give a counterexample.**

5. All roses are red
Incorrect. There are yellow roses.

6. A number is divisible by 4 if its last two digits are divisible by 4.
Correct.

7. The difference of two numbers is always less than at least one of the numbers.
Incorrect. $8 - (-7) = 15$

**Describe the next figure in each pattern. Then draw the figure.**

8. a square with 4 dots

9. a circle inside a square

10. a triangle divided into 4 triangles with the lower right one shaded

11. the third figure rotated 90° clockwise



## Reteaching

The sum of two numbers is always at least as great as either number. Is the statement correct or incorrect? If incorrect, give a counterexample.

Try some examples.

$2 + 8 = 10$ $10 \geq 8$ and $10 \geq 2$

$365 + 241 = 606$ $606 \geq 365$ and $606 \geq 241$

The conjecture seems correct. Try different kinds of numbers. Although the numbers in the second trial are much larger than those in the first, all are whole numbers. Try zero, fractions, and negative numbers.

$56 + 0 = 56$ $56 \geq 56$ and $56 \geq 0$

$\frac{3}{8} + \frac{1}{8} = \frac{1}{2}$ $\frac{1}{2} \geq \frac{3}{8}$ and $\frac{1}{2} \geq \frac{1}{8}$

$-4 + 7 = 3$ $3 \geq -4$ but 3 is not at least as great as 7

The conjecture is incorrect and $-4 + 7 = 3$ is a counterexample.

**Is each conjecture correct or incorrect? If incorrect give a counterexample?**

1. The difference of two numbers is less than or equal to each number.
Incorrect. $6 - (-4) = 10$

2. The sum of two negative numbers is always less than each number.
Correct.

3. The sum of 5 and any positive integer is divisible by 5.
Incorrect. $4 + 5 = 9$

4. A number is divisible by 10 if its last digit is 0.
Correct.

5. The sum of a number and its absolute value is always 0.
Incorrect. $2 + |2| = 4$

6. The next number in the pattern 2, 4, 8, ... is 10.
Incorrect. The next number is 16.

7. Every even number is divisible by 4.
Incorrect. 6 is even, but not divisible by 4.

8. The next number in the pattern 5, 3, 1, ... is $-1$.
Correct.



## Enrichment

Occasionally, a scientist discovers a pattern of numbers which seems to suggest a natural law. The scientist must prove that the pattern is not simply accidental but that there is a reason behind it.

The table lists the planets known in 1772, and their relative distances from the sun, taking the earth's distance as 10. In that year the astronomer Johann Bode discovered an amazing pattern of numbers that closely matched the planetary distances.

| Planet | Relative Distance (Earth = 10) |
|---|---|
| Mercury | 5 |
| Venus | 7 |
| Earth | 10 |
| Mars | 16 |
| Jupiter | 52 |
| Saturn | 98 |

1. To find Bode's pattern, start with 1.5 and double each term.
1.5, 3, 6, 12, 24, 48, 96

2. Now add 4 to each term: 5.5, 7, 10, 16, 28, 52, 100

3. With one exception, note the close correlation between the pattern and the relative distances in the table.
a. Two planetary distances are off slightly. Which two?
Mercury and Saturn
b. What is the exception?
There is no planet corresponding to the pattern term 28.

4. In 1781, Uranus was discovered at a relative distance of 196 from the Sun. Calculate the next number in Bode's pattern in Exercise 2. 196
Does the pattern correctly predict the discovery of Uranus? yes

5. In 1801, Ceres, the first and largest of the asteroids or "minor" planets, was discovered at a relative distance of 28.
Does the pattern correctly predict the discovery of Ceres? yes

6. In 1846, the planet Neptune was discovered at a relative distance of 301. Had Bode discovered a law of planetary distance? Explain.
No; the next term after 196 (Uranus) is 388. To fit the pattern, Neptune would have to be much farther away.

# 1-8

## Getting Ready

**Resources** A complete list of resources for this lesson is on p. 1H.

### Daily Skills Warm-Up

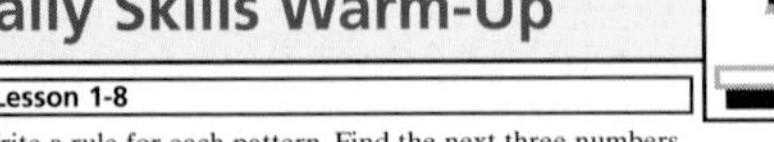

**Lesson 1-8**

Write a rule for each pattern. Find the next three numbers in the pattern.

1. 8, 11, 14, 17, …
   Start with 8 and add 3 repeatedly; 20, 23, 26
2. 1, 5, 4, 8, 7, …
   Add 4, then alternately subtract 1; 11, 10, 14
3. 1, 3, 6, 8, 16, …
   Add 2, then alternately multiply by 2; 18, 36, 38
4. How many half-hour periods are there between 1 P.M. and 4 P.M.? 6

### Background for the Lesson

Effective problem solvers can analyze their own thinking. They take time to reflect on the process that they use to solve a problem, instead of hurrying to find an answer. In this way they increase their knowledge about the problem-solving process and learn from each problem they solve. Looking for a pattern is one of many problem solving strategies, one that is common in both daily life and mathematics. Patterns and consistency are basic to the structure of mathematics.

## 1 Focus

### Connecting to Students' Lives

Ask students if they have ever found out about the score of their school's basketball game before the score was printed in the next morning's newspaper. Many students may have watched the game or heard about it from their friends who watched it. Have students comment on the different ways the news of the score could spread.

### Connecting to Prior Knowledge

In the previous lesson, students learned how to write a rule for a number pattern by giving the starting number and the repeated operations. Remind students to apply that skill as part of their problem solving strategy for the problems in this lesson.





# 1-8

# Look for a Pattern

**Problem Solving Strategies**

Account for All Possibilities
Draw a Diagram
Look for a Pattern
Make a Model
Make a Table
Simplify a Problem
Simulate a Problem
Solve by Graphing
Try, Test, Revise
Use Multiple Strategies
Work Backward
Write an Equation
Write a Proportion

*Math Strategies in Action*

What do songs on the radio, computer code, and your body's DNA have in common?

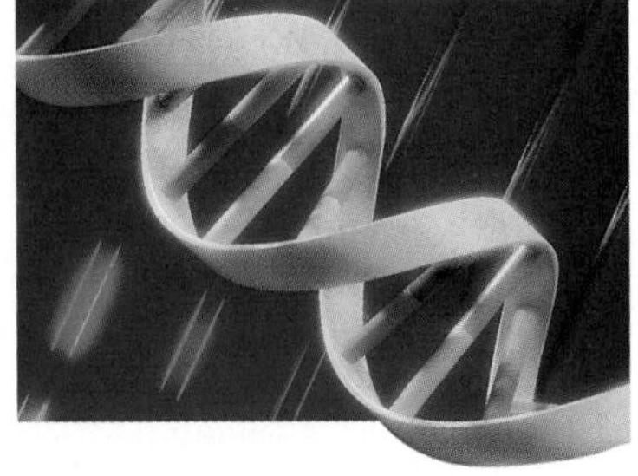

All are based on patterns. Radio uses patterns of electromagnetic waves. Computer code consists of patterns of numbers. Your DNA is made up of molecules that repeat in special patterns.

You can solve many types of problems by finding and using patterns. Making predictions from patterns is a form of inductive reasoning.

**SAMPLE PROBLEM**

News spreads quickly at Riverdell High. Each student who hears a story repeats it 15 minutes later to two students who have not yet heard it, and then tells no one else.

Suppose one student hears some news at 8:00 A.M. How many students will know the news at 9:00 A.M.?

### Read

1. How many students does each student tell? 2 students
2. How long does the news take to reach the second and third students? 15 min

### Plan

Make a table to organize the numbers. Then look for a pattern.

3. How many *new* students hear the news at 8:15 A.M.? 2 students
4. How many 15-minute periods are there between 8:00 A.M. and 9:00 A.M.? 4 periods



# Tools to Monitor Progress

### BEFORE THE LESSON

**To check prerequisite skills:**

- Multiplying whole numbers

**Skills Handbook,** p. 725

**Skills Intervention Kit,** Whole Numbers

### DURING THE LESSON

**To check understanding:**

- **Additional Sample Problem**
  Each student on a committee with five members shakes hands with every other member. How many handshakes will there be in all? 10

## Solve

The pattern is to add the number of new students to the number who already know.

$1 + 2 = 3$ the number who know at 8:15
$3 + 4 = 7$ the number who know at 8:30

Make a table and extend the pattern to 9:00.

| Time | 8:00 | 8:15 | 8:30 | 8:45 | 9:00 |
|---|---|---|---|---|---|
| Number of new students told | 1 | 2 | 4 | 8 | 16 |
| Number of students who know | 1 | 1 + 2 = 3 | 3 + 4 = 7 | 7 + 8 = 15 | 15 + 16 = 31 |

By 9:00 A.M., 31 students know the news.

## Look Back

One way to check a solution is to solve the problem by another method. You can use a *tree diagram* to show the pattern visually.

| Time | New Students | Students Who Know |
|---|---|---|
| 8:00 | 1 | 1 |
| 8:15 | 2 | 3 |
| 8:30 | 4 | 7 |
| 8:45 | 8 | 15 |
| 9:00 | 16 | 31 |

5. Describe two ways to find the number of students who know the news at 9:15 A.M. Answers may vary. Sample: Extend the table. Extend the diagram.
6. Suppose you want to continue the pattern beyond 9:15. Which would work better, a table or a tree diagram? Explain. A table; it would be difficult to draw all the branches of the tree.
7. There are 251 students at Riverdell High. By what time will every student know the news? 9:45 A.M.



# 2 Teach

## Teaching Notes

Have one student shake hands with two other students, and then each of those two shake hands with two more, and so on. Ask a volunteer to make a drawing on the board to reflect what happened as students discuss the numbers in this pattern.

### Sample Problem

**Build understanding.** At 8:00 A.M., how many students know the news? 1 At 8:15 A.M., how many? 3 At 8:30 A.M., how many? 7

**ELL** Ask a student who is familiar with computer code or DNA to share knowledge with others in the class about the patterns these examples contain.

**Math Reasoning** Before students start the Exercises, ask them to reflect on their own problem-solving process. Discuss which method helped them the most: acting out, explaining in words, making a table, or drawing a tree diagram. Point out that there are many problem solving methods, and no particular method is the best for everyone.

**Extension** Ask students to suggest real-life examples that are similar to the sample problem. One relevant area would be the spread of a communicable disease; another might be the acceptance of a new technology.

**Error Prevention** Students often make errors in seeing what happens at the beginning of the pattern. Remind them to read carefully and to check their table or decision tree against what the problem says.

- **Additional Sample Problem**
  Seventy-two band members are lining up for a parade. How many ways can they line up in equal rows if each row must have 4 or more members but no more than 8?. 3 ways; 18 rows of 4; 12 rows of 6; 9 rows of 8

## AFTER THE LESSON

**To assess knowledge:**
**Lesson Quiz**

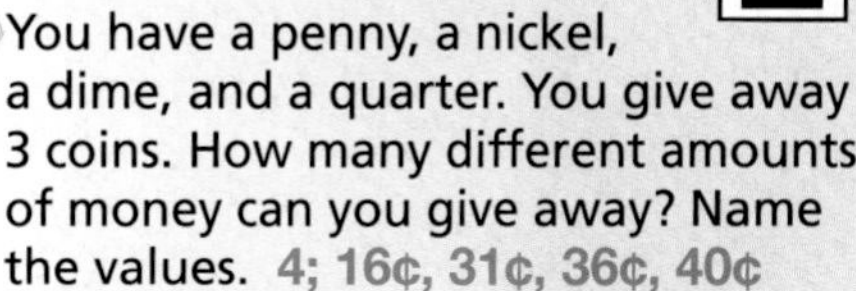

Solve using any strategy.
You have a penny, a nickel, a dime, and a quarter. You give away 3 coins. How many different amounts of money can you give away? Name the values. 4; 16¢, 31¢, 36¢, 40¢

- For enrichment and reteaching options see Resources on p. 1H.

# 3 Practice/Assess

## Assignment Guide

**Core** 1–10

Mixed Review can be assigned at any time for maintenance.

## Exercises

**Exercise 3** Ask students who have difficulty with this exercise to compare the first line with the second. Help them to see that the first factor has decreased by one and the second factor has increased by one.

**Exercise 4** Some students may find it helpful to model this problem with counters.

## ✪ Challenge

A species of bacteria reproduce by dividing every 30 minutes. Starting with a single bacterium, how many bacteria will there be after 3 hours? 64

## Closure

You can use patterns to solve problems.

## Daily Cumulative Review

**Write a rule for each pattern. Find the next three numbers in each pattern.** *(Lesson 1-7)*

1. 6, 11, 16, 21, 26, 31, 36
   Rule: Start with 6 and add 5 repeatedly.
2. 1, 2, 4, 8, 16, 32, 64, 128
   Rule: Start with 1 and multiply by 2 repeatedly.
3. −35, −27, −19, −11, −3, 5, 13
   Rule: Start with −35 and add 8 repeatedly.

**Use a rule to find each difference.** *(Lesson 1-6)*

4. $7 - 16$ −9
5. $-15 - 21$ −36
6. $170 - (-65)$ 235
7. $-71 - (-56)$ −15
8. $-37 - (-36)$ −1
9. $-36 - 8 - (-42)$ −2

**Mixed Review**

**Insert grouping symbols to make each number sentence true.**

10. $(8 - 6) \cdot 6 = 12$ (1-2)
11. $(6 + 3) \cdot (9 + 3) = 108$ (1-2)
12. $4 \cdot 2 \cdot 3 - (4 \cdot 6) = 0$ (1-2)

**Find the average for each set of data.** *(From Last Year)*

13. 15, 26, 32, 19, 25, 21 23
14. 87, 67, 98, 84, 94 86

**Find each product or quotient.** *(From Last Year)*

15. $72 \div 9$ 8
16. $8 \cdot 5$ 40
17. $7 \times 4$ 28
18. $6 \cdot 6$ 36
19. $21 \div 7$ 3
20. $\frac{54}{6}$ 9





# Exercises

## Check Understanding

**Solve by looking for a pattern.**

1. *Data Analysis* Caroline is training for a swim meet. The graph shows the number of laps per day she swims each week. If she keeps to this training pattern, how many laps per day will Caroline swim in week 8? 36 laps/day

2. *Patterns* Students are to march in a parade. There will be one first-grader, two second-graders, three third-graders, and so on through the twelfth grade. How many students will march in the parade? 78 students

3. a. *Number Sense* Complete. Then look for a pattern.

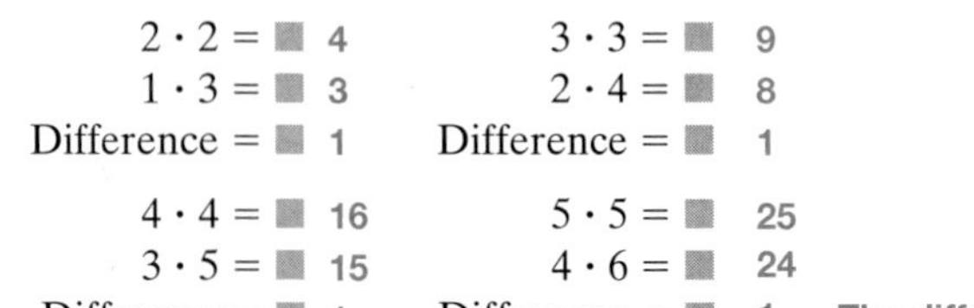
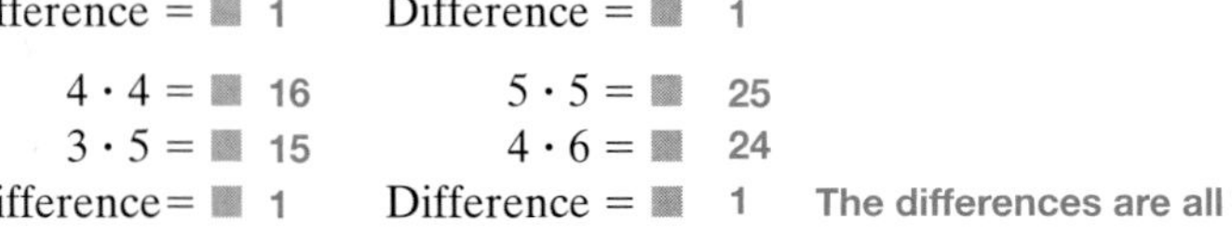

$2 \cdot 2 = ■$ 4 $\quad 3 \cdot 3 = ■$ 9
$1 \cdot 3 = ■$ 3 $\quad 2 \cdot 4 = ■$ 8
Difference = ■ 1 $\quad$ Difference = ■ 1

$4 \cdot 4 = ■$ 16 $\quad 5 \cdot 5 = ■$ 25
$3 \cdot 5 = ■$ 15 $\quad 4 \cdot 6 = ■$ 24
Difference = ■ 1 $\quad$ Difference = ■ 1 The differences are all 1.

   b. Which is greater, $10 \cdot 12$ or $11 \cdot 11$? How much is the difference? $11 \cdot 11$; 1 greater
   c. *Mathematical Reasoning* Suppose you know that $47 \cdot 47 = 2{,}209$. Use this to find $46 \cdot 48$. 2,208
   d. Suppose you know that $64 \cdot 66 = 4{,}224$. Use this to find $65 \cdot 65$. 4,225

4. Suppose that every day you save twice as many pennies as you saved the day before. You start by saving one penny on January 1. How much money will you have in all by January 10? $10.23

## Practice and Problem Solving

**Solve using any strategy.**

5. Roland has an appointment tomorrow at 8:45 A.M. He wants to arrive at least fifteen minutes early. It takes him one hour to get ready and 45 minutes to drive to the appointment. At what time should Roland plan to get up? 6:45 A.M.



## Alternative Assessment

Have students create a number pattern similar to the example in this lesson. Then, ask them to write a word problem that uses the number pattern.

6. *Geometry* You can cut a pizza into two pieces with one straight cut. With two cuts you can get four pieces. Three cuts give a maximum of seven pieces. What is the maximum number of pieces with four cuts? With five cuts? 11 pieces; 16 pieces

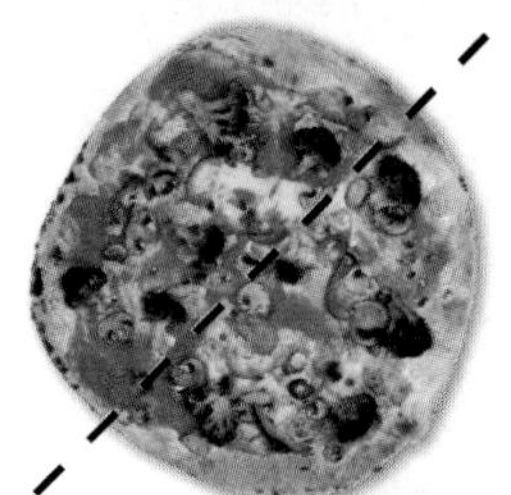

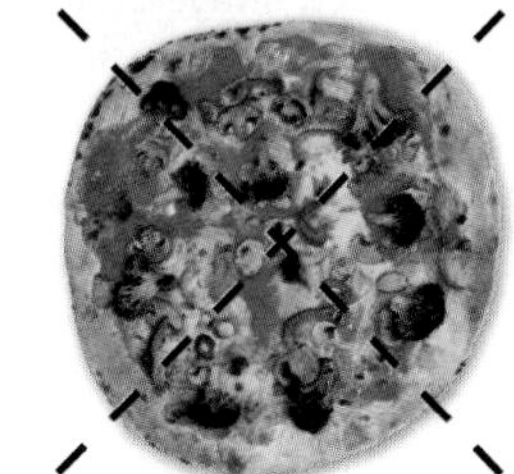

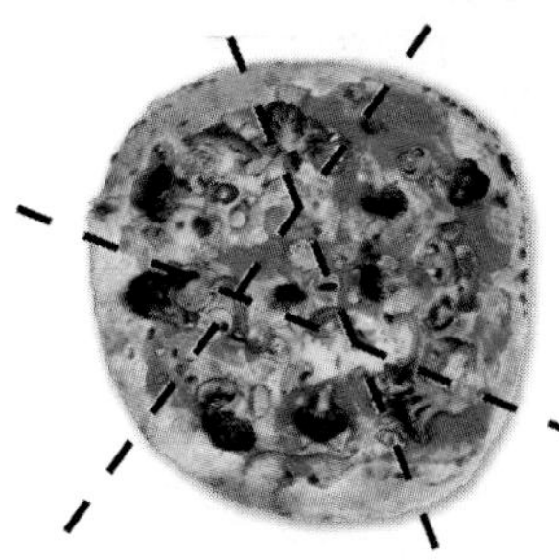

7. A restaurant offers a buffet dinner at group prices. It costs \$10 for one person, \$20 for two, \$29 for three, \$37 for four, \$44 for five, and so on.
   a. How much does a buffet dinner for 8 cost? How much does a group of eight save if its members eat together rather than alone? \$59; \$21
   b. The buffet costs the restaurant \$6 per person. How large a group can the restaurant serve without losing money? 10 people

8. Jayne has 3 quarters, 2 dimes, a nickel, and 2 pennies in her pocket. How many different amounts of money can she make using some or all of these coins? 62

9. One edition of *Alice's Adventures in Wonderland* has 352 pages. How many 4's were used in the page numbers? 75 4's

10. A woman jogging at 6 mi/h passes a man biking in the opposite direction at 12 mi/h. If they maintain their speeds, how far from each other will they be 10 min after passing? 3 mi

## Mixed Review

*Geometry* **Describe the next figure in each pattern. Then draw the figure.** ***(Lesson 1-7)***

11.

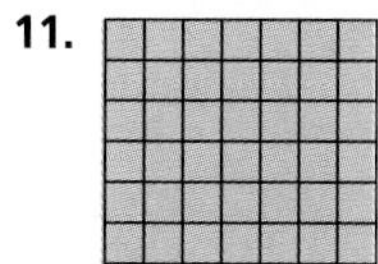

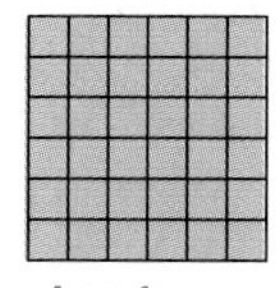

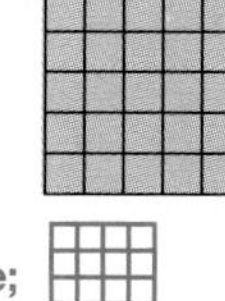

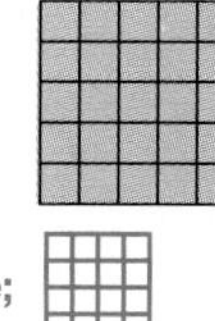

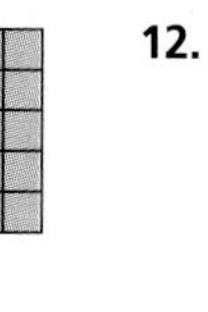

a $4 \times 4$ square;

12.

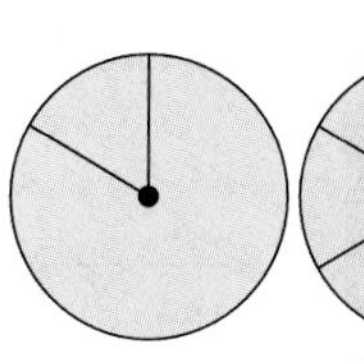

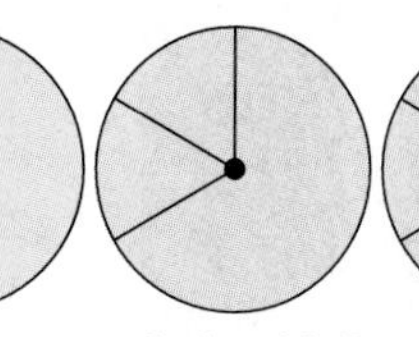

a circle with 5 radii;

**Evaluate each expression for $m = 1$ and $n = 4$.** ***(Lesson 1-3)***

13. $4m - n$ 0

14. $4(n + 2) + m$ 25

15. $11n - 5$ 39

16. $mn + 13$ 17

17. *Weather* At midnight, the temperature was $-5°$F. By dawn, the temperature had risen 14 degrees. What was the temperature at dawn? ***(Lesson 1-5)*** 9°F



## Practice

**Solve using any strategy.**

1. Each row in a window display of floppy disk cartons contains two more boxes than the row above. The first row has one box.
   a. Complete the table.

| Row Number | 1 | 2 | 3 | 4 | 5 | 6 |
|---|---|---|---|---|---|---|
| Boxes in the row | 1 | 3 | 5 | 7 | 9 | 11 |
| Total boxes in the display | 1 | 4 | 9 | 16 | 25 | 36 |

   b. Describe the pattern in the numbers you wrote. The total in the display is the row number multiplied by itself (the row number squared).
   c. Find the number of rows in a display containing the given number of boxes.
   81 9 144 12 400 20
   d. Describe how you can use the number of boxes in the display to calculate the number of rows. The number of rows is the square root of the number of boxes in the display.

2. A computer multiplied nine 100 times. You can use patterns to find the ones' digit of the product.
$$\underbrace{9 \times 9 \times 9 \times 9 \times \cdots \times 9}_{100 \text{ times}}$$
   a. Find the ones' digit when nine is multiplied:
   1 time 9 2 times 1 3 times 9 4 times 1
   b. Describe the pattern. When 9 is multiplied an even number of times the ones' digit is 1. When 9 is multiplied an odd number of times the ones' digit is 9.
   c. What is the ones' digit of the computer product? 1

3. Use the method of Exercise 2 to find the ones' digit of the product when 4 is multiplied by itself 100 times. 6



## Reteaching

Margarita learned to dig clams over her vacation and got steadily better at finding clams each day. On the first day she found 2 clams, on the second day 5 clams, and on the third day 8. If she continued to improve at the same rate, how many clams did she find on the sixth day?

Make a table to organize the numbers. Then look for a pattern.

| Day | 1 | 2 | 3 | 4 | 5 | 6 |
|---|---|---|---|---|---|---|
| Clams | 2 | 5 | 8 | 11 | 14 | 17 |
| More than day before | 0 | 3 | 3 | 3 | 3 | 3 |

Margarita found 17 clams on the sixth day.

---

Phillipe got steadily better at playing ping pong on his vacation. The table shows the number of games he won the first three days. If he continued to improve at the same rate, how many games would he win on the sixth day?

1. Complete the table.

| Day | 1 | 2 | 3 | 4 | 5 | 6 |
|---|---|---|---|---|---|---|
| Games Won | 3 | 5 | 7 | 9 | 11 | 13 |
| More than day before | 0 | 2 | 2 | 2 | 2 | 2 |

2. Solve the problem.
   Phillipe would win 13 games on the sixth day.

Jennifer improved her bike riding distance steadily while preparing for a race. The table shows the distance in miles she rode during the first three weeks of training. If she continues to improve at the same rate, how many miles will she be able to ride in the sixth week? How many more miles did she ride in week 6 than she rode in week 5?

3. Complete the table.

| Week | 1 | 2 | 3 | 4 | 5 | 6 |
|---|---|---|---|---|---|---|
| Miles Traveled | 3 | 4 | 6 | 9 | 13 | 18 |
| More than week before | 0 | 1 | 2 | 3 | 4 | 5 |

4. Solve the problems.
   Jennifer rode 18 miles in the sixth week.
   Jennifer rode 5 miles more in week 6 than in week 5.



## Enrichment

Two of the most important factors influencing temperature are elevation and latitude. (Latitude is position on the earth's surface measured in degrees north or south of the equator, from 0° to 90°.)

*Elevation Rule*
For every 300-ft gain in elevation, subtract 1° F.

*Latitude Rule*
For every 2 degrees of latitude north or south of the equator, subtract 3° F.

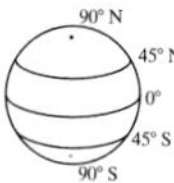


**In Exercises 1–10, elevations and latitudes are approximate.**

| Location | Latitude | Altitude (ft) |
|---|---|---|
| Albuquerque, NM | 35°N | 5,100 |
| Chicago, IL | 42°N | 0 |
| Mount Massive, CO | 40°N | 14,400 |
| Portland, ME | 43°N | 0 |

1. On average, how much warmer is Albuquerque than Portland due to latitude? 12°
2. On average, how much colder is Albuquerque than Portland due to altitude? 17°
3. Find the net difference. 5°
4. Which city is colder? By how much? Albuquerque; 5°F
5. How much warmer is Mount Massive than Chicago due to latitude? 3°
6. How much colder is Mount Massive than Chicago due to altitude? 48°
7. Find the net difference. 45°
8. Which location is colder? By how much? Mount Massive; 45°F

**Solve**

9. Moscow, Russia has a latitude of 56°N and an altitude of 400 ft. Mexico City, Mexico, has a latitude of 20°N and an altitude of 7,300 ft. Which location is colder? By how much?
   Moscow, Russia; 31°F
10. Peking, China, has a latitude of 40°N and an altitude of 150 ft. St. Louis, Missouri, has a latitude of 38°N and an altitude of 450 ft. Which location is colder? By how much?
   Peking, China; 2°F

# 1-9

## Getting Ready

**Resources** A complete list of resources for this lesson is on p. 1H.

### Daily Skills Warm-Up

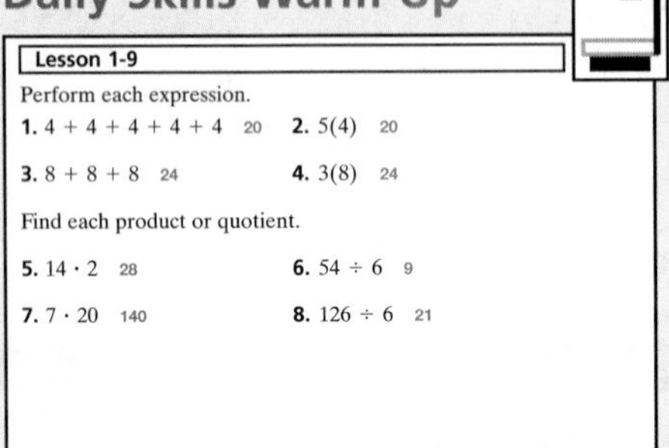
Lesson 1-9

Perform each expression.

1. 4 + 4 + 4 + 4 + 4   20
2. 5(4)   20
3. 8 + 8 + 8   24
4. 3(8)   24

Find each product or quotient.

5. 14 · 2   28
6. 54 ÷ 6   9
7. 7 · 20   140
8. 126 ÷ 6   21

### Background for the Lesson

The product of two negative integers is positive. This rule often seems counter-intuitive. There are few simple real-world situations that involve multiplying two negative numbers. So, using patterns to find products and quotients of integers provides an example that shows the reasons behind the sign of the product. To find $-1(-3)$ with a pattern, start with a product you know:

$$\begin{aligned} 2(-3) &= -6 \\ 1(-3) &= -3 \\ 0(-3) &= 0 \\ -1(-3) &= 3 \end{aligned}$$

## 1 Focus

### Investigate

Have students discuss what patterns they see in the completed table.

### Connecting to Students' Lives

Ask students if they have ever played video games in an arcade. Many games cost a quarter to play. Each time you play you add −25¢ to the total amount of money you have. Suppose you start with $5. To find how much money you have after playing six games, you add 500 + −25 + −25 + −25 + −25 + −25 + −25.





# 1-9 Multiplying and Dividing Integers

**What You'll Learn**

1. To multiply integers using repeated addition, patterns, and rules
2. To divide integers

**. . . And Why**

To solve real-world problems involving deep-sea exploration and currency

## Investigate

PREPARING TO MULTIPLY INTEGERS

1. Copy and complete the table. The first row is done for you.

| Multiplication | Repeated Addition | Sum |
|---|---|---|
| 3 · (−5) | −5 + (−5) + (−5) | −15 |
| 5 · (−4) | ■ −4 + (−4) + (−4) + (−4) + (−4); | ■ −20 |
| 2 · (−8) | ■ −8 + (−8); | ■ −16 |
| 4 · (−10) | ■ −10 + (−10) + (−10) + (−10); | ■ −40 |

2. What do you notice about the signs of the sums? They are all negative.
3. *Inductive Reasoning* What does the pattern suggest about the product of a positive integer and a negative integer? It is negative.

## PART 1 Multiplying Integers

You can think of multiplication as repeated addition.

REAL-WORLD CONNECTION

**EXAMPLE 1**

*Deep Sea Exploration* **After it is launched from a boat, *Deep Rover* descends 60 ft/min. Where is it in relation to sea level 3 min after its launch?**

Use a number line to show repeated addition.

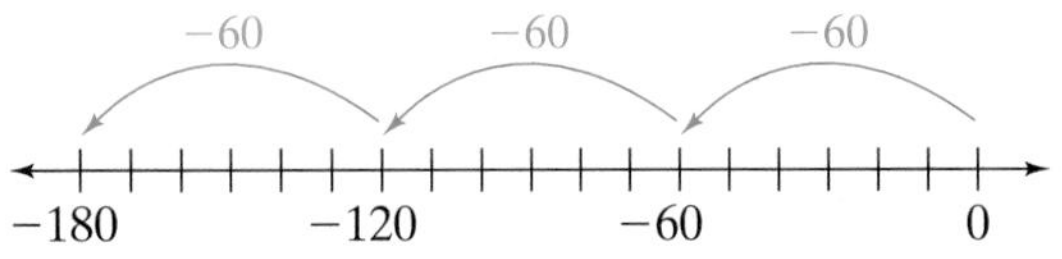


$3(-60) = (-60) + (-60) + (-60) = -180$

*Deep Rover* is at −180 feet, or 180 feet below sea level.

Scientists explore the deep waters of the Pacific Ocean in *Deep Rover*, a submersible designed for research.

■ **TRY THIS** Simplify each product.

4. 2(−6) −12
5. 4(−3) −12
6. 7(−2) −14



# Tools to Monitor Progress

### BEFORE THE LESSON

**To check prerequisite skills:**

- Multiplying and dividing whole numbers

**Skills You Need**, p. 1

**Skills Handbook**, pp. 725–726

**Skills Intervention Kit**, Whole Numbers

### DURING THE LESSON

**To check understanding:**

**Try This** exercises on student page

- **Additional Example 1**

A mountain climber descends from a peak at the rate of 2 miles an hour. Write an expression with repeated addition to show how far he is from the top of the mountain after 4 hours.

(−2) + (−2) + (−2) + (−2); −8 mi

You can use patterns to simplify the product of a negative number and a positive number, or the product of two negative numbers.

### EXAMPLE 2

*Patterns* **Use a pattern to find each product.**

**a.** $-2(5)$

$2(5) = 10$ Start with products you know.
$1(5) = 5$
$0(5) = 0$
$-1(5) = -5$ Continue the pattern.
$-2(5) = -10$

**b.** $-2(-5)$

$2(-5) = -10$
$1(-5) = -5$
$0(-5) = 0$
$-1(-5) = 5$
$-2(-5) = 10$

**Writing Math**

Symbols for multiplication:

| | |
|---|---|
| × | $-2 \times 2$ |
| · | $-2 \cdot 2$ |
| ( ) | $-2(3)$ |
| * | $-2 * 3$ |

**TRY THIS**

7. *Patterns* Use a pattern to simplify $-3(-4)$. 12

By inductive reasoning, the patterns from Example 2 suggest rules for multiplying integers.

**Multiplying Integers**

The product of two integers with the same sign is positive.
The product of two integers with different signs is negative.
The product of zero and any integer is zero.

| Examples | | |
|---|---|---|
| | $3(4) = 12$ | $3(-4) = -12$ |
| | $-3(-4) = 12$ | $-3(4) = -12$ |
| | $3(0) = 0$ | $-4(0) = 0$ |

### EXAMPLE 3

**Multiply $-3 \cdot 5(-4)$.**

$-3 \cdot 5(-4) = -15(-4)$ Multiply from left to right. The product of a negative integer and a positive integer is negative.

$= 60$ Multiply. The product of two negative integers is positive.

**TRY THIS** Simplify each product.

8. $-4 \cdot 8(-2)$ 64 9. $6(-3)(5)$ −90 10. $-7 \cdot (-14) \cdot 0$ 0



# 2 Teach

## Part 1 Teaching Notes

Students will understand and remember the rules for multiplying integers when they have actually written down and reflected on the patterns that explain the rules.

### Example 1

**Build understanding.** Ask: Where is the Deep Rover 1 minute after launch? 2 minutes after launch? at −60 ft; at −120 ft

**ELL** Ask a volunteer to explain what the term *submersible* means in the context of Example 1.

### Example 2

**Build understanding.** Ask: As you go down column a., what happens to the product? It decreases by 5 each time.

### Example 3

**Build understanding.** Ask: Why was $-3 \cdot 5$ multiplied first? Multiplication is done from left to right.

- **Additional Examples 2–3**
  Multiply $7(-2)(-3)$. 42
- **Additional Example 4**
  Use the table to find the average difference between the values for 1994–1997. −27¢

**AFTER THE LESSON**

**To assess knowledge:**

**Lesson Quiz**

Find each product or quotient.

1. $-7(-3)$ 21
2. $-36 \div (-9)$ 4
3. $-12 \cdot 2$ −24
4. $7(-3)$ −21
5. $-6 \cdot (-2) \cdot (-1)$ −12

- For enrichment and reteaching options see Resources on p. 1H.

## Part 2 Teaching Notes

To show why division by zero is undefined, remind students that they can check $\frac{10}{2} = 5$ by multiplying 2 • 5 to get 10. Then ask them to try checking $\frac{10}{0} = 0$ by multiplying 0 • 0. Zero does not equal 10. Then ask them to try checking any other quotient of an integer divided by zero in the same way. Nothing checks, so division by zero is undefined.

### Example 4

**Build understanding.** Ask: How do you find the average of 3, 8, and 4? **Find the sum of the addends and divide by the number of addends; the average is 5.**

**Extension** Ask students to find how much U.S. currency a Canadian tourist could get for $5 Canadian in 1996. **5 • 74, or $3.70**

**Error Prevention** A common error is to write the answer with the wrong sign when multiplying three or more numbers. Show students that they can write just the signs and circle the pairs of negative multipliers to help them decide on the sign of the final product.

**Connecting to History** The Hindus introduced negative numbers about A.D. 700, but Europeans were reluctant to use them for many years. One of the earliest examples of the use of signed numbers in Europe occurs in Germany in the fifteenth century. Mathematicians of the seventeenth and eighteenth century called negative numbers "absurd" and "false."



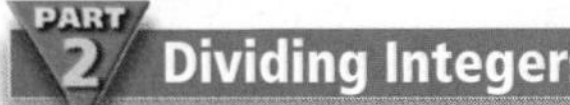

## Dividing Integers

The rules for dividing integers are similar to those for multiplying.

**Dividing Integers**

The quotient of two integers with the same sign is positive.
The quotient of two integers with opposite signs is negative.
Remember that division by zero is undefined.

| Examples | $12 \div 3 = 4$ | $12 \div (-3) = -4$ |
|---|---|---|
| | $-12 \div (-3) = 4$ | $-12 \div 3 = -4$ |

**DATA ANALYSIS** CONNECTION

### Example 4

*Currency* **Find the average of the differences in the values of a Canadian dollar and a U.S. dollar for 1994–1998.**

**Value of Dollars (U.S. cents)**

| Year | Canadian Dollar | U.S. Dollar | Difference |
|---|---|---|---|
| 1994 | 73 | 100 | −27 |
| 1995 | 73 | 100 | −27 |
| 1996 | 74 | 100 | −26 |
| 1997 | 72 | 100 | −28 |
| 1998 | 68 | 100 | −32 |

SOURCES: Bank of Canada; *The World Almanac*

$\frac{-27 + (-27) + (-26) + (-28) + (-32)}{5}$ Write an expression for the average.

$= \frac{-140}{5}$ Use the order of operations. The fraction bar acts as a grouping symbol.

$= -28$ The quotient of a negative integer and a positive integer is negative.

For 1994–1998, the average difference was −28¢. The Canadian dollar was worth an average of 28¢ less than the U.S. dollar.

**Try This** Simplify each quotient.

**11.** $-32 \div 8$ −4 **12.** $-48 \div (-6)$ 8 **13.** $-56 \div (-4)$ 14

**14.** Find the average of 4, −3, −5, 2, and −8. −2

# Exercises

## Check Understanding

**Write each sum as a product. Find the product.**

1. $(-9) + (-9) + (-9) + (-9)$ 4(−9); −36
2. $(-5) + (-5) + (-5) + (-5) + (-5)$ 5(−5); −25

**Without computing, tell whether each product or quotient is *positive* or *negative*. Explain your reasoning.**

3. $-6(-20)$ Positive; the integers have the same sign.
4. $7(-83)$ Negative; the integers have opposite signs.
5. $39 \div (-3)$ Negative; the integers have opposite signs.
6. $-3(8)(-24)$ Positive; the first product is negative, so the second is a product of integers with the same sign.

**Simplify each expression.**

7. $-3 \cdot 10$ −30
8. $-25 \div 5$ −5
9. $4(-11)$ −44
10. $-90 \div (-9)$ 10

11. a. What is the product of −6 and −1? 6
    b. How are that product and −6 related? They are opposites.
    c. *Inductive Reasoning* Complete: The product of any integer and −1 is the __?__ of the integer. opposite

## Practice and Problem Solving

*Mental Math* **Find each product or quotient.**

12. $-5(-3)$ 15
13. $-6 \cdot 10$ −60
14. $-10 \cdot 0$ 0
15. $24 \div (-24)$ −1
16. $18 \div (-1)$ −18
17. $-120 \div 12$ −10

*Choose* **Use repeated addition, patterns, or rules to find each product or quotient.**

18. $24(-16)(-32)$ 12,288
19. $-9(-8)(-5)$ −360
20. $0(-12) \cdot 4$ 0
21. $|-2| \cdot (-7)$ −14
22. $-59(-79)$ 4,661
23. $243(-88)$ −21,384
24. $8 \cdot 3(-4)$ −96
25. $-38 \div (-2)$ 19
26. $-200 \div 25$ −8
27. $-18(-12)$ 216
28. $38(-2)$ −76
29. $-72 \div 6$ −12
30. $1{,}000 \div (-50)$ −20
31. $-33 \div 11$ −3
32. $225 \div (-15)$ −15
33. $-58 \div (-1)$ 58
34. $-72 \div (-8)$ 9
35. $5{,}959 \div (-101)$ −59
36. $\frac{-1{,}225}{35}$ −35
37. $\frac{3{,}132}{-36}$ −87
38. $\frac{-56 \cdot 12}{-24}$ 28

39. Write a number sentence for the product shown on the number line. $5 \cdot (-2) = -10$

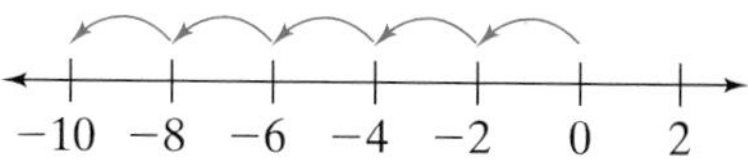




# 3 Practice/Assess

## Assignment Guide

To provide flexible scheduling, this lesson can be divided into parts.

**Part 1**
**Core** 1–4, 6–7, 9, 11–14, 18–24, 27–28, 39, 44–45, 59, 62, 65
**Extension** 40–43, 50, 60–61

**Part 2**
**Core** 5, 8, 10, 15–17, 25–26, 29–38, 46–49, 54–58, 63–64
**Extension** 51–53, 66

Mixed Review can be assigned at any time for maintenance.

## Exercises

**Exercises 18–30** Remind students that they can use whichever method helps them understand the mathematics. Later they will learn ways to make their calculations faster.

**Exercises 31–38** Tell students to take the time to decide which operation they are doing (addition or multiplication, for example) before they calculate.

## Alternative Assessment

Have students write in their journals their own informal explanation for how to multiply two negative integers.

## Daily Cumulative Review

**Use a pattern to solve each problem.** *(Lesson 1-8)*

1. Dominic is setting up chairs for the school play. He put 2 chairs in the first row. After that, each row had 2 more chairs than the one in front of it. He made 10 rows. How many chairs did Dominic need? 110 chairs
2. The local pizza place is having a sale on medium pizzas. If you buy 2 mediums for \$12.00, each additional medium pizza is only \$5.00. How much would 8 medium pizzas cost? \$42.00

**Write a rule for each pattern. Find the next three numbers in each pattern.** *(Lesson 1-7)*

3. $2, 2\frac{1}{2}, 3, 3\frac{1}{2},$ 4, $4\frac{1}{2}$, 5
   Rule: Start with 2 and add $\frac{1}{2}$ repeatedly.
4. 1, 4, 8, 11, 15, 18, 22, 25
   Rule: Start with 1. Alternate adding 3 and adding 4 repeatedly.
5. 4, 4, 8, 12, 20, 32, 52, 84
   Rule: Start with 4 and add the number that comes before it.

**Mixed Review**

**Graph each set of numbers on the number line. Then order the numbers from least to greatest.**

6. −3, 1, −5 *(1-4)* — −5, −3, 1
7. 2, −4, −2 *(1-4)* — −4, −2, 2

**Evaluate each expression.**

8. $45 - (n - 8)$, for $n = 25$ *(1-3)* 28
9. $d - 3h + \frac{h}{2}$, for $d = 15, h = 4$ *(1-3)* 5

## Challenge

Simplify the product.
$-9(-3) \cdot 4 \cdot |-2|(-1)$ −216

## Closure

To multiply or divide integers, you multiply or divide the absolute values of the integers. If the integers have the same sign, the product or quotient is positive. If the integers have different signs, the product or quotient is negative.

**Name the point on the number line that is the graph of each product.**

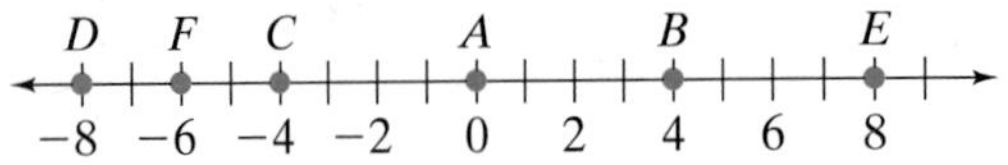


40. $-2 \cdot 0$ *A*
41. $4(-2)$ *D*
42. $|-2| \cdot |-2|$ *B*
43. $2(-2)$ *C*

**Compare. Use >, <, or = to complete each statement.**

44. $(-9)(-6) \;\blacksquare\; 8(-10)$ >
45. $5(-2) \;\blacksquare\; (-6)(-1)$ <
46. $-10 \div (-2) \;\blacksquare\; 25 \div (-5)$ >
47. $-(-15 \div 5) \;\blacksquare\; -100 \div (-20)$ <
48. $|-25| \div |-5| \;\blacksquare\; |-25 \div (-5)|$ =
49. $-|-28| \div 7 \;\blacksquare\; -28 \div (-7)$ <

*Open-ended* **Simplify each pair of expressions. Then write an integer whose value is between the values of the expressions.** 50–53. Intermediate values may vary. Samples are given.

50. $-2 \cdot (-2)$ and $2 \cdot 4$ 4 and 8; 7
51. $10 + (-7)$ and $10 \div (-5)$ 3 and −2; −1
52. $121 \div (-11)$ and $|-7| - |7|$ −11 and 0; −6
53. $50 + (-48)$ and $80 \div (-20)$ 2 and −4; 1

**For each group, find the average.**

54. temperatures: −9°C, −12°C, 9°C, 4°C, −2°C −2°C
55. football yardage: 10, −5, 7, 9, −11 2 yd
56. golf scores: −3, 4, 2, 1, −4, −1, 3, −2 0
57. bank balances: \$200, −\$85, \$120, \$200, \$280 \$143
58. feet above and below sea level: 135, −56, 92, −29, −88, −60 −1
59. *Weather* The temperature dropped 5 degrees each hour for 7 h. Use an integer to represent the total change in temperature. −35
60. *Investing* The price of one share of a stock fell \$3 each day for 12 days.
    a. What was the total change in price of a share of the stock? −\$36
    b. The original stock price was \$76 per share. What was the price after the drop? \$40 per share
61. a. *Inductive Reasoning* Will the sign be positive or negative for the product of three negative integers? Of four negative integers? Of five negative integers? negative; positive; negative
    b. *Writing* Use inductive reasoning to write a rule for the sign of the product of more than two negative integers. See above right.
62. A scuba diver descended to a depth of 50 feet in 25 seconds. Write an integer to represent the average number of feet per second the diver traveled. −2

61. If there are an even number of negative integers, the sign of the product will be positive; otherwise, the sign will be negative.

63. What integer multiplied by $-8$ equals $-96$? 12

64. What integer multiplied by 9 equals $-135$? $-15$

65. What two integers have a sum of negative ten and a product of negative seventy-five? $-15, 5$

66. *Mathematical Reasoning* If $a$ and $b$ are positive integers, and $x$ and $y$ are negative integers, what is the sign of $\frac{a+b}{x+y}$? Explain. Negative; the numerator is positive, and the denominator is negative, so the quotient is negative.

## Mixed Review

**Compare. Use >, <, or = to complete each statement.** ***(Lessons 1-5 and 1-6)***

67. $-3 + (-8)$ ■ $12 - (-6)$ <

68. $-9 + 13$ ■ $24 - 30$ >

69. $|-6| - |12|$ ■ $-8 + |-12|$ <

**Write a variable expression for each word phrase.** ***(Lesson 1-1)***

70. the product of $y$ and 60 $60y$

71. 50 decreased by a number $50 - n$

72. the quotient of $d$ and 5 $\frac{d}{5}$

73. *Choose a Strategy* How many whole numbers between 10 and 200 have exactly two identical digits? 36

## Checkpoint 2 — Lessons 1-5 through 1-9

**Simplify each expression.**

1. $3 + (-11)$ $-8$
2. $12 - (-8)$ 20
3. $-9 \cdot 5$ $-45$
4. $-64 \div (-8)$ 8
5. $-8(-3)(3)$ 72
6. $|-3| \cdot 8 \div (-2)$ $-12$

*Open-ended* **Use integers to complete each equation.** 7–9. Answers may vary. Samples are given.

7. ■ + ■ = $-7$ $3 + (-10) = -7$
8. ■ $- (-20) =$ ■ $2 - (-20) = 22$
9. ■ · ■ = $-40$ $8 \cdot (-5) = -40$

*Patterns* **Find the next three numbers in each pattern.**

10. $-7, -2, 3, 8,$ ■, ■, ■ 13, 18, 23
11. $1, 3, 9, 27,$ ■, ■, ■ 81, 243, 729

12. **TEST PREP** What is the average temperature for the five days? A

| Day | Mon. | Tue. | Wed. | Thu. | Fri. |
|---|---|---|---|---|---|
| Temperature | −3°F | 2°F | 1°F | −4°F | −6°F |

A. −2°F B. −1°F C. 2°F D. 1°F

See also Extra Practice section.



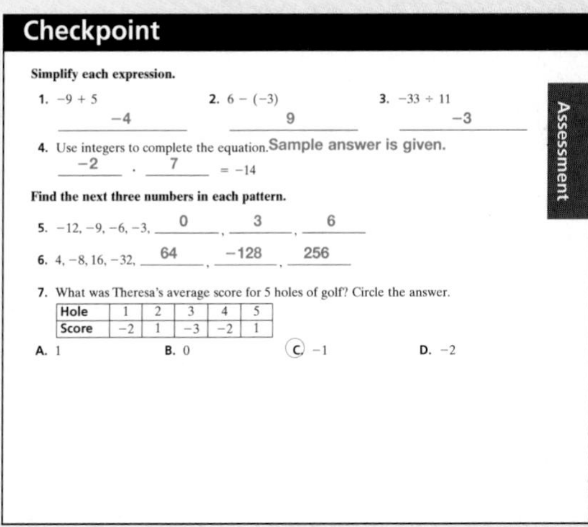
Checkpoint

Assessment

**Simplify each expression.**

1. $-9 + 5$ $-4$
2. $6 - (-3)$ 9
3. $-33 \div 11$ $-3$

4. Use integers to complete the equation. Sample answer is given.
$-2 \cdot 7 = -14$

**Find the next three numbers in each pattern.**

5. −12, −9, −6, −3, 0, 3, 6
6. 4, −8, 16, −32, 64, −128, 256

7. What was Theresa's average score for 5 holes of golf? Circle the answer.

| Hole | 1 | 2 | 3 | 4 | 5 |
|---|---|---|---|---|---|
| Score | −2 | 1 | −3 | −2 | 1 |

A. 1 B. 0 (C.) −1 D. −2

## Practice

**Use repeated addition, patterns, or rules to find each product or quotient.**

1. $23 \cdot 16$ 368
2. $8 \cdot 7(-6)$ $-336$
3. $-17 \cdot 3$ $-51$
4. $-24 \div 4$ $-6$
5. $-65 \div 5$ $-13$
6. $117 \div (-1)$ $-117$
7. $-30 \div (-6)$ 5
8. $-21 \div (-3)$ 7
9. $63 \div (-21)$ $-3$
10. $5(-1)(-9)$ 45
11. $-6(-3) \cdot 2$ 36
12. $-3 \cdot 7(-2)$ 42
13. $\frac{1,512}{-42}$ $-36$
14. $\frac{-4,875}{-65}$ 75
15. $\frac{-15(-3)}{-9}$ $-5$

**Compare. Use >, <, or = to complete each statement.**

16. $-7(5)$ [<] $-6 \cdot (-6)$
17. $-20 \cdot (-5)$ [=] $10 \cdot |-10|$
18. $3(-6)$ [=] $-3(6)$
19. $121 \div (-11)$ [<] $-45 \div (-6)$
20. $-40 \div 8$ [=] $40 \div (-8)$
21. $-54 \div 9$ [>] $21 \div (-3)$

**For each group, find the average.**

22. temperatures: 6°, −15°, −24°, 3°, −25° −11°
23. bank balances: \$52, −\$7, \$20, −\$63, −\$82 −\$16
24. stock price changes: \$6, −\$6, −\$9, \$1, \$3 −\$1
25. golf scores: −2, 0, 3, −2, −3, 1, −4 −1
26. elevations (ft): −120, 168, −60, −42, −36 −18 ft

**Write a multiplication or division sentence to answer the question.**

27. The temperature dropped 4° each hour for 3 hours. What was the total change in temperature?
$3(-4) = -12$; The temperature dropped a total of 12°.



## Reteaching

Multiplying and dividing integers is very similar to multiplying and dividing whole numbers. Just remember the two basic rules for determining the sign of the product or quotient.

**Rule 1:** The product or quotient of two integers with the *same sign* is positive.

**Rule 2:** The product or quotient of two integers with *opposite signs* is negative.

**Find each product or quotient.**

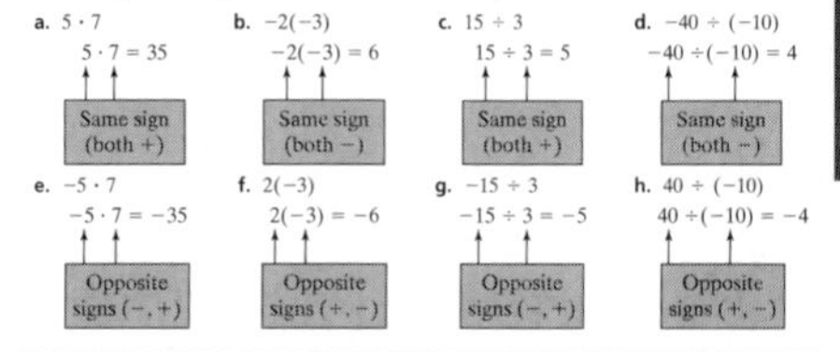


**Complete the table. The first row has been done for you.**

| | | Same or Opposite sign? | Sign of product or quotient | Product or quotient |
|---|---|---|---|---|
| | −5 · 12 | Opposite | Negative | −60 |
| 1. | −91 ÷ (−13) | Same | Positive | 7 |
| 2. | 6 · 8 | Same | Positive | 48 |
| 3. | 72 ÷ −9 | Opposite | Negative | −8 |
| 4. | −3(−6) | Same | Positive | 18 |
| 5. | −18 ÷ 2 | Opposite | Negative | −9 |
| 6. | 11 · (−5) | Opposite | Negative | −55 |
| 7. | 52 ÷ 4 | Same | Positive | 13 |
| 8. | −12(6) | Opposite | Negative | −72 |



## Enrichment

**A. Finger Multiplication**

Adding on your fingers is easy. Here is how to *multiply* numbers from 6 to 10 using your fingers.

**Example** Multiply: $9 \cdot 8$

**Solution** Imagine the fingers of both hands are numbered from 6 (thumb) to 10 (little finger). Touch finger 9 on one hand to finger 8 on the other hand. Bend any fingers beyond the touching fingers.

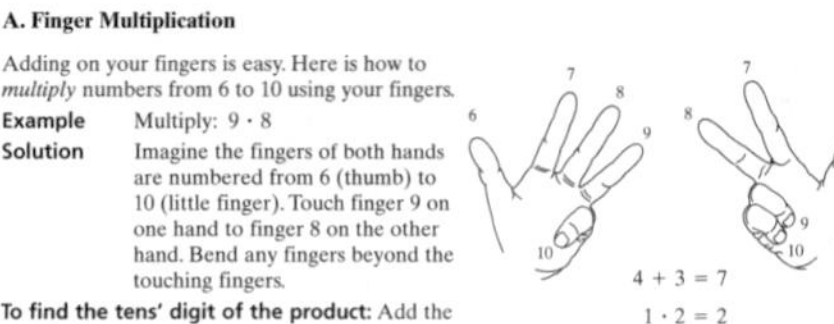


**To find the tens' digit of the product:** Add the upright fingers.

**To find the ones' digit of the product:** Multiply the number of bent fingers on one hand times the number of bent fingers on the other hand.

**Product:** 72

**Use your fingers to multiply.**

1. $7 \cdot 8$ 56
2. $9 \cdot 9$ 81
3. $9 \cdot 7$ 63
4. $6 \cdot 8$ 48

**B. Binary Multiplication**

Using only multiplication and division by 2, you can find the product of any two numbers.

**Example** Multiply: $39(-13)$

**Solution** Write the factors side by side.

On the left side, divide by 2, dropping any remainder. On the right side multiply by 2. Continue until you reach 1 on the left.

| | |
|---|---|
| 39 | −13 |
| 19 | −26 |
| 9 | −52 |
| 4 | −104 |
| 2 | −208 |
| 1 | −416 |

List those numbers from the right side that are positioned across from the odd numbers on the left side. Add them.

−13
−26
−52
−416

Product: −507

**Find each product using binary multiplication.**

5. $22 \cdot 17$ 374
6. $45(-25)$ −1,125
7. $68(-33)$ −2,244
8. $75(-41)$ −3,075

# 1-10

## Getting Ready

**Key Terms and Symbols** coordinate plane, *x*-axis, *y*-axis, quadrants, ordered pair, origin, *x*-coordinate, *y*-coordinate

**Resources** A complete list of resources for this lesson is on p. 1H.

### Daily Skills Warm-Up

**Lesson 1-10**

Graph each set of numbers on a number line. Then order the numbers from least to greatest.

1. $-2, 1, -5$  $-5, -2, 1$
2. $0, 2, -4$  $-4, 0, 2$
3. $-3, 3, -2$  $-3, -2, 3$
4. $-1, -5, -8$  $-8, -5, -1$

Describe the next figure in the pattern. Then draw the figure.

5\.

A five-sided figure

### Background for the Lesson

The Cartesian coordinate system was developed in the seventeenth century by Pierre de Fermat (1601–1665) and René Descartes (1596–1650). This system uses two perpendicular number lines to identify any point in a plane. The lines intersect at the origin, or zero point. An ordered pair of numbers names each point in the plane. The pair is called *ordered* because the first number of the pair always gives the horizontal distance from zero on the *x*-axis, and the second number of the pair, in order, gives the vertical distance from zero on the *y*-axis.

## 1 Focus

### Connecting to Prior Knowledge

Remind students that left is the negative direction on a horizontal number line. Ask them which direction seems reasonable for negative numbers on a vertical number line.

# 1-10 The Coordinate Plane

**What You'll Learn**

1. To name coordinates and quadrants in the coordinate plane
2. To graph points in the coordinate plane

**. . . And Why**

To use a graph to define locations of points

## PART 1 Naming Coordinates and Quadrants

A **coordinate plane** is formed by the intersection of two number lines. The horizontal number line is called the ***x*-axis** and the vertical number line is called the ***y*-axis.**

The *x*- and *y*-axes divide the coordinate plane into four **quadrants.**

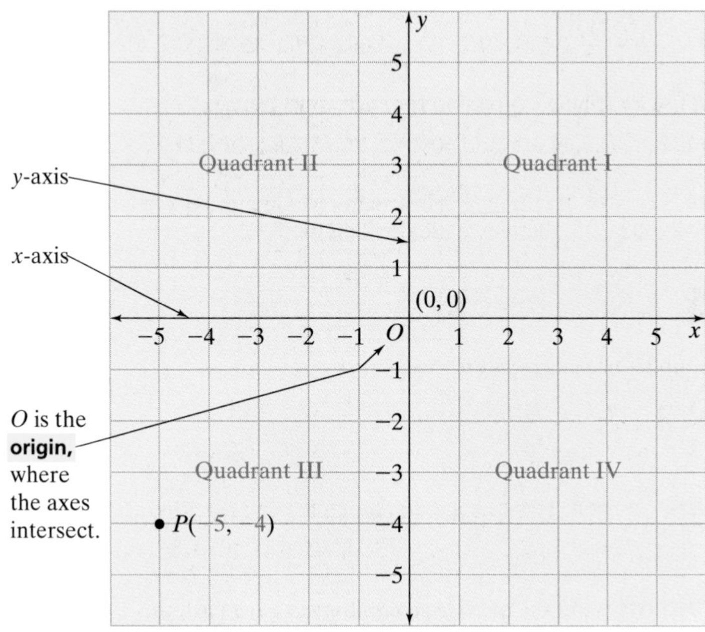


An **ordered pair** gives the coordinates and location of a point. The ordered pair $(-5, -4)$ identifies point *P* in Quadrant III above.

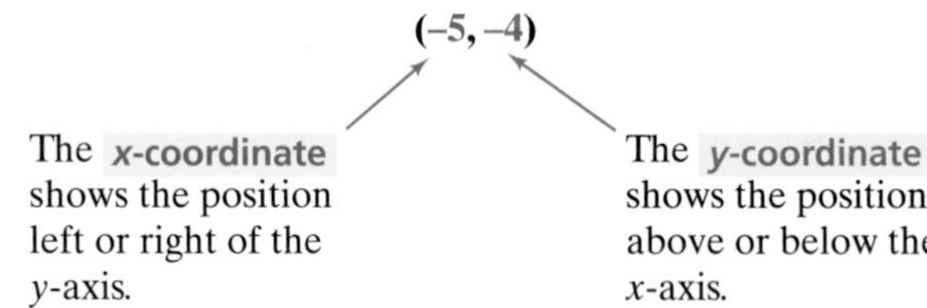

(−5, −4)
The x-coordinate shows the position left or right of the y-axis.
The y-coordinate shows the position above or below the x-axis.




## Tools to Monitor Progress

**BEFORE THE LESSON**

**To check prerequisite skills:**

- Graphing on a number line

**Skills Intervention Kit,** Pre-Algebra Basics

**DURING THE LESSON**

**To check understanding:**

**Try This** exercises on student page

- **Additional Example 1**

  In which quadrant is point *G* (–2, –3) located? **Quadrant III**

## EXAMPLE 1

**Write the coordinates of point *A*. In which quadrant is point *A* located?**

Point *A* is located 2 units to the left of the *y*-axis. So the *x*-coordinate is –2. The point is 1 unit above the *x*-axis. So the *y*-coordinate is 1.

The coordinates of point *A* are $(-2, 1)$. Point *A* is located in Quadrant II.

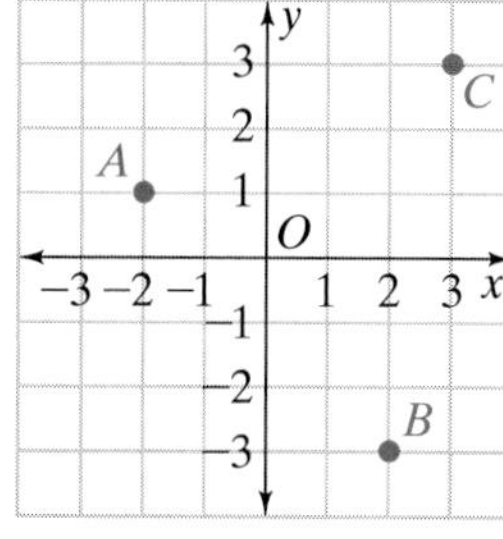


### TRY THIS

1. Use the graph in Example 1. Write the coordinates of *B* and *C*. (2, −3); (3, 3)
2. Identify the quadrants in which *B* and *C* are located. Quadrant IV; Quadrant I

## PART 2 Graphing Points

To graph a point $A(x, y)$ in a coordinate plane, you graph the ordered pair $(x, y)$.

## EXAMPLE 2

**Graph point $R(3, -5)$.**

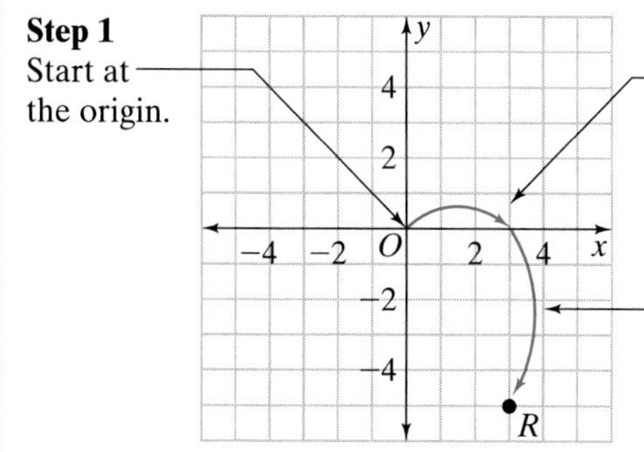


3a–b.

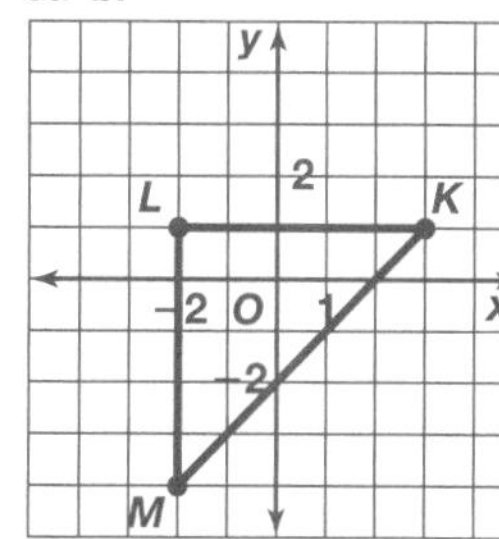


### TRY THIS

3. a. Graph these points on one coordinate plane: $K(3, 1)$, $L(-2, 1)$, and $M(-2, -4)$. See right.
   b. *Geometry* Draw lines to connect points *K*, *L*, and *M*. Describe the figure that results. See right.

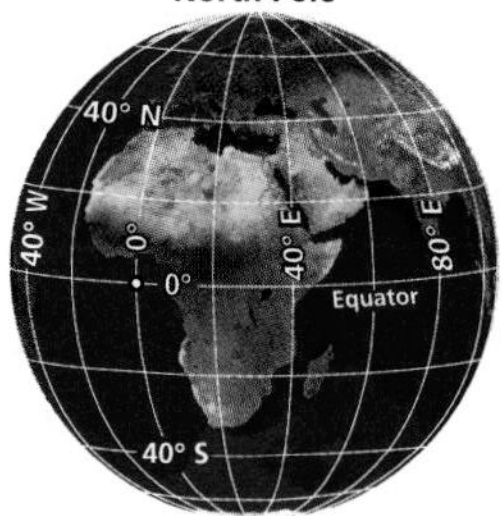


***Geography*** Latitude and longitude are measurements in a coordinate system that locates every point on Earth's surface.



# 2 Teach

## PART 1 Part 1 Teaching Notes

Ask students to compare the way the quadrants are numbered with the way the hands of a clock move. Have them identify the numbers for the quadrants and make sure they understand that Quadrant II is in a counter-clockwise direction from Quadrant I.

### Example 1

**Build understanding.** Ask: What kind of numerals are used to label the quadrants? Roman numerals

**ELL** Explain that the coordinates are called an ordered pair because the order matters: (2, 3) is not the same point as (3, 2).

**Connecting to Technology** The Global Positioning System (GPS) is a system of satellites and radio receivers that can accurately locate a point on Earth within a few meters. GPS receivers are used in many planes and ships, and in some cars. There are even hand-held units that can be carried by hikers.

## PART 2 Part 2 Teaching Notes

Have students locate a point that has a coordinate of zero. Ask them to point to the origin.

### Example 2

**Build understanding.** Ask: What does the first number in the ordered pair tell you? how far, and in which direction, to move on the horizontal axis from the origin

**Auditory Learning** As students plot points, they often find it helpful to say aloud the horizontal and vertical moves.

**Extension** Challenge students to name a square by giving the coordinates of its corners. Answers will vary.

**Error Prevention** A common error is to use the first coordinate to move up or down on the *y*-axis. It may help students to remember that *x* and *y* are in alphabetical order, so the *x* value always comes first.

- **Additional Example 2**
  Graph point $M(-3, 3)$.

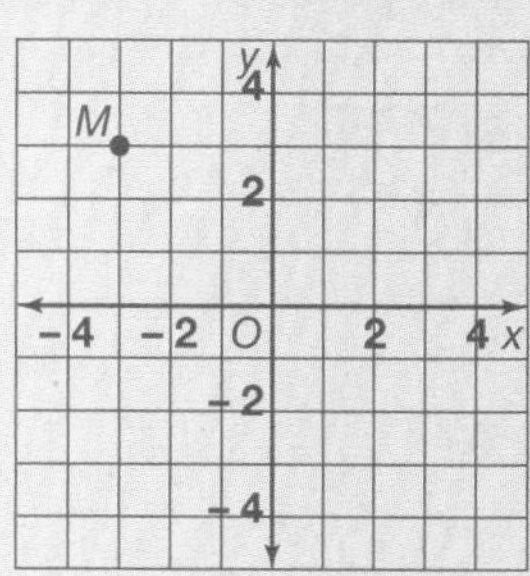


### AFTER THE LESSON

**To assess knowledge: Lesson Quiz**

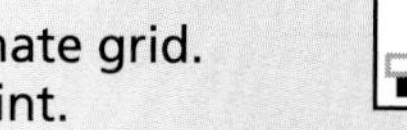

Draw a coordinate grid. Graph each point.

1. $S(2, 3)$
2. $T(2, -3)$
3. $U(-2, 3)$
4. $K(0, 3)$
5. $L(3, 0)$

- For enrichment and reteaching options see Resources on p. 1H.

1–5. See back of book.

# 3 Practice/Assess

## Assignment Guide

To provide flexible scheduling, this lesson can be divided into parts.

**Part 1**
Core 1–9, 16–37
Extension 53–56

**Part 2**
Core 10–15, 38–52, 59
Extension 57–58, 60–61

Mixed Review can be assigned at any time for maintenance.

**ELL** Verify that students understand that graphing a point means to draw it on the coordinate grid.

### Exercises

**Exercises 27–30** Suggest that students test a numeric example, for instance, (2, −3) for Exercise 27, to check their answer.

**Test Prep Exercise 31** Students may want to make a quick sketch of the coordinate system and number the quadrants to help them answer.

**Exercise 51–52** Ask students to recall what they know about a square. four equal sides, four right angles

# Exercises

## Check Understanding

**Write the coordinates of each point.**

1. $T$ (0, −7)
2. $V$ (−4, 1)
3. $M$ (1, −4)
4. $K$ (2, 6)

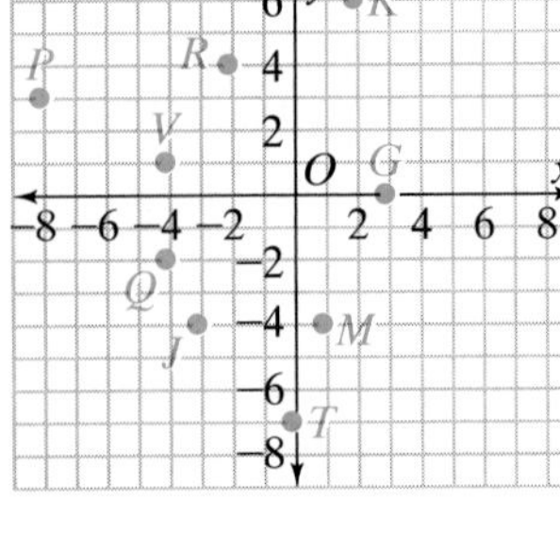

**Name the point with the given coordinates.**

5. $(-3, -4)$ J
6. $(3, 0)$ G
7. $(-2, 4)$ R
8. $(-4, -2)$ Q
9. What ordered pair names the origin? (0, 0)

**Draw a coordinate plane. Graph each point.** 10–15. See margin.

10. $A(-1, 3)$
11. $B(-4, -1)$
12. $C(2, 5)$
13. $D(2, -2)$
14. $F(0, 6)$
15. $G(6, 0)$

## Practice and Problem Solving

**Name the point with the given coordinates.**

16. $(3, 2)$ Q
17. $(0, -5)$ F
18. $(2, 3)$ M
19. $(-2, -3)$ P

**Write the coordinates of each point.**

20. $A$ (2, −3)
21. $B$ (−2, 3)
22. $C$ (−5, 0)
23. $D$ (6, 6)

*Mental Math* **Write the coordinates of each point.**

24. the point 5 units to the left of the $y$-axis and 2 units below the $x$-axis (−5, −2)
25. the point on the $y$-axis 4 units below the $x$-axis (0, −4)
26. the point on the $x$-axis 3 units to the right of the origin (3, 0)

*Mental Math* **In which quadrant does $P(x, y)$ lie?**

27. $x$ is positive and $y$ is negative. IV
28. $x$ is positive and $y$ is positive. I
29. $x$ is negative and $y$ is positive. II
30. $x$ is negative and $y$ is negative. III



### Daily Cumulative Review

**Use rules to find each product or quotient.** *(Lesson 1-9)*

1. 24 ÷ (−3) −8
2. −7 · 6 −42
3. (−8)(−4) 32
4. 6 · 6(−2) −72
5. −81 ÷ (−3) 27
6. |−6| · (−4) −24

**Use a pattern to solve each problem.** *(Lesson 1-8)*

7. Macy receives $15 per week allowance. She wants to buy a CD player that costs $89. She already has $17.75. How many weeks will it take her to earn enough money to buy the CD player? 5 weeks
8. When Carl bought his pet snake, it was 10 inches long. Since then, the snake has grown 3 inches per month. Carl has had his pet snake for 5 months. How long is his pet snake now? 25 inches

**Mixed Review**

**Is each conjecture correct or incorrect? If incorrect, give a counterexample.**

9. Mammals do not fly. (1-7) incorrect; bats are mammals, and they do fly.
10. A rectangle is a parallelogram. (1-7) correct
11. The sum of a negative number and a positive number is always negative. (1-7) incorrect; −3 + 8 = 5

**Simplify each expression.**

12. |−3,000| (1-4) 3,000
13. −|−87| (1-4) −87
14. the opposite of 54 (1-4) −54

**Simplify each expression.**

15. 17 + 3 × 5 (1-2) 32
16. 16 ÷ 4 · 6 (1-2) 24
17. (21 + 9) ÷ 3 ÷ 2 (1-2) 5



### Alternative Assessment

Have students draw a triangle on a coordinate system so that each vertex is in a different quadrant. Then ask them to label each vertex with its ordered pair and to give the number of the quadrant that does not contain a vertex.

10–15.

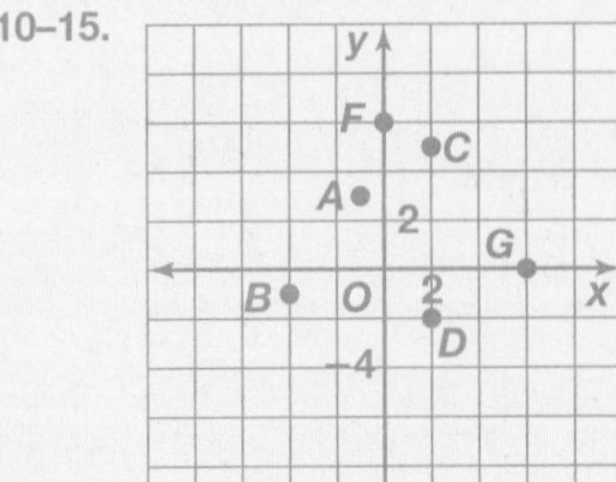

31. **TEST PREP** Fill in the blanks: $P(a, b)$ is in quadrant III. The value of $a$ must be __?__. The value of $b$ must be __?__. D

A. positive; positive
B. positive; negative
C. negative; positive
D. negative; negative

**In which quadrant or on which axis does each ordered pair lie?**

32. $(13, 25)$ I
33. $(-17, -2)$ III
34. $(x, y)$ if $x = 0, y > 0$ (positive) $y$-axis
35. $(x, y)$ if $x > 0, y < 0$ IV
36. $(x, y)$ if $x < 0, y > 0$ II
37. $(0, |-2|)$ (positive) $y$-axis

**Draw a coordinate plane. Graph each point.** 38–46. See margin.

38. $F(-3, 2)$
39. $G(-5, -2)$
40. $H(1, 7)$
41. $K(5, -6)$
42. $L(0, 0)$
43. $N(7, 0)$
44. $P(-1, -3)$
45. $Q(1, 1)$
46. $R(0, -4)$

*Geometry* **Graph and connect the points in the order given. Connect the last point to the first. Name the figure.** 47–50. See margin.

47. $(2, 2), (2, -1), (-5, -1), (-5, 2)$ rectangle
48. $(-4, 1), (1, 1), (-3, -1)$ triangle
49. $(2, -4), (7, -1), (4, 4), (-1, 1)$ square
50. $(-1, 2), (1, 5), (7, 5), (5, 2)$ parallelogram

*Geometry* ***PQRS* is a square. Find the coordinates of *S*.**

51. $P(-5, 0), Q(0, 5), R(5, 0), S(■, ■)$ (0, −5)
52. $P(-1, 3), Q(4, 3), R(4, -2), S(■, ■)$ (−1, −2)

*Geography* **On a map, coordinates are given in degrees of longitude and latitude. Use the map below for Exercises 53–55.**

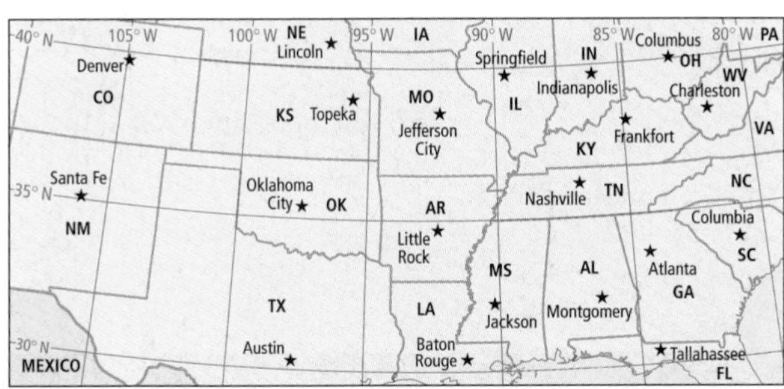


SAMPLE The longitude of Little Rock, Arkansas, is about 92° W and the latitude is about 34° N.

53. Find the longitude and latitude of Jackson, Mississippi. about 90° W, 32° N
54. Find the longitude and latitude of Topeka, Kansas. about 96° W, 39° N
55. What city is located near 85° W, 38° N? Frankfort, KY



## Challenge

What figure is formed when you connect in order the points (−4, −3), (4, −3), (4, 3), and (−4, 3)? a rectangle

## Closure

An ordered pair gives the coordinates of a point on a coordinate plane. The first number, or $x$-coordinate, shows the position to the left or right of the $y$-axis. The $y$-coordinate shows the position above or below the $x$-axis.

48.

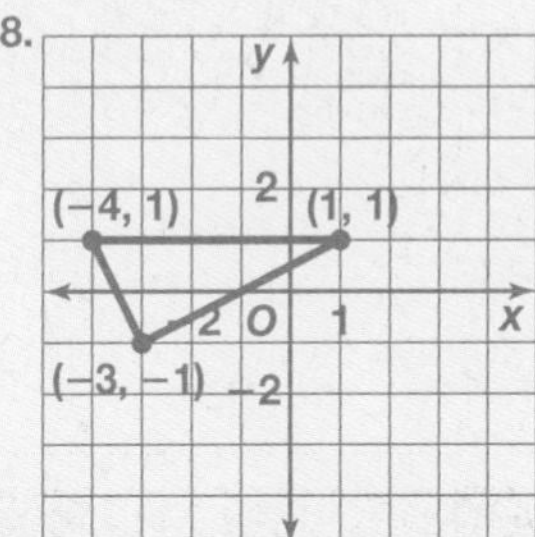


49.

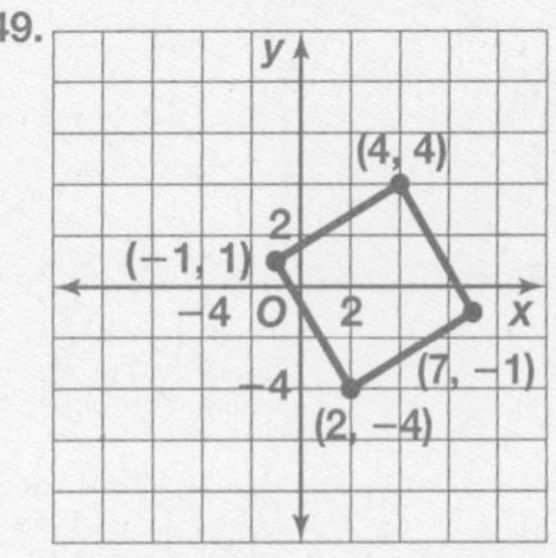


50.

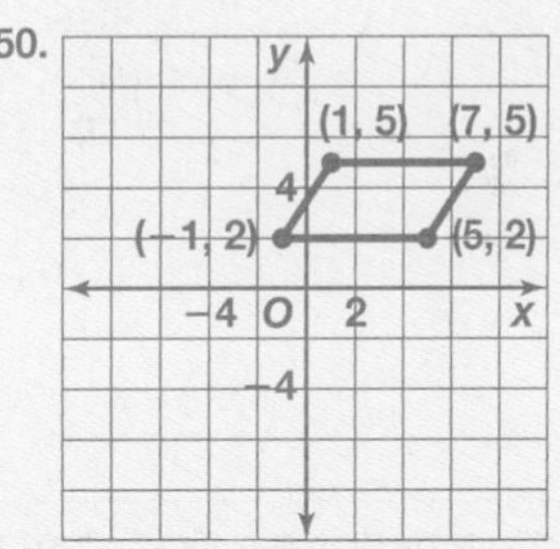

38–46.

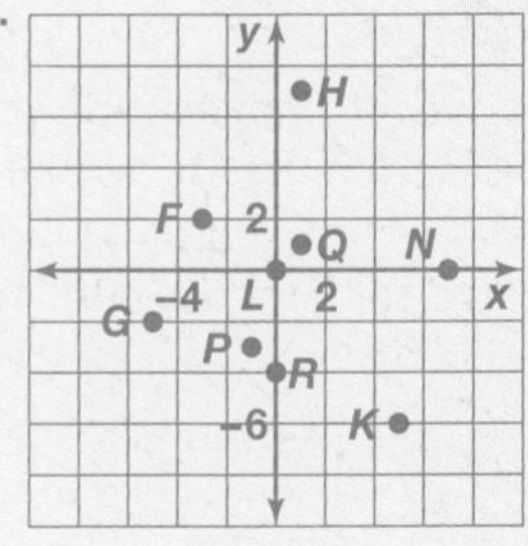


47.

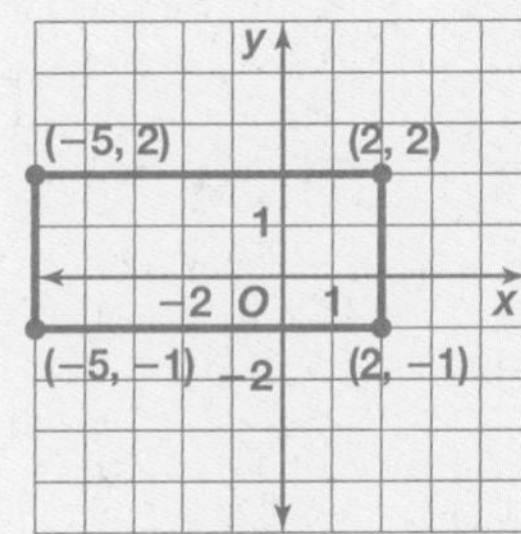

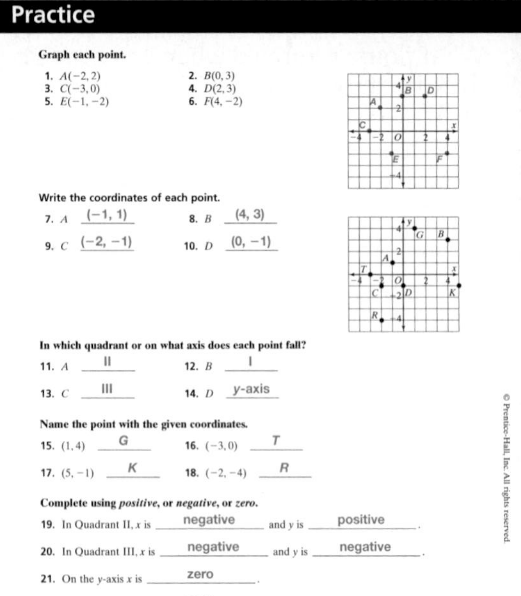

## Practice

Graph each point.

1. $A(-2, 2)$ 2. $B(0, 3)$
3. $C(-3, 0)$ 4. $D(2, 3)$
5. $E(-1, -2)$ 6. $F(4, -2)$

Write the coordinates of each point.

7. $A$ (−1, 1) 8. $B$ (4, 3)
9. $C$ (−2, −1) 10. $D$ (0, −1)

In which quadrant or on what axis does each point fall?

11. $A$ II 12. $B$ I
13. $C$ III 14. $D$ y-axis

Name the point with the given coordinates.

15. (1, 4) G 16. (−3, 0) T
17. (5, −1) K 18. (−2, −4) R

Complete using *positive*, or *negative*, or *zero*.

19. In Quadrant II, $x$ is negative and $y$ is positive.
20. In Quadrant III, $x$ is negative and $y$ is negative.
21. On the $y$-axis $x$ is zero.
22. On the $x$-axis $y$ is zero.



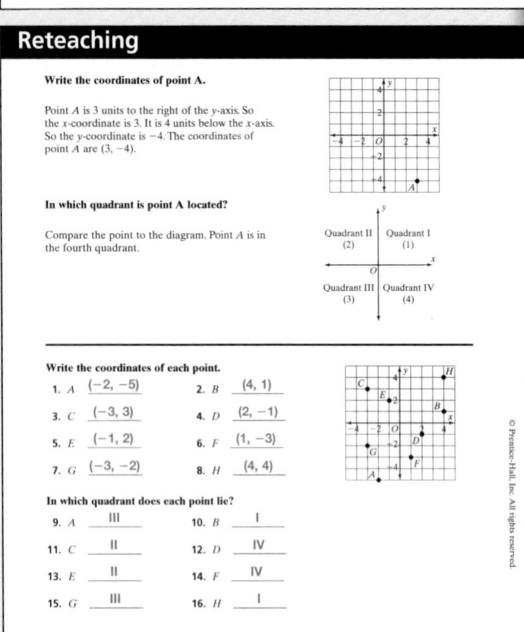

## Reteaching

Write the coordinates of point A.

Point $A$ is 3 units to the right of the $y$-axis. So the $x$-coordinate is 3. It is 4 units below the $x$-axis. So the $y$-coordinate is −4. The coordinates of point $A$ are (3, −4).

In which quadrant is point A located?

Compare the point to the diagram. Point $A$ is in the fourth quadrant.



Write the coordinates of each point.

1. $A$ (−2, −5) 2. $B$ (4, 1)
3. $C$ (−3, 3) 4. $D$ (2, −1)
5. $E$ (−1, 2) 6. $F$ (1, −3)
7. $G$ (−3, −2) 8. $H$ (4, 4)

In which quadrant does each point lie?

9. $A$ III 10. $B$ I
11. $C$ II 12. $D$ IV
13. $E$ II 14. $F$ IV
15. $G$ III 16. $H$ I



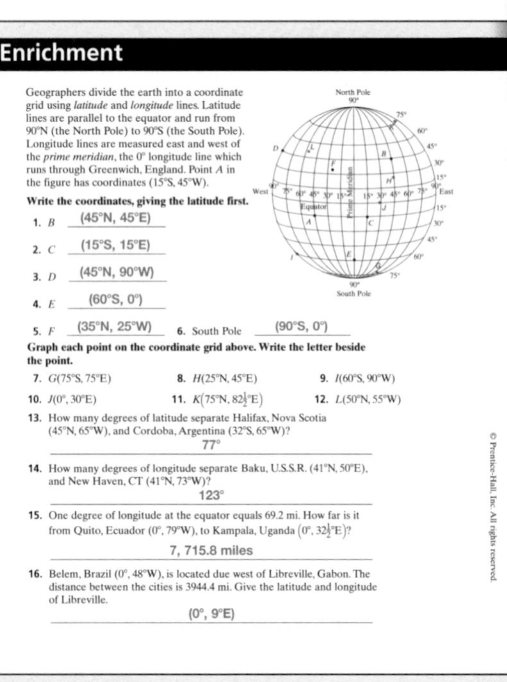

## Enrichment

Geographers divide the earth into a coordinate grid using *latitude* and *longitude* lines. Latitude lines are parallel to the equator and run from 90°N (the North Pole) to 90°S (the South Pole). Longitude lines are measured east and west of the *prime meridian*, the 0° longitude line which runs through Greenwich, England. Point $A$ in the figure has coordinates (15°S, 45°W).



Write the coordinates, giving the latitude first.

1. $B$ (45°N, 45°E)
2. $C$ (15°S, 15°E)
3. $D$ (45°N, 90°W)
4. $E$ (60°S, 0°)
5. $F$ (35°N, 25°W) 6. South Pole (90°S, 0°)

Graph each point on the coordinate grid above. Write the letter beside the point.

7. $G$(75°S, 75°E) 8. $H$(25°N, 45°E) 9. $I$(60°S, 90°W)
10. $J$(0°, 30°E) 11. $K$(75°N, 82½°E) 12. $L$(50°N, 55°W)
13. How many degrees of latitude separate Halifax, Nova Scotia (45°N, 65°W), and Cordoba, Argentina (32°S, 65°W)? 77°
14. How many degrees of longitude separate Baku, U.S.S.R. (41°N, 50°E), and New Haven, CT (41°N, 73°W)? 123°
15. One degree of longitude at the equator equals 69.2 mi. How far is it from Quito, Ecuador (0°, 79°W), to Kampala, Uganda (0°, 32½°E)? 7,715.8 miles
16. Belem, Brazil (0°, 48°W), is located due west of Libreville, Gabon. The distance between the cities is 3944.4 mi. Give the latitude and longitude of Libreville. (0°, 9°E)



56. ***Mathematical Reasoning*** Assume that $a \neq b$. Do $(a, b)$ and $(b, a)$ describe the same point? Explain. Explanations may vary. Sample: No; since $a$ and $b$ describe positions on two number lines, $(a, b)$ and $(b, a)$ describe different points (unless $a = b$).
57. Write the coordinates of four points in the coordinate plane that are 3 units from the origin. Graph the points. See back of book.
58. ***Open-ended*** Draw a dot-to-dot picture on a coordinate grid. Write the coordinates of the points in order. Exchange coordinates with a classmate and draw the other's picture. Check students' work.

***Geometry*** **Use one coordinate plane for Exercises 59–61.** 59–60. See back of book.

59. Graph the points $(-2, 1), (-2, 3), (1, 3)$, and $(1, 1)$. Connect them in the order given. Connect the last point to the first.
60. Transform the coordinates of Exercise 59 as described below. Graph and connect each new set of coordinates. Use a different color for each set.
    a. Multiply each $x$-coordinate by $-1$.
    b. Multiply each $y$-coordinate by $-1$.
    c. Multiply each coordinate by $-1$.
    d. Multiply each coordinate by 2.
61. ***Writing*** Compare each figure in Exercise 60 to the figure in Exercise 59. Write a short paragraph describing your results. 60a shifts the figure right 1 unit; 60b shifts it down 4 units; 60c shifts it right 1 unit and down 4 units; 60d doubles its dimensions.

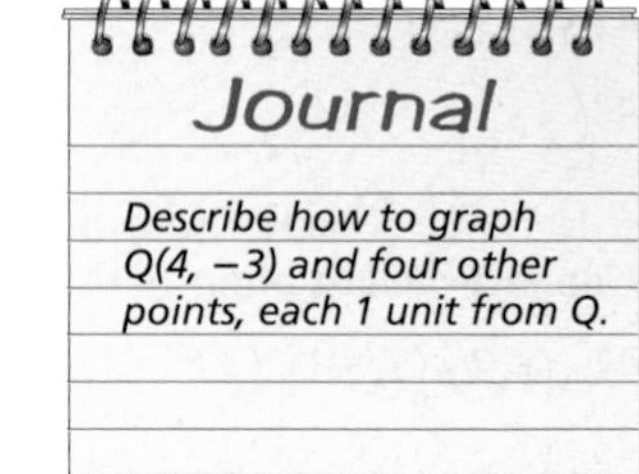

Journal
Describe how to graph Q(4, −3) and four other points, each 1 unit from Q.



## Mixed Review

**Find each product or quotient.** *(Lesson 1-9)*

62. $-11 \cdot 11$ −121
63. $-432 \div 48$ −9
64. $\frac{0}{-56}$ 0

**Write the value of each expression.** *(Lesson 1-4)*

65. $|-8|$ 8
66. $-|-95|$ −95
67. the opposite of 12 −12
68. A submarine at sea level dives 800 ft and then another 125 ft. Find the submarine's final depth. *(Lesson 1-5)* −925 ft

## Chapter Project 1 — Activity 3 Creating

Codes don't always use numbers or letters. In "The Adventure of the Dancing Men," the detective Sherlock Holmes used deductive reasoning to decipher the code at the right. It substitutes stick figures for letters. Using the substitution symbols of your choice, invent a cipher. Use it to write a message. Don't forget to provide the key!

See also Extra Practice section.

### Project Activity 3

**Creating** You may wish to have students illustrate their cipher and message with either sketches or pictures cut from magazines. Ask each student to have a partner decode the message to check the work.

# Cure for the Common Code

**Invent a Secret Code** The Project Activities on pages 16, 33, and 54 will help you complete your project. Here is a checklist to help you gather the different parts.

- ✔ your decoding of the ASCII message
- ✔ your letter in Caesar Cipher
- ✔ a cipher of your own creation, including a message and key

Make a poster to display the cipher you invented. Explain how it works. Include a sample of the cipher and its English translation. You may wish to use a table to illustrate the cipher's key.

***Reflect and Revise***

Ask a friend or someone at home to review your poster. Are your explanations and illustrations clear? If necessary, make changes to improve your poster.

## *Web Extension*

**Visit Prentice Hall's Web site. You'll find some interesting links and ideas related to codes. You'll also be able to share information about your project.**

**www.phschool.com**

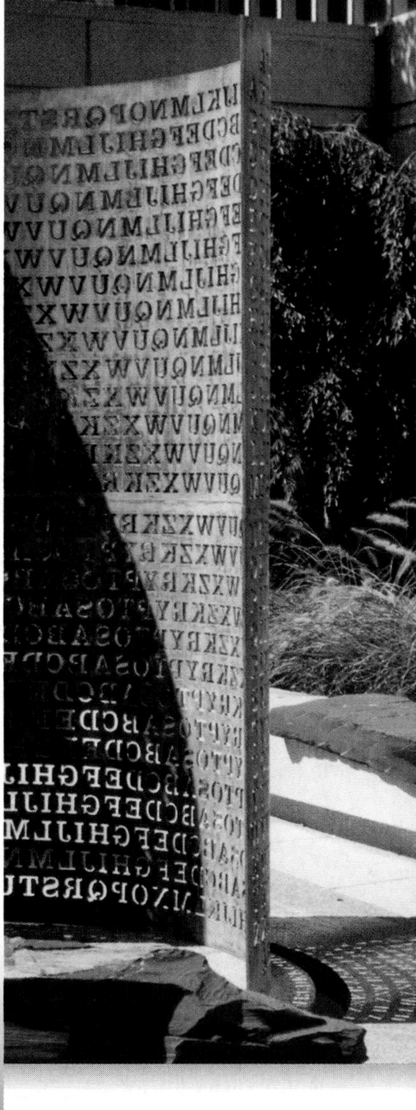

**Project Day** You may wish to plan a project day on which students share their completed projects. Encourage students to explain their process as well as their product.

**Block Scheduling** If you have block scheduling or extended periods, you may wish to intersperse the sharing of projects over Days 4 and 5 between the completion of one lesson and the start of a new lesson.

### Project Notebook

Have students review their project work and bring their notebooks up to date. Call attention to the fact that they can share their projects with other students through the Web site **www.phschool.com**.

Be sure students include in their notebooks their completed Project Manager and Scoring Rubric forms.

**Portfolio** Students may wish to include their projects and/or their project notebooks in their portfolios.

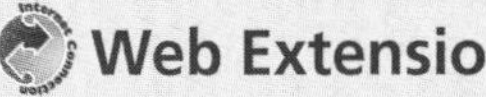


### Tell Us About Your Project

Students may wish to share their projects with other students on the Web site: **www.phschool.com**.

### Scoring Rubric

**3** You translate the ASCII code accurately and use the Caesar Cipher correctly to write a letter. Your poster is complete, descriptive, well-organized, and easy to read. Your cipher is creative, accurate, and not overly complicated.

**2** You make minor errors in translating the ASCII code, in using the Caesar Cipher, or in inventing your own code. Your poster is complete and descriptive, but could be better organized or easier to read.

**1** You translate codes incorrectly. Your poster is incomplete and lacks organization.

**0** Major elements of the project are incomplete or missing.

### Resources

Glossary, p. 748
Extra Practice, p. 710

For a complete list of resources for the chapter, see pp. 1F–H.

# Wrap Up

## Key Terms

absolute value (p. 18)
conjecture (p. 35)
coordinate plane (p. 50)
counterexample (p. 37)
evaluate (p. 13)
integers (p. 18)
inductive reasoning (p. 35)
opposites (p. 18)
order of operations (p. 8)
ordered pair (p. 50)
origin (p. 50)
quadrants (p. 50)
variable (p. 4)
variable expression (p. 4)
$x$-axis (p. 50)
$x$-coordinate (p. 50)
$y$-axis (p. 50)
$y$-coordinate (p. 50)

## Graphic Organizer

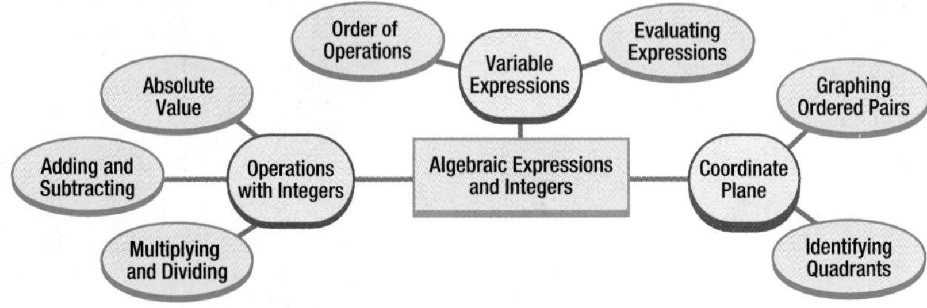


## Variables and Expressions — 1-1

*Summary* A **variable** is a letter that stands for a number. A **variable expression** is a mathematical phrase that uses variables, numerals, and operation symbols.

**Write a variable expression for each word phrase.**

1. twenty-five less than $x$ $x - 25$
2. the product of $n$ and 3 $3n$
3. two more than $y$ $y + 2$
4. ten decreased by $t$ $10 - t$
5. a number $n$ increased by 5 $n + 5$
6. a number $x$ divided by 4 $\frac{x}{4}$

## The Order of Operations — 1-2

*Summary* To simplify a numerical expression, follow the **order of operations.**
1. Work inside grouping symbols.
2. Multiply and divide in order from left to right.
3. Add and subtract in order from left to right.

**Simplify each expression.**

7. $3 \cdot 7 + 6 \div 2$ 24
8. $(4 + 8) \div 2 \cdot 2$ 12
9. $9 \cdot 5 - 4(12 \div 6)$ 37

## ■ *Evaluating Expressions* 1-3

*Summary* To **evaluate** a variable expression, substitute a number for each variable. Use the order of operations to simplify.

**Evaluate each expression.**

**10.** $3x + 4$ for $x = 5$ 19

**11.** $15 + 10 \div n$ for $n = 5$ 17

**12.** $(y - 6)2$ for $y = 16$ 20

**13.** $4(4 + m)$ for $m = 6$ 40

**14.** $15t \cdot 10$ for $t = 3$ 450

**15.** $z + [15 - (z - 1)]$ for $z = 4$ 16

## ■ *Integers and Absolute Value* 1-4

*Summary* **Integers** are the set of whole numbers and their **opposites.** The **absolute value** of an integer is its distance from zero on a number line. On a number line, the integer farther to the right is the greater integer.

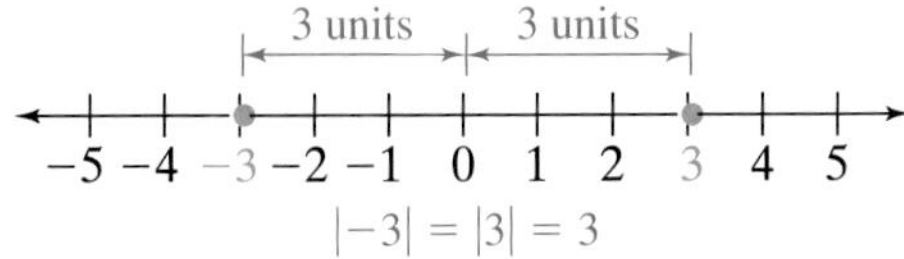


**Simplify each expression.**

**16.** the opposite of 17 −17

**17.** $|-1{,}000|$ 1,000

**18.** the absolute value of negative nine 9

**19.** the opposite of the absolute value of 12 −12

**Compare. Use >, <, or = to complete each statement.**

**20.** $-7$ ■ $-9$ >

**21.** $0$ ■ $-3$ >

**22.** $|-5|$ ■ $|5|$ =

**23.** $-6$ ■ $2$ <

**24.** *Writing* Explain how you would use integers to describe the changing elevation of a hot-air balloon. Answers may vary. Sample: Positive integers would indicate rising while negative integers would indicate falling.

## ■ *Adding and Subtracting Integers* 1-5 and 1-6

*Summary* To add integers with the *same* sign, add their absolute values. The sum has the same sign as the integers. To add integers with *different* signs, find the difference of their absolute values. The sum has the sign of the integer with the greater absolute value. To subtract an integer, add its opposite.

**Simplify each expression.**

**25.** $8 + (-15)$ −7

**26.** $-9 + 21$ 12

**27.** $9 - (-5)$ 14

**28.** $-7 - 4$ −11

**29.** $-62 - (-59) - 24$ −27

**30.** $14 + (-9) + (-20)$ −15

**31.** $-4 + 12 + (-3) + (-6)$ −1



**Portfolio** Students may wish to include their completed work for the Wrap Up in their portfolios.

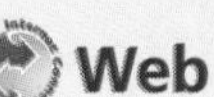

### Web Site

Students can find self-assessment materials on the Web site **www.phschool.com.**

## Inductive Reasoning — 1-7

**Summary** **Inductive reasoning** is making conclusions based on patterns you observe. A conclusion reached by inductive reasoning is a **conjecture.**

**Write a rule for each pattern. Find the next three numbers in the pattern.**

**32.** $0, 6, 12, 18, \ldots$ 24, 30, 36
Start with 0 and add 6 repeatedly.

**33.** $-18, -9, 0, 9, \ldots$ 18, 27, 36
Start with $-18$ and add 9 repeatedly.

**34.** $\frac{1}{2}, 1, 1\frac{1}{2}, 2, \ldots$ $2\frac{1}{2}$, 3, $3\frac{1}{2}$
Start with $\frac{1}{2}$ and add $\frac{1}{2}$ repeatedly.

## Look for a Pattern — 1-8

**Summary** You can use patterns to solve problems.

**35.** Suppose you plan to save \$12 per week. You have already saved \$7.50. In how many weeks will you have saved at least \$100? 8 weeks

**36.** A four-line classified ad costs \$28 for a week. Each additional line costs \$10.50. What is the weekly cost of a 12-line ad? \$112

## Multiplying and Dividing Integers — 1-9

**Summary** To multiply or divide integers, multiply or divide the absolute values of the integers. If the integers have the same sign, the product or quotient is positive. If the integers have different signs, the product or quotient is negative.

**Multiply or divide.**

**37.** $7(-6)$ $-42$ **38.** $250 \div (-50)$ $-5$ **39.** $(-9)(-8)$ 72 **40.** $-56 \div (-8)$ 7

**41.** $-120 \div 40$ $-3$ **42.** $-15(11)$ $-165$ **43.** $\frac{-64}{8}$ $-8$ **44.** $(-5)(-7)$ 35

## Graphing in the Coordinate Plane — 1-10

**Summary** A **coordinate plane** is formed by the intersection of two number lines. The ***x*-axis** and the ***y*-axis** divide the coordinate plane into four **quadrants.** An **ordered pair** gives the coordinates of a point. The ***x*-coordinate** shows the position left or right of the $y$-axis. The ***y*-coordinate** shows the position above or below the $x$-axis.

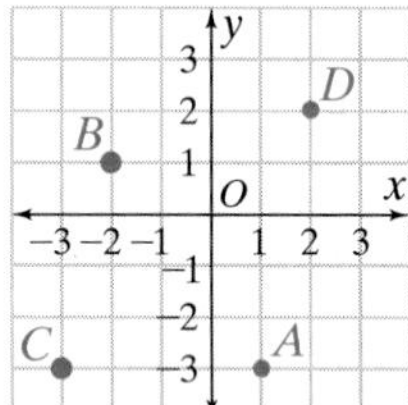


**Write the coordinates of each point.**

**45.** $A$ (1, −3) **46.** $B$ (−2, 1) **47.** $C$ (−3, −3) **48.** $D$ (2, 2)



## Chapter Assessment Form A Page 1

**Circle the answer.**

1. Which of the following statements is true?
   A. $-8 > -7$ B. $9 < 3$
   (C.) $0 > -3$ D. $0 > 4$
2. The product $(-3)(5)(-8)(15)$ is:
   (F.) positive G. negative
   H. zero J. Not Here
3. In which quadrant does the point $(-5, 12)$ lie?
   A. I (B.) II C. III D. IV
4. Let $a$ be any integer, except zero. Which statement is *never* true?
   F. $|a| = -a$ G. $|a| > 0$
   H. $a > -a$ (J.) $-|a| = |a|$

**Write your answer.**

5. Graph the integers $-3, 4, -2$ on a number line. Then order the numbers from least to greatest.
   −5 −4 −3 −2 −1 0 1 2 3 4 5
   −3, −2, 4
6. Write a variable expression for the word phrase: *five subtracted from a number n.*
   $n - 5$

**Evaluate each expression for the given values of the variables.**

7. $10a - 3$, for $a = 5$ 47
8. $3z + 2xy$, for $x = 2$, $y = 5$, and $z = 7$ 41

**Simplify each expression.**

9. $|-18|$ 18
10. $-5 + (-9)$ −14
11. $-3 - (-7)$ 4
12. $-4(-11)$ 44
13. $\frac{28}{-2}$ −14
14. $7 + 2 \cdot 8 \div 4$ 11
15. $6 + (7 \cdot 3) - 8 \div 2$ 23



## Chapter Assessment Form A Page 2

**Write the coordinates of each point.**

16. $A$ (−3, −2)
17. $B$ (4, −5)

y
4
2
x
−4 −2 O 2 4
−2
A
−4
B

18. A mail-order company charges \$12 for each t-shirt. Shipping costs \$5 per order.
    a. Write a variable expression for the cost of ordering $x$ number of t-shirts.
       $12x + 5$
    b. Evaluate the expression to find the cost of ordering 3 t-shirts.
       \$41
19. A student takes in 2,300 calories and burns 2,500 calories. Find the net calories.
    −200 calories
20. Write a rule for the pattern below. Find the next two numbers in the pattern.
    1, 2, 3, 6, 7, 14, 15, 30, 31
    Rule: Start with 1, alternately multiply by 2 and add 1.
21. Suppose you have \$8. After you get your allowance you have \$20. At the end of the week you have \$10. You get your allowance and have \$22. At the end of that week you have \$12. You get your allowance and have \$24. If you follow the same pattern, how much money should you have at the end of the third week?
    \$14
22. Explain what steps you would use to simplify $2 + 3(9 - 5)$.
    Sample answer is shown. 1) Perform the subtraction 9 − 5 in parentheses to get 4. 2) Multiply 3 times 4 to get 12. 3) Add 2 and 12 to get 14.



Assessment

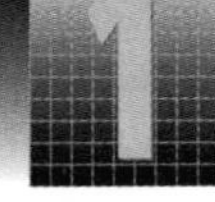

# Assessment

**Write an expression for each phrase.**

1. a number $n$ increased by nineteen $n + 19$
2. ten less than negative three $-3 - 10$
3. the product of $x$ and negative five $-5x$
4. 5 more than the opposite of $y$ $-y + 5$

**Evaluate each expression for the given values of the variables.**

5. $3a + 5$, for $a = -5$ $-10$
6. $5m + 9 + 7n$, for $m = 8$ and $n = 1$ 56
7. $3|x - y| + x$, for $x = 1$ and $y = 8$ 22
8. $20 - 2(a - b)$, for $a = 3$ and $b = 2$ 18

**Simplify each expression.**

9. $|-5|$ 5
10. opposite of $-9$ 9
11. opposite of 7 $-7$
12. $|15|$ 15

**Use >, <, or = to complete each sentence.**

13. $-6 \blacksquare -5$ $<$
14. $8 \blacksquare -10$ $>$
15. $-3 \blacksquare 3$ $<$
16. $0 \blacksquare -7$ $>$

**Simplify each expression.**

17. $15 + (-7)$ 8
18. $-8 - (-12)$ 4
19. $-9(-7)$ 63
20. $54 \div (-6)$ $-9$
21. $-6 \cdot 48$ $-288$
22. $\frac{-56}{-7}$ 8
23. $119 - (-24)$ 143
24. $-47 + (-21)$ $-68$
25. $-83 + 17$ $-66$
26. $5(-12)(-3)(-1)$ $-180$
27. $2|14 - (-9)|$ 46
28. $8 \cdot 6 \div (2 + 1)$ 16
29. $4 + 7 \cdot 2 + 8$ 26
30. $16 - 2 \cdot (5 + 3)$ 0

**In which quadrant or on which axis does each point lie?**

31. $(-5, 7)$ II
32. $(0, -4)$ (negative) $y$-axis
33. $(-8, -6)$ III

**Write the coordinates of each point.**

34. $F$ $(-3, 2)$
35. $G$ $(1, -2)$
36. $H$ $(2, 0)$
37. $J$ $(-2, -2)$

38. A shirt costs \$15 and jeans cost \$25.
    a. Write an expression for the cost of $j$ jeans and $s$ shirts. $25j + 15s$
    b. Evaluate the expression to find the cost of three pairs of jeans and five shirts. \$150
    c. How many pairs of jeans can you buy for \$60? 2
39. Which statement is *always* true? D
    A. The absolute value of an integer is equal to the opposite of the integer.
    B. The absolute value of an integer is greater than zero.
    C. An integer is greater than its opposite.
    D. A positive integer is greater than a negative integer.
40. A submarine was 250 m below sea level. It rose 75 m. Use an integer to describe the new depth of the submarine. $-175$
41. Write a rule for the pattern below. Find the next two numbers in the pattern. Start with 100 and alternately subtract 10 and 5.
    100, 90, 85, 75, 70, 60, ... 55, 45, 40
42. You are in an elevator on the seventh floor. You go down 4 floors, and then up 8 floors. Then you go down 3 floors and up 9 floors. The elevator goes down again, and you get off. According to the pattern, on which floor are you now? 15th floor
43. *Writing* Describe how to order the integers 2, −6, 9, 0, and −13 from least to greatest. Place them on a number line and write them as they appear from left to right.



## Chapter Assessment

**Resources** For a complete list of resources for this chapter, see pp. 1F–H.

### Chapter Assessment Form B Page 1

**Circle the answer.**

1. Which of the following statements is true?
   A. $5 > 7$ B. $0 < -2$
   (C.) $-4 < -1$ D. $-3 > -3$
2. The product $(2)(-5)(-7)(-17)$ is:
   F. positive (G.) negative
   H. zero J. Not Here
3. In which quadrant does the point $(14, -3)$ lie?
   A. I B. II C. III (D.) IV
4. Let $a$ be any integer. Which statement is *always* true?
   F. $|a| = -a$ (G.) $|a| \geq 0$
   H. $a > -a$ J. $-|a| = |a|$

**Write your answer.**

5. Graph the integers −1, 0, 4, −4 on a number line. Then order the numbers from least to greatest.
   −5 −4 −3 −2 −1 0 1 2 3 4 5
   −4, −1, 0, 4
6. Write a variable expression for the word phrase: *four times some number n.* $4n$

**Evaluate each expression for the given values of the variables.**

7. $9 + 4m$, for $m = 3$ 21
8. $11a - 7b$, for $a = 4, b = 6$ 2

**Simplify each expression.**

9. the opposite of $-6$ 6
10. $2 + (-11)$ $-9$
11. $-8 - 4$ $-12$
12. $-7(15)$ $-105$
13. $\frac{-60}{-4}$ 15
14. $4 + 2 \cdot 8 \div 4$ 8
15. $(3 + 2) \cdot 4 \div (3 - 1)$ 10



### Chapter Assessment Form B Page 2

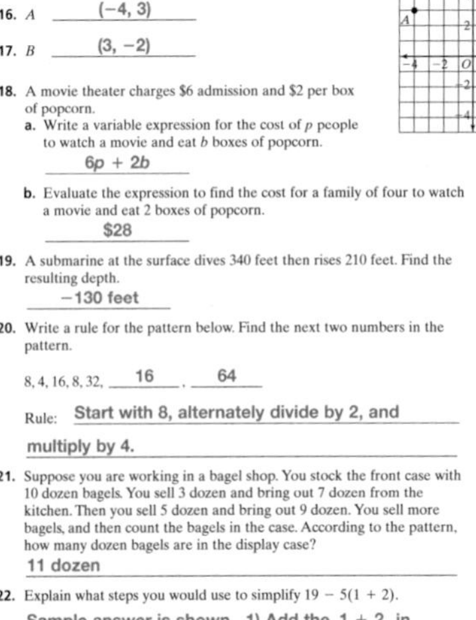

**Write the coordinates of each point.**

16. $A$ $(-4, 3)$
17. $B$ $(3, -2)$
18. A movie theater charges \$6 admission and \$2 per box of popcorn.
    a. Write a variable expression for the cost of $p$ people to watch a movie and eat $b$ boxes of popcorn. $6p + 2b$
    b. Evaluate the expression to find the cost for a family of four to watch a movie and eat 2 boxes of popcorn. \$28
19. A submarine at the surface dives 340 feet then rises 210 feet. Find the resulting depth. −130 feet
20. Write a rule for the pattern below. Find the next two numbers in the pattern.
    8, 4, 16, 8, 32, 16, 64
    Rule: Start with 8, alternately divide by 2, and multiply by 4.
21. Suppose you are working in a bagel shop. You stock the front case with 10 dozen bagels. You sell 3 dozen and bring out 7 dozen from the kitchen. Then you sell 5 dozen and bring out 9 dozen. You sell more bagels, and then count the bagels in the case. According to the pattern, how many dozen bagels are in the display case? 11 dozen
22. Explain what steps you would use to simplify $19 - 5(1 + 2)$.
    Sample answer is shown. 1) Add the 1 + 2 in parentheses to get 3. 2) Multiply 5 times 3 to get 15. 3) Subtract 15 from 19 to get 4.



Assessment

# Cumulative Review

## Cumulative Review Page 1

**Circle the answer.**

1. Sean has $s$ dollars which is \$8 more than Tina. Which expression gives the amount of money Tina has in dollars?
   A. $s + 8$ B. $8 - s$
   (C.) $s - 8$ D. $8s$
2. Marie bought 8 flower pots for \$5 each and sold 4 for \$7 each. Which expression gives Marie's net expenses?
   F. $(8 + 5)(4 + 7)$ (G.) $(8 \cdot 5) - (4 \cdot 7)$
   H. $(8 + 4) \cdot (5 + 7)$ J. $(8 - 4)(7 - 5)$
3. Evaluate $a + 9$, for $a = 11$.
   (A.) 20 B. 2
   C. 99 D. 19
4. Which statement is true?
   F. −2 is greater than 1 G. $|-7|$ is less than −6
   (H.) −8 is less than $|-8|$ J. −5 is less than −6
5. Find the sum of −5 and −4.
   A. 9 B. 1
   C. −1 (D.) −9
6. Which expression has a value that is different from the value of the other expressions?
   F. $2 - 8$ (G.) $-2 + 8$
   H. $2 + (-8)$ J. $-|8 - 2|$
7. Find $-12 + (-17)$
   A. 29 B. −5
   C. 5 (D.) −29
8. Find $-3 - (-15)$
   (F.) 12 G. −18
   H. −12 J. 18
9. Which statement is *not* true?
   A. $|-9 + 3| = 6$ B. $|-4| < |1 - 6|$
   (C.) $|-4| < 0$ D. $|-7| < |-8|$
10. In which quadrant do the coordinates $(-5, 2)$ lie?
   F. I (G.) II
   H. III J. IV



Assessment

## Cumulative Review Page 2

11. Write a rule for the pattern and find the next two numbers in the pattern.
   3, 6, 5, 10, 9, 18, 17
   Start with 3, alternately multiply by 2 and subtract 1.
12. There are 12 eggs in a dozen. Write an expression for the number of dozens in $e$ eggs. $\frac{e}{12}$
13. Simplify $7 \cdot 3 - 4 - (3 + 2) - 1$ 11
14. Insert grouping symbols to make the number sentence true.
   $2 \cdot (6 + 5) - 4 \cdot 2 = 14$
15. Graph $|-4|, -3, |-2|, 0$ and $-1$ on the number line. Then order the numbers from least to greatest.
   −5 −4 −3 −2 −1 0 1 2 3 4 5
   $-3, -1, 0, |-2|, |-4|$
16. Evaluate $\frac{h + 4}{j}$, for $h = 14$ and $j = 3$. 6
17. Find $|-8| \cdot (-2)$ −16
18. Find $-36 \div 3$ −12
19. Write the coordinates of each point.
   $A$ (−2, −4)
   $B$ (3, −2)
   $C$ (−4, 1)
20. Explain the difference between a numerical expression and a variable expression.
   A numerical expression uses numerals and operation symbols. A variable expression uses these and variables.



# 1 Cumulative Review

**Preparing for Algebra**

**Choose the best answer.**

1. A bridge is $t$ years old. Which expression gives the age of the bridge 5 years ago? A
   A. $t - 5$
   B. $5 - t$
   C. $t + 5$
   D. $\frac{t}{5}$
2. A florist sold five plants for \$7 each and two wreaths for \$12 each. Which expression gives the sales total? H
   F. $(5 + 7) \cdot (2 + 12)$
   G. $(5 \cdot 7)(2 + 12)$
   H. $5 \cdot 7 + 2 \cdot 12$
   J. $5 \cdot (7 + 12)$
3. Evaluate $12a$ for $a = 4$. C
   A. 8 B. 16
   C. 48 D. 3
4. Which statement is true? F
   F. −2 is less than 2.
   G. −6 is greater than −4.
   H. $|-5|$ is greater than 6.
   J. −7 is greater than $|-6|$.
5. Find the sum of −4 and −3. A
   A. −7 B. 1
   C. 7 D. −1
6. Which expression has a value that is different from the value of the other expressions? H
   F. $9 - 3$
   G. $|3 - 9|$
   H. $-9 - 3$
   J. $9 + (-3)$
7. Find $-10 + (-18)$. A
   A. −28 B. −8
   C. 8 D. 28
8. Find $-20 - (-9)$. F
   F. −11 G. −29
   H. 29 J. 11
9. Which statement is *not* true? D
   A. $|-3| > |-2|$
   B. $|-5| < |1 - 7|$
   C. $|-6 + 2| = |4|$
   D. $|-1| < 0$
10. In which quadrant does the point with the coordinates $(-3, -4)$ lie? H
   F. I
   G. II
   H. III
   J. IV

**For Exercises 11–19, show your work.**

11. Write a rule for the pattern 1, −2, 4, −8, . . . Find the next two numbers in the pattern. 16, −3
   Start with 1 and multiply by −2 repeatedly.
12. The number of boys $b$ on the swim team is one fifth of the number of girls. Write a variable expression for the number of girls on the team. $5b$
13. Simplify $6 \cdot 2 - 5 - (2 + 2) - 1$. 2
14. Insert grouping symbols to make the number sentence true. $3 \cdot (4 + 6) - 2 \cdot 3 = 24$ o
   $3 \cdot 4 + 6 - 2 \cdot 3 = 24$ $3 \cdot 4 + (6 - 2) \cdot 3 = 24$
15. On a number line, graph $|-5|, -2, 0, |-3|$, and 1. See below.
16. Evaluate $\frac{c + a}{2}$ for $a = 3$ and $c = 8$. 5.5
17. Find $|-3| \cdot (-4)$. −12
18. Find $-44 \div 2$. −22
19. Write the coordinates of points $A$, $B$, and $C$.
   (−2, 3); (0, 0); (2, −2)

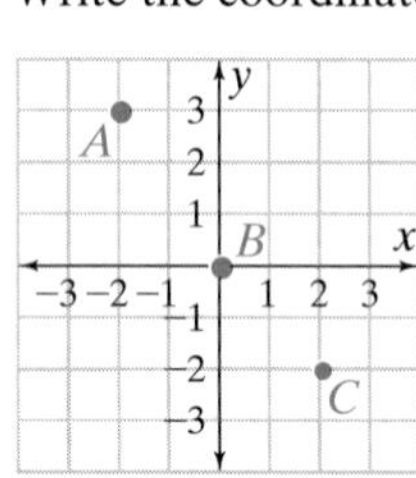


15. −2 0 1 $|-3|$ $|-5|$



| Item | Chapter/ Lesson | Review Topic |
|---|---|---|
| 1, 3, 12, 16 | 1-1, 1-3 | Variables and Expressions; Evaluating Expressions |
| 2, 13, 14 | 1-2 | Order of Operations |
| 4–9, 15, 17, 18 | 1-4, 1-5, 1-6, 1-9 | Integers and Absolute Value; Adding, Subtracting, Multiplying, and Dividing Integers |
| 11 | 1-7 | Inductive Reasoning |
| 10, 19 | 1-10 | Coordinate Plane |

CHAPTER 2

# Solving One-Step Equations and Inequalities

## Content Overview for Chapter 2

Chapter 2 introduces the basic algebraic properties needed to solve equations. You can use the Associative Properties to change grouping. You can use the Commutative Properties to change order. The Identity Properties state that adding zero to an expression does not change its value, and that multiplying an expression by 1 does not change its value. You can use the Distributive Property to multiply a number by each term of a sum or difference.

You can apply properties to simplify a variable expression by replacing it with an equivalent expression with as few terms as possible. You can write an equation to model a situation. An equation with numerical expressions is true or false. An equation with at least one variable is an open sentence. A solution of the open sentence is a value of a variable that makes the equation true. To solve an equation, you can use inverse operations and the properties of equality to get the variable alone on one side of the equation.

To graph an inequality, use a number line. Use an open dot for $>$ and $<$. Use a closed dot for $\geq$ and $\leq$. To solve a one-step inequality, use inverse operations and the properties of inequality to get the variable alone on one side of the inequality. When multiplying or dividing each side of an inequality by a negative number, reverse the direction of the inequality symbol.

## Making Connections

| Lesson | Interdisciplinary and Real-World Connections | Math Integration |
|---|---|---|
| 2-1 | Geography | Arithmetic |
| 2-2 | Geography | Arithmetic |
| 2-3 | Biology | Algebra |
| 2-4 | Language | Algebra |
| 2-5 | Health, Astronomy, Physics | Algebra |
| 2-6 | Statistics | Data Analysis |
| 2-7 | Biology | Problem Solving, Geometry, Number Theory |
| 2-8 | Nutrition | Data Analysis |
| 2-9 | Computer Science | Algebra |
| 2-10 | Engineering | Algebra |

**SCHOOL/HOME CONNECTION**
English and Spanish versions are available in the *Help at Home* book of copy masters.

**Helper's Page** You will find detailed instruction, more examples, and

**Student Page** Review Exercises for Lessons 2-1 to 2-3

**Name each property shown.** *(Lesson 2-1)*

1. ____________ equals

2. ____________ equals

***Mental Math*** **Simplify each expression.** *(Lesson 2-1)*

3. $84 + 9 + 6 =$ ______
4. $14 + (-8) + 7 + (-6) =$ ______
5. $3 \cdot 5 \cdot 7 \cdot 8 =$ ______
6. $25 \cdot 19 \cdot 4 =$ ______

**Use the Distributive Property to multiply mentally.** *(Lesson 2-2)*

7. $6(57) =$ ____________
8. $31(97) =$ ____________

**Use the Distributive Property and mental math to solve this problem.** *(Lesson 2-2)*

9. You buy 4 bottles of shampoo for $.89 each. How much do you pay in all?

$.89

**Simplify each expression.** *(Lesson 2-3)*

10. $8x - 5x + 4$
11. $-2x + 7(4 + x)$

12. **Test Prep** Which shows the Commutative Property of Multiplication? *(Lesson 2-1)*
A. $6(x + 5) = 6x + 30$
B. $6(x + 5) = (x + 5)6$
C. $6(x + 5) = 6(5 + x)$
D. $6(x + 5) = 6$

Helper: ____________ Comments: ____________

**Helper's Page** You will find detailed instruction, more examples, and

**Student Page** Review Exercises for Lessons 2-4 to 2-9

**Write an equation for each sentence. Is each equation true, false, or an open sentence?** *(Lesson 2-4)*

1. Seven more than $-5$ is 2. ______ ______
2. The quotient of 15 and a number $n$ is 3. ______ ______
3. The product of negative 8 and 2 is negative 6. ______ ______

**Solve each equation.** *(Lessons 2-5 and 2-6)*

4. $y + 5 = 1$ $y =$ ______
5. $x - 9 = 3$ $x =$ ______
6. $4k = -24$ $k =$ ______
7. $\frac{a}{-6} = 2$ $a =$ ______

**Use the *Try, Test, Revise* strategy to solve the problem.** *(Lesson 2-7)*

8. A florist charged $21 for a bouquet of 5 daisies and 8 roses. Another time, she charged $16 for 8 daisies and 4 roses. You are working in the florist shop. How much does 1 rose cost? 1 daisy?

**Write the inequality shown in each graph.** *(Lesson 2-8)*

9. ____________
−5 −4 −3 −2 −1 0 1 2 3 4 5

10. ____________
−5 −4 −3 −2 −1 0 1 2 3 4 5

**Solve each inequality.** *(Lesson 2-9)*

11. $n - 12 > 9$ ______
12. $7 + t \leq 4$ ______

13. **Test Prep** Which is *not* a solution of $x - 8 < 2$? *(Lesson 2-9)*
A. 4 B. 9 C. 11 D. 8

Helper: ____________ Comments: ____________

CHAPTER 2

# Chapter 2 at a Glance

To accommodate flexible scheduling, most lessons are divided into parts. Assignment Options are given in the Teacher's Edition for each lesson.

| Pages | Lesson | NCTM | Parts |
|---|---|---|---|
| 64–68 | **Lesson 2-1** **Properties of Numbers** | 1, 2, 6, 8, 9, 10 | Part 1 Identifying Properties<br>Part 2 Using Properties |
| 69–73 | **Lesson 2-2** **The Distributive Property** | 1, 2, 6, 8, 9, 10 | Part 1 Numerical Expressions<br>Part 2 Variable Expressions<br>**Project Activity 1** |
| 74–77 | **Lesson 2-3** **Simplifying Variable Expressions** | 1, 2, 6, 7, 8, 9, 10 | Part 1 Identifying Parts of a Variable Expression<br>Part 2 Simplifying Variable Expressions<br>**Checkpoint 1** |
| 94–97 | **Lesson 2-7** **Problem Solving Strategy** | 1, 2, 3, 4, 6, 7, 8, 9, 10 | Try, Test, Revise<br>**Math at Work** |
| 100–103 | **Lesson 2-8** **Data Analysis: Inequalities and Their Graphs** | 1, 2, 3, 6, 8, 9, 10 | Part 1 Graphing Inequalities<br>Part 2 Writing Inequalities |
| 104–107 | **Lesson 2-9** **Solving One-Step Inequalities by Adding or Subtracting** | 1, 2, 6, 8, 9, 10 | Part 1 Solving Inequalities by Subtracting<br>Part 2 Using Addition to Solve Inequalities<br>**Checkpoint 2** |

## Pacing Options

This chart suggests pacing for only the core lessons and their parts, and it is provided merely as a possible guide. It will help you determine how much time you have in your schedule to cover other features, such as the Chapter Project, Math Toolboxes, Standardized Test Prep, Wrap Up, and Assessment.

| | Day 1 | Day 2 | Day 3 | Day 4 | Day 5 | Day 6 | Day 7 | Day 8 | Day 9 | Day 10 | Day 11 |
|---|---|---|---|---|---|---|---|---|---|---|---|
| **Traditional** (40–45 min. class periods) | 2–1 (1) | 2–1 (2) | 2–2 (1) | 2–2 (2) | 2–3 (1), 2–3 (2) | 2–4 (1), 2–4 (2) | 2–5 (1) | 2–5 (2) | 2–6 (1), 2–6 (2) | 2–7 | 2–8 (1), 2–8 (2) |
| **Pre-Algebra Over 2 Years** (40–45 min. class periods) | 2–1 (1) | 2–1 (2) | 2–1 (2) | 2–2 (1) | 2–2 (1) | 2–2 (2) | 2–3 (1) | 2–3 (2) | 2–3 (2) | 2–4 (1) | 2–4 (2) |
| **Block Scheduling** (90 min. class periods) | 2–1 (1) (2), 2–2 (1) (2) | 2–3 (1) (2), 2–4 (1) (2) | 2–5 (1) (2), 2–6 (1) (2) | 2–7, 2–8 (1), 2–8 (2) | 2–9 (1) (2), 2–10 (1) (2) | | | | | | |

| Pages 78–81 | Lesson 2-4 Variables and Equations |
|---|---|
| NCTM 1, 2, 6, 8, 9, 10 | Part 1 Classifying Types of Equations<br>Part 2 Checking Equations Using Substitution |

| Pages 84–88 | Lesson 2-5 Solving Equations by Adding or Subtracting |
|---|---|
| NCTM 1, 2, 4, 6, 8, 9, 10 | Part 1 Using Subtraction to Solve Equations<br>Part 2 Using Addition to Solve Equations |

| Pages 89–92 | Lesson 2-6 Data Analysis: Solving Equations by Multiplying or Dividing |
|---|---|
| NCTM 1, 2, 4, 6, 8, 9, 10 | Part 1 Using Division to Solve Equations<br>Part 2 Using Multiplication to Solve Equations<br>▼ Project Activity 2 |

| Pages 108–112 | Lesson 2-10 Solving One-Step Inequalities by Multiplying or Dividing |
|---|---|
| NCTM 1, 2, 6, 8, 9, 10 | Part 1 Solving Inequalities Using Division<br>Part 2 Solving Inequalities Using Multiplication<br>▼ Project Activity 3 |

**NCTM STANDARDS 2000**

1 Number and Operations
2 Algebra
3 Geometry
4 Measurement
5 Data Analysis and Probability
6 Problem Solving
7 Reasoning and Proof
8 Communication
9 Connections
10 Representation

| Day 12 | Day 13 | Day 14 | Day 15 | Day 16 | Day 17 | Day 18 | Day 19 | Day 20 | Day 21 | Day 22 | Day 23 | Day 24 |
|---|---|---|---|---|---|---|---|---|---|---|---|---|
| 2-9 ▼1 2-9 ▼2 | 2-10 ▼1 2-10 ▼2 | | | | | | | | | | | |
| 2-5 ▼1 | 2-5 ▼1 | 2-5 ▼2 | 2-6 ▼1 | 2-6 ▼2 | 2-7 | 2-7 | 2-8 ▼1 | 2-8 ▼2 | 2-9 ▼1 | 2-9 ▼2 | 2-10 ▼1 | 2-10 ▼2 |

**Block Scheduling Notes**

Consider these suggestions:

- **Day 3** Before starting Lesson 2-5, teach Math Toolbox 1, p. 82.
- **Day 4** Before starting Lesson 2-7, teach the Standardized Test Prep, p. 93.
- **Day 4** Before completing Lesson 2-8, teach Math Toolbox 1, p. 98.
- **Day 5** Before starting Lesson 2-9, begin presentations for Finish the Project

# Math Background

## Lessons 2-1 and 2-2

### Properties of Numbers

The Order of Operations states an agreed-upon convention about which operations in an expression are performed before the others. The properties in these lessons state the various ways an expression can be renamed without changing its value. Generally, you will apply these properties first to simplify calculations, and then you will use the order of operations as you actually perform the calculations.

Here is a summary of the key properties.

Commutative Property

| | |
|---|---|
| $a + b = b + a$ | of Addition |
| $ab = ba$ | of Multiplication |

Associative Property

| | |
|---|---|
| $(a + b) + c = a + (b + c)$ | of Addition |
| $(ab)c = a(bc)$ | of Multiplication |

Notice that each one of these properties involves only *one* operation, either addition or multiplication. A third property combines *two* operations. This property is sometimes called the Distributive Property of Multiplication over Addition.

Distributive Property
$a(b + c) = ab + ac$

The following identity properties define the results of adding and multiplying by 1 and by 0.

Identity Properties

| | |
|---|---|
| $a + 0 = a$ | of Addition |
| $a \bullet 1 = a$ | of Multiplication |

These identity properties state that adding 0 or multiplying by 1 leaves a number *identical* in value to its original value.

## Lesson 2-3

### Simplifying Variable Expressions

When plus or minus signs separate an algebraic expression into parts, each part is called a *term*. $3x + 7y + 2x + 8 - 4y$ has 5 terms.

Terms with no variables, such as 8 in this example, are called *constants.* The numerical multipliers of the variables (3, 7, 2, and $-4$ in this example) are called numerical *coefficients.* The terms with identical variables are called *like terms.* When the like terms are combined, this example simplifies to $5x + 3y + 8$, an expression with three terms. When a term includes no numerical coefficient, the coefficient is understood to be 1, so $x$ means $1x$.

## Lesson 2-4

### Variables and Equations

An equation is a mathematical sentence that contains an equal sign (=). An equation with at least one variable is an open sentence. An equation can be always true $x + x = 2x$ or $4 \bullet 5 = 20$, always false $x + 1 = x$ or $2 + 3 = 6$, or sometimes true $x - 3 = 2$ (if $x = 5$) and sometimes false (if $x$ equals any other number).

To solve an equation such as $3x - 2 = 4$ means to find the set of all the values for $x$ that will, when substituted for $x$, make the equation true. For linear equations with one variable, such as this example, there will be only one value for $x$ (in this example, $x = 2$).

A true equation remains true if you add, subtract, multiply, or divide (by a non-zero number) *both sides* of the equation by the *same* number.

If $a = b$, then
$a + c = b + c$
$a - c = b - c$
$ca = cb$
$a \div c = b \div c \; (c \neq 0)$

To keep an equation (or an inequality) in balance, you must perform the same operation with the same number on both sides of the equation.

## LESSONS 2-5 AND 2-6
### Solving Equations

Linear equations with one variable have only one solution. To find this solution, first simplify by using the properties and the order of operations to rewrite without grouping symbols and to collect like terms. Then, isolate the variable by using *inverse* operations. Addition and subtraction are inverse operations; multiplication and division are inverse operations.

There are two inverse properties.
$a + (-a) = 0$ and
$a \bullet (\frac{1}{a}) = 1, (a \neq 0)$
Note that 0 does not have a multiplicative inverse.

Division by zero is undefined. Students are often interested in a proof of why division by zero is undefined.
$\frac{a}{b} = c$ means that $b \bullet c = a$, for example, $\frac{10}{2} = 5$ means that $2 \bullet 5 = 10$. It follows that $\frac{10}{0} = c$ would mean that $0 \bullet c = 10$, but there is no number $c$ that would make this sentence true. This argument generalizes to any number, $a$, instead of 10. A similar argument shows that $\frac{0}{0}$ is also undefined. $\frac{0}{0} = 3$ would mean that $0 \bullet 3 = 0$, which is true. However, $\frac{0}{0} = 4$ means that $0 \bullet 4 = 0$, which is true. These two results lead to the conclusion that, since $\frac{0}{0} = 3$ and $\frac{0}{0} = 4$, then by the transitive property, $3 = 4$ which is clearly not true! (The Transitive Property says that if $a = b$ and $b = c$, then $a = c$.) So this attempt to define division by zero leads to a false conclusion. Division by zero is undefined; no meaningful and consistent definition is possible.

## LESSONS 2-7 AND 2-8
### Inequalities and Their Graphs

An inequality is a mathematical sentence that contains $<, \leq, >$, or $\geq$. As with an equation, the solution to an inequality is the set of numbers that, when substituted for the variable, make the inequality true. Unlike equations, however, a linear inequality may have more than one number in the solution set.

Inequalities such as $x > -3$ can be graphed on a number line, using an open circle to show that $-3$ is *not* included in the set of values that makes the sentence true.

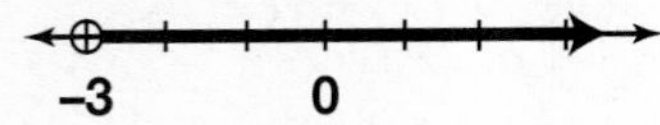


## LESSONS 2-9 AND 2-10
### Solving One-Step Inequalities

In order to solve a simple equality, you can apply inequality properties that are, for addition and subtraction, similar to the equality properties.

If $a < b$, then
$a + c < b + c$ and
$a - c < b - c$.

If $a > b$, then
$a + c > b + c$ and
$a - c > b - c$.

If $c > 0$, and $a > b$, then $ac > cb$ and
$a \div c > b \div c$.
If $c > 0$ and $a < b$, then $ac < cb$ and
$a \div c < b \div c$.

However, there is one key difference. To multiply or divide an inequality by a negative number, you must *reverse* the direction of the inequality. For example, $-2 > -3$ but $-1(-2) < -1(-3)$ because $2 < 3$.

If $c < 0$, and $a > b$, then $ac < cb$ and
$a \div c < b \div c$.
Similarly, if $c < 0$, and $a < b$, then $ac > cb$ and
$a \div c > b \div c$.

For professional development tips visit our Web site **www.phschool.com**.

# Monitoring Progress

## Universal Access

### ▶ *Preventing a Student from Falling Behind*

These resources are particularly helpful in preventing a student from falling behind his or her appropriate math level. For a complete list of resources for this chapter, see page 61H.

#### Skills You Need for Chapter 2

Student Edition, p. 61
Teacher's Edition, p. 61

- Order of operations with integers
- Inverse operations
- Comparing numbers

#### Skills Handbook

Student Edition, pp. 723–741
Teacher's Edition, pp. 723–741

- Dividing Whole Numbers, p. 726
- Working with Integers, p. 741

#### Reteaching Worksheets

There is a Reteaching worksheet for every lesson in this chapter.

- Chapter 2 Support File, Teaching Resources box
- See TE p. 61H for a complete list of resources.

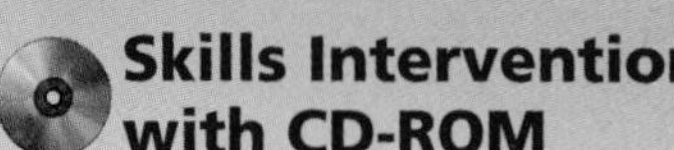

#### Skills Intervention Kit with CD-ROM

| For | Use |
|---|---|
| Lessons 2-1, 2-3, 2-4 | Pre-Algebra Basics |

#### Daily Cumulative Review Blackline Masters

There is a Daily Cumulative Review worksheet for every lesson in this chapter.

See TE p. 61H for a complete list of resources.

### ▶ *Accommodating Diverse Learning Styles*

#### Tactile Learning

Use algebra tiles to model subtracting the same number from each side of an equation. (Lesson 2-5)

Walk the graph of an inequality on a number line marked on the floor. (Lesson 2-8)

#### Advanced Learner

Every lesson has at least one challenge problem.

Explain why zero is not a multiplicative identity. (Lesson 2-1)

#### ELL (English Language Learner)

Discuss how remembering the meaning of *commuting* to work can help to remember the name of the Commutative Property. (Lesson 2-1)

#### Auditory Learning

Work with a partner to practice reading and writing inequalities. (Lesson 2-9)

#### Visual Learning

Create tables or charts to organize data before trying to find solutions. (Lesson 2-7)

Circle inequalities as a reminder to reverse the direction of the inequality symbol when dividing or multiplying by a negative number. (Lesson 2-10)

# Aligning Assessment with Instruction

## Assessment Options

| | Chapter Opener | 2-1 | 2-2 | 2-3 | 2-4 | 2-5 | 2-6 | 2-7 | 2-8 | 2-9 | 2-10 | End |
|---|---|---|---|---|---|---|---|---|---|---|---|---|
| Chapter Project | ■ | | ■ | | | | ■ | | | | ■ | ■ |
| Try This Exercises | | ■ | ■ | ■ | ■ | ■ | ■ | ■ | ■ | ■ | ■ | |
| Mixed Reviews | | ■ | ■ | ■ | ■ | ■ | ■ | ■ | ■ | ■ | ■ | |
| Checkpoints | | | | ■ | | | | | | ■ | | |
| Writing | | | ■ | ■ | ■ | ■ | ■ | | ■ | ■ | ■ | ■ |
| Chapter Assessment | | | | | | | | | | | | ■ |
| Cumulative Review | | | | | | | | | | | | ■ |
| Standardized Test Prep | | ■ | | ■ | ■ | ■ | | | ■ | ■ | ■ | |
| | Standardized Test Prep, p. 93 | | | | | | | | | | | |
| Computer Item Generator | Can be used to create custom-made practice pages or assessment pages at any time. | | | | | | | | | | | |

### Test-Taking Tips on Transparencies

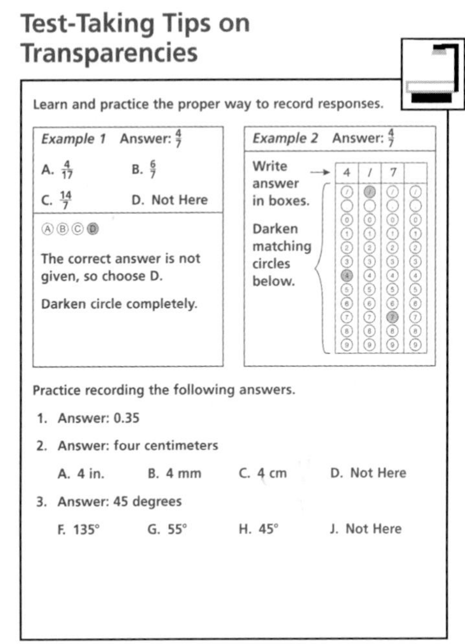

Learn and practice the proper way to record responses.

*Example 1* Answer: $\frac{4}{7}$

A. $\frac{4}{17}$ B. $\frac{6}{7}$
C. $\frac{14}{7}$ D. Not Here

Ⓐ Ⓑ Ⓒ Ⓓ

The correct answer is not given, so choose D.

Darken circle completely.

*Example 2* Answer: $\frac{4}{7}$

Write answer in boxes. → 4 / 7

Darken matching circles below.

Practice recording the following answers.

1. Answer: 0.35
2. Answer: four centimeters
   A. 4 in. B. 4 mm C. 4 cm D. Not Here
3. Answer: 45 degrees
   F. 135° G. 55° H. 45° J. Not Here

*Use with Standardized Test Prep and Chapter Assessments.*

## Correlation to Standardized Tests

| Lesson | | CAT5 | CTBS/5 TerraNova™ | ITBS | MAT7 | SAT9 | LOCAL OBJECTIVES |
|---|---|---|---|---|---|---|---|
| 2-1 | Properties of Numbers | | | ■ | | ■ | |
| 2-2 | The Distributive Property | | | ■ | | ■ | |
| 2-3 | Simplifying Variable Expressions | | ■ | | | ■ | |
| 2-4 | Variables and Equations | | | | ■ | ■ | |
| 2-5 | Solving Equations by Adding or Subtracting | | | | ■ | ■ | |
| 2-6 | Solving Equations by Multiplying and Dividing | | | | ■ | ■ | |
| 2-7 | Problem Solving Strategy: Try, Test, Revise | | | | ■ | ■ | |
| 2-8 | Inequalities and Their Graphs | | | | ■ | ■ | |
| 2-9 | Solving One-Step Inequalities by Adding or Subtracting | | | | ■ | ■ | |
| 2-10 | Solving One-Step Inequalities by Multiplying or Dividing | | | | ■ | ■ | |

**CAT5** California Achievement Test, 5th edition
**CTBS TerraNova** Comprehensive Test of Basic Skills, 5th edition
**ITBS** Iowa Test of Basic Skills, Form M
**MAT7** Metropolitan Achievement Test, 7th edition
**SAT** Stanford Achievement Test, Advanced 1

For other standardized test correlations, follow the link to your state at **www.phschool.com**.

# Resources for Chapter 2

| | TEACHING RESOURCES BOX | | | | | | | | | | | | | | |
|---|---|---|---|---|---|---|---|---|---|---|---|---|---|---|---|
| | CHAPTER 2 SUPPORT FILE | | | | | | | | | | | | | | |
| | Practice | Reteach | Enrichment | Project Manager | Checkpoints | Cumulative Review | Chapter Assessment | Alternative Assessment | Cumulative Assessment | Lesson Planners Plus | Daily Cum Review | Teaching Transparencies | Warm-Up Transparencies | Help at Home | SE Answers on Transparencies |
| Begin Chapter | | | | ■ | | | | | | ■ | | 9 | | | |
| 2-1 | ■ | ■ | ■ | | | | | | | ■ | ■ | 39 | ■ | | ■ |
| 2-2 | ■ | ■ | ■ | | | | | | | ■ | ■ | 16, 39 | ■ | | ■ |
| 2-3 | ■ | ■ | ■ | | ■ | | | | | ■ | ■ | 40 | ■ | ■ | ■ |
| 2-4 | ■ | ■ | ■ | | | | | | | ■ | ■ | | ■ | | ■ |
| 2-5 | ■ | ■ | ■ | | | | | | | ■ | ■ | 8, 41 | ■ | | ■ |
| 2-6 | ■ | ■ | ■ | | | | | | | ■ | ■ | | ■ | | ■ |
| 2-7 | ■ | ■ | ■ | | | | | | | ■ | ■ | 19, 42 | ■ | | ■ |
| 2-8 | ■ | ■ | ■ | | | | | | | ■ | ■ | 7, 43 | ■ | | ■ |
| 2-9 | ■ | ■ | ■ | | ■ | | | | | ■ | ■ | | ■ | ■ | ■ |
| 2-10 | ■ | ■ | ■ | | | | | | | ■ | ■ | | ■ | | ■ |
| End Chapter | | | | | | ■ | ■ (2 forms) | ■ | After Ch. 3, 6, 9, 13 | | | | | | |

**Also available for use with the chapter:**

Solution Key
Computational Practice Skills Booklet
Mathematics Standardized Test Prep, Student Edition and Teacher's Edition
Overhead Manipulatives Kit
Practice Workbook
Algebra Readiness Kit
Student Manipulatives Kit
Test-Taking Tips on Transparencies
Assessment Success Kit
Teaching Aids and Letters
Graphing Calculator Handbook
Spanish Resources
Success-Building Puzzle and Problem Masters

## TECHNOLOGY

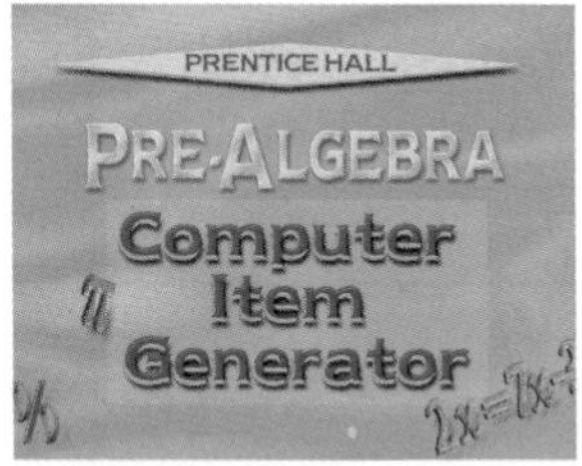


**Computer Item Generator with Standardized Test Prep**

CD-ROM with an unlimited supply of questions with varying degrees of difficulty for customized practice sheets, quizzes, and tests.

**Resource Pro® with Planning Express®**

CD-ROM with complete classroom planning tool and teaching resources for customizing and planning lessons.

**Interactive Math Lessons and Tools**

CD-ROM with lessons and tools to make abstract concepts visual and accessible.

**Student Tutorial**

Test preparation software for students on CD-ROM with management system for teachers; includes Secondary Math Lab Toolkit™.

**Secondary Math Lab Toolkit™ with Integrated Math Labs**

Integrated software package with linkable math tools for exploring key concepts.

**Also available for use with the chapter:**

Math Blaster® Pre-Algebra CD-ROM
Video Fieldtrips, Vol. I: Algebra Applications
Video Fieldtrips, Vol. II: Geometry Applications
Wide World of Mathematics CD-ROM
Wide World of Mathematics Video

### *Web Extension*

**www.phschool.com**

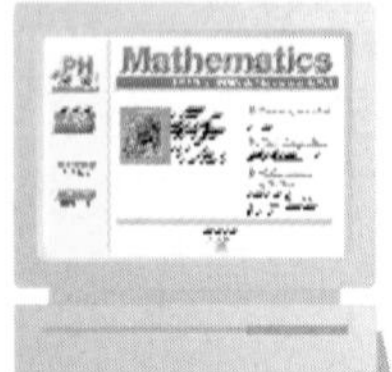


**For Students**
- Chapter Support with Internet Links
- Internet Activities

**For Teachers**
- Curriculum Support
- Professional Development
- Product Information
- Regional Support Information

# Skills You Need for Chapter 2

## ▶ Order of operations with integers

Use before Lesson 2-2.

**Simplify each expression.**

1. $5 \cdot 2 + 5 \cdot 3$ 25
2. $7(6 - 2)$ 28
3. $10 \cdot 3 - 5 \cdot 3$ 15
4. $-(34 + 76)$ −110
5. $4(6) + 4(3)$ 36
6. $-4(12 - 16)$ 16
7. $7(8) - 10(8)$ −24
8. $11 \cdot 9 - 6 \cdot 9$ 45
9. $-2 \cdot 3 - 2 \cdot 7$ −20
10. $6 \cdot (-9) - 3(-9)$ −27
11. $4(12) + 4(6)$ 72
12. $12(-14 + 8)$ −72
13. $(24 - 15)(-2)$ −18
14. $-5(3) - (-5)(2)$ −5
15. $(72 - 81)(5)$ −45

## ▶ Inverse operations

Use before Lessons 2-5 and 2-6.

**Complete the related equations.**

16. ■ + 5 = 8 (3); 8 − ■ = 5 (3)
17. 20 − ■ = 9 (11); 9 + ■ = 20 (11)
18. −2 + ■ = 3 (5); 3 − ■ = −2 (5)
19. 90 − ■ = 55 (35); 55 + ■ = 90 (35)
20. 20 − ■ = 23 (−3); 23 + ■ = 20 (−3)
21. ■ + 12 = −7 (−19); −7 − ■ = 12 (−19)
22. 5 · ■ = 30 (6); 30 ÷ ■ = 5 (6)
23. 3 · ■ = 75 (25); 75 ÷ ■ = 3 (25)
24. 72 ÷ ■ = 12 (6); 12 · ■ = 72 (6)
25. 100 ÷ 20 = ■ (5); 20 · ■ = 100 (5)
26. 2 · ■ = −14 (−7); −14 ÷ ■ = 2 (−7)
27. −36 ÷ ■ = −6 (6); −6 · ■ = −36 (6)
28. ■ · (−10) = −70 (7); −70 ÷ ■ = −10 (7)
29. 52 ÷ ■ = 4 (13); 4 · ■ = 52 (13)

## ▶ Comparing numbers

Use before Lesson 2-8.

**Compare. Use >, <, or = to complete each statement.**

30. 6 ■ 16 (<)
31. 5 ■ −5 (>)
32. 36 ■ 15 (>)
33. −52 ■ −21 (<)
34. 0 ■ −8 (>)
35. −7 ■ 3 (<)
36. 12 + 3 ■ 19 − 4 (=)
37. 5(4) ■ 7 (>)
38. 18 − 27 ■ −34 + 12 (>)
39. 27 ÷ 9 ■ 6 · 2 (<)
40. −2 · 6 ■ 4 · (−3) (=)
41. −8 ÷ 2 ■ 9 ÷ 3 (<)
42. 8(−5) ■ 100 − 65 (<)
43. 3(−2)(−4) ■ 4(−3)(2) (>)
44. 6 ÷ (10 − 8) ■ 1 + 5 (<)



# Skills You Need

### Order of operations with integers

**In Lesson 2-2** students will use the Distributive Property to simplify expressions with integers.

### Inverse operations

**In Lesson 2-5** students will solve equations by adding or subtracting using inverse operations.

**In Lesson 2-6** students will solve equations by multiplying or dividing using inverse operations.

### Comparing numbers

**In Lesson 2-8** students will graph inequalities that compare quantities.

# Skills Trace

| SKILL | INTRODUCED | DEVELOPED IN LESSON(S) | REVIEWED/REINFORCED |
|---|---|---|---|
| Identifying and using properties | 2-1 | 2-2, 2-3 | pp. 73, 77, 97, 112 |
| Characteristics of variable expressions and equations | 2-3 | 2-4 | pp. 81, 88, 107, 135, 145, 149, 179, 249, 678 |
| Solving one-step equations with inverse operations | 2-5 | 2-6, 3-5, 5-7, 5-8 | pp. 92, 97, 140, 145, 228, 299 |
| Writing, solving, and graphing one-step inequalities | 2-8 | 2-9, 2-10 | pp. 107, 112, 126, 155, 175, 201, 263, 402, 425 |

# Solving One-Step Equations and Inequalities

## Connecting to Students' Lives

Ask students if they have ever been on a see-saw or teeter-totter. Ask what they did to balance the see-saw if the weight on one side was heavier than that on the other side. Probably they added people to the lighter side. In this project, students construct an equal-arm balance, similar to a see-saw, to compare the mass of several coins.

## Interdisciplinary Connections

The Chapter Project connects math and science. You may want to display pictures or information about coins (perhaps including coins from other countries) and the United States Mint in the classroom.

## About the Project

The Chapter Project directs students to apply their knowledge of equations and graphing to data they gather about the mass of coins by using an equal-arm balance.

CHAPTER 2

# Solving One-Step Equations and Inequalities

**What you'll learn in this chapter:**

- How to use the Distributive Property
- How to write and solve equations
- How to write, solve, and graph inequalities

***Web Extension***
**www.phschool.com**

**For Students**
Chapter Support with Internet links
Interactive Activities

**For Teachers**
Curriculum Support
Professional Development
Product Information
Regional Support Information

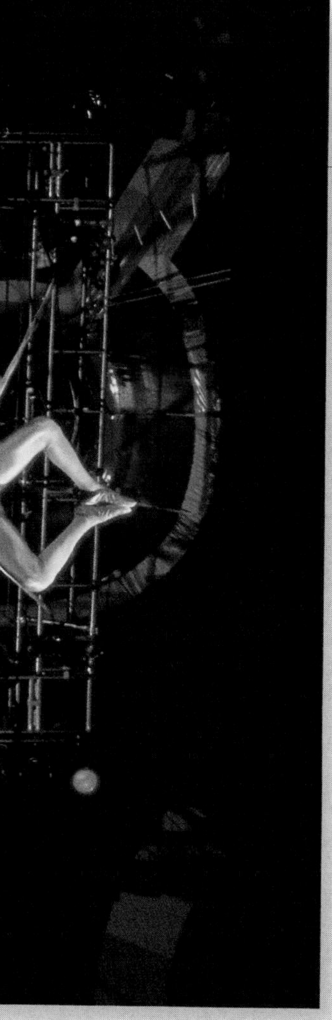

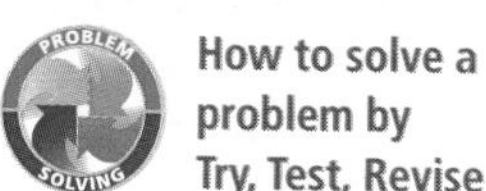


How to solve a problem by Try, Test, Revise

CHAPTER PROJECT 2

# DON'T LOSE YOUR BALANCE!

Have you ever used a balance in your science class? Balances make very precise measurements in science, industry, and government. The United States Mint, for example, ensures that the coins it produces meet exact specifications. You can make your own version of a balance and use it to compare the masses of different objects.

***Make a Balance Scale*** For the chapter project, you will make a simple balance scale. You will use it to write and solve equations and inequalities for the masses of different coins.

### *Steps to help you complete the project*


p. 73 ACTIVITY: CREATING

p. 92 ACTIVITY: CALCULATING

p. 112 ACTIVITY: GRAPHING

p. 113 FINISHING THE CHAPTER PROJECT

***Web Extension***
**www.phschool.com**

## Scoring Rubric

**3** You write and solve all equations and inequalities accurately. Your graph shows the possible mass of a quarter correctly. Your diagrams are complete, descriptive, well-organized, and easy to read.

**2** You make minor errors in your equations, inequalities, or graph. Your diagrams are complete and descriptive, but could be better organized or easier to read.

**1** You set up and solve your equations and inequalities inaccurately. Your diagrams are incomplete and lack organization.

**0** Major elements of the project are incomplete or missing.

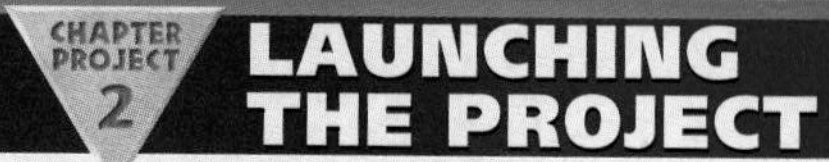


*The Chapter Project is optional and may be assigned at your discretion.*

Ask students:

- Have you ever seen a balance scale or equal-arm scale in a science laboratory?
- How do you think scientists, such as physicists and chemists, or medical technologists and pharmacists, use math to help them do their work?
- How might you use math to compare the mass of coins on an equal-arm balance?

Distribute a copy of the Project Manager and Scoring Rubric to help students get an overview of the project.

Review the scoring rubric with students.

## Project Notebook

Encourage students to keep all project-related materials in a separate folder or notebook. Call attention to the fact that they will find much useful information on the Web site **www.phschool.com**.

**Tracking the Project** Set benchmark deadlines for students to show you their work in progress.

*Available in the Chapter 2 Support File in the Teaching Resources box.*

### Project Manager and Scoring Rubric

**Getting Started** You will be making diagrams to compare the weights of different coins. Read about the project in your textbook. As you work on the project, you will need a ruler, a pencil, several coins including pennies, nickels, and quarters, materials to make your diagrams, and writing materials.

**Checklist and Suggestions**

| | | |
|---|---|---|
| ❏ | Make your balance scale. | Be sure to find the right balance point. |
| ❏ | Write and solve an equation to find the mass of a penny. | Choose a variable to represent the mass of the penny. |
| ❏ | Write and solve two inequalities for the mass of a quarter. | Remember that a nickel has a mass of about 5 grams. |
| ❏ | Graph your inequalities on the same number line. | The actual mass of the quarter is in the range where the two graphs overlap. |
| ❏ | Make your diagrams. | Draw coins on a balance scale. |
| ❏ | Share your diagrams with the class. | Check each other's work and provide suggestions. |

**Scoring Rubric**

**3** You write and solve all equations and inequalities accurately. Your graph shows the possible mass of a quarter correctly. Your diagrams are complete, descriptive, well-organized, and easy to read.

**2** You make minor errors in your equations, inequalities or graph. Your diagrams are complete and descriptive, but could be better organized or easier to read.

**1** You set up and solve your equations and inequalities inaccurately. Your diagrams are incomplete and lack organization.

**0** Major elements of the project are incomplete or missing.

**Your Evaluation of the Project** Evaluate your work, based on the Scoring Rubric.

**Teacher's Evaluation of the Project**

# 2-1

## Getting Ready

**Key Terms and Symbols**
Commutative Properties of Addition and Multiplication, Associative Properties of Addition and Multiplication, Identity Properties of Addition and Multiplication, additive identity, multiplicative identity

**Resources** A complete list of resources for this lesson is on p. 61H.

### Daily Skills Warm-Up

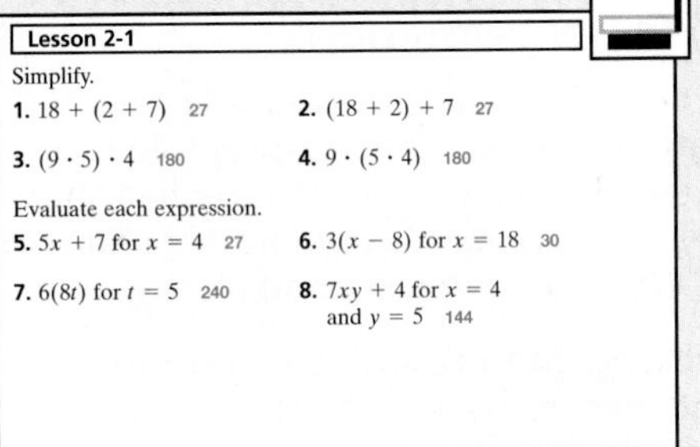

Lesson 2-1

Simplify.

1. $18 + (2 + 7)$ 27
2. $(18 + 2) + 7$ 27
3. $(9 \cdot 5) \cdot 4$ 180
4. $9 \cdot (5 \cdot 4)$ 180

Evaluate each expression.

5. $5x + 7$ for $x = 4$ 27
6. $3(x - 8)$ for $x = 18$ 30
7. $6(8t)$ for $t = 5$ 240
8. $7xy + 4$ for $x = 4$ and $y = 5$ 144

### Background for the Lesson

The Commutative and Associative Properties of Addition and Multiplication say that when adding numbers or multiplying numbers, you can do the operation in any order, and you can change the grouping. These properties apply when there is a single operation, either addition or multiplication. With mixed operations, use the order of operations also. These properties help you do mental math.

## 1 Focus

### Connecting to Students' Lives

Ask students to explain the mental math they might use to compute the amount of change for the purchase of a hot dog for $2.37 if they give the clerk $3.00.

### Connecting to Prior Knowledge

Students know from Lessons 1-5 and 1-9 how to add and multiply integers. In this lesson they use those skills with the Associative and Commutative Properties. In Lesson 2-3, they apply the properties to simplifying variable expressions.

# 2-1 Properties of Numbers

**What You'll Learn**

1. To identify properties of addition and multiplication
2. To use properties to solve problems

**. . . And Why**

To find answers quickly using mental math

## PART 1 Identifying Properties

The sum of 6 and 4 is the same as the sum of 4 and 6. Similarly, the product of 9 and 5 is the same as the product of 5 and 9. These suggest the following properties.

**Commutative Properties of Addition and Multiplication**

Changing the order of the values you are adding or multiplying does not change the sum or product.

| Arithmetic | Algebra |
|---|---|
| $6 + 4 = 4 + 6$ | $a + b = b + a$ |
| $9 \cdot 5 = 5 \cdot 9$ | $a \cdot b = b \cdot a$ |

You can also change the grouping of numbers before you add or multiply them.

**Associative Properties of Addition and Multiplication**

Changing the grouping of the values you are adding or multiplying does not change the sum or product.

| Arithmetic | Algebra |
|---|---|
| $(2 + 7) + 3 = 2 + (7 + 3)$ | $(a + b) + c = a + (b + c)$ |
| $(9 \cdot 4)5 = 9(4 \cdot 5)$ | $(ab)c = a(bc)$ |

**Quick Review**

When you use the order of operations, you do operations within grouping symbols first.

REAL-WORLD  CONNECTION

**EXAMPLE 1**

**Carlos rented a set of golf clubs for $7 and a golf cart for $12. He paid a greens fee of $23. Find his total cost.**

You can use the Associative Property of Addition to find the total cost in two different ways.

$(7 + 12) + 23 = 19 + 23 = 42$ Add 7 and 12 first.

$7 + (12 + 23) = 7 + 35 = 42$ Add 12 and 23 first.

Carlos's total cost was $42.



# Tools to Monitor Progress

**BEFORE THE LESSON**

**To check prerequisite skills:**

- Combining integers

**Skills Intervention Kit,** Pre-Algebra Basics

**DURING THE LESSON**

**To check understanding:**

**Try This** exercises on student page

- **Additional Example 1**
  After spending $42, Carlos bought a bottle of water for $2 and a chef salad for $8. What was the total cost for his golf game and meal? $52

■ **TRY THIS**

1. You go out with friends. You spend $6 for dinner, $8 for a movie, and $4 for popcorn. Find your total cost. Explain which property or properties you used. $18; see below right.

When you add a number and 0, the sum equals the original number. The **additive identity** is 0. When you multiply a number and 1, the product equals the original number. The **multiplicative identity** is 1.

**Identity Properties of Addition and Multiplication**

The sum of any number and zero is the original number. The product of any number and 1 is the original number.

| Arithmetic | Algebra |
|---|---|
| $12 + 0 = 12$ | $a + 0 = a$ |
| $10 \cdot 1 = 10$ | $a \cdot 1 = a$ |

1. Explanations may vary. Sample:
$6 + 8 + 4$
$= 6 + (8 + 4)$ Assoc. Prop. of Add.
$= 6 + (4 + 8)$ Comm. Prop. of Add.
$= (6 + 4) + 8$ Assoc. Prop. of Add.
$= 10 + 8$ Add within parentheses.
$= 18$ Add.

■ **EXAMPLE 2**

**Name each property shown.**

**a.** $5 \cdot 7 = 7 \cdot 5$ Commutative Property of Multiplication
**b.** $c \cdot 1 = c$ Identity Property of Multiplication
**c.** $7 + a = a + 7$ Commutative Property of Addition
**d.** $5(xy) = (5x)y$ Associative Property of Multiplication

■ **TRY THIS** Name each property shown.

**2.** $3 + 6 = 6 + 3$ Comm. Prop. of Add. **3.** $8 = 1 \times 8$ Ident. Prop. of Mult. **4.** $(3z)m = 3(zm)$ Assoc. Prop. of Mult.

## PART 2 Using Properties

You can use properties and mental math to help you find sums.

■ **EXAMPLE 3**

**Use mental math to simplify $(81 + 6) + 9$.**

$(81 + 6) + 9$
$= (6 + 81) + 9$ Use the Commutative Property of Addition.
$= 6 + (81 + 9)$ Use the Associative Property of Addition.
$= 6 + 90$ Add within parentheses.
$= 96$ Add.

Look for combinations that equal 10 or a multiple of 10, since they are easier to use in calculating mentally.



# 2 Teach

## PART 1 Part 1 Teaching Notes

Explain that the Commutative and Associative Properties are consistent with the order of operations because these properties apply to doing only one operation several times.

### ■ Example 1

**Build understanding.** What is a greens fee? a fee you pay to use the golf course

**ELL** Have a volunteer explain what it means if a person commutes to work. Then have students discuss how this can help them remember the name of the Commutative Property.

### ■ Example 2

**Build understanding.** Ask: What is it about the Identity Property in item b. that is identical or remains the same? c

## PART 2 Part 2 Teaching Notes

Using the properties makes mental math easier. Write the following expression on the board: $2 \times 27 \times 5$. Show students how to use the properties of multiplication to change this expression into $27 \times (2 \times 5)$ or $27 \times 10$. Multiplying by 10 is easy with mental math.

### ■ Example 3

**Build understanding.** Ask: How does grouping 81 and 9 together make this expression easier to simplify? Combinations that make 10 are easier to do mentally.

- **Additional Example 2**
Name each property shown.
**a.** $17 + x + 3 = 17 + 3 + x$
**b.** $(36 \times 2)10 = 36(2 \times 10)$
**c.** $km = (km) \times 1$
**d.** $(103 + 26) + 4 = 103 + (26 + 4)$
a. Comm. Add.; b. Assoc. Mult.; c. Ident. Mult.; d. Assoc. Add.
- **Additional Examples 3–5**
Use mental math to simplify $20 \cdot 13 \cdot 5 \cdot 2$. 2,600

## AFTER THE LESSON

**To assess knowledge:**
**Lesson Quiz**

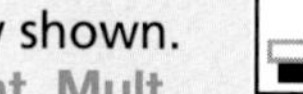

Name each property shown.
**1.** $d \times 1 = d$ Ident. Mult.
**2.** $3 + (2 + 5) = (3 + 2) + 5$ Assoc. Prop. of Add.
**3.** $f \times g = g \times f$ Comm. Mult.
**4.** $32 + 45 + 102 = 45 + 32 + 102$ Comm. Add.

- For enrichment and reteaching options see Resources on p. 61H.

**Tactile Learning** Have students model expressions using counters or algebra tiles so that they physically move or regroup the objects to reinforce the concepts.

**Error Prevention** Students may assume that the Commutative and Associative Properties also work for subtraction and division. Have students create their own subtraction and division examples to find out for themselves that these properties are not true for all operations.

### Example 4

**Build understanding.** Ask: Why is the 1.65 moved? because 1.65 and 0.35 add to 2.00, making the mental math easier

### Example 5

**Build understanding.** Ask: How do you know the first step is an example of the Commutative Property? because the order of 4 and 9 is changed

**Extension** Challenge students to explain why zero is not a multiplicative identity. Multiplying by zero does not leave the number identical, or unchanged.

**Error Prevention** Encourage students for whom mental math is difficult to use the properties in this lesson to make expressions easier.

**Try This** Use mental math to simplify each expression.

**5.** $6 + 27 + 14$ 47

**6.** $8 + 0 + 2 + (-7)$ 3

**7.** $5 + 12 + 18 + 5$ 40

**8.** $19 + (-30) + 21$ 10

REAL-WORLD CONNECTION

## Example 4

**Suppose you buy the school supplies shown at the left. Use mental math to find the cost of these supplies.**

| | |
|---|---|
| $1.65 + 0.85 + 0.35$ | |
| $= 0.85 + 1.65 + 0.35$ | Use the Commutative Property of Addition. |
| $= 0.85 + (1.65 + 0.35)$ | Use the Associative Property of Addition. |
| $= 0.85 + 2.00$ | Add within parentheses. |
| $= 2.85$ | Add. |

The cost of the school supplies is $2.85.

*Need Help?* For help with adding decimals, see Skills Handbook, p. 730.

**Try This**

**9.** Use the supermarket receipt and mental math to find the cost of the groceries. $6.30

SOUTH STREET MARKET
527-5817

| DATE 08.03.00 | THU |
|---|---|
| 1 GALLON MILK | $2.30 |
| BREAD | $1.80 |
| APPLES | $2.20 |

You can also use mental math to help you find products.

## Example 5

**Use mental math to simplify $(4 \cdot 9) \cdot 5$.**

| | |
|---|---|
| $(4 \cdot 9) \cdot 5 = (9 \cdot 4) \cdot 5$ | Use the Commutative Property of Multiplication. |
| $= 9 \cdot (4 \cdot 5)$ | Use the Associative Property of Multiplication. |
| $= 9 \cdot 20$ | Multiply within parentheses. |
| $= 180$ | Multiply. |

**Try This** Use mental math to simplify each expression.

**10.** $25 \cdot (3 \cdot 4)$ 300

**11.** $3 \cdot 1 \cdot 5 \cdot 8$ 120

**12.** $2(-8)(15)$ −240

**13.** $5 \cdot 9 \cdot 6 \cdot (-2)$ −540

# Exercises

## CHECK UNDERSTANDING

**Name each property shown.**

1. $27 + 6 = 6 + 27$ Comm. Prop. of Add.
2. $0 + 8 = 8$ Ident. Prop. of Add.
3. $(6 \cdot 15)2 = 6(15 \cdot 2)$ Assoc. Prop. of Mult.
4. $(12r)s = 12(rs)$ Assoc. Prop. of Mult.
5. $999 \cdot 1 = 999$ Ident. Prop. of Mult.
6. ● · ▲ = ▲ · ● Comm. Prop. of Mult.

**Which two numbers would you combine first? Explain.**

7. $5 + 36 + 95$ 5 and 95; they are easiest to add.
8. $5 \cdot 17 \cdot 2$ 5 and 2; they are easiest to multiply.
9. $50(-2)43$ 50 and (−2); they are easiest to multiply.

*Mental Math* **Simplify each expression.**

10. $10 \cdot 13 \cdot (-10)$ −1,300
11. $23 + (-15) + 85$ 93
12. $25 + 157 + (-75)$ 107
13. $(5)(-20)(66)$ −6,600
14. $140 + 17 + (-60)$ 97
15. $30 \cdot 30 \cdot 6$ 5,400
16. *Critical Thinking* How do reordering and regrouping help you to add mentally? Include examples. Answers may vary. Sample: Reordering and regrouping can put numbers in positions in which they are easier to combine. Example: 83 + 194 + 17 is easier to simplify if the 83 and 17 are added first. 4 · 17 · 5 is easier to simplify if the 4 and 5 are multiplied first.

## PRACTICE AND PROBLEM SOLVING

**Name each property shown.**

17. ● + ▲ = ▲ + ● Comm. Prop. of Add.
18. $8(3 \cdot 2) = (8 \cdot 3)2$ Assoc. Prop. of Mult.
19. $5 + 8 = 8 + 5$ Comm. Prop. of Add.
20. $(6x)y = 6(xy)$ Assoc. Prop. of Mult.
21. $6 \cdot 1 = 6$ Ident. Prop. of Mult.
22. $ab = ba$ Comm. Prop. of Mult.
23. $999 + 0 = 999$ Ident. Prop. of Add.
24. $(3 \cdot 4)(25) = 3(4 \cdot 25)$ Assoc. Prop. of Mult.
25. $a \cdot 1 = 1 \cdot a$ Comm. Prop. of Mult.
26. $(6 + 5) + x = 6 + (5 + x)$ Assoc. Prop. of Add.
27. ✪ $(3 + 2)(4 + 5) = (4 + 5)(3 + 2)$ Comm. Prop. of Mult.

*Mental Math* **Simplify each expression.**

28. $62 + 3 + 7$ 72
29. $25 \cdot 4 \cdot 8$ 800
30. $24 + 0 + (-16)$ 8
31. $10 \cdot 37 \cdot 10$ 3,700
32. $35 + 15 + (-8)$ 42
33. $5 \cdot 1 \cdot 20$ 100
34. $730 + 693 + 270$ 1,693
35. $5 \cdot 50 \cdot 20 \cdot (-2)$ −10,000
36. $15 + 13 + (-25) + 12$ 15
37. $125 + 18 + 75 + 162$ 380
38. $4 \cdot 6 \cdot 25 \cdot 50 \cdot 2$ 60,000
39. $17 + 17 + (-2) + 3$ 35

*Mental Math* **Evaluate each expression.**

40. ✪ $x(y \cdot z)$, for $x = 4, y = -7$, and $z = 5$ −140
41. ✪ $t(u)(-v)$, for $t = 3, u = -10$, and $v = 8$ 240
42. ✪ $a + b + c$, for $a = 14, b = -52$, and $c = 26$ −12
43. ✪ $d(v)(d)$, for $d = 5$ and $v = -4$ −100



# 3 Practice/Assess

## Assignment Guide

To provide flexible scheduling, this lesson can be divided into parts.

**Part 1**

**Core** 1–6, 17–26, 44–45

✪ **Extension** 27

**Part 2**

**Core** 7–16, 28–39, 47–48

✪ **Extension** 40–43, 46

Mixed Review can be assigned at any time for maintenance.

## Exercises

**Test Prep Exercise 45** Suggest that students first recall what the Associative Property is to help them eliminate incorrect choices.

## ✪ Challenge

Simplify the following expression:
$17 + 7 \times 8 + 23$. 96

## Closure

Use the Commutative Property to change order. Use the Associative Property to change grouping. Adding zero to an expression does not change its value. Multiplying an expression by 1 does not change its value.

## Alternative Assessment

Have students describe a real-world situation, including an example expression, in which they could make mental math easier by applying the properties.

## Daily Cumulative Review

**Name the point with the given coordinates.** *(Lesson 1-10)*

1. (1, 5) E
2. (0, 3) G
3. (−2, 1) A
4. (−3, 0) D
5. (−5, −2) C
6. (5, −3) F

**Compare. Use >, <, or = to complete each statement.** *(Lesson 1-9)*

7. $(-4)(-3)$ [<] $(-3)(-5)$
8. $-15 \div (-3)$ [>] $35 \div (-7)$
9. $-56 \div 8$ [=] $-|-56| \div 8$
10. $7(-7)$ [<] $(-9)(-5)$

**Mixed Review**

**Use rules to find each difference.**

11. (1-6) $-87 - (-9)$ −78
12. (1-6) $43 - (-14)$ 57
13. (1-6) $-73 - 25$ −98
14. (1-6) $-760 - 70 - (-30)$ −800
15. (1-6) $-50 - (-30) - 20$ −40
16. (1-6) $450 - (-40) - (-30)$ 520

**Simplify each expression.**

17. (1-2) $[16 \div (8 - 4)]8$ 32
18. (1-2) $(48 - 12) \div 6$ 6
19. (1-2) $3(4 + 7)$ 33
20. (1-2) $3[12 - (2 \cdot 6)] + 4$ 4
21. (1-2) $[(6 + 3) \cdot 2] - 5$ 13
22. (1-2) $(78 - 24) \div 6 \div 3$ 3

**Write a rule for the pattern. Find the next three numbers in the pattern.**

23. (1-7) −13, −6, 1, 8, 15, 22, 29
Rule: Start with −13 and add 7 repeatedly.

## Practice

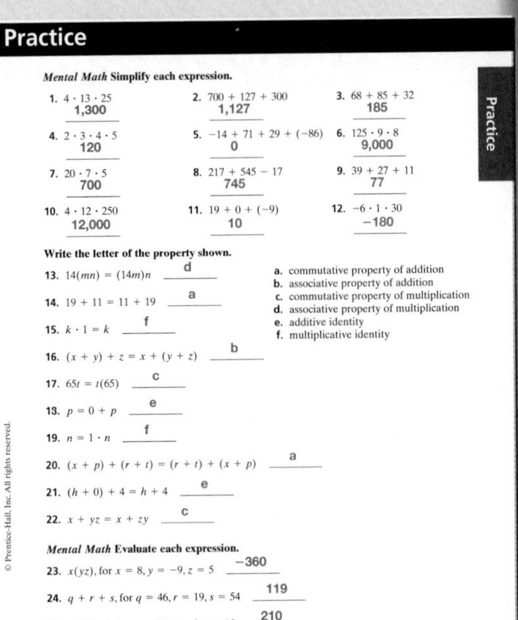

*Mental Math* **Simplify each expression.**

1. $4 \cdot 13 \cdot 25$ **1,300**
2. $700 + 127 + 300$ **1,127**
3. $68 + 85 + 32$ **185**
4. $2 \cdot 3 \cdot 4 \cdot 5$ **120**
5. $-14 + 71 + 29 + (-86)$ **0**
6. $125 \cdot 9 \cdot 8$ **9,000**
7. $20 \cdot 7 \cdot 5$ **700**
8. $217 + 545 - 17$ **745**
9. $39 + 27 + 11$ **77**
10. $4 \cdot 12 \cdot 250$ **12,000**
11. $19 + 0 + (-9)$ **10**
12. $-6 \cdot 1 \cdot 30$ **−180**

**Write the letter of the property shown.**

a. commutative property of addition
b. associative property of addition
c. commutative property of multiplication
d. associative property of multiplication
e. additive identity
f. multiplicative identity

13. $14(mn) = (14m)n$ **d**
14. $19 + 11 = 11 + 19$ **a**
15. $k \cdot 1 = k$ **f**
16. $(x + y) + z = x + (y + z)$ **b**
17. $65t = t(65)$ **c**
18. $p = 0 + p$ **e**
19. $n = 1 \cdot n$ **f**
20. $(x + p) + (r + t) = (r + t) + (x + p)$ **a**
21. $(h + 0) + 4 = h + 4$ **e**
22. $x + yz = x + zy$ **c**

*Mental Math* **Evaluate each expression.**

23. $x(yz)$, for $x = 8, y = -9, z = 5$ **−360**
24. $q + r + s$, for $q = 46, r = 19, s = 54$ **119**
25. $a(b)(-c)$, for $a = 7, b = -2, c = 15$ **210**



## Reteaching

**Properties of numbers help make mental computations easier.**

Use mental math to simplify $1.84 + $.76 + $.16.
Since 0.84 + 0.16 = 1, it is easier to add $1.84 and $.16 first.

| | |
|---|---|
| $1.84 + 0.76 + 0.16$ | |
| $= 1.84 + (0.16 + 0.76)$ | Use the commutative property of addition. |
| $= (1.84 + 0.16) + 0.76$ | Use the associative property of addition. |
| $= 2.00 + 0.76$ | Add within parentheses. |
| = $2.76 | Add. |

Use mental math to simplify $5 \cdot 13 \cdot 20 \cdot 2$.
Since $5 \cdot 20 = 100$, it is easier to multiply 5 and 20 first.

| | |
|---|---|
| $5 \cdot 13 \cdot 20 \cdot 2$ | |
| $= (13 \cdot 5) \cdot 20 \cdot 2$ | Use the commutative property of multiplication. |
| $= 13 \cdot (5 \cdot 20) \cdot 2$ | Use the associative property of multiplication. |
| $= 13 \cdot 100 \cdot 2$ | Multiply within parentheses. |
| $= 13 \cdot (200)$ | Multiply. |
| $= 2,600$ | Multiply. |

**Use mental math to simplify each expression.**

1. $198 + 15 + 302$ **515**
2. $16 + 27 + (-16)$ **27**
3. $4 \cdot 7 \cdot 25$ **700**
4. $2 \cdot 6 \cdot 5$ **60**
5. $18 + (-8) + 11$ **21**
6. $5 \cdot 9 \cdot 8$ **360**
7. $21 + 4 + (-1)$ **24**
8. $1,242 + 125 + 58$ **1,425**
9. $50 \cdot 13 \cdot 2$ **1,300**
10. $(-209) + 576 + (-91)$ **276**
11. $17 + 9 + 13 + 6$ **45**
12. $125 \cdot 353 \cdot 8$ **353,000**



## Enrichment

Suppose ⊙ is a relationship between two quantities. The following properties may hold for ⊙.

| Property | Statement |
|---|---|
| Reflexive | $a \odot a$. |
| Symmetric | If $a \odot b$, then $b \odot a$. |
| Transitive | If $a \odot b$ and $b \odot c$, then $a \odot c$. |

**Example** Which of the properties hold for the relationship ">"?

**Solution** Substitute > in each of the above statements. Substitute values for $a$ and $b$. If you can find a single example for which the statement is not true, then the relationship does not have the given property. If every example you try produces a true statement, the relationship appears to have the given property.

Reflexive: $a > a$
Test: Is $5 > 5$? No. The relationship ">" is not reflexive.

Symmetric: If $a > b$, then $b > a$.
Test: $8 > 6$. Is $6 > 8$? No. The relationship ">" is not symmetric.

Transitive: If $a > b$ and $b > c$, then $a > c$.
Test: $10 > 7$ and $7 > 3$. Is $10 > 3$? Yes.
$-1 > -2$ and $-2 > -5$. Is $-1 > -5$? Yes.
$12 > -3$ and $-3 > -6$. Is $12 > -6$? Yes.
The relationship ">" appears to be transitive.

**Test the relationship for the reflexive, symmetric, and transitive properties. Tell which properties, if any, appear to hold. Write *R*, *S*, or *T*.**

1. = ***R, S, T***
2. ≥ ***R, T***
3. "is older than" ***T***
4. "is the father of" **none**
5. "is the sister of" ***S, T***
6. "has the same zip code as" ***R, S, T***
7. "dances with" ***S***
8. "has the same color hair as" ***R, S, T***
9. "sings to" ***R***
10. "is as tall as" ***R, S, T***





44. ***Mathematical Reasoning*** Are there commutative and associative properties for subtraction and division? Justify your answer. **No; for subtraction, for example $6 - 4 \neq 4 - 6$ and $6 - (3 - 1) \neq (6 - 3) - 1$; for division, $12 \div 3 \neq 3 \div 12$; and $(20 \div 4) \div 2 \neq 20 \div (4 \div 2)$.**

45. **TEST PREP** Which equation shows the Associative Property of Addition? **B**
   A. $8 + 6 + 7 = 8 + 7 + 6$
   B. $10 + 5 + 15 + 6 = 10 + (5 + 15) + 6$
   C. $9 + 0 + (-1) = 9 + (-1)$
   D. $17 \cdot (-2) \cdot 1 \cdot 9 = 17 \cdot (-2) \cdot 9$

46. ***Critical Thinking*** As the first step in evaluating the expression $3 \cdot 4 + 2 \div (-2)$, can you use the Associative Property of Addition to find $4 + 2$? Explain. **Answers may vary. Sample: No; $3 \cdot 4$ must be found first by the order of operations.**

***Math in the Media*** **Use the article below for Exercises 47 and 48. Write an expression and simplify it.**

### A Fair Fare in Alaska

Railroads are a popular means of transportation in Alaska. One scenic train route travels 356 miles from Anchorage to Fairbanks. It includes a stop in Denali Park, where you can see the tallest mountain in the United States, Mount McKinley. A one-way fare for the 12-hour trip is $154 in the summer and $120 in the spring and fall. A one-way fare for the 7.5-hour trip from Anchorage to Denali Park is $102 in the summer, and $84 in the spring and fall. Children's fares are half the fares for adults.

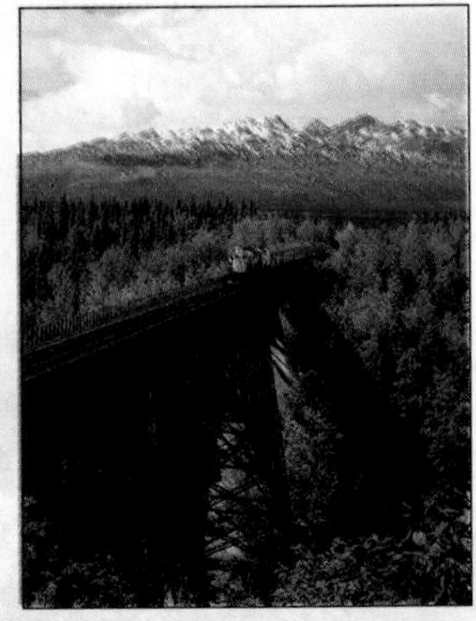

47. ***Mental Math*** A family with two adults and two children plans to travel round trip from Anchorage to Fairbanks. How much will the trip cost in the summer? In the fall? **$924; $720.**

48. a. A group of three adults and two children plan to travel round trip from Anchorage to Denali Park. How much will the trip cost in the fall? **$672**
   b. How much more would the trip cost them in the summer? **$144**

## Mixed Review

**In which quadrant of a coordinate plane does the graph of each ordered pair lie? *(Lesson 1-10)***

49. $(5, 3)$ **I**
50. $(-1, 4)$ **II**
51. $(-6, -3)$ **III**
52. $(8, -1)$ **IV**
53. $(-4, 17)$ **II**
54. $(1, -3)$ **IV**

**Simplify each expression. *(Lesson 1-2)***

55. $3 \cdot 5 + 3 \cdot 15$ **60**
56. $4 \cdot 7 + 4 \cdot 11$ **72**
57. $5 \cdot 22 - 5 \cdot 2$ **100**

58. Lin worked 4 hours per day for 3 days to build a model bridge. How many hours did she spend on the project? ***(Lesson 1-9)*** **12 h**


See also Extra Practice section.

# The Distributive Property

# 2-2

## What You'll Learn

1. To use the Distributive Property with numerical expressions
2. To use the Distributive Property with algebraic expressions

## . . . And Why

To solve real-world multiplication problems using mental math

## Investigate

EXPLORING THE DISTRIBUTIVE PROPERTY

You can find the total area of two rectangles by two methods.

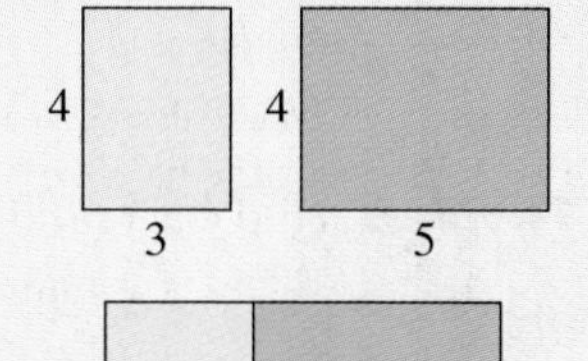


1. Method 1: Find the area of each rectangle. Then find the sum of the areas. 12; 20; 32
2. Method 2: Combine the two into one large rectangle. Find its length. Find its width. Then find its area. 8; 4; 32

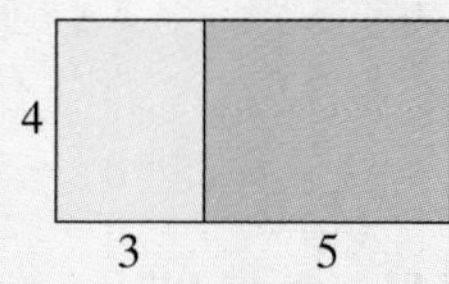


3. On a piece of paper, draw and label the dimensions of three rectangles with the same width and different lengths. Repeat Method 1 and Method 2 with each pair of rectangles. What do you notice about your results?

Check students' work; the results using the two methods are the same.

## PART 1 Numerical Expressions

The Investigate above shows different ways to find the sum of the areas of two rectangles. This shows the *Distributive Property*, which combines multiplication with addition or subtraction.

### Distributive Property

To multiply a sum or difference, multiply each number within the parentheses by the number outside the parentheses.

| Arithmetic | Algebra |
|---|---|
| $3(2 + 6) = 3(2) + 3(6)$ | $a(b + c) = ab + ac$ |
| $(2 + 6)3 = 2(3) + 6(3)$ | $(b + c)a = ba + ca$ |
| $6(7 - 4) = 6(7) - 6(4)$ | $a(b - c) = ab - ac$ |
| $(7 - 4)6 = 7(6) - 4(6)$ | $(b - c)a = ba - ca$ |



# Tools to Monitor Progress

## BEFORE THE LESSON

**To check prerequisite skills:**

- Order of operations with integers

**Skills You Need,** p. 61

## DURING THE LESSON

**To check understanding:**

**Try This** exercises on student page

- **Additional Example 1**

  Use the distributive property to find 15(110) mentally. 1,650

- **Additional Example 2**

  Joaquin bought 5 mangoes for 37¢ each. How much did he spend? $1.85

# 2-2

## Getting Ready

**Key Terms and Symbols**
Distributive Property

**Materials** algebra tiles

**Resources** A complete list of resources for this lesson is on p. 61H.

### Daily Skills Warm-Up

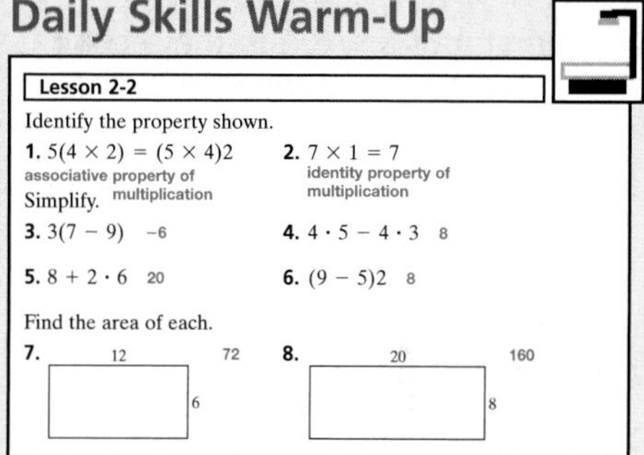
Lesson 2-2

Identify the property shown.

1. $5(4 \times 2) = (5 \times 4)2$ associative property of multiplication
2. $7 \times 1 = 7$ identity property of multiplication

Simplify.

3. $3(7 - 9)$ −6
4. $4 \cdot 5 - 4 \cdot 3$ 8
5. $8 + 2 \cdot 6$ 20
6. $(9 - 5)2$ 8

Find the area of each.

7. 12 by 6 rectangle — 72
8. 20 by 8 rectangle — 160

### Background for the Lesson

The Distributive Property refers to the relationship between two operations. With 6(2 + 3), you can either add first and then multiply by 6 or multiply 6(2) and 6(3) first and then find the sum. The multiplier 6 is distributed to both the 2 and the 3.

## 1 Focus

### Investigate

Ask: Does the expression 4(3 + 5) represent the combined area of the two rectangles? yes Ask: Would this expression work if one of the rectangles had a width other than 4? no How could you then find the total area of the two rectangles? Use Method 1.

### Connecting to Prior Knowledge

Discuss the differences between the Associative and Commutative Properties in the previous lesson and the Distributive Property. Emphasize particularly how many different operations are involved in each property.

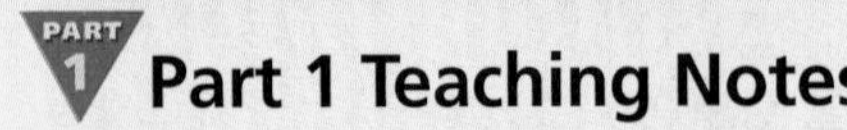

# 2 Teach

## Part 1 Teaching Notes

Have students find the value of both sides of the example equations to verify that they are indeed equal. These concrete results help to reinforce the abstract concept of the Distributive Property.

### Example 1

**Build understanding.** Ask: Why is 102 rewritten as 100 + 2 instead of, for example, 99 + 3? **The numbers 100 and 2 are easy multipliers.**

### Example 2

**Build understanding.** Ask: In the second step, why do you do the multiplication before the subtraction? **order of operations**

### Example 3

**Build understanding.** Ask: Does the Distributive Property work both ways? Can you rewrite the difference as a product? **yes; 8(10)**

**Auditory Learning** Suggest that students take turns reading aloud a question from the Try This to a partner, who then writes the simplified expression using the Distributive Property.

**Connection to Measurement**
A carpenter needs to cut 3 boards that are 13 inches long, and 3 boards that are 17 inches long from a single board. Use the distributive property to find the total length of the uncut board.
**3(13 + 17) or 90 in.**

You can use the Distributive Property to multiply mentally.

### Example 1

**Use the Distributive Property to find 20(102) mentally.**

| | |
|---|---|
| $20(102) = 20(100 + 2)$ | Write 102 as (100 + 2). |
| $20(100 + 2) = 20 \cdot 100 + 20 \cdot 2$ | Use the Distributive Property. |
| $= 2{,}000 + 40$ | Multiply. |
| $= 2{,}040$ | Add. |

**Try This** Find each product mentally.

4. (53)50 **2,650**  5. $30 \cdot 104$ **3,120**  6. $9 \cdot 199$ **1,791**

REAL-WORLD  CONNECTION

### Example 2

**The PTA served 397 people at a pancake breakfast. How many pancakes did the PTA serve?**

| | |
|---|---|
| $(397)4 = (400 - 3)4$ | Write 397 as (400 − 3). |
| $= 400 \cdot 4 - 3 \cdot 4$ | Use the Distributive Property. |
| $= 1{,}600 - 12$ | Multiply. |
| $= 1{,}588$ | Subtract. |

The PTA served 1,588 pancakes.



**Try This**

7. Your club sold calendars for $7. Club members sold 204 calendars. How much money did they raise? **$1,428**

### Example 3

**Simplify 8(15) − 8(5).**

| | |
|---|---|
| $8(15) - 8(5) = 8(15 - 5)$ | Use the Distributive Property. |
| $= 8(10)$ | Subtract within parentheses. |
| $= 80$ | Multiply. |

**Try This** Simplify each expression.

8. 7(21) + 7(9) **210**  9. 12(52) − 12(62) **−120**  10. (16)7 − (11)7 **35**



- **Additional Example 3**
  Simplify 11(23) − 11(7). **176**
- **Additional Example 4**
  Use models to multiply $(4 - 3x)4$.
  **$16 - 12x$**
- **Additional Example 5**
  Multiply each expression.
  a. $-9(2 - 8y)$ **$-18 + 72y$**
  b. $(5m + 6)11$ **$55m + 66$**

## AFTER THE LESSON

**To assess knowledge:**
**Lesson Quiz**
Use the Distributive Property to simplify.

1. 15(203) **3,045**
2. 7(180) **1,260**
3. 6(26) − 6(16) **60**
4. $(8a - 4)9$ **$72a - 36$**
5. $2(14 + y)$ **$28 + 2y$**

- For enrichment and reteaching options see Resources on p. 61H.

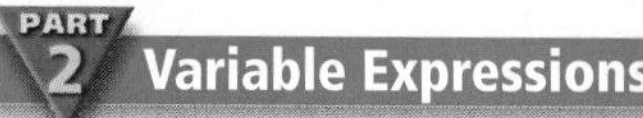

## Variable Expressions

You can use algebra tiles to model the Distributive Property with variable expressions. Use a green rectangular tile to represent a variable.

### Example 4

**Use models to multiply $3(2x + 5)$.**

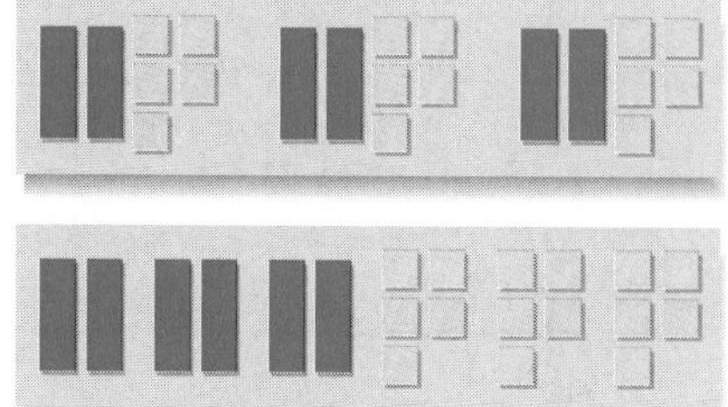

Model three groups of $2x + 5$.

Use the Commutative Property of Addition.

So $3(2x + 5) = 6x + 15$.

**Try This** Use models to multiply.

**11.** $4(2x - 3)$ $8x - 12$ **12.** $3(x + 4)$ $3x + 12$ **13.** $(3x + 1)2$ $6x + 2$

In Example 4, notice that 3 multiplies both $2x$ and 5. That is, $3(2x + 5) = 3(2x) + 3(5)$.

### Example 5

**Multiply.**

**a.** $-5(4x - 3)$

$-5(4x - 3) = -5(4x) - (-5)(3)$ Use the Distributive Property.

$= -20x - (-15)$ Multiply.

$= -20x + 15$ Simplify.

**b.** $(2x + 5)7$

$(2x + 5)7 = (2x)7 + (5)7$ Use the Distributive Property.

$= 14x + 35$ Multiply.

**Try This** Multiply.

**14.** $2(7 + 3d)$ $14 + 6d$ **15.** $(6m + 1)(3)$ $18m + 3$ **16.** $-3(5t - 2)$ $-15t + 6$

**Quick Review**

(light tile) represents 1.
(dark tile) represents $-1$.

**Reading Math**

When a teacher distributes paper to the students in a class, each student gets some. Similarly, when a number is distributed over a sum or difference, each value within the parentheses is multiplied by the number.



## Part 2 Teaching Notes

Have students model $2(x + 1)$ with algebra tiles. Show that the result is two $x$ tiles and two unit tiles because the 2 is distributed as a multiplier to both $x$ and 1.

### Example 4

**Build understanding.** Ask: Why must there be three groups of $2x + 5$? The expression $2x + 5$ is multiplied by 3.

### Example 5

**Build understanding.** Ask: In part a. why does $-(-15)$ become $+15$? Subtracting is the same as adding the opposite, and 15 is the opposite of $-15$.

**Extension** Challenge students to multiply 3(10,523) mentally. 31,569

**Error Prevention** Remind students to apply the rules for combining integers when they use the Distributive Property to multiply a numeric or algebraic expression by a negative number.

# 3 Practice/Assess

## Assignment Guide

To provide flexible scheduling, this lesson can be divided into parts.

**▼ Part 1**
**Core** 1, 5–8, 9–18, 21–26, 44–46, 49
**✪ Extension** 19–20

**▼ Part 2**
**Core** 2–4, 27–36, 38–40, 47–48, 50
**✪ Extension** 37, 41–43

Mixed Review can be assigned at any time for maintenance.

## Exercises

**Exercises 27–28** Help students recall that a green rectangular tile represents a variable.

**Exercises 41–43** Students need to recall the Commutative and Associative Properties that they learned in Lesson 2-1.

## ✪ Challenge

Multiply $3x(15 - 7)$. $45x - 21x$ or $24x$

## Closure

Use the Distributive Property to multiply a number outside the parentheses by each term of a sum or difference.

## Daily Cumulative Review

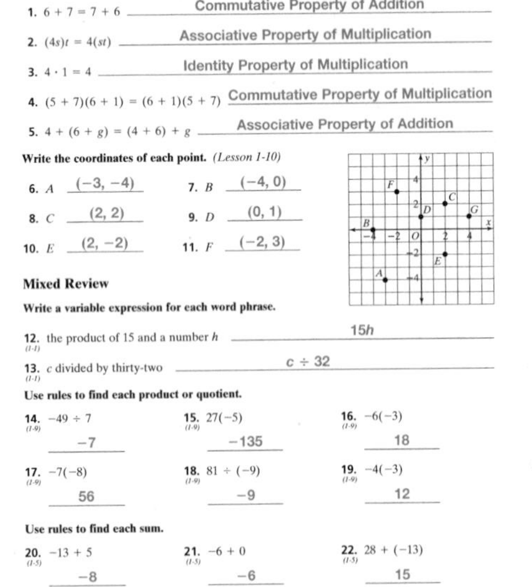

**Name each property.** *(Lesson 2-1)*

1. $6 + 7 = 7 + 6$ Commutative Property of Addition
2. $(4s)t = 4(st)$ Associative Property of Multiplication
3. $4 \cdot 1 = 4$ Identity Property of Multiplication
4. $(5 + 7)(6 + 1) = (6 + 1)(5 + 7)$ Commutative Property of Multiplication
5. $4 + (6 + g) = (4 + 6) + g$ Associative Property of Addition

**Write the coordinates of each point.** *(Lesson 1-10)*

6. $A$ $(-3, -4)$ 7. $B$ $(-4, 0)$
8. $C$ $(2, 2)$ 9. $D$ $(0, 1)$
10. $E$ $(2, -2)$ 11. $F$ $(-2, 3)$



**Mixed Review**

**Write a variable expression for each word phrase.**

12. *(1-1)* the product of 15 and a number $h$ $15h$
13. *(1-1)* $c$ divided by thirty-two $c \div 32$

**Use rules to find each product or quotient.**

14. *(1-9)* $-49 \div 7$ $-7$
15. *(1-9)* $27(-5)$ $-135$
16. *(1-9)* $-6(-3)$ $18$
17. *(1-9)* $-7(-8)$ $56$
18. *(1-9)* $81 \div (-9)$ $-9$
19. *(1-9)* $-4(-3)$ $12$

**Use rules to find each sum.**

20. *(1-5)* $-13 + 5$ $-8$
21. *(1-5)* $-6 + 0$ $-6$
22. *(1-5)* $28 + (-13)$ $15$



# Exercises

## Check Understanding

**Copy and complete each statement.**

1. $12(3 + 5) = \blacksquare \cdot 3 + \blacksquare \cdot 5$ 12; 12
2. $(y - 6)z = y \cdot \blacksquare - 6 \cdot \blacksquare$ z; z
3. $a(3 - b) = \blacksquare 3 - \blacksquare b$ a; a
4. $6 \cdot b + 12 \cdot b = (6 + 12)\blacksquare$ b

*Mental Math* **Use the Distributive Property to simplify.**

5. $6(23)$ 138
6. $7(48)$ 336
7. $5(18)$ 90
8. $13(101)$ 1,313

## Practice and Problem Solving

*Mental Math* **Use the Distributive Property to simplify.**

9. $6(52)$ 312
10. $(104)(9)$ 936
11. $8(98)$ 784
12. $(6)(83)$ 498
13. $(208)4$ 832
14. $5(1{,}005)$ 5,025
15. $7(3) + 7(5)$ 56
16. $2(9) - 3(9)$ −9
17. $6(4) + 6(8)$ 72
18. $9(3) - (2)(3)$ 21
✪ 19. $(-4)(7) + (-4)(-9)$ 8
✪ 20. $3(9) - 3(5) + 3(6)$ 30
21. $12 \cdot 27 - 12 \cdot 24$ 36
22. $3 \cdot 5 + 27 \cdot 5$ 150
23. $(8) \cdot 11 + (-13) \cdot 11$ −55
24. $13 \cdot (-3) - 7 \cdot (-3)$ −18
25. $-32 \cdot 6 + 29 \cdot 6$ −18
26. $4 \cdot 19 - 4 \cdot (11)$ 32

**Write an expression using parentheses for each model. Then multiply.**

27. 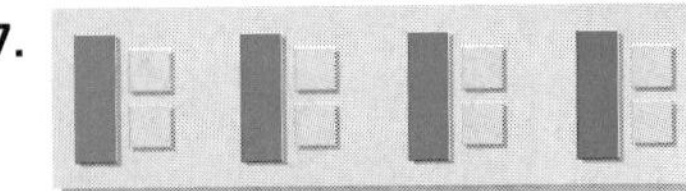
$4(x + 2)$; $4x + 8$

28. 
$3(3x - 1)$; $9x - 3$

**Use models to multiply.**

29. $7(t - 5)$ $7t - 35$
30. $(v - 3)4$ $4v - 12$
31. $2(7z + 3)$ $14z + 6$
32. $(2 + 3d)5$ $10 + 15d$

**Use the Distributive Property to multiply.**

33. $4(b + 5)$ $4b + 20$
34. $9(2h - 1)$ $18h - 9$
35. $-3(2t + 6)$ $-6t - 18$
36. $-7(-3n + 2)$ $21n - 14$
✪ 37. $-8(6 - c)$ $-48 + 8c$
38. $3(5 - 3w)$ $15 - 9w$
39. $(4 - t)(-7)$ $-28 + 7t$
40. $-5(-m + 6)$ $5m - 30$

**Name each property shown.**

✪ 41. $m[t + (-t)] = mt + m(-t)$ Dist. Prop.
✪ 42. $m[t + (-t)] = m(-t + t)$ Comm. Prop. of Add.
✪ 43. $m[t + (-t)] = [t + (-t)]m$ Comm. Prop. of Mult.



## Alternative Assessment

Ask students to write a quiz that has several multiplication expressions using the Distributive Property. Have them record the answers on a separate piece of paper. Then have students exchange their quizzes.

**Solve using mental math.**

44. A theater sold out its evening performances four nights in a row. The theater has 294 seats. How many people attended the theater in the four nights? 1,176 people

45. *Geography* If you drove from Atlanta, Georgia, to Los Angeles, California, and back, how many miles would you travel? 3,888 mi

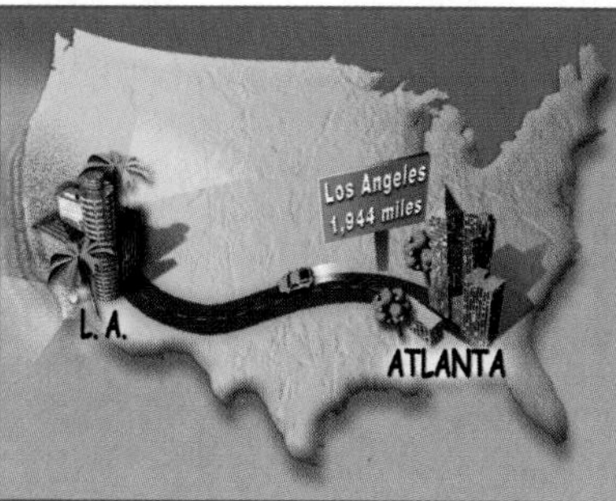

46. You rent three videos for $2.95 each. How much do you pay in all? $8.85

47. *Writing* Explain how to use the Distributive Property to multiply $6(3r + 4s)$. Answers may vary. Sample: Multiply $3r$ and $4s$ by 6, and then write the sum: $18r + 24s$.

48. *Error Analysis* Suppose your friend wrote $7(2m + t) = 14m + t$. What error did your friend make? My friend didn't distribute the 7 to the $t$.

49. *Open-ended* Use three integers to write an expression that you can simplify using the Distributive Property. Then simplify your expression. Answers may vary. Sample: $18(100 + 4) = 1{,}800 + 72$, or 1,872

50. *Mathematical Reasoning* Explain why $c(a + b) = (a + b)c$. Use the Comm. Prop. of Mult.

## Mixed Review

**Name the property shown.** ***(Lesson 2-1)***

51. $3(6 \cdot 2) = 3(2 \cdot 6)$ Comm. Prop. of Mult.
52. $8 = 8 + 0$ Ident. Prop. of Add.
53. $4(8 \cdot 3) = (4 \cdot 8)3$ Assoc. Prop. of Mult.
54. $1 \cdot 3 = 3$ Ident. Prop. of Mult.

**Evaluate each expression.** ***(Lesson 1-3)***

55. $7 - m$, for $m = 6$ 1
56. $6t + 1$, for $t = -2$ −11
57. $c \div 3 - 5$, for $c = 6$ −3

58. You have $120 in your checking account. In one month, you deposit $30, write a check for $21, withdraw $20, and deposit $45. Find your balance at the end of the month. ***(Lessons 1-5 and 1-6)*** $154

## Chapter Project 2 — Activity 1 Creating

Use a ruler and a pencil to make a simple balance scale like the one pictured. Find the balance point near the center of the ruler. Label it *Zero*. Label points four inches in each direction from the balance point *Mass 1* and *Mass 2*. Practice using your balance scale by placing one penny at Mass 1 and another at Mass 2.

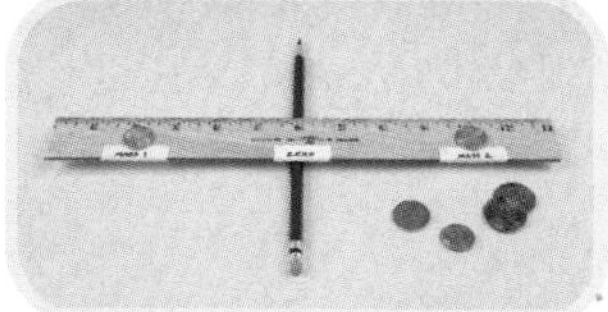

See also Extra Practice section.



## Project Activity 1

**Creating** Some students may not be aware of the difference between weight, commonly used in the conventional system of measurement, and mass, used in the metric system. Weight is gravitational force, so a person's mass is the same on Earth and the Moon, but the weight would be less on the Moon, which has less gravitational force than Earth.

## Practice

**Write an expression using parentheses for each model. Then multiply.**

1. $3(4x + 2) = 12x + 6$
2. $2(5x + 3) = 10x + 6$

**Multiply each expression.**

3. $6(h - 4)$ $6h - 24$
4. $(p + 3)5$ $5p + 15$
5. $-3(x + 8)$ $-3x - 24$
6. $(4 - y)(-9)$ $-36 + 9y$
7. $2(7n - 11)$ $14n - 22$
8. $-10(-a + 5)$ $10a - 50$

**Use the distributive property to simplify.**

9. $98 \cdot 7$ $(100 - 2)7 = 700 - 14 = 686$
10. $9 \cdot 28$ $9(30 - 2) = 270 - 18 = 252$
11. $78 \cdot 8$ $(80 - 2)8 = 640 - 16 = 624$
12. $7(2{,}009)$ $7(2{,}000 + 9) = 14{,}000 + 63 = 14{,}063$
13. $899 \cdot 5$ $(900 - 1)5 = 4{,}500 - 5 = 4{,}495$
14. $30 \cdot 105$ $30(100 + 5) = 3{,}000 + 150 = 3{,}150$
15. $8 \cdot 5 - 12 \cdot 5$ $(8 - 12)5 = -20$
16. $7 \cdot 10 + 7(-3)$ $7[10 + (-3)] = 49$
17. $-4(3) + (-4)(6)$ $-4(3 + 6) = -36$
18. $6(8) + 6(-2)$ $6[8 + (-2)] = 36$

**Solve using mental math.**

19. A shipping container holds 144 boxes. How many boxes can be shipped in 4 containers? 576 boxes



## Reteaching

According to the *distributive property*, you distribute or "pass out" a multiplication to each part of a sum or difference in parentheses. In $2(a + b) = 2a + 2b$, we "pass out" the 2 by multiplying it by both the $a$ and the $b$.

Multiply $6(x - 9)$ and $(4 - h)(-3)$.

$$6(x - 9) = 6x - 6(9) = 6x - 54$$

$$(4 - h)(-3) = 4(-3) - h(-3) = -12 - (-3h) = -12 + 3h = 3h - 12$$

**Complete with the appropriate number or variable.**

1. $12(5 + 9) = 12 \cdot 5 +$ 12 $\cdot 9$
2. $(3 - 8)7 =$ 3 $\cdot 7 - 8 \cdot$ 7
3. $z(a - b - c) =$ z $\cdot a - z \cdot$ b − z · c
4. $[14 + (-3)]7 = 14 \cdot$ 7 + (−3) $\cdot 7$
5. $p[(-3) + n] = p \cdot$ (−3) + p · n

**Multiply each expression.**

6. $4(x + 5) =$ $4x + 20$
7. $(6 - m)(-4) =$ $4m - 24$
8. $s(-6 + t) =$ $st - 6s$
9. $8(j - 2k + l) =$ $8j - 16k + 8l$
10. $(z - 4)(-5) =$ $20 - 5z$
11. $9[(-7) - y] =$ $-63 - 9y$



## Enrichment

A *term* is part of an expression. Terms are separated by addition and subtraction symbols. A *binomial* is an expression with two terms.

| Binomials | Not binomials |
| --- | --- |
| $2 + 7$ | $12n$ (only one term) |
| $3x + 4y$ | $6 + 5k - 3py$ (three terms) |
| $-7k - 9$ | $-(2g)$ (terms not separated by + or −) |

You can multiply binomials using the distributive property.

**Complete the following to find the product $(a + b)(c + d)$.**
*Hint:* Think of $a + b$ as a single quantity. Distribute $a + b$ to both $c$ and $d$.

1. $(a + b)(c + d) = (a + b)($ c $) + (a + b)($ d $)$
$= ac +$ bc $+ ad +$ bd

To multiply two binomials, multiply each of the terms in the first binomial by each of the terms in the second binomial.

**Example** Find the product: $(3 + k)(m - 4)$

**Solution** $(3 + k)(m - 4) = (3 + k)m - (3 + k)(4)$
$= 3 \cdot m + k \cdot m - 3 \cdot 4 - k \cdot 4$
$= 3m + km - 12 - 4k$

**Find the product.**

2. $(h + w)(c + d)$ $hc + wc + hd + wd$
3. $(5 + p)(9 + t)$ $45 + 9p + 5t + pt$
4. $(x + y)(7 - m)$ $7x + 7y - mx - my$
5. $(n - 5)(y - 6)$ $ny - 5y - 6n + 30$

You can use binomials to find the product of two numbers.

$$12 \times 8 = (10 + 2)(10 - 2) = 10 \cdot 10 + 2 \cdot 10 - 10 \cdot 2 - 2 \cdot 2 = 100 + 20 - 20 - 4 = 96$$

**Find the product by multiplying two binomials.**

6. $23 \times 17 = (20 + 3)(20 - 3) =$ $400 + 60 - 60 - 9 = 391$
7. $55 \times 45 = (50 + 5)(50 - 5) =$ $2{,}500 + 250 - 250 - 25 = 2{,}475$

# 2-3

## Getting Ready

**Key Terms and Symbols**
simplify, deductive reasoning
term, constant, like terms, coefficient

**Materials** algebra tiles

**Resources** A complete list of resources for this lesson is on p. 61H.

### Daily Skills Warm-Up

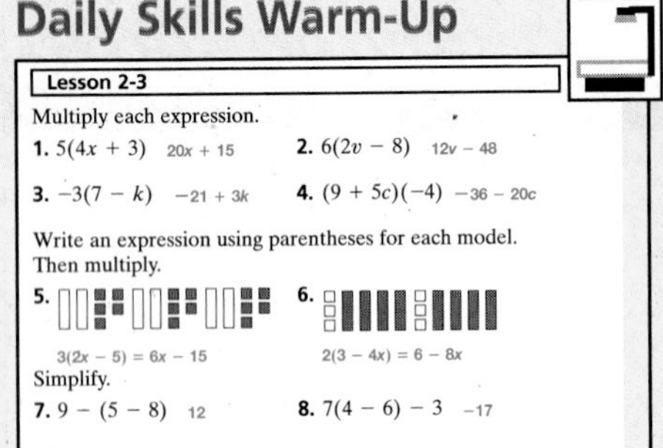

Lesson 2-3

Multiply each expression.

1. $5(4x + 3)$ $20x + 15$
2. $6(2v - 8)$ $12v - 48$
3. $-3(7 - k)$ $-21 + 3k$
4. $(9 + 5c)(-4)$ $-36 - 20c$

Write an expression using parentheses for each model. Then multiply.

5. $3(2x - 5) = 6x - 15$
6. $2(3 - 4x) = 6 - 8x$

Simplify.

7. $9 - (5 - 8)$ $12$
8. $7(4 - 6) - 3$ $-17$

### Background for the Lesson

Plus and minus signs separate an expression into *terms*. This means that $2 + x + 8$ has three terms. In contrast, $xyz$ consists of just one term. *Like terms* can be combined because the variables in like terms are the same, although the numeric coefficients may be different. The terms $3a$ and $-7a$ are like terms, even though the coefficients 3 and -7 are different.

## 1 Focus

### Connecting to Students' Lives

Discuss examples of grouping similar items together, such as on supermarket shelves or in dresser drawers.

### Connecting to Prior Knowledge

In Lesson 2-2, students learned to use the Distributive Property to simplify numeric expressions. In this lesson they apply properties to simplify a variable expression. In Lesson 2-4, students use what they have learned about variable expressions to write and solve equations.



# 2-3 Simplifying Variable Expressions

**What You'll Learn**

1. To identify parts of a variable expression
2. To simplify expressions

**. . . And Why**

To extend addition and subtraction skills to include variables

## PART 1 Identifying Parts of a Variable Expression

The diagram shows the possible parts of a variable expression.

A **term** is a number or the product of a number and variable(s).

$7a + 4a + 3b - 6$ ← A **constant** is a term that has no variable.

**Like terms** have identical variables.

A **coefficient** is a number that multiplies a variable.

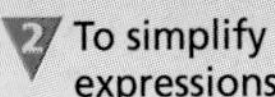

When you have a variable expression that includes subtraction, you can rewrite the expression using only addition. This will help you find the coefficient(s) and constant(s).

$5x - 3y + z - 2$

$= 5x + (-3y) + z + (-2)$ Rewrite subtraction as adding opposites.

$= 5x + (-3y) + 1z + (-2)$ Identity Property of Multiplication

Rewriting the expression using addition shows that the coefficients are 5, −3, and 1. The constant is −2. Notice that the sign between terms in the original expression determines whether a coefficient or constant is positive or negative.

**EXAMPLE 1**

**Name the coefficients, the like terms, and the constants in $3m - 2n + n - 4$.**

Coefficients: 3, −2, and 1  Like terms: $-2n$ and $n$  Constant: −4

**TRY THIS** Name the coefficients, any like terms, and constants.

1. $6 + 2s + 4s$ 2, 4; $2s$, $4s$; 6
2. $-4x$ −4; none; none
3. $9m + 2r - 2m + r$ 9, 2, −2, 1; $9m$ and $-2m$, $2r$ and $r$; none

## PART 2 Simplifying Variable Expressions

You **simplify** a variable expression by replacing it with an equivalent expression that has as few terms as possible.



# Tools to Monitor Progress

**BEFORE THE LESSON**

**To check prerequisite skills:**

- Combining integers

**Skills Intervention Kit,** Pre-Algebra Basics

**DURING THE LESSON**

**To check understanding:**

**Try This** exercises on student page

- **Additional Example 1**
  Name the coefficients, the like terms, and the constants in $7x + y - 2x - 7$. 7, 1, −2; $7x$, $-2x$; −7
- **Additional Example 2**
  Simplify $9 + 4f + 3 + 2f$. $6f + 12$

## Example 2

**Simplify $2x + 4 + 3x$.**

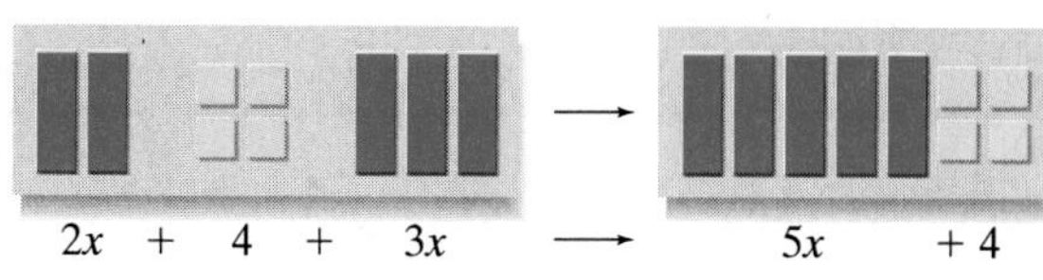


**Try This**

4. Use tiles to simplify $3a + 2 + 4a - 1$. $7a + 1$

You can also use the Distributive Property to combine like terms.

## Example 3

**Simplify $5y + y$.**

$5y + y = 5y + 1y$ Use the Identity Property of Multiplication.
$= (5 + 1)y$ Use the Distributive Property.
$= 6y$ Simplify.

**Try This** Simplify each expression.

5. $8a + 5a$ $13a$
6. $3b - b$ $2b$
7. $-4m - 9m$ $-13m$

**Deductive reasoning** is the process of reasoning logically from given facts to a conclusion. As you use properties, rules, and definitions to justify the steps in a problem, you are using deductive reasoning.

## Example 4

**Simplify $4g + 3(3 + g)$.**

$4g + 3(3 + g) = 4g + 9 + 3g$ Use the Distributive Property.
$= 4g + 3g + 9$ Use the Commutative Property of Addition.
$= (4 + 3)g + 9$ Use the Distributive Property to combine like terms.
$= 7g + 9$ Simplify.

**Try This** Simplify each expression. Justify each step.

8. $6y + 4m - 7y + m$ $-y + 5m$
9. $4x + 3 - 2(5 + x)$ $2x - 7$



- **Additional Example 3**
  Simplify $2b + b - 4$. $3b - 4$
- **Additional Example 4**
  Simplify $(7 - 3x)5 + 20x$. $5x + 35$

### AFTER THE LESSON

**To assess knowledge:**
**Lesson Quiz**

Name coefficients, like terms, and constants.

1. $4f - 2f + 3$ 4, −2; $4f$, $-2f$; 3
2. $z + 2y - 14$ 1, 2; none; −14

Simplify each expression.

3. $3(a + c - 1) - 2c$ $3a + c - 3$
4. $4(4v) - 4(v - 9)$ $12v + 36$

- For enrichment and reteaching options see Resources on p. 61H.

# 2 Teach

## Part 1 Teaching Notes

Students often find the vocabulary of mathematics intimidating. Help students devise creative ways to remember the definitions of these new terms. For example, the phrase *constants don't vary* may help students remember that constants do not have variables.

### Example 1

**Building understanding.** Ask: How do you know that $n$ has a coefficient of 1? Identity Property of Multiplication

## Part 2 Teaching Notes

You may wish to have students write expressions on a sheet of paper and cut out the separate terms with scissors. They can then rearrange the pieces to group like terms and constants.

### Example 2

**Building understanding.** Ask: How is the number of variable tiles related to the coefficients in this expression? The number of tiles equals the sum of the coefficients.

### Example 3

**Building understanding.** Ask: What is the same about the terms $5y$ and $y$? the variable What is different about these two terms? the coefficients

### Example 4

**Building understanding.** Ask: Which terms get multiplied by 3? those inside the parentheses: 3 and $g$

**Extension** Explain how it is possible to apply the Commutative or Associative Property of Addition to an expression in which the operation is subtraction. Change the subtraction operation to adding the opposite.

**Error Prevention** For variables that have an understood or unwritten coefficient of 1, suggest that students write a 1 in front of these variables to help them remember the coefficient.

# 3 Practice/Assess

## Assignment Guide

To provide flexible scheduling, this lesson can be divided into parts.

**▼ Part 1**

**Core** 1–4, 11–16, 39
**✪ Extension** 38

**▼ Part 2**

**Core** 5–10, 17–30, 36, 37, 40, 41
**✪ Extension** 31–35

Mixed Review can be assigned at any time for maintenance.

## Exercises

**Exercises 11–16** Remind students that the sign between the terms determines whether a coefficient or constant is positive or negative.

**Test Prep Exercise 39** Notice that the correct answer must have only two like terms, but may have more than two terms in the expression.

## ✪ Challenge

Simplify $x(y + 8y + 3)$.
$= xy + 8xy + 3x$
$= 9xy + 3x$

## Closure

To simplify a variable expression, replace it with an equivalent expression with as few terms as possible.

### Daily Cumulative Review

**Use the Distributive Property to simplify.** *(Lesson 2-2)*

1. $(5)(62)$ 310
2. $(307)4$ 1,228
3. $3(7) + 3(5)$ 36
4. $8(5) - 8(2)$ 24
5. $9(2) - (-3)(2)$ 24
6. $(-4)(5) + (-4)(-2)$ −12

**Name each property.** *(Lesson 2-1)*

7. $y \cdot 1 = y$ Identity Property of Multiplication
8. $mn = nm$ Commutative Property of Multiplication
9. $894 + 0 = 894$ Identity Property of Addition
10. $(5 + 7) + 3 = 5 + (7 + 3)$ Associative Property of Addition
11. $8 + p = p + 8$ Commutative Property of Addition

**Mixed Review**

**Tell whether each expression is a numerical expression or a variable expression. For a variable expression, name the variable.**

12. $58 - t + 21$ (1-1) variable expression; $t$
13. $144 \div 12$ (1-1) numerical expression
14. $19 \cdot x$ (1-1) variable expression; $x$

**Evaluate.**

15. $4a + 6$, for $a = 3$ (1-3) 18
16. $t + 15$, for $t = 4$ (1-3) 19
17. $w \div 3$, for $w = 24$ (1-3) 8

**Is the statement correct or incorrect? If incorrect, give a counterexample.**

18. The product of three negative numbers is always a positive number. (1-7) incorrect; $-1(-2)(-3) = -6$



# Exercises

## Check Understanding

**Name the coefficients, any like terms, and any constants.**

1. $3x + 5y - 3$ 3; 5; none; −3
2. $2x - 7$ 2; none; −7
3. $4x - 7x + 3x$ 4, −7, 3; $4x$, $-7x$, $3x$; none
4. $6xy - 5xy$ 6, −5; $6xy$, $-5xy$; none

**Copy and complete each equation.**

5. $6a + 4a + 7 = (6■ + 4■) + 7$ *a, a*
$= (6 + 4)■ + 7$ *a*
$= 10■ + 7$ *a*

6. $8m - 3 - 9m = 8m - 9■ - 3$ *m*
$= (8 - 9)■ - 3$ *m*
$= -1■ - 3$ *m*

**Simplify each expression.**

7. $2r - 5 + 6r$ $8r - 5$
8. $12a + a$ $13a$
9. $2x + 5x + 3$ $7x + 3$
10. $4 + 2m - m$ $4 + m$

## Practice and Problem Solving

**Name the coefficients, any like terms, and any constants.**

11. $5a + 8a$ 5, 8; $5a$, $8a$; none
12. $6a - 2b + b$ 6, −2, 1; $-2b$, $b$; none
13. $-3x - 8$ −3; none; −8
14. $6ab + 8 + ab$ 6, 1; $6ab$, $ab$; 8
15. $12 - 4x + 7w - 9x - w$ −4, 7, −9, −1; $-4x$ and $-9x$, $7w$ and $-w$; 12
16. $a + 2a + 3a - 4a$ 1, 2, 3, −4; $a$, $2a$, $3a$, $-4a$; none

**Write an expression for each model. Simplify the expression.**

17.
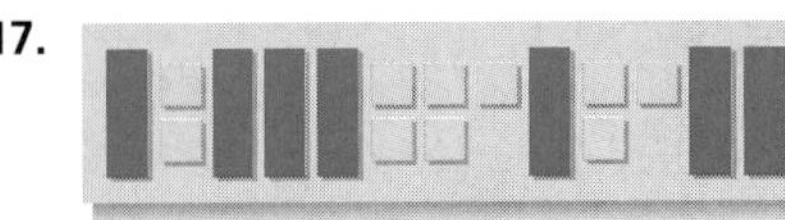
$x + 2 + 3x + 5 + x + 3 + 2x$; $7x + 10$

18. $2x + 1 + x - 4 + 4x + 1$; $7x - 2$

**Simplify each expression.**

19. $4a - 3 + 5a$ $9a - 3$
20. $t - 3t + 2t + 4$ 4
21. $5 + y - 3y$ $-2y + 5$
22. $4 + 3a + 2$ $3a + 6$
23. $4m + 3 - 5m + m$ 3
24. $r + 3 - 6r + r$ $-4r + 3$
25. $8z + 8y + 3z$ $11z + 8y$
26. $-4(a + 3) - a$ $-5a - 12$
27. $3(g + 5) + 2g$ $5g + 15$
28. $4(w + 2x) + 9(-4w)$ $-32w + 8x$
29. $(2t + 4)3 + 6(-5t) - (-8)$ $-24t + 20$
30. $-12(5x) + 3(-7x) - x$ $-82x$

***Mathematical Reasoning*** **Justify each step.**

✪31. $3x + 2 + 5x - 3 = 3x + 5x + 2 - 3$ Comm. Prop. of Add.
$= (3 + 5)x + 2 - 3$ Dist. Prop.
$= 8x + 2 - 3$ Add within parentheses.
$= 8x - 1$ Simplify.

✪32. $6(2x + y) + 2y = 12x + 6y + 2y$ Dist. Prop.
$= 12x + (6 + 2)y$ Dist. Prop.
$= 12x + 8y$ Add within parentheses.



## Alternative Assessment

Give students the following list:
coefficients: −4, 6, 1
like terms: $6w$, $w$
constants: 2, −3
Have them use this information to construct a variable expression and simplify it.
sample answer:
$6w + 2 + w - 3 - 4x = 7w - 4x - 1$

**Simplify each expression. Justify each step.**

★33. $3a + 2a + a$ 6a ★34. $w + 3w + 4$ 4w + 4 ★35. $18 + 6(9k - 13)$ 54k − 60

**Write an expression for each situation. Simplify if possible.**

36. Juan bought supplies for his new gecko. He bought four plants for $p$ dollars each. He also bought a 10-gallon tank for $10 and a water dish for $3. $4p + 10 + 3$; $4p + 13$

37. Jaleesa bought three folders for $b$ cents each and two report covers for $c$ cents each. She also bought a binder for $1.89. $3b + 2c + 189$

★38. *Writing* The expression $10bc$ has two variables. Explain why $10bc$ is not two terms. Answers may vary. Sample: Terms are separated by plus or minus signs.

39. **TEST PREP** Which expression has exactly two like terms? A
A. $3t + 1 - t$ B. $7 + 2m$ C. $8q + 3p$ D. $6r + r - 9r$

40. *Error Analysis* Your friend simplified $x + y + xy$ to $2xy$. What error did your friend make? Answers may vary. Sample: My friend added $x + y$ to get $xy$.

41. *Open-ended* Use the variables $r$ and $s$ to write a variable expression. Evaluate your expression for $r = 2$ and $s = -5$. Answers may vary. Sample: $3r - 4s + 1$; 27

## Mixed Review

*Mental Math* **Use the Distributive Property to find each product.** *(Lesson 2-2)*

42. $8(102)$ 816 43. $54 \cdot 6$ 324 44. $19(30)$ 570 45. $(41)(9)$ 369

46. *Choose a Strategy* A pair of rock climbers start up a 1,000-ft cliff. After one hour, they have gone up 160 ft. After two hours, they have gone up 320 ft. If they continue at this pace, how far will they have gone after five hours? 800 ft

## Checkpoint 1 — Lessons 2-1 through 2-3

**Name each property shown.**

1. $3 \cdot (-6) = -6 \cdot 3$ Comm. Prop. of Mult.
2. $(3a)b = 3(ab)$ Assoc. Prop. of Mult.
3. $17 \cdot 1 = 17$ Ident. Prop. of Mult.
4. $6 + 0 = 0 + 6$ Comm. Prop. of Add.
5. $(3 + 2)(4 - 7) = (4 - 7)(3 + 2)$ Comm. Prop. of Mult.
6. $4(3 - 12) = 4 \cdot 3 - 4 \cdot 12$ Dist. Prop.

**Simplify each expression.**

7. $3(a + 2a)$ 9a 8. $9y - 3y + 12y$ 18y 9. $7(2w) + 2(w - 3)$ 16w − 6

10. **TEST PREP** Which expression simplifies to $3xy + z$? B
A. $3x + z + 3y$ B. $2xy + z + xy$ C. $3xyz$ D. $3(x + y) + z$

See also Extra Practice section.



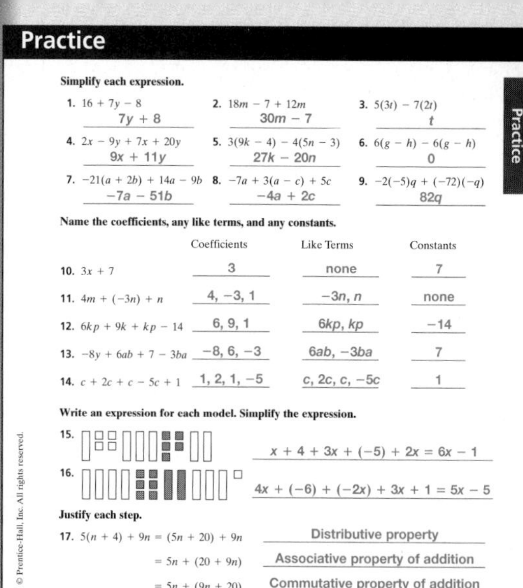

## Practice

**Simplify each expression.**

1. $16 + 7y - 8$ 7y + 8
2. $18m - 7 + 12m$ 30m − 7
3. $5(3t) - 7(2t)$ t
4. $2x - 9y + 7x + 20y$ 9x + 11y
5. $3(9k - 4) - 4(5n - 3)$ 27k − 20n
6. $6(g - h) - 6(g - h)$ 0
7. $-21(a + 2b) + 14a - 9b$ −7a − 51b
8. $-7a + 3(a - c) + 5c$ −4a + 2c
9. $-2(-5)q + (-72)(-q)$ 82q

**Name the coefficients, any like terms, and any constants.**

| | Coefficients | Like Terms | Constants |
|---|---|---|---|
| 10. $3x + 7$ | 3 | none | 7 |
| 11. $4m + (-3n) + n$ | 4, −3, 1 | −3n, n | none |
| 12. $6kp + 9k + kp - 14$ | 6, 9, 1 | 6kp, kp | −14 |
| 13. $-8y + 6ab + 7 - 3ba$ | −8, 6, −3 | 6ab, −3ba | 7 |
| 14. $c + 2c + c - 5c + 1$ | 1, 2, 1, −5 | c, 2c, c, −5c | 1 |

**Write an expression for each model. Simplify the expression.**

15. $x + 4 + 3x + (-5) + 2x = 6x - 1$

16. $4x + (-6) + (-2x) + 3x + 1 = 5x - 5$

**Justify each step.**

17. $5(n + 4) + 9n = (5n + 20) + 9n$ Distributive property
$= 5n + (20 + 9n)$ Associative property of addition
$= 5n + (9n + 20)$ Commutative property of addition
$= (5n + 9n) + 20$ Associative property of addition
$= (5 + 9)n + 20$ Distributive property
$= 14n + 20$ Addition



## Reteaching

Simplify $5n + (-n - 4)(-2)$.

$5n + (-n - 4)(-2)$
$= 5n + (-n)(-2) - 4(-2)$ Use the distributive property.
$= 5n + 2n + 8$ Multiply. Think of $-4(-2)$ as $+(-4)(-2)$.
$= (5 + 2)n + 8$ Use distributive property to combine like terms.
$= 7n + 8$ Add.

**Complete each equation.**

1. $9a - 7a + 5$
$= (9 - 7)$ a $+ 5$
$=$ 2 $a + 5$

2. $5k - 4 - 8k$
$= 5k - 8$ k $- 4$
$= (5 - 8)$ k $- 4$
$=$ −3k $- 4$

**Simplify each expression.**

3. $12a + 4 - 10a$ 2a + 4
4. $7 + x - 7x$ 7 − 6x
5. $2(n - 4) + 3$ 2n − 5
6. $-3(a + 5) + 9$ −3a − 6
7. $5(2y + 1) - 7y$ 3y + 5
8. $2(4 - 3t) - (-3) + 2t$ 11 − 4t
9. $8c + 5(c - 3)$ 13c − 15
10. $-2(-4 - 3s)$ 6s + 8
11. $q(-3) + 3(2 + q)$ 6
12. $(3 + k)(-4) - 5k$ −9k − 12
13. $(-3)(1 - 2n) + 2(n + 4)$ 8n + 5
14. $9p - 3(5p + 2) + 6$ −6p



## Enrichment

In 1976, Captain Elden Joersz set the world aircraft speed record. On July 28, 1976, Captain Joersz flew an SR-71 Blackbird at Beale Air Force Base in California. How fast did Captain Joersz fly?

To find out, simplify each expression. Find the answer in the digital read-out and shade the region containing the answer.

1. $9x + (-5x)$ 4x
2. $-7y + 12y$ 5y
3. $-17p + 12p - 11p$ −16p
4. $3(2a + 5a)$ 21a
5. $4(3f) - 8f$ 4f
6. $n(8 + 6 - 19)$ −5n
7. $-2(4x) + 7x$ −x
8. $7(3f - 2g) + 14(g - f)$ 7f
9. $-15y + 11y - 9y$ −13y
10. $-3[12p + (-7p)]$ −15p
11. $-2n(5 - 7) + 3(3n)$ 13n
12. $6(b - a) + 2(4a - 3b)$ 2a
13. $-9(4f - 6f) + (-15f)$ 3f
14. $8(5 - n) - 19 + 17n - 21$ 9n
15. $8(3x - 2y) + 4[(-3x) + 4y]$ 12x
16. $-5p + 3p - 2p - 9p + 7p - 3p$ −9p
17. $-9(7y - 8y) + 12(6y - 7y)$ −3y
18. $8(5a - 4n + 3p) - 4(6p - 8n + 11a)$ −4a

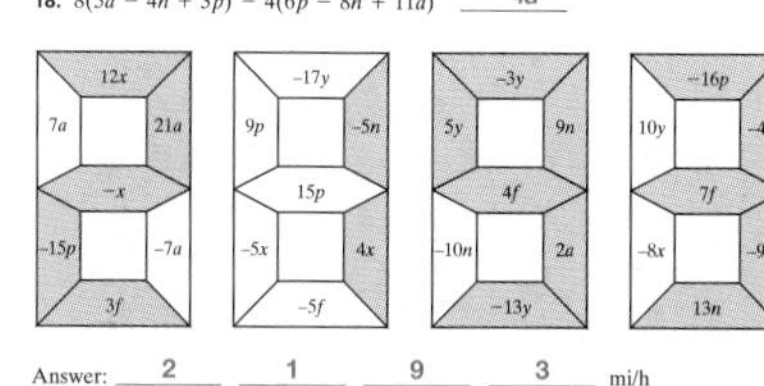


Answer: 2 1 9 3 mi/h



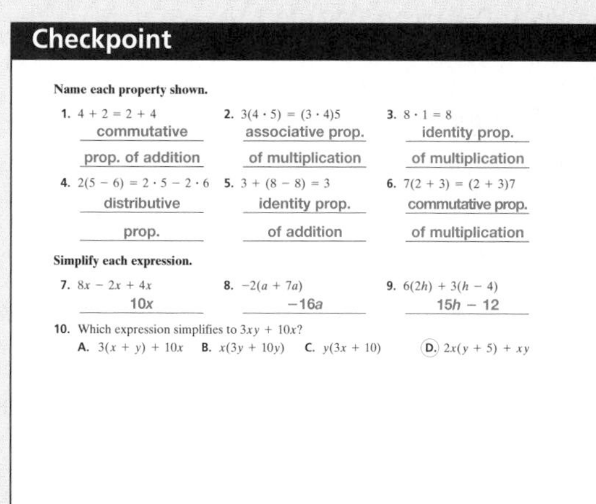

## Checkpoint

**Name each property shown.**

1. $4 + 2 = 2 + 4$ commutative prop. of addition
2. $3(4 \cdot 5) = (3 \cdot 4)5$ associative prop. of multiplication
3. $8 \cdot 1 = 8$ identity prop. of multiplication
4. $2(5 - 6) = 2 \cdot 5 - 2 \cdot 6$ distributive prop.
5. $3 + (8 - 8) = 3$ identity prop. of addition
6. $7(2 + 3) = (2 + 3)7$ commutative prop. of multiplication

**Simplify each expression.**

7. $8x - 2x + 4x$ 10x
8. $-2(a + 7a)$ −16a
9. $6(2h) + 3(h - 4)$ 15h − 12

10. Which expression simplifies to $3xy + 10x$?
A. $3(x + y) + 10x$ B. $x(3y + 10y)$ C. $y(3x + 10)$ (D.) $2x(y + 5) + xy$

# 2-4

## Getting Ready

### Key Terms and Symbols

equation, open sentence, solution

**Resources** A complete list of resources for this lesson is on p. 61H.

### Daily Skills Warm-Up

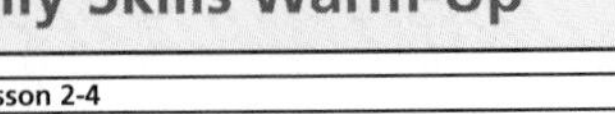

Lesson 2-4

Write a variable expression for each word phrase.

1. twenty less than a number $x$ $x - 20$
2. five times the quantity 7 plus $h$ $5(7 + h)$

Tell whether each expression is a numerical expression or a variable expression. For a variable expression, name the variable.

3. $7 + 9(2 + 6)$ numerical expression
4. $19 - 6 + h$ variable expression; $h$
5. $8m - 4$ variable expression; $m$
6. $5 + 5 + 5 + 5$ numerical expression

### Background for the Lesson

An equation can be always true ($3 + 1 = 4$), or always false ($4 - 3 = 9$), or open ($x + 3 = 7$). The equation $x + 5 = 8$ is an open sentence. When $x$ has a value of 3, then the equation is true. When $x$ has a value of 1, the equation is false. You solve the equation when you find the value for $x$ that makes the equation true. That value is called the solution.

## 1 Focus

### Connecting to Students' Lives

Remind students that they have used equations when they found the distance or the area by using formulas.

### Connecting to Prior Knowledge

In Lesson 2-3, students learned to simplify variable expressions. In this lesson, students use those skills as they write and solve equations. In Lesson 2-5, students solve equations by adding or subtracting.

# 2-4 Variables and Equations

**What You'll Learn**

1. To classify types of equations
2. To check equations using substitution

**. . . And Why**

To check solutions of equations

## PART 1 Classifying Types of Equations

An **equation** is a mathematical sentence with an equal sign. Here are three of the ways you will see equations in this book.

| | |
|---|---|
| $9 + 2 = 11$ | a numerical expression equal to a numerical expression |
| $x + 7 = 37$ | a variable expression equal to a numerical expression |
| $a + (-3) = 2a + 5$ | a variable expression equal to a variable expression |

An equation with a numerical expression equal to another numerical expression is either *true* or *false*. An equation with one or more variables is an **open sentence.**

### EXAMPLE 1

**Is each equation *true, false,* or an *open sentence?***

**a.** $6 + 12 = 18$ true, because $18 = 18$

**b.** $6 = 4 + 3$ false, because $6 \neq 7$

**c.** $6y = -3 + 5y$ an open sentence, because there is a variable

**TRY THIS** Is each equation *true, false,* or an *open sentence?*

**1.** $9 - 7 = 3$ false **2.** $8 + x = 2$ open **3.** $4 \cdot 5 = 20$ true

You can write a mathematical word sentence as an equation.

### EXAMPLE 2

**Write an equation for *Nine times the opposite of five is forty-five.* Is the equation true, false, or an open sentence?**

| Words | nine | times | the opposite of five | is | forty-five |
|---|---|---|---|---|---|
| ↓ | 9 | times | $-5$ | is | 45 |
| Equation | 9 | $\cdot$ | $(-5)$ | $=$ | 45 |

Since $9 \cdot (-5) = -45$ and $-45 \neq 45$, the equation is false.

**Writing Math**

The phrases *is equal to* and *equals* indicate you should use the equal sign. The verb *is* often indicates you should use the equal sign also.



## Tools to Monitor Progress

**BEFORE THE LESSON**

**To check prerequisite skills:**

- Combining integers

**Skills Intervention Kit,** Pre-Algebra Basics

**DURING THE LESSON**

**To check understanding:**

**Try This** exercises on student page

- **Additional Example 1**
  Is each equation true, false, or an open sentence?
  a. $3(b - 8) = 12$ open sentence
  b. $7 - (-6) = 1$ false
  c. $-9 + 5 = -4$ true

■ **Try This**

4. Write an equation for *Twenty minus x is three.* Is the equation true, false, or an open sentence? $20 - x = 3$; open

## Part 2 Checking Equations Using Substitution

A **solution** is a value for a variable that makes an equation true. You substitute a number for a variable to determine whether the number is a solution of the equation.

### Example 3

**Is 30 a solution of the equation $170 + x = 200$?**

$$170 + x = 200$$
$$170 + 30 \stackrel{?}{=} 200 \quad \text{Substitute 30 for } x.$$
$$200 = 200$$

Yes, 30 is a solution of the equation.

■ **Try This** Is the given number a solution of the equation?

5. $8 + t = 2t; 1$ no

6. $9 - m = 3; 6$ yes

REAL-WORLD CONNECTION

### Example 4

**A diver's equipment weighs 35 lb. The diver plus the equipment weighs 165 lb. Can the diver's weight be 200 lb?**

| | | | | | |
|---|---|---|---|---|---|
| **Words** | weight of diver | plus | weight of equipment | is | 165 lb |
| | Let $d$ = weight of diver. | | | | |
| **Equation** | $d$ | + | 35 | = | 165 |

$$d + 35 = 165$$
$$200 + 35 \stackrel{?}{=} 165 \quad \text{Substitute 200 for the variable.}$$
$$235 \neq 165$$

No, the diver's weight cannot be 200 lb.

■ **Try This**

7. A tent weighs 6 lb. Your backpack and the tent weigh 33 lb. Use an equation to find whether the backpack weighs 27 lb.
$b + 6 = 33$; $27 + 6 = 33$ ✓; Yes, the backpack weighs 27 lb.

A scuba tank can hold 63 $ft^3$ of compressed air. It weighs 29 lb when full.



# 2 Teach

## Part 1 Teaching Notes

Discuss the meaning of *equal*. Point out that the appearance or form may be different but equal expressions have the same *value*.

### ■ Example 1

**Build understanding.** Ask: How might you change part b. to make it true? Sample answer: Change 4 to 3.

### ■ Example 2

**Build understanding.** Ask: What word in the sentence means *equals*? is

## Part 2 Teaching Notes

If a volleyball player is injured, the coach may substitute, or replace, the injured player with another. Help students see that when they substitute a number for a variable in an equation, they replace the variable with the number.

### ■ Example 3

**Build understanding.** Ask: What kind of equation is $170 + x = 200$? open sentence

### ■ Example 4

**Build understanding.** Ask: What does the abbreviation *lb* mean? pound

**Extension** Challenge students to explain whether it would be possible for an equation to have more than one solution. Yes; for example: $|x| = 1$; Both $x = 1$ and $x = -1$ make the equation true.

**Error Prevention** Remind students to check whether the solution to an equation is reasonable. Example 4 shows a solution that is not reasonable.

**Visual Learning** Before they substitute a value, have students circle the variable in an equation on their paper.

- **Additional Example 2**
  Write an equation for "A number added to six times the number is the opposite of forty-two."
  $6x + x = -42$
- **Additional Examples 3–4**
  Airline passengers are allowed to take 20 kg of luggage on a plane trip. If a passenger has one suitcase that weighs 12 kg and a bag that weighs 4 kg, can she take a briefcase that weighs 5 kg? no

### AFTER THE LESSON

**To assess knowledge: Lesson Quiz**

1. Is this equation true, false, or an open sentence?
   $b + 3b - 1 = 15$ open sentence

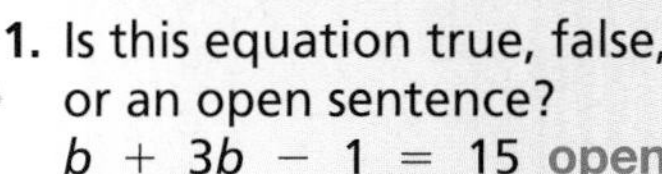

2. Can eight books that are 3 in. thick be stacked inside a box that is 12 in. tall? no

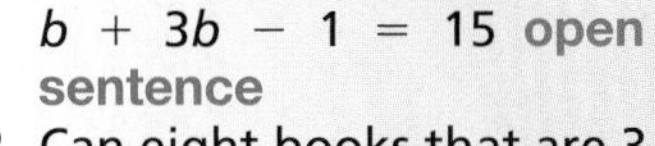

- For enrichment and reteaching options see Resources on p. 61H.

# 3 Practice/Assess

## Assignment Guide

To provide flexible scheduling, this lesson can be divided into parts.

**▼ Part 1**

**Core** 1–7, 11–16, 18–19, 29–33, 39–40

✪ **Extension** 17, 41

**▼ Part 2**

**Core** 8–10, 20–28, 37–38

✪ **Extension** 34–36

Mixed Review can be assigned at any time for maintenance.

## Exercises

**Exercises 20–28** Suggest that students test whether the given number would be a reasonable solution by estimating.

**Test Prep Exercise 39** Simplify each numeric equation before you select a response. Decide whether the variable equation is an open sentence.

## ✪ Challenge

What are the solutions to these equations? **a.** $x = x$ **b.** $0y = 0$
any number

## Closure

You can write an equation to model a situation. An equation with numerical expressions is true or false. An equation with at least one variable is an open sentence. A solution of an open sentence is a value of a variable that makes the equation true.

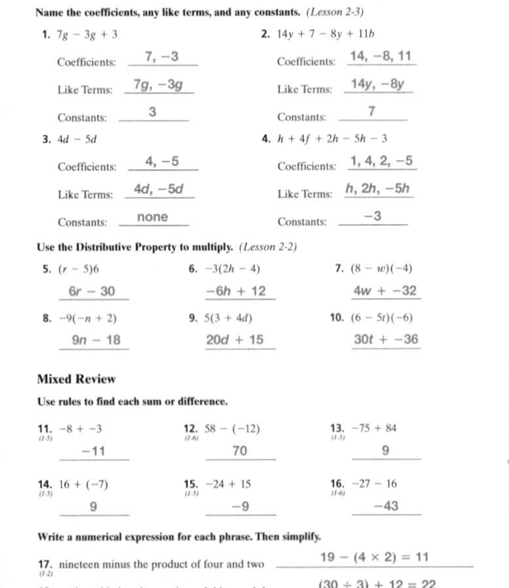

**Daily Cumulative Review**

**Name the coefficients, any like terms, and any constants.** *(Lesson 2-3)*

1. $7g - 3g + 3$
   Coefficients: 7, −3
   Like Terms: $7g, -3g$
   Constants: 3
2. $14y + 7 - 8y + 11b$
   Coefficients: 14, −8, 11
   Like Terms: $14y, -8y$
   Constants: 7
3. $4d - 5d$
   Coefficients: 4, −5
   Like Terms: $4d, -5d$
   Constants: none
4. $h + 4f + 2h - 5h - 3$
   Coefficients: 1, 4, 2, −5
   Like Terms: $h, 2h, -5h$
   Constants: −3

**Use the Distributive Property to multiply.** *(Lesson 2-2)*

5. $(r - 5)6$ — $6r - 30$
6. $-3(2h - 4)$ — $-6h + 12$
7. $(8 - w)(-4)$ — $4w + -32$
8. $-9(-n + 2)$ — $9n - 18$
9. $5(3 + 4d)$ — $20d + 15$
10. $(6 - 5t)(-6)$ — $30t + -36$

**Mixed Review**

**Use rules to find each sum or difference.**

11. (1-5) $-8 + -3$ — $-11$
12. (1-6) $58 - (-12)$ — 70
13. (1-5) $-75 + 84$ — 9
14. (1-5) $16 + (-7)$ — 9
15. (1-5) $-24 + 15$ — $-9$
16. (1-6) $-27 - 16$ — $-43$

**Write a numerical expression for each phrase. Then simplify.**

17. (1-2) nineteen minus the product of four and two — $19 - (4 \times 2) = 11$
18. (1-2) twelve added to the quotient of thirty and three — $(30 \div 3) + 12 = 22$



# Exercises

## CHECK UNDERSTANDING

**Determine whether each statement is true or false. Explain.**

1. An equation can be false. True; for example, $3 + 2 = 7$.
2. $3w - 7$ is an open sentence. False; $3w - 7$ is not an equation.
3. An open sentence must contain a variable. True; by definition, an open sentence is one that contains a variable.
4. $4 + 2x = 12$ is an open sentence. True; it contains a variable.

**Is each equation *true, false,* or an *open sentence*?**

5. $15 = 3 \cdot 5$ true
6. $4x - 8 = 25$ open
7. $3(-9) = -36 + 6$ false

**Replace *c* with −2. State whether the resulting equation is true or false.**

8. $c + 5 = 3$ true
9. $24 = 2c + 29$ false
10. $c \div 2 - 8 = 3(-3)$ true

## PRACTICE AND PROBLEM SOLVING

**Is each equation *true, false,* or an *open sentence*?**

11. $6 - 10 = 22 - 18$ false
12. $18 = -3(-6)$ true
13. $20 + 3x = 42$ open
14. $4c - 12 = 20$ open
15. $37 - 17 = 2 \cdot 10$ true
16. $36 \div 6 + 1 = 5 + 3$ false
17. ✪ $6[-3 - (-5)] = 2(-4 + 10)$ true
18. $-24(-2) = 18(4 + 2)$ false
19. $-9 + x = 50 \div 10 + 3$ open

**Is the given number a solution of the equation?**

20. $4 + d = 6; 2$ yes
21. $12 = 26 \div x; 14$ no
22. $-x - 5 = 6; 1$ no
23. $20 - c = 12; 8$ yes
24. $8 = 2a + 3; 0$ no
25. $3 + 2t = 7; 4$ no
26. $3b \div 18 = 2; 12$ yes
27. $3a = 12 + a; 6$ yes
28. $2m = m + 6; 4$ no

**Write an equation for each sentence. Is the equation *true, false,* or an *open sentence*?**

29. Four times the opposite of five equals negative twenty. $4(-5) = -20$; true
30. The product of negative twenty and nine is negative eleven. $(-20)(9) = -11$; false
31. The sum of fifteen and a number *n* is fifty. $15 + n = 50$; open
32. Forty-eight divided by twelve equals three. $48 \div 12 = 3$; false
33. Twenty-five equals a number *v* plus fifteen. $25 = v + 15$; open



## Alternative Assessment

Have students write two number riddles that describe open sentences with the equation and solution for each riddle. Sample answer: I am a number that when added to seven equals ten. What am I? $x + 7 = 10$, $x = 3$.

*Number Sense* **Which of the numbers are reasonable substitutions for each variable? Justify your reasoning.** 34–36. Answers may vary. Samples are given.

**34.** Let $p$ represent the number of passengers on a fifty-passenger school bus. Can $p$ be 30? $27\frac{1}{2}$? $-5$? 48? 30 or 48; both are counting numbers less than 50.

**35.** Let $c$ represent the number of coins with a value of one dollar. Can $c$ be 5 quarters? 10 dimes? 100 pennies? 17 nickels? 10 dimes or 100 pennies; both have a value of one dollar.

**36.** Let $d$ represent the day of a month. Can $d$ be 15? 56? 28? 0? 15 or 28; all months have at least 28 days.

**Write an equation. Is the given value a solution?**

**37.** A veterinarian weighs 140 lb. When she steps on a scale carrying a husky, the scale shows 192 lb. Let $d$ represent the weight of the dog. Does the dog weigh 52 lb? $140 + d = 192$; yes

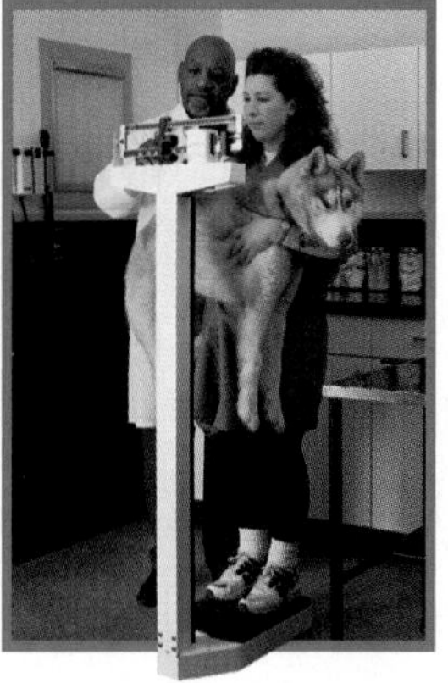

The veterinarian weighs 140 lb without the dog. She weighs 192 lb with the dog.

**38.** A recipe calls for 4 c of flour. You have 20 c of flour. Let $r$ represent the flour you have left after making the recipe. Is the remaining amount of flour 18 c? $20 - 4 = r$; no

**39.** **TEST PREP** Which equation is false? A

A. $3 + (-7) = 10$ B. $6 \div 2 = 3$ C. $8 \cdot 2 - 15 = 1$ D. $7w = 3w + 12$

**40.** *Writing* Equations can be true or false. Can an expression be true or false? Explain. No; an expression is not a sentence.

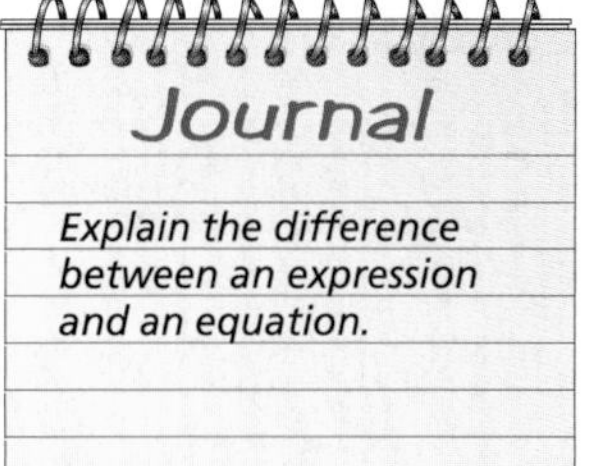

Journal
Explain the difference between an expression and an equation.

**41.** *Language* Some word sentences are similar to equations.

a. The sentence *Abraham Lincoln was an American president* is true. Write two other true sentences. See below.

b. The sentence *Eleanor Roosevelt was an American president* is false. Write two other false sentences. See below.

c. The sentence *He is a professional baseball player* is open. It is not clear to whom the word *he* refers. Write two other open sentences. Sample: She has new shoes. It has six legs.

41a. Sample: London is the capital of England. Water is made of hydrogen and oxygen. 41b. Sample: Hawaii is in the Atlantic Ocean. Potatoes are a fruit.

## MIXED REVIEW

**Simplify each expression.** *(Lesson 2-3)*

**42.** $6m + 7 - 2m + 1$ $4m + 8$ **43.** $-8t + 4t - 19$ $-4t - 19$ **44.** $3w + 5k - 4w + k$ $6k - w$

**Evaluate each expression for $a = 3$ and $b = 2$.** *(Lesson 1-3)*

**45.** $a + 2b$ 7 **46.** $a - b + 15$ 16 **47.** $(3b - 2a) \div 4$ 0 **48.** $3(b + 2) - 4$ 8

**49.** *Choose a Strategy* Larissa ran 15 mi per week before she decided to train for a marathon. The first week of training she ran 17 mi. The second week she ran 19 mi. If she continued her pattern, how far did she run the fifth week? 25 mi

See also Extra Practice section.

## Practice

**Is the given number a solution of the equation?**

1. $9k = 10 - k; -1$ no
2. $-7r - 15 = -2r; -3$ yes
3. $3g \div (-6) = 5 - g; -10$ no
4. $-3p = 4p + 35; -5$ yes
5. $8 - e = 2e - 16; 8$ yes
6. $5 - 15s = 8 - 16s; 3$ yes
7. $2(x - 2) - 5x = 5(2 - x); 7$ yes
8. $6a + 3 = 3(3a - 2); 4$ no

**Is each equation true, false, or an open sentence?**

9. $14 = x - 9$ open sentence
10. $8 + 7 = 10$ false
11. $4 - 15 = 22 - 33$ true
12. $5 + x = 90 \div 9 + 4$ open sentence
13. $-7(5 - 9) = 19 - 3(-3)$ true
14. $6(5 - 8) = 2(10 - 1)$ false

**Write an equation for each sentence. Is each equation true, false, or an open sentence.**

15. One fifth of a number $n$ is equal to $-7$.
$\frac{1}{5}n = -7$; open sentence
16. The product of 13 and $-7$ is $-91$.
$13(-7) = -91$; true
17. Fifty-four divided by six equals negative nine.
$54 \div 6 = -9$; false
18. Seven less than the product of a number $z$ and 3 is equal to 4.
$3z - 7 = 4$; open sentence

**Write an equation. Is the given value a solution?**

19. A truck driver drove 468 miles on Tuesday. That was 132 miles farther than she drove on Monday. Let $d$ represent the distance she drove on Monday. Did she drive 600 miles on Monday?
$d + 132 = 468$; no

## Reteaching

You earned \$84 at \$6 an hour. Let $h$ be the number of hours you worked. Can $h$ be 12? Can $h$ be 14?

Write an equation.

Words: Rate of pay · Hours worked = Total pay

Equation: $6 \cdot h = 84$

$6h = 84$

Substitute 12 for $h$.

$6(12) \stackrel{?}{=} 84$

$72 \neq 84$

No, you did not work 12 hours.

Substitute 14 for $h$.

$6(14) \stackrel{?}{=} 84$

$84 = 84$

Yes, you worked 14 hours.

**Write an equation. Is the given value a solution?**

1. You rode 180 miles at 60 miles per hour. Let $t$ be the time it took. Can $t$ be 4 hours?
$60t = 180$; No, it did not take 4 hours.
2. Ernie scored 8 more points than Mike scored. Ernie scored 20 points. Let $p$ be the number of points Mike scored. Can $p$ be 12?
$20 = p + 8$; Yes, Mike scored 12 points.
3. Each person in your class contributed a quart of punch for the school dance. You divided them into gallon containers and got 5 gallons. Let $q$ be the number of quarts you started with. Could $q$ be 20? (*Hint:* There are 4 quarts in a gallon.)
$\frac{q}{4} = 5$; Yes, you started with 20 qts.
4. You typed a 600 word essay in 12 minutes. Let $w$ be the number of words you can type in one minute. Can $w$ be 60?
$12w = 600$; No, you cannot type 60 words in one minute.

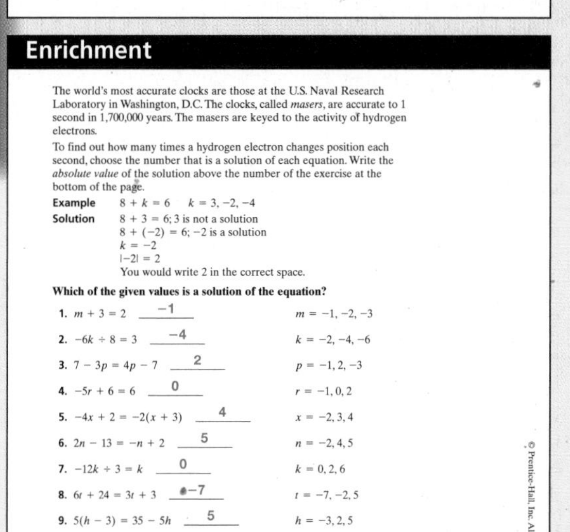

## Enrichment

The world's most accurate clocks are those at the U.S. Naval Research Laboratory in Washington, D.C. The clocks, called *masers*, are accurate to 1 second in 1,700,000 years. The masers are keyed to the activity of hydrogen electrons.

To find out how many times a hydrogen electron changes position each second, choose the number that is a solution of each equation. Write the *absolute value* of the solution above the number of the exercise at the bottom of the page.

**Example** $8 + k = 6$ $k = 3, -2, -4$

**Solution** $8 + 3 = 6$; 3 is not a solution
$8 + (-2) = 6$; $-2$ is a solution
$k = -2$
$|-2| = 2$
You would write 2 in the correct space.

**Which of the given values is a solution of the equation?**

1. $m + 3 = 2$ $-1$ $m = -1, -2, -3$
2. $-6k \div 8 = 3$ $-4$ $k = -2, -4, -6$
3. $7 - 3p = 4p - 7$ 2 $p = -1, 2, -3$
4. $-5r + 6 = 6$ 0 $r = -1, 0, 2$
5. $-4x + 2 = -2(x + 3)$ 4 $x = -2, 3, 4$
6. $2n - 13 = -n + 2$ 5 $n = -2, 4, 5$
7. $-12k \div 3 = k$ 0 $k = 0, 2, 6$
8. $6t + 24 = 3t + 3$ $-7$ $t = -7, -2, 5$
9. $5(h - 3) = 35 - 5h$ 5 $h = -3, 2, 5$
10. $-m - 1 = 0$ $-1$ $m = -1, 0, 2$
11. $8(9 - 2y) = -4y$ 6 $y = -4, 3, 6$
12. $5e + 36 = e$ $-9$ $e = -12, -9, -4$
13. $17 - 9c = -3(c + 3) + 2$ 4 $c = 2, 3, 4$

Answer: $\frac{1}{1}$, $\frac{4}{2}$ $\frac{2}{3}$ $\frac{0}{4}$, $\frac{4}{5}$ $\frac{5}{6}$ $\frac{0}{7}$, $\frac{7}{8}$ $\frac{5}{9}$ $\frac{1}{10}$, $\frac{6}{11}$ $\frac{9}{12}$ $\frac{4}{13}$ times per second

## MATH TOOLBOX

### Using Models with Equations

This Math Toolbox shows how to use algebra tiles to model and to solve equations.

### Math Background

Modeling equations with algebra tiles provides a concrete representation of the abstract ideas involved in solving equations. When you work with algebra tiles, it is important to realize that the green rectangle that represents the variable is one unit wide, but its length is unknown, so that you cannot equate the length to exactly either 4, 5, or 6 unit tiles.

### Teaching Notes

**Error Prevention** Students may need to be reminded to model the opposite of a unit or a variable by turning over the tile.

**Monitoring Progress** Discuss why you can always remove a zero pair of tiles or add a zero pair to just one side of the equation.

**Block Scheduling** If you have block scheduling or extended periods, you may wish to insert this Math Toolbox lesson between the completion of Part 1 of Lesson 2-4 and the beginning of Part 2 of Lesson 2-4.

## MATH TOOLBOX

Modeling
*Before Lesson 2-5*

# *Using Models with Equations*

You can model an equation using algebra tiles. Use a green rectangular tile to represent the variable. Here are some examples.

**Equation 1**

$x + 3 = 4$

**Equation 2**

$x + 3 = -3$

**Model each equation.** 1–6. See margin.

1. $x + 3 = 5$
2. $z + 2 = -6$
3. $y + 1 = 4$
4. $-3 = a - 4$
5. $2b + 2 = 8$
6. $3 + 3x = -6$

To solve an equation, get the variable alone on one side of the equal sign. Often you can do this by removing the same number of tiles from each side.

Here's how to solve $x + 3 = 7$.

Model the equation.

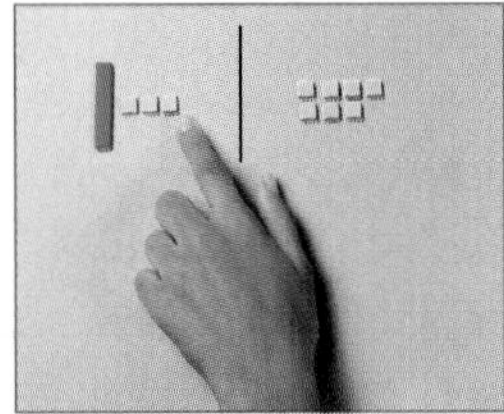

Solve by removing 3 tiles from each side.

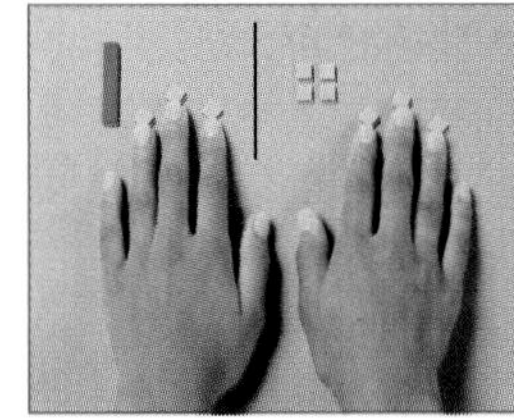

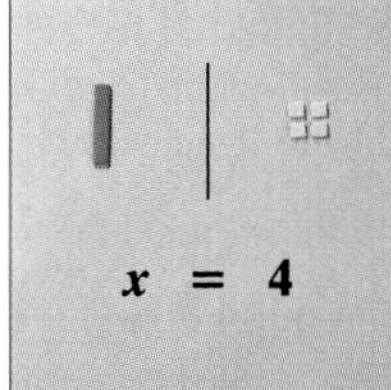


**Check** $x + 3 = 7$
$4 + 3 \stackrel{?}{=} 7$ Replace $x$ with 4.
$7 = 7$ ✔

**Model and solve each equation.** 7–12. See margin for models.

7. $x + 3 = 6$ $x = 3$
8. $m + 2 = 8$ $m = 6$
9. $1 = 1 + d$ $d = 0$
10. $-4 + y = -7$ $y = -3$
11. $-1 + p = -5$ $p = -4$
12. $w - 2 = -3$ $w = -1$



• **Additional Example**
Model and solve the equation $3 + x - 2 = -4$. $x = -5$

1.

2.
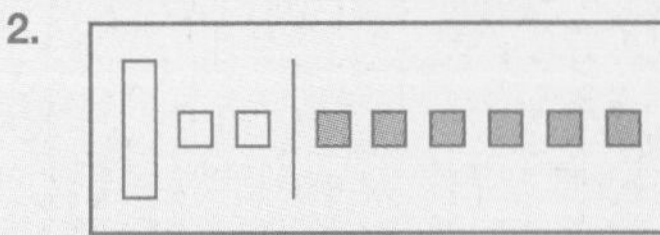

3.
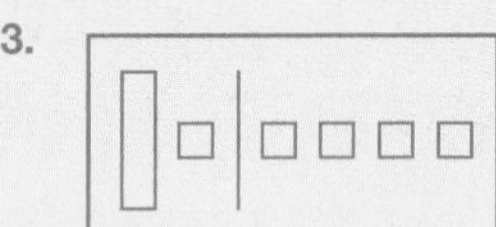

4.
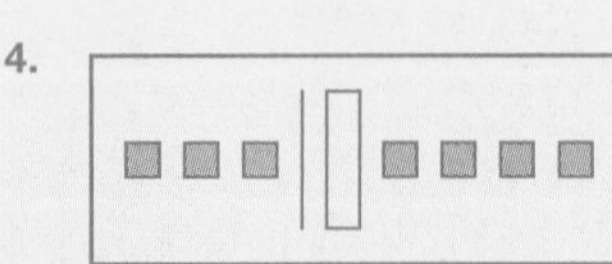

5.
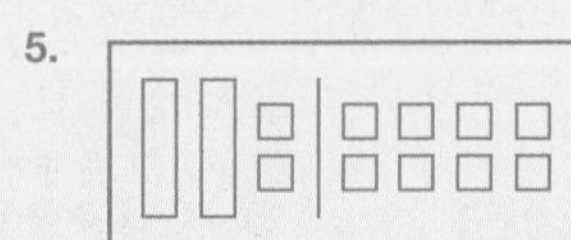

*Modeling* **Write and solve the equation for each model.**

**13.** 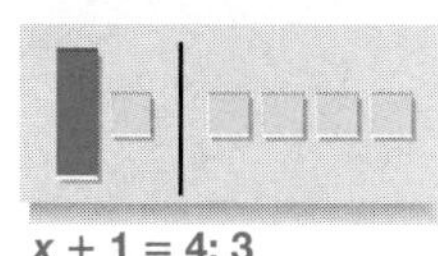
$x + 1 = 4; 3$

**14.** 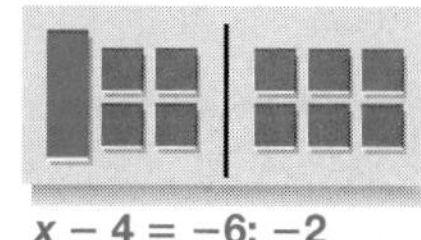
$x - 4 = -6; -2$

**15.** 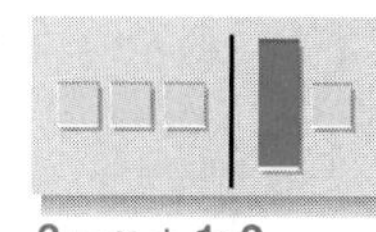
$3 = x + 1; 2$

Sometimes you cannot remove the same number of tiles from each side. You may need to add tiles to create zero pairs. Here's how to solve $x + 2 = -4$.

Model the equation.

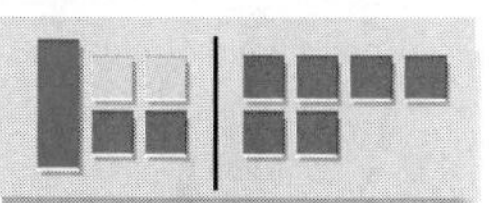
Add $-2$ to each side.

**Quick Review**

is a zero pair.

Remove zero pairs.

$x = -6$

**Check** $x + 2 = -4$
$-6 + 2 \stackrel{?}{=} -4$ Replace $x$ with $-6$.
$-4 = -4$ ✔

**Model and solve each equation.** 16–21. See margin for models.

**16.** $y + 2 = -2$ $y = -4$

**17.** $x + 5 = 2$ $x = -3$

**18.** $n + 7 = 1$ $n = -6$

**19.** $-1 = k + 3$ $k = -4$

**20.** $x - 4 = 5$ $x = 9$

**21.** $2 = z - 3$ $z = 5$

*Modeling* **Write and solve the equation for each model.**

**22.** 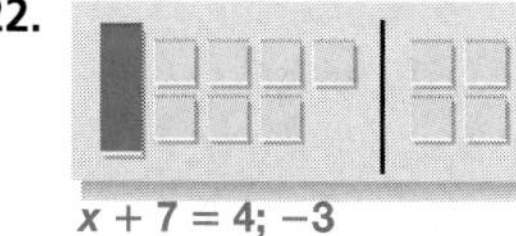
$x + 7 = 4; -3$

**23.** 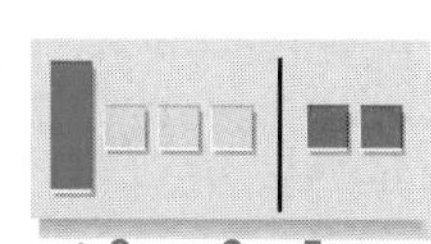
$x + 3 = -2; -5$

**24.** 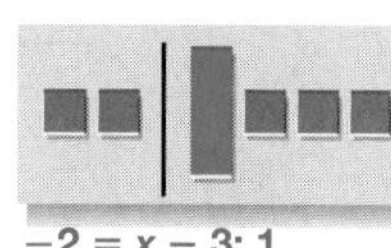
$-2 = x - 3; 1$

**25.** *Critical Thinking* Write two different equations that have the solution modeled at the right.
Answers may vary. Samples: $x + 1 = 4$; $x - 1 = 2$

12. 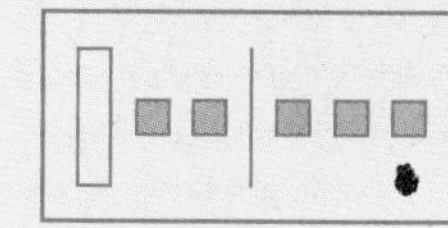

16. 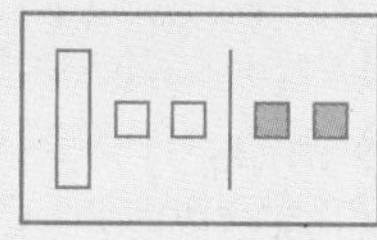

17. 

18. 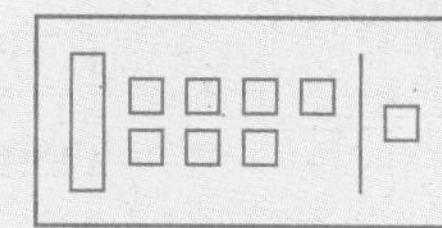

19. 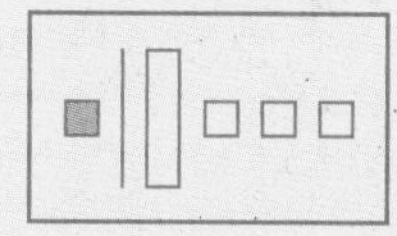

20. 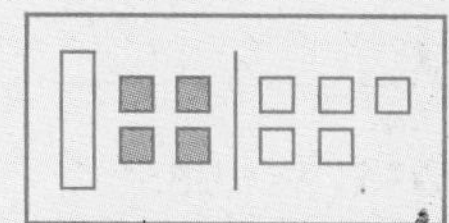

21. 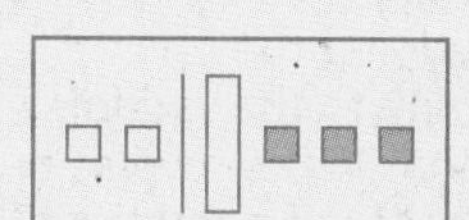

6. 

7. 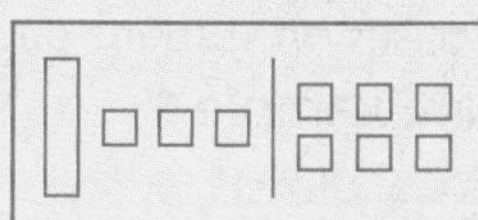

8. 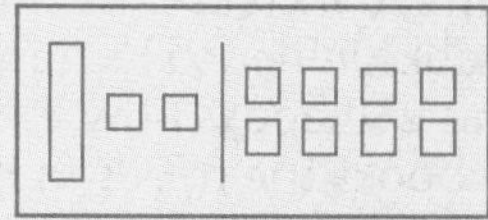

9. 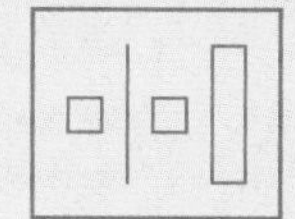

10. 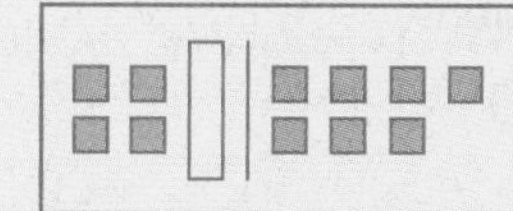

11. 

# 2-5

## Getting Ready

### Key Terms and Symbols

inverse operations, Subtraction Property of Equality, Addition Property of Equality

**Resources:** A complete list of resources for this lesson is on p. 61H.

### Daily Skills Warm-Up

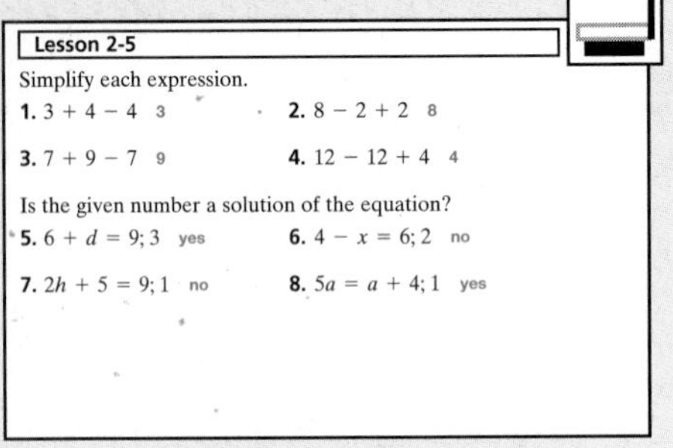

Lesson 2-5

Simplify each expression.

**1.** $3 + 4 - 4$ 3 **2.** $8 - 2 + 2$ 8

**3.** $7 + 9 - 7$ 9 **4.** $12 - 12 + 4$ 4

Is the given number a solution of the equation?

**5.** $6 + d = 9; 3$ yes **6.** $4 - x = 6; 2$ no

**7.** $2h + 5 = 9; 1$ no **8.** $5a = a + 4; 1$ yes

### Background for the Lesson

To solve an equation, isolate the variable on one side by undoing the operations that have been done to the variable. Undo the operations in the reverse order from that of the order of operations. In $x - 3 = 5$, you undo the subtraction of 3 by adding 3 to both sides of the equation. Always do the same thing to both sides of the equation to maintain the equality.

## 1 Focus

### Connecting to Students' Lives

Have a student describe what happens when one of the two people on a seesaw gets off. Lead students to see that an equation is like a seesaw. It becomes unbalanced if something is taken away from or added to only one side and not the other.

### Connecting to Prior Knowledge

In Lesson 2-4, students verified given solutions to equations by substituting the solution for the variable. In this lesson, they learn to solve equations by adding or subtracting. In Lesson 2-6 they add to their skills the procedures for solving equations by multiplying or dividing.

# 2-5 Solving Equations by Adding or Subtracting

**What You'll Learn**

1. To solve one-step equations using subtraction
2. To solve one-step equations using addition

**. . . And Why**

To model real-world situations such as problems involving health

## PART 1 Using Subtraction to Solve Equations

Balancing an equation is like balancing a barbell. If you add weight to or subtract weight from one side of the bar, you must do the same on the other side.

Subtract 5 lb from each side.

As you can see in the photos, the barbell remains balanced when the same weight is removed from each side.

In previous math courses, you used related equations like $3 + 5 = 8$ and $8 - 3 = 5$. These equations show that addition and subtraction undo each other.

When you solve an equation, your goal is to get the variable alone on one side of the equation. The value on the other side tells you the solution of the original equation. You use **inverse operations,** which undo each other to get the variable alone.

**Subtraction Property of Equality**

You can subtract the same number from each side of an equation.

| Arithmetic | Algebra |
|---|---|
| $10 = 2(5)$ | If $a = b$, |
| $10 - 5 = 2(5) - 5$ | then $a - c = b - c$. |

After you solve an equation, check your result in the original equation to make sure your solution is correct.



# Tools to Monitor Progress

**BEFORE THE LESSON**

**To check prerequisite skills:**

- Inverse operations

**Skills You Need,** p. 61

**DURING THE LESSON**

**To check understanding:**

**Try This** exercises on student page

- **Additional Example 1**
  Solve $y + 5 = 13$. $y = 8$
- **Additional Example 2**
  Larissa wants to increase the number of comic books in her collection to 327. She has 250 books now. Find how many books she needs to buy.
  $250 + x = 327$; 77 books

## Example 1

**Solve $x + 6 = 4$.**

**Method 1**

$$x + 6 = 4$$
$$x + 6 - 6 = 4 - 6 \quad \text{Subtract 6 from each side.}$$
$$x = -2 \quad \text{Simplify.}$$

**Method 2**

$$\begin{array}{r} x + 6 = \phantom{-}4 \\ \underline{-6} \quad \underline{-6} \\ x = -2 \end{array}$$

**Check** $x + 6 = 4$

$-2 + 6 \stackrel{?}{=} 4$ Replace $x$ with $-2$.

$4 = 4$ ✔

**Try This** Solve each equation.

1. $x + 8 = 3$ $-5$
2. $5 = d + 1$ $4$
3. $c + (-4) = -5$ $-1$

You can write and solve equations describing real-world situations. To help check, decide whether your solution is reasonable using the original problem.

**REAL-WORLD**  **CONNECTION**

## Example 2

*Health* **Fred's target heart rate is 130 beats/min. This is 58 beats/min more than his resting heart rate. Find his resting heart rate.**

**Words** target rate is 58 more than resting rate

Let $r$ = resting heart rate.

**Equation** $130 = 58 + r$

$$130 = 58 + r$$
$$130 - 58 = 58 + r - 58 \quad \text{Subtract 58 from each side.}$$
$$130 - 58 = r + 58 - 58 \quad \text{Use the Commutative Property of Addition.}$$
$$72 = r \quad \text{Simplify.}$$

Fred's resting heart rate is 72 beats per minute.

**Check** Is the answer reasonable? The resting heart rate plus 58 beats per minute should be 130 beats per minute. $72 + 58 = 130$. The answer is reasonable.

Here is one method for estimating your target heart-rate range: Begin by subtracting your age from 220. Then multiply the result by 0.6 and 0.8 to find the lower and upper limits of your heart-rate range.

**Try This**

4. Cora measures her heart rate at 123 beats per minute. This is 55 beats per minute more than her resting heart rate $r$. Write and solve an equation to find Cora's resting heart rate. $123 = r + 55$; 68 beats/min



- **Additional Example 3**
  Solve $c - 23 = -40$. $c = -17$
- **Additional Example 4**
  Sergio bought a turkey sandwich for \$4.20. He also bought an orange. The orange cost \$3.40 less than the sandwich. How much did the orange cost?
  $x + \$3.40 = \$4.20$; \$.80

### AFTER THE LESSON

**To assess knowledge:**

**Lesson Quiz**

Solve each equation.

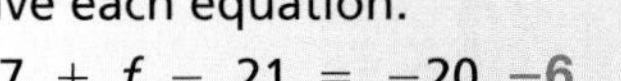

1. $7 + f - 21 = -20$ $-6$

2. $67 = g - (-36)$ $31$
3. Ricky rides his bike 12 mi every day. He stops after 7 mi to rest. How much farther does he have to ride? 5 mi

- For enrichment and reteaching options see Resources on p. 61H.

# 2 Teach

## Part 1 Teaching Notes

Explain that the procedures in solving an equation must result in equivalent equations at every step.

### Example 1

**Build understanding.** Ask: Which property of addition allows you to rewrite $x + 6 - 6$ as $x$? Ident. Prop. Add.

**Tactile Learning** Have students use algebra tiles to model subtracting the same number from each side of an equation.

**ELL** Write the words *equivalent* and *equal* on the board. Point out that both words are variations of the same root word. Ask students to connect this to the meaning of each word.

### Example 2

**Build understanding.** Ask: Why is 58 subtracted from both sides of the equation? to isolate the variable by undoing the addition of 58 to $r$

## Part 2 Teaching Notes

Have students discuss how the Addition Property of Equality is similar to the Subtraction Property of Equality.

### Example 3

**Build understanding.** Ask: Why is adding 12 to each side of the equation the first step? to isolate the variable $b$

### Example 4

**Build understanding.** Ask: Which cost more, the TV or the VCR? the TV

**Extension** Challenge students to describe how they would solve $8 + r - 4 = 25$. Steps will vary. $r = 21$

**Error Prevention** Students may fail to use the correct sign when applying inverse operations. Tell students to copy the original equation carefully and to verify that they are using the inverse operation.

# 3 Practice/Assess

## Assignment Guide

To provide flexible scheduling, this lesson can be divided into parts.

▼ **Part 1**
**Core** 1, 3–4, 6–8, 12–19, 21, 34–35, 37–38, 47
✪ **Extension** 20, 22, 29

▼ **Part 2**
**Core** 2, 5, 9–11, 23–27, 31–33, 36, 39–46
✪ **Extension** 28, 30

Mixed Review can be assigned at any time for maintenance.

## Exercises

**Exercise 12** Remind students that the word problems that they write need to have realistic quantities or measurements.

**Test Prep Exercise 41** Suggest that students ask themselves questions like these: Which team won more games? Will you add or subtract from the Tigers' 22 games?

## ✪ Challenge

Solve $15 - s = 2s = 13$

## Closure

To solve an equation, use an inverse operation and the properties of equality to get the variable alone on one side of the equation.

### Daily Cumulative Review

**Is each equation true, false, or an open sentence?** *(Lesson 2-4)*

1. $6 + 8y = 30$ open sentence
2. $8 \cdot 5 = 85 - 45$ true equation
3. $-4(-6) = 3(-t + 8)$ open sentence
4. $42 \div 7 - 2 = 7 - 4$ false equation

**Simplify each expression.** *(Lesson 2-3)*

5. $4k - 5k + 4 + 3k$ $2k + 4$
6. $8(3p - 2) - p$ $23p - 16$
7. $3(3 - g) + (-4g)$ $-7g + 9$
8. $-2(4a) - 3(b + 2a)$ $-14a - 3b$
9. $-5(3r) + 4(-6d) + d$ $-23d + -15r$
10. $5h + 4c - 2h + 2$ $4c + 3h + 2$
11. $7n - 7 - n + 5n$ $11n - 7$
12. $6g - 8b + 3g$ $-8b + 9g$
13. $2(k - 7) + 5k$ $7k - 14$

**Mixed Review**

**Use rules to find each product or quotient.**

14. (1-9) $-45 \div 9$ $-5$
15. (1-9) $-14(-2)$ $28$
16. (1-9) $\frac{56}{(-7)}$ $-8$
17. (1-9) $4(-3)$ $-12$
18. (1-9) $(-72) \div (-8)$ $9$
19. (1-9) $-12 \cdot 6$ $-72$

**Write an integer to represent each situation.**

20. (1-4) 3,000 ft below sea level $-3{,}000$ ft
21. (1-4) a debt of \$34 $-\$34$
22. (1-4) win by 4 points $4$

## PART 2 Using Addition to Solve Equations

When you solve an equation involving subtraction, *add* the same number to each side of the equation.

### Addition Property of Equality

You can add the same number to each side of an equation.

| Arithmetic | Algebra |
|---|---|
| $8 = 2(4)$ | If $a = b$, |
| $8 + 3 = 2(4) + 3$ | then $a + c = b + c$. |

### EXAMPLE 3

**Solve $b - 12 = -49$.**

$b - 12 = -49$
$b - 12 + 12 = -49 + 12$ Add 12 to each side.
$b = -37$ Simplify.

**TRY THIS** Solve each equation.

**5.** $y - 5 = 8$ 13 **6.** $p - 30 = 42$ 72 **7.** $98 = x - 14$ 112

REAL-WORLD CONNECTION

### EXAMPLE 4

**Your friend's VCR cost \$328 less than her TV. Her VCR cost \$179. How much did her TV cost?**

**Words** cost of VCR was \$328 less than cost of TV

Let $t$ = the cost of the TV.

**Equation** 179 = $t$ − 328

$179 = t - 328$
$179 + 328 = t - 328 + 328$ Add 328 to each side.
$507 = t$ Simplify.

Your friend's TV cost \$507.

**Writing Math**

When you go from words to an equation, the order of the math symbols may be different from the order of the words:

- ten fewer than $n$ → $n - 10$
- eight less than $r$ → $r - 8$
- $n$ times 5 → $5n$

**TRY THIS** Write and solve an equation for this situation.

**8.** A softcover book costs \$17 less than its hardcover edition. The softcover costs \$5. How much does the hardcover cost? $h - 17 = 5$; \$22

86 Chapter 2 Solving One-Step Equations and Inequalities

## Alternative Assessment

Write several variable equations on the board, such as $b + 5 = 7$ and $-8 = y - 3$. Ask students to write and explain the steps that are necessary to find equivalent equations with the variable alone on one side.

# Exercises

## Check Understanding

**Copy and complete the steps for solving each equation.**

1. $x + 8 = 15$
   $x + 8 - ■ = 15 - ■$ 8, 8
   $x = ■$ 7

2. $y - 3 = -5$
   $y - 3 + ■ = -5 + ■$ 3, 3
   $y = ■$ −2

**State the first step in solving each equation.**

3. $a + 8 = 12$ Subtract 8 from each side.
4. $54 + x = 98$ Subtract 54 from each side.
5. $34 = c - 19$ Add 19 to each side.

**Solve each equation.**

6. $6 + b = 9$ 3
7. $x + 35 = 15$ −20
8. $3 = n + 4$ −1
9. $d - 4 = -7$ −3
10. $c - 34 = 20$ 54
11. $-25 = q - 10$ −15

12. *Open-ended* Write two word problems that can be solved using the equation $x + 15 = -18$. Check students' work.

## Practice and Problem Solving

**Solve each equation.**

13. $c + 9 = 37$ 28
14. $b + 24 = 19$ −5
15. $65 = n + 34$ 31
16. $47 = 7 + y$ 40
17. $450 = a + 325$ 125
18. $h + 35 = 15$ −20
19. $298 + n = 924$ 626
20. $-45 = x + (-3)$ −42
21. $89 + y = 112$ 23
22. $e + (-43) = -45$ −2
23. $a - 4 = -5$ −1
24. $r - 3 = 8$ 11
25. $x - 366 = -415$ −49
26. $-27 = w - 14$ −13
27. $z - 100 = 100$ 200
28. $n - 29 - 16 = 246$ 291
29. $34 + p + 112 = 78 - 7$ −75
30. $183 + k - 20 = -15$ −178

*Mental Math* **Use mental math to solve each equation.**

31. $5 = d - 1$ 6
32. $40 = g - 20$ 60
33. $b + 15 = -5$ −20
34. $130 = 30 + s$ 100
35. $x + 800 = 500$ −300
36. $100 = x - 25$ 125

**Write and solve an equation for each sentence.**

37. Negative six plus $y$ equals eighteen. $-6 + y = 18$; 24
38. Twelve equals the sum of $n$ and twenty-three. $12 = n + 23$; −11
39. Negative five equals $x$ minus eight. $-5 = x - 8$; 3
40. The number $a$ minus five is negative eight. $a - 5 = -8$; −3

## Practice

**Use mental math to solve each equation.**

1. $-52 = -52 + k$  $k = 0$
2. $837 = p + 37$  $p = 800$
3. $x - 155 = 15$  $x = 170$
4. $180 = 80 + n$  $n = 100$
5. $2{,}000 + y = 9{,}500$  $y = 7{,}500$
6. $81 = x - 19$  $x = 100$
7. $111 + f = 100$  $f = -11$
8. $w - 6 = -16$  $w = -10$

**Solve each equation.**

9. $m - 17 = -8$  $m = 9$
10. $k - 55 = 67$  $k = 122$
11. $-44 + n = 36$  $n = 80$
12. $-36 = p - 91$  $p = 55$
13. $x - 255 = 671$  $x = 926$
14. $19 = c - (-12)$  $c = 7$
15. $x + 14 = 21$  $x = 7$
16. $31 = p + 17$  $p = 14$
17. $-19 = k + 9$  $k = -28$
18. $87 + y = 19$  $y = -68$
19. $36 + n = 75$  $n = 39$
20. $-176 = h + (-219)$  $h = 43$
21. $41 + k = 7$  $k = -34$
22. $1{,}523 + c = 2{,}766$  $c = 1{,}243$
23. $-88 + z = 0$  $z = 88$
24. $-33 + (-7) = 29 + m$  $m = -69$
25. $t + (-2) = -66$  $t = -64$
26. $-390 + x = 11 - 67$  $x = 334$
27. The combined enrollment in the three grades at Jefferson Middle School is 977. There are 356 students in the seventh grade and 365 in the eighth grade. Write and solve an equation to find how many students are in the ninth grade.

Equation $356 + 365 + n = 977$

Solution 256 students



## Reteaching

Solve $x - 9 = 2$ and $x + 8 = 3$.

Since the 9 is subtracted from $x$, do the inverse and add 9 to both sides of the equation.

$x - 9 = 2$
$x - 9 + 9 = 2 + 9$
$x = 11$

In $x + 8 = 3$, 8 is added to $x$. So, subtract 8 from both sides of the equation.

$x + 8 = 3$
$x + 8 - 8 = 3 - 8$
$x = -5$

**Solve each equation.**

1. $17 + m = 21$  $m = 4$
2. $y - 34 = 43$  $y = 77$
3. $t + 9 = -9$  $t = -18$
4. $15 = z + 6$  $z = 9$
5. $r + 7 = -16$  $r = -23$
6. $68 = p - 41$  $p = 109$
7. $144 + g = 78$  $g = -66$
8. $311 = y - 281$  $y = 592$
9. $-11 + b = -11$  $b = 0$
10. $s + 31 = 14$  $s = -17$
11. $24 = k - 2$  $k = 26$
12. $8 + f = 30$  $f = 22$
13. $37 = z - 3$  $z = 40$
14. $a + 19 = -82$  $a = -101$
15. $18 + n - 7 = 44$  $n = 33$
16. $15 = 7 + h + 14$  $h = -6$



## Enrichment

The equation $x + y = 16$ has many solutions.
$x = 9, y = 7 \rightarrow x + y = 16$
$x = 22, y = -6 \rightarrow x + y = 16$

The equations $x - y = 6$ also has many solutions.
$x = 13, y = 7 \rightarrow x - y = 6$
$x = 24, y = 18 \rightarrow x - y = 6$

Only one pair of numbers solves *both* equations: $x = 11, y = 5$
$x + y \stackrel{?}{=} 16$  $x - y \stackrel{?}{=} 6$
$11 + 5 = 16$  $11 - 5 = 6$

**Answer these questions to find the pair of numbers that solves both of the following equations.**

Equation 1: $x + y = 8$  Equation 2: $x - y = 20$

1. Find $x$ in Equation 1 if $y = -4$  12
   Find $x$ in Equation 2 if $y = -4$  16
2. Find $x$ in Equation 1 if $y = -5$  13
   Find $x$ in Equation 2 if $y = -5$  15
3. Find $x$ in Equation 1 if $y = -6$  14
   Find $x$ in Equation 2 if $y = -6$  14
4. Write the pair of numbers that solves both equations.
   $x =$ 14, $y =$ −6

**Complete the table to find the pair of numbers that solves both equations.**

5. Equation 1: $x + y = -6$  Equation 2: $x - y = -12$

| y | 1 | 2 | 3 | 4 | 5 |
|---|---|---|---|---|---|
| x (Equation 1) | −7 | −8 | −9 | −10 | −11 |
| x (Equation 2) | −11 | −10 | −9 | −8 | −7 |

Solution: $x =$ −9, $y =$ 3





41. **TEST PREP** This year, the Newville Tigers won six games more than the Wilton Panthers won. The Tigers won 22 games. Which equation *cannot* be used to find the number of games the Panthers won? D
   **A.** $b + 6 = 22$  **B.** $22 - b = 6$  **C.** $22 = 6 + b$  **D.** $b - 6 = 22$

**Use the table at the right for Exercises 42 and 43.**

| Planet | Approximate Distance from Sun (millions of kilometers) |
|---|---|
| Mercury | 58 |
| Venus | 108 |
| Earth | ■ |
| Mars | ■ |
| Jupiter | 778 |
| Saturn | 1,429 |
| Uranus | 2,871 |
| Neptune | 4,504 |
| Pluto | 5,914 |

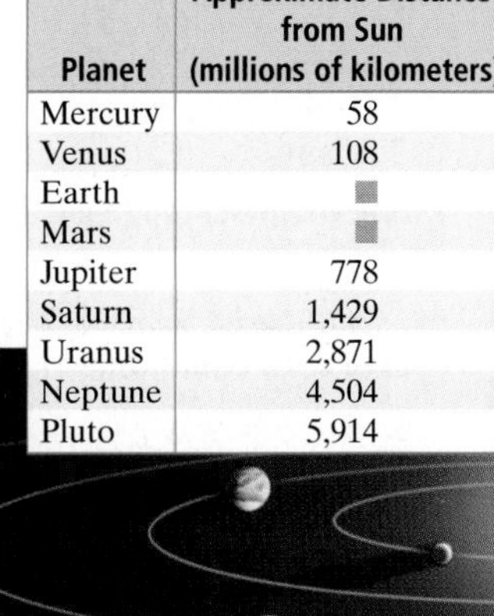

42. *Astronomy* The average distance from the sun to Jupiter is 550 million km greater than the average distance from the sun to Mars. Write and solve an equation to find Mars's average distance $d$ from the sun. $778 = d + 550$; 228 million km
43. *Astronomy* The distance from Venus to the sun is 42 million km less than Earth's average distance from the sun. Write and solve an equation to find Earth's average distance $d$ from the sun. $108 = d - 42$; 150 million km
44. *Error Analysis* A student solved the equation $x - 6 = -6$. His solution was $-12$. What error did the student make? The student subtracted (rather than added) 6 on the right side.
45. *Writing* To solve $x + 25 = -22$, one student subtracted 25 from each side. Another student added $-25$ to each side. Will both methods work? Explain. Yes; subtracting a number is the same as adding its opposite.
46. In 1996, 487 million people across the world spoke English. This was 512 million people fewer than the number who spoke Mandarin Chinese. Write and solve an equation to find the number of people $n$ who spoke Mandarin Chinese. $487 = n - 512$; 999 million people
47. *Physics* The speed of sound through steel is 5,200 meters per second (m/s). This is 2,520 m/s faster than the speed of sound through silver. Write and solve an equation to find the speed $s$ of sound through silver. $5{,}200 = s + 2{,}520$; 2,680 m/s

## Mixed Review

**Is each equation *true, false,* or an *open sentence?* (Lesson 2-4)**

48. $x + 2 = 4$ open sentence
49. $4 = 6 - 2$ true
50. $5 - 3 = 7 - 4$ false

**Evaluate. (Lesson 1-3)**

51. $6n$, for $n = 8$ 48
52. $\frac{k}{20}$, for $k = 140$ 7
53. $50x$, for $x = 8$ 400

54. *Patterns* Deric studied math for 1 min the first week of school, and then doubled his study time each week. How many minutes did he study in the tenth week? (Lesson 1-7) 512 min



See also Extra Practice section.

DATA ANALYSIS CONNECTION

# Solving Equations by Multiplying or Dividing

2-6

## Using Division to Solve Equations

Division and multiplication are inverse operations. You can solve an equation that involves multiplication by using the Division Property of Equality.

**Division Property of Equality**

If you divide each side of an equation by the same nonzero number, the two sides remain equal.

| Arithmetic | Algebra |
|---|---|
| $6 = 3(2)$ | If $a = b$ and $c \neq 0$, |
| $\frac{6}{3} = \frac{3(2)}{3}$ | then $\frac{a}{c} = \frac{b}{c}$. |

### What You'll Learn

1. To solve one-step equations using division
2. To solve one-step equations using multiplication

### . . . And Why

To model real-world situations such as population growth

DATA ANALYSIS CONNECTION

### Example 1

*Statistics* **The United States population in 1998 was twice the population in 1943. Find the 1943 population in millions.**

**Words** 1998 population was twice 1943 population

Let $p$ = population in 1943.

**Equation** $270 = 2 \cdot p$

$270 = 2p$

$\frac{270}{2} = \frac{2p}{2}$ Divide each side by 2.

$135 = p$ Simplify.

The United States population in 1943 was 135 million people.

**Check** Is the answer reasonable? Twice the 1943 population should be the 1998 population. Since $135 \cdot 2 = 270$, the answer is reasonable.

270 million
? million
1943
1998

U.S. Population Growth

**Try This** Solve each equation.

1. $4x = 84$ 21
2. $91 = 7y$ 13
3. $12w = 108$ 9



# 2-6

## Getting Ready

### Key Terms and Symbols
Division Property of Equality, Multiplication Property of Equality

**Resources** A complete list of resources for this lesson is on p. 61H.

### Daily Skills Warm-Up

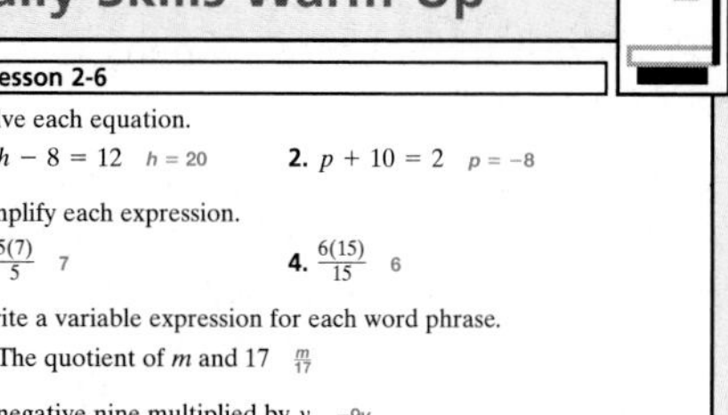

Lesson 2-6

Solve each equation.

1. $h - 8 = 12$ $h = 20$
2. $p + 10 = 2$ $p = -8$

Simplify each expression.

3. $\frac{5(7)}{5}$ 7
4. $\frac{6(15)}{15}$ 6

Write a variable expression for each word phrase.

5. The quotient of $m$ and 17 $\frac{m}{17}$
6. negative nine multiplied by $y$ $-9y$

### Background for the Lesson

The Division Property of Equality states that you can divide each side of an equation by the same *nonzero* value. Divisors are restricted to *nonzero* values because division *by zero* is not defined.

## 1 Focus

### Connecting to Students' Lives

Ask students if they have ever shared the total cost, perhaps of a meal or a video, equally with a group of friends. Tell students that they can represent the amount each friend owes with an equation.

### Connecting to Prior Knowledge

In Lesson 2-5, students learned to solve equations by adding or subtracting. In this lesson, students add the procedures of multiplying or dividing to solve equations. In Lessons 2-9 and 2-10, students apply these techniques to solving inequalities.

# Tools to Monitor Progress

### BEFORE THE LESSON

**To check prerequisite skills:**

- Inverse operations

**Skills You Need,** p. 61

### DURING THE LESSON

**To check understanding:**

**Try This** exercises on student page

- **Additional Example 1**

A dozen marker pens cost $21. What is the price of one marker pen?
$12p = 21$; $1.75

- **Additional Example 2**

Solve $-2v = -24$.

$\frac{-2v}{-2} = \frac{-24}{-2}$

$v = 12$

# 2 Teach

## Part 1 Teaching Notes

Elicit the fact that the solution to an equation does not depend on whether the variable is on the left or right side of the equal sign. Show students that the solutions of these equations are the same.

$2x = 10 \qquad 10 = 2x$

$x = 5 \qquad 5 = x$

### Example 1

**Build understanding.** Ask: What must you do to the 1943 population for it to equal the 1998 population? **Multiply by 2.**

**ELL** Point out that "twice" means a value is multiplied by 2.

### Example 2

**Build understanding.** Ask: Why is each side of the equation divided by 5? **to keep the equation balanced and to get the variable alone on one side of the equation**

## Part 2 Teaching Notes

Remind students how multiplication and division are related: $3 \times 4 = 12$; $12 \div 4 = 3$; and $12 \div 3 = 4$. These two operations are inverse operations; they undo each other.

### Example 3

**Build understanding.** Ask: Why is the solution a positive number? **A negative times a negative gives a positive product.**

**Extension** Challenge students to explain what happens when they multiply each side of an equation by zero. **You get the true equation 0 = 0.**

**Error Prevention** A common error is to divide one side of the equation by a number while multiplying the other side by the same number. Remind students that they must use the same operation and number on both sides of the equation.

### EXAMPLE 2

**Solve $5r = -20$.**

$5r = -20$

$\frac{5r}{5} = \frac{-20}{5}$ Divide each side by 5.

$r = -4$ Simplify.

**Check** $5r = -20$

$5 \cdot (-4) \stackrel{?}{=} -20$ Replace $r$ with $-4$.

$-20 = -20$ ✔

**TRY THIS** Solve each equation.

**4.** $-3b = 24$ −8 **5.** $96 = -8n$ −12 **6.** $-4d = -56$ 14

## PART 2 Using Multiplication to Solve Equations

When you multiply each side of an equation by the same number, the two sides remain equal.

**Multiplication Property of Equality**

You can multiply each side of an equation by the same number.

| Arithmetic | Algebra |
|---|---|
| $12 = 3(4)$ | If $a = b$, |
| $12 \cdot 2 = 3(4) \cdot 2$ | then $ac = bc$. |

**Reading Math**

The equation $\frac{x}{-9} = -3$ is read as "$x$ divided by negative nine equals negative three."

### EXAMPLE 3

**Solve $\frac{x}{-9} = -3$.**

$\frac{x}{-9} = -3$

$-9\left(\frac{x}{-9}\right) = -9(-3)$ Multiply each side by −9.

$x = 27$ Simplify.

**TRY THIS** Solve each equation.

**7.** $\frac{r}{-5} = 10$ −50 **8.** $\frac{s}{-6} = 54$ −324 **9.** $-30 = \frac{t}{20}$ −600



**• Additional Example 3**

Solve $\frac{x}{8} = -5$.

$\frac{x}{8} = -5$

$8\left(\frac{x}{8}\right) = 8(-5)$

$x = -40$

## AFTER THE LESSON

**To assess knowledge: Lesson Quiz**

Solve each equation.

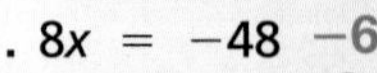

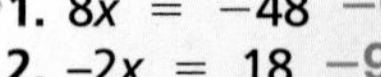

1. $8x = -48$ −6
2. $-2x = 18$ −9
3. $108 = 9x$ 12
4. $\frac{v}{3} = 14$ 42
5. $-6 = n \div 4$ −24

• For enrichment and reteaching options see Resources on p. 61H.

# Exercises

## CHECK UNDERSTANDING

**State the first step in solving each equation.**

1. $6x = 96$ Divide each side by 6.
2. $32 = c \cdot 3$ Divide each side by 3.
3. $\frac{r}{-5} = -4$ Multiply each side by −5.

**Solve each equation.**

4. $8x = -48$ −6
5. $108 = 9x$ 12
6. $-75 = -15x$ 5
7. $\frac{v}{3} = 14$ 42
8. $-6 = \frac{n}{4}$ −24
9. $\frac{m}{-2} = -20$ 40

10. *Critical Thinking* You can divide each side of an equation by the same *nonzero* value. Explain what would result from the equation $4 \cdot 0 = 5 \cdot 0$ if you could divide each side by zero and if $\frac{0}{0} = 1$. Answers may vary. Sample: 4 = 5

## PRACTICE AND PROBLEM SOLVING

*Mental Math* **Is −3 a solution of each equation? Explain.**

11. $-6 = 2m$ yes; $-6 = 2(-3)$
12. $\frac{b}{-3} = 1$ yes; $\frac{-3}{-3} = 1$
13. $\frac{-18}{k} = -6$ no; $\frac{-18}{-3} \neq -6$
14. $3t = 9$ no; $3(-3) \neq 9$

**Solve each equation.**

15. $4a = 28$ 7
16. $-2b = 30$ −15
17. $-45 = 9a$ −5
18. $15c = 90$ 6
19. $5w = 95$ 19
20. $-28 = 7m$ −4
21. $-10d = 100$ −10
22. $125 = 25d$ 5
23. $\frac{m}{4} = 13$ 52
24. $\frac{b}{-6} = 20$ −120
25. $-2 = \frac{d}{8}$ −16
26. $\frac{v}{3} = -4$ −12
27. $-50 = \frac{n}{-6}$ 300
28. $9 = \frac{n}{8}$ 72
29. $\frac{w}{12} = -2$ −24
30. $\frac{r}{9} = -8$ −72

*Mental Math* **Solve each equation.**

31. $20b = 2{,}000$ 100
32. $75m = -7{,}500$ −100
33. $\frac{v}{-50} = 300$ −15,000
34. $3{,}823 = \frac{s}{100}$ 382,300

**For what values of $x$ is each equation true?**

35. $|x| = 7$ 7, −7
36. $2|x| = 8$ 4, −4
37. $-3|x| = -9$ 3, −3
38. $\frac{|x|}{3} = 2$ 6, −6

**Solve for $x$.**

39. $x - a = b$ $b + a$
40. $a + x = b$ $b - a$
41. $ax = b$ $\frac{b}{a}, a \neq 0$
42. $\frac{x}{a} = b$ $ab, a \neq 0$



# 3 Practice/Assess

## Assignment Guide

To provide flexible scheduling, this lesson can be divided into parts.

**Part 1**

**Core** 1–2, 4–6, 10–11, 14–22, 31–32, 43–44, 46, 48–49
**Extension** 35–37, 39–41

**Part 2**

**Core** 3, 7–9, 12–13, 23–30, 33–34, 45, 47
**Extension** 38, 42

Mixed Review can be assigned at any time for maintenance.

## Exercises

**Exercises 4–9** Ask students who are having difficulty what operation they must do to get the variable alone on one side of the equation.

**Exercises 39–42** Remind students that although there are 3 variables, they are solving for $x$.

## Challenge

Multiplication equations have the form $ax = b$. If $b$ is 134, what whole numbers are possible for $a$ and $x$? 2 and 67

## Closure

To solve an equation, use an inverse operation and the properties of equality to get the variable alone on one side of the equation.

## Daily Cumulative Review

**Solve each equation.** *(Lesson 2-5)*

1. $x + 6 = 32$ $x = 26$
2. $t - 4 = 16$ $t = 20$
3. $-35 = p - 19$ $-16 = p$
4. $267 = f + 189$ $78 = f$
5. $-76 = w + (-13)$ $-63 = w$
6. $q - 176 = -326$ $q = -150$

**Write an equation for each sentence. Is each equation true, false, or an open sentence?** *(Lesson 2-4)*

7. The sum of twenty-one and a number $f$ is thirty-seven. $21 + f = 37$; open sentence
8. The product of six and negative fifteen is ninety. $6(-15) = 90$; false equation
9. Sixty-four divided by eight equals eight. $64 \div 8 = 8$; true equation
10. Fifteen minus twenty-one equals the product of negative two and three. $15 - 21 = (-2)(3)$; true equation

**Mixed Review**

**Use a pattern to solve each problem.**

11. (1-8) Each day Mr. Harrison added 2 math problems to his students' assignment. The first day he assigned 6 problems. He gave 12 assignments in the month of February. How many math problems did the students have on the last assignment? 28 problems
12. (1-8) Tony was supposed to wash the dishes every night after dinner. He told his little brother that if he helped wash the dishes then he would give him some marbles. He would give him 2 the first night and then double the amount each time he helped. How many marbles altogether did Tony have to give his brother after 7 nights of helping to do the dishes? 254 marbles



## Alternative Assessment

Have students write three equations involving multiplication or division in which one or both numbers are negative. Have students explain how they can predict the sign of the solution.

**Write an equation for each sentence. Solve for the variable.**

**43.** The product of negative twenty and $y$ is one hundred. $-20y = 100; -5$

**44.** Negative six multiplied by $q$ equals one hundred eight. $-6q = 108; -18$

**45.** Thirteen equals the quotient of $x$ divided by three. $13 = \frac{x}{3}; 39$

**46.** Use the table at the right. The number of students in grades 1–8 is four times the number of students in kindergarten. Write and solve an equation to find the number of students $s$ in kindergarten. $32 = 4s$; 8 million students

**U.S. School Enrollment**

| Grades | Millions of Students |
|---|---|
| Kindergarten | ■ |
| 1–8 | 32 |
| 9–12 | 16 |

SOURCE: U.S. Bureau of the Census

**47.** One of the world's tallest office buildings is in Malaysia. The building has 88 stories. The height of the 88 stories is 1,232 ft. What is the height of one story? 14 ft

**48.** ***Writing*** How are the procedures to solve $3x = 9$ and $x + 3 = 9$ alike? How are they different? Answers may vary. Sample: You do something to each side of the equation. You divide by 3 in the first equation; you subtract 3 in the second.

**49.** ***Open-ended*** Write a question that can be solved using the equation $5x = 45$. Check students' work.

## MIXED REVIEW

**Solve each equation.** *(Lesson 2-5)*

**50.** $-4 = a + 7$ $-11$ **51.** $n - 5 = 12$ 17 **52.** $t - (-4) = -15$ $-19$ **53.** $y + 10 = 12$ 2

**Write a variable expression for each word phrase.** *(Lesson 1-1)*

**54.** three less than $a$ $a - 3$ **55.** 7 times a number $n$ $7n$

**56.** Suppose you start hiking from a point 92 ft below sea level and break for lunch on a hilltop that is 1,673 ft above sea level. What is your change in elevation? *(Lesson 1-5)* increase of 1,765 ft

## CHAPTER PROJECT 2 — ACTIVITY 2 CALCULATING

Place a nickel at Mass 1 on your balance scale. At Mass 2, place as many pennies as you need to balance the scale. The nickel has a mass of about 5 g. Write and solve an equation to find the mass of a penny.



See also Extra Practice section.

### Project Activity 2

**Calculating** Suggest that students center the coins on the mark for Mass 1 or Mass 2. Students may wish to try a different nickel to see if they get significantly different results. Ask them to conjecture whether two nickels might have different weights on a more precise balance scale.

## Practice

**Solve each equation.**

1. $\frac{k}{-5} = -5$ $k = 25$
2. $-3 = \frac{n}{7}$ $n = -21$
3. $\frac{x}{12} = 0$ $x = 0$
4. $-6 = \frac{m}{-2}$ $m = 12$
5. $\frac{y}{-4} = -12$ $y = 48$
6. $\frac{s}{30} = 6$ $s = 180$
7. $\frac{1}{9}z = 0$ $z = 0$
8. $-\frac{m}{55} = 1$ $m = -55$
9. $-3x = 18$ $x = -6$
10. $-56 = 8y$ $y = -7$
11. $8p = -8$ $p = -1$
12. $-4s = -32$ $s = 8$
13. $14h = 42$ $h = 3$
14. $-175 = 25g$ $g = -7$
15. $-42 = 6m$ $m = -7$
16. $-2x = 34$ $x = -17$
17. $\frac{x}{-9} = -11$ $x = 99$
18. $216 = 9w$ $w = 24$
19. $-17v = -17$ $v = 1$
20. $-161 = 23t$ $t = -7$
21. $56h = 3{,}136$ $h = 56$
22. $20 = \frac{e}{-25}$ $e = -500$
23. $4{,}200 = 30x$ $x = 140$
24. $\frac{y}{-21} = -21$ $y = 441$
25. $\frac{m}{-3} = 21$ $m = -63$
26. $4{,}000 = \frac{x}{-40}$ $x = -160{,}000$
27. A bamboo tree grew 3 in. per day. Write and solve an equation to find how many days $d$ it took the tree to grow 144 in.
    Equation: $3d = 144$ Solution: 48 days
28. Carl drove 561 miles. His car averages 33 miles per gallon of gas. Write and solve an equation to find how much gas $g$ Carl's car used.
    Equation: $33g = 561$ Solution: 17 gallons

**For what values of $y$ is each equation true?**

29. $-5|y| = -25$ $-5, 5$
30. $\frac{|y|}{2} = 28$ $-56, 56$
31. $9|y| = 27$ $-3, 3$



## Reteaching

Solve $4x = -32$.

$4x = -32$

Since 4 is multiplied by $x$, divide both sides of the equation by 4.

$4x = -32$

$\frac{4x}{4} = \frac{-32}{4}$

$x = -8$

Solve $\frac{x}{-5} = -9$.

$\frac{x}{-5} = -9$

Since $x$ is divided by $-5$, multiply both sides of the equation by $-5$.

$\frac{x}{-5} = -9$

$-5\frac{x}{-5} = -5(-9)$

$x = 45$

**Solve each equation.**

1. $7m = 35$ $m = 5$
2. $\frac{b}{8} = -3$ $b = -24$
3. $90 = 10k$ $k = 9$
4. $1 = \frac{n}{14}$ $n = 14$
5. $100 = -20n$ $n = -5$
6. $\frac{p}{15} = 5$ $p = 75$
7. $-87{,}654y = 0$ $y = 0$
8. $\frac{m}{4} = -12$ $m = -48$
9. $-10a = 10$ $a = -1$
10. $\frac{z}{-4} = 16$ $z = -64$
11. $350t = -700$ $t = -2$
12. $11j = 121$ $j = 11$
13. $\frac{r}{-7} = 13$ $r = -91$
14. $-7{,}650 = 10c$ $c = -765$
15. $23 = \frac{w}{3}$ $w = 69$
16. $125 = 25g$ $g = 5$



## Enrichment

You can use variable expressions and the distributive property to analyze mathematical puzzles and determine why they work.

**Carry out the following directions for three different integers.**

| | | | |
|---|---|---|---|
| 1. Choose any integer. | 2 | −4 | 17 |
| 2. Add 7. | 9 | 3 | 24 |
| 3. Multiply by 3. | 27 | 9 | 72 |
| 4. Subtract the original number. | 25 | 13 | 55 |
| 5. Subtract 11. | 14 | 2 | 44 |
| 6. Divide by 2. | 7 | 1 | 22 |
| 7. Subtract the original number. | 5 | 5 | 5 |

8. What unusual result did you obtain? The final result is always 5.

To discover why you obtain this result, choose $n$ as your original number. Since $n$ is a variable, it represents every number that can possibly be chosen.

**Write variable expressions for each direction in the puzzle.**

9. Add 7 to $n$. $n + 7$
10. Multiply this quantity by 3 using the distributive property. $3n + 21$
11. Subtract $n$, the original number. $2n + 21$
12. Subtract 11. $2n + 10$
13. Divide by 2. (Note that you must divide both terms by 2.) $n + 5$
14. Subtract $n$, the original number. 5

You will obtain this result for every possible value of $n$.

**Write your own mathematical puzzle, trade with a partner, and solve.**

Answers may vary.

# Standardized Test Prep

## Multiple Choice

**Choose the best answer.**

1. The graph shows life expectancies in selected countries. Which conclusion is reasonable? D

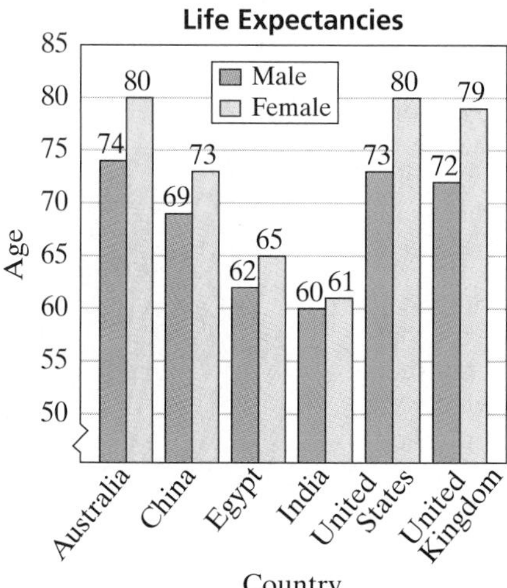


A. The country in which a person lives has little influence on life expectancy.
B. A female in Australia lives about as long as a male in China.
C. The oldest male known to live in India is 60, while the oldest female is 61.
D. Females live longer than males.

2. Use the graph above. Which conjecture is *false?* F
F. A male in Egypt lives half as long as a female in Australia.
G. A male in India lives almost as long as a female in India.
H. Males in the United States and in the United Kingdom have about the same life expectancy.
J. Females in the United States and in Australia have the same life expectancy.

3. During the riverside cleanup Marisa filled three times the number of bags Kevin filled. If $b$ represents the number of bags Kevin filled, which expression gives the number of bags Marisa filled? A
A. $3b$ B. $b - 3$ C. $b + 3$ D. $\frac{b}{3}$

4. Which expression is *not* equivalent to $m(p + q)$? F
F. $mp + q$ G. $m(q + p)$
H. $(p + q)m$ J. $mp + mq$

5. Which expression gives the area of the figure? A

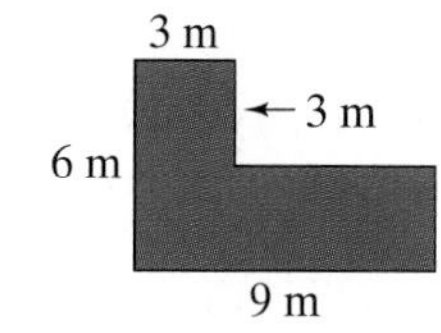


A. $(3 \cdot 3) + (9 \cdot 3)$
B. $(6 \cdot 9) - (3 \cdot 3)$
C. $(3 \cdot 3) + (6 \cdot 9)$
D. $6 + 3 + 3 + 6 + 3 + 9$

6. Which statement is true for the expression $5a - 3b - b - 1$? J
F. The expression is equivalent to $5a - 2b - 1$.
G. The coefficients are all negative.
H. The expression has three terms and two variables.
J. The coefficients are 5, −3, and −1.

## Free Response

**For Exercises 7–9, show your work.**

7. Use the pattern below. 987,654,321

$1 \cdot 8 + 1 = 9$
$12 \cdot 8 + 2 = 98$
$123 \cdot 8 + 3 = 987$
$1{,}234 \cdot 8 + 4 = 9{,}876$

Find the value of $123{,}456{,}789 \cdot 8 + 9$.

8. Answers may vary. Sample: $8 \cdot 9 = 72$; $8 \cdot 5 + 8 \cdot 4 = 40 + 32 = 72$

8. Show two ways to simplify $8(5 + 4)$. See above.

9. *Open-ended* Write an expression with four terms using variables $t$ and $z$. Evaluate your expression for $t = -3$ and $z = 7$.
Answers may vary. Sample: $t + z + tz - 1$; −18



# Standardized Test Prep

Standardized tests, such as those administered for state assessment, SAT9, TerraNova™, ITBS, MAT7, or CAT5, may include multiple choice questions, free-response questions, and open-ended questions.

**Multiple Choice Questions** are followed usually by four choices, one of which is correct.

**Exercises 1–6** are multiple choice questions.

**Free-Response Questions** do not give answer choices. Student must provide the one correct answer on their own.

**Exercises 7–9** are free-response questions.

**Open-Ended Questions** allow for more than one solution. Students must construct their own responses instead of choosing from possible answers.

**Exercise 9** is an open-ended question.

## Resources

See p. 61G for a list of assessment options.

## Test-Taking Tip

When a question has a graph or diagram, read carefully all the labels and information in the graphic. Make sure you understand what is pictured before you consider the answer choices.

### Test-Taking Tips on Transparency

Learn and practice the proper way to record responses.

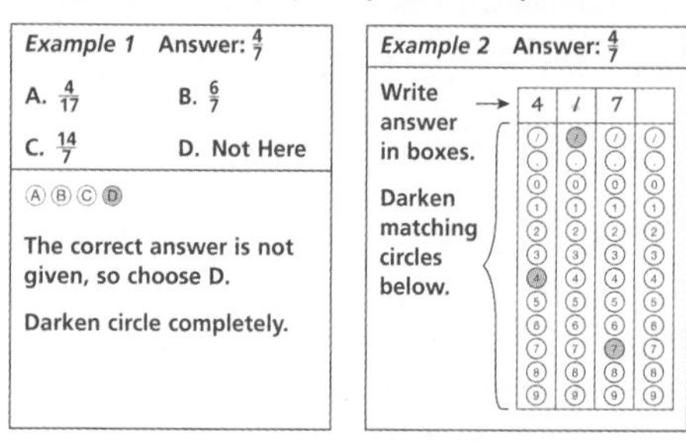

Example 1 Answer: 4/7
A. 4/17
B. 6/7
C. 14/7
D. Not Here
The correct answer is not given, so choose D.
Darken circle completely.
Example 2 Answer: 4/7
Write answer in boxes.
Darken matching circles below.


Practice recording the following answers.

1. Answer: 0.35
2. Answer: four centimeters
A. 4 in. B. 4 mm C. 4 cm D. Not Here
3. Answer: 45 degrees
F. 135° G. 55° H. 45° J. Not Here

# 2-7

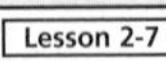

## Getting Ready

**Resources** A complete list of resources for this lesson is on p. 61H.

### Daily Skills Warm-Up

Lesson 2-7

Evaluate each expression.

1. $x + y$ when $x = 70$ and $y = 30$ 100
2. $4x + 3y$ when $x = 70$ and $y = 30$ 370
3. $a + b + c$ when $a = 4, b = 6$ and $c = 2$ 12
4. $5a + 10b + 20c$ when $a = 4, b = 6$ and $c = 2$ 120
5. Is 300 a solution to $x + (x + 200) = 1000$? no
6. Is 400 a solution to $x + (x + 200) = 1000$? yes

### Background for the Lesson

Try, Test, and Revise problem solving strategy is common in the world outside of the classroom. It is used by everyone—from infants who are just discovering their world to scientists making discoveries that change our world. In this strategy, a "try" is a careful and reasonable trial solution, not merely a random or wild speculation.

## 1 Focus

### Connecting to Students' Lives

Ask students if they have entered a contest to find the number of marbles in a jar for a prize. While testing the number may be difficult, there are often ways to increase the accuracy of the estimate by using math.

### Connecting to Prior Knowledge

In Lesson 2-6, students practiced solving equations. In this lesson, they apply those skills to problem solving. In Lesson 2-9, students solve problems with inequalities as well as equations.

# Try, Test, Revise

**Problem Solving Strategies**

- Account for All Possibilities
- Draw a Diagram
- Look for a Pattern
- Make a Model
- Make a Table
- Simplify a Problem
- Simulate a Problem
- Solve by Graphing
- Try, Test, Revise
- Use Multiple Strategies
- Work Backward
- Write an Equation
- Write a Proportion

*Math Strategies in Action* Did you know that meteorologists use weather balloons to collect data? They use the temperature, humidity, and other data in mathematical models to bring you the daily weather forecast. As more data become available—from weather balloons and satellites, for example—the models, and therefore the weather reports, become more accurate.

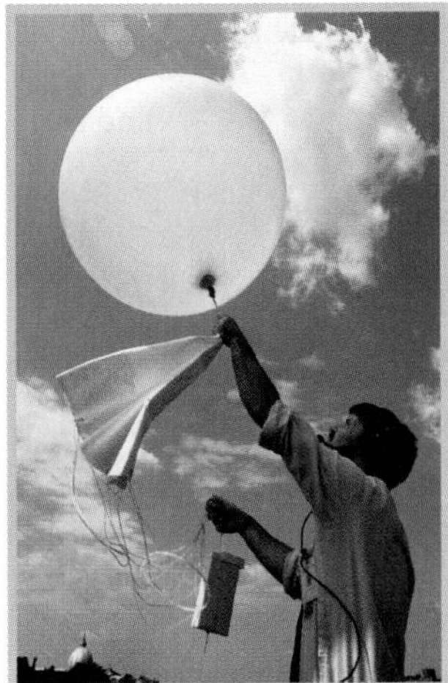

Similarly, in math problems, you can make an initial conjecture. You can test your conjecture. If it is not the right answer, you can use what you learn from your first conjecture to make a better second conjecture.

**SAMPLE PROBLEM**

The theater club at school put on a play. For one performance, it sold 133 tickets and raised \$471. Tickets cost \$4 for adults and \$3 for students. How many student tickets and how many adult tickets did the club sell?

### Read

Look at the given information to make an informed conjecture.

1. How much does each type of ticket cost? adult \$4; student \$3
2. How many tickets did the club sell for the performance? 133 tickets
3. How much money did the club raise from ticket sales for this performance? \$471

### Plan

Make a conjecture, and then test it. Use what you learn from your conjecture to make a better second conjecture.



# Tools to Monitor Progress

**BEFORE THE LESSON**

**To check prerequisite skills:**

- Working with integers

**Skills Handbook,** p. 741

**DURING THE LESSON**

**To check understanding:**

- **Additional Sample Problem**
  During the intermission of the play, the theater club sold cups of popcorn and sodas. The club sold 79 cups of popcorn and 96 sodas for a total of \$271. What was the selling price of a cup of popcorn? of a soda? **popcorn: \$1, soda: \$2**

4. When you make a conjecture for how many adult tickets were sold, how can you use your conjecture to find how many student tickets could have been sold? **Subtract the number of adult tickets from 133.**

5. By what number do you multiply your conjecture of adult tickets sold to find how much money was made on adult tickets? **4**

### Solve

You can organize conjectures in a table. As a first conjecture, try making about half the tickets adult tickets.

| Adult Tickets | Student Tickets | Total Money (in dollars) | |
|---|---|---|---|
| 60 | 133 − 60 = 73 | 60(4) + 73(3) = 240 + 219 = 459 | The total is too low. Increase the number of adult tickets. |
| 80 | 133 − 80 = 53 | 80(4) + 53(3) = 320 + 159 = 479 | The total is too high. Decrease the number of adult tickets. |
| 70 | 133 − 70 = 63 | 70(4) + 63(3) = 280 + 189 = 469 | The total is very close. Increase the number of adult tickets. |
| 72 | 133 − 72 = 61 | 72(4) + 61(3) = 288 + 183 = 471 | The total is correct. |

There were 72 adult tickets and 61 student tickets sold.

### Look Back

Is it possible to solve the problem in another way? Consider using logical reasoning.

- The less expensive ticket is \$3. So the theater club would get 133 · \$3 = \$399 if all the tickets sold were student tickets.
- \$471 − \$399 = \$72. The theater club actually raised \$72 more than if they had sold only student tickets.
- Since adult tickets are \$1 more than student tickets, there must have been 72 adult tickets sold.
- 133 − 72 = 61. There were 61 student tickets sold.
- Since 72 · 4 + 61 · 3 = 471, the solution 72 adult tickets and 61 student tickets is correct.

6. Suppose the club sold the same number of tickets, but raised \$452. How many tickets of each type did the theater club sell? **53 adult tickets, 80 student tickets**



## 2 Teach

Effective problem solving requires students to organize their tries and calculations. Explain that in order to make good second and third tries, the information you test in the first try must be recorded.

### Sample Problem

**Build understanding.** Ask: Why was the first try that about half of the tickets were for adults and half for children? **Sample answer: This is a reasonable guess for the audience at a school play.**

**ELL** Help students pronounce and understand the meaning of the math vocabulary word *conjecture*. A conjecture is a tentative or temporary answer that is then checked and, perhaps, changed to be more accurate.

**Visual Learning** Students benefit from creating tables or charts to organize their data before they begin trying to find solutions.

**Connecting to Science**

Scientists solve problems and make new discoveries by using a system similar to the Try, Test, Revise method. They call this system the scientific method. They start with a hypothesis, a tentative assumption. They then do experiments to test the hypothesis. Many different scientists must test and verify a hypothesis many times before it is considered to be true.

**Extension** Challenge students to give examples of types of math problems for which the Try, Test, Revise method would not be an effective way to find a solution.

**Error Prevention** Students may think that they have the correct solution to their problem because their final answer and original try are the same. Explain to students that a confirmed try is not an answer check. Students should carefully check their arithmetic for errors and verify that their solution answers the original question in the problem.

**• Additional Sample Problem**

Karen made a border design with a total of 26 triangles and rectangles. If there were 92 sides in the figures, how many triangles and how many rectangles did she use? **12 triangles; 14 rectangles**

**AFTER THE LESSON**

**To assess knowledge: Lesson Quiz**

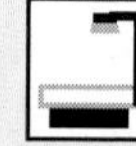

Solve using any strategy.

1. Three consecutive integers have a sum of −9 and a product of −24. What are the three integers? **−2, −3, −4**

- For enrichment and reteaching options see Resources on p. 61H.

# 3 Practice/Assess

## Assignment Guide

**Core** 1–9, 11–13
✪ **Extension** 10

Mixed Review can be assigned at any time for maintenance.

## Exercises

**Exercise 1** Have students write a list of all of the types of coins Bonnie could possibly have. Remind them to include half-dollars.

**Exercises 4–13** Remind students that they can use any strategy to solve these problems.

## ✪ Challenge

Challenge students to solve Exercise 7 by writing an equation and solving it. $\frac{r}{3} = 16$, $r$ (Rafi's age) $= 48$

## Closure

You can solve some problems by trying an answer. Use each incorrect conjecture to make a better estimate of the correct answer.

## Daily Cumulative Review

**Solve each equation.** *(Lesson 2-6)*

1. $-6h = 36$ — $h = -6$
2. $3t = 27$ — $t = 9$
3. $-56 = 8k$ — $-7 = k$
4. $\frac{g}{-3} = 7$ — $g = -21$
5. $\frac{b}{9} = 5$ — $b = 45$
6. $-20 = \frac{d}{5}$ — $-100 = d$

**Solve each equation.** *(Lesson 2-5)*

7. $r - 350 = 350$ — $r = 700$
8. $665 + y = 796$ — $y = 131$
9. $-543 = j + -193$ — $-350 = j$
10. $99 = 25 + z + (-12)$ — $86 = z$
11. $u + (-73) + 13 = 36$ — $u = 96$
12. $342 + m - 176 = -272$ — $m = -438$
13. $453 + w = -264$ — $w = -717$
14. $p - 34 = -23$ — $p = 11$
15. $69 = -45 + x$ — $114 = x$

**Mixed Review**

**Graph each set of numbers on a number line. Then order the numbers from least to greatest.**

16. (1-4) $-2, 3, -4$ — $-4, -2, 3$
17. (1-4) $5, -3, 4$ — $-3, 4, 5$

**Compare. Use >, <, or = to complete each statement.**

18. (1-4) $-9$ [<] $-6$
19. (1-4) $7$ [>] $-6$
20. (1-4) $8$ [>] $4$

**Simplify each expression.**

21. (2-3) $3 - 7y + 6$ — $-7y + 9$
22. (2-3) $t + 7t - 8 - 2t$ — $6t - 8$
23. (2-3) $-7(u - 4) + 2$ — $-7u + 30$



# Exercises

## Check Understanding

**Use the *Try, Test, Revise* strategy to solve each problem.**

1. Bonnie has 16 coins in her pocket worth \$1.50. What are two different combinations of coins she could have in her pocket? Answers may vary. Samples: 14 dimes, 2 nickels; 2 quarters, 6 dimes, 8 nickels
2. A cashier's drawer has some \$5 bills, some \$10 bills, and some \$20 bills. There are 15 bills worth a total of \$185. How many \$5 bills, \$10 bills, and \$20 bills are there? 1, 10, and 4, or 3, 7, and 5, or 5, 4, and 6, or 7, 1, and 7
3. The Smiths have two children. The sum of their ages is 23. The product of their ages is 132. How old are the children? 11 years and 12 years

## Practice and Problem Solving

**Solve using any strategy.**

4. A movie theater sells senior and child tickets for \$3, and other tickets for \$6.50. One day, the theater sold 445 tickets. It made \$2,518. How many of each kind of ticket did it sell? 107 senior and child tickets, 338 others
5. *Geometry* A rectangular vegetable garden has a length of 5 ft and a width of 8 ft. The length is increased by 2 ft. By how many square feet does the area increase? 16 ft$^2$
6. Trains leave New York for Boston every 40 min. The first train leaves at 5:20 A.M. What departure time is closest to 12:55 P.M.? 12:40 P.M.
7. Lovell is 16 years old. Lovell's age is the same as Rafi's age divided by three. How old is Rafi? 48 years
8. *Number Theory* A number multiplied by itself and then by itself again gives $-1{,}000$. What is the number? $-10$
9. In a group of quarters and nickels, there are four more nickels than quarters. How many nickels and quarters are there if the coins are worth \$2.30? 11 nickels, 7 quarters
10. ✪ *Biology* A certain bacteria doubles the number of its cells every 20 min. A scientist puts 50 cells in a culture disk. How many cells will be in the culture dish after 2 h? 3,200 cells
11. The sum of the page numbers on two facing pages is 245. The product of the numbers is 15,006. What are the page numbers? 122, 123



## Alternative Assessment

Ask students to write in their journals a description of how they might teach someone else how to use Try, Test, Revise method of solving problems.

12. A student bought some compact discs for $12 each and some books for $5 each. She spent $39 in all on five items. How many of each item did she buy? 2 CDs, 3 books

13. Two runners ran as a team in a 5,000 m relay race. The first runner ran 500 m farther than the second runner. How many meters did each run? 2,750 m, 2,250 m

## Mixed Review

**Solve each equation.** *(Lesson 2-6)*

14. $\frac{m}{4} = 52$ 208
15. $-32 = -16y$ 2
16. $63 = \frac{t}{-3}$ −189
17. $3x = -18$ −6

**Identify each property shown.** *(Lessons 2-1 and 2-2)*

18. $8 + (-6 + 17) = [8 + (-6)] + 17$ Assoc. Prop. of Add.
19. $1{,}879 \cdot 1 = 1{,}879$ Ident. Prop. of Mult.
20. $8(52 - 37) = 8(52) - 8(37)$ Dist. Prop.
21. $-19 + 37 + (-31) = -19 + (-31) + 37$ Comm. Prop. of Add.

22. *Weather* The sound of thunder travels about one mile in five seconds. Suppose a bolt of lightning strikes 3 mi away from you. How long does it take for the sound of the thunder to reach you? about 15 s *(Lesson 1-9)*

## Math at Work

### Nurse

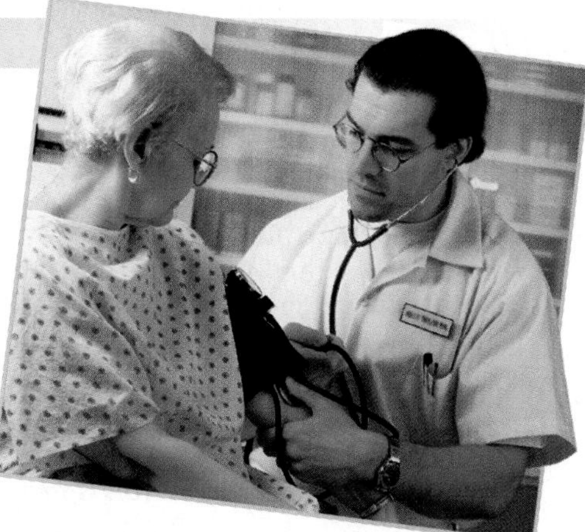

Anyone who has been in a hospital knows that nurses are patients' principal caregivers. Nurses dispense medication, monitor patients' progress, and tend to patients' daily medical needs.

Mathematics plays an important role in a nurse's duties. The nurse compares a patient's blood pressure reading against established norms and draws a conclusion about the result. Nurses also solve math problems when they convert one unit of measure of medication to another, and then calculate the total amount of various medications needed for a patient in their care.

For more information about careers in nursing, visit the Prentice Hall Web site. **www.phschool.com**



### Math at Work

If you have block scheduling or extended class periods, have small groups of students research the math used in nursing by contacting local hospitals, doctors' offices, nurses' professional associations, nursing services, or a nurses' training program at a local college to set up an interview with a nurse to discuss how nurses use math on the job.

Students can find additional information on the Web site **www.phschool.com**.

## Practice

**Use the Try, Test, Revise strategy to solve each problem.**

1. The length of a rectangle is 9 in. greater than the width. The area is 36 in.$^2$ Find the dimensions. 3 in by 12 in

Sample guesses are shown.

| Width | 1 | 2 | 3 | | | |
|---|---|---|---|---|---|---|
| Length | 10 | 11 | 12 | | | |
| Area | 10 | 22 | 36 | | | |

2. Shari Williams, a basketball player, scored 30 points on 2-point and 3-point goals. She hit 5 more 2-pointers than 3-pointers. How many of each did she score? 4 3-pointers; 9 2-pointers

Sample guesses are shown.

| 3-pointers | 1 | 2 | 3 | 4 | | |
|---|---|---|---|---|---|---|
| 2-pointers | 6 | 7 | 8 | 9 | | |
| points | 15 | 20 | 25 | 30 | | |

3. The sums and products of pairs of integers are given. Find each pair of integers.

a. sum = −12, product = 36 −6, −6
b. sum = −12, product = 35 −7, −5
c. sum = −12, product = 32 −8, −4
d. sum = −12, product = 11 −11, −1
e. sum = −12, product = 0 −12, 0

4. Jess had 3 more nickels than dimes for a total of $1.50. How many of each coin did he have? 9 dimes; 12 nickels

5. A brush cost $2 more than a comb. The brush and a comb together cost $3.78. Find the cost of each. brush $2.89; comb $.89

6. The hard-cover edition of a book cost 3 times as much as the paperback edition. Both editions together cost $26.60. Find the cost of each. paperback $6.65; hardcover $19.95



## Reteaching

On vacation, your family spent 4 hours driving 220 miles across a state. Part of the time you drove on a scenic state highway at 40 miles per hour. The rest of the time you drove on an interstate at 60 miles per hour. How long did you drive on each type of highway?

Try 3 hours on the state highway. That leaves 1 hour on the interstate. In 3 hours, at 40 miles per hour, you travel 120 miles. In 1 hour, at 60 miles per hour, you drive 60 miles. That is a total of 180 miles, which is not enough. You must have spent more time on the interstate.

Organize the conjectures in a table.

| Hours on State Hwy | Hours on Interstate | Distance on State Hwy | Distance on Interstate | Total Distance |
|---|---|---|---|---|
| 3 | 1 | 3(40) = 120 | 1(60) = 60 | 120 + 60 = 180 |
| 2 | 2 | 2(40) = 80 | 2(60) = 120 | 80 + 120 = 200 |
| 1 | 3 | 1(40) = 40 | 3(60) = 180 | 40 + 180 = 220 |

Your family traveled one hour on the state highway and three hours on the interstate highway.

**Solve using the Try, Test, Revise strategy. Organize your guesses in the table.**

1. The Wolverines scored 42 points in a football game. They scored 2 more field goals (3 points each) than touchdowns (6 points each). How many field goals and touchdowns did they score? 6 field goals and 4 touchdowns

Possible guesses are shown.

| Touchdowns | Fieldgoals | Points from Touchdowns | Points from Fieldgoals | Total Points |
|---|---|---|---|---|
| 1 | 3 | 6 | 9 | 15 |
| 2 | 4 | 12 | 12 | 24 |
| 3 | 5 | 18 | 15 | 33 |
| 4 | 6 | 24 | 18 | 42 |



## Enrichment

In many problems, you have used the Try, Test, Revise strategy to find two numbers. Here is a classic problem that involves finding three numbers. Finding three numbers is more complicated than finding two, but you can still do it by using the Try, Test, Revise strategy.

A farmer sold cows for $100 apiece, sheep for $20, and rabbits for $1. The farmer sold 100 animals in all and earned exactly $2,000.

**Complete to find the number of each type of animal sold.**

1. Let $c$ = the number of cows sold, $s$ = the number of sheep sold, and $r$ = the number of rabbits sold. Write an equation using $c$, $s$, and $r$ expressing the total number of animals sold. $c + s + r = 100$

2. Write a variable expression for:

a. the amount of money earned on the sale of cows $100c$
b. the amount of money earned on the sale of sheep $20s$
c. the amount of money earned on the sale of rabbits $r$

3. Use the above expressions to write an equation expressing the total amount of money the farmer earned. $100c + 20s + r = 2{,}000$

4. How do you know that the number of cows is less than 20? 20 cows would bring in $2,000, but 100 animals were sold.

5. Complete the table.

| Number of cows sold | 14 | 15 | 16 | 17 | 18 | 19 |
|---|---|---|---|---|---|---|
| Number of sheep sold | 3 | 5 | 6 | 8 | 9 | 2 |
| Number of rabbits sold | 83 | 80 | 78 | 75 | 73 | 79 |
| Amount earned | $1,543 | $1,680 | $1,798 | $1,935 | $2,053 | $2,019 |

6. Find the values in the table which produce earnings closest to $2,000. Adjust them using guess and test until you find the correct answer.

Number of cows 19 Number of sheep 1 Number of rabbits 80

## MATH TOOLBOX

### Data and Graphs

This Math Toolbox shows how to use a spreadsheet to create line and bar graphs.

### Math Background

A graph often shows the relationship between data expressed as related pairs more quickly and effectively than a table of data. Changes such as growth or decline are obvious at a glance, and unusual data stands out more than in a list. When one of the sets of numbers represents time, you usually use a line graph. A bar graph effectively uses the area of a bar to represent the relative sizes of different sets of data. The bars of a bar graph may be either horizontal or vertical. If there are no spaces between the bars, the bar graph is also called a *histogram*.

## Teaching Notes

**Error Prevention** Check the graph to make sure that no mistakes were made as the data was typed into the program.

**Monitoring Progress** Help students use the choices offered by the program effectively. For example, the program may have more than one way to distinguish the lines in the double line graph.

**Block Scheduling** If you have block scheduling or extended periods, you may wish to insert this Math Toolbox lesson between the completion of Part 1 of Lesson 2-8 and the beginning of Part 2 of Lesson 2-8.

# MATH TOOLBOX

Technology

*Before Lesson 2-8*

## *Data and Graphs*

Sometimes a graph will help you analyze data. You can use a spreadsheet program to create different types of graphs. First, enter the data in a spreadsheet. Then use a graphing tool to create an appropriate graph.

### EXAMPLE 1

**The spreadsheet gives the voting-age populations in thousands for two states. Graph the data in the spreadsheet.**

| | A | B | C |
|---|---|---|---|
| 1 | Year | Arizona | Georgia |
| 2 | 1988 | 2,610 | 4,631 |
| 3 | 1990 | 2,696 | 4,791 |
| 4 | 1992 | 2,812 | 5,006 |
| 5 | 1994 | 2,923 | 5,159 |
| 6 | 1996 | 3,094 | 5,396 |

Row 3 contains voting-age populations of both states in 1990.

Cell B3 contains the voting-age population of Arizona in 1990.

Column B contains the voting-age population of Arizona.

Choose an appropriate type of graph from your spreadsheet program. Line graphs are often useful to display changes in data over a period of time. Since the data show changes over time for two states, use a double line graph.

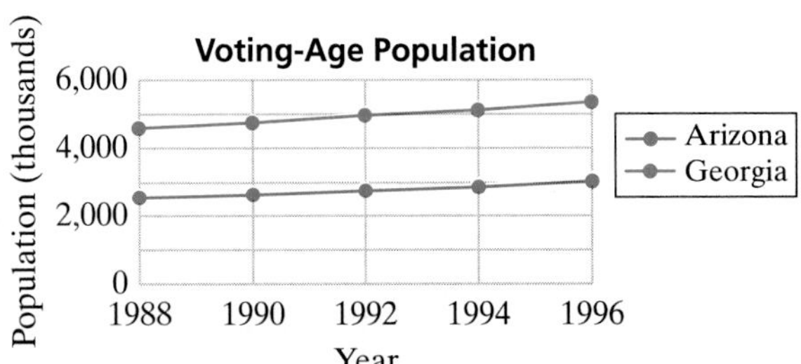


1. Use a spreadsheet to graph the data below. See margin.

**Average Prices Farmers Received**

| Year | 1990 | 1991 | 1992 | 1993 | 1994 | 1995 | 1996 | 1997 |
|---|---|---|---|---|---|---|---|---|
| Price for Turkey (¢/lb) | 39.4 | 38.4 | 37.7 | 39.0 | 40.4 | 41.6 | 43.3 | 39.9 |
| Price for Chicken (¢/lb) | 32.6 | 30.8 | 31.8 | 34.0 | 35.0 | 34.4 | 38.1 | 37.7 |

SOURCE: U.S. Department of Agriculture



- **Additional Example 1**
  Write a description of data you might gather at your school to find the answer to a research question and describe how you would graph it.
- **Additional Example 2**
  Write a description of data you might gather at your home to find the answer to a research question and describe how you would graph it.

## EXAMPLE 2

**The spreadsheet gives population data for five states. Graph the data in the spreadsheet.**

| | A | B | C |
|---|---|---|---|
| 1 | | Age 25 to 34 | Age 75 to 84 |
| 2 | California | 5,285 | 1,229 |
| 3 | Florida | 1,968 | 958 |
| 4 | Illinois | 1,764 | 517 |
| 5 | New York | 2,767 | 825 |
| 6 | Texas | 2,882 | 638 |

Bar graphs are often useful in comparing amounts. Since the data in the spreadsheet show populations for two age ranges, use a double bar graph.

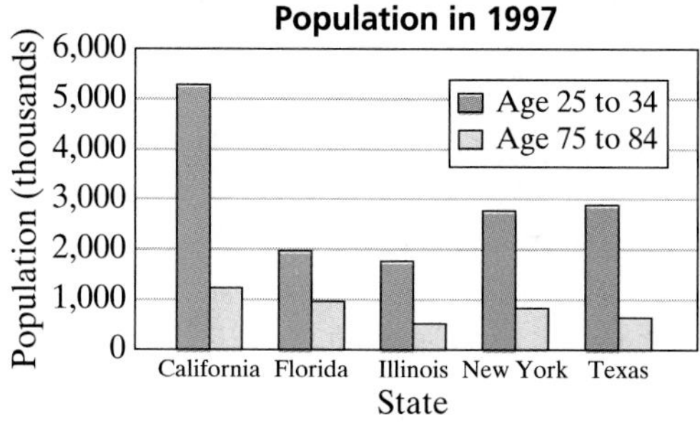


**2. a.** Use a spreadsheet to make a graph of the postage rate data below. See margin.

**Postage Rates**

| Sent from the United States to | First Class 1-oz Letter (¢) | Postcard (¢) |
|---|---|---|
| United States | 33 | 20 |
| Canada | 52 | 40 |
| Mexico | 46 | 35 |
| All other countries | 100 | 50 |

SOURCE: U.S. Postal Service

**b.** *Data Analysis* Use the graph you made in part (a). Which bar is tallest? Explain why. b. bar for 1-oz letters to countries other than U.S., Canada, and Mexico; reasons may vary. Sample: postage for 1-oz letters costs more than for postcards.

**3.** *Writing* Explain when you would use a line graph and when you would use a bar graph to display a data set. Answers may vary. Sample: Use a line graph to show change over time. Use a bar graph to compare quantities.



1. Graphs may vary. Sample:

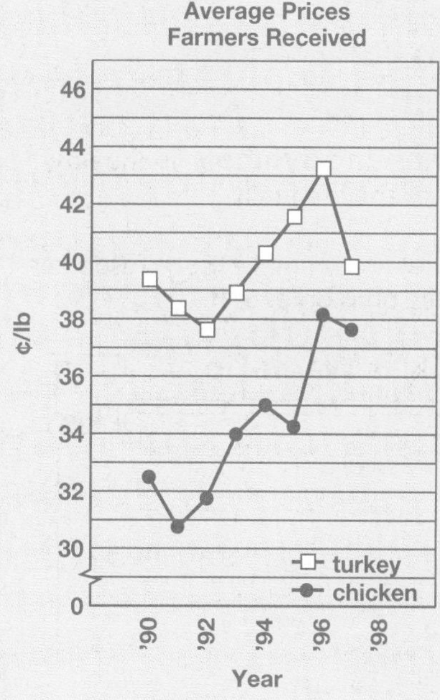


2. Graphs may vary. Sample:

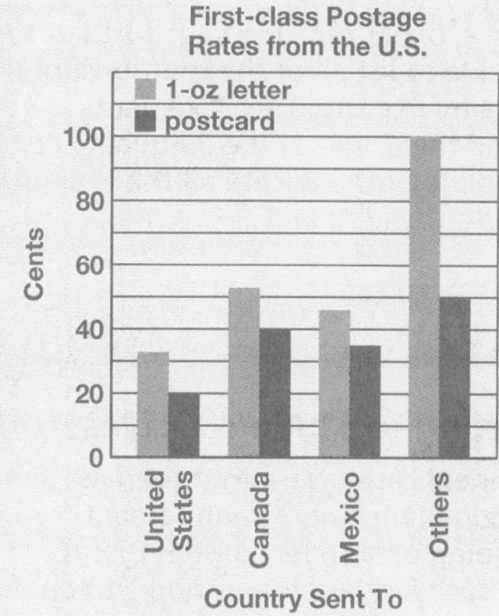

# 2-8

## Getting Ready

**Key Terms and Symbols** inequality, solution of the inequality

**Resources** A complete list of resources for this lesson is on p. 61H.

### Daily Skills Warm-Up

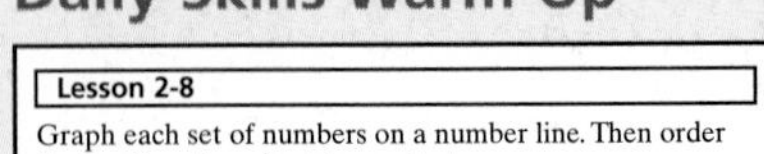

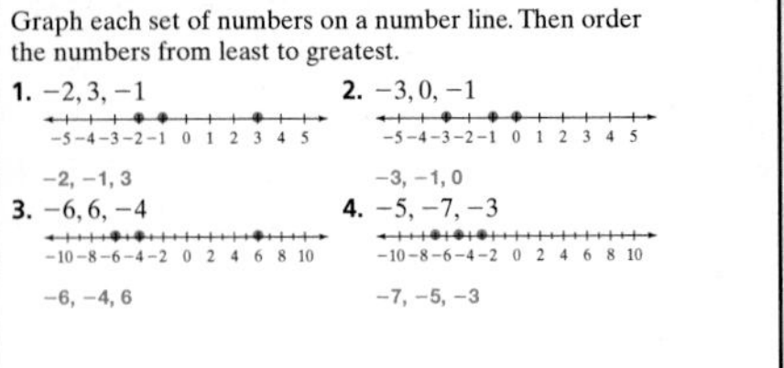

Lesson 2-8

Graph each set of numbers on a number line. Then order the numbers from least to greatest.

1. −2, 3, −1 — −2, −1, 3
2. −3, 0, −1 — −3, −1, 0
3. −6, 6, −4 — −6, −4, 6
4. −5, −7, −3 — −7, −5, −3

### Background for the Lesson

The equation $x = 1$ only has one solution: 1. However, the inequality $x < 1$ has an infinite number of solutions consisting of all numbers less than 1, for example: $\frac{1}{2}$, 0, −0.7, − 9, and so forth. It is impossible to list all of the solutions for an inequality like this. The statement $x < 1$ and the graph of the inequality on a number line both indicate all the solutions to the inequality.

## 1 Focus

### Connecting to Students' Lives

Ask if students are aware that there is often a minimum height requirement for people going on a roller coaster. Discuss whether such a ride requires riders to be exactly a certain height or at least a certain height. Help students conclude that in some problems or situations a range of values may be a correct answer.

### Connecting to Prior Knowledge

In Lesson 2-4, students learned the definition of the solution for an equation. In this lesson they graph the solutions for inequalities. In Lessons 2-9 and 2-10, students learn to solve inequalities by adding, subtracting, multiplying, or dividing.



# 2-8 Inequalities and Their Graphs

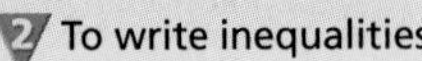

**What You'll Learn**

1. To graph inequalities
2. To write inequalities

**. . . And Why**

To model real-world situations such as problems involving nutrition

## PART 1 Graphing Inequalities

An **inequality** is a mathematical sentence that contains $>, <, \geq, \leq$, or $\neq$. Some inequalities contain a variable. Any number that makes an inequality true is a **solution of the inequality.** For example, −4 is a solution of $y \geq -5$ because $-4 \geq -5$.

You can graph the solutions of an inequality on a number line.

**Reading Math**

Read > as "is greater than."
Read < as "is less than."
Read ≥ as "is greater than or equal to."
Read ≤ as "is less than or equal to."

### Example 1

**Graph the solutions of each inequality on a number line.**

**a.** $y < 3$

An open dot shows that 3 is *not* a solution.

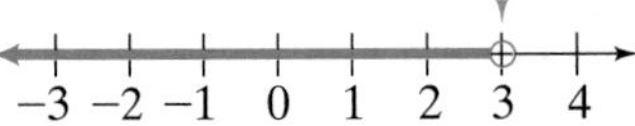

Shade all the points to the left of 3.

**b.** $x > -1$

An open dot shows that −1 is *not* a solution.

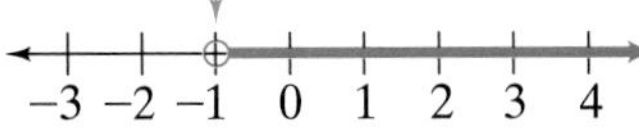

Shade all the points to the right of −1.

**c.** $a \leq -2$

A closed dot shows that −2 *is* a solution.

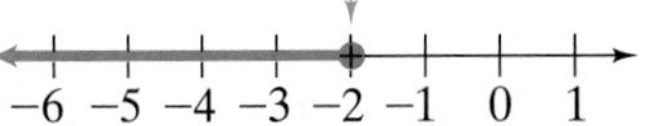

Shade all the points to the left of −2.

**d.** $-6 \leq g$

A closed dot shows that −6 *is* a solution.

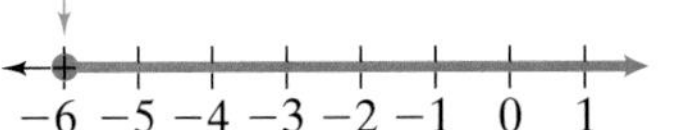

Shade all the points to the right of −6.

**Try This** Graph the solutions of each inequality.

1. $z < -2$
2. $4 > t$
3. $a \leq -5$
4. $2 \geq c$

1–4. See margin.



## Tools to Monitor Progress

### BEFORE THE LESSON

**To check prerequisite skills:**

- Comparing numbers

**Skills You Need,** p. 61

### DURING THE LESSON

**To check understanding:**

**Try This** exercises on student page

- **Additional Examples 1–2**

Write an inequality for the graph.

$x \geq -3$

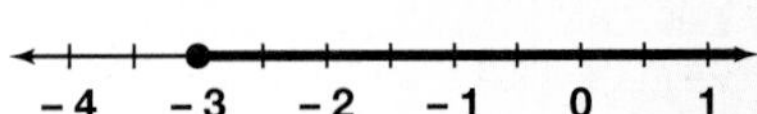

## Writing Inequalities

You can write an inequality for a graph.

### Example 2

**Write the inequality shown in each graph.**

**a.** 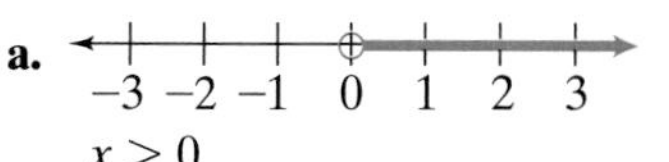
$x > 0$

**b.** 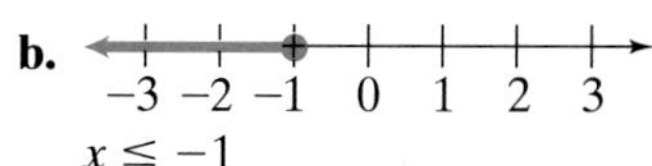
$x \leq -1$

### Try This

**5.** Write an inequality for the graph below. $x \geq 3$

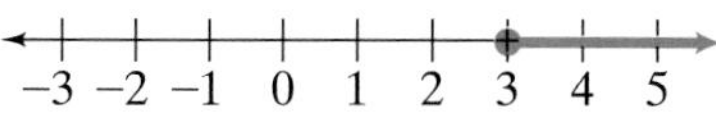

You can write an inequality to describe a real-world situation. Keep in mind that *at most* means "less than or equal to" and *at least* means "greater than or equal to."

**DATA ANALYSIS** CONNECTION

### Example 3

*Nutrition* **Food can be labeled *low sodium* only if it meets the requirement established by the federal government. Use the table to write an inequality for this requirement.**

| Label | Definition |
|---|---|
| Sodium-free food | Less than 5 mg per serving |
| Very low sodium food | At most 35 mg per serving |
| Low-sodium food | At most 140 mg per serving |

**Words** — a serving of low-sodium food | has at most | 140 mg sodium

Let $s$ = number of milligrams of sodium in a serving of low-sodium food.

**Inequality** — $s$ $\leq$ $140$

### Try This

**6.** Use the table in Example 3. A food is labeled sodium free. Write an inequality for $n$, the number of milligrams of sodium in a serving of sodium-free food. $n < 5$

# 2 Teach

## Part 1 Teaching Notes

Point out the parts of the graph of an inequality on a number line: the starting place (open or closed dot), the shaded line, and the arrow at the end.

### Example 1

**Build understanding.** Ask: What words do you use for the symbol <? for >? for ≤? less than, greater than, less than or equal to

## Part 2 Teaching Notes

Point out that an arrow to the right is associated with an inequality that has the variable greater than (or greater than or equal to) the starting number. An arrow to the left is associated with an inequality that has the variable less than (or less than or equal to) the starting number.

### Example 2

**Build understanding.** Ask: What is a sample number that is part of the solution for $x > 0$? Answers will vary, but should be any number greater than zero.

### Example 3

**Build understanding.** Ask: Is the sodium in a very low sodium food less than 35 mg or less than or equal to that amount? less than or equal to 35 mg

**Extension** Ask: Are there any fractions in the solution to $x \leq 1$? If so, name one. Yes; sample answers: $\frac{1}{2}$, $-\frac{1}{2}$.

**Error Prevention** A common error in graphing inequalities relates to drawing the dot at the beginning of the graph as either open or closed. Remind students to check the inequality symbol and to draw a closed dot if the symbol is ≤ or ≥ and to draw an open dot if the symbol is < or >.

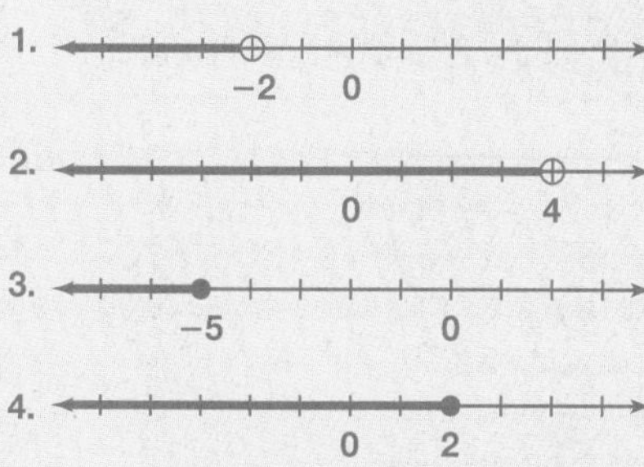

- **Additional Example 3**
  Use the table in Example 3 to write an inequality for a very low sodium food. $v \leq 35$

### AFTER THE LESSON

**To assess knowledge:**
**Lesson Quiz**
Graph the solutions.

**1.** $-7 \geq w$

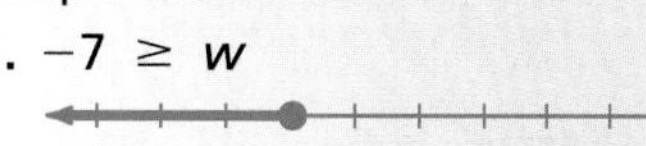

Write an inequality for the graph.

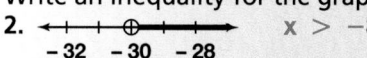

**2.** 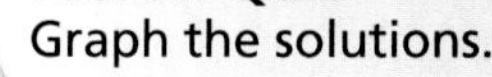 $x > -30$

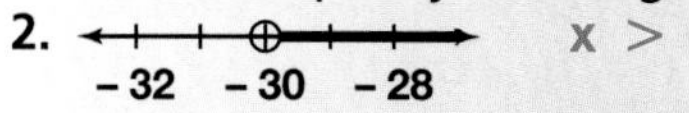

- For enrichment and reteaching options see Resources on p. 61H.

# 3 Practice/Assess

## Assignment Guide

To provide flexible scheduling, this lesson can be divided into parts.

**Part 1**
**Core** 1–4, 9–19
**Extension** 20

**Part 2**
**Core** 5–8, 21–29, 31–33, 37, 39
**Extension** 30, 34–36, 38

Mixed Review can be assigned at any time for maintenance.

**Tactile Learning** Mark a number line on the floor with masking tape. Have students walk the graph of their inequalities and place a shaded circle of paper or a circle of wire (or pipe cleaner) to show an closed or open dot.

### Exercises

**Test Prep Exercise 29** Students can immediately eliminate any choices that do not have the ≤ or ≥ symbol.

### Challenge

Challenge students to draw a graph of numbers that are both ≥ −1 and are also ≤ 1 (or between −1 and 1 inclusive).

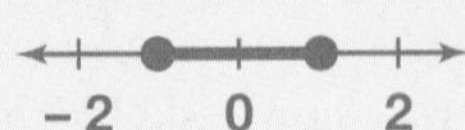


### Closure

To graph an inequality, use a number line. Use an open dot for > and <. Use a closed dot for ≥ and ≤.

### Daily Cumulative Review

**Solve using any strategy.** *(Lesson 2-7)*

1. Maxine is between 30 and 45 years old. The sum of the digits in her age is 11. How old is Maxine? 38 years old
2. Marty has dimes and nickels in his pocket. He has 2 times as many nickels as dimes. How many dimes and nickels are there if he has $3.20 in his pocket? 16 dimes and 32 nickels

**Solve each equation.** *(Lesson 2-6)*

3. $12m = 132$   $m = 11$
4. $-25p = 125$   $p = -5$
5. $-63 = 3v$   $-21 = v$
6. $\frac{p}{12} = -3$   $p = -36$
7. $\frac{r}{-3} = 6$   $r = -18$
8. $-9 = \frac{e}{-7}$   $63 = e$
9. $-3x = 60$   $x = -20$
10. $\frac{y}{4} = -2$   $y = -8$
11. $-72 = 8z$   $-9 = z$

**Mixed Review**

**Find each sum or difference.**

12. $-20 - 15$ (1-6)   $-35$
13. $-12 + (-14)$ (1-5)   $-26$
14. $0 + (-4)$ (1-5)   $-4$
15. $34 + (-12)$ (1-5)   $22$
16. $13 - 25$ (1-6)   $-12$
17. $-18 + 21$ (1-5)   $3$

**Write an expression for each quantity.**

18. the number of days in 5 weeks (1-1)   $5 \times 7$
19. the number of inches in 3 feet (1-1)   $3 \times 12$



# Exercises

## Check Understanding

**Match each inequality with its graph.**

1. $x \geq -4$ D
2. $x \leq -4$ A
3. $x > -4$ B
4. $x < -4$ C

A. (number line: −5 −4 −3 −2 −1 0 1 2 3)
B. (number line: −5 −4 −3 −2 −1 0 1)
C. (number line: −5 −4 −3 −2 −1 0 1)
D. (number line: −7 −6 −5 −4 −3 −2 −1 0 1)

**Write an inequality for each sentence.**

5. $x$ is less than 5. $x < 5$
6. $y$ is more than −3. $y > -3$
7. $b$ is less than or equal to 8. $b \leq 8$
8. *Critical Thinking* Explain how you know whether the endpoint of the graph of an inequality should be a solid dot or an open dot. Answers may vary. Sample: Use solid dot for ≥ and ≤; use open dot for > and <.

## Practice and Problem Solving

**Graph the solutions of each inequality on a number line.** 9–20. See margin.

9. $x < 7$
10. $y > 2$
11. $a < 3$
12. $c < 1$
13. $z > -3$
14. $x > 1$
15. $m \leq -4$
16. $b \geq 6$
17. $p \leq 4$
18. $a \geq -2$
19. $j \geq -1$
20. $j \leq 0.6$

**Write an inequality for each graph.**

21. (number line: −1 0 1 2 3 4) $x \geq 2$
22. (number line: −3 −2 −1 0 1 2) $x < 0$
23. (number line: −5 −4 −3 −2 −1 0) $x > -4$
24. (number line: −3 −2 −1 0 1 2 3) $x \leq -2$

**Write an inequality for each sentence.**

25. A number $c$ is at least twelve. $c \geq 12$
26. The total $t$ is greater than seven. $t > 7$
27. The price $p$ is not more than $30. $p \leq 30$
28. A number $n$ is positive. $n > 0$
29. **TEST PREP** Which inequality represents *A number t is greater than or equal to −8?* A
A. $-8 \leq t$   B. $t > -8$   C. $t \leq -8$   D. $-8 \geq t$
30. *Mathematical Reasoning* Compare. Use > or < to complete each statement.
a. If $a < b$, then $b$ ■ $a$. >
b. If $x > y$, and $y > z$, then $x$ ■ $z$. >



### Alternative Assessment

Have students make a chart of four examples, one for each type, <, ≤, >, ≥, and write each example in three different ways: as words, as symbols, and as a graph.

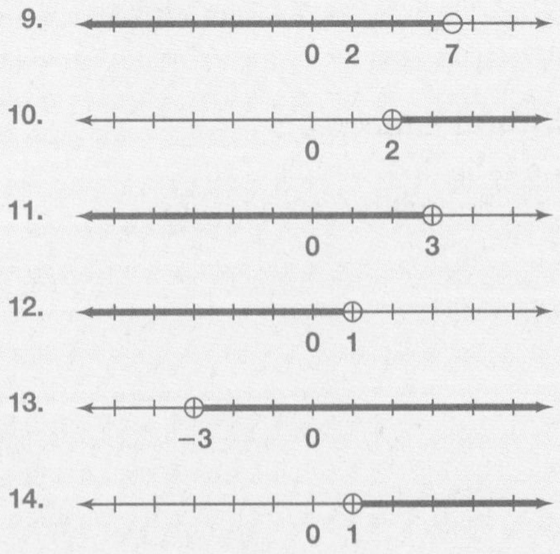

9. (number line: 0 2 7)
10. (number line: 0 2)
11. (number line: 0 3)
12. (number line: 0 1)
13. (number line: −3 0)
14. (number line: 0 1)

**Write an inequality for each situation.**

31. Fewer than 45 people attended a show. Let $n$ be the number of people who attended the show. $n < 45$

32. *Nutrition* High-fiber foods have at least 5 g of fiber per serving. Let $f$ be the number of grams of fiber per serving of high-fiber food. $f \geq 5$

33. A student pays for three movie tickets with a twenty-dollar bill and gets change back. Let $t$ be the cost of a movie ticket. $3t < 20$

**Use a variable to write an inequality for each situation.**
34–37. Variables may vary. Samples are given.

34.

$t$ = weight in tons; $t \leq 3$

35.

$s$ = speed in mi/h; $s \leq 25$

36.

$h$ = height in feet; $h \geq 4$

37. *Writing* Explain why graphing the solutions of an inequality is more efficient than listing all the solutions of the inequality. See below.

38. *Critical Thinking* No more than 50 students walked in a walkathon. Let $s$ be the number of students. Determine which numbers are reasonable values for $s$: 40, $45\frac{1}{2}$, 50, and 55. 40 and 50

39. *Open-ended* Describe a situation that you could represent with an inequality. Then write the inequality. Check students' work.

37. Answers may vary. Sample: Graphing can show infinitely many solutions.

*Explain how an inequality with one variable differs from an equation with one variable.*

## Mixed Review

**Solve each equation.** *(Lessons 2-5 and 2-6)*

40. $x - 5 = 29$ 34
41. $7y = 35$ 5
42. $t \div 12 = 6$ 72
43. $8 + m = -3$ −11

**Simplify each expression.** *(Lesson 2-3)*

44. $6 - 5s + 4s + 3$ $9 - s$
45. $n + (n + 2) + (n + 4)$ $3n + 6$

46. Write a variable expression for the number of weeks in $y$ years. *(Lesson 1-1)* $52y$

See also Extra Practice section.



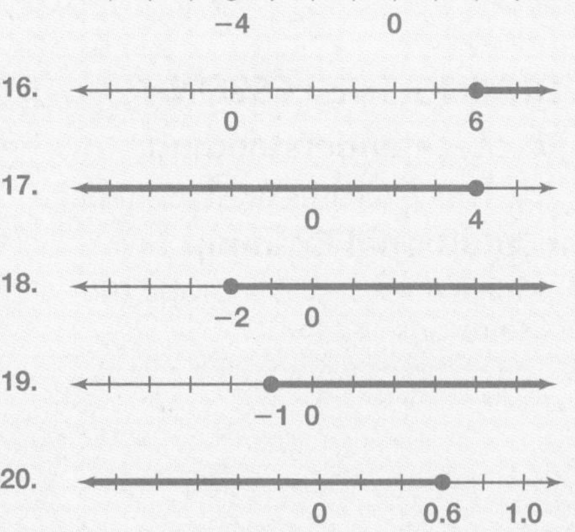


## Practice

**Write an inequality for each sentence.**

1. The total $t$ is less than sixteen. $t < 16$
2. A number $h$ is not less than 7. $h \geq 7$
3. The price $p$ is less than or equal to $25. $p \leq 25$
4. A number $n$ is negative. $n < 0$

**Write an inequality for each graph.**

5. (number line −8 to 2) $x \leq -7$
6. (number line −16 to 4) $x > -11$
7. (number line −5 to 5) $x < 2$
8. (number line −5 to 5) $x \geq -3$

**Graph the solutions of each inequality on a number line.**

9. $x < -2$
10. $y \geq -1$
11. $k > 1$
12. $p \leq 4$

**Write an inequality for each situation.**

13. Everyone in the class is under 13 years old. Let $x$ be the age of a person in the class. $x < 13$
14. The speed limit is 60 miles per hour. Let $s$ be the speed of a car driving within the limit. $s \leq 60$
15. You have $4.50 to spend on lunch. Let $c$ be the cost of your lunch. $c \leq \$4.50$

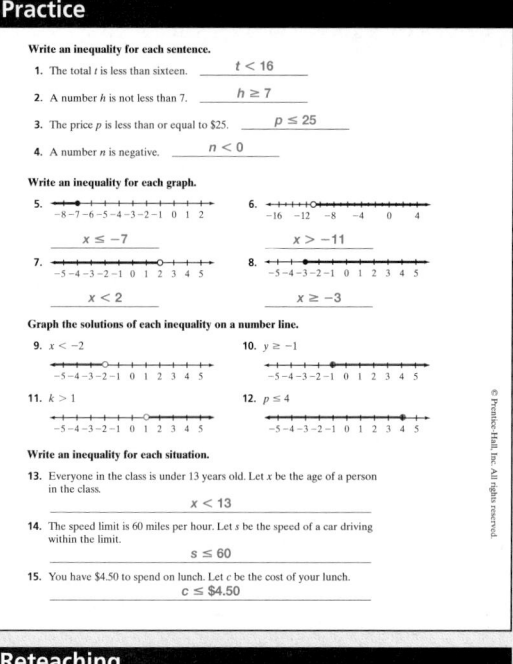

## Reteaching

Write an inequality for each graph.

a. (number line −5 to 5)

The open dot indicates 2 is not a solution. However, every number less than 2 is a solution. Thus, $x < 2$. Check by testing a point. Since 1 is shaded, try it. Is $1 < 2$? Yes.

b. (number line −5 to 5)

The closed dot indicates −1 is a solution. Every number greater than −1 is also a solution. Thus, $x \geq -1$. Check by testing a point. Since 2 is shaded, try it. Is $2 \geq -1$? Yes.

**Write an inequality for each graph.**

1. $x \geq -2$
2. $x \leq -3$
3. $x < 6$
4. $x > -5$
5. $x \geq 4$
6. $x > 0$
7. $x < -1$
8. $x \geq 2$
9. $x > 3$
10. $x \leq 0$



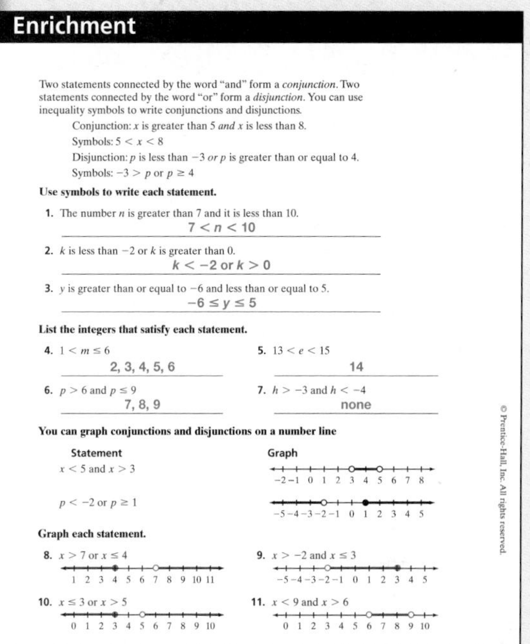

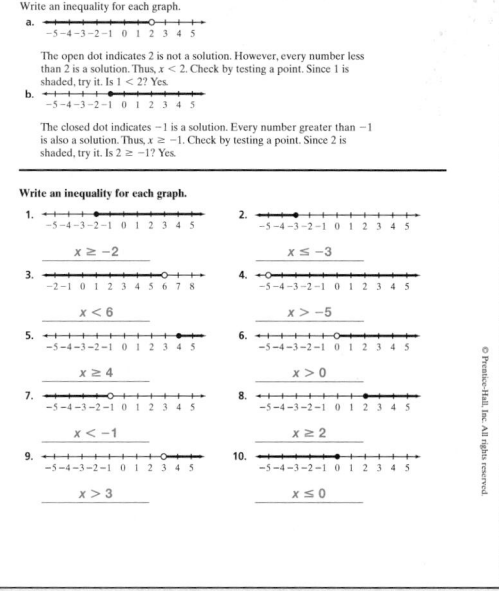

## Enrichment

Two statements connected by the word "and" form a *conjunction*. Two statements connected by the word "or" form a *disjunction*. You can use inequality symbols to write conjunctions and disjunctions.

Conjunction: $x$ is greater than 5 *and* $x$ is less than 8.
Symbols: $5 < x < 8$
Disjunction: $p$ is less than −3 *or* $p$ is greater than or equal to 4.
Symbols: $-3 > p$ or $p \geq 4$

**Use symbols to write each statement.**

1. The number $n$ is greater than 7 and it is less than 10. $7 < n < 10$
2. $k$ is less than −2 or $k$ is greater than 0. $k < -2$ or $k > 0$
3. $y$ is greater than or equal to −6 and less than or equal to 5. $-6 \leq y \leq 5$

**List the integers that satisfy each statement.**

4. $1 < m \leq 6$ 2, 3, 4, 5, 6
5. $13 < e < 15$ 14
6. $p > 6$ and $p \leq 9$ 7, 8, 9
7. $h > -3$ and $h < -4$ none

**You can graph conjunctions and disjunctions on a number line**

| Statement | Graph |
|---|---|
| $x < 5$ and $x > 3$ | (number line −2 to 8) |
| $p < -2$ or $p \geq 1$ | (number line −5 to 5) |

**Graph each statement.**

8. $x > 7$ or $x \leq 4$
9. $x > -2$ and $x \leq 3$
10. $x \leq 3$ or $x > 5$
11. $x < 9$ and $x > 6$

# 2-9

## Getting Ready

**Key Terms and Symbols** Subtraction Property of Inequality, Addition Property of Inequality

**Resources** A complete list of resources for this lesson is on p. 61H.

### Daily Skills Warm-Up

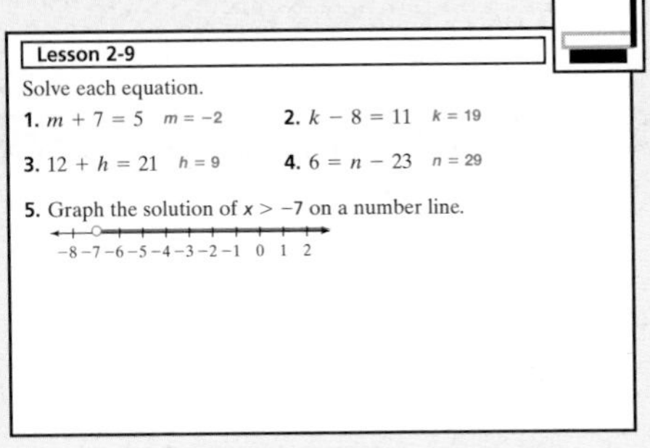

Lesson 2-9
Solve each equation.
1. m + 7 = 5   m = −2
2. k − 8 = 11   k = 19
3. 12 + h = 21   h = 9
4. 6 = n − 23   n = 29
5. Graph the solution of x > −7 on a number line.
−8 −7 −6 −5 −4 −3 −2 −1 0 1 2


### Background for the Lesson

Solving an inequality by addition or subtraction uses the same procedures as solving an equation by addition or subtraction. The Subtraction and Addition Properties of Inequality are exactly like their counterparts—the Subtraction and Addition Properties of Equality. The same number can be added or subtracted to both sides of an inequality without changing the inequality. The result is an equivalent inequality.

## 1 Focus

### Connecting to Prior Knowledge

In Lesson 2-5, students learned how to solve equations by adding or subtracting the same value on each side of an equation. In this lesson, they apply the same procedure to solving one-step inequalities. In Lesson 2-10, they will learn to solve inequalities by multiplying or dividing.

# Solving One-Step Inequalities by Adding or Subtracting

**What You'll Learn**

1. To solve one-step inequalities using subtraction
2. To solve one-step inequalities using addition

**. . . And Why**

To model problems involving computers

## Part 1 Solving Inequalities by Subtracting

Solving an inequality is similar to solving an equation. You want to get the variable alone on one side of the inequality.

You can see from the number line that if you subtract 2 from each side of the inequality $-1 < 2$, the resulting inequality $-3 < 0$ is still true.

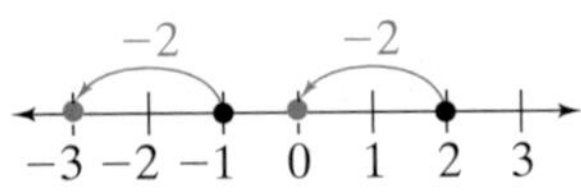


**Subtraction Property of Inequality**

You can subtract the same number from each side of an inequality.

| Arithmetic | Algebra |
|---|---|
| $7 > 4$, so $7 - 3 > 4 - 3$ | If $a > b$, then $a - c > b - c$. |
| $6 < 9$, so $6 - 2 < 9 - 2$ | If $a < b$, then $a - c < b - c$. |

### Example 1

**Solve each inequality. Graph the solutions.**

**a.** $n + 8 \geq 19$

$n + 8 \geq 19$

$n + 8 - 8 \geq 19 - 8$ Subtract 8 from each side.

$n \geq 11$ Simplify.

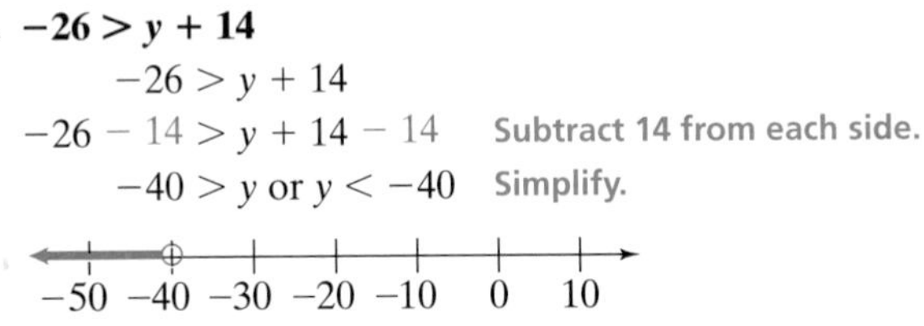


**b.** $-26 > y + 14$

$-26 > y + 14$

$-26 - 14 > y + 14 - 14$ Subtract 14 from each side.

$-40 > y$ or $y < -40$ Simplify.

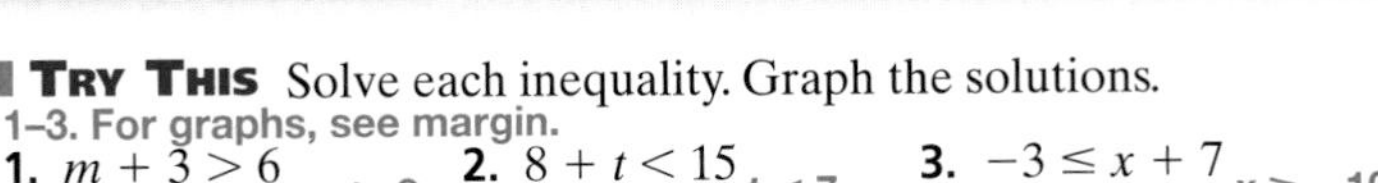


**Test Prep TIP**

You can use the related equation to check that you solved an inequality correctly. For example, use $-26 = y + 14$ for $-26 > y + 14$. Substitute the boundary point, $-40$, into the equation. Since $-26 = -40 + 14$, you solved correctly. You must also check that the inequality symbol in your solution is correct.

**Try This** Solve each inequality. Graph the solutions.

1–3. For graphs, see margin.

1. $m + 3 > 6$ $m > 3$
2. $8 + t < 15$ $t < 7$
3. $-3 \leq x + 7$ $x \geq -10$



## Tools to Monitor Progress

**BEFORE THE LESSON**

**To check prerequisite skills:**

- Working with integers

**Skills Handbook,** p. 741

**DURING THE LESSON**

**To check understanding:**

**Try This** exercises on student page

- **Additional Example 1**

  Solve $4 + s < 12$. Graph the solutions. $s < 8$;

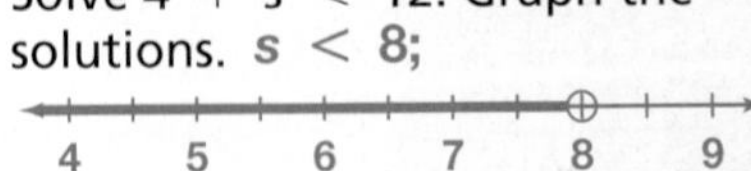

REAL-WORLD CONNECTION

## EXAMPLE 2

**Nearly 32 megabytes (MB) of memory are available for running your computer. If its basic systems require 12.1 MB, how much memory is available for other programs?**

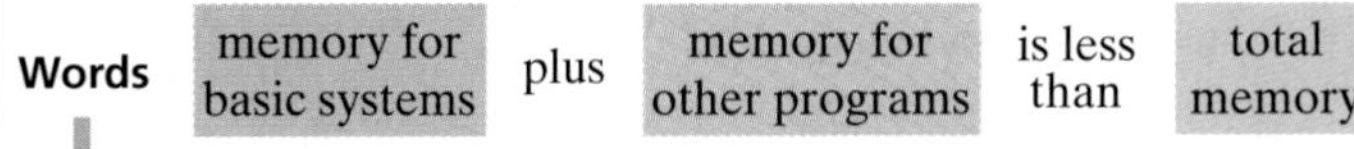


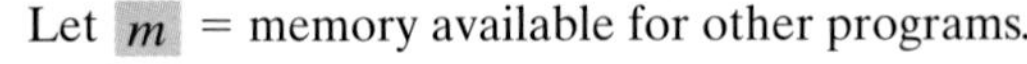


Inequality $12.1 \quad + \quad m \quad < \quad 32$

$12.1 + m < 32$

$12.1 - 12.1 + m < 32 - 12.1$ Subtract 12.1 from each side.

$m < 19.9$ Simplify.

Less than 19.9 MB of memory is available for other programs.

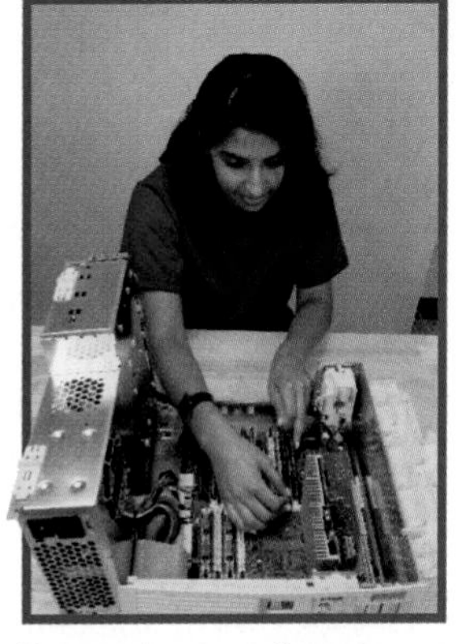

You can increase the memory of a computer by adding more memory chips. These chips have multiples of 8 megabytes of extra memory.

### TRY THIS

4. An airline lets you check up to 65 lb of luggage. One suitcase weighs 37 lb. How much can another suitcase weigh? $\leq 28$ lb

## PART 2 Using Addition to Solve Inequalities

To solve an inequality involving subtraction, use addition.

**Addition Property of Inequality**

You can add the same number to each side of an inequality.

| Arithmetic | Algebra |
|---|---|
| $7 > 3$, so $7 + 4 > 3 + 4$ | If $a > b$, then $a + c > b + c$. |
| $2 < 5$, so $2 + 6 < 5 + 6$ | If $a < b$, then $a + c < b + c$. |

## EXAMPLE 3

**Solve $n - 15 < 3$.**

$n - 15 < 3$

$n - 15 + 15 < 3 + 15$ Add 15 to each side.

$n < 18$ Simplify.

### TRY THIS Solve each inequality.

5. $m - 13 > 29$ $m > 42$
6. $v - 4 \leq 7$ $v \leq 11$
7. $t - 5 \geq 11$ $t \geq 16$



# 2 Teach

## PART 1 Part 1 Teaching Notes

As students graph their solutions, they may be able to visualize the graph more accurately if they first say the inequality by beginning with the variable. To read $8 > p$, say "$p$ is less than 8."

### Example 1

**Build understanding.** Ask: What must you do to isolate the variable on one side of the inequality? Subtract 8 from both sides.

### Example 2

**Build understanding.** Ask: Might the computer use more than 12.1 MB to run basic systems? yes

## PART 2 Part 2 Teaching Notes

Have students compare the Addition Property of Inequality to the Subtraction Property of Inequality.

### Example 3

**Build understanding.** Ask: Would you still add 15 to each side if the inequality was greater than rather than less than? Explain. Yes, because the Addition Property of Inequality is true regardless of the direction of the inequality sign.

**Extension** Ask: How would you change $x + 13 - 4 \geq 7$ into the equivalent inequality $x \geq -2$? Subtract 9 from both sides of the inequality.

**Error Prevention** Students may reverse the operation that they do to isolate the variable on one side of the equation when they work on the opposite side. In $x + 3 < 7$, students may mistakenly add 3 to the right side of the inequality, resulting in an inequality that is not equivalent to the original.

- **Additional Example 2**
  Suppose your computer's hard drive has a total capacity of 6.1 gigabytes (GB). The files you have stored on the hard drive occupy no more than 1.2 GB. How much storage space is left for other files? $s \geq 4.9$; At least 4.9 GB are left.
- **Additional Example 3**
  Solve $-10 < -13 + q$. $3 < q$

### AFTER THE LESSON

**To assess knowledge:**

**Lesson Quiz**

Solve each inequality.

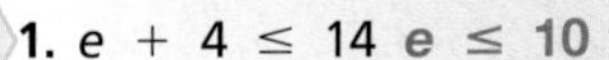

3. A number $q$ plus the opposite of 5 is less than or equal to 0. $q \leq 5$

- For enrichment and reteaching options see Resources on p. 61H.

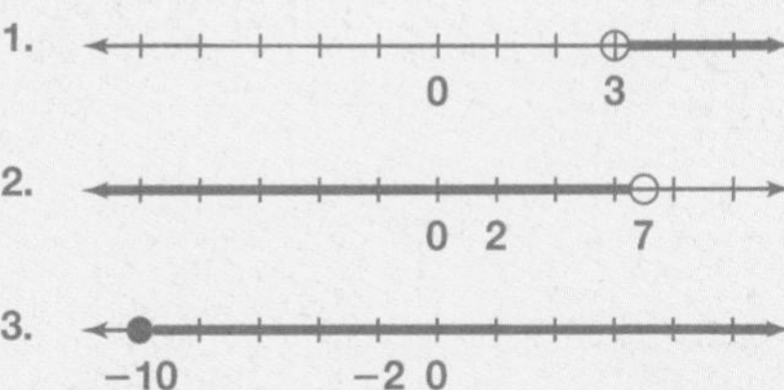

# 3 Practice/Assess

## Assignment Guide

To provide flexible scheduling, this lesson can be divided into parts.

**▼ Part 1**

**Core** 2, 5–6, 8–13, 25–26, 28–29, 31–32

**✪ Extension** 14–15, 23

**▼ Part 2**

**Core** 1, 3–4, 7, 16–21, 27, 30

**✪ Extension** 22, 24

Mixed Review can be assigned at any time for maintenance.

## Exercises

**Exercises 25–32** When writing inequalities from word problems, remind students to check whether to include "or equal to."

**Test Prep Exercise 30** Students may wish to select an example value for $x$ and for $y$ and then use these numbers to test the answer choices.

## ✪ Challenge

Solve $37 + n - 51 < 23 - 84$.
$n < -47$

## Closure

To solve a one-step inequality, use inverse operations and the properties of inequality to get the variable alone on one side of the inequality.

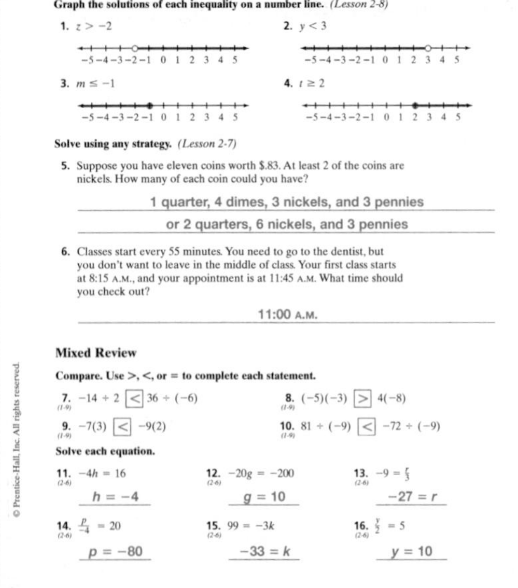

**Daily Cumulative Review**

**Graph the solutions of each inequality on a number line.** *(Lesson 2-8)*

1. $z > -2$
2. $y < 3$
3. $m \leq -1$
4. $t \geq 2$

**Solve using any strategy.** *(Lesson 2-7)*

5. Suppose you have eleven coins worth \$.83. At least 2 of the coins are nickels. How many of each coin could you have?
   1 quarter, 4 dimes, 3 nickels, and 3 pennies or 2 quarters, 6 nickels, and 3 pennies
6. Classes start every 55 minutes. You need to go to the dentist, but you don't want to leave in the middle of class. Your first class starts at 8:15 A.M., and your appointment is at 11:45 A.M. What time should you check out?
   11:00 A.M.

**Mixed Review**

**Compare. Use >, <, or = to complete each statement.**

7. (1-9) $-14 \div 2$ [<] $36 \div (-6)$
8. (1-9) $(-5)(-3)$ [>] $4(-8)$
9. (1-9) $-7(3)$ [<] $-9(2)$
10. (1-9) $81 \div (-9)$ [<] $-72 \div (-9)$

**Solve each equation.**

11. (2-6) $-4h = 16$ $h = -4$
12. (2-6) $-20g = -200$ $g = 10$
13. (2-6) $-9 = \frac{r}{3}$ $-27 = r$
14. (2-6) $\frac{p}{-4} = 20$ $p = -80$
15. (2-6) $99 = -3k$ $-33 = k$
16. (2-6) $\frac{y}{2} = 5$ $y = 10$



# Exercises

## Check Understanding

**What was done to the first inequality to get the second inequality?**

1. $x - 5 \geq 6; x \geq 11$
   Each side had 5 added.
2. $x + 8 \leq 11; x \leq 3$
   Each side had 8 subtracted.

**Solve each inequality. Graph the solutions.** 3–6. For graphs, see margin.

3. $n - 12 \leq 3$ $n \leq 15$
4. $x - 8 > -2$ $x > 6$
5. $w + 5 < 12$ $w < 7$
6. $2 > 9 + a$ $a < -7$

7. *Discussion* Explain how you know whether to add or subtract a number from each side to solve an inequality. Answers may vary. Sample: Use the inverse of the operation shown in the inequality.

## Practice and Problem Solving

**Solve each inequality. Graph the solutions.** 8. See margin. 9–22. See back of book.

8. $x + 6 \geq 7$ $x \geq 1$
9. $2 + m \leq 2$ $m \leq 0$
10. $6 < y + 19$ $y > -13$
11. $18 \leq 20 + w$ $w \geq -2$
12. $5 + x > -7$ $x > -12$
13. $16 + t < 42$ $t < 26$
14. ✪ $7.1 + r > 10.8$ $r > 3.7$
15. ✪ $9 < b + 3.7$ $b > 5.3$
16. $r - 4 \leq 3$ $r \leq 7$
17. $x - 7 < -15$ $x < -8$
18. $c - 9 > -5$ $c > 4$
19. $6 \leq h - 10$ $h \geq 16$
20. $w - 8 < -3$ $w < 5$
21. $3 \leq y - 5$ $y \geq 8$
22. ✪ $u - 3.5 \geq 8.9$ $u \geq 12.4$

*Mathematical Reasoning* **Justify each step.**

✪ 23.

| | |
|---|---|
| $4 + a + 3 > 16$ | |
| $4 + 3 + a > 16$ | Comm. Prop. of Add. |
| $7 + a > 16$ | Simplify. |
| $7 - 7 + a > 16 - 7$ | Subt. Prop. of Inequality |
| $a > 9$ | Simplify. |

✪ 24.

| | |
|---|---|
| $m - 2(8 - 5) \leq -9$ | |
| $m - 2(3) \leq -9$ | Subt. within parentheses |
| $m - 6 \leq -9$ | Simplify. |
| $m - 6 + 6 \leq -9 + 6$ | Add. Prop. of Inequality |
| $m \leq -3$ | Simplify. |

**Write an inequality for each sentence. Then solve the inequality.**

25. Thirteen plus a number $n$ is greater than fifteen. $13 + n > 15; n > 2$
26. The sum of a number $w$ and three is less than or equal to ten. $w + 3 \leq 10; w \leq 7$
27. Eleven subtracted from a number $b$ is less than negative twelve. $b - 11 < -12; b < -1$
28. The total weight limit for a truck is 100,000 lb. The truck weighs 36,000 lb empty. What is the most that the truck's load $w$ can weigh? 64,000 lb



## Alternative Assessment

Have students explain why the solution to an inequality can be a range of numbers.

3. 

4. 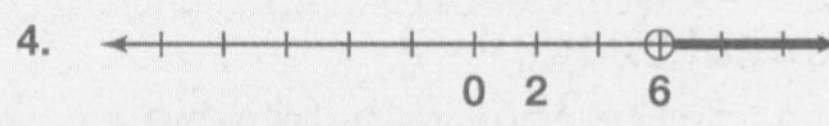


5. 0 2 7

6. 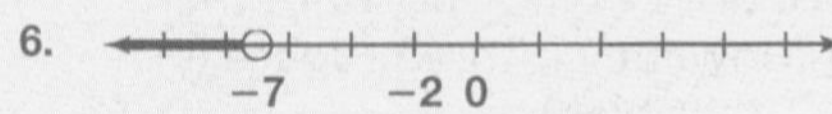


8. 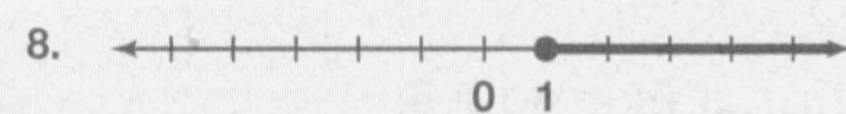

**29.** *Writing* Are $m > -2$ and $-2 < m$ both solutions to $m + 4 > 2$? Explain. Yes; solving $m + 4 > 2$ gives $m > -2$, which can also be written $-2 < m$.

**30.** **TEST PREP** If $x$ and $y$ are positive and $x > y$, which is true? A

A. $x > \frac{x + y}{2}$  B. $y > \frac{x + y}{2}$  C. $x = \frac{x + y}{2}$  D. $x < \frac{x + y}{2}$

**31.** *Budgeting* You are saving to buy a bicycle that will cost at least \$120. Your parents give you \$45 toward the bicycle. Write an inequality to find how much money $m$ you will have to save. $45 + m \geq 120$; at least \$75

**32.** Use the table at the right. Suppose your computer's basic system uses at least 12 MB of memory.

a. You want to have your e-mail active while you work on a paper with your word processor. How much memory $m$ must your computer have? at least 27.6 MB

b. If you also want to search the Web for data at the same time, how much memory $m$ must your computer have? at least 36.9 MB

**Computer Memory**

| Application | Memory Requirement |
|---|---|
| Word processor | 11.2 MB |
| Spreadsheet | 5.3 MB |
| Web browser | 9.3 MB |
| E-mail | 4.4 MB |

## Mixed Review

**Graph the solutions of each inequality.** *(Lesson 2-8)*

**33.** $x < 2$  **34.** $x \geq -5$  **35.** $y \leq 4$  **36.** $m > 0$

33–36. See margin.

**Simplify each expression.** *(Lesson 2-3)*

**37.** $4x + 6 - 2x + 7$ $2x + 13$  **38.** $9 - 5r + 2(r - 3)$ $3 - 3r$  **39.** $-4 - 5t + t - 10$ $-4t - 14$

**40.** Write an integer to represent a debt of \$35. *(Lesson 1-4)* $-35$

## Checkpoint 2

**Lessons 2-4 through 2-9**

**Is each equation *true, false,* or an *open sentence?***

**1.** $4 + 15 = 27 - 8$ true  **2.** $-30 = 9w$ open  **3.** $|9 - 10| = 8 - 9$ false

**Solve each equation or inequality.**

**4.** $y - 3 = -7$ $-4$  **5.** $x + 4 = 8$ 4  **6.** $7t = 42$ 6  **7.** $m \div 8 = -4$ $-32$

**8.** $-90 = 10f$ $-9$  **9.** $m + 5 > -4$ $m > -9$  **10.** $r - 12 < 7$ $r < 19$  **11.** $9 \leq 3 + a$ $a \geq 6$

**12.** *Open-ended* Describe a situation that can be modeled using an inequality. Write the inequality. Check students' work.

**13.** *Choose a Strategy* You have some quarters, dimes, and pennies. You have eight coins worth \$.77 altogether. How many of each type of coin do you have? 1 quarter, 5 dimes, 2 pennies



33.
34.
35.
36.

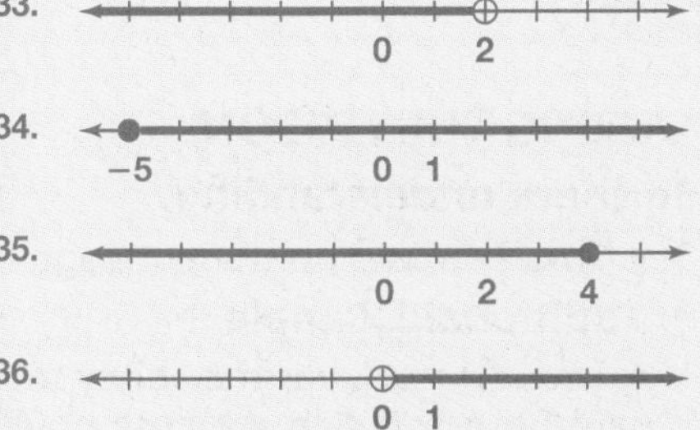


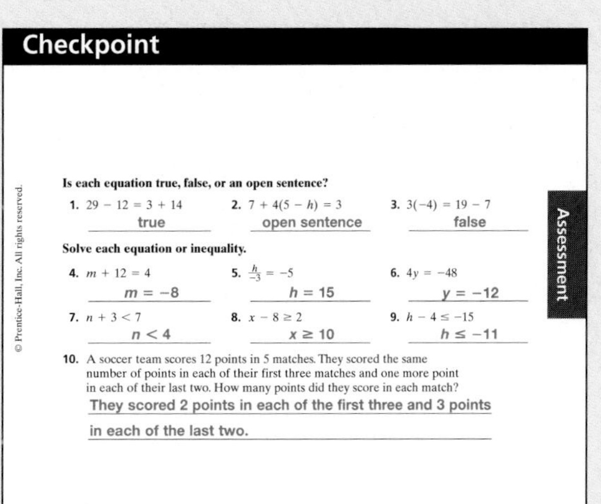

## Checkpoint

**Is each equation true, false, or an open sentence?**

1. $29 - 12 = 3 + 14$ true
2. $7 + 4(5 - h) = 3$ open sentence
3. $3(-4) = 19 - 7$ false

**Solve each equation or inequality.**

4. $m + 12 = 4$ $m = -8$
5. $\frac{h}{-3} = -5$ $h = 15$
6. $4y = -48$ $y = -12$
7. $n + 3 < 7$ $n < 4$
8. $x - 8 \geq 2$ $x \geq 10$
9. $h - 4 \leq -15$ $h \leq -11$

10. A soccer team scores 12 points in 5 matches. They scored the same number of points in each of their first three matches and one more point in each of their last two. How many points did they score in each match? They scored 2 points in each of the first three and 3 points in each of the last two.

Assessment



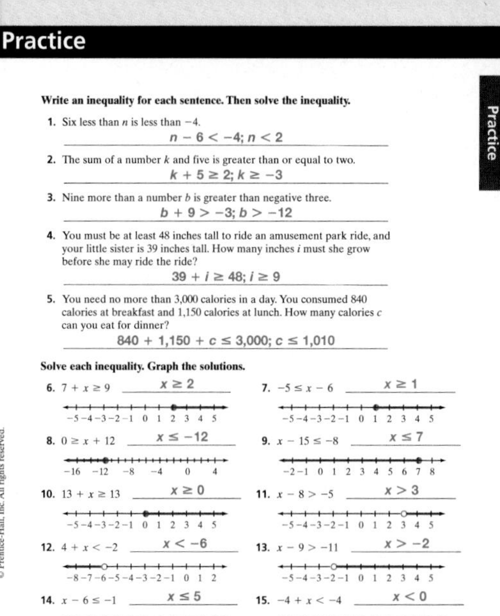

## Practice

**Write an inequality for each sentence. Then solve the inequality.**

1. Six less than $n$ is less than $-4$. $n - 6 < -4$; $n < 2$
2. The sum of a number $k$ and five is greater than or equal to two. $k + 5 \geq 2$; $k \geq -3$
3. Nine more than a number $b$ is greater than negative three. $b + 9 > -3$; $b > -12$
4. You must be at least 48 inches tall to ride an amusement park ride, and your little sister is 39 inches tall. How many inches $i$ must she grow before she may ride the ride? $39 + i \geq 48$; $i \geq 9$
5. You need no more than 3,000 calories in a day. You consumed 840 calories at breakfast and 1,150 calories at lunch. How many calories $c$ can you eat for dinner? $840 + 1{,}150 + c \leq 3{,}000$; $c \leq 1{,}010$

**Solve each inequality. Graph the solutions.**

6. $7 + x \geq 9$ $x \geq 2$
7. $-5 \leq x - 6$ $x \geq 1$
8. $0 \geq x + 12$ $x \leq -12$
9. $x - 15 \leq -8$ $x \leq 7$
10. $13 + x \geq 13$ $x \geq 0$
11. $x - 8 > -5$ $x > 3$
12. $4 + x < -2$ $x < -6$
13. $x - 9 > -11$ $x > -2$
14. $x - 6 \leq -1$ $x \leq 5$
15. $-4 + x < -4$ $x < 0$

Practice



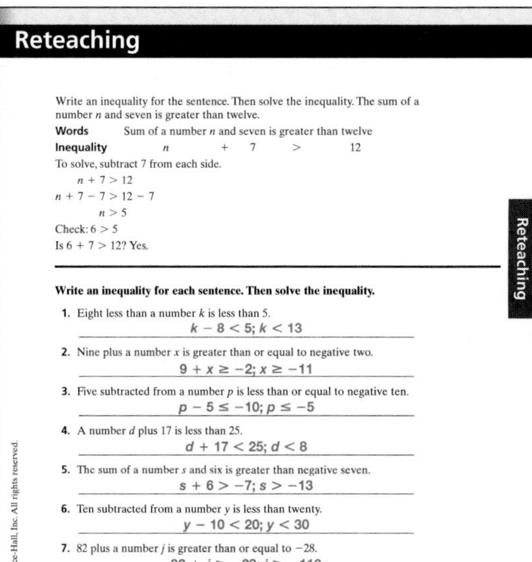

## Reteaching

Write an inequality for the sentence. Then solve the inequality. The sum of a number $n$ and seven is greater than twelve.

**Words** Sum of a number $n$ and seven is greater than twelve

**Inequality** $n$ + 7 > 12

To solve, subtract 7 from each side.

$n + 7 > 12$

$n + 7 - 7 > 12 - 7$

$n > 5$

Check: $6 > 5$

Is $6 + 7 > 12$? Yes.

**Write an inequality for each sentence. Then solve the inequality.**

1. Eight less than a number $k$ is less than 5. $k - 8 < 5$; $k < 13$
2. Nine plus a number $x$ is greater than or equal to negative two. $9 + x \geq -2$; $x \geq -11$
3. Five subtracted from a number $p$ is less than or equal to negative ten. $p - 5 \leq -10$; $p \leq -5$
4. A number $d$ plus 17 is less than 25. $d + 17 < 25$; $d < 8$
5. The sum of a number $s$ and six is greater than negative seven. $s + 6 > -7$; $s > -13$
6. Ten subtracted from a number $y$ is less than twenty. $y - 10 < 20$; $y < 30$
7. 82 plus a number $j$ is greater than or equal to $-28$. $82 + j \geq -28$; $j \geq -110$
8. A number $n$ minus 9 is less than or equal to $-23$. $n - 9 \leq -23$; $n \leq -14$
9. Nineteen less than a number $h$ is greater than three. $h - 19 > 3$; $h > 22$

Reteaching



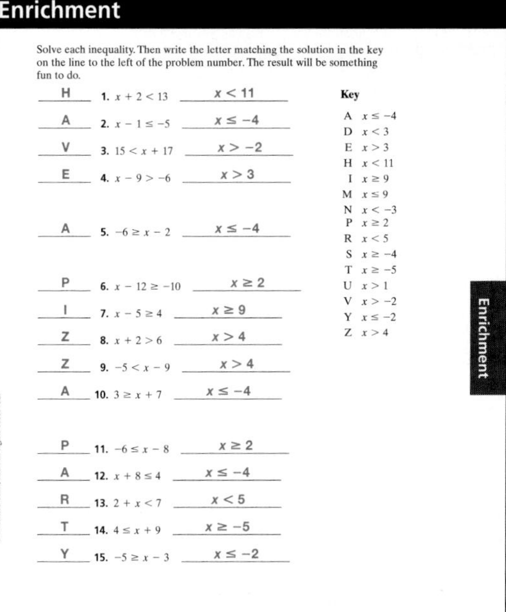

## Enrichment

Solve each inequality. Then write the letter matching the solution in the key on the line to the left of the problem number. The result will be something fun to do.

H 1. $x + 2 < 13$ $x < 11$
A 2. $x - 1 \leq -5$ $x \leq -4$
V 3. $15 < x + 17$ $x > -2$
E 4. $x - 9 > -6$ $x > 3$
A 5. $-6 \geq x - 2$ $x \leq -4$
P 6. $x - 12 \geq -10$ $x \geq 2$
I 7. $x - 5 \geq 4$ $x \geq 9$
Z 8. $x + 2 > 6$ $x > 4$
Z 9. $-5 < x - 9$ $x > 4$
A 10. $3 \geq x + 7$ $x \leq -4$
P 11. $-6 \leq x - 8$ $x \geq 2$
A 12. $x + 8 \leq 4$ $x \leq -4$
R 13. $2 + x < 7$ $x < 5$
T 14. $4 \leq x + 9$ $x \geq -5$
Y 15. $-5 \geq x - 3$ $x \leq -2$

**Key**

A $x \leq -4$
D $x < 3$
E $x > 3$
H $x < 11$
I $x \geq 9$
M $x \leq 9$
N $x < -3$
P $x \geq 2$
R $x < 5$
S $x \geq -4$
T $x \geq -5$
U $x > 1$
V $x > -2$
Y $x \leq -2$
Z $x > 4$

Enrichment

# 2-10

## Getting Ready

**Key Terms and Symbols** Division Properties of Inequality, Multiplication Properties of Inequality

**Resources** A complete list of resources for this lesson is on p. 61H.

### Daily Skills Warm-Up

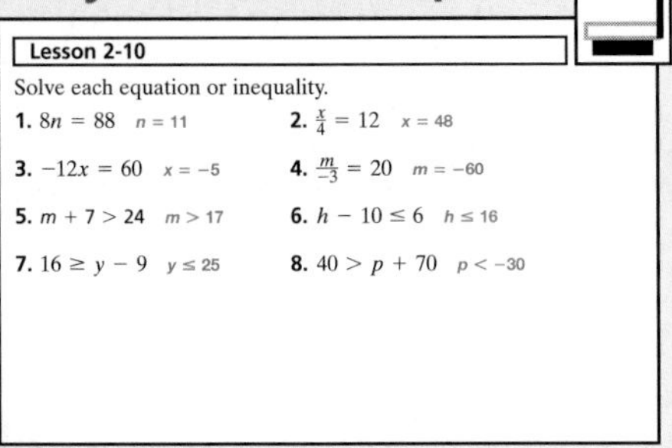
Lesson 2-10

Solve each equation or inequality.

1. $8n = 88$ $n = 11$
2. $\frac{x}{4} = 12$ $x = 48$
3. $-12x = 60$ $x = -5$
4. $\frac{m}{-3} = 20$ $m = -60$
5. $m + 7 > 24$ $m > 17$
6. $h - 10 \le 6$ $h \le 16$
7. $16 \ge y - 9$ $y \le 25$
8. $40 > p + 70$ $p < -30$

### Background for the Lesson

When you solve inequalities by multiplying or dividing both sides by a negative number, you change the direction of the inequality symbol. For example, the inequality $2 < 4$ is true. Multiply both sides by $-1$. The result without reversing the sign is the false statement $-2 < -4$. When you multiply or divide an inequality by a negative number, you must always also reverse the direction of the inequality symbol so that the new inequality is equivalent to the original.

## 1 Focus

### Investigate

Draw a number line on the board. Mark 6 and 12 on the number line. Point out that the number to the right, 12, is the greater. Graph $-6$ and $-12$ on the number line. Show students that the greater number, $-6$, is still to the right.

### Connecting to Prior Knowledge

In Lesson 2-9, students solved one-step inequalities by adding or subtracting. In this lesson, they solve inequalities by multiplying or dividing. In Lesson 3-6, students use multiplying or dividing to solve equations with decimals.



# 2-10 Solving One-Step Inequalities by Multiplying or Dividing

**What You'll Learn**

1. To solve one-step inequalities using division
2. To solve one-step inequalities using multiplication

**. . . And Why**

To model real-world problems involving transportation

## *Investigate*

SOLVING INEQUALITIES

Explore what happens when you divide each side of an inequality by a number.

1. Simplify each expression at the right. Replace each ■ with > or <.
2. *Patterns* Does the direction of the inequality symbol stay the same as you divide each side of an inequality by the given numbers? Explain your reasoning. No; the inequality symbol switches direction when you divide by a negative number.

$6 \div 3$ ■ $12 \div 3$ <
$6 \div 2$ ■ $12 \div 2$ <
$6 \div 1$ ■ $12 \div 1$ <
$6 \div (-1)$ ■ $12 \div (-1)$ >
$6 \div (-2)$ ■ $12 \div (-2)$ >
$6 \div (-3)$ ■ $12 \div (-3)$ >

## PART 1 Solving Inequalities Using Division

You can solve an inequality that involves multiplication by dividing each side of the inequality by a nonzero number.

**Division Properties of Inequality**

If you divide each side of an inequality by a positive number, the direction of an inequality symbol is unchanged.

| Arithmetic | Algebra |
|---|---|
| $3 < 6$, so $\frac{3}{3} < \frac{6}{3}$ | If $a < b$ and $c$ is positive, then $\frac{a}{c} < \frac{b}{c}$. |
| $8 > 2$, so $\frac{8}{2} > \frac{2}{2}$ | If $a > b$ and $c$ is positive, then $\frac{a}{c} > \frac{b}{c}$. |

If you divide each side of an inequality by a negative number, *the direction of the inequality symbol is reversed.*

| Arithmetic | Algebra |
|---|---|
| $6 < 12$, so $\frac{6}{-3} > \frac{12}{-3}$ | If $a < b$ and $c$ is negative, then $\frac{a}{c} > \frac{b}{c}$. |
| $16 > 8$, so $\frac{16}{-4} < \frac{8}{-4}$ | If $a > b$ and $c$ is negative, then $\frac{a}{c} < \frac{b}{c}$. |



## Tools to Monitor Progress

**BEFORE THE LESSON**

**To check prerequisite skills:**

- Dividing whole numbers

**Skills Handbook**, p. 726

**Skills Intervention Kit**, Whole Numbers

**DURING THE LESSON**

**To check understanding:**

**Try This** exercises on student page

- **Additional Example 1**

A 1-ton (t) truck has the ability to haul 1 t, or 2,000 lb. At most, how many television sets could the truck carry, if each one weighs 225 lb? 8 television sets

REAL-WORLD CONNECTION

## EXAMPLE 1

*Engineering* **An elevator can carry up to 2,500 lb. Suppose the weight of an average adult is 150 lb. At most how many average-sized adults can safely ride the elevator at the same time?**

| | | | | | |
|---|---|---|---|---|---|
| **Words** | the number of adults | times | 150 lb | is less than or equal to | 2,500 lb |
| | Let $x$ = number the number of adults. | | | | |
| **Inequality** | $x$ | $\cdot$ | 150 lb | $\leq$ | 2,500 |

$150x \leq 2{,}500$

$\frac{150x}{150} \leq \frac{2{,}500}{150}$ Divide each side by 150.

$x \leq 16.\overline{6}$ Simplify. Round the answer down to find a whole number of people.

At most 16 average adults can safely ride an elevator at one time.

**Check** Is the answer reasonable? The total weight of 16 average adults is $16(150) = 2{,}400$ lb, which is less than 2,500 lb but so close that another adult could not ride. The answer is reasonable.

Express elevators can travel as fast as 1,800 ft/min.

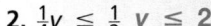

**TRY THIS** Solve each inequality.

**3.** $4x > 40$ $x > 10$ **4.** $-21 \geq 3m$ $m \leq -7$ **5.** $36 \geq -9t$ $t \geq -4$

## 2 Solving Inequalities Using Multiplication

You can solve inequalities that involve division.

### Multiplication Properties of Inequality

If you multiply each side of an inequality by a positive number, the direction of the inequality symbol is unchanged.

| Arithmetic | Algebra |
|---|---|
| $3 < 4$, so $3(5) < 4(5)$ | If $a < b$ and $c$ is positive, then $ac < bc$. |
| $7 > 2$, so $7(6) > 2(6)$ | If $a > b$ and $c$ is positive, then $ac > bc$. |

If you multiply each side of an inequality by a negative number, *the direction of the inequality symbol is reversed.*

| Arithmetic | Algebra |
|---|---|
| $6 < 9$, so $6(-2) > 9(-2)$ | If $a < b$ and $c$ is negative, then $ac > bc$. |
| $7 > 5$, so $7(-3) < 5(-3)$ | If $a > b$ and $c$ is negative, then $ac < bc$. |



# 2 Teach

## Part 1 Teaching Notes

Help students understand why the direction of the inequality symbol must be reversed when dividing by a negative number. Have students divide several numerical inequalities by negative numbers. They will soon see that the inequality is false after the division unless the sign is reversed to maintain equivalence.

### Example 1

**Build understanding.** Ask: Would 10 adults be too many? would 20? no; yes

## Part 2 Teaching Notes

Ask students to hypothesize whether they must change the direction of the inequality symbol when they multiply both sides of an inequality by a negative number. Have volunteers go to the board to multiply a numeric inequality to test their hypothesis.

**Reading/Writing Math** Make sure students understand that "reversing the direction of the inequality symbol" means the same thing as "reversing the inequality." Confusion may occur because the same phrase is sometimes used for rewriting $4 < x$ as $x > 4$.

**Error Prevention** Have students write rules for dividing or multiplying inequalities on a note card. Make sure students include examples of how to change the direction of the inequality on their note cards. Suggest that students refer to their note cards as they solve inequalities.

- **Additional Example 2**
  Solve $\frac{1}{-8}z \leq -2$. $z \geq 16$

## AFTER THE LESSON

**To assess knowledge:**
**Lesson Quiz**
Solve each inequality.

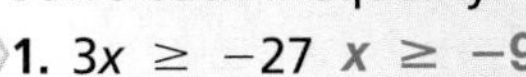

1. $3x \geq -27$ $x \geq -9$
2. $\frac{1}{4}y \leq \frac{1}{2}$ $y \leq 2$
3. $-5w > 15$ $w < -3$
4. $\frac{-x}{5} \leq 0$ $x \geq 0$
5. $4f > -12$ $f > -3$

- For enrichment and reteaching options see Resources on p. 61F.

## Example 2

**Build understanding.** Ask: Why does $\frac{t}{-4}$ multiplied by $-4$ equal $t$? because $\frac{-4}{-4} = 1$ and $1 \cdot t = t$

**Visual Learning** Help students identify inequalities where they will divide or multiply by a negative number. Suggest that they circle the inequality as a reminder to reverse the direction of the inequality symbol.

## Different Ways to Solve a Problem

**Build understanding.** Ask: Is dividing $-3x$ by $-3$ the same as adding $3x$ to $-3x$? Explain. No; dividing $-3x$ by $-3$ equals $x$, but $3x$ added to $-3x$ equals zero.

**Extension** Ask: What would happen to an inequality if both sides were multiplied by zero? The value of each side would be zero; the new inequality would not be equivalent to the original.

**Error Prevention** A common error occurs when students reverse the inequality every time they see a negative sign. For example, students may solve $6x > -12$ incorrectly as $x < -2$. Suggest that students substitute values from their solution into the original inequality to check.

**Connecting to Geometry** Inequalities are often used to describe geometric figures. For example, an acute angle is an angle that measures less than 90°. An obtuse angle is an angle that measures greater than 90°, but less than 180°.



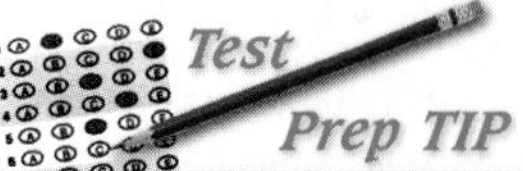


You can check whether the inequality symbol in your solution is correct. For example, for the inequality $\frac{t}{-4} \geq 7$, choose a number that is less than $-28$, such as $-32$. Substitute $-32$ into the original inequality. Since $\frac{-32}{-4} = 8$ and 8 is greater than 7, the inequality symbol in the solution is correct.

### EXAMPLE 2

**Solve $\frac{t}{-4} \geq 7$.**

$\frac{t}{-4} \geq 7$

$-4\left(\frac{t}{-4}\right) \leq -4(7)$ Multiply each side by $-4$ and reverse the inequality symbol.

$t \leq -28$ Simplify.

**TRY THIS** Solve each inequality.

6. $\frac{m}{4} \geq 2$ $m \geq 8$
7. $\frac{t}{-3} < 7$ $t > -21$
8. $5 < \frac{r}{7}$ $r > 35$

## Different Ways to Solve a Problem

**Solve $-3x < 12$.**

**Method 1**

Divide each side by $-3$ and reverse the direction of the inequality symbol.

$-3x < 12$

$\frac{-3x}{-3} > \frac{12}{-3}$

$x > -4$

**Method 2**

Rewrite the inequality so the coefficient of the variable is positive.

$-3x < 12$

$-3x + 3x < 12 + 3x$

$0 < 12 + 3x$

$0 - 12 < 3x + 12 - 12$

$-12 < 3x$

$\frac{-12}{3} < \frac{3x}{3}$

$-4 < x$, or $x > -4$

**Choose a Method**

1. Which method would you use to solve this inequality? Explain. Answers may vary. Sample: Method 1; it uses fewer steps.
2. Solve $18 < -6x$ using Method 1 or Method 2. $x < -3$

# Exercises

## Check Understanding

**What happens to the inequality symbol when you do the following to each side of an inequality?**

**1.** subtract a negative number unchanged
**2.** multiply by a positive number unchanged
**3.** divide by a negative number reverses
**4.** multiply by a negative number reverses

**What was done to the first inequality to get the second?**

**5.** $4x \geq 48; x \geq 12$ Divide each side by 4.
**6.** $8 > -4x; -2 < x$ Divide each side by −4.
**7.** $\frac{1}{3}x \leq 18; x \leq 54$ Multiply each side by 3.

**Solve each inequality.**

**8.** $-2x < 14$ $x > -7$
**9.** $3t > 21$ $t > 7$
**10.** $\frac{x}{-6} > 3$ $x < -18$
**11.** $\frac{m}{6} \leq -18$ $m \leq -108$

**12.** *Critical Thinking* The rules for multiplying and dividing both sides of an inequality do not mention zero. Discuss why. Answers may vary. Sample: Multiplying each side by zero can give the inequality $0 > 0$. Division by zero is not defined.

## Practice and Problem Solving

**Solve each inequality.**

**13.** $6m > 24$ $m > 4$
**14.** $-4x \leq -16$ $x \geq 4$
**15.** $9x \leq 27$ $x \leq 3$
**16.** $-3x < 0$ $x > 0$
**17.** $18 < -2m$ $m < -9$
**18.** $64 \leq -8k$ $k \leq -8$
**19.** $7m > 28$ $m > 4$
**20.** $-r \geq 21$ $r \leq -21$
**21.** $\frac{1}{2}x \geq -3$ $x \geq -6$
**22.** $\frac{x}{3} \geq 5$ $x \geq 15$
**23.** $\frac{y}{4} > 3$ $y > 12$
**24.** $\frac{r}{-4} > 2$ $r < -8$
**25.** $\frac{b}{3} \geq -31$ $b \geq -93$
**26.** $6 > \frac{q}{-3}$ $q > -18$
**27.** $20 < \frac{v}{6}$ $v > 120$
**28.** $-3 \geq \frac{g}{-7}$ $g \geq 21$

*Mathematical Reasoning* **Justify each step.**

**29.**
$$-7m \leq -28$$
$$\frac{-7m}{-7} \geq \frac{-28}{-7} \quad \text{Div. Prop. of Ineq.}$$
$$m \geq 4 \quad \text{Simplify.}$$

**30.**
$$\frac{a}{3} > 12$$
$$\left(\frac{a}{3}\right)(3) > 12(3) \quad \text{Mult. Prop. of Ineq.}$$
$$a > 36 \quad \text{Simplify.}$$

**31.** *Error Analysis* Your friend solved $3x > -12$ as shown at the right. What error did your friend make? My friend reversed the direction of the inequality when dividing each side by a positive number.

$$3x > -12$$
$$\frac{3x}{3} < \frac{-12}{3}$$
$$x < -4$$

**32.** Determine whether each number is a solution of $-2x \leq -4$.
**a.** 3 yes **b.** −2 no **c.** 0 no **d.** 10 yes



# 3 Practice/Assess

## Assignment Guide

To provide flexible scheduling, this lesson can be divided into parts.

**Part 1**
**Core** 1, 3, 5–6, 8–9, 13–20, 31–34, 39
**Extension** 29, 37, 40

**Part 2**
**Core** 2, 4, 7, 10–12, 21–28, 35–36, 38
**Extension** 30

Mixed Review can be assigned at any time for maintenance.

## Exercises

**Exercises 13–28** Remind students to ask themselves "Am I multiplying or dividing both sides by a negative number?"

**Test Prep Exercise 38** Students may wish to solve each answer choice before selecting one.

## Challenge

Solve $-2\left(\frac{x}{-3}\right) - 2 \leq 4$. $x \leq 9$

## Closure

To solve a one-step inequality, use inverse operations and the properties of inequality to get the variable alone on one side of the inequality. When multiplying or dividing each side of an inequality by a negative number, reverse the direction of the inequality symbol.

## Daily Cumulative Review

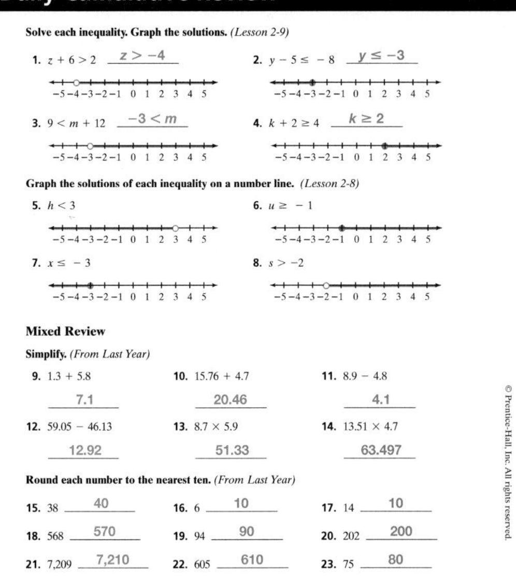

**Solve each inequality. Graph the solutions.** *(Lesson 2-9)*

**1.** $z + 6 > 2$ $z > -4$
**2.** $y - 5 \leq -8$ $y \leq -3$
**3.** $9 < m + 12$ $-3 < m$
**4.** $k + 2 \geq 4$ $k \geq 2$

**Graph the solutions of each inequality on a number line.** *(Lesson 2-8)*

**5.** $h < 3$
**6.** $u \geq -1$
**7.** $x \leq -3$
**8.** $s > -2$

**Mixed Review**

**Simplify.** *(From Last Year)*

**9.** 1.3 + 5.8 7.1
**10.** 15.76 + 4.7 20.46
**11.** 8.9 − 4.8 4.1
**12.** 59.05 − 46.13 12.92
**13.** 8.7 × 5.9 51.33
**14.** 13.51 × 4.7 63.497

**Round each number to the nearest ten.** *(From Last Year)*

**15.** 38 40
**16.** 6 10
**17.** 14 10
**18.** 568 570
**19.** 94 90
**20.** 202 200
**21.** 7,209 7,210
**22.** 605 610
**23.** 75 80



## Alternative Assessment

Have students write an explanation addressed to a student who was absent to tell why they must reverse the inequality symbol whenever they multiply or divide both sides of an inequality by the same negative number.

## Practice

**Write an inequality for each sentence. Then solve the inequality.**

1. The product of $k$ and $-5$ is no more than 30. $-5k \le 30; k \ge -6$
2. Half of $p$ is at least $-7$. $\frac{1}{2}p \ge -7; p \ge -14$
3. The product of $k$ and 9 is no more than 18. $9k \le 18; k \le 2$
4. One-third of $p$ is at least $-17$. $\frac{1}{3}p \ge -17; p \ge -51$
5. The opposite of $g$ is at least $-5$. $-g \ge -5; g \le 5$

**Solve each inequality.**

6. $-5x < 10$ $x > -2$
7. $\frac{x}{4} > 1$ $x > 4$
8. $-8 < -8x$ $x < 1$
9. $\frac{1}{3}x > -2$ $x > -6$
10. $48 \ge -12x$ $x \ge -4$
11. $\frac{1}{3}x < -6$ $x < -18$
12. $\frac{x}{5} < -4$ $x < -20$
13. $-x \le 2$ $x \ge -2$

**Determine whether each number is a solution of $7 \ge -3k$.**

14. 2 yes 15. $-2$ yes 16. 0 yes 17. $-3$ no

**Justify each step.**

18. $-5n \ge 45$

$\frac{-5n}{-5} \le \frac{45}{-5}$ Divide each side by $-5$ and reverse the inequality symbol.

$n \le -9$ Simplify.



## Reteaching

Solve $5x < -40$.

$5x < -40$

Since 5 and $x$ are multiplied, use a division property of inequality and divide both sides by 5.

$5x < -40$

$\frac{5x}{5} < \frac{-40}{5}$

$x < -8$

Solve $\frac{x}{-4} \ge 3$.

Since $x$ is divided by $-4$, use a multiplication property of inequality and multiply both sides by $-4$.

When you multiply both sides of an inequality by a negative number, you must reverse the direction of the inequality symbol.

$\frac{x}{-4} \ge 3$

$(-4)\frac{x}{-4} \le (-4)3$

$x \le -12$

**Solve each inequality.**

1. $7n \ge 42$ $n \ge 6$
2. $-3m < 27$ $m > -9$
3. $\frac{x}{3} > 7$ $x > 21$
4. $\frac{y}{4} \le 8$ $y \le 32$
5. $\frac{q}{-2} < 5$ $q > -10$
6. $-n \ge 2$ $n \le -2$
7. $27 \le 3k$ $k \ge 9$
8. $6 \ge \frac{d}{7}$ $d \le 42$
9. $\frac{r}{-9} < 12$ $r > -108$
10. $-13 < \frac{h}{-3}$ $h < 39$
11. $-15 \ge -3z$ $z \ge 5$
12. $2f \le -27$ $f \le -\frac{27}{2}$



## Enrichment

What is a heptagon?

To find out, solve each inequality in the diagram below. Use a ruler to connect each inequality with its solution. When you have finished, you will have drawn a heptagon in the center of the square. Shade the heptagon and tell what it is in the space below the drawing.

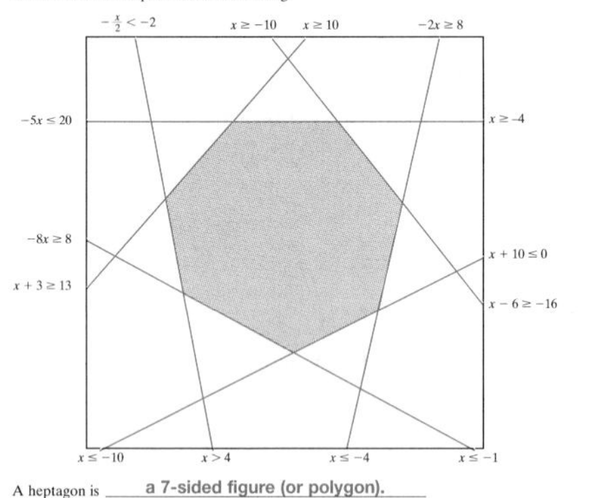


A heptagon is a 7-sided figure (or polygon).



**Write an inequality for each sentence. Then solve the inequality.**

33. The product of negative two and a number $a$ is greater than ten. $-2a > 10; a < -5$
34. A number $t$ multiplied by seven is less than or equal to twenty-one. $7t \le 21; t \le 3$
35. A number $b$ divided by four is greater than or equal to three. $\frac{b}{4} \ge 3; b \ge 12$
36. The quotient of a number $v$ divided by negative five is less than nine. $\frac{v}{-5} < 9; v > -45$
37. *Open-ended* Write a problem that you would solve using the inequality $5m \le 15$. Check students' work.
38. **TEST PREP** Which inequality has the same solutions as $\frac{a}{4} < -20$? D

    A. $4d > 80$ B. $\frac{m}{-2} < -40$ C. $-2r < -40$

    D. $\frac{z}{-2} > 40$ E. $4c < -80$
39. *Writing* Explain how solving $-4t < 32$ is different from solving $4t < -32$. Answers may vary. Sample: You have to divide by $-4$ instead of 4.
40. In Georgia, for every 18 four-year-old children in day care there must be at least one teacher. At one day care center, 56 four-year-olds are signed up for next year. At least how many teachers must the center have to teach four-year-olds next year? 4 teachers

## Mixed Review

**Solve each inequality.** *(Lesson 2-9)*

41. $6 + t > 17$ $t > 11$
42. $m - 4 \le 6$ $m \le 10$
43. $-9 \ge r + 5$ $r \le -14$
44. $11 > v - 12$ $v < 23$

**Name each property shown.** *(Lessons 2-1 and 2-2)*

45. $-12(100 - 3) = -12(100) - 12(-3)$ Dist. Prop.
46. $102 + 34 + 98 = 102 + 98 + 34$ Comm. Prop. of Add.
47. *Weather* The high temperature one day in January was 34°F, and the low temperature was −7°F. What was the difference between the high and the low temperatures that day? *(Lesson 1-6)* 41°F

## Chapter Project 2 — Activity 3 Graphing

On your balance scale, place two quarters at Mass 1 and two nickels at Mass 2. Write and solve an inequality for the mass of a quarter. Then add another nickel at Mass 2. Write and solve a second inequality for the mass of a quarter. Graph your two solutions on one number line.


See also Extra Practice section.

### Project Activity 3

**Graphing** Remind students that they learned in Activity 2 that the mass of a nickel is about 5 g. Discuss the fact that you can compare the mass, the value, the area, and the thickness of a quarter and a nickel. This means that the problem "compare the size of a quarter and nickel" would need to be stated in more precise math language.

# DON'T LOSE YOUR BALANCE!

**Make a Balance Scale** The Activities on pages 73, 92, and 112 will help you complete your project. Here is a checklist to help you gather the different parts.

- ✔ your balance scale
- ✔ your equation and solution for the mass of a penny
- ✔ your inequalities, solutions, and graph for the mass of a quarter

Draw diagrams to show your balance scale and your balancing experiments. For each diagram, include the names of the coins, the equation or inequality you solved, and the solution. For the inequalities, include your graph.

***Reflect and Revise***

Ask a friend or someone at home to review your diagrams. Are they clearly labeled? Are the equation, inequalities, graph, and solutions correct? If necessary, make changes to improve your diagrams.

### *Web Extension*

**Visit Prentice Hall's Web site. You'll find some interesting links and ideas related to scales. You'll also be able to share information about your project.**

**www.phschool.com**

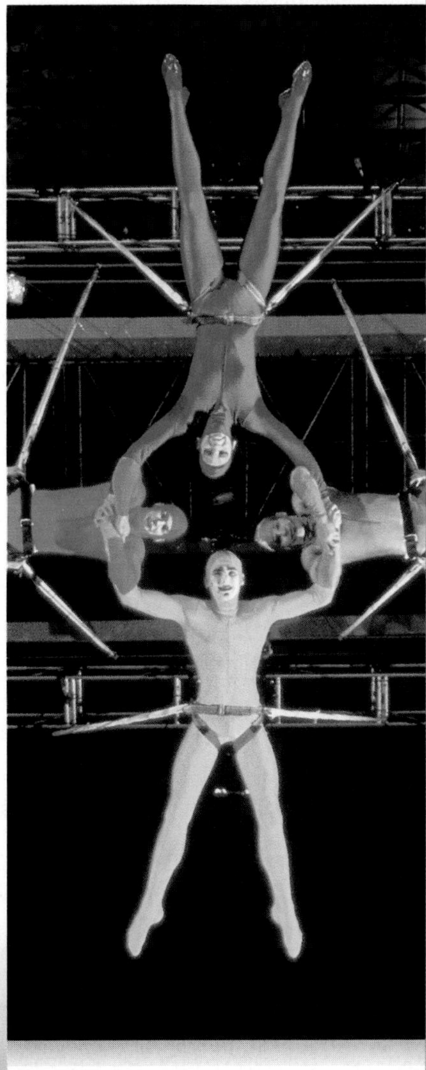



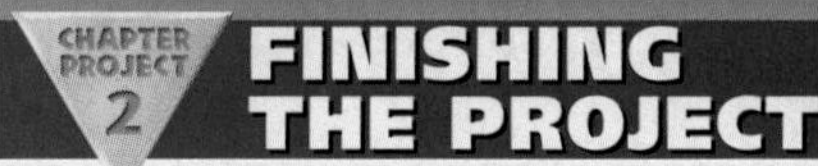


**Project Day** You may wish to plan a project day on which students share their completed projects. Encourage students to explain their process as well as their product.

**Block Scheduling** If you have block scheduling or extended periods, you may wish to intersperse the sharing of projects over Days 4 and 5 between the completion of one lesson and the start of a new lesson.

## Project Notebook

Have students review their project work and bring their notebooks up to date. Call attention to the fact that they can share their projects with other students through the Web site **www.phschool.com**.

Be sure students include in their notebooks their completed Project Manager and Scoring Rubric forms.

**Portfolio** Students may wish to include their projects and/or their project notebooks in their portfolios.

## Web Extension

**ll Us About Your Project**

ıdents may wish to share their projects th other students on the Web site: **ww.phschool.com**.

## Scoring Rubric

**3** You write and solve all equations and inequalities accurately. Your graph shows the possible mass of a quarter correctly. Your diagrams are complete, descriptive, well-organized, and easy to read.

**2** You make minor errors in your equations, inequalities, or graph. Your diagrams are complete and descriptive, but could be better organized or easier to read.

**1** You set up and solve your equations and inequalities inaccurately. Your diagrams are incomplete and lack organization.

**0** Major elements of the project are incomplete or missing.

# Wrap Up

## Resources

Glossary, p. 748
Extra Practice, p. 711

For a complete list of resources for the chapter, see p. 61H.

# Wrap Up

## Key Terms

Addition Property
of Equality (p. 86)
of Inequality (p. 105)
additive identity (p. 65)
Associative Properties of Addition and Multiplication (p. 64)
coefficient (p. 74)
Commutative Properties of Addition and Multiplication (p. 64)
constant (p. 74)
deductive reasoning (p. 75)
Distributive Property (p. 69)
Division Property
of Equality (p. 89)
of Inequality (p. 108)
equation (p. 78)
Identity Properties of Addition and Multiplication (p. 65)
inequality (p. 100)
inverse operations (p. 84)
like terms (p. 74)
Multiplication Property
of Equality (p. 90)
of Inequality (p. 109)
multiplicative identity (p. 65)
open sentence (p. 78)
simplify (p. 74)
solution (p. 79)
solution of the inequality (p. 100)
Subtraction Property
of Equality (p. 84)
of Inequality (p. 104)
term (p. 74)

## Graphic Organizer

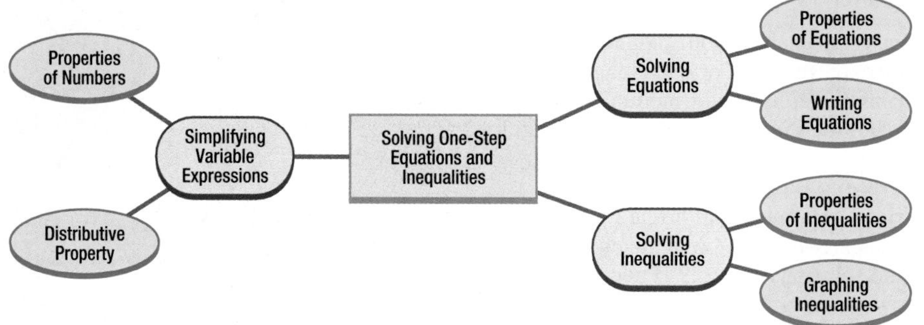


## Properties of Numbers 2-1

*Summary* Use the **Commutative Property** to change order. Use the **Associative Property** to change grouping. Adding zero to an expression does not change its value. Multiplying an expression by 1 does not change its value.

**Simplify each expression. Justify each step.**

**1.** $58 + 16 + 2 + 4$ 80
**2.** $4 \cdot 7 \cdot 25 \cdot 1$ 700
**3.** $125 + 347 + 75$ 547
**4.** $(20 \cdot 65) \cdot 5$ 6,500
**5.** $10 \cdot 15 \cdot 2$ 300
**6.** $37 + 0 + (5 + 63)$ 105

## The Distributive Property 2-2

*Summary* Use the **Distributive Property** to multiply a number outside parentheses by each term of a sum or difference.

*Mental Math* **Use the Distributive Property to simplify.**

**7.** 9(96) 864 **8.** 8(62) 496 **9.** (43)(9) 387

**Use the Distributive Property to multiply.**

**10.** $4(w + 9)$ $4w + 36$ **11.** $(2 + 4a)12$ $24 + 48a$ **12.** $-7(6 - 2m)$ $-42 + 14m$

**13.** **TEST PREP** Which product equals $3t - 12$? D

**A.** $4(t - 3)$ **B.** $(3 - t)4$ **C.** $(4 - t)3$ **D.** $3(t - 4)$

## Simplifying Variable Expressions 2-3

*Summary* To **simplify** a variable expression, replace it with an equivalent expression with as few terms as possible.

**Simplify each expression.**

**14.** $8a + 7 - 11a$ $7 - 3a$ **15.** $3(w + 3) + 4w$ $7w + 9$ **16.** $6 + x - 4x + 3$ $9 - 3x$

**17.** $19 - 4(5n + 1) - 4n$ $15 - 24n$ **18.** $10 + 7k - 2(3k + 5)$ $k$ **19.** $-7(2r - 1) + 3(8 - r)$ $31 - 17r$

**20.** *Writing* Explain how to determine whether terms are like terms. Check whether the variable parts of the terms are identical.

## Variables and Equations 2-4

*Summary* You can write an **equation** to model a situation. An equation with numerical expressions is true or false. An equation with at least one variable is an **open sentence.** A **solution** of an open sentence is a value of a variable that makes the equation true.

**Write an equation for each sentence. Is each equation *true, false,* or an *open sentence?***

**21.** Thirty-two plus five equals the product of six and six. $32 + 5 = 6 \cdot 6$; false

**22.** A number $t$ divided by seventeen equals the opposite of three. $\frac{t}{17} = -3$; open

**23.** The product of four and twenty equals eighty. $4 \cdot 20 = 80$; true

**24.** The admission price to an art museum increased by \$1.75 to \$6.50. Let $p$ be the original admission price. Write an equation to model the situation. $p + 1.75 = 6.50$



**Portfolio** Students may wish to include their completed work for the Wrap Up in their portfolios.

Students can find self-assessment materials on the Web site: **www.phschool.com.**

## ■ Solving One-Step Equations — 2-5 and 2-6

*Summary* To solve an equation, use an **inverse operation** and the **properties of equality** to get the variable alone on one side of the equation.

**Solve each equation.**

**25.** $6 + y = 17$ 11 **26.** $-2 = a - 10$ 8 **27.** $3x = -15$ −5

**28.** $\frac{m}{9} = 3$ 27 **29.** $\frac{w}{4} = 32$ 128 **30.** $40 = -5b$ −8

## ■ Try, Test, Revise — 2-7

*Summary* You can solve some problems by trying an answer. Use each incorrect conjecture to make a better estimate of the correct answer.

**31.** Marcella and Danilo went to a bookstore. Marcella bought 2 notebooks and 3 pens for $14.50. Danilo bought 1 notebook and 2 pens for $7.50. How much does 1 notebook cost? $6.50

## ■ Inequalities and Their Graphs — 2-8

*Summary* To graph an **inequality,** use a number line. Use an open dot for > and <. Use a closed dot for ≥ and ≤.

**Graph the solutions of each inequality.** 32–35. See margin.

**32.** $m > 5$ **33.** $t \geq -2$ **34.** $0 < r$ **35.** $w \leq 6$

**Write an inequality for each sentence.**

**36.** The temperature $t$ is less than zero degrees. $t < 0$

**37.** The height $h$ is greater than twelve feet. $h > 12$

## ■ Solving One-Step Inequalities — 2-9 and 2-10

*Summary* To solve a one-step inequality, use inverse operations and the **properties of inequality** to get the variable alone on one side of the inequality. When multiplying or dividing each side of an inequality by a negative number, *reverse* the direction of the inequality symbol.

**Solve each inequality.**

**38.** $n - 4 > 10$ $n > 14$ **39.** $t + 6 \geq 3$ $t \geq -3$ **40.** $-3 < r + 5$ $r > -8$ **41.** $-5 \leq k - 7$ $k \geq 2$

**42.** $6s \leq 18$ $s \leq 3$ **43.** $\frac{m}{3} < -2$ $m < -6$ **44.** $-d > 14$ $d < -14$ **45.** $\frac{c}{-4} \geq -9$ $c \leq 36$



32. 0 2 5

33. −2 0

34. 0 2

35. 0 6

## Chapter Assessment Form A Page 1

**Circle the letter of the best answer.**

1. Which word describes the equation $17 = t - 5$?
A. true B. false (C.) open D. not given

2. Which property does $a + 11 = 11 + a$ illustrate?
A. commutative property of multiplication
(B.) commutative property of addition
C. associative property of multiplication
D. associative property of addition

3. Which of the following is a solution of the equation $5x + 4 = 14$?
(A.) 2 B. −2 C. 3 D. 1

4. Which is *not* equal to $2(x + 5)$?
A. $2x + 10$ B. $(x + 5)2$ C. $2(5 + x)$ (D.) $2x + 5$

**Simplify. Use the commutative, associative and distributive properties.**

5. $175 + 37 + 25$
$= 175 + (25 + 37) = (175 + 25) + 37 = 200 + 37 = 237$

6. $50(11 \cdot 2)$
$= 50(2 \cdot 11) = (50 \cdot 2)11 = 100 \cdot 11 = 1{,}100$

7. $12(99)$
$= 12(100 - 1) = 1{,}200 - 12 = 1{,}188$

**Simplify each expression.**

8. $12n + (-3k) + 2n - 5k$ $14n - 8k$

9. $(-3y + 2x)(-2) + y + (-x)$ $7y - 5x$

**Solve each equation.**

10. $x - 9 = 14$ $x = 23$

11. $b + 14 = 22$ $b = 8$

12. $-5z = -45$ $z = 9$

13. $\frac{m}{-7} = 14$ $m = -98$



## Chapter Assessment Form A Page 2

14. The speed of a human is 7 mi/h more than that of a jackal. Write and solve an equation to find the speed of a jackal $j$?

| Animal | Speed (nearest mi/h) |
|---|---|
| cheetah | 70 |
| human | 28 |
| lion | 50 |
| elk | 48 |

$28 = j + 7$

$j = 21$ mi/h

**Write an inequality for the situation. Graph the solutions.**

15. The number of students $s$ in the class is less than 35.
$s < 35$

30 31 32 33 34 35 36 37 38 39 40

**Solve each inequality.**

16. $8 + y < -6$ $y < -14$

17. $-5 > k - 3$ $k < -2$

18. $\frac{n}{8} \geq -2$ $n \geq -16$

19. $-4z \geq -12$ $z \leq 3$

20. Central Middle School sold 50 tickets for one night of the school play. Student tickets sold for $2 each and adult tickets sold for $3 each. They took in $135. How many of each type of ticket did they sell?
35 adult tickets and 15 student tickets

21. Write a word problem to describe the equation. $12n = 108$
Sample answer: Marcus gathered 108 eggs. How many dozen is that?



Assessment

# Assessment

**Is each equation *true, false,* or an *open sentence?***

1. $24 = 3(-8)$ false
2. $5x + 28 = 153$ open
3. $18(-7 \div 7) = (-2)(9)$ true
4. $-6 + 15 = (120 \div 20) - (5 - 8)$ true

**Simplify. Use the Commutative and the Associative Properties.**

5. $50 \cdot 38 \cdot 2$ 3,800
6. $45 + 62 + 55$ 162
7. $2 \cdot 27 \cdot 5$ 270
8. $99 + (-7) + 101$ 193

9. **TEST PREP** Which property does $3 + (7 + 2) = (3 + 7) + 2$ show? E
   - A. Commutative Property of Addition
   - B. Identity Property of Addition
   - C. Distributive Property
   - D. Commutative Property of Multiplication
   - E. Associative Property of Addition

**Simplify each expression.**

10. $2(x + y) - 2y$ $2x$
11. $5a + 2b + 3a - 7b$ $8a - 5b$
12. $3(2r - 5) + 8(r + 2)$ $14r + 1$
13. $(-2c + 3d)(-5) + 3(-2c) - (-8d)$ $4c - 7d$

**Solve each equation.**

14. $k - 23 = 17$ 40
15. $\frac{t}{-5} = 15$ $-75$
16. $y \div 12 = -3$ $-36$
17. $7w = -217$ $-31$
18. $-9 + a = 11$ 20
19. $n - 2 = 13$ 15
20. $120 = 38 + p$ 82
21. $w \cdot (-2) = 14$ $-7$
22. $r + 6 = 30$ 24
23. $m - 7 = -3$ 4
24. $9t = 18$ 2
25. $-3f = -42$ 14
26. $5 = \frac{s}{-7}$ $-35$
27. $\frac{h}{12} = 12$ 144

**For Exercises 28 and 29, write and solve an equation.**

28. *Architecture* The length of a room is 4 m greater than the width. The perimeter of the room is 28 m. Find the width of the room. $w + w + 4 + w + w + 4 = 28$; 5 m
29. Brian bought a used bike for \$25 less than its original price. He paid a total of \$88 for the bike. What was the original price of the bike? $p - 25 = 88$; \$113
30. *Writing* How are the rules for solving inequalities similar to those for solving equations? How are they different? See below.

**Write an inequality for each situation. Graph the solutions.** 31–35. For graphs, see margin.

31. The total $t$ is greater than 5. $t > 5$
32. The perimeter $p$ is less than 64. $p < 64$
33. The number of passengers $p$ on the bus is no more than 45. $p \le 45$
34. The number of students $s$ that ran in the road race was not less than 55. $s \ge 55$
35. The number of questions $q$ answered correctly is at most 49. $q \le 49$

**Solve each inequality.**

36. $5 \le x + 1$ $x \ge 4$
37. $3a > 4$ $a > \frac{4}{3}$
38. $y - 6 < 9$ $y < 15$
39. $-2n \le 10$ $n \ge -5$
40. $\frac{b}{3} \ge \frac{1}{3}$ $b \ge 1$
41. $\frac{p}{-2} < -5$ $p > 10$
42. $r + 8 > 12$ $r > 4$
43. $j - 7 \le 24$ $j \le 31$
44. $h - 5 \ge -16$ $h \ge -11$
45. $8 + b < -3$ $b < -11$
46. $3k \le -27$ $k \le -9$
47. $\frac{h}{4} > 16$ $h > 64$
48. $9 < \frac{a}{6}$ $a > 54$
49. $-7z < 21$ $z > -3$

30. Answers may vary. Sample: They are alike except that to multiply or divide each side of an inequality by a negative number, you must reverse the inequality symbol.



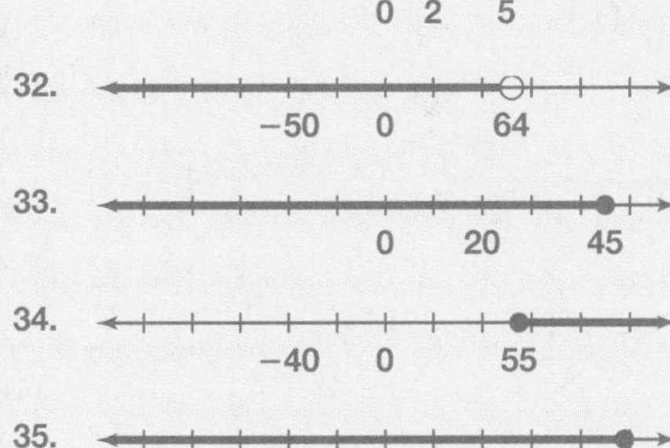


## Chapter Assessment

**Resources** For a complete list of resources for this chapter, see p. 61H.

### Chapter Assessment Form B Page 1

**Circle the letter of the best answer.**

1. Which word describes the equation $-12 = -2(2 - 8)$?
   A. true (B.) false C. open D. not given
2. Which property does $2(5y) = (2 \cdot 5)y$ illustrate?
   (A.) associative property of multiplication
   B. associative property of addition
   C. commutative property of multiplication
   D. commutative property of addition
3. Which of the following is a solution to the equation $4x - 1 = 11$?
   A. $-2$ B. 4 C. 2 (D.) 3
4. Which is *not* equal to $3(x + 7)$
   A. $(x + 7)3$ (B.) $3x + 7$ C. $3x + 21$ D. $3(7 + x)$

**Simplify. Use the commutative, associative, and distributive properties.**

5. $197 + 48 + 3$
   $= 197 + (3 + 48) = (197 + 3) + 48 = 200 + 48 = 248$
6. $4 \cdot 19 \cdot 25$
   $= 4(25 \cdot 19) = (4 \cdot 25)19 = 100 \cdot 19 = 1{,}900$
7. $15(102)$
   $= 15(100 + 2) = 1{,}500 + 30 = 1{,}530$

**Simplify each expression.**

8. $2z + 5z - 3y + y$ $7z - 2y$
9. $6(2a - 3b) + 2(-4b + 2) - 3$ $12a - 26b + 1$

**Solve each equation.**

10. $j - 12 = 24$ $j = 36$
11. $-7 = 14 + b$ $b = -21$
12. $315 = -15y$ $y = -21$
13. $\frac{m}{-4} = -8$ $m = 32$



### Chapter Assessment Form B Page 2

14. The Romanche Gap is 2,578 m deeper than the Ionian Basin in the Mediterranean Sea. Write and solve an equation to find how deep $d$ the Ionian Basin is.

| Area of Atlantic Ocean | Depth (m) |
|---|---|
| Puerto Rico Trench | 8,605 |
| Cayman Trench | 7,535 |
| Brazil Basin | 6,119 |
| South Sandwich Trench | 8,325 |
| Romanche Gap | 7,728 |

$7{,}728 = d + 2{,}578$

$d = 5{,}150$ m

**Write an inequality for the situation. Graph the solutions.**

15. The number of questions $q$ on the test is not more than 20.
    $q \le 20$
    15 16 17 18 19 20 21 22 23 24 25

**Solve each inequality.**

16. $-2 + n \le 7$ $n \le 9$
17. $-11 < x - 4$ $x > -7$
18. $5k \ge -45$ $k \ge -9$
19. $\frac{m}{-3} > 10$ $m < -30$
20. Ali and Keesha found a sale in a sporting goods store. Ali spent \$33 on 2 pair of shorts and 3 packages of socks. Keesha spent \$27 on 1 pair of shorts and 5 packages of socks. How much does one of each item cost?
    \$12 for a pair of shorts and \$3 for a package of socks
21. Write a word problem to describe the equation. $n - 15 = 25$?
    Sample answer: Maurice spent \$15 less than Whitney. If Maurice spent \$25, how much did Whitney spend?



Assessment

# Cumulative Review

## Cumulative Review Page 1

**Circle the letter of the best answer.**

1. You earn $d$ dollars working 40 hours. Which expression describes how much you earn per hour?
   A. $\frac{40}{d}$ (B.) $\frac{d}{40}$ C. $40d$ D. $d + 40$
2. Which equation shows the commutative property of multiplication?
   A. $5 \cdot 0 = 0$ (B.) $ab = ba$ C. $3 + 2 = 2 + 3$ D. $(ab)c = a(bc)$
3. Kara ran 3 miles a day for 5 days and 4 miles a day for 2 days. Which expression shows the total distance she ran?
   A. $3 + 5 + 4 + 2$ B. $(3 + 4)5 + 2$
   (C.) $(3 \cdot 5) + (4 \cdot 2)$ D. $7 \cdot 5 + 7 \cdot 2$
4. Solve $s + 12 = -8$
   A. 4 B. 20 (C.) −20 D. −4
5. Evaluate $4(a + b)$, for $a = 11$ and $b = 4$.
   A. 32 B. 88 C. 28 (D.) 60
6. Which integer is *not* a solution of $h + 4 < 9$?
   (A.) 6 B. 2 C. −3 D. −5
7. Find $22 + (-8)$.
   A. −30 B. −14 (C.) 14 D. 30
8. Which symbol makes $15 - (-7)$ ______ $-2(11)$ a true statement?
   (A.) > B. < C. = D. +
9. Which group is in order from least to greatest?
   A. 6, 3, −3, −6 B. −8, |−8|, 4, 5
   C. |−15|, −10, 5, 10 (D.) −5, −2, |−2|, 7

**Use the distributive property to simplify each expression.**

10. 8(106) = 8(100 + 6) = 800 + 48 = 848
11. 4(98) = 4(100 − 2) = 400 − 8 = 392

**Simplify each expression.**

12. $9 - 2x + 9x + 6$ $7x + 15$
13. $5 - 2(m + 3) - m$ $-3m - 1$



Assessment

## Cumulative Review Page 2

**Write an expression for the situation. Then simplify.**

14. Lisa and John paid 75¢ each to enter the carnival. Lisa bought 8 ride tickets for $c$ cents each. John bought 6 ride tickets for $c$ cents each.
    $75 + 75 + 8c + 6c = 14c + 150$
15. Is the equation $5(7 + 2) - 40 = 8$ true, false, or an open sentence?
    false

**Solve each equation.**

16. $h - 6 = 27$ $h = 33$
17. $16 + m = 36$ $m = 20$
18. $\frac{a}{8} = 6$ $a = 48$
19. $-4r = 56$ $r = -14$
20. Graph $x > -5$.
    −5 −4 −3 −2 −1 0 1 2 3 4 5

**Solve each inequality.**

21. $19 > y + 7$ $y < 12$
22. $j - 12 < -23$ $j < -11$
23. $\frac{x}{11} \le -4$ $x \le -44$
24. $-5h \le -50$ $h \ge 10$
25. Explain how you can use the commutative and associative properties to add 19 + 28 + 81 mentally.
    19 + 28 + 81 = 19 + (81 + 28) by the commutative property
    = (19 + 81) + 28 by the associative property
    = 100 + 28
    = 128



# 2 Cumulative Review

**Preparing for Algebra**

**Choose the best answer.**

1. You make \$8.00 per hour. Each week you work $n$ hours. Which expression describes your weekly pay? D
   A. $\frac{n}{8}$ B. $8 - n$
   C. $n + 8$ D. $8n$
2. Which equation shows the Associative Property of Addition? B
   A. $9 + 7 + 8 = 9 + 8 + 7$
   B. $(8 + 3) + 13 = 8 + (3 + 13)$
   C. $12 + (-4) + 0 = 12 + (-4)$
   D. $19 \cdot (-3) \cdot 1 = 19 \cdot (-3)$
3. Mara ordered 5 bags of seed for \$7 each and 3 wildflower seed kits for \$9 each. She also paid a \$13 shipping fee. Which expression shows the total cost? B
   A. $5 + 7 + 3 + 9 + 13$
   B. $(5 \cdot 7) + (3 \cdot 9) + 13$
   C. $(5 + 3)16 + 13$
   D. $(5 \cdot 7 + 13) + (3 \cdot 9 + 13)$
4. Solve $r + 43 = -45$. D
   A. −2 B. 2 C. 88 D. −88
5. Evaluate $5(n + m)$ for $n = 12$ and $m = 6$. C
   A. 30 B. 66 C. 90 D. 810
6. Which integer is *not* a solution of $p + 12 < 16$? A
   A. 4 B. 3 C. −4 D. −28
7. Which group is in order from least to greatest? C
   A. 4, 2, −2, −4
   B. |−3|, |−4|, −5, 6
   C. −7, 1, 4, |−12|
   D. −3, 4, −5, 6, −7
8. Find $-23 + (-12)$. D
   A. −11 B. 11 C. 35 D. −35
9. Which symbol makes the statement true? A
   $11 - (-4)$ ■ $-6 - 12$
   A. > B. < C. = D. ≤
10. *Writing* Simplify $25 \cdot 7 \cdot 4$. Explain how you can use the Commutative and Associative Properties to multiply mentally. See below.

**Use the Distributive Property to simplify each expression.**

11. 7(58) 406
12. 6(92) 552
13. 5(1,002) 5,010

**Simplify each expression.**

14. $3c - 4c + 11$ $11 - c$
15. $6(t + 7) + t$ $7t + 42$
16. $-5(n + 9) - n$ $-6n - 45$
17. $8 - 4(s + 2) - s$ $-5s$

**Write an expression for each situation. Then simplify.**

18. Lana bought juice for \$3.25 and some fruit for \$5.25. She also bought five beach passes for $x$ dollars each. 3.25 + 5.25 + 5x; 5x + 8.50
19. Chung bought six brushes for $b$ dollars each and two tubes of paint for $p$ dollars each. He also bought paper for \$7.59. 6b + 2p + 7.59

**Is each equation *true, false,* or an *open sentence?***

20. $8(8 \div 2) = 32$ true
21. $18 = (2 \cdot 7) + 6$ false
22. $5x = 3 + 2x$ open
23. $14 - 1 = 52 \div 4$ true

**Solve each equation.**

24. $b - 7 = 21$ 28
25. $18 + n = 37$ 19
26. $\frac{c}{7} = 8$ 56
27. $-9r = 108$ −12

**Graph each inequality.** 28–29. See margin.

28. $j < 4$
29. $t \ge -3$

**Solve each inequality.**

30. $24 > b + 17$ $b < 7$
31. $x - 9 < -14$ $x < -5$
32. $\frac{r}{13} \ge 3$ $r \ge 39$
33. $-4s \ge -56$ $s \le 14$

10. 700; explanations may vary. Sample: Use the Commutative Property to write $25 \cdot 4 \cdot 7$. Then use the Associative Property to write $(25 \cdot 4) \cdot 7$.



| Item | Chapter/ Lesson | Review Topic |
|---|---|---|
| 1, 3, 5, 7, 8, 9 | 1-1, 1-2, 1-3, 1-4, 1-5, 1-6 | Algebraic Expressions and Integers |
| 4, 6, 20–33 | 2-1, 2-2, 2-3, 2-4, 2-5, 2-6, 2-8, 2-9, 2-10 | Solving One-Step Equations and Inequalities |
| 2, 10–19 | 2-3, 2-4 | Simplifying Expressions; Variables and Equations |

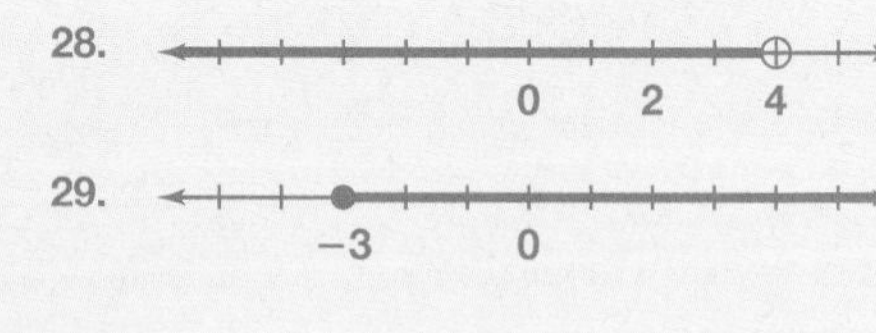

CHAPTER 3

# Decimals and Equations

## Content Overview for Chapter 3

Chapter 3 begins with lessons on rounding decimals and estimating decimal sums, differences, products, and quotients. You can estimate decimals by rounding or by front-end estimating. To estimate sums you can also use clustering. You can estimate a quotient of two decimals using compatible numbers.

You can apply the skill of estimating decimal products and quotients to finding the mean, median, and mode. A measure of central tendency describes a collection of data. The mean is the sum of the items divided by the number of items. The median is the middle value or the mean of the two middle values when the data are written in order. The mode is the item that occurs most often.

An outlier is an item that is much greater or less than the rest.

You can apply the skill of solving equations from Chapter Two to using formulas.
A formula is an equation that shows the relationship between two or more quantities. The quantities are represented by variables. You can use formulas to find such things as perimeter, area, and distance. You can also solve one-step equations by using inverse operations and the properties of equality to get the variable alone on one side of the equation.

The metric system of measurement uses the decimal system to relate units to one another. To measure, you must choose an appropriate unit of measure.

## Making Connections

| Lesson | Interdisciplinary and Real-World Connections | Math Integration |
|---|---|---|
| 3-1 | Statistics, Geography | Arithmetic |
| 3-2 | Health | Data Analysis |
| 3-3 | Nutrition | Data Analysis |
| 3-4 | Geometry, Biology | Measurement |
| 3-5 | Astronomy | Algebra |
| 3-6 | Sports | Statistics |
| 3-7 | Geography, Earth Science | Measurement |
| 3-8 | Art and Design | Problem Solving |

**SCHOOL/HOME CONNECTION**
English and Spanish versions are available in the *Help at Home* book of copy masters.

*Helper's Page* You will find detailed instruction, more examples, and

*Student Page* *Review Exercises for Lessons 3-1 to 3-4*

**Estimate using front-end estimation.** *(Lesson 3-1)*

1. $12.59 + $18.95
2. 38.61 − 11.47
3. 4.63 + 1.852

**Determine whether each product or quotient is reasonable. If it is not reasonable, write a reasonable result.** *(Lesson 3-2)*

4. 6.952(4.15) = 2.88508 ______
5. $59.22 ÷ 12.6 = $4.70 ______
6. 25.48(0.316) = 8.05168 ______

**Find the mean, median, and mode. Round to the nearest tenth where necessary.** *(Lesson 3-3)*

7. Money earned mowing grass: $25, $18, $30, $25, $20
   mean: ______ median: ______ mode: ______
8. High temperatures each day for a week: 55°, 62°, 61°, 61°, 58°, 59°, 59°
   mean: ______ median: ______ mode: ______

**Use the formula $P = 2l + 2w$. Find the perimeter of each rectangle.** *(Lesson 3-4)*

9. 6 in. by 7 in. ______
10. 9 cm by 5 cm ______
11. 28 mm by 46 mm ______

12. **Test Prep** Which of the following is the best estimate of 138.95 ÷ 6.85? *(Lesson 3-2)*
    A. 2 B. 2.2 C. 20 D. 22 ______

Helper: ______ Comments: ______

*Helper's Page* You will find detailed instruction, more examples, and

*Student Page* *Review Exercises for Lessons 3-5 to 3-7*

**Solve each equation.** *(Lessons 3-5 and 3-6)*

1. $n + 4.3 = 2.7$ $n =$ ______
2. $-7.6 = y + 1.02$ $y =$ ______
3. $a - (-2.5) = -4.1$ $a =$ ______
4. $x - 3.6 = -4.8$ $x =$ ______
5. $4h = 9.6$ $h =$ ______
6. $-13.6 = -1.7w$ $w =$ ______
7. $3.4m = -8.16$ $m =$ ______
8. $\frac{b}{-0.4} = 14.7$ $b =$ ______
9. $\frac{z}{-8.2} = -5.03$ $z =$ ______

**Complete each statement.** *(Lesson 3-7)*

10. 1.25 km = ____ m
11. 0.53 L = ____ mL
12. 346 g = ____ kg
13. 65 mm = ____ cm
14. 42 cm = ____ m
15. 8.4 g = ____ mg

16. **Test Prep** Which is the best metric unit to use to measure the amount of gasoline in a car's gas tank? *(Lesson 3-7)*
    A. centimeter B. meter C. milliliter D. liter ______

Helper: ______ Comments: ______

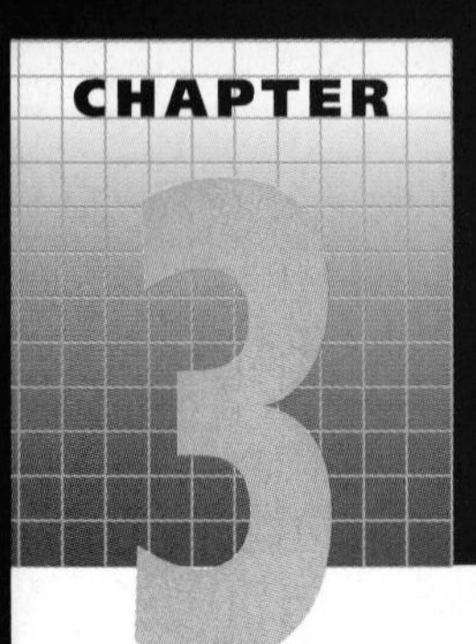

# Chapter 3 at a Glance

To accommodate flexible scheduling, most lessons are divided into parts. Assignment Options are given in the Teacher's Edition for each lesson.

**Lesson 3-1**
**Rounding and Estimating**
Pages 122–126
NCTM 1, 2, 4, 6, 7, 8, 9
Part 1 Rounding Decimals
Part 2 Estimating Sums and Differences

**Lesson 3-2**
**Estimating Decimal Products and Quotients**
Pages 127–130
NCTM 1, 2, 4, 6, 8, 9
Part 1 Estimating Products
Part 2 Estimating Quotients

**Lesson 3-3**
**Data Analysis: Mean, Median, and Mode**
Pages 131–135
NCTM 1, 2, 4, 5, 8, 9
Part 1 Finding Mean, Median, and Mode
Part 2 Choosing the Best Measure
**Project Activity 1**

**Lesson 3-7**
**Measurement: Using the Metric System**
Pages 150–155
NCTM 1, 2, 4, 6, 8, 9, 10
Part 1 Identifying Appropriate Metric Measures
Part 2 Converting Units
**Checkpoint 2**
**Project Activity 3**

**Lesson 3-8**
**Problem Solving Strategy**
Pages 159–162
NCTM 1, 2, 6, 7, 8, 9, 10
Simplify a Problem
**Math at Work**

## Pacing Options

This chart suggests pacing for only the core lessons and their parts, and it is provided merely as a possible guide. It will help you determine how much time you have in your schedule to cover other features, such as the Chapter Project, Math Toolboxes, Standardized Test Prep, Wrap Up, and Assessment.

| | Day 1 | Day 2 | Day 3 | Day 4 | Day 5 | Day 6 | Day 7 | Day 8 | Day 9 | Day 10 | Day 11 |
|---|---|---|---|---|---|---|---|---|---|---|---|
| **Traditional** (40–45 min. class periods) | 3–1 (1), 3–1 (2) | 3–2 (1), 3–2 (2) | 3–3 (1), 3–3 (2) | 3–4 (1), 3–4 (2) | 3–5 (1), 3–5 (2) | 3–6 (1), 3–6 (2) | 3–7 (1) | 3–7 (2) | 3–8 | | |
| **Pre-Algebra Over 2 Years** (40–45 min. class periods) | 3–1 (1) | 3–1 (2) | 3–1 (2) | 3–2 (1) | 3–2 (1) | 3–2 (2) | 3–3 (1) | 3–3 (1) | 3–3 (2) | 3–4 (1) | 3–4 (2) |
| **Block Scheduling** (90 min. class periods) | 3–1 (1, 2), 3–2 (1, 2) | 3–3 (1, 2), 3–4 (1, 2) | 3–5 (1, 2), 3–6 (1, 2) | 3–7 (1), 3–7 (2), 3–8 | | | | | | | |

| Pages 137–140 | Lesson 3-4 Measurement: Using Formulas |
|---|---|
| NCTM 1, 2, 3, 4, 6, 8, 9, 10 | Part 1 Substituting into Formulas<br>Part 2 Using a Perimeter Formula<br>**Checkpoint 1** |

| Pages 142–145 | Lesson 3-5 Solving Equations by Adding or Subtracting Decimals |
|---|---|
| NCTM 1, 2, 3, 6, 8, 9, 10 | Part 1 Using Subtraction to Solve Equations<br>Part 2 Using Addition to Solve Equations |

| Pages 146–149 | Lesson 3-6 Solving Equations by Multiplying or Dividing Decimals |
|---|---|
| NCTM 1, 2, 3, 6, 8, 9, 10 | Part 1 Using Division to Solve Equations<br>Part 2 Using Multiplication to Solve Equations<br>**Project Activity 2** |

**NCTM STANDARDS 2000**

1 Number and Operations
2 Algebra
3 Geometry
4 Measurement
5 Data Analysis and Probability
6 Problem Solving
7 Reasoning and Proof
8 Communication
9 Connections
10 Representation

| Day 12 | Day 13 | Day 14 | Day 15 | Day 16 | Day 17 | Day 18 | Day 19 | Day 20 | Day 21 | Day 22 | Day 23 | Day 24 |
|---|---|---|---|---|---|---|---|---|---|---|---|---|
| 3–5 1 | 3–5 1 | 3–5 2 | 3–6 1 | 3–6 1 | 3–6 2 | 3–7 1 | 3–7 1 | 3–7 2 | 3–8 | 3–8 | | |

**Block Scheduling Notes**

Consider these suggestions:

- **Day 2** After completing Part 1 of Lesson 3-3 and before starting Part 2, teach Math Toolbox 1, p. 136.
- **Day 3** After completing Part 1 of Lesson 3-5 and before starting Part 2, teach Math Toolbox 2, p. 141.
- **Day 4** After completing Part 1 of Lesson 3-7 and before starting Part 2, teach Math Toolbox 3, p. 156.
- **Day 4** Before starting Lesson 3-8, teach the Standardized Test Prep, p. 158.

# Math Background

## Lesson 3-1
### Rounding and Estimating

Working with decimals requires an understanding of how the various decimal places are named. The names for the decimal places, 10 (ten) and 0.1 (tenth) differ only by two letters, but ten is 100 times greater than one-tenth. Notice in the place value system (as the following diagram shows) that it is the ones place (followed by the decimal point) that is the center of this system. One in the first place to the left of the decimal has no partner to the right of the decimal. Students may be confused if they think of the decimal point itself as the center, or dividing line, between units and decimal fractions.

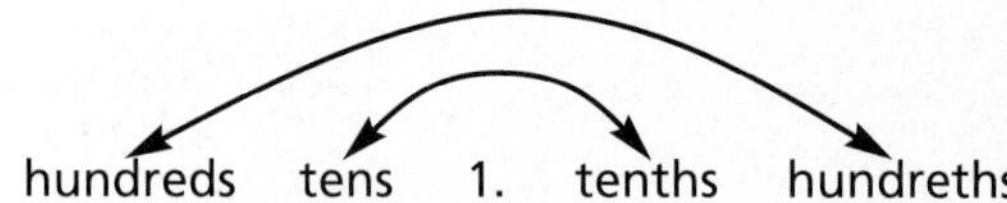


In computations with decimals, you often need to use only a certain number of decimal places. For example, even though the odometer of the car measures in tenths, people most often round this number to the nearest mile.

Consider the number 3.467. If you want to round it to the nearest tenth, you are essentially asking, "Is 3.467 closer to 3.400 or 3.500?" (Notice that the number 3.450 would be the same distance from both these choices.)

When rounding to a particular place, look at the digit immediately to the right of that place. If it is less than 5, do not change the digit in the place you are rounding to, and drop all digits to the right of that place. If the digit to the right of the place you are rounding to is greater than or equal to 5, increase by 1 the digit in the place you are rounding to, and drop the digits to the right of it.

Students sometimes mistakenly think that rounding is kind of a "rolling process" beginning at the far right digit. This mistake leads them to round 3.247 to the nearest tenth by first increasing the 4 to a 5 (because of the 7) to get 3.25 and then increasing the 2 to a 3 because of this 5. This results in the wrong conclusion that 3.247 rounds to 3.3 even though it is clearly closer to 3.200 than to 3.300.

## Lesson 3-2
### Estimating Decimal Products and Quotients

With the increased use of calculators and computers in various occupations, the life skill of estimating has taken on new importance. Because it is so easy to push the wrong key, you must be able to look at the result on the calculator and judge whether or not it is a reasonable solution.

There is no one right way to estimate. Valid estimates made by two different people often differ; an estimate is not a precise answer. However, to make sure that students are using a reasonable process in their estimations, ask them to explain how they arrived at their estimates. This also provides an opportunity to help students practice using the language of mathematics in their explanations.

## Lesson 3-3
### Mean, Median, and Mode

In everyday language, the word "average" is ambiguous. In the more precise language of mathematics, the mean, the median, or the mode of a set of numbers may be used to represent an "average" value. Finding the mean, median, and mode are all ways to summarize the data. A measure that summarizes a whole set of measurements by representing the approximate center of the distribution is called a *measure of central tendency.*

The most familiar measure of central tendency is the *mean.* When you add a set of grades and divide by how many grades there are, you are finding the mean. The mean is the only measure of central tendency that is dependent upon the exact value of every measurement. A change in any measurement will produce a change in the mean.

Less familiar is the mode, which is simply the number that occurs most often.

The median is the middle number in a distribution where all the numbers are arranged in order from greatest to least. If there are an even number of data items, the median is the mean of the middle two numbers. The median is often used when incomes or housing prices are given. Mathematicians have other more precise ways of defining the median to reflect repeated numbers, but these are used only in advanced statistical analysis.

## LESSON 3-4

### Using Formulas

In this lesson, students substitute values in formulas to solve for one variable. Later they will apply their skills in solving equations to restating a formula in different forms, as shown here.

$d = rt; r = \frac{d}{t}; t = \frac{d}{r}$

## LESSONS 3-5 AND 3-6

### Solving One-Step Equations with Decimals

In these lessons, students apply to equations with decimals what they know about using inverse operations and these properties of equality.

If $a = b$, then
$a + c = b + c$
$a - c = b - c$
$ca = cb$
$a \div c = b \div c, (c \neq 0)$

Remind students that they are also applying the two inverse properties.

$a + (-a) = 0$ and
$a \bullet (\frac{1}{a}) = 1, (a \neq 0)$
as they solve these equations.

## LESSONS 3-7

### Using the Metric System

The English, or Customary system, uses the concept of weight (measured in pounds) while the metric system uses the concept of mass. Mass is the amount of material that can be measured on a balance. Weight is the gravitational force exerted by the given amount of material.

weight = gravitational force
weight = mass • acceleration due to gravity

Weight depends on mass and gravity. An astronaut that weighs 150 pounds on Earth weighs 25 pounds on the moon, where the gravitational pull is $\frac{1}{6}$ that of Earth.The astronaut is weightless in space. But in all three places, the astronaut would balance a mass of 68.2 kilograms.

As long as the measurements are made on Earth, a mass of 1 kilogram weighs approximately 2.2 pounds.

For professional development tips visit our Web site **www.phschool.com**.

# Monitoring Progress

## Universal Access

### ▶ Preventing a Student from Falling Behind

These resources are particularly helpful in preventing a student from falling behind his or her appropriate math level. For a complete list of resources for this chapter, see page 119H.

#### Skills You Need for Chapter 3

Student Edition, p. 119
Teacher's Edition, p. 119

- Rounding numbers
- Comparing and ordering decimals
- Operations with decimals
- Multiplying and dividing by multiples of 10

#### Skills Handbook

Student Edition, pp. 723–741
Teacher's Edition, pp. 723–741

- Rounding Whole Numbers, p. 724
- Working with Decimals, pp. 728, 729, 730, 731, 733, 735
- Multiply/Divide by Powers of 10, p. 734
- Working with Integers, p. 741

#### Reteaching Worksheets

There is a Reteaching worksheet for every lesson in this chapter.

- Chapter 3 Support File, Teaching Resources box
- See TE p. 119H for a complete list of resources

#### Skills Intervention Kit with CD-ROM

| For | Use |
|---|---|
| Lessons 3-1, 3-3 | Whole Numbers |
| Lessons 3-5, 3-6 | Decimals |
| Lessons 3-7, 3-8 | Measurement |

#### Daily Cumulative Review Blackline Masters

There is a Daily Cumulative Review worksheet for every lesson in this chapter.

- See TE p. 119H for a complete list of resources.

### ▶ Accommodating Diverse Learning Styles

#### Tactile Learning

Use a meter stick and masking tape to put a length of tape on the floor or wall of the classroom and label it at 10 cm, 50 cm, and 1m. (Lesson 3-7)

#### Advanced Learner

Every lesson has at least one challenge problem.

Write a variable equation in which the variable is multiplied by a decimal and also subtracted from a decimal, then solving the equation. (Lesson 3-6)

#### ELL (English Language Learner)

Listen and speak carefully to avoid confusing *hundreds* and *hundredths.* (Lesson 3-1)

#### Auditory Learning

Read decimals aloud using and to indicate the decimal point. (Lesson 3-1)

Say equations to hear the name of an operation to be undone. (Lesson 3-6)

#### Visual Learning

Circle the number that keeps the variable from being isolated on one side. (Lesson 3-5)

Build a model of a problem. (Lesson 3-8)

# Aligning Assessment with Instruction

## Assessment Options

| | Chapter Opener | 3-1 | 3-2 | 3-3 | 3-4 | 3-5 | 3-6 | 3-7 | 3-8 | End |
|---|---|---|---|---|---|---|---|---|---|---|
| Chapter Project | ■ | | | ■ | | | ■ | ■ | | ■ |
| Try This Exercises | | ■ | ■ | ■ | ■ | ■ | ■ | ■ | ■ | |
| Mixed Reviews | | ■ | ■ | ■ | ■ | ■ | ■ | ■ | ■ | |
| Checkpoints | | | | | ■ | | | ■ | | |
| Writing | | ■ | ■ | ■ | | ■ | ■ | ■ | ■ | ■ |
| Chapter Assessment | | | | | | | | | | ■ |
| Cumulative Review | | | | | | | | | | ■ |
| Standardized Test Prep | | ■ | ■ | ■ | ■ | ■ | | ■ | | |
| | Standardized Test Prep, p. 158 | | | | | | | | | |
| Computer Item Generator | Can be used to create custom-made practice pages or assessment pages at any time. | | | | | | | | | |

### Test-Taking Tips on Transparencies

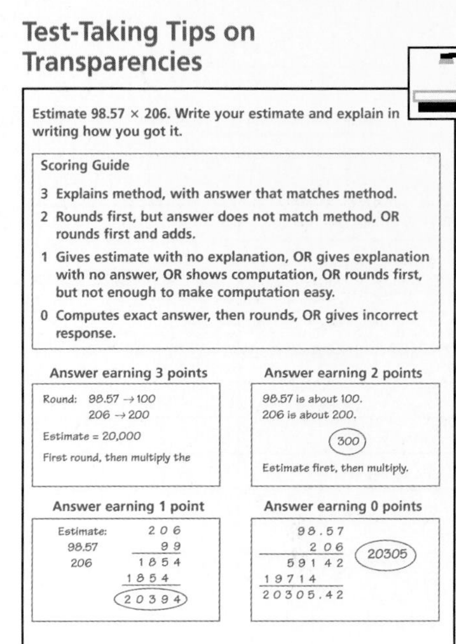
Estimate 98.57 × 206. Write your estimate and explain in writing how you got it.

Scoring Guide

3 Explains method, with answer that matches method.
2 Rounds first, but answer does not match method, OR rounds first and adds.
1 Gives estimate with no explanation, OR gives explanation with no answer, OR shows computation, OR rounds first, but not enough to make computation easy.
0 Computes exact answer, then rounds, OR gives incorrect response.

Answer earning 3 points: Round: 98.57 → 100, 206 → 200. Estimate = 20,000. First round, then multiply the

Answer earning 2 points: 98.57 is about 100. 206 is about 200. 300. Estimate first, then multiply.

Answer earning 1 point: Estimate: 98.57, 206; 206 × 99 = 1854, 1854, 20394

Answer earning 0 points: 98.57 × 206 = 59142, 19714, 20305.42; 20305

*Use with Standardized Test Prep and Chapter Assessments.*

## Correlation to Standardized Tests

| Lesson | | CAT5 | CTBS/5 TerraNova™ | ITBS | MAT7 | SAT9 | LOCAL OBJECTIVES |
|---|---|---|---|---|---|---|---|
| 3-1 | Rounding and Estimating | ■ | | ■ | ■ | ■ | |
| 3-2 | Estimating Decimal Products and Quotients | ■ | | ■ | ■ | ■ | |
| 3-3 | Mean, Median, and Mode | ■ | ■ | ■ | ■ | ■ | |
| 3-4 | Using Formulas | ■ | ■ | ■ | | ■ | |
| 3-5 | Solving Equations by Adding or Subtracting Decimals | | | | | ■ | |
| 3-6 | Solving Equations by Multiplying or Dividing Decimals | | | | | ■ | |
| 3-7 | Using the Metric System | ■ | ■ | ■ | ■ | ■ | |
| 3-8 | Problem Solving Strategy: Simplify a Problem | | | | | ■ | |

**CAT5** California Achievement Test, 5th edition
**CTBS TerraNova** Comprehensive Test of Basic Skills, 5th edition
**ITBS** Iowa Test of Basic Skills, Form M
**MAT7** Metropolitan Achievement Test, 7th edition
**SAT** Stanford Achievement Test, Advanced 1

For other standardized test correlations, follow the link to your state at **www.phschool.com**.

# Resources for Chapter 3

| | TEACHING RESOURCES BOX | | | | | | | | | | | | | | |
|---|---|---|---|---|---|---|---|---|---|---|---|---|---|---|---|
| | CHAPTER 3 SUPPORT FILE | | | | | | | | Cumulative Assessment | Lesson Planners Plus | Daily Cum Review | Teaching Transparencies | Warm-Up Transparencies | Help at Home | SE Answers o Transparencie |
| | Practice | Reteach | Enrichment | Project Manager | Checkpoints | Cumulative Review | Chapter Assessment | Alternative Assessment | | | | | | | |
| Begin Chapter | | | | ■ | | | | | | ■ | | | | | |
| 3-1 | ■ | ■ | ■ | | | | | | | ■ | ■ | 44 | ■ | | ■ |
| 3-2 | ■ | ■ | ■ | | | | | | | ■ | ■ | | ■ | | ■ |
| 3-3 | ■ | ■ | ■ | | | | | | | ■ | ■ | 45 | ■ | | ■ |
| 3-4 | ■ | ■ | ■ | | ■ | | | | | ■ | ■ | 3, 46 | ■ | ■ | ■ |
| 3-5 | ■ | ■ | ■ | | | | | | | ■ | ■ | | ■ | | ■ |
| 3-6 | ■ | ■ | ■ | | | | | | | ■ | ■ | | ■ | | ■ |
| 3-7 | ■ | ■ | ■ | | ■ | | | | | ■ | ■ | 47 | ■ | ■ | ■ |
| 3-8 | ■ | ■ | ■ | | | | | | | ■ | ■ | 19 | ■ | | ■ |
| End Chapter | | | | | | ■ | ■ (2 forms) | ■ | After Ch. 3, 6, 9, 13 | | | | | | |

**Also available for use with the chapter:**

Solution Key
Computational Practice Skills Booklet
Mathematics Standardized Test Prep, Student Edition and Teacher's Edition
Overhead Manipulatives Kit
Practice Workbook
Algebra Readiness Kit
Student Manipulatives Kit
Test-Taking Tips on Transparencies
Assessment Success Kit
Teaching Aids and Letters
Graphing Calculator Handbook
Spanish Resources
Success-Building Puzzle and Problem Masters

## TECHNOLOGY

**Computer Item Generator with Standardized Test Prep**

CD-ROM with an unlimited supply of questions with varying degrees of difficulty for customized practice sheets, quizzes, and tests.

**Resource Pro® with Planning Express®**

CD-ROM with complete classroom planning tool and teaching resources for customizing and planning lessons.

**Interactive Math Lessons and Tools**

CD-ROM with lessons and tools to make abstract concepts visual and accessible.

**Student Tutorial**

Test preparation software for students on CD-ROM with management system for teachers; includes Secondary Math Lab Toolkit™.

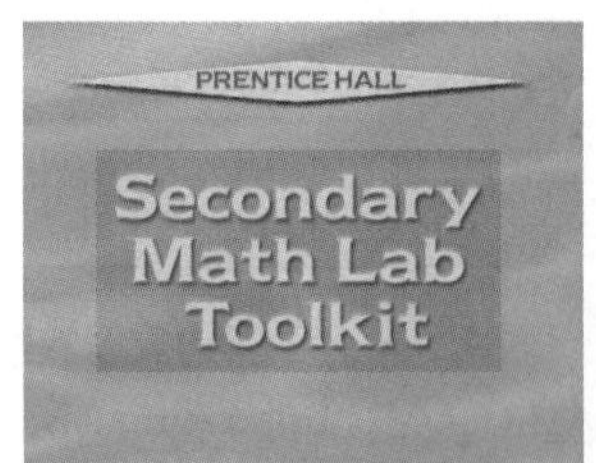


**Secondary Math Lab Toolkit™ with Integrated Math Labs**

Integrated software package with linkable math tools for exploring key concepts.

**Also available for use with the chapter:**

Math Blaster® Pre-Algebra CD-ROM
Video Fieldtrips, Vol. I: Algebra Applications
Video Fieldtrips, Vol. II: Geometry Applications
Wide World of Mathematics CD-ROM
Wide World of Mathematics Video

### *Web Extension*

**www.phschool.com**

**For Students**
- Chapter Support with Internet Links
- Internet Activities

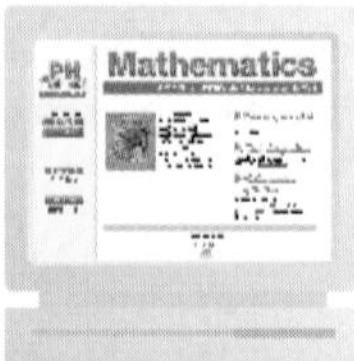


**For Teachers**
- Curriculum Support
- Professional Development
- Product Information
- Regional Support Information

# Skills You Need for Chapter 3

### Rounding numbers
Use before Lessons 3-1 and 3-2.

**Round each number to the nearest ten.**

1. 37 40
2. 12 10
3. 9 10
4. 2 0
5. 49 50
6. 105 110
7. 207 210
8. 602 600
9. 834 830
10. 6,009 6,010
11. 3 0
12. 45 50

### Comparing and ordering decimals
Use before Lesson 3-3.

**Compare. Use >, <, or = to complete each statement.**

13. 10.5 ■ 1.05 >
14. 8.792 ■ 8.972 <
15. 12.74 ■ 12.751 <
16. 0.96 ■ 1.32 <
17. 7.641 ■ 7.593 >
18. 6.3 ■ 6.38 <
19. 5.001 ■ 5.02 <
20. −9.871 ■ −10.3 >
21. −27.619 ■ −27.7 >
22. 14.0352 ■ 14.3052 <
23. 1.956 ■ 2.989 <
24. −24 ■ −23.68 <

**Order each group of decimals from least to greatest.**

25. 3.25, 4.19, 3.8, 4.91 — 3.25, 3.8, 4.19, 4.91
26. 8.35, 8.349, 8.351, 9.25 — 8.349, 8.35, 8.351, 9.25
27. 12.09, 12.01, 12.9, 12.1 — 12.01, 12.09, 12.1, 12.9
28. 0.02, 0.017, 0.201, 0.0201 — 0.017, 0.02, 0.0201, 0.201
29. −1.4, −1.04, −1.401, −14.1 — −14.1, −1.401, −1.4, −1.04
30. −2.3, −3.2, −3.19, −2.8 — −3.2, −3.19, −2.8, −2.3

### Operations with decimals
Use before Lessons 3-5 and 3-6.

**Simplify.**

31. $3.4 + 8.09$ 11.49
32. $9.32 - 7.65$ 1.67
33. $5.6 + 9.3$ 14.9
34. $8 - 4.93$ 3.07
35. $0.59 + 3.06$ 3.65
36. $5.8 - 4.92$ 0.88
37. $10.579 + 4.638$ 15.217
38. $2.19 - 0.984$ 1.206
39. $3.4 \cdot 2.1$ 7.14
40. $\frac{14.4}{1.2}$ 12
41. $(1.001)(6.7)$ 6.7067
42. $16.25 \div 2.5$ 6.5
43. $(6.1)(8.7)$ 53.07
44. $40.02 \div 5.8$ 6.9
45. $10.4 \cdot 5.3$ 55.12
46. $\frac{77.38}{7.3}$ 10.6

### Multiplying and dividing by multiples of 10
Use before Lesson 3-7.

**Simplify.**

47. $9.87 \cdot 10$ 98.7
48. $5.32 \cdot 100$ 532
49. $0.3 \cdot 1{,}000$ 300
50. $15.407 \cdot 10{,}000$ 154,070
51. $0.8 \div 10$ 0.08
52. $8.42 \div 100$ 0.0842
53. $16.1 \div 1{,}000$ 0.0161
54. $12.09 \div 10{,}000$ 0.001209
55. $0.087 \cdot 10$ 0.87
56. $157.4 \cdot 100$ 15,740
57. $1{,}430 \div 10$ 143
58. $1.89 \div 100$ 0.0189



## Skills You Need

### Rounding numbers
**In Lessons 3-1 and 3-2** students will use rounding to estimate quantities with decimals.

### Comparing and ordering decimals
**In Lesson 3-3** students will use decimals as they find the mean, median, and mode.

### Operations with decimals
**In Lessons 3-5 and 3-6** students will solve equations involving decimals.

### Multiplying and dividing by multiples of 10
**In Lesson 3-7** students will apply multiples of 10 as they use the metric system.

## Skills Trace

| SKILLS | INTRODUCED | DEVELOPED IN LESSON(S) | REVIEWED/REINFORCED |
|---|---|---|---|
| Estimating | 3-1 | 3-2 | pp. 130, 135, 162, 189, 207, 317 |
| Finding and using mean, median, and mode of data | 3-3 | 12-2 | pp. 140, 179, 239, 293, 611 |
| Substituting with formulas | 3-4 | 3-5 | pp. 145, 213 |
| Solving one-step equations containing decimals | 3-5 | 3-6 | pp. 149, 184, 189, 258, 268, 304, 408 |
| Converting metric units | 3-7 | 6-3 | pp. 162, 175 |

# Decimals and Equations

## Connecting to Students' Lives

Ask students if they have traveled to another country. Ask if they bought any souvenirs or spent any of their own money. Ask them how they reacted to the prices they saw in other currencies.

## Interdisciplinary Connections

The Chapter Project connects math and social studies. You may want to display pictures or information about other countries and their currencies.

## About the Project

The Chapter Project directs students to apply their knowledge of decimals and converting units to estimating the cost of various items in other currencies.

**What you'll learn in this chapter:**

- How to estimate with decimals
- How to solve equations with decimals
- How to convert metric units of measure



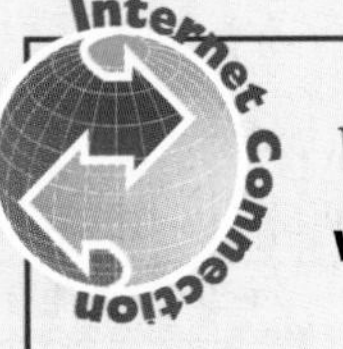


*Web Extension*
**www.phschool.com**

**For Students**
Chapter Support with Internet links
Interactive Activities

**For Teachers**
Curriculum Support
Professional Development
Product Information
Regional Support Information

CHAPTER PROJECT 3

# CURRENCY EVENTS

When you are shoppping, of course you want to know how much an item costs before you decide to buy it! When you travel in another country, you need to "translate" the cost into its value in U.S. dollars.

***Compare Currencies*** For the chapter project, you will research currency exchange rates and calculate prices in different currencies. You will make a poster that shows prices in U.S. dollars and in the currencies of three other countries.

*Steps to help you complete the project*


p. 135 ACTIVITY: ESTIMATING

p. 149 ACTIVITY: RESEARCHING

p. 155 ACTIVITY: CALCULATING

p. 163 FINISHING THE CHAPTER PROJECT

*Web Extension*
**www.phschool.com**

How to solve a problem by simplifying the problem

## Scoring Rubric

**3** You calculate all costs accurately. Your poster is complete, colorful, well-organized, and easy to read.

**2** You make minor errors when calculating costs. Your poster is complete and colorful, but could be organized better or easier to read.

**1** You find inaccurate costs. Your poster is incomplete and lacks organization.

**0** Major elements of the project are incomplete or missing.

*The Chapter Project is optional and may be assigned at your discretion.*

Ask students:

- Have you ever been outside the United States?
- How did you know the cost of the goods and food that were for sale?
- How did you know how much to pay and how to count your change?

Distribute a copy of the Project Manager and Scoring Rubric to help students get an overview of the project.

Review the scoring rubric with students.

### Project Notebook

Encourage students to keep all project-related materials in a separate folder or notebook. Call attention to the fact that they will find much useful information on the Web site **www.phschool.com.**

**Tracking the Project** Set benchmark deadlines for students to show you their work in progress.

*Available in the Chapter 3 Support File in the Teaching Resources box.*

### Project Manager and Scoring Rubric

**Getting Started** You will be creating a poster with the cost of items in U.S. dollars and three other currencies. Read about the project in your textbook. As you work on the project, you will need a calculator, a newspaper, materials to make your poster, and materials to record your calculations.

**Checklist and Suggestions**

| | | |
|---|---|---|
| ❑ | Estimate the costs in U.S. dollars of two items given in pesos. | You can either multiply or divide. |
| ❑ | Research foreign currency exchange rates. | Look in the business section of a newspaper or on the internet. |
| ❑ | Find advertisements for two items from a newspaper. | Choose colorful advertisements for things you might like to buy. |
| ❑ | Find the cost of the items from your advertisements in the currencies of three countries other than the U.S. | Choose countries you might like to visit. |
| ❑ | Make your poster. | Plan the layout first. |
| ❑ | Share your poster with the class. | Check each other's work and provide suggestions. |

**Scoring Rubric**

**3** You calculate all costs accurately. Your poster is complete, colorful, well-organized, and easy to read.

**2** You make minor errors when calculating costs. Your poster is complete and colorful, but could be organized better or easier to read.

**1** You find inaccurate costs. Your poster is incomplete and lacks organization.

**0** Major elements of the project are incomplete or missing.

**Your Evaluation of the Project** Evaluate your work, based on the Scoring Rubric.

**Teacher's Evaluation of the Project**

# 3-1

## Getting Ready

**Resources** A complete list of resources for this lesson is on p. 119H.

### Daily Skills Warm-Up

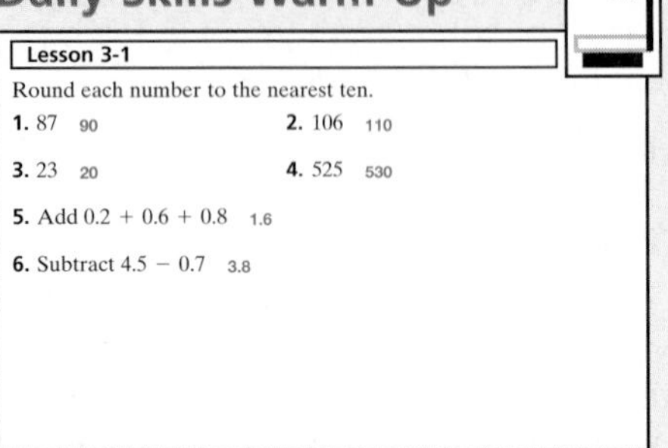

Lesson 3-1

Round each number to the nearest ten.

1. 87 90
2. 106 110
3. 23 20
4. 525 530
5. Add 0.2 + 0.6 + 0.8 1.6
6. Subtract 4.5 − 0.7 3.8

### Background for the Lesson

To round a decimal number, look at the digit to the right of the place you are rounding. If the number to the right is 5 or more, increase by 1 the number in that place. If the number to the right is less than 5, do not increase that number. Then drop the digits in all the places beyond the place to which you are rounding. For example, rounding 34.546 to the tenths place results in 34.5, and rounding to the hundredths place results in 34.55, while rounding to the nearest tens gives 30.

## 1 Focus

### Investigate

Ask students for examples of estimation situations.

### Connecting to Students' Lives

The amount of sales tax may be rounded up or down to the nearest cent, or it may be always rounded up to the nearest cent. For example, if the tax is 8.25 cents, the store may add 8 or 9 cents to your purchase. Discuss your local sales tax rate if there is one.

### Connecting to Prior Knowledge

In previous courses, students learned to round whole numbers. In this lesson, students round decimal numbers. In Lesson 3-2, students will use rounding



# 3-1 Rounding and Estimating

**What You'll Learn**

1. To round decimals
2. To estimate sums and differences

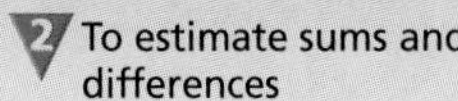

**. . . And Why**

To understand and apply appropriate estimation strategies in a variety of situations

## *Investigate*

ESTIMATING IN THE REAL WORLD

Some real-world problems require only an estimate for an answer. Others require an exact answer. Decide whether each situation needs an estimate or an exact answer. Explain your reasoning.

1–4. Answers may vary. Samples are given.

1. a headline noting the number of people living in China
   Estimate; an exact count of such a large population is not possible.
2. the amount of money a babysitter charges per hour
   Exact; the babysitter should be paid fairly.
3. the width of a window screen
   Exact; the screen needs to fit.
4. the distance from Earth to the moon
   Estimate; the distance is always changing.

## PART 1 Rounding Decimals

You can round decimal numbers when you don't need exact values.

**Quick Review**

| Ones | . | Tenths | Hundredths | Thousandths | Ten-thousandths |
|---|---|---|---|---|---|
| 4 | . | 2 | 6 | 8 | 3 |

### EXAMPLE 1

**a. Round 4.2683 to the nearest tenth.**

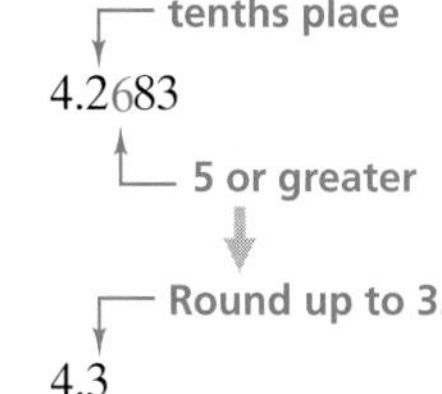


**b. Round 4.2683 to the nearest integer.**

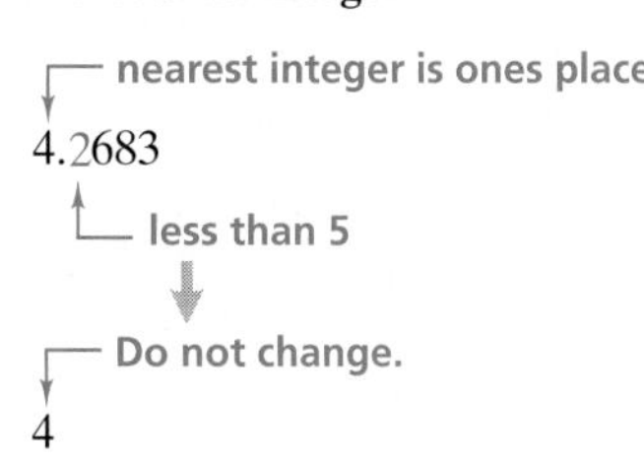


**TRY THIS** Identify the underlined place value. Then round each number to that place value.

5. 38.41 tenths; 38.4
6. 0.7772 ones; 1
7. 7,098.56 tenths; 7,098.6
8. 274.9434 thousandths; 274.943
9. 5.025 tenths; 5.0
10. 9.851 hundredths; 9.85



## Tools to Monitor Progress

**BEFORE THE LESSON**

**To check prerequisite skills:**

- Rounding numbers

**Skills You Need,** p. 119

**Skills Handbook,** p. 724

**Skills Intervention Kit,** Whole Numbers

**DURING THE LESSON**

**To check understanding:**

**Try This** exercises on student page

- **Additional Example 1**
  a. Round 8.7398 to the nearest tenth. 8.7
  b. Round 8.7398 to the nearest integer. 9

## Estimating Sums and Differences

You can estimate an answer before you calculate it to make sure your answer is reasonable. If the answer is close to the estimate, then you know it is probably correct.

The symbol ≈ means "is approximately equal to."

**Write** $126 ≈ $130

**Read** $126 is approximately equal to $130.

One way to estimate is to round all numbers to the same place value.

*Need Help?* For help with decimal place value or adding and subtracting decimals, see Skills Handbook, pp. 727 and 730.

### Example 2

**Estimate to find whether each answer is reasonable.**

| **a. Calculation** | | **Estimate** | **b. Calculation** | | **Estimate** |
|---|---|---|---|---|---|
| $135.95 | ≈ | $140 | 464.90 | ≈ | 460 |
| $15.90 | ≈ | $20 | −125.73 | ≈ | −130 |
| +$24.05 | ≈ | +$20 | 339.17 | | 330 |
| $275.90 | | $180 | | | |

a. The answer is not close to the estimate. It is *not* reasonable.

b. The answer is close to the estimate. It is reasonable.

**Try This** Estimate.

**11.** 355.302 + 204.889 about 560 **12.** 453.56 − 230.07 about 220

A *front-end estimate* is often closer to the exact sum than an estimate you find by rounding. First add the front-end digits. Round to estimate the sum of the remaining digits. Then combine estimates.

REAL-WORLD CONNECTION

### Example 3

**The carrots cost $2.71, the red peppers cost $1.73, and the broccoli cost $1.10. Estimate the total cost of the vegetables.**

Add the front-end digits. →

| | | | |
|---|---|---|---|
| 1.10 | ⟶ | .10 | Estimate by rounding. |
| 1.73 | ⟶ | .70 | |
| +2.71 | ⟶ | .70 | |
| 4 | + | 1.50 = 5.50 | |

The total cost is about $5.50.

**Try This** Estimate using front-end estimation.

**13.** 6.75 + 2.2 + 9.58 about 18.6 **14.** $1.07 + $2.49 + $7.40 about $11



to help them estimate decimal products and quotients.

## 2 Teach

### Part 1 Teaching Notes

The place to the right of the ones place is called *tenths*. The place to the left of the ones place is called *tens*. This means that the ones place (not the decimal point) is the center of the naming pattern for number places.

#### Example 1

**Build understanding.** Ask: In part b., is 4.2683 closer to 4 or to 5? 4

**ELL** Point out that only a *th* separates *hundreds* from *hundredth*. So, it is important to listen and speak carefully to avoid confusing these names of number places.

**Technology Option** You may want to have students explore how several different kinds of calculators round decimal numbers.

### Part 2 Teaching Notes

Remind students that they probably often use estimates to decide if they have enough money for a planned purchase.

#### Example 2

**Build understanding.** Ask: How far is $135.95 from $130? from $140? $5.95; $4.05

#### Example 3

**Build understanding.** Ask: How can you tell which digits are the front-end digits? They are in front of (or to the left of) the decimal point.

**• Additional Example 4**

Estimate by clustering the total electric charges: March: $81.75; April: $79.56; May: $80.89. about $240

### AFTER THE LESSON

**To assess knowledge: Lesson Quiz**

Round to the underlined place value.

**1.** 6.<u>5</u>57 6.6 **2.** 3.04<u>4</u>8 3.04

Estimate.

**3.** $4.95 + $0.89 about $6.00

**4.** 4.589 + 5.098 + 5.179 about 15

- For enrichment and reteaching options see Resources on p. 119H.

## ■ Example 4

**Build understanding.** Ask: What was the greatest monthly charge? the least? $16.05; $14.90

**Extension** Challenge students to write five numbers that cluster around the current local cost of a gallon of gasoline.

**Error Prevention** When rounding to a specified place value, students may start at the end of the number and round each place. This incorrect method may give the wrong answer. For example, in rounding 5.44548 to the nearest tenth, if the student starts with 8 and rounds each digit to the left in succession, the answer might appear to be 5.5. This answer is incorrect because 5.44548 is closer to 5.4 than to 5.5. Point out that 5.45000 would be halfway between these two numbers, and 5.44548 is less than 5.45000. Remind students to underline the specified place value and to consider only the digit to the right of the underlined place.

**Auditory Learning** Have students practice reading decimals aloud, using *and* to indicate the decimal point.

**Math Reasoning** In scientific rounding, if the first digit to be dropped is 5, you go up if the digit to the right of the 5 is odd but not if the digit to the right of the 5 is even. What is the effect of this kind of rounding? When a 5 occurs, half the time you go up, half down. So the effect of rounding is more even, and it builds in less error.

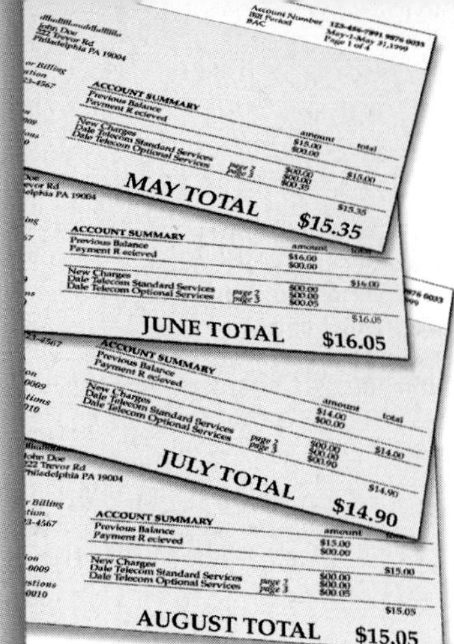


You can also use *clustering* to estimate the sum of several numbers that are close to one value.

### ■ Example 4

*Telephone Service* **Estimate the total long-distance charge for the months of May, June, July, and August shown at the left.**

The values cluster around $15. ⟶ $15 \cdot 4 = 60$ (four months)

The long-distance charge is about $60.00.

■ **Try This** Estimate using clustering.

**15.** $4.50 + $5.20 + $5.55 about $15

**16.** 26.7 + 26.2 + 24.52 + 25.25 + 23.9 about 125

In this lesson, you have seen several methods for finding a reasonable estimate. Here are two methods used for the same situation.

## ■ Different Ways to Solve a Problem

**Estimate the total cost of four items priced at $4.39, $3.75, $4.96, and $2.40.**

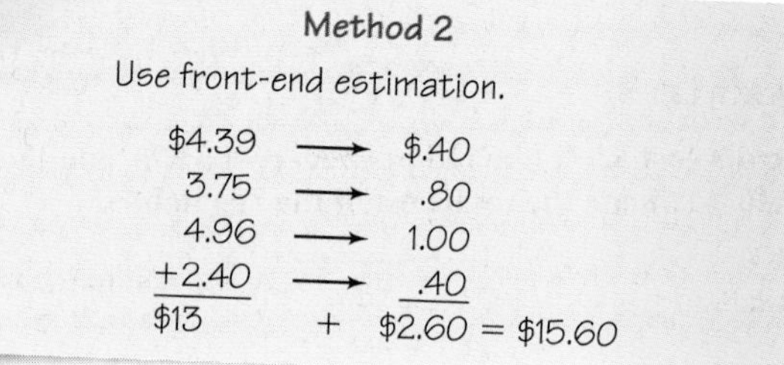

Method 1
Round each price to the nearest dollar. Then add.
$4.39 + $3.75 + $4.96 + $2.40
$4 + $4 + $5 + $2 = $15


Method 2

Use front-end estimation.

| | | |
|---|---|---|
| $4.39 | ⟶ | $.40 |
| 3.75 | ⟶ | .80 |
| 4.96 | ⟶ | 1.00 |
| +2.40 | ⟶ | .40 |
| $13 | + | $2.60 = $15.60 |

**Choose a Method**

1. Which method would you use to estimate the cost of the items? Explain. Answers may vary. Sample: Front-end; it will probably give an answer closer to the actual cost.
2. Find the exact cost. Which estimate is nearer the exact cost? $15.50; front-end estimate

# Exercises

## CHECK UNDERSTANDING

**Round to the underlined place value.**

1. $27.3\underline{8}56$ 27.39
2. $0.91\underline{2}2$ 0.912
3. $1{,}04\underline{5}.98$ 1,046
4. $345.\underline{6}78$ 345.7

**Estimate by rounding.**

5. $37.99 − $27.32 about $11
6. 1.58 + 17.0244 about 19
7. 72.98 − 28.301 about 45

**Estimate using front-end estimation.**

8. $6.04 + $3.45 + $4.43 about $13.90
9. $5.92 + $4.07 about $10
10. 9.89 + 2.43 + 8.37 about 20.7

**Estimate by clustering.**

11. 44.87 + 42.712 + 43.5 about $129
12. $9.50 + $8.45 + $9.08 about $27
13. 0.18 + 0.23 + 0.19 about 0.60
14. *Open-ended* Describe a situation in which a rounded answer is appropriate. Then describe one in which an exact answer is necessary. Answers may vary. Sample: the number of hours I studied last month; the amount I have to pay for a purchase

## PRACTICE AND PROBLEM SOLVING

**Round to the underlined place value.**

15. $1.\underline{5}28$ 1.5
16. $4{,}652.9\underline{8}7$ 4,652.99
17. $\underline{0}.5834$ 1
18. $33.3\underline{0}4$ 33.30

**Estimate by rounding.** Answers may vary. Samples are given.

19. $4.89 + $3.87 about $9
20. 8.974 + 2.154 about 11
21. $16.81 + $11.49 about $28
22. 102.44 + 48.35 about 150
23. $5.65 − $2.25 about $4
24. 600 − 209.52 about 400
25. 0.08 + 17.02 about 17
26. 27.4 + 16.02 about 43

**Estimate using front-end estimation.**

27. 14.39 + 79.102 about 93.5
28. $38.59 + $15.28 about $53.90
29. 78.87 + 11.49 about 90.4
30. $412.44 + $72.23 about $484.60
31. 7.04 + 2.45 about 9.5
32. 7.54 + 3.02 about 10.5
33. 2.298 + 7.750 about 10.1
34. 6.79 + 4.041 about 10.8

**Estimate by clustering.**

35. $7.43 + $7.05 + $6.95 + $7.29 about $28
36. 15.4 + 16 + 15.9 + 16.25 + 15.7 about 80
37. 800 + 810.5 + 807.35 + 803.9 about 3,220
38. 54.23 + 56.12 + 57.98 + 55.55 about 220



# 3 Practice/Assess

## Assignment Guide

To provide flexible scheduling, this lesson can be divided into parts.

**Part 1**
**Core** 1–4, 15–18

**Part 2**
**Core** 5–14, 19–49, 52
**Extension** 50–51

Mixed Review can be assigned at any time for maintenance.

## Exercises

**Exercise 18** Keep the final zero in the answer to show that you rounded the number to the hundredths place.

**Test Prep Exercise 52** Remind students to practice their estimating skills instead of doing the exact calculation. On a test they may run out of time if they actually do the calculation.

## Challenge

Estimate 24.96 − 8.02 + 6.3. about 23; estimates may differ.

## Closure

You can estimate the sum or difference of decimals by rounding, front-end estimating, or clustering.

## Alternative Assessment

Ask students to draw a cartoon that explains how the symbol for *is approximately equal to* differs in form and meaning from the symbol for *equals*.

## Daily Cumulative Review

**Solve each inequality.** *(Lesson 2-10)*

1. $24 < -6u$ $-4 > u$
2. $30 \geq \frac{t}{-6}$ $-180 \leq t$
3. $-6w \leq 18$ $w \geq -3$
4. $-2n > 32$ $n < -16$
5. $5y \geq 35$ $y \geq 7$
6. $\frac{r}{4} < 13$ $r < 52$
7. $-8 \leq \frac{p}{-4}$ $32 \geq p$
8. $-7h < 56$ $h > -8$
9. $\frac{a}{8} \geq 5$ $a \geq 40$

**Write an inequality for each sentence. Then solve each inequality.** *(Lesson 2-9)*

10. The sum of a number $p$ and negative eight is greater than or equal to twenty-four. $p + (-8) \geq 24$; $p \geq 32$
11. Twelve subtracted from a number $s$ is greater than negative fourteen. $s - 12 > -14$; $s > -2$
12. Negative twenty-four plus a number $k$ is less than or equal to negative three. $-24 + k \leq -3$; $k \leq 21$
13. Thirty subtracted from a number $r$ is less than negative twenty. $r - 30 < -20$; $r < 10$

**Mixed Review**

**Estimate each product by rounding to the underlined place value.** *(From Last Year)*

14. 28 × 31 900
15. 91 × 55 5,400
16. 87 × 98 9,000
17. 231 × 461 100,000
18. 752 × 498 400,000
19. 321 × 241 60,000

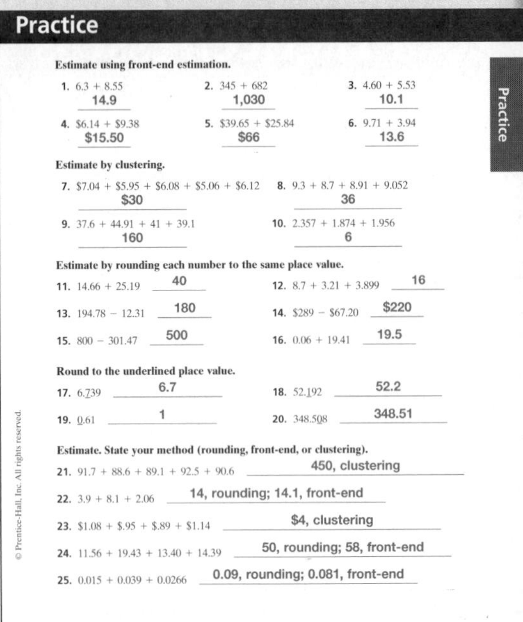

## Practice

**Estimate using front-end estimation.**

1. 6.3 + 8.55 — 14.9
2. 345 + 682 — 1,030
3. 4.60 + 5.53 — 10.1
4. \$6.14 + \$9.38 — \$15.50
5. \$39.65 + \$25.84 — \$66
6. 9.71 + 3.94 — 13.6

**Estimate by clustering.**

7. \$7.04 + \$5.95 + \$6.08 + \$5.06 + \$6.12 — \$30
8. 9.3 + 8.7 + 8.91 + 9.052 — 36
9. 37.6 + 44.91 + 41 + 39.1 — 160
10. 2.357 + 1.874 + 1.956 — 6

**Estimate by rounding each number to the same place value.**

11. 14.66 + 25.19 — 40
12. 8.7 + 3.21 + 3.899 — 16
13. 194.78 − 12.31 — 180
14. \$289 − \$67.20 — \$220
15. 800 − 301.47 — 500
16. 0.06 + 19.41 — 19.5

**Round to the underlined place value.**

17. 6.739 — 6.7
18. 52.192 — 52.2
19. 0.61 — 1
20. 348.508 — 348.51

**Estimate. State your method (rounding, front-end, or clustering).**

21. 91.7 + 88.6 + 89.1 + 92.5 + 90.6 — 450, clustering
22. 3.9 + 8.1 + 2.06 — 14, rounding; 14.1, front-end
23. \$1.08 + \$.95 + \$.89 + \$1.14 — \$4, clustering
24. 11.56 + 19.43 + 13.40 + 14.39 — 50, rounding; 58, front-end
25. 0.015 + 0.039 + 0.0266 — 0.09, rounding; 0.081, front-end



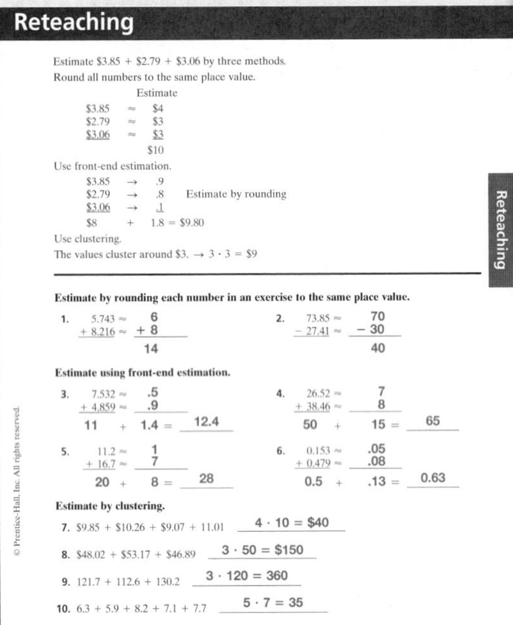

## Reteaching

Estimate \$3.85 + \$2.79 + \$3.06 by three methods.

Round all numbers to the same place value.

Estimate

\$3.85 ≈ \$4
\$2.79 ≈ \$3
\$3.06 ≈ \$3
\$10

Use front-end estimation.

\$3.85 → .9
\$2.79 → .8 Estimate by rounding
\$3.06 → .1
\$8 + 1.8 = \$9.80

Use clustering.

The values cluster around \$3. → 3 · 3 = \$9

**Estimate by rounding each number in an exercise to the same place value.**

1. 5.743 ≈ 6; + 8.216 ≈ + 8; 14
2. 73.85 ≈ 70; − 27.41 ≈ − 30; 40

**Estimate using front-end estimation.**

3. 7.532 ≈ .5; + 4.859 ≈ .9; 11 + 1.4 = 12.4
4. 26.52 ≈ 7; + 38.46 ≈ 8; 50 + 15 = 65
5. 11.2 ≈ 1; + 16.7 ≈ 7; 20 + 8 = 28
6. 0.153 ≈ .05; + 0.479 ≈ .08; 0.5 + .13 = 0.63

**Estimate by clustering.**

7. \$9.85 + \$10.26 + \$9.07 + 11.01 — 4 · 10 = \$40
8. \$48.02 + \$53.17 + \$46.89 — 3 · 50 = \$150
9. 121.7 + 112.6 + 130.2 — 3 · 120 = 360
10. 6.3 + 5.9 + 8.2 + 7.1 + 7.7 — 5 · 7 = 35



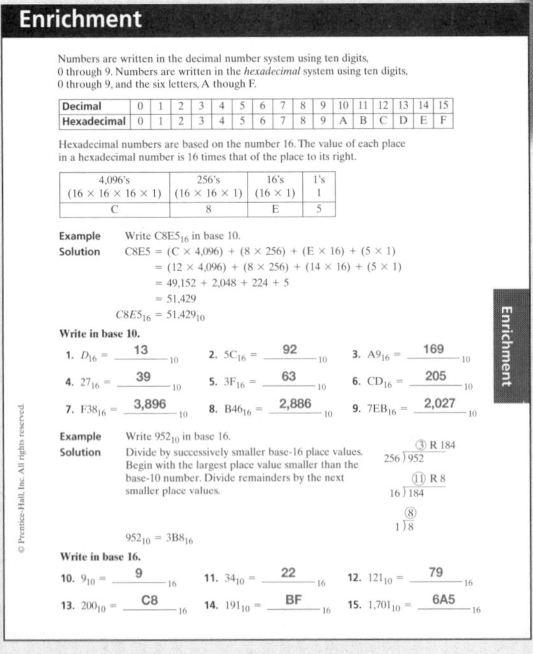

## Enrichment

Numbers are written in the decimal number system using ten digits, 0 through 9. Numbers are written in the *hexadecimal* system using ten digits, 0 through 9, and the six letters, A though F.

| Decimal | 0 | 1 | 2 | 3 | 4 | 5 | 6 | 7 | 8 | 9 | 10 | 11 | 12 | 13 | 14 | 15 |
|---|---|---|---|---|---|---|---|---|---|---|---|---|---|---|---|---|
| Hexadecimal | 0 | 1 | 2 | 3 | 4 | 5 | 6 | 7 | 8 | 9 | A | B | C | D | E | F |

Hexadecimal numbers are based on the number 16. The value of each place in a hexadecimal number is 16 times that of the place to its right.

| 4,096's (16 × 16 × 16 × 1) | 256's (16 × 16 × 1) | 16's (16 × 1) | 1's 1 |
|---|---|---|---|
| C | 8 | E | 5 |

**Example** Write $C8E5_{16}$ in base 10.

**Solution** C8E5 = (C × 4,096) + (8 × 256) + (E × 16) + (5 × 1)
= (12 × 4,096) + (8 × 256) + (14 × 16) + (5 × 1)
= 49,152 + 2,048 + 224 + 5
= 51,429

$C8E5_{16} = 51{,}429_{10}$

**Write in base 10.**

1. $D_{16}$ = 13$_{10}$
2. $5C_{16}$ = 92$_{10}$
3. $A9_{16}$ = 169$_{10}$
4. $27_{16}$ = 39$_{10}$
5. $3F_{16}$ = 63$_{10}$
6. $CD_{16}$ = 205$_{10}$
7. $F38_{16}$ = 3,896$_{10}$
8. $B46_{16}$ = 2,886$_{10}$
9. $7EB_{16}$ = 2,027$_{10}$

**Example** Write $952_{10}$ in base 16.

**Solution** Divide by successively smaller base-16 place values. Begin with the largest place value smaller than the base-10 number. Divide remainders by the next smaller place values.

256 ) 952 = ③ R 184
16 ) 184 = ⑪ R 8
1 ) 8 = ⑧

$952_{10} = 3B8_{16}$

**Write in base 16.**

10. $9_{10}$ = 9$_{16}$
11. $34_{10}$ = 22$_{16}$
12. $121_{10}$ = 79$_{16}$
13. $200_{10}$ = C8$_{16}$
14. $191_{10}$ = BF$_{16}$
15. $1{,}701_{10}$ = 6A5$_{16}$





**Estimate. State the method you used.**
39-46. Answers may vary. Samples are given.

39. \$8.99 + \$8.01 about \$17; rounding
40. 2.3 + 2.3 + 4.56 about 9.2; front-end
41. \$89.90 − \$49.29 about \$40; rounding
42. 102.54 − 74.75 about 25; rounding
43. 20.55 − 1.48 about 20; rounding
44. \$11.97 − \$2.29 about \$10; rounding
45. \$19.01 + \$10.99 + \$7.49 about \$37.50; front-end
46. 6.57 + 5.99 + 5.70 + 6.25 about 24; clustering

47. *Statistics* In 1990, the population of the state of Georgia was 6.8 million. In 1950, the population was 3.44 million. About how much greater was Georgia's population in 1990 than in 1950? about 3.4 million

48. *Geography* Lake Superior, the largest of the Great Lakes, has an area of 31,760 mi$^2$. Lake Erie, the smallest of the Great Lakes, has an area of 9,920 mi$^2$. About how much larger is Lake Superior than Lake Erie? about 22,000 mi$^2$

Lake Erie
Lake Superior

49. *Weather* Mobile, Alabama, has an average annual rainfall of 63.96 in. The average annual rainfall in San Francisco, California, is 19.70 in. About how much more rain falls each year in Mobile than in San Francisco? about 44 in.

50. *Error Analysis* You used a calculator to find 383.8 − 21.9. Your estimate was 360, but your display reads 164.8. How could you have gotten 164.8 on your calculator? Subtract 219 instead of 21.9.

51. *Writing* You have \$11.50 to buy two presents. You find one item that costs \$7.43. Another item costs \$4.41. What estimation strategy will help you decide whether you have enough money to buy both? Explain. Answers may vary. Sample: front-end; it gives an estimate of \$11.80, so I don't have enough money.

52. **TEST PREP** Choose the phrase that best completes the statement. The sum of \$12.45 and \$7.65 is __?__. B
A. less than \$20.00 B. greater than \$20.00 C. an integer D. greater than \$25.00

## Mixed Review

**Solve each inequality.** ***(Lesson 2-10)***

53. $9x \leq 27$ $x \leq 3$
54. $4x < 16$ $x < 4$
55. $-6k > -24$ $k < 4$
56. $-3y \leq 0$ $y \geq 0$

**Simplify.** ***(Lesson 1-9)***

57. $(-2)(-2)$ 4
58. $4(-3)$ −12
59. $6(-5)$ −30
60. $-8 \div 2$ −4

61. *Choose a Strategy* Ming's model vehicle collection contains 4-wheeled trucks and 2-wheeled bikes. She owns an even number of vehicles, and they have 26 wheels in all. If Ming has a little more than twice as many bikes as trucks, how many of each does she own? 7 bikes; 3 trucks



See also Extra Practice section.

# Estimating Decimal Products and Quotients

## Part 1 Estimating Products

You can use mental math to estimate products and quotients. It is a good idea to estimate answers to check your calculations.

**EXAMPLE 1**

**Estimate 7.65 · 3.2.**

$7.65 \approx 8$ $3.2 \approx 3$ Round to the nearest integer.

$8 \cdot 3 = 24$ Multiply.

$7.65 \cdot 3.2 \approx 24$

**TRY THIS** Estimate each product.

1. 4.72 · 1.8 about 10
2. 17.02 · 3.78 about 68
3. 8.25 · 19.8 about 160

REAL-WORLD CONNECTION

**EXAMPLE 2**

**Arlene bought 6 yd of fabric to make a Lone Star quilt. The fabric cost $6.75/yd. The sales clerk charged Arlene $45.90 before tax. Did the clerk make a mistake? Explain.**

$6.75 \approx 7$ Round to the nearest dollar.

$7 \cdot 6 = 42$ Multiply 7 times 6, the number of yards of fabric.

The sales clerk made a mistake. Since $6.75 < 7$, the actual cost should be less than the estimate. The clerk should have charged Arlene less than $42.00 before tax.

**TRY THIS**

4. You buy 8 rolls of film for your camera. Each roll costs $4.79. Estimate the cost of the film before tax. about $40

The quilter is working on a Lone Star quilt. The quilt is 7.8 ft wide and 8.5 ft long.

## 3-2

**What You'll Learn**

1. To estimate products
2. To estimate quotients

**. . . And Why**

To determine the reasonableness of a calculation



# Tools to Monitor Progress

**BEFORE THE LESSON**

**To check prerequisite skills:**

- Rounding numbers

**Skills You Need,** p. 119

**Skills Handbook,** p. 724

**Skills Intervention Kit,** Whole Numbers

**DURING THE LESSON**

**To check understanding:**

**Try This** exercises on student page

- **Additional Example 1**
  Estimate 6.43 • 4.7. 30
- **Additional Example 2**
  Joshua bought 3 yd of fabric to make a flag. The fabric cost $5.65/yd. The clerk said his total was $14.95 before tax. Did the clerk make a mistake? Explain. Yes; the total should be more than 3 • 5.

# 3-2

## Getting Ready

**Key Terms and Symbols** compatible numbers

**Resources** A complete list of resources for this lesson is on p. 119H.

### Daily Skills Warm-Up

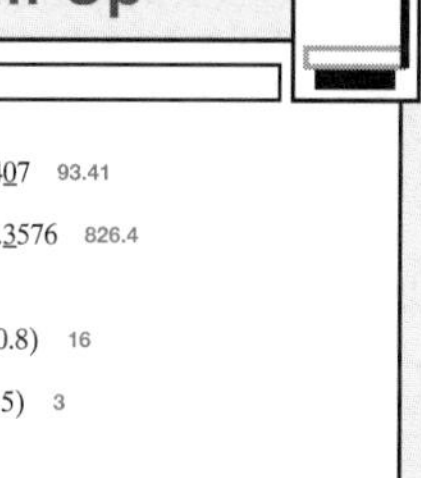

Lesson 3-2

Round to the underlined place.

| | |
|---|---|
| 1. 3.716 3.7 | 2. 93.407 93.41 |
| 3. 0.623 1 | 4. 826.3576 826.4 |

Simplify.

| | |
|---|---|
| 5. 40(5) 200 | 6. 20(0.8) 16 |
| 7. 2.4 ÷ 6 0.4 | 8. 6(0.5) 3 |

### Background for the Lesson

You use rounding as an important step in estimating products. When you multiply decimals, round each decimal to the nearest integer. Then multiply the integers to get an estimate. Estimating an answer is particularly important when you use a calculator. It is easy to accidentally press a wrong key. Beginning with an estimate of the correct answer helps you recognize whether the calculator answer is reasonable.

## 1 Focus

### Connecting to Students' Lives

Discuss with students how they estimate the total cost when they buy several identical items at the supermarket.

### Connecting to Prior Knowledge

In Lesson 3-1, students learned to round decimals. In this lesson, they use those skills to estimate decimal products and quotients. In Lesson 3-3, students will apply this to finding the mean, median, and mode.

# 2 Teach

## Part 1 Teaching Notes

One of the most important skills for a wise consumer is the ability to spot the accidental mistakes in a sales slip or restaurant check. This skill depends on estimating.

### Example 1

**Build understanding.** Ask: One of these numbers has digits in the tenths and hundredths places. Why does the digit in the hundredths place make no difference when you round to the nearest integer? **Only the next digit to the right, in the tenths place, makes a difference in rounding to the nearest integer.**

### Example 2

**Build understanding.** Ask: What is the approximate cost of 1 yd of fabric? of 2 yd? **$7; $14**

## Part 2 Teaching Notes

To demonstrate compatible numbers, ask students to compare dividing 20 by 5 and dividing 19 by 4.

### Example 3

**Build understanding.** Ask: A kilogram is about 2.2 lb. Does one bowling pin weigh more than or less than 2 lb? **more**

**Connecting to Science** Mass is the measure of matter in an object. Weight is the result of the force of gravity on an object. A person on the Moon has the same mass as on Earth, but the person weighs much less because of low gravity on the moon.

### Example 4

**Build understanding.** Ask: Why is 17.931 rounded to 16? **because 16 and 8 are compatible numbers**

**Extension** Challenge students to use fact families (such as $4 \div 2$, $40 \div 2$) to write a list of five pairs of compatible numbers for mental division.

## Part 2 Estimating Quotients

When dividing, remember these names for the parts of a division sentence.

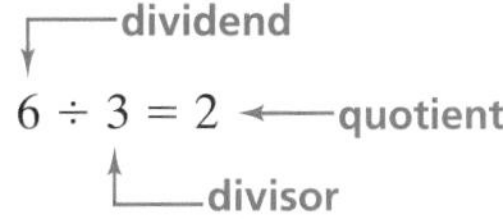


When dividing, you can use *compatible numbers* to estimate quotients. **Compatible numbers** are numbers that are easy to divide mentally. When you estimate a quotient, first round the divisor, and then round the dividend to a compatible number.

### Example 3

*Measurement* **A bowling ball has a mass of 5.61 kg. A bowling pin has a mass of 1.57 kg. How many bowling pins are about equal in mass to one bowling ball? Estimate 5.61 ÷ 1.57.**

| | |
|---|---|
| $1.57 \approx 2$ | Round the divisor. |
| $5.61 \approx 6$ | Round the dividend to a multiple of 2 that is close to 5.61. |
| $6 \div 2 = 3$ | Divide. |

The mass of three bowling pins is about equal to that of one bowling ball.

1.57 kg
5.61 kg

**Try This** Estimate each quotient.

5. $38.9 \div 1.79$ about 19
6. $11.95 \div 2.1$ about 6
7. $82.52 \div 4.25$ about 20

You can estimate to determine the reasonableness of results.

You can sometimes use estimation to eliminate possible responses on a multiple choice test.

Solve $8.19 \div 2.1$.

A. 39 B. 3.9
C. 4.1 D. 0.041

If you estimate $8 \div 2 \approx 4$, then you know you can eliminate choices A and D.

### Example 4

*Number Sense* **Is 2.15 a reasonable quotient for 17.931 ÷ 8.34?**

| | |
|---|---|
| $8.34 \approx 8$ | Round the divisor. |
| $17.931 \approx 16$ | Round the dividend to a multiple of 8 that is close to 17.931. |
| $16 \div 8 = 2$ | Divide. |

Since 2.15 is close to the estimate 2, it is reasonable.

**Try This** Use estimation. Is each quotient reasonable?

8. $1.564 \div 2.3 = 0.68$ yes
9. $26.0454 \div 4.98 = 52.3$ no



- **Additional Example 3**
  The cost to ship one yearbook is $3.12. The total cost for a shipment was $62.40. Estimate to find how many books were in the shipment. **20**
- **Additional Example 4**
  Is 3.29 a reasonable quotient for $31.423 \div 5.94$? Explain. **no; $30 \div 6 = 5$**

### AFTER THE LESSON

**To assess knowledge:**

**Lesson Quiz**

Estimate each product or quotient.

1. $4.78 ÷ 0.891 **about $5**
2. 983.24 • 2.41 **about 2,000**
3. −5.89 ÷ (−2.7) **about 2**
4. 24.69 • 0.7 **about 25**
5. 20.498 • 4.908 **about 100**

- For enrichment and reteaching options see Resources on p. 119H.

# Exercises

## Check Understanding

**Estimate each product.**

1. $4.562 \cdot 7.02$ about 35
2. $11.15 \cdot 4.44$ about 44
3. $6.3 \cdot 9.2$ about 54
4. $24.5 \cdot 4.2$ about 100

**Estimate each quotient using compatible numbers.**

5. $3.9 \div 2.1$ about 2
6. $0.33 \div 0.14$ about 2
7. $19.56 \div 0.71$ about 20
8. $\$585 \div 11.75$ about \$50
9. *Number Sense* Explain how you would find a reasonable estimate for $14.90 \div 4.56$. Answers may vary. Sample: 14.90 is about 15, and 4.56 is about 5, so $14.90 \div 4.56 \approx 15 \div 5$, or 3.

## Practice and Problem Solving

**Estimate each product or quotient.**

10. $329.08 \cdot 56$ about 18,000
11. $0.98 \cdot 40.05$ about 40
12. $92.81 \cdot 48.33$ about 4,500
13. $16.2 \cdot 9.21$ about 144
14. $32.57 \cdot 4.2$ about 120
15. $193.7 \cdot 1.78$ about 400
16. $876.66 \cdot 39.34$ about 36,000
17. $16.33 \cdot 3.5$ about 64
18. $120.32 \div 4.948$ about 24
19. $\$2.97 \div 0.64$ about \$5
20. $9.418 \div 1.583$ about 5
21. $7.95 \div 2.1$ about 4
22. $9.392 \div 2.9$ about 3
23. $\$32.43 \div 4.68$ about \$6
24. ✪ $-483.09 \div 72$ about $-7$
25. ✪ $-7.75 \div (-1.97)$ about 4

**Determine whether each product or quotient is reasonable. If it is not reasonable, find a reasonable result.**

26. $7.008 \cdot 3.2 = 22.4256$ reasonable
27. $102.6 \div 22.5 = 45.6$ not reasonable; 4.56
28. $\$32.40 \div 4.80 = \$67.50$ not reasonable; \$6.75
29. $-46.82(-1.5) = 702.3$ not reasonable; 70.23
30. $6.009(-11.9) = -71.5071$ reasonable
31. $1.76(0.18) = 3.168$ not reasonable; 0.3168

32. ✪ *Open-ended* Write an expression that includes a product of decimals. Estimate the value of your expression. Check students' work.

33. *Gas Mileage* Shari is planning a 450-mi car trip. Her car can travel about 39 mi on a gallon of gasoline. Gasoline costs \$1.19/gal. About how much will the gas cost for her trip? about \$12

34. **TEST PREP** Greta ran the 400-m dash in 49.07 s. If Greta ran at a constant rate, how many meters did she run in one second? C
    A. between 9 m and 10 m
    B. between 10 m and 11 m
    C. between 8 m and 9 m
    D. between 11 m and 12 m

35. *Writing* Two people estimate the product $\$1.99 \cdot 8.5$. Is it necessary that they get the same estimate? Explain. Answers may vary. Sample: No. $\$2 \cdot 9 = \$18$ will give one estimate. A closer estimate is $(\$2 \cdot 8) + (\$2 \cdot 0.5) = \$16 + \$1 = \$17$.



# 3 Practice/Assess

## Assignment Guide

To provide flexible scheduling, this lesson can be divided into parts.

▼ **Part 1**
**Core** 1–4, 10–17, 26, 29–31, 35–36, 38, 40
✪ **Extension** 32

▼ **Part 2**
**Core** 5–9, 18–23, 27–28, 33–34, 37, 39
✪ **Extension** 24–25, 41

Mixed Review can be assigned at any time for maintenance.

## Exercises

**ELL** Encourage students to read 0.98 as "ninety-eight hundredths" rather than as "oh point nine eight" so that they attach meaning to the math symbols.

**Test Prep Exercise 34** Estimate the answer before looking at the answer choices. Then compare the estimate to the answer choices to find one that fits.

## ✪ Challenge

Estimate.
798.603 ÷ 0.9054. 800

## Closure

You can estimate a product or a quotient of two decimals using compatible numbers.

## Daily Cumulative Review

**Estimate using front-end estimation.** *(Lesson 3-1)*

1. \$5.25 + \$3.14 = \$8.40
2. \$31.47 − \$16.22 = \$15.30
3. 0.73 + 3.08 = 3.80
4. 347.12 − 134.01 = 213.10
5. \$58.32 + \$12.56 = \$70.90
6. 13.93 − 7.29 = 6.60

**Write an inequality for each sentence. Then solve each inequality.** *(Lesson 2-10)*

7. A number *h* multiplied by negative six is greater than or equal to eighteen. $-6h \geq 18; h \leq -3$
8. The quotient of a number *w* and three is greater than negative six. $w \div 3 > -6; w > -18$
9. The product of four and a number *x* is less than or equal to negative twenty-four. $4x \leq -24; x \leq -6$
10. A number *y* divided by negative two is greater than or equal to five. $y \div (-2) \geq 5; y \leq -10$

**Mixed Review**

**Order the following data from least to greatest.**

11. (1-4) 6, 3, −1, 7, −2, 5 — −2, −1, 3, 5, 6, 7
12. (1-4) 10, −9, 8, 7, 5, −3, 2 — −9, −3, 2, 5, 7, 8, 10
13. (1-4) 0, 2, −4, 7, −3, 6, 4 — −4, −3, 0, 2, 4, 6, 7

**Simplify each expression.**

14. (1-2) (12 + 15 + 12) ÷ 3 — 13
15. (1-2) (4 + 6 + 5) ÷ 3 — 5
16. (1-2) (1 + 3 + 2 + 2) ÷ 4 — 2



## Alternative Assessment

Ask students to write beside the numbers the mental steps they use while estimating a product and a quotient.

## Practice

**Determine whether each product or quotient is reasonable. If it is not reasonable, find a reasonable result.**

1. 62.77(29.8) = 187.0546 no; 1800
2. 16.132 ÷ 2.96 = 54.5 no; 5
3. (47.89)(6.193) = 296.5828 yes
4. 318.274 ÷ 4.07 = 78.2 yes
5. 2.65(−0.84) = −0.2226 no; −2.4
6. −38.6(−1.89) = 7.2954 no; 80
7. 6,355 ÷ 775 = 8.2 yes
8. 1,444.14 ÷ 67.8 = 213 no; 20
9. 1.839(6.3) = 115.857 no; 12
10. 3.276 ÷ 0.63 = 5.2 yes

**Estimate each product or quotient.**

11. 8.73 · 6.01 54
12. 11.042(4.56) 55
13. 197.4 · 2.85 600
14. 675.1 · 0.051 35
15. 479.2(3.2) 1500
16. 712.9 · 0.41 280
17. 11.57 ÷ 3.09 4
18. 43.68 ÷ 8.7 5
19. 29.5 ÷ 5.1 6
20. \$41.09 ÷ \$6.88 6
21. 148.8 ÷ 9.8 15
22. \$76.77 ÷ \$24.19 3
23. Apples cost \$.89 per lb. Estimate the cost of three 5-lb bags. \$15
24. You buy 3 dinners that are \$6.85 each. Before tax and tip, the total is \$25.42. Is this total correct? Explain.
    No, 6.85 ≈ 7; the total should be less than 3 · 7 = \$21.
25. You worked 18 hours last week and received \$92.70 in your paycheck. Estimate your hourly pay.
    \$5



## Reteaching

Estimate \$3.14 ÷ \$0.75.
Round 0.75. Since 5 is 5 or greater, add one to the 7, so 0.75 ≈ 0.8.
Round 3.14 to a compatible number, one that is easy to divide by 0.8. Since 8 · 4 = 32, round 3.14 to 3.2.
Mentally divide 3.2 ÷ 0.8 = 4
Thus \$3.14 ÷ 0.75 ≈ \$4.

**Estimate each quotient using compatible numbers.**
Accept all reasonable answers.

1. 15.831 ÷ 7.87 ≈ 16 ÷ 8 = 2
2. 163.7 ÷ 0.46 ≈ 150 ÷ 0.5 = 300
3. −472 ÷ 78.6 ≈ −480 ÷ 80 = −6
4. 11.45 ÷ 3.2 ≈ 12 ÷ 3 = 4
5. 549.7 ÷ 51.4 ≈ 550 ÷ 50 = 11
6. −9.6 ÷ (−1.854) ≈ −10 ÷ ( −2 ) = 5
7. 6.39 ÷ (−0.82) ≈ 6.4 ÷ ( −0.8 ) = −8
8. −31.8 ÷ 0.56 ≈ −30 ÷ 0.6 = −50
9. 336.4 ÷ (−4.23) ≈ 320 ÷ ( −4 ) = −80
10. 82.56 ÷ 8.72 ≈ 81 ÷ 9 = 9
11. −62.31 ÷ 14.89 −60 ÷ 15 = −4
12. 25.8 ÷ 6.72 ≈ 24 ÷ 6 = 4
13. 131 ÷ 42.1 ≈ 120 ÷ 40 = 3
14. 1.53 ÷ 0.28 ≈ 1.5 ÷ 0.3 = 5
15. 6,243 ÷ (−75) ≈ 6,300 ÷ ( −70 ) = −90



## Enrichment

The answer to each problem is correct but the digits in each problem are scrambled. Unscramble the digits and write them in the correct order in the empty boxes.

1. 137 + 825 = 629 → 371 + 258 = 629
2. 8765 − 4329 = 2384 → 5678 − 3294 = 2384
3. 2273 + 8365 = 9405 → 3722 + 5683 = 9405
4. 91.4 × 63.8 = 748.84 → 19.4 × 38.6 = 748.84
5. 1.52 × 6.39 = 35.4816 → 5.12 × 6.93 = 35.4816
6. 3.71 ) 67.027 = 2.9 → 7.13 ) 20.677 = 2.9





36. *Consumer Awareness* You review your sales slip after buying 4 CDs that cost \$14.95 each. Before tax, the total was \$77.80. Is this total correct? Explain. No; \$14.95 × 4 ≈ \$15 × 4 = \$60. The total, \$77.80, is too far from this estimate.

*Data Analysis* **Use the table below for Exercises 37–39.**

**Hospital Staff Wages (40-h week)**

| Occupation | Dallas, TX | Washington, DC |
|---|---|---|
| Physical Therapist | \$733.20 | \$655.20 |
| Pharmacist | \$793.60 | \$851.60 |
| Nurse | \$606.80 | \$714.80 |

SOURCE: *The American Almanac of Jobs and Salaries*

37–38. Answers may vary: Samples are given. See above right.

37. Estimate the hourly wage for each staff position.
38. Estimate the yearly salary for each staff position.

37. physical therapist: about \$18/h in Dallas, about \$16/h in Washington, D.C.; pharmacist: about \$20/h in Dallas, about \$21/h in Washington, D.C.; nurse: about \$15/h in Dallas, about \$18/h in Washington, D.C.

38. physical therapist: about \$35,000 in Dallas and in Washington D.C.; pharmacist: about \$40,000 in Dallas and \$45,000 in Washington D.C.; nurse: about \$30,000 in Dallas and \$35,000 in Washington, D.C.

39. How much more per hour does a physical therapist in Dallas, Texas make than a physical therapist in Washington, D.C.? about \$2

**Journal**
Describe a real-world situation in which you would use estimation to check the reasonableness of a calculation.

40. *Health* Humans breathe about 15 breaths in a minute. The average breath at rest contains 0.76 liters of air. About how many liters of air will you breathe while at rest for 25 minutes? about 300 L

41. *Mathematical Reasoning* You estimate 21.2 ÷ 3.75 to be 5. Your friend estimates the quotient to be 7. Explain how the two estimates can be different and yet both be reasonable. I rounded to 20 ÷ 4. My friend used compatible numbers, 21 ÷ 3.

## MIXED REVIEW

**Estimate each sum or difference.** *(Lesson 3-1)*

42. \$2.99 + \$6.01 about \$9
43. 12.3 + 12.3 + 14.56 about 39
44. \$25.90 − \$5.79 about \$20
45. 1,242.24 − 24.05 about 1,220
46. 18.95 − 7.48 about 12
47. \$7.47 − \$5.50 about \$2

**In which quadrant or on which axis of a coordinate plane does each ordered pair lie?** *(Lesson 1-10)*

48. (2, 4) Quadrant I
49. (−5, −3) Quadrant III
50. (8, −6) Quadrant IV
51. (0, 8) *y*-axis
52. (−9, −2) Quadrant III
53. (−5, 0) *x*-axis

54. *Choose a Strategy* A bus trip from Sacramento to Los Angeles takes 7 h 40 min. If the bus leaves Sacramento at 11:40 A.M., at what time will it arrive in Los Angeles? 7:20 P.M.



See also Extra Practice section.

# Mean, Median, and Mode

## PART 1 Finding Mean, Median, and Mode

*Mean*, *median*, and *mode* are **measures of central tendency** of a collection of data. Consider the data 2, 3, 4, 5, 8, 8, and 12.

The **mean** is the sum of the data items divided by the number of data items.

$$\text{mean} = \frac{2+3+4+5+8+8+12}{7} = \frac{42}{7}$$
$$\text{mean} = 6$$

The **median** is the middle number when data items are written in order and there are an odd number of data items. For an even number of data items, the median is the mean of the two middle numbers.

2 3 4 5 8 8 12 (5 ↑ median)

The **mode** is the data item that occurs most often. There can be one mode, more than one mode, or no mode.

2 3 4 5 8 8 12 (8 8 mode)

### What You'll Learn

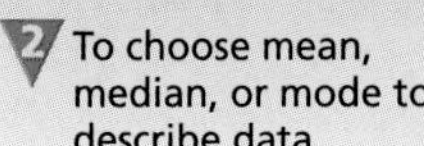

1. To find mean, median, and mode
2. To choose mean, median, or mode to describe data

### . . . And Why

To apply different averages to consumer issues

REAL-WORLD CONNECTION

### EXAMPLE 1

**Six elementary students are participating in a one-week Readathon to raise money for a good cause. Use the graph at the right. Find the (a) mean, (b) median, and (c) mode.**

**a. Mean:** $\frac{\text{sum of data items}}{\text{number of data items}} = \frac{40+45+48+50+50+69}{6}$
$= \frac{292}{6}$
$= 48.66\ldots$

Rounded to the nearest tenth, the mean is 48.7.

**b. Median:** 40 45 48 50 50 59 Write the data in order.

$\frac{48+50}{2} = 49$ Find the mean of the two middle numbers.

The median is 49.

**c. Mode:** Find the data item that occurs most often.
The mode is 50.

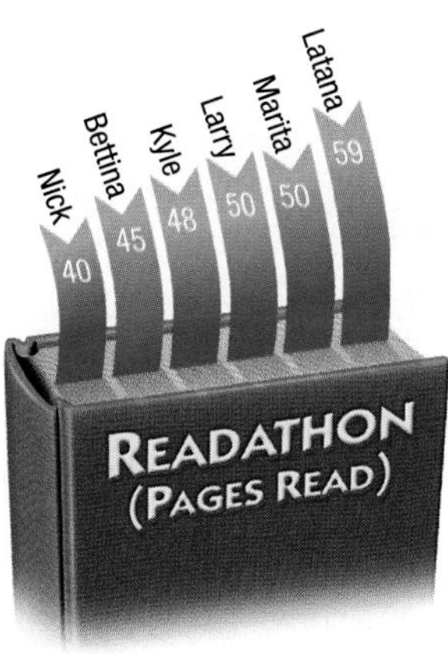




# Tools to Monitor Progress

## BEFORE THE LESSON

**To check prerequisite skills:**

- Working with integers

**Skills Handbook,** p. 741

**Skills Intervention Kit,** Whole Numbers

## DURING THE LESSON

**To check understanding:**

**Try This** exercises on student page

- **Additional Example 1**

  Find the mean, median, and mode of the pages read (from the table) if you leave out Latana's pages.
  **46.6; 48; 50**

# 3-3

## Getting Ready

**Key Terms and Symbols** measures of central tendency, mean, mode, median, outlier

**Resources** A complete list of resources for this lesson is on p. 119H.

### Daily Skills Warm-Up

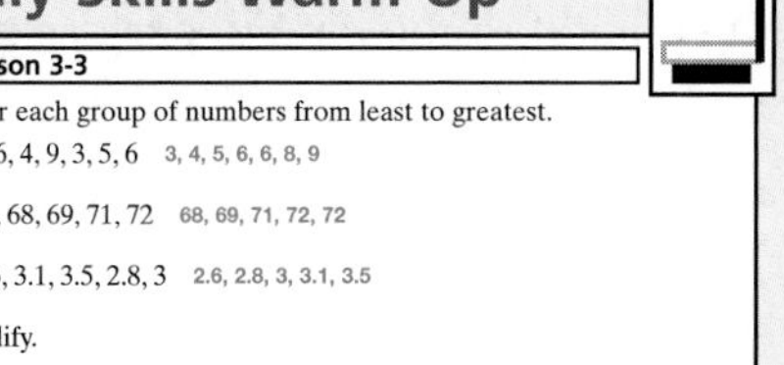

Lesson 3-3

Order each group of numbers from least to greatest.

1. 8, 6, 4, 9, 3, 5, 6 3, 4, 5, 6, 6, 8, 9
2. 72, 68, 69, 71, 72 68, 69, 71, 72, 72
3. 2.6, 3.1, 3.5, 2.8, 3 2.6, 2.8, 3, 3.1, 3.5

Simplify.

4. $\frac{2+3+5+7+1+6}{6}$ 4
5. $\frac{38+25+33+24}{4}$ 30
6. $\frac{11+9+12+21+5}{5}$ 11.6
7. $\frac{247+168+185}{3}$ 200

### Background for the Lesson

There are three common ways to use one number to represent a body of data: the mean, the median, and the mode. The mean is the arithmetic average. The median is the middle value when you arrange the data in order. The mode can be thought of as the fashion—the data item (or items) that occurs most often. Extreme data values (very large or very small), known as *outliers*, do not affect the median and the mode, but they may make a major difference in the mean.

## 1 Focus

### Connecting to Students' Lives

Any of the measures of central tendency can be called an *average*, but the average most students are familiar with is the mean. Ask students for examples of averages they use in their daily lives, such as averaging scores or grades.

### Connecting to Prior Knowledge

In Lesson 3-2, students learned to estimate decimal products and quotients. In this lesson they apply these skills to finding the mean, median, and mode. In the Toolbox that follows, they apply estimating skills as they use a calculator to find the mean and median.

# 2 Teach

## Part 1 Teaching Notes

You can think of a measure of the central tendency of a set of data, such as the mean, as a way to use a single number (the mean) to represent all the data.

### Example 1

**Build understanding.** Ask: What single number do you think best represents the Readathon data? sample answer: 49

### Example 2

**Build understanding.** Ask: What value could you add to the data in part a. so that the set would then have a mode? any value in the set; sample answer: $2.40

### Example 3

**Build understanding.** Ask: Which single number do you think best represents the data, the mean with the outlier or the mean without the outlier? Explain. Answers will vary.

## Part 2 Teaching Notes

The *best* measure of central tendency is the one that summarizes the information most usefully. Ask yourself which of the measures best represents all the data in a fair and accurate way.

### Example 4

**Build understanding.** Ask: Why is the mean not always the best way to represent data? The data may not be numerical, or an outlier may significantly influence the mean.

**Extension** Challenge students to write a set of five data points that has a different mean, median, and mode.

**Error Prevention** Students may try to find the middle value, or median, without first arranging the data in order. Remind students always to order the data before finding the median.

**TRY THIS** Find the mean, median, and mode.

1. 12 14 26 37 8 14
   18.5, 14, 14
2. 2.3 4.3 3.2 2.9 2.7 2.3
   2.95, 2.8, 2.3

### EXAMPLE 2

**How many modes, if any, does each have?**

**a. $1.50 $2.00 $2.25 $2.40 $3.50 $4.00**
No values are the same, so there is no mode.

**b. 2 3 6 <u>8</u> <u>8</u> 10 11 12 <u>14</u> <u>14</u> 18 20**
Both 8 and 14 appear more often than the other data items. Since they appear the same number of times, there are two modes.

**c. grape, grape, banana, nectarine, <u>strawberry</u>, <u>strawberry</u>, <u>strawberry</u>, orange, watermelon**
Strawberry appears most often. There is one mode.

**TRY THIS** Find the number of modes.

3. 11 9 7 7 8 8 13 11
   3 modes
4. 38.5 55.4 45.3 38.5 68.4
   1 mode

An **outlier** is a data value that is much higher or lower than the other data values. An outlier can affect the mean of a group of data.

DATA ANALYSIS CONNECTION

### EXAMPLE 3

**Use the data in the Central America map at the left.**

**a. Which data value is an outlier?**
The data value for El Salvador, 27%, is an outlier. It is an outlier because it is 12% away from the closest data value.

**b. How does the outlier affect the mean?**

$\frac{78}{7} \approx 11.1$ Find the mean with the outlier.

$\frac{51}{6} = 8.5$ Find the mean *without* the outlier.

$11.1 - 8.5 = 2.6$

The outlier raises the mean about 2.6 points.

**Percent of Land That Can Be Farmed in Central American Countries**

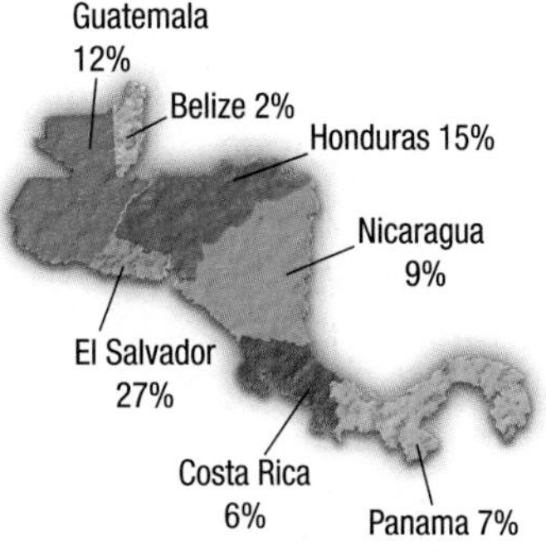


SOURCE: *The New York Times Almanac*

**TRY THIS** Find an outlier in each group of data below and tell how it affects the mean. Round to the nearest tenth.

5. 9 10 12 13 8 9 31 9
   31; raises the mean by 2.6
6. 1 17.5 18 19.5 16 17.5
   1; lowers the mean by 2.8



- **Additional Example 4**
  Which measure of central tendency best describes each situation?
  a. average hours of sleep per night mean
  b. most popular color of shirt mode
  c. times school buses arrive at school median

## AFTER THE LESSON

**To assess knowledge: Lesson Quiz**

Which measure of central tendency best describes each situation?

1. number of legs on the animals in the zoo mode
2. favorite digit (from 0 to 9) of the students in a class mode

- For enrichment and reteaching options see Resources on p. 119H.

## PART 2 Choosing the Best Measure

One measure of central tendency may be better than another to describe data. For example, consider the wages of the employees shown at the right. Here are the measures of central tendency.

Mode: \$5.50
Mean: \$7.50
Median: \$6.10

| Employees' Hourly Wages | |
|---|---|
| \$5.50 | \$6.20 |
| \$5.50 | \$6.30 |
| \$5.50 | \$8.00 |
| \$6.00 | \$17.00 |

The mode is the lowest wage listed. So the mode does not describe the data well.

The mean is above the hourly wage of all but two workers. The mean is influenced by the outlier, \$17.

The median is the best measure of central tendency here since it is not influenced by the outlier.

### EXAMPLE 4

**Which measure of central tendency best describes each situation? Explain.**

**a. the favorite movies of students in the eighth grade**
Mode; since the data are not numerical, the mode is the appropriate measure. When determining the most frequently chosen item, or when the data are not numerical, use the mode.

**b. the daily high temperatures during a week in July**
Mean; since daily high temperatures in July are not likely to have an outlier, mean is the appropriate measure. When the data have no outliers, use the mean.

**c. the distances students in your class travel to school**
Median; since one student may live much farther from school than the majority of students, the median is the appropriate measure. When an outlier may significantly influence the mean, use the median.

**Reading Math**

To help you recall that *median* means "middle number," think of the green, grassy *median strip* in the middle of a divided highway.

### TRY THIS

7. a. *Comparison Shopping* Toshio found the following prices for sport shirts: \$20, \$26, \$27, \$28, \$21, \$42, \$18, and \$20. Find the mean, median, and mode for the shirt prices. \$25.25, \$23.50, \$20
   b. *Reasoning* Which measure of central tendency best describes the data? Justify your reasoning. Answers may vary. Sample: Median; the mode is equal to the two smallest data values, and the outlier (\$42) affects the mean too much.



# 3 Practice/Assess

## Assignment Guide

To provide flexible scheduling, this lesson can be divided into parts.

**Part 1**
**Core** 1–2, 5–8, 19, 20

**Part 2**
**Core** 3–4, 9–18
**Extension** 21, 22

Mixed Review can be assigned at any time for maintenance.

## Exercises

**Test Prep Exercise 19** The word average can refer to any one of the three measures of central tendency. Most often it is used instead of mean.

## Challenge

Change just one of these data values to increase the mean by 5 but leave the mode and median unchanged: 10, 25, 30, 15, 20. Change 30 to 55.

## Closure

A measure of central tendency describes a collection of data. The mean is the sum of the items divided by the number of items. The median is the middle value or the mean of the two middle values when the data are written in order. The mode is the item that occurs most often. An outlier is an item that is much greater or less than the rest.

## Daily Cumulative Review

**Estimate each product or quotient.** *(Lesson 3-2)*
Answers may vary. Accept any reasonable answer.

1. $56.82 \cdot 23.18$ about 1,311
2. $14.03 \div 6.79$ about 2
3. $0.92 \cdot 5.8$ about 6
4. $\$24.93 \div 5.19$ about \$5
5. $4.931 \div 1.4$ about 5
6. $37.12 \cdot 3.8$ about 148
7. $-0.9 \cdot 20.31$ about −20
8. $5.803 \div 1.69$ about 3
9. $15.12 \cdot 27$ about 405

**Estimate by clustering.** *(Lesson 3-1)*

10. $12.7 + 13.4 + 12.9 + 13.1 + 13.7$ about 65
11. $\$45.67 + \$44.21 + \$45.55 + \$44.95$ about \$180
12. $301 + 298.4 + 302.98 + 308.8$ about 1,200
13. $63.27 + 64.73 + 58.31 + 60.01$ about 240
14. $\$29.67 + \$31.20 + \$30.55 + \$31.95$ about \$120
15. $72.7 + 73 + 72.9 + 73.1 + 72.7$ about 365

**Mixed Review**

**Evaluate.**

16. (1-3) $8cd$, for $c = 1, d = 2$ 16
17. (1-3) $18 - (z - 3)$, for $z = 7$ 14
18. (1-3) $4(r + s)$, for $r = 8, s = 3$ 44
19. (1-3) $8 \div d + 4$, for $d = 2$ 8

**Replace $x$ with −3. State whether the resulting equation is true or false.**

20. (2-4) $36 = 3x + 41$ false
21. (2-4) $3x \div 3 + 4 = 2(6)$ false
22. (2-4) $7(3) + x = 18$ true

# Exercises

## Check Understanding

**Find the mean, median, and mode. When the answer is not an integer, round to the nearest tenth. Identify any outliers.**

1. 37 4 7 3 11 9 13 5
   11.1, 8, none; outlier: 37

2. 126 123 115 125 123
   122.4, 123, 123; outlier: 115

**Find the mean, median, and mode. Which measure of central tendency best describes the data? Explain.**

3. minutes on the Internet
   50 63 59 85 367 48 112, 61, none; median; there is no mode, and the outlier (367) affects the mean too much.

4. heights of students in inches
   51 45 47 48 50 50 50 52 49.1, 50, 50; mean (or mode); there are no outliers.

## Practice and Problem Solving

**Find the mean, median, and mode. When the answer is not an integer, round to the nearest tenth. Identify any outliers.**

16. 70.7, 75.5, 72; median; the outlier (40) affects the mean too much.

5. 47 56 57 63 89 44 56
   58.9, 56, 56; outlier: 89

6. 3,456 560 435 456
   1,226.8, 508, none; outlier: 3,456

7. 4 5 2 3 2 3 3 3 1 1 3
   2.7, 3, 3; no outliers

8. 5.6 6.8 1.2 6.5 7.9 6.5
   5.8, 6.5, 6.5; outlier: 1.2

**Which measure of central tendency best describes each situation? Explain.** 9–14. Answers may vary. Samples are given.

9. numbers of apples in 2-lb bags
   Mean; there likely are no outliers.

10. favorite brands of jeans of 14-year-olds
    Mode; the data are not numerical.

11. ages of students in a fifth-grade classroom
    Mean; there likely are no outliers.

12. most common shoe color in a classroom
    Mode; the data are not numerical.

13. widths of computer screens at a bank
    Mean; there likely are no outliers.

14. number of pets owned by your classmates
    Median; there could easily be outliers.

**Find the mean, median, and mode. When the answer is not an integer, round to the nearest tenth. Which measure of central tendency best describes the data? Explain.** 15. 13.5, 14.5, 13.5 and 15; median; the outlier (7) affects the mean too much.

15. weight of backpacks in pounds
    14.5 7 13.5 15 15 16 13.5

16. resting heart rate in beats per minute
    79 72 80 81 40 72 See above.

17. numbers of raisins in cookies
    20 1 18 19 14 18 15, 18, 18; median (or mode); the outlier (1) affects the mean too much.

18. temperatures (°F) on race days
    53° 53° 55° 45° 47° 51° 57° 58° 52.4, 53, 53; mean (or mode); there are no outliers.

19. **TEST PREP** The average cost of a meal at the Grand Plaza is $20. Which of the following statements *cannot* be true? D
    A. The cost of four meals is greater than $20.
    B. Some meals cost less than $10.
    C. Each meal costs exactly $20.
    D. Each meal costs more than $20.



## Alternative Assessment

Have students use data sets from their daily lives, such as time spent over 5 days doing homework, to explain in their own words the differences between the three measures of central tendency.

**Use the table at the right for Exercises 20–22. Round your answers to the nearest tenth where necessary.**

**Fat and Calorie Content**
(per 2-tablespoon serving)

| Seed or Nut | Fat (g) | Calories |
|---|---|---|
| Peanut | 8.9 | 104 |
| Pecan | 9.1 | 90 |
| Pistachio | 7.9 | 92 |
| Pumpkin | 7.9 | 93 |
| Sunflower | 8.9 | 102 |
| Walnut | 7.7 | 80 |

SOURCE: *The T-Factor Fat Gram Counter*

**20.** *Data Analysis* You make a mixture using the same amount of each kind of seed and nut.
   a. What is the mean number of grams of fat in a 2-tablespoon serving of the mixture? 8.4 g
   b. What is the mean number of calories in a 2-tablespoon serving of the mixture? 93.5 calories

**21.** a. *Writing* Describe two different mixtures that use a total of 8 tablespoons. a–b. Check students' work.
   b. *Open-ended* Which recipe has the lower mean fat content for a 2-tablespoon serving?

**22.** *Nutrition* A mixture of equal amounts of pumpkin seeds, sunflower seeds, and pistachios contains 12 tablespoons in all. How many grams of fat and how many calories does the mixture contain? 49.4 g, 574 calories

## MIXED REVIEW

**Estimate each product or quotient.** *(Lesson 3-2)*

**23.** $9.01 ÷ $1.42 about 6 **24.** $7.5 \cdot 89.1$ about 720 **25.** $37.32 \div 5.99$ about 6 **26.** $12.56 · $2.99 about $39.00

**Simplify each expression.** *(Lesson 2-3)*

**27.** $6x + 8 + 2$ $6x + 10$ **28.** $5z + 4x + 3z$ $4x + 8z$ **29.** $x - 4t + 2t + 5$ $x - 2t + 5$

**30.** *Choose a Strategy* Karen sells children's hats for $4 and adults' hats for $7. On Saturday, she sold 120 hats, and she collected $720. How many adults' hats did she sell? 80 adults' hats

CHAPTER PROJECT 3

## ACTIVITY 1 ESTIMATING

Suppose you visit Mexico, and you want to estimate the cost of a jacket in U.S. dollars. The jacket costs 1,258 pesos. The exchange rate is $.117 = 1 peso or 8.54 pesos = $1. The 1,258-peso jacket is worth $147.19. When you shop, you can estimate the price in dollars by either multiplying or dividing.

Multiply: 1,258 pesos · $.117/peso ≈ 1,258 · $.10 = $125.80
Divide: 1,258 pesos ÷ 8.54 pesos/dollar ≈ 1,200 ÷ 8/$1 = $150

Estimate the price in dollars of a shirt that costs 326 pesos and of a souvenir that costs 45 pesos.

See also Extra Practice section.



## Project Activity 1

**Estimating** Encourage students to use the equations given in the text to help them write a procedure, they can easily remember, such as "Change pesos to approximate dollars by dividing by 10."

## Practice

1. There were 8 judges at a gymnastics competition. Kathleen received these scores for her performance on the uneven parallel bars:
   8.9, 8.7, 8.9, 9.2, 8.8, 8.2, 8.9, 8.8
   a. Find these statistics: mean 8.8 median 8.85 mode 8.9
   b. Which measure of central tendency best describes the data? Explain.
   Answers may vary. All are reasonable. The mean is slightly lowered by the score of 8.2.
   c. Why do you think that the highest and lowest judge's scores are disregarded in tallying the total score in a gymnastics competition?
   This eliminates scores that are not representative of the majority.

**Find the mean, median, and mode. Round to the nearest tenth where necessary. Identify any outliers.**

| | Data | Mean | Median | Mode | Outliers |
|---|---|---|---|---|---|
| 2. | 8, 15, 9, 7, 4, 5, 9, 11 | 8.5 | 8.5 | 9 | 15 |
| 3. | 70, 61, 28, 40, 60, 72, 25, 31, 64, 63 | 51.4 | 60.5 | none | none |
| 4. | 4.9, 5.7, 6.0, 5.3, 4.8, 4.9, 5.3, 4.7, 4.9, 5.6, 5.1 | 5.2 | 5.1 | 4.9 | none |
| 5. | 271, 221, 234, 240, 271, 234, 213, 253, 155 | 232.4 | 234 | 234 & 271 | 155 |
| 6. | 0, 2, 3, 3, 3, 4, 4, 5 | 3 | 3 | 3 | none |

**Use the data in the table. Round to the nearest tenth where necessary.**

| Peak | Height (ft) |
|---|---|
| Mont Blanc | 15,771 |
| Monte Rosa | 15,203 |
| Dom | 14,911 |
| Liskamm | 14,852 |
| Weisshom | 14,780 |

7. What is the mean height of the five highest European mountains? 15,103.4 ft
8. What is the median height? 14,911 ft
9. Is any of the heights an outlier? Explain.
   Mont Blanc is over 500 ft higher than Monte Rosa.



## Reteaching

In 1995, eight states had pupil-teacher ratios that were close to the U.S. average of 17.3. Use the table at the right. Find the **a)** mean, **b)** median, and **c)** mode.

| State | Pupils per Teacher |
|---|---|
| Arkansas | 17.1 |
| Illinois | 17.1 |
| Indiana | 17.5 |
| Louisiana | 17.0 |
| Mississippi | 17.5 |
| New Mexico | 17.0 |
| Ohio | 17.1 |
| Pennsylvania | 17.0 |

a. Mean: $\frac{\text{sum of data items}}{\text{number of data items}}$
   $= \frac{17.1 + 17.1 + 17.5 + 17.0 + 17.5 + 17.0 + 17.1 + 17.0}{8}$
   $= \frac{137.3}{8} = 17.1625$
   Rounded to the nearest tenth, the mean is 17.2.
b. Median: Write the data in order.
   17.0, 17.0, 17.0, [17.1, 17.1,] 17.1, 17.5, 17.5
   $\frac{17.1 + 17.1}{2} = 17.1$ Find the mean of the two middle numbers. The median is 17.1
c. Mode: Find the data item that occurs most often.
   Both 17.0 and 17.1 occur 3 times. The modes are 17.0 and 17.1.

**Find the mean, median, and mode. Round to the nearest tenth where necessary.**

| | | mean | median | mode |
|---|---|---|---|---|
| 1. | 14.2 14.7 14.3 14.6 | 14.5 | 14.45 | none |
| 2. | 8 7 3 5 9 2 4 7 | 5.6 | 6 | 7 |
| 3. | 37 42 51 28 36 | 38.8 | 37 | none |
| 4. | 1.1 1.8 2.6 1.8 1.9 2.6 | 2.0 | 1.85 | 1.8 & 2.6 |

The world's largest body of freshwater is formed by the Great Lakes of North America. Use the table of depths at the right. Find the following statistics. Round to the nearest tenth where necessary.

| Lake | Depth (in ft) |
|---|---|
| Superior | 1,333 |
| Michigan | 923 |
| Huron | 750 |
| Erie | 210 |
| Ontario | 802 |

5. mean: 803.6 ft
6. median: 802 ft
7. mode: none



## Enrichment

**Solve. Round to the nearest tenth, if necessary.**

1. Leon must have a mean score of 90 on his math quizzes to earn an A. So far, he has received grades of 88, 85, 91, 92, 94, 81, 86, and 98. What grade must he earn on his final quiz?
   95
2. The median of the following set of data is 6: 1, 8, 7, 1, 6, 8, 3, 6. What number from the set of data can you subtract 1 from so that the median of the resulting set will be $5\frac{1}{2}$?
   6
3. There are twelve girls and eight boys in a math class. The girls' mean score on the final exam was 83.5. The boys' mean score was 81.5. What was the mean for the entire class? Hint: First find the total points scored by all members of the class.
   82.7
4. The mode of the following set of data is 23: 19, 5, 23, $x$, 17. What is the mean?
   17.4
5. The median of the following set of data is 26: 17, $y$, 49, 13. Find $y$.
   35
6. The total weight of all the students in a class is 3,159 lb. The mean weight of the students is 117 lb. How many students are there in the class?
   27
7. Ramon, Jake, and Pearl are all less than 50 years old. The age difference between the youngest person and the oldest person is 15. The mode of their ages is 37. What is their mean age? What is their median age?
   32, 37
8. There are five one-digit numbers in a set of data. The mean of the numbers is 3. A mode is 1. The median is 4. What are the numbers?
   1, 1, 4, 4, 5

## MATH TOOLBOX

### Mean and Median on a Calculator

This Math Toolbox shows how to use a calculator to find the mean and median for a set of data.

### Math Background

The mean (also called the arithmetic average) is the measure found by adding together all the data points and dividing by the total number of data points. For example, suppose that a group of people are given 8, 4, 10, and 2 cookies each. Clearly this is an unfair distribution of the cookies. If you redistribute the cookies so that each person has the same number (6), this is a fair distribution. The mean (6) is the number that represents a fair or equal distribution of the data. The median is the middle of the data when the data points are in order. Half of the data points are greater than (or equal to) the median and half are less than (or equal to) the median.

## Teaching Notes

**Error Prevention** Remind students that the mean is dependent on the exact value of each data point.

**Monitoring Progress** Have student partners watch as the partner presses the keys to make sure they use the correct ones.

**Block Scheduling** If you have block scheduling or extended periods, you may wish to insert this Math Toolbox lesson between the completion of Part 1 of Lesson 3-3 and the beginning of Part 2 of Lesson 3-3.

# MATH TOOLBOX

*Technology*
*After Lesson 3-3*

## *Mean and Median on a Graphing Calculator*

You can use a graphing calculator to find means and medians.

### EXAMPLE

**Find (a) the mean and (b) the median number of acres in Ohio zoos.**

**Zoos in Ohio**

| Zoo | Number of Acres | Number of Species |
|---|---|---|
| Cincinnati Zoo | 70 | 712 |
| Cleveland Metroparks Zoo | 165 | 599 |
| Columbus Zoo | 90 | 650 |
| Toledo Zoological Gardens | 62 | 633 |

SOURCE: *The World Almanac*

**a.** To use the mean function, press 2nd STAT ▶ ▶ 3.

Then press 2nd { and enter the data, separated by commas. End by pressing 2nd } ).

Press ENTER to calculate the mean.

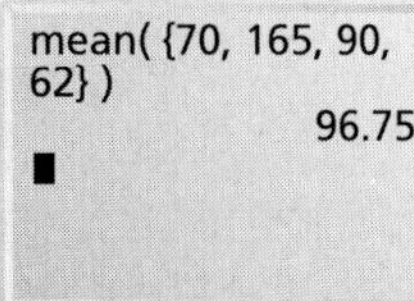


The mean is about 97 acres.

**b.** To use the median function, press 2nd STAT ▶ ▶ 4.

Then press 2nd { and enter the data, separated by commas. End the list by pressing 2nd } ).

Press ENTER to calculate the median.

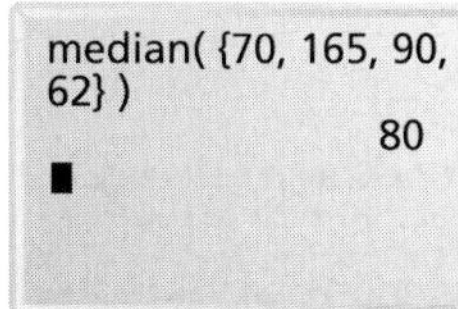


The median is 80 acres.

**Use a calculator to find the mean and median.**

1. number of species in Ohio zoos **648.5 species; 641.5 species**
2. 85°F, 79°F, 80°F, 75°F, 82°F **80.2°F; 80°F**
3. \$3.75, \$4.50, \$9.25, \$4.70, \$5.90 **\$5.62; \$4.70**
4. 100, 95, 82, 102, 78, 76 **about 88.8; 88.5**
5. **Miles of Atlantic Coastline by State**

| State | DE | FL | GA | ME | MD | MA | NH | NJ | NY | NC | RI | SC | VA |
|---|---|---|---|---|---|---|---|---|---|---|---|---|---|
| Miles | 28 | 580 | 100 | 228 | 31 | 192 | 13 | 130 | 127 | 301 | 40 | 187 | 112 |

**about 159 mi; 127 mi**

SOURCE: National Oceanic and Atmospheric Administration, U.S. Dept. of Commerce



### • Additional Example

Use a calculator to find the mean and median.
5.6 ft, 3.2 ft, 8.9 ft, 1.7 ft **mean: 4.85 ft; median: 4.4 ft**

# Using Formulas

3-4

## Substituting into Formulas

A **formula** is an equation that shows a relationship between quantities that are represented by variables.

An important formula in math and science is $d = rt$, where $d$ is the distance, $r$ is the speed, and $t$ is the time spent traveling.

REAL-WORLD  CONNECTION

### EXAMPLE 1

**Suppose you travel 162 miles in 3 hours. Use the formula $d = rt$ to find your average speed.**

| | |
|---|---|
| $d = rt$ | Write the formula. |
| $162 = (r)(3)$ | Substitute 162 for $d$ and 3 for $t$. |
| $\frac{162}{3} = \frac{3r}{3}$ | Divide each side by 3. |
| $54 = r$ | Simplify. |

Your average speed is 54 mi/h.

**TRY THIS** Use the formula $d = rt$. Find $d$, $r$, or $t$.

1. $d = 273$ mi, $t = 9.75$ h  $r = 28$ mi/h
2. $d = 540.75$ in., $r = 10.5$ in./yr  $t = 51.5$ yr

 CONNECTION

### EXAMPLE 2

**You can estimate the temperature outside using the chirps of a cricket. Use the formula $F = \frac{n}{4} + 37$, where $n$ is the number of chirps a cricket makes in one minute, and $F$ is the temperature in degrees Fahrenheit. Estimate the temperature when a cricket chirps 100 times in a minute.**

| | |
|---|---|
| $F = \frac{n}{4} + 37$ | Write the formula. |
| $F = \frac{100}{4} + 37$ | Replace $n$ with 100. |
| $F = 25 + 37$ | Divide. |
| $F = 62$ | Add. |

The temperature is about 62°F.

**What You'll Learn**

1. To substitute into formulas
2. To use the formula for the perimeter of a rectangle

**. . . And Why**

To use formulas to find perimeters, areas, and rates of speed

The chirping calls of crickets have been recorded at temperatures ranging from 45°F to 100°F.



# 3-4

## Getting Ready

**Key Terms and Symbols** formula, perimeter

**Resources** A complete list of resources for this lesson is on p. 119H.

### Daily Skills Warm-Up

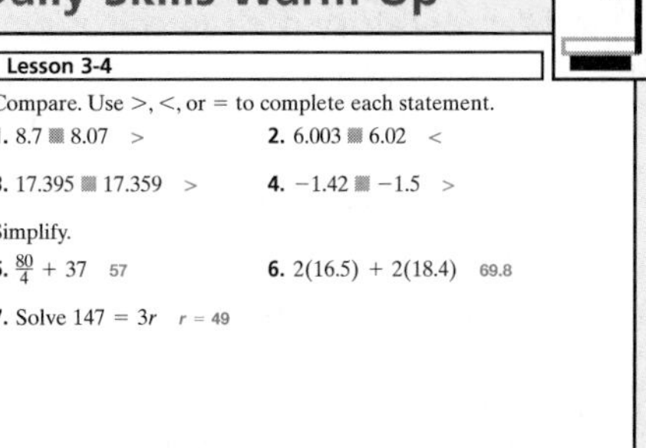

Lesson 3-4

Compare. Use >, <, or = to complete each statement.

1. 8.7 ■ 8.07  >
2. 6.003 ■ 6.02  <
3. 17.395 ■ 17.359  >
4. −1.42 ■ −1.5  >

Simplify.

5. $\frac{80}{4} + 37$  57
6. 2(16.5) + 2(18.4)  69.8
7. Solve 147 = 3r  r = 49

### Background for the Lesson

A formula is an open sentence equation that often has more than one variable. You use a formula to tell how certain quantities in the real world are related to each other. You cannot solve a formula, such as $d = rt$, until you know three facts about the formula: (1) what the variables represent, (2) the value of one or more of the variables, and (3) the units for each quantity represented in the formula. Once you know (1) that $d$ is the distance, $r$ is the rate or speed, and $t$ is the time, and (2 and 3) that $r$ is 30 miles per hour and $t$ is 4 hours, then you can substitute values and units in the formula and solve for the distance in miles.

## 1 Focus

### Connecting to Students' Lives

Discuss with students any formulas they have used at home, perhaps for area or to find the distance traveled.

### Connecting to Prior Knowledge

In Lessons 2-5 and 2-6, students learned to solve equations. In this lesson, students solve equations that are formulas. In Lessons 3-5 and 3-6, students extend their skills to solving equations that involve decimals.

# Tools to Monitor Progress

### BEFORE THE LESSON

**To check prerequisite skills:**

- Adding and subtracting decimals
- Multiplying decimals
- Dividing decimals

**Skills You Need,** p. 119

**Skills Handbook,** pp. 730, 731, 733, 735

**Skills Intervention Kit,** Decimals

### DURING THE LESSON

**To check understanding:**

**Try This** exercises on student page

- **Additional Example 1**
  Suppose you ride your bike 18 mi in 3 h. Use the formula $d = rt$ to find your average speed. 6 mi/h
- **Additional Example 2**
  Use the formula $F = \frac{n}{4} + 37$ to estimate the temperature when a cricket chirps 76 times in a minute. 56°F

# 2 Teach

## Part 1 Teaching Notes

Discuss that $r$ is used to represent the speed because the speed is sometimes called the *rate*, or the *rate of travel.*

### Example 1

**Build understanding.** Ask: What operation is implied by writing $r$ next to $t$, as in $rt$? Multiply the variables.

### Example 2

**Build understanding.** Ask: What is the estimated temperature if $n$ is 4 chirps per minute? Use mental math. 38°F

## Part 2 Teaching Notes

Discuss with students why you can choose either dimension to be the length by having them draw and label some example rectangles.

### Example 3

**Build understanding.** Ask: Could the room have different dimensions, but still have the same perimeter? Explain. Yes; the room could have any dimensions as long as $2l + 2w = 62$.

**Tactile Learning** Have students make rectangles with masking tape on the floor and then walk around the perimeter, naming the lengths and widths as they go.

**Extension** Challenge students to write a formula to find the perimeter of a square.

**Connecting to Geometry** You can find many quantities in geometry that are involved in formulas. Perimeters, areas, and volumes are some of the most common. Suggest that students use reference sources to find such formulas for different geometric figures.

**Try This** Use the formula $F = \frac{n}{4} + 37$ to estimate the temperature in degrees Fahrenheit for each situation.

3. 96 chirps/min 61°F
4. 88 chirps/min 59°F
5. 66 chirps/min 53.5°F

## Part 2 Using a Perimeter Formula

The **perimeter** of a figure is the distance around the figure. You can find the perimeter of a rectangle by adding the lengths of the four sides, or by using the formula $P = 2\ell + 2w$, where $\ell$ is the length and $w$ is the width. For rectangles, it does not matter which dimension you choose to be the length or the width.

**MEASUREMENT** CONNECTION

### Example 3

**Find the perimeter of the room. Use the formula for the perimeter of a rectangle, $P = 2\ell + 2w$.**

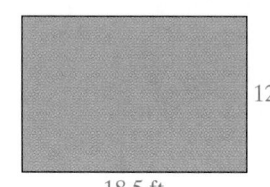

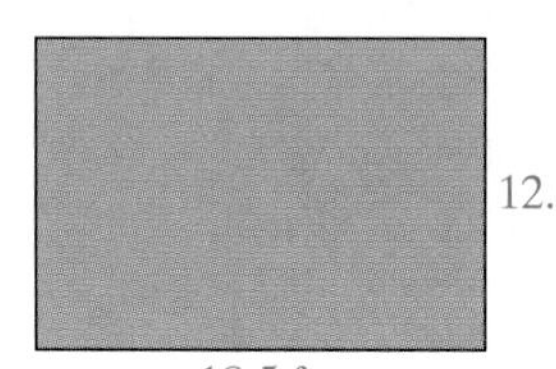


$P = 2\ell + 2w$ Write the formula.
$P = 2(18.5) + 2(12.5)$ Replace $\ell$ with 18.5 and $w$ with 12.5.
$P = 37 + 25$ Multiply.
$P = 62$ Add.

The perimeter of the room is 62 ft.

**Try This** Find the perimeter of each rectangle.

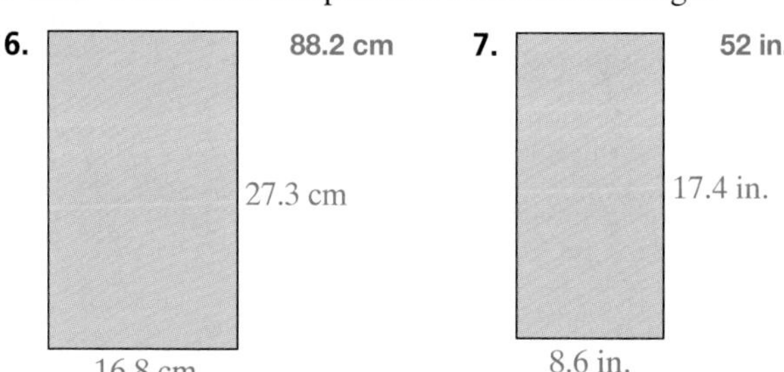




- **Additional Example 3**
  Find the perimeter of a rectangular tabletop with a length of 14.5 in. and a width of 8.5 in. 46 in.

## AFTER THE LESSON

**To assess knowledge:**
**Lesson Quiz**

Use the formula $p = 4s$ to find the perimeter of a square with the side $s$.

1. $s = 5.6$ m 22.4 m
2. $s = 9.3$ in. 37.2 in.
3. Find the side of a square with a perimeter of 164 yd. 41 yd

- For enrichment and reteaching options see Resources on p. 119H.

# Exercises

## Check Understanding

**Use the formula $F = \frac{n}{4} + 37$ to find the temperature.**

1. 120 chirps/min 67°F
2. 80 chirps/min 57°F
3. 92 chirps/min 60°F
4. 64 chirps/min 53°F

**Use the formula $d = rt$. Find $d$, $r$, or $t$.**

5. $r = 38.5$ m/h, $t = 12.5$ h $d = 481.25$ m
6. $d = 2{,}730$ mi, $t = 9.75$ h $r = 280$ mi/h
7. $d = 596.39$ cm, $r = 2.3$ cm/s $t = 259.3$ s
8. $d = 10.2$ ft, $r = 0.5$ ft/h $t = 20.4$ h
9. The pronghorn antelope can run 0.73 mi/min. Use the formula $d = rt$ to find how far a pronghorn antelope can travel in 8 min at this speed. 5.84 mi

## Practice and Problem Solving

**Given that $C$ is the temperature in degrees Celsius, use the formula $F = 1.8C + 32$ to find each temperature $F$ in degrees Fahrenheit.**

10. $C = 58$ 136.4°F
11. $C = 14$ 57.2°F
12. $C = -89$ −128.2°F
13. $C = 56$ 132.8°F
14. $C = 72$ 161.6°F

**Use the formula $P = 2\ell + 2w$. Find the perimeter of each rectangle.**

15. 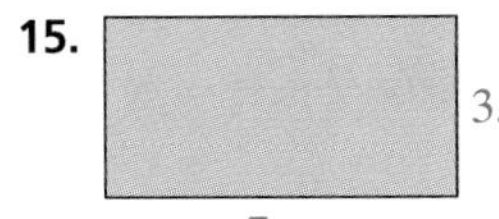

21 m

16. 

74 cm

17. 6 yd; 15.6 yd
43.2 yd

18. Use the formula for the area of a rectangle, $A = \ell w$. Find the area of each rectangle in Exercises 15–17. 24.5 m$^2$; 288.96 cm$^2$; 93.6 yd$^2$

19. *Geometry* The top surface of the world's longest rectangular strawberry shortcake was 175.33 ft long and 4 ft wide.
   a. Use the formula $A = \ell w$. Find the area of the top surface of the shortcake. 701.32 ft$^2$
   b. What was the perimeter of the top surface of the shortcake? 358.66 ft

20. *Measurement* The state of Colorado is nearly rectangular in shape. Find the approximate area of the state using the formula $A = \ell w$. 105,300 mi$^2$

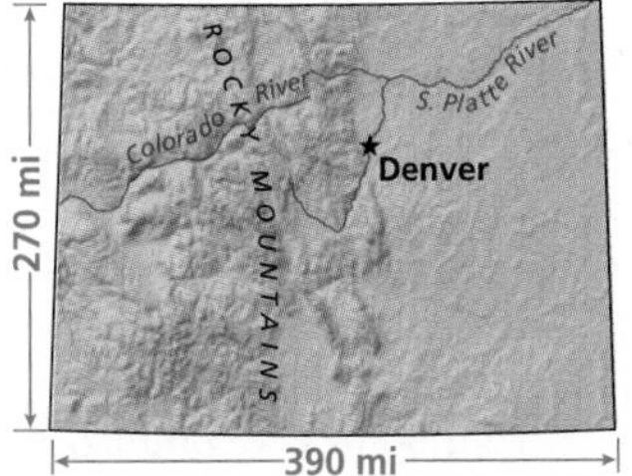




# 3 Practice/Assess

## Assignment Guide

To provide flexible scheduling, this lesson can be divided into parts.

**Part 1**
Core 1–14, 18, 22
Extension 21

**Part 2**
Core 15–17
Extension 19–20

Mixed Review can be assigned at any time for maintenance.

## Exercises

**Error Prevention** Exercises 5–9
Students may substitute the incorrect value. Suggest that they first copy the formula and then rewrite it carefully with the substitutions.

## Challenge

Use the formula $C = \frac{F - 32}{1.8}$ to find the temperature in degrees Celsius when the temperature in degrees Fahrenheit is 104°. $C = 40°$

## Closure

A formula is an equation that shows the relationship between two or more quantities. The quantities are represented by variables. You can use formulas to find such things as perimeter, area, and distance.

## Alternative Assessment

Ask students to write a formula for finding the total number of nickels, $n$, that are equal in value to $q$ quarters. Then have them write and solve a problem that uses their formula.

## Daily Cumulative Review

**Find the mean, median, and mode. Round to the nearest tenth where needed. Identify any outliers.** *(Lesson 3-3)*

1. 6 7 2 5 6 5 7 8 5 5 6
   Mean 5.6 Median 6
   Mode 5 Outliers 2
2. 1.8 1.4 1.5 1.3 10.7 1.3
   Mean 3 Median 1.5
   Mode 1.3 Outliers 10.7
3. 81 87 92 56 80 90 92 81
   Mean 82.4 Median 84
   Mode 81, 92 Outliers 56
4. \$456 \$425 \$798 \$397 \$402
   Mean \$495.60 Median \$425
   Mode none Outliers \$798

**Estimate each product or quotient.** *(Lesson 3-2)*
Answers may vary. Accept any reasonable answer.

5. $294.9 \cdot 3.08$ about 900
6. \$148.03 ÷ 51.19 about \$3
7. $29.2 \cdot 1.8$ about 60
8. $18.3 \div 5.89$ about 3
9. $199.7 \div 48.3$ about 4
10. \$14.62 · 2.1 about \$30

**Mixed Review**

**Solve each equation.**

11. (2-5) $b + 34 = 23$ $b = -11$
12. (2-5) $369 + c = 452$ $c = 83$
13. (2-5) $-4 = h - 2$ $-2 = h$
14. (2-5) $t - 7 = -11$ $t = -4$
15. (2-5) $n + (-6) = -12$ $n = -6$
16. (2-5) $-12 = d - 5$ $-7 = d$

**Simplify.**

17. (1-4) $|24|$ 24
18. (1-4) $|-4|$ 4
19. (1-4) the opposite of −11 11

**21.** A giant tortoise travels about 0.17mi/h on land. If a tortoise travels at a constant speed, how far can he travel in 2.5 h? 0.425 mi

The weight of a giant tortoise hatchling is 0.001 of an adult's weight of 500 lb.

**22. a.** ***Estimation*** You can *estimate* a temperature in degrees Fahrenheit using the formula $F = 2 \cdot C + 30$, where $C$ represents the temperature in degrees Celsius (°C). What is the approximate temperature in degrees Fahrenheit when it is 3°C? 5°C? 25°C? 36°F; 40°F; 80°F

**b.** ***Mathematical Reasoning*** Is this formula better for estimating higher temperatures or lower temperatures? Explain. See below right.

## Mixed Review

**Find the mean, median, and mode. When the answer is not an integer, round to the nearest integer. Which measure of central tendency best describes the data?** *(Lesson 3-3)*

**23.** minutes of homework
8 125 154 120 105 125 106 min, 123 min, 125 min; median

**24.** number of mL per container
250 250 355 355 375 250 306 mL, 303 mL, 250 mL; mean

**Solve each equation.** *(Lesson 2-5)*

**25.** $c + 8 = 41$ 33 **26.** $b + 32 = 19$ −13 **27.** $98 = n + 42$ 56

22b. Lower temperatures; for 10°C, the estimation formula gives the correct Fahrenheit temperature. The more the temperature differs from 10°C, the greater the difference between the estimate and the actual Fahrenheit temperatures.

**28.** ***Patterns*** Which equation describes the relationship between the variables in the table? *(Lesson 1-7)* B

| $n$ | 14 | 16 | 18 | 20 |
|---|---|---|---|---|
| $t$ | 7 | 8 | 9 | 10 |

**A.** $n = t + 2$ **B.** $n = 2t$
**C.** $t = n \cdot 2$ **D.** $t \div 2 = n$

## Checkpoint 1

**Lessons 3-1 through 3-4**

**Round each number to the underlined place value.**

**1.** 15.6571 15.66 **2.** 0.8914 0.891 **3.** 7,022.56 7,023 **4.** 345.678 345.7

**Estimate.**

**5.** $3.7 \cdot 8.06$ about 32 **6.** $17.25 + 6.66$ about 24 **7.** $8.7 - 9.6$ about −1 **8.** $4.21 \div 0.7$ about 6

**Find the mean, median, and mode.**

**9.** 47, 56, 58, 63
56, 57, no mode

**10.** 1, 4, 1, 3, 1, 2, 3, 2, 1, 2
2, 2, 1

**11.** $10.20, $1.50, $2.70, $1.80
$4.05, $2.25, no mode

**12.** **TEST PREP** The path at the right is made of segments that are all the same length. The shortest distance from point $C$ to point $D$ is 7.2 m. What is the distance from point $C$ to point $D$ on the path shown? B

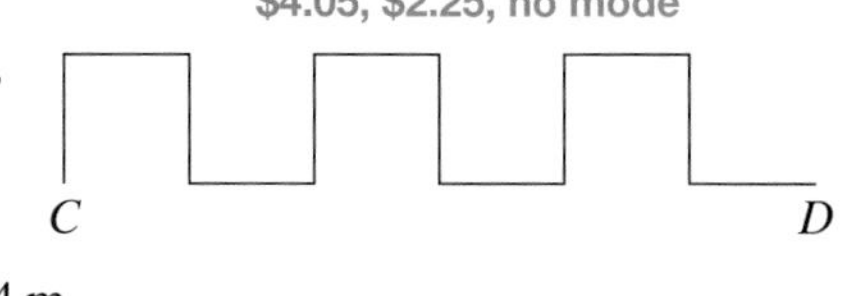



**A.** 6.2 m **B.** 14.4 m **C.** 21.6 m **D.** 144.4 m



See also Extra Practice section.

## Practice

**Use the formula $P = 2l + 2w$. Find the perimeter of each rectangle.**

1. 27 m (9 m by 4.5 m)
2. 13 ft (5.2 ft by 1.3 ft)
3. 35.2 cm (12.9 cm by 4.7 cm)

**Use the formula $A = lw$. Find the area of each rectangle above.**

4. 40.5 sq m
5. 6.76 sq ft
6. 60.63 sq cm

7. Use the formula $d = rt$ to find how far each animal in the table can travel in 5 seconds.

| Animal | Speed (ft/s) | Distance in 5 s (ft) |
|---|---|---|
| Pronghorn antelope | 89.5 | 447.5 |
| Wildebeest | 73.3 | 366.5 |
| Gray fox | 61.6 | 308 |
| Wart hog | 44.0 | 220 |
| Wild turkey | 22.0 | 110 |
| Chicken | 13.2 | 66 |

8. While vacationing on the Mediterranean Sea, Angie recorded the temperature several times during a 24-hour period. She used a thermometer in the lobby of her hotel. It was a beautiful day. Use the formula $F = 1.8C + 32$ to change the temperatures Angie recorded from Celsius to Fahrenheit.

| Time | Temperature (°C) | Temperature (°F) |
|---|---|---|
| 4:00 A.M. | 19 | 66.2 |
| 8:00 A.M. | 22 | 71.6 |
| 12:00 P.M. | 30 | 86 |
| 4:00 P.M. | 28 | 82.4 |
| 8:00 P.M. | 24 | 75.2 |
| 12:00 A.M. | 20 | 68 |



## Reteaching

Given that $C$ is the temperature in degrees Celsius, use the formula $F = 1.8C + 32$ to find the temperature $F$ in degrees Fahrenheit. What is the temperature in degrees Fahrenheit for a temperature of 18° in Celsius?

$F = 1.8C + 32$ Write the formula.
$F = 1.8(18) + 32$ Substitute 18 for $C$.
$F = 32.4 + 32$ Simplify.
$F = 64.4°$

The temperature is 64.4° Fahrenheit, or 64.4°F.

**Find the temperature in degrees Fahrenheit for each temperature in degrees Celsius.**

1. $C = 4°$ $F = 1.8($ 4 $) + 32 =$ 7.2 $+ 32 =$ 39.2°F
2. $C = 40°$ $F = 1.8($ 40 $) + 32 =$ 72 $+ 32 =$ 104°F
3. $C = 22°$ $F = 1.8($ 22 $) + 32 =$ 39.6 $+ 32 =$ 71.6°F
4. $C = 35°$ $F = 1.8($ 35 $) + 32 =$ 63 $+ 32 =$ 95°F
5. $C = -6°$ $F = 1.8($ −6 $) + 32 =$ −10.8 $+ 32 =$ 21.2°F
6. $C = -24°$ $F = 1.8($ −24 $) + 32 =$ −43.2 $+ 32 =$ −11.2°F

**Given that $F$ is the temperature in degrees Fahrenheit, the formula $C = (F - 32)/1.8$ is the temperature $C$ in degrees Celsius. Find the temperature in degrees Celsius for each temperature in degrees Fahrenheit.**

7. $F = 68°$ $C = ($ 68 $- 32)/1.8 =$ 36 $/1.8 =$ 20°C
8. $F = 17.6°$ $C = ($ 17.6 $- 32)/1.8 =$ −14.4 $/1.8 =$ −8°C
9. $F = 5°$ $C = ($ 5 $- 32)/1.8 =$ −27 $/1.8 =$ −15°C
10. $F = 57.2°$ $C = ($ 57.2 $- 32)/1.8 =$ 25.2 $/1.8 =$ 14°C
11. $F = 32°$ $C = ($ 32 $- 32)/1.8 =$ 0 $/1.8 =$ 0°C
12. $F = 212°$ $C = ($ 212 $- 32)/1.8 =$ 180 $/1.8 =$ 100°C



## Enrichment

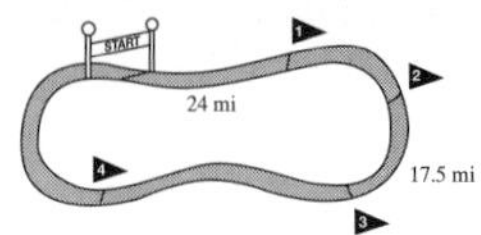



**Solve these problems about Maria's car-rally performance.**

1. Maria left the starting line at 8:30 A.M. and drove at an average rate of 40 mi/h. What time did she arrive at Checkpoint 1?
9:06 A.M.

2. She continued to Checkpoint 2, taking 20 min to make the trip at an average rate of 48 mi/h. How far is it between Checkpoints 1 and 2? What time did she arrive at Checkpoint 2?
16 mi; 9:26 A.M.

3. Maria needed 25 min to drive the leg between Checkpoints 2 and 3. What was her average rate of speed? What time did she arrive at Checkpoint 3?
42 mi/h; 9:51 A.M.

4. Between Checkpoints 3 and 4, Maria used 1.44 gal of gas and averaged 25 mi/gal. Her average speed was 54 mi/h. Find the distance between Checkpoints 3 and 4. What time did she arrive at Checkpoint 4?
36 mi; 10:31 A.M.

5. Maria arrived back at the starting line at 11:16 A.M., traveling the final leg of the rally course at an average rate of 46 mi/h. Find the length of the final leg.
34.5 mi

6. Find the length of the entire course, the length of time it took Maria to finish, and her average overall speed. If necessary, round answers to the nearest hundredth.
128 mi; 2.77 h; 46.21 mi/h



## Checkpoint

Practice

**Round to the underlined place value.**

1. 17.9264 — 17.93
2. 0.4821 — 0.5
3. 6,328.54 — 6,329

**Estimate.**

4. $2.8 \cdot 9.03$ — 27
5. $3.6 - 4.8$ — −1
6. $5.42 \div 0.89$ — 6

7. Find the mean, median, and mode: $8.75, $2.39, $3.01, $2.69, $3.45
mean $4.06 median $3.01 mode none

8. If the figure has a perimeter of 24 inches, what is its area?
A. 6 square in. B. 12 square in.
(C.) 24 square in. D. 48 square in.

*Technology*
*After Lesson 3-4*

# *Formulas in a Spreadsheet*

You can use a computer spreadsheet to evaluate formulas. Look at the spreadsheet at the right. In the spreadsheet, the algebraic formula $d = rt$ is evaluated for $r = 50$ mi/h and $t = 3$ h.

| | A | B | C |
|---|---|---|---|
| 1 | r | t | d |
| 2 | 50 | 3 | 150 |

The spreadsheet formula "=A2*B2" is used to calculate $d = rt$. The spreadsheet formula means that the value in cell C2 equals the value in cell A2 times the value in cell B2.

In spreadsheet formulas the asterisk symbol * means multiply. The slash symbol / means divide.

## EXAMPLE

**Use a spreadsheet and the formula $P = 2\ell + 2w$ to find the perimeter $P$ of a rectangle. Evaluate the formula for a length $\ell$ of 7.8 in. and a width $w$ of 2.6 in.**

| | A | B | C |
|---|---|---|---|
| 1 | $\ell$ | w | P |
| 2 | 7.8 | 2.6 | 20.8 |

← Use the spreadsheet formula =2*A2+2*B2.

The perimeter is about 21 in.

**Use a spreadsheet to find each perimeter.**

1. $\ell = 5.6$ in., $w = 7.9$ in. **27 in.**
2. $\ell = 12.7$ in., $w = 15.6$ in. **56.6 in.**
3. $\ell = 0.2$ in., $w = 1.3$ in. **3 in.**

**Use a spreadsheet to evaluate the formula $t = d \div r$ for the given values of $d$ and $r$.**

4. $d = 250$ mi, $r = 5$ mi/h **50 h**
5. $d = 1{,}400$ mi, $r = 50$ mi/h **28 h**
6. $d = 4{,}500$ mi, $r = 250$ mi/h **18 h**

**Write a spreadsheet formula for each algebraic formula.**

7. to find $A$, using $A = 0.5bh$ **=0.5*A2*B2**
8. to find $P$, using $P = 4a$ **=4*A2**
9. to find $y$, using $y = mx + b$ **=A2*B2+C2**
10. a. *Open-ended* Use a spreadsheet to evaluate the formula $A = \ell w$. How does the value of $A$ change as you double the value of $\ell$ while keeping $w$ unchanged? **It doubles.**
    b. How does the value of $A$ change as you double the values of both $\ell$ and $w$? **It is multiplied by 4.**



MATH TOOLBOX

## Formulas in a Spreadsheet

This Math Toolbox shows how to use a computer spreadsheet to evaluate a formula.

## Math Background

You can use spreadsheet software to help you perform repeated calculations where you do the same math operations over and over, but with different numbers. You express the repeated calculations as a formula. You type the numbers you want to use into the spreadsheet, which then substitutes the given values for the variables and calculates the results.

## Teaching Notes

**Error Prevention** Remind students that the results will only be as accurate as their typing of the formula and values.

**Monitoring Progress** Students can test whether they have done the spreadsheet correctly by using simple data, such as $l = 5$ and $w = 4$, where they know the correct answer.

**Block Scheduling** If you have block scheduling or extended periods, you may wish to insert this Math Toolbox lesson between the completion of Part 1 of Lesson 3-5 and the beginning of Part 2 of Lesson 3-5.

- **Additional Example**
  Use a spreadsheet to evaluate the formula $i = prt$ for $p = \$100$, $r = 0.06$, $t = 2$ years. **\$12**

# 3-5

## Getting Ready

**Resources** A complete list of resources for this lesson is on p. 119H.

### Daily Skills Warm-Up

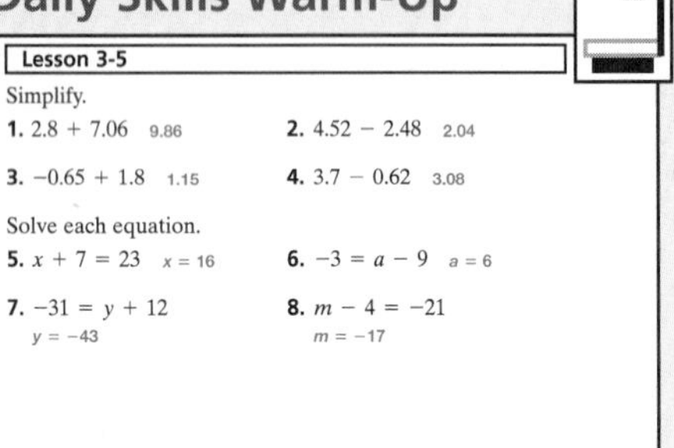

Lesson 3-5

Simplify.

1. $2.8 + 7.06$ 9.86
2. $4.52 - 2.48$ 2.04
3. $-0.65 + 1.8$ 1.15
4. $3.7 - 0.62$ 3.08

Solve each equation.

5. $x + 7 = 23$ $x = 16$
6. $-3 = a - 9$ $a = 6$
7. $-31 = y + 12$ $y = -43$
8. $m - 4 = -21$ $m = -17$

### Background for the Lesson

When you use a calculator to add and subtract decimals (when solving equations), first estimate the answer to help you catch mistakes you might have made when entering the numbers. When you add and subtract decimals without a calculator, line up the decimal points carefully and check your work to catch mistakes. Check addition problems by subtracting. Check subtraction by adding.

$$\begin{array}{r} 56.8 \\ +12.5 \\ \hline 69.3 \\ -12.5 \\ \hline 56.8 \end{array} \qquad \begin{array}{r} 23.7 \\ -3.8 \\ \hline 19.9 \\ +3.8 \\ \hline 23.7 \end{array}$$

## 1 Focus

### Connecting to Prior Knowledge

In Lesson 2-5, students learned to solve equations by adding or subtracting. In this lesson, they extend this to solving equations with decimals. In Lesson 2-6, they will solve equations by multiplying or dividing decimals.

**Technology Option** Some calculators have both a subtract key (−) and a change-sign key (+/−). Students probably know to use the subtract key when subtracting numbers. Tell students that the change-sign key makes numbers they have entered negative. Enter a number (4) then press the change sign key to get (−4).

# 3-5 Solving Equations by Adding or Subtracting Decimals

### What You'll Learn

1. To solve one-step decimal equations involving addition
2. To solve one-step decimal equations involving subtraction

### . . . And Why

To model real-world situations in astronomy and money management

## PART 1 Using Subtraction to Solve Equations

You can use the Subtraction Property of Equality to solve an equation. Remember to subtract the same number from each side of the equation.

### EXAMPLE 1

**Solve $n + 4.5 = -9.7$.**

$n + 4.5 = -9.7$

$n + 4.5 - 4.5 = -9.7 - 4.5$ Subtract 4.5 from each side.

$n = -14.2$ Simplify.

**Check** $n + 4.5 = -9.7$

$-14.2 + 4.5 \stackrel{?}{=} -9.7$ Replace $n$ with $-14.2$.

$-9.7 = -9.7$ ✔

**TRY THIS** Solve each equation.

1. $x + 4.9 = 18.8$ 13.9
2. $14.73 = -24.23 + b$ 38.96

MEASUREMENT CONNECTION

### EXAMPLE 2

*Astronomy* **A communications satellite is circling Earth. Use the diagram below to find the approximate distance from the satellite to the moon.**

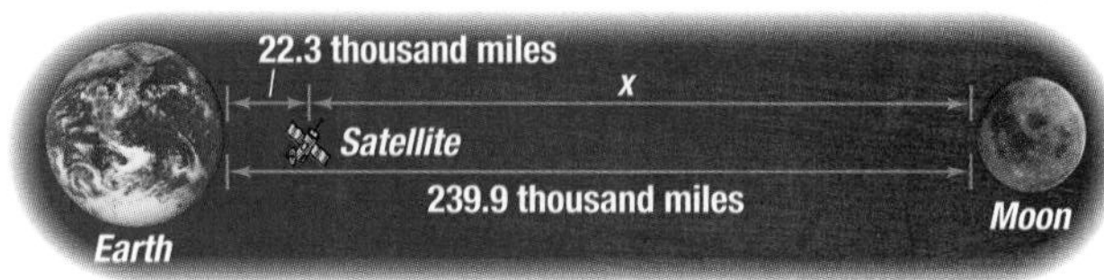


$22.3 + x = 239.9$

$22.3 + x - 22.3 = 239.9 - 22.3$ Subtract 22.3 from each side.

$x = 217.6$ Simplify.

$x \approx 218$ Round to the nearest integer.

The distance from the satellite to the moon is about 218 thousand mi.

A communications satellite follows a circular path that is 22.3 thousand miles above Earth, orbiting above the equator. This *geostationary* orbit allows the satellite to maintain a fixed position above Earth.



## Tools to Monitor Progress

### BEFORE THE LESSON

**To check prerequisite skills:**

- Operations with decimals

**Skills You Need,** p. 119

**Skills Handbook,** p. 730

**Skills Intervention Kit,** Decimals

### DURING THE LESSON

**To check understanding:**

**Try This** exercises on student page

- **Additional Example 1**
  Solve $6.8 + p = -9.7$. $-16.5$
- **Additional Example 2**
  Ping has a board that is 14.5 ft long. She saws off a piece that is 8.75 ft long. Sketch a diagram. Then write an equation and solve it to find the length of the piece that is left. 5.75 ft

■ **TRY THIS**

3. *Analyzing Markup* A store's cost plus markup is the price you pay for an item. Suppose a pair of shoes costs a store \$35.48. You pay \$70. Write and solve an equation to find the store's markup. $35.48 + m = 70$; \$34.52

## PART 2 Using Addition to Solve Equations

You can also use the Addition Property of Equality to solve equations. Remember to add the same number to each side of the equation.

### EXAMPLE 3

**Solve $k - 14.4 = -18.39$.**

$k - 14.4 = -18.39$

$k - 14.4 + 14.4 = -18.39 + 14.4$ Add 14.4 to each side.

$k = -3.99$ Simplify.

*Need Help?* For help with adding and subtracting decimals, see Skills Handbook, p. 730.

■ **TRY THIS** Solve each equation.

4. $n - 5.85 = 15.25$ 21.1
5. $-10 = c - 2.6$ −7.4

REAL-WORLD CONNECTION

### EXAMPLE 4

*Personal Finance* **Danzel wrote a check for \$76.85. His new account balance is \$235.00. What was his previous balance?**

**Words** previous balance minus check is new balance

Let $p$ = previous balance.

**Equation** $p$ − 76.85 = 235

$p - 76.85 = 235$

$p - 76.85 + 76.85 = 235 + 76.85$ Add 76.85 to each side.

$p = 311.85$ Simplify.

Danzel had \$311.85 in his account before he wrote the check.

■ **TRY THIS**

6. You spent \$14.95 for a new shirt. You now have \$12.48. Write and solve an equation to find how much money you had before you bought the shirt. $x - 14.95 = 12.48$; \$27.43



# 2 Teach

## Part 1 Teaching Notes

Although the text shows subtraction of decimals on one line: −9.7 − 4.5, students may find decimal subtraction easier by stacking the numbers one under the other. Remind them to decide first on the sign of the result.

### ■ Example 1

**Build understanding.** Before you do any calculating, tell what kind of number (positive or negative) $n$ must be. negative

### ■ Example 2

**Build understanding.** Describe a communication satellite and its use. a man-made object containing instruments used to bounce signals from one location on Earth to another

## Part 2 Teaching Notes

Remind students that the Addition Property of Equality states that if you add the same number to each side of an equation, the two sides remain equal. Students may find it easier to stack the decimals they are adding.

### ■ Example 3

**Build understanding.** Ask: What integer is a good estimate for the value of $k$? −4

### ■ Example 4

**Build understanding.** Ask: When Danzel writes a check, is he adding to or subtracting from the balance in his checkbook? subtracting from

**Extension** Challenge students to explain why the Addition Property of Equality is used to solve an equation that has a number subtracted from the variable.

**Visual Learning** Suggest that students circle the number that keeps the variable from being isolated on one side.

- **Additional Example 3**
  Solve $-23.34 = q - 16.99$. −6.35
- **Additional Example 4**
  After Alejandro wrote a check for \$49.98, the balance in his checking account was \$169.45. What was the previous balance? \$219.43

**AFTER THE LESSON**

**To assess knowledge:**

**Lesson Quiz**

Solve each equation.

1. $a + 10 = 7.9$ −2.1
2. $-1.01 = c - 9$ 7.99
3. $s - (-2.6) = 1.6$ −1
4. $3.02 + d = 2.91$ −0.11
5. $-23.7 = 13.3 + g$ −37

- For enrichment and reteaching options see Resources on p. 119H.

# 3 Practice/Assess

## Assignment Guide

To provide flexible scheduling, this lesson can be divided into parts.

▼ Part 1

**Core** 1, 3–4, 6–8, 12–14, 16–18, 22–25

✪ **Extension** 31, 35–36

▼ Part 2

**Core** 2, 5, 9–11, 15, 19–21, 26–30, 33–34

✪ **Extension** 32

Mixed Review can be assigned at any time for maintenance.

## Exercises

**Error Prevention** Students may forget to perform the same operation on each side of an equation. Remind students that the rewritten equation must always be equivalent to the original equation.

**Test Prep Exercise 34** Students may find it helpful to ask themselves this question: Is the value of $p$ greater or less than $12.30?

## ✪ Challenge

Solve $-5.2 + x + 3.06 = -9.8$. $-7.66$

## Closure

To solve a one-step equation, use inverse operations and the properties of equality to get the variable alone on one side of the equation.

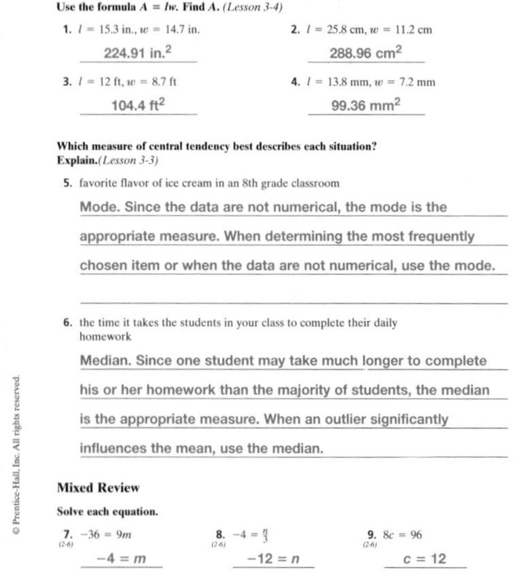

**Daily Cumulative Review**

**Use the formula $A = lw$. Find $A$.** *(Lesson 3-4)*

1. $l = 15.3$ in., $w = 14.7$ in. — 224.91 in.$^2$
2. $l = 25.8$ cm, $w = 11.2$ cm — 288.96 cm$^2$
3. $l = 12$ ft, $w = 8.7$ ft — 104.4 ft$^2$
4. $l = 13.8$ mm, $w = 7.2$ mm — 99.36 mm$^2$

**Which measure of central tendency best describes each situation? Explain.** *(Lesson 3-3)*

5. favorite flavor of ice cream in an 8th grade classroom

   Mode. Since the data are not numerical, the mode is the appropriate measure. When determining the most frequently chosen item or when the data are not numerical, use the mode.

6. the time it takes the students in your class to complete their daily homework

   Median. Since one student may take much longer to complete his or her homework than the majority of students, the median is the appropriate measure. When an outlier significantly influences the mean, use the median.

**Mixed Review**

**Solve each equation.**

7. *(2-6)* $-36 = 9m$ — $-4 = m$
8. *(2-6)* $-4 = \frac{n}{3}$ — $-12 = n$
9. *(2-6)* $8c = 96$ — $c = 12$

**Compare. Use >, <, or = to complete each statement.**

10. *(1-9)* $-24 \div (-6)$ [=] $|-32| \div 8$
11. *(1-9)* $5(-5)$ [<] $(-6)(-4)$



# Exercises

## CHECK UNDERSTANDING

**Complete the steps for each equation.**

1. $x + 1.2 = 15$
   $x + 1.2 - \blacksquare = 15 - \blacksquare$ 1.2, 1.2
   $x = \blacksquare$ 13.8

2. $y - 3.33 = 12.42$
   $y - 3.33 + \blacksquare = 12.42 + \blacksquare$ 3.33, 3.33
   $y = \blacksquare$ 15.75

**State the first step in solving each equation.**

3. $a + 8.5 = 12.53$ Subtract 8.5 from each side, or add $-8.5$ to each side.
4. $54.2 + x = 98$ Subtract 54.2 from each side, or add $-54.2$ to each side.
5. $3.4 = c - 1.9$ Add 1.9 to each side.

**Solve each equation.**

6. $6.35 + b = 9.89$ 3.54
7. $x + 0.035 = 0.915$ 0.88
8. $12.13 = n + 1.4$ 10.73
9. $d - 4.9 = 18.8$ 23.7
10. $c - 19.2 = 24$ 43.2
11. $-2.5 = q - 1.7$ $-0.8$

12. *Critical Thinking* Do the equations $x + 2.4 = 1.5$ and $x + 24 = 15$ have the same solution? Explain. No; the solution of the first equation is $-0.9$, while the solution of the second equation is $-9$.

## PRACTICE AND PROBLEM SOLVING

*Mental Math* **Use mental math to solve each equation.**

13. $1.60 = 0.40 + s$ 1.2
14. $x + 8.8 = 9.9$ 1.1
15. $5.5 = x - 5.5$ 11

**Solve each equation.**

16. $c + 9 = 3.7$ $-5.3$
17. $b + 7.6 = 23$ 15.4
18. $43.6 = n + 17.5$ 26.1
19. $-5.6 = y - 8$ 2.4
20. $4.035 = a - 3.25$ 7.285
21. $h - (-1.5) = 1.5$ 0
22. $n + (-7) = -7.08$ $-0.08$
23. $-32 = x + (-8.05)$ $-23.95$
24. $9.03 + y = 1.12$ $-7.91$
25. $e + (-7.8) = -6.7$ 1.1
26. $a - 108.8 = -203$ $-94.2$
27. $r - 0.832 = 8.67$ 9.502
28. $4.093 = d - 12$ 16.093
29. $4.3 = g - 1$ 5.3
30. $b - (-1.5) = -9$ $-10.5$

*Mathematical Reasoning* **Justify each step. Write the property or operation used to complete each step.**

✪31. $p + 8.9 + (-7.2) = 54$
   $p + 1.7 = 54$ Simplify.
   $p + 1.7 - 1.7 = 54 - 1.7$ Sub. Prop. of Equality
   $p = 52.3$ Simplify.

✪32. $81.3 + k - 4.13 = -15$
   $k + 81.3 - 4.13 = -15$ Comm. Prop. of Add.
   $k + 77.17 = -15$ Simplify.
   $k + 77.17 - 77.17 = -15 - 77.17$ Sub. Prop. of Equality
   $k = -92.17$ Simplify.



## Alternative Assessment

Have each student write an equation in which a negative decimal equals the variable plus a decimal. Then have each student write the solution on another piece of paper. Have students exchange equations, and solve, and then check.

**33.** *Error Analysis* A student solved an equation as shown at the right. Explain the student's error. The student should have added 1.6 to each side.

$$x - 1.6 = -6$$
$$x - 1.6 + 1.6 = -6 - 1.6$$
$$x = -7.6$$

**34.** **TEST PREP** Mira sold a basketball card for $12.30. This was $2.50 more than the price she paid for the card. Which equation *cannot* be used to find the original price $p$ of the card? B

**A.** $p + 2.50 = 12.30$ **B.** $p - 2.50 = 12.30$
**C.** $12.30 = 2.50 + p$ **D.** $12.30 - 2.50 = p$

**35.** *Writing* Explain how you would use the Addition Property of Equality to solve $x + 1.8 = -4.7$. Add −1.8 to each side.

*Math in the Media* **Use the cartoon below for Exercise 36.**

***Dilbert* by Scott Adams**

SOURCE: ©1993 United Features Syndicate, Inc.

**36. a.** *Critical Thinking* You can find the amount of money the clerk owes Dilbert by solving the equation $\$1.89 + x = \$7.14$. How much does the clerk owe Dilbert? $5.25

**b.** *Open-ended* Dilbert did not want to receive change that included pennies. What was another amount of money Dilbert could have given the cashier? Answers may vary. Sample: $7.39

## Mixed Review

**Use the formula $A = \ell w$. Find $A$.** ***(Lesson 3-4)***

**37.** $\ell = 23.4$ in., $w = 15.8$ in. 369.72 in.$^2$

**38.** $\ell = 5.5$ cm, $w = 7$ cm 38.5 cm$^2$

**Solve each equation.** ***(Lesson 2-6)***

**39.** $6a = 24$ 4

**40.** $-2b = 60$ −30

**41.** $-81 = 9a$ −9

**42.** $3c = 39$ 13

**43.** A large juice costs $.83. A small juice costs $.57. Ida buys one juice each school day. If Ida buys small juices instead of large juices, how much money will she save each week? ***(Lesson 2-2)*** $1.30


See also Extra Practice section.




## Practice

Practice

**Solve each equation.**

**1.** $3.8 = n - 3.62$ $n = 7.42$

**2.** $x - 19.7 = -17.48$ $x = 2.22$

**3.** $12.5 = t - 3.55$ $t = 16.05$

**4.** $k - 263.48 = -381.09$ $k = -117.61$

**5.** $9.36 + k = 14.8$ $k = 5.44$

**6.** $-22 = p + 13.7$ $p = -35.7$

**7.** $y + 3.85 = 2.46$ $y = -1.39$

**8.** $-13.8 = h + 15.603$ $h = -29.403$

**9.** $y - 48.763 = 0$ $y = 48.763$

**10.** $6.21 = e + (-3.48)$ $e = 9.69$

**11.** $x + (-0.0025) = 0.0024$ $x = 0.0049$

**12.** $-58.109 = v - 47.736$ $v = -10.373$

**13.** $x + 82.7 = 63.5$ $x = -19.2$

**14.** $-0.08 = f + 0.07$ $f = -0.15$

**15.** $0 = a + 27.98$ $a = -27.98$

**16.** $117.345 + m = 200$ $m = 82.655$

**17.** $z - 81.6 = -81.6$ $z = 0$

**18.** $5.4 = t + (-6.1)$ $t = 11.5$

**19.** $-4.095 + b = 18.665$ $b = 22.76$

**20.** $4.87 = n + 0.87$ $n = 4$

**Use mental math to solve each equation.**

**21.** $k + 23.7 = 23.7$ $k = 0$

**22.** $5.63 = n + 1.63$ $n = 4$

**23.** $x - 3.2 = 4.1$ $x = 7.3$

**24.** $p - 0.7 = 9.3$ $p = 10$

**25.** $6.75 + c = 12.95$ $c = 6.2$

**26.** $-1.09 = j - 4.99$ $j = 3.9$



## Reteaching

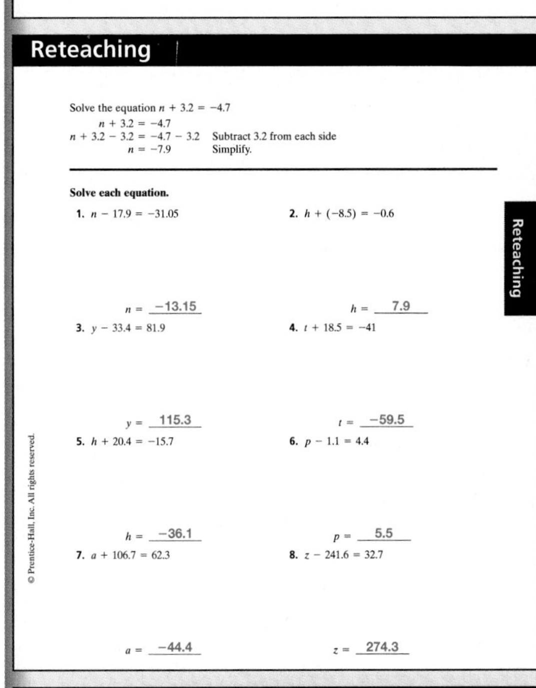

Reteaching

Solve the equation $n + 3.2 = -4.7$

$n + 3.2 = -4.7$
$n + 3.2 - 3.2 = -4.7 - 3.2$ Subtract 3.2 from each side
$n = -7.9$ Simplify.

**Solve each equation.**

**1.** $n - 17.9 = -31.05$ $n =$ −13.15

**2.** $h + (-8.5) = -0.6$ $h =$ 7.9

**3.** $y - 33.4 = 81.9$ $y =$ 115.3

**4.** $t + 18.5 = -41$ $t =$ −59.5

**5.** $h + 20.4 = -15.7$ $h =$ −36.1

**6.** $p - 1.1 = 4.4$ $p =$ 5.5

**7.** $a + 106.7 = 62.3$ $a =$ −44.4

**8.** $z - 241.6 = 32.7$ $z =$ 274.3



## Enrichment

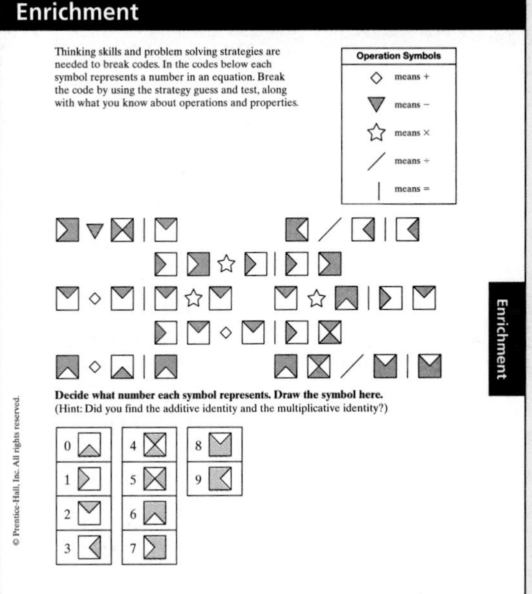

Enrichment

Thinking skills and problem solving strategies are needed to break codes. In the codes below each symbol represents a number in an equation. Break the code by using the strategy guess and test, along with what you know about operations and properties.



**Decide what number each symbol represents. Draw the symbol here.**
(Hint: Did you find the additive identity and the multiplicative identity?)

# 3-6

## Getting Ready

**Resources** A complete list of resources for this lesson is on p. 119H.

### Daily Skills Warm-Up

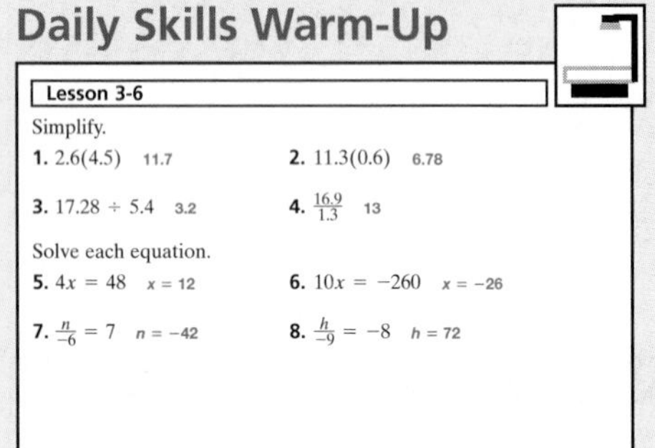
Lesson 3-6

Simplify.

1. $2.6(4.5)$ 11.7
2. $11.3(0.6)$ 6.78
3. $17.28 \div 5.4$ 3.2
4. $\frac{16.9}{1.3}$ 13

Solve each equation.

5. $4x = 48$ $x = 12$
6. $10x = -260$ $x = -26$
7. $\frac{n}{-6} = 7$ $n = -42$
8. $\frac{h}{-9} = -8$ $h = 72$

### Background for the Lesson

Division and multiplication are inverse operations that undo each other. To solve the equation $1.2x = 4.2$, divide each side by 1.2 to isolate the variable on one side. You can then rewrite the original equation as the equivalent equation $x = 3.5$. To check this solution, substitute the value 3.5 for the variable $x$ to see if 3.5 makes the original equation true. The number you use to multiply or divide each side must be a *nonzero* number. If you try to multiply or divide each side of an equation by the number zero, the result is not an equation that is equivalent to the original.

## 1 Focus

### Connecting to Students' Lives

Ask students where they are most likely to use decimal numbers. Remind them that most money transactions involve decimals.

### Connecting to Prior Knowledge

Help students recall that, in Lesson 2-6, they solved equations by multiplying or dividing integers. The process is the same when the equation contains decimals.

# 3-6 Solving Equations by Multiplying or Dividing Decimals

**What You'll Learn**

1. To solve one-step decimal equations involving multiplication
2. To solve one-step decimal equations involving division

**. . . And Why**

To model real-world situations in business

## PART 1 Using Division to Solve Equations

Division undoes multiplication. You can solve an equation involving multiplication by dividing.

### EXAMPLE 1

**Solve $0.9r = -5.4$.**

$$0.9r = -5.4$$

$$\frac{0.9r}{0.9} = \frac{-5.4}{0.9} \quad \text{Divide each side by 0.9.}$$

$$r = -6 \quad \text{Simplify.}$$

**Check**

$$0.9r = -5.4$$

$$0.9(-6) \stackrel{?}{=} -5.4 \quad \text{Replace } r \text{ with } -6.$$

$$-5.4 = -5.4 \checkmark$$

**TRY THIS** Solve each equation.

1. $0.8x = -1.6$ −2
2. $1.15 = 2.3x$ 0.5
3. $-81.81 = -0.9n$ 90.9

REAL-WORLD CONNECTION

### EXAMPLE 2

**An oil field produces an average of 16.8 thousand barrels of crude oil per day. About how many days will it take to produce 200 thousand barrels?**

| | | | | | |
|---|---|---|---|---|---|
| **Words** | daily barrel production | times | number of days | equals | 200 thousand barrels |
| | Let $d$ = number of days. | | | | |
| **Equation** | 16.8 | · | $d$ | = | 200 |

$$16.8d = 200$$

$$\frac{16.8d}{16.8} = \frac{200}{16.8} \quad \text{Divide each side by 16.8.}$$

$$d = 11.904\ldots \quad \text{Simplify.}$$

$$d \approx 12 \quad \text{Round to the nearest integer.}$$

The field will take about 12 days to produce 200 thousand barrels.



## Tools to Monitor Progress

### BEFORE THE LESSON

**To check prerequisite skills:**

- Operations with decimals

**Skills You Need,** p. 119

**Skills Handbook,** pp. 731, 733, 735

**Skills Intervention Kit,** Decimals

### DURING THE LESSON

**To check understanding:**

**Try This** exercises on student page

- **Additional Example 1**
  Solve $-6.4 = 0.8b$. −8
- **Additional Example 2**
  Every day the school cafeteria uses an average of 85.8 gallons of milk. About how many days will it be before the cafeteria uses the 250 gallons in the refrigerator? **about 3 days**

■ **TRY THIS**

4. You paid $7.70 to mail a package that weighed 5.5 lb. Write and solve an equation to find the cost per pound. $5.5p = 7.7$; $1.40

## PART 2 Using Multiplication to Solve Equations

To solve an equation involving division, multiply each side by the same nonzero number.

### EXAMPLE 3

**Solve $\frac{m}{-7.2} = -12.5$.**

$$\frac{m}{-7.2} = -12.5$$

$$\frac{m}{-7.2}(-7.2) = -12.5(-7.2) \quad \text{Multiply each side by } -7.2.$$

$$m = 90 \quad \text{Simplify.}$$

■ **TRY THIS** Solve each equation.

5. $\frac{r}{-6.0} = 0.5$ $-3$
6. $\frac{s}{2.5} = 5$ $12.5$
7. $-80 = \frac{t}{4.5}$ $-360$

**DATA ANALYSIS** CONNECTION

### EXAMPLE 4

*Batting Averages* **The 1923 baseball season was one of Babe Ruth's best years. He was at bat 522 times and had a batting average of 0.393, rounded to the nearest thousandth. The batting average formula is $a = \frac{h}{n}$, where $a$ is the batting average, $h$ is the number of hits, and $n$ is the number of times at bat. Use the formula to find the number of hits Babe Ruth made.**

$$a = \frac{h}{n}$$

$$0.393 = \frac{h}{522} \quad \text{Replace } a \text{ with 0.393 and } n \text{ with 522.}$$

$$(0.393)(522) = \frac{h}{522}(522) \quad \text{Multiply each side by 522.}$$

$$h = 205.146 \quad \text{Simplify.}$$

$$h \approx 205 \quad \text{Since } h \text{ (hits) represents an integer, round to the nearest integer.}$$

Babe Ruth made 205 hits.

During his professional career Babe Ruth was at bat 8,399 times and had a batting average of 0.342. About how many hits did he have? about 2,870 hits

■ **TRY THIS**

8. Suppose your batting average is 0.222. You have batted 54 times. How many hits do you have? 12 hits



# 2 Teach

## PART 1 Part 1 Teaching Notes

Ask students how they would solve the equation $9y = -27$. Help them recall using the Division Property of Equality to rewrite the original equation as the equivalent equation $y = -3$. Remind them to check by substituting $-3$ to test whether $9(-3)$ does equal $-27$.

### ■ Example 1

**Build understanding.** Look at the equation and predict whether the value of *r* will be a positive or a negative number. negative

### ■ Example 2

**Build understanding.** Ask: Estimate—will it take more than 10 days to produce 200 barrels? yes, a little more than 10 days

## PART 2 Part 2 Teaching Notes

Discuss with students why the number you use to divide or multiply each side of an equation must be a *nonzero* number.

### ■ Example 3

**Build understanding.** Ask: What has been done to the variable *m*? It has been divided by $-7.2$. What undoes this? multiplying each side by $-7.2$

### ■ Example 4

**Build understanding.** Ask: What are the steps in rounding 205.146 to the nearest integer? Underline the digit in the ones place; look at the digit to the right; since it is less than 5, drop all the digits to the right of the underlined digit.

**Extension** Challenge students to write a variable equation in which the variable is multiplied by a decimal and also subtracted from a decimal. Then have students solve the equation.

- **Additional Example 3**
  Solve $-37.5 = \frac{c}{-1.2}$. 45
- **Additional Example 4**
  A little league player has a batting average of 0.133 (rounded to the nearest thousandth) and was at bat 15 times. Use the batting average formula to find how many hits she made. 2

### AFTER THE LESSON

**To assess knowledge:**

**Lesson Quiz**

Solve each equation.

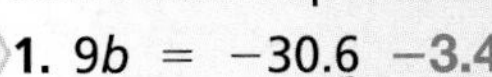

1. $9b = -30.6$ $-3.4$

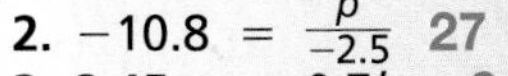

2. $-10.8 = \frac{p}{-2.5}$ 27
3. $2.45 = -0.7k$ $-3.5$
4. $\frac{t}{3.07} = 240$ 736.8
5. $y \div (-0.3) = 146.7$ $-44.01$

- For enrichment and reteaching options see Resources on p. 119H.

# 3 Practice/Assess

## Assignment Guide

To provide flexible scheduling, this lesson can be divided into parts.

**Part 1**

**Core** 1, 3, 6–8, 11–19, 28, 31–32

**Extension** 35, 38

**Part 2**

**Core** 2, 4–5, 9–10, 20–27, 29–30, 33–34

**Extension** 36–37

Mixed Review can be assigned at any time for maintenance.

## Exercises

**Error Prevention** Suggest that students write the operation sign (÷ or ×) with the number on each side so that they do the same operation on both sides.

**Auditory Learning** **Exercise 4** Students can say the equations softly to themselves so that they hear the name of the operation to be undone.

## Challenge

Solve the batting average formula $a = \frac{h}{n}$ for $n$. $n = \frac{h}{a}$

## Closure

To solve a one-step equation, use inverse operations and the properties of equality to get the variable alone on one side of the equation.

## Daily Cumulative Review

**Solve each equation.** *(Lesson 3-5)*

1. $x + 7.4 = 16$ — $x = 8.6$
2. $-23.8 = t + 15.2$ — $-39 = t$
3. $-7.8 = w - 3$ — $-4.8 = w$
4. $p - 2.653 = 5.832$ — $p = 8.485$
5. $56.87 = a - (-13.79)$ — $43.08 = a$
6. $u + (-34) = -34.3$ — $u = -0.3$
7. $d - 14.66 = -3.45$ — $d = 11.21$
8. $-15.4 = n + (-23.7)$ — $8.3 = n$
9. $-19.4 = k + (-45.6)$ — $26.2 = k$

**Evaluate each formula for the values given.** *(Lesson 3-4)*

10. perimeter of a rectangle: $P = 2l + 2w$ when $l = 12$ in., $w = 6$ in. — $P = 36$ in.
11. distance: $d = rt$ when $r = 25$ mi/h, $t = 4$ h — $d = 100$ mi
12. circumference: $C = 2\pi r$ when $r = 6$ cm; use 3.14 for $\pi$ — $C = 37.68$ cm
13. area of a rectangle: $A = lw$ when $l = 3$ ft, $w = 2$ ft — $A = 6\text{ ft}^2$

**Mixed Review**

**Write the coordinates of each point.**

14. the point 7 units to the right of the $y$-axis and 4 units below the $x$-axis *(1-10)* — (7, −4)
15. the point on the $y$-axis 3 units below the $x$-axis *(1-10)* — (−3, 0)
16. the point 5 units below the $x$-axis and 6 units to the left of the $y$-axis *(1-10)* — (−6, −5)

**Find each product or quotient.** *(From Last Year)*

17. $36 \times 1{,}000$ — 36,000
18. $270 \div 10$ — 27
19. $739 \times 100$ — 73,900



# Exercises

## Check Understanding

**Complete the steps for each equation.**

1. $0.8x = 1.5$
   $(0.8x) \div \blacksquare = 1.5 \div \blacksquare$ (0.8; 0.8)
   $x = \blacksquare$ (1.875)

2. $\frac{d}{4.5} = -3$
   $\blacksquare \cdot \frac{d}{4.5} = \blacksquare(-3)$ (4.5; 4.5)
   $d = \blacksquare$ (−13.5)

**State the first step in solving each equation.**

3. $0.9x = -0.54$ Divide each side by 0.9.
4. $\frac{y}{0.6} = 1.2$ Multiply each side by 0.6.
5. $1.5 = d \div 15$ Multiply each side by 15.
6. $-1.2 = -0.4m$ Divide each side by −0.4.

**Solve each equation.**

7. $-0.5y = -0.73$ 1.46
8. $0.8x = 0.448$ 0.56
9. $\frac{n}{2.3} = -4.8$ −11.04
10. $0.97 = \frac{c}{-2}$ −1.94

11. a. *Error Analysis* Harry found 324.8 as a solution for the equation $4x = 81.2$. What was Harry's error? Harry multiplied by 4 instead of dividing each side by 4.
    b. How could Harry have used estimation to check whether his answer was reasonable? Answers may vary. Sample: He could have compared his result, 324.8, to the estimate $81.2 \div 4 \approx 20$.

## Practice and Problem Solving

**Solve each equation.**

12. $2x = -4.88$ −2.44
13. $-0.3y = 7.53$ −25.1
14. $6.4x = 0.2816$ 0.044
15. $-5.1z = -11.73$ 2.3
16. $1.92 = 1.6s$ 1.2
17. $0.004m = 0.12$ 30
18. $3.2n = 27.52$ 8.6
19. $2.21 = 1.7w$ 1.3
20. $\frac{n}{1.7} = 0.22$ 0.374
21. $\frac{k}{2.01} = 0.04$ 0.0804
22. $4.5 = m \div (-3.3)$ −14.85
23. $-33.04 = \frac{z}{-0.03}$ 0.9912
24. $-0.45 = x \div 12$ −5.4
25. $\frac{m}{0.89} = 3{,}488$ 3,104.32
26. $\frac{w}{-3.4} = -25.5$ 86.7
27. $120 = \frac{v}{3.8}$ 456

*Mental Math* **Solve each equation.**

28. $0.7x = 2.8$ 4
29. $9 = \frac{a}{1.5}$ 13.5
30. $\frac{m}{7.08} = -100$ −708
31. $10{,}000r = 483.08$ 0.048308

**Write an equation for each sentence. Solve for the variable.**

32. The product of a number $n$ and −7.3 is 30.66. Find the value of $n$. $-7.3n = 30.66$; −4.2
33. The quotient of a number $n$ divided by −4.5 equals 200.6. Find the value of $n$. $n \div (-4.5) = 200.6$; −902.7
34. A number $n$ divided by −2.35 equals 400.9. Find the value of $n$. $n \div (-2.35) = 400.9$; −942.115



## Alternative Assessment

Have students create a chart or diagram that describes how they decide which of the four equality properties to use when they solve a decimal equation.

35. *Measurement* If you know a length $\ell$ in meters, you can multiply the length by 3.28 to find the length in feet $f$.
   a. Write an equation to model this situation. $f = 3.28\ell$
   b. A tree is 7.5 m tall. Use your equation to find this height in feet. 24.6 ft
   c. A bookshelf is 6 ft tall. What is this height in meters? about 1.83 m
   d. A room in your home is 12 ft long and 15 ft wide. Use your equation and the formula for the area of a rectangle to find the area of the room in square meters. Round your answer to the nearest tenth. 16.7 $m^2$

36. *Number Sense* The weight of a record-setting onion was 12.25 lb. An average-sized onion weighs 0.5 lb. About how many average-sized onions have a total weight equal to the record-setting onion? Round your answer to the nearest integer. 24 (or 25) onions

37. a. Your batting average is 0.244, and you have been at bat 82 times. How many hits do you have? 20 hits
   b. *Writing* Why is it necessary to round your answer in part (a) to the nearest integer? You can have only a whole number of hits.

38. *Mathematical Reasoning* Find values for $x$ and $y$ that satisfy $xy = 0.42$ and $x + y = 1.3$. $x = 0.6, y = 0.7$ (or $x = 0.7, y = 0.6$)

## Mixed Review

**Solve each equation.** *(Lesson 3-5)*

39. $c + 9 = 3.7$ −5.3
40. $b + 7.6 = 23$ 15.4
41. $43.6 = n + 17.5$ 26.1
42. $-5.6 = y - 8$ 2.4
43. $4.035 = a - 3.25$ 7.285
44. $h - (-3.5) = 1.5$ −2

**Is the given number a solution of the equation?** *(Lesson 2-4)*

45. $20 - c = 12; c = 8$ yes
46. $8 = 2a + 3; a = 0$ no
47. $2m = m + 6; m = 4$ no

48. a. *Patterns* Multiply $99 \cdot 24$, $99 \cdot 25$, and $99 \cdot 26$. *(Lesson 1-7)* 2,376, 2,475, 2,574
   b. Describe the pattern you found in part (a). Answers may vary. Sample: 99 times a number is 100 times the number less one of the number.
   c. Use the pattern to evaluate $99 \cdot 27$. 2,673

CHAPTER PROJECT 3

## Activity 2 Researching

In the business section of a newspaper or on the Internet, find today's foreign currency exchange rates. Keep the chart to use for your project.

Cut out advertisements from a newspaper for two items. Make sure the advertisements include the costs of the items.

See also Extra Practice section.



## Project Activity 2

**Researching** You may want to bring some copies of newspapers to class for students to use. Encourage students to select advertisements for items that interest them, or that a visitor might want to buy on a trip to this country.

## Practice

**Use mental math to solve each equation.**

1. $0.7h = 4.2$ $h = 6$
2. $\frac{x}{2.5} = -3$ $x = -7.5$
3. $38.7 = -100k$ $k = -0.387$
4. $-45.6e = -4.56$ $e = 0.1$

**Solve each equation.**

5. $\frac{p}{2.9} = 0.55$ $p = 1.595$
6. $9.1 = \frac{x}{-0.7}$ $x = -6.37$
7. $-6.4 = \frac{y}{8.5}$ $y = -54.4$
8. $\frac{k}{-1.2} = -0.07$ $k = 0.084$
9. $277.4 = \frac{n}{3.5}$ $n = 970.9$
10. $\frac{e}{-0.76} = 2{,}809$ $e = -2{,}134.84$
11. $\frac{a}{27} = -32.3$ $a = -872.1$
12. $\frac{p}{-1.52} = -3{,}600$ $p = 5{,}472$
13. $-9k = 2.34$ $k = -0.26$
14. $-12.42 = 0.03p$ $p = -414$
15. $-7.2y = 61.2$ $y = -8.5$
16. $-0.1035 = 0.23n$ $n = -0.45$
17. $1.5m = 3.03$ $m = 2.02$
18. $-0.007h = 0.2002$ $h = -28.6$
19. $8.13t = -100.812$ $t = -12.4$
20. $0.546 = 0.42y$ $y = 1.3$

**Write an equation for each sentence. Solve for the variable.**

21. The opposite of seventy-five hundredths times some number $n$ equals twenty-four thousandths. Find the value of $n$.
$-0.75n = 0.024; n = -0.032$

22. A number $n$ divided by −3.88 equals negative two thousand. Find the value of $n$.
$\frac{n}{-3.88} = -2{,}000; n = 7{,}760$

23. Four hundredths times some number $n$ equals thirty-three and four tenths. Find the value of $n$.
$0.04n = 33.4; n = 835$

24. The product of some number $n$ and −0.26 equals 169.39. Find the value of $n$.
$-0.26n = 169.39; n = -651.5$



## Reteaching

Solve the equations $0.7x = -2.8$ and $\frac{x}{1.5} = 0.2$

| | |
|---|---|
| $0.7x = -2.8$ | Write the equation |
| $\frac{0.7x}{0.7} = \frac{-2.8}{0.7}$ | Divide each side by 0.7 |
| $x = -4$ | Simplify |
| $\frac{x}{1.5} = 0.2$ | Write the equation |
| $\frac{x}{1.5}(1.5) = 0.2(1.5)$ | Multiply each side by 1.5 |
| $x = 0.3$ | Simplify |

**Solve each equation.**

1. $4x = -2.44$ $x =$ −0.61
2. $1.8x = 5.76$ $x =$ 3.2
3. $\frac{h}{-1.05} = -0.36$ $h =$ 0.378
4. $\frac{z}{-0.02} = 5.9$ $z =$ −0.118
5. $4.25y = 0.85$ $y =$ 0.2
6. $\frac{n}{-1.9} = 24.6$ $n =$ −46.74
7. $\frac{r}{8.04} = 1.55$ $r =$ 12.462
8. $11.32a = -39.62$ $a =$ −3.5



## Enrichment

Each judge in a diving competition grades every dive from 0 to 10, with 10 representing a perfect dive. High and low scores are thrown out. (If there are duplications of high and low scores, only one of the duplicated scores is thrown out.) The remaining scores are added and their sum is multiplied by the degree of difficulty.

| Degrees of Difficulty | | | |
|---|---|---|---|
| Position: | Tuck | Pike | Layout |
| Forward $1\frac{1}{2}$ somersault | 1.4 | 1.7 | 2.1 |
| Back double somersault | 1.9 | 2.2 | 2.5 |
| Reverse dive | 1.5 | 1.7 | 1.8 |
| Inward $2\frac{1}{2}$ somersault | 2.8 | — | — |
| Back $1\frac{1}{2}$ somersault $2\frac{1}{2}$ twist | — | 3.1 | — |

1. A back double somersault in the tuck position is awarded these scores: 6, 5, 7, 7, 8, 6, 7, 6
   a. Which scores should be thrown out? 5 and 8
   b. Find the total score for the dive. 74.1

**Complete.**

| | Dive | Position | Judge's scores | Diver's score |
|---|---|---|---|---|
| 2. | Reverse | Layout | 6, 8, 6, 8, 7, 7, 6, 6 | 72 |
| 3. | Forward $1\frac{1}{2}$ somersault | Pike | 3, 4, 6, 4, 5, 5, 3, 7 | 45.9 |
| 4. | Inward $2\frac{1}{2}$ somersault | Tuck | 9, 9, 8, 7, 8, 7, 9, 9 | 140 |

5. A diver received scores of 6, 9, 7, 9, 7, 7, 8, and 5 and earned a total score of 136.4. What dive did the diver perform?
Back $1\frac{1}{2}$ somersault $2\frac{1}{2}$ twist

6. To win, a diver needs to score 110 points on her final dive. She thinks she could average 7.5 points from each of the 8 judges. What degree of difficulty should she attempt?
2.5 or greater

# 3-7

## Getting Ready

**Resources** A complete list of resources for this lesson is on p. 119H.

### Daily Skills Warm-Up

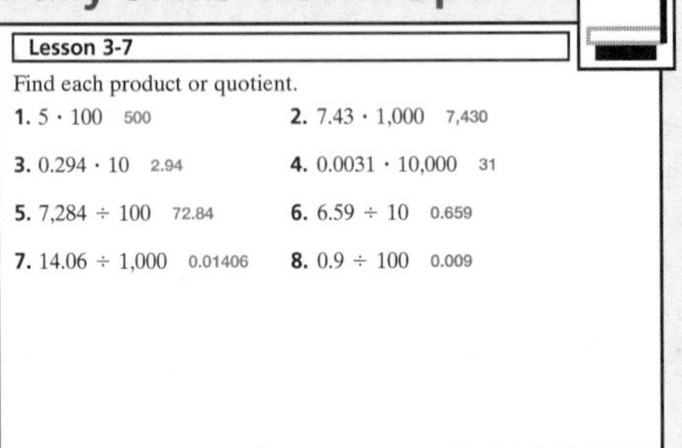

Lesson 3-7

Find each product or quotient.

1. 5 · 100 500
2. 7.43 · 1,000 7,430
3. 0.294 · 10 2.94
4. 0.0031 · 10,000 31
5. 7,284 ÷ 100 72.84
6. 6.59 ÷ 10 0.659
7. 14.06 ÷ 1,000 0.01406
8. 0.9 ÷ 100 0.009

### Background for the Lesson

Today nearly all the countries of the world use the metric system or SI (Système Internationale) for measurement. Even the common Customary system units of measurement used in the United States are defined in terms of metric units by the National Institute of Standards and Technology. The meter is officially defined as the distance a certain wavelength of light travels in a minute fraction of a second. The kilogram is defined as the mass of a platinum-iridium sphere that is kept in France, though some scientists are working to redefine the kilogram as the mass of an exact number of a certain type of atom. The liter is a unit that is derived from the meter. One liter is equal to the volume of 1,000 cubic centimeters.

## 1 Focus

### Connecting to Students' Lives

Ask students to relate where they have seen metric measurements used. Examples could include automotive repair or track and field events.

### Connecting to Prior Knowledge

In Lesson 3-2, students made estimates using decimals. In this lesson they use decimals in using metric system. In Lesson 4-9, students will extend these skills as they learn about scientific notation.



# 3-7 Using the Metric System

**What You'll Learn**

1. To identify appropriate metric measures
2. To convert metric units

**. . . And Why**

To understand metric measures and to measure everyday objects

## PART 1 Identifying Appropriate Metric Measures

Knowing the approximate size of each metric unit of measure will allow you to choose an appropriate unit.

**Metric Units of Measurement**

| Type | Unit | Reference Example |
|---|---|---|
| Length | millimeter (mm) | about the thickness of a dime |
| | centimeter (cm) | about the width of a thumbnail |
| | meter (m) | about the distance from a doorknob to the floor |
| | kilometer (km) | a little more than one half mile |
| Capacity | milliliter (mL) | about 5 drops of water |
| | liter (L) | a little more than a quart of milk |
| Mass | milligram (mg) | about the mass of a speck of sawdust |
| | gram (g) | about the mass of a paper clip |
| | kilogram (kg) | about one half the mass of this math book |

**EXAMPLE 1**

**Choose an appropriate metric unit.**

**a. height of a classroom chalkboard**

Meter; the height of a chalkboard is about twice the distance from the floor to a doorknob.

**b. mass of a backpack filled with books**

Kilogram; a backpack filled with books is many times the mass of this textbook.

**c. capacity of a birdbath**

Liter; several quart bottles of water would fill a birdbath.

**TRY THIS** Choose an appropriate metric unit. Explain your choice. 1-4. See left.

1. length of a broom
2. the mass of an energy bar
3. mass of a horse
4. capacity of a car's gas tank

1. Centimeter; a meter is too large unless you use fractional parts of a meter; millimeters are too small.
2. Gram; an energy bar has a mass of several grams, but it is much less than 1 kilogram.
3. Kilogram; a horse is very heavy, so grams are too small.
4. Liter; a gas tank holds several liters, so milliliters are too small.



# Tools to Monitor Progress

### BEFORE THE LESSON

**To check prerequisite skills:**

- Multiplying and dividing by multiples of 10

**Skills You Need,** p. 119

**Skills Handbook,** p. 734

**Skills Intervention Kit,** Measurement

### DURING THE LESSON

**To check understanding:**

**Try This** exercises on student page

- **Additional Example 1**
  Choose an appropriate metric unit for each: the width of this textbook; the mass of a pair of glasses; the capacity of a thimble. cm; g; mL
- **Additional Example 2**
  Choose a reasonable estimate.
  a. capacity of a drinking glass: 500 L or 500 mL 500 mL

## EXAMPLE 2

*Estimation* **Choose a reasonable estimate. Explain your choice.**

**a. capacity of a juice box: 200 mL or 200 L**
200 mL; the juice box holds less than a quart of milk.

**b. length of a new pencil: 15 cm or 15 m**
15 cm; the length of a pencil would be about 15 widths of a thumbnail.

**c. mass of a small tube of toothpaste: 100 g or 100 kg**
100 g; the mass is about the same as a box of paper clips.

**TRY THIS** Choose a reasonable estimate.

5. distance between two cities: 50 mm or 50 km **50 km**
6. amount of liquid that an eyedropper holds: 10 mL or 10 L **10 mL**

## PART 2 Converting Units

The metric system uses a decimal system to relate different units to each other. Look down the metric units chart below. The units highlighted in yellow are the units most often used. As you read from left to right, each unit is 10 times the size of the unit before it.

| | milli- | centi- | deci- | UNIT | deka- | hecto- | kilo- |
|---|---|---|---|---|---|---|---|
| **Length** | millimeter (mm) | centimeter (cm) | decimeter (dm) | meter (m) | dekameter (dam) | hectometer (hm) | kilometer (km) |
| **Capacity** | milliliter (mL) | centiliter (cL) | deciliter (dL) | liter (L) | dekaliter (daL) | hectoliter (hL) | kiloliter (kL) |
| **Mass** | milligram (mg) | centigram (cg) | decigram (dg) | gram (g) | dekagram (dag) | hectogram (hg) | kilogram (kg) |

You can convert from one unit to another by multiplying or dividing by 10; 100; 1,000 and so on.

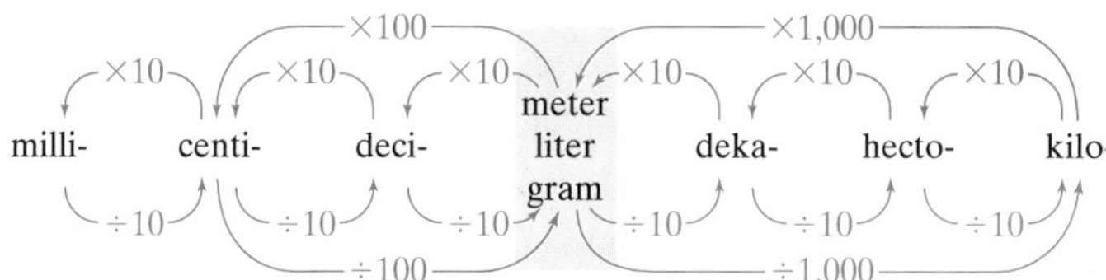




# 2 Teach

## Part 1 Teaching Notes

Elicit the fact that the basic units of measure in the metric system are the meter, the liter, and the gram.

### Example 1

**Build understanding.** Ask: Is the height of an automobile greater than or less than one meter? **greater than**

**ELL** Have students familiar with languages other than English share the words for metric units in their languages. Discuss similarities.

### Example 2

**Build understanding.** Name something that is equivalent to a liter. **sample answer: quart-size milk carton** Can you imagine the capacity of a juice box being equal to 200 milk cartons? **no**

## PART 2 Part 2 Teaching Notes

Point out that conversion within the metric system is much easier than in the Customary system. In the metric system, you multiply or divide by 10 (or multiples of 10).

### Example 3

**Build understanding.** Ask: Why do you multiply by 1,000 to change from liters to milliliters? **There are 1,000 mL in 1 L.**

**Reading Math** Remind students that they may have learned in previous math courses that the prefix *centi-* means hundredths, *milli-* means thousandths, and *kilo-* means thousand.

**b.** length of a hair clip: 12 m or 12 cm **12 cm**
**c.** mass of a pair of workboots: 1 kg or 1 g **1 kg**

- **Additional Example 3**

Complete each statement.
**a.** 7,603 mL = ■ L **7.603**
**b.** 457 cm = ■ m **4.57**

- **Additional Example 4**

A blue whale was caught in 1931 that was 2,900 cm long. What was its length in meters? **29 m**

## AFTER THE LESSON

### To assess knowledge: Lesson Quiz

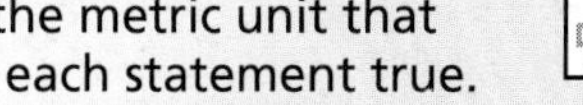

Write the metric unit that makes each statement true.

1. 23 kg = 23,000 ■ **g**
2. 970 cm = 9.7 ■ **m**

Complete each statement.

3. ■ g = 42 mg **0.042**
4. ■ km = 5,000 m **5**

- For enrichment and reteaching options see Resources on p. 119H.

## Example 4

**Build understanding.** Ask: Why do you divide 2,300 by 1,000? There are 1,000 m in 1 km.

**Tactile Learning** Have students use a meter stick and masking tape to put a length of tape (and label it) one meter long on the floor or wall of the classroom. Have them use a centimeter ruler to do the same thing for various lengths such as 10 cm and 50 cm.

**Extension** What unit of measure is used on the road signs in Canada and Mexico that give the distance to the next town? km

**Connecting to History** The metric system was set up in 1790 by the French Academy of Science. At the time there was much discussion about what number should be used as a base. Both 12 and 11 were seriously considered before base 10 won and was adopted.

**Advanced Learners** Have students discuss in writing the pros and cons of converting the Customary system of measurements used in the United States to the metric system.

To convert from one unit to another in the metric system, find the relationship between the two units. Remember to multiply if you are going from a larger unit to a smaller unit (there will be more of the smaller units) and to divide if you are going from a smaller unit to a larger unit (there will be fewer of the larger units).

*Need Help?* For help with multiplying and dividing decimals by powers of 10, see Skills Handbook, p. 734.

### EXAMPLE 3

*Mental Math* **Complete each statement.**

**a. 4.35 L = ■ mL**

4.35 · 1,000 = 4,350 — To convert liters to milliliters, multiply by 1,000.

4.35 L = 4,350 mL

**b. 914 cm = ■ m**

914 ÷ 100 = 9.14 — To convert centimeters to meters, divide by 100.

914 cm = 9.14 m

**TRY THIS** Complete each statement.

7. 35 mL = ■ L 0.035
8. ■ g = 250 kg 250,000
9. ■ cm = 68 m 6,800

REAL-WORLD CONNECTION

### EXAMPLE 4

*Geography* **The ancient Incan city of Machu Picchu is located in Peru. Its altitude is about 2,300 m above sea level. What is Machu Picchu's altitude in kilometers?**

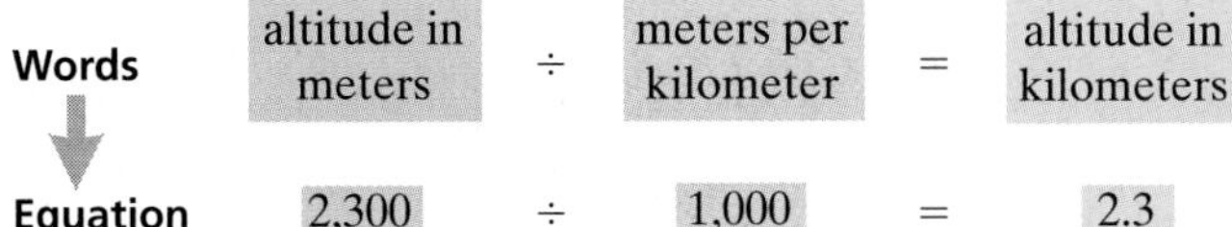

| | | | | | |
|---|---|---|---|---|---|
| Words | altitude in meters | ÷ | meters per kilometer | = | altitude in kilometers |
| Equation | 2,300 | ÷ | 1,000 | = | 2.3 |

Machu Picchu is about 2.3 km above sea level.

The ancient city of Machu Picchu (c. 1450–1550) is located in Peru's Andes Mountains. One of the few major pre-Columbian ruins found nearly intact, Machu Picchu was designated a World Heritage site in 1983.

**TRY THIS**

10. The record for the highest a kite has flown is 3.8 km. Find the height of the kite in meters. 3,800 m
11. *Number Sense* You have a recipe that requires 0.25 L of milk. Your measuring cup is marked only in milliliters. How many milliliters of milk do you need? 250 mL

# Exercises

## CHECK UNDERSTANDING

**Match each quantity with an appropriate metric measurement.**

| | | | |
|---|---|---|---|
| **1.** length of your thumb C | | **A.** 1 g | |
| **2.** mass of a book F | | **B.** 100 m | |
| **3.** length of a soccer field B | | **C.** 6 cm | |
| **4.** amount of water in a fishbowl E | | **D.** 15 mL | |
| **5.** mass of a sewing needle A | | **E.** 4 L | |
| **6.** amount of fluid in a straw D | | **F.** 1 kg | |

*Mental Math* **Complete each statement.**

**7.** 54 m = ■ cm 5,400 **8.** ■ L = 234 mL 0.234 **9.** 12 g = ■ kg 0.012 **10.** ■ m = 3.01 km 3,010

**11.** *Geography* The shortest street in the world is Elgin Street, in Bacup, England. It is 518 cm long. How many meters long is it? 5.18 m

## PRACTICE AND PROBLEM SOLVING

**Choose an appropriate metric unit of measure. Explain your choice.** 12–17. See above.

**12.** mass of a banana **13.** depth of Lake Michigan **14.** length of a small calculator

**15.** mass of a car **16.** width of a highway **17.** quantity of water in a spoon

12. Gram; a banana is well under a kilogram, so kilograms are too large.
13. Meter; the depth is less than a kilometer, so kilometers are too large.
14. Centimeter; the length is much less than a meter and much more than a millimeter, so meters are too large and millimeters are too small.
15. Kilogram; a car is very heavy, so grams are too small.
16. Meter; the width is much less than a kilometer and much more than a centimeter, so kilometers are too large and centimeters are too small.
17. Milliliter; a spoon holds much less than a liter, so a liter is too large.

**Choose a reasonable estimate. Explain your choice.**

**18.** the mass of a small dog: 5 g or 5 kg 5 kg; 5 g is about the mass of a nickel.

**19.** amount of liquid you should drink daily: 2,000 mL or 2,000 L 2,000 mL; 2,000 L is about 2,000 qt and 2,000 mL ≈ 2 qt.

**20.** the mass of a box of cereal: 350 mg or 350 g 350 g; 350 mg is less than the mass of a paper clip.

**21.** the width of a sidewalk: 150 cm or 150 m 150 cm; 150 m is greater than the length of a football field.

**22.** the length of 24 city blocks: 2 m or 2 km 2 km; 2 m can be walked in 3 or 4 steps.

**23.** the mass of a thumbtack: 1 mg or 1 g 1 g; 1 mg is closer to the mass of a speck of sawdust.

**Write the metric unit that makes each statement true.**

**24.** 9.03 ■ = 9,030 mm m **25.** 890 cm = 8.9 ■ m **26.** 130,000 ■ = 1.3 km cm



# 3 Practice/Assess

## Assignment Guide

To provide flexible scheduling, this lesson can be divided into parts.

▼ Part 1
**Core** 1–6, 12–23, 50

▼ Part 2
**Core** 7–11, 24–38, 46–48, 51–52
✪ **Extension** 39–45, 49, 53

Mixed Review can be assigned at any time for maintenance.

## Exercise

**Exercises 39–44** Suggest that students first look for measurements that are the same kind (length, mass, capacity).

**Test Prep Exercise 50** Have students envision a bird larger than an eagle.

## ✪ Challenge

Change 0.005 L to mL. 5 mL

## Closure

The metric system of measurement uses a decimal system to relate units to one another. To measure, you must choose an appropriate unit of measure.

## Alternative Assessment

Have students write a list of their estimates for the length, mass, and capacity in metric units of familiar objects in the classroom or around the school.

## Daily Cumulative Review

**Solve each equation.** *(Lesson 3-6)*

1. $5y = 3.25$ $y = 0.65$
2. $13.11 = 2.3n$ $5.7 = n$
3. $\frac{m}{3.4} = -5.6$ $m = -19.04$
4. $-0.032b = 0.08$ $b = -2.5$
5. $-54.02 = u \div 2.1$ $-113.442 = u$
6. $\frac{p}{13} = -0.34$ $p = -4.42$
7. $a \cdot -9.3 = 50.22$ $a = -5.4$
8. $-6.3z = 34.65$ $z = -5.5$
9. $g \div 3.72 = 8.37$ $g = 31.1364$

**Solve each equation.** *(Lesson 3-5)*

10. $5.6 = t - 4.7$ $10.3 = t$
11. $7.36 + w = 9.52$ $w = 2.16$
12. $v - (-3.6) = 2.5$ $v = -1.1$
13. $-76 = m + (-35.54)$ $-40.46 = m$
14. $12.435 = h - 13.65$ $26.085 = h$
15. $k + (-4) = -3.2$ $k = 0.8$

**Mixed Review**

**Solve using any strategy.**

16. (2-7) The school fundraiser made $3,445. There were 438 items sold. Each t-shirt sold for $9 and each mug sold for $5.50. How many of each item did they sell?
296 t-shirts and 142 mugs

17. (1-8) Mary wants to plant zinnias in her triangular shaped garden. At the point of the triangle she will put 1 zinnia. She will add 1 zinnia to each of the previous rows. She will have room for 10 rows. How many zinnias will Mary need to buy?
55 zinnias

*Mental Math* **Complete each statement.**

27. 0.25 m = ■ cm 25
28. ■ mL = 7.3 L 7,300
29. 595 g = ■ kg 0.595
30. 900,500 mL = ■ L 900.5
31. 35 m = ■ km 0.035
32. ■ m = 875 cm 8.75
33. 9,120 mg = ■ g 9.12
34. 900 km = ■ m 900,000
35. 5 g = ■ kg 0.005
36. ■ cm = 13 km 1,300,000
37. ■ km = 562,300 cm 5.623
38. 301 kg = ■ mg 301,000,000

*Number Sense* **Match each measurement in the first column with its equivalent measurement in the second column.**

| | |
|---|---|
| 39. 0.015 km E | A. 15,000 mL |
| 40. 1,500 cm E | B. 150 cm |
| 41. 150,000 mg C | C. 150 g |
| 42. 0.15 L F | D. 1.5 kg |
| 43. 15 L A | E. 15 m |
| 44. 1,500 g D | F. 150 mL |
| | G. 150 kg |
| | H. 0.15 mL |

49. Camille multiplied 6,392 g by 1,000, so she changed grams to milligrams. To change grams to kilograms she should have *divided* 6,392 by 1,000 to find 6.392 kg.

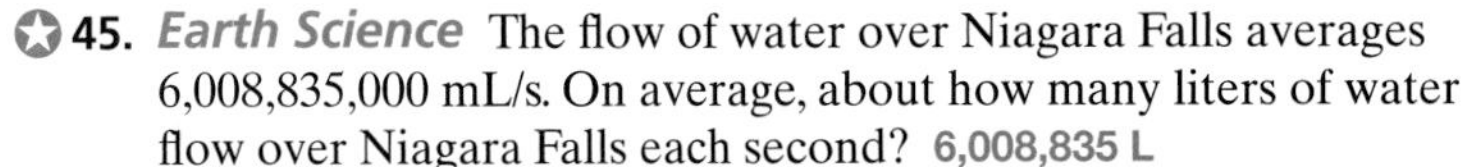

45. *Earth Science* The flow of water over Niagara Falls averages 6,008,835,000 mL/s. On average, about how many liters of water flow over Niagara Falls each second? 6,008,835 L

46. The world's longest model train has 650 cars and is 0.695 km long. How many meters long is the train? 695 m

47. *Nutrition* A world-record grapefruit had a mass of 3,068 g. What was its mass in kilograms? 3.068 kg

48. *Zoology* A hippopotamus is so large that it has a stomach 304.8 cm long, yet it is agile enough to outrun a human. How long is the stomach of a hippopotamus in meters? 3.048 m

49. *Error Analysis* One of the world's largest pearls had a mass of 6,392 g. Camille wrote in her report that the pearl had a mass of 6,392,000 kg. What was her error? See above right.

50. **TEST PREP** The albatross has the greatest wingspan of any bird. A reasonable wingspan for an albatross would be _?_. C
A. 335 km B. 335 m C. 335 cm D. 3.35 cm

51. *Writing* The prefix *kilo-* means "one thousand," and the prefix *milli-* means "one thousandth." What do the prefixes tell you about *kilometer* and *kilogram,* and *milliliter* and *milligram?* A kilometer is 1,000 meters, a kilogram is 1,000 grams, a milliliter is 0.001 liter, and a milligram is 0.001 gram.

52. *Measurement* What part of a second is a millisecond? 0.001

One of the world's first hydroelectric power plants was built at Niagara Falls. The present-day plant is capable of producing 2,100,000 kilowatts of electricity. A 100-watt light bulb, left on for ten hours, uses 1 kilowatt-hour.

53. a. *Physical Fitness* You walk about 3 mi/h. Approximately how many kilometers can you walk in an hour? 5 to 6 km
b. How many meters can you walk in an hour? 5,000 to 6,000 m

## MIXED REVIEW

**Estimate each product or quotient.** *(Lesson 3-2)*

**54.** 28.134 ÷ 3.75 about 7 **55.** 8.517 · 9.82 about 90 **56.** 101.49 ÷ 9.51 about 10

**Solve each inequality.** *(Lessons 2-9 and 2-10)*

**57.** $a - 5 \geq 16$ $a \geq 21$ **58.** $n + 8 < -7$ $n < -15$ **59.** $-3r \leq 21$ $r \geq -7$

**60.** *Data Analysis* Clinton Bailey, Sr., holds the record for knot tying. He tied six different rope knots in 8.1 s. Write and solve an equation to find his average time per knot. *(Lesson 3-6)* $6t = 8.1$ or $t = \frac{8.1}{6}$; 1.35 s/knot

## CHECKPOINT 2 Lessons 3-5 through 3-7

**Solve each equation.**

**1.** $0.5m = 0.125$ 0.25 **2.** $y - 135.43 = -5.43$ 130 **3.** $d \div 0.3 = 28.5$ 8.55

**4.** $12.2 = 4x$ 3.05 **5.** $29.25 = 4.5w$ 6.5 **6.** $k + 870.9 = 1{,}000.5$ 129.6

**Choose the most reasonable estimate. Explain your choice.**

**7.** height of a standard house window: 1.5 cm or 1.5 m 1.5 m; 1.5 cm is a little wider than the width of a thumbnail.

**8.** capacity of a shampoo bottle: 500 mL or 500 L 500 mL; 500 L would be about 500 qt.

**Complete each statement.**

**9.** 95 mL = ■ L 0.095 **10.** ■ cm = 76.5 km 7,650,000 **11.** ■ km = 675 m 0.675 **12.** 7.1 kg = ■ g 7,100

**13.** The world's smallest horse had a mass of only 9.1 kg. What was the mass of the horse in grams? 9,100 g

CHAPTER PROJECT 3

## ACTIVITY 3 CALCULATING

Use the foreign currency exchange rate chart and the advertisements you found for Activity 2. Find the cost of each item in the currencies of three countries other than the United States.

See also Extra Practice section.



## Project Activity 3

**Calculating** Suggest that students make a table to show the cost of each item in the three countries and the United States.

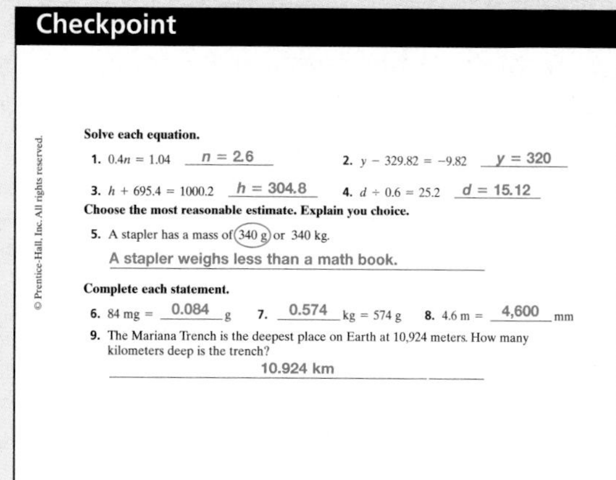

### Checkpoint

**Solve each equation.**

1. $0.4n = 1.04$ $n = 2.6$
2. $y - 329.82 = -9.82$ $y = 320$
3. $h + 695.4 = 1000.2$ $h = 304.8$
4. $d \div 0.6 = 25.2$ $d = 15.12$

**Choose the most reasonable estimate. Explain you choice.**

5. A stapler has a mass of (340 g) or 340 kg.
A stapler weighs less than a math book.

**Complete each statement.**

6. 84 mg = 0.084 g
7. 0.574 kg = 574 g
8. 4.6 m = 4,600 mm
9. The Mariana Trench is the deepest place on Earth at 10,924 meters. How many kilometers deep is the trench?
10.924 km



### Practice

**Write the metric unit that makes each statement true.**

1. 7.84 cm = 78.4 mm
2. 423 m = 0.423 km
3. 2.8 m = 280 cm
4. 6.5 km = 650,000 cm

**Complete each statement.**

5. 3.4 cm = 34 mm
6. 197.5 cm = 1.975 m
7. 7 L = 7,000 mL
8. 5,247 mg = 5.247 g
9. 87 g = 0.087 kg
10. 9,246 mL = 9.246 L

**Choose a reasonable estimate. Explain your choice.**

11. The amount of water a cup would hold: (250 mL) 250 L
A cup would hold less than a quart.
12. The mass of a bag of apples: 2 g (2 kg)
A bag of apples weighs more than this math book.
13. The height of your kitchen table: (68 cm) 68 m
The height is less than a yard.

**Choose an appropriate metric unit. Explain your choice.**

14. distance between two cities
kilometer; Cities are usually miles apart.
15. the mass of a pencil
gram; A pencil weighs a little more than a paper clip.
16. the capacity of an automobile's gas tank
liters; A tank usually holds between 10 and 20 gal.
17. One Olympic event is the 1,500-meter run. How many kilometers is this?
1.5
18. A fish pond holds 2,500 liters of water. How many kiloliters is this?
2.5



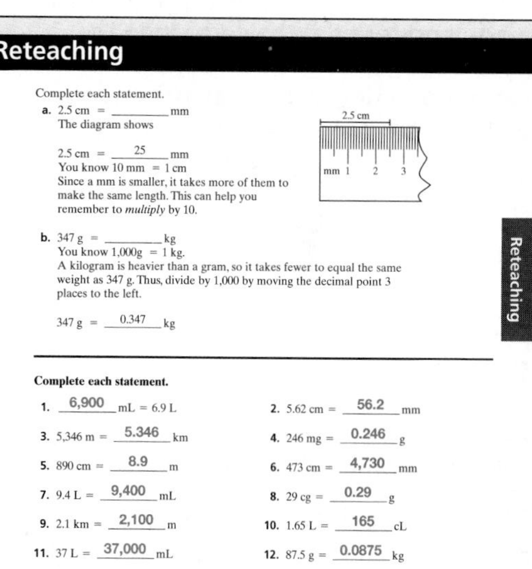

### Reteaching

Complete each statement.

a. 2.5 cm = ____ mm
The diagram shows

2.5 cm = 25 mm
You know 10 mm = 1 cm
Since a mm is smaller, it takes more of them to make the same length. This can help you remember to *multiply* by 10.



b. 347 g = ____ kg
You know 1,000g = 1 kg.
A kilogram is heavier than a gram, so it takes fewer to equal the same weight as 347 g. Thus, divide by 1,000 by moving the decimal point 3 places to the left.

347 g = 0.347 kg

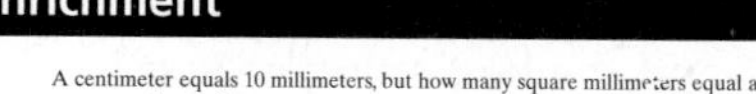

**Complete each statement.**

1. 6,900 mL = 6.9 L
2. 5.62 cm = 56.2 mm
3. 5,346 m = 5.346 km
4. 246 mg = 0.246 g
5. 890 cm = 8.9 m
6. 473 cm = 4,730 mm
7. 9.4 L = 9,400 mL
8. 29 cg = 0.29 g
9. 2.1 km = 2,100 m
10. 1.65 L = 165 cL
11. 37 L = 37,000 mL
12. 87.5 g = 0.0875 kg
13. 797 mm = 0.797 m
14. 1.75 km = 175,000 cm
15. 3,926 mg = 3.926 g
16. 0.71 kL = 710 L
17. 9,836 cm = 0.09836 km
18. 17.9 g = 17,900 mg



### Enrichment

A centimeter equals 10 millimeters, but how many square millimeters equal a square centimeter?

1. A square centimeter is shown on the right. How many squares that are a millimeter on a side fit inside it?
1 square centimeter (sq cm) = 100 square millimeters (sq mm)

**Complete the table. You can draw diagrams to help. Look for a pattern.**

| | Unit | In | | |
|---|---|---|---|---|
| | | sq cm | sq m | sq km |
| 2. | sq mm | 100 | 1,000,000 | 1,000,000,000,000 |
| 3. | sq cm | 1 | 10,000 | 10,000,000,000 |
| 4. | sq m | 0.0001 | 1 | 1,000,000 |

**Complete.**

5. 2 sq cm = 200 sq mm
6. 3.4 sq cm = 340 sq mm
7. 5 sq km = 5,000,000 sq m
8. 7.45 sq km = 7,450,000 sq m
9. 68.4 sq m = 68,400,000 sq mm
10. 476.9 sq km = 476,900,000,000,000 sq mm
11. 8.4 sq m = 84,000 sq cm
12. 0.5 sq m = 500,000 sq mm
13. 9 sq cm = 0.0009 sq m
14. 6.1 sq km = 61,000,000,000 sq cm

## MATH TOOLBOX

### Precision and Significant Digits

This Math Toolbox shows how to indicate the precision of a measurement and use significant digits.

### Math Background

A significant digit is one that indicates the result of some measurement. Digits other than zero are always significant. If a zero indicates that a measurement was made and found to be zero, then the zero is significant. For example, if the weight of a dog is given as 102 pounds, all the digits are significant. However, if the weight of an elephant is given as 12,000 pounds, the last three digits may not be significant, depending on the accuracy of the measurement.

## Teaching Notes

**Error Prevention** **Exercise 5** Explain that it is not more accurate to use more decimal places in a calculation that results from measured quantities.

**Monitoring Progress** Have students name aloud the less precise measurement in Exercises 6–9 before they do the calculation.

**Block Scheduling** If you have block scheduling or extended periods, you may wish to insert this Math Toolbox lesson between the completion of Part 1 of Lesson 3-7 and the beginning of Part 2 of Lesson 3-7.

## MATH TOOLBOX

*Extension*
After Lesson 3-7

# *Precision and Significant Digits*

The pin at the right measures about 5 cm. A more precise measurement is 4.5 cm. An even more precise measurement is 46 mm. The smaller the units on the scale of a measuring instrument, the more precise the measurement is.

### EXAMPLE 1

**Choose the more precise measurement.**

**a. 5 g or 8 mg**
Since a milligram is a smaller unit of measure than a gram, 8 mg is more precise than 5 g.

**b. 2.72 m or 3.5 m**
A hundredth of a meter is a smaller unit of measure than a tenth of a meter. So 2.72 m is more precise than 3.5 m.

**Choose the more precise measurement.**

**1.** 3 m or 5.2 m 5.2 m
**2.** 8 mL or 9.5 L 8 mL
**3.** 1.89 km or 8.7 cm 8.7 cm
**4.** 1.9 kg or 1.87 kg 1.87 kg

**5.** *Error Analysis* Your friend says that 4.35 km is more precise than 5.2 cm because a hundredths unit is a smaller unit than a tenths unit. What mistake did your friend make? Answers may vary. Sample: My friend ignored the unit of measurement.

A calculation will be only as precise as the least precise measurement used in the calculation. So, round your results to match the precision of the least precise measurement.

### EXAMPLE 2

**Add the lengths 6.31 m, 5.447 m, and 2.8 m.**

$6.31 + 5.447 + 2.8 = 14.557$
Rounded to tenths $\approx 14.6$ m

The least precise measurement is 2.8 m. Round the sum to the nearest tenth of a meter.

**Find each sum or difference. Round to the place value of the less precise measurement.**

**6.** 5.6 g + 8 g 14 g
**7.** 8.35 kg + 6.2 kg 14.6 kg
**8.** 8.2 km − 1.75 km 6.5 km
**9.** 9 cm − 2.3 cm 7 cm



- **Additional Example**
A rectangular tile measures 6.3 cm by 14 cm. What is the area of the tile? Use significant digits. 88 cm²

Digits that represent an actual measurement are *significant digits*. Nonzero digits (1–9) are always significant. The rules below will help you decide whether a zero is a significant digit.

| Type of Number | Which Zeros Are Significant | Example |
|---|---|---|
| decimal numbers between 0 and 1 | Zeros to the left of *all* the nonzero digits are not significant. All other zeros are significant. | significant digits<br>0.006040<br>not significant digits |
| positive integers | Zeros to the right of *all* the nonzero digits are not significant. Zeros between nonzero digits are significant. | significant digits<br>203,400<br>not significant digits |
| noninteger decimal numbers greater than 1 | All zeros are significant. | significant digits<br>350.07050 |

## Example 3

**How many significant digits are in 0.0504 m?**

The 5 and the 4 are significant. The zero between them is significant. The other zeros are not significant. There are three significant digits.

**Determine the number of significant digits in each measurement.**

**10.** 0.069 m
2 significant digits

**11.** 100.5 L
4 significant digits

**12.** 3,400 kL
2 significant digits

**13.** 5.2100 km
5 significant digits

When you multiply or divide measurements, round your answer to match the least number of significant digits in the problem.

## Example 4

**A survey of a plot for a new house measures 152.6 m by 121 m. What is the area of the plot? Use significant digits.**

3 significant digits

$152.6 \cdot 121 = 18{,}464.6$ ← Multiply.

4 significant digits

The area is 18,500 $m^2$. ← Round the area to 3 significant digits.

**Find each product or quotient. Use significant digits.**

**14.** 1,234 in. · 31 in.
38,000 $in.^2$

**15.** 0.0702 ft · 227 ft
15.9 $ft^2$

**16.** 16,250 m ÷ 14.5 s
1,120 m/s

**17.** 132.5 cm · 43.2 cm
5,720 $cm^2$

# Standardized Test Prep

Standardized tests, such as those administered for state assessment, SAT9, TerraNova™, ITBS, MAT7, or CAT5, may include multiple choice questions, free-response questions, and open-ended questions.

**Multiple Choice Questions** are followed usually by four choices, one of which is correct.

**Exercises 1–8** are multiple choice questions.

**Free-Response Questions** do not give answer choices. Student must provide the one correct answer on their own.

**Exercises 9–10** are free-response questions.

**Open-Ended Questions** allow for more than one solution. Students must construct their own responses instead of choosing from possible answers.

**Exercise 11** is an open-ended question.

## Resources

See p. 119G for a list of assessment options.

## Test-Taking Tip

When a question involves more than one step, carefully do the calculations before you consider the answer choices.

### Test-Taking Tips on Transparency

Estimate 98.57 × 206. Write your estimate and explain in writing how you got it.

Scoring Guide

3 Explains method, with answer that matches method.

2 Rounds first, but answer does not match method, OR rounds first and adds.

1 Gives estimate with no explanation, OR gives explanation with no answer, OR shows computation, OR rounds first, but not enough to make computation easy.

0 Computes exact answer, then rounds, OR gives incorrect response.

**Answer earning 3 points**

Round: 98.57 → 100
206 → 200
Estimate = 20,000
First round, then multiply the

**Answer earning 2 points**

98.57 is about 100.
206 is about 200.
300
Estimate first, then multiply.

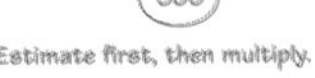

**Answer earning 1 point**

Estimate: 98.57 206
206 × 99 = 1854, 1854 → 20394

**Answer earning 0 points**

98.57 × 206 = 59142 + 19714 → 20305.42 → 20305

# Standardized Test Prep

## Multiple Choice

**Choose the best answer.**

1. Every year Tyrone gets a raise as shown in the table.

| Year | Hourly Wage |
|---|---|
| 1997 | \$10.15 |
| 1998 | \$10.75 |
| 1999 | \$11.35 |
| 2000 | \$11.95 |

The best prediction of Tyrone's hourly wage for the year 2001 is __?__. A
A. \$12.55 B. \$13.15
C. \$12.35 D. \$12.15

2. Five men on the same team ran the 100-m dash. Their times were 11.6 s, 10.2 s, 9.9 s, 10.6 s, and 11.9 s. What was the mean time for the team members? F
F. 10.84 s G. 10.5 s
H. 54.2 s J. 13.55 s

3. A number $t$ divided by $-2.35$ is equal to 400.9. Find $t$. B
A. 170.596 B. $-942.115$
C. $-170.596$ D. 942.115

4. Ms. Manfre's drive from Middletown took 4.5 hours. Her average speed was 60 mi/h and she used one of the roads shown. To which town did she drive? H

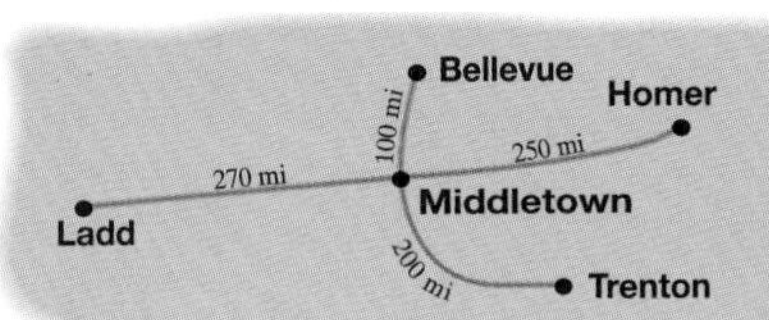


F. Bellevue G. Homer
H. Ladd J. Trenton

5. Solve $k - (-4.6) = 23.345$. B
A. $-18.745$ B. 18.745
C. $-27.945$ D. 27.945

6. With a \$20 bill, you buy 2 dozen bagels at \$5.49 per dozen and 3 containers of cream cheese for \$2.75 each. How much change should you receive? H
F. \$19.23 G. \$2.27
H. \$.77 J. \$1.26

7. In 1998, Mary Meagher set the women's world swimming record for the 100-m butterfly. She swam the distance in 57.93 s. On average, how long did she take to swim 10 m? B
A. between 4 s and 5 s
B. between 5 s and 6 s
C. between 6 s and 7 s
D. between 7 s and 8 s

8. What is the greatest precision that can be measured using this ruler? H

F. nearest meter
G. nearest centimeter
H. nearest millimeter
J. nearest tenth of a millimeter

## Free Response

**For Exercises 9–11, show your work.**

9. Mario had $d$ dollars in his bank account when he wrote a check for \$40.65. He now has \$182.33 in his account. Write and solve an equation to find how much money Mario originally had in his bank account. $d - 40.65 = 182.33$; \$222.98

10. The sum of two numbers is 14. The product of the numbers is 24. Find the two numbers. 2, 12

11. *Open-ended* Describe two situations in which an estimate would be preferred over an exact amount. Check students' work.

# Simplify a Problem

3-8

*Math Strategies in Action*

Scientists often encounter problems that are very complicated. When they work to develop a new vaccine or develop a new method to fight disease, they usually work on smaller or simpler pieces of the problem first. Sometimes when you solve a problem, it helps to solve other problems that have similar conditions. Here is a well-known problem that shows you how to use this strategy.

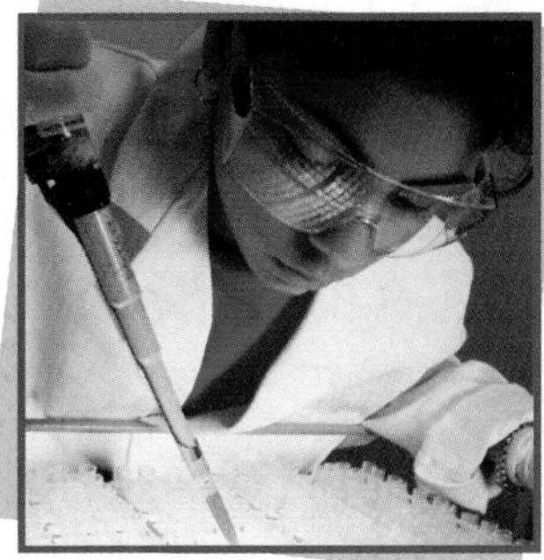

### Problem Solving Strategies

- Account for All Possibilities
- Draw a Diagram
- Look for a Pattern
- Make a Model
- Make a Table
- Simplify a Problem
- Simulate a Problem
- Solve by Graphing
- Try, Test, Revise
- Use Multiple Strategies
- Work Backward
- Write an Equation
- Write a Proportion

### Sample Problem

A snail is trying to escape from a well 10 ft deep. The snail can climb 2 ft each day, but each night it slides back 1 ft. How many days will the snail take to climb out of the well?

### Read

A snail needs to climb 10 ft to escape from a well. It can climb 2 ft per day. At night the snail slides back 1 ft.

1. How far up the well will the snail be after the first day and the first night? 1 ft
2. How far up the well will the snail be after the second day? 3 ft
3. How far up the well will the snail be after the second day and the second night? 2 ft

### Plan

At first you might think that the snail progresses 1 ft each day and will therefore take 10 days to escape. This answer is wrong, however, because it leaves out an important part of the problem.



# 3-8

## Getting Ready

**Resources** A complete list of resources for this lesson is on p. 119H.

### Daily Skills Warm-Up

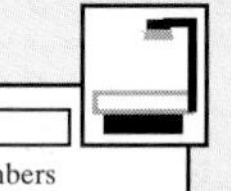

Lesson 3-8

Write a rule for each pattern. Find the next three numbers in the pattern.

1. 0, 2, 1, 3, 2, 4, 3 ... Add 2 then alternately subtract 1. 5, 4, 6
2. 2, 6, 4, 8, 6, 10, 8 ... Add 4 then alternately subtract 2. 12,10,14

How many cuts would it take to divide the pipe into each number of sections?

3. 3 sections 2 cuts
4. 6 sections 5 cuts

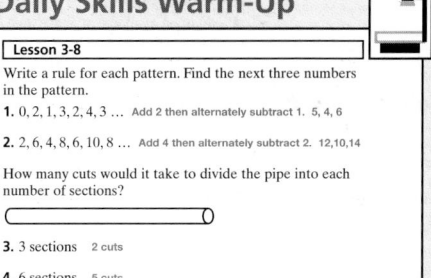

### Background for the Lesson

You can often solve a difficult math problem by breaking it into simpler pieces. For example, if a problem involves fractions, you can simplify it by substituting integers. Frequently you can grasp problems involving patterns if you draw a sketch or diagram to model the situation in the problem.

## 1 Focus

### Connecting to Students' Lives

Ask students if they have made a scrapbook or school report where they had to figure out problems involving the numbering of pages and placement of pictures.

### Connecting to Prior Knowledge

In Lessons 1-8 and 2-7, students practiced the problem solving strategies of Look for a Pattern and Try, Test, Revise. In this lesson, they learn to use the strategy of Simplify a Problem. In Lesson 4-1, they will learn the strategy Account for All Possibilities.

## Tools to Monitor Progress

### BEFORE THE LESSON

**To check prerequisite skills:**

- Working with integers

**Skills Handbook,** p. 741

**Skills Intervention Kit,** Measurement

### DURING THE LESSON

**To check understanding:**

- **Additional Sample Problem**
  Marta gives her sister one penny on the first day of September, two pennies on the second day, and four pennies on the third day. She continues to double the number of pennies each day. What is the date when Marta gives her sister $10.24 in pennies? September 11th

# 2 Teach

## Teaching Notes

Review the basic problem solving plan: Read, Plan, Solve, Look Back. Elicit the fact that more than one strategy might be used to solve a problem.

### Sample Problem

**Build understanding.** Ask: What progress is the snail making? **1 ft per day and night**

**Visual Learning** Suggest that students build a model of the problem.

**Extension** Challenge students to write a similar problem using events in their daily lives.

Try to solve a simpler problem. Change the problem to a simpler one based on a 3-ft well, and then try a 4-ft well to see if there is a pattern.

### Solve

| Time | 3-ft Well | 4-ft Well |
|---|---|---|
| Day 1 | Up 2 ft from bottom | Up 2 ft from bottom |
| Night 1 | Up 1 ft from bottom | Up 1 ft from bottom |
| Day 2 | Up 3 ft from bottom; OUT! | Up 3 ft from bottom |
| Night 2 | | Up 2 ft from bottom |
| Day 3 | | Up 4 ft from bottom; OUT! |

4. Using the information from the simpler 3-ft well and 4-ft well problems, describe the pattern. **The number of days it takes to get out is 1 less than the depth of the well in feet.**
5. How many days will the snail take to escape from the 10-ft well? **9 days**

### Look Back

You can check your answer by drawing a diagram.

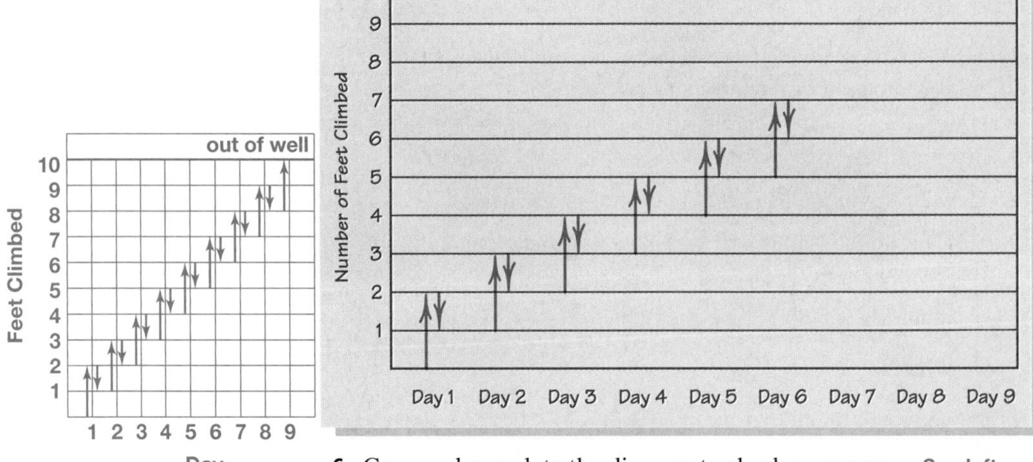


6. Copy and complete the diagram to check your answer. **See left.**



- **Additional Sample Problem**
  If a team loses a game in a soccer tournament, it is eliminated. There are 32 teams. How many games are scheduled to determine the league champion? **31 games**

## AFTER THE LESSON

**To assess knowledge:**
**Lesson Quiz**
Solve using any strategy.
On Monday, Jon reads p. 45 of his book and continues to read until he finishes p. 89. How many pages does he read on Monday?
**89 − 45 + 1, or 45 pages**

- For enrichment and reteaching options see Resources on p. 119H.

# Exercises

## CHECK UNDERSTANDING

**Solve by simplifying each problem.**

1. You decide to number the 58 pages in your journal from 1 to 58. How many digits do you have to write? 107 digits
2. *Sports* In a tennis tournament, each athlete plays one match against each of the other athletes. There are 12 athletes scheduled to play in the tournament. How many matches will be played? 66 matches
3. *Geometry* What is the total number of triangles in the figure at the right? 13 triangles

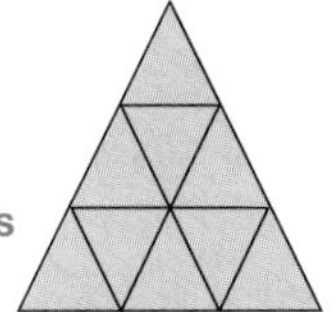

8. 21 house numbers; explanations may vary. Sample: There is 1 single-digit number that has a 5. The two-digit numbers have 9 numbers that end in 5, and there are 9 other numbers in the 50s. From 100 to 120, there are 2 numbers that have a 5. In all, there are 1 + 9 + 9 + 2 = 21 numbers that contain at least one digit 5.

## PRACTICE AND PROBLEM SOLVING

**Solve using any strategy.**

4. What is the total number of squares in the figure at the right? 55 squares

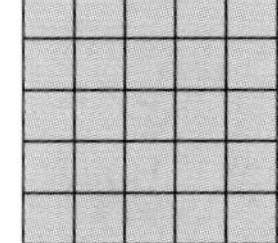

5. There are 10 girls and 8 boys at a party. A cartoonist wants to sketch a picture of each boy with each girl. How many cartoon sketches are required? 80 sketches
6. A rancher wants to build a fence for a square lot with dimensions of 50 yd by 50 yd. He wants to install a fence post every 5 yd. How many fence posts will he need? 40 fence posts
7. *Construction* To accommodate a wheelchair, a builder installed counter tops that are 0.75 ft lower than the original ones. The new counter tops are 2.5 ft high. How high were the original counter tops? 3.25 ft
8. *Writing* The houses on your street are numbered 1 to 120. No numbers are skipped. How many house numbers contain at least one digit 5? Explain your strategy. See above.
9. Before the use of computers, typesetters used metal pieces of type to print each letter in a word and each digit in a number. For example, three pieces of type—1, 4, and 8—were used to create the page number 148. How many pieces of type would be needed to set the page numbers 1 through 476? 1,320 pieces

Metal type is set upside down and from right to left in a composing stick. It would have taken a typesetter about 66 seconds to set the type for one line of this page.

# 3 Practice/Assess

## Assignment Guide

**Core** 1–7, 10–12
**Extension** 8, 9

Mixed Review can be assigned at any time for maintenance.

## Exercises

**Error Prevention** Students sometimes make errors because they do not carefully consider the situation at the beginning and the end of the problem. Remind them to pay special attention to the start and end of a pattern.

**Exercise 2** Students can model this problem by using string to join 12 people to each of the others.

**Tactile Learning** **Exercise 5** Students can model this with 18 index cards, each labeled with the name of a girl or a boy.

## Challenge

Solve using any strategy.
Han and Ping each have some horses. Han says, "If you give me one of yours, we will have the same number." Ping replies, "No, you give me one of yours and then I will have twice as many as you do." How many horses do they each have at the beginning? Han: 5, Ping: 7

## Closure

When a problem is complicated, you can solve related simpler problems to better understand the problem.

## Daily Cumulative Review

**Choose an appropriate metric unit of measure. Explain your answer.** *(Lesson 3-7)*

1. width of a dictionary
centimeters; answers may vary.
2. mass of an adult
kilograms; answers may vary.
3. length of a football field
meters; answers may vary.

**Write an equation for each sentence. Solve for the variable.** *(Lesson 3-6)*

4. The quotient of some number $h$ and −6.7 equals 36.18. Find the value of $h$.
$h \div -6.7 = 36.18; h = -242.406$
5. A number $w$ divided by −3.75 equals 124.5. Find the value of $w$.
$w \div -3.75 = 124.5; w = -466.875$
6. The product of some number $d$ and −2.4 is 45.36. Find the value of $d$.
$-2.4d = 45.36; d = -18.9$

**Mixed Review**

**Find each quotient.** *(From Last Year)*

7. 98 ÷ 2 49
8. 65 ÷ 5 13
9. 230 ÷ 10 23
10. 72 ÷ 3 24
11. 117 ÷ 9 13
12. 108 ÷ 3 36



## Alternative Assessment

Have students select which problem they liked best in this lesson and explain why it was their favorite. Ask them to describe their problem solving strategies as they worked that problem.

## Practice

**Solve using any strategy.**

1. A house-number manufacturer sold numbers to retail stores for $.09 per digit. A hardware store bought enough digits for two of every house number from 1 to 999. How many digits did the store purchase for house numbers:

 a. 1–9 18 b. 10–99 360 c. 100–999 5,400

 d. Find the total cost of the house numbers. $520.02

2. A tic-tac-toe diagram uses 2 vertical lines and 2 horizontal lines to create 9 spaces. How many spaces can you create using:

 a. 1 vertical line and 1 horizontal line 4

 b. 2 vertical lines and 1 horizontal line 6

 c. 3 vertical lines and 3 horizontal line 16

 d. 4 vertical lines and 5 horizontal lines 30

 e. 17 vertical lines and 29 horizontal lines 540

3. Each side of each triangle in the figure has length 1 cm. The perimeter (the distance around) the first triangle is 3 cm. Find the perimeter of the figure formed by connecting:

 a. 2 triangles 4 cm b. 3 triangles 5 cm

 c. 4 triangles 6 cm d. 50 triangles 52 cm

4. At the inauguration, the President was honored with a 21-gun salute. The report from each gunshot lasted 1 s. Four seconds elapsed between shots. How long did the salute last?

 101 s

5. Bernie began building a model airplane on day 7 of his summer vacation and finished building it on day 65. He worked on the plane each day. How many days did it take?

 59 days



## Reteaching

You have 12 meters of ribbon to cut into half-meter pieces. How many cuts do you need to make?

Simplify the problem. Suppose you only had 3 meters of ribbon. Use a diagram.

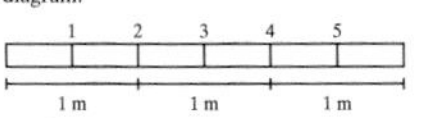


Although you will get 6 pieces of ribbon (2 · 3), you need to make only 5 cuts.

With 12 meters of ribbon, you would get 24 pieces with 23 cuts.

**Solve by simplifying the problem.**

1. A plumber charges $25 to weld two pipes together. Pipe comes in 4-foot pieces and you need one piece 60 feet long. How much will it cost to have enough 4-foot pieces welded together? Fill in the table first.

| Length of Pipe | Number of Welds |
|---|---|
| 8 | 1 |
| 12 | 2 |
| 16 | 3 |
| 20 | 4 |
| 60 | 14 |

 $350

2. How many digits are used to number the pages of a 425-page book? Fill in the table first.

| Page Number | Number of Pages | Digits |
|---|---|---|
| 1–9 | 9 | 9 |
| 10–99 | 90 | 180 |
| 100–425 | 326 | 978 |

 Total digits: 1,167

3. You are serving fruit in small bowls at a luncheon. You decide to place one slice of melon and a spoonful of one type of berry in each bowl. You have three types of melon and four types of berries available. How many different combinations of melon and berries can you make?

 12



## Enrichment

0.1 mi. 0.1 mi. 0.2 mi. 0.4 mi. 0.8 mi.

A party of explorers is stranded in the desert at ⊠. Water supplies, 10 in all, have previously been buried at increasingly greater distances from the party's camp, as shown on the map. In order to gauge how long the party can survive, the leader must calculate the difficulty of retrieving the water from the supplies.

1. Write a rule that the leader can use to calculate the distances between water supplies.

 Each distance is twice the previous distance.

2. Find the round-trip distances from camp to:

 supply 1 0.2 mi supply 2 0.4 mi supply 3 0.8 mi

 supply 4 1.6 mi supply 5 3.2 mi supply 6 6.4 mi

3. Because of their weakened condition, water-retrieval parties can travel at a rate of only 0.2 mi/h. Find the round-trip times from camp to:

 supply 1 1 h supply 2 2 h supply 3 4 h

 supply 4 8 h supply 5 16 h supply 6 32 h

4. The leader wished to calculate the total amount of time the party would spend retrieving water from all 10 supplies. Find the time needed to retrieve the indicated supplies.

 the first 1 1 h the first 2 3 h the first 3 7 h

 the first 4 15 h the first 5 31 h the first 6 63 h

5. The leader stumbled onto a simple method for calculating total water-retrieval times.

 Complete: (2) − 1 = 1

 (2 × 2) − 1 = 3

 (2 × 2 × 2) − 1 = 7

 (2 × 2 × 2 × 2) − 1 = 15

6. Use the leader's method to calculate the total amount of time the party will need to retrieve all 10 water supplies.

 1,023 h



10. The school store buys pencils for $.20 each. It sells the pencils for $.25 each. How much profit does the store make if it sells five dozen pencils? $3

11. *Population* The population of Rancho Cucamonga, California, is 117,000 people. The area of Rancho Cucamonga is 37.8 mi$^2$. Find the population density, the number of people per square mile. about 3,095 people/mi$^2$

12. You are hiking with three friends. You pass a group of six hikers going the other way. Each person in one group greets each person in the other group. How many greetings are there? 24 greetings

### MIXED REVIEW

*Measurement* **Complete each statement.** *(Lesson 3-7)*

13. 27 cm = ■ m 0.27
14. 5,200 km = ■ m 5,200,000
15. 2,000 mg = ■ g 2
16. 0.5 L = ■ mL 500
17. 3 m = ■ cm 300
18. 6 kg = ■ mg 6,000,000

**Estimate using front-end estimation.** *(Lesson 3-1)*

19. $3.75 + $25.50 + $17.23 about $46.50
20. $9.54 + $1.25 about $10.80

21. *Choose a Strategy* Your test scores so far this semester are 100, 90, 82, 96, and 78. You have one more test to take. After you complete the last test, what is your highest possible average? 91

### Math at Work

#### Woodworker

Woodworkers cut, shape, assemble, and finish wood to create tables, chairs, and other types of furniture. To create these items, woodworkers must plan and carry out many individual steps in sequence.

Machines used in professional woodworking shops cut and shape wood with great precision. The most sophisticated machines use computer-controlled programs. Woodworkers can enhance their skills by taking mathematics and computer courses that develop their ability to think three-dimensionally.

For more information about woodworking, visit the Prentice Hall Web site. www.phschool.com

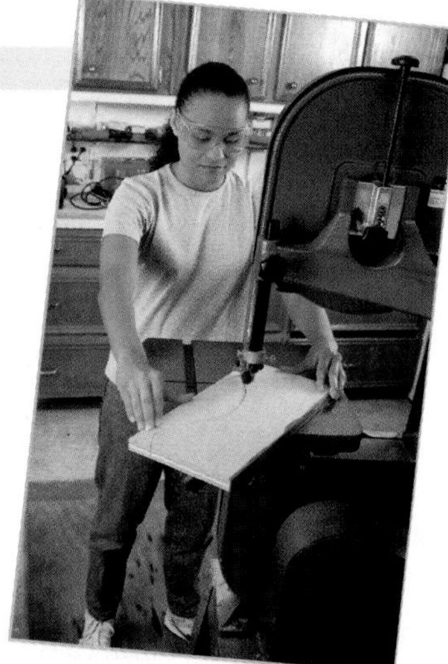



See also Extra Practice section.

### Math at Work

If you have block scheduling or extended class periods, have small groups of students research building furniture and the math that is involved. Suggest that students contact a community college to find out what kinds of math is involved in courses in woodworking. Students may also wish to interview furniture builders with questions about the math they use.

Students can find additional information on the Web site **www.phschool.com**.

# CURRENCY EVENTS

**Compare Currencies** The Project Activities on pages 135, 149, and 155 will help you complete your project. Here is a checklist to help you gather the different parts.

- ✔ the cost of a shirt and a souvenir, in U.S. dollars and Mexican pesos
- ✔ a currency exchange rate chart
- ✔ two advertisements that include prices in U.S. dollars
- ✔ your calculations of the costs of the advertised items in the currencies of other countries

Make a poster that displays your results. Include a title. Identify the name of each currency you used, its exchange rate, and the country in which the currency is used.

*Reflect and Revise*

Have a friend review your poster. Does it have all the information listed above? Is it organized and easy to interpret? Are your calculations accurate? If necessary, make changes to improve your work.

### *Web Extension*

**Visit Prentice Hall's Web site. You'll find some interesting links and ideas related to currency exchange rates. You'll also be able to share information about your project.**
**www.phschool.com**

## FINISHING THE PROJECT

**Project Day** You may wish to plan a project day on which students share their completed projects. Encourage students to explain their process as well as their product.

**Block Scheduling** If you have block scheduling or extended periods, you may wish to intersperse the sharing of projects over Days 3 and 4 between the completion of one lesson and the start of a new lesson.

### Project Notebook

Have students review their project work and bring their notebooks up to date. Call attention to the fact that they can share their projects with other students through the Web site **www.phschool.com**.

Be sure students include in their notebooks their completed Project Manager and Scoring Rubric forms.

**Portfolio** Students may wish to include their projects and/or their project notebooks in their portfolios.

### Web Extension

**Tell Us About Your Project**

Students may wish to share their projects with other students on the Web site: **www.phschool.com.**

### Scoring Rubric

3 You calculate all costs accurately. Your poster is complete, colorful, well-organized, and easy to read.
2 You make minor errors when calculating costs. Your poster is complete and colorful, but could be organized better or easier to read.
1 You find inaccurate costs. Your poster is incomplete and lacks organization.
0 Major elements of the project are incomplete or missing.

# Wrap Up

## Resources

Glossary, p. 748
Extra Practice, p. 712

For a complete list of resources for the chapter, see p. 119H.

## Quarterly Assessment Form A Page 1

**Circle the letter of the best answer.**

1. What is the opposite of $|-3|$?
   **(A.)** $-3$ B. 0
   C. 3 D. $\frac{1}{3}$
2. Evaluate $8y - 3$, for $y = -2$.
   F. 13 **(G.)** $-19$
   H. 3 J. $-13$
3. Which property does the equation $(6 - 4)3 = 6 \cdot 3 - 4 \cdot 3$ illustrate?
   A. cumulative
   B. associative property of multiplication
   **(C.)** distributive property
   D. associative property of addition
4. Simplify $4a + 5(2c - a)$.
   F. $3a + 10c$ **(G.)** $-a + 10c$
   H. $9a + 10c$ J. $-a + 5c$
5. Which equation has a solution of $-3$?
   A. $2b - 4 = 2$ **(B.)** $-b - 4 = -1$
   C. $4 + (-b) = 1$ D. $2b - 1 = 5$
6. Solve the equation $84 = -4t$.
   F. $t = -504$ G. $t = -12$
   H. $t = -14$ **(J.)** $t = -21$
7. Round 13.4256 to the nearest tenth.
   **(A.)** 13.4 B. 13.5
   C. 13.43 D. 10
8. Estimate $4.789 + 3.002 + 9.117$.
   **(F.)** 17 G. 21
   H. 37 J. 16
9. Estimate $73.41 \div 26.005$.
   A. 0.3 B. 30
   **(C.)** 3 D. 0.03
10. Where does the point $(-5, -8)$ lie?
    F. Quadrant I G. Quadrant II
    **(H.)** Quadrant III J. Quadrant IV
11. What is the variable expression for *two more than three times a number?*
    A. $2n + 3$ B. $(n + 3) + 2$
    C. $2(n + 3)$ **(D.)** $3n + 2$
12. The graph shows the solutions to which inequality?
    −10 −8 −6 −4 −2 0 2 4 6 8 10
    F. $x > 6$ G. $x \leq 6$
    **(H.)** $x < 6$ J. $x \geq 6$
13. How far can a plane fly in 3.5 h at a speed of 595 mi/h? Use $d = rt$.
    **(A.)** 2,082.5 mi B. 170 mi
    C. 4,165 mi D. 1,700 mi
14. A bottle holds 0.5 L of juice. How many milliliters is that?
    F. 0.0005 mL G. 50 mL
    H. 5,000 mL **(J.)** 500 mL
15. Which set has numbers in order from least to greatest?
    A. $|-10|, -7, 2, 6$
    B. $4, -|-3|, |-6|, -1$
    **(C.)** $-8, -|-4|, 0, |-9|$
    D. $-5, |-1|, -12, 3$
16. Simplify $\frac{5 + 2(9 - 4)}{3}$.
    5



## Quarterly Assessment Form A Page 2

**Solve each equation or inequality.**

17. $x - 9 \leq 6$ $x \leq 15$
18. $-3x \geq 33$ $x \leq -11$
19. $y + 7.4 = 3.4$ $y = -4$
20. $n \div -4.2 = -16.8$ $n = 70.56$

**Use the data in the table.**

21. Find the mean. 53.46
22. Find the median. 52.2
23. Find the mode. 52.2
24. Identify any outliers 58.4

| Maurice's Times in 100-meter Freestyle Swim | |
|---|---|
| Meet Number | Time (s) |
| 1 | 52.2 |
| 2 | 51.8 |
| 3 | 58.4 |
| 4 | 52.7 |
| 5 | 52.2 |

25. The temperature was 15° below zero when it rose 7 degrees. Use an integer to describe the new temperature. $-8°$
26. Write a rule for the pattern below. Find the next two numbers in the pattern.
    12, 9, 6, 3, 0, −3
    Start with 12 and subtract 3 repeatedly.
27. You want a two-dip ice cream cone with two different flavors of ice cream. How many different combinations can you choose if the ice cream store has:
    a. 4 flavors of ice cream? 6
    b. 12 flavors of ice cream? 66
    c. 20 flavors of ice cream? 190
28. Explain how to use the distributive property to find 64($1.02) mentally.
    $64(1.02) = 64(1) + 64(0.02) = 64 + 1.28 = \$65.28$
29. Write a word problem that could be solved with the equation $c + 1.02 = 13.48$.
    Sample answer is shown. Tricia spent $1.02 more than Carlos. If she spent $13.48, how much did Carlos spend?





# 3 Wrap Up

## Key Terms

compatible numbers (p. 128)
formula (p. 137)
mean (p. 131)
measures of central tendency (p. 131)
median (p. 131)
metric system (p. 150)
mode (p. 131)
perimeter (p. 138)
outlier (p. 132)

## Graphic Organizer

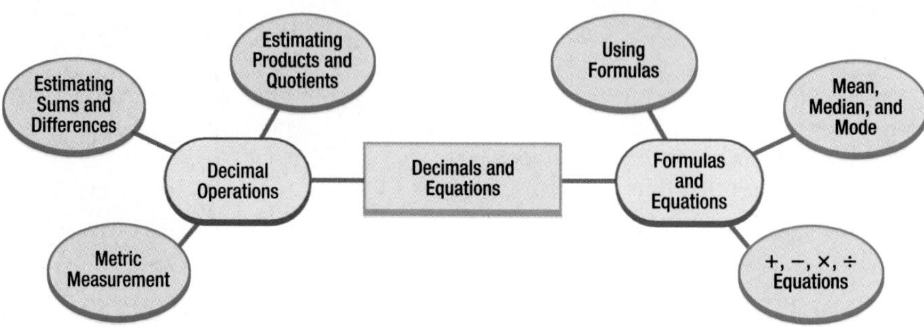


## Rounding and Estimating 3-1

**Summary** You can estimate the sum of decimals by rounding, front-end estimating, or clustering.

You can estimate the difference of decimals by rounding.

**Estimate each sum or difference. State which method you used.**
1–9. Answers may vary. Samples are given.

1. $3.14 + 6.952$ about 10; front-end
2. $10.2538 - 6.095$ about 4; rounding
3. $14.451 + 9.736$ about 24; rounding
4. $14.27 - 4.268$ about 10; rounding
5. $20.681 + 19.39 + 20.56$ about 60; clustering
6. $12.814 - 6.3791$ about 7; rounding
7. $9.0426 + 2.7182$ about 11.7; front-end
8. $21.9384 - 15.639$ about 6; rounding
9. $6.257 + 6.129 + 6.34$ about 18; clustering
10. ***Writing*** Explain when you would use each method to estimate a sum of decimals. Use examples. Answers may vary. Sample: I use rounding when only a rough answer is needed and the numbers are not clustered. I use front-end estimation when I need a more accurate estimate of a sum. I use clustering when there are 3 or more numbers and there is one number that they are all close to.
11. **TEST PREP** Which strategy is not appropriate to estimate $5.57 + 5.021 + 4.98$? C
    A. $5.57 + 5.021 + 4.98 \approx 5 \cdot 3 = 15$
    B. $5.57 + 5.021 + 4.98 \approx 6 + 5 + 5 = 16$
    C. $5.57 + 5.021 + 4.98 \approx 10.591 + 4 = 14.591$
    D. $5.57 + 5.021 + 4.98 \approx 14 + 0.6 + 0 + 1 = 15.6$

## Estimating Decimal Products and Quotients 3-2

*Summary* You can estimate a product by rounding. You can estimate a quotient of two decimals by using **compatible numbers.**

**Estimate each product or quotient.**

12. 8.15(6.04) about 48
13. 19.28 ÷ 5.439 about 4
14. 1.9 · 4.92 about 10
15. 25.1 ÷ 4.87 about 5
16. 12.497 · 0.894 about 12
17. 59.3581 ÷ 11.5304 about 6
18. 3.59(−2.3291) about −8
19. −17.45 ÷ 3.059 about −6
20. (−2.0936)(−5.6892) about 12

## Mean, Median, and Mode 3-3

*Summary* You can use a **measure of central tendency** to describe a collection of data. The **mean** is the sum of the data items divided by the number of data items. The **median** is the middle value or the mean of the two middle values when the data are written in order. The **mode** is the data item that occurs most often. An **outlier** is a data item that is much greater or much less than the rest of the data items.

**Find the mean, median, and mode. When an answer is not an integer, round to the nearest tenth. Identify any outliers.**

21. 2, 3, 6, 2, 8, 9, 5, 10, 4, 5
5.4, 5, 2 and 5; no outliers
22. 16.1, 16.3, 15.9, 16.2, 16.3, 16.3, 15.8
16.1, 16.2, 16.3; no outliers
23. 32, 35, 31, 57, 33, 30, 34
36, 33, none; outlier: 57
24. 0.1, 7.9, 0.2, 0.3, 0.1, 0.2, 0.1, 0.1, 0.3
1.0, 0.2, 0.1; outlier: 7.9

**Which measure of central tendency best describes each situation? Explain.** Answers may vary. Samples are given.

25. the favorite radio stations of teenagers in your neighborhood
Mode; the data are not numerical.
26. the numbers of videos owned by students in your class
Median; there could easily be outliers.
27. the prices of 8-oz containers of yogurt at six local grocery stores
Mean; there likely are no outliers.

## Using Formulas 3-4

*Summary* A **formula** is an equation that shows a relationship between quantities that are represented by variables. You can use formulas to find such things as **perimeter**, area, and distance.

**Evaluate each formula for the values given.**

28. distance: $d = rt$
when $r = 35$ mi/h and $t = 2$ h 70 mi
29. area of a rectangle: $A = \ell w$
when $\ell = 16$ mm and $w = 24$ mm 384 mm$^2$
30. Circumference: $C = 2\pi r$
when $r = 6$ in. Use 3.14 for $\pi$. 37.68 in.
31. perimeter of a square: $P = 4s$
when $s = 13$ cm 52 cm



**Portfolio** Students may wish to include their completed work for the Wrap Up in their portfolios.

**Web Site**

Students can find self-assessment materials on the Web site: **www.phschool.com.**

### Quarterly Assessment Form B Page 1

**Circle the letter of the best answer.**

1. What is the opposite of $-|-5|$?
A. −5 **(B.)** 5
C. 0 D. $\frac{1}{5}$
2. Evaluate $4z - 3$, for $z = -4$.
**(F.)** −19 G. 13
H. −13 J. 19
3. Which illustrates the commutative property of multiplication?
A. $2(3 + 4) = 2 \cdot 3 + 2 \cdot 4$
B. $2(3 \cdot 4) = (2 \cdot 3)4$
**(C.)** $2(3 \cdot 4) = (3 \cdot 4)2$
D. $2(3 + 4) = 2(4 + 3)$
4. Simplify $3(n - 5) + n - 5$.
F. $-2n - 7$ G. $4n - 10$
**(H.)** $4n - 20$ J. $-2n - 10$
5. Which equation has a solution of −5?
A. $3 - k = -2$ B. $-k + 1 = 4$
C. $k - 3 = 8$ **(D.)** $4k + 12 = -8$
6. Solve the equation $-24 = \frac{k}{-4}$.
F. $k = -12$ **(G.)** $k = 96$
H. $k = -8$ J. $k = 6$
7. Round 3.40563 to the nearest tenth.
**(A.)** 3.4 B. 3.4056
C. 3.41 D. 3.5
8. Estimate $5.6 \times 9.06$.
F. 90 **(G.)** 54
H. 10 J. 45
9. Estimate $7.231 + (-3.778)$.
**(A.)** 3 B. 11
C. 28 D. 5
10. Where does the point (9, −6) lie?
F. Quadrant I G. Quadrant II
H. Quadrant III **(J.)** Quadrant IV
11. Which word phrase describes the equation $4(x - 5) + 3 = 3$?
A. five less than some number times four is equal to three
**(B.)** three more than four times the quantity $x - 5$ equals three
C. three is equal to four times the quantity $x + 5$ less three
D. not given
12. The graph shows the solutions to which inequality?
−20 −15 −10 −5 0 5 10 15 20
F. $x < -10$ G. $x \leq -10$
**(H.)** $x > -10$ J. $x \geq -10$
13. Use the formula $C = \frac{F - 32}{1.8}$ to find the Celsius temperature equal to −13°F.
**(A.)** −25°C B. −10°C
C. −24.4°C D. 10°C
14. A bottle of juice has 250 mg of vitamin C. How many grams is that?
F. 250,000 g G. 25 g
H. 2.5 g **(J.)** 0.25 g
15. Which set has numbers in order from least to greatest?
A. $-3, |-5|, 0, 3$
**(B.)** $-12, -|-9|, |-1|, 4$
C. $-|-6|, -4, |-8|, 2$
D. $-5, -6, 0, 3$
16. Simplify $8 - 2(12 - 10)$.
4



### Quarterly Assessment Form B Page 2

**Solve each equation or inequality.**

17. $x + 3 > 15$ $x > 12$
18. $\frac{n}{-2} \leq 7$ $n \geq -14$
19. $y - 1.5 = -3.7$ $y = -2.2$
20. $-2.8k = 16.8$ $k = -6$

**Use the data in the table.**

21. Find the mean. 75.25
22. Find the median. 76.5
23. Find the mode. 76.5
24. Identify outliers. 70.25

| Keesha's High Jumps | |
|---|---|
| Track Meet | Height (in.) |
| 1 | 75.25 |
| 2 | 77.75 |
| 3 | 76.5 |
| 4 | 70.25 |
| 5 | 76.5 |

25. During one day, a company had $2,000 income and $3,500 debits. Use an integer to describe the company's balance for that day. −$1,500
26. Write a rule for the pattern below. Find the next two numbers in the pattern.
15, 10, 5, 0, −5, −10
Start with 15 and subtract 5 repeatedly.
27. What coins do you have if you have:
a. 4 coins and 25 cents? 1 dime and 3 nickels
b. 10 coins and 40 cents? 2 dimes, 3 nickels, and 5 pennies
c. 11 coins and 75 cents? 1 quarter, 4 dimes, 1 nickel, and 5 pennies
28. Explain how to use the distributive property to find 26($.98).
26(0.98) = 26(1 − 0.02) = 26 − 0.52 = $25.48
29. Write a word problem that could be solved with the equation $4.8c = 33.60$.
Sample answer is shown. Manuel bought some notebooks that cost $4.80 each. He spent $33.60 before tax. How many notebooks did he buy?

## Solving One-Step Equations with Decimals — 3-5 and 3-6

*Summary* To solve a one-step equation, use an inverse operation and the properties of equality to get the variable alone on one side of the equation.

**Solve each equation.**

**32.** $n + 3.8 = 10.9$ 7.1
**33.** $y - 6.72 = 2.53$ 9.25
**34.** $h + 0.67 = -1.34$ −2.01
**35.** $t - 2.7 = -3.5$ −0.8
**36.** $12.9 + x = 3.8$ −9.1
**37.** $5.7 = b - 4.9$ 10.6
**38.** $6.3m = 15.75$ 2.5
**39.** $a \div 4.9 = 8.33$ 40.817
**40.** $v \cdot 7.1 = 80.23$ 11.3
**41.** $c \div 12.5 = 77.5$ 968.75
**42.** $-5.7z = 110.58$ −19.4
**43.** $d \div 4.75 = -38.95$ −185.0125

**44.** **TEST PREP** Which equation has the solution 3.2? C
**A.** $-2x = 6.4$
**B.** $5.1 + a = 1.9$
**C.** $t - 1.56 = 1.64$
**D.** $w \div 0.8 = 2.56$
**E.** Not here

## Using the Metric System — 3-7

*Summary* The **metric system** of measurement uses a decimal system to relate units to one another. To measure, you must choose an appropriate unit of measure. 45. Meter; a kilometer is too large unless you use fractional parts of a kilometer; centimeters are too small.

**Choose an appropriate metric unit of measure. Explain each choice.**

**45.** height of a building See above.
**46.** mass of a bicycle Kilogram; a bicycle is heavy, so grams are too small.
**47.** amount of milk in a glass Milliliter; a liter is about the same as a quart, so liters are too large.

*Mental Math* **Complete each statement.**

**48.** 0.85 m = ■ cm 85
**49.** 160 mL = ■ L 0.160
**50.** 2.3 m = ■ cm 230
**51.** 1.6 kg = ■ g 1,600
**52.** 0.62 L = ■ mL 620
**53.** 80 g = ■ kg 0.080

**54.** **TEST PREP** Which unit is appropriate to measure the height of a mature oak tree? D
**A.** centimeter **B.** kilogram **C.** liter **D.** meter

## Simplify a Problem — 3-8

*Summary* When a problem is complicated, you can solve related simpler problems to better understand the problem.

**55.** A school's lockers are numbered 1 to 100. One hundred students enter the school one at a time. The first student opens the lockers. The second student closes the even-numbered lockers. The third student either closes or opens every third locker, and so on. After all the students have passed the lockers, which lockers are open? 1, 4, 9, 16, 25, 36, 49, 64, 81, 100



### Chapter Assessment Form A Page 1

**Circle the letter of the best answer.**

1. Which of the following is the best estimate of $7.78 + 12.003$?
   A. 17 B. 18 C. 19 (D.) 20
2. Which of the following is the best estimate of $8.79 - 2.49$?
   F. 5 G. 6 (H.) 6.3 J. 7
3. Which of the following is the best estimate of $4.2 \cdot 10.85$?
   A. 40 (B.) 44 C. 50 D. 55
4. Which of the following is the best estimate of $31.8 \div 5.9$?
   (F.) 5 G. 6 H. 7 J. 8
5. Which of the following is the most appropriate metric unit to measure your mass?
   A. mg B. g (C.) kg D. L
6. Which of the following is the most appropriate metric unit to measure the length of you fingers?
   F. mm G. km H. m (J.) cm
7. A set of data has a mean of 25 and an outlier of 4. You find the mean without the outlier. Which of the following best describes your new mean?
   A. The new mean is the same as the original mean.
   B. The new mean is the same as the median.
   (C.) The new mean is greater than the original mean.
   D. The new mean is less than the original mean.

**Solve each equation.**

8. $y - 4.7 = 12.52$ $y = 17.22$
9. $2.97 = x + 1.6$ $x = 1.37$
10. $\frac{n}{15} = 0.24$ $n = 3.6$
11. $-3.5z = 2.31$ $z = -0.66$



### Chapter Assessment Form A Page 2

**Use the rectangle for 12 and 13.**

2.5 m
8.6 m

12. Use the formula $P = 2l + 2w$ to find the perimeter of the rectangle. 22.2 m
13. Use the formula $A = lw$ to find the area of the rectangle. 21.5 sq m

**Complete.**

14. 9.6 L = 9,600 mL
15. 37.9 g = 0.0379 kg
16. The amount of rain we got last month was 2 inches more than what we got this month. We got 3.5 inches last month. Write an equation and solve to find how much rain we got this month. $3.5 = r + 2$; 1.5 in
17. There are 24 students in a class which has 2 representatives to Student Council. How many different sets of two representatives can the class have? 276

**Use the data in the table.**

18. Find the mean. 3.42
19. Find the median 3.6
20. Find the mode. 3.6
21. Identify any outliers. 1.4

| Normal April Precipitation | |
|---|---|
| City | Precipitation inches |
| Atlanta, GA | 4.3 |
| Boston, MA | 3.6 |
| Chicago, IL | 3.6 |
| New York, NY | 4.2 |
| San Francisco, CA | 1.4 |

22. Which is the best measure of central tendency? Explain. Answers may vary. The median and mode are both good. The mean is a little low because of the outlier.

Assessment

# Assessment

**Estimate.** 1–10. Answers may vary.

1. $6.43 - 4.079$ about 2.3
2. $2.06 + 3.91$ about 6
3. $5.97 - 1.674$ about 4.3
4. $6.025 + 0.35$ about 6.4
5. $8.54 + 2.3$ about 10.8
6. $6.25 \cdot 9.87$ about 60
7. $12.89 \div 3.04$ about 4
8. $1.76 \cdot 3.93$ about 8
9. $4.96 \div 2.49$ about 2
10. $3.2 \cdot 14.69$ about 45

**Find the mean, median, and mode. When an answer is not an integer, round to the nearest tenth. Identify any outliers.**

11. 11, 12, 9, 13, 10, 12, 11, 14, 12 — 11.6, 12, 12; no outliers
12. 5.3, 5.6, 5.2, 5.0, 5.4, 5.6, 5.1, 5.0 — 5.3, 5.3, 5.0 and 5.6; no outliers
13. 10.6, 9.8, 11.6, 29.1, 3.4, 11.4, 12.7 — 12.7, 11.4, no mode; outliers: 3.4 and 29.1
14. 8.7, 8.5, 8.7, 8.5, 8.6, 8.5, 8.7, 8.6 — 8.6, 8.6, 8.5 and 8.7; no outliers

**Evaluate each formula for the given values.**

15. area of a rectangle: $A = \ell w$ when $\ell = 3.8$ in. and $w = 1.5$ in. $5.7$ in.$^2$
16. perimeter of a square: $P = 4s$ when $s = 4.7$ cm 18.8 cm
17. perimeter of a rectangle: $P = 2\ell + 2w$ when $\ell = 2.9$ m and $w = 6.05$ m 17.9 m

**Solve each equation.**

18. $x + 7.8 = 12.5$ 4.7
19. $n - 5.9 = 0.5$ 6.4
20. $4.1 + c = -1.2$ −5.3
21. $d - 6.3 = 11$ 17.3
22. $-9.7 + h = 10.3$ 20
23. $m \div 2.7 = 14.58$ 39.366
24. $h \cdot 4.7 = 30.55$ 6.5
25. $b \div (-7.8) = -79.56$ 620.568
26. $-3.4t = 30.94$ −9.1

**Write an appropriate metric unit of measure for each quantity.**

27. the height of a truck meter
28. the capacity of a standard shampoo bottle milliliter
29. the mass of a pineapple kilogram
30. the width of a paperback book centimeter

**Complete.**

31. 4.5 m = ■ cm 450
32. 68 mL = ■ L 0.068
33. 90 kg = ■ g 90,000
34. 6,700 cm = ■ m 67
35. 4 L = ■ mL 4,000
36. 50.2 g = ■ kg 0.0502

**For exercises 37 and 38, write an equation, and then solve.**

37. You have a \$20 bill. You buy gloves for \$6.50. How much money do you now have? $6.50 + m = 20$; \$13.50
38. The fastest speed recorded for a reptile on land is 9.7 m/s for a spiny-tailed iguana. At this rate, how far could a spiny-tailed iguana travel in 12 s? $d = 9.7(12)$; 116.4 m
39. *Geography* Madrid and Barcelona are cities in Spain. The distance between them is 636,000 m. What is this in kilometers? 636 km
40. You have an 18-ft metal pipe. How many cuts must you make to cut the pipe into 2-ft-long pieces? 8 cuts
41. *Data Analysis* Which measure of central tendency best describes the weights of the dogs in one neighborhood? B
    15 lb, 20 lb, 18 lb, 27 lb, 15 lb, 70 lb
    A. mean B. median
    C. mode D. all of the above
42. *Writing* Explain how the outlier in the data set affects the mean.
    3, 2, 6, 3, 5, 4, 15, 4, 3
    The outlier 15 raises the mean by 1.2.



## Chapter Assessment

**Resources** For a complete list of resources for this chapter, see p. 119H.

### Chapter Assessment Form B Page 1

**Circle the letter of the best answer.**

1. Which of the following is the best estimate of $5.36 + 2.71$?
   A. 7 B. 8 (C.) 8.1 D. 8.2
2. Which of the following is the best estimate of $16.82 - 4.39$?
   F. 12 (G.) 13 H. 14 J. 11
3. Which of the following is the best estimate of $10.3 \cdot 7.8$?
   A. 77 B. 88 C. 70 (D.) 80
4. Which of the following is the best estimate of $34.2 \div 4.6$?
   (F.) 7 G. 8 H. 6 J. 9
5. Which of the following is the most appropriate metric unit to measure the amount of water in your body?
   A. mm B. m C. ml (D.) L
6. Which of the following is the most appropriate metric unit to measure the length of your eyelashes?
   F. m (G.) mm H. km J. cm
7. A set of data has a mean of 35 and an outlier of 100. You find the mean without the outlier. Which of the following best describes your new mean?
   A. The new mean is the same as the original mean.
   B. The new mean is the same as the median.
   C. The new mean is greater than the original mean.
   (D.) The new mean is less than the original mean.

**Solve each equation.**

8. $t - (-3.04) = -4.23$ $t = -7.27$
9. $16.784 = y + 4.56$ $y = 12.224$
10. $-0.8 = \frac{x}{4.4}$ $x = -3.52$
11. $-0.9x = -1.44$ $x = 1.6$



### Chapter Assessment Form B Page 2

**Use the rectangle for 12 and 13.**



12. Use the formula $P = 2l + 2w$ to find the perimeter of the rectangle. 26.2 cm
13. Use the formula $A = lw$ to find the area of the rectangle. 34.2 sq cm

**Complete.**

14. 9.2 L = 9,200 mL
15. 42.8 m = 0.0428 km
16. Steven and Marisa drove 351 miles at an average rate of 54 miles per hour. Write an equation and solve to find how much time $t$ it took. $351 = 54t$; 6.5 h
17. A rectangular garden is 36 feet by 45 feet. A gardener needs to plant a shrub every 3 feet all the way around the garden. How many shrubs does the garden need? 54 shrubs

**Use the data in the table.**

18. Find the mean. 11.6
19. Find the median 11.5
20. Find the mode. 11.5 and 11.8
21. Identify any outliers. none

| 100-meter Race | |
|---|---|
| Name | Time (seconds) |
| Gail | 11.5 |
| Ayla | 11.4 |
| Olga | 11.8 |
| Marsha | 11.5 |
| Tina | 11.8 |

22. Which is the best measure of central tendency? Explain. Answers may vary. The mean and median are both good. The two modes include almost all of the data.



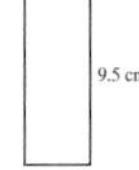

Assessment

## Cumulative Review Page 1

**Circle the letter of the best answer.**

1. Find the value of $36 \div (-2) + 4 \cdot 3$.
   A. $-42$ B. 42 (C.) $-6$ D. 6
2. Evaluate $3m + \frac{n}{5}$, for $m = 4$ and $n = 35$.
   F. 5 G. 7 H. 12 (J.) 19
3. Simplify $12 - (-3) + 4(3 - 1)$.
   (A.) 23 B. 38 C. 26 D. 17
4. Which equation does not have $-2$ for a solution?
   F. $16 = -8n$ G. $\frac{z}{2} = -1$ (H.) $y + 2 = -4$ J. $8 + x = 6$
5. What is the first step in solving $x - 8 = 4$?
   A. subtract 4 from each side B. add 4 to each side
   C. subtract 8 from each side (D.) add 8 to each side
6. Round 123.5673 to the nearest tenth.
   F. 120 (G.) 123.6 H. 123.57 J. 123.5
7. Find the number of hours it would take to drive 168 mi at an average rate of 48 mi/h. Use the formula $d = rt$.
   A. $-3.75$ h (B.) 3.5 h C. 3.25 h D. 3.75 h
8. Solve $m - 5.07 = 7.23$.
   F. $m = -2.16$ G. $m = 12.93$ (H.) $m = 12.3$ J. $m = -2.16$
9. Solve $-3t = 0.174$.
   A. $t = 0.058$ B. $t = 3.174$ C. $t = -0.522$ (D.) $-0.058$
10. Which is an expression for the total area of the figure?
    F. $7 + (x + 3)$ G. $x + 21$
    H. $7x + 3$ (J.) $7(x + 3)$

    x 3
    7
11. A medium size apple weighs about 225 grams. How many medium apples would it take to make 1.5 kilograms?
    (A.) 7 B. 6 C. 5 D. 2
12. Write an inequality for the sentence, "A number $n$ is greater than or equal to $-4$."
    $n \geq -4$



Assessment

## Cumulative Review Page 2

a. Find the mean. 88.6

b. Find the median. 86

c. Find the mode. 86

14. Karl is 124 centimeters tall. How many meters is that?
    1.24 m

**Solve each equation.**

15. Solve $x - 5.04 = -12.43$. $x = -7.39$
16. Solve $\frac{n}{-3.2} = 1.6$. $n = -5.12$
17. Write and solve an equation to find $x$. Seven times a number $x$ is equal to two hundred eighty.
    $7x = 280; x = 40$
18. A catalog company charges $.95 per pound to ship orders. Explain how you can estimate the shipping cost of the items listed in the table.

| Item | Weight |
|---|---|
| pants | 1.1 lb |
| shorts | 0.8 lb |
| sweatshirt | 1.4 lb |
| shirt | 0.93 lb |

All the weights cluster around one pound, so the total weight is about $4 \cdot 1 = 4$ lbs. The cost is approximately $1 per pound, so the cost of shipping is about $4.

# Cumulative Review

Preparing for Algebra

**Choose the best answer.**

1. Find the value of $4 \cdot 6 + 2 \div 2$. C
   A. 24 B. 13
   C. 25 D. 16
2. Evaluate $4a + \frac{c}{4}$ for $a = 5$ and $c = 20$. J
   F. 12 G. 84
   H. 36 J. 25
3. Simplify $-4(-15 + 5)$. C
   A. $-80$ B. $-40$
   C. 40 D. 80
4. What replacement for $a$ will make the equation $4a - 8 = 24$ true? J
   F. $-4$ G. 4
   H. $-8$ J. 8
5. Which is an expression for the total area of the figure? C

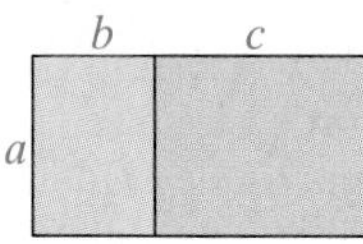


   A. $a \cdot (b \cdot c)$ B. $a + (b + c)$
   C. $a(b + c)$ D. $2a + 2c + 2c$
6. What is the first step in solving $\frac{x}{-9} = -3$? H
   F. Multiply each side by $-3$.
   G. Divide each side by $-3$.
   H. Multiply each side by $-9$.
   J. Divide each side by $-9$.
7. Which inequality matches the sentence *A number y is less than or equal to 6?* D
   A. $6 < y$ B. $6 \leq y$
   C. $y \geq 6$ D. $y \leq 6$
8. Find the mean. F
   250, 280, 240, 230, 270, 240, 270, 240, 230, 250
   F. 250 G. 245
   H. 240 J. 230
9. Round 6.55901 to the nearest tenth. B
   A. 6.5 B. 6.6
   C. 6.55 D. 6.56
10. Use the formula $d = rt$. Find $d$ when $r = 48$ mi/h and $t = 3.5$ h. F
    F. 168 mi G. 13.71 mi
    H. 0.073 mi J. 192 mi
11. Solve $x - 2.5 = -5$. A
    A. $-2.5$ B. 7.5
    C. $-7.5$ D. 12.5
12. Solve $2.8t = 56.98$. G
    F. 2.035 G. 20.35
    H. 159.544 J. 15.95
13. Solve $5.6 = x + 3.5$. B
    A. 9.1 B. 2.1
    C. 9.2 D. 8.5
14. Your car engine needs about 1.5 L of oil. A can of oil contains 946 mL. How many cans should you buy? G
    F. 1 can G. 2 cans
    H. 3 cans J. 4 cans
15. A Swedish coin minted in 1644 has a mass of 19,750 g. What is the coin's mass in kilograms? C
    A. 19,750,000 kg B. 197.5 kg
    C. 19.75 kg D. 1,975,000 kg

**For Exercises 16–18, show your work.**

16. A number $x$ divided by six is equal to three hundred. Write and solve an equation to find $x$. $x \div 6 = 300$; 1,800
17. Grapes cost $1.99/lb. Explain how you can estimate the total cost of three bunches of grapes that weigh 1.3 lb, 2.6 lb, and 1.9 lb. See above left.
18. *Writing* Are all formulas equations? Are all equations formulas? Explain.
    Answers may vary. Sample: A formula is a type of equation. All formulas are equations, but not all equations are formulas.

17. Answers may vary. Sample: Use rounding to estimate the total weight, and then multiply the result by the rounded price ($2).



| Item | Chapter/ Lesson | Review Topic |
|---|---|---|
| 1–3 | 1-2, 1-3, 1-5, 1-6, 1-9 | Algebraic Expressions and Integers |
| 4–7, 11–13, 16 | 2-2, 2-4, 2-6, 2-8 | Solving One-Step Equations and Inequalities |
| 8–10, 14–15, 17–18 | 3-1, 3-2, 3-3, 3-4, 3-5, 3-6, 3-7 | Rounding and Estimating |

CHAPTER 4

# Factors, Fractions, and Exponents

## Content Overview for Chapter 4

In the first lesson of Chapter 4, you use divisibility tests to find factors of whole numbers. One integer is a factor of a number if it divides that number with no remainder. One integer is divisible by another if the remainder is 0 when you divide.

An exponent is a number or symbol that you place to the upper right of the base. To simplify an expression that has an exponent, remember that the base is the number used as a factor and the exponent shows the number of times the base is used as a factor. To multiply numbers or variables with the same base, add the exponents. To raise a power to a power, multiply the exponents. To divide numbers or variables with the same nonzero base, subtract the exponents. Scientific notation is a way to write numbers as the product of two factors: a power of 10, and a decimal.

To multiply numbers in scientific notation, group the decimals, group the powers of ten, multiply, and then put the answer in scientific notation.

A prime number is a positive integer greater than 1 with only two factors, 1 and itself. A positive integer greater than 1 with more than two factors is a composite number. The prime factorization of a composite number is the product of its prime factors. The greatest common factor (GCF) of two or more expressions is the greatest factor the expressions have in common. You can use the GCF to write a fraction in simplest form. A fraction is in simplest form when the numerator and the denominator have no factors in common other than 1. A rational number is any number you can write as a quotient of two integers, $\frac{a}{b}$, where $b$ is not zero.

## Making Connections

| Lesson | Interdisciplinary and Real-World Connections | Math Integration |
|---|---|---|
| 4-1 | Music | Arithmetic |
| 4-2 | Language | Geometry |
| 4-3 | Photography | Algebra |
| 4-4 | Health | Data Analysis |
| 4-5 | Economics | Problem Solving, Geometry |
| 4-6 | Science | Algebra |
| 4-7 | Geophysics | Algebra, Arithmetic, Geometry |
| 4-8 | Seismology | Algebra, Arithmetic |
| 4-9 | Chemistry, Zoology | Measurement |

**SCHOOL/HOME CONNECTION**
English and Spanish versions are available in the *Help at Home* book of copy masters.

**Helper's Page** You will find detailed instruction, more examples, and

**Student Page** *Review Exercises for Lessons 4-1 to 4-4*

**List all the factors of each number.** *(Lesson 4-1)*

1. 30 ______ 2. 48 ______

3. 119 ______ 4. 19 ______

**Simplify each expression.** *(Lesson 4-2)*

5. $(-10)^3$ ______ 6. $-6^2 + 3 \cdot 2^3$ ______

7. $4(8 - 5)^2$ ______ 8. $18 + (4 + 2)^2 \div 3$ ______

**Find the GCF.** *(Lesson 4-3)*

9. 55, 95 ______ 10. 42, 70 ______

11. $18m^2n^2, 24m^2n$ ______ 12. $36a^2b^3, 35a^2b$ ______

**Write in simplest form.** *(Lesson 4-4)*

13. $\frac{30}{48}$ ______ 14. $\frac{9mn}{12m^2}$ ______

15. **Test Prep** Which number is divisible by both 3 and 5? *(Lesson 4-1)*
A. 7,218 B. 9,430 C. 8,310 D. 5,245 ______

Helper: ______ Comments: ______

**Helper's Page** You will find detailed instruction, more examples, and

**Student Page** *Review Exercises for Lessons 4-5 to 4-8*

**Solve the problem by accounting for all possibilities.** *(Lesson 4-5)*

1. A pizza shop has traditional, thin, and thick crusts. Their toppings are mushrooms, pepperoni, sausage, and green peppers. Suppose you eat there every day. For how many days could you order a different one-topping pizza? Complete the list below to solve the problem.

traditional: mushrooms, pepperoni, sausage, green peppers
thin
thick

**Evaluate. Write in simplest form.** *(Lesson 4-6)*

2. $\frac{a}{b}$ for $a = -5$ and $b = 35$ ______ 3. $\frac{x - y}{-3}$ for $x = 3$ and $y = 12$ ______

4. $\frac{4m - 9}{n}$ for $m = 11$ and $n = 7$ ______ 5. $\frac{-3a}{b^2}$ for $a = 16$ and $b = 4$ ______

**Simplify each expression.** *(Lessons 4-7 and 4-8)*

6. $3x^3 \cdot 5x^4$ ______ 7. $(m^7)^2$ ______

8. $8h^3 \cdot (-3h^2)$ ______ 9. $\frac{n^9}{n^4}$ ______

10. $x^{-4}y^3$ ______ 11. $(-8)^0$ ______

12. **Test Prep** What rational number corresponds to $A$ on the number line? *(Lesson 4-6)*

A; −1, 0, 1

A. $-\frac{5}{8}$ B. $-\frac{1}{2}$ C. $-\frac{3}{4}$ D. $\frac{3}{4}$ ______

Helper: ______ Comments: ______

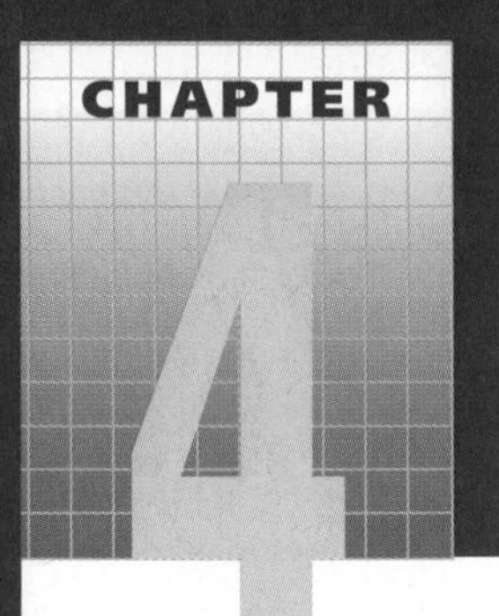

# Chapter 4 at a Glance

To accommodate flexible scheduling, most lessons are divided into parts. Assignment Options are given in the Teacher's Edition for each lesson.

| Pages 172–175 | Lesson 4-1 Divisibility and Factors |
|---|---|
| NCTM 1, 2, 6, 8, 9 | Part 1 Using Divisibility Tests<br>Part 2 Finding Factors<br>Project Activity 1 |

| Pages 176–179 | Lesson 4-2 Exponents |
|---|---|
| NCTM 1, 2, 6, 8, 10 | Part 1 Using Exponents<br>Part 2 Using the Order of Operations with Exponents |

| Pages 180–184 | Lesson 4-3 Prime Factorization and Greatest Common Factor |
|---|---|
| NCTM 1, 2, 6, 8, 9 | Part 1 Finding Prime Factorizations<br>Part 2 Finding the Greatest Common Factor |

| Pages 198–201 | Lesson 4-7 Exponents and Multiplication |
|---|---|
| NCTM 1, 2, 6, 8, 9, 10 | Part 1 Multiplying Powers with the Same Base<br>Part 2 Finding a Power of a Power<br>Math at Work |

| Pages 203–207 | Lesson 4-8 Exponents and Division |
|---|---|
| NCTM 1, 2, 6, 8, 9, 10 | Part 1 Dividing Expressions Containing Exponents<br>Part 2 Simplifying Expressions with Integer Exponents<br>Checkpoint 2 |

| Pages 208–213 | Lesson 4-9 Measurement: Scientific Notation |
|---|---|
| NCTM 1, 2, 4, 6, 8, 9, 10 | Part 1 Writing and Evaluating Scientific Notation<br>Part 2 Calculating with Scientific Notation |

## Pacing Options

This chart suggests pacing for only the core lessons and their parts, and it is provided merely as a possible guide. It will help you determine how much time you have in your schedule to cover other features, such as the Chapter Project, Math Toolboxes, Standardized Test Prep, Wrap Up, and Assessment.

| | Day 1 | Day 2 | Day 3 | Day 4 | Day 5 | Day 6 | Day 7 | Day 8 | Day 9 | Day 10 | Day 11 |
|---|---|---|---|---|---|---|---|---|---|---|---|
| **Traditional** (40–45 min. class periods) | 4-1 (1), 4-1 (2) | 4-2 (1), 4-2 (2) | 4-3 (1) | 4-3 (2) | 4-4 (1), 4-4 (2) | 4-5 | 4-6 (1), 4-6 (2) | 4-7 (1), 4-7 (2) | 4-8 (1), 4-8 (2) | 4-9 (1) | 4-9 (2) |
| **Pre-Algebra Over 2 Years** (40–45 min. class periods) | 4–1 (1) | 4–1 (2) | 4–2 (1) | 4–2 (2) | 4–3 (1) | 4–3 (1) | 4–3 (2) | 4–4 (1) | 4–4 (1) | 4–4 (2) | 4–5 |
| **Block Scheduling** (90 min. class periods) | 4–1 (1) (2), 4–2 (1) (2) | 4–3 (1) (2), 4–4 (1) (2) | 4–5, 4–6 (1), 4–6 (2) | 4–7 (1), 4–7 (2), 4–8 (2) | 4–8 (2), 4–9 (1), 4–9 (2) | | | | | | |

| Pages 186–189 | Lesson 4-4<br>Simplifying Fractions |
|---|---|
| NCTM<br>1, 2, 6, 8, 9, 10 | Part 1 Finding Equivalent Fractions<br>Part 2 Writing Fractions in Simplest Form<br>**Checkpoint 1** |

| Pages 190–193 | Lesson 4-5<br>Problem Solving Strategy |
|---|---|
| NCTM<br>1, 2, 5, 6, 7, 8, 9, 10 | Account for All Possibilities<br>**Project Activity 2** |

| Pages 194–197 | Lesson 4-6<br>Rational Numbers |
|---|---|
| NCTM<br>1, 2, 6, 8, 9, 10 | Part 1 Identifying and Graphing Rational Numbers<br>Part 2 Evaluating Fractions Containing Variables<br>**Project Activity 3** |

**NCTM STANDARDS 2000**

1 Number and Operations
2 Algebra
3 Geometry
4 Measurement
5 Data Analysis and Probability
6 Problem Solving
7 Reasoning and Proof
8 Communication
9 Connections
10 Representation

| Day 12 | Day 13 | Day 14 | Day 15 | Day 16 | Day 17 | Day 18 | Day 19 | Day 20 | Day 21 | Day 22 | Day 23 | Day 24 |
|---|---|---|---|---|---|---|---|---|---|---|---|---|
| 4–5 | 4–6 1 | 4-6 2 | 4–7 1 | 4–7 1 | 4-7 2 | 4-8 1 | 4-8 1 | 4-8 2 | 4–9 1 | 4-9 1 | 4-9 2 | |

**Block Scheduling Notes**

Consider these suggestions:

- **Day 2** Before starting Lesson 4-4, teach Math Toolbox 1, p. 185.
- **Day 3** After completing Lesson 4-6, begin presentations for Finish the Project.
- **Day 4** Before starting Lesson 4-8, teach the Standardized Test Prep, p. 202.
- **Day 5** After completing Lesson 4-9, teach Math Toolbox 2, p. 214.

# Math Background

## Lesson 4-1
### Divisibility and Factors

To say that 12 is divisible by 3 means that 12 counters can be divided into 3 piles, each of which has the same number (4) of counters in it. However, it is difficult to extend this concrete definition to the negative integers. Another way to think of the divisibility of integers is that the distance on a number line from 0 to 12 can be represented as three line segments of equal length, one after the other, and that the length of each of these segments is an integer. This definition extends naturally to include those integers to the left of 0. These concrete representations of divisibility can be expressed more abstractly by saying that one integer is divisible by another if the remainder when you divide is 0.

The integer divisors of an integer are called the *factors* of that integer. This idea is expanded further in Lesson 4-3, where students learn that a prime number is an integer other than 1 that has only two factors, itself and 1. The *prime factors* of an integer are its factors greater than 1 that can only be factored into themselves and 1. This means that the *prime* factors of 12 are 2, 2, and 3. *All* the factors of 12 are 1, 2, 3, 4, 6, and 12.

The *fundamental theorem of arithmetic* states that every integer greater than one can be expressed as a product of prime factors in one and only one way (except for the order in which the factors may be listed). This means that writing 12 as $2 \bullet 2 \bullet 3$ is a unique way of expressing 12.

## Lesson 4-2
### Exponents

You can recognize an exponent by how it is written in three ways: it is always written to the *right* of the number that is its **base;** the writing is *smaller* for the exponent; and the exponent is written so that it is *raised* above the base.

Students may find it useful to think of an exponent as saying "write the base as a factor to multiply as many times as the exponent indicates." You can interpret $3^4$ as saying "write the number 3 four times and multiply" so that $3^4 = 3 \bullet 3 \bullet 3 \bullet 3$, or 81.

An exponent applies only to the base to which it is attached, so
$-3^4 = -(3^4)$ or $-81$ while
$(-3)^4 = (-3) \bullet (-3) \bullet (-3) \bullet (-3)$ or 81.

## Lesson 4-3
### Prime Factorization and Greatest Common Factor

Integers that are not prime numbers, that is, integers that have a factor other than 1 and the number itself, are called *composite* numbers. The integer 1 is neither prime nor composite.

The *greatest common factor* is the largest factor common to a given set of integers. For example, the set of numbers 48, 60, and 96 has these factors 1, 2, 3, 4, 6, and 12 in common, but 12 is the greatest common factor of 48, 60, and 96.

## Lesson 4-4
### Simplifying Fractions

Equivalent fractions have the same value; they name the same number on a number line. Since 4 and 9 have no common factors, $\frac{4}{9}$ cannot be expressed in simpler form. A fraction is in simplest form when the numerator and denominator have no factors in common other than 1.

You can write a fraction such as $\frac{x}{y}$ in simplest form by finding the greatest common factor for *x* and *y*. For example, $\frac{6}{10} = \frac{2 \cdot 3}{2 \cdot 5}$, which can be written as $\frac{2}{2} \bullet \frac{3}{5}$ because $\frac{a}{b} \bullet \frac{c}{d} = \frac{ac}{bd}$ $(b, d \neq 0)$ or $1 \bullet \frac{3}{5}$ because $\frac{a}{a} = 1$ $(a \neq 0)$, and finally as $\frac{3}{5}$ because $1a = a$.

A shorter form of this same reasoning is expressed in the *cancellation law for fractions,* which simply says that $\frac{ac}{bc} = \frac{a}{b}$ ($b, c \neq 0$).

## LESSON 4-6
### Rational Numbers

A *rational number* is a number that can be written as the *ratio* of two integers. Notice that the word *rational* contains the word *ratio*.

Any decimal that ends, such as 3.567 or 0.00011, can be written as a ratio of integers: $\frac{3,567}{1,000}$ or $\frac{11}{100,000}$.

Any decimal that repeats a set of digits, such as $0.333\overline{3}$ (where the bar over the 3 indicates that it repeats without stopping) or $2.456456\overline{456}$, can be written as a ratio of integers.

For example, set $x = 2.456456\overline{456}$.

$$\begin{aligned} \text{Then } 1000x &= 2456.456\overline{456} \\ -\ (x &= 2.456\overline{456})\text{ gives} \\ \hline 999x &= 2454.000 \text{ so} \\ x &= \frac{2,454}{999}\text{, which is clearly a rational number.} \end{aligned}$$

You can use a similar procedure for any decimal that repeats a set of digits by choosing a multiple of 10 that has the same number of zeroes as there are digits in the repeating portion.

However, an unending decimal that has a pattern without a repeating set of digits, such as 1.020020002000020000002 . . . , is not rational, even though you can always predict the next digit. Similarly, a decimal that goes on forever, such as $\pi$ without repeating or forming a pattern, is also irrational. Some students may have been incorrectly taught that $\pi$ is equal to $\frac{22}{7}$, and so they may mistakenly think that $\pi$ is rational. The fraction $\frac{22}{7}$ is only an approximation to the value of $\pi$. The number $\pi$ is an irrational number.

## LESSONS 4-7 AND 4-8
### Exponents and Multiplication and Division

Students can easily remember when to add exponents and when to multiply them if they take a moment to write an example in expanded form.

$a^2 \bullet a^3$ means $(a \bullet a) \bullet (a \bullet a \bullet a)$, which is clearly $a^5$. However,

$(a^2)^3$ means $(a^2 \bullet a^2 \bullet a^2)$ or $(a \bullet a \bullet a \bullet a \bullet a \bullet a)$, which is $a^6$.

Students can also remember the rules for division with exponents if they write the problem in expanded form.

$\frac{a^3}{a^2} \bullet \frac{a \cdot a \cdot a}{a \cdot a} = a$

Therefore, $\frac{a^3}{a^2} = a^{3-2}$, or $a^1$.

## LESSON 4-9
### Scientific Notation

A number is written in scientific notation when it is written as the product of a number greater than or equal to 1 and less than 10 multiplied by a power of 10. When a number is written in scientific notation, a zero or positive exponent on 10 indicates that the number is greater than 1. A negative exponent on 10 indicates that the number is less than 1.

For example:
The weight of Earth in tons is $6.6 \times 10^{21}$, and the diameter of the hydrogen atom in cm is $1.016 \times 10^{-8}$. In standard notation, these numbers are 6,600,000,000,000,000,000,000 and 0.00000001016.

The exponent on 10 tells you to make the first part of the number larger or smaller by that many decimal places.

For professional development tips visit our Web site **www.phschool.com**.

# Monitoring Progress

## Universal Access

### ▶ Preventing a Student from Falling Behind

These resources are particularly helpful in preventing a student from falling behind his or her appropriate math level. For a complete list of resources for this chapter, see page 169H.

#### Skills You Need for Chapter 4

Student Edition, p. 169
Teacher's Edition, p. 169

- Dividing whole numbers
- Multiplying three or more factors
- Recalling multiplication facts
- Reading and writing fractions

#### Skills Handbook

Student Edition, pp. 723–741
Teacher's Edition, pp. 723–741

- Multiplying, Dividing Whole Numbers, pp. 725–726
- Powers of Ten, p. 734
- Writing Equivalent Fractions, p. 737
- Working with Integers, p. 741

#### Reteaching Worksheets

There is a Reteaching worksheet for every lesson in this chapter.

- Chapter 4 Support File, Teaching Resources box
- See TE p. 169H for a complete list of resources.

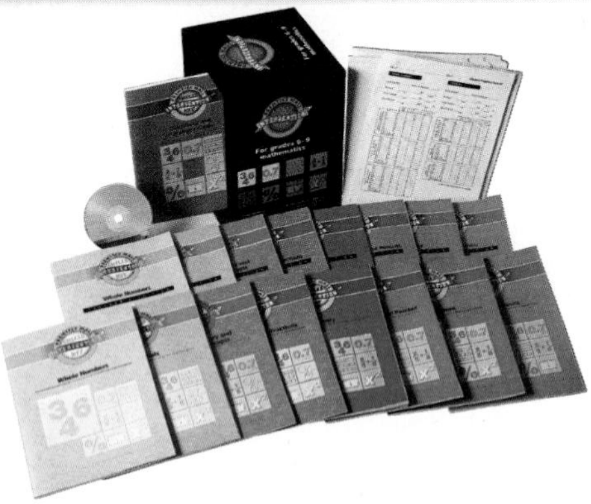

####  Skills Intervention Kit with CD-ROM

| For | Use |
|---|---|
| Lessons 4-1, 4-3 | Whole Numbers |
| Lesson 4-4 | Fractions |
| Lesson 4-5 | Pre-Algebra Basics |
| Lessons 4-6, 4-9 | Number Theory and Fraction Concepts |

#### Daily Cumulative Review Blackline Masters

There is a Daily Cumulative Review worksheet for every lesson in this chapter.

See TE p. 169H for a complete list of resources.

### ▶ Accommodating Diverse Learning Styles

#### Tactile Learning

Use paper plates to model slices of *pizza*, then label the slices with appropriate fractions and compare to find combinations of equivalent slices. (Lesson 4-4)

#### Advanced Learner

Every lesson has at least one challenge problem.

Write a formula to predict the number of pictures needed by a group of *n* friends with the pictures taken two people at a time. (Lesson 4-5)

#### ELL (English Language Learner)

Understand the meanings of each word in the phrase represented by GCF. (Lesson 4-3)

Remember that $\frac{1}{2}$ is not "one twoth" but "one half." (Lesson 4-4)

#### Auditory Learning

Say powers aloud before rewriting expressions using exponents. (Lesson 4-2)

Work with a partner with one reading the equation, including the blank and the other suggesting a response for the blank. (Lesson 4-7)

#### Visual Learning

Draw a sketch to model possible arrangements for 48 band members. (Lesson 4-3)

Compare the numerator and denominator carefully before simplifying an expression. (Lesson 4-8)

# Aligning Assessment with Instruction

## Assessment Options

| | Chapter Opener | 4-1 | 4-2 | 4-3 | 4-4 | 4-5 | 4-6 | 4-7 | 4-8 | 4-9 | End |
|---|---|---|---|---|---|---|---|---|---|---|---|
| Chapter Project | ■ | | | ■ | | | ■ | | | | ■ |
| Try This Exercises | | ■ | ■ | ■ | ■ | ■ | ■ | ■ | ■ | ■ | |
| Mixed Reviews | | ■ | ■ | ■ | ■ | ■ | ■ | ■ | ■ | ■ | |
| Checkpoints | | | | | ■ | | | | ■ | | |
| Writing | | ■ | ■ | ■ | ■ | ■ | ■ | ■ | | ■ | ■ |
| Chapter Assessment | | | | | | | | | | | ■ |
| Cumulative Review | | | | | | | | | | | ■ |
| Standardized Test Prep | | ■ | ■ | ■ | ■ | ■ | | ■ | ■ | | |
| | Standardized Test Prep, p. 202 | | | | | | | | | | |
| Computer Item Generator | Can be used to create custom-made practice pages or assessment pages at any time. | | | | | | | | | | |

### Test-Taking Tips on Transparencies

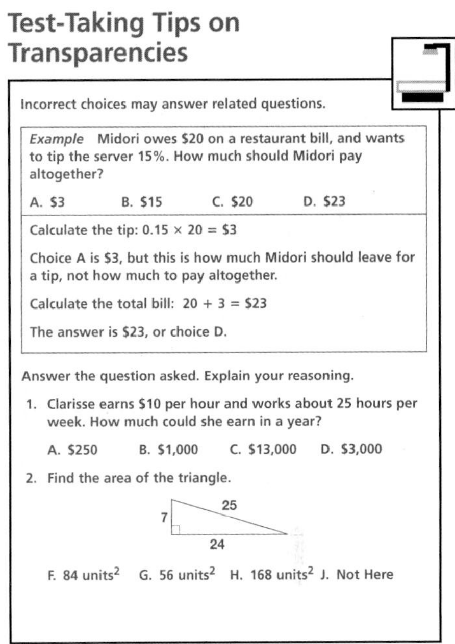
Incorrect choices may answer related questions.

*Example* Midori owes $20 on a restaurant bill, and wants to tip the server 15%. How much should Midori pay altogether?

A. $3 B. $15 C. $20 D. $23

Calculate the tip: $0.15 \times 20 = \$3$

Choice A is $3, but this is how much Midori should leave for a tip, not how much to pay altogether.

Calculate the total bill: $20 + 3 = \$23$

The answer is $23, or choice D.

Answer the question asked. Explain your reasoning.

1. Clarisse earns $10 per hour and works about 25 hours per week. How much could she earn in a year?

   A. $250 B. $1,000 C. $13,000 D. $3,000

2. Find the area of the triangle.



   F. 84 units$^2$ G. 56 units$^2$ H. 168 units$^2$ J. Not Here

*Use with Standardized Test Prep and Chapter Assessments.*

## Correlation to Standardized Tests

| Lesson | | CAT5 | CTBS/5 TerraNova™ | ITBS | MAT7 | SAT9 | LOCAL OBJECTIVES |
|---|---|---|---|---|---|---|---|
| 4-1 | Divisibility and Factors | ■ | ■ | ■ | ■ | ■ | |
| 4-2 | Exponents | ■ | ■ | | ■ | ■ | |
| 4-3 | Prime Factorization and Greatest Common Factor | ■ | ■ | ■ | ■ | ■ | |
| 4-4 | Simplifying Fractions | | | | | ■ | |
| 4-5 | Problem Solving Strategy: Account for All Possibilities | | | | | ■ | |
| 4-6 | Rational Numbers | | | | | ■ | |
| 4-7 | Exponents and Multiplication | ■ | ■ | | ■ | ■ | |
| 4-8 | Exponents and Division | | | | | ■ | |
| 4-9 | Scientific Notation | | | | | ■ | |

**CAT5** California Achievement Test, 5th edition
**CTBS TerraNova** Comprehensive Test of Basic Skills, 5th edition
**ITBS** Iowa Test of Basic Skills, Form M
**MAT7** Metropolitan Achievement Test, 7th edition
**SAT** Stanford Achievement Test, Advanced 1

For other standardized test correlations, follow the link to your state at **www.phschool.com**.

# Resources for Chapter 4

| | TEACHING RESOURCES BOX | | | | | | | | | | | | | | |
|---|---|---|---|---|---|---|---|---|---|---|---|---|---|---|---|
| | CHAPTER 4 SUPPORT FILE | | | | | | | | | | | | | | |
| | Practice | Reteach | Enrichment | Project Manager | Checkpoints | Cumulative Review | Chapter Assessment | Alternative Assessment | Cumulative Assessment | Lesson Planners Plus | Daily Cum Review | Teaching Transparencies | Warm-Up Transparencies | Help at Home | SE Answers Transparen |
| Begin Chapter | | | | ■ | | | | | | ■ | | | | | |
| 4-1 | ■ | ■ | ■ | | | | | | | ■ | ■ | | ■ | | ■ |
| 4-2 | ■ | ■ | ■ | | | | | | | ■ | ■ | 18, 22 | ■ | | ■ |
| 4-3 | ■ | ■ | ■ | | | | | | | ■ | ■ | 21, 48 | ■ | | ■ |
| 4-4 | ■ | ■ | ■ | | ■ | | | | | ■ | ■ | 30, 31 | ■ | ■ | ■ |
| 4-5 | ■ | ■ | ■ | | | | | | | ■ | ■ | 19 | ■ | | ■ |
| 4-6 | ■ | ■ | ■ | | | | | | | ■ | ■ | 21, 49 | ■ | | ■ |
| 4-7 | ■ | ■ | ■ | | | | | | | ■ | ■ | 50 | ■ | | ■ |
| 4-8 | ■ | ■ | ■ | | ■ | | | | | ■ | ■ | 50, 51 | ■ | ■ | ■ |
| 4-9 | ■ | ■ | ■ | | | | | | | ■ | ■ | 10, 52 | ■ | | ■ |
| End Chapter | | | | | | ■ | ■ (2 forms) | ■ | After Ch. 3, 6, 9, 13 | | | | | | |

Also available for use with the chapter:

Solution Key
Computational Practice Skills Booklet
Mathematics Standardized Test Prep, Student Edition and Teacher's Edition
Overhead Manipulatives Kit
Practice Workbook
Algebra Readiness Kit
Student Manipulatives Kit
Test-Taking Tips on Transparencies
Assessment Success Kit
Teaching Aids and Letters
Graphing Calculator Handbook
Spanish Resources
Success-Building Puzzle and Problem Masters

## TECHNOLOGY

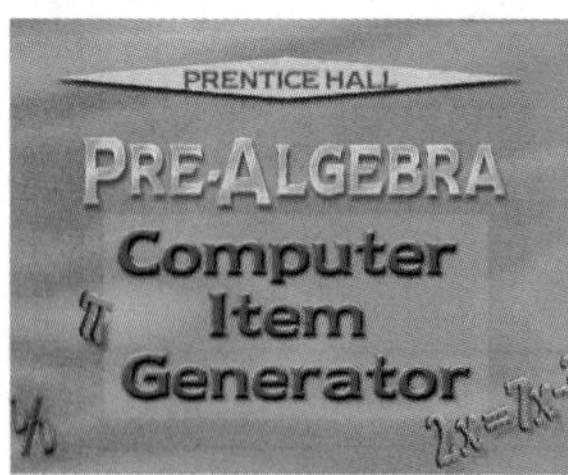


**Computer Item Generator with Standardized Test Prep**
CD-ROM with an unlimited supply of questions with varying degrees of difficulty for customized practice sheets, quizzes, and tests.

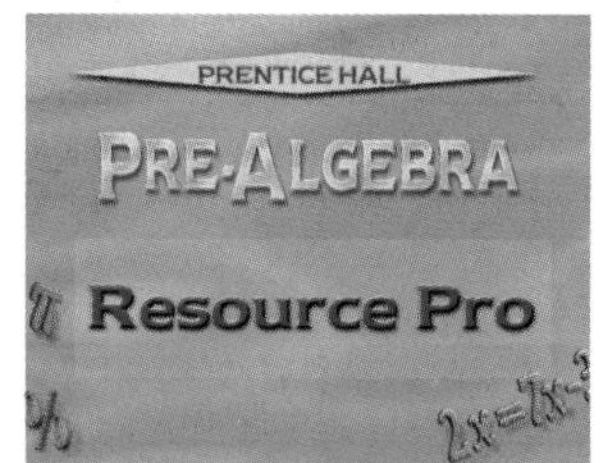


**Resource Pro® with Planning Express®**
CD-ROM with complete classroom planning tool and teaching resources for customizing and planning lessons.

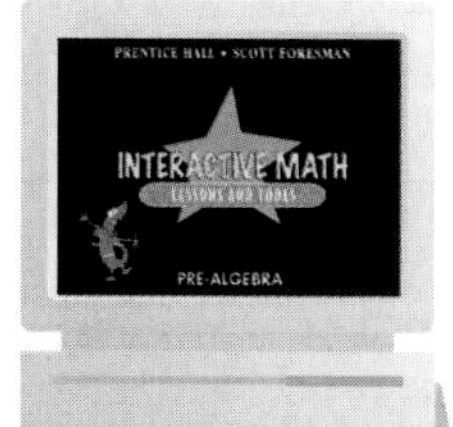


**Interactive Math Lessons and Tools**
CD-ROM with lessons and tools to make abstract concepts visual and accessible.

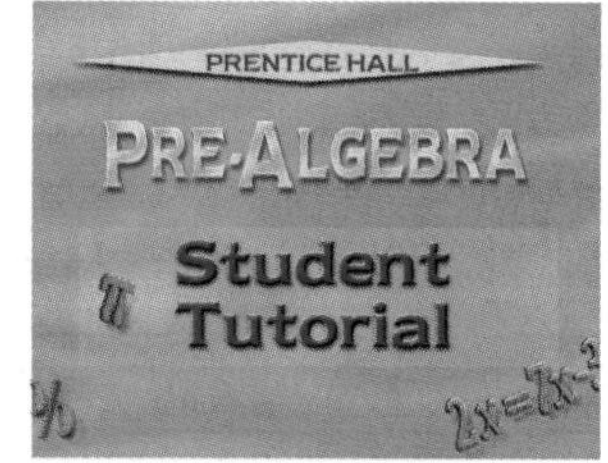


**Student Tutorial**
Test preparation software for students on CD-ROM with management system for teachers; includes Secondary Math Lab Toolkit™.

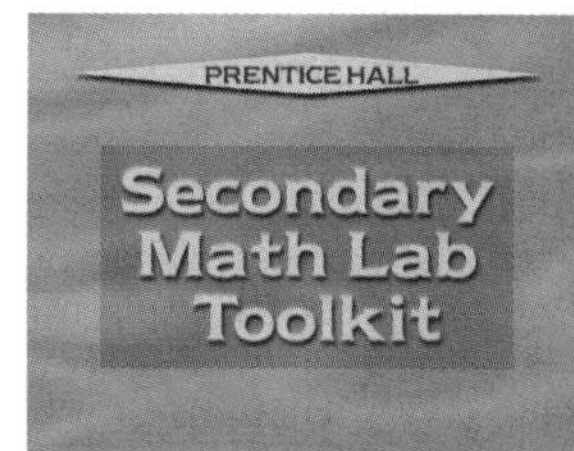


**Secondary Math Lab Toolkit™ with Integrated Math Labs**
Integrated software package with linkable math tools for exploring key concepts.

Also available for use with the chapter:

Math Blaster® Pre-Algebra CD-ROM
Video Fieldtrips, Vol. I: Algebra Applications
Video Fieldtrips, Vol. II: Geometry Applications
Wide World of Mathematics CD-ROM
Wide World of Mathematics Video

***Web Extension***
**www.phschool.com**

**For Students**
- Chapter Support with Internet Links
- Internet Activities

**For Teachers**
- Curriculum Support
- Professional Development
- Product Information
- Regional Support Information

# Skills You Need for Chapter 4

## ▶ Dividing whole numbers

Use before Lesson 4-1.

**Find each quotient.**

1. $720 \div 8$ 90
2. $7200 \div 8$ 900
3. $6\overline{)132}$ 22
4. $3\overline{)147}$ 49
5. $\frac{189}{9}$ 21
6. $\frac{450}{10}$ 45
7. $424 \div 2$ 212
8. $5\overline{)135}$ 27
9. $10\overline{)1300}$ 130
10. $700 \div 5$ 140
11. $\frac{273}{3}$ 91
12. $92 \div 4$ 23

## ▶ Multiplying three or more factors

Use before Lesson 4-2.

**Find each product.**

13. $12 \cdot 12 \cdot 12$ 1,728
14. $8 \cdot 8 \cdot 8$ 512
15. $9 \cdot 9 \cdot 9 \cdot 9$ 6,561
16. $5 \cdot 5 \cdot 5 \cdot 5 \cdot 5 \cdot 5$ 15,625
17. $(-4)(-4)(-4)$ −64
18. $(-2)(-2)(-2)(-2)(-2)(-2)$ 64

## ▶ Recalling multiplication facts

Use before Lesson 4-3.

**Write two numbers that, when multiplied, result in each product.**

19–33. Answers may vary. Samples are given.

19. 12 2, 6
20. 45 9, 5
21. 18 3, 6
22. 63 9, 7
23. 24 6, 4
24. 50 2, 25
25. 32 16, 2
26. 81 9, 9
27. 54 6, 9
28. 60 6, 10
29. 28 4, 7
30. 56 7, 8
31. 44 4, 11
32. 36 9, 4
33. 72 8, 9

## ▶ Reading and writing fractions

Use before Lesson 4-4.

**Write two fractions to describe each model.**

34. 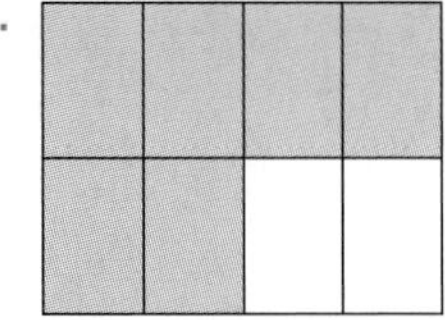 $\frac{6}{8}, \frac{3}{4}$

35. 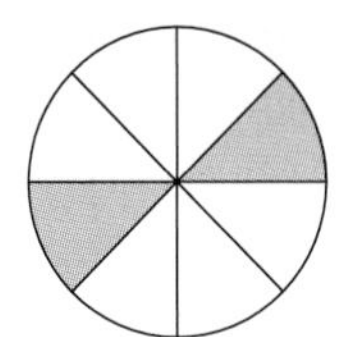 $\frac{2}{8}, \frac{1}{4}$

36. 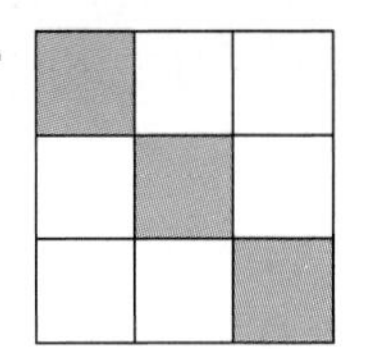 $\frac{3}{9}, \frac{1}{3}$



# Skills You Need

### Dividing whole numbers

**In Lesson 4-1** students will use divisibility tests and find factors by dividing whole numbers.

### Multiplying three or more factors

**In Lesson 4-2** students will use exponents to show repeated multiplication.

### Recalling multiplication facts

**In Lesson 4-3** students will find the prime factorization of a number by recalling multiplication facts.

### Reading and writing fractions

**In Lesson 4-4** students will find equivalent fractions and write them in simplest form.

# Skills Trace

| SKILL | INTRODUCED | DEVELOPED IN LESSON(S) | REVIEWED/REINFORCED |
|---|---|---|---|
| Finding factors and the GCF (greatest common factor) of two numbers | 4-1 | 4-3 | pp. 179, 189, 537, 563 |
| Combining numbers with exponents; finding a power of a power | 4-2 | 4-7, 4-8, 5-9 | pp. 184, 213, 217, 239, 263, 313 |
| Simplifying and evaluating fractions | 4-4 | 4-6 | pp. 193, 201, 239, 244, 326 |
| Using scientific notation | 4-9 | 4-9 | pp. 228, 309, 395, 569 |

CHAPTER 4

# Factors, Fractions and Exponents

### Connecting to Students' Lives

Ask students about their experiences with time and calendars. Ask if they have ever seen pictures of the Mayan calendar stones or any unusual types of calendars.

### Interdisciplinary Connections

The Chapter Project connects math and history. You may want to display historical pictures or other information about time and calendars.

### About the Project

The Chapter Project directs students to use their creativity and math skills to devise a calendar of their own.

CHAPTER 4

Factors, Fractions, and Exponents

**What you'll learn in this chapter:**

- How to simplify expressions with exponents
- How to simplify fractions
- How to write and calculate in scientific notation

***Web Extension***
**www.phschool.com**

**For Students**
Chapter Support with Internet links
Interactive Activities

**For Teachers**
Curriculum Support
Professional Development
Product Information
Regional Support Information

CHAPTER PROJECT 4

# TIME AFTER TIME

On the morning of the summer solstice, the sun rises directly over one of the stones at Stonehenge in southern England. Just as a sundial tells the time of day, Stonehenge tells the time of year.

A calendar may involve several astronomical events. For example, our day is based on Earth's rotation, while our year is based on Earth's movement around the sun. Over the centuries, people have come up with many different calendars.

***Design a Calendar*** For the chapter project, you will investigate calendars and adjustments to calendars. Then you will design your own calendar. Your final project will be a sample of your calendar and an explanation of your calendar.

### *Steps to help you complete the project*


p. 175 ACTIVITY: INVESTIGATING

p. 193 ACTIVITY: ANALYZING

p. 197 ACTIVITY: DESIGNING

p. 215 FINISHING THE CHAPTER PROJECT

***Web Extension***
**www.phschool.com**

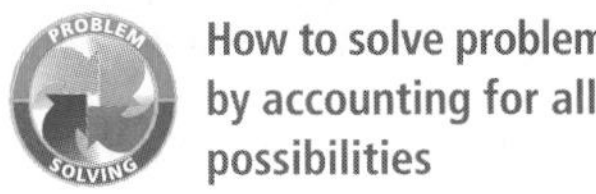


How to solve problems by accounting for all possibilities

## LAUNCHING THE PROJECT

*The Chapter Project is optional and may be assigned at your discretion.*

Ask students:

- Why do we have a 24-hour day?
- Does everyone work or go to school in the morning and sleep at night?
- How would your life be different if you or your parents worked at night?

Distribute a copy of the Project Manager and Scoring Rubric to help students get an overview of the project.

Review the scoring rubric with students.

### Project Notebook

Encourage students to keep all project-related materials in a separate folder or notebook. Call attention to the fact that they will find much useful information on the Web site **www.phschool.com**.

**Tracking the Project** Set benchmark deadlines for students to show you their work in progress.

*Available in the Chapter 4 Support File in the Teaching Resources box.*

**Project Manager and Scoring Rubric**

**Getting Started** You will be designing your own calendar and writing a description of your design to present to your class. Read about the project in your textbook. As you work on the project, you will need a calculator, materials to record your calculations, and materials to display your calendar.

**Checklist and Suggestions**

| | | |
|---|---|---|
| ❑ | Investigate the Egyptian calendar. | Find the factors of 360 and of 365. |
| ❑ | Analyze leap years. | Find the number of seconds in a solar year and in a non-leap year. |
| ❑ | Design your own calendar. | Think about factors. |
| ❑ | Justify your decisions in designing your calendar. | Explain your reasons thoroughly and clearly. |
| ❑ | Decide how to display your calendar and prepare a sample. | You can use a table, graph, number line, spreadsheet, or another format. |
| ❑ | Write the final description of your design. | Be clear, specific, and thorough. |

**Scoring Rubric**

3 You design your calendar using logical time periods. You make accurate calculations and explain them thoroughly. You present your calendar effectively.

2 You design your calendar using logical time periods. You make minor errors in accuracy of your calculations. You present clear explanations, but your presentation could be better organized or more thorough.

1 You do not consider the role of factors in designing your calendar. Your calculations are inaccurate. Your calendar sample could be neater and more accurate. Explanations lack detail.

0 Major elements of the project are incomplete or missing.

**Your Evaluation of the Project** Evaluate your work, based on the Scoring Rubric.

**Teacher's Evaluation of the Project**



## Scoring Rubric

**3** You design your calendar using logical time periods. You make accurate calculations and explain them thoroughly. You present your calendar effectively.

**2** You design your calendar using logical time periods. You make minor errors in accuracy of your calculations. You present clear explanations, but your presentation could be better organized or more thorough.

**1** You do not consider the role of factors in designing your calendar. Your calculations are inaccurate. Your calendar sample could be neater and more accurate. Explanations lack detail.

**0** Major elements of the project are incomplete or missing.

# 4-1

## Getting Ready

**Key Terms and Symbols** divisible; Divisibility Rules for 2, 5, and 10; Divisibility Rules for 3 and 9; factors

**Resources** A complete list of resources for this lesson is on p. 169H.

### Daily Skills Warm-Up

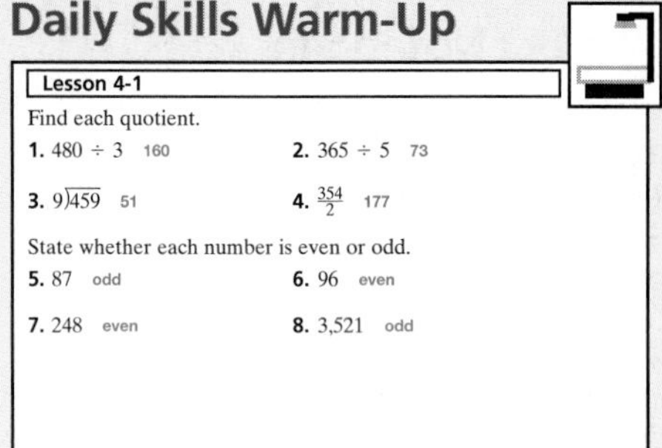
Lesson 4-1

Find each quotient.

1. 480 ÷ 3 160
2. 365 ÷ 5 73
3. $9\overline{)459}$ 51
4. $\frac{354}{2}$ 177

State whether each number is even or odd.

5. 87 odd
6. 96 even
7. 248 even
8. 3,521 odd

### Background for the Lesson

One integer is *divisible* by another integer if the quotient is an integer. So 6 is not divisible by 4 because the quotient, 1.5, is not an integer. If the quotient of two integers is an integer, then the quotient and the divisor are *factors* of the first integer: 6 ÷ 3 = 2 means that 3 and 2 are factors of 6. You can tell some factors by inspection: 2 is a factor of any integer ending in an even digit; 5 is a factor of any integer ending in 5 or 0; 10 is a factor of any integer ending in 0. Other tests for factors involve finding the sum of the digits.

## 1 Focus

### Connecting to Students' Lives

Ask if students have ever formed equal groups of four in class and discovered that there were one or more students not in a group.

### Connecting to Prior Knowledge

In a previous course, students learned to multiply and divide whole numbers. In this lesson, they use divisibility tests to find factors of whole numbers. In Lesson 4-3, students find prime factors and greatest common factors.

# 4-1 Divisibility and Factors

**What You'll Learn**

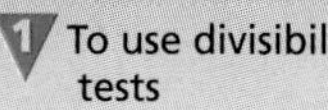

1. To use divisibility tests
2. To find factors

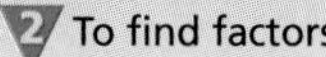

**. . . And Why**

To use divisibility tests to quickly find factors of numbers

## PART 1 Using Divisibility Tests

One integer is **divisible** by another if the remainder is 0 when you divide. Because 18 ÷ 3 = 6, 18 is divisible by 3. You can test for divisibility using mental math.

**Divisibility Rules for 2, 5, and 10**

An integer is divisible by

- 2 if it ends in 0, 2, 4, 6, or 8.
- 5 if it ends in 0 or 5.
- 10 if it ends in 0.

*Even* numbers end in 0, 2, 4, 6, or 8 and are divisible by 2.
*Odd* numbers end in 1, 3, 5, 7, or 9 and are not divisible by 2.

### EXAMPLE 1

**Is the first number divisible by the second?**

**a. 567 by 2** No, 567 doesn't end in 0, 2, 4, 6, or 8.
**b. 1,015 by 5** Yes, 1,015 ends in 5.
**c. 111,120 by 10** Yes, 111,120 ends in 0.

**TRY THIS** Is the first number divisible by the second? Explain.

**1.** 160 by 5 **2.** 56 by 10 **3.** 53 by 2 **4.** 1,118 by 2

1–4. See left.

1. Yes; 160 ends in 0.
2. No; 56 does not end in 0.
3. No; 53 does not end in 0, 2, 4, 6, or 8.
4. Yes; 1,118 ends in 8.

To see a pattern for divisibility by 3 and 9, look at the following table.

| Number | Sum of digits | Is the sum divisible by 3? | Is the sum divisible by 9? | Is the number divisible by 3? | Is the number divisible by 9? |
|---|---|---|---|---|---|
| 282 | 2 + 8 + 2 = 12 | Yes | No | Yes | No |
| 468 | 4 + 6 + 8 = 18 | Yes | Yes | Yes | Yes |
| 215 | 2 + 1 + 5 = 8 | No | No | No | No |
| 1,017 | 1 + 0 + 1 + 7 = 9 | Yes | Yes | Yes | Yes |

The pattern suggests the following rules for divisibility by 3 and 9.



## Tools to Monitor Progress

### BEFORE THE LESSON

**To check prerequisite skills:**

- Dividing whole numbers

**Skills You Need,** p. 169

**Skills Handbook,** p. 726

**Skills Intervention Kit,** Whole Numbers

### DURING THE LESSON

**To check understanding:**

**Try This** exercises on student page

- **Additional Example 1**

Is the first number divisible by the second?

**a.** 1,028 by 2 yes, even
**b.** 572 by 5 no, doesn't end in 0 or 5
**c.** 275 by 10 no, doesn't end in 0

### Divisibility Rules for 3 and 9

An integer is divisible by
- 3 if the sum of its digits is divisible by 3.
- 9 if the sum of its digits is divisible by 9.

### EXAMPLE 2

**Is the first number divisible by the second?**

**a. 567 by 3** Yes, 5 + 6 + 7 = 18; 18 is divisible by 3.
**b. 1,015 by 9** No, 1 + 0 + 1 + 5 = 7; 7 is not divisible by 9.

**TRY THIS** Is the first number divisible by the second? Explain.

**5.** 64 by 9 **6.** 472 by 3 **7.** 174 by 3 **8.** 43,542 by 9
5–8. See right.

5. No; the sum of the digits, 10, is not divisible by 9.
6. No; the sum of the digits, 13, is not divisible by 3.
7. Yes; the sum of the digits, 12, is divisible by 3.
8. Yes; the sum of the digits, 18, is divisible by 9.

## PART 2 Finding Factors

The photo at the right shows all the rectangles you can form with 12 squares. Each of the rectangles has an area of 12 square units. Their dimensions, 1, 2, 3, 4, 6, and 12, are the *factors* of 12. One integer is a **factor** of another integer if it divides that integer with remainder zero.

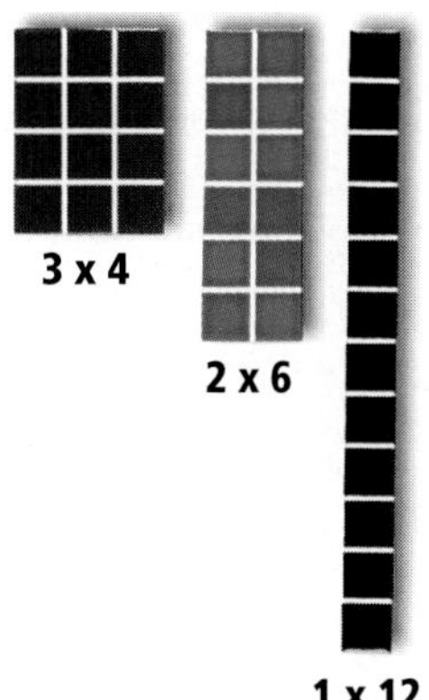

REAL-WORLD CONNECTION

### EXAMPLE 3

**There are 20 choral students singing at a school concert. Each row of singers must have the same number of students. If there are at least 5 students in each row, what are all the possible arrangements?**

1 · 20, 2 · 10, 4 · 5 Find the factors of 20.

There can be 1 row of 20 students, 2 rows of 10 students, or 4 rows of 5 students.

**TRY THIS** List the positive factors of each number.

**9.** 10 1, 2, 5, 10 **10.** 21 1, 3, 7, 21 **11.** 24 1, 2, 3, 4, 6, 8, 12, 24 **12.** 31 1, 31

**13.** What are the possible arrangements for Example 3 if there are 36 students singing at the concert? 1 row of 36 students, 2 rows of 18 students, 3 rows of 12 students, 4 rows of 9 students, or 6 rows of 6 students



# 2 Teach

## Part 1 Teaching Notes

Divisible means *divides evenly with no remainder.* Any integer can be divided by another. For example, 25 is not divisible by 2, but 25 can still be divided by 2. The quotient of 25 and 2 will have a remainder since 25 is not divisible by 2.

### Example 1

**Build understanding.** Ask: Can you tell just by looking at an integer whether it is divisible by 2 or 5 or 10? yes; by 2 if it is even; by 5 if it ends in 0 or 5; by 10 if it ends in 0

### Example 2

**Build understanding.** Ask: What do you have to do to test divisibility by 3 or 9? Find the sum of the digits.

**Advanced Learners** Challenge students to explain why any integer that is divisible by 9 is also divisible by 3. Any integer that can be written as 9*y* (where *y* is some integer) can also be written as 3(3*y*).

**Error Prevention** Students may mistakenly assume that the "sum of the digits" rule can be extended to test for divisibility by any integer. Suggest that they test 43 for divisibility by 7 to discover that the rule cannot be extended to divisibility by all integers.

## Part 2 Teaching Notes

Every integer has at least two factors, 1 and the number itself. The integer 1 is always a factor because any integer is divisible by 1. Any integer is also divisible by itself, with a quotient of 1.

### Example 3

**Build understanding.** Ask: Why did the final answer to the problem not include 20 rows of 1 student or 10 rows of 2 students? There must be at least 5 students in each row.

**Extension** Ask: Why can't 0 be a factor of any integer? Division by zero is undefined, and 0(*y*) can only be zero.

### • Additional Example 3

Ms. Washington's class is on the school's front steps for their class photo. Each row must have the same number of students. There are 35 students in the class. How can Ms. Washington arrange the students into rows if there must be at least 5 students, but no more than 10 students, in each row?
5 rows of 7 students or 7 rows of 5 students

### AFTER THE LESSON

**To assess knowledge: Lesson Quiz**

State whether each number is divisible by 2, 3, 5, 9, or 10.

1. 18 2, 3, 9
2. 90 2, 3, 5, 9, 10
3. 81 3, 9

List all the factors of the number.

4. 36 1, 2, 3, 4, 6, 9, 12, 18, 36

- For enrichment and reteaching options see Resources on p. 169H.

# 3 Practice/Assess

## Assignment Guide

To provide flexible scheduling, this lesson can be divided into parts.

**Part 1**

**Core** 1–7, 14–25, 50–51

✪ **Extension** 26–30, 49

**Part 2**

**Core** 8–13, 31–46, 52–53

✪ **Extension** 47–48

Mixed Review can be assigned at any time for maintenance.

### Exercises

**Exercises 31–48** Remind students that all integers have at least two factors, 1 and the number itself.

**Tactile Learning Exercises 52–53** Students can arrange counters or tiles into groups to model these problems.

### ✪ Challenge

State whether 6,854,567,940 is divisible by 2, 3, 5, 9, or 10. What single integer could you divide by (with a calculator) to test this? 2, 3, 5, 9, 10; 90

### Closure

One integer is divisible by another if the remainder is 0 when you divide. Divisibility tests can help you find factors. One integer is a factor of a number if it divides that number with no remainder.

### Daily Cumulative Review

**Solve using any strategy.** *(Lesson 3-8)*

1. Carson is planting petunias along the fence in her backyard. She wants them to be equally spaced. Carson plants the first petunia against the left end of the fence. She then plants a petunia every 1.5 ft. If the fence is 60.5 ft long , what is the greatest number of petunias she can plant?

   41 petunias

2. Mrs. Smith's class is working on a variety of science experiments. Each student must complete one experiment with each of the other students in the class. There are 12 students in the class. How many different groups will be made by the end of the experiments? Each pair of students can only be together once.

   66 groups

**Complete each statement.** *(Lesson 3-7)*

3. 3,785 mg = 3.785 g
4. 540 km = 540,000 m
5. 4,100 mL = 4.1 L
6. 4,800 g = 4.8 kg
7. 2.458 km = 245,800 cm
8. 56 mL = 0.056 L

**Mixed Review**

**Simplify each expression.**

9. (1-2) 8(5 + 6) 88
10. (1-2) $4 + 3 \cdot (12 \div 6)$ 10
11. (1-2) $(27 - 12) \div 5$ 3

**Evaluate.**

12. (1-3) $7(b + c)$, for $b = 5, c = 3$ 56
13. (1-3) $45 - (h - 32)$, for $h = 57$ 20

**Solve each inequality.**

14. (2-10) $4k \le 64$ $k \le 16$
15. (2-10) $-a > 31$ $a < -31$
16. (2-10) $\frac{m}{-5} \le 4$ $m \ge -20$



# Exercises

## Check Understanding

**Test whether each number is divisible by 2, 3, 5, 9, or 10.**

**1.** 20 2, 5, 10 **2.** 37 none **3.** 45 3, 5, 9 **4.** 99 3, 9 **5.** 240 2, 3, 5, 10 **6.** 333 3, 9

**7. a.** Which of the following numbers are divisible by both 2 and 3? 66 and 4,710

10 66 898 4,710 975

**b.** Which of the numbers above are divisible by 6? 66 and 4,710

**c.** Using your results, write a divisibility rule for 6. An integer is divisible by 6 if it is divisible by 2 and 3.

**List the positive factors of each number.**

**8.** 8 1, 2, 4, 8 **9.** 16 1, 2, 4, 8, 16 **10.** 23 1, 23 **11.** 54 1, 2, 3, 6, 9, 18, 27, 54 **12.** 75 1, 3, 5, 15, 25, 75 **13.** 68 1, 2, 4, 17, 34, 68

## Practice and Problem Solving

**Test whether each number is divisible by 2, 3, 5, 9, or 10.**

**14.** 10 2, 5, 10 **15.** 23 none **16.** 75 3, 5 **17.** 90 2, 3, 5, 9, 10 **18.** 111 3 **19.** 131 none

**20.** 288 2, 3, 9 **21.** 300 2, 3, 5, 10 **22.** 52 2 **23.** 891 3, 9 **24.** 4,805 5 **25.** 437,684 2

✪ **26. a.** Copy and complete the table.

| Number | Last two digits | Are the last two digits divisible by 4? | Is the number divisible by 4? |
|---|---|---|---|
| 136 | 36 | Yes | Yes |
| 1,268 | 68 | Yes | Yes |
| 314 | 14 | No | No |
| 1,078 | ■78 | ■no | ■no |
| 696 | ■96 | ■yes | ■yes |

**b.** *Critical Thinking* Write a divisibility rule for 4. An integer is divisible by 4 if its last 2 digits are divisible by 4.

**Write the missing digit to make each number divisible by 9.**

✪ **27.** 22■,034 7 ✪ **28.** 3■,817 8 ✪ **29.** 2,03■,371 2 ✪ **30.** 1■,111 5

**List the positive factors of each number.**

**31.** 4 1, 2, 4 **32.** 1 1 **33.** 6 1, 2, 3, 6 **34.** 14 1, 2, 7, 14 **35.** 15 1, 3, 5, 15 **36.** 17 1, 17

**37.** 22 1, 2, 11, 22 **38.** 25 1, 5, 25 **39.** 28 1, 2, 4, 7, 14, 28 **40.** 32 1, 2, 4, 8, 16, 32 **41.** 35 1, 5, 7, 35 **42.** 37 1, 37

**43.** 50 1, 2, 5, 10, 25, 50 **44.** 53 1, 53 **45.** 72 **46.** 108 ✪ **47.** 144 ✪ **48.** 157 1, 157

45. 1, 2, 3, 4, 6, 8, 9, 12, 18, 24, 36, 72
46. 1, 2, 3, 4, 6, 9, 12, 18, 27, 36, 54, 108
47. 1, 2, 3, 4, 6, 8, 9, 12, 16, 18, 24, 36, 48, 72, 144



### Alternative Assessment

Have students create a poem or rap that explains these divisibility rules. Ask volunteers to share their results with the class.

49. *Mathematical Reasoning* If $a$ is divisible by 2, what can you conclude about $a + 1$? Justify your answer. Answers may vary. Sample: $a + 1$ is not divisible by 2. Dividing by 2 will leave a remainder of 1.

50. *Writing* If a number is divisible by 9, is it also divisible by 3? Explain how you reached your conclusion. Explanations may vary. Sample: Yes; a number divisible by 9 has 3 as a factor.

51. *Open-ended* Deandrea has a trick for remembering her PIN (personal identification number), the secret number used with a bank card. The number formed by the first two digits is divisible by 3. The number formed by the last two digits is divisible by 5. Write two four-digit numbers that could be Deandrea's PIN. Answers may vary. Sample: 0345, 7890

52. There are 126 people in a workshop. The leader wants to put people into groups. Each group needs to have the same number of people. There must be at least 5 groups but not more than 20 groups. List the possible numbers of groups and the number of people in each group. 6, 7, 9, 14, 18; 21, 18, 14, 9, 7

53. John made oatmeal cookies for a class bake sale. The cookies need to be distributed evenly on 2 or more plates. If each plate gets at least 7 cookies, what are the possible combinations for the totals below? See right.
   a. 42 cookies  b. 56 cookies  c. 60 cookies

53a. 2 plates of 21 cookies, 3 plates of 14 cookies, 6 plates of 7 cookies

53b. 2 plates of 28 cookies, 4 plates of 14 cookies, 7 plates of 8 cookies, 8 plates of 7 cookies

53c. 2 plates of 30 cookies, 3 plates of 20 cookies, 4 plates of 15 cookies, 5 plates of 12 cookies, 6 plates of 10 cookies

## Mixed Review

**Complete each statement.** *(Lesson 3-7)*

54. 240 ■ = 24,000 mg g

55. 18.2 km = 1,820,000 ■ cm

56. 3.8 ■ = 0.0038 g mg

**Evaluate.** *(Lesson 1-3)*

57. $3y + 3$, for $y = 8$ 27

58. $4(2 + a)$, for $a = 10$ 48

59. $xyz$, for $x = 3, y = 7$, and $z = 2$ 42

60. You have \$5 to spend at the grocery store. You need \$2.89 for a gallon of milk. Write an inequality to show how much money $m$ you can spend on a box of cereal. *(Lesson 2-9)* $m \leq \$2.11$

## Activity 1 Investigating

The ancient Egyptian calendar divided a year into 12 months of 30 days each, with 5 extra days at the end. Why do you think the Egyptians based their calendar on 360, rather than 365? What are some other ways they could have organized a 360-day year into months? Why do you think the Egyptians chose 12 months of 30 days?

See also Extra Practice section.



## Project Activity 1

**Investigating** To help students answer these questions, you might pose this problem: If you knew that a group of students might have 2, 3, 5, or 6 people, and you wanted to have a number of cookies you could share equally with these people, how many cookies could you bring to the group to do this? 30 or a multiple of 30

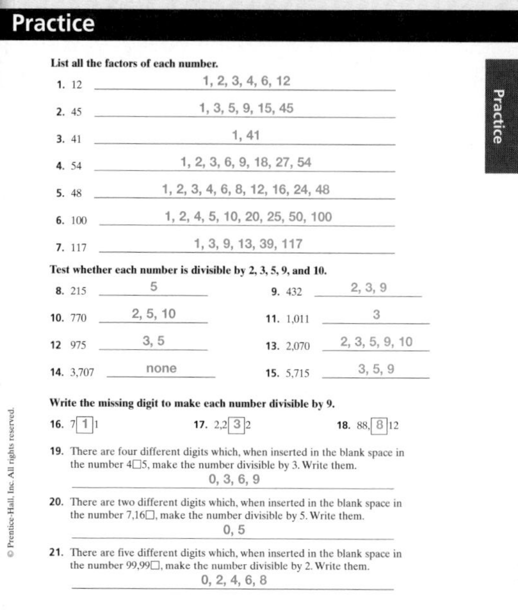

## Practice

**List all the factors of each number.**

1. 12 1, 2, 3, 4, 6, 12
2. 45 1, 3, 5, 9, 15, 45
3. 41 1, 41
4. 54 1, 2, 3, 6, 9, 18, 27, 54
5. 48 1, 2, 3, 4, 6, 8, 12, 16, 24, 48
6. 100 1, 2, 4, 5, 10, 20, 25, 50, 100
7. 117 1, 3, 9, 13, 39, 117

**Test whether each number is divisible by 2, 3, 5, 9, and 10.**

8. 215 5
9. 432 2, 3, 9
10. 770 2, 5, 10
11. 1,011 3
12. 975 3, 5
13. 2,070 2, 3, 5, 9, 10
14. 3,707 none
15. 5,715 3, 5, 9

**Write the missing digit to make each number divisible by 9.**

16. 7[1]1  17. 2,2[3]2  18. 88,[8]12

19. There are four different digits which, when inserted in the blank space in the number 4□5, make the number divisible by 3. Write them. 0, 3, 6, 9

20. There are two different digits which, when inserted in the blank space in the number 7,16□, make the number divisible by 5. Write them. 0, 5

21. There are five different digits which, when inserted in the blank space in the number 99,99□, make the number divisible by 2. Write them. 0, 2, 4, 6, 8



## Reteaching

Find all the factors of 30.

Start with 1 and 30.
Is 30 divisible by 2? Yes, it ends in 0.
List 2 and 15.
Is 30 divisible by 3? Yes, the sum of the digits, 3, is divisible by 3.
List 3 and 10.
Is 30 divisible by 4? No, $4 \cdot 7 = 28$ and $4 \cdot 8 = 32$.
Is 30 divisible by 5? Yes, it ends in 0.
List 5 and 6.
When you list all the factors in order, the pairs with products of 30 form a symmetric pattern.

**1, 2, 3, 5, 6, 10, 15, 30**

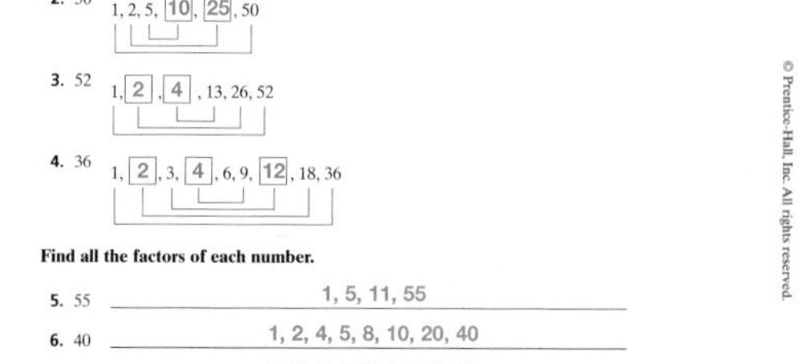

**Fill in the boxes to find all the factors for each number.**

1. 34 1, 2, [17], 34
2. 50 1, 2, 5, [10], [25], 50
3. 52 1, [2], [4], 13, 26, 52
4. 36 1, [2], 3, [4], 6, 9, [12], 18, 36

**Find all the factors of each number.**

5. 55 1, 5, 11, 55
6. 40 1, 2, 4, 5, 8, 10, 20, 40
7. 42 1, 2, 3, 6, 7, 14, 21, 42
8. 48 1, 2, 3, 4, 6, 8, 12, 16, 24, 48



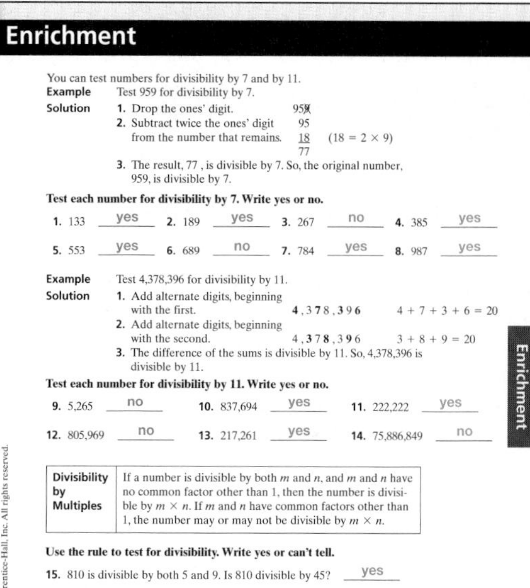

## Enrichment

You can test numbers for divisibility by 7 and by 11.

**Example** Test 959 for divisibility by 7.

**Solution**
1. Drop the ones' digit. 95~~9~~
2. Subtract twice the ones' digit from the number that remains. 95 − 18 = 77 $(18 = 2 \times 9)$
3. The result, 77, is divisible by 7. So, the original number, 959, is divisible by 7.

**Test each number for divisibility by 7. Write yes or no.**

1. 133 yes  2. 189 yes  3. 267 no  4. 385 yes
5. 553 yes  6. 689 no  7. 784 yes  8. 987 yes

**Example** Test 4,378,396 for divisibility by 11.

**Solution**
1. Add alternate digits, beginning with the first. **4**,3**7**8,**3**9**6** $4 + 7 + 3 + 6 = 20$
2. Add alternate digits, beginning with the second. 4,**3**7**8**,3**9**6 $3 + 8 + 9 = 20$
3. The difference of the sums is divisible by 11. So, 4,378,396 is divisible by 11.

**Test each number for divisibility by 11. Write yes or no.**

9. 5,265 no  10. 837,694 yes  11. 222,222 yes
12. 805,969 no  13. 217,261 yes  14. 75,886,849 no

| Divisibility by Multiples | If a number is divisible by both $m$ and $n$, and $m$ and $n$ have no common factor other than 1, then the number is divisible by $m \times n$. If $m$ and $n$ have common factors other than 1, the number may or may not be divisible by $m \times n$. |
|---|---|

**Use the rule to test for divisibility. Write yes or can't tell.**

15. 810 is divisible by both 5 and 9. Is 810 divisible by 45? yes
16. 3,654 is divisible by both 7 and 9. Is 3,654 divisible by 63? yes
17. 3,720 is divisible by both 6 and 8. Is 3,720 divisible by 48? can't tell
18. 189 is divisible by both 3 and 9. Is 189 divisible by 27? can't tell

# 4-2

## Getting Ready

**Key Terms and Symbols** exponents, power

**Resources** A complete list of resources for this lesson is on p. 169H.

### Daily Skills Warm-Up

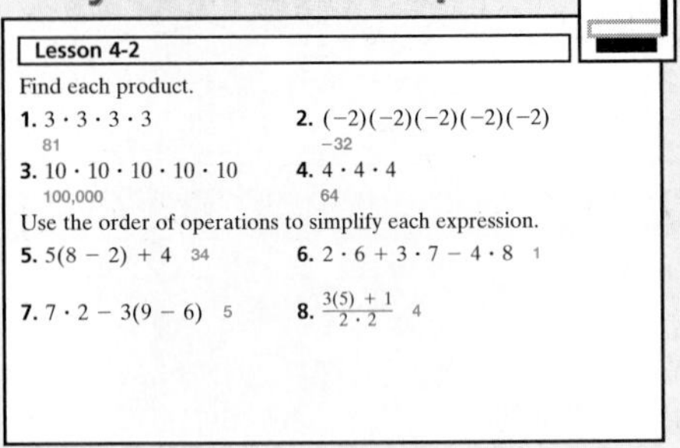

Lesson 4-2

Find each product.

1. $3 \cdot 3 \cdot 3 \cdot 3$ 81
2. $(-2)(-2)(-2)(-2)(-2)$ $-32$
3. $10 \cdot 10 \cdot 10 \cdot 10 \cdot 10$ 100,000
4. $4 \cdot 4 \cdot 4$ 64

Use the order of operations to simplify each expression.

5. $5(8 - 2) + 4$ 34
6. $2 \cdot 6 + 3 \cdot 7 - 4 \cdot 8$ 1
7. $7 \cdot 2 - 3(9 - 6)$ 5
8. $\frac{3(5) + 1}{2 \cdot 2}$ 4

### Background for the Lesson

An *exponent* is a number or symbol that you place to the upper right of another number or symbol called the *base*. The word *power* can also mean the exponent: $x^2$ in words is "*x* squared" or "*x* to the second power." You can think of $x^2$ as writing *x* down two times and then multiplying. So, $2^4 = 2 \bullet 2 \bullet 2 \bullet 2$, or 16. You can say the expression $2^2$ as "two squared," and the expression $2^3$ as "two cubed." An exponent of 1 leaves the base unchanged: $x^1 = x$; $5^1 = 5$. Any base with an exponent of 0 equals 1: $x^0 = 1$; $5^0 = 1$.

## 1 Focus

### Connecting to Prior Knowledge

Students have learned to find the area of a square by multiplying the length of a side by itself. Area is expressed in square units. Help students see a connection between this and the expression $x^2$, or *x* squared, that uses 2 as the exponent. In Lesson 4-7, students will multiply numbers with exponents.

# Exponents

**What You'll Learn**

1. To use exponents
2. To use the order of operations with exponents

**. . . And Why**

To use exponents as an efficient way of writing products of a repeated factor, for example $5 \cdot 5 \cdot 5$ as $5^3$

## PART 1 Using Exponents

You can use **exponents** to show repeated multiplication.

$$2^6 = 2 \cdot 2 \cdot 2 \cdot 2 \cdot 2 \cdot 2 = 64$$

exponent; base; power; the value of the expression; The base is used as a factor six times.

A **power** has two parts, a base and an exponent. The expression $2^6$ is read as "two to the sixth power."

| Power | Verbal Expression | Value |
|---|---|---|
| $12^1$ | *Twelve to the first power* | 12 |
| $6^2$ | *Six to the second power,* or *six squared* | $6 \bullet 6 = 36$ |
| $(0.2)^3$ | *Two tenths to the third power,* or *two tenths cubed* | $(0.2)(0.2)(0.2) = 0.008$ |
| $-7^4$ | *The opposite of the quantity seven to the fourth power* | $-(7 \bullet 7 \bullet 7 \bullet 7) = -2{,}401$ |
| $(-8)^5$ | *Negative eight to the fifth power* | $(-8)(-8)(-8)(-8)(-8) = -32{,}768$ |

**Reading Math**

Words in mathematics often have quite different everyday meanings. The word *base* can refer to the foundation of a building, or a starting point in a board game. How are these meanings similar to the use of the word *base* you see in this lesson?

### EXAMPLE 1

**Write using exponents.**

**a.** $(-5)(-5)(-5)$

$(-5)^3$ — Include the negative sign within parentheses.

**b.** $-2 \cdot a \cdot b \cdot a \cdot a$

$-2 \cdot a \cdot a \cdot a \cdot b$ — Rewrite the expression using the commutative and associative properties.

$-2a^3b$ — Write $a \cdot a \cdot a$ using exponents.

**TRY THIS** Write using exponents.

1. $6 \cdot 6 \cdot 6$ $6^3$
2. $(-3)(-3)(-3)(-3)$ $(-3)^4$
3. $4 \cdot y \cdot x \cdot y$ $4xy^2$



## Tools to Monitor Progress

**BEFORE THE LESSON**

**To check prerequisite skills:**

- Multiplying three or more factors

**Skills You Need,** p. 169

**Skills Handbook,** p. 725

**Skills Intervention Kit,** Whole Numbers

**DURING THE LESSON**

**To check understanding:**

**Try This** exercises on student page

- **Additional Example 1**

Write using exponents.

**a.** $(-11)(-11)(-11)(-11)$ $(-11)^4$

**b.** $-5 \bullet x \bullet x \bullet y \bullet y \bullet x$ $-5x^3y^2$

## EXAMPLE 2

REAL-WORLD CONNECTION

*Science* **A microscope can magnify a specimen $10^3$ times. How many times is that?**

$10^3 = 10 \cdot 10 \cdot 10$ — The exponent indicates that the base 10 is used as a factor 3 times.

$= 1{,}000$ — Multiply.

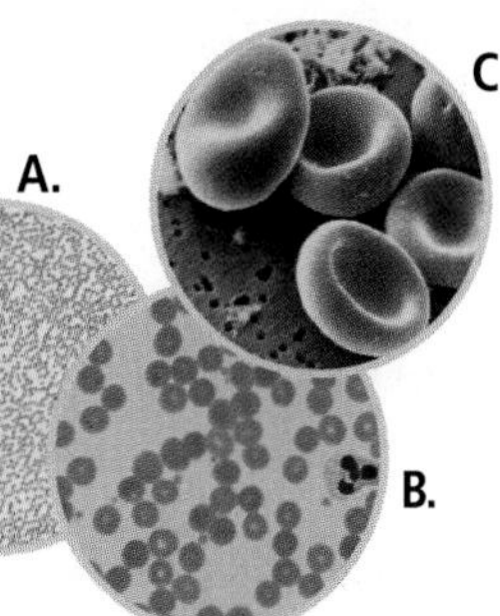


Human blood cells are shown here magnified (A)$10^2$ times, (B) $10^3$ times, and (C) $10^4$ times.

### TRY THIS

4. Simplify $6^2$. 36

5. Evaluate $-a^4$ and $(-a)^4$, for $a = 2$. $-16$, 16

## PART 2 Using the Order of Operations with Exponents

You can extend the order of operations to include exponents.

**Order of Operations**

1. Work inside grouping symbols.
2. Simplify any terms with exponents.
3. Multiply and divide in order from left to right.
4. Add and subtract in order from left to right.

## EXAMPLE 3

**a. Simplify $4(3 + 2)^2$.**

$4(3 + 2)^2 = 4(5)^2$ — Work within parentheses first.

$= 4 \cdot 25$ — Simplify $5^2$.

$= 100$ — Multiply.

**b. Evaluate $-2x^3 + 4y$, for $x = -2$ and $y = 3$.**

$-2x^3 + 4y = -2(-2)^3 + 4(3)$ — Replace $x$ with $-2$ and $y$ with 3.

$= -2(-8) + 4(3)$ — Simplify $(-2)^3$.

$= 16 + 12$ — Multiply from left to right.

$= 28$ — Add.

**Reading Math**

The expression $4(3 + 2)^2$ is read as "four times the square of the quantity three plus two."

### TRY THIS

6. Simplify $2 \cdot 5^2 + 4 \cdot (-3)^3$. $-58$

7. Evaluate $3(a)^2 + 6$, for $a = -5$. 81



# 2 Teach

## PART 1 Part 1 Teaching Notes

Have students practice writing expressions with exponents as multiplication problems.

### Example 1

**Build understanding.** Ask: Why do you use an exponent of 3? **because the base is written as a factor 3 times**

### Example 2

**Build understanding.** Ask: What do the exponent and the number of zeros in the product have in common? **The exponent is 3 and there are 3 zeros in the product.**

**Error Prevention** Students may multiply the base by the exponent when they simplify, to write $3^4$ incorrectly as 12 instead of 81. Make sure students say the expression carefully as "three to the fourth power" and not as "three-four."

## PART 2 Part 2 Teaching Notes

Point out that the exponent affects only what it touches, either the parentheses or the base. In $-2^3$, the exponent does not affect the negative sign, so $-2^3$ can be rewritten as $-(2^3)$, or $-8$.

### Example 3

**Build understanding.** Ask: Which operation is done first, simplifying terms with exponents or multiplying? **simplifying exponents**

**Extension** Challenge students to evaluate $2^0$ by completing this table.

| $2^3$ | 2 • 2 • 2 | 8 |
|---|---|---|
| $2^2$ | 2 • 2 | 4 |
| $2^1$ | 2 | 2 |
| $2^0$ | 1 | 1 |

**Error Prevention** You can suggest that students add to the memory device Please, My Dear Aunt Sally (from Lesson 1-2) by changing it to Please Excuse My Dear Aunt Sally, where the "E" in Excuse reminds them to simplify Exponents. Suggest to students that they use parentheses when they are substituting values for variables so that they do not forget negative signs.

- **Additional Example 2**
  Suppose a certain galaxy is $10^4$ light-years from Earth. How many light-years is that?
  **10,000 light-years**
- **Additional Example 3**
  Evaluate $7(w + 3)^3 + w$ for $w = -5$. $-61$

## AFTER THE LESSON

**To assess knowledge:**

**Lesson Quiz**

Write using exponents.

1. $x \cdot y \cdot z \cdot x \cdot z$ $x^2yz^2$

Simplify the expression.

2. $a \cdot b \cdot b \cdot b \cdot 3$ $3ab^3$

Evaluate the expression.

3. $(g^3 - 7)^2 \cdot 5 + 1$, for $g = 3$ 2,001

- For enrichment and reteaching options see Resources on p. 169H.

# 3 Practice/Assess

## Assignment Guide

To provide flexible scheduling, this lesson can be divided into parts.

▼ **Part 1**

**Core** 1–6, 9, 12–22, 30–32, 44–45, 47, 50–51, 54

✪ **Extension** 48–49, 52–53

▼ **Part 2**

**Core** 7–8, 10–11, 23–29, 35–40, 46

✪ **Extension** 41–43, 55

Mixed Review can be assigned at any time for maintenance.

## Exercises

**Auditory Learning Exercises 13–18** Students can say the powers aloud to themselves before they rewrite the expressions using exponents.

**Test Prep Exercise 45** Determine whether the first negative sign in answer choices A. and C. is affected by the exponent.

## ✪ Challenge

Simplify $\frac{2(5+2)^3}{(-8+15)^2 \cdot 14}$. 1

## Closure

To simplify an expression that has an exponent, remember the base is the number used as a factor and the exponent shows the number of times the base is used as a factor.

# Exercises

## Check Understanding

**Write using exponents.**

1. $8 \cdot 8 \cdot 8$ $8^3$
2. $r \cdot r \cdot r \cdot r \cdot s \cdot s$ $r^4s^2$
3. $-7 \cdot a \cdot a \cdot 3 \cdot b$ $-21a^2b$

**Simplify each expression.**

4. $4^3$ 64
5. $0.5^2$ 0.25
6. $-3^2$ −9
7. $3(4+2)^2$ 108
8. $49 - (4 \cdot 2)^2$ −15

**Evaluate each expression.**

9. $b^2$, for $b = 9$ 81
10. $(x+4)^2$, for $x = 3$ 49
11. $2m^2 + n$, for $m = -3$ and $n = 4$ 22
12. *Critical Thinking* Are $-6^2$ and $(-6)^2$ equal? Explain. No; $-6^2$ is −36 while $(-6)^2$ is 36.

## Practice and Problem Solving

**Write using exponents.**

13. $5 \cdot 5 \cdot a \cdot a$ $25a^2$
14. $x \cdot x \cdot y \cdot y \cdot z$ $x^2y^2z$
15. $-5 \cdot x \cdot x \cdot 3 \cdot y \cdot y$ $-15x^2y^2$
16. $(-7)(-7)(-7)$ $(-7)^3$
17. $c \cdot b \cdot 4 \cdot b \cdot b$ $4b^3c$
18. $d$ cubed $d^3$

**Simplify each expression.**

19. $5^3$ and $3^5$ 125 and 243
20. $10^3$ and $10^6$ 1,000 and 1,000,000
21. $-1^8$ and $(-1)^8$ −1 and 1
22. $-2^4$ and $(-2)^3$ −16 and −8
23. $-3^2 + 5 \cdot 2^3$ 31
24. $2(9-4)^2$ 50
25. $(-4)(-6)^2(2)$ −288
26. $25 - (3 \cdot 2)^2$ −11
27. $15 + (4+6)^2 \div 5$ 35
28. $(12-3)^2 \div (2^2 - 1^2)$ 27
29. $(4+8)^2 \div 4^2$ 9

**Evaluate each expression.**

30. $a^2$, for $a = 8$ 64
31. $r^2$, for $r = 0.6$ 0.36
32. $h^3$, for $h = -4$ −64
33. ✪ $(-x)^5$, for $x = -1$ 1
34. ✪ $b^2$, for $b = -0.9$ 0.81
35. $-6m^2$, for $m = 2$ −24
36. $3a^2 - 2$, for $a = 5$ 73
37. $5k^2$, for $k = 1.2$ 7.2
38. $c^3 + 4$, for $c = -6$ −212
39. $xy^2$, for $x = 3$ and $y = 4$ 48
40. $8 - x^3$, for $x = -2$ 16
41. ✪ $3(2m+5)^2$, for $m = 2$ 243
42. ✪ $4(2y-3)^2$, for $y = 5$ 196
43. ✪ $y^2 + 2y + 5$, for $y = -6$ 29
44. *Mental Math* Given that $2^{10} = 1{,}024$, find $2^{11}$ mentally. 2,048
45. **TEST PREP** Which expression equals 1? D
    A. $-1^2$  B. $(-1)^3$  C. $-(-1)^2$  D. $|-1|^3$



## Alternative Assessment

Ask students to write a number such as 64 as an expression with an exponent, for example, $4^3$. Ask them to write other expressions for the number if possible, such as $2^6$.

## Daily Cumulative Review

**List all the factors of each number.** *(Lesson 4-1)*

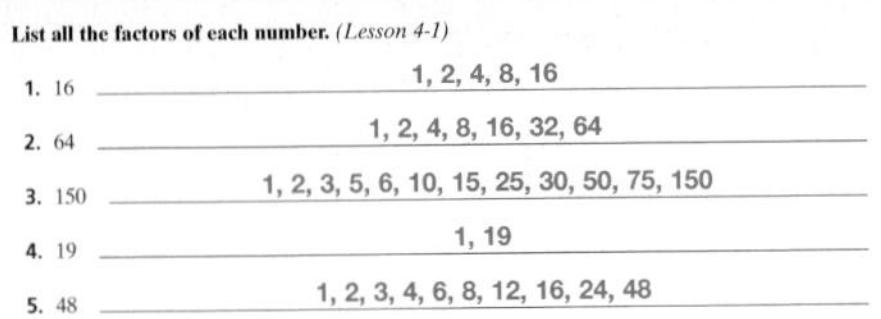

1. 16 1, 2, 4, 8, 16
2. 64 1, 2, 4, 8, 16, 32, 64
3. 150 1, 2, 3, 5, 6, 10, 15, 25, 30, 50, 75, 150
4. 19 1, 19
5. 48 1, 2, 3, 4, 6, 8, 12, 16, 24, 48

**Solve using any strategy.** *(Lesson 3-8)*

6. Marcus went to buy a pair of jeans. The sign above the rack read, "$12.25 off original price." The price at the cash register, before tax, was $35.78. How much was the original price of the jeans? $48.03

**Mixed Review**

**Name the point with the given coordinates.**

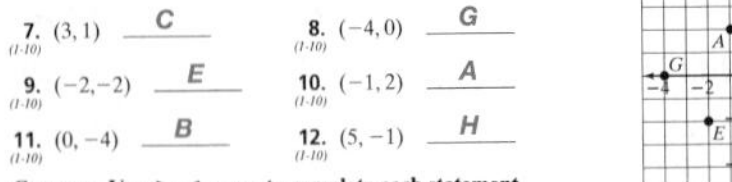

7. (3, 1) *(1-10)* C
8. (−4, 0) *(1-10)* G
9. (−2, −2) *(1-10)* E
10. (−1, 2) *(1-10)* A
11. (0, −4) *(1-10)* B
12. (5, −1) *(1-10)* H

**Compare. Use >, <, or = to complete each statement.**

13. $13 + (-7) > -9 + 12$ *(1-5)*
14. $-20 + 7 < |-45| + (-32)$ *(1-5)*
15. $|-13| > -5 + 8$ *(1-5)*
16. $|74| = |-74|$ *(1-4)*
17. $|-12| < |-15|$ *(1-4)*
18. $-8 > -10$ *(1-4)*
19. $-23 + (-4) < 5 + (-22)$ *(1-5)*
20. $-43 < -42$ *(1-4)*
21. $3(-3) < (-4)(2)$ *(1-9)*
22. $-25 \div (-5) = -30 \div (-6)$ *(1-9)*
23. $|-14| \div |-2| = |-14 \div -2|$ *(1-9)*

46. Read the word phrase that follows:
the square of $a$ increased by the sum of twice $a$ and 3.
a. Write a variable expression for the word phrase. $a^2 + 2a + 3$
b. Evaluate the expression for $a = 7$. 66

47. *Error Analysis* A student gives $ab^3$ as an answer when asked to write the expression $ab \cdot ab \cdot ab$ using exponents. What is the student's error?
The student didn't use parentheses around $ab$.

48. a. Copy and complete the table at the right.
b. For what value(s) of $n$ is each sentence true?
$4^n = n^4$ 2, 4 $\quad 4^n < n^4$ 3 $\quad 4^n > n^4$ 1

| $n$ | $4n$ | $4^n$ | $n^4$ |
|---|---|---|---|
| 1 | | | |
| 2 | | | |
| 3 | | | |
| 4 | | | |

48a.
4, 4, 1
8, 16, 16
12, 64, 81
16, 256, 256

49. *Inductive Reasoning* Evaluate $(-1)^m$ for $m = 2$, 4, and 6. Then, evaluate $(-1)^m$ for $m = 1, 3$, and 5. Write a conjecture about the sign of an even power of a negative number. Then write a conjecture about the sign of an odd power of a negative number.

49. An even power of a negative number is positive. An odd power of a negative number is negative.

*Geometry* **Use the diagrams at the right.**

50. A square has sides of length 5 in. What is its area? 25 in.$^2$

51. A cube has a side length of 6 in. What is its volume? 216 in.$^3$

52. What is the length of a side of a square with an area of 64 in.$^2$? 8 in.

53. What is the side length of a cube with a volume of 64 in.$^3$? 4 in.

SAMPLE

$s = 3$ in.
Area $= s^2$
$= 9$ in.$^2$

$s = 3$ in.
Volume $= s^3$
$= 27$ in.$^3$

54. *Language* Why do you think *squared* and *cubed* are used to indicate the second power and the third power? Answers may vary. Sample: A number *squared* is the area of a square. A number *cubed* is the volume of a cube.

55. *Mathematical Reasoning* Are $5x^2y$ and $5xy^2$ the same for all values of $x$ and $y$? Justify your answer. No; $5x^2y$ for $x = 1$ and $y = 2$ is 10, but $5xy^2$ for $x = 1$ and $y = 2$ is 20.

## MIXED REVIEW

**Test whether each number is divisible by 2, 3, 5, 9, or 10.** ***(Lesson 4-1)***

56. 36 2, 3, 9 $\quad$ 57. 135 3, 5, 9 $\quad$ 58. 171 3, 9 $\quad$ 59. 190 2, 5, 10 $\quad$ 60. 253 none

**Simplify each expression.** ***(Lesson 2-3)***

61. $3x - 2y + x$ $\;4x - 2y$ $\quad$ 62. $w + 8 - 4w - 15$ $\;-3w - 7$ $\quad$ 63. $9a + 2(a - 5) + 3$ $\;11a - 7$

64. Sara's grades are 79, 83, 74, 86, and 93. What is the mean? ***(Lesson 3-3)*** 83

See also Extra Practice section.



## Practice

**Evaluate each expression.**

1. $m^4$, for $m = 5$ ___625___
2. $(5a)^3$, for $a = -1$ ___−125___
3. $-(2p)^2$, for $p = 7$ ___−196___
4. $-n^6$, for $n = 2$ ___−64___
5. $b^6$ for, $b = -1$ ___1___
6. $(e - 2)^3$, for $e = 11$ ___729___
7. $(6 + h^2)^2$, for $h = 3$ ___225___
8. $x^2 + 3x - 7$, for $x = -4$ ___−3___
9. $y^3 - 2y^2 + 3y - 4$, for $y = 5$ ___86___

**Write using exponents.**

10. $3 \cdot 3 \cdot 3 \cdot 3$ ___$3^4$___
11. $k \cdot k \cdot k \cdot k \cdot k$ ___$k^5$___
12. $(-9)(-9)(-9)m \cdot m \cdot m$ ___$(-9)^3m^3$___
13. $g \cdot g \cdot g \cdot g \cdot h$ ___$g^4h$___
14. $7 \cdot a \cdot a \cdot b \cdot b \cdot b$ ___$7a^2b^3$___
15. $-8 \cdot m \cdot n \cdot n \cdot 2 \cdot m \cdot m$ ___$-16m^3n^2$___
16. $d \cdot (-3) \cdot e \cdot e \cdot d \cdot (-3) \cdot e$ ___$(-3)^2d^2e^3$___

**Simplify each expression.**

17. $(-2)^3$ and $-2^3$ ___−8 ; −8___
18. $0^{12}$ ___0___
19. $2^8$ and $4^4$ ___256; 256___
20. $-5^2 + 4 \cdot 2^3$ ___7___
21. $3(8 - 6)^2$ ___12___
22. $-6^2 + 2 \cdot 3^2$ ___−18___
23. $(-2)(-5)^2(3)$ ___−150___
24. $24 + (11 - 3)^2 \div 4$ ___40___
25. $(17 - 3)^2 \div (4^2 - 3^2)$ ___28___
26. $(5 + 10)^2 \div 5^2$ ___9___
27. $4^3 \div (2^5 - 4^2)$ ___4___
28. $(-1)^5 \cdot (2^4 - 13)^2$ ___−9___



## Reteaching

Evaluate $(-x)^2$, $-x^2$, and $2(x - 4)^2 + 1$ when $x = 9$.

Substitute 9 for $x$ in $(-x)^2$.
$(-9)^2 = (-9)(-9) = 81$

Substitute 9 for $x$ in $-x^2$.
$-9^2 = -(9 \cdot 9) = -81$

Substitute 9 for $x$ in $2(x - 4)^2 + 1$.

| | |
|---|---|
| $2(x - 4)^2 + 1 = 2(9 - 4)^2 + 1$ | Substitute 9 for $x$. |
| $= 2(5)^2 + 1$ | Work within parentheses first. |
| $= 2(25) + 1$ | Simplify $(5)^2$. |
| $= 50 + 1$ | Multiply. |
| $= 51$ | Add. |

**Evaluate each expression.**

1. $(-a)^2$, for $a = 10$ $\;(-$___10___$)^2 =$ ___100___
2. $-a^2$, for $a = 10$ $\;-$___10___$^2 =$ ___−100___
3. $a^2$, for $a = -10$ $\;($___−10___$)^2 =$ ___100___
4. $-a^2$, for $a = -10$ $\;-($___−10___$)^2 =$ ___−100___
5. $-3m^2$, for $m = 5$ $\;-3($___5___$)^2 = -3($___25___$) =$ ___−75___
6. $2n^2 - 4$, for $n = 3$ $\;2($___3___$)^2 - 4 = 2($___9___$) - 4$
$= ($___18___$) - 4 =$ ___14___
7. $5(2h - 4)^2$, for $h = 4$ $\;5(2 \cdot$ ___4___ $- 4)^2 = 5($___8___ $- 4)^2$
$= 5($___4___$)^2 = 5($___16___$) =$ ___80___
8. $xy^2$, for $x = 7, y = 2$ $\;($___7___$)($___2___$)^2 = ($___7___$)($___4___$)$
$=$ ___28___



Reteaching

## Enrichment

**Complete the patterns. Then use your results to make the indicated predictions.**

1. $5^1 =$ ___5___
$5^2 =$ ___25___
$5^3 =$ ___125___
Predict:
the tens' digit of $5^{74}$ ___2___

2. $6^1 =$ ___6___
$6^2 =$ ___36___
$6^3 =$ ___216___
Predict:
the ones' digit of $6^{113}$ ___6___

3. $4^1 =$ ___4___
$4^2 =$ ___16___
$4^3 =$ ___64___
$4^4 =$ ___256___
Predict:
the ones' digit of $4^{29}$ ___4___
the ones' digit of $4^{82}$ ___6___

4. $9^1 =$ ___9___
$9^2 =$ ___81___
$9^3 =$ ___729___
$9^4 =$ ___6,561___
Predict:
the ones' digit of $9^{114}$ ___1___
the ones' digit of $9^{223}$ ___9___

5. $2^1 =$ ___2___ $\quad 2^5 =$ ___32___
$2^2 =$ ___4___ $\quad 2^6 =$ ___64___
$2^3 =$ ___8___ $\quad 2^7 =$ ___128___
$2^4 =$ ___16___ $\quad 2^8 =$ ___256___
Predict:
the ones' digit of $2^{84}$ ___6___
the ones' digit of $2^{43}$ ___8___

6. $1^2 =$ ___1___
$11^2 =$ ___121___
$111^2 =$ ___12,321___
$1{,}111^2 =$ ___1,234,321___
Predict:
$11{,}111^2$ ___123,454,321___
$111{,}111^2$ ___12,345,654,321___

7. Study the pattern of the ones' digits in the powers of 3 and the powers of 7. Then predict the ones' digit of each number.
a. $3^{50}$ ___9___ $\quad$ b. $7^{101}$ ___7___
c. $3^{81}$ ___3___ $\quad$ d. $7^{44}$ ___1___

# 4-3

## Getting Ready

**Key Terms and Symbols** prime number, composite number, prime factorization, greatest common factor (GCF)

**Resources** A complete list of resources for this lesson is on p. 169H.

### Daily Skills Warm-Up

**Lesson 4-3**

Write two numbers that, when multiplied, result in each product. Sample answers are shown.

1. 20 4 and 5
2. 35 5 and 7
3. 7 1 and 7
4. 15 3 and 5

State whether each number is divisible by 2, 3, 5, 9, or 10.

| | 2 | 3 | 5 | 9 | 10 |
|---|---|---|---|---|---|
| 5. 347 | no | no | no | no | no |
| 6. 255 | no | yes | yes | no | no |
| 7. 470 | yes | no | yes | no | yes |
| 8. 549 | no | yes | no | yes | no |

### Background for the Lesson

A *prime number* is any positive integer, other than 1, that has exactly two factors: 1 and itself. All positive integers greater than one that are not prime are *composite numbers.* The number 1 is neither prime nor composite because it has only one factor, namely itself. Every composite number has more than two factors. For example, 4 (the first composite number, since 2 and 3 are prime) has three factors, 1, 2, and 4.

## 1 Focus

### Investigate

You may want to have students use graph paper to help them draw rectangles with the given numbers of unit squares.

### Connecting to Prior Knowledge

In Lesson 4-1, students learned about divisibility rules and factors, and in Lesson 4-2 they learned about exponents. In this lesson they will find prime factors using divisibility rules and write greatest common factors (GCF) using exponents.

# Prime Factorization and Greatest Common Factor

### What You'll Learn

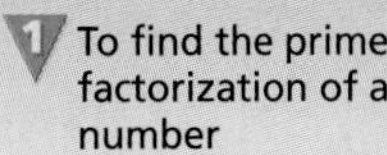

1. To find the prime factorization of a number

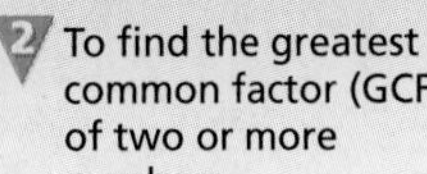

2. To find the greatest common factor (GCF) of two or more numbers

**. . . And Why**

To compute with fractions

## Investigate

EXPLORING PRIME NUMBERS

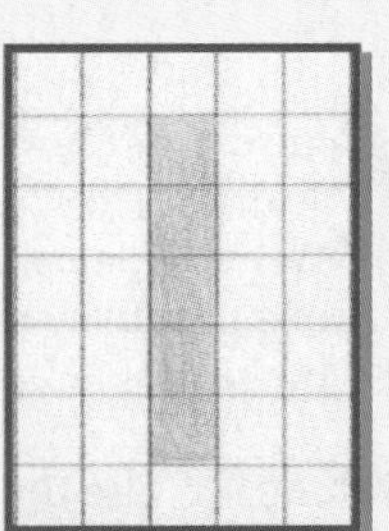

The diagram shows the only rectangle you can make with integer side lengths and an area of 5 square units. Work with a partner. Find the number of rectangles you can make with each number of unit squares: 2, 3, 4, 5, 6, 7, 8, 9, and 10.

1. For which numbers of squares is only one rectangle possible? 2, 3, 5, 7
2. For which numbers of squares is more than one rectangle possible? 4, 6, 8, 9, 10
3. List the dimensions of the rectangles you can make with each of the following numbers of unit squares: 13, 15, 17, 19, and 21. 1 by 13; 1 by 15, 3 by 5; 1 by 17; 1 by 19; 1 by 21, 3 by 7

## PART 1 Finding Prime Factorizations

A **prime number** is a positive integer greater than 1 with exactly two factors, 1 and the number itself. The numbers 2, 3, 5, and 7 are prime numbers.

A **composite number** is a positive integer greater than 1 with more than two factors. The numbers 4, 6, 8, 9, and 10 are composite numbers. The number 1 is neither prime nor composite.

**Test Prep TIP**

To check whether a number is prime, look for prime factors in order, starting with 2. When you get to a prime whose square is greater than the original number, you can stop. For 23, check 2 and 3. Then stop at 5, since $5^2 > 23$. Since 2, 3, and 5 are not factors of 23, 23 is prime.

### EXAMPLE 1

**Tell whether each number is *prime* or *composite*.**

**a. 23** Prime; it has only 2 factors, 1 and 23.
**b. 129** Composite; it has more than two factors, 1, 3, 43, and 129.

### TRY THIS

4. Which numbers from 10 to 20 are prime? Are composite? 11, 13, 17, 19; 10, 12, 14, 15, 16, 18, 20



# Tools to Monitor Progress

### BEFORE THE LESSON

**To check prerequisite skills:**

- Recalling multiplication facts

**Skills You Need,** p. 169

**Skills Handbook,** p. 725

**Skills Intervention Kit,** Whole Numbers

### DURING THE LESSON

**To check understanding:**

**Try This** exercises on student page

- **Additional Example 1**
  Tell whether each number is prime or composite.
  a. 46 composite
  b. 2,825 composite
  c. 13 prime

Writing a composite number as a product of its prime factors shows the **prime factorization** of the number. You can use a *factor tree* to find prime factorizations. Write the final factors in increasing order from left to right. Use exponents to indicate repeated factors.

### EXAMPLE 2

**Use a factor tree to write the prime factorization of 825.**

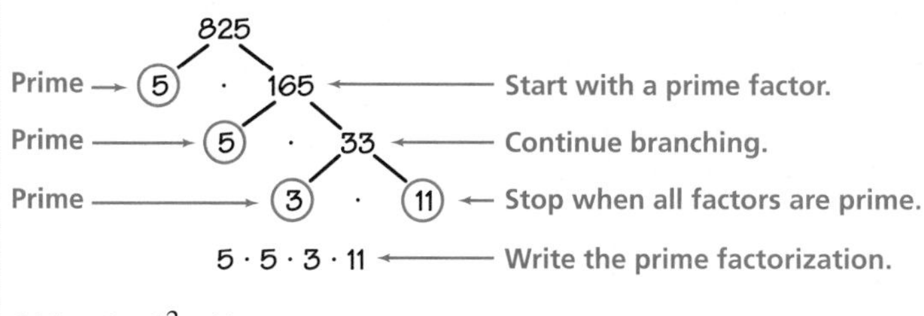

825
Prime → 5 · 165 ← Start with a prime factor.
Prime → 5 · 33 ← Continue branching.
Prime → 3 · 11 ← Stop when all factors are prime.
5 · 5 · 3 · 11 ← Write the prime factorization.

$825 = 3 \cdot 5^2 \cdot 11$ Use exponents to write the prime factorization.

**TRY THIS** Write the prime factorization of each number.

**5.** 72 $2^3 \cdot 3^2$ **6.** 150 $2 \cdot 3 \cdot 5^2$ **7.** 225 $3^2 \cdot 5^2$ **8.** 236 $2^2 \cdot 59$

## PART 2 Finding the Greatest Common Factor

Any factors that are the same for two or more numbers are *common factors*. The greatest of these common factors is called the **greatest common factor (GCF).** You can use prime factorization to find the GCF of two or more numbers or expressions. If there are no prime factors in common, the GCF is 1.

### EXAMPLE 3

**Find the GCF of each pair of expressions.**

**a. 40 and 60**

$40 = 2^3 \cdot 5$
$60 = 2^2 \cdot 3 \cdot 5$

Write the prime factorizations.

Find the common factors. Use the lesser power of the common factors.

$GCF = 2^2 \cdot 5 = 20$

The GCF of 40 and 60 is 20.

**b. $6a^3b$ and $4a^2b$**

$6a^3b = 2 \cdot 3 \cdot a^3 \cdot b$
$4a^2b = 2 \cdot 2 \cdot a^2 \cdot b$

$GCF = 2 \cdot a^2 \cdot b = 2a^2b$

The GCF of $6a^3b$ and $4a^2b$ is $2a^2b$.

# 2 Teach

## Part 1 Teaching Notes

Help students see that the number 1 does not fit the definition of either a prime or a composite number, since 1 has only one factor, itself. This means that 1 is neither composite nor prime.

### Example 1

**Build understanding.** Ask: When you test whether or not a number is prime, why can you stop dividing when you find a third factor for the number? **If a number has more than two factors, you know it is composite.**

**Error Prevention** Give students the following steps to use when they check for primes:

- If the number > 2 and even, it is not prime (because it has a factor of 2).
- If the number > 1 and odd, check for divisibility by 3, 5, 7, 11, and so on.
- Stop checking when a factor squared > the number. For example, since 7 • 7 > 37, you don't have to test whether 11 is a factor of 37 because, if it were, 37 would have to equal 11 times some number < 11, and you have already tested all of those.

**Connecting to History** It is not known exactly when prime numbers were first recognized. The Greek mathematicians Euclid and Eratosthenes studied them as early as 300 B.C.

### Example 2

**Build understanding.** Ask: Why is 5 a good prime factor to start with when you find the prime factorization of 825? **because 825 ends in 5**

**Error Prevention** Remind students that the prime factorization of a number contains only prime numbers. Even though 9 • 8 is a factorization of 72, it is not a *prime* factorization because 9 and 8 are not prime.

## Part 2 Teaching Notes

Ask students to read GCF as "greatest common factor" instead of saying just the letters, so they will learn the meaning of this acronym.

**Additional Example 2**

Use a factor tree to write the prime factorization of 273. **3 • 7 • 13**

**Additional Example 3**

Find the GCF of each pair of expressions.

a. 24 and 30 **6**

b. $36ab^2$ and $81b$ **$9b$**

**AFTER THE LESSON**

**To assess knowledge:**

**Lesson Quiz**

Tell whether each is prime or composite.

1. 123 **composite**

Find the GCF for each pair.

2. $8sr^4$ and $12s^2rq$ **$4sr$**
3. $62b^3c^2d$ and $31b^2c^3d$ **$31b^2c^2d$**

- For enrichment and reteaching options see Resources on p. 169H.

## Example 3

**Build understanding.** Ask: What is the *greatest* number that divides evenly into both 40 and 60? Compare this to the GCF of 40 and 60. 20; The greatest number that divides both 40 and 60 is the same as the greatest factor they have in common.

**ELL** Discuss the meaning of each word in the phrase represented by GCF. Compare the *greatest* common factor to other *common* factors. Explain that a common factor is shared by both numbers.

## Different Ways to Solve a Problem

**Build understanding.** Ask: Why is it a good idea to write the factors in ascending order? It is easier to find the common factors.

**Visual and Tactile Learning** Suggest that students draw a sketch or use counters to model possible arrangements for 48 band members.

**Error Prevention** Students who use Method 1 to find the GCF may overlook some factors. Prime factorization ensures that no factors are overlooked.

**Extension** Ask: What is the GCF for two numbers if one of them is prime, for example, 30 and 3, 5 and 16, or 7 and 11? The GCF will be either the prime number or 1.

**TRY THIS** Use prime factorizations to find each GCF.

**9.** 8, 20 4 **10.** 12, 87 3 **11.** $12r^3, 8r$ $4r$ **12.** $15m^2n, 45m$ $15m$

You can find the GCF of two or more numbers or expressions by listing factors or by using prime factorizations.

## Different Ways to Solve a Problem

**A parade organizer wants each marching band to have the same number of band members in each row. The bands have 48, 32, and 56 band members. What is the greatest number of band members possible for each row?**

A parade organizer wants bands with 90 members, 108 members, and 72 members to have the same number of members in each row. What is the greatest number of members possible for each row? 18 members

**Method 1**

List the factors of each number. Then find the greatest factor the numbers have in common.

48: 1, 2, 3, 4, 6, (8), 12, 16, 24, 48

32: 1, 2, 4, (8), 16, 32

56: 1, 2, 4, 7, (8), 14, 28, 56

The GCF of 48, 32, and 56 is 8. The greatest possible number of band members in each row is 8.

**Method 2**

Find the prime factorization of each number. Then find the least power of all common prime factors.

48: $2^4 \cdot 3$

32: $2^5$

56: $2^3 \cdot 7$

The GCF of 48, 32, and 56 is $2^3$, or 8. The greatest possible number of band members in each row is 8.

**Choose a Method**

1. Which method do you prefer to find the GCF? Explain why. Answers may vary. Sample: Method 2; it ensures that factors aren't missed.
2. Which method would you use to find the GCF of 4, 8, and 24? Of 54, 27, and 36? Explain why. Answers may vary. Sample: Method 1; Method 2; the lists are very short for 4, 8, and 24; not so for 54, 27, and 36.

# Exercises

## CHECK UNDERSTANDING

**Is each number *prime* or *composite?* For each composite number, write the prime factorization.**

1. 27 composite; $3^3$
2. 19 prime
3. 31 prime
4. 38 composite; $2 \cdot 19$
5. 45 composite; $3^2 \cdot 5$
6. 53 prime
7. 87 composite; $3 \cdot 29$
8. 93 composite; $3 \cdot 31$
9. 125 composite; $5^3$
10. 360 composite; $2^3 \cdot 3^2 \cdot 5$

**Find each GCF.**

11. 10, 45 5
12. 6, 8, 12 2
13. 42, 65 1
14. $14c^2, 35c$ $7c$
15. $3y^2, 24y^3$ $3y^2$

16. *Critical Thinking* To find the prime factorization of 225, one student started by using the prime factor 3. Another started by using the prime factor 5. Does starting with different numbers make any difference in the prime factorization? Explain. Explanations may vary. Sample: No; there is only one prime factorization for a number.

## PRACTICE AND PROBLEM SOLVING

**Is each number *prime, composite,* or *neither?* For each composite number, write the prime factorization.**

17. 8 composite; $2^3$
18. 17 prime
19. 2 prime
20. 34 composite; $2 \cdot 17$
21. 1 neither
22. 29 prime
23. 115 composite; $5 \cdot 23$
24. 186 composite; $2 \cdot 3 \cdot 31$
25. 49 composite; $7^2$
26. 621 composite; $3^3 \cdot 23$
27. ✪ 253 composite; $11 \cdot 23$
28. ✪ 1,575 composite; $3^2 \cdot 5^2 \cdot 7$

**Find each GCF.**

29. 14, 21 7
30. 25, 100 25
31. 57, 84 3
32. 54, 144 18
33. 8, 16, 20 4
34. 12, 18, 21 3
35. 90, 900 90
36. 143, 169 13
37. $z, z^2$ $z$
38. $5a, 35a$ $5a$
39. $18c^3, 24c^3$ $6c^3$
40. $180a^2, 210a$ $30a$
41. $48r^2s, 63s$ $3s$
42. $6m^3n, 8mn^2$ $2mn$
43. $27x^2y^3, 46x^2y$ $x^2y$
44. $25b^2c, 42bc$ $bc$

45. *Puzzle* Find the integers that fit the following conditions:
    - They are between 44 and 53.
    - The sums of their digits are prime.
    - They have more than three factors. 50, 52

46. *Writing* Explain how to find the prime factorization of 50.

    46. Answers may vary. Sample: Divide 50 by the prime factor 5, and then divide the quotient, 10, by the prime factor 5. Collect all the prime factors to get the prime factorization $2 \cdot 5^2$.

47. **TEST PREP** For which expressions is the GCF 12? B

    A. 3 and 4
    B. $24x^2$ and $36y$
    C. $12xy$ and $24y$
    D. $3x$ and $12x$



## Alternative Assessment

Tell students that $3^2 \bullet 5a^2b$ is the GCF of two variable expressions. Have students write one possibility for the variable expressions. sample answer: $90a^3b^2$ and $45a^2b$

# 3 Practice/Assess

## Assignment Guide

To provide flexible scheduling, this lesson can be divided into parts.

**Part 1**

**Core** 1–10, 16–26, 45–46
✪ **Extension** 27–28

**Part 2**

**Core** 11–15, 29–44, 47–48, 54–57
✪ **Extension** 49–53

Mixed Review can be assigned at any time for maintenance.

## Exercises

**Test Prep Exercise 47** Consider the variables as well as the numbers to find the GCF.

## ✪ Challenge

Find the GCF of $97ab^2c^3$ and $131ad^2e^3$. *a*

## Closure

A prime number is a positive integer greater than 1 with only two factors, 1 and itself. A positive integer greater than 1 with more than two factors is a composite number. The prime factorization of a composite number is the product of its prime factors.

The greatest common factor (GCF) of two or more expressions is the greatest factor the expressions have in common. You can list factors or use prime factorization to find the GCF of two or more expressions.

## Daily Cumulative Review

**Simplify each expression.** *(Lesson 4-2)*

1. $5^4 + 3^2$ 634
2. $6^1 + (-2)^5$ −26
3. $3(7-5)^4$ 48
4. $(-2)^4(3)(4)$ 192
5. $16 - (2 \cdot 2)^5$ −1,008
6. $-7^2 - 1^4$ −50

**State whether each number is divisible by 2, 3, 5, 9, or 10.** *(Lesson 4-1)*

7. 18 2, 3, 9
8. 27 3, 9
9. 270 2, 3, 5, 9, 10
10. 135 3, 5, 9
11. 500 2, 5, 10
12. 6,726 2, 3

**Mixed Review**

**Solve each inequality. Graph the solutions.**

13. $6 + h > -4$ (2-9) $h > -10$

    −12 −10 −8 −6 −4 −2 0 2 4 6 8

14. $n - 13 \le -11$ (2-9) $n \le 2$

    −5 −4 −3 −2 −1 0 1 2 3 4 5

**Write a variable expression for each word phrase.**

15. the product of 18 and a number $b$ (1-1) $18b$
16. the number of inches in $k$ feet (1-1) $12 \times k$
17. the sum of $c$ and seven (1-1) $c + 7$

**Is each equation true, false, or an open sentence?**

18. $19 = 6(-3) + 1$ (2-4) false equation
19. $-4 + k = 15 \div 5$ (2-4) open sentence
20. $46 - 23 = 7(3) + 2$ (2-4) true equation

**Solve each equation.**

21. $m + 3.56 = -5.4$ (3-5) $m = -8.96$
22. $-14 = d + (-5.8)$ (3-5) $-8.2 = d$
23. $v - (-3.65) = -5.42$ (3-5) $v = -9.07$

## Practice

Practice

**Find each GCF.**

1. 8, 12 4
2. 36, 54 18
3. 63, 81 9
4. 69, 92 23
5. 15, 28 1
6. 21, 35 7
7. $30m$, $36n$ 6
8. $75x^3y^2$, $100xy$ $25xy$
9. 15, 24, 30 3
10. 48, 80, 128 16
11. $36hk^3$, $60k^2m$, $84k^4n$ $12k^2$
12. $2mn$, $4m^2n^2$ $2mn$

**Is each number prime, composite, or neither? For each composite, write the prime factorization.**

13. 75 composite; $3 \cdot 5^2$
14. 152 composite; $2^3 \cdot 19$
15. 432 composite; $2^4 \cdot 3^3$
16. 588 composite; $2^2 \cdot 3 \cdot 7^2$
17. 160 composite; $2^5 \cdot 5$
18. 108 composite; $2^2 \cdot 3^3$
19. 19 prime
20. 143 composite; $11 \cdot 13$
21. 531 composite; $3^2 \cdot 59$
22. 369 composite; $3^2 \cdot 41$
23. 83 prime
24. 137 prime
25. The numbers 3, 5, and 7 are factors of $n$. Find four other factors of n besides 1.
 15, 35, 21, 105
26. For which expressions is the GCF $8x$?
 A. $2xy$ and $4x^2$ (B.) $16x^2$ and $24xy$ C. $8x^3$ and $4x$ D. $24x^2$ and $48x^3$



## Reteaching

Find the GCF of 36 and 54.

$36 = 2^2 \cdot 3^2 = 2 \cdot 2 \cdot 3 \cdot 3$ write the prime factorization
$54 = 2 \cdot 3^3 = 2 \cdot 3 \cdot 3 \cdot 3$

find the common factors

$GCF = 2 \cdot 3 \cdot 3 = 2 \cdot 3^2 = 18$
Notice 2 is the lesser power of $2^2$ and 2, and $3^2$ is the lesser power of $3^2$ and $3^3$.

**Find the GCF.**

1. 50 = $2 \cdot 5^2$
 35 = $5 \cdot 7$
 GCF = 5
2. 75 = $3 \cdot 5^2$
 30 = $2 \cdot 3 \cdot 5$
 GCF = $3 \cdot 5 = 15$
3. 48 = $2^4 \cdot 3$
 60 = $2^2 \cdot 3 \cdot 5$
 GCF = $2^2 \cdot 3 = 12$
4. 45 = $3^2 \cdot 5$
 72 = $2^3 \cdot 3^2$
 GCF = $3^2 = 9$
5. 98 = $2 \cdot 7^2$
 42 = $2 \cdot 3 \cdot 7$
 GCF = $2 \cdot 7 = 14$
6. 24 = $2^3 \cdot 3$
 80 = $2^4 \cdot 5$
 GCF = $2^3 = 8$
7. 315 = $3^2 \cdot 5 \cdot 7$
 360 = $2^3 \cdot 3^2 \cdot 5$
 GCF = $3^2 \cdot 5 = 45$
8. 156 = $2^2 \cdot 3 \cdot 13$
 208 = $2^4 \cdot 13$
 GCF = $2^2 \cdot 13 = 52$



## Enrichment

Enrichment

1. Find the factors of 23. 1, 23
2. Find the factors of 24. 1, 2, 3, 4, 6, 8, 12, 24

As the above examples show, two numbers may have greatly different numbers of factors, even though the numbers are nearly equal.

3. How many factors does 23 have? 2
4. How many factors does 24 have? 8

You can use prime factorizations to find out how many factors a number has.

**Example** How many factors does 40 have?

**Solution**
1. Write the prime factorization. $40 = 2^3 \cdot 5^1$
2. Take each exponent and add 1. $3 + 1 = 4$; $1 + 1 = 2$
3. Multiply the sums. $4 \times 2 = 8$
 40 has 8 factors.

**Complete the table. The first one is done for you.**

| | Number | Prime Factorization | Number of Factors | Factors |
|---|---|---|---|---|
| | 6 | $2 \cdot 3$ | 4 | 1, 2, 3, 6 |
| 5. | 44 | $2^2 \cdot 11$ | 6 | 1, 2, 4, 11, 22, 44 |
| 6. | 91 | $7 \cdot 13$ | 4 | 1, 7, 13, 91 |
| 7. | 125 | $5^3$ | 4 | 1, 5, 25, 125 |
| 8. | 54 | $2 \cdot 3^3$ | 8 | 1, 2, 3, 6, 9, 18, 27, 54 |
| 9. | 664 | $2^3 \cdot 83$ | 8 | 1, 2, 4, 8, 83, 166, 332, 664 |
| 10. | 369 | $3^2 \cdot 41$ | 6 | 1, 3, 9, 41, 123, 369 |
| 11. | 475 | $5^2 \cdot 19$ | 6 | 1, 5, 19, 25, 95, 475 |
| 12. | 222 | $2 \cdot 3 \cdot 37$ | 8 | 1, 2, 3, 6, 37, 74, 111, 222 |



48. *Open-ended* The GCF of 36 and $x$ is 6. What are two possible values for $x$? Answers may vary. Sample: 6, 36

**Two numbers are *relatively prime* if their GCF is 1. Is each pair of numbers relatively prime? Explain.**

SAMPLE 8, 17 Yes, 8 and 17 are relatively prime. The GCF is 1.
7, 35 No, 7 and 35 are not relatively prime. The GCF is 7.

49. 3, 20 Yes; the GCF is 1.
50. 9, 42 No; the GCF is 3.
51. 13, 52 No; the GCF is 13.
52. 24, 47 Yes; the GCF is 1.
53. 52, 65 No; the GCF is 13.

54. Simon is covering a wall with equal-sized tiles that can't be cut into smaller pieces. The area he wishes to cover is 66 in. high by 72 in. wide. What is the largest square tile that Simon can use? 6 in. by 6 in.

55. A math teacher and a science teacher combine their first-period classes for a group activity. The math class has 24 students and the science class has 16 students. The teachers need to divide the students into groups of the same size. Each group must have the same number of math students. Find the greatest number of groups possible. 8 groups

56. A photography club is practicing developing techniques. One set of negatives contains 32 negatives and another contains 48 negatives. Each set can be divided equally among the members present. List all the possible numbers of members present. What is the greatest possible number? 1, 2, 4, 8, 16; 16 members

57. Organizers for a high school graduation have set up chairs in two sections. They put 126 chairs for graduates in the front section and 588 chairs for guests in the back section. If all rows have the same number of chairs, what is the greatest number of chairs possible for a row? 42 chairs

## Mixed Review

**Evaluate for $x = 2$ and $y = 5$. *(Lesson 4-2)***

58. $x^2y$ 20
59. $xy^2$ 50
60. $x^2 + y^2$ 29
61. $x^4 - y$ 11

**Solve each equation. *(Lesson 3-6)***

62. $3x = 5.4$ 1.8
63. $-0.5a = 4.35$ −8.7
64. $4.32 = 1.6y$ 2.7
65. $-8m = -74.4$ 9.3

66. *Choose a Strategy* A store manager ordered three times as many books as magazines. She ordered a total of 108 books and magazines. How many books did she order? 81 books

 See also Extra Practice section.

Extension
*After Lesson 4-3*

# *Venn Diagrams*

You can use a *Venn diagram* to show relationships among collections of objects or numbers. Each collection is represented by a circle. The *intersection*, or overlap, of two circles indicates what is common to both collections.

## EXAMPLE 1

**School coaches plan to send notices to all students playing fall or winter sports. How many notices do they need to send?**

**Students in Sports**

| Season | Students |
|---|---|
| Fall | 155 |
| Winter | 79 |
| Both fall and winter | 28 |

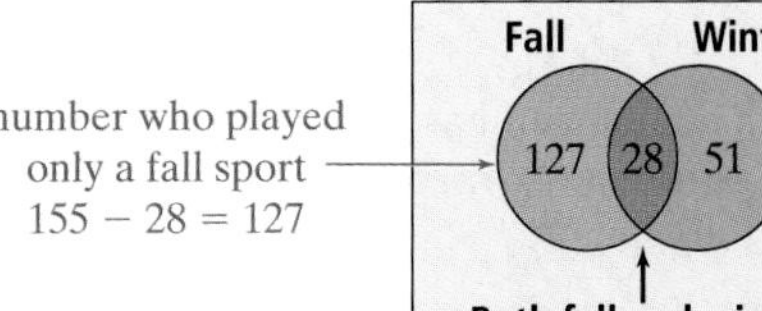


Add all three numbers to find the number of notices needed.

$127 + 28 + 51 = 206$

The coaches need to send 206 notices.

1. In a class of 38 students, 32 are wearing jeans, 21 are wearing T-shirts, and 15 are wearing both. Find how many students are wearing jeans and something other than a T-shirt. 17 students

You can use a Venn diagram to find the GCF of two numbers.

## EXAMPLE 2

**Find the GCF of 30 and 84.**

Include the common prime factors of 30 and 84 in the intersection.

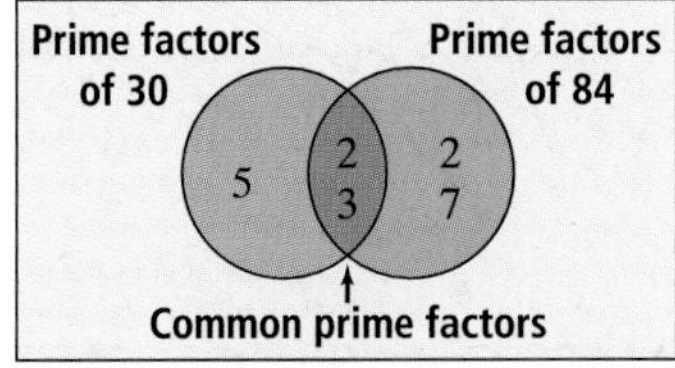


The GCF is the product of the factors in the intersection.

The GCF is $2 \cdot 3$, or 6.

**Draw a Venn diagram to find each GCF.**

2. 24, 56 8
3. 35, 49 7
4. 36, 84 12
5. 72, 108 36





## Venn Diagrams

This Math Toolbox shows how to use a Venn diagram to picture relationships.

## Math Background

Venn diagrams are geometric figures you can use to picture sets and set relations. These diagrams are called Venn diagrams in honor of John Venn, an English mathematician in the late nineteenth century. The size and shape of the diagrams do not matter. Sometimes a rectangle is used to represent the universal (or entire) set, and circles are used to represent subsets of the universal set.

## Teaching Notes

**Error Prevention** As you find the GCF, verify the product of the numbers in each circle and which numbers the circles share.

**Monitoring Progress** To make sure that students understand, check their diagrams for Exercise 2 before they continue with the others.

**Block Scheduling** If you have block scheduling or extended periods, you may wish to teach this Math Toolbox lesson with Lesson 4-3.

- **Additional Example**
  Draw a Venn diagram to find each GCF.
  60, 42 6

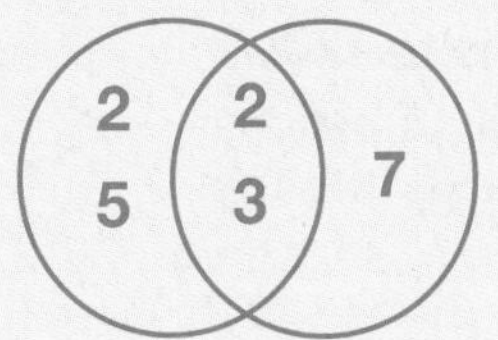

# 4-4

## Getting Ready

**Key Terms and Symbols** equivalent fractions, simplest form

**Resources** A complete list of resources for this lesson is on p. 169H.

### Daily Skills Warm-Up

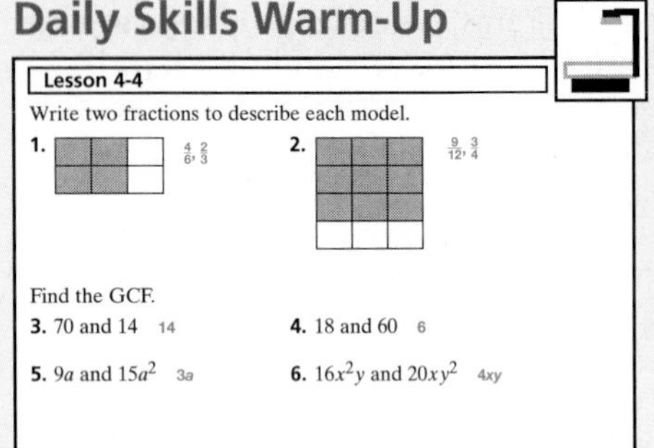
Lesson 4-4
Write two fractions to describe each model.
1. $\frac{4}{6}, \frac{2}{3}$  2. $\frac{9}{12}, \frac{3}{4}$

Find the GCF.
3. 70 and 14 14
4. 18 and 60 6
5. $9a$ and $15a^2$ $3a$
6. $16x^2y$ and $20xy^2$ $4xy$

### Background for the Lesson

Equivalent fractions represent equal values; they name the same place on a number line. When you multiply or divide both the numerator and the denominator of a fraction by the same nonzero number, the result is equivalent to the original fraction. The fractions $\frac{3}{4}$ and $\frac{9}{12}$ are equivalent because $\frac{3}{4} \bullet \frac{3}{3} = \frac{9}{12}$. When you multiply or divide the numerator and the denominator by the same number, you are actually multiplying or dividing the fraction by 1. That's because $\frac{3}{3}$ (or $\frac{a}{a}$ for any nonzero $a$) equals 1.

## 1 Focus

### Connecting to Students' Lives

Two United States coins are named with fractions: the quarter and half dollar. These names come from the fact that the coins are valued at $\frac{1}{4}$ and $\frac{1}{2}$ of one dollar. Rewrite these decimal values as the fractions $\frac{25}{100}$ and $\frac{50}{100}$. Ask students how these fractions compare to $\frac{1}{4}$ and $\frac{1}{2}$.

### Connecting to Prior Knowledge

In Lesson 4-3, students found the GCF for a set of numbers. In this lesson, they use the GCF to write a fraction in simplest form.

# 4-4 Simplifying Fractions

**What You'll Learn**

1. To find equivalent fractions
2. To write fractions in simplest form

**. . . And Why**

To recognize equivalent forms of a fraction, such as $\frac{24}{30}$ and $\frac{4}{5}$

## Part 1 Finding Equivalent Fractions

Each fraction bar below represents one whole. The blue bar is divided into four equal parts. The orange bar is divided into twelve equal parts.

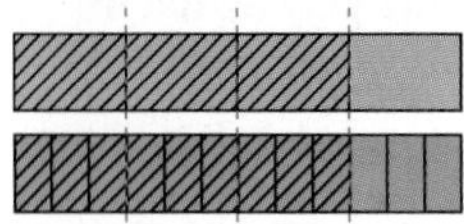

$\frac{3}{4}$ of the bar is shaded.

$\frac{9}{12}$ of the bar is shaded.

$\frac{3}{4} = \frac{3 \cdot 3}{4 \cdot 3} = \frac{9}{12}$

The fraction bars show that $\frac{3}{4} = \frac{9}{12}$. The fractions $\frac{3}{4}$ and $\frac{9}{12}$ are **equivalent fractions** because they describe the same part of a whole.

You can find equivalent fractions by multiplying or dividing the numerator and denominator by the same nonzero factor.

**Reading Math**

Most fraction names are made by adding *th* or *ths* to the denominator. You read $\frac{1}{4}$ as "one fourth," $\frac{2}{5}$ as "two fifths," and $\frac{8}{10}$ as "eight tenths." Halves and thirds are two exceptions.

### EXAMPLE 1

**Find two fractions equivalent to $\frac{4}{12}$.**

**a.** $\frac{4}{12} = \frac{4 \cdot 3}{12 \cdot 3} = \frac{12}{36}$

**b.** $\frac{4}{12} = \frac{4 \div 4}{12 \div 4} = \frac{1}{3}$

The fractions $\frac{12}{36}$ and $\frac{1}{3}$ are both equivalent to $\frac{4}{12}$.

1–3. Answers may vary. Samples are given.

**TRY THIS** Find two fractions equivalent to each fraction.

1. $\frac{5}{15}$ $\frac{1}{3}, \frac{10}{30}$
2. $\frac{10}{12}$ $\frac{5}{6}, \frac{20}{24}$
3. $\frac{14}{20}$ $\frac{7}{10}, \frac{28}{40}$

## Part 2 Writing Fractions in Simplest Form

A fraction is in **simplest form** when the numerator and the denominator have no factors in common other than 1. You can use the GCF to write a fraction in simplest form.



## Tools to Monitor Progress

### BEFORE THE LESSON

**To check prerequisite skills:**

- Reading and writing fractions

**Skills You Need,** p. 169

**Skills Handbook,** p. 737

**Skills Intervention Kit,** Operations with Fractions

### DURING THE LESSON

**To check understanding:**

**Try This** exercises on student page

- **Additional Example 1**
  Find two fractions equivalent to $\frac{18}{21}$. sample answers: $\frac{6}{7}$ and $\frac{36}{42}$

REAL-WORLD CONNECTION

### EXAMPLE 2

*Statistics* **You survey your friends about their favorite sandwich and find that 8 out of 12, or $\frac{8}{12}$, prefer peanut butter. Write this fraction in simplest form.**

The GCF of 8 and 12 is 4.

$\frac{8}{12} = \frac{8 \div 4}{12 \div 4}$ Divide the numerator and denominator by the GCF, 4.

$= \frac{2}{3}$ Simplify.

The favorite sandwich of $\frac{2}{3}$ of your friends is peanut butter.

The average American child will eat 1,500 peanut butter and jelly sandwiches by the time she or he graduates from high school.

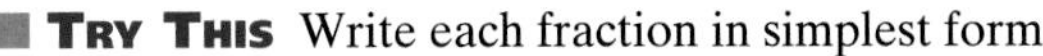

**TRY THIS** Write each fraction in simplest form.

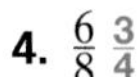

**4.** $\frac{6}{8}$ $\frac{3}{4}$ **5.** $\frac{9}{12}$ $\frac{3}{4}$ **6.** $\frac{28}{35}$ $\frac{4}{5}$

You can simplify fractions that contain variables. In this book, assume that no expression for a denominator equals zero.

### EXAMPLE 3

**Write in simplest form.**

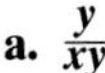

**a.** $\frac{y}{xy}$

$\frac{y}{xy} = \frac{y^1}{xy_1}$ Divide the numerator and denominator by the common factor, *y*.

$= \frac{1}{x}$ Simplify.

**b.** $\frac{3ab^2}{12ac}$

$\frac{3ab^2}{12ac} = \frac{3 \cdot a \cdot b \cdot b}{2 \cdot 2 \cdot 3 \cdot a \cdot c}$ Write as a product of prime factors.

$= \frac{3^1 \cdot a^1 \cdot b \cdot b}{2 \cdot 2 \cdot {}_1 3 \cdot {}_1 a \cdot c}$ Divide the numerator and denominator by the common factors.

$= \frac{b \cdot b}{2 \cdot 2 \cdot c}$ Simplify.

$= \frac{b \cdot b}{4 \cdot c}$ Simplify.

$= \frac{b^2}{4c}$

**Test Prep TIP**

You will see the directions *write in lowest terms* on some tests. This is another way of saying "write in simplest form."

**TRY THIS** Write in simplest form.

**7.** $\frac{b}{abc}$ $\frac{1}{ac}$ **8.** $\frac{2mn}{6m}$ $\frac{n}{3}$ **9.** $\frac{24x^2y}{8xy}$ $3x$



## 2 Teach

### Part 1 Teaching Notes

**Tactile Learning** Have students in small groups use paper plates and scissors to cut different plates, or *pizzas,* into 2, 3, 4, 6, and 8 equal *slices.* Have them label the slices with the appropriate fraction and compare to find combinations of equivalent slices.

#### Example 1

**Build understanding.** Ask: What happens if you multiply 4 times 3 then divide 12 by 3? **The resulting fraction is not equivalent to the original; do the *same operation* with the *same number* to both parts of the original fraction.**

**ELL** Call attention to the note in the margin of the text page. Point out that $\frac{1}{2}$ is *not* "one twoth" as you might expect from the pattern of fraction names, but is "one half" instead.

### Part 2 Teaching Notes

To find the *simplest form* of a fraction, first find the GCF of the numerator and denominator and then divide both numerator and denominator by that GCF.

#### Example 2

**Build understanding.** Ask: Why not *multiply* the numerator and denominator of $\frac{8}{12}$ by the GCF? **The fraction is equivalent, but not in simplest form.**

**Error Prevention** Students may divide the terms of a fraction by different numbers. Have them write the factor by which they divide in both the numerator and the denominator.

#### Example 3

**Build understanding.** Ask: In part a, why do you simplify the numerator *y* to 1? $y \div y = 1$

**Extension** Ask: If the numerator of a fraction is a prime number, is the fraction in simplest form? **Not necessarily; the prime number may be a factor of the denominator.**

- **Additional Example 2**
You learn that 21 out of the 28 students in a class, or $\frac{21}{28}$, buy their lunches in the cafeteria. Write this fraction in its simplest form. $\frac{3}{4}$
- **Additional Example 3**
Write in simplest form.
**a.** $\frac{p}{2p}$ $\frac{1}{2}$
**b.** $\frac{14q^2rs^3}{8qrs^2}$ $\frac{7qs}{4}$

### AFTER THE LESSON

**To assess knowledge:**

**Lesson Quiz**

Find two fractions equivalent to the fraction.

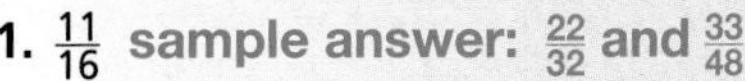

**1.** $\frac{11}{16}$ **sample answer:** $\frac{22}{32}$ **and** $\frac{33}{48}$

Write in simplest form.

**2.** $\frac{wx^4y^8}{w^2x^3y}$ $\frac{xy^7}{w}$

- For enrichment and reteaching options see Resources on p. 169H.

# 3 Practice/Assess

## Assignment Guide

To provide flexible scheduling, this lesson can be divided into parts.

**Part 1**
**Core** 1–5, 12–17, 40
✪ **Extension** 38

**Part 2**
**Core** 6–11, 18–33, 36–37, 39, 41
✪ **Extension** 34–35, 42–44

Mixed Review can be assigned at any time for maintenance.

### Exercises

**ELL Exercise 38** Students may mistakenly interpret the problem to be two different halves of the same pizza. Point out and explain the words *different* and *same*.

**Test Prep Exercise 40** An equivalent fraction does not have to be in simplest form.

### ✪ Challenge

Write $\frac{25x^2yz^3y}{5(5zx^2y^2z^2)}$ in its simplest form. 1

### Closure

Equivalent fractions describe the same part of a whole and look alike when they are in simplest form. A fraction is in simplest form when the numerator and the denominator have no factors in common other than 1. You can use the GCF to write a fraction in simplest form. You can also write the numerator and denominator as products of prime factors.

### Daily Cumulative Review

**Is each number prime or composite? If composite, write the prime factorization.** *(Lesson 4-3)*

1. 48 composite; $2^4 \cdot 3$
2. 17 prime
3. 93 composite; $3 \cdot 31$
4. 72 composite; $2^3 \cdot 3^2$
5. 435 composite; $3 \cdot 5 \cdot 29$
6. 2,965 composite; $5 \cdot 593$

**Evaluate each expression.** *(Lesson 4-2)*

7. $k^3 + 5$, for $k = 4$ 69
8. $(-m)^2$, for $m = -2$ 4
9. $(5 + a^2)^2$, for $a = 3$ 196
10. $-8d^3$, for $d = 2.1$ −74.088
11. $bw^3$, for $b = 6$, $w = 3$ 162
12. $z^2 + 2$, for $z = -0.7$ 2.49

**Mixed Review**

13. (2-7) The Johnsons bought two winter coats. The sum of their prices is $77. The product of their prices is $1,440. How much did each cost? $32 and $45

14. (3-8) The school is participating in a fundraiser. For every 5 books the students sell, the library receives 1 book. How many books will the library receive if the students sell 8 dozen books? 19 books

**Round to the underlined place value.**

15. (3-1) 10.5123 11
16. (3-1) 67,321.9681 67,321.97
17. (3-1) 109.7063 109.71
18. (3-1) 0.453 0.45
19. (3-1) 28.960 29.0
20. (3-1) 5,764.51 5,800

**Complete each statement.**

21. (3-7) 673 cm = 6.73 m
22. (3-7) 8,790 mg = 8.79 g
23. (3-7) 4,400 mL = 4.4 L



# Exercises

## Check Understanding

**Find two fractions equivalent to each fraction.** 1–5. Answers may vary. Samples are given.

1. $\frac{2}{8}$ $\frac{1}{4}, \frac{4}{16}$
2. $\frac{8}{10}$ $\frac{4}{5}, \frac{16}{20}$
3. $\frac{3}{9}$ $\frac{1}{3}, \frac{2}{6}$
4. $\frac{8}{36}$ $\frac{2}{9}, \frac{16}{72}$
5. $\frac{15}{30}$ $\frac{1}{2}, \frac{2}{4}$

**Write in simplest form.**

6. $\frac{3}{9}$ $\frac{1}{3}$
7. $\frac{4}{10}$ $\frac{2}{5}$
8. $\frac{12}{48}$ $\frac{1}{4}$
9. $\frac{2x}{3x}$ $\frac{2}{3}$
10. $\frac{4km^2}{12k}$ $\frac{m^2}{3}$

11. Write the numerator and denominator of $\frac{24}{32}$ as products of prime factors. Then use the prime factors to write $\frac{24}{32}$ in simplest form. $\frac{2 \cdot 2 \cdot 2 \cdot 3}{2 \cdot 2 \cdot 2 \cdot 2 \cdot 2} = \frac{3}{4}$

## Practice and Problem Solving

**Find two fractions equivalent to each fraction.** 12–17. Answers may vary. Samples are given.

12. $\frac{4}{8}$ $\frac{1}{2}, \frac{2}{4}$
13. $\frac{4}{10}$ $\frac{2}{5}, \frac{8}{20}$
14. $\frac{5}{20}$ $\frac{1}{4}, \frac{2}{8}$
15. $\frac{10}{16}$ $\frac{5}{8}, \frac{20}{32}$
16. $\frac{18}{20}$ $\frac{9}{10}, \frac{36}{40}$
17. $\frac{25}{100}$ $\frac{1}{4}, \frac{2}{8}$

**Write in simplest form.**

18. $\frac{2}{10}$ $\frac{1}{5}$
19. $\frac{4}{12}$ $\frac{1}{3}$
20. $\frac{6}{15}$ $\frac{2}{5}$
21. $\frac{15}{25}$ $\frac{3}{5}$
22. $\frac{8}{14}$ $\frac{4}{7}$
23. $\frac{18}{32}$ $\frac{9}{16}$
24. $\frac{20}{30}$ $\frac{2}{3}$
25. $\frac{12}{16}$ $\frac{3}{4}$
26. $\frac{14}{42}$ $\frac{1}{3}$
27. $\frac{3b}{5b}$ $\frac{3}{5}$
28. $\frac{6m}{15m}$ $\frac{2}{5}$
29. $\frac{24x}{16}$ $\frac{3x}{2}$
30. $\frac{8pr}{12p}$ $\frac{2r}{3}$
31. $\frac{14a^2}{24a}$ $\frac{7a}{12}$
32. $\frac{4bc}{16b}$ $\frac{c}{4}$
33. $\frac{40ab}{5ab}$ 8
34. ✪ $\frac{5t}{10t^2}$ $\frac{1}{2t}$
35. ✪ $\frac{x^2y}{3yz}$ $\frac{x^2}{3z}$

36. You share a fishing tackle box with some friends. Of the 20 fishing lures in the box, 5 belong to you. What fraction of the lures belong to you? Write in simplest form. $\frac{1}{4}$

37. *Error Analysis* A student claims $\frac{65}{91}$ is in simplest form. What prime factor do the numerator and denominator still have in common? 13

38. ✪ *Writing* Does $\frac{1}{2}$ of one pizza represent the same amount as $\frac{1}{2}$ of another pizza? Justify your answer. Answers may vary. Sample: Yes, as long as the pizzas are the same size and weight.

39. *Open-ended* Write two fractions whose simplest form is $\frac{3x}{5}$. Answers may vary. Sample: $\frac{6x}{10}, \frac{3xy}{5y}$

40. **TEST PREP** Which fraction is equivalent to $\frac{ab}{5}$? B

A. $\frac{10ab}{50a}$  B. $\frac{15a^2b}{75a}$  C. $\frac{25ab^2}{5b}$  D. $\frac{45a^3b}{15a^2}$



### Alternative Assessment

Have students create a diagram or sketch that models the fact that the fraction $\frac{6}{8}$ and its simplest form are equivalent.

41. *Health* Doctors suggest that most people need about 8 h of sleep each night to stay healthy. What fraction of the day is this? Write your answer in simplest form. $\frac{1}{3}$

*Data Analysis* **Use the table at the right. Write each fraction in simplest form.**

42. In 1997, what fraction of U.S. households had PCs (personal computers)? $\frac{11}{25}$

43. In 1997, what fraction of U.S. households had PCs and modems? $\frac{9}{25}$

44. In 1998, what fraction of U.S. households with PCs were on-line? (Assume a household must have a PC in order to be on-line.) $\frac{9}{16}$

**PC and On-Line Households in the U.S. (millions)**

| | | | Projected | |
|---|---|---|---|---|
| **Households** | **1997** | **1998** | **1999** | **2000** |
| Total households | 100 | 101 | 102 | 103 |
| Households with PCs | 44 | 48 | 52 | 55 |
| Households with PCs and modems | 36 | 42 | 48 | 51 |
| On-line households | 21 | 27 | 33 | 36 |

SOURCE: *The Wall Street Journal Almanac 1999*

## Mixed Review

**Find each GCF.** *(Lesson 4-3)*

45. 10, 12 2
46. 28, 60 4
47. $14a, 21a$ $7a$
48. $24x^2, 40x^3$ $8x^2$

**Solve each equation.** *(Lesson 3-5)*

49. $y + 3.23 = 5.85$ 2.62
50. $b - 2.13 = 9.9$ 12.03
51. $12.8 + z = 6.47$ −6.33

52. *Estimation* A damaged oil tanker spilled 34.7 million gallons of crude oil over 4 days. On average, about how many gallons did the tanker spill each day? *(Lesson 3-2)* 9 million gallons

## Checkpoint 1

**Lessons 4-1 through 4-4**

**Test whether each number is divisible by 2, 3, 5, 9, or 10.**

1. 30 2, 3, 5, 10
2. 54 2, 3, 9
3. 48 2, 3
4. 161 none
5. 2,583 3, 9

**Evaluate each expression.**

6. $x^2$, for $x = 8$ 64
7. $a^3$, for $a = 5$ 125
8. $-2z^2$, for $z = -3$ −18

**Write in simplest form.**

9. $\frac{8}{16}$ $\frac{1}{2}$
10. $\frac{14}{21}$ $\frac{2}{3}$
11. $\frac{16}{28}$ $\frac{4}{7}$
12. $\frac{3a}{12a}$ $\frac{1}{4}$
13. $\frac{2xy}{x}$ $2y$

14. *Open-ended* Write two expressions whose GCF is $5a^2$. Answers may vary. Sample: $5a^2$, $10a^2$

See also Extra Practice section.



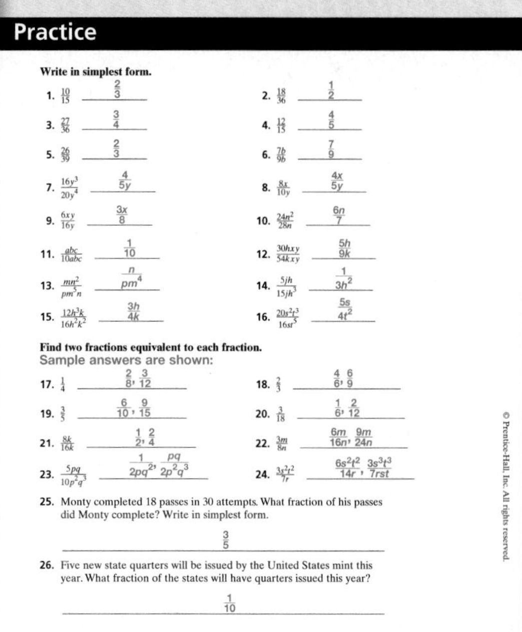

## Practice

**Write in simplest form.**

1. $\frac{10}{15}$ $\frac{2}{3}$
2. $\frac{18}{36}$ $\frac{1}{2}$
3. $\frac{27}{36}$ $\frac{3}{4}$
4. $\frac{12}{15}$ $\frac{4}{5}$
5. $\frac{26}{39}$ $\frac{2}{3}$
6. $\frac{7b}{9b}$ $\frac{7}{9}$
7. $\frac{16y^3}{20y^4}$ $\frac{4}{5y}$
8. $\frac{8x}{10y}$ $\frac{4x}{5y}$
9. $\frac{6xy}{16y}$ $\frac{3x}{8}$
10. $\frac{24n^2}{28n}$ $\frac{6n}{7}$
11. $\frac{abc}{10abc}$ $\frac{1}{10}$
12. $\frac{30hxy}{54kxy}$ $\frac{5h}{9k}$
13. $\frac{mn^2}{pm^5n}$ $\frac{n}{pm^4}$
14. $\frac{5jh}{15jh^3}$ $\frac{1}{3h^2}$
15. $\frac{12h^3k}{16h^2k^2}$ $\frac{3h}{4k}$
16. $\frac{20s^2t^3}{16st^5}$ $\frac{5s}{4t^2}$

**Find two fractions equivalent to each fraction.**
Sample answers are shown:

17. $\frac{1}{4}$ $\frac{2}{8}, \frac{3}{12}$
18. $\frac{2}{3}$ $\frac{4}{6}, \frac{6}{9}$
19. $\frac{3}{5}$ $\frac{6}{10}, \frac{9}{15}$
20. $\frac{3}{18}$ $\frac{1}{6}, \frac{2}{12}$
21. $\frac{8k}{16k}$ $\frac{1}{2}, \frac{2}{4}$
22. $\frac{3m}{8n}$ $\frac{6m}{16n}, \frac{9m}{24n}$
23. $\frac{5pq}{10p^2q^3}$ $\frac{1}{2pq^2}, \frac{pq}{2p^2q^3}$
24. $\frac{3s^2t^2}{7r}$ $\frac{6s^2t^2}{14r}, \frac{3s^3t^3}{7rst}$

25. Monty completed 18 passes in 30 attempts. What fraction of his passes did Monty complete? Write in simplest form.
$\frac{3}{5}$

26. Five new state quarters will be issued by the United States mint this year. What fraction of the states will have quarters issued this year?
$\frac{1}{10}$



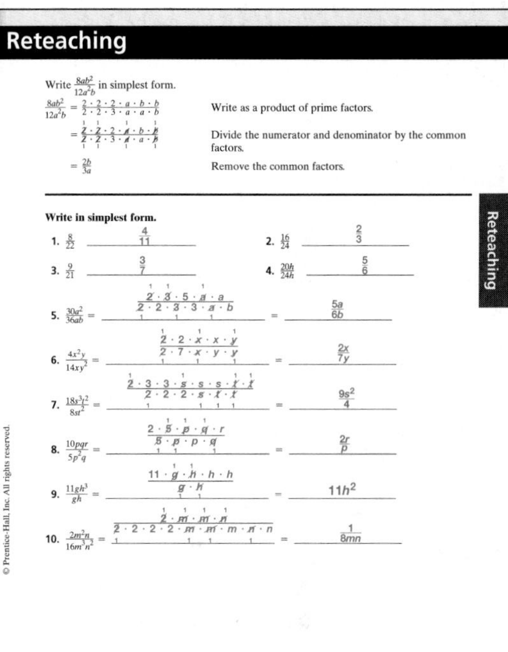

## Reteaching

Write $\frac{8ab^2}{12a^2b}$ in simplest form.

$\frac{8ab^2}{12a^2b} = \frac{2 \cdot 2 \cdot 2 \cdot a \cdot b \cdot b}{2 \cdot 2 \cdot 3 \cdot a \cdot a \cdot b}$ Write as a product of prime factors.

$= \frac{\cancel{2} \cdot \cancel{2} \cdot 2 \cdot \cancel{a} \cdot b \cdot \cancel{b}}{\cancel{2} \cdot \cancel{2} \cdot 3 \cdot \cancel{a} \cdot a \cdot \cancel{b}}$ Divide the numerator and denominator by the common factors.

$= \frac{2b}{3a}$ Remove the common factors.

**Write in simplest form.**

1. $\frac{8}{22}$ $\frac{4}{11}$
2. $\frac{16}{24}$ $\frac{2}{3}$
3. $\frac{9}{21}$ $\frac{3}{7}$
4. $\frac{20h}{24h}$ $\frac{5}{6}$
5. $\frac{30a^2}{36ab} = \frac{\cancel{2} \cdot \cancel{3} \cdot 5 \cdot \cancel{a} \cdot a}{\cancel{2} \cdot 2 \cdot \cancel{3} \cdot 3 \cdot \cancel{a} \cdot b} = \frac{5a}{6b}$
6. $\frac{4x^2y}{14xy^2} = \frac{\cancel{2} \cdot 2 \cdot \cancel{x} \cdot x \cdot \cancel{y}}{\cancel{2} \cdot 7 \cdot \cancel{x} \cdot y \cdot \cancel{y}} = \frac{2x}{7y}$
7. $\frac{18s^3t^2}{8st^2} = \frac{\cancel{2} \cdot 3 \cdot 3 \cdot \cancel{s} \cdot s \cdot s \cdot \cancel{t} \cdot \cancel{t}}{\cancel{2} \cdot 2 \cdot 2 \cdot \cancel{s} \cdot \cancel{t} \cdot \cancel{t}} = \frac{9s^2}{4}$
8. $\frac{10pqr}{5p^2q} = \frac{2 \cdot \cancel{5} \cdot \cancel{p} \cdot \cancel{q} \cdot r}{\cancel{5} \cdot \cancel{p} \cdot p \cdot \cancel{q}} = \frac{2r}{p}$
9. $\frac{11gh^3}{gh} = \frac{11 \cdot \cancel{g} \cdot \cancel{h} \cdot h \cdot h}{\cancel{g} \cdot \cancel{h}} = 11h^2$
10. $\frac{2m^2n}{16m^3n^2} = \frac{\cancel{2} \cdot \cancel{m} \cdot \cancel{m} \cdot \cancel{n}}{\cancel{2} \cdot 2 \cdot 2 \cdot 2 \cdot \cancel{m} \cdot \cancel{m} \cdot m \cdot \cancel{n} \cdot n} = \frac{1}{8mn}$



Reteaching

## Checkpoint

**Test whether each number is divisible by 2, 3, 5, 9, and 10.**

1. 93 3 only
2. 156 2 and 3
3. 4,230 2, 3, 5, 9, and 10

**Evaluate each expression.**

4. $a^2$, for $a = 7$ 49
5. $x^3$, for $x = -1$ −1
6. $-3h^2$, for $h = -5$ −75

**Write in simplest form.**

7. $\frac{12}{15}$ $\frac{4}{5}$
8. $\frac{22}{33}$ $\frac{2}{3}$
9. $\frac{9a}{18a}$ $\frac{1}{2}$

10. Write two pairs of expressions whose GCF is $3x^2$.
Sample answers are shown:

$6x^2$ and $9x^3$; $9x^2$ and $3x^3$

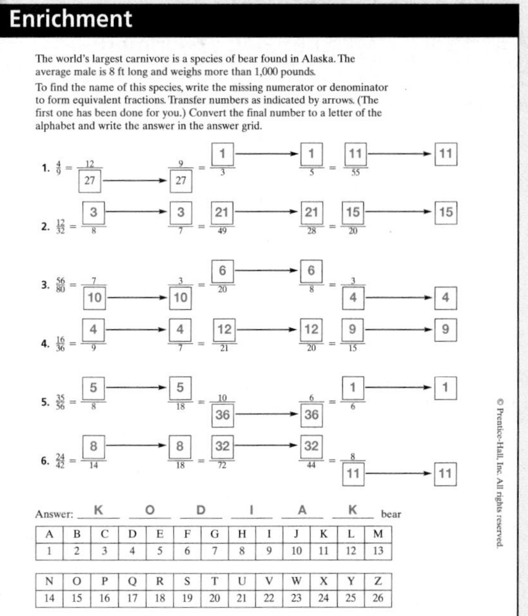

## Enrichment

The world's largest carnivore is a species of bear found in Alaska. The average male is 8 ft long and weighs more than 1,000 pounds.

To find the name of this species, write the missing numerator or denominator to form equivalent fractions. Transfer numbers as indicated by arrows. (The first one has been done for you.) Convert the final number to a letter of the alphabet and write the answer in the answer grid.

1. $\frac{4}{9} = \frac{12}{27}$ → $\frac{9}{27} = \frac{1}{3}$ → $\frac{1}{5} = \frac{11}{55}$ → 11
2. $\frac{12}{32} = \frac{3}{8}$ → $\frac{3}{7} = \frac{21}{49}$ → $\frac{21}{28} = \frac{15}{20}$ → 15
3. $\frac{56}{80} = \frac{7}{10}$ → $\frac{3}{10} = \frac{6}{20}$ → $\frac{6}{8} = \frac{3}{4}$ → 4
4. $\frac{16}{36} = \frac{4}{9}$ → $\frac{4}{7} = \frac{12}{21}$ → $\frac{12}{20} = \frac{9}{15}$ → 9
5. $\frac{35}{56} = \frac{5}{8}$ → $\frac{5}{18} = \frac{10}{36}$ → $\frac{6}{36} = \frac{1}{6}$ → 1
6. $\frac{24}{42} = \frac{8}{14}$ → $\frac{8}{18} = \frac{32}{72}$ → $\frac{32}{44} = \frac{8}{11}$ → 11

Answer: K O D I A K bear

| A | B | C | D | E | F | G | H | I | J | K | L | M |
|---|---|---|---|---|---|---|---|---|---|---|---|---|
| 1 | 2 | 3 | 4 | 5 | 6 | 7 | 8 | 9 | 10 | 11 | 12 | 13 |

| N | O | P | Q | R | S | T | U | V | W | X | Y | Z |
|---|---|---|---|---|---|---|---|---|---|---|---|---|
| 14 | 15 | 16 | 17 | 18 | 19 | 20 | 21 | 22 | 23 | 24 | 25 | 26 |

# 4-5

## Getting Ready

**Resources** A complete list of resources for this lesson is on p. 169H.

### Daily Skills Warm-Up

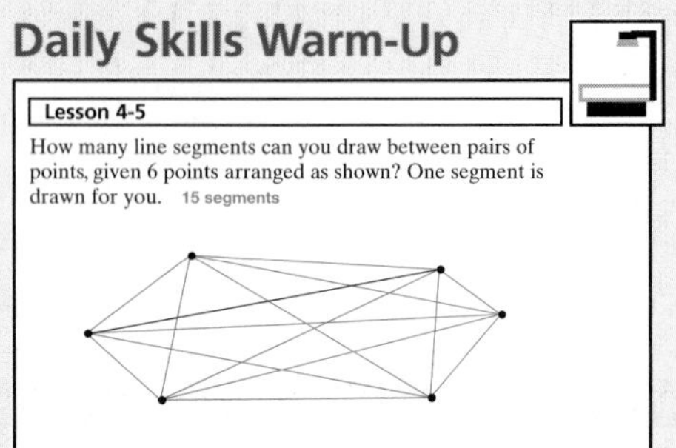
Lesson 4-5

How many line segments can you draw between pairs of points, given 6 points arranged as shown? One segment is drawn for you. 15 segments

### Background for the Lesson

One problem solving strategy is to account for all possibilities. When you solve a problem with this strategy, you carefully organize the data so that you can accurately and completely count the possibilities. If lists and diagrams are not neatly drawn and systematically arranged, it is easy to miss one or more of the possibilities, or to count one twice.

## 1 Focus

### Connecting to Students' Lives

Ask students to describe some of the ways they organize data in their daily lives, for example, class schedules, assignment lists, to-do lists, shopping lists, and budgets. Have students describe how they benefit from keeping their data organized.

### Connecting to Prior Knowledge

In Lesson 4-3, students used a factor tree to account for all possibilities in the prime factorization of a number. In this lesson, students learn more about how to account for all possibilities. In Lesson 5-6, they learn the problem solving strategy of working backward.

# 4-5 Account for All Possibilities

**Problem Solving Strategies**



***Math Strategies in Action*** Have you ever lost something that you just couldn't find anywhere? Don't you usually discover that you didn't check *every* place you could, even when you thought you had?

Even for a situation like losing a TV remote control, making a list of places to search might help.

In some problems, you need to count the possibilities. To solve these problems, you need to be sure that you have found every possible combination. Organized lists and diagrams help you to keep track of possibilities as you find them.

**SAMPLE PROBLEM**

Mandy, Jim, Keisha, Darren, Lin, Chris, and Jen are friends. They want to take pictures of themselves with two people in each picture. How many pictures do they need to take?

### Read

1. What do you need to find? the number of pictures that must be taken
2. How many people are there in all? 7 people
3. How many people will be in each photograph? 2 people

### Plan

To make sure that you account for everyone, make an organized list.



# Tools to Monitor Progress

### BEFORE THE LESSON

**To check prerequisite skills:**

- Working with integers

**Skills Handbook,** p. 741

**Skills Intervention Kit,** Pre-Algebra Basics

### DURING THE LESSON

**To check understanding:**

- **Additional Sample Problem**
  A committee of five members wants to choose three representatives from the committee to present their conclusions to the class. How many different groups of three representatives could they choose? 10

## Solve

First pair Mandy with each of her six friends. Next, pair Jim with each of the five friends left. Since Mandy and Jim have already been paired, you don't need to count them again.

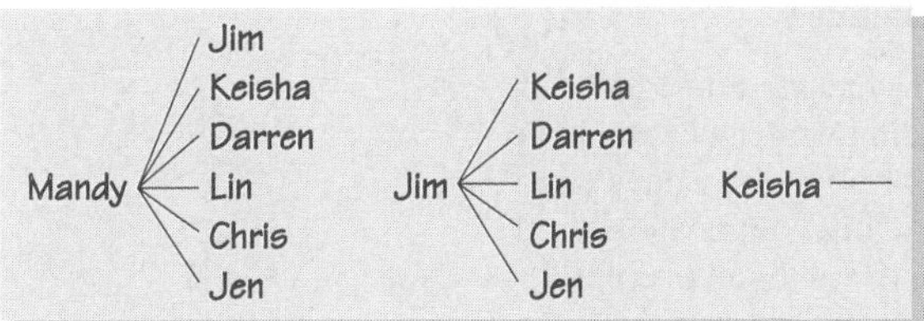


4. Copy and complete the list of paired friends. See below right.
5. What pattern do you see? Each successive "tree" has one less "branch."
6. How many pictures do they need to take? 21 pictures
7. Suppose Mandy and nine friends paired up for pictures. Using the pattern suggested above, find how many pictures there would be. 45 pictures

## Look Back

Another way to solve this problem is to use a diagram. Draw line segments to show all possible pairs of friends.

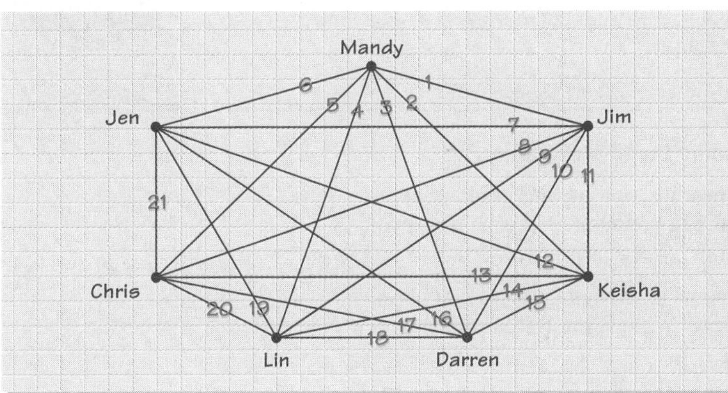


There are 21 line segments. This shows there are 21 pairs of friends.

4. Keisha — Darren, Lin, Chris, Jen
Darren — Lin, Chris, Jen
Lin — Chris, Jen
Chris — Jen



# 2 Teach

## Teaching Notes

**Visual Learning** Place some unsorted different-colored algebra tiles on a surface. Tell the class that you need to know how many tiles there are of each different color. Ask a volunteer to come up and arrange the tiles to make them easier to count. Discuss how the arrangement makes it easier to get a fast and accurate count.

### ■ Sample Problem

**Build understanding.** Ask: How can you be sure that the same two people will not be in two different pictures? When you make a list of paired friends, you leave out the ones who have already been paired.

**Error Prevention** Students may count one pair twice by mistake. For example, Mandy and Jim make up a pair for one picture, but students may also count the pair Jim and Mandy. Point out that the order does not matter in this problem.

**Extension** Ask: One of the group of seven friends suggests that they will have to take fewer pictures if they put three people in every picture, then take a picture of each possible combination of three people. Is this true? Explain your answer. No; with 3 people in each picture, they will need to take 35 pictures to get all possible combinations of 3 people.

**Connecting to Statistics** The collection, manipulation, analysis, and classification of data is part of a branch of mathematics called *statistics.* Some of the problems in this lesson deal with statistical analysis of data. Students will learn more about data analysis in later chapters.

• **Sample Problem**
Suppose you have 10 different CDs to play. Your CD player holds three CDs. How many different sets of three CDs can you select? 120 sets

### AFTER THE LESSON

**To assess knowledge: Lesson Quiz**

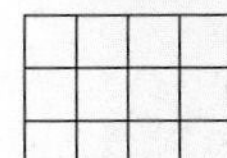

1. Each small box is a square. What is the number of different squares shown? 17

• For enrichment and reteaching options see Resources on p. 169H.

# 3 Practice/Assess

## Assignment Guide

**Core** 1–5, 7, 9–10, 12
✪ **Extension** 6, 8, 11

Mixed Review can be assigned at any time for maintenance.

### Exercises

**Error Prevention Exercises 1–4** You may wish to have students work together in cooperative groups.

**Test Prep Exercise 10** The area of a rectangle is the length times the width, so 36 = *lw*.

### ✪ Challenge

Write a formula for the sample problem that predicts the number of pictures needed by a group of *n* friends with the pictures taken two people at a time. The formula should work no matter how many friends they add to the group.
$\frac{n(n-1)}{2}$

### Closure

To account for all possibilities in a word problem, make an organized list or a diagram to keep track of possibilities as you find them.

# Exercises

## Check Understanding

**Solve each problem by accounting for all possibilities.**

1. A sandwich shop serves turkey, ham, tuna, chicken, and egg salad sandwiches. You can have any sandwich using white, wheat, or rye bread. Suppose you eat there every day. For how many days can you order a sandwich that is different from any you have ordered before? Copy and complete the list below to solve the problem. 15 days

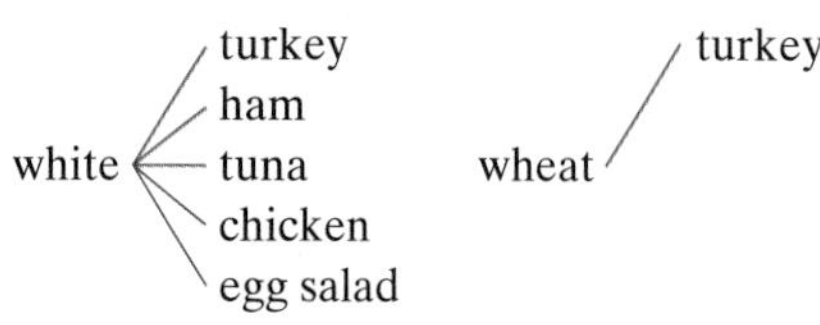

2. You throw three darts at the target shown at the right. If each dart hits the target, what possible point totals can you score? 30, 24, 21, 18, 15, 12, 9, 6, 3
3. *Patterns* Eight people are at a party. Everyone shakes hands once with everyone else. How many handshakes are there altogether? 28 handshakes
4. You have one penny, one nickel, one dime, and one quarter. How many different amounts of money can you make using one or more of these coins? 15 amounts of money

## Practice and Problem Solving

**Solve each problem by accounting for all possibilities.**

5. You have pepperoni, mushrooms, onions, and green peppers. How many different pizzas can you make by using one, two, three, or four of the toppings? 15 pizzas
6. ✪ There are seven softball teams in a league. Each team plays each of the other teams twice. What is the total number of games played? 42 games
7. Four candidates run for president of the student council. Three other candidates run for vice-president. How many different ways can the two offices be filled? 12 ways



### Alternative Assessment

Have students write a list of steps to use when they solve problems involving possibilities.

### Daily Cumulative Review

**Write in simplest form.** *(Lesson 4-4)*

1. $\frac{2}{6}$ $\frac{1}{3}$
2. $\frac{4}{20}$ $\frac{1}{5}$
3. $\frac{60}{80}$ $\frac{3}{4}$
4. $\frac{7m}{56m}$ $\frac{1}{8}$
5. $\frac{h^2}{15h}$ $\frac{h}{15}$
6. $\frac{6s^2n}{64sn}$ $\frac{3s}{32}$

**Find the GCF.** *(Lesson 4-3)*

7. 15, 45 15
8. 36, 81 9
9. 18, 56, 90 2
10. $12n^4, 32n^4$ $4n^4$
11. $12b^2, 156b^4$ $12b^2$
12. $22s^4x^3, 48s^4x$ $2s^4x$

**Mixed Review**

**Evaluate.**

13. (1-3) $\frac{b+c}{3}$, for $b = 16, c = 5$ 7
14. (1-3) $ghy$, for $g = 3, h = 6, y = 2$ 36
15. (1-3) $6v - 5$, for $v = 5$ 25
16. (1-3) $9(n + m)$, for $n = 6, m = 8$ 126

**Graph each set of numbers on the number line. Then order the numbers from least to greatest.**

17. (1-4) −2, 6, −5
−5 −2 6
−7 −5 −3 −1 0 1 3 5 7
−5, −2, 6
18. (1-4) −2, −4, −6
−6 −4 −2
−7 −5 −3 −1 0 1 3 5 7
−6, −4, −2

**Write a rule for each pattern. Find the next three numbers in the pattern.**

19. (1-7) 81, 77, 89, 85, 97, 93, 105, 101, 113
Rule: Start with 81. Alternate subtracting 4 and adding 12.

**Compare. Use >, <, or = to complete each statement.**

20. (1-2) (15 − 3) · 3 [>] 15 − 3 · 3
21. (1-2) 14 − 2 + 7 [>] 14 − (2 + 7)

**Solve using any strategy.**

8. Copy the diagram at the right. Using the paths shown, Jill can walk to Trisha's house in many different ways. Draw each route that is four blocks long. How can you be sure that you have found all possible routes? See below right. Answers may vary. Sample: I was systematic in drawing the routes.

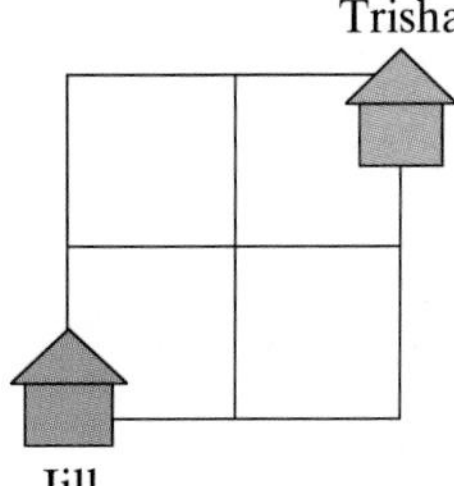


9. *Geometry* You have 24 feet of fence to make a rectangular garden. Each side will measure a whole number of feet. How many different-sized rectangular gardens can you make? 6

10. **TEST PREP** How many different rectangles are there with an area of 36 cm$^2$ if the side lengths, in centimeters, are integers? D

    A. 1 B. 3 C. 4 D. 5

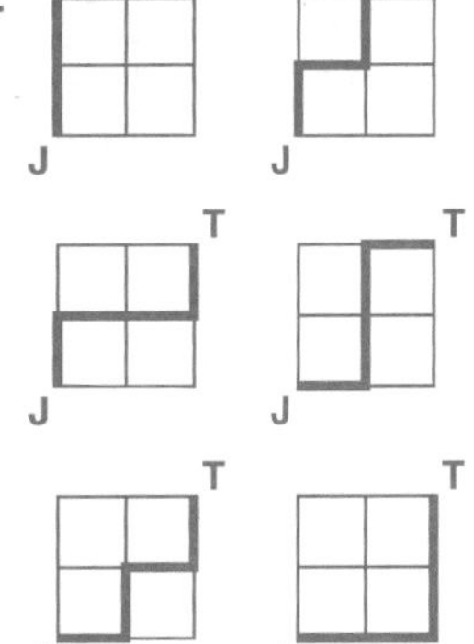


11. a. Five workers take 12 hours to do a job. The number of person-hours the job requires is the number of hours the job would take one person to do. How many person-hours does the job require?

    b. In how many hours could 20 workers do the job?

    a. 60 person-hours b. 3 h

12. *Patterns* The bottom row of a stack of blocks contains 11 blocks. The row above it contains 9 blocks. The next higher row contains 7 blocks. The rows continue in this pattern, and the top row contains a single block. How many blocks does the stack contain in all? 36 blocks

## Mixed Review

**Write in simplest form.** *(Lesson 4-4)*

13. $\frac{6}{12}$ $\frac{1}{2}$ 14. $\frac{10}{40}$ $\frac{1}{4}$ 15. $\frac{6a^2}{15}$ $\frac{2a^2}{5}$ 16. $\frac{14a^3}{28a^2}$ $\frac{a}{2}$

**Write a rule for each pattern.** *(Lesson 1-7)*

17. 10, 20, 30, . . . Start with 10; add 10 repeatedly.
18. 8, 5, 2, −1, . . . Start with 8; subtract 3 repeatedly.
19. 2, 6, 18, 54, . . . Start with 2; multiply by 3 repeatedly.

20. *Choose a Strategy* Elki has read the first 60 pages of a book. When he has read 35 more pages, he will have read half the book. How many pages are in the book? 190 pages

## Activity 2 Analyzing

No calendar uses the exact solar year, which is 365 days, 5 hours, 48 minutes, 46 seconds. What problems arise from rounding a year to 365 days? A *leap year* has an extra day to adjust for the rounding. Explain why leap years occur at four-year intervals.



## Project Activity 2

**Analyzing** To help students get started on answering these questions, suggest that they calculate what the excess time over exactly 365 days will be for 2 years and for 3 years, rounded to the nearest hour.

## Practice

**Solve each problem by accounting for all possibilities.**

1. A baseball team has 4 pitchers and 3 catchers. How many different pitcher-catcher combinations are possible? One way to solve this problem is to make a list like the one started below. Finish the list.
   12

| | |
|---|---|
| P1-C1 | P2-C1 |
| P1-C2 | P2-C2 |
| P1-C3 | P2-C3 |
| P3-C1 | P4-C1 |
| P3-C2 | P4-C2 |
| P3-C3 | P4-C3 |

2. The baseball team has 2 first basemen, 3 second basemen, and 2 third basemen. How many combinations of the three positions are possible?
   12
3. A quarter is tossed 3 times. In how many different orders can heads and tails be tossed?
   8
4. A quarter is tossed 4 times. In how many different orders can heads and tails be tossed?
   16
5. Curtains are manufactured in 3 different styles and 5 different colors.
   a. How many different style-color combinations are possible?
   15
   b. The curtains are produced in 2 different fabrics. How many different style-color-fabric combinations are possible?
   30



Practice

## Reteaching

A taco shop serves beef, chicken, or bean burritos. You can have any burrito on a corn or a flour tortilla and with or without hot sauce. How many different burritos does the shop serve?

The different burritos are listed in the table at the right. To be sure all possibilities are counted, all the beef burritos are listed first. Within those, the two types of beef burritos on a corn tortilla are listed first. The pattern is continued with chicken and then bean burritos.

| Filling | Tortilla | Hot Sauce |
|---|---|---|
| beef | corn | yes |
| beef | corn | no |
| beef | flour | yes |
| beef | flour | no |
| chicken | corn | yes |
| chicken | corn | no |
| chicken | flour | yes |
| chicken | flour | no |
| bean | corn | yes |
| bean | corn | no |
| bean | flour | yes |
| bean | flour | no |

**Solve each problem by accounting for all possibilities.**

1. Kara and Karl love steak, fried chicken, hamburgers, mashed potatoes, and french fries. They like green beans and peas. How many different meals including a meat, potatoes, and a green vegetable can they make from these choices? List all possibilities in the table to find the number of different meals.
   12 meals
2. What is the most money you can have in coins and not be able to make change for a dollar? Hint: You do not have to have each kind of coin.
   $1.19

| Meat | Potato | Vegetable |
|---|---|---|
| steak | mashed | beans |
| steak | mashed | peas |
| steak | fries | beans |
| steak | fries | peas |
| chicken | mashed | beans |
| chicken | mashed | peas |
| chicken | fries | beans |
| chicken | fries | peas |
| hamburger | mashed | beans |
| hamburger | mashed | peas |
| hamburger | fries | beans |
| hamburger | fries | peas |
| | | |
| | | |
| | | |



## Enrichment

A coin is tossed 2 times. The organized list shows that 4 orders of heads (H) and tails (T) are possible.

| 1st toss | 2nd toss |
|---|---|
| H | H |
| H | T |
| T | H |
| T | T |

1. In how many of the 4 possible orders will the following occur?
   a. 0 heads 1 b. exactly 1 heads 2 c. 2 heads 1

The organized list shows that eight orders of heads and tails are possible if a coin is tossed three times.

| 1st | 2nd | 3rd |
|---|---|---|
| H | H | H |
| H | H | T |
| H | T | H |
| H | T | T |
| T | H | H |
| T | H | T |
| T | T | H |
| T | T | T |

2. In how many of the eight possible orders will the following occur?
   a. 0 heads 1
   b. exactly 1 head 3
   c. exactly 2 heads 3
   d. exactly 3 heads 1
3. The above results show that there are four possible outcomes when a coin is tossed twice and eight outcomes when it is tossed three times.
   a. Complete: $4 = 2^{2}$ $8 = 2^{3}$
   b. State a rule involving powers of 2 that gives the number of possible outcomes when a coin is tossed $n$ times.
   The number of outcomes when a coin is tossed $n$ times is $2^n$.

**Suppose a coin is tossed four times.**

4. How many outcomes are possible? 16
5. The pattern of numbers shown here is called Pascal's triangle. Explain how the numbers in each row are calculated.
   Each entry is the sum of the two entries above.
6. Compare your answers to Exercises 1 and 2 with rows 3 and 4 of Pascal's triangle. What do you notice?
   They are the same.
7. When a coin is tossed 4 times in how many of the outcomes does exactly 2 heads occur?
   6

1
1 1
1 2 1
1 3 3 1
1 4 6 4 1
1 5 10 10 5 1
1 6 15 20 15 6 1

Enrichment

# 4-6

## Getting Ready

**Key Terms** rational number

**Resources** A complete list of resources for this lesson is on p. 169H.

### Daily Skills Warm-Up

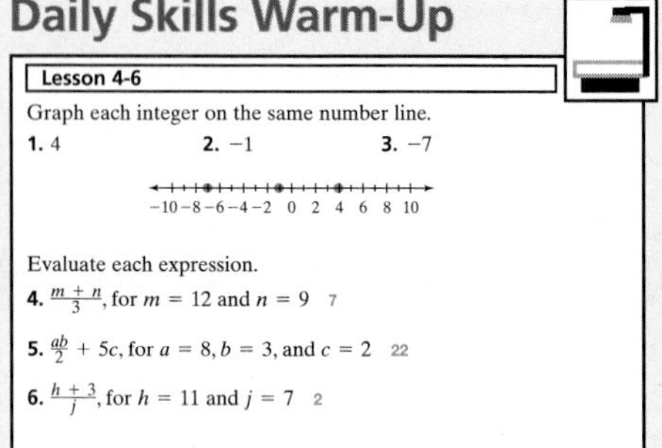

Lesson 4-6

Graph each integer on the same number line.

1. 4 2. −1 3. −7

−10 −8 −6 −4 −2 0 2 4 6 8 10

Evaluate each expression.

4. $\frac{m+n}{3}$, for $m = 12$ and $n = 9$ 7

5. $\frac{ab}{2} + 5c$, for $a = 8$, $b = 3$, and $c = 2$ 22

6. $\frac{h+3}{j}$, for $h = 11$ and $j = 7$ 2

### Background for the Lesson

A *rational* number is any number that you can write as the *ratio* of two integers, $\frac{x}{y}$, with the divisor $y$ not equal to zero. A decimal number that ends is rational (4, 4.1, 0.444, 4.00004). A number that has a *repeating set of digits* is rational. Often a bar over the digits indicates the repeating set of digits ($0.\overline{3}$, $6.\overline{12}$, $0.\overline{3487}$). In decimal form, the rational number $\frac{1}{16}$ ends: $\frac{1}{16} = 0.0625$. The number $\frac{2}{7}$ is equal to $0.\overline{285714}$, which has a repeating pattern of six digits.

## 1 Focus

### Connecting to Students' Lives

Ask students to think of the last time they used a fraction outside the classroom, perhaps as a shoe size, money, a measurement, or a share of a sandwich. Students will learn that fractions belong to a set of numbers known as the rational numbers.



# 4-6 Rational Numbers

**What You'll Learn**

1. To identify and graph rational numbers
2. To evaluate fractions containing variables

**. . . And Why**

To use rational numbers in real-world situations, such as problems involving rates

## Part 1 Identifying and Graphing Rational Numbers

A **rational number** is any number you can write as a quotient $\frac{a}{b}$ of two integers, where $b$ is not zero. The diagram below shows rational numbers.

Notice that all integers are rational numbers. This is true because you can write any integer $a$ as $\frac{a}{1}$.

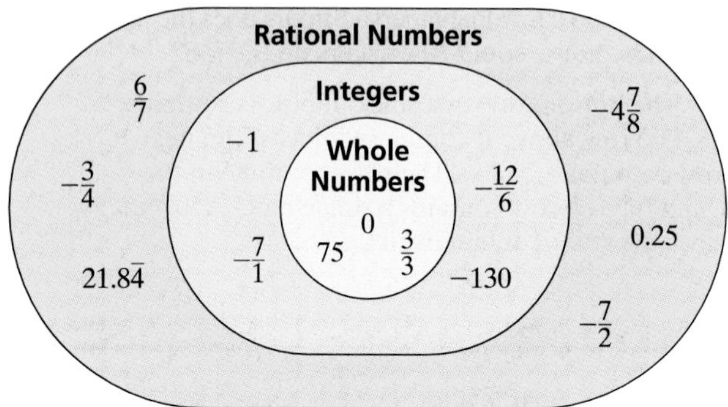


Here are three ways you can write a negative rational number.

$$-\frac{7}{9} = \frac{-7}{9} = \frac{7}{-9}$$

For each rational number, there are an unlimited number of equivalent fractions.

**Quick Review**

The quotient of two integers with the same sign is positive.

The quotient of two integers with opposite signs is negative.

**EXAMPLE 1**

**Write two lists of fractions equivalent to $\frac{1}{2}$.**

$\frac{1}{2} = \frac{2}{4} = \frac{3}{6} = \cdots$ Numerators and denominators are positive.

$\frac{1}{2} = \frac{-1}{-2} = \frac{-2}{-4} = \cdots$ Numerators and denominators are negative.

**TRY THIS** Write three fractions equivalent to each fraction.

1–4. Answers may vary. Samples are given.

1. $\frac{1}{3}$ $\frac{2}{6}, \frac{-2}{-6}, \frac{-1}{-3}$
2. $-\frac{4}{5}$ $-\frac{8}{10}, \frac{-4}{5}, \frac{4}{-5}$
3. $\frac{5}{8}$ $\frac{10}{16}, \frac{-10}{-16}, \frac{-5}{-8}$
4. $-\frac{1}{2}$ $-\frac{2}{4}, \frac{-1}{2}$



## Tools to Monitor Progress

**BEFORE THE LESSON**

**To check prerequisite skills:**

- Writing equivalent fractions

**Skills Handbook,** p. 737

**Skills Intervention Kit,** Number Theory and Fraction Concepts

**DURING THE LESSON**

**To check understanding:**

**Try This** exercises on student page

- **Additional Example 1**

  Write two lists of fractions equivalent to $\frac{2}{3}$.

  $\frac{2}{3} = \frac{4}{6} = \frac{6}{9} = \ldots$

  $\frac{2}{3} = \frac{-2}{-3} = \frac{-4}{-6} = \ldots$

You can graph rational numbers on a number line.

### Example 2

**Graph each rational number on a number line.**

**a.** $\frac{1}{2}$ **b.** $-\frac{8}{10}$ **c.** 1 **d.** $-0.2$

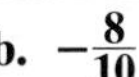

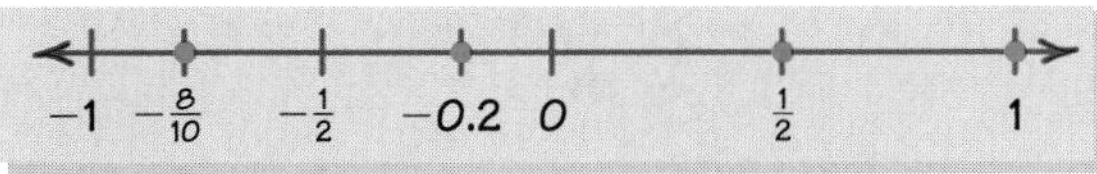


**Try This** Graph each rational number on the same number line.

**5.** $-\frac{1}{2}$ **6.** $-\frac{4}{10}$ **7.** $-2$ **8.** 0.9

5–8.

## Part 2 Evaluating Fractions Containing Variables

To evaluate fractions with variables, remember that a fraction bar is a grouping symbol. First, substitute for the variables and simplify the expressions in the numerator and denominator. Then, write the fraction in simplest form.

Simplify the numerator. → Simplify the denominator. → $\frac{1+9+2}{2-5} = \frac{12}{-3} = -4$

REAL-WORLD CONNECTION

### Example 3

*Science* **The speed of a car changes from 37 ft/s to 102 ft/s in five seconds. What is its acceleration in feet/second² (ft/s²)? Use the formula $a = \frac{f-i}{t}$, where $a$ is acceleration, $f$ is final speed, $i$ is initial speed, and $t$ is time.**

$a = \frac{f-i}{t}$ Use the acceleration formula.

$= \frac{102-37}{5}$ Substitute.

$= \frac{65}{5}$ Subtract.

$= 13$ Write in simplest form.

The car's acceleration is 13 ft/s².

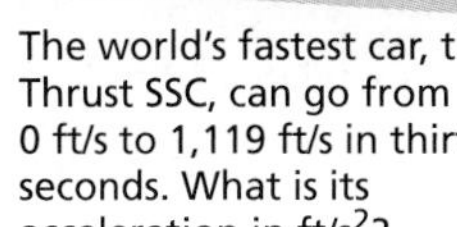

The world's fastest car, the Thrust SSC, can go from 0 ft/s to 1,119 ft/s in thirty seconds. What is its acceleration in ft/s²? 373 ft/s²

**Try This** Evaluate each expression for $a = 6$ and $b = -5$.

**9.** $\frac{a+b}{-3}$ $-\frac{1}{3}$ **10.** $\frac{7-b}{3a}$ $\frac{2}{3}$ **11.** $\frac{a+9}{b}$ $-3$



# 2 Teach

## Part 1 Teaching Notes

The diagram shows that all whole numbers and integers are also rational numbers. Have volunteers give examples of whole numbers and integers written as the ratio of integers. Then have other volunteers give examples of rational numbers that are not integers or whole numbers.

### Example 1

**Build understanding.** Ask: Why isn't $\frac{-2}{-4}$ a negative number? The quotient of two integers with the same sign is positive.

**Error Prevention** The definition of a rational number says that you *can* write it as the ratio of two integers. A number such as 13 is rational, even though it is not written in the form of a fraction.

### Example 2

**Build understanding.** Ask: Where on a number line will you graph rational numbers that are positive? that are negative? positives to the right of zero; negatives to the left of zero

## Part 2 Teaching Notes

Explain that even though division precedes addition and subtraction in the order of operations, they must complete all operations grouped in the numerator and denominator before the fraction can be written in simplest form.

### Example 3

**Build understanding.** Ask: In the formula for acceleration, what must be done before the fraction can be written in simplest form? Subtract initial speed from final speed.

**Extension** Describe the steps you would use to evaluate this fraction: $\frac{3 \cdot 2 + 8}{12 - 2}$. Do the multiplication in the numerator, then the addition, then the subtraction in the denominator, then write the fraction in simplest form.

- **Additional Example 2**
Graph each rational number on a number line.
**a.** $\frac{1}{3}$ **b.** $-\frac{3}{4}$ **c.** 0.5 **d.** 0

−1.5 −1 −.5 0 .5 1 1.5

- **Additional Example 3**
A fast sports car can accelerate from a stop to 90 ft/s in 5 s. What is its acceleration? 18 ft/s²

## AFTER THE LESSON

### To assess knowledge:

**Lesson Quiz**

Write three fractions equivalent to the fraction.

**1.** $\frac{5}{6}$ sample answer: $\frac{-5}{-6} = \frac{10}{12} = \frac{15}{18}$

Evaluate the expression for $x = 7$ and $y = 22$. Write in simplest form.

**2.** $\frac{-9}{x-y}$ $\frac{3}{5}$

- For enrichment and reteaching options see Resources on p. 169H.

# 3 Practice/Assess

## Assignment Guide

To provide flexible scheduling, this lesson can be divided into parts.

**Part 1**
Core 1–5, 10–18, 25–28
Extension 30–33, 37

**Part 2**
Core 6–9, 19–24, 29
Extension 34–36

Mixed Review can be assigned at any time for maintenance.

## Exercises

**Exercise 25** Suggest that there may be one or more choices that are incorrect on the basis of the sign alone.

**ELL Exercises 34–36** Read the directions for these exercises carefully.

## Challenge

When $a$ and $b$ are integers, what must be true of $b$ for $\frac{a}{b}$ to be a rational number? $b \neq 0$

## Closure

Equivalent fractions look alike when they are in simplest form. A fraction is in simplest form when the numerator and the denominator have no factors in common other than 1. You can use the GCF to write a fraction in simplest form. A rational number is any number you can write as a quotient of two integers, $\frac{a}{b}$, where $b$ is not zero.

## Daily Cumulative Review

**Solve each problem by accounting for all possibilities.** *(Lesson 4-5)*

1. Chris has 6 different colors of cupcake sprinkles. He wants to sprinkle each of his cupcakes with two different colors. What is the maximum number of combinations he could have? 15 combinations
2. You have strawberry, vanilla, chocolate, and chocolate chip ice cream. How many different double dip cones can you make? You can have 2 of the same flavor on a cone. 10 cones

**Find two fractions equivalent to each fraction.** *(Lesson 4-4)* Answers may vary.

3. $\frac{3}{6}$ $\frac{1}{2}, \frac{6}{12}$
4. $\frac{4}{16}$ $\frac{1}{4}, \frac{8}{32}$
5. $\frac{75}{100}$ $\frac{3}{4}, \frac{150}{200}$
6. $\frac{10}{12}$ $\frac{5}{6}, \frac{30}{36}$
7. $\frac{3}{15}$ $\frac{1}{5}, \frac{6}{30}$
8. $\frac{5}{25}$ $\frac{1}{5}, \frac{10}{50}$

**Mixed Review**

**Simplify each expression.**

9. (4-2) $(-3)(-4)^2(3)$ −144
10. (4-2) $(-5)^2 + 2 \cdot 1^2$ 27
11. (4-2) $6^2 + 6^5$ 7,812
12. (4-2) $2(7-3)^2$ 32
13. (4-2) $76 - (4 \cdot 2)^2$ 12
14. (4-2) $14 + (3+7)^2 \div 2^2$ 39

**Find each product.**

15. (1-9) $7 \cdot 5(-3)$ −105
16. (1-9) $-4(-6)(-2)$ −48
17. (1-9) $-8(9)(-3)$ 216

**Evaluate each formula for the values given.**

18. (3-4) perimeter of a square: $P = 4s$ when $s = 3$ ft. $P = 12$ ft
19. (3-4) distance: $d = rt$ when $r = 17$ mi/h, $t = 5$ h. $d = 85$ mi



# Exercises

26b. Explanations may vary. Sample: No; between any two numbers you can find another number, so there is no limit to the number of rational numbers between 0 and $\frac{1}{2}$.

## Check Understanding

**Write three fractions equivalent to each fraction.** 1–5. Answers may vary. Samples are given.

1. $\frac{1}{6}$ $\frac{2}{12}, \frac{-2}{-12}, \frac{-1}{-6}$
2. $\frac{3}{5}$ $\frac{6}{10}, \frac{-6}{-10}, \frac{-3}{-5}$
3. $-\frac{5}{9}$ $-\frac{10}{18}, \frac{-5}{9}, \frac{5}{-9}$
4. $\frac{2}{8}$ $\frac{1}{4}, \frac{-1}{-4}, \frac{-2}{-8}$
5. $-\frac{4}{4}$ $-\frac{1}{1}, -\frac{2}{2}, -\frac{3}{3}$

**Evaluate for $a = -4$ and $b = -6$. Write in simplest form.**

6. $\frac{a}{b}$ $\frac{2}{3}$
7. $\frac{a+9}{b}$ $-\frac{5}{6}$
8. $\frac{b+a}{3a}$ $\frac{5}{6}$
9. $\frac{2a+b}{20}$ $-\frac{7}{10}$

## Practice and Problem Solving

**Write three fractions equivalent to each fraction.** 10–14. Answers may vary. Samples are given.

10. $\frac{3}{4}$ $\frac{6}{8}, \frac{-6}{-8}, \frac{-3}{-4}$
11. $-\frac{2}{5}$ $-\frac{4}{10}, \frac{-2}{5}, \frac{2}{-5}$
12. $\frac{4}{12}$ $\frac{1}{3}, \frac{-1}{-3}, \frac{-4}{-12}$
13. $-\frac{12}{27}$ $-\frac{4}{9}, \frac{-12}{27}, \frac{12}{-27}$
14. $\frac{7}{11}$ $\frac{14}{22}, \frac{-14}{-22}, \frac{-7}{-11}$

**Graph the rational numbers below on the same number line.**

15. $\frac{1}{10}$
16. $-\frac{3}{5}$
17. 2
18. $-0.3$

15–18. −2, $-\frac{3}{5}$, −0.3, 0, $\frac{1}{10}$, 1, 2

**Evaluate. Write in simplest form.**

19. $\frac{m}{n}$, for $m = -2$ and $n = 8$ $-\frac{1}{4}$
20. $\frac{m-n}{-12}$, for $m = -3$ and $n = 6$ $\frac{3}{4}$
21. $\frac{3m-11}{n}$, for $m = 7$ and $n = 14$ $\frac{5}{7}$
22. $\frac{y}{-x}$, for $x = 5$ and $y = -4$ $\frac{4}{5}$
23. $\frac{-2y}{x^2}$, for $x = 9$ and $y = 3$ $-\frac{2}{27}$
24. $\frac{y(xy-7)}{10}$, for $x = 6$ and $y = 2$ 1

25. Which of the following rational numbers are equivalent to $-\frac{4}{5}$? $\frac{4}{-5}, \frac{-12}{15}, -\frac{16}{20}, \frac{-4}{-5}$ $\frac{4}{-5}, \frac{-12}{15}, -\frac{16}{20}$

26a. Answers may vary. Sample: $\frac{1}{3}, \frac{1}{4}$

26. a. *Open-ended* Write two rational numbers between 0 and $\frac{1}{2}$.
    b. *Critical Thinking* Is there any limit to the number of rational numbers between 0 and $\frac{1}{2}$? Explain. See above.
27. *Writing* Can two different fractions that are written in simplest form be equivalent to each other? Explain. See margin.
28. *Mathematical Reasoning* What are three fractions equivalent to $\frac{a}{b}$? Justify your answers. See below.
29. *Science* The formula $s = \frac{1{,}600}{d^2}$ gives the strength $s$ of a radio signal at a distance $d$ miles from the transmitter. What is the strength at 5 mi? Write your answer in simplest form. 64

What is the strength of a radio signal at 10 miles from a transmitter? 16

28. Answers may vary. Sample: $\frac{-a}{-b}, \frac{2a}{2b}$, and $\frac{-2a}{-2b}$ all simplify to $\frac{a}{b}$ so they are equivalent to $\frac{a}{b}$.



## Alternative Assessment

Have students draw a concept map (similar to the one that opens the lesson, but without looking at that one) of the set of rational numbers, integers, and whole numbers, with examples in each area.

27. No; if equivalent, you could multiply the numerator and denominator of one fraction by the same nonzero number to get the other, meaning that the numerator and the denominator of the other fraction have a common factor.

**Write the opposite and the absolute value of each number.**

**SAMPLE** Find the opposite and absolute value of $-\frac{3}{5}$.

Opposite:

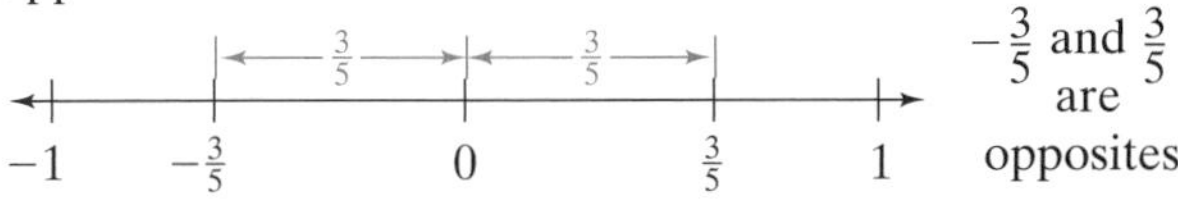

$-\frac{3}{5}$ and $\frac{3}{5}$ are opposites.

Absolute value:

$\left|-\frac{3}{5}\right| = \frac{3}{5}$

30. $-\frac{5}{6}$ $\frac{5}{6}, \frac{5}{6}$  31. $\frac{2}{3}$ $-\frac{2}{3}, \frac{2}{3}$  32. $\frac{-4}{5}$ $\frac{4}{5}, \frac{4}{5}$  33. $\frac{1}{4}$ $-\frac{1}{4}, \frac{1}{4}$

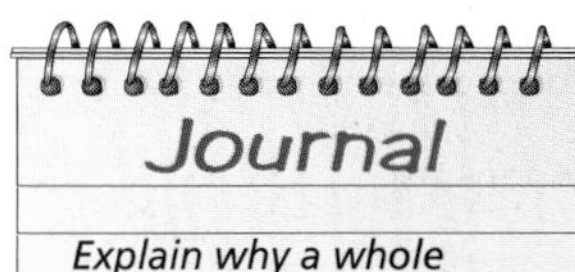

Journal
Explain why a whole number is an integer and an integer is a rational number.


*Mathematical Reasoning* **For positive integers *a* and *b*, tell whether each statement is *always* true. If the statement is not always true, give a counterexample.**

34. $\frac{a^2}{b} > \frac{a}{b}$ Not always true; for $a = 1$, $\frac{1^2}{b} = \frac{1}{b}$.

35. $\frac{3a}{3b} = \frac{a}{b}$ always true

36. $\frac{a^2}{b^2} > \frac{a}{b}$ Not always true; for $a = 1 = b$, $\frac{1^2}{1^2} = \frac{1}{1}$.

37. *Open-ended* Write two rational numbers between −3 and −2. Answers may vary. Sample: $-2\frac{1}{2}, -2\frac{1}{3}$

## MIXED REVIEW

**Write the integer represented by each point on the number line.** ***(Lesson 1-4)***

38. *A* −1  39. *B* 1  40. *C* −4  41. *D* −2

**Multiply or divide.** ***(Lesson 1-9)***

42. $-7 \cdot 4$ −28  43. $19(-5)$ −95  44. $-124 \div (-4)$ 31  45. $-204 \div 6$ −34

46. *Choose a Strategy* Lucia has 4 pairs of pants, 5 shirts, and 2 sweaters. How many different three-piece outfits can she make? 40 three-piece outfits

## ACTIVITY 3 DESIGNING

Design your own calendar. Use what you have learned about multiples and factors to decide how to divide your calendar year into shorter periods. Will your calendar have months? Weeks? Justify your decisions.

See also Extra Practice section.



## Project Activity 3

**Designing** Encourage students to think of new and different approaches that have not been tried before. Begin by considering how they would like their time to be structured. Consider whether lights and electricity might suggest a calendar different from the ones people invented when there was no artificial light.

## Practice

**Graph the rational numbers below on the same number line.**

1. $\frac{3}{4}$  2. $-\frac{1}{4}$  3. −0.5  4. 0.3

**Evaluate. Write in simplest form.**

5. $\frac{x}{y}$, for $x = 12, y = 21$ $\frac{4}{7}$
6. $\frac{n}{n+p}$, for $n = 9, p = 6$ $\frac{3}{5}$
7. $\frac{k}{k^2+4}$, for $k = 6$ $\frac{3}{20}$
8. $\frac{x-y}{-21}$, for $x = -2, y = 5$ $\frac{1}{3}$
9. $\frac{m}{-n}$, for $m = 6, n = 7$ $-\frac{6}{7}$
10. $\frac{x(xy-8)}{60}$, for $x = 3, y = 9$ $\frac{19}{20}$

**Write three fractions equivalent to each fraction.** Sample answers are shown:

11. $\frac{5}{7}$ $\frac{-5}{-7}, \frac{10}{14}, \frac{-10}{-14}$
12. $\frac{22}{33}$ $\frac{2}{3}, \frac{-2}{-3}, \frac{4}{6}$
13. $\frac{24}{30}$ $\frac{4}{5}, \frac{-4}{-5}, \frac{-24}{-30}$
14. $\frac{6}{16}$ $\frac{3}{8}, \frac{-3}{-8}, \frac{-6}{-16}$

15. Which of the following rational numbers are equal to $-\frac{17}{10}$? $-17, -1.7, -\frac{34}{20}, 0.17$ $-1.7, -\frac{34}{20}$

16. Which of the following rational numbers are equal to $\frac{3}{5}$? $\frac{12}{20}, \frac{-3}{-5}, 0.3, \frac{6}{10}$ $\frac{12}{20}, \frac{-3}{-5}, \frac{6}{10}$

17. Which of the following rational numbers are equal to $\frac{12}{15}$? $\frac{4}{5}, \frac{40}{50}, -\frac{8}{10}, \frac{8}{10}$ $\frac{4}{5}, \frac{40}{50}, \frac{8}{10}$

18. The weight *w* of an object in pounds is related to its distance *d* from the center of Earth by the equation $w = \frac{320}{d^2}$, where *d* is in thousands of miles. How much does the object weigh at sea level which is about 4,000 miles from the center of Earth? 20 lb



## Reteaching

Evaluate $\frac{a+7}{b}$, for $a = 9$ and $b = -2$. Write in simplest form.

$\frac{a+7}{b} = \frac{9+7}{-2}$ Substitute.

$= \frac{16}{-2}$ Add.

$= -8$ Write in simplest form.

**Evaluate. Write in simplest form.**

1. $\frac{a}{b}$, for $a = -12$ and $b = 6$ −2
2. $\frac{m-n}{-4}$, for $m = -5$ and $n = 3$ 2
3. $\frac{2x-5}{y}$, for $x = 6$ and $y = 21$ $\frac{1}{3}$
4. $\frac{h}{h^2-2}$, for $h = 4$ $\frac{2}{7}$
5. $\frac{n}{2m-8}$, for $m = 2$ and $n = 10$ $-\frac{5}{2}$
6. $\frac{x}{3y+4}$, for $x = 4$ and $y = 6$ $\frac{2}{11}$
7. $\frac{-r-s}{s+2}$, for $r = -4$ and $s = 2$ $\frac{1}{2}$
8. $\frac{j^2-k}{k}$, for $j = 4$ and $k = -12$ $-\frac{7}{3}$
9. $\frac{10+f^2}{3f}$, for $f = 6$ $\frac{23}{9}$
10. $\frac{z+2}{z^2-4}$, for $z = 6$ $\frac{1}{4}$
11. $\frac{a^2+b^2}{2a+b}$, for $a = 4$ and $b = -3$ 5
12. $\frac{e}{f^2-2f+1}$, for $e = -6$ and $f = 5$ $-\frac{3}{8}$
13. $\frac{17-u^2}{v^2-4v}$, for $u = -3$ and $v = 2$ −2
14. $\frac{-50}{2x^2-3x+5}$, for $x = -1$ −5
15. $\frac{y^3-4y+6}{y^3}$, for $y = -2$ $-\frac{3}{4}$

Reteaching



## Enrichment

**Complete the table for the values of *m* and *n* given. Then try several pairs of values of your own.**

| | $m$ | $n$ | $\frac{m^2-n^2}{m+n}$ | $m-n$ |
|---|---|---|---|---|
| 1. | 5 | 2 | 3 | 3 |
| 2. | 8 | 2 | 6 | 6 |
| 3. | 3 | 10 | −7 | −7 |
| 4. | 6 | 1 | 5 | 5 |
| 5. | 12 | 2 | 10 | 10 |

Sample answers are shown. (rows 4–5)

6. What do you notice? $\frac{m^2-n^2}{m+n} = m - n$

7. Complete the table and look for a pattern. Sample answers are shown:

| $a$ | 2 | 4 | 7 | 10 | 8 | −2 | 1 |
|---|---|---|---|---|---|---|---|
| $\frac{a^2+2a-15}{a-3}$ | 7 | 9 | 12 | 15 | 13 | 3 | 6 |

8. Describe the pattern. $\frac{a^2-2a-15}{a-3} = a + 5$

9. What happens if you try $a = 3$?

Sample answer is shown: You cannot evaluate the fraction because the denominator evaluates to zero. The fraction is undefined.

# 4-7

## Getting Ready

**Resources** A complete list of resources for this lesson is on p. 169H.

### Daily Skills Warm-Up

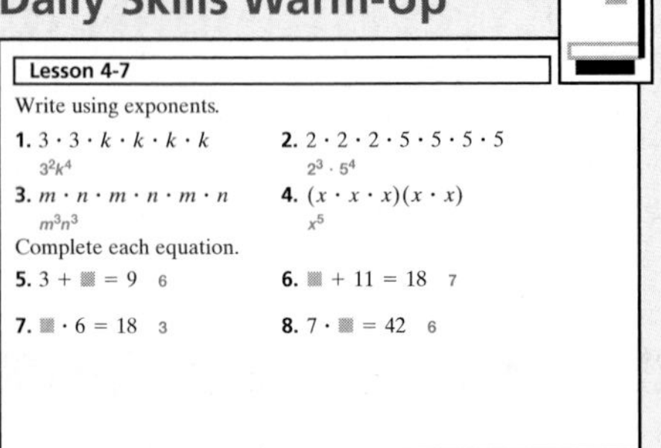
Lesson 4-7

Write using exponents.

1. $3 \cdot 3 \cdot k \cdot k \cdot k \cdot k$ $3^2k^4$
2. $2 \cdot 2 \cdot 2 \cdot 5 \cdot 5 \cdot 5 \cdot 5$ $2^3 \cdot 5^4$
3. $m \cdot n \cdot m \cdot n \cdot m \cdot n$ $m^3n^3$
4. $(x \cdot x \cdot x)(x \cdot x)$ $x^5$

Complete each equation.

5. $3 + ■ = 9$ 6
6. $■ + 11 = 18$ 7
7. $■ \cdot 6 = 18$ 3
8. $7 \cdot ■ = 42$ 6

### Background for the Lesson

Exponents indicate repeated multiplication. You can write $5 \bullet 5 \bullet 5$ as $5^3$. The exponent tells you how many times to use the base as a factor. When you multiply two powers with the same base, you are putting more factors in the product. The product $5^3 \bullet 5^4$ becomes $(5 \bullet 5 \bullet 5) \bullet (5 \bullet 5 \bullet 5 \bullet 5)$, or $5^7$. To multiply two powers with the same base, you use the sum of the exponents with the same base. So, $5^3 \bullet 5^4 = 5^{3+4}$, or $5^7$. To raise a power to a power, you can write out the factors like this: $(5^3)^4 = 5^3 \bullet 5^3 \bullet 5^3 \bullet 5^3$. This shows that to raise a power to a power, you multiply the exponents: $(5^3)^4 = 5^{3 \bullet 4}$, or $5^{12}$.

## 1 Focus

### Connecting to Students' Lives

Remind students that they have probably used metric measurements. Grams and kilograms and other metric units are related to each other by powers of 10. For example, one kilogram is $10^3$ grams.

### Connecting to Prior Knowledge

In Lesson 4-2, students learned to use exponents to show repeated multiplication. In this lesson, they learn how to multiply numbers with exponents. In Lesson 4-8, they will learn about exponents and division.

# 4-7 Exponents and Multiplication

**What You'll Learn**

1. To multiply powers with the same base
2. To find a power of a power

**. . . And Why**

To efficiently simplify expressions with exponents

## Part 1 Multiplying Powers with the Same Base

In Lesson 4-2 you learned how to use exponents to indicate repeated multiplication. What happens when you multiply two powers with the same base, such as $7^2$ and $7^3$?

$$7^2 \cdot 7^3 = (7 \cdot 7) \cdot (7 \cdot 7 \cdot 7) = 7^5$$

Notice that $7^2 \cdot 7^3 = 7^{2+3} = 7^5$. In general, when you multiply powers with the same base, you can add the exponents.

**Multiplying Powers with the Same Base**

To multiply numbers or variables with the same base, add the exponents.

| Arithmetic | Algebra |
|---|---|
| $2^3 \cdot 2^4 = 2^{3+4} = 2^7$ | $a^m \cdot a^n = a^{m+n}$, for positive integers $m$ and $n$. |

You *simplify* an expression by doing as many of the indicated operations as possible.

**Quick Review**

$3 = 3^1$

$a = a^1$

### Example 1

**Simplify each expression.**

**a.** $\mathbf{3 \cdot 3^3}$

$3^1 \cdot 3^3 = 3^{1+3}$ Add the exponents of powers with the same base.

$= 3^4$

$= 81$ Simplify.

**b.** $\mathbf{a^5 \cdot a \cdot b^2}$

$a^5 \cdot a^1 \cdot b^2 = a^{5+1}b^2$ Add the exponents of powers with the same base.

$= a^6b^2$ Simplify.

**Try This** Simplify each expression.

1. $2^2 \cdot 2^3$ 32
2. $m^5 \cdot m^7$ $m^{12}$
3. $x^2 \cdot x^3 \cdot y \cdot y^4$ $x^5y^5$



## Tools to Monitor Progress

**BEFORE THE LESSON**

**To check prerequisite skills:**

- Using exponents

**Skills Intervention Kit,** Number Theory and Fraction Concepts

**DURING THE LESSON**

**To check understanding:**

**Try This** exercises on student page

- **Additional Example 1**

  Simplify each expression.

  a. $5^2 \bullet 5^3$ 3,125

  b. $x^5 \bullet y^2 \bullet x^7 \bullet y$ $x^{12}y^3$

## Example 2

**Simplify $-2x^2 \cdot 3x^5$.**

$-2x^2 \cdot 3x^5 = -2 \cdot 3 \cdot x^2 \cdot x^5$ Use the Commutative Property of Multiplication.

$= -6x^{2+5}$ Add the exponents.

$= -6x^7$ Simplify.

**Try This** Simplify each expression.

4. $6a^3 \cdot 3a$ $18a^4$ 5. $-5c^2 \cdot -3c^7$ $15c^9$ 6. $4x^2 \cdot 3x^4$ $12x^6$

## Part 2 Finding a Power of a Power

You can find the power of a power by using the rule for Multiplying Powers with the Same Base.

$(7^2)^3 = (7^2) \cdot (7^2) \cdot (7^2)$ $7^2$ is used as a base 3 times.

$= 7^{2+2+2}$ When multiplying powers with the same base, add the exponents.

$= 7^6$

Notice that $(7^2)^3 = 7^{2 \cdot 3} = 7^6$. You can raise a power to a power by multiplying the exponents.

### Finding a Power of a Power

To find a power of a power, multiply the exponents.

| Arithmetic | Algebra |
|---|---|
| $(2^3)^4 = 2^{3 \cdot 4} = 2^{12}$ | $(a^m)^n = a^{m \cdot n}$, for positive integers $m$ and $n$. |

## Example 3

**Simplify each expression.**

**a.** $(3^2)^3$

$(3^2)^3 = (3)^{2 \cdot 3}$ ← Multiply the exponents. →

$= (3)^6$ ← Simplify the exponent. →

$= 729$ ← Simplify.

**b.** $(a^6)^2$

$(a^6)^2 = a^{6 \cdot 2}$

$= a^{12}$

**Try This** Simplify each expression.

7. $(2^4)^2$ 256 8. $(c^5)^4$ $c^{20}$ 9. $(m^3)^2$ $m^6$

### Test Prep TIP

When in doubt, write it out! If you are unsure about the rules for multiplying powers, write the powers out. For instance, write $x^2 \cdot x^5$ as $(x \cdot x) \cdot (x \cdot x \cdot x \cdot x \cdot x)$. This simplifies to $x^7$.

### Reading Math

You read $(3^2)^3$ as "three squared to the third power." You read $(a^6)^2$ as "$a$ to the sixth power squared."



# 2 Teach

## Part 1 Teaching Notes

Have students write out all the factors of a power, changing $6^2 \cdot 6^3$ into $(6 \cdot 6) \cdot (6 \cdot 6 \cdot 6)$ and then to $6^5$. After several examples, ask students what the rule seems to be.

### Example 1

**Build understanding.** Ask: Why can you rewrite 3 as $3^1$? because $3^1 = 3$

### Example 2

**Build understanding.** Ask: What does the Commutative Property of Multiplication say? You can interchange factors you are multiplying without changing the product.

**Error Prevention** Students may multiply the bases to incorrectly write $2^3 \cdot 2^5$ as $4^8$. Have them write out the factors $(2 \cdot 2 \cdot 2) \cdot (2 \cdot 2 \cdot 2 \cdot 2 \cdot 2) = 2^8$ to show the base is unchanged.

## Part 2 Teaching Notes

Students may wonder whether to add or multiply the exponents. Writing out a short example showing all the factors is a way to verify the correct operation.

**Technology Option** After you introduce the method of multiplying exponents when finding the power of a power, you may want to have students check this method with calculators. Ask some students to find $(7^2)^3$ using a calculator and ask others to find $7^6$ using a calculator, and then compare answers.

**Extension** Challenge students to predict what to do with exponents when dividing powers with the same base. Subtract the exponents.

- **Additional Example 2**
  Simplify $3a^3 \cdot -5a^4$. $-15a^7$
- **Additional Example 3**
  Simplify each expression.
  a. $(-2^3)^3$ $-512$
  b. $(g^5)^4$ $g^{20}$

### AFTER THE LESSON

**To assess knowledge:**

**Lesson Quiz**

Simplify each expression.

1. $2^2 \cdot 2^3$ 32
2. $g^2 \cdot h^2 \cdot h^4 \cdot h$ $g^2h^7$
3. $4r^6s \cdot 7r^3s^5$ $28r^9s^6$
4. $-(2^2)^5$ $-1,024$
5. $(v^3)^8$ $v^{24}$

- For enrichment and reteaching options see Resources on p. 169H.

# 3 Practice/Assess

## Assignment Guide

To provide flexible scheduling, this lesson can be divided into parts.

▼ Part 1
**Core** 1–5, 9–20, 26–29, 43–44
✪ **Extension** 45–48

▼ Part 2
**Core** 6–8, 21–25, 30–38, 40, 42
✪ **Extension** 39, 41

Mixed Review can be assigned at any time for maintenance.

## Exercises

**Auditory Learning Exercises 26–33** Suggest that students work with a partner for these exercises. Ask one of the pair of students to read the equation, including the blank. Then have the other student suggest a response for the blank.

**Test Prep Exercise 40** Use the exponent rules to examine the first three choices to see if one of them is correct before taking the time to multiply 2 by itself 13 times to check answer choice D.

## ✪ Challenge

Simplify $a^5 \cdot a^{12} \cdot b^{21} \cdot (b^0)^9$. $a^{17}b^{21}$

## Closure

To multiply numbers or variables with the same base, add the exponents. To raise a power to a power, multiply the exponents.

### Daily Cumulative Review

**Graph the rational numbers on the number line.** *(Lesson 4-6)*

1. $1, -0.8, \frac{4}{10}, -\frac{3}{10}$

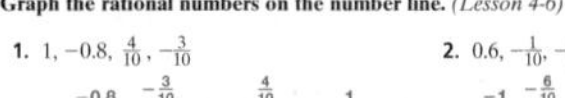

2. $0.6, -\frac{1}{10}, -1, -\frac{7}{10}$

3. $2, -1.4, 1\frac{3}{10}, -1\frac{1}{2}$

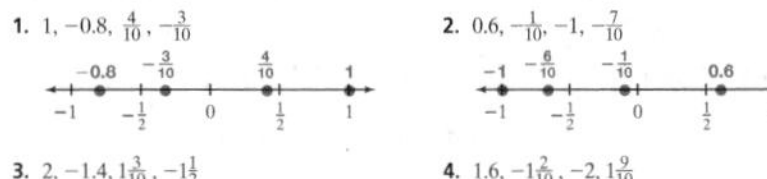

4. $1.6, -1\frac{2}{10}, -2, 1\frac{9}{10}$

**Solve each problem by accounting for all possibilities.** *(Lesson 4-5)*

5. Jason needs to wash the dishes, study for a history test, do his math homework, and take a shower before he goes to bed. The order in which he does these activities does not matter. In how many different ways can he do these activities? 24 ways

**Mixed Review**

**Write the coordinates of each point.**

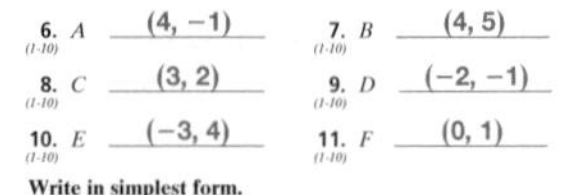

6. $A$ (4, −1)   7. $B$ (4, 5)
8. $C$ (3, 2)   9. $D$ (−2, −1)
10. $E$ (−3, 4)   11. $F$ (0, 1)

**Write in simplest form.**

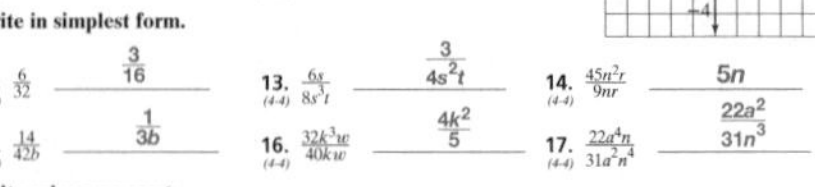

12. $\frac{6}{32}$ $\frac{3}{16}$   13. $\frac{6s}{8s^3t}$ $\frac{3}{4s^2t}$   14. $\frac{45n^2r}{9nr}$ $5n$
15. $\frac{14}{42b}$ $\frac{1}{3b}$   16. $\frac{32k^3w}{40kw}$ $\frac{4k^2}{5}$   17. $\frac{22a^4n}{31a^2n^4}$ $\frac{22a^2}{31n^3}$

**Write using exponents.**

18. $4 \cdot 4 \cdot 4 \cdot d \cdot d$ $4^3d^2$   19. $h \cdot h \cdot 3 \cdot h$ $3h^3$   20. $w \cdot x \cdot w \cdot y$ $w^2xy$



# Exercises

## Check Understanding

**Simplify each expression.**

1. $4^2 \cdot 4$ 64
2. $a^2 \cdot a^5$ $a^7$
3. $x^4 \cdot y \cdot x^5 \cdot y$ $x^9y^2$
4. $7b^3 \cdot 4b^4$ $28b^7$
5. $-9c^2 \cdot (-2c^8)$ $18c^{10}$
6. $(10^3)^2$ 1,000,000
7. $(x^3)^4$ $x^{12}$
8. $(m^6)^4$ $m^{24}$
9. *Critical Thinking* Can $x^6y^7$ be simplified? Explain. No; the bases are not the same.

## Practice and Problem Solving

**Simplify each expression.**

10. $10^2 \cdot 10^5$ 10,000,000
11. $2^2 \cdot 2^5$ 128
12. $x^4 \cdot x^4$ $x^8$
13. $a^{10} \cdot a \cdot a^2$ $a^{13}$
14. $(x^2)(y^5)(x)$ $x^3y^5$
15. $m^{50} \cdot m^2$ $m^{52}$
16. $5x^3 \cdot 2x^6$ $10x^9$
17. $4y^7 \cdot 6y^4$ $24y^{11}$
18. $(-2a^2)(-2a^2)$ $4a^4$
19. $9b^2 \cdot (-4b)^2$ $144b^4$
20. $-7x^6 \cdot -5x^8$ $35x^{14}$
21. $(2^2)^3$ 64
22. $(3^2)^4$ 6,561
23. $(c^2)^8$ $c^{16}$
24. $(x^5)^7$ $x^{35}$
25. $(m^5)^5$ $m^{25}$

**Complete each equation.**

26. $8^2 \cdot 8^{\blacksquare} = 8^9$ 7
27. $5^6 \cdot 5^{\blacksquare} = 5^{14}$ 8
28. $c^{\blacksquare} \cdot c^4 = c^{11}$ 7
29. $x^{\blacksquare} \cdot x^{12} = x^{15}$ 3
30. $(2^2)^{\blacksquare} = 2^6$ 3
31. $(9^{\blacksquare})^4 = 9^{16}$ 4
32. $(a^{\blacksquare})^9 = a^{27}$ 3
33. $(y^7)^{\blacksquare} = y^{35}$ 5

**Compare. Use >, <, or = to complete each statement.**

34. $5^5 \blacksquare (5^3)^2$ <
35. $7^2 \cdot 7^5 \blacksquare (7^6)^2$ <
36. $(2^3)^3 \blacksquare 2^6$ >
37. $25^2 \blacksquare (5^2)^2$ =
38. $(2^7)^7 \blacksquare (2^{25})^2$ <
39. ✪ $(4^3 \cdot 4^2)^3 \blacksquare 4^9$ >

40. **TEST PREP** Which expression is equivalent to $2^{13}$? B
A. $(2^3)^{10}$ B. $2^5 \cdot 2^8$ C. $2^1 \cdot 2^{13}$ D. 8,190

41. ✪ *Mathematical Reasoning* Are $-(2^3)^2$ and $(-2^3)^2$ equivalent? Justify your answer. No; $-(2^3)^2$ is −64 but $(-2^3)^2$ is 64.

42. *Open-ended* A megabyte is $2^{20}$ bytes. Use exponents to write $2^{20}$ in four different ways. Answers may vary. Sample: $2^{20}$, $(2^2)^{10}$, $(2^4)^5$, $2^2 \cdot 2^{18}$

43. *Writing* Explain why $x^8 \cdot x^2$ is equivalent to $x^5 \cdot x^5$. Both $x^8 \cdot x^2$ and $x^5 \cdot x^5$ are equivalent to $x^{10}$.

44. *Error Analysis* Marcos thinks that $x^4 + x^4$ simplifies to $2x^4$. Doug thinks that $x^4 + x^4$ simplifies to $x^8$. Which result is correct? Explain. Explanations may vary. Sample: $2x^4$; the two terms are being added, not multiplied.



## Alternative Assessment

Have students demonstrate and explain with examples both the rule for multiplying powers with the same base and the rule for raising a power to a power.

45. *Critical Thinking* Is $2^{30}$ or $2^{16}$ twice the value of $2^{15}$? Explain. $2^{16}$; $2^{16} = 2^{1+15} = 2 \cdot 2^{15}$

*Geometry* **Find the area of each rectangle.**

46. 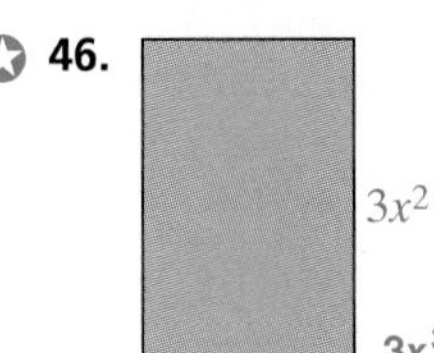

$3x^3$

47. 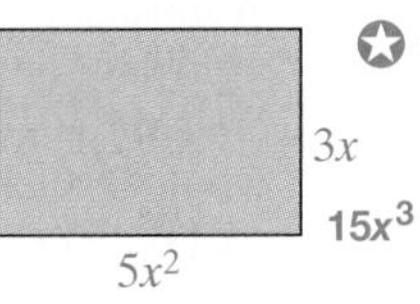

$15x^3$

48. 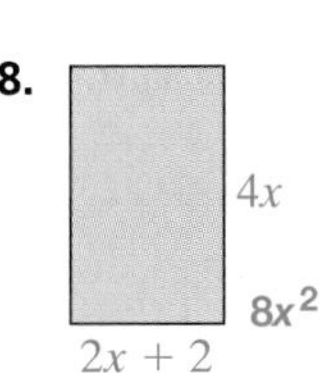

$8x^2 + 8x$

52. 

53.–55. 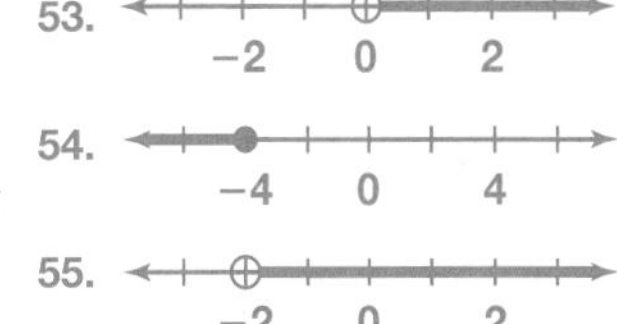


## Mixed Review

**Evaluate. Write in simplest form.** ***(Lesson 4-6)***

49. $\frac{a}{b+1}$, for $a = -4$ and $b = 7$ $-\frac{1}{2}$

50. $\frac{x-5}{y+8}$, for $x = -7$ and $y = 10$ $-\frac{2}{3}$

51. $\frac{mn}{m-6}$, for $m = 4$ and $n = 2$ $-4$

**Graph the solutions of each inequality on a number line.** ***(Lesson 2-8)*** See above right.

52. $x < -3$

53. $a > 0$

54. $y \leq -4$

55. $b > -2$

56. The Scotts are getting ready for a barbeque. They buy 8 lb of hamburger at \$1.50/lb and 10 lb of chicken at \$1.25/lb. Write and simplify an expression that shows the total cost. ***(Lesson 1-2)*** 8(1.50) + 10(1.25); \$24.50

## Math at Work

### Geophysicist

Geophysicists study Earth's surface, including the history of Earth's crust and rock formations. They search for oil, natural gas, minerals, and underground water. They also work to solve environmental problems. In addition, they study what makes up Earth's interior, as well as its magnetic, electrical, and gravitational forces. They often study earthquakes and volcanoes.

Geophysicists use physics and mathematics in their studies. Much of their work involves measurement. They use instruments to track sound waves, gravity, energy waves, and magnetic fields. Exponents appear in the data that geophysicists gather because they often work with very large numbers.

For more information about careers in geophysics, visit the Prentice Hall Web site.
www.phschool.com



## Math at Work

**Geophysicist** If you have block scheduling or extended class periods, have small groups of students research the training and math involved in being a geophysicist. Suggest that students contact a college to find out what math courses are required for this career. Students may also wish to interview a geophysicist with questions about the math they use.

Students can find additional information on the Web site **www.phschool.com**.

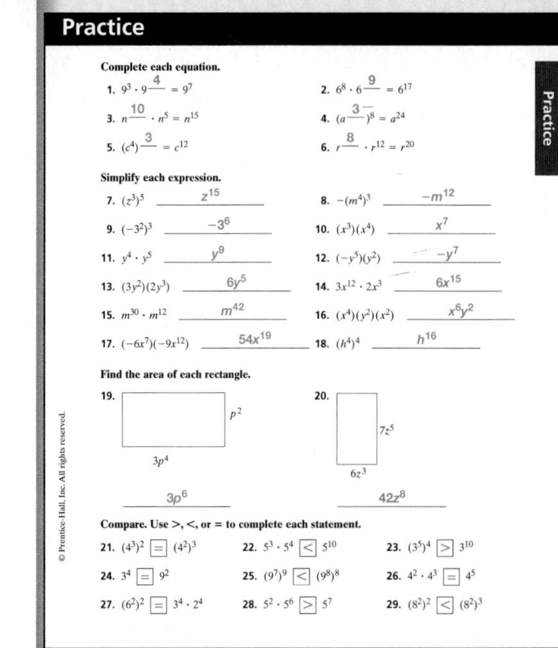

## Practice

**Complete each equation.**

1. $9^3 \cdot 9^{\underline{4}} = 9^7$
2. $6^8 \cdot 6^{\underline{9}} = 6^{17}$
3. $n^{\underline{10}} \cdot n^5 = n^{15}$
4. $(a^{\underline{3}})^8 = a^{24}$
5. $(c^4)^{\underline{3}} = c^{12}$
6. $r^{\underline{8}} \cdot r^{12} = r^{20}$

**Simplify each expression.**

7. $(z^3)^5$ $z^{15}$
8. $-(m^4)^3$ $-m^{12}$
9. $(-3^2)^3$ $-3^6$
10. $(x^3)(x^4)$ $x^7$
11. $y^4 \cdot y^5$ $y^9$
12. $(-y^5)(y^2)$ $-y^7$
13. $(3y^2)(2y^3)$ $6y^5$
14. $3x^{12} \cdot 2x^3$ $6x^{15}$
15. $m^{30} \cdot m^{12}$ $m^{42}$
16. $(x^4)(y^2)(x^2)$ $x^6y^2$
17. $(-6x^7)(-9x^{12})$ $54x^{19}$
18. $(h^4)^4$ $h^{16}$

**Find the area of each rectangle.**

19. $p^2$ by $3p^4$ — $3p^6$

20. $7z^5$ by $6z^3$ — $42z^8$

**Compare. Use >, <, or = to complete each statement.**

21. $(4^3)^2$ = $(4^2)^3$
22. $5^3 \cdot 5^4$ < $5^{10}$
23. $(3^5)^4$ > $3^{10}$
24. $3^4$ = $9^2$
25. $(9^7)^9$ < $(9^8)^8$
26. $4^2 \cdot 4^3$ = $4^5$
27. $(6^2)^2$ = $3^4 \cdot 2^4$
28. $5^2 \cdot 5^6$ > $5^7$
29. $(8^2)^2$ < $(8^2)^3$



## Reteaching

Simplify $m^3 \cdot m^4$ and $(n^2)^3$.

The base of $m^3$ is $m$ and the base of $m^4$ is $m$. So, they have the same base. To multiply variables with the same base, add the exponents.

$m^3 \cdot m^4 = m^{3+4} = m^7$

This rule works because you are combining 3 factors of $m$ and 4 factors of $m$.

$m^3 \cdot m^4 = (m \cdot m \cdot m) \cdot (m \cdot m \cdot m \cdot m) = m^7$

Simplifying $(n^2)^3$ involves raising a power $(n^2)$ to a power. To find a power of a power, multiply the exponents.

$(n^2)^3 = n^{2 \cdot 3} = n^6$

This rule works because you are using $n^2$ as a factor 3 times.

$(n^2)^3 = n^2 \cdot n^2 \cdot n^2 = (n \cdot n) \cdot (n \cdot n) \cdot (n \cdot n) = n^6$

**Simplify each expression. Show an intermediate step.**

1. $4^7 \cdot 4^2 = (4 \cdot 4 \cdot 4 \cdot 4 \cdot 4 \cdot 4 \cdot 4) \cdot (4 \cdot 4) = 4^9$
2. $a^3 \cdot a^6 = (a \cdot a \cdot a) \cdot (a \cdot a \cdot a \cdot a \cdot a \cdot a) = a^9$
3. $3x^2 \cdot 4x^5 = (3 \cdot x \cdot x) \cdot (4 \cdot x \cdot x \cdot x \cdot x \cdot x) = 12x^7$
4. $3^4 \cdot 3^3 = (3 \cdot 3 \cdot 3 \cdot 3) \cdot (3 \cdot 3 \cdot 3) = 3^7$
5. $y^5 \cdot y^3 = (y \cdot y \cdot y \cdot y \cdot y) \cdot (y \cdot y \cdot y) = y^8$
6. $7r^4 \cdot 3r^2 = (7 \cdot r \cdot r \cdot r \cdot r) \cdot (3 \cdot r \cdot r) = 21r^6$
7. $(5^3)^4 = 5^3 \cdot 5^3 \cdot 5^3 \cdot 5^3 = 5^{12}$
8. $(h^2)^5 = h^2 \cdot h^2 \cdot h^2 \cdot h^2 \cdot h^2 = h^{10}$
9. $(m^4)^8 = m^4 \cdot m^4 \cdot m^4 \cdot m^4 \cdot m^4 \cdot m^4 \cdot m^4 \cdot m^4 = m^{32}$
10. $(x^3y^2)^3 = x^3y^2 \cdot x^3y^2 \cdot x^3y^2 = x^9y^6$
11. $(2s^4t^5)^4 = 2s^4t^5 \cdot 2s^4t^5 \cdot 2s^4t^5 \cdot 2s^4t^5 = 16s^{16}t^{20}$
12. $(-pqr^2)^3 = -pqr^2 \cdot (-pqr^2) \cdot (-pqr^2) = -p^3q^3r^6$



## Enrichment

**Solve.**

1. $9^{99}$ is a very great number, but you can write an even greater one using three nines. What is the greatest number that can be written using three nines? (Written out, this number contains over 300 million digits.)
   $9^{(9^9)}$

2. Every person has 2 parents, $2^2$ grandparents, $2^3$ great-grandparents, and so on. There are, on average, 25 years in each generation.
   a. Use exponents to write the number of ancestors you had in the generation in which Columbus landed in America.
   $2^{20}$
   b. Circle the number closest to your answer to Part a.
   40 100 1,000 (1,000,000)

**Circle the letter of the best estimate.**

3. the height of a stack of $10^6$ pennies
   A. 1 yd B. 100 yd (C.) 1 mi D. 1 million mi
4. the weight of a stack of $10^6$ dollar bills
   F. 1 lb G. 10 lb H. 100 lb (J.) 1 ton
5. the length of time in $10^9$ minutes
   A. 1 day B. 1 yr C. 100 yr (D.) 2,000 years
6. the number of years in $10^7$ days
   F. 1 yr G. 1 million years H. 10 years (J.) 30,000 years

A sheet of paper is about 0.003 in. thick. Suppose you folded a sheet of paper in half the given number of times. What factor would you multiply 0.003 by to find the thickness of the folded sheet? Write the factor in exponential form.

7. once $2^1$
8. twice $2^2$
9. 50 times $2^{50}$
10. You could not actually fold a piece of paper in half 50 times. However, if you were able to do so, circle the best estimate of the thickness of the folded sheet.
   F. 1 ft G. 1 mi H. 1,000 mi (J.) 50,000,000 mi

## Standardized Test Prep

Standardized tests, such as those administered for state assessment, SAT9, TerraNova™, ITBS, MAT7, or CAT5, may include multiple choice questions, free-response questions, and open-ended questions.

**Multiple Choice Questions** are followed usually by four choices, one of which is correct.

**Exercises 1–6** are multiple choice questions.

**Free-Response Questions** do not give answer choices. Student must provide the one correct answer on their own.

**Exercises 7, 9–10** are free-response questions.

**Open-Ended Questions** allow for more than one solution. Students must construct their own responses instead of choosing from possible answers.

**Exercise 8** is an open-ended question.

### Resources

See p. 169G for a list of assessment options.

### Test-Taking Tip

When a question has a word emphasized, such as *not*, pay careful attention to the form of the question. Check to make sure that you haven't answered the opposite of the question that was asked.

### Test-Taking Tips on Transparency

Incorrect choices may answer related questions.

*Example* Midori owes $20 on a restaurant bill, and wants to tip the server 15%. How much should Midori pay altogether?

A. $3 B. $15 C. $20 D. $23

Calculate the tip: 0.15 × 20 = $3

Choice A is $3, but this is how much Midori should leave for a tip, not how much to pay altogether.

Calculate the total bill: 20 + 3 = $23

The answer is $23, or choice D.

Answer the question asked. Explain your reasoning.

1. Clarisse earns $10 per hour and works about 25 hours per week. How much could she earn in a year?

   A. $250 B. $1,000 C. $13,000 D. $3,000

2. Find the area of the triangle.

   7, 25, 24

   F. 84 units² G. 56 units² H. 168 units² J. Not Here





## Standardized Test Prep

### Multiple Choice

**Choose the best answer.**

1. Which is the prime factorization of 90? A
   A. $2 \cdot 3^2 \cdot 5$ B. $2 \cdot 5 \cdot 9$
   C. $3 \cdot 3 \cdot 5^2$ D. $2 \cdot 45$

2. Which equation is true? G
   F. $(3 \cdot 6)^2 = (3 \cdot 6)(3 \cdot 6)(3 \cdot 6)$
   G. $(3 \cdot 6)^2 = 3^2 \cdot 6^2$
   H. $(3 + 6)^2 = 3^2 + 6^2$
   J. $(3 - 6)^2 = 3^2 - 6^2$

3. A rectangular skateboard park has 5 curbs, 2 ramps, and a perimeter of 480 yd. The width of the park is $2s$ and the length is $3s$, where $s$ equals 48 yd. What are the width and length of the park? B
   A. 48 yd and 72 yd B. 96 yd and 144 yd
   C. 120 yd and 2 yd D. 60 yd and 40 yd

4. The diagram below shows the numbers of students in the school play, the comedy troupe, and the debate club.

   *S*: students

   *P*: play members

   *C*: comedy troupe members

   *D*: debate club members

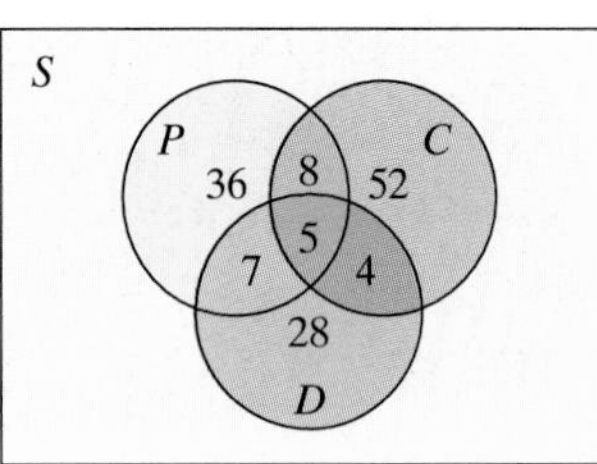


   How many students are in the play and the debate club but *not* in the comedy troupe? H
   F. 4 students G. 5 students
   H. 7 students J. 12 students

5. A musician receives a "platinum CD" award if one million copies of an album are sold. A CD is 1.5 mm thick. How high would a stack of 1 million CDs be? C
   A. 1,500,000 cm
   B. 150,000 m
   C. 1.5 km
   D. 15 km

6. What is the total number of squares in the figure below? H

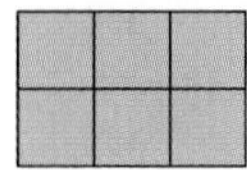

   F. 6 G. 7
   H. 8 J. 9

### Free Response

**For Exercises 7–10, show your work.**

7. Complete the pattern.

| Gold Measure | Gold Content |
|---|---|
| 24-karat | $\frac{24}{24} = 1$ |
| 22-karat | $\frac{22}{24} = \frac{11}{12}$ |
| 18-karat | $\frac{18}{24} = \frac{3}{4}$ |
| 14-karat | $\frac{14}{24} = ■$ $\frac{7}{12}$ |
| 9-karat | $\frac{9}{24}$ ■ $= \frac{3}{8}$ |

9. Explanations may vary. Sample: $-5^4$ is negative and $(-5)^4$ is positive.

8. *Open-ended* The GCF of three numbers is 6. What are three possible values for the numbers? Answers may vary. Sample: 6, 12, 18

9. Explain why $-5^4$ and $(-5)^4$ are not equal. See above right.

10. Choose an even number between 10 and 20 and an odd number between 50 and 60. Find the difference between the two numbers. Will the digit in the ones place of the difference be even or odd? Explain. Odd; an odd number minus an even number is odd.

# Exponents and Division

4-8

## PART 1 Dividing Expressions Containing Exponents

### What You'll Learn

1. To divide expressions containing exponents
2. To simplify expressions with integer exponents

### . . . And Why

To divide and simplify expressions with exponents efficiently

In Lesson 4-7, you learned that you add exponents to multiply powers with the same base. To divide powers with the same base, you subtract exponents. Here's why.

$$\frac{7^8}{7^3} = \frac{7 \cdot 7 \cdot 7 \cdot 7 \cdot 7 \cdot 7 \cdot 7 \cdot 7}{7 \cdot 7 \cdot 7}$$ Expand the numerator and denominator.

$$= \frac{\overset{1}{\cancel{7}} \cdot \overset{1}{\cancel{7}} \cdot \overset{1}{\cancel{7}} \cdot 7 \cdot 7 \cdot 7 \cdot 7 \cdot 7}{\underset{1}{\cancel{7}} \cdot \underset{1}{\cancel{7}} \cdot \underset{1}{\cancel{7}}}$$ Divide common factors.

$$= 7^5$$

Notice that $\frac{7^8}{7^3} = 7^{8-3}$, or $7^5$. This suggests the following rule.

**Dividing Powers with the Same Base**

To divide numbers or variables *with the same nonzero base,* you subtract exponents.

| Arithmetic | Algebra |
|---|---|
| $\frac{4^5}{4^2} = 4^{5-2} = 4^3$ | $\frac{a^m}{a^n} = a^{m-n}$, for $a \neq 0$ and positive integers $m$ and $n$. |

### EXAMPLE 1

**Simplify each expression.**

**a.** $\frac{3^8}{3^5}$ **b.** $\frac{a^4}{a^2}$

| a. | | b. |
|---|---|---|
| $\frac{3^8}{3^5} = 3^{8-5}$ | ← Subtract the exponents. → | $\frac{a^4}{a^2} = a^{4-2}$ |
| $= 3^3$ | ← Simplify the exponent. → | $= a^2$ |
| $= 27$ | ← Simplify. | |

**TRY THIS** Simplify each expression.

**1.** $\frac{10^7}{10^4}$ 1,000 **2.** $\frac{x^{25}}{x^{18}}$ $x^7$ **3.** $\frac{12m^5}{3m}$ $4m^4$



# Tools to Monitor Progress

## BEFORE THE LESSON

**To check prerequisite skills:**

- Using exponents

**Skills Intervention Kit,** Number Theory and Fraction Concepts

## DURING THE LESSON

**To check understanding:**

**Try This** exercises on student page

- **Additional Example 1**
  Simplify each expression.
  **a.** $\frac{4^{12}}{4^8}$ 256 **b.** $\frac{w^{18}}{w^{13}}$ $w^5$
- **Additional Example 2**
  Simplify each expression.
  **a.** $\frac{(-12)^{73}}{(-12)^{73}}$ 1 **b.** $\frac{8s^{20}}{32s^{20}}$ $\frac{1}{4}$

# 4-8

## Getting Ready

**Resources** A complete list of resources for this lesson is on p. 169H.

### Daily Skills Warm-Up

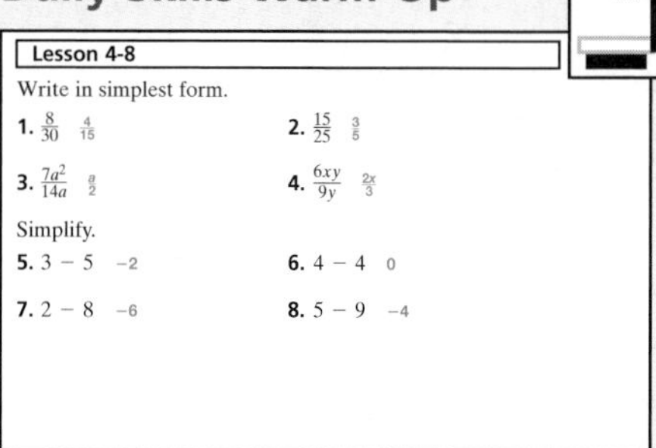

Lesson 4-8

Write in simplest form.

**1.** $\frac{8}{30}$ $\frac{4}{15}$ **2.** $\frac{15}{25}$ $\frac{3}{5}$

**3.** $\frac{7a^2}{14a}$ $\frac{a}{2}$ **4.** $\frac{6xy}{9y}$ $\frac{2x}{3}$

Simplify.

**5.** $3 - 5$ $-2$ **6.** $4 - 4$ 0

**7.** $2 - 8$ $-6$ **8.** $5 - 9$ $-4$

### Background for the Lesson

The laws of exponents describe what happens when you use positive integer exponents. Negative and zero exponents are defined to maintain consistency with these laws. The fraction $\frac{x^2}{x^2}$ is defined to be 1 (when $x \neq 0$), and the exponent laws say that $\frac{x^2}{x^2}$ is also $x^{2-2}$ or $x^0$. In order to be consistent, these two expressions ($x^0$ and 1) for the same value $\left(\frac{x^2}{x^2}\right)$ must be equal, so $x^0$ is defined to be one.

## 1 Focus

### Connecting to Prior Knowledge

In Lesson 4-4, students simplified fractions with exponents by dividing the numerator and denominator by the common factors: $\frac{y}{xy} = \frac{1}{x}$. In this lesson they learn to use a rule to make the division shorter. In Lesson 5-4, they will learn about dividing fractions.

# 2 Teach

## Part 1 Teaching Notes

Have students work through several examples of dividing powers by expanding the numerator and denominator and then dividing common factors. Examples with the factors written out enable students to develop understanding, so they will not be dependent just on memorized rules.

### Example 1

**Build understanding.** Ask: What is the first thing you must do before you subtract the exponents? **Check that the base is the same for both the divisor and dividend.**

**Error Prevention** Students may not subtract in the correct order. Explain that division with exponents means subtracting the exponent in the denominator from the exponent in the numerator. Reversing this order produces an incorrect result.

## Part 2 Teaching Notes

Students have seen only whole number exponents. Now they simplify expressions with integer exponents, including negatives and zero. The meaning of these follows directly from the definitions already established for exponents.

**Error Prevention** Another way to help students with the concept of zero as an exponent is to explain it with a pattern such as this one.

$$10^3 = 1{,}000$$
$$10^2 = 100$$
$$10^1 = 10$$
$$10^0 = 1$$

## Simplifying Expressions with Integer Exponents

What happens when you divide powers with the same base and get zero as an exponent? Consider $\frac{3^4}{3^4}$.

$$\frac{3^4}{3^4} = 3^{4-4} = 3^0 \qquad \frac{3^4}{3^4} = \frac{\cancel{3}^1 \cdot \cancel{3}^1 \cdot \cancel{3}^1 \cdot \cancel{3}^1}{{}_1\cancel{3} \cdot {}_1\cancel{3} \cdot {}_1\cancel{3} \cdot {}_1\cancel{3}} = \frac{1}{1} = 1$$

Notice that $\frac{3^4}{3^4} = 3^0$ and $\frac{3^4}{3^4} = 1$. This suggests the following rule.

**Zero as an Exponent**

| Arithmetic | Algebra |
|---|---|
| $3^0 = 1$ | $a^0 = 1$, for $a \neq 0$. |

### EXAMPLE 2

**Simplify each expression.**

**a.** $\frac{(-8)^2}{(-8)^2}$

$\frac{(-8)^2}{(-8)^2} = (-8)^{2-2}$ Subtract the exponents.

$= (-8)^0$

$= 1$ Simplify.

**b.** $\frac{6^3}{18b^3}$

$\frac{6b^3}{18b^3} = \frac{1}{3}b^0$ Subtract the exponents. Simplify $\frac{6}{18}$.

$= \frac{1}{3} \cdot 1$ Simplify $b^0$.

$= \frac{1}{3}$ Multiply.

**TRY THIS** Simplify each expression.

**4.** $43^0$ 1 **5.** $\frac{5^2x^6}{5x^6}$ 5 **6.** $\frac{x^5y^6}{x^5y^3}$ $y^3$ **7.** $5x^0$ 5

What happens when you divide powers with the same base and get a negative exponent? Consider $\frac{3^2}{3^4}$.

$$\frac{3^2}{3^4} = 3^{2-4} = 3^{-2} \qquad \frac{3^2}{3^4} = \frac{\cancel{3}^1 \cdot \cancel{3}^1}{{}_1\cancel{3} \cdot {}_1\cancel{3} \cdot 3 \cdot 3} = \frac{1}{3^2}$$

Notice $\frac{3^2}{3^4} = 3^{-2}$ and $\frac{3^2}{3^4} = \frac{1}{3^2}$. This suggests the following rule.



- **Additional Example 3**
  Simplify each expression.
  **a.** $\frac{6^{12}}{6^{14}}$ $\frac{1}{36}$
  **b.** $\frac{z^4}{z^{15}}$ $\frac{1}{z^{11}}$
- **Additional Example 4**
  Write $\frac{a^2b^3}{ab^{15}}$ without a fraction bar.
  $ab^{-12}$

## AFTER THE LESSON

**To assess knowledge:**

**Lesson Quiz**

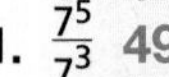

Simplify each expression.

**1.** $\frac{7^5}{7^3}$ 49

**2.** $\frac{-15b^5c^3}{60b^3c^2}$ $-\frac{1}{4}b^2c$

Write the expression without a fraction bar.

**3.** $\frac{6n^{14}}{3n^{24}}$ $2n^{-10}$

- For enrichment and reteaching options see Resources on p. 169H.

| Negative Exponents | |
|---|---|
| **Arithmetic** | **Algebra** |
| $3^{-2} = \frac{1}{3^2}$ | $a^{-n} = \frac{1}{a^n}$, for $a \neq 0$ |

A hummingbird has a mass of about $10^{-2}$ kg, or $\frac{1}{10^2}$ kg. To *simplify* $10^{-2}$, you write $\frac{1}{100}$ or 0.01. So the hummingbird has a mass of 0.01 kg. When you simplify an expression such as $x^{-2}$, you write it as $\frac{1}{x^2}$, using no negative exponents.

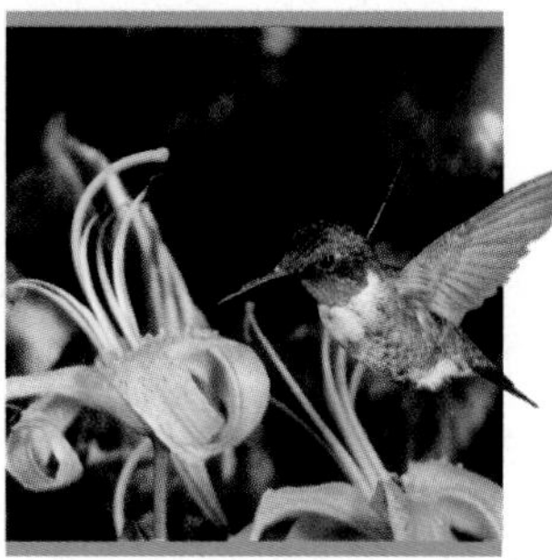

Hummingbirds may range from 0.0022 kg to 0.02 kg in mass.

## EXAMPLE 3

**Simplify each expression.**

**a.** $\frac{5^6}{5^8}$

$\frac{5^6}{5^8} = 5^{6-8}$ ←Subtract the exponents.

$= 5^{-2}$

$= \frac{1}{5^2}$ ←Write with a positive exponent.

$= \frac{1}{25}$ ←Simplify.

**b.** $\frac{m^2}{m^5}$

$\frac{m^2}{m^5} = m^{2-5}$ ←Subtract the exponents.

$= m^{-3}$

$= \frac{1}{m^3}$ ←Write with a positive exponent.

**TRY THIS** Simplify each expression.

**8.** $\frac{4^5}{4^7}$ $\frac{1}{16}$ **9.** $\frac{a^4}{a^6}$ $\frac{1}{a^2}$ **10.** $\frac{3y^8}{9y^{12}}$ $\frac{1}{3y^4}$

You can also write an expression such as $\frac{1}{x^2}$ so that there is no fraction bar.

## EXAMPLE 4

**Write $\frac{x^2y^3}{x^3y}$ without a fraction bar.**

$\frac{x^2y^3}{x^3y} = x^{2-3}y^{3-1}$ Use the rule for Dividing Powers with the Same Base.

$= x^{-1}y^2$ Subtract the exponents.

**TRY THIS** Write each expression without a fraction bar.

**11.** $\frac{b^3}{b^9}$ $b^{-6}$ **12.** $\frac{m^3n^2}{m^6n^8}$ $m^{-3}n^{-6}$ **13.** $\frac{xy^5}{x^5y^3}$ $x^{-4}y^2$



### Example 2

**Build understanding.** Ask: Look at part a. before it is simplified. Compare the numerator and denominator. What does this mean about the value of the fraction? **They are the same; the fraction must be equal to 1.**

**Visual Learning** Suggest that students compare the numerator and denominator carefully before they begin simplifying an expression. If they are the same, then the expression is always equal to 1.

**Reading Math** Read $x^{-4}$ as "x to the negative fourth power."

### Example 3

**Build understanding.** Ask: Before you simplify, how can you tell that these expressions can be written with a negative exponent? **The exponent in the denominator is larger than the exponent in the numerator.**

### Example 4

**Build understanding.** Ask: If a variable has a negative exponent when an expression is *not* written in fractional form, where will you see the variable in a fraction written without negative exponents? **in the denominator**

**Extension** Ask: The variables $x$ and $-x$ are opposites. Is $x^{-1}$ the opposite of $x^1$? Explain how you know. **No, opposites, or additive inverses, add to zero. The expressions $x^{-1}$ (or $\frac{1}{x}$) and $x^1$ or ($x$) multiply to 1, so they are multiplicative inverses, or reciprocals.**

**Error Prevention** Students often think that an expression with a negative exponent must be a negative number. Point out that $3^{-2} = \frac{1}{3^2}$ which is $\frac{1}{9}$, a positive number.

# 3 Practice/Assess

## Assignment Guide

To provide flexible scheduling, this lesson can be divided into parts.

**Part 1**
**Core** 1–4, 16–24, 41–44
✪ **Extension** 25, 57

**Part 2**
**Core** 5–15, 26–38, 45–56
✪ **Extension** 39–40

Mixed Review can be assigned at any time for maintenance.

## Exercises

**Error Prevention Exercises 16–40**
Suggest that students write each expression on their paper and, before they simplify, underline the exponents to be subtracted and circle the numbers to be divided.

## ✪ Challenge

Simplify $\frac{1}{x^{-1}}$. $x$

## Closure

To multiply numbers or variables with the same base, add the exponents. To raise a power to a power, multiply the exponents. To divide numbers or variables with the same nonzero base, subtract the exponents.

## Daily Cumulative Review

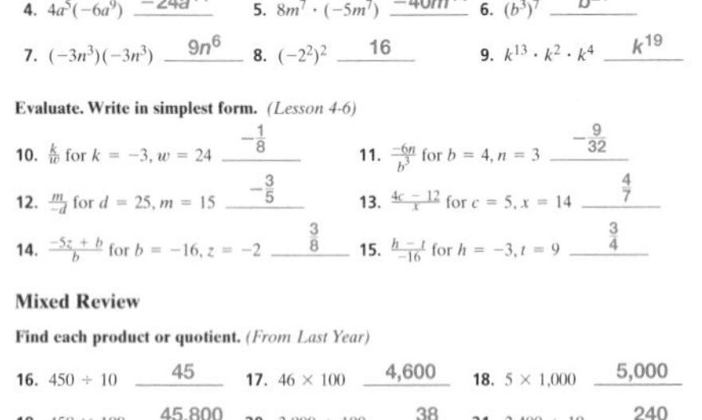

**Simplify each expression.** *(Lesson 4-7)*

1. $3^2 \cdot 3^5$ 2,187
2. $v^{13} \cdot v^4$ $v^{17}$
3. $(n^8)(s^4)(n^3)$ $n^{11}s^4$
4. $4a^5(-6a^9)$ $-24a^{14}$
5. $8m^7 \cdot (-5m^7)$ $-40m^{14}$
6. $(b^3)^7$ $b^{21}$
7. $(-3n^3)(-3n^3)$ $9n^6$
8. $(-2^2)^2$ 16
9. $k^{13} \cdot k^2 \cdot k^4$ $k^{19}$

**Evaluate. Write in simplest form.** *(Lesson 4-6)*

10. $\frac{k}{w}$ for $k = -3, w = 24$ $-\frac{1}{8}$
11. $\frac{-6n}{b^3}$ for $b = 4, n = 3$ $-\frac{9}{32}$
12. $\frac{m}{-d}$ for $d = 25, m = 15$ $-\frac{3}{5}$
13. $\frac{4c - 12}{x}$ for $c = 5, x = 14$ $\frac{4}{7}$
14. $\frac{-5z + b}{b}$ for $b = -16, z = -2$ $\frac{3}{8}$
15. $\frac{h - t}{-16}$ for $h = -3, t = 9$ $\frac{3}{4}$

**Mixed Review**

**Find each product or quotient.** *(From Last Year)*

16. $450 \div 10$ 45
17. $46 \times 100$ 4,600
18. $5 \times 1{,}000$ 5,000
19. $458 \times 100$ 45,800
20. $3{,}800 \div 100$ 38
21. $2{,}400 \div 10$ 240

**Solve each equation.**

22. $-78 = c + (-45.35)$ (3-5) $-32.65 = c$
23. $7.86 + k = 12.45$ (3-5) $k = 4.59$
24. $x - (-43.21) = 17.83$ (3-5) $x = -25.38$
25. $-0.65b = 3.25$ (3-6) $b = -5$
26. $5.65 = z \div (-0.02)$ (3-6) $-0.113 = z$
27. $0.002v = 0.36$ (3-6) $v = 180$

**Write a numerical expression for each of the following. Then find the sum.**

28. negative four plus the opposite of six (1-5) $(-4) + (-6) = -10$
29. You borrow $50, and then you pay back $34. (1-5) $-\$50 + \$34 = -\$16$
30. positive nine plus the opposite of eleven (1-5) $9 + (-11) = -2$



# Exercises

## Check Understanding

**Simplify each expression.**

1. $\frac{2^5}{2^2}$ 8
2. $\frac{h^6}{h^2}$ $h^4$
3. $\frac{6y^7}{10y^2}$ $\frac{3y^5}{5}$
4. $\frac{m^4n^3}{m^6n^2}$ $\frac{n}{m^2}$
5. $(-4)^0$ 1
6. $\frac{10b^8}{2b^8}$ 5
7. $\frac{m^2}{m^6}$ $\frac{1}{m^4}$
8. $2^{-3}$ $\frac{1}{8}$
9. $\frac{4a^3}{20a^6}$ $\frac{1}{5a^3}$
10. $\frac{x^5y^4}{x^2y^9}$ $\frac{x^3}{y^5}$

**Write each expression without a fraction bar.**

11. $\frac{y^4}{y^7}$ $y^{-3}$
12. $\frac{a^2b^4}{a^8b^2}$ $a^{-6}b^2$
13. $\frac{m^5n^6}{m^7n^8}$ $m^{-2}n^{-2}$
14. $\frac{xy^2}{x^4y^9}$ $x^{-3}y^{-7}$
15. $\frac{b^{12}c^5}{b^6c^{10}}$ $b^6c^{-5}$

## Practice and Problem Solving

**Simplify each expression.**

16. $\frac{6^2}{6^1}$ 6
17. $\frac{11^5}{11^3}$ 121
18. $\frac{(-2)^{14}}{(-2)^{11}}$ $-8$
19. $\frac{x^7}{x^3}$ $x^4$
20. $\frac{b^3}{b^2}$ $b$
21. $\frac{a^{27}}{a^{19}}$ $a^8$
22. $\frac{200m^{200}}{100m^{100}}$ $2m^{100}$
23. $\frac{18x^{20}}{36x^{12}}$ $\frac{x^8}{2}$
24. $\frac{w^{12}z^{15}}{w^8z^8}$ $w^4z^7$
25. ✪ $\frac{42a^6b^7}{7a^3b^3}$ $6a^3b^4$
26. $3^0$ 1
27. $\frac{b^5}{b^8}$ $\frac{1}{b^3}$
28. $\frac{5^3}{5^3}$ 1
29. $8^{-1}$ $\frac{1}{8}$
30. $\frac{7^3}{7^5}$ $\frac{1}{49}$
31. $a^{-4}$ $\frac{1}{a^4}$
32. $\frac{6^7}{6^{11}}$ $\frac{1}{1{,}296}$
33. $\frac{(-2)^4}{(-2)^4}$ 1
34. $(-2)^0$ 1
35. $\frac{a^2}{a^7}$ $\frac{1}{a^5}$
36. $\frac{6x^2}{x^4}$ $\frac{6}{x^2}$
37. $\frac{2y^3}{8y^7}$ $\frac{1}{4y^4}$
38. $x^{-3}y^2$ $\frac{y^2}{x^3}$
39. ✪ $\frac{5x^2}{10x^{-5}}$ $\frac{x^7}{2}$
40. ✪ $5b^{-7}$ $\frac{5}{b^7}$

**Complete each equation.**

41. $\frac{4^{■}}{4^3} = 4^5$ 8
42. $\frac{x^6}{x^{■}} = x^4$ 2
43. $\frac{14x^5}{7x^3} = 2x^{■}$ 2
44. $\frac{10^5}{10^{■}} = 1$ 5
45. $\frac{1}{8^2} = 8^{■}$ $-2$
46. $\frac{1}{a^3} = a^{■}$ $-3$
47. $\frac{y^{■}}{y^9} = y^{-4}$ 5
48. $\frac{1}{-27} = (-3)^{■}$ $-3$

**Write each expression without a fraction bar.**

49. $\frac{x^3}{x^5}$ $x^{-2}$
50. $\frac{a^9b^3}{a^7b^8}$ $a^2b^{-5}$
51. $\frac{m^9n^3}{m^2n^{10}}$ $m^7n^{-7}$
52. $\frac{x^4y}{x^8y^3}$ $x^{-4}y^{-2}$
53. $\frac{b^{14}c^2}{b^9c^{11}}$ $b^5c^{-9}$
54. *Writing* Explain why $3^{-2}$ is not a negative number. $3^{-2} = \frac{1}{3^2} = \frac{1}{9}$, which is positive.
55. *Error Analysis* A student wrote that $-5^0 = 1$. What was the student's error? The student thought that the base was $-5$.
56. *Open-ended* Write three different quotients that equal $5^{-7}$. Answers may vary. Sample: $\frac{1}{5^7}, \frac{5}{5^8}, \frac{x}{5^7x}$



## Alternative Assessment

Ask groups of students to develop a board game in which the players have to simplify expressions with exponents to advance through the game.

★ 57. *Science* The *magnitude* of an earthquake is a measure of the amount of energy released. An earthquake of magnitude 6 releases about 30 times as much energy as an earthquake of magnitude 5.

The magnitude of the 1989 earthquake in Loma Prieta, California, was about 7. The magnitude of the 1933 earthquake in Sanriku, Japan, was about 9. Simplify $\frac{30^9}{30^7}$ to find how many times as much energy was released in the Sanriku earthquake. 900 times as much

The photo shows damage from the Loma Prieta, California, earthquake of October 17, 1989.

## MIXED REVIEW

**Simplify each expression.** *(Lesson 4-7)*

58. $5^2 \cdot 5$ 125
59. $x^7 \cdot x^2$ $x^9$
60. $(y^{12})(y^8)$ $y^{20}$
61. $2a^9 \cdot 8a^7$ $16a^{16}$

**Estimate using front-end estimation.** *(Lesson 3-1)*

62. $5.68 + 3.24$ about 8.9
63. $17.86 + 2.321$ about 20.2
64. $20.2 + 5.8$ about 26.0
65. $42.8 + 7.6$ about 51

66. *Choose a Strategy* The sum of three consecutive integers is 264. What are the three integers? 87, 88, 89

## CHECKPOINT 2

Lessons 4-5 through 4-8

**Write three fractions equivalent to each fraction.**

1. $\frac{3}{12}$ $\frac{1}{4}, \frac{-1}{-4}, \frac{2}{8}$
2. $\frac{12}{36}$ $\frac{1}{3}, \frac{-1}{-3}, \frac{2}{6}$
3. $\frac{49}{70}$ $\frac{7}{10}, \frac{-7}{-10}, \frac{14}{20}$
4. $\frac{18}{28}$ $\frac{9}{14}, \frac{-9}{-14}, \frac{-18}{-28}$
5. $\frac{4}{5}$ $\frac{8}{10}, \frac{-8}{-10}, \frac{-4}{-5}$

**Evaluate for $a = 4$ and $b = -6$. Write in simplest form.**

6. $\frac{a}{2b}$ $-\frac{1}{3}$
7. $\frac{b+a}{a}$ $-\frac{1}{2}$
8. $\frac{a-b}{15}$ $\frac{2}{3}$
9. $\frac{b-a}{a^2}$ $-\frac{5}{8}$
10. $\frac{3a+b}{24}$ $\frac{1}{4}$

**Graph the rational numbers below on the same number line.**

11–15. (number line from −1 to 1 with points at −0.8, $-\frac{2}{10}$, $\frac{1}{2}$, 0.6, $\frac{9}{10}$; labels −1, 0, 1)

11. $-0.8$
12. $\frac{1}{2}$
13. $0.6$
14. $-\frac{2}{10}$
15. $\frac{9}{10}$

**Simplify each expression.**

16. $2^3 \cdot 2^4$ 128
17. $(x^5)^{10}$ $x^{50}$
18. $\frac{18a^4}{3a^2}$ $6a^2$
19. $\frac{x^3}{x^8}$ $\frac{1}{x^5}$
20. $\frac{a^3b^5}{a^9b^5}$ $\frac{1}{a^6}$

21. **TEST PREP** What is the simplest form of $\frac{12a^{35}}{36a^{50}}$? C

A. $\frac{1}{3}a^{85}$ B. $\frac{1}{3a^{85}}$ C. $\frac{1}{3a^{15}}$ D. $\frac{1}{3}a^{15}$

22. If 12 of 16 students vote to do a project, what fraction of the students is this? Write the fraction in simplest form. $\frac{3}{4}$

See also Extra Practice section.



## Practice

**Complete each equation.**

1. $\frac{8^n}{8^7} = 8^2$, $n =$ 9
2. $\frac{12x^5}{4x} = 3x^n$, $n =$ 4
3. $\frac{1}{h^5} = h^n$, $n =$ −5
4. $\frac{p^n}{p^8} = p^{-6}$, $n =$ 2
5. $\frac{1}{81} = 3^n$, $n =$ −4
6. $\frac{12^4}{12^n} = 1$, $n =$ 4

**Simplify each expression.**

7. $\frac{a^3}{a^7}$ $\frac{1}{a^4}$
8. $\frac{j^5}{j^6}$ $\frac{1}{j}$
9. $\frac{x^7}{x^7}$ 1
10. $\frac{k^5}{k^9}$ $\frac{1}{k^4}$
11. $\frac{9x^8}{12x^5}$ $\frac{3x^3}{4}$
12. $\frac{2f^{10}}{f^5}$ $2f^5$
13. $\frac{3y^4}{6y^{-4}}$ $\frac{y^8}{2}$
14. $n^{-5}$ $\frac{1}{n^5}$
15. $\frac{3xy^4}{9xy}$ $\frac{y^3}{3}$
16. $(-15)^0$ 1
17. $\frac{15h^6k^3}{5hk^2}$ $3h^5k$
18. $4b^{-6}$ $\frac{4}{b^6}$

**Write each expression without a fraction bar.**

19. $\frac{a^7}{a^{10}}$ $a^{-3}$
20. $\frac{4x^2y}{2x^3}$ $2x^{-1}y$
21. $\frac{x^3y^4}{x^9y^2}$ $x^{-6}y^2$
22. $\frac{12mn}{12m^3n^5}$ $m^{-2}n^{-4}$
23. $\frac{16s^2t^4}{8s^5t^3}$ $2s^{-3}t$
24. $\frac{21e^4f^2}{7e^2}$ $3e^2f^2$

25. Write three different quotients that equal $4^{-5}$.
Sample answers are shown: $\frac{1}{4^5}, \frac{4^2}{4^7}, \frac{4^{-4}}{4}$



## Reteaching

Simplify $\frac{a^3}{a^3}$ and $\frac{m^2}{m^6}$.

To divide variables with the same non-zero base, you subtract the exponents.

$\frac{a^3}{a^3} = a^{3-3}$ Subtract the exponents.
$= a^0$ Simplify the exponent.

However, $\frac{a^3}{a^3} = 1$ as long as $a$ is not zero, just like $\frac{2}{2} = 1$, $\frac{9}{9} = 1$ and so on.

So $\frac{a^3}{a^3} = 1$ and $a^0 = 1$.

$\frac{m^2}{m^6} = m^{2-6}$ Subtract the exponents.
$= m^{-4}$ Simplify the exponent.

However, $\frac{m^2}{m^6} = \frac{\cancel{m} \cdot \cancel{m}}{\cancel{m} \cdot \cancel{m} \cdot m \cdot m \cdot m \cdot m} = \frac{1}{m^4}$

So, $\frac{m^2}{m^6} = \frac{1}{m^4}$ and $m^{-4} = \frac{1}{m^4}$.

The *simplified* forms are 1 and $\frac{1}{m^4}$.

**Simplify each expression.**

1. $\frac{7^8}{7^2}$ $7^6$
2. $\frac{x^5}{x}$ $x^4$
3. $5^0$ 1
4. $n^{-3}$ $\frac{1}{n^3}$
5. $x^{-2}y^4$ $\frac{y^4}{x^2}$
6. $6a^{-3}$ $\frac{6}{a^3}$
7. $(-4)^0$ 1
8. $\frac{b^3}{b^8}$ $\frac{1}{b^5}$
9. $\frac{y^2}{y^9}$ $\frac{1}{y^7}$
10. $7s^{-5}t^{-3}$ $\frac{7}{s^5t^3}$
11. $\frac{3^{18}}{3^3}$ $3^{15}$
12. $(-729)^0$ 1
13. $\frac{z^7}{z^{34}}$ $\frac{1}{z^{27}}$
14. $4e^3f^{-2}$ $\frac{4e^3}{f^2}$



## Enrichment

The entries in each row, column, and diagonal in the basic magic square add to 15. By adding or subtracting the same number to or from the entries in the basic magic square, you can create a new one. The second magic square, which adds to −6, was created by subtracting 7 from the entries in the basic square.

Basic Magic Square

| 2 | 7 | 6 |
|---|---|---|
| 9 | 5 | 1 |
| 4 | 3 | 8 |

subtract →

| −5 | 0 | −1 |
|---|---|---|
| 2 | −2 | −6 |
| −3 | −4 | 1 |

**Complete the magic square using the basic magic square.**

1.

| 37 | 42 | 41 |
|---|---|---|
| 44 | 40 | 36 |
| 39 | 38 | 43 |

Sum = 120

2.

| −17 | −12 | −13 |
|---|---|---|
| −10 | −14 | −18 |
| −15 | −16 | −11 |

Sum = −42

3.

| −8 | −3 | −4 |
|---|---|---|
| −1 | −5 | −9 |
| −6 | −7 | −2 |

Sum = −15

Magic square entries can be used as exponents to create multiplication magic squares, or *multi-magic squares*.

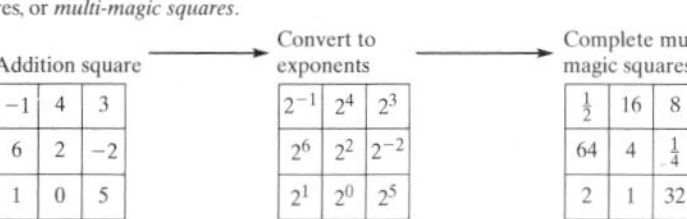

Addition square → Convert to exponents → Complete multi-magic squares

| −1 | 4 | 3 |
|---|---|---|
| 6 | 2 | −2 |
| 1 | 0 | 5 |

| $2^{-1}$ | $2^4$ | $2^3$ |
|---|---|---|
| $2^6$ | $2^2$ | $2^{-2}$ |
| $2^1$ | $2^0$ | $2^5$ |

| $\frac{1}{2}$ | 16 | 8 |
|---|---|---|
| 64 | 4 | $\frac{1}{4}$ |
| 2 | 1 | 32 |

4. Find the product for the multi-magic square above. 64

Complete the multi-magic square. In Exercise 5, note that $32 = 2^5$.

5.

| $\frac{1}{4}$ | 8 | 4 |
|---|---|---|
| 32 | 2 | $\frac{1}{8}$ |
| 1 | $\frac{1}{2}$ | 16 |

Product = 8

6.

| $\frac{1}{16}$ | 2 | 1 |
|---|---|---|
| 8 | $\frac{1}{2}$ | $\frac{1}{32}$ |
| $\frac{1}{4}$ | $\frac{1}{8}$ | 4 |

Product = $\frac{1}{8}$

7.

| $\frac{1}{8}$ | 4 | 2 |
|---|---|---|
| 16 | 1 | $\frac{1}{16}$ |
| $\frac{1}{2}$ | $\frac{1}{4}$ | 8 |

Product = 1



## Checkpoint

**Write three fractions equivalent to each fraction.** Sample answers are shown:

1. $\frac{2}{9}$ $\frac{-2}{-9}, \frac{4}{18}, \frac{-4}{-18}$
2. $\frac{8}{10}$ $\frac{-8}{-10}, \frac{4}{5}, \frac{-4}{-5}$

**Evaluate for $a = 3$ and $b = -5$. Write in simplest form.**

3. $\frac{a}{3b}$ $-\frac{1}{5}$
4. $\frac{a+b}{2}$ −1
5. $\frac{a-b}{24}$ $\frac{1}{3}$

**Graph the rational numbers below on the same number line.**

6. $-0.7$
7. $\frac{4}{5}$
8. $-\frac{3}{10}$

(number line from −1.0 to 1.0 with points at −0.7, $-\frac{3}{10}$, $\frac{4}{5}$; labels −1.0, 0, 1.0)

**Simplify each expression.**

9. $5^3 \cdot 5^8$ $5^{11}$
10. $(a^3)^4$ $a^{12}$
11. $\frac{x^2y^5}{x^4y^2}$ $\frac{y^3}{x^2}$

12. If 15 out of 20 students vote to go to the science museum, what fraction of the students want to go to the museum? Write the fraction in simplest form. $\frac{3}{4}$

# 4-9

## Getting Ready

**Key Terms and Symbols** scientific notation, standard notation

**Resources** A complete list of resources for this lesson is on p. 169H.

### Daily Skills Warm-Up

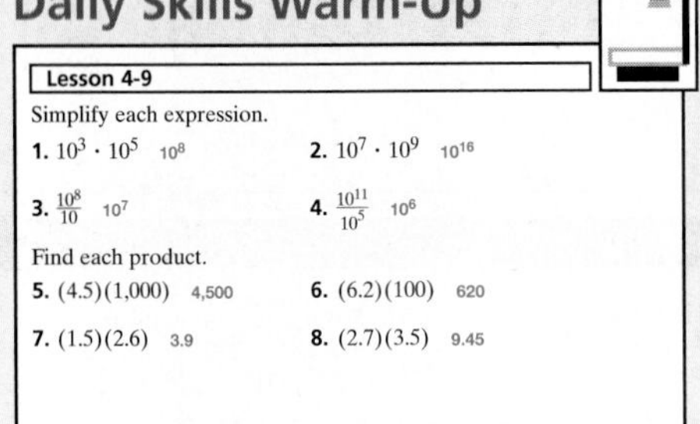

Lesson 4-9

Simplify each expression.

1. $10^3 \cdot 10^5$ $10^8$
2. $10^7 \cdot 10^9$ $10^{16}$
3. $\frac{10^8}{10}$ $10^7$
4. $\frac{10^{11}}{10^5}$ $10^6$

Find each product.

5. (4.5)(1,000) 4,500
6. (6.2)(100) 620
7. (1.5)(2.6) 3.9
8. (2.7)(3.5) 9.45

### Background for the Lesson

In scientific notation, you rewrite any number as a product of two factors: the first is a number greater than or equal to 1 and less than 10 and the second is a power of 10. The number 347.1 (in decimal notation) becomes $3.471 \times 10^2$ in scientific notation. Scientific notation often uses the times sign $\times$ instead of the multiplying dot to avoid confusion with the decimal point. A long number such as 0.00000000456 becomes $4.56 \times 10^{-9}$. The exponent on 10 equals the number of places the decimal has been moved. A positive exponent indicates that the original number was greater than or equal to 1. A negative exponent indicates that the original number was less than 1.

## 1 Focus

### Connecting to Students' Lives

Ask students to think about calculating the volume of water in the nearest lake. In this chapter, they will learn a way to make such very large (or very small) numbers more manageable.

### Connecting to Prior Knowledge

Students will use the rules in Lessons 4-7 and 4-8 for multiplying and dividing exponents in scientific notation.





# 4-9 Scientific Notation

**What You'll Learn**

1. To write and evaluate numbers in scientific notation
2. To calculate with scientific notation

**. . . And Why**

To use scientific notation for recording very large or very small numbers, such as the weight of the Great Pyramid or the mass of a hydrogen atom

## *Investigate*

EXPLORING SCIENTIFIC NOTATION

**1.** Copy and complete the chart below.

| | | | |
|---|---|---|---|
| $5 \times 10^4$ | $= 5 \times 10{,}000$ | $= 50{,}000$ | |
| $5 \times 10^3$ | $= 5 \times 1{,}000$ | $=$ ■ 5,000 | |
| $5 \times 10^2$ | $= 5 \times$ ■ 100 | $=$ ■ 500 | |
| $5 \times 10^1$ | $= 5 \times$ ■ 10 | $=$ ■ 50 | |
| $5 \times 10^0$ | $= 5 \times$ ■ 1 | $=$ ■ 5 | |
| $5 \times 10^{-1}$ | $= 5 \times \frac{1}{10}$ | $= 5 \times 0.1$ | $= 0.5$ |
| $5 \times 10^{-2}$ | $= 5 \times$ ■ $\frac{1}{100}$ | $= 5 \times 0.01$ | $= 0.05$ |
| $5 \times 10^{-3}$ | $= 5 \times$ ■ $\frac{1}{1{,}000}$ | $= 5 \times$ ■ 0.001 | $= 0.005$ |
| $5 \times 10^{-4}$ | $= 5 \times$ ■ $\frac{1}{10{,}000}$ | $= 5 \times$ ■ 0.0001 | $=$ ■ 0.0005 |

**2.** *Patterns* Describe the pattern you see in your chart. See below.

**3. a.** Based on the pattern you see, simplify $5 \times 10^7$. 50,000,000

**b.** Simplify $5 \times 10^{-6}$. 0.000005

2. Answers may vary. Sample: As the exponent of 10 decreases by 1, the product becomes $\frac{1}{10}$ as great.

## PART 1 Writing and Evaluating Scientific Notation

**Scientific notation** is a shorthand way of writing numbers using powers of 10. You write a number in scientific notation as the product of two factors.

$$7{,}500{,}000{,}000{,}000 = 7.5 \times 10^{12}$$

Second factor is a power of 10.

First factor is greater than or equal to 1, but less than 10.

*Need Help?* For help with multiplying by powers of ten, see Skills Handbook, p. 734.

Scientific notation lets you know the size of a number without having to count digits. For example, if the exponent of 10 is 6, the number is in the millions. If the exponent is 9, the number is in the billions.



# Tools to Monitor Progress

**BEFORE THE LESSON**

**To check prerequisite skills:**

- Using exponents

**Skills Handbook,** p. 734

**Skills Intervention Kit,** Number Theory and Fraction Concepts

**DURING THE LESSON**

**To check understanding:**

**Try This** exercises on student page

- **Additional Examples 1–4**

Write each number in scientific notation.

**a.** $0.1070 \times 10^{12}$ $1.07 \times 10^{11}$

**b.** $515.0 \times 10^{-4}$ $5.15 \times 10^{-2}$

## Example 1

**About 4,200,000 people visit the Statue of Liberty every year. Write this number in scientific notation.**

4,200,000 (6 places) — Move the decimal point to get a decimal greater than 1 but less than 10.

4.2 — Drop the zeros after the 2.

$4.2 \times 10^6$ — The decimal point moved 6 places to the left. Use 6 as the exponent of 10.

**Try This** Write each number in scientific notation.

**4.** 54,500,000 $5.45 \times 10^7$  **5.** 723,000 $7.23 \times 10^5$  **6.** 602,000,000,000 $6.02 \times 10^{11}$

In scientific notation, you use a negative exponent to write a number between 0 and 1.

## Example 2

**Write 0.000079 in scientific notation.**

0.000079 (5 places) — Move the decimal point to get a decimal greater than 1 but less than 10.

7.9 — Drop the zeros before the 7.

$7.9 \times 10^{-5}$ — The decimal point moved 5 places to the right. Use −5 as the exponent of 10.

**Try This** Write each number in scientific notation.

**7.** 0.00021 $2.1 \times 10^{-4}$  **8.** 0.00000005 $5 \times 10^{-8}$  **9.** 0.0000000000803 $8.03 \times 10^{-11}$

You can change expressions from scientific notation to **standard notation** by simplifying the product of the two factors.

## Example 3

**Write each number in standard notation.**

**a.** $8.9 \times 10^5$  **b.** $2.71 \times 10^{-6}$

| a. | | b. |
|---|---|---|
| 8.90000 | Add zeros while moving the decimal point. | 000002.71 |
| 890,000 | Rewrite in standard notation. | 0.00000271 |

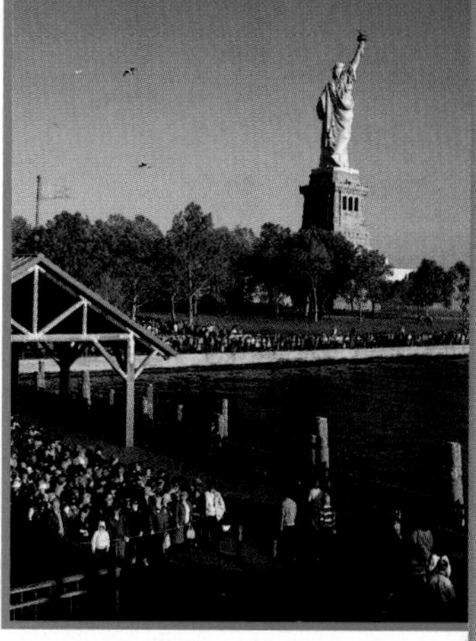

The total weight of the Statue of Liberty is about 450,000 lb. Write this number in scientific notation. $4.5 \times 10^5$ lb



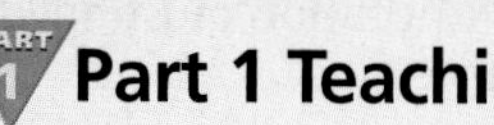

# 2 Teach

## Part 1 Teaching Notes

The numbers $75 \times 10^{11}$ and $0.75 \times 10^{13}$ have the same value, but neither is in scientific notation. The first factor in scientific notation is a number greater than or equal to 1 and less than 10, as in $7.5 \times 10^{12}$.

### Example 1

**Build understanding.** Ask: The original number is greater than 1. What does this tell you about the exponent on 10? It will be positive.

### Example 2

**Build understanding.** Ask: The original number is less than 1. What does this tell you about the exponent on 10? It will be negative.

### Example 3

**Build understanding.** Ask: Which of the two numbers is greater? Explain how you know. $8.9 \times 10^5$, because it has a positive exponent

**Connecting to Science** In chemistry, the mole is an amount of any element that is equal in grams to that element's atomic weight. Scientists have determined through experiments that the number of atoms in one mole of any element is equal to approximately $6.02 \times 10^{23}$. This number is called *Avogadro's number,* named after the Italian physicist Amadeo Avogadro (1776–1856).

### • Additional Examples 5–7

In chemistry, one mole of any element contains approximately $6.02 \times 10^{23}$ atoms. If each hydrogen atom weighs approximately $1.67 \times 10^{-27}$ kg, approximately how much does one mole of hydrogen weigh? $1.01 \times 10^{-3}$ kg

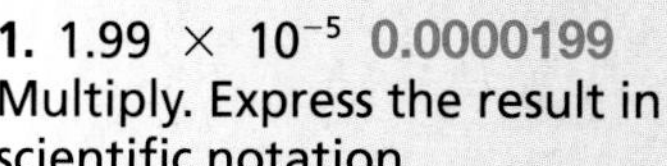

### After the Lesson

**To assess knowledge:**
**Lesson Quiz**

Write in standard notation.

**1.** $1.99 \times 10^{-5}$ 0.0000199

Multiply. Express the result in scientific notation.

**2.** $(14 \times 10^6)(4 \times 10^{-4})$ $5.6 \times 10^3$

- For enrichment and reteaching options see Resources on p. 169H.

## Example 4

**Build understanding.** Ask: A number written in scientific notation must have a digit in which place? the ones place

## Example 5

**Build understanding.** Ask: Explain why you cannot order these numbers by simply looking at the exponents. They are not in scientific notation.

## Part 2 Teaching Notes

Show students that multiplying numbers in scientific notation is just like multiplying expressions with powers that have the same base. Remind them that when you multiply powers, you add the exponents.

## Example 6

**Build understanding.** Ask: What must be true about bases before you can add exponents? Explain why this is not a problem with numbers in scientific notation. The bases must be the same; the base is always 10.

**Error Prevention** After multiplying two numbers that are in scientific notation, make sure students rewrite the product in scientific notation if necessary.

## Example 7

**Build understanding.** Ask: Why is $11.5 \times 10^9$ not the correct answer? It is not in scientific notation.

**Extension** The number called a *googol* is written with a 1 followed by 100 zeros. The number was named by the mathematician Edward Kasner after he asked his nine-year-old nephew what he should call a number with 100 zeros. How would you write one googol in scientific notation? $1.0 \times 10^{100}$



**TRY THIS** Write each number in standard notation.

**10.** $3.21 \times 10^7$ 32,100,000 **11.** $5.9 \times 10^{-8}$ 0.000000059 **12.** $1.006 \times 10^{10}$ 10,060,000,000

For a number to be in scientific notation, the digit in front of the decimal must be between 1 and 10.

### EXAMPLE 4

**Write each number in scientific notation.**

**a.** $\mathbf{0.37 \times 10^{10}}$

$0.37 \times 10^{10} = 3.7 \times 10^{-1} \times 10^{10}$ Write 0.37 as $3.7 \times 10^{-1}$.

$= 3.7 \times 10^9$ Add the exponents.

**b.** $\mathbf{453.1 \times 10^8}$

$453.1 \times 10^8 = 4.531 \times 10^2 \times 10^8$ Write 453.1 as $4.531 \times 10^2$.

$= 4.531 \times 10^{10}$ Add the exponents.

**TRY THIS** Write each number in scientific notation.

**13.** $16 \times 10^5$ $1.6 \times 10^6$ **14.** $0.203 \times 10^6$ $2.03 \times 10^5$ **15.** $7{,}243 \times 10^{12}$ $7.243 \times 10^{15}$

You can compare and order numbers using scientific notation. First compare the powers of 10, and then compare the decimals.

### EXAMPLE 5

**Order $0.064 \times 10^8$, $312 \times 10^2$, and $0.58 \times 10^7$ from least to greatest.**

Write each number in scientific notation.

| $0.064 \times 10^8$ | $312 \times 10^2$ | $0.58 \times 10^7$ |
|---|---|---|
| ↓ | ↓ | ↓ |
| $6.4 \times 10^6$ | $3.12 \times 10^4$ | $5.8 \times 10^6$ |

Order the powers of 10. Arrange the decimals with the same power of 10 in order.

$3.12 \times 10^4$ $5.8 \times 10^6$ $6.4 \times 10^6$

Write the original numbers in order.

$312 \times 10^2, 0.58 \times 10^7, 0.064 \times 10^8$

**TRY THIS** Order from least to greatest.

**16.** $526 \times 10^7, 18.3 \times 10^6, 0.098 \times 10^9$ $18.3 \times 10^6, 0.098 \times 10^9, 526 \times 10^7$

**17.** $8 \times 10^{-9}, 14.7 \times 10^{-7}, 0.22 \times 10^{-10}$ $0.22 \times 10^{-10}, 8 \times 10^{-9}, 14.7 \times 10^{-7}$

## PART 2 Calculating with Scientific Notation

You can multiply numbers in scientific notation using the rule for Multiplying Powers with the Same Base.

### EXAMPLE 6

**Multiply $3 \times 10^{-7}$ and $9 \times 10^{3}$. Express the result in scientific notation.**

| | |
|---|---|
| $(3 \times 10^{-7})(9 \times 10^{3}) = 3 \times 9 \times 10^{-7} \times 10^{3}$ | Use the Commutative Property of Multiplication. |
| $= 27 \times 10^{-7} \times 10^{3}$ | Multiply 3 and 9. |
| $= 27 \times 10^{-4}$ | Add the exponents. |
| $= 2.7 \times 10^{1} \times 10^{-4}$ | Write 27 as $2.7 \times 10^{1}$. |
| $= 2.7 \times 10^{-3}$ | Add the exponents. |

**TRY THIS** Multiply. Express each result in scientific notation.

18. $(4 \times 10^{4})(6 \times 10^{6})$ $2.4 \times 10^{11}$
19. $(7.1 \times 10^{-8})(8 \times 10^{4})$ $5.68 \times 10^{-3}$

Computations with scientific notation often occur in real-world situations that involve very large or very small numbers.

REAL-WORLD CONNECTION

### EXAMPLE 7

*Measurement* **The Great Pyramid of Giza in Egypt contains about $2.3 \times 10^{6}$ blocks of stone. On average, each block weighs about $5 \times 10^{3}$ lb. About how many pounds of stone does the Great Pyramid contain?**

| | |
|---|---|
| $(2.3 \times 10^{6})(5 \times 10^{3})$ | Write a multiplication problem. |
| $= 2.3 \times 5 \times 10^{6} \times 10^{3}$ | Use the Commutative Property of Multiplication. |
| $= 11.5 \times 10^{6} \times 10^{3}$ | Simplify. |
| $= 11.5 \times 10^{9}$ | Add the exponents. |
| $= 1.15 \times 10^{1} \times 10^{9}$ | Write 11.5 as $1.15 \times 10^{1}$. |
| $= 1.15 \times 10^{10}$ | Add the exponents. |

The Great Pyramid contains more than $1.15 \times 10^{10}$ lb of stone.

**TRY THIS**

20. *Chemistry* A hydrogen atom has a mass of $1.67 \times 10^{-27}$ kg. What is the mass of $6 \times 10^{3}$ hydrogen atoms? Express the result in scientific notation. $1.002 \times 10^{-23}$ kg

# 3 Practice/Assess

## Assignment Guide

To provide flexible scheduling, this lesson can be divided into parts.

**Part 1**
**Core** 1–10, 14–31, 36, 40, 42–43
**Extension** 32, 41

**Part 2**
**Core** 11–13, 33–35
**Extension** 37–39

Mixed Review can be assigned at any time for maintenance.

## Exercises

**Exercises 29–32** Remind students that the numbers must be in scientific notation before the exponents can be compared.

## Challenge

A *googolplex* is the number 1 followed by the number of zeros equal to a googol. How would you write this number in scientific notation? 1.0 times 10 to the googol power

## Closure

Scientific notation is a way to write numbers as the product of two factors, a power of 10 and a decimal. To multiply numbers in scientific notation, group the decimals, group the powers of ten, multiply, and then put the answer in scientific notation.

# Exercises

## Check Understanding

**Write each number in scientific notation.**

1. 8,900,000,000 $8.9 \times 10^9$
2. 0.000631 $6.31 \times 10^{-4}$
3. 555,900,000 $5.559 \times 10^8$
4. $0.09 \times 10^{12}$ $9 \times 10^{10}$

**Write each number in standard notation.**

5. $5.94 \times 10^7$ 59,400,000
6. $2.104 \times 10^{-8}$ 0.00000002104
7. $1.2 \times 10^5$ 120,000
8. $7.2 \times 10^{-4}$ 0.00072

**Order from least to greatest.**

9. $16 \times 10^9, 2.3 \times 10^{12}, 0.065 \times 10^{11}$ $0.065 \times 10^{11}, 16 \times 10^9, 2.3 \times 10^{12}$
10. $253 \times 10^{-9}, 3.7 \times 10^{-8}, 12.9 \times 10^{-7}$ $3.7 \times 10^{-8}, 253 \times 10^{-9}, 12.9 \times 10^{-7}$

**Multiply. Express each result in scientific notation.**

11. $(5 \times 10^6)(6 \times 10^2)$ $3 \times 10^9$
12. $(4.3 \times 10^3)(2 \times 10^8)$ $8.6 \times 10^{11}$
13. $(9 \times 10^3)(7 \times 10^8)$ $6.3 \times 10^{12}$

## Practice and Problem Solving

**Write each number in scientific notation.**

14. 55,000 $5.5 \times 10^4$
15. 0.000006 $6 \times 10^{-6}$
16. 0.00209 $2.09 \times 10^{-3}$
17. $52.8 \times 10^9$ $5.28 \times 10^{10}$
18. Pluto is 5 billion km from the sun. $5 \times 10^9$ km
19. A nanometer is 0.000000001 meter. $1 \times 10^{-9}$ m
20. A house spider weighs about 0.0001 kg. $1 \times 10^{-4}$ kg
21. The length of a grain of salt is about 0.004 in. $4 \times 10^{-3}$ in.

**Write each number in standard notation.**

22. $9 \times 10^2$ 900
23. $8.43 \times 10^6$ 8,430,000
24. $2 \times 10^{-4}$ 0.0002
25. $6.02 \times 10^{-7}$ 0.0000006
26. One light year is $5.88 \times 10^{12}$ mi. 5,880,000,000,000 mi
27. Fingernails grow $7.14 \times 10^{-3}$ cm per day. 0.00714 cm
28. The most venomous scorpion delivers $9 \times 10^{-6}$ oz of venom per bite. 0.000009 oz

**Order from least to greatest.**

29. $10^9, 10^{-8}, 10^5, 10^{-6}, 10^0$ $10^{-8}, 10^{-6}, 10^0, 10^5, 10^9$
30. $65 \times 10^4, 432 \times 10^3, 2.996 \times 10^4$ $2.996 \times 10^4, 432 \times 10^3, 65 \times 10^4$
31. $55.8 \times 10^{-5}, 782 \times 10^{-8}, 9.1 \times 10^{-5}, 1{,}009 \times 10^2, 0.8 \times 10^{-4}$ $782 \times 10^{-8}, 0.8 \times 10^{-4}, 9.1 \times 10^{-5}, 55.8 \times 10^{-5}, 1{,}009 \times 10^2$
32. $0.16 \times 10^7, 1{,}600 \times 10^6, 1.6 \times 10^5, 160 \times 10^8, 0.0016 \times 10^6$ $0.0016 \times 10^6, 1.6 \times 10^5, 0.16 \times 10^7, 1{,}600 \times 10^6, 160 \times 10^8$

**Multiply. Express each result in scientific notation.**

33. $(3 \times 10^2)(2 \times 10^2)$ $6 \times 10^4$
34. $(6 \times 10^3)(4 \times 10^1)$ $2.4 \times 10^5$
35. $(8 \times 10^{-3})(2.5 \times 10^{-2})$ $2 \times 10^{-4}$



## Daily Cumulative Review

**Simplify each expression.** *(Lesson 4-8)*

1. $5^0$ 1
2. $\frac{12^6}{12^2}$ 20,736
3. $\frac{a^{13}}{a^{11}}$ $a^2$
4. $\frac{(-3)^5}{(-3)^5}$ 1
5. $4^{-1}$ $\frac{1}{4}$
6. $\frac{18m^8x^5}{20m^3x^2}$ $\frac{9m^5x^3}{10}$

**Complete each expression.** *(Lesson 4-7)*

7. $3^2 \cdot 3^{\boxed{11}} = 3^{13}$
8. $7^6 \cdot 7^{\boxed{17}} = 7^{23}$
9. $n^{\boxed{6}} \cdot n^{15} = n^{21}$
10. $(6^3)^{\boxed{6}} = 6^{18}$
11. $(g^4)^{\boxed{7}} = g^{28}$
12. $(4^{\boxed{2}})^4 = 4^8$

**Mixed Review**

**Compare. Use >, <, or = to complete each statement.**

13. (1-4) $3 \boxed{>} 0$
14. (1-4) $-1 \boxed{<} 1$
15. (1-4) $-15 \boxed{>} -18$
16. (1-4) $-3 \boxed{>} -9$
17. (1-4) $-25 \boxed{<} -21$
18. (1-4) $-17 \boxed{<} 13$

**Find two fractions equivalent to each fraction.** Answers may vary.

19. (4-4) $\frac{1}{4}$ $\frac{2}{8}, \frac{3}{12}$
20. (4-4) $\frac{3}{7}$ $\frac{6}{14}, \frac{9}{21}$
21. (4-4) $\frac{2}{9}$ $\frac{4}{18}, \frac{6}{27}$
22. (4-4) $\frac{5}{6}$ $\frac{10}{12}, \frac{15}{18}$
23. (4-4) $\frac{1}{8}$ $\frac{2}{16}, \frac{3}{24}$
24. (4-4) $\frac{2}{3}$ $\frac{4}{6}, \frac{6}{9}$

**Is each number prime or composite? If composite, write the prime factorization.**

25. (4-3) 83 prime
26. (4-3) 72 composite; $2^3 \cdot 3^2$
27. (4-3) 725 composite; $5^2 \cdot 29$
28. (4-3) 244 composite; $2^2 \cdot 61$

**Name each property shown.**

29. (2-1) $456 + 0 = 456$ Identity Property of Addition
30. (2-1) $(7b)z = 7(bz)$ Associative Property of Multiplication
31. (2-1) $(5 + 4)(6 + 2) = (6 + 2)(5 + 4)$ Commutative Property of Multiplication



## Alternative Assessment

Have a contest between groups of students to see which group can find the smallest living organism in a reference source. Have the groups record the weight and length of the organism in scientific notation.

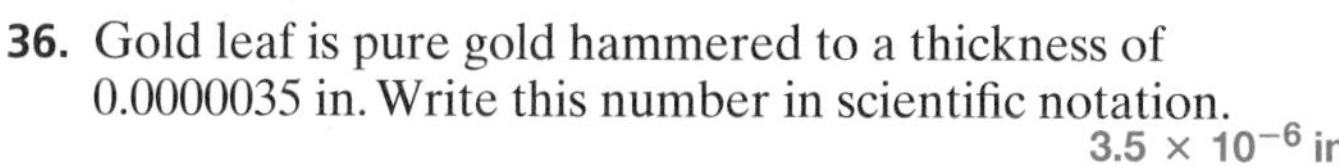

36. Gold leaf is pure gold hammered to a thickness of 0.0000035 in. Write this number in scientific notation. $3.5 \times 10^{-6}$ in.

**Solve. Write each result in scientific notation.**

37. *Zoology* An ant weighs about $2 \times 10^{-5}$ lb. There are about $10^{15}$ ants on Earth. How many pounds of ants are on Earth? $2 \times 10^{10}$ lb

38. *Statistics* The population density of India is about $8.33 \times 10^{2}$ people per square mile. The area of India is $1.2 \times 10^{6}$ mi$^2$. What is the approximate population of India? $9.996 \times 10^{8}$

39. *Health Care* In the year 2005, the population of the United States will be about 296 million. Health expenditures will be about $7,350 per person. In total, about how much will the United States spend on health care in 2005? about $\$2.18 \times 10^{12}$

*Math in the Media* **Use the article for Exercises 40–41.**

40. Express the moon's distance from Earth in scientific notation. $3.8 \times 10^{5}$ km

41. a. Express the distance from Earth to the moon in meters, using scientific notation. $3.8 \times 10^{8}$ m
    b. How many 0.5-meter footsteps are there from here to the moon? Express in scientific notation. $7.6 \times 10^{8}$ footsteps

42. *Open-ended* Describe a situation where you would use standard notation for a large number instead of scientific notation. Explain the reason for your choice. Check students' work.

43. *Writing* Explain how to write each number in scientific notation. 43a–b. Answers may vary. Samples are given.
    a. 0.00043 Move the decimal point 4 places to the right and write $4.3 \times 10^{-4}$.
    b. $523.4 \times 10^{5}$ Write $523.4 \times 10^{5} = 5.234 \times 10^{2} \times 10^{5} = 5.234 \times 10^{7}$.

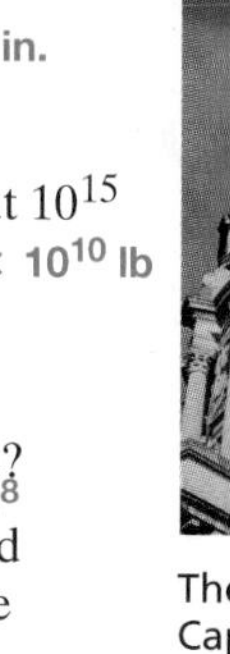

The dome of the Georgia State Capitol building has had two applications of gold leaf for a total of 103 oz. of 23-karat gold.

## One Giant Leap

On July 20, 1969, Neil Armstrong and Edwin "Buzz" Aldrin, Jr. were the first people to set foot on the moon. With his first step, Armstrong announced over the radio, "That's one small step for a man, one giant leap for mankind."

The moon is about 380,000 km from Earth. The footsteps the astronauts left on the moon will probably be visible for at least 10 million years.

## Mixed Review

**Simplify each expression.** *(Lesson 4-8)*

44. $\frac{10^7}{10^9}$ $\frac{1}{100}$

45. $\frac{x^3y}{xy}$ $x^2$

46. $\frac{15b^2}{10b^5}$ $\frac{3}{2b^3}$

47. $\frac{9m^7}{3m^5n}$ $\frac{3m^2}{n}$

**Use the formula $d = rt$. Find $d$, $r$, or $t$.** *(Lesson 3-4)*

48. $r = 46.2$ m/h, $t = 2.75$ h 127.05 m

49. $d = 4.68$ ft, $t = 5.2$ h 0.9 ft/h

50. $d = 988$ cm, $r = 6.5$ cm/s 152 s

51. A chime clock strikes once at one o'clock, twice at two o'clock, and so on. In a twelve-hour period, what is the total number of chimes the clock strikes? 78 chimes

See also Extra Practice section.



## Practice

**Write each number in standard notation.**

1. $3.77 \times 10^4$ 37,700
2. $8.5 \times 10^3$ 8,500
3. $9.002 \times 10^{-5}$ 0.00009002
4. $1.91 \times 10^{-3}$ 0.00191

**Write each number in scientific notation.**

5. Pluto is about 3,653,000,000 mi from the sun. $3.653 \times 10^9$
6. There are 63,360 in. in a mile. $6.336 \times 10^4$
7. At its closest, Mercury is about 46,000,000 km from the sun. $4.6 \times 10^7$
8. 77,250,000 $7.725 \times 10^7$
9. 526,000 $5.26 \times 10^5$
10. 8 billion $8 \times 10^9$
11. 8,100,000 $8.1 \times 10^6$
12. 0.00000073 $7.3 \times 10^{-7}$
13. 0.000903 $9.03 \times 10^{-4}$

**Multiply. Express each result in scientific notation.**

14. $(2 \times 10^5)(3 \times 10^2)$ $6 \times 10^7$
15. $(1.5 \times 10^5)(4 \times 10^9)$ $6 \times 10^{14}$
16. $(6 \times 10^{-4})(1.2 \times 10^{-3})$ $7.2 \times 10^{-7}$
17. $(5 \times 10^3)(1.7 \times 10^{-5})$ $8.5 \times 10^{-2}$

**Order from least to greatest.**

18. $72 \times 10^5$, $6.9 \times 10^6$, $23 \times 10^5$ — $23 \times 10^5$, $6.9 \times 10^6$, $72 \times 10^5$
19. $19 \times 10^{-3}$, $2.5 \times 10^{-4}$, $1.89 \times 10^{-4}$ — $1.89 \times 10^{-4}$, $2.5 \times 10^{-4}$, $19 \times 10^{-3}$
20. An ounce is 0.00003125 tons. Write this number in scientific notation. $3.125 \times 10^{-5}$
21. A century is 3,153,600,000 seconds. Write this number in scientific notation. $3.1536 \times 10^9$



## Reteaching

Write each number in scientific notation, then multiply. (8,600,000)(0.0042)

8.6 is between 1 and 10

$8{,}600{,}000. = 8.6 \times 10^6$

6 places to the left

4.2 is between 1 and 10

$0.0042 = 4.2 \times 10^{-3}$

3 places to the right

| | |
|---|---|
| $(8.6 \times 10^6)(4.2 \times 10^{-3}) = 8.6 \times 4.2 \times 10^6 \times 10^{-3}$ | Use the commutative property of multiplication. |
| $= 36.12 \times 10^6 \times 10^{-3}$ | Multiply 8.6 and 4.2. |
| $= 36.12 \times 10^3$ | Add the exponents. |
| $= 3.612 \times 10^1 \times 10^3$ | Write 36.12 as $3.612 \times 10^1$. |
| $= 3.612 \times 10^4$ | Add the exponents. |

**Write each number in scientific notation**

1. 745 million $7.45 \times 10^8$
2. 0.00034 $3.4 \times 10^{-4}$
3. 888,200,000 $8.882 \times 10^8$
4. 5,700 $5.7 \times 10^3$

**Multiply. Write your result using scientific notation.**

5. $(1.6 \times 10^6)(3.7 \times 10^4)$ $5.92 \times 10^{10}$
6. $(3 \times 10^{-4})(2 \times 10^{-5})$ $6 \times 10^{-9}$
7. $72{,}000 \times 143{,}000$ $1.0296 \times 10^{10}$
8. $(2.3 \times 10^{-2})(1.5 \times 10^4)$ $3.45 \times 10^2$



## Enrichment

**Solve. Write your answers in scientific notation unless otherwise directed.**

1. An unmanned spacecraft sets out to explore the moon, Jupiter, and Alpha Centauri, the closest star in our galaxy. A typical rocket travels about 20,000 mi/h. Write this number in scientific notation. $2 \times 10^4$ mi/h
2. The trip to the moon will take about 12 h. Use your answer to Exercise 1 and the formula $d = rt$ to find the distance to the moon in scientific notation. $2.4 \times 10^5$ mi
3. The trip from the moon to Jupiter will take about 24,000 h.
   a. Write the number of hours in scientific notation $2.4 \times 10^4$ h
   b. Find the distance from the moon to Jupiter. $4.8 \times 10^8$ mi
   c. Write the number of days the journey will take in standard notation. (1 day = 24h) 1,000 days
4. From Earth, the trip to Alpha Centauri will take about $1.25 \times 10^9$ h. Find the distance to Alpha Centauri. $2.5 \times 10^{13}$ mi
5. The most distant star in the Milky Way is about $2.5 \times 10^4$ times as far from Earth as Alpha Centauri. Find the distance to this star. $6.25 \times 10^{17}$ mi

## MATH TOOLBOX

### Scientific Notation with Calculators

This Math Toolbox explains how a graphing calculator uses scientific notation to show numbers too long to display in standard notation.

### Math Background

Many calculators display an *E* in the window to show that the number that follows is the *Exponent* you place on 10 when you write that quantity in scientific notation. To demonstrate this, put the calculator in *SCI* mode (if necessary) and enter the digits of a very large number in standard notation (ignoring the commas). Then press the equal key. For example, enter 960,345,823,581,002 and press the equal key. Some calculators will display 9.60345824E9 or $9.60345824^{09}$. This is the same as $9.6035 \times 10^9$ (rounded). Many non-graphing calculators will not let you enter a number like 960,345,823,581,002.

## Teaching Notes

**Error Prevention** You do not use commas when you enter a number in the calculator. Before pressing another key, check the digits in the window to make sure that you pressed the keys correctly.

**Monitoring Progress** Each kind of calculator works just a little differently. Help students use the procedures that apply on the calculators they are using.

**Block Scheduling** If you have block scheduling or extended periods, you may wish to teach this Math Toolbox lesson with Lesson 4-9.

## MATH TOOLBOX

Technology

*After Lesson 4-9*

# *Scientific Notation with Calculators*

When you enter a number with more digits than a calculator can display, the calculator translates the number into scientific notation. E11 in the output below means "$\times 10^{11}$."

112,345,678,999 ENTER → 1.12345679E11 The display shows the number rounded.

You can use a calculator to calculate with numbers in scientific notation.

### EXAMPLE 1

**Use a calculator to find $(9.8 \times 10^5)(4.56 \times 10^4)$.**

9.8E5*4.56E4

4.4688E10

Use 2nd EE to multiply by a power of 10.

The product is $4.4688 \times 10^{10}$.

### EXAMPLE 2

**Use a calculator to find $3.9 \times 10^{-7} + 4.7 \times 10^{-8}$.**

3.9E-7+4.7E-8

4.37E-7

Use (-) to enter a negative sign.

The sum is $4.37 \times 10^{-7}$.

1. $1.4976 \times 10^{11}$
2. $4.8000697 \times 10^{10}$
3. $2.0196 \times 10^{16}$
4. $1.401098901 \times 10^{-7}$
5. $9.338 \times 10^{23}$
6. $7.089807 \times 10^{10}$
7. $6.19 \times 10^{-5}$
8. $6.795 \times 10^{-4}$
9. $1.1907 \times 10^{-12}$

**Use a calculator to add, subtract, multiply, or divide.** 1–9. See above.

1. $1.5 \times 10^{11} - 2.4 \times 10^8$
2. $6.97 \times 10^5 + 4.8 \times 10^{10}$
3. $(1.02 \times 10^9)(1.98 \times 10^7)$
4. $(5.1 \times 10^3) \div (3.64 \times 10^{10})$
5. $(2.8 \times 10^{13})(3.335 \times 10^{10})$
6. $9.807 \times 10^7 + 7.08 \times 10^{10}$
7. $7.1 \times 10^{-5} - 9.1 \times 10^{-6}$
8. $3.5 \times 10^{-6} + 6.76 \times 10^{-4}$
9. $(2.43 \times 10^{-3})(4.9 \times 10^{-10})$
10. $(1.08 \times 10^4) \div (7.3 \times 10^{-7})$
11. $(5.01 \times 10^{-3})(8.5 \times 10^{-8})$
12. $1.99 \times 10^{-5} - 3.81 \times 10^{-4}$

See margin for 10–12.



- **Additional Example**

Use a calculator to find $(3.4 \times 10^{-3} + 4.5 \times 10^3) \div 9.2 \times 10^3$. Give the result in scientific notation and standard notation.
$4.8913 \times 10^{-1}$; 0.489130804

10. $1.479452055 \times 10^{10}$

11. $4.2585 \times 10^{-10}$

12. $-3.611 \times 10^{-4}$

# TIME AFTER TIME

**Design a Calendar** The Project Activity sections on pages 175, 193, and 197 will help you complete your project. Here is a checklist to help you gather the different parts.

✔ investigation of Egyptian calendar

✔ analysis of leap years

✔ your calendar design

Calendars are usually displayed in table form. You could also use a graph, a spreadsheet, a number line, or another format. Prepare a sample of your calendar and a written description of your design for presentation to your class.

***Reflect and Revise***

Ask a friend to review your calendar and your presentation. Is your calendar workable? Is it attractively presented? Are your explanations clear? If necessary, make changes to improve your calendar and presentation.

## *Web Extension*

**Visit Prentice Hall's Web site. You'll find some interesting links and ideas related to calendars. You'll also be able to share information about your project.**
**www.phschool.com.**



## CHAPTER PROJECT 4 FINISHING THE PROJECT

**Project Day** You may wish to plan a project day on which students share their completed projects. Encourage students to explain their process as well as their product.

**Block Scheduling** If you have block scheduling or extended periods, you may wish to intersperse the sharing of projects over Days 3, 4, and 5 between the completion of one lesson and the start of a new lesson.

### Project Notebook

Have students review their project work and bring their notebooks up to date. Call attention to the fact that they can share their projects with other students through the Web site **www.phschool.com**.

Be sure students include in their notebooks their completed Project Manager and Scoring Rubric forms.

**Portfolio** Students may wish to include their projects and/or their project notebooks in their portfolios.

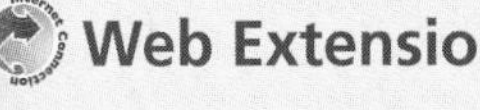

### Web Extension

**Tell Us About Your Project**

Students may wish to share their projects with other students on the Web site: **www.phschool.com**

### Scoring Rubric

**3** You design your calendar using logical time periods. You make accurate calculations and explain them thoroughly. You present your calendar effectively.

**2** You design your calendar using logical time periods. You make minor errors in accuracy of your calculations. You present clear explanations, but your presentation could be better organized or more thorough.

**1** You do not consider the role of factors in designing your calendar. Your calculations are inaccurate. Your calendar sample could be neater and more accurate. Explanations lack detail.

**0** Major elements of the project are incomplete or missing.

## Wrap Up

### Resources

Glossary, p. 748
Extra Practice, p. 713

For a complete list of resources for the chapter, see p. 169H.

# 4 Wrap Up

## Key Terms

base (p. 176)
composite number (p. 180)
divisible (p. 172)
equivalent fractions (p. 186)
exponents (p. 176)
factor (p. 173)
greatest common factor (GCF) (p. 181)
power (p. 176)
prime number (p. 180)
prime factorization (p. 181)
rational number (p. 194)
scientific notation (p. 208)
simplest form (p. 186)
standard notation (p. 209)

## Graphic Organizer

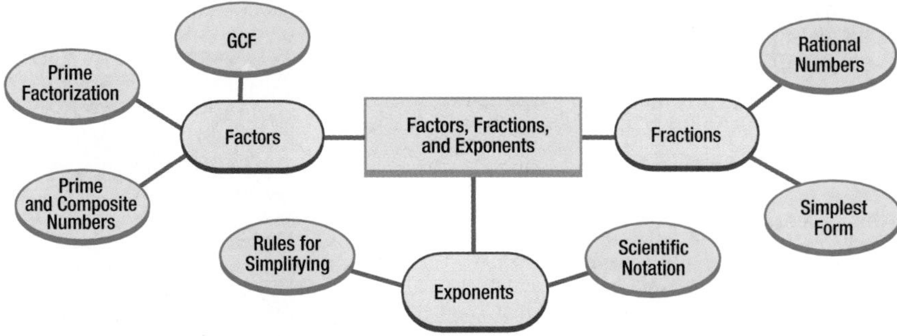


## Divisibility and Factors 4-1

*Summary* One integer is **divisible** by another if the remainder is 0 when you divide. Divisibility tests help you find factors. One integer is a **factor** of another integer if it divides that integer with remainder zero.

**List the positive factors of each number.**

1. 12 1, 2, 3, 4, 6, 12
2. 30 1, 2, 3, 5, 6, 10, 15, 30
3. 42 1, 2, 3, 6, 7, 14, 21, 42
4. 72 1, 2, 3, 4, 6, 8, 9, 12, 18, 24, 36, 72
5. 111 1, 3, 37, 111
6. 252 1, 2, 3, 4, 6, 7, 9, 12, 14, 18, 21, 28, 36, 42, 63, 84, 126, 252

## Exponents 4-2

*Summary* To simplify an expression that has an **exponent,** remember the **base** is the number used as a factor. The exponent shows the number of times the base is used as a factor.

**Simplify each expression.**

7. $2^3$ 8
8. $3(10 - 7)^2$ 27
9. $28 + (1 + 5)^2 \cdot 4$ 172
10. $-5^2$ −25

**Evaluate each expression.**

11. $x^2$, for $x = 11$ 121
12. $7m^2 - 5$, for $m = 3$ 58
13. $(2a + 1)^2$, for $a = -4$ 49
14. $b^2$, for $b = -4$ 16

## Prime Factorization and Greatest Common Factor 4-3

*Summary* A **prime number** is a positive integer greater than 1 with only two factors, 1 and itself. A positive integer greater than 1 with more than two factors is a **composite number.** The **prime factorization** of a composite number is the product of its prime factors.

The **greatest common factor (GCF)** of two or more expressions is the greatest factor the expressions have in common. You can list factors or use prime factorization to find the GCF of two or more expressions.

**Is each number *prime, composite,* or *neither?* For each composite number, write the prime factorization. Use exponents where possible.**

**15.** 13 prime **16.** 20 composite; $2^2 \cdot 5$ **17.** 73 prime **18.** 110 composite; $2 \cdot 5 \cdot 11$ **19.** 87 composite; $3 \cdot 29$

**Find the GCF.**

**20.** 16, 60 4 **21.** 36, 81, 27 9 **22.** 15, 17, 30 1 **23.** $3x^2y, 9x^2$ $3x^2$ **24.** $8a^2b, 14ab^2$ $2ab$

**25.** *Writing* Why is the GCF of two or more positive integers never greater than the least of the numbers? No factor of a positive integer is greater than the integer.

## Simplifying Fractions 4-4

*Summary* **Equivalent fractions** describe the same part of a whole. A fraction is in **simplest form** when the numerator and the denominator have no factors in common other than 1. You can use the GCF of the numerator and denominator to write a fraction in simplest form.

**Write in simplest form.**

**26.** $\frac{3}{15}$ $\frac{1}{5}$ **27.** $\frac{10}{20}$ $\frac{1}{2}$ **28.** $\frac{16}{52}$ $\frac{4}{13}$ **29.** $\frac{28}{40}$ $\frac{7}{10}$ **30.** $\frac{21}{33}$ $\frac{7}{11}$ **31.** $\frac{9}{54}$ $\frac{1}{6}$

**32.** $\frac{xy}{y}$ $x$ **33.** $\frac{25m}{5m}$ 5 **34.** $\frac{2y}{8y}$ $\frac{1}{4}$ **35.** $\frac{2c}{5c}$ $\frac{2}{5}$ **36.** $\frac{9x^2}{27x}$ $\frac{x}{3}$ **37.** $\frac{36bc}{9c}$ $4b$

## Account for All Possibilities 4-5

*Summary* To account for all possibilities in a word problem, make an organized list or a diagram to keep track of possibilities as you find them.

**38.** *School* Every day in class, Mike, Don, Tameka, and Rosa sit in the four desks in the last row of desks. Each day they sit in a different order. How many days can they do this before they repeat a previous pattern? 24 days



**Portfolio** Students may wish to include their completed work for the Wrap Up in their portfolios.

**Web Site**

Students can find self-assessment materials on the Web site: **www.phschool.com.**

## Rational Numbers

4-6

*Summary* A **rational number** is any number you can write as a quotient $\frac{a}{b}$ of two integers, where $b$ is not zero.

39–42. Number line: −2, $-\frac{5}{10}$, 0, 1, 2; −0.6, $\frac{2}{10}$

**Graph the rational numbers below on the same number line.**

39. 2
40. −0.6
41. $-\frac{5}{10}$
42. $\frac{2}{10}$

**Evaluate each expression for $a = -5$ and $b = -2$. Write in simplest form.**

43. $\frac{b}{a}$ $\frac{2}{5}$
44. $\frac{a+b}{4b}$ $\frac{7}{8}$
45. $\frac{b-a}{a-b}$ −1
46. $\frac{b^2}{a}$ $-\frac{4}{5}$

## Properties of Exponents

4-7 and 4-8

*Summary* To multiply numbers or variables with the same base, add the exponents. To raise a power to a power, multiply the exponents. To divide numbers or variables with the same nonzero base, subtract the exponents.

**Simplify each expression.**

47. $2^4 \cdot 2^3$ 128
48. $7a^4 \cdot 3a^2$ $21a^6$
49. $b \cdot c^2 \cdot b^6 \cdot c^2$ $b^7c^4$
50. $(x^3)^5$ $x^{15}$
51. $(y^4)^5$ $y^{20}$
52. $\frac{4^8}{4^2}$ 4,096
53. $\frac{b^2}{b^4}$ $\frac{1}{b^2}$
54. $\frac{28xy^7}{32xy^{12}}$ $\frac{7}{8y^5}$

## Scientific Notation

4-9

*Summary* **Scientific notation** is a way to write numbers as the product of two factors, a power of 10 and a decimal greater than or equal to 1, but less than 10. To multiply numbers in scientific notation, multiply the decimals, multiply the powers of ten, and then put the result in scientific notation.

**Write each number in scientific notation.**

55. 2,000,000 $2 \times 10^6$
56. 458,000,000 $4.58 \times 10^8$
57. 0.0000007 $7 \times 10^{-7}$
58. 0.0000000059 $5.9 \times 10^{-9}$

**Write each number in standard notation.**

59. $8 \times 10^{11}$ 800,000,000,000
60. $3.2 \times 10^{-6}$ 0.0000032
61. $1.119 \times 10^7$ 11,190,000
62. $5 \times 10^{-12}$ 0.000000000005

**Order from least to greatest.**

63. $3{,}644 \times 10^9, 12 \times 10^{11}, 4.3 \times 10^{10}$ $4.3 \times 10^{10}, 12 \times 10^{11}, 3{,}644 \times 10^9$
64. $58 \times 10^{-10}, 8 \times 10^{-10}, 716 \times 10^{-10}$ $8 \times 10^{-10}, 58 \times 10^{-10}, 716 \times 10^{-10}$

**Multiply. Express each result in scientific notation.**

65. $(4 \times 10^9)(6 \times 10^6)$ $2.4 \times 10^{16}$
66. $(5 \times 10^7)(3.6 \times 10^3)$ $1.8 \times 10^{11}$



### Chapter Assessment Form A Page 1

**Circle the letter of the best answer.**

1. Evaluate $3^5$.
   A. 15 B. 125 (C.) 243 D. 81
2. Evaluate $8 - 3^2$.
   F. −25 G. 25 H. 1 (J.) −1
3. Evaluate $cd^2$ for $c = 3$ and $d = -1$.
   A. −3 (B.) 3 C. −9 D. 9
4. Simplify $y^3 \cdot y^2 \cdot y^4$.
   (F.) $y^9$ G. $y^{24}$ H. $24y^4$ J. $2y^7$
5. Simplify $\frac{h^3}{h^8}$.
   A. $h^2$ B. $\frac{3}{8}h$ C. $h^5$ (D.) $\frac{1}{h^5}$
6. Simplify $(x^5)^2$.
   (F.) $x^{10}$ G. $x^7$ H. $2x^5$ J. $x^{25}$
7. Simplify $\frac{5x^3y^4}{15xy^6}$.
   A. $3x^2y^2$ (B.) $\frac{x^2}{3y^2}$ C. $\frac{x^3}{3y}$ D. $3x^3y^2$
8. Express 207,500 in scientific notation.
   F. $2.75 \times 10^5$ G. $2.075 \times 10^6$ (H.) $2.075 \times 10^5$ J. $2.75 \times 10^6$
9. Express $7.02 \times 10^{-5}$ in standard notation.
   A. 702,000 B. 70,200 C. 0.00000702 (D.) 0.0000702
10. 38,220 is *not* divisible by which of the following?
   F. 2 G. 3 H. 5 (J.) 9
11. In which of the following are the numbers in order from least to greatest?
   A. $5 \times 10^{-4}, 40 \times 10^{-5}, 0.6 \times 10^{-3}$ (B.) $7.2 \times 10^{-6}, 6.8 \times 10^{-5}, 73 \times 10^{-6}$
   C. $4.2 \times 10^{-3}, 45 \times 10^{-4}, 0.32 \times 10^{-2}$ D. $9.8 \times 10^{-2}, 8.4 \times 10^{-3}, 85 \times 10^{-2}$
12. List all the factors of 110. 1, 2, 5, 10, 11, 22 , 55, 110

**Is each number prime or composite? For each composite number, write the prime factorization.**

13. 63 composite; $3^2 \cdot 7$
14. 23 prime

**Find each GCF.**

15. 18, 35 1
16. $4x^2y^3, 6xy^2$ $2xy^2$

Assessment



### Chapter Assessment Form A Page 2

**Write in simplest form.**

17. $\frac{21}{35}$ $\frac{3}{5}$
18. $\frac{9m^3n^2}{18mn}$ $\frac{m^2n}{2}$

**Graph the numbers below on the same number line.**

19. $\frac{3}{10}$
20. $-\frac{2}{5}$
21. −0.7

Number line: −1.0, 0, 1.0; −0.7, $-\frac{2}{5}$, $\frac{3}{10}$

22. Evaluate for $a = 8$ and $b = -3$. Write in simplest form. $\frac{a+4b}{6}$
   $-\frac{2}{3}$
23. Multiply. Write the result in scientific notation. $(1.8 \times 10^5)(3 \times 10^4)$
   $5.4 \times 10^9$
24. For lunch, you must choose a sandwich, a piece of fruit, and a drink. Your choices include a ham sandwich, tuna sandwich, or cheese sandwich; an apple or an orange; and skim milk, whole milk, fruit juice, or bottled water. How many combinations of choices are possible?
   24
25. Explain why $2^{-3} = \frac{1}{2^3}$. Sample answer is shown:
   $\frac{2^2}{2^5} = 2^{2-5} = 2^{-3}$
   Also, $\frac{2^2}{2^5} = \frac{2 \cdot 2}{2 \cdot 2 \cdot 2 \cdot 2 \cdot 2} = \frac{1}{2^3}$
   So, $2^{-3} = \frac{1}{2^3}$ since $\frac{2^2}{2^5}$ can not have two different values.

# Assessment

**Test whether each number is divisible by 2, 3, 5, 9, or 10.**

1. 36 2, 3, 9
2. 100 2, 5, 10
3. 270 2, 3, 5, 9, 10
4. 84 2, 3
5. 555 3, 5
6. 49 none

**List all the factors of each number.**

7. 16 1, 2, 4, 8, 16
8. 30 1, 2, 3, 5, 6, 10, 15, 30
9. 41 1, 41
10. 23 1, 23
11. 55 1, 5, 11, 55
12. 64 1, 2, 4, 8, 16, 32, 64

**Simplify each expression.**

13. $5^3$ 125
14. $2^0 \cdot 2^3$ 8
15. $3^2 + 3^3$ 36
16. $4^2 \cdot 1^3$ 16
17. $(-9)^2$ 81
18. $(7 - 6)^4$ 1
19. $-2(3 + 2)^2$ −50
20. $12 - 4^2$ −4

21. *Writing* A number written in scientific notation is doubled. Must the exponent of the power of 10 change? Explain. See below.

**Evaluate for $a = -2$ and $b = 3$.**

22. $(a \cdot b)^2$ 36
23. $a^2b$ 12
24. $b^3 \cdot b^0$ 27
25. $(a + b)^5$ 1
26. $b^2 - a$ 11
27. $2(a^2 + b^3)$ 62

**Is each number *prime* or *composite?* For each composite number, write the prime factorization.**

28. 24 composite; $2^3 \cdot 3$
29. 17 prime
30. 42 composite; $2 \cdot 3 \cdot 7$
31. 54 composite; $2 \cdot 3^3$
32. 72
33. 100

32. composite; $2^3 \cdot 3^2$

33. composite; $2^2 \cdot 5^2$

**Find each GCF.**

34. 56, 96 8
35. 36, 60 12
36. 14, 25 1
37. $15x, 24x^2$ $3x$
38. $14a^2b^3, 21ab^2$ $7ab^2$

**Simplify.**

39. $\frac{4}{16}$ $\frac{1}{4}$
40. $\frac{44}{52}$ $\frac{11}{13}$
41. $\frac{15}{63}$ $\frac{5}{21}$
42. $\frac{a^3}{a^2}$ $a$
43. $\frac{5b^4}{b}$ $5b^3$
44. $\frac{8m^4n^2}{40mn}$ $\frac{m^3n}{5}$

21. Answers may vary. Sample: Yes, if the decimal between 1 and 10 is at least 5, doubling the original number will increase the exponent of 10 by 1.

**Graph the numbers on the same number line.**

45–48. [number line marked −1, $-\frac{1}{2}$, −0.3, 0, $\frac{1}{10}$, 1]

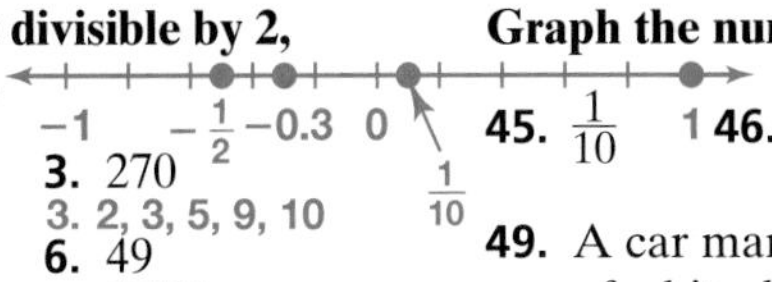

45. $\frac{1}{10}$
46. $-0.3$
47. $-\frac{1}{2}$
48. 1

49. A car manufacturer offers exterior colors of white, blue, red, black, and silver. The manufacturer offers interior colors of black and silver. How many different styles are there? 10 styles

**Evaluate for $x = 4$ and $y = -3$. Write in simplest form.**

50. $\frac{2y}{x^2}$ $-\frac{3}{8}$
51. $\frac{xy}{5x}$ $-\frac{3}{5}$
52. $\frac{(x + y)^3}{x}$ $\frac{1}{4}$
53. $\frac{x + 3y}{10}$ $-\frac{1}{2}$
54. $\frac{y^2 - x}{5}$ 1
55. $\frac{x - y}{x + y}$ 7

**Simplify each expression.**

56. $a^4 \cdot a$ $a^5$
57. $(y^3)^6$ $y^{18}$
58. $x^3 \cdot x^6 \cdot y^2$ $x^9y^2$
59. $(a^3)^2$ $a^6$
60. $6b^7 \cdot 5b^2$ $30b^9$
61. $\frac{9^8}{9^2}$ 531,441
62. $\frac{6a^7}{15a^3}$ $\frac{2a^4}{5}$
63. $\frac{b^8}{b^{11}}$ $\frac{1}{b^3}$
64. $\frac{2x^2y^5}{8x^3y^5}$ $\frac{1}{4x}$

**Write each number in scientific notation.**

65. 43,000,000 $4.3 \times 10^7$
66. 6,000,000,000 $6 \times 10^9$
67. 0.0000032 $3.2 \times 10^{-6}$
68. 0.00000000099 $9.9 \times 10^{-10}$

**Write each number in standard notation.**

69. $5 \times 10^5$ 500,000
70. $3.812 \times 10^{-7}$ 0.0000003812
71. $9.3 \times 10^8$ 930,000,000
72. $1.02 \times 10^{-9}$ 0.00000000102

**Order from least to greatest.**

73. $3 \times 10^{10}, 742 \times 10^7, 0.006 \times 10^{12}$ See below.
74. $85 \times 10^{-7}, 2 \times 10^{-5}, 0.9 \times 10^{-8}$ $0.9 \times 10^{-8}, 85 \times 10^{-7}, 2 \times 10^{-5}$

**Multiply. Express each result in scientific notation.**

75. $(3 \times 10^{10})(7 \times 10^8)$ $2.1 \times 10^{19}$
76. $(8.3 \times 10^6)(3 \times 10^5)$ $2.49 \times 10^{12}$

73. $0.006 \times 10^{12}, 742 \times 10^7, 3 \times 10^{10}$



## Chapter Assessment

**Resources** For a complete list of resources for this chapter, see p. 169H.

### Chapter Assessment Form B Page 1

1. Evaluate $2^7$.
   (A.) 128  B. 144  C. 48  D. 14
2. Evaluate $7 - 3^2$.
   F. 2  (G.) −2  H. 16  J. −16
3. Evaluate $(x + y)^3$, for $x = -2$ and $y = 5$.
   A. 117  B. −27  (C.) 27  D. 343
4. Simplify $h^3 \cdot h \cdot h^4$.
   F. $h^{12}$  (G.) $h^8$  H. $3h^5$  J. $12h^4$
5. Simplify $\frac{m^2}{m^9}$.
   A. $m^4$  B. $\frac{2}{9}m$  C. $m^7$  (D.) $\frac{1}{m^7}$
6. Simplify $(y^3)^3$.
   F. $y^2$  G. $3y^3$  H. $y^6$  (J.) $y^9$
7. Simplify $\frac{6x^7y^2}{8x^2y^5}$.
   (A.) $\frac{3x^5}{4y^3}$  B. $\frac{3}{4}x^5y^3$  C. $\frac{3x^3}{4y^2}$  D. $\frac{3}{4}x^3y^2$
8. Express 17,000 in scientific notation.
   F. $1.7 \times 10^2$  G. $17 \times 10^3$  (H.) $1.7 \times 10^4$  J. $1.7 \times 10^3$
9. Express $5.50 \times 10^{-6}$ in standard notation.
   A. 550,000  B. 5,500,000  C. 0.00000055  (D.) 0.0000055
10. 87,430 is *not* divisible by which of the following?
    F. 2  (G.) 3  H. 5  J. 10
11. In which of the following are the numbers in order from least to greatest?
    A. $6 \times 10^{-4}, 70 \times 10^{-5}, 0.5 \times 10^{-3}$  B. $3.6 \times 10^{-3}, 39 \times 10^{-4}, 0.35 \times 10^{-2}$
    (C.) $8.3 \times 10^{-6}, 0.85 \times 10^{-5}, 7.8 \times 10^{-5}$  D. $1.7 \times 10^{-2}, 2.6 \times 10^{-3}, 21 \times 10^{-2}$

**Write your answer.**

12. List all the factors of 70 1, 2, 5, 7, 10, 14, 35, 70

**Is each number prime or composite? For each composite number, write the prime factorization.**

13. 37 prime
14. 99 composite; $3^2 \cdot 11$

**Find the GCF.**

15. 36, 70 2
16. $6xy^4, 9x^3y^3$ $3xy^3$



Assessment

### Chapter Assessment Form B Page 2

**Write in simplest form.**

17. $\frac{35}{40}$ $\frac{7}{8}$
18. $\frac{8m^4n^3}{24mn}$ $\frac{m^3n^2}{3}$

**Graph the numbers below on the same number line.**

19. $\frac{7}{10}$
20. $-\frac{3}{5}$
21. −0.2

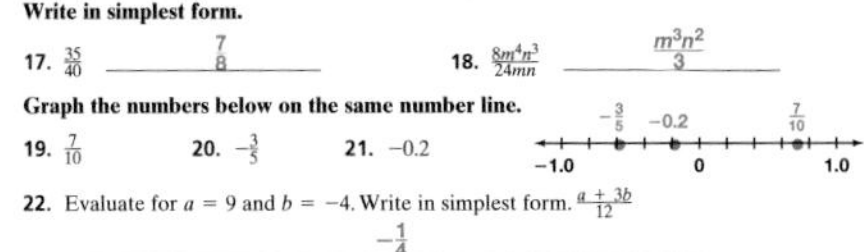


22. Evaluate for $a = 9$ and $b = -4$. Write in simplest form. $\frac{a + 3b}{12}$
    $-\frac{1}{4}$
23. Multiply. Write your result using scientific notation. $(2.1 \times 10^3)(4 \times 10^5)$
    $8.4 \times 10^8$
24. Suppose your school colors are red and light blue. You can get warm-up suits for the basketball team with either red, light blue, or white as the main color. The logo and other detailing comes in black or dark blue. You can also get the suits with or without a vertical stripe. How many choices do you have?
    12
25. Explain why $b^2 = (-b)^2$ for any number $b$. Sample answer is shown:
    $(-b)^2 = (-b)(-b) = b^2$, since the product of two negative numbers is positive.

# Cumulative Review

## Cumulative Review Page 1

**Circle the letter of the best answer.**

1. Simplify $-3 + 2 \cdot 4 - 2$.
   A. $-2$ (B.) $3$ C. $1$ D. $-6$
2. What is the opposite of 19?
   F. $-1$ G. $\frac{1}{19}$ H. $19$ (J.) $-19$
3. Simplify $5 + (-4) + (-5)$.
   (A.) $-4$ B. $14$ C. $-14$ D. $-10$
4. Simplify $-2y - (3k - 2y) + 3k$.
   (F.) $0$ G. $4y - 6k$ H. $4y$ J. $6k - 4y$
5. Which integer is *not* a solution of $36 + x > 14$?
   A. $5$ B. $-20$ (C.) $-22$ D. $-16$
6. Which number is divisible by both 3 and 2?
   F. 68,211 G. 45,305 H. 28,000 (J.) 58,404
7. Which expression is equivalent to $-6 \cdot m \cdot m \cdot n \cdot 3 \cdot m$?
   A. $-6m^3 + 3n$ (B.) $-18m^3n$ C. $-18mn^3$ D. $-18 \cdot 3m \cdot n$
8. Which expression is the GCF of $12x^3$ and $32xy$?
   F. $93x^3y$ G. $96x^4y$ (H.) $4x$ J. $4xy$
9. Which is equivalent to $\frac{m^4n^5}{m^6n^2}$?
   A. $m^2n^3$ (B.) $m^{-2}n^3$ C. $m^2n^{-3}$ D. $m^{-2}n^{-3}$
10. Evaluate $\frac{4m - 5}{n}$ for $m = 5, n = 25$.
    F. $5$ G. $3$ H. $\frac{5}{3}$ (J.) $\frac{3}{5}$
11. Simplify $x^6 \cdot y^2 \cdot x^3 \cdot y$.
    A. $x^3y$ B. $x^2y$ (C.) $x^9y^3$ D. $x^{18}y^2$
12. Simplify $\frac{w^{10}y^{12}z}{w^6z^5}$.
    (F.) $\frac{w^4y^{12}}{z^4}$ G. $\frac{w^{16}y^{12}}{z^6}$ H. $w^{16}y^{12}z^6$ J. $w^4y^{12}z^4$
13. Simplify $5^{-2}$.
    A. $-10$ B. $25$ C. $-25$ (D.) $\frac{1}{25}$
14. Which is true?
    F. $14 > 9 \cdot 3$ G. $-26 - 12 = 38$
    H. $4[-5 - (-2)] = (-2)6$ (J.) $50 - (-3 \cdot 5) \geq 55$



## Cumulative Review Page 2

15. Which expression is equal to $x^{14}$?
    A. $x^7 + x^7$ (B.) $(x^7)^2$ C. $(x^7)^7$ D. $x^2 \cdot x^7$
16. Which symbol makes $(5^3)^4$ ☐ $5^3 \cdot 5^4$ true?
    F. $<$ (G.) $>$ H. $=$ J. none
17. Write a variable expression using parentheses for the total area of the rectangle. Then find the area for $x = 5$.
    $6(x + 3)$; 48

    x 3 6

18. The quotient of a number $n$ and 3.2 is negative twenty-five hundredths. Write and solve an equation to find $n$.
    $\frac{n}{3.2} = -0.25$
    $n = -0.8$
19. List all the factors of 56.
    1, 2, 4, 7, 8, 14, 28, 56
20. A restaurant offers a breakfast special of one egg, toast, and orange or tomato juice for $1.79. The egg may be poached, scrambled, or fried. List all the breakfast special combinations that are available. How many are there? Explain how you know you have them all.
    poached egg with orange juice and toast
    poached egg with tomato juice and toast
    scrambled egg with orange juice and toast
    scrambled egg with tomato juice and toast
    fried egg with orange juice and toast
    fried egg with tomato juice and toast
    There are 6 combinations. List them in an organized way.



Assessment



**Choose the best answer.**

1. Simplify $2(11 + 7 \cdot 2)$. B
   A. 72 B. 50
   C. 36 D. 78
2. What is the opposite of $-3$? J
   F. $-9$ G. 9
   H. 0.3 J. 3
3. Simplify $-8 + (-8) - (-8)$. C
   A. $-16$ B. 8
   C. $-8$ D. $-24$
4. Simplify $(4c - 5c) + (7 - 2)$. G
   F. $c + 5$ G. $-c + 5$
   H. $9c + 5$ J. $c - 5$
5. Which integer is *not* a solution of $25 + t < 19$? A
   A. $-6$ B. $-43$
   C. $-7$ D. $-8$
6. Which sentence is true? H
   F. $16 \geq 2 \cdot 9$
   G. $-36 - 10 = 4(5)$
   H. $5[-6 - (-2)] = 2 \cdot (-5)2$
   J. $32 - (-4 \cdot 6) \leq 54$
7. Which number is divisible by both 3 and 9? D
   A. 95,500 B. 36,089
   C. 24,000 D. 45,288
8. Which expression is equivalent to $-8 \cdot n \cdot n \cdot n \cdot 4 \cdot t$? F
   F. $-32n^3t$ G. $-8n^3 + 4t$
   H. $-32 \cdot 3n \cdot t$ J. $-32nt^3$
9. Which expression is the GCF of $24x^3$ and $64x$? D
   A. $1{,}536x^4$ B. $4x^4$
   C. $40x^2$ D. $8x$
10. Which expression is equal to $x^{12}$? J
    F. $x^6 + x^6$ G. $(x^4)^8$
    H. $x^2 \cdot x^6$ J. $x^6 \cdot x^6$
11. Which expression is equivalent to $\frac{x^3y^7}{x^5y^2}$? A
    A. $x^{-2}y^5$ B. $x^2y^5$
    C. $x^{-2}y^{-5}$ D. $x^2y^{-5}$
12. Evaluate $\frac{3m - 12}{n}$, for $m = 8$ and $n = 4$. G
    F. 0 G. 3
    H. 4 J. $\frac{24m - 12}{4}$
13. Which symbol makes $7^2 \cdot 7^5$ ■ $(7^5)^2$ true? B
    A. $>$ B. $<$ C. $=$ D. $\geq$
14. Simplify $x^5 \cdot y \cdot x^5 \cdot y$. J
    F. $(x^{25})(2y)$ G. $x^5y^2$
    H. $2x^5y$ J. $x^{10}y^2$
15. Simplify $\frac{w^{12}y^{15}z}{w^9y^7}$. A
    A. $w^3y^8z$ B. $w^{21}y^{22}z$
    C. $\frac{w^{21}y^{22}z}{wz}$ D. $\frac{w^3y^8z}{wz}$
16. Simplify $2^{-3}$. G
    F. $-6$ G. $\frac{1}{8}$
    H. $-8$ J. 6

**For Exercises 17–20, show your work.**

17. Write a variable expression for the length of the red segment. Then find the length of the segment for $a = 7$. $4a$; 28

    a a a a

18. The product of negative 6.2 and a number $k$ is negative seventy and sixty-eight hundredths. Write and solve an equation to find $k$. $-6.2k = -70.68$; 11.4
19. List the positive factors of 54. 1, 2, 3, 6, 9, 18, 27, 54
20. The school store sells erasers for \$.05, \$.10, and \$.15. List all the ways that you could spend exactly \$.45 on erasers. See back of book.



| Item | Chapter/ Lesson | Review Topic |
|---|---|---|
| 1, 2, 3, 4, 17 | 1-1, 1-2, 1-4, 1-6, 2-3 | Algebraic Expressions and Integers |
| 5, 6 | 2-9, 2-10 | Solving One-Step Inequalities |
| 18, 20 | 3-5, 3-6 | Decimals and Equations |
| 7–16, 19 | 4-1, 4-2, 4-3, 4-4 4-6, 4-7, 4-8 | Factors, Fractions, and Exponents |

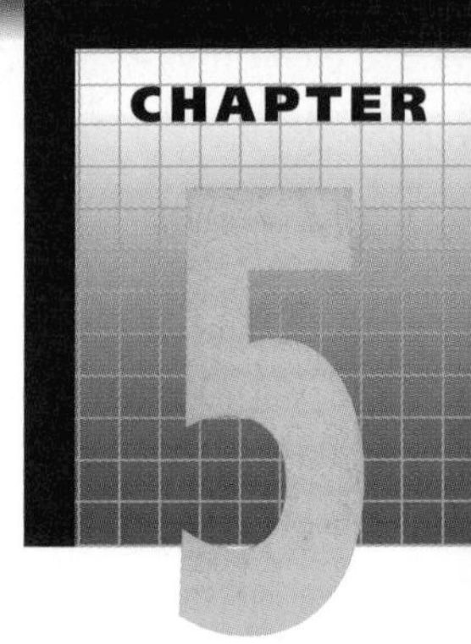


# Operations with Fractions

## Content Overview for Chapter 5

Chapter 5 starts by showing how to compare fractions by writing them as equivalent fractions using the LCM of the denominators. You can also compare fractions by changing them to decimal form.

To add or subtract fractions and mixed numbers, first write the fractions with a common denominator, then add or subtract the numerators. To multiply fractions, multiply their numerators and their denominators. To divide fractions, multiply the first fraction by the reciprocal of the second fraction. You can use dimensional analysis, the multiplication of fractions, to convert units of measure in the customary system of measurement.

You can use your knowledge of adding, subtracting, multiplying, and dividing fractions to solve equations that contain fractions.

To raise a product to a power, raise each factor to the power. To raise a quotient to a power, raise both the numerator and the denominator to the power.

## Making Connections

| Lesson | Interdisciplinary and Real-World Connections | Math Integration |
|---|---|---|
| 5-1 | Home Economics | Geometry |
| 5-2 | Zoology, Consumer Issues | Algebra |
| 5-3 | Meteorology | Algebra |
| 5-4 | Construction | Geometry |
| 5-5 | Geography, History | Measurement |
| 5-6 | History | Problem Solving, Geometry |
| 5-7 | Environment | Algebra |
| 5-8 | Biology, Astronomy | Algebra |
| 5-9 | Consumerism | Geometry |

**SCHOOL/HOME CONNECTION**
English and Spanish versions are available in the *Help at Home* book of copy masters.

**Helper's Page** You will find detailed instruction, more examples, and

**Student Page** *Review Exercises for Lessons 5-1 to 5-3*

**Compare. Use $<$, $>$, or $=$ to complete each statement.** *(Lesson 5-1)*

1. $\frac{5}{9}$ ☐ $\frac{2}{3}$
2. $-\frac{5}{8}$ ☐ $-\frac{5}{16}$
3. $-\frac{3}{5}$ ☐ $-\frac{7}{10}$

**Write each fraction or mixed number as a decimal.** *(Lesson 5-2)*

4. $\frac{7}{40}$ ____
5. $-2\frac{3}{25}$ ____
6. $\frac{1}{6}$ ____

**Write as a fraction or mixed number in simplest form.** *(Lesson 5-2)*

7. 0.375 ____
8. 5.75 ____
9. $0.\overline{45}$ ____

**Find each sum or difference.** *(Lesson 5-3)*

10. $\frac{6}{17} + \frac{15}{17}$ ____
11. $\frac{6}{7} - \frac{1}{2}$ ____
12. $2\frac{3}{4} + 3\frac{5}{8}$
13. $5\frac{1}{9} - 2\frac{2}{3}$
14. **Test Prep** Which group of rational numbers is in order from least to greatest? *(Lesson 5-2)*
    A. $-\frac{5}{9}, -0.5, -0.4, -\frac{4}{9}$
    B. $-0.5, -0.4, -\frac{5}{9}, -\frac{4}{9}$
    C. $-\frac{5}{9}, -0.5, -\frac{4}{9}, -0.4$
    D. $-0.5, -\frac{5}{9}, -0.4, -\frac{4}{9}$ ____

Helper: ____ Comments: ____

**Helper's Page** You will find detailed instruction, more examples, and

**Student Page** *Review Exercises for Lessons 5-4 to 5-8*

**Find each product or quotient.** *(Lesson 5-4)*

1. $1\frac{2}{3} \cdot \left(-2\frac{1}{5}\right)$ ____
2. $5\frac{1}{7} \div 1\frac{5}{7}$ ____

**Use estimation, mental math, or paper and pencil to convert from one unit to the other.** *(Lesson 5-5)*

3. $4\frac{1}{3}$ ft = ____ in.
4. 18 pt = ____ gal
5. 54 oz = ____ lb

**Work backward to solve the problem.** *(Lesson 5-6)*

6. Juan wants to be at camp by 3:30 P.M. to meet some friends. It normally takes Juan and his family $2\frac{1}{2}$ hours to get to camp. The family usually stops for 15 minutes on the way. Juan wants to allow an additional 15 minutes of travel time in case there are traffic delays. What time should Juan and his family leave their home to get Juan to camp? ____

**Solve each equation.** *(Lessons 5-7 and 5-8)*

7. $x - \frac{2}{3} = 2\frac{1}{6}$ $x =$ ____
8. $m - 1\frac{6}{7} = 2\frac{1}{14}$ $m =$ ____
9. $y + 3\frac{1}{9} = 4\frac{2}{3}$ $y =$ ____
10. $a + 7\frac{1}{4} = 3\frac{3}{8}$ $a =$ ____
11. $\frac{11}{12}n = 1\frac{5}{6}$ $n =$ ____
12. $-2\frac{1}{4}b = \frac{3}{8}$ $b =$ ____
13. **Test Prep** Which of the following is a reasonable measure for the amount of water in a pond? *(Lesson 5-5)*
    A. 6,000 c B. 6,000 pt C. 6,000 qt D. 6,000 gal ____

Helper: ____ Comments: ____

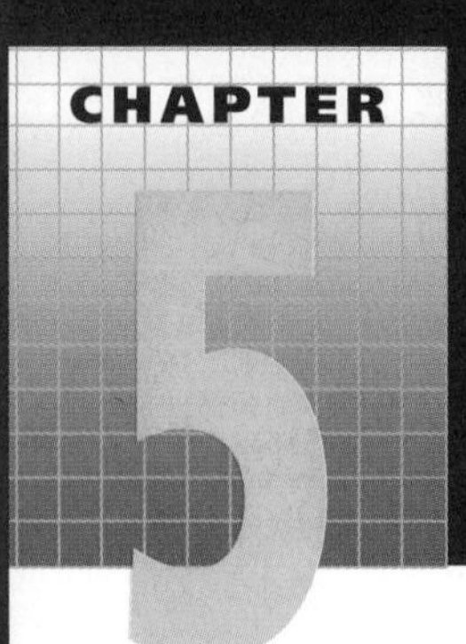

# Chapter 5 at a Glance

To accommodate flexible scheduling, most lessons are divided into parts. Assignment Options are given in the Teacher's Edition for each lesson.

| Pages | Lesson | NCTM | Parts |
|---|---|---|---|
| 224–228 | **Lesson 5-1** Comparing and Ordering Fractions | 1, 2, 6, 8, 9, 10 | Part 1 Finding the Least Common Multiple<br>Part 2 Comparing Fractions<br>▽ **Project Activity 1** |
| 229–233 | **Lesson 5-2** Fractions and Decimals | 1, 6, 7, 8, 9, 10 | Part 1 Writing Fractions as Decimals<br>Part 2 Writing Decimals as Fractions |
| 235–239 | **Lesson 5-3** Adding and Subtracting Fractions | 1, 2, 6, 8, 9, 10 | Part 1 Adding and Subtracting Fractions<br>Part 2 Adding and Subtracting Mixed Numbers<br>**Checkpoint 1** |
| 255–258 | **Lesson 5-7** Solving Equations by Adding or Subtracting Fractions | 1, 2, 6, 8, 9, 10 | Part 1 Using Subtraction to Solve Equations<br>Part 2 Using Addition to Solve Equations |
| 259–263 | **Lesson 5-8** Solving Equations by Multiplying Fractions | 1, 2, 6, 8, 9, 10 | Part 1 Using Multiplication to Solve Equations<br>Part 2 Solving Equations with Mixed Numbers<br>**Checkpoint 2**<br>▽ **Project Activity 3** |
| 265–268 | **Lesson 5-9** Powers of Products and Quotients | 1, 2, 6, 8, 9, 10 | Part 1 Finding Powers of Products<br>Part 2 Finding Powers of Quotients<br>▽ **Project Activity 4** |

## Pacing Options

This chart suggests pacing for only the core lessons and their parts, and it is provided merely as a possible guide. It will help you determine how much time you have in your schedule to cover other features, such as the Chapter Project, Math Toolboxes, Standardized Test Prep, Wrap Up, and Assessment.

| | Day 1 | Day 2 | Day 3 | Day 4 | Day 5 | Day 6 | Day 7 | Day 8 | Day 9 | Day 10 | Day 11 |
|---|---|---|---|---|---|---|---|---|---|---|---|
| **Traditional** (40–45 min. class periods) | 5–1 ▽1 | 5–1 ▽2 | 5–2 ▽1 | 5–2 ▽2 | 5–3 ▽1, 5–3 ▽2 | 5–4 ▽1 | 5–4 ▽2 | 5–5 ▽1, 5–5 ▽2 | 5–6 | 5–7 ▽1, 5–7 ▽2 | 5–8 ▽1, 5–8 ▽2 |
| **Pre-Algebra Over 2 Years** (40–45 min. class periods) | 5–1 ▽1 | 5–1 ▽1 | 5–1 ▽2 | 5–1 ▽2 | 5–2 ▽1 | 5–2 ▽1 | 5–2 ▽2 | 5–2 ▽2 | 5–3 ▽1 | 5–3 ▽1 | 5–3 ▽2 |
| **Block Scheduling** (90 min. class periods) | 5–1 ▽1, 5–1 ▽2, 5–2 ▽1 | 5–2 ▽2, 5–3 ▽1, 5–3 ▽2 | 5–4 ▽1 ▽2, 5–5 ▽1 ▽2 | 5–6, 5–7 ▽1, 5–7 ▽2 | 5–8 ▽1 ▽2, 5–9 ▽1 ▽2 | | | | | | |

| Pages 240–244 | Lesson 5-4 Multiplying and Dividing Fractions |
|---|---|
| NCTM 1, 2, 6, 7, 8, 9, 10 | Part 1 Multiplying Rational Numbers<br>Part 2 Dividing Rational Numbers |

| Pages 245–249 | Lesson 5-5 Measurement: Using Customary Units of Measurement |
|---|---|
| NCTM 1, 4, 6, 8, 9, 10 | Part 1 Identifying Appropriate Measures<br>Part 2 Converting Units<br>**Math At Work** |

| Pages 251–254 | Lesson 5-6 Problem Solving Strategy |
|---|---|
| NCTM 1, 2, 4, 6, 8, 9, 10 | Work Backward<br>**Project Activity 2** |

**NCTM STANDARDS 2000**

1 Number and Operations
2 Algebra
3 Geometry
4 Measurement
5 Data Analysis and Probability
6 Problem Solving
7 Reasoning and Proof
8 Communication
9 Connections
10 Representation

| Day 12 | Day 13 | Day 14 | Day 15 | Day 16 | Day 17 | Day 18 | Day 19 | Day 20 | Day 21 | Day 22 | Day 23 | Day 24 |
|---|---|---|---|---|---|---|---|---|---|---|---|---|
| 5–9 1, 5–9 2 | | | | | | | | | | | | |
| 5–3 2 | 5–4 1 | 5–4 1 | 5–4 2 | 5–4 2 | 5–5 1 | 5–5 2 | 5–6 | 5–7 1 | 5–7 2 | 5–8 1 | 5–8 2 | 5–9 1, 5–9 2 |

**Block Scheduling Notes**

Consider these suggestions:

- **Day 2** Before starting Lesson 5-3, teach Math Toolbox 1, p. 234.
- **Day 3** After completing Lesson 5-4, begin presentations for Finish the Project.
- **Day 4** Before starting Lesson 5-6, teach Math Toolbox 2, p. 250.
- **Day 5** Before starting Lesson 5-9, teach the Standardized Test Prep, p. 264.

# Math Background

## Lesson 5-1

### Comparing and Ordering Fractions

If *a, b,* and *c* are whole numbers, and if $ab = c$, then $c$ is a multiple of $a$ and $b$. For example, $5 \bullet 6 = 30$, so 30 is a multiple of 5 and 6.

A number that is a multiple of two or more given whole numbers is a common multiple of the numbers. For example, 30 is a common multiple of 5 and 6 and also of 2 and 15.

The least common multiple (LCM) of two or more numbers (other than zero) is the least number that is a common multiple of the numbers. For example, 10 and 12 have the common multiples 60, 120, 180, and 240, but the least common multiple of 10 and 12 is 60.

If two numbers are relatively prime (having no factor in common) then the least common multiple is the product of the two numbers.

## Lesson 5-2

### Fractions and Decimals

Any fraction that is the ratio of two integers can be converted to a decimal fraction by dividing the numerator by the denominator. If this division reaches a point when there is no remainder, the decimal fraction is called a *terminating decimal.* A terminating decimal can always be written as the ratio of two integers.

## Lesson 5-3

### Adding and Subtracting Fractions

There are many ways to model fractions. One way is to use a number line. The following number line shows line segments modeling $\frac{1}{2}$ (above) and $\frac{1}{3}$ (below).

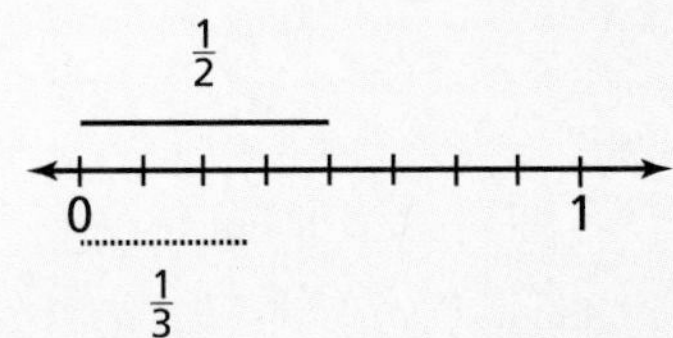


When these two line segments are placed end to end to model $\frac{1}{2} + \frac{1}{3}$, you can see immediately that the sum of these two fractions is not found by adding the numerators and adding the denominators, which would give $\frac{2}{5}$ (approximated by the line underneath).

$$\frac{1}{2} + \frac{1}{3} = \frac{5}{6}$$

0 1

$\frac{2}{5}$

This model shows graphically and clearly the common errors made in adding these fractions. The model also shows the correct sum of $\frac{5}{6}$. This model can help students build an intuitive understanding about the addition and subtraction of fractions, even before they calculate a lowest common denominator. The algebraic rule, or algorithm, for adding is this: $\frac{a}{b} + \frac{c}{d} = \frac{ad + bc}{bd}$. Students may gain an understanding of the process of adding or subtracting fractions using the lowest common denominators by writing out prime factors.

$$\frac{3}{4} + \frac{1}{6} = \frac{3}{2^2} + \frac{1}{2 \cdot 3} = \frac{3 \cdot 3}{2^2 \cdot 3} + \frac{1 \cdot 2}{2 \cdot 3 \cdot 2} =$$

$$\frac{9}{2^2 \cdot 3} + \frac{2}{2^2 \cdot 3} = \frac{11}{2^2 \cdot 3} = \frac{11}{12}$$

## Lesson 5-4

### Multiplying and Dividing Fractions

The process for multiplying fractions seems intuitively reasonable for most students. $\frac{a}{b} \times \frac{c}{d} = \frac{ac}{bd}$

The process for dividing fractions is not obvious. When you divide 14 counters into 2 equal groups, each group has 7 counters. This demonstrates that $14 \div 2 = 7$ is equivalent to finding one-half of 14.

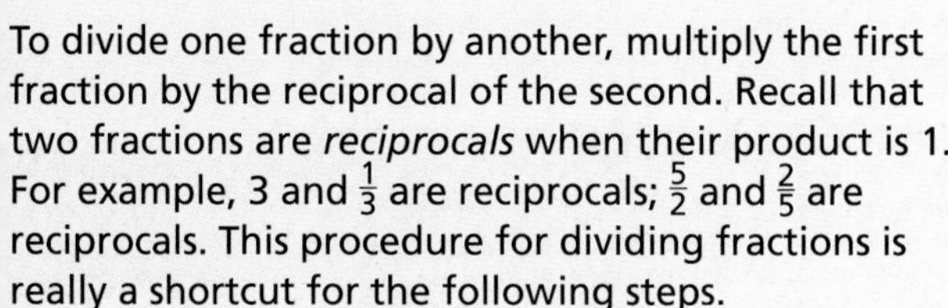

To divide one fraction by another, multiply the first fraction by the reciprocal of the second. Recall that two fractions are *reciprocals* when their product is 1. For example, 3 and $\frac{1}{3}$ are reciprocals; $\frac{5}{2}$ and $\frac{2}{5}$ are reciprocals. This procedure for dividing fractions is really a shortcut for the following steps.

$\frac{1}{2} \div \frac{1}{3} = \frac{\frac{1}{2}}{\frac{1}{3}}$, which is $\frac{\frac{1}{2} \times \frac{3}{1}}{\frac{1}{3} \times \frac{3}{1}} = \frac{\frac{3}{2}}{1}$, which is $\frac{3}{2}$.

# Lesson 5-5

## Using Customary Units of Measurement

The United States customary system of measurement (sometimes called the English system of measure) is based on the U. S. customary yard as a standard. The standard U.S. yard is currently defined to be $\frac{3600}{3937}$ of the standard meter.

Systems of measurement are used to measure length, weight, mass, volume, temperature , and time. The *accuracy* of a measurement tells how correctly a measurement is made. An accurate scale gives the same reading every time and is adjusted to match standard weights. The *precision* of a measurement tells how closely, or finely, the measurement is made. The precision tells you the smallest units on the measuring device that was used. Bathroom scales, for example, are much less precise that the scales used in a laboratory. The *greatest possible error* in a measurement is related to the precision of a measuring device; the greatest possible error is one-half the smallest unit on the device.

# Lesson 5-7

## Solving Equations by Adding or Subtracting Fractions

The process by which you solve an equation containing a fraction is very similar to the previous process for solving one-step equations with integers. To isolate the variable, you use inverse operations to undo what has been done to the variable.

$x + \frac{1}{3} = \frac{2}{5}$

$x + \frac{1}{3} - \frac{1}{3} = \frac{2}{5} - \frac{1}{3}$

$x = \frac{2}{5} - \frac{1}{3}$

$x = \frac{2 \cdot 3 - 1 \cdot 5}{3 \cdot 5}$

$x = \frac{1}{15}$

# Lesson 5-8

## Solving Equations by Multiplying Fractions

You can solve an equation such as $3x = 12$ by using inverse operations (dividing by 3) or by multiplying both sides by the reciprocal of 3, which is the fraction $\frac{1}{3}$.

$$3x = 12$$

$$\frac{1}{3}(3x) = \frac{1}{3}(12), \text{ so } x = 4$$

# Lesson 5-9

## Powers of Products and Quotients

To raise a product to a power, you raise each factor to the power, so $(ab)^m = a^m b^m$. This means that $(2 \bullet 3)^2 = 2^2 \bullet 3^2$, or 4(9), which is 36. Notice that the rule for raising a product (or quotient) to a power does *not* apply to raising a sum to a power, for example, $(2 + 3)^2 \neq 2^2 + 3^2$.

For professional development tips visit our Web site **www.phschool.com**.

# Monitoring Progress

## Universal Access

### ▶ Preventing a Student from Falling Behind

These resources are particularly helpful in preventing a student from falling behind his or her appropriate math level. For a complete list of resources for this chapter, see page 221H.

#### Skills You Need for Chapter 5

Student Edition, p. 221
Teacher's Edition, p. 221

- Reading and writing fractions
- Writing fractions and decimals
- Solving equations
- Finding the GCF

#### Skills Handbook

Student Edition, pp. 723–741
Teacher's Edition, pp. 723–741

- Multiplying Whole Numbers, p. 725
- Dividing Whole Numbers, p. 726

#### Reteaching Worksheets

There is a Reteaching worksheet for every lesson in this chapter.

- Chapter 5 Support File, Teaching Resources box
- See TE p. 221H for a complete list of resources.

#### Skills Intervention Kit with CD-ROM

| For | Use |
|---|---|
| Lessons 5-1, 5-3, 5-4 | Fraction Concepts |
| Lesson 5-2 | Decimals |
| Lesson 5-5 | Measurement |
| Lesson 5-6 | Fraction Operations |
| Lessons 5-7, 5-8, 5-9 | Pre-Algebra Basics |

#### Daily Cumulative Review Blackline Masters

There is a Daily Cumulative Review worksheet for every lesson in this chapter.

See TE p. 221H for a complete list of resources.

### ▶ Accommodating Diverse Learning Styles

#### Tactile Learning

Use fraction bars to add and subtract fractions. (Lesson 5-3)

Examine objects used to measure length, capacity, and weight. (Lesson 5-5)

#### Advanced Learner

Every lesson has at least one challenge problem.

#### ELL (English Language Learner)

Understand the terms *least common multiple* and *least common denominator.* (Lesson 5-1)

Discuss how the abbreviation lb came to b used for pound. (Lesson 5-5)

#### Auditory Learning

Listen to a partner reading decimals and fractions. (Lesson 5-2)

Say "I need to add . . . to each side" as you work problems. (Lesson 5-7)

#### Visual Learning

Graph fractions on a number line. (Lesson 5-1)

Model portions of cookies or pizzas. (Lesson 5-4)

# Aligning Assessment with Instruction

## Assessment Options

| | Chapter Opener | 5-1 | 5-2 | 5-3 | 5-4 | 5-5 | 5-6 | 5-7 | 5-8 | 5-9 | End |
|---|---|---|---|---|---|---|---|---|---|---|---|
| Chapter Project | ■ | ■ | | | | | ■ | | ■ | ■ | ■ |
| Try This Exercises | | ■ | ■ | ■ | ■ | ■ | ■ | ■ | ■ | ■ | |
| Mixed Reviews | | ■ | ■ | ■ | ■ | ■ | ■ | ■ | ■ | ■ | |
| Checkpoints | | | | ■ | | | | | ■ | | |
| Writing | | | ■ | | ■ | ■ | | ■ | ■ | ■ | ■ |
| Chapter Assessment | | | | | | | | | | | ■ |
| Cumulative Review | | | | | | | | | | | ■ |
| Standardized Test Prep | | | | ■ | ■ | ■ | | ■ | ■ | | |
| | Standardized Test Prep, p. 264 | | | | | | | | | | |
| Computer Item Generator | Can be used to create custom-made practice pages or assessment pages at any time. | | | | | | | | | | |

### Test-Taking Tips on Transparencies

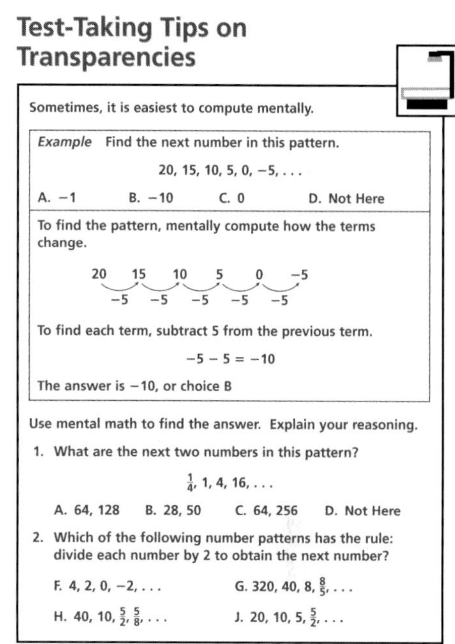
Sometimes, it is easiest to compute mentally.

*Example* Find the next number in this pattern.

20, 15, 10, 5, 0, −5, . . .

A. −1 B. −10 C. 0 D. Not Here

To find the pattern, mentally compute how the terms change.

20 15 10 5 0 −5
−5 −5 −5 −5 −5

To find each term, subtract 5 from the previous term.

−5 − 5 = −10

The answer is −10, or choice B

Use mental math to find the answer. Explain your reasoning.

1. What are the next two numbers in this pattern?

   $\frac{1}{4}$, 1, 4, 16, . . .

   A. 64, 128 B. 28, 50 C. 64, 256 D. Not Here

2. Which of the following number patterns has the rule: divide each number by 2 to obtain the next number?

   F. 4, 2, 0, −2, . . . G. 320, 40, 8, $\frac{8}{5}$, . . .
   H. 40, 10, $\frac{5}{2}$, $\frac{5}{8}$, . . . J. 20, 10, 5, $\frac{5}{2}$, . . .

*Use with Standardized Test Prep and Chapter Assessments.*

## Correlation to Standardized Tests

| Lesson | | CAT5 | CTBS/5 TerraNova™ | ITBS | MAT7 | SAT9 | LOCAL OBJECTIVES |
|---|---|---|---|---|---|---|---|
| 5-1 | Comparing and Ordering Fractions | ■ | | ■ | ■ | ■ | |
| 5-2 | Fractions and Decimals | | ■ | ■ | ■ | ■ | |
| 5-3 | Adding and Subtracting Fractions | ■ | ■ | ■ | ■ | ■ | |
| 5-4 | Multiplying and Dividing Fractions | ■ | ■ | ■ | ■ | ■ | |
| 5-5 | Using Customary Units of Measurement | ■ | ■ | ■ | ■ | ■ | |
| 5-6 | Problem Solving Strategy: Work Backward | | ■ | | | ■ | |
| 5-7 | Solving Equations by Adding or Subtracting Fractions | | | | | ■ | |
| 5-8 | Solving Equations by Multiplying Factions | | | | | ■ | |
| 5-9 | Powers and Products of Quotients | | | | | ■ | |

**CAT5** California Achievement Test, 5th edition
**CTBS TerraNova** Comprehensive Test of Basic Skills, 5th edition
**ITBS** Iowa Test of Basic Skills, Form M
**MAT7** Metropolitan Achievement Test, 7th edition
**SAT** Stanford Achievement Test, Advanced 1

For other standardized test correlations, follow the link to your state at **www.phschool.com**.

# Resources for Chapter 5

| | TEACHING RESOURCES BOX | | | | | | | | | | | | | | |
|---|---|---|---|---|---|---|---|---|---|---|---|---|---|---|---|
| | CHAPTER 5 SUPPORT FILE | | | | | | | | | | | | | | |
| | Practice | Reteach | Enrichment | Project Manager | Checkpoints | Cumulative Review | Chapter Assessment | Alternative Assessment | Cumulative Assessment | Lesson Planners Plus | Daily Cum Review | Teaching Transparencies | Warm-Up Transparencies | Help at Home | SE Answers on Transparencies |
| Begin Chapter | | | | ■ | | | | | | ■ | | | | | |
| 5-1 | ■ | ■ | ■ | | | | | | | ■ | ■ | 31, 32, 53 | ■ | | ■ |
| 5-2 | ■ | ■ | ■ | | | | | | | ■ | ■ | 33, 34 | ■ | | ■ |
| 5-3 | ■ | ■ | ■ | | ■ | | | | | ■ | ■ | 35 | ■ | ■ | ■ |
| 5-4 | ■ | ■ | ■ | | | | | | | ■ | ■ | 54 | ■ | | ■ |
| 5-5 | ■ | ■ | ■ | | | | | | | ■ | ■ | 17 | ■ | | ■ |
| 5-6 | ■ | ■ | ■ | | | | | | | ■ | ■ | 55 | ■ | | ■ |
| 5-7 | ■ | ■ | ■ | | | | | | | ■ | ■ | | ■ | | ■ |
| 5-8 | ■ | ■ | ■ | | ■ | | | | | ■ | ■ | | ■ | ■ | ■ |
| 5-9 | ■ | ■ | ■ | | | | | | | ■ | ■ | | ■ | | ■ |
| End Chapter | | | | | | ■ | ■ (2 forms) | ■ | After Ch. 3, 6, 9, 13 | | | | | | |

Also available for use with the chapter:

Solution Key
Computational Practice Skills Booklet
Mathematics Standardized Test Prep, Student Edition and Teacher's Edition
Overhead Manipulatives Kit
Practice Workbook
Algebra Readiness Kit
Student Manipulatives Kit
Test-Taking Tips on Transparencies
Assessment Success Kit
Teaching Aids and Letters
Graphing Calculator Handbook
Spanish Resources
Success-Building Puzzle and Problem Masters

## Technology

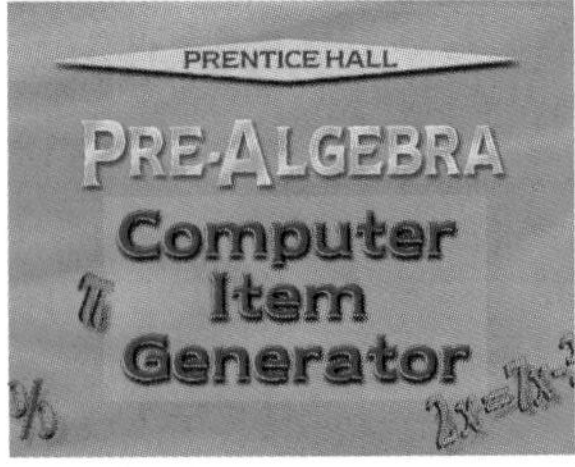


**Computer Item Generator with Standardized Test Prep**

CD-ROM with an unlimited supply of questions with varying degrees of difficulty for customized practice sheets, quizzes, and tests.

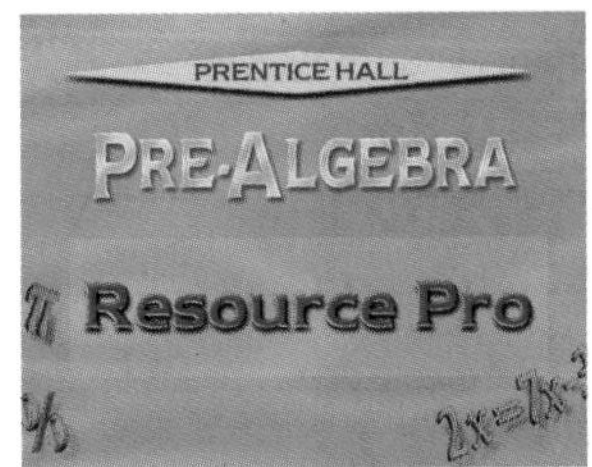


**Resource Pro® with Planning Express®**

CD-ROM with complete classroom planning tool and teaching resources for customizing and planning lessons.

**Interactive Math Lessons and Tools**

CD-ROM with lessons and tools to make abstract concepts visual and accessible.

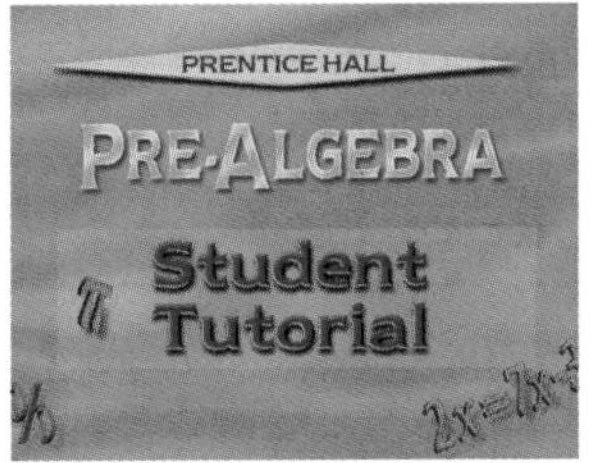


**Student Tutorial**

Test preparation software for students on CD-ROM with management system for teachers; includes Secondary Math Lab Toolkit™.

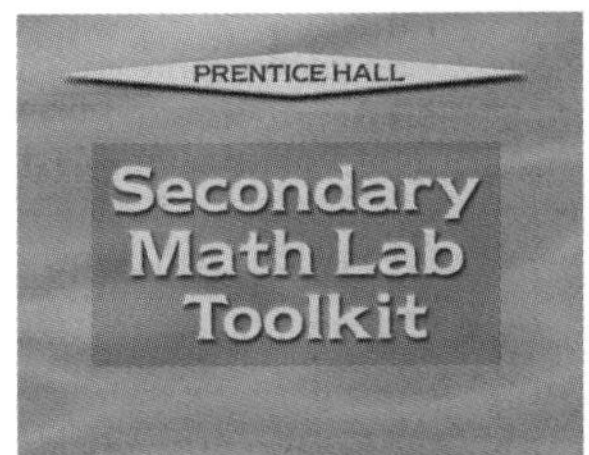


**Secondary Math Lab Toolkit™ with Integrated Math Labs**

Integrated software package with linkable math tools for exploring key concepts.

Also available for use with the chapter:

Math Blaster® Pre-Algebra CD-ROM
Video Fieldtrips, Vol. I: Algebra Applications
Video Fieldtrips, Vol. II: Geometry Applications
Wide World of Mathematics CD-ROM
Wide World of Mathematics Video

### *Web Extension*

**www.phschool.com**

**For Students**
- Chapter Support with Internet Links
- Internet Activities

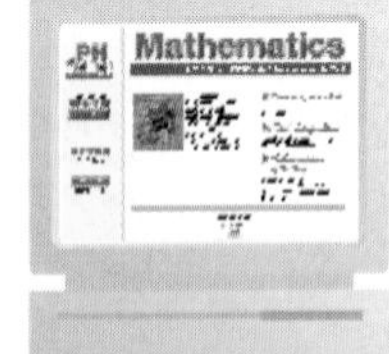


**For Teachers**
- Curriculum Support
- Professional Development
- Product Information
- Regional Support Information

# Skills You Need for Chapter 5

### ▶ *Reading and writing fractions* — Use before Lesson 5-1.

1–4. Answers may vary. Sample answers are given.

**Write two equivalent fractions to describe each model.**

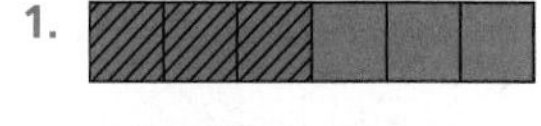

1. $\frac{1}{2}, \frac{3}{6}$
2. $\frac{8}{12}, \frac{2}{3}$
3. $\frac{2}{5}, \frac{4}{10}$
4. $\frac{3}{4}, \frac{6}{8}$

### ▶ *Writing fractions and decimals* — Use before Lesson 5-2.

**Write each fraction in simplest form.**

5. $\frac{10}{12}$ $\frac{5}{6}$
6. $\frac{8}{20}$ $\frac{2}{5}$
7. $-\frac{32}{16}$ $-2$
8. $\frac{25}{200}$ $\frac{1}{8}$
9. $-\frac{120}{125}$ $-\frac{24}{25}$
10. $\frac{15}{45}$ $\frac{1}{3}$
11. $\frac{-20}{-75}$ $\frac{4}{15}$
12. $\frac{16}{124}$ $\frac{4}{31}$
13. $-\frac{18}{81}$ $-\frac{2}{9}$
14. $-\frac{10}{65}$ $-\frac{2}{13}$
15. $\frac{14}{84}$ $\frac{1}{6}$
16. $\frac{55}{77}$ $\frac{5}{7}$

**Divide. Write each quotient as a decimal.**

17. $27 \div 5$ 5.4
18. $6 \div 10$ 0.6
19. $10 \div 16$ 0.625
20. $9 \div 12$ 0.75
21. $15 \div 40$ 0.375

### ▶ *Solving equations* — Use before Lessons 5-2, 5-7 and 5-8.

**Solve each equation.**

22. $x + 1.8 = 3$ 1.2
23. $n - 41 = 19$ 60
24. $27.2 = 3.5 + y$ 23.7
25. $a \div (-3) = 15$ $-45$
26. $-19 = p + 21$ $-40$
27. $6t = 9$ 1.5
28. $40 = z - 34$ 74
29. $8d = 64$ 8
30. $-0.89 = \frac{x}{2}$ $-1.78$

### ▶ *Finding the greatest common factor* — Use before Lesson 5-3.

**Find the GCF of each group of numbers.**

31. 3, 15 3
32. 16, 20 4
33. 12, 36 12
34. 11, 30 1
35. 30, 500 10
36. 45, 80 5
37. 27, 72 9
38. 55, 121 11
39. 30, 40, 210 10
40. 14, 28, 84 14



# Skills You Need

## Reading and writing fractions

**In Lesson 5-1** students will order fractions by finding the least common denominator to compare them.

## Writing fractions and decimals

**In Lesson 5-2** students will write fractions as decimals and terminating and repeating decimals as fractions.

## Solving equations

**In Lessons 5-7 and 5-8** students will solve equations by adding, subtracting, and multiplying fractions.

## Finding the greatest common factor

**In Lesson 5-3** students will use the greatest common factor to simplify while adding and subtracting fractions.

# Skills Trace

| SKILL | INTRODUCED | DEVELOPED IN LESSON(S) | REVIEWED/REINFORCED |
|---|---|---|---|
| Finding the least common multiple and comparing fractions | 5-1 | 5-2 | pp. 233, 281, 468 |
| Writing fractions as decimals and various kinds of decimals as fractions | 5-2 | 6-5 | pp. 239, 293, 299, 303 |
| Adding, subtracting, multiplying, and dividing fractions and mixed numbers | 5-3 | 5-4 | pp. 244, 249, 258, 263, 288, 317, 321, 447, 483, 508, 519 |
| Using customary units of measurement | 5-5 | 5-5 | pp. 258, 263 |
| Solving equations by adding, subtracting, multiplying, and dividing fractions and mixed numbers | 5-7 | 5-8 | pp. 263, 268, 431 |
| Finding powers of products and quotients | 5-9 | 5-9 | pp. 550, 569 |

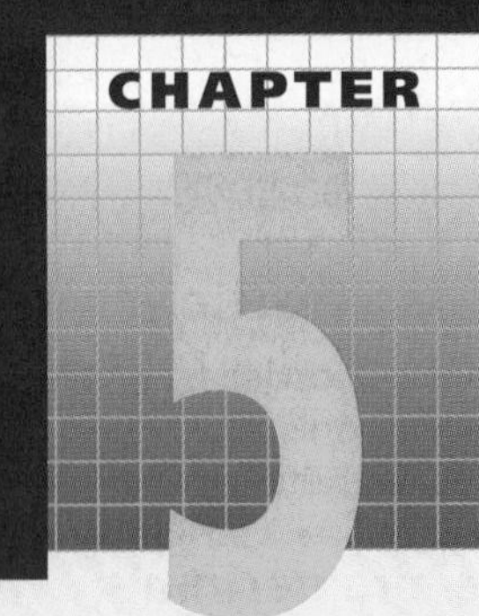

# Operations with Fractions

## Connecting to Students' Lives

Discuss where the numbers that indicate sizes (for shoes, shirts, socks, hats, and so forth) come from, and what they indicate.

## Interdisciplinary Connections

The Chapter Project connects math, history, and clothing. You may want to display shoe advertisements and information about number systems based on 12 or 60 or bases other than 10.

## About the Project

The Chapter Project directs students to apply their knowledge of fractions to examining the relationship between shoe sizes and measurements.

CHAPTER 5

# Operations with Fractions

**What you'll learn in this chapter:**

- How to perform operations with fractions
- How to solve equations with fractions
- How to find powers of products and quotients

222 Chapter 5

*Web Extension*
**www.phschool.com**

**For Students**
Chapter Support with Internet links
Interactive Activities

**For Teachers**
Curriculum Support
Professional Development
Product Information
Regional Support Information

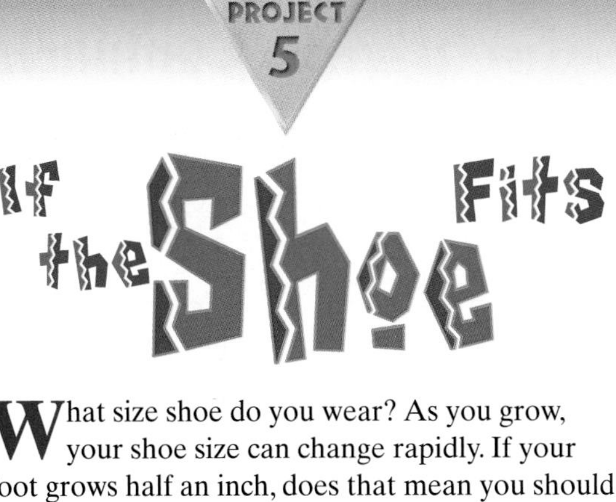


# If the Shoe Fits

What size shoe do you wear? As you grow, your shoe size can change rapidly. If your foot grows half an inch, does that mean you should get shoes that are a half-size larger?

The scale we use for sizing shoes is from the *duodecimal,* or base 12, number system. For that reason, a size chart could come in handy.

***Make a Comparison Chart*** For the chapter project, you will make measurements and calculations that relate women's shoe sizes, men's shoe sizes, and shoe lengths. Your final project will be a convenient comparison chart that you can distribute to your friends and family and to shoe stores.

### *Steps to help you complete the project*


p. 228 Activity: Researching
p. 254 Activity: Creating
p. 263 Activity: Investigating
p. 268 Activity: Calculating
p. 269 Finishing the Chapter Project

***Web Extension***
**www.phschool.com**

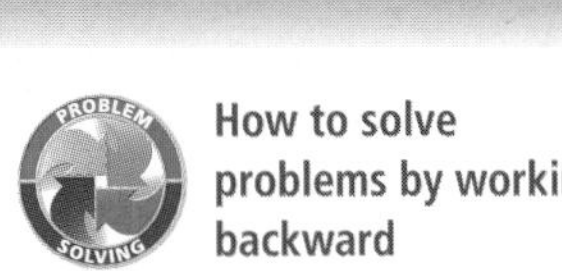

How to solve problems by working backward

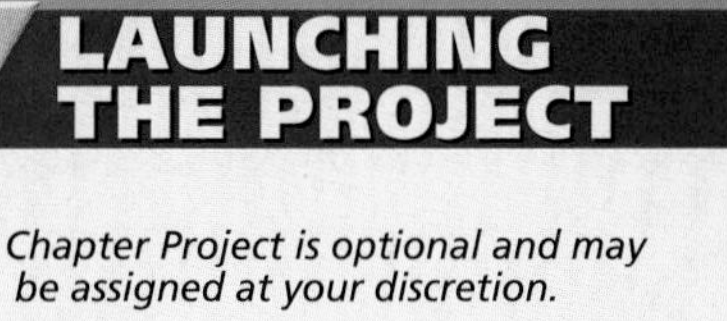


*The Chapter Project is optional and may be assigned at your discretion.*

Ask students:

- What numbers are used for children's shoe sizes? for teenagers? for adults?
- Is a shoe that is size 6 half as long as a shoe that is size 12?
- Where did our system of shoe sizes come from?

Distribute a copy of the Project Manager and Scoring Rubric to help students get an overview of the project.

Review the scoring rubric with students.

## Project Notebook

Encourage students to keep all project-related materials in a separate folder or notebook. Call attention to the fact that they will find much useful information on the Web site **www.phschool.com.**

**Tracking the Project** Set benchmark deadlines for students to show you their work in progress.

## Scoring Rubric

3 You calculate all numbers in your chart accurately. You prepare your chart so it is neat, easy to read, simply presented, and eye-pleasing. You organize your calculations so they are easy to follow.

2 You make minor errors when calculating numbers for your chart. Your chart is complete and basically accurate, but it could be neater or easier to read. You present clear calculations, but they could be better organized.

1 You calculate numbers in your chart inaccurately. Your chart could be neater and easier to read. Your calculations are difficult to follow due to lack of organization.

0 Major elements of the project are incomplete or missing.

*Available in the Chapter 5 Support File in the Teaching Resources box.*

### Project Manager and Scoring Rubric

**Getting Started** You will be creating a chart comparing shoe length to shoe size for both men and women. Read about the project in your textbook. As you work on the project, you will need a 12-inch ruler, materials to make your comparison chart, and materials to record your calculations.

**Checklist and Suggestions**

| | Checklist | Suggestions |
|---|---|---|
| ❑ | Research examples of the duodecimal system in everyday life. | Look for everyday situations where you use multiples of 12. |
| ❑ | Compare men's and women's shoe sizes. | Plan your final chart. |
| ❑ | Calculate your shoe size based on the length of your shoe. | Use the formula given for your gender. |
| ❑ | Compare your calculated size to the label on your shoe. | If the sizes are not the same, measure again more carefully. |
| ❑ | Calculate the shoe length of each whole and half-size in your chart. | Use the formula given for each gender. |
| ❑ | Complete your chart. | Make it neat and easy to read. |

**Scoring Rubric**

3 You calculate all numbers in your chart accurately. You prepare your chart so it is neat, easy to read, simply presented, and eye-pleasing. You organize your calculations so they are easy to follow.

2 You make minor errors when calculating numbers for your chart. Your chart is complete and basically accurate, but it could be neater or easier to read. You present clear calculations, but they could be better organized.

1 You calculate numbers in your chart incorrectly. Your chart could be neater and easier to read. Your calculations are difficult to follow due to lack of organization.

0 Major elements of the project are incomplete or missing.

**Your Evaluation of the Project** Evaluate your work, based on the Scoring Rubric.

**Teacher's Evaluation of the Project**

# 5-1

## Getting Ready

**Key Terms and Symbols** multiple, least common multiple (LCM), least common denominator (LCD)

**Resources** A complete list of resources for this lesson is on p. 221H.

### Daily Skills Warm-Up

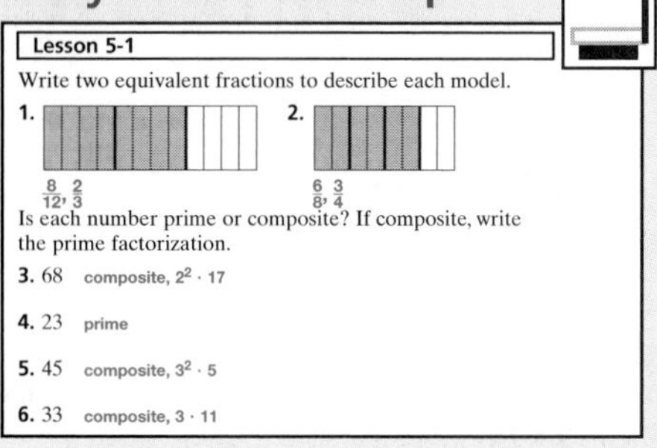

Lesson 5-1

Write two equivalent fractions to describe each model.

1. $\frac{8}{12}, \frac{2}{3}$ 2. $\frac{6}{8}, \frac{3}{4}$

Is each number prime or composite? If composite, write the prime factorization.

3. 68 composite, $2^2 \cdot 17$

4. 23 prime

5. 45 composite, $3^2 \cdot 5$

6. 33 composite, $3 \cdot 11$

### Background for the Lesson

When you find the least common multiple (LCM) of two numbers, such as 6 and 10, you find the smallest (least) multiple that they share (or have in common). The numbers 6 and 10 share the multiple 120 (because 6 • 20 is 120 and 10 • 12 is 120); but their *least* common multiple is 30. One way to find the LCM of two numbers is to list multiples of both numbers in ascending order until one multiple appears in both lists. For larger numbers, it is faster to find the prime factors of each number. The LCM consists of all the factors that appear in either number raised to the greatest power that appears in any one of the numbers.

## 1 Focus

### Connecting to Students' Lives

Discuss ways students have counted by twos or fives when counting objects such as coins.

### Connecting to Prior Knowledge

In Lesson 4-3, students learned that the GCF is the greatest common factor. In this lesson, students learn that the Least Common Multiple (LCM) is the lowest common multiple.

5-1

### What You'll Learn

1 To find the least common multiple

2 To compare fractions

### . . . And Why

To understand how fractions are used in real-world situations, such as comparing team records

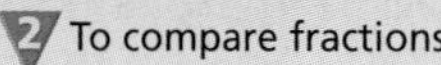

# Comparing and Ordering Fractions

## PART 1 Finding the Least Common Multiple

A **multiple** of a number is the product of that number and any nonzero whole number.

Multiples of 4: 4, 8, (12), 16, 20, (24), 28, 32, (36), . . .

Multiples of 6: 6, (12), 18, (24), 30, (36), 42, . . .

The numbers 12, 24, and 36 are *common multiples* of 4 and 6. The common multiple 12 is their **least common multiple (LCM).**

REAL-WORLD  CONNECTION

### EXAMPLE 1

**Today both the school baseball and school soccer teams had games. The baseball team plays every 6 days. The soccer team plays every 5 days. When will both teams have games on the same day again?**

6, 12, 18, 24, (30), 36, . . . List the multiples of 6.

5, 10, 15, 20, 25, (30), . . . List the multiples of 5.

The LCM is 30. In 30 days both teams will have games again.

**TRY THIS** Find the LCM.

1. 3, 4 12 2. 4, 5 20 3. 3, 4, 5 60

You can also use prime factorization to find the LCM.

### EXAMPLE 2

**Find the LCM of 12 and 40.**

$12 = 2^2 \cdot (3)$, $40 = (2^3) \cdot (5)$ Write the prime factorizations.

$\text{LCM} = 2^3 \cdot 3 \cdot 5$ Use the greatest power of each factor.

$= 120$ Multiply.

The LCM of 12 and 40 is 120.



# Tools to Monitor Progress

### BEFORE THE LESSON

**To check prerequisite skills:**

- Reading and writing fractions

**Skills You Need,** p. 221

**Skills Handbook,** p. 725

**Skills Intervention Kit,** Number Theory and Fraction Concepts

### DURING THE LESSON

**To check understanding:**

**Try This** exercises on student page

- **Additional Examples 1–3**

  Find the LCM of $5a^4$ and $15a$. $15a^4$

- **Additional Example 4**

  Graph and compare this pair of fractions. $\frac{3}{14}, \frac{7}{14}$

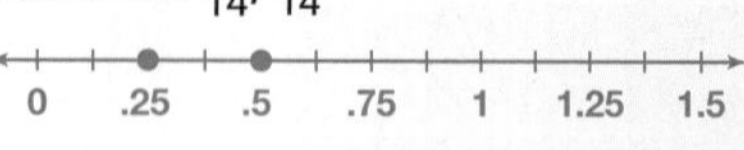

$\frac{3}{14} < \frac{7}{14}$

**TRY THIS** Use prime factorization to find the LCM.

**4.** 6, 16 48 **5.** 9, 15 45 **6.** 12, 15, 18 180

You can find the LCM of a variable expression.

### EXAMPLE 3

**Find the LCM of $6a^2$ and $18a^3$.**

$6a^2 = (2) \cdot 3 \cdot a^2$
$18a^3 = 2 \cdot (3^2) \cdot (a^3)$ — Write the prime factorizations.

$\text{LCM} = 2 \cdot 3^2 \cdot a^3$ — Use the greatest power of each factor.
$= 18a^3$ — Multiply.

The LCM of $6a^2$ and $18a^3$ is $18a^3$.

**TRY THIS** Find the LCM.

**7.** $12x, 15xy$ $60xy$ **8.** $8m^2, 14m^4$ $56m^4$ **9.** $25y^2, 15x$ $75xy^2$

## PART 2 Comparing Fractions

You can use a number line to compare fractions.

### EXAMPLE 4

**Graph and compare each pair of fractions.**

**a.** $\frac{9}{11}, \frac{6}{11}$

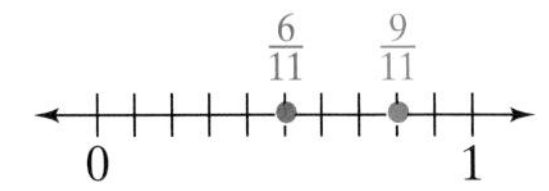


$\frac{9}{11}$ is to the right of $\frac{6}{11}$, so $\frac{9}{11} > \frac{6}{11}$.

**b.** $-\frac{1}{2}, -\frac{1}{10}$

$-\frac{1}{2}$, $-\frac{1}{10}$, $-1$, $0$

$-\frac{1}{2}$ is to the left of $-\frac{1}{10}$, so $-\frac{1}{2} < -\frac{1}{10}$.

**TRY THIS** Use a number line to compare each pair of fractions.

**10.** $\frac{4}{9}, \frac{2}{9}$ $\frac{2}{9} < \frac{4}{9}$ **11.** $-\frac{4}{9}, -\frac{2}{9}$ $-\frac{4}{9} < -\frac{2}{9}$ **12.** $-\frac{4}{9}, \frac{2}{9}$ $-\frac{4}{9} < \frac{2}{9}$



# 2 Teach

## PART 1 Part 1 Teaching Notes

Discuss the two methods of Example 1 and 2. Suggest that listing the multiples may be easier for lesser numbers while prime factorization may be easier for greater numbers.

### Example 1

**Build understanding.** Ask: What is the next common multiple of 5 and 6? Describe the pattern for how often the baseball and soccer teams play on the same day. **60; They play on the same day every 30 days.**

### Example 2

**Build understanding.** Ask: How could you verify that the LCM you found through prime factorization is correct? **List the multiples of both numbers in order until one number occurs in both lists.**

**Error Prevention** If one number factors to $2^2 \cdot 7$ and a second number factors to $2^3 \cdot 7$, students sometimes incorrectly think that the LCM is $2^5 \cdot 7$. Help them see that the correct LCM of $2^3 \cdot 7$ is also divisible by both numbers. $2^5 \cdot 7$ is not the *least* common multiple.

### Example 3

**Build understanding.** Ask: Why is the LCM in this case equal to one of the variable expressions? **because one of the variable expressions, $6a^2$, is a factor of the other, $18a^3$**

**Extension** What rule will always give you the LCM of two prime numbers? **The LCM of two prime numbers will always be the product of the two numbers.**

## PART 2 Part 2 Teaching Notes

Remind students that multiplying both the numerator and denominator of a fraction by the same number is the same as multiplying the fraction by 1.

### Additional Examples 5–6

Order $\frac{3}{7}, \frac{1}{4}$, and $\frac{2}{3}$ from least to greatest. $\frac{1}{4} < \frac{3}{7} < \frac{2}{3}$

### AFTER THE LESSON

**To assess knowledge:**

**Lesson Quiz**

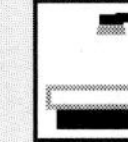

Find the LCM of each pair of numbers.

**1.** 8, 6 24
**2.** 12, 16 48

Compare or order the fractions from least to greatest.

**3.** $\frac{3}{16}, -\frac{8}{10}$, and $-\frac{3}{16}$ $-\frac{8}{10} < -\frac{3}{16} < \frac{3}{16}$

- For enrichment and reteaching options see Resources on p. 221H.

## Example 4

**Build understanding.** Ask: On a number line, the greater of two numbers, regardless of the signs of the numbers, is on which side of the lesser number? **The greater is to the right of the lesser.**

## Example 5

**Build understanding.** Ask: Why do you need to find the LCM of 8 and 10? **So you can rewrite the two fractions with the same denominator in order to compare them.**

**ELL** Make sure students are comfortable with the meaning of the terms *least common multiple* and *least common denominator* before you substitute the acronyms LCM and LCD.

## Example 6

**Build understanding.** Ask: If you compared only $\frac{1}{2}$ and $\frac{2}{5}$, explain why the LCD would be different from 20. **The LCM of 2 and 5 is 10, which would make 10 the LCD of the two fractions.**

**Visual Learning** For students who have difficulty comparing or ordering fractions, suggest that they graph their fractions on a number line after they find the LCD so they can see which one is to the right.

**Technology Option** You may want to have students explore ways to use the calculator to aid in finding the LCM. One way is to divide the multiples of the greater number by the lesser number until there is a whole number quotient.

## Challenge

Find the LCM of 6 and 7, and of 9 and 4. Write a rule for finding the LCM of two numbers that are relatively prime (have no common factors). **42; 36; The LCM is the product of the two numbers.**

### Reading Math

The LCD is sometimes called the *lowest common denominator.*

When fractions have different denominators, rewrite the fractions with a common denominator. Then compare the numerators. The **least common denominator (LCD)** of two or more fractions is the LCM of the denominators.

### EXAMPLE 5

**The math team won $\frac{5}{8}$ of its competitions and the debate team won $\frac{7}{10}$ of its competitions. Which team won the greater fraction of competitions?**

**Step 1** Find the LCM of 8 and 10.

$8 = 2^3$ and $10 = 2 \cdot 5$

$\text{LCM} = 2^3 \cdot 5 = 40$

**Step 2** Write equivalent fractions with a denominator of 40.

$\frac{5 \cdot 5}{8 \cdot 5} = \frac{25}{40}$

$\frac{7 \cdot 4}{10 \cdot 4} = \frac{28}{40}$

**Step 3** Compare the fractions.

$\frac{25}{40} < \frac{28}{40}$, so $\frac{5}{8} < \frac{7}{10}$.

The debate team won the greater fraction of competitions.

High school debate teams can have as few as 8 debates and as many as 20 debates in a school year. If the school in Example 5 had 20 debates, how many did they win? 14

**TRY THIS** Compare each pair of fractions.

13. $\frac{6}{7}, \frac{4}{5}$ $\frac{6}{7} > \frac{4}{5}$

14. $\frac{2}{3}, \frac{3}{4}$ $\frac{2}{3} < \frac{3}{4}$

15. $\frac{3}{4}, \frac{7}{10}$ $\frac{3}{4} > \frac{7}{10}$

### EXAMPLE 6

**Order $\frac{1}{2}, \frac{3}{4}$, and $\frac{2}{5}$ from least to greatest.**

$\frac{1}{2} = \frac{1 \cdot 10}{2 \cdot 10} = \frac{10}{20}$

$\frac{3}{4} = \frac{3 \cdot 5}{4 \cdot 5} = \frac{15}{20}$

$\frac{2}{5} = \frac{2 \cdot 4}{5 \cdot 4} = \frac{8}{20}$

The LCM of 2, 4, and 5 is 20. Use 20 as the common denominator.

$\frac{8}{20} < \frac{10}{20} < \frac{15}{20}$, so $\frac{2}{5} < \frac{1}{2} < \frac{3}{4}$.

**TRY THIS** Order from least to greatest.

16. $\frac{2}{3}, \frac{1}{6}, \frac{5}{12}$ $\frac{1}{6} < \frac{5}{12} < \frac{2}{3}$

17. $\frac{3}{10}, \frac{1}{5}, \frac{1}{2}, \frac{7}{12}$ $\frac{1}{5} < \frac{3}{10} < \frac{1}{2} < \frac{7}{12}$

# Exercises

## CHECK UNDERSTANDING

**Find the LCM of each pair of numbers.**

**1.** 10, 45 90 **2.** 6, 9 18 **3.** 12, 20 60 **4.** 5, 9 45

**Compare. Use >, <, or = to complete each statement.**

**5.** $\frac{5}{8}$ ■ $\frac{3}{4}$ < **6.** $\frac{7}{15}$ ■ $\frac{2}{3}$ < **7.** $\frac{1}{2}$ ■ $\frac{4}{8}$ = **8.** $-\frac{5}{18}$ ■ $-\frac{1}{3}$ >

**Order from least to greatest.**

**9.** $\frac{7}{9}, \frac{3}{9}, \frac{5}{9}$ $\frac{3}{9} < \frac{5}{9} < \frac{7}{9}$ **10.** $\frac{1}{2}, \frac{1}{3}, \frac{1}{4}$ $\frac{1}{4} < \frac{1}{3} < \frac{1}{2}$ **11.** $\frac{2}{5}, \frac{2}{3}, \frac{2}{7}$ $\frac{2}{7} < \frac{2}{5} < \frac{2}{3}$ **12.** $\frac{2}{5}, \frac{3}{7}, \frac{1}{3}, \frac{2}{4}$ $\frac{1}{3} < \frac{2}{5} < \frac{3}{7} < \frac{2}{4}$

**13.** You need $\frac{5}{8}$ yd of fabric for a craft project. You find a piece marked $\frac{2}{3}$ yd. Is the piece long enough? Explain. Yes; $\frac{2}{3} > \frac{5}{8}$.

## PRACTICE AND PROBLEM SOLVING

**Find the LCM of each group of numbers or expressions.**

**14.** 10, 36 180 **15.** 20, 36 180 **16.** 7, 12 84 **17.** 5, 6 30

**18.** 5, 6, 7 210 **19.** 45, 120, 150 1,800 **20.** 8, 14, 20 280 **21.** 2, 5, 12, 15 60

**22.** $12x, 40$ $120x$ **23.** $8x, 25y$ $200xy$ **24.** $6a^3, 8a$ $24a^3$ **25.** $16a, 18ab, 21a^2$ $1{,}008a^2b$

*Mental Math* **Compare. Use >, <, or = to complete each statement.**

**26.** $-\frac{3}{19}$ ■ $\frac{1}{200}$ < **27.** $\frac{(-1)\cdot(-1)}{3}$ ■ $\frac{1}{3}$ = **28.** $\frac{9}{11}$ ■ $\frac{7}{11}$ > **29.** $\frac{-2}{-7}$ ■ $\frac{4}{14}$ =

**30.** $\frac{8}{8}$ ■ $\frac{3}{3}$ = **31.** $\frac{2}{10}$ ■ $\frac{2}{100}$ > **32.** $\frac{2}{5}$ ■ $3\frac{2}{5}$ < **33.** $\frac{-4}{-17}$ ■ $-\frac{5}{2}$ >

**Compare. Use >, <, or = to complete each statement.**

**34.** $\frac{7}{14}$ ■ $\frac{3}{6}$ = **35.** $\frac{5}{6}$ ■ $\frac{3}{4}$ > **36.** $\frac{6}{8}$ ■ $\frac{7}{9}$ < **37.** $\frac{1}{6}$ ■ $\frac{1}{8}$ >

**38.** $-\frac{7}{9}$ ■ $-\frac{2}{3}$ < **39.** $-\frac{19}{24}$ ■ $-\frac{5}{6}$ > **40.** $\frac{8}{5}$ ■ $\frac{3}{2}$ > **41.** $-\frac{3}{8}$ ■ $-\frac{6}{16}$ =

**42.** $\frac{1}{3}$ ■ $\frac{3}{4}$ < **43.** $-\frac{1}{5}$ ■ $-\frac{1}{7}$ < **44.** $\frac{2}{3}$ ■ $\frac{3}{4}$ < **45.** $\frac{10}{11}$ ■ $\frac{4}{5}$ >

**46.** $\frac{3}{8}$ ■ $\frac{15}{24}$ < **47.** $\frac{3}{8}$ ■ $\frac{5}{12}$ < **48.** $\frac{1}{2}$ ■ $\frac{2}{4}$ = **49.** $-\frac{7}{12}$ ■ $-\frac{28}{48}$ =



# 3 Practice/Assess

## Assignment Guide

To provide flexible scheduling, this lesson can be divided into parts.

**Part 1**
**Core** 1–4, 14–25, 50
**Extension** 52

**Part 2**
**Core** 5–13, 26–49, 51
**Extension** 53

Mixed Review can be assigned at any time for maintenance.

## Exercises

**Exercises 26–33** Remind students to use mental math to compare the fractions in these exercises. Mentally locating the approximate position of the fractions on a number line may help.

## Challenge

Compare $\frac{7}{120}$ and $\frac{8}{125}$. Explain why comparing 7 • 125 and 8 • 120 is one way to find the answer. You are comparing these fractions with like denominators: $\frac{7 \cdot 125}{120 \cdot 125} < \frac{8 \cdot 120}{125 \cdot 120}$.

## Closure

A multiple of a number is the product of that number and any whole number. A common multiple of any group of numbers is a number that is a multiple of all the numbers. The common multiple with the least value is the least common multiple (LCM) of the numbers. To compare fractions, use the LCM as the least common denominator (LCD) and write equivalent fractions.

## Daily Cumulative Review

**Write each number in scientific notation.** *(Lesson 4-9)*

**1.** 0.000465 $4.65 \times 10^{-4}$ **2.** 23,920,000,000 $2.392 \times 10^{10}$ **3.** $0.003 \times 10^9$ $3.0 \times 10^6$

**4.** 3,677,000,000 $3.677 \times 10^9$ **5.** $353.1 \times 10^6$ $3.531 \times 10^8$ **6.** 0.00707 $7.07 \times 10^{-3}$

**Simplify each expression.** *(Lesson 4-8)*

**7.** $\frac{(-3)^5}{(-3)^3}$ 9 **8.** $7^0$ 1 **9.** $r^{-6}s^3$ $\frac{s^3}{r^6}$

**10.** $\frac{64a^7b^8}{8a^4b^4}$ $8a^3b^4$ **11.** $\frac{14m^{17}n^{15}}{28m^3n^{14}}$ $\frac{m^{14}n}{2}$ **12.** $6v^{-8}$ $\frac{6}{v^8}$

**Mixed Review**

**Round to the underlined place value.**

**13.** (3-1) 7.6392 7.64 **14.** (3-1) 32.73201 32.7 **15.** (3-1) 463.2951 463.30

**Write in simplest form.**

**16.** (4-4) $\frac{12}{18}$ $\frac{2}{3}$ **17.** (4-4) $\frac{9}{15}$ $\frac{3}{5}$ **18.** (4-4) $\frac{14}{56}$ $\frac{1}{4}$

**Divide. Write each quotient as a decimal.** *(From Last Year)*

**19.** 28 ÷ 5 5.6 **20.** 16 ÷ 5 3.2 **21.** 12 ÷ 15 0.8

**22.** 9 ÷ 16 0.5625 **23.** 39 ÷ 6 6.5 **24.** 42 ÷ 8 5.25

**Solve each equation.**

**25.** (2-6) $6a = 30$ $a = 5$ **26.** (2-6) $-3x = 12$ $x = -4$ **27.** (2-6) $15v = 105$ $v = 7$



## Alternative Assessment

Have students write a paragraph in their math journals explaining how they can use the LCD to compare or order fractions. Ask students to include an example of comparison of fractions.

## Practice

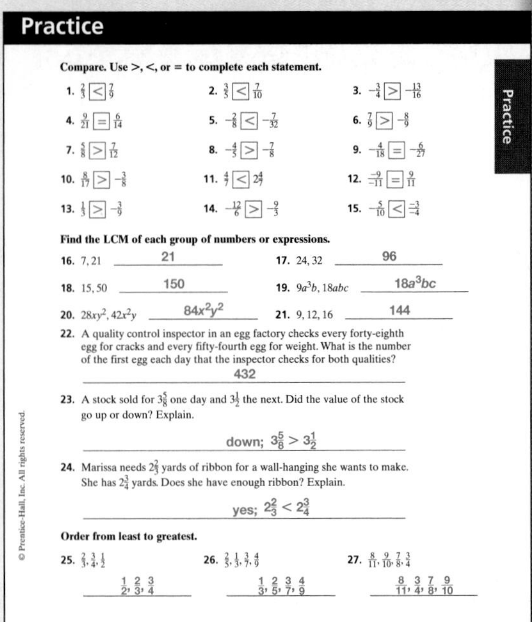

Compare. Use >, <, or = to complete each statement.

1. $\frac{2}{3}$ [<] $\frac{7}{9}$
2. $\frac{3}{5}$ [<] $\frac{7}{10}$
3. $-\frac{3}{4}$ [>] $-\frac{13}{16}$
4. $\frac{9}{21}$ [=] $\frac{6}{14}$
5. $-\frac{2}{8}$ [<] $-\frac{7}{32}$
6. $\frac{7}{9}$ [>] $-\frac{8}{9}$
7. $\frac{5}{8}$ [>] $\frac{7}{12}$
8. $-\frac{4}{5}$ [>] $-\frac{7}{8}$
9. $-\frac{4}{18}$ [=] $-\frac{6}{27}$
10. $\frac{8}{17}$ [>] $-\frac{3}{8}$
11. $\frac{4}{7}$ [<] $2\frac{4}{7}$
12. $\frac{-9}{-11}$ [=] $\frac{9}{11}$
13. $\frac{1}{3}$ [>] $-\frac{3}{9}$
14. $-\frac{12}{6}$ [>] $-\frac{9}{3}$
15. $-\frac{5}{10}$ [<] $\frac{-3}{-4}$

Find the LCM of each group of numbers or expressions.

16. 7, 21 — 21
17. 24, 32 — 96
18. 15, 50 — 150
19. $9a^3b$, $18abc$ — $18a^3bc$
20. $28xy^2$, $42x^2y$ — $84x^2y^2$
21. 9, 12, 16 — 144
22. A quality control inspector in an egg factory checks every forty-eighth egg for cracks and every fifty-fourth egg for weight. What is the number of the first egg each day that the inspector checks for both qualities? — 432
23. A stock sold for $3\frac{5}{8}$ one day and $3\frac{1}{2}$ the next. Did the value of the stock go up or down? Explain. — down; $3\frac{5}{8} > 3\frac{1}{2}$
24. Marissa needs $2\frac{2}{3}$ yards of ribbon for a wall-hanging she wants to make. She has $2\frac{3}{4}$ yards. Does she have enough ribbon? Explain. — yes; $2\frac{2}{3} < 2\frac{3}{4}$

Order from least to greatest.

25. $\frac{2}{3}, \frac{3}{4}, \frac{1}{2}$ — $\frac{1}{2}, \frac{2}{3}, \frac{3}{4}$
26. $\frac{2}{5}, \frac{1}{3}, \frac{3}{7}, \frac{4}{9}$ — $\frac{1}{3}, \frac{2}{5}, \frac{3}{7}, \frac{4}{9}$
27. $\frac{8}{11}, \frac{9}{10}, \frac{7}{8}, \frac{3}{4}$ — $\frac{8}{11}, \frac{3}{4}, \frac{7}{8}, \frac{9}{10}$



## Reteaching

Compare $\frac{2}{27}$ and $\frac{1}{18}$. Also compare $-\frac{2}{27}$ and $-\frac{1}{18}$.

Step 1: Find the LCM of 27 and 18
$27 = 3^3$ and $18 = 2 \cdot 3^2$
$\text{LCM} = 2 \cdot 3^3 = 54$

Step 2: Write equivalent fractions with a denominator of 54.
$\frac{2 \cdot 2}{27 \cdot 2} = \frac{4}{54}$
$\frac{1 \cdot 3}{18 \cdot 3} = \frac{3}{54}$

Step 3: Compare the fractions.
$4 > 3$, so
$\frac{4}{54} > \frac{3}{54}$ or $\frac{2}{27} > \frac{1}{18}$.
Since $-4 < -3$
$-\frac{4}{54} < -\frac{3}{54}$ or $-\frac{2}{27} < -\frac{1}{18}$.

**Find the LCD of each pair of fractions. Write equivalent fractions using the LCD and compare. Use >, <, or = to complete each statement.**

1. $\frac{2}{9}, \frac{1}{6}$ — $\frac{4}{18}$ [>] $\frac{3}{18}$
2. $\frac{5}{8}, \frac{3}{4}$ — $\frac{5}{8}$ [<] $\frac{6}{8}$
3. $-\frac{2}{3}, -\frac{5}{6}$ — $-\frac{4}{6}$ [>] $-\frac{5}{6}$
4. $-\frac{5}{18}, -\frac{2}{9}$ — $-\frac{5}{18}$ [<] $-\frac{4}{18}$
5. $\frac{7}{12}, \frac{11}{18}$ — $\frac{21}{36}$ [<] $\frac{22}{36}$
6. $\frac{13}{20}, \frac{11}{15}$ — $\frac{39}{60}$ [<] $\frac{44}{60}$
7. $-\frac{11}{20}, -\frac{22}{40}$ — $-\frac{22}{40}$ [=] $-\frac{22}{40}$
8. $\frac{6}{25}, \frac{1}{5}$ — $\frac{6}{25}$ [>] $\frac{5}{25}$
9. $\frac{15}{28}, \frac{4}{7}$ — $\frac{15}{28}$ [<] $\frac{16}{28}$
10. $\frac{5}{9}, \frac{11}{21}$ — $\frac{35}{63}$ [>] $\frac{33}{63}$
11. $\frac{5}{17}, \frac{15}{51}$ — $\frac{15}{51}$ [=] $\frac{15}{51}$
12. $-\frac{5}{12}, -\frac{13}{30}$ — $-\frac{25}{60}$ [>] $-\frac{26}{60}$



## Enrichment

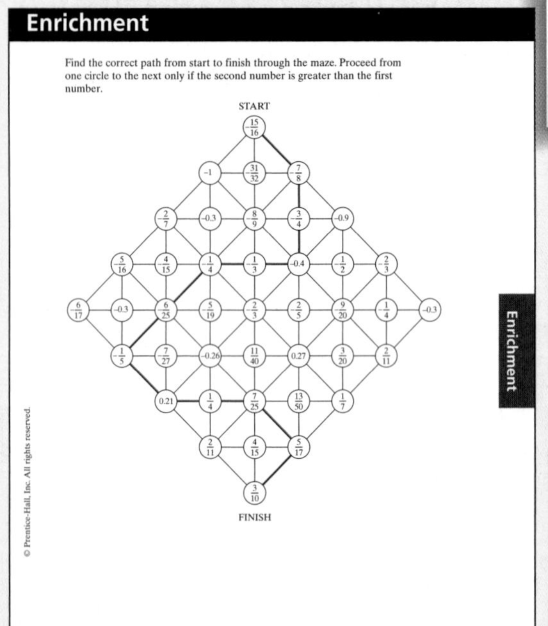

Find the correct path from start to finish through the maze. Proceed from one circle to the next only if the second number is greater than the first number.





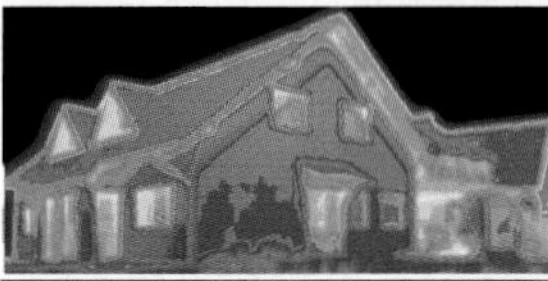

**50.** The manager of Frank's Snack Shop buys hot dogs in packages of 36. He buys hot dog buns in packages of 20. He cannot buy part of a package. What is the least number of packages of each product he can buy to have an equal number of hot dogs and buns? 5 packages hotdogs and 9 packages buns

**51.** *Construction* The *R-value* of a building material measures how well the material keeps heat in or out. The greater the R-value, the better the insulating capability. Use the table at the right. List the materials in order from greatest to least R-value.
wood shingle, siding, plywood, asphalt shingle, brick, stucco

| Material | R-value |
|---|---|
| $\frac{3}{8}$-in. plywood | $\frac{1}{2}$ |
| Asphalt roof shingle | $\frac{5}{12}$ |
| Common brick | $\frac{1}{4}$ |
| Stucco | $\frac{1}{6}$ |
| Wood bevel siding | $\frac{3}{4}$ |
| Wood roof shingle | $\frac{11}{12}$ |

**52.** *Geometry* You have tiles that measure 4 in. by 5 in. What is the smallest square region you can cover without cutting or overlapping the tiles? 20 in. by 20 in.

**53.** Suppose you and your brother shared two 12-in. pizzas, a mushroom pizza cut into 8 slices and a cheese pizza cut into 6 slices. If you ate 5 slices of the mushroom pizza, and your brother ate 3 slices of the cheese pizza, who ate more pizza? you

## Mixed Review

**Write in scientific notation.** *(Lesson 4-9)*

**54.** 5,000,000 $5 \times 10^6$ **55.** 0.001394 $1.394 \times 10^{-3}$ **56.** 8,900,000 $8.9 \times 10^6$ **57.** 0.000005 $5 \times 10^{-6}$

**Find each GCF.** *(Lesson 4-3)*

**58.** 24, 42 6 **59.** 16, 52 4 **60.** $25c, 55c^2$ $5c$ **61.** $90xy, 45x^2$ $45x$

**62.** *History* The first modern Olympics took place in 1896 in Athens, Greece. One hundred years later, 197 nations participated in the Olympics in Atlanta, Georgia. This was 184 more nations than at the first Olympics. Solve the equation $x + 184 = 197$ to find the number of nations participating in the first Olympics. *(Lesson 2-5)* 13 nations

## Chapter Project 5 — Activity 1 Researching

We still use the *duodecimal*, or base 12, system. For example, 12 in. = 1 ft. Research some other examples of the duodecimal system. Describe how they appear in your everyday life.



See also Extra Practice section.

### Project Activity 1

**Researching** Students may suggest measuring items in dozens as one example of the base 12 system. Discuss the possible advantages of base 12 over base 10, such as the number of factors.

# Fractions and Decimals

5-2

## PART 1 Writing Fractions as Decimals

**What You'll Learn**

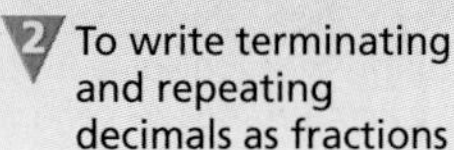

1. To write fractions as decimals
2. To write terminating and repeating decimals as fractions

**. . . And Why**

To use fractions and decimals in real-world situations, such as buying food

You can write a fraction as a decimal by dividing the numerator by the denominator. When the division ends with a remainder of zero, the quotient is called a **terminating decimal.**

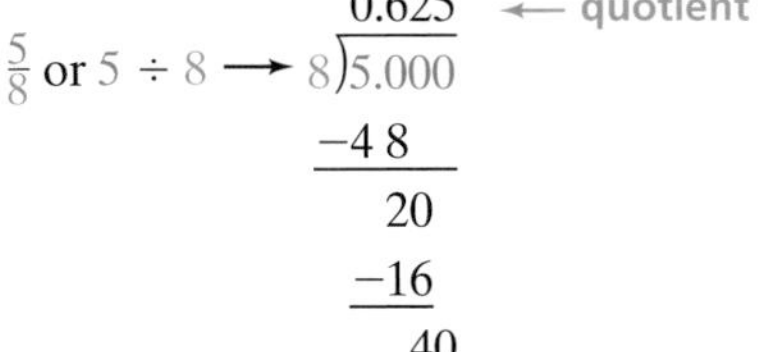

$\frac{5}{8}$ or $5 \div 8 \rightarrow 8\overline{)5.000}$ — quotient 0.625

$-4\,8$

$20$

$-16$

$40$

$-40$

$0$ ← remainder

The quotient of $5 \div 8$ ends with a remainder of zero. So 0.625 is a terminating decimal.

REAL-WORLD CONNECTION

### EXAMPLE 1

*Consumer Issues* **A customer at a delicatessen asks for $\frac{3}{4}$ lb of potato salad. The scale reads 0.75. Is the customer getting the amount of potato salad she requested?**

$\frac{3}{4} = 3 \div 4 = 0.75$

Since $\frac{3}{4} = 0.75$, the customer is getting the right amount of potato salad.

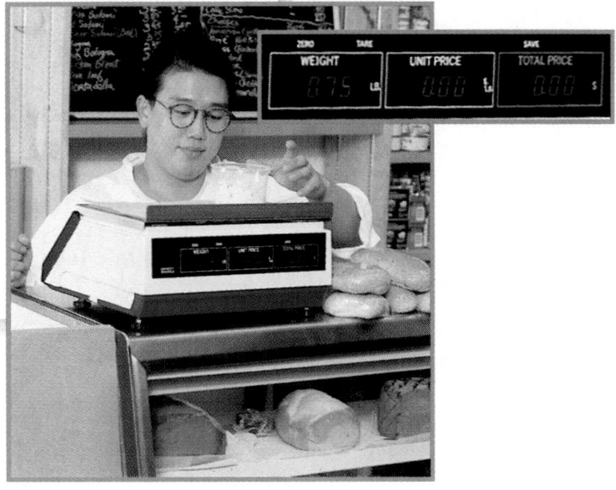


**TRY THIS** Write each fraction or mixed number as a decimal.

1. $\frac{1}{4}$ 0.25
2. $1\frac{7}{8}$ 1.875
3. $3\frac{3}{10}$ 3.3
4. $\frac{3}{5}$ 0.6



# 5-2

## Getting Ready

**Key Terms and Symbols** terminating decimal, repeating decimal

**Resources** A complete list of resources for this lesson is on p. 221H.

### Daily Skills Warm-Up

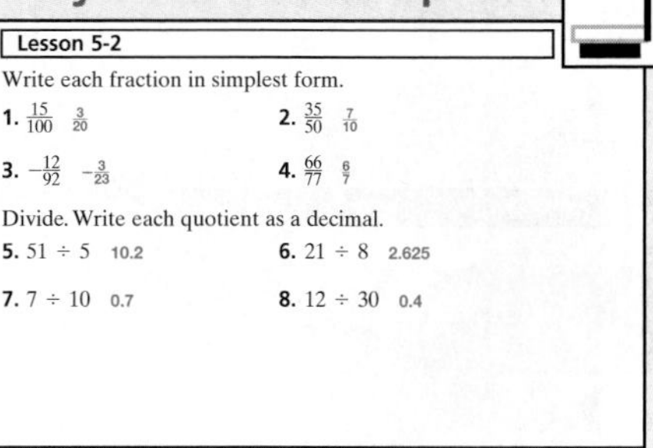

Lesson 5-2

Write each fraction in simplest form.

1. $\frac{15}{100}$ $\frac{3}{20}$
2. $\frac{35}{50}$ $\frac{7}{10}$
3. $-\frac{12}{92}$ $-\frac{3}{23}$
4. $\frac{66}{77}$ $\frac{6}{7}$

Divide. Write each quotient as a decimal.

5. $51 \div 5$ 10.2
6. $21 \div 8$ 2.625
7. $7 \div 10$ 0.7
8. $12 \div 30$ 0.4

### Background for the Lesson

A rational number is any number that can be expressed in the form $\frac{a}{b}$, where $a$ is any integer, and $b$ is any nonzero integer. Both terminating and repeating decimals are rational numbers that can be written as the ratio of two integers. Some repeating decimals have just a few digits in the block of digits that repeats, such as $0.\overline{34}$ or $\frac{34}{99}$. The number $\frac{2}{7}$ has a block of six digits that repeats: $\frac{2}{7}$ is $0.\overline{285714}$. Decimals that neither terminate nor have a block of repeating numbers are irrational numbers and cannot be written as the ratio of integers. Both $\pi$ and $\sqrt{2}$ are irrational.

## 1 Focus

### Connecting to Students' Lives

Discuss with students the fact that at many supermarkets the weight/price stickers for produce and meats show fractions of a pound in decimal form, such as 2.75 lb.

### Connecting to Prior Knowledge

In Lesson 5-1, students learned how to order fractions using LCD. In this lesson, students order fractions by changing them to decimal form. In Lessons 5-3 and 5-4, they will combine fractions.

## Tools to Monitor Progress

### BEFORE THE LESSON

**To check prerequisite skills:**

- Writing fractions and decimals
- Solving equations

**Skills You Need,** p. 221

**Skills Handbook,** p. 727

**Skills Intervention Kit,** Decimals

### DURING THE LESSON

**To check understanding:**

**Try This** exercises on student page

- **Additional Example 1**

The fuel tank for Scott's lawn mower holds $\frac{1}{2}$ gal of gas. When he bought gas at the service station, the pump read 0.4. Did Scott get his tank full? Explain. no, because $\frac{1}{2} = 0.5$

# 2 Teach

## Part 1 Teaching Notes

Point out that the repeating block of digits for terminating decimals may be even longer than five digits. For this reason, when students divide the numerator by the denominator they should continue until there is a zero remainder, or a remainder repeats.

### Example 1

**Build understanding.** Ask: Which part of the fraction becomes the divisor when you change a fraction to a decimal? **the denominator**

### Example 2

**Build understanding.** Ask: If the bar covers four digits, how many digits repeat? Explain. **4; The bar covers the block of digits that repeats.**

**Error Prevention** Students may fail to divide when writing fractions as decimals. They may simply write $\frac{2}{5}$ as 0.25, moving the numerator and denominator to the right of the decimal point. Remind students that the fraction bar indicates the division they must do to write a fraction as a decimal, 2 divided by 5.

### Example 3

**Build understanding.** Ask: How can you use mental math to begin ordering the fractions? **1.1 is greatest because it is the only number greater than 1. $\frac{1}{4}$ must be the next greatest because the other two numbers are negative.**

When the same block of digits in a decimal repeats without end, the decimal is called a **repeating decimal.** The block of digits that repeats can be one digit or more than one digit.

*Calculator HINT*

Enter 2 ÷ 3 into your calculator. If the last digit in the display is 7, your calculator rounds. If the last digit in the display is 6, your calculator doesn't round.

### Example 2

**Write each fraction as a decimal. State the block of digits that repeats.**

**a.** $\frac{2}{3}$

$2 \div 3 = 0.66666\ldots$ ← Divide.

$= 0.\overline{6}$ ← Place a bar over the digit or block of digits that repeats.

$\frac{2}{3} = 0.\overline{6}$; the digit that repeats is 6.

**b.** $\frac{15}{11}$

$15 \div 11 = 1.36363\ldots$ ← Divide.

$= 1.\overline{36}$ ← Place a bar over the digit or block of digits that repeats.

$\frac{15}{11} = 1.\overline{36}$; the block of digits that repeats is 36.

**Try This** Write each fraction as a decimal. State whether the decimal is *terminating* or *repeating*. If the decimal repeats, state the block of digits that repeats.

**5.** $\frac{7}{9}$ $0.\overline{7}$; repeating; 7 **6.** $\frac{21}{22}$ $0.9\overline{54}$; repeating; 54 **7.** $\frac{11}{8}$ 1.375; terminating **8.** $\frac{8}{11}$ $0.\overline{72}$; repeating; 72

When you compare and order decimals and fractions, it may be helpful to write the fractions as decimals first.

### Example 3

**Write the numbers from least to greatest.**

$\frac{1}{4}, -0.2, -\frac{3}{5}, 1.1$

$1 \div 4 = 0.25$
$-3 \div 5 = -0.6$ } Change the fractions to decimals.

$-0.6 < -0.2 < 0.25 < 1.1$ Compare the decimals.

From least to greatest, the numbers are $-\frac{3}{5}$, $-0.2$, $\frac{1}{4}$, and 1.1.

**Try This** Order from least to greatest.

**9.** $0.2, \frac{4}{5}, \frac{7}{10}, 0.5$ $0.2, 0.5, \frac{7}{10}, \frac{4}{5}$

**10.** $-\frac{1}{8}, -0.75, -\frac{1}{4}, -0.375$ $-0.75, -0.375, -\frac{1}{4}, -\frac{1}{8}$



- **Additional Examples 2–3**
  Write $-0.8, \frac{3}{12}, -\frac{5}{4}$, and 0.125 from least to greatest.
  $-\frac{5}{4} < -0.8 < 0.125 < \frac{3}{12}$
- **Additional Example 4**
  Write 1.72 as a mixed number in simplest form. $1\frac{18}{25}$
- **Additional Example 5**
  Write $0.\overline{18}$ as a fraction in simplest form. $\frac{2}{11}$

### AFTER THE LESSON

**To assess knowledge:**

**Lesson Quiz**

Order from least to greatest.

**1.** $\frac{6}{5}, -\frac{1}{3}, 0.625, -0.35$
$-0.35 < -\frac{1}{3} < 0.625 < \frac{6}{5}$

Write as a fraction or mixed number in simplest form.

**2.** 3.85 $3\frac{17}{20}$

- For enrichment and reteaching options see Resources on p. 221H.

## PART 2 Writing Decimals as Fractions

Reading a decimal correctly provides a way to write a fraction.

| Decimal | Read | Fraction |
|---|---|---|
| 0.43 | "forty-three hundredths" | $\frac{43}{100}$ |

If a decimal is greater than 1, you can write it as a mixed number.

### Example 4

**Write 1.12 as a mixed number in simplest form.**

$1.12 = 1\frac{12}{100}$ Keep the whole number 1. Write twelve hundredths as a fraction.

$= 1\frac{12 \div 4}{100 \div 4}$ Divide the numerator and denominator of the fraction by the GCF, 4.

$1.12 = 1\frac{3}{25}$ Simplify.

**Try This** Write each decimal as a mixed number in simplest form.

**11.** 1.75 $1\frac{3}{4}$ **12.** 3.004 $3\frac{1}{250}$ **13.** 2.32 $2\frac{8}{25}$

You can use algebra to write a repeating decimal as a fraction.

### Example 5

**Write $0.\overline{72}$ as a fraction in simplest form.**

$n = 0.\overline{72}$ Let the variable $n$ equal the decimal.

$100n = 72.\overline{72}$ Because 2 digits repeat, multiply each side by $10^2$, or 100.

$$\begin{aligned} 100n &= 72.\overline{72} \\ - \quad n &= -0.\overline{72} \\ \hline 99n &= 72 \end{aligned}$$

The Subtraction Property of Equality allows you to subtract an equal quantity from each side of an equation. So, subtract to eliminate $0.\overline{72}$.

$\frac{99n}{99} = \frac{72}{99}$ Divide each side by 99.

$n = \frac{72 \div 9}{99 \div 9}$ Divide the numerator and denominator by the GCF, 9.

$= \frac{8}{11}$ Simplify.

As a fraction in simplest form, $0.\overline{72} = \frac{8}{11}$.

**Try This** Write each decimal as a fraction in simplest form.

**14.** $0.\overline{7}$ $\frac{7}{9}$ **15.** $0.\overline{54}$ $\frac{6}{11}$ **16.** $0.\overline{213}$ $\frac{71}{333}$

**Quick Review**

The properties of equality allow you to perform the same operation on each side of an equation.



## PART 2 Part 2 Teaching Notes

To review how to read a decimal number, write 5.37 on the board. Ask a student to read the number. Remind students that the correct way to read the number is, "five and thirty-seven hundredths," instead of the more informal, "five point three seven." Naming the place value makes it easier to write the decimal as a fraction.

### Example 4

**Build understanding.** Ask: Why do you keep 1 as a whole number? It is the whole number part of the mixed number.

### Example 5

**Build understanding.** Ask: What number would you multiply both sides of the equation by if there were three digits in the repeating block? 1,000

**Extension** Write 0.672154 as a fraction, without writing it in simplest form. $\frac{672{,}154}{1{,}000{,}000}$

**Reading Math** Point out to students that it is important to include the fact that a decimal repeats when they read aloud a repeating decimal. The decimal $1.\overline{36}$ is read, "one and thirty-six hundredths, repeating the thirty-six."

**Auditory Learning** In pairs, have one partner read a decimal while the other writes the decimal as a fraction. Then, one partner reads a fraction as the other writes the fraction as a decimal. Make sure each partner gets a chance to read and write both fractions and decimals.

**Connecting to Economics** In 1997, the Board of Directors of the New York Stock Exchange voted to begin trading stocks in decimal prices rather than fractional prices. Previously, a stock that was valued at \$65.25 per share was priced on the exchange as $65\frac{1}{4}$. The smallest fraction of a dollar allowed for trade was $\frac{1}{8}$. The year 2000 was chosen as the starting date for the decimal pricing.

# 3 Practice/Assess

## Assignment Guide

To provide flexible scheduling, this lesson can be divided into parts.

**Part 1**

**Core** 1–10, 16–37, 51–52, 54–55
**Extension** 50

**Part 2**

**Core** 11–15, 38–46, 53
**Extension** 47–49, 56

Mixed Review can be assigned at any time for maintenance.

## Exercises

**Exercise 35** The repeating decimal $0.\overline{6} = \frac{2}{3}$ while $0.66666666 \approx \frac{2}{3}$. The repeating decimal is exactly equal to the fraction. Without the bar to show repeating, the decimal is only approximately equal to the fraction.

## Challenge

Write $\frac{1}{17}$ as a decimal. Hint: it is a repeating decimal. $0.\overline{0588235294117647}$

## Closure

To write a fraction as a decimal, divide the numerator by the denominator. If the division has a remainder of zero, the decimal is called a terminating decimal. If the division produces a repeating block of digits, the decimal is written with an overbar. Reading a decimal correctly is one way to write it as a fraction. To write a repeating decimal as a fraction, use algebra to eliminate the repeating part.

## Daily Cumulative Review

**Find the LCM of each group of numbers or expressions.** *(Lesson 5-1)*

1. 15, 20 60
2. 3, 11 33
3. 6, 7, 9 126
4. 60, 75, 100 300
5. $32a$, 40 $160a$
6. $6n^4, 9n^2$ $18n^4$
7. 11, 15 165
8. 3, 6, 9, 12 36
9. $8x^6, 30x^5$ $120x^6$

**Write each number in standard notation.** *(Lesson 4-9)*

10. $5 \times 10^{-6}$ 0.000005
11. $4.07 \times 10^9$ 4,070,000,000
12. $9.43 \times 10^{-5}$ 0.0000943
13. $1.356 \times 10^{-7}$ 0.0000001356
14. $8.9 \times 10^8$ 890,000,000
15. $6.04 \times 10^{-4}$ 0.000604

**Mixed Review**

**Use rules to find each sum or difference.**

16. (1-5) $-17 + 5$ $-12$
17. (1-5) $2 + (-9)$ $-7$
18. (1-5) $-4 + (-13)$ $-17$
19. (1-6) $-14 - 12$ $-26$
20. (1-6) $24 - (-16)$ 40
21. (1-6) $15 - 26$ $-11$
22. (1-5) $5 + (-26)$ $-21$
23. (1-6) $9 - 17$ $-8$
24. (1-5) $-35 + (-21)$ $-56$

**Is each number prime or composite? If composite, write the prime factorization.**

25. (4-3) 27 composite; $3^3$
26. (4-3) 14 composite; $2 \cdot 7$
27. (4-3) 90 composite; $2 \cdot 3^2 \cdot 5$
28. (4-3) 79 prime

**Multiply each expression.**

29. (2-2) $6(d + 5)$ $6d + 30$
30. (2-2) $(3v - 6)(-7)$ $-21v + 42$
31. (2-2) $8(2 - 4g)$ $-32g + 16$
32. (2-2) $-3(-w + 9)$ $3w - 27$
33. (2-2) $-5(5 - h)$ $5h - 25$
34. (2-2) $(7 + 4k)3$ $12k + 21$



# Exercises

## Check Understanding

**Write each fraction as a decimal.**

1. $\frac{7}{25}$ 0.28
2. $\frac{3}{5}$ 0.6
3. $-\frac{5}{8}$ −0.625
4. $-\frac{1}{6}$ $-0.1\overline{6}$
5. $\frac{2}{9}$ $0.\overline{2}$
6. $\frac{16}{24}$ $0.\overline{6}$

**Compare. Use >, <, or = to complete each statement.**

7. $\frac{1}{2}$ ■ 1.2 <
8. $\frac{7}{8}$ ■ 0.875 =
9. $\frac{3}{5}$ ■ 0.25 >
10. $\frac{1}{8}$ ■ 0.375 <

**Write each decimal as a fraction or mixed number in simplest form.**

11. 0.1 $\frac{1}{10}$
12. 5.36 $5\frac{9}{25}$
13. 2.55 $2\frac{11}{20}$
14. $0.\overline{5}$ $\frac{5}{9}$
15. $2.\overline{15}$ $2\frac{5}{33}$

16. In the school band, $\frac{6}{27}$ of the members play the clarinet. Write $\frac{6}{27}$ as a fraction in simplest form and as a decimal. $\frac{2}{9}$; $0.\overline{2}$

## Practice and Problem Solving

**Write each fraction or mixed number as a decimal.**

17. $\frac{9}{20}$ 0.45
18. $5\frac{3}{8}$ 5.375
19. $2\frac{5}{16}$ 2.3125
20. $6\frac{1}{4}$ 6.25
21. $\frac{1}{25}$ 0.04
22. $3\frac{4}{5}$ 3.8
23. $-\frac{31}{100}$ −0.31
24. $\frac{33}{22}$ 1.5
25. $\frac{1}{3}$ $0.\overline{3}$
26. $\frac{7}{11}$ $0.\overline{63}$
27. $\frac{13}{20}$ 0.65
28. $-\frac{3}{11}$ $-0.\overline{27}$
29. $\frac{4}{9}$ $0.\overline{4}$
30. $-\frac{11}{12}$ $-0.91\overline{6}$
31. $\frac{3}{50}$ 0.06

**Order from least to greatest.**

32. $1.2, \frac{3}{5}, -0.5, \frac{9}{10}$ $-0.5, \frac{3}{5}, \frac{9}{10}, 1.2$
33. $\frac{1}{2}, \frac{3}{2}, \frac{5}{2}, 0.3$ $0.3, \frac{1}{2}, \frac{3}{2}, \frac{5}{2}$
34. $-\frac{1}{4}, -\frac{1}{8}, -0.75, -0.625$ $-0.75, -0.625, -\frac{1}{4}, -\frac{1}{8}$
35. $\frac{2}{3}, \frac{2}{5}, \frac{5}{6}, 0.\overline{06}$ $0.0\overline{6}, \frac{2}{5}, \frac{2}{3}, \frac{5}{6}$
36. $-\frac{7}{10}, -\frac{8}{10}, -0.77, -0.\overline{77}$ $-\frac{8}{10}, -0.\overline{77}, -0.77, -\frac{7}{10}$
37. $2.1, \frac{22}{10}, 2.01, \frac{22}{11}$ $\frac{22}{11}, 2.01, 2.1, \frac{22}{10}$

**Write as a fraction or mixed number in simplest form.**

38. 0.35 $\frac{7}{20}$
39. 6.8 $6\frac{4}{5}$
40. 0.05 $\frac{1}{20}$
41. −3.9 $-3\frac{9}{10}$
42. 0.27 $\frac{27}{100}$
43. 0.272727 $\frac{272,727}{1,000,000}$
44. $0.\overline{27}$ $\frac{3}{11}$
45. $-0.\overline{3}$ $-\frac{1}{3}$
46. $-0.\overline{8}$ $-\frac{8}{9}$
47. $1.1\overline{9}$ $1\frac{1}{5}$
48. $0.0\overline{6}$ $\frac{1}{15}$
49. $0.1\overline{83}$ $\frac{91}{495}$

50. *Number Sense* The number of digits that repeat in a repeating decimal is called the *period* of the decimal. The period of $0.\overline{3}$ is 1.
   a. Write $\frac{5}{7}$, $\frac{4}{13}$, and $\frac{7}{15}$ as decimals. $0.\overline{714285}, 0.\overline{307692}, 0.4\overline{6}$
   b. What is the period of each decimal you wrote in part (a)? 6, 6, 1



## Alternative Assessment

Have students in pairs measure five objects around the room and record their inch measurements in fractions. Then have them convert their fractions to decimals, rounded to hundredths. Then, have pairs exchange decimal measurements and convert the decimal measurements back to fractional measurements.

51. *Zoology* In 1995, there were about 70,200 cats registered with the Cat Fancier's Association. Of these, about 44,700 were Persians. What part of the registered cats were Persians? Write your answer as a fraction in simplest form and as a decimal rounded to the nearest hundredth. $\frac{149}{234}$; 0.64

52. Batting averages are usually expressed as decimals. Sarah got 32 hits in 112 times at bat. Lizzie got 26 hits in 86 times at bat.
   a. Find their batting averages, to the nearest thousandth. Sarah: 0.286; Lizzie: 0.302
   b. Based on their batting averages, who is more likely to get a hit? Explain. Lizzie; 0.302 > 0.286

53. *Number Sense* Copy and complete the tables of some commonly used fractions and decimals. Write the fractions in simplest form.

| Fraction | ■ $\frac{1}{8}$ | ■ $\frac{1}{4}$ | $\frac{3}{8}$ | $\frac{1}{2}$ | ■ $\frac{5}{8}$ | $\frac{3}{4}$ | $\frac{7}{8}$ |
|---|---|---|---|---|---|---|---|
| Decimal | 0.125 | 0.25 | ■ 0.375 | ■ 0.5 | 0.625 | ■ 0.75 | ■ 0.875 |

| Fraction | $\frac{1}{5}$ | ■ $\frac{2}{5}$ | ■ $\frac{3}{5}$ | $\frac{4}{5}$ |
|---|---|---|---|---|
| Decimal | ■ 0.2 | 0.4 | ■ 0.6 | 0.8 |

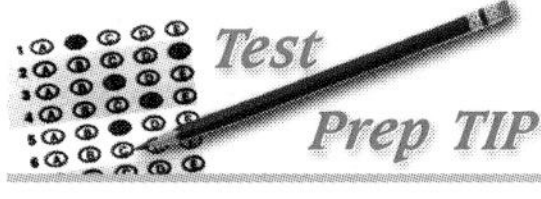


You can work faster during a test if you memorize the decimals for commonly used fractions.

54. *Carpentry* A carpenter has a bolt with diameter $\frac{5}{32}$ in. Will the bolt fit in a hole made by a drill bit with diameter 0.2 in.? Justify your reasoning. Yes; the bolt has diameter 0.15625 in., which is less than 0.2 in.

55. *Writing* Is 3.010010001... a repeating decimal? Explain. No; there is no block of digits that repeats.

56. *Critical Thinking* Seth had just finished a division problem on his calculator when the telephone rang. He got distracted. When he looked back at the calculator, all he could see was the display 0.04040404. What might have been the numbers Seth divided? Explain. 4 ÷ 99 since $0.\overline{04} = \frac{4}{99}$

## MIXED REVIEW

**Write each group of fractions from least to greatest.** ***(Lesson 5-1)***

57. $-\frac{1}{3}, \frac{2}{3}, -\frac{5}{6}, \frac{1}{6}$ $-\frac{5}{6}, -\frac{1}{3}, \frac{1}{6}, \frac{2}{3}$

58. $\frac{5}{8}, \frac{3}{8}, \frac{1}{5}, \frac{3}{5}, \frac{1}{8}$ $\frac{1}{8}, \frac{1}{5}, \frac{3}{8}, \frac{3}{5}, \frac{5}{8}$

59. $-\frac{4}{7}, -\frac{1}{14}, -\frac{3}{14}, -\frac{6}{7}$ $-\frac{6}{7}, -\frac{4}{7}, -\frac{3}{14}, -\frac{1}{14}$

**Change each number to an improper fraction.** ***(Previous course)***

60. $3\frac{2}{3}$ $\frac{11}{3}$

61. $1\frac{5}{6}$ $\frac{11}{6}$

62. $10\frac{3}{7}$ $\frac{73}{7}$

63. $7\frac{5}{8}$ $\frac{61}{8}$

64. $4\frac{7}{10}$ $\frac{47}{10}$

65. *Geography* Lake Mead Reservoir, located between Arizona and Nevada, has a capacity of 34,850,000,000 m$^3$. Write this number in scientific notation. ***(Lesson 4-9)*** $3.485 \times 10^{10}$

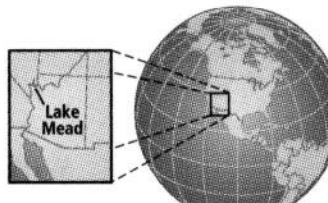


See also Extra Practice section.



## Practice

**Write as a fraction or mixed number in simplest form.**

1. 0.4 $\frac{2}{5}$
2. 0.75 $\frac{3}{4}$
3. 0.16 $\frac{4}{25}$
4. 2.34 $2\frac{17}{50}$
5. 0.09 $\frac{9}{100}$
6. 8.8 $8\frac{4}{5}$

**Write each fraction or mixed number as a decimal.**

7. $\frac{17}{20}$ 0.85
8. $\frac{7}{8}$ 0.875
9. $-\frac{9}{16}$ −0.5625
10. $3\frac{1}{8}$ 3.125
11. $6\frac{9}{32}$ 6.28125
12. $2\frac{87}{125}$ 2.696
13. $\frac{13}{25}$ 0.52
14. $4\frac{31}{50}$ 4.62
15. $-\frac{7}{12}$ $-0.58\overline{3}$
16. $\frac{4}{9}$ $0.\overline{4}$
17. $\frac{5}{18}$ $0.2\overline{7}$
18. $\frac{15}{11}$ $1.\overline{36}$

**Order from least to greatest**

19. $0.4, \frac{3}{5}, \frac{1}{2}, \frac{3}{10}$ $\frac{3}{10}, 0.4, \frac{1}{2}, \frac{3}{5}$
20. $-\frac{3}{8}, -\frac{3}{4}, -0.38, -0.6$ $-\frac{3}{4}, -0.6, -0.38, -\frac{3}{8}$
21. $\frac{1}{4}, -\frac{1}{5}, 0.2, \frac{2}{5}$ $-\frac{1}{5}, 0.2, \frac{1}{4}, \frac{2}{5}$
22. Write an improper fraction with the greatest possible value using each of the digits 5, 7, and 9 once. Write this as a mixed number and as a decimal.
   $\frac{97}{5} = 19\frac{2}{5} = 19.4$

**Write each decimal as a fraction or mixed number in simplest form.**

23. $10.0\overline{7}$ $10\frac{7}{90}$
24. 3.44 $3\frac{11}{25}$
25. $-4.\overline{27}$ $-4\frac{3}{11}$
26. 0.09 $\frac{9}{100}$
27. 0.375 $\frac{3}{8}$
28. $0.2\overline{43}$ $\frac{241}{990}$

**Compare. Use <, >, or = to complete each statement.**

29. $\frac{5}{6}$ [>] 0.8
30. $\frac{7}{11}$ [<] 0.65
31. $4.\overline{2}$ [=] $4\frac{2}{9}$
32. $-\frac{3}{11}$ [<] −0.25
33. $0.\overline{80}$ [=] $\frac{80}{99}$
34. −0.43 [>] $-\frac{7}{16}$



## Reteaching

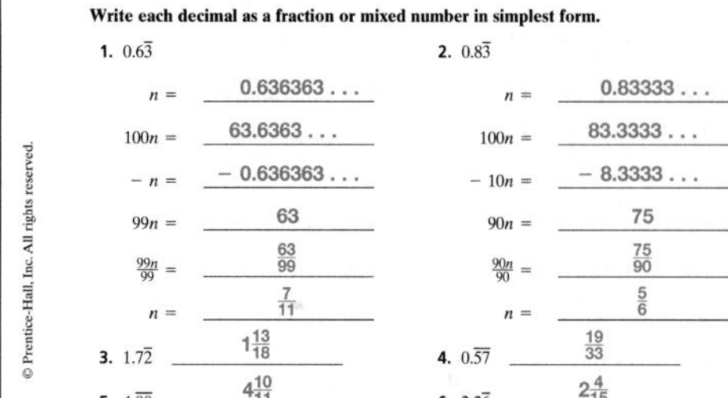

Write $1.5\overline{3}$ as a mixed number in simplest form.

| | |
|---|---|
| $n = 1.533333\ldots$ | Let the variable $n$ equal the decimal. Note that the bar is over only the 3 so only the 3 repeats. |
| $100n = 153.3333\ldots$ | Multiply each side by $10^2$ or 100 to bring one of the repeating 3's left of the decimal. |
| $10n = 15.3333\ldots$ | Multiply each side by 10 so the repeating 3's will subtract out. |
| $100n = 153.3333\ldots$ <br> $-10n = -15.3333\ldots$ | Subtract to eliminate the repeating 3's. |
| $90n = 138$ | Solve the new equation |
| $\frac{90n}{90} = \frac{138}{90}$ | Divide each side by 90. |
| $n = 1\frac{48}{90}$ | |
| $n = 1\frac{48 \div 6}{90 \div 6}$ | Divide the numerator and denominator by the GCF, 6. |
| $= 1\frac{8}{15}$ | |

Reteaching

**Write each decimal as a fraction or mixed number in simplest form.**

1. $0.\overline{63}$
   $n =$ 0.636363 . . .
   $100n =$ 63.6363 . . .
   $-n =$ − 0.636363 . . .
   $99n =$ 63
   $\frac{99n}{99} =$ $\frac{63}{99}$
   $n =$ $\frac{7}{11}$

2. $0.8\overline{3}$
   $n =$ 0.83333 . . .
   $100n =$ 83.3333 . . .
   $-10n =$ − 8.3333 . . .
   $90n =$ 75
   $\frac{90n}{90} =$ $\frac{75}{90}$
   $n =$ $\frac{5}{6}$

3. $1.7\overline{2}$ $1\frac{13}{18}$
4. $0.\overline{57}$ $\frac{19}{33}$
5. $4.\overline{90}$ $4\frac{10}{11}$
6. $2.2\overline{6}$ $2\frac{4}{15}$



## Enrichment

Recall that you can indicate repeating digits in a decimal by writing a bar over the repeating digits.

**Example** $\frac{1}{3} = 0.33333\ldots$ Shorthand: $\frac{1}{3} = 0.\overline{3}$

**Example** $\frac{51}{110} = 0.4636363\ldots$ Shorthand: $\frac{51}{110} = 0.4\overline{63}$

Use your calculator to do the following exercises.

**Write as a decimal, using a bar.**

1. $\frac{17}{18}$ $0.9\overline{4}$
2. $\frac{3}{11}$ $0.\overline{27}$
3. $\frac{14}{55}$ $0.2\overline{54}$
4. $\frac{8}{33}$ $0.\overline{24}$
5. $\frac{68}{153}$ $0.\overline{4}$
6. $\frac{7{,}067}{990}$ $7.1\overline{38}$

When only nines appear in a denominator, you can predict the decimal equivalent of a fraction.

**Write as a decimal.**

7. $\frac{4}{9}$ $0.\overline{4}$
8. $\frac{7}{9}$ $0.\overline{7}$
9. $\frac{2}{9}$ $0.\overline{2}$
10. $\frac{5}{9}$ $0.\overline{5}$
11. Predict the decimal equivalent of $\frac{8}{9}$. $0.\overline{8}$
12. Find the answer using your calculator. $0.\overline{8}$

**Write as a decimal.**

13. $\frac{37}{99}$ $0.\overline{37}$
14. $\frac{82}{99}$ $0.\overline{82}$
15. $\frac{5}{99}$ $0.\overline{05}$
16. $\frac{61}{99}$ $0.\overline{61}$
17. Predict the decimal equivalent of $\frac{47}{99}$. $0.\overline{47}$
18. Find the answer using your calculator. $0.\overline{47}$

**Write as a decimal.**

19. $\frac{571}{999}$ $0.\overline{571}$
20. $\frac{7}{999}$ $0.\overline{007}$
21. $\frac{365}{999}$ $0.\overline{365}$
22. $\frac{998}{999}$ $0.\overline{998}$
23. Predict the decimal equivalent of $\frac{135}{999}$. $0.\overline{135}$
24. Find the answer using your calculator. $0.\overline{135}$
25. Predict the decimal equivalent of $\frac{8{,}705}{99{,}999}$. $0.\overline{08705}$

## MATH TOOLBOX

### Estimating with Fractions and Mixed Numbers

This Math Toolbox shows how to round to estimate calculations involving fractions and mixed numbers.

### Math Background

Before you begin a fraction calculation, first estimate an approximate answer. Compare this estimate to the final answer to help you find and correct errors in your calculations. Estimating answers is particularly important on the job, where many people use a calculator to help them find solutions to problems. Estimating is also useful when taking standardized tests.

## Teaching Notes

**Error Prevention** Check to see which operation (addition, subtraction, multiplication, division) you will use before you start to estimate.

**Monitoring Progress** Have student partners explain to each other the reasoning in their estimates.

**Block Scheduling** If you have block scheduling or extended periods, you may wish to insert this Math Toolbox lesson between the completion of Part 1 of Lesson 5-2 and the beginning of Part 2 of Lesson 5-2.

## MATH TOOLBOX

*Review*
*Before Lesson 5-3*

# *Estimating with Fractions and Mixed Numbers*

You can round to estimate sums and differences involving fractions and mixed numbers. In one method, you round the fraction or fraction part of a mixed number to $0, \frac{1}{2}$, or 1.

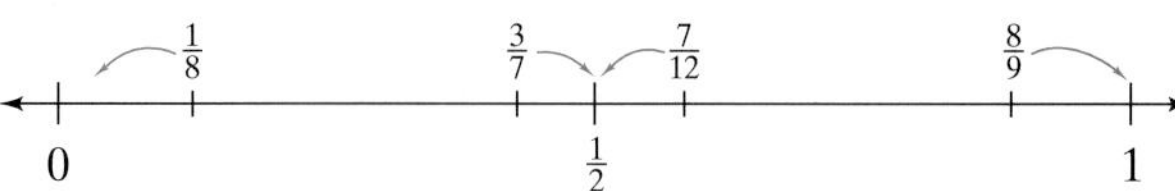


Round to 0 when the numerator is less than half of the denominator.

Round to $\frac{1}{2}$ when the numerator is about half the denominator.

Round to 1 when the numerator and denominator are almost equal.

### EXAMPLE 1

**a. Estimate $\frac{5}{6} + \frac{5}{12}$.**

$\frac{5}{6} \approx 1$

$+\frac{5}{12} \approx \frac{1}{2}$

$1\frac{1}{2}$

**b. Estimate $\frac{9}{20} - \frac{1}{5}$.**

$\frac{9}{20} \approx \frac{1}{2}$

$-\frac{1}{5} \approx 0$

$\frac{1}{2}$

← Round each fraction. →

← Add or subtract. →

You can get reasonable estimates when multiplying by rounding to the nearest whole number. For division, use compatible numbers.

### EXAMPLE 2

**a. Estimate $16\frac{1}{5} \div 2\frac{3}{4}$.**

$16\frac{1}{5} \div 2\frac{3}{4}$ — $2\frac{3}{4}$ rounds to 3. A number compatible with 3 and close to $16\frac{1}{5}$ is 15.

$15 \div 3 = 5$ Divide.

**b. Estimate $4\frac{1}{8} \cdot 1\frac{9}{10}$.**

$4\frac{1}{8} \cdot 1\frac{9}{10}$ — If the fractional part is greater than $\frac{1}{2}$, round up.

$4 \cdot 2 = 8$ Multiply.

**Estimate the value of each expression.** 1–8. Answers may vary. Sample answers are given.

1. $\frac{2}{3} + \frac{7}{8}$ 2
2. $5\frac{1}{12} - 2\frac{7}{9}$ 2
3. $\frac{1}{5} + 3\frac{5}{8}$ 4
4. $4\frac{11}{24} - \frac{7}{12}$ 4
5. $\frac{11}{12} \cdot 4$ 4
6. $6\frac{8}{9} \div 1\frac{1}{5}$ 7
7. $10\frac{1}{10} \div 4\frac{7}{8}$ 2
8. $2\frac{4}{5} \cdot 5$ 15

234 Math Toolbox

- **Additional Examples**

a. Estimate $\frac{3}{7} - \frac{7}{27}$. $\frac{1}{4}$

b. Estimate $3\frac{7}{8} \cdot 2\frac{2}{9}$. 8

# Adding and Subtracting Fractions

# 5-3

## What You'll Learn

1 To add or subtract fractions

2 To add or subtract mixed numbers

## . . . And Why

To apply fraction skills to a variety of situations, such as cooking

## Investigate

USING MODELS TO ADD FRACTIONS

Use the models to answer each question below.

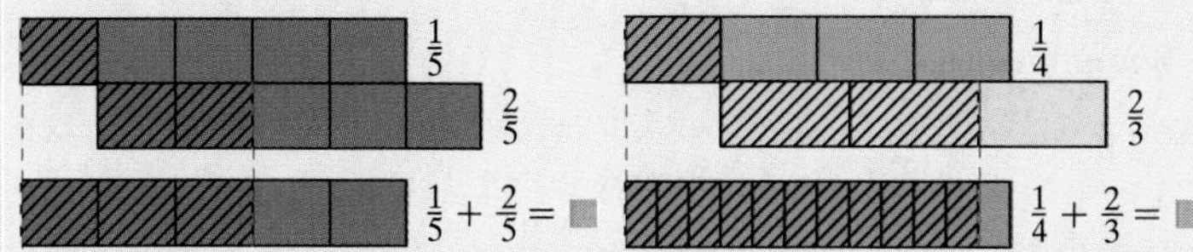


1. a. Refer to the model for $\frac{1}{5}+\frac{2}{5}$. What fraction does $\frac{1}{5}+\frac{2}{5}$ equal?
   b. *Mathematical Reasoning* Write a conjecture about how to find the numerator and denominator of a fraction that is the sum of two fractions with the same denominator.
2. a. Refer to the model for $\frac{1}{4}+\frac{2}{3}$. What fraction does $\frac{1}{4}+\frac{2}{3}$ equal?
   b. Can you add the numerators to find the sum? Explain.
   c. Can you add the denominators to find the sum? Explain.

1a. $\frac{3}{5}$
b. Answers may vary. Sample: Keep the denominator the same and add the numerators.
2a. $\frac{11}{12}$
b. No; $1 + 2 = 3$, but the correct numerator is 11.
c. No; $4 + 3 = 7$, but the correct denominator is 12.

## PART 1 Adding and Subtracting Fractions

In the model for $\frac{1}{5}+\frac{2}{5}$ above, you can see that the sum (or difference) of fractions with the same denominator is the sum (or difference) of the numerators. The denominators do not change.

### EXAMPLE 1

**Find each sum or difference.**

**a.** $\frac{1}{8}+\frac{3}{8}$

$\frac{1}{8}+\frac{3}{8}=\frac{1+3}{8}$ Add or subtract the numerators.

$=\frac{4}{8}=\frac{1}{2}$ Simplify.

**b.** $\frac{9}{x}-\frac{7}{x}$

$\frac{9}{x}-\frac{7}{x}=\frac{9-7}{x}$

$=\frac{2}{x}$

**TRY THIS** Find each sum or difference.

3. $\frac{3}{7}+\frac{1}{7}$ $\frac{4}{7}$
4. $\frac{2}{k}+\frac{3}{k}$ $\frac{5}{k}$
5. $\frac{7}{10}-\frac{3}{10}$ $\frac{2}{5}$
6. $\frac{11}{y}+\left(-\frac{5}{y}\right)$ $\frac{6}{y}$



# 5-3

## Getting Ready

**Materials** paper, scissors

**Resources** A complete list of resources for this lesson is on p. 221H.

### Daily Skills Warm-Up

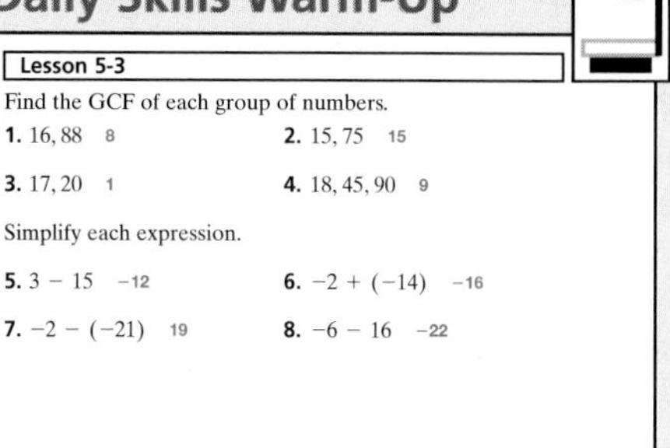

Lesson 5-3

Find the GCF of each group of numbers.

1. 16, 88 8
2. 15, 75 15
3. 17, 20 1
4. 18, 45, 90 9

Simplify each expression.

5. $3 - 15$ $-12$
6. $-2 + (-14)$ $-16$
7. $-2 - (-21)$ $19$
8. $-6 - 16$ $-22$

### Background for the Lesson

To add or subtract fractions with like denominators, place the sum or difference of the denominators over the common denominator. To add or subtract fractions with unlike denominators, you first rewrite the fractions so that they both have a common denominator. The easiest common denominator to use is the least one, the LCD. To add or subtract mixed numbers, you separately add or subtract the fractional parts and the whole number parts.

## 1 Focus

### Investigate

Help students see from the fraction model activity that they have used a model to find the sum of fractions with unlike denominators. Now they will use a mathematical procedure to do the same thing.

### Connecting to Prior Knowledge

In Lesson 5-1, students learned that they can compare fractions with unlike denominators by rewriting the fractions with the LCD. In this lesson, students learn to add and subtract fractions by using the LCD. In Lesson 5-4, they will learn to multiply and divide fractions.

# Tools to Monitor Progress

## BEFORE THE LESSON

**To check prerequisite skills:**

- Finding the greatest common factor

**Skills You Need,** p. 221

**Skills Handbook,** p. 739

**Skills Intervention Kit,** Number Theory and Fraction Concepts

## DURING THE LESSON

**To check understanding:**

**Try This** exercises on student page

- **Additional Example 1**

  Find each sum or difference.

  a. $\frac{4}{9}+\frac{2}{9}$ $\frac{2}{3}$

  b. $\frac{12}{b}-\frac{5}{b}$ $\frac{7}{b}$

- **Additional Example 2**

  Find each sum or difference.

  a. $\frac{1}{6}-\frac{3}{4}$ $-\frac{7}{12}$

  b. $\frac{2}{y}+\frac{5}{16}$ $\frac{32+5y}{16y}$

# 2 Teach

## Part 1 Teaching Notes

Review the meaning of LCM (least common multiple) and LCD (least common denominator) with students, asking them for examples.

### Example 1

**Build understanding.** Ask: In part a., why can you rewrite $\frac{4}{8}$ as $\frac{1}{2}$? Divide both the numerator and denominator of $\frac{4}{8}$ by 4 to get $\frac{1}{2}$, the equivalent fraction in simplest form.

### Example 2

**Build understanding.** Ask: In part b., what is the common denominator for the fractions? 48

**Error Prevention** Students sometimes try to use the rules for multiplying fractions when adding fractions, so they add the numerators and the denominators. Have students use models to convince them that $\frac{1}{2}$ of a sheet of paper plus $\frac{1}{3}$ of the same sheet is much more than $\frac{2}{5}$ of the sheet.

**Alternative Method** After students add or subtract fractions, suggest that they check their answers by converting the fractions to decimals and performing the operation again. Convert the decimal answer back to a fraction to compare answers.

## Part 2 Teaching Notes

Suggest that students write the whole number parts of the mixed numbers separately before they add the fractional parts. Point out that estimating first helps prevent errors in the final answer.

### Example 3

**Build understanding.** Ask: How can you tell that $\frac{53}{12}$ is greater than one? The numerator is greater than the denominator.

**Tactile Learning** Show students how to use fraction bars to help them add or subtract fractions.



Before you can add or subtract fractions with unlike denominators, first write the fractions with a common denominator. The method shown below works with subtraction also.

| Arithmetic | | Algebra | |
|---|---|---|---|
| | $\frac{2}{3} + \frac{1}{5}$ | | $\frac{a}{b} + \frac{c}{d}$ |
| | $\frac{2}{3} \cdot \frac{5}{5} + \frac{1}{5} \cdot \frac{3}{3}$ | | $\frac{a}{b} \cdot \frac{d}{d} + \frac{c}{d} \cdot \frac{b}{b}$ |
| | $\frac{10}{15} + \frac{3}{15}$ | | $\frac{ad}{bd} + \frac{bc}{bd}$ |
| | $\frac{13}{15}$ | | $\frac{ad + bc}{bd}$ |

### EXAMPLE 2

**Simplify each difference.**

**a.** $\frac{1}{8} - \frac{5}{6}$

$\frac{1}{8} - \frac{5}{6} = \frac{1 \cdot 6 - 8 \cdot 5}{8 \cdot 6}$ Rewrite using a common denominator.

$= \frac{6 - 40}{48}$ Use the Order of Operations to simplify.

$= \frac{-34}{48} = -\frac{17}{24}$ Simplify.

**b.** $\frac{1}{8} - \frac{5x}{6}$

$\frac{1}{8} - \frac{5x}{6} = \frac{1 \cdot 6 - 8 \cdot 5x}{8 \cdot 6}$

$= \frac{6 - 40x}{48}$

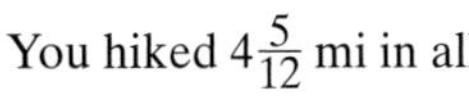

Quick Review

$\frac{-17}{24} = -\frac{17}{24}$

**TRY THIS** Write each sum or difference in simplest form.

7. $\frac{2}{3} - \frac{1}{5}$ $\frac{7}{15}$
8. $-\frac{7}{8} + \frac{3}{4}$ $-\frac{1}{8}$
9. $\frac{3}{7} + \frac{2}{m}$ $\frac{3m + 14}{7m}$

## PART 2 Adding and Subtracting Mixed Numbers

Before you add or subtract mixed numbers, write the mixed numbers as improper fractions.

REAL-WORLD CONNECTION

### EXAMPLE 3

**Suppose you hiked $2\frac{2}{3}$ mi near Mt. Shasta and then another $1\frac{3}{4}$ mi to your campsite. How far did you hike in all?**

$2\frac{2}{3} + 1\frac{3}{4} = \frac{8}{3} + \frac{7}{4}$ Write mixed numbers as improper fractions.

$= \frac{8 \cdot 4 + 3 \cdot 7}{3 \cdot 4}$ Rewrite using a common denominator.

$= \frac{32 + 21}{12}$ Use the Order of Operations to simplify.

$= \frac{53}{12} = 4\frac{5}{12}$ Write as a mixed number.

You hiked $4\frac{5}{12}$ mi in all.

Mt. Shasta, in northern California, is 14,162 ft high. The Avalanche Gulch route up the mountain is 6 mi long from Bunny Flat to the summit, and the elevation gain is more than 7,000 ft.



- **Additional Example 3**

Suppose one day you rode a bicycle for $3\frac{1}{2}$ hours, and jogged for $1\frac{1}{4}$ hours. How long did you exercise on that day? $4\frac{3}{4}$ h

## AFTER THE LESSON

**To assess knowledge: Lesson Quiz**

Find each sum or difference.

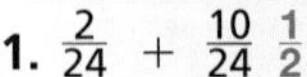

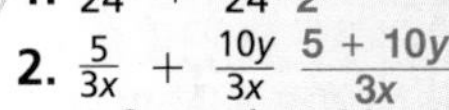

1. $\frac{2}{24} + \frac{10}{24}$ $\frac{1}{2}$
2. $\frac{5}{3x} + \frac{10y}{3x}$ $\frac{5 + 10y}{3x}$
3. $-\frac{3}{5} - \frac{1}{3}$ $-\frac{14}{15}$
4. $\frac{4d}{7} + -\frac{3}{2c}$ $\frac{8cd - 21}{14c}$
5. $16\frac{3}{4} - 11\frac{1}{8}$ $5\frac{5}{8}$

- For enrichment and reteaching options see Resources on p. 221H.

■ **TRY THIS** Find each sum.

**10.** $5\frac{3}{4} + \frac{7}{8}$ $6\frac{5}{8}$ **11.** $25\frac{1}{3} + 3\frac{5}{6}$ $29\frac{1}{6}$ **12.** $2\frac{3}{8} + \frac{7}{16}$ $2\frac{13}{16}$

**13.** A recipe for punch calls for $1\frac{1}{2}$ qt of orange juice, $1\frac{1}{4}$ qt of ginger ale, and $\frac{3}{4}$ qt of cranberry juice. How many quarts of punch will the recipe make? $3\frac{1}{2}$ qt

*Need Help?* For help with mixed numbers and improper fractions, see Skills Handbook, page 738.

You can subtract mixed numbers in more than one way.

## ■ Different Ways to Solve a Problem

**You are making banana bread for a bake sale, using the recipe at the right. You have $1\frac{3}{4}$ c of sugar left in a bag of sugar. How much more sugar do you need?**

**Method 1**

You write both mixed numbers as improper fractions.

$$2\frac{1}{2} - 1\frac{3}{4} = \frac{5}{2} - \frac{7}{4}$$
$$= \frac{5 \cdot 4 - 2 \cdot 7}{2 \cdot 4}$$
$$= \frac{20 - 14}{8}$$
$$= \frac{\not{6}^{3}}{\not{8}_{4}} = \frac{3}{4}$$

You need $\frac{3}{4}$ c more sugar.

**Banana Bread**

| | |
|---|---|
| 5 ripe bananas | 3½ cups flour |
| 4 eggs | 2 tsp baking soda |
| 1 cup shortening | 1 tsp salt |
| 2½ cups sugar | 1½ cups chopped walnuts, optional |
| 3 tsp vanilla | |

**Method 2**

You write $2\frac{1}{2}$ as $2\frac{2}{4}$, and then rewrite it as $1\frac{6}{4}$ before subtracting.

$$2\frac{1}{2} - 1\frac{3}{4} = 2\frac{2}{4} - 1\frac{3}{4}$$
$$= 1\frac{6}{4} - 1\frac{3}{4}$$
$$= \frac{3}{4}$$

You need $\frac{3}{4}$ c more sugar.

**Choose a Method** 1–2. Answers may vary. Sample answers are given above.

1. For the problem above, which method do you prefer? Explain.
2. Which method would you use to find $2\frac{4}{7} - 1\frac{9}{14}$? Which method would you use to find $-2\frac{1}{2} - 1\frac{3}{4}$? Explain your choices.

1. Method 1; writing both mixed numbers as improper fractions is easier than renaming $2\frac{1}{2}$ as $1\frac{6}{4}$.
2. Method 1 because writing both mixed numbers as improper fractions is easier than renaming $2\frac{4}{7}$; method 2 because I need only to find common denominators and then use addition.



### ■ Different Ways to Solve a Problem

**Build understanding.** Ask: What is the total amount of sugar you need for the recipe? Estimate how much more you need. $2\frac{1}{2}$ c; less than 1 c

**Extension** How would you subtract a mixed number from a whole number? For example, find the difference $6 - 2\frac{11}{16}$. sample answers: $5 + \frac{16}{16} - 2 + \frac{11}{16}$; $\frac{6}{1} - \frac{43}{16}$

# 3 Practice/Assess

## Assignment Guide

To provide flexible scheduling, this lesson can be divided into parts.

**Part 1**
**Core** 1–4, 10–22, 40–42
✪ **Extension** 33, 35–39, 45

**Part 2**
**Core** 5–9, 23–32, 43–44
✪ **Extension** 34

Mixed Review can be assigned at any time for maintenance.

## Exercises

**Exercises 10–28** Remind students to check that the denominators of the two fractions are the same before they add or subtract the numerators.

**Test Prep Exercise 40** Answer choices B. and C. can be eliminated because the results must be negative. Then compare the fractions in answer choices A. and D.

## ✪ Challenge

Find the difference $25\frac{7}{12} - \left(-18\frac{13}{18}\right)$. $44\frac{11}{36}$

## Closure

To add or subtract fractions and mixed numbers, first write the fractions with a common denominator, then add or subtract the numerators. You may need to rename a mixed number or change it to an improper fraction before subtracting.

## Daily Cumulative Review

**Write each fraction or mixed number as a decimal.** *(Lesson 5-2)*

1. $3\frac{2}{9}$ $3.\overline{2}$
2. $-\frac{6}{11}$ $-0.\overline{54}$
3. $-2\frac{7}{8}$ $-2.875$
4. $\frac{25}{10}$ $2.5$
5. $-\frac{16}{5}$ $-3.2$
6. $\frac{2}{3}$ $0.\overline{6}$

**Compare. Use <, >, or = to complete each statement.** *(Lesson 5-1)*

7. $\frac{6}{9}$ [>] $\frac{1}{3}$
8. $-\frac{3}{4}$ [>] $-\frac{7}{8}$
9. $\frac{7}{12}$ [<] $\frac{3}{4}$
10. $-\frac{3}{4}$ [<] $-\frac{2}{3}$
11. $\frac{4}{16}$ [=] $\frac{3}{12}$
12. $\frac{2}{9}$ [<] $\frac{3}{8}$
13. $-\frac{16}{64}$ [<] $\frac{17}{28}$
14. $\frac{4}{4}$ [>] $\frac{4}{8}$
15. $-\frac{1}{5}$ [<] $-\frac{1}{6}$

**Mixed Review**

**Write in simplest form.**

16. $\frac{8}{12}$ $\frac{2}{3}$ (4-4)
17. $\frac{16}{80}$ $\frac{1}{5}$ (4-4)
18. $\frac{6x}{30x}$ $\frac{1}{5}$ (4-4)
19. $\frac{16}{24}$ $\frac{2}{3}$ (4-4)
20. $\frac{48}{104}$ $\frac{6}{13}$ (4-4)
21. $\frac{26}{46}$ $\frac{13}{23}$ (4-4)

**Find each product or quotient.**

22. $-6(-45)$ $270$ (1-9)
23. $7 \cdot (-23)$ $-161$ (1-9)
24. $15 \div (-3)$ $-5$ (1-9)
25. $14 \div (-14)$ $-1$ (1-9)
26. $-16(0)$ $0$ (1-9)
27. $-24 \div (-6)$ $4$ (1-9)

**Write an inequality for each sentence.**

28. The total $d$ is less than 7. $d < 7$ (2-8)
29. The number $m$ is at least 2 dozen. $m \geq 24$ (2-8)

**Solve each equation.**

30. $-17 = m + (-45.6)$ $28.6 = m$ (3-5)
31. $s - (-3.6) = 2.1$ $s = -1.5$ (3-5)
32. $a + 23.6 = 17.9$ $a = -5.7$ (3-5)



# Exercises

## Check Understanding

**Find each sum or difference.**

1. $\frac{3}{16} + \frac{7}{16}$ $\frac{5}{8}$
2. $\frac{3}{4} - \frac{2}{3}$ $\frac{1}{12}$
3. $\frac{7m}{3} + \frac{5m}{3}$ $4m$
4. $\frac{5x}{7} - \frac{2x}{7}$ $\frac{3x}{7}$
5. $5\frac{3}{4} - 2\frac{1}{8}$ $3\frac{5}{8}$
6. $\frac{4}{16} + 1\frac{3}{8}$ $1\frac{5}{8}$
7. $10\frac{1}{8} + 3\frac{3}{4}$ $13\frac{7}{8}$
8. $1\frac{7}{9} - \frac{17}{18}$ $\frac{5}{6}$

9. *Crafts* A dollmaker cuts a piece of lace $8\frac{5}{8}$ in. long from a piece $10\frac{1}{2}$ in. long. How many inches of lace are left? $1\frac{7}{8}$ in.

## Practice and Problem Solving

**Find each sum or difference.**

10. $\frac{5}{11} + \frac{4}{11}$ $\frac{9}{11}$
11. $\frac{11}{12} - \frac{7}{12}$ $\frac{1}{3}$
12. $\frac{7}{8} + \frac{5}{8}$ $1\frac{1}{2}$
13. $\frac{3}{10} - \frac{7}{10}$ $-\frac{2}{5}$
14. $\frac{9}{10} + \frac{3}{4}$ $1\frac{13}{20}$
15. $\frac{2}{x} + \frac{3}{x}$ $\frac{5}{x}$
16. $-\frac{3}{10} - \frac{5}{100}$ $-\frac{7}{20}$
17. $\frac{12}{15} + \frac{1}{2}$ $1\frac{3}{10}$
18. $\frac{3}{n} - \frac{3}{10}$ $\frac{30 - 3n}{10n}$
19. $\frac{7}{d} + \frac{2d}{3}$ $\frac{21 + 2d^2}{3d}$
20. $\frac{12}{20} - \frac{1}{4}$ $\frac{7}{20}$
21. $\frac{5}{8y} - \frac{2}{8y}$ $\frac{3}{8y}$
22. $\frac{x}{6} + \frac{2x}{12}$ $\frac{x}{3}$
23. $3\frac{3}{4} + 2\frac{1}{4}$ $6$
24. $1\frac{5}{9} - 1\frac{2}{9}$ $\frac{1}{3}$
25. $3\frac{5}{8} + 2\frac{7}{12}$ $6\frac{5}{24}$
26. $-6\frac{1}{6} + \left(-2\frac{2}{9}\right)$ $-8\frac{7}{18}$
27. $1\frac{3}{4} - 2\frac{7}{8}$ $-1\frac{1}{8}$
28. $1\frac{5}{8} - \frac{3}{5} + 2\frac{1}{4}$ $3\frac{11}{40}$

*Estimation* **Estimate each sum or difference.** 29–32. Answers may vary. Sample answers are given.

29. $2\frac{1}{3} + 7\frac{1}{8}$ $9$
30. $25\frac{5}{18} - 9\frac{11}{17}$ $15$
31. $-4\frac{7}{8} + 15\frac{1}{10}$ $10$
32. $15\frac{3}{4} + 31\frac{1}{2}$ $48$

*Mental Math* **Find each sum.**

✪ 33. $\frac{3}{4} + \frac{3}{8} + \frac{1}{4}$ $1\frac{3}{8}$
✪ 34. $2\frac{5}{7} + 1\frac{2}{5} + 3\frac{2}{7}$ $7\frac{2}{5}$
✪ 35. $\frac{2}{7} + \frac{x}{2} + \left(-\frac{2}{7}\right)$ $\frac{x}{2}$

**Use prime factors to simplify each expression.**

SAMPLE $\frac{1}{14} + \frac{1}{4} = \frac{1}{2 \cdot 7} + \frac{1}{2^2} = \frac{1 \cdot 2}{2 \cdot 7 \cdot 2} + \frac{1 \cdot 7}{2^2 \cdot 7} = \frac{2}{2^2 \cdot 7} + \frac{7}{2^2 \cdot 7} = \frac{2 + 7}{2^2 \cdot 7} = \frac{9}{28}$

✪ 36. $\frac{5}{6} + \frac{7}{9}$ $1\frac{11}{18}$
✪ 37. $\frac{7}{24} - \frac{15}{90}$ $\frac{1}{8}$
✪ 38. $\frac{-5}{63} + \frac{-7}{99}$ $-\frac{104}{693}$
✪ 39. $\frac{2}{28} + \frac{1}{49}$ $\frac{9}{98}$

40. **TEST PREP** Which sum or difference is greater than 0? D
   A. $-\frac{7}{8} + \frac{3}{4}$
   B. $-\frac{7}{8} - \frac{3}{4}$
   C. $-\frac{7}{8} + \left(-\frac{3}{4}\right)$
   D. $\frac{7}{8} + \left(-\frac{3}{4}\right)$

41. *Error Analysis* Explain how the error in $\frac{3}{8} + \frac{2}{8} = \frac{5}{16}$ was made. Tell how the sum should be found. Answers may vary. Sample: The denominators were added; add numerators only.



## Alternative Assessment

Have students write their own quiz for this lesson. Include problems involving adding and subtracting fractions with like denominators, unlike denominators, and mixed numbers. Consider using student-generated problems on the actual quiz for the class.

42. First-class postage in the United States costs 33¢ for 1 oz. Your letter weighs $\frac{3}{4}$ oz. Do you need extra postage to include a newspaper clipping that weighs $\frac{3}{8}$ oz? Explain. **Yes; $\frac{3}{4} + \frac{3}{8} = 1\frac{1}{8}$, and $1\frac{1}{8}$ oz > 1 oz.**

43. Yesterday a fisherman caught a fish that weighed $6\frac{3}{4}$ lb. Today he caught a fish that weighs $8\frac{1}{4}$ lb. How much heavier is today's fish than yesterday's fish? **$1\frac{1}{2}$ lb**

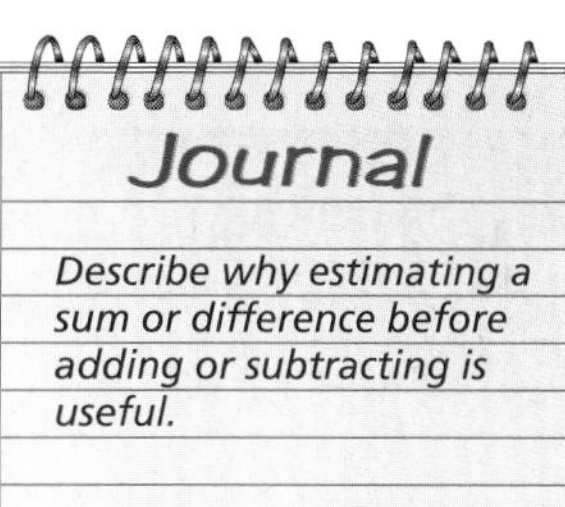

Journal
Describe why estimating a sum or difference before adding or subtracting is useful.


44. *Weather* There were three snowstorms last winter. The storms dropped $3\frac{1}{2}$ in., $6\frac{1}{2}$ in., and $10\frac{3}{4}$ in. of snow. What was the combined snowfall of the three storms? **$20\frac{3}{4}$ in.**

45. *Algebra* Dora and Paul have a collection of $x$ marbles. Dora has $\frac{x}{3}$ of the marbles. What fraction of the marbles does Paul have? **$\frac{2x}{3}$**

## Mixed Review

**Order from least to greatest.** ***(Lesson 5-2)***

46. $\frac{5}{8}, \frac{4}{7}, \frac{3}{6}$ **$\frac{3}{6}, \frac{4}{7}, \frac{5}{8}$**

47. $\frac{2}{3}$, 0.6, 0.66 **0.6, 0.66, $\frac{2}{3}$**

48. $\frac{10}{9}, \frac{9}{10}, -\frac{9}{10}, -\frac{10}{9}$ **$-\frac{10}{9}, -\frac{9}{10}, \frac{9}{10}, \frac{10}{9}$**

**Simplify each expression.** ***(Lesson 4-7)***

49. $x \cdot x^2$ **$x^3$**

50. $y^3 \cdot y^5$ **$y^8$**

51. $(x^3)^4$ **$x^{12}$**

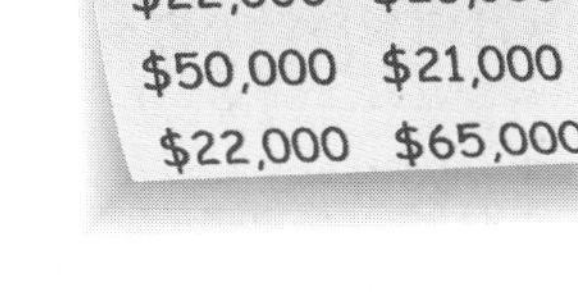

**10 Salaries at Company A**

| | |
|---|---|
| \$26,000 | \$62,000 |
| \$30,000 | \$22,000 |
| \$22,000 | \$26,000 |
| \$50,000 | \$21,000 |
| \$22,000 | \$65,000 |

52. *Data Analysis* Use the data at the right. Find the mean, median, and mode of the annual salaries. Which statistic would you use to encourage someone to take a job at Company A? ***(Lesson 3-3)*** **\$34,600, \$26,000, \$22,000; mean**

## Checkpoint 1 — Lessons 5-1 through 5-3

**Find the LCM of each pair of numbers.**

1. 30 and 50 **150**
2. 10 and 100 **100**
3. 1 and 5 **5**
4. 15 and 20 **60**
5. 27 and 32 **864**

**Compare. Use >, <, or = to complete each statement.**

6. $\frac{2}{3}$ ■ $\frac{2}{5}$ **>**
7. $\frac{1}{4}$ ■ 0.36 **<**
8. $-1.65$ ■ $-1\frac{5}{8}$ **<**
9. $-\frac{1}{5}$ ■ $-\frac{1}{8}$ **<**
10. $2\frac{2}{3}$ ■ $2\frac{4}{6}$ **=**

**Write each fraction or mixed number as a decimal and each decimal as a fraction in simplest form.**

11. $\frac{51}{100}$ **0.51**
12. 0.012 **$\frac{3}{250}$**
13. $1\frac{1}{4}$ **1.25**
14. $0.\overline{3}$ **$\frac{1}{3}$**
15. $\frac{5}{6}$ **$0.8\overline{3}$**
16. $0.\overline{51}$ **$\frac{17}{33}$**

17. **TEST PREP** Which expression is equal to $\frac{1}{3} + \frac{1}{6}$? **B**

A. $\frac{1}{2} + \frac{2}{4}$ B. $\frac{1}{4} + \frac{2}{8}$ C. $\frac{1}{5} + \frac{2}{10}$ D. $\frac{1}{7} + \frac{2}{14}$

See also Extra Practice section.



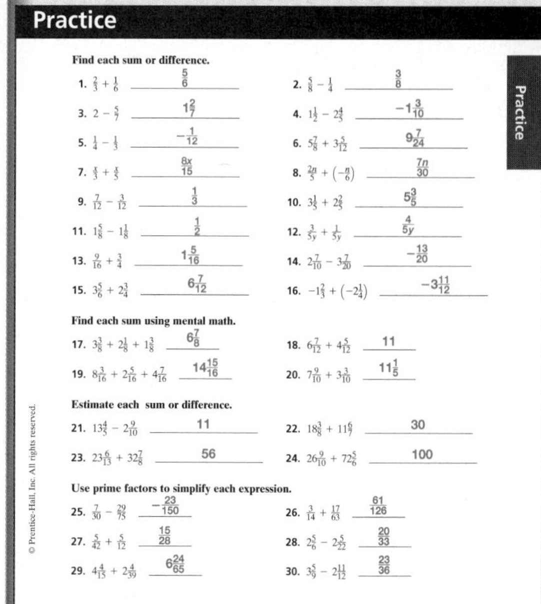

## Practice

**Find each sum or difference.**

1. $\frac{2}{3} + \frac{1}{6}$ **$\frac{5}{6}$**
2. $\frac{5}{8} - \frac{1}{4}$ **$\frac{3}{8}$**
3. $2 - \frac{5}{7}$ **$1\frac{2}{7}$**
4. $1\frac{1}{2} - 2\frac{4}{5}$ **$-1\frac{3}{10}$**
5. $\frac{1}{4} - \frac{1}{3}$ **$-\frac{1}{12}$**
6. $5\frac{7}{8} + 3\frac{5}{12}$ **$9\frac{7}{24}$**
7. $\frac{x}{3} + \frac{x}{5}$ **$\frac{8x}{15}$**
8. $\frac{2n}{5} + \left(-\frac{n}{6}\right)$ **$\frac{7n}{30}$**
9. $\frac{7}{12} - \frac{3}{12}$ **$\frac{1}{3}$**
10. $3\frac{1}{5} + 2\frac{2}{5}$ **$5\frac{3}{5}$**
11. $1\frac{5}{8} - 1\frac{1}{8}$ **$\frac{1}{2}$**
12. $\frac{3}{5y} + \frac{1}{5y}$ **$\frac{4}{5y}$**
13. $\frac{9}{16} + \frac{3}{4}$ **$1\frac{5}{16}$**
14. $2\frac{7}{10} - 3\frac{7}{20}$ **$-\frac{13}{20}$**
15. $3\frac{5}{6} + 2\frac{3}{4}$ **$6\frac{7}{12}$**
16. $-1\frac{2}{3} + \left(-2\frac{1}{4}\right)$ **$-3\frac{11}{12}$**

**Find each sum using mental math.**

17. $3\frac{3}{8} + 2\frac{1}{8} + 1\frac{3}{8}$ **$6\frac{7}{8}$**
18. $6\frac{7}{12} + 4\frac{5}{12}$ **11**
19. $8\frac{3}{16} + 2\frac{5}{16} + 4\frac{7}{16}$ **$14\frac{15}{16}$**
20. $7\frac{9}{10} + 3\frac{3}{10}$ **$11\frac{1}{5}$**

**Estimate each sum or difference.**

21. $13\frac{4}{5} - 2\frac{9}{10}$ **11**
22. $18\frac{3}{8} + 11\frac{6}{7}$ **30**
23. $23\frac{6}{13} + 32\frac{7}{8}$ **56**
24. $26\frac{9}{10} + 72\frac{5}{6}$ **100**

**Use prime factors to simplify each expression.**

25. $\frac{7}{30} - \frac{29}{75}$ **$-\frac{23}{150}$**
26. $\frac{3}{14} + \frac{17}{63}$ **$\frac{61}{126}$**
27. $\frac{5}{42} + \frac{5}{12}$ **$\frac{15}{28}$**
28. $2\frac{5}{6} - 2\frac{5}{22}$ **$\frac{20}{33}$**
29. $4\frac{4}{15} + 2\frac{4}{39}$ **$6\frac{24}{65}$**
30. $3\frac{5}{9} - 2\frac{11}{12}$ **$\frac{23}{36}$**



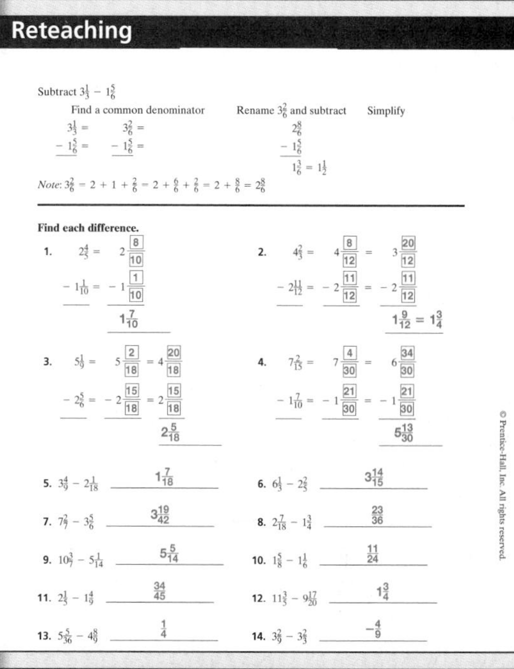

## Reteaching

Subtract $3\frac{1}{3} - 1\frac{5}{6}$

Find a common denominator: $3\frac{1}{3} = 3\frac{2}{6}$; $-1\frac{5}{6} = -1\frac{5}{6}$

Rename $3\frac{2}{6}$ and subtract: $2\frac{8}{6} - 1\frac{5}{6}$

Simplify: $1\frac{3}{6} = 1\frac{1}{2}$

*Note:* $3\frac{2}{6} = 2 + 1 + \frac{2}{6} = 2 + \frac{6}{6} + \frac{2}{6} = 2 + \frac{8}{6} = 2\frac{8}{6}$

**Find each difference.**

1. $2\frac{4}{5} = 2\frac{8}{10}$; $-1\frac{1}{10} = -1\frac{1}{10}$; **$1\frac{7}{10}$**
2. $4\frac{2}{3} = 4\frac{8}{12} = 3\frac{20}{12}$; $-2\frac{11}{12} = -2\frac{11}{12} = -2\frac{11}{12}$; **$1\frac{9}{12} = 1\frac{3}{4}$**
3. $5\frac{1}{9} = 5\frac{2}{18} = 4\frac{20}{18}$; $-2\frac{5}{6} = -2\frac{15}{18} = 2\frac{15}{18}$; **$2\frac{5}{18}$**
4. $7\frac{2}{15} = 7\frac{4}{30} = 6\frac{34}{30}$; $-1\frac{7}{10} = -1\frac{21}{30} = -1\frac{21}{30}$; **$5\frac{13}{30}$**
5. $3\frac{4}{9} - 2\frac{1}{18}$ **$1\frac{7}{18}$**
6. $6\frac{1}{3} - 2\frac{2}{5}$ **$3\frac{14}{15}$**
7. $7\frac{2}{7} - 3\frac{5}{6}$ **$3\frac{19}{42}$**
8. $2\frac{7}{18} - 1\frac{3}{4}$ **$\frac{23}{36}$**
9. $10\frac{3}{7} - 5\frac{1}{14}$ **$5\frac{5}{14}$**
10. $1\frac{5}{8} - 1\frac{1}{6}$ **$\frac{11}{24}$**
11. $2\frac{1}{5} - 1\frac{4}{9}$ **$\frac{34}{45}$**
12. $11\frac{3}{5} - 9\frac{17}{20}$ **$1\frac{3}{4}$**
13. $5\frac{5}{36} - 4\frac{8}{9}$ **$\frac{1}{4}$**
14. $3\frac{2}{9} - 3\frac{2}{3}$ **$-\frac{4}{9}$**



## Checkpoint

**Find the LCM of each pair of numbers.**

1. 16 and 14 **112**
2. 40 and 50 **200**
3. 7 and 11 **77**

**Compare. Use <, >, and = to complete each statement.**

4. $\frac{2}{7}$ **>** $\frac{2}{8}$
5. $\frac{2}{9}$ **<** 0.24
6. $-1\frac{2}{3}$ **>** $-1\frac{5}{6}$

**Write each fraction or mixed number as a decimal and each decimal as a fraction in simplest form.**

7. $1\frac{3}{5}$ **1.6**
8. $0.\overline{6}$ **$\frac{2}{3}$**
9. $\frac{5}{18}$ **$0.2\overline{7}$**

10. *Test Prep* Which expression is equal to $\frac{1}{4} + \frac{1}{2}$?

A. $\frac{1}{3} + \frac{2}{3}$ B. $\frac{1}{16} + \frac{5}{8}$ C. $\frac{3}{8} + \frac{5}{16}$ **(D.)** $\frac{2}{3} + \frac{1}{12}$

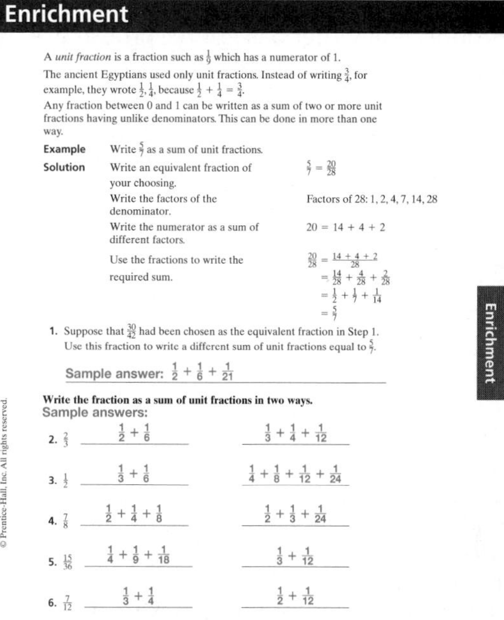

## Enrichment

A *unit fraction* is a fraction such as $\frac{1}{9}$ which has a numerator of 1.

The ancient Egyptians used only unit fractions. Instead of writing $\frac{3}{4}$, for example, they wrote $\frac{1}{2}, \frac{1}{4}$, because $\frac{1}{2} + \frac{1}{4} = \frac{3}{4}$.

Any fraction between 0 and 1 can be written as a sum of two or more unit fractions having unlike denominators. This can be done in more than one way.

**Example** Write $\frac{5}{7}$ as a sum of unit fractions.

**Solution**

Write an equivalent fraction of your choosing. $\frac{5}{7} = \frac{20}{28}$

Write the factors of the denominator. Factors of 28: 1, 2, 4, 7, 14, 28

Write the numerator as a sum of different factors. $20 = 14 + 4 + 2$

Use the fractions to write the required sum. $\frac{20}{28} = \frac{14 + 4 + 2}{28} = \frac{14}{28} + \frac{4}{28} + \frac{2}{28} = \frac{1}{2} + \frac{1}{7} + \frac{1}{14} = \frac{5}{7}$

1. Suppose that $\frac{30}{42}$ had been chosen as the equivalent fraction in Step 1. Use this fraction to write a different sum of unit fractions equal to $\frac{5}{7}$.

**Sample answer: $\frac{1}{2} + \frac{1}{6} + \frac{1}{21}$**

**Write the fraction as a sum of unit fractions in two ways.**

**Sample answers:**

2. $\frac{2}{3}$ **$\frac{1}{2} + \frac{1}{6}$** **$\frac{1}{3} + \frac{1}{4} + \frac{1}{12}$**
3. $\frac{1}{2}$ **$\frac{1}{3} + \frac{1}{6}$** **$\frac{1}{4} + \frac{1}{8} + \frac{1}{12} + \frac{1}{24}$**
4. $\frac{7}{8}$ **$\frac{1}{2} + \frac{1}{4} + \frac{1}{8}$** **$\frac{1}{2} + \frac{1}{3} + \frac{1}{24}$**
5. $\frac{15}{36}$ **$\frac{1}{4} + \frac{1}{9} + \frac{1}{18}$** **$\frac{1}{3} + \frac{1}{12}$**
6. $\frac{7}{12}$ **$\frac{1}{3} + \frac{1}{4}$** **$\frac{1}{2} + \frac{1}{12}$**

# 5-4

## Getting Ready

**Key Terms and Symbols** reciprocals

**Materials** paper for folding

**Resources** A complete list of resources for this lesson is on p. 221H.

### Daily Skills Warm-Up

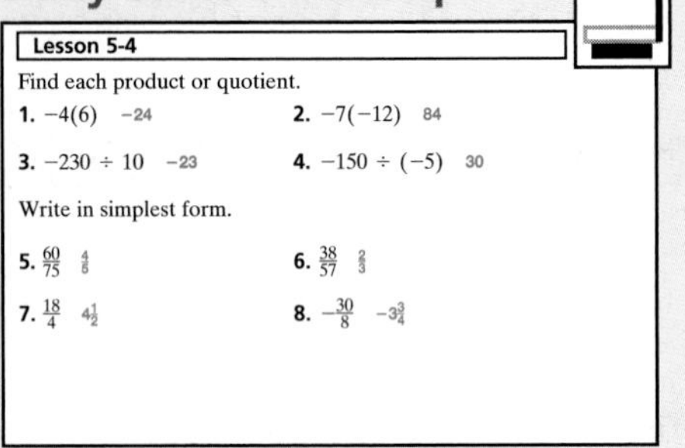

Lesson 5-4

Find each product or quotient.

1. $-4(6)$ $-24$
2. $-7(-12)$ $84$
3. $-230 \div 10$ $-23$
4. $-150 \div (-5)$ $30$

Write in simplest form.

5. $\frac{60}{75}$ $\frac{4}{5}$
6. $\frac{38}{57}$ $\frac{2}{3}$
7. $\frac{18}{4}$ $4\frac{1}{2}$
8. $-\frac{30}{8}$ $-3\frac{3}{4}$

### Background for the Lesson

Multiply fractions by first multiplying the numerators and then multiplying the denominators. To multiply mixed numbers, first rewrite them as improper fractions. To make multiplication easier, simplify the fractions by dividing the common factors.

Dividing by 2 is the same as multiplying by $\frac{1}{2}$. In general, dividing by a number is the same as multiplying by its *reciprocal* (or *multiplicative inverse*). The numbers 2 and $\frac{1}{2}$ are reciprocals because their product is 1. Other pairs of reciprocals are $x$ and $\frac{1}{x}$, $\frac{2}{3}$ and $\frac{3}{2}$, and 23 and $\frac{1}{23}$.

## 1 Focus

### Investigate

Explain to students that while arithmetic is exact, folding paper is not. This paper model only approximates the product.

### Connecting to Students' Lives

Ask students what items in a supermarket are sold in halves, quarters, or other fractions, such as a half-gallon carton of milk, or a quarter pound of butter. In this lesson students learn how they could find the total amount of milk in three half-gallon cartons by multiplying fractions.





# 5-4 Multiplying and Dividing Fractions

**What You'll Learn**

1. To multiply fractions
2. To divide fractions

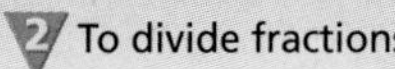

**. . . And Why**

To use fractions in finding area

## *Investigate*

MODELING MULTIPLICATION OF FRACTIONS

Use paper folding to find $\frac{2}{3}$ of $\frac{1}{4}$, or $\frac{2}{3} \cdot \frac{1}{4}$.

1. Fold a sheet of paper into fourths as shown. Shade $\frac{1}{4}$ of it. See left.
2. Now unfold the paper and fold it into thirds as shown in the second picture. Shade $\frac{2}{3}$ of it. See left.
3. **a.** Count the total number of rectangles. 12
   **b.** How many did you shade twice? 2
   **c.** What fraction of all the rectangles is this? $\frac{2}{12}$
4. Use your model to complete: $\frac{2}{3} \cdot \frac{1}{4} = \frac{■}{■}$ $\frac{2}{12}$
5. *Modeling* Use paper folding and shading to find $\frac{3}{4} \cdot \frac{1}{2}$. $\frac{3}{8}$

1.

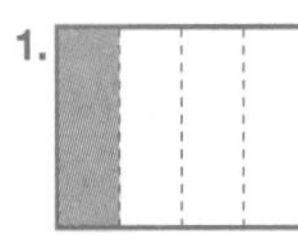

2.

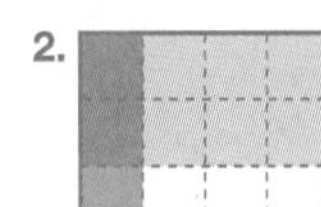

## PART 1 Multiplying Rational Numbers

To multiply fractions, first multiply their numerators and multiply their denominators. Then write the result in simplest form.

**EXAMPLE 1**

**Find $\frac{3}{7} \cdot \frac{4}{5}$.**

$\frac{3}{7} \cdot \frac{4}{5} = \frac{3 \cdot 4}{7 \cdot 5}$ ← Multiply the numerators. ← Multiply the denominators.

$= \frac{12}{35}$ Simplify.

**TRY THIS** Find each product.

6. $\frac{2}{5}\left(\frac{1}{3}\right)$ $\frac{2}{15}$
7. $-\frac{5}{6} \cdot \frac{2}{3}$ $-\frac{5}{9}$
8. $\frac{7}{8} \cdot \frac{5}{9}$ $\frac{35}{72}$
9. $-\frac{1}{4}\left(-\frac{3}{8}\right)$ $\frac{3}{32}$



## Tools to Monitor Progress

### BEFORE THE LESSON

**To check prerequisite skills:**

- Multiplying whole numbers

**Skills Handbook,** p. 740

**Skills Intervention Kit,** Number Theory and Fraction Concepts

### DURING THE LESSON

**To check understanding:**

**Try This** exercises on student page

- **Additional Example 1**
  Find $\frac{2}{3} \cdot \frac{5}{7}$. $\frac{10}{21}$
- **Additional Example 2**
  Find $\frac{5}{w} \cdot \frac{3w}{17}$. $\frac{15}{17}$
- **Additional Example 3**
  Keesha's desktop is a rectangle $3\frac{1}{2}$ ft long and $1\frac{1}{2}$ ft wide. What is the area of her desktop? $5\frac{1}{4}$ ft$^2$

When a numerator and a denominator have common factors, you can simplify before multiplying.

### EXAMPLE 2

**a. Find $\frac{9}{15} \cdot \frac{5}{9}$.**

$\frac{9}{15} \cdot \frac{5}{9} = \frac{{}^{1}\cancel{9}}{{}_{3}\cancel{15}} \cdot \frac{{}^{1}\cancel{5}}{{}_{1}\cancel{9}}$ Divide the common factors.

$= \frac{1}{3}$ Multiply.

**b. Find $\frac{y}{4} \cdot \frac{8}{11}$.**

$\frac{y}{4} \cdot \frac{8}{11} = \frac{y}{{}_{1}\cancel{4}} \cdot \frac{\cancel{8}^{2}}{11}$ Divide the common factors.

$= \frac{2y}{11}$ Multiply.

**TRY THIS** Find each product.

10. $\frac{2}{3} \cdot \frac{6}{7}$ $\frac{4}{7}$
11. $-\frac{5}{14} \cdot \frac{21}{25}$ $-\frac{3}{10}$
12. $\frac{2x}{9} \cdot \frac{3}{4}$ $\frac{x}{6}$

To multiply mixed numbers, first write them as improper fractions. Then simplify before multiplying, if possible.

**REAL-WORLD**  CONNECTION

### EXAMPLE 3

*Geometry* **Central Park in New York City is a rectangle. It is approximately $2\frac{1}{2}$ mi long and $\frac{1}{2}$ mi wide. What is the area of Central Park?**

$A = 2\frac{1}{2} \cdot \frac{1}{2}$ Area of a rectangle = length · width

$= \frac{5}{2} \cdot \frac{1}{2}$ Write $2\frac{1}{2}$ as an improper fraction, $\frac{5}{2}$.

$= \frac{5}{4}$ Multiply.

$= 1\frac{1}{4}$ Write as a mixed number.

The area of Central Park is about $1\frac{1}{4}$ mi$^2$.

Central Park is a rectangle. The angle of the photo makes two sides appear not to be parallel.

**TRY THIS** Find each product.

13. $3\frac{3}{4} \cdot \frac{2}{5}$ $1\frac{1}{2}$
14. $\frac{2}{3} \cdot 1\frac{2}{7}$ $\frac{6}{7}$
15. $\left(-2\frac{5}{6}\right) \cdot 1\frac{3}{5}$ $-4\frac{8}{15}$



## 2 Teach

### Part 1 Teaching Notes

Students will soon realize that simplifying before they multiply, when possible, saves steps.

#### Example 1

**Build understanding.** Ask: Why was the fraction $\frac{12}{35}$ not simplified further? **There is no factor common to both 12 and 35 other than 1.**

#### Example 2

**Build understanding.** Ask: Why do you write a 1 above the 5 (in part a.) when you divide? **because 5 ÷ 5 = 1**

#### Example 3

**Build understanding.** Ask: What are the steps in writing $2\frac{1}{2}$ to the improper fraction $\frac{5}{2}$? **Rewrite 2 as $\frac{4}{2}$ and add $\frac{1}{2}$ to get $\frac{5}{2}$.**

**Extension** Explain the difference between adding $\frac{1}{2}$ and $\frac{1}{3}$ and multiplying the same two fractions. **Before you can add, you must rewrite the fractions so they have the same denominator. Multiplication does not require like denominators.**

**Error Prevention** Suggest that students first determine the sign of the product before doing the multiplication.

**Connecting to Geometry** Formulas for area sometimes involve multiplication of fractions. The formula for the area of a triangle is $a = \frac{1}{2}bh$, where $b$ is the length of the base, and $h$ is the height, or altitude, to that base.

- **Additional Example 4**
  Find each quotient.
  a. $\frac{3}{5} \div \frac{7}{10}$ $\frac{6}{7}$
  b. $\frac{27}{8q} \div \frac{9}{4q}$ $\frac{3}{2}$ or $1\frac{1}{2}$
- **Additional Example 5**
  Find $4\frac{1}{2} \div (-3\frac{3}{8})$. $-1\frac{1}{3}$

**AFTER THE LESSON**

**To assess knowledge:**

**Lesson Quiz**

Simplify each expression.

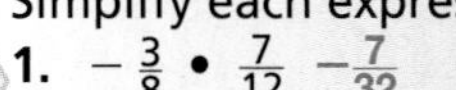

1. $-\frac{3}{8} \cdot \frac{7}{12}$ $-\frac{7}{32}$

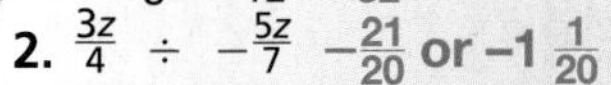

2. $\frac{3z}{4} \div -\frac{5z}{7}$ $-\frac{21}{20}$ or $-1\frac{1}{20}$

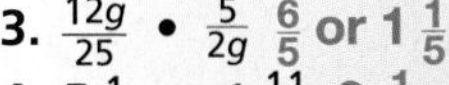

3. $\frac{12g}{25} \cdot \frac{5}{2g}$ $\frac{6}{5}$ or $1\frac{1}{5}$

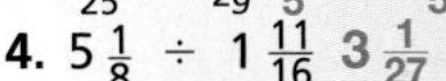

4. $5\frac{1}{8} \div 1\frac{11}{16}$ $3\frac{1}{27}$

- For enrichment and reteaching options see Resources on page 221H.

## Part 2 Teaching Notes

Help students understand why dividing is the same as multiplying by the reciprocal. Give several models and examples, as in the following strategies.

**Visual Learning** Use three circular pieces of paper to model three large cookies or pizzas. If each portion is to be half of a circle, how many portions are there? Help students connect this model to the abstract representation: $3 \div \frac{1}{2}$.

**Alternative Method** Write the following expression on the board: $8 \div 2$. Make sure students agree that the quotient is 4. Then, rewrite the 8 and the 2 as fractions: $\frac{8}{1} \div \frac{2}{1}$. Compare this expression to the expression $\frac{8}{1} \bullet \frac{1}{2}$ which has a product of 4.

### Example 4

**Build understanding.** Ask: In part b., why is there no $x$ in the answer? $\frac{x}{x}$ is 1; 1 is the multiplicative identity.

### Example 5

**Build understanding.** Ask: How does dividing mixed numbers differ from multiplying mixed numbers? To divide, you rewrite the problem as multiplying by the reciprocal of the divisor. Multiplication does not require the use of reciprocals.

**Error Prevention** Students often make only one of the two changes required to rewrite a division problem. Remind them both to rewrite division as multiplication and to rewrite the divisor as its reciprocal.

## Dividing Rational Numbers

Asking "What is $3 \div \frac{1}{2}$?" is the same as asking "How many halves are in three wholes?" Look at the oranges below.

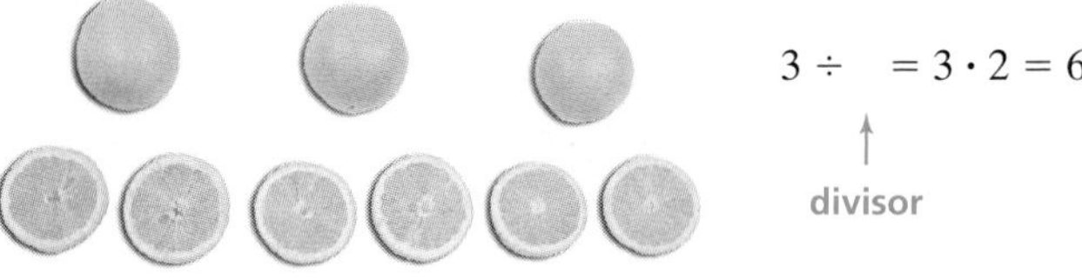

$3 \div \frac{1}{2} = 3 \cdot 2 = 6$

divisor

**Reading Math**

Reciprocals are also called *multiplicative inverses.*

Numbers like $\frac{1}{2}$ and 2 $\left(\text{or } \frac{2}{1}\right)$ are **reciprocals** because their product is 1. To divide fractions, rewrite the division as a related multiplication in which you multiply by the reciprocal of the divisor.

### Example 4

**a. Find $\frac{2}{9} \div \frac{2}{5}$.**

$\frac{2}{9} \div \frac{2}{5} = \frac{2}{9} \cdot \frac{5}{2}$ Multiply by the reciprocal of the divisor.

$= \frac{\overset{1}{\cancel{2}}}{9} \cdot \frac{5}{\underset{1}{\cancel{2}}}$ Divide the common factors.

$= \frac{5}{9}$ Simplify.

**b. Find $\frac{x}{3} \div \frac{x}{4}$.**

$\frac{x}{3} \div \frac{x}{4} = \frac{x}{3} \cdot \frac{4}{x}$

$= \frac{\overset{1}{\cancel{x}}}{3} \cdot \frac{4}{\underset{1}{\cancel{x}}}$

$= \frac{4}{3} = 1\frac{1}{3}$

■ **Try This** Find each quotient.

**16.** $\frac{5}{8} \div \frac{2}{3}$ $\frac{15}{16}$ **17.** $-\frac{1}{4} \div \frac{1}{2}$ $-\frac{1}{2}$ **18.** $\frac{5x}{9} \div \frac{10x}{27}$ $1\frac{1}{2}$

To divide mixed numbers, change the mixed numbers to improper fractions before multiplying by the reciprocal of the divisor.

### Example 5

**Find $1\frac{3}{4} \div \left(-2\frac{5}{8}\right)$.**

$1\frac{3}{4} \div \left(-2\frac{5}{8}\right) = \frac{7}{4} \div \left(-\frac{21}{8}\right)$ Change to improper fractions.

$= \frac{7}{4} \cdot \left(-\frac{8}{21}\right)$ Multiply by $-\frac{8}{21}$, the reciprocal of $-\frac{21}{8}$.

$= \frac{\overset{1}{\cancel{7}}}{\underset{1}{\cancel{4}}} \cdot -\frac{\overset{2}{\cancel{8}}}{\underset{3}{\cancel{21}}} = -\frac{2}{3}$ Divide the common factors. Simplify.

■ **Try This** Find each quotient.

**19.** $1\frac{1}{3} \div \frac{5}{6}$ $1\frac{3}{5}$ **20.** $-1\frac{3}{5} \div 1\frac{1}{5}$ $-1\frac{1}{3}$ **21.** $12\frac{1}{2} \div 1\frac{2}{3}$ $7\frac{1}{2}$

# Exercises

## Check Understanding

**Find each product.**

1. $\frac{2}{3} \cdot \frac{1}{5}$ $\frac{2}{15}$
2. $-\frac{1}{2}\left(\frac{3}{8}\right)$ $-\frac{3}{16}$
3. $5\frac{7}{8} \cdot \frac{6}{7}$ $5\frac{1}{28}$
4. $2\frac{3}{4} \cdot 1\frac{1}{5}$ $3\frac{3}{10}$
5. $\left(-\frac{7}{8}\right)\left(-\frac{4}{5}\right)$ $\frac{7}{10}$
6. $3\frac{2}{5} \cdot 1\frac{2}{3}$ $5\frac{2}{3}$
7. $\frac{12y}{25} \cdot \frac{5}{6}$ $\frac{2y}{5}$
8. $\frac{9}{10} \cdot \frac{15x}{3}$ $\frac{9x}{2}$

**Find each quotient.**

9. $\frac{1}{2} \div \frac{1}{3}$ $1\frac{1}{2}$
10. $\frac{5}{8} \div \frac{3}{4}$ $\frac{5}{6}$
11. $-\frac{3}{4} \div \frac{1}{3}$ $-2\frac{1}{4}$
12. $\frac{11}{12} \div \left(-\frac{7}{8}\right)$ $-1\frac{1}{21}$
13. $12\frac{2}{3} \div \frac{3}{4}$ $16\frac{8}{9}$
14. $1\frac{3}{8} \div 2\frac{1}{16}$ $\frac{2}{3}$
15. $-1\frac{7}{11} \div \frac{9}{11}$ $-2$
16. $-3\frac{2}{3} \div \left(-2\frac{4}{9}\right)$ $1\frac{1}{2}$

17. One granola bar weighs $1\frac{1}{2}$ oz. How much does a box of 6 granola bars weigh? 9 oz

## Practice and Problem Solving

**Find each product.**

18. $\frac{4}{7} \cdot \frac{3}{5}$ $\frac{12}{35}$
19. $\frac{5}{9}\left(\frac{9}{10}\right)$ $\frac{1}{2}$
20. $1\frac{2}{5} \cdot 2\frac{2}{7}$ $3\frac{1}{5}$
21. $\frac{6x}{7} \cdot \frac{1}{3}$ $\frac{2x}{7}$
22. $\left(-\frac{2}{3}\right)\left(\frac{11}{13}\right)$ $-\frac{22}{39}$
23. $-1\frac{1}{4} \cdot 6\frac{2}{3}$ $-8\frac{1}{3}$
24. $\frac{8}{9} \cdot \frac{15}{28}$ $\frac{10}{21}$
25. $-\frac{2}{3} \cdot \frac{9}{10}$ $-\frac{3}{5}$
26. $\frac{4}{t} \cdot \frac{3t}{8}$ $1\frac{1}{2}$
27. $\frac{4a}{9} \cdot \frac{3}{10}$ $\frac{2a}{15}$
28. $1\frac{3}{5} \cdot \left(-2\frac{1}{2}\right)$ $-4$
29. $\left(-\frac{7}{12}\right)\left(-\frac{5}{6}\right)$ $\frac{35}{72}$

**Find each quotient.**

30. $\frac{3}{4} \div \frac{8}{9}$ $\frac{27}{32}$
31. $\frac{3}{4} \div \frac{1}{2}$ $1\frac{1}{2}$
32. $3\frac{1}{2} \div \frac{4}{21}$ $18\frac{3}{8}$
33. $\frac{1}{x} \div \frac{3}{x}$ $\frac{1}{3}$
34. $-\frac{1}{2} \div \frac{2}{3}$ $-\frac{3}{4}$
35. $\frac{10}{13} \div \frac{15}{26}$ $1\frac{1}{3}$
36. $\frac{2t}{5} \div \frac{2}{5}$ $t$
37. $-\frac{5}{6} \div \frac{4}{9}$ $-1\frac{7}{8}$
38. $\frac{4}{9x} \div \frac{2}{3x}$ $\frac{2}{3}$
39. $1\frac{4}{5} \div \left(-1\frac{1}{2}\right)$ $-1\frac{1}{5}$
40. $6\frac{2}{3} \div \frac{8}{9}$ $7\frac{1}{2}$
41. $\frac{2}{5} \div \frac{15}{16}$ $\frac{32}{75}$

*Choose* **Use paper and pencil or mental math to simplify each expression.**

42. $\frac{1}{2} \cdot \frac{2}{5}$ $\frac{1}{5}$
43. $\frac{1}{2} \div \frac{2}{5}$ $1\frac{1}{4}$
44. $10 \cdot \frac{1}{4}$ $2\frac{1}{2}$
45. $10 \div \frac{1}{4}$ $40$
46. $\frac{5}{8} \cdot \frac{3}{5}$ $\frac{3}{8}$
47. $\frac{5}{8} \div \frac{3}{5}$ $1\frac{1}{24}$
48. $\frac{2}{7} \cdot \frac{12}{49}$ $\frac{24}{343}$
49. $\frac{2}{7} \div \frac{12}{49}$ $1\frac{1}{6}$



# 3 Practice/Assess

## Assignment Guide

To provide flexible scheduling, this lesson can be divided into parts.

**Part 1**

**Core** 1–8, 17–29, 50, 52

**Extension** 56

**Part 2**

**Core** 9–16, 30–49, 51, 57–58

**Extension** 53–55

Mixed Review can be assigned at any time for maintenance.

## Exercises

**Exercises 42–49** Remind students to rewrite the division as multiplying by the reciprocal of the divisor *before* they try to divide by a factor common to the numerator and denominator.

**Test Prep Exercise 57** Recall that for the quotient of two numbers to be 1, the two numbers must be equivalent.

## Challenge

Find $\frac{4}{\frac{2}{3}}$. 6

## Closure

To multiply fractions, multiply their numerators and their denominators. To divide fractions, multiply the first fraction by the reciprocal of the second fraction. To multiply or divide mixed numbers, write them as improper fractions before multiplying or dividing.

## Alternative Assessment

Have students write a letter explaining to a friend, with examples, why dividing by a number is the same as multiplying by the reciprocal of that number.

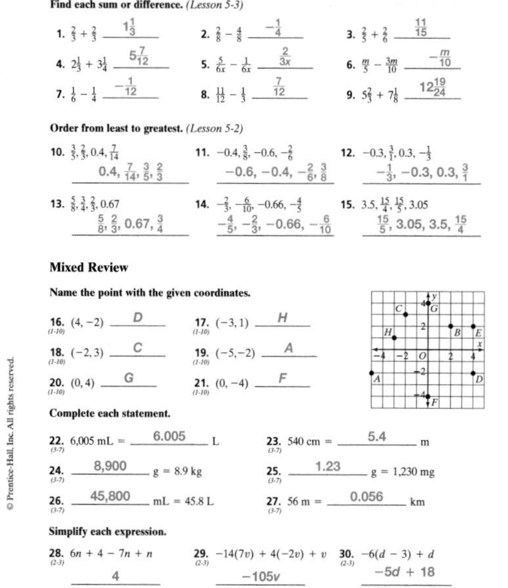

**Daily Cumulative Review**

**Find each sum or difference.** *(Lesson 5-3)*

1. $\frac{2}{3} + \frac{2}{3}$ $1\frac{1}{3}$
2. $\frac{2}{8} - \frac{4}{8}$ $-\frac{1}{4}$
3. $\frac{2}{5} + \frac{2}{6}$ $\frac{11}{15}$
4. $2\frac{1}{3} + 3\frac{1}{4}$ $5\frac{7}{12}$
5. $\frac{5}{6x} - \frac{1}{6x}$ $\frac{2}{3x}$
6. $\frac{m}{5} - \frac{3m}{10}$ $-\frac{m}{10}$
7. $\frac{1}{6} - \frac{1}{4}$ $-\frac{1}{12}$
8. $\frac{11}{12} - \frac{1}{3}$ $\frac{7}{12}$
9. $5\frac{2}{3} + 7\frac{1}{8}$ $12\frac{19}{24}$

**Order from least to greatest.** *(Lesson 5-2)*

10. $\frac{3}{5}, \frac{2}{3}, 0.4, \frac{7}{14}$ — $0.4, \frac{7}{14}, \frac{3}{5}, \frac{2}{3}$
11. $-0.4, \frac{3}{8}, -0.6, -\frac{2}{6}$ — $-0.6, -0.4, -\frac{2}{6}, \frac{3}{8}$
12. $-0.3, \frac{3}{1}, 0.3, -\frac{1}{3}$ — $-\frac{1}{3}, -0.3, 0.3, \frac{3}{1}$
13. $\frac{5}{8}, \frac{3}{4}, \frac{2}{3}, 0.67$ — $\frac{5}{8}, \frac{2}{3}, 0.67, \frac{3}{4}$
14. $-\frac{2}{3}, -\frac{6}{10}, -0.66, -\frac{4}{5}$ — $-\frac{4}{5}, -\frac{2}{3}, -0.66, -\frac{6}{10}$
15. $3.5, \frac{15}{4}, \frac{15}{5}, 3.05$ — $\frac{15}{5}, 3.05, 3.5, \frac{15}{4}$

**Mixed Review**

**Name the point with the given coordinates.**

16. (1-10) $(4, -2)$ D
17. (1-10) $(-3, 1)$ H
18. (1-10) $(-2, 3)$ C
19. (1-10) $(-5, -2)$ A
20. (1-10) $(0, 4)$ G
21. (1-10) $(0, -4)$ F



**Complete each statement.**

22. (3-7) 6,005 mL = 6.005 L
23. (3-7) 540 cm = 5.4 m
24. (3-7) 8,900 g = 8.9 kg
25. (3-7) 1.23 g = 1,230 mg
26. (3-7) 45,800 mL = 45.8 L
27. (3-7) 56 m = 0.056 km

**Simplify each expression.**

28. (2-3) $6n + 4 - 7n + n$ 4
29. (2-3) $-14(7v) + 4(-2v) + v$ $-105v$
30. (2-3) $-6(d - 3) + d$ $-5d + 18$

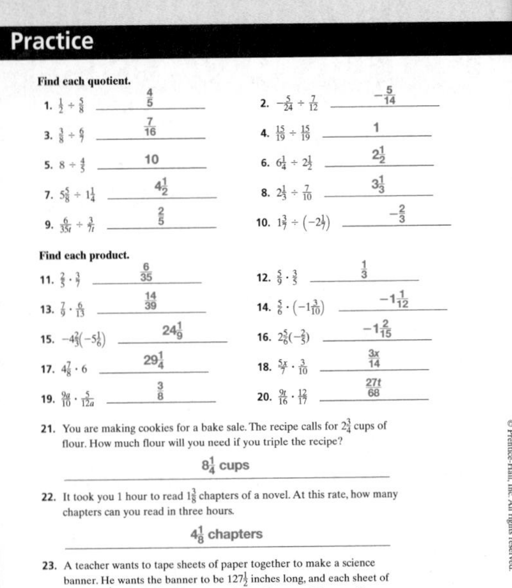

## Practice

**Find each quotient.**

1. $\frac{1}{2} \div \frac{5}{8}$ $\frac{4}{5}$
2. $-\frac{5}{24} \div \frac{7}{12}$ $-\frac{5}{14}$
3. $\frac{3}{8} \div \frac{6}{7}$ $\frac{7}{16}$
4. $\frac{15}{19} \div \frac{15}{19}$ $1$
5. $8 \div \frac{4}{5}$ $10$
6. $6\frac{1}{4} \div 2\frac{1}{2}$ $2\frac{1}{2}$
7. $5\frac{5}{8} \div 1\frac{1}{4}$ $4\frac{1}{2}$
8. $2\frac{1}{3} \div \frac{7}{10}$ $3\frac{1}{3}$
9. $\frac{6}{35t} \div \frac{3}{7t}$ $\frac{2}{5}$
10. $1\frac{3}{7} \div \left(-2\frac{1}{7}\right)$ $-\frac{2}{3}$

**Find each product.**

11. $\frac{2}{5} \cdot \frac{3}{7}$ $\frac{6}{35}$
12. $\frac{5}{9} \cdot \frac{3}{5}$ $\frac{1}{3}$
13. $\frac{7}{9} \cdot \frac{6}{13}$ $\frac{14}{39}$
14. $\frac{5}{6} \cdot \left(-1\frac{3}{10}\right)$ $-1\frac{1}{12}$
15. $-4\frac{2}{3}\left(-5\frac{1}{6}\right)$ $24\frac{1}{9}$
16. $2\frac{5}{6}\left(-\frac{2}{5}\right)$ $-1\frac{2}{15}$
17. $4\frac{7}{8} \cdot 6$ $29\frac{1}{4}$
18. $\frac{5x}{7} \cdot \frac{3}{10}$ $\frac{3x}{14}$
19. $\frac{9a}{10} \cdot \frac{5}{12a}$ $\frac{3}{8}$
20. $\frac{9t}{16} \cdot \frac{12}{17}$ $\frac{27t}{68}$

21. You are making cookies for a bake sale. The recipe calls for $2\frac{3}{4}$ cups of flour. How much flour will you need if you triple the recipe?
$8\frac{1}{4}$ cups

22. It took you 1 hour to read $1\frac{3}{8}$ chapters of a novel. At this rate, how many chapters can you read in three hours.
$4\frac{1}{8}$ chapters

23. A teacher wants to tape sheets of paper together to make a science banner. He wants the banner to be $127\frac{1}{2}$ inches long, and each sheet of paper is $8\frac{1}{2}$ inches wide. How many sheets of paper will he need?
15 sheets



## Reteaching

Find $3\frac{2}{3} \cdot 1\frac{4}{5}$

| | |
|---|---|
| $3\frac{2}{3} \cdot 1\frac{4}{5} = \frac{11}{3} \cdot \frac{9}{5}$ | Change to improper fractions. |
| $= \frac{11}{\cancel{3}_1} \cdot \frac{\cancel{9}^3}{5}$ | Divide the common factors. |
| $= \frac{33}{5} = 6\frac{3}{5}$ | Simplify. |

Find $-1\frac{1}{2} \div 2\frac{1}{4}$

| | |
|---|---|
| $-1\frac{1}{2} \div 2\frac{1}{4} = -\frac{3}{2} \div \frac{9}{4}$ | Change to improper fractions. |
| $= -\frac{\cancel{3}^1}{\cancel{2}_1} \cdot \frac{\cancel{4}^2}{\cancel{9}_3}$ | Multiply by the reciprocal. |
| $= -\frac{1}{1} \cdot \frac{2}{3}$ | Divide the common factors. |
| $= -\frac{2}{3}$ | Simplify. |

Check your sign with the original problem. A negative times a positive has a negative product.

**Find each product.**

1. $\frac{7}{9} \cdot \frac{3}{7} =$ $\frac{1}{3}$
2. $2\frac{1}{5} \cdot \left(-1\frac{1}{11}\right) =$ $-2\frac{2}{5}$
3. $-3\frac{7}{8} \cdot 2\frac{2}{3} =$ $-10\frac{1}{3}$
4. $5\frac{1}{7} \cdot 4\frac{2}{3} =$ $24$

**Find each quotient.**

5. $-\frac{6}{11} \div \frac{4}{11} =$ $-1\frac{1}{2}$
6. $1\frac{1}{6} \div 2\frac{1}{3} =$ $\frac{1}{2}$
7. $-4\frac{1}{5} \div \left(-1\frac{3}{4}\right) =$ $2\frac{2}{5}$
8. $-6\frac{1}{8} \div \frac{7}{3} =$ $-2\frac{5}{8}$

Reteaching



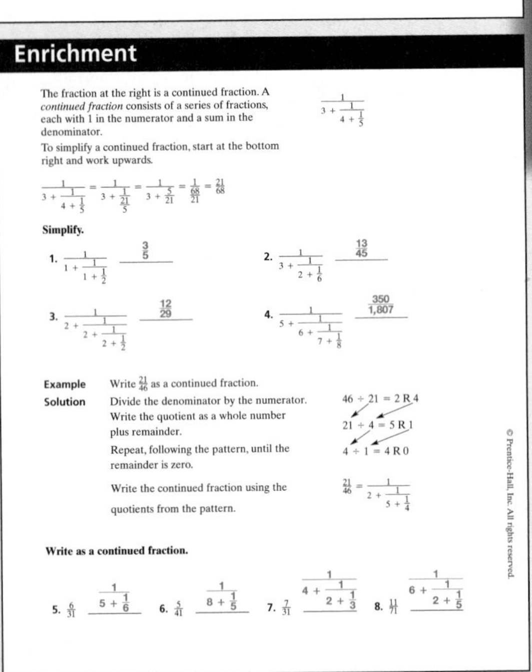

## Enrichment

The fraction at the right is a continued fraction. A *continued fraction* consists of a series of fractions, each with 1 in the numerator and a sum in the denominator.

$$\frac{1}{3 + \frac{1}{4 + \frac{1}{5}}}$$

To simplify a continued fraction, start at the bottom right and work upwards.

$$\frac{1}{3 + \frac{1}{4 + \frac{1}{5}}} = \frac{1}{3 + \frac{1}{\frac{21}{5}}} = \frac{1}{3 + \frac{5}{21}} = \frac{1}{\frac{68}{21}} = \frac{21}{68}$$

**Simplify.**

1. $\frac{1}{1 + \frac{1}{1 + \frac{1}{2}}}$ $\frac{3}{5}$
2. $\frac{1}{3 + \frac{1}{2 + \frac{1}{6}}}$ $\frac{13}{45}$
3. $\frac{1}{2 + \frac{1}{2 + \frac{1}{2 + \frac{1}{2}}}}$ $\frac{12}{29}$
4. $\frac{1}{5 + \frac{1}{6 + \frac{1}{7 + \frac{1}{8}}}}$ $\frac{350}{1{,}807}$

**Example** Write $\frac{21}{46}$ as a continued fraction.

**Solution** Divide the denominator by the numerator. Write the quotient as a whole number plus remainder.
$46 \div 21 = 2 \text{ R } 4$

Repeat, following the pattern, until the remainder is zero.
$21 \div 4 = 5 \text{ R } 1$
$4 \div 1 = 4 \text{ R } 0$

Write the continued fraction using the quotients from the pattern.
$\frac{21}{46} = \frac{1}{2 + \frac{1}{5 + \frac{1}{4}}}$

**Write as a continued fraction.**

5. $\frac{6}{31}$ $\frac{1}{5 + \frac{1}{6}}$
6. $\frac{5}{41}$ $\frac{1}{8 + \frac{1}{5}}$
7. $\frac{7}{31}$ $\frac{1}{4 + \frac{1}{2 + \frac{1}{3}}}$
8. $\frac{11}{71}$ $\frac{1}{6 + \frac{1}{2 + \frac{1}{5}}}$



50. Suppose you charge \$4.50/h for baby-sitting. How much will you earn baby-sitting for $3\frac{1}{2}$ hours? **\$15.75**

51. *Construction* A cable television crew has to install cable along a road $1\frac{1}{2}$ mi long. The crew takes a day to install each $\frac{1}{4}$ mi of cable. How many days will the installation take? **6 days**

52. A cheetah can run as fast as 64 mi/h. At that speed, how far could a cheetah run in $\frac{1}{16}$ h? $\frac{1}{30}$ h? **4 mi; $2\frac{2}{15}$ mi**

53. You are hiking along a trail that is $13\frac{1}{2}$ mi long. You plan to rest every $2\frac{1}{4}$ mi. How many rest stops will you make? **5 rest stops**

54. a. *Patterns* Find each quotient: $\frac{1}{2} \div 2, \frac{1}{2} \div 3, \frac{1}{2} \div 4,$ and $\frac{1}{2} \div 5$. **$\frac{1}{4}, \frac{1}{6}, \frac{1}{8}, \frac{1}{10}$**
    b. *Writing* Explain what happens to the quotients as the divisor increases in value. **The quotients decrease.**

**Quick Review**

divisor
$6 \div 2 = 3$
dividend quotient

55. *Critical Thinking* Write a multiplication equation and a division equation that you could use to show the result of cutting four melons into eight equal slices each. **Answers may vary. Sample: $4 \cdot 8 = 32$; $4 \div \frac{1}{8} = 32$**

56. *Open-ended* Find two fractions greater than $\frac{1}{2}$ with a product less than $\frac{1}{2}$. **Answers may vary. Sample: $\frac{4}{7}, \frac{3}{4}$**

57. **TEST PREP** Which quotient does *not* equal 1? **D**
    A. $2\frac{3}{4} \div \frac{11}{4}$  B. $\frac{3}{8} \div 0.375$  C. $\frac{7}{8} \div \frac{7}{8}$  D. $-1\frac{2}{3} \div \left(-\frac{3}{5}\right)$

58. a. Write an expression for the following: The product of $\frac{1}{2}a$ and 3 is decreased by the quotient $a \div (-4)$. **$3\left(\frac{1}{2}a\right) - \frac{a}{-4}$**
    b. Evaluate your expression for $a = 3$. **$5\frac{1}{4}$**

## Mixed Review

**Add or subtract.** *(Lesson 5-3)*

59. $\frac{4}{5} + \frac{6}{7}$ **$1\frac{23}{35}$**
60. $\frac{10}{13} - \frac{25}{26}$ **$-\frac{5}{26}$**
61. $-\frac{3}{10} + \frac{3}{5}$ **$\frac{3}{10}$**
62. $\frac{16}{21} - \frac{5}{7}$ **$\frac{1}{21}$**

**Simplify each fraction.** *(Lesson 4-4)*

63. $\frac{10}{12}$ **$\frac{5}{6}$**
64. $\frac{24}{40}$ **$\frac{3}{5}$**
65. $\frac{45}{10}$ **$4\frac{1}{2}$**
66. $\frac{12}{50}$ **$\frac{6}{25}$**
67. $\frac{34}{51}$ **$\frac{2}{3}$**
68. $\frac{105}{135}$ **$\frac{7}{9}$**

69. *Choose a Strategy* You spent $\frac{1}{4}$ of your money on lunch. After lunch, you gave half of what you had left to a friend, and then you spent \$3 on a book. You have \$4.50 left. How much money did you have before lunch? **\$20**



See also Extra Practice section.

# Using Customary Units of Measurement

# 5-5

## PART 1 Identifying Appropriate Units of Measure

### What You'll Learn

1. To identify appropriate customary units
2. To convert customary units

### . . . And Why

To use the customary system in solving consumer problems

Most people in the United States use the *customary system* of measurement.

**Customary Units of Measure**

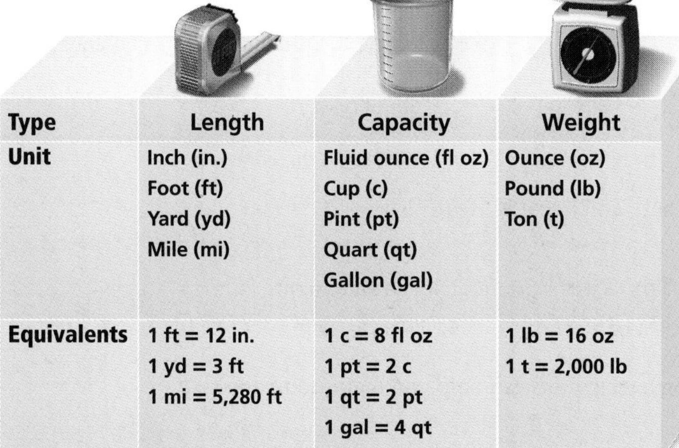

| Type | Length | Capacity | Weight |
|---|---|---|---|
| **Unit** | Inch (in.)<br>Foot (ft)<br>Yard (yd)<br>Mile (mi) | Fluid ounce (fl oz)<br>Cup (c)<br>Pint (pt)<br>Quart (qt)<br>Gallon (gal) | Ounce (oz)<br>Pound (lb)<br>Ton (t) |
| **Equivalents** | 1 ft = 12 in.<br>1 yd = 3 ft<br>1 mi = 5,280 ft | 1 c = 8 fl oz<br>1 pt = 2 c<br>1 qt = 2 pt<br>1 gal = 4 qt | 1 lb = 16 oz<br>1 t = 2,000 lb |

In order to measure an object, you should choose an appropriate unit of measure.

**EXAMPLE 1**

**Choose an appropriate unit of measure. Explain your choice.**

**a. weight of a truck** Measure its weight in tons because a truck is very heavy.

**b. length of a hallway rug** Measure its length in feet or yards because the length is too great to measure in inches.

**TRY THIS** Choose an appropriate unit of measure. Explain. See right.

1. capacity of a swimming pool
2. weight of a baby
3. length of a pencil
4. capacity of an eyedropper

1. Yard; it is the largest customary unit of length smaller than the length of a pool.
2. Pound; it is the largest customary unit of weight smaller than the weight of a baby.
3. Inch; it is the largest customary unit of length smaller than the length of a pencil.
4. Fluid ounce; it is the smallest customary unit of capacity. An eyedropper may hold a fraction of a fluid ounce.



# Tools to Monitor Progress

**BEFORE THE LESSON**

**To check prerequisite skills:**

- Multiplying and dividing fractions

**Skills Handbook,** p. 740

**Skills Intervention Kit,** Measurement

**DURING THE LESSON**

**To check understanding:**

**Try This** exercises on student page

- **Additional Example 1**

Choose an appropriate unit of measure. Explain your choice.

**a.** weight of a hummingbird **ounces; A hummingbird is very light.**

**b.** length of a soccer field **yards; A soccer field is quite long, but it is not a mile.**

# 5-5

## Getting Ready

**Key Terms and Symbols** conversion factors, dimensional analysis

**Resources** A complete list of resources for this lesson is on p. 221H.

### Daily Skills Warm-Up

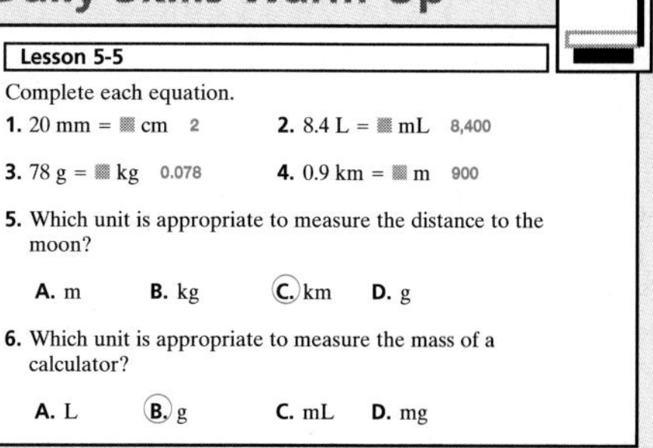

Lesson 5-5

Complete each equation.

1. 20 mm = ■ cm 2
2. 8.4 L = ■ mL 8,400
3. 78 g = ■ kg 0.078
4. 0.9 km = ■ m 900
5. Which unit is appropriate to measure the distance to the moon?
   A. m B. kg (C.) km D. g
6. Which unit is appropriate to measure the mass of a calculator?
   A. L (B.) g C. mL D. mg

### Background for the Lesson

To convert units of measure, you can use a unit fraction that equals one (such as $\frac{1 \text{ ft}}{12 \text{ in.}}$, or $\frac{12 \text{ in.}}{1 \text{ ft}}$). A fraction like this is called a *conversion factor*. The process you use to decide which conversion factor to use is called *dimensional analysis*. To convert 42 in. to feet, notice that inches is the unit you want to convert. Use the unit fraction that will *divide* the inches: $\frac{1 \text{ ft}}{12 \text{ in.}}$. The conversion expression is: $\frac{42 \text{ in.}}{1} \bullet \frac{1 \text{ ft}}{12 \text{ in.}}$. The inches *divide* to 1, so the result is $\frac{42 \text{ ft}}{12}$, or $\frac{7}{2}$ ft, which equals $3\frac{1}{2}$ ft.

## 1 Focus

### Connecting to Students' Lives

Discuss when students have used a unit of measurement. Ask a student to use a yard stick and a 1-foot ruler to demonstrate the number of feet in a yard. In this lesson, students convert units with the familiar units of inches, feet, and yards.

### Connecting to Prior Knowledge

Students learned how to multiply fractions in Lesson 5-4. In this lesson, students use the multiplication of fractions to convert between units of measurement.

# 2 Teach

## Part 1 Teaching Notes

Make sure that students understand how to read the abbreviations used in the bottom row of the table of customary measurements. Ask why *in.* is the only abbreviation that uses a period. It could be confused with the word *in*.

**ELL** The abbreviation *lb* may be difficult for students to associate with *pound*. Ask if they have seen a picture of the constellation Libra, a set of balance scales. The abbreviation comes from the Latin word *libra* for a scale used to measure weight.

### Example 1

**Build understanding.** Ask: How heavy would an object be before you started to use tons instead of pounds to measure its weight? somewhere near 2,000 lb (1 t)

**Tactile Learning** As you discuss customary units, have students examine actual objects used to measure length, capacity, and weight, such as measuring cups, rulers, and weights. Examining a container that holds a cup helps students conceptualize that amount.

**Error Prevention** Remind students that ounces and fluid ounces are different units. The *fluid* in fluid ounces is a reminder that the fluid ounce is a unit of liquid capacity, while the ounce is a unit of weight.

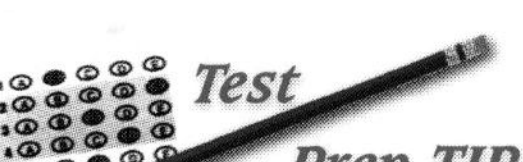

**Test Prep TIP**

You can work faster during tests if you memorize common conversions.

## Part 2 Converting Units

You can use *conversion factors* to change from one unit of measure to another. The process of analyzing units to decide which conversion factors to use is called **dimensional analysis.** You use equivalent units to write a conversion factor. For example, since 12 in. = 1 ft, the fraction $\frac{12\text{ in.}}{1\text{ ft}} = 1$. You can use $\frac{12\text{ in.}}{1\text{ ft}}$ to convert from feet to inches.

### Example 2

**Use dimensional analysis to convert 10 quarts to gallons.**

| | |
|---|---|
| $10\text{ qt} = \frac{10\text{ qt}}{1} \cdot \frac{1\text{ gal}}{4\text{ qt}}$ | Use a conversion factor that changes quarts to gallons. |
| $= \frac{{}^{5}\cancel{10}\,\cancel{\text{qt}} \cdot 1\text{ gal}}{{}_{2}\cancel{4}\,\cancel{\text{qt}}}$ | Divide the common factors and units. |
| $= \frac{5}{2}\text{ gal}$ | Simplify. |
| $= 2\frac{1}{2}\text{ gal}$ | Write as a mixed number. |

There are $2\frac{1}{2}$ gal in 10 qt.

**Try This** Complete each statement.

5. 14 oz = ■ lb $\frac{7}{8}$
6. 14 in. = ■ ft $1\frac{1}{6}$
7. 14 pt = ■ qt 7

Converting units can help you make comparisons.

REAL-WORLD CONNECTION

### Example 3

*Consumer Issues* **At Store A, a $4\frac{1}{4}$-lb bag of cashews costs \$15.99. Store B charges the same price for a 76-oz bag of cashews. Which store gives you more for your money?**

| | |
|---|---|
| $4\frac{1}{4}\text{ lb} = \frac{17}{4}\text{ lb} \cdot \frac{16\text{ oz}}{1\text{ lb}}$ | Use a conversion factor that changes pounds to ounces. |
| $= \frac{17}{{}_{1}\cancel{4}}\,\cancel{\text{lb}} \cdot \frac{{}^{4}\cancel{16}\text{ oz}}{1\,\cancel{\text{lb}}}$ | Divide the common factors and units. |
| $= 68\text{ oz}$ | Multiply. |

Since 76 oz > 68 oz, Store B gives you more for your money.

**Try This** Complete each statement.

8. $3\frac{1}{2}$ lb = ■ oz 56
9. $3\frac{1}{2}$ yd = ■ ft $10\frac{1}{2}$
10. $3\frac{1}{2}$ pt = ■ c 7



- **Additional Example 2**
  Use dimensional analysis to convert 68 fluid ounces to cups. $8\frac{1}{2}$ c
- **Additional Example 3**
  Fred's fruit stand sells homemade lemonade in $6\frac{1}{2}$-pt bottles for \$1.99. Jill's fruit stand sells homemade lemonade in $3\frac{1}{2}$-qt containers for the same price. At which stand do you get the most lemonade for your money? Jill's; $6\frac{1}{2}$ pt is $3\frac{1}{4}$ qt.

## AFTER THE LESSON

### To assess knowledge:

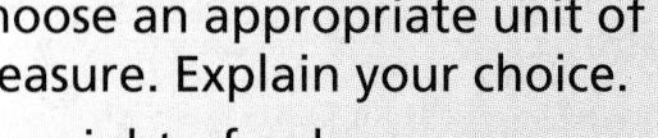

**Lesson Quiz**

Choose an appropriate unit of measure. Explain your choice.

1. weight of a dog
pounds

Use dimensional analysis to convert from one unit to the other.

2. $1\frac{1}{2}$ mi = ■ ft 7,920

- For enrichment and reteaching options see Resources on p. 221H.

# Exercises

## Check Understanding

*Estimation* **Match each situation with a possible measure.**

1. height of a 7-year-old C
2. weight of a bag of apples B
3. width of your palm F
4. amount of water in a vase D
5. weight of a peach E
6. amount of juice in a child's cup A

A. 4 fl oz
B. 4 lb
C. 4 ft
D. 4 c
E. 4 oz
F. 4 in.

*Mental Math* **Complete each equation.**

7. 1,000 lb = ■ t $\frac{1}{2}$
8. $\frac{1}{2}$ yd = ■ ft $1\frac{1}{2}$
9. 3 qt = ■ gal $\frac{3}{4}$
10. 16,000 oz = ■ lb 1,000
11. $\frac{1}{2}$ mi = ■ ft 2,640
12. 3 gal = ■ qt 12
13. You have a 24-fl oz bottle of water and a 2-pt bottle of water. How much water do you have altogether? 56 fl oz, or $3\frac{1}{2}$ pt

## Practice and Problem Solving

**Should each item be measured by *length, weight,* or *volume?***

14. a hair ribbon length
15. a package of meat weight
16. a bottle of juice volume
17. a bag of oranges weight
18. a zipper length
19. the contents of an eyedropper volume

**Choose an appropriate unit of measure. Explain your choice.** 20–25. Explanations may vary. Sample explanations are given.

20. weight of a paper clip Ounce; it is closest to the weight of a paper clip.
21. volume of a baby bottle Fluid ounce; baby bottles are usually marked in fluid ounces.
22. distance to Australia See below.
23. length of a sports field Yard; it is the largest customary unit of length less than the length of a sports field.
24. volume of a cooking pot Quart; it is the largest customary unit of volume less than the volume of most cooking pots.
25. weight of a medium-sized fish Pound; it is the largest customary unit of weight less than the weight of a medium-sized fish.

**Is each measurement reasonable? If not, give a reasonable measurement.**

26. A textbook weighs 2 oz. no; 2 lb
27. You drink about 10 gal of liquid per day. no; 10 pt
28. The street is 25 ft wide. yes
29. A sewing needle is about 2 ft long. no; 2 in.

22. Mile; it is the largest customary unit of distance less than the distance to Australia.

## Part 2 Teaching Notes

Point out that the units in dimensional analysis are necessary parts of the conversion fractions. You multiply and divide the units like variables in order to find the unit of the result.

### Example 2

**Build understanding.** Ask: How do you choose the unit fraction by which to multiply? **Use capacity equivalents in the chart to write a fraction (equal to 1) that will divide the qt and leave gal.**

### Example 3

**Build understanding.** Explain how you could answer this question if you converted the weight of the 76-oz bag to pounds. **You could compare the weight of the bags in pounds, rather than ounces.**

**Extension** Ask students to write the unit fractions that might be used to convert fl oz to gal and oz to t. $\frac{1 \text{ gal}}{128 \text{ fl oz}}$; $\frac{1 \text{ t}}{32{,}000 \text{ oz}}$

# 3 Practice/Assess

## Assignment Guide

To provide flexible scheduling, this lesson can be divided into parts.

**Part 1**

**Core** 1–6, 14–29, 65

✪ **Extension** 70

**Part 2**

**Core** 7–13, 30–60, 66–69

✪ **Extension** 61–64

Mixed Review can be assigned at any time for maintenance.

## Exercises

**Exercises 20–25** Students may suggest metric units. Remind them that this lesson is about customary units.

**Test Prep Exercise 65** You can eliminate answer choices A. and D. as unreasonable. Convert answer choice C. to feet to compare with answer choice B.

## ✪ Challenge

27 t = ■ oz 864,000

## Closure

To convert units of measure in the customary system of measurement, use dimensional analysis.

*Number Sense* **Match each measurement from the first group with an equivalent amount from the second group.**

| | |
|---|---|
| **30.** 15 mi G | **A.** 30,000 lb |
| **31.** 15 t A | **B.** $\frac{3}{400}$ t |
| **32.** 15 in. C | **C.** $1\frac{1}{4}$ ft |
| **33.** 15 fl oz F | **D.** $7\frac{1}{2}$ pt |
| **34.** 15 c D | **E.** $7\frac{1}{2}$ qt |
| **35.** 15 lb B | **F.** $1\frac{7}{8}$ c |
| **36.** 15 pt E | **G.** 79,200 ft |

*Choose* **Use estimation, mental math, or paper and pencil to convert from one unit to the other.**

**37.** 9 lb 2 oz = ■ oz 146 **38.** 4 ft = ■ in. 48 **39.** 28 in. = ■ ft $2\frac{1}{3}$

**40.** 5 c = ■ pt $2\frac{1}{2}$ **41.** 5 t = ■ lb 10,000 **42.** 3 gal = ■ qt 12

**43.** 2,640 ft = ■ mi $\frac{1}{2}$ **44.** 3,000 lb = ■ t $1\frac{1}{2}$ **45.** $10\frac{1}{2}$ lb = ■ oz 168

**46.** $5\frac{1}{2}$ mi = ■ ft 29,040 **47.** $7\frac{1}{2}$ c = ■ fl oz 60 **48.** 3 yd 2 ft = ■ ft 11

**49.** $6\frac{1}{4}$ gal = ■ qt 25 **50.** $\frac{3}{4}$ lb = ■ oz 12 **51.** 13 pt = ■ qt $6\frac{1}{2}$

**52.** 70 fl oz = ■ c $8\frac{3}{4}$ **53.** 1 ft 9 in. = ■ in. 21 **54.** 18 qt = ■ gal $4\frac{1}{2}$

**55.** 50 oz = ■ lb $3\frac{1}{8}$ **56.** $3\frac{1}{2}$ qt = ■ pt 7 **57.** 12 pt = ■ c 24

**58.** 20 c = ■ qt 5 **59.** $1\frac{1}{3}$ yd = ■ in. 48 **60.** $\frac{1}{5}$ t = ■ oz 6,400

**Complete each equation.**

✪ **61.** $2\frac{1}{4}$ yd = $6\frac{3}{4}$ ■ ft ✪ **62.** 6 qt = $1\frac{1}{2}$ ■ gal ✪ **63.** 100 lb = $\frac{1}{20}$ ■ t ✪ **64.** 6 c = 48 ■ fl oz

**65.** **TEST PREP** The great white shark is the world's largest predatory fish. A reasonable measurement for its length would be __?__. B

**A.** 18 in. **B.** 18 ft **C.** 18 yd **D.** 18 mi

**66. a.** *Geography* The Mississippi River is about 19,747,200 ft long. What is a better unit of measure? mile

**b.** Find the length of the Mississippi using the unit of measure you named in part (a). about 3,740 mi

**67.** *Error Analysis* Suzanne claims a quarter-pound hamburger is heavier than a 6-oz hamburger. Explain why she is incorrect.

A quarter pound is $\frac{1}{4}$ of 16 oz, or 4 oz, and 4 oz < 6 oz.



## Daily Cumulative Review

**Find each product or quotient.** *(Lesson 5-4)*

**1.** $-\frac{3}{4} \cdot -\frac{1}{3}$ $\frac{1}{4}$ **2.** $\frac{8a}{9} \cdot \frac{1}{2}$ $\frac{4a}{9}$ **3.** $-\frac{2}{3} \div \frac{5}{6}$ $-\frac{4}{5}$

**4.** $\left(\frac{9}{15}\right)\left(-\frac{5}{12}\right)$ $-\frac{1}{4}$ **5.** $\frac{4}{5} \div \frac{4}{5}$ 1 **6.** $-1\frac{3}{4} \div \left(-1\frac{1}{2}\right)$ $1\frac{1}{6}$

**7.** $\frac{30}{40} \cdot \frac{4}{15}$ $\frac{1}{5}$ **8.** $\frac{7}{15x} \div \frac{14}{30x}$ 1 **9.** $\frac{2}{b} \div \frac{3}{b}$ $\frac{2}{3}$

**Find each sum or difference.** *(Lesson 5-3)*

**10.** $\frac{3}{14} + \frac{1}{7}$ $\frac{5}{14}$ **11.** $\frac{8}{17y} - \frac{4}{17y}$ $\frac{4}{17y}$ **12.** $\frac{2a}{10} + \frac{4a}{15}$ $\frac{7a}{15}$

**13.** $-3\frac{1}{3} + \left(-1\frac{2}{9}\right)$ $-4\frac{5}{9}$ **14.** $\frac{2}{13} - \frac{1}{16}$ $\frac{19}{208}$ **15.** $\frac{6}{8} - \frac{2}{7}$ $\frac{13}{28}$

**Mixed Review**

**Use a pattern to solve the problem.**

**16.** *(1-8)* A local sporting goods store is having a sale on jerseys. Each jersey costs $11.75 and for every 3 jerseys purchased, you can buy a fourth jersey for $8.50. How much would it cost the Tigers football team to purchase 37 jerseys? $405.50

**Solve the problem by accounting for all possibilities.**

**17.** *(4-5)* There are five football teams in a league. Each team plays each of the other teams three times. What is the total number of games played? 30 games

**Simplify each expression.**

**18.** *(1-2)* 42 ÷ 7 × 3 18 **19.** *(1-2)* 78 − 24 ÷ 6 ÷ 2 76 **20.** *(1-2)* 7 · 2 + 3 · 6 32

**Write a rule for each pattern. Find the next three numbers in the pattern.**

**21.** *(1-7)* 1, 7, 5, 11, 9, 15, 13, 19, 17

Rule: Start with 1. Alternate adding 6 and subtracting 2.

**22.** *(1-7)* 3.75, 4.25, 4.75, 5.25, 5.75, 6.25, 6.75

Rule: Start with 3.75. Add 0.5 repeatedly.



## Alternative Assessment

In groups of three or four, have students create a poster to describe the customary measurements. Posters might include a table of measurements, similar to the one that starts the lesson, and photos or drawings of items with their measurement given in two different units. Old magazines and newspapers are good sources for the images on the posters.

**68.** *Hiking* You are hiking a 2-mi-long trail. You pass by a sign showing that you have hiked 1,000 ft. How many feet are left? 9,560 ft

**69.** *Reasoning* A student converted 8 cups to pints. His answer was 16 pints. Use dimensional analysis to determine whether the student's answer is reasonable. $8 \text{ c} \cdot \frac{1 \text{ pt}}{2 \text{ c}} = 4$ pt; the student's answer is not reasonable.

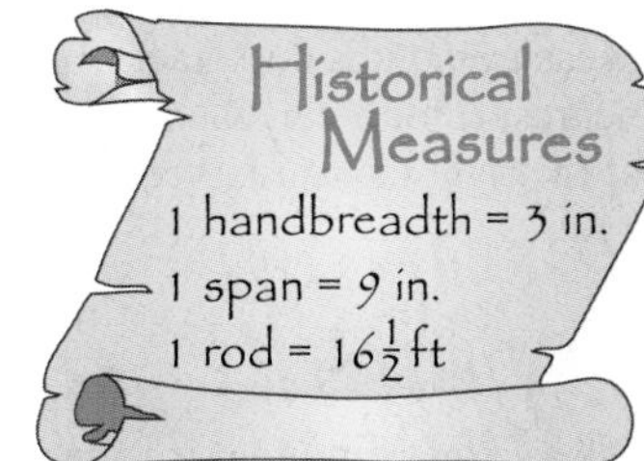

 **70.** *History* People once measured length in *handbreadths, spans,* and *rods.* a–b. Check students' work.

a. *Open-ended* Measure the length of an object. Give the length in *handbreadths, spans,* and *rods.*

b. *Writing* Consider the measurements you made in part (a). Which unit of measure is the most appropriate for the item you chose? Explain.

## Mixed Review

**Multiply or divide.** *(Lesson 5-4)*

**71.** $\frac{9}{11} \div 2\frac{7}{11}$ $\frac{9}{29}$ **72.** $1\frac{5}{7} \cdot 1\frac{1}{2}$ $2\frac{4}{7}$ **73.** $\frac{9}{10} \div \frac{3}{4}$ $1\frac{1}{5}$ **74.** $2\frac{2}{5} \cdot 3\frac{2}{3}$ $8\frac{4}{5}$

**Simplify each expression.** *(Lesson 2-3)*

**75.** $3x + (-2x) + 3y$ $x + 3y$ **76.** $10 - 3t - 4t$ $10 - 7t$ **77.** $2y - 5y$ $-3y$

**78.** *Choose a Strategy* In a single-elimination softball tournament each team plays until it loses. Eight teams are playing in a single-elimination tournament. How many games must be played? 7 games

## Math at Work

### Technical Artist

Technical artists prepare the drawings used by manufacturing and construction workers. The drawings give visual guidelines and technical details of products, buildings, and structures. Technical artists specify dimensions and materials to be used in the building process, and state procedures and processes to be followed. Many technical artists use computer-aided design (CAD) systems to prepare plans. Since they draw technical plans to scale, fractions and operations with fractions are an important part of their work.

For more information about careers in design, visit the Prentice Hall Website. www.phschool.com



## Math at Work

f you have block scheduling or extended class periods, have small groups of students research technical artists, CAD programs, and the math that is involved in this work. Suggest that students contact a community college to find out what kinds of math are involved in courses related to this career. Students may also wish to interview technical artists with questions about the math they use.

Students can find additional information on the Web site **www.phschool.com**.

## Practice

**Use estimation, mental math, or paper and pencil to convert from one unit to the other.**

1. 2 gal 2 qt = 10 qt
2. 3 yd = 9 ft
3. 1 ft 8 in. = 20 in.
4. $\frac{3}{5}$ t = 1200 lb
5. 30 in. = $2\frac{1}{2}$ ft
6. 20 fl oz = $2\frac{1}{2}$ c
7. 20 oz = $1\frac{1}{4}$ lb
8. $2\frac{1}{2}$ pt = 5 c
9. $1\frac{1}{8}$ lb = 18 oz
10. 7920 ft = $1\frac{1}{2}$ mi

**Is each measurement reasonable? If not, give a reasonable measurement.**

11. A glass of milk holds about 8 pt.
A glass of milk holds about 8 fl oz.
12. A newborn baby weighs about $7\frac{1}{2}$ oz.
A newborn weighs about $7\frac{1}{2}$ lb.
13. A phonebook is $\frac{3}{4}$ ft wide.
Reasonable

**Choose an appropriate unit of measure. Explain your choice.**

14. weight of a whale
ton; A whale is very heavy.
15. sugar in a cookie recipe
cup; Cookies have about a cup of sugar.
16. length of a mouse
inch; A mouse is small.

**Should each item be measured by *length*, *weight*, or *capacity*?**

17. amount of soup in a can
capacity
18. height of a can
length
19. heaviness of a can
weight
20. diameter of a can
length



## Reteaching

Use dimensional analysis to convert 36 ounces to pounds.

$36 \text{ oz} = \frac{36 \text{ oz}}{1} \cdot \frac{1 \text{ lb}}{16 \text{ oz}}$ Multiply by a fraction that is equal to one and compares pounds to ounces.

$= \frac{\overset{9}{\cancel{36}} \cancel{\text{oz}} \cdot 1 \text{ lb}}{1 \cdot \underset{4}{\cancel{16}} \cancel{\text{oz}}}$ Divide the common factors and units.

$= \frac{9}{4} \text{ lb} = 2\frac{1}{4} \text{ lb}$ Simplify.

There are $2\frac{1}{4}$ lb in 36 oz.

**Convert from one unit to the other.**

1. 12 fl oz = $1\frac{1}{2}$ c
2. 42 in = $3\frac{1}{2}$ ft
3. 6,600 ft = $1\frac{1}{4}$ mi
4. 5,000 lb = $2\frac{1}{2}$ t
5. $3\frac{1}{8}$c = 25 fl oz
6. $2\frac{3}{8}$lb = 38 oz
7. 2 gal 2 qt = 10 qt
8. 1 yd 2 ft = 5 ft
9. 2 ton 800 lb = 4,800 lb
10. 15 qt = $3\frac{3}{4}$ gal
11. 23 pt = $2\frac{7}{8}$ gal
12. 81 in. = $2\frac{1}{4}$ yd



## Enrichment

American Forests maintains a national Register of Big Trees. The organization lists the "National Champion" tree of each species, which is the largest known tree of that kind by total mass. The table lists ten National Champion trees that American Forests has selected as noteworthy.

1. Complete the table.

**National Champion Trees**

| Tree Type | Girth 4.5 ft from ground | | Height | | Location |
|---|---|---|---|---|---|
| | Inches | Feet | Feet | Yards | |
| American Beech | 279 | $23\frac{1}{4}$ | 115 | $38\frac{1}{3}$ | Harwood, MD |
| Black Willow | 400 | $33\frac{1}{3}$ | 76 | $25\frac{1}{3}$ | Grand Traverse County, MI |
| Coast Douglas-Fir | 438 | $36\frac{1}{2}$ | 329 | $109\frac{2}{3}$ | Coos County, OR |
| Coast Redwood | 867 | $72\frac{1}{4}$ | 313 | $104\frac{1}{3}$ | Prairie Creek, CA |
| Giant Sequoia | 998 | $83\frac{1}{6}$ | 275 | $91\frac{2}{3}$ | Sequoia National Park, CA |
| Loblolly Pine | 188 | $15\frac{2}{3}$ | 148 | $49\frac{1}{3}$ | Warren, AZ |
| Pinyon Pine | 213 | $17\frac{3}{4}$ | 69 | 23 | Cuba, NM |
| Sugar Maple | 233 | $19\frac{5}{12}$ | 87 | 29 | Kingston, NM |
| Sugar Pine | 442 | $36\frac{5}{6}$ | 232 | $77\frac{1}{3}$ | Dorrington, CA |
| White Oak | 374 | $31\frac{1}{6}$ | 79 | $26\frac{1}{3}$ | Wye Mills State Park, MD |

2. Which units were most appropriate for measuring the girth and the height of these giant trees? Explain.
Sample answer: The larger units are more appropriate, but the people at American Forests probably wanted to avoid fractions.

# MATH TOOLBOX

### Greatest Possible Error

This Math Toolbox shows how to find the greatest possible error for a measurement.

### Math Background

The numbers in abstract mathematics problems (such as 5.67 + 3.45) are exact. Numbers that result from taking a *measurement* (length, weight, volume, and so forth) are always approximate. The accuracy of the measurement increases when you use more accurate instruments, but no measurement can be exact. A *count,* on the other hand, can be exact (for example, the number of chairs in the room). Every measurement is, in effect, rounded. The *greatest possible error* in a measurement is one-half of the unit to which the measurement is rounded.

## Teaching Notes

**Error Prevention** Have two students measure the length of the same piece of paper with two different instruments (a 12-inch ruler and a yard stick, for example) to demonstrate that measurements are approximate.

**Monitoring Progress** Review the meaning of the unit abbreviations in the exercises.

**Block Scheduling** If you have block scheduling or extended periods, you may wish to insert this Math Toolbox lesson between the completion of Part 1 of Lesson 5-5 and the beginning of Part 2 of Lesson 5-5.

# MATH TOOLBOX

*Extension*

*After Lesson 5-5*

## *Greatest Possible Error*

Measurement is not exact. To the nearest centimeter, each segment at the right measures 3 cm.

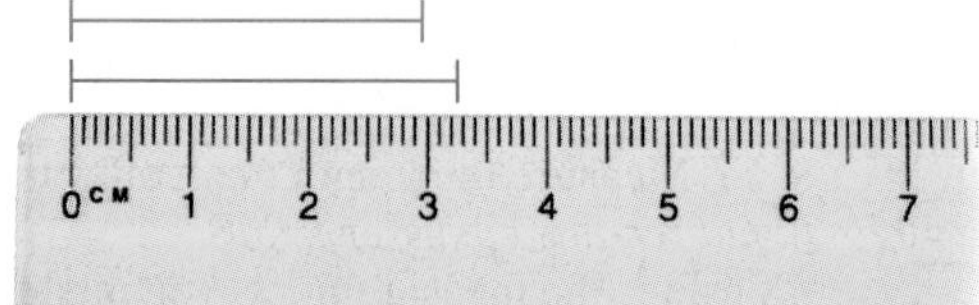


When a measurement is rounded to the nearest centimeter, it can vary from the actual length by as much as one half centimeter. The *greatest possible error* of a measurement is half the unit used for measuring.

**EXAMPLE**

**Find the greatest possible error for each measurement.**

**a. $1\frac{1}{2}$ in.** The measurement is to the nearest $\frac{1}{2}$ in.
Since $\frac{1}{2} \cdot \frac{1}{2} = \frac{1}{4}$, the greatest possible error is $\frac{1}{4}$ in.

**b. 15.6 L** The measurement is to the nearest tenth of a liter.
Since $\frac{1}{2} \cdot 0.1 = 0.05$, the greatest possible error is 0.05 L.

**c. 3.004 mm** The measurement is to the nearest 0.001 mm.
Since $\frac{1}{2} \cdot 0.001 = 0.0005$, the greatest possible error is 0.0005 mm.

**Find the greatest possible error for each measurement.**

1. 45.98 mg 0.005 mg
2. $12\frac{1}{4}$ in. $\frac{1}{8}$ in.
3. 54.4 cm 0.05 cm
4. $1\frac{3}{4}$ c $\frac{1}{8}$ c
5. 3 ft $\frac{1}{2}$ ft
6. 9 g $\frac{1}{2}$ g
7. 12.3 L 0.05 L
8. 15.575 mm 0.0005 mm
9. $24\frac{1}{2}$ yd $\frac{1}{4}$ yd
10. 500 m 50 m
11. $10\frac{1}{8}$ oz $\frac{1}{16}$ oz
12. $3\frac{1}{16}$ in. $\frac{1}{32}$ in.
13. *Geometry* A rectangle measures 12 cm by 10.5 cm. What is the greatest possible error for each measurement? 0.5 cm, 0.05 cm
14. *Carpentry* A carpenter is cutting a table leg that is $2\frac{1}{4}$ ft long.
    a. What is the greatest possible error? $\frac{1}{8}$ ft
    b. *Writing* Is the greatest possible error acceptable in this situation? Explain. No; $\frac{1}{8}$ ft is 1.5 in., an error that could cause the table to wobble.



### • Additional Example

Find the greatest possible error for each measurement.

a. 23.5 cm 0.05 cm
b. $2\frac{1}{3}$ yd $\frac{1}{6}$ yd
c. 47 in. 0.5 in.

# 5-6 Work Backward

*Math Strategies in Action* In England in the 1800s, many wealthy people had mazes made of hedges constructed in their gardens. Some of the mazes still exist today. The hedges are so high you can't see over them unless you stand on a bench. You have to remember the path you followed to get to the center of the maze and work backward to get out.

Working backward from known information will sometimes help you solve a problem.

## Sample Problem

You are planning to go to a baseball game that starts at 1:00 P.M. You want to arrive half an hour early. Your walk to the train station is about 10 minutes long. The train ride to the city takes $\frac{3}{4}$ of an hour. After you arrive in the city, you will need to walk for about 10 more minutes to get to the stadium. What time should you plan to leave?

### Read

Think about the information you are given.

1. What do you want to find? the time you should leave home
2. What is your arrival time? 12:30 P.M.
3. How much time will you spend walking to the train? 10 min
4. How much time will you spend on the train? $\frac{3}{4}$ h
5. How much time will you spend walking from the train? 10 min

**Problem Solving Strategies**

- Account for All Possibilities
- Draw a Diagram
- Look for a Pattern
- Make a Model
- Make a Table
- Simplify a Problem
- Simulate a Problem
- Solve by Graphing
- Try, Test, Revise
- Use Multiple Strategies
- Work Backward
- Write an Equation
- Write a Proportion



# 5-6

## Getting Ready

**Resources** A complete list of resources for this lesson is on p. 221H.

### Daily Skills Warm-Up

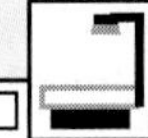

Lesson 5-6

Find each time.

1. $\frac{3}{4}$ hour before 2:00 1:15
2. $\frac{1}{2}$ hour after 3:05 3:35
3. $\frac{1}{2}$ hour before 7:10 6:40
4. $1\frac{1}{2}$ hours after 10:40 12:10
5. 38 minutes after 8:45 9:23
6. 17 minutes before 5:04 4:47

### Background for the Lesson

In many problem solving situations, it may be helpful to work backward to solve the problem. Often, these situations involve time or a known end quantity. To solve these problems, begin with what you know and then work backward to find the beginning.

## 1 Focus

### Connecting to Students' Lives

Ask students to explain how they know what time they need to wake up in the morning in order to get to school on time. Help them see that the time they wake up depends on when school starts, how long it takes to travel to school, and how long it takes to get ready to leave.

## Tools to Monitor Progress

### BEFORE THE LESSON

**To check prerequisite skills:**

- Operations with fractions

**Skills Handbook,** p. 739

**Skills Intervention Kit,** Operations with Fractions

### DURING THE LESSON

**To check understanding:**

- **Additional Sample Problem**
  a. Your flight leaves the airport at 10:00 A.M. You must arrive an hour early to check your luggage. The drive to the airport takes about 90 minutes. What time should you plan to leave home? 7:30 A.M.

# 2 Teach

One key skill for solving problems is to understand the situation before you begin to calculate. Urge students to take the time to read and read again until they have grasped the story that the problem tells. Then they may wish to use a chart to help organize the known information.

## Sample Problem

**Build understanding.** Ask: What would you have to know if the question was "Will you arrive on time?" and you were going to solve this problem by working forward? **You would need to know the time you planned to leave. The rest of the problem would stay the same.**

**Error Prevention** Students may, because they choose the incorrect operation, rush into calculation before they visualize the problem. For example, you add travel times to find out how long a trip will take, but you subtract that sum from the arrival time to find the time you should leave. Suggest that students determine which operations they should use before they begin to do calculations.

**Extension** I am thinking of a number. When you double my number and then add 5, you get 23. What is my number? **9**

**Reading Math** Students may have difficulty translating English words and phrases into mathematical operations. For example, students may not realize that, "You want to arrive half an hour early," means to subtract 30 minutes from the start of the event. Have students keep a list of words and phrases and their corresponding operations in their math journals. Encourage students to look at the list before they begin to solve a word problem.

### Plan

You know that the series of events must end at 1:00 P.M. Work backward to find when the events must begin.

### Solve

Move the hands of a clock to find your departure time.

**6.** Write the starting time for each event. **See beneath each clock.**

You should leave home at 11:25 A.M.

### Look Back

Check the departure time. Find the total time needed.

10 min + 45 min + 10 min + 30 min = 95 min

Add 95 minutes to your departure time.

```
  11: 25
+  0: 95
  11:120     120 min = 2 h
```

11:120 = 2 hours after 11:00, or 1:00 P.M.

Since the game starts at 1 P.M., your departure time is correct.



**b.** Your flight leaves the airport at 10:00 A.M. You must arrive an hour early to check your luggage. The drive to the airport takes about 90 minutes. A stop for breakfast takes about 30 minutes. It will take about 15 minutes to park and get to the terminal. What time should you plan to leave home? **6:45 A.M.**

## AFTER THE LESSON

### To assess knowledge: Lesson Quiz

Solve by working backward.

Jason has a total of 212 sheep now. Last spring, 52 lambs were born, but 9 died. How many sheep did he have before the lambs were born? **169**

- For enrichment and reteaching options see Resources on p. 221H.

# Exercises

## Check Understanding

**Work backward to solve each problem.**

1. Eduardo wants to finish mowing lawns at 3:00 P.M. on Saturday. It takes $1\frac{1}{2}$ h to mow the first lawn, and twice as long to mow the lawn next door. The lawn across the street takes $1\frac{1}{2}$ h to mow. Eduardo plans to take a $\frac{1}{2}$-h break between the second and third lawns. What time should he plan to start mowing? 8:30 A.M.
2. Siobhan's family is planning a trip to the Grand Canyon. It will take 5 h of driving. In addition, her family is planning to make three $\frac{1}{2}$-h stops. They want to arrive at 3:30 P.M. What time should they plan to leave? 9:00 A.M.
3. Korin is going to a movie. The movie begins at 1:00 P.M. She has a 15-minute walk to the bus from her home and a 5-minute walk from the bus to the movie. The bus ride takes 38 min. What is the latest bus she can take to make the movie? the 12:15 P.M. bus

| BUS DEPARTURE TIMES | |
|---|---|
| 10:10 A.M. | 12:05 P.M. |
| 10:30 A.M. | 12:15 P.M. |
| 11:00 A.M. | 12:25 P.M. |
| 11:35 A.M. | 12:40 P.M. |

## Practice and Problem Solving

**Solve using any strategy.**

4. You have two nickels, three dimes, and a quarter. Using at least one of each coin, how many different amounts of money can you make? 6 different amounts
5. *Geometry* Zach's rectangular garden measures 12 ft by 10 ft. He puts a stake in each corner and one every 2 ft along each side. How many stakes are there in all? 22 stakes



# 3 Practice/Assess

## Assignment Guide

**Core** 1–7, 10
**Extension** 8–9

Mixed Review can be assigned at any time for maintenance.

## Exercises

**Exercises 1–3** Remind students to use the same problem solving steps—Read, Plan, Solve, Look Back—that they used to solve the sample problem.

## Challenge

Work backward to find the missing portion of the equation. $\frac{■}{5} \div \frac{3}{■} = 2\frac{2}{3}$ $\frac{4}{5} \div \frac{3}{10}$; Any two factors whose product is 40 will work.

## Closure

To solve some problems, you have to work backward.

## Alternative Assessment

Ask students to write a word problem that uses their school morning routines, complete with times, that they can solve by working backward.

## Daily Cumulative Review

**Is each measurement reasonable? If not, give a reasonable measurement.** *(Lesson 5-5)*

1. A steak weighs 2 oz. no; 16 oz
2. A pencil is about 8 ft long. no; 8 in.
3. A bathtub holds about 45 pt of water. no; 45 gal
4. A door is about 3 ft wide. yes

**Find each product or quotient.** *(Lesson 5-4)*

5. $-\frac{3}{4} \div \frac{1}{2}$ $-1\frac{1}{2}$
6. $\frac{7}{8a} \cdot \frac{4}{5}$ $\frac{7}{10a}$
7. $-\frac{3}{5}\left(-\frac{7}{9}\right)$ $\frac{7}{15}$
8. $\frac{2}{r} \cdot \frac{6r}{13}$ $\frac{12}{13}$
9. $\frac{2}{5} \div \frac{3}{25}$ $3\frac{1}{3}$
10. $-\frac{7}{8} \div \frac{5}{16}$ $-2\frac{4}{5}$

**Mixed Review**

**Solve each equation.**

11. (2-5) $h + 34 = 18$ $h = -16$
12. (2-5) $c - 15 = 38$ $c = 53$
13. (2-5) $17 = b + 23$ $-6 = b$
14. (2-5) $f - 42 = 18$ $f = 60$
15. (2-5) $39 = p - 56$ $95 = p$
16. (3-5) $6.3 = m + 2.1$ $4.2 = m$
17. (3-5) $12.3 = s + 13.9$ $-1.6 = s$
18. (3-5) $k - 3.541 = 7.732$ $k = 11.273$
19. (3-5) $w - 0.034 = 0.982$ $w = 1.016$

**List all the factors of each number.**

20. (4-1) 30 1, 2, 3, 5, 6, 10, 15, 30
21. (4-1) 110 1, 2, 5, 10, 11, 22, 55, 110

**Solve each inequality.**

22. (2-9) $4.2 + c > 9.1$ $c > 4.9$
23. (2-9) $6.4 \geq d - 5.5$ $11.9 \geq d$
24. (2-9) $z + 3.9 < 4.7$ $z < 0.8$

## Practice

**Work backward to solve each problem.**

1. Manuel's term paper is due on March 31. He began doing research on March 1. He intends to continue doing research for 3 times as long as he has done already. Then he will spend a week writing the paper and the remaining 3 days typing. What day is it? (Assume he will finish typing on March 30.) March 5
2. A disc jockey must allow time for 24 minutes of commercials every hour, along with 4 minutes for news, 3 minutes for weather, and 2 minutes for public-service announcements. If each record lasts an average of 3 minutes, how many records per hour can the DJ play? 9 records per hour
3. Margaret is reading the 713-page novel *War and Peace*. When she has read twice as many pages as she has read already, she will be 119 pages from the end. What page is she on now? page 198
4. On Monday the low temperature at the South Pole dropped 9°F from Sunday's low. On Tuesday it fell another 7°, then rose 13° on Wednesday and 17° more on Thursday. Friday it dropped 8° to −50°F. What was Sunday's low temperature? −56°F
5. Each problem lists the operations performed on $n$ to produce the given result. Find $n$.
   a. Multiply by 3, add 4, divide by 5, subtract 6; result, −1. $n =$ 7
   b. Add 2, divide by 3, subtract 4, multiply by 5; result, 35. $n =$ 31
   c. Multiply by 2, add 7, divide by 17; result, 1. $n =$ 5
   d. Divide by 3, add 9, multiply by 2, subtract 12; result, 4. $n =$ −3
   e. Subtract 2, divide by 5, add 7, multiply by 3; result, 30. $n =$ 17



## Reteaching

Jody, Karl, and Kara want to buy a pizza. Jody said she can pay half the cost. Karl said he can pay $\frac{1}{3}$ of what was left after Jody paid half. Kara said she could pay the remaining $4. How much does the pizza cost?

Work backward.

Kara will pay $4. This is $\frac{2}{3}$ of what is left after Jody pays half, since Karl pays $\frac{1}{3}$ and $1 - \frac{1}{3} = \frac{2}{3}$. Let $h$ equal half the cost of the pizza.

$\frac{2}{3}h = 4$

Use try, test, revise strategy to find $h = 6$.

Thus, Jody pays $6 and Karl pays $\frac{1}{3} \cdot 6 = \$2$.

The pizza costs $6 + 2 + 4 = \$12$.

1. Steven, Lisa, and Mark want to buy a pizza. Steven said he could pay twice as much as Lisa. Mark said he could pay the remaining $3, which is $1 less than Lisa's share. How much does the pizza cost?
   a. How much is Mark paying? $3
   b. How much is Lisa paying? $4
   c. How much is Steven paying? $8
   d. How much does the pizza cost? $15
2. On Wednesday Olga's parents said she owed them too much money to borrow anymore. On Thursday, she paid her parents $15 she earned babysitting. On Friday she borrowed $5 to go to a movie. On Saturday, she paid them the $12 she earned babysitting. Then her debt was down to $22. How much did she owe on Wednesday? $44
3. Yuki, Mollie, Brandon, and Anna share an apple pie for desert. Brandon eats half the amount Mollie eats. Yuki eats four times as much pie as Brandon. Mollie eats $\frac{1}{4}$ of the pie. How much does Anna eat? $\frac{1}{8}$ of the pie



Reteaching

## Enrichment

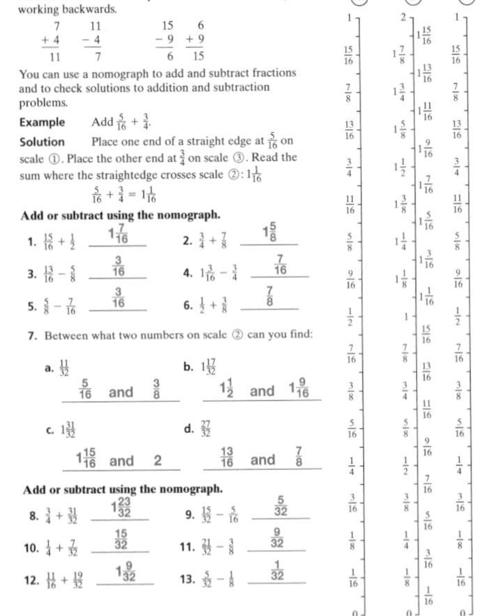

Addition and subtraction problems can be checked by working backwards.

$7 + 4 = 11$, $11 - 4 = 7$; $15 - 9 = 6$, $6 + 9 = 15$

You can use a nomograph to add and subtract fractions and to check solutions to addition and subtraction problems.

**Example** Add $\frac{5}{16} + \frac{3}{4}$.

**Solution** Place one end of a straight edge at $\frac{5}{16}$ on scale ①. Place the other end at $\frac{3}{4}$ on scale ③. Read the sum where the straightedge crosses scale ②: $1\frac{1}{16}$

$\frac{5}{16} + \frac{3}{4} = 1\frac{1}{16}$

**Add or subtract using the nomograph.**

1. $\frac{15}{16} + \frac{1}{2}$ $1\frac{7}{16}$
2. $\frac{3}{4} + \frac{7}{8}$ $1\frac{5}{8}$
3. $\frac{13}{16} - \frac{5}{8}$ $\frac{3}{16}$
4. $1\frac{3}{16} - \frac{3}{4}$ $\frac{7}{16}$
5. $\frac{5}{8} - \frac{7}{16}$ $\frac{3}{16}$
6. $\frac{1}{2} + \frac{3}{8}$ $\frac{7}{8}$
7. Between what two numbers on scale ② can you find:
   a. $\frac{11}{32}$ $\frac{5}{16}$ and $\frac{3}{8}$
   b. $1\frac{17}{32}$ $1\frac{1}{2}$ and $1\frac{9}{16}$
   c. $1\frac{31}{32}$ $1\frac{15}{16}$ and 2
   d. $\frac{27}{32}$ $\frac{13}{16}$ and $\frac{7}{8}$

**Add or subtract using the nomograph.**

8. $\frac{3}{4} + \frac{31}{32}$ $1\frac{23}{32}$
9. $\frac{15}{32} - \frac{5}{16}$ $\frac{5}{32}$
10. $\frac{1}{4} + \frac{7}{32}$ $\frac{15}{32}$
11. $\frac{21}{32} - \frac{3}{8}$ $\frac{9}{32}$
12. $\frac{11}{16} + \frac{19}{32}$ $1\frac{9}{32}$
13. $\frac{5}{32} - \frac{1}{8}$ $\frac{1}{32}$





6. You spent half of your money at the amusement park and had $15 left. How much money did you have originally? $30
7. ***Patterns*** Describe the pattern of the numbers below. Then find the next three numbers in the pattern. Start with $\frac{2}{3}$ and add $\frac{3}{4}$ repeatedly;
   $\frac{2}{3}, 1\frac{5}{12}, 2\frac{1}{6}, 2\frac{11}{12}, ■, ■, ■, \ldots$ $3\frac{2}{3}, 4\frac{5}{12}, 5\frac{1}{6}$
8. Several freshmen tried out for the school track team.
   After Round 1, $\frac{1}{2}$ of the freshmen were eliminated.
   After Round 2, $\frac{1}{3}$ of those remaining were eliminated.
   After Round 3, $\frac{1}{4}$ of those remaining were eliminated.
   After Round 4, $\frac{1}{5}$ of those remaining were eliminated.
   After Round 5, $\frac{1}{6}$ of those remaining were eliminated.
   The 10 freshmen who remained made it onto the track team. How many freshmen originally tried out? 60 freshmen
9. ***Number Sense*** Use the equation at the right and the numbers 1, 1, 1, 2, 3, 5, and 6. Make four different true equations.
   $\frac{■}{■} + \frac{■}{■} = \frac{■}{■}$
   9. Answers may vary. Sample: $\frac{1}{2} + \frac{1}{3} = \frac{5}{6}, \frac{1}{3} + \frac{1}{6} = \frac{1}{2}, \frac{3}{1} + \frac{2}{1} = \frac{5}{1}, \frac{1}{2} + \frac{3}{6} = \frac{1}{1}$.
10. Pump A can fill a tank in 12 min. Pump B can fill the same tank in 20 min.
    a. How many tanks can each pump fill in 60 min? A 5 tanks; B 3 tanks
    b. How many tanks can the two pumps fill in 60 min? 8 tanks
    c. Working together, how long would it take the two pumps to fill one tank? 7.5 min

## Mixed Review

**Simplify each expression.** ***(Lessons 5-4 and 1-9)***

11. $\frac{1}{3} \div \frac{5}{6}$ $\frac{2}{5}$
12. $1\frac{2}{3} \div 1\frac{1}{9}$ $1\frac{1}{2}$
13. $\frac{2}{5} \cdot (-20)$ −8
14. $\frac{4}{9} \cdot \frac{5}{12}$ $\frac{5}{27}$
15. $\frac{3}{4} \div 8$ $\frac{3}{32}$
16. $-\frac{1}{6} \cdot (-12)$ 2
17. $-8 \cdot 5$ −40
18. $2 \cdot 3 \cdot (-4) \cdot 5$ −120
19. $-1(-1)$ 1
20. $-56 \div 8$ −7
21. $100 \div (-2)$ −50
22. $-100 \div (-10)$ 10
23. ***Estimation*** You want to buy three shirts for $15.95 each. Estimate the total cost of the shirts. ***(Lesson 3-2)*** about $48

## Chapter Project 5 — Activity 2 Creating

Shoes come in whole and half sizes. Shoe sizes for men and women are different, however. For shoes of equal length, a woman's shoe is one size larger than a man's shoe. Make a chart that compares men's and women's shoe sizes, including half sizes, from 1 to 15.



### Project Activity 2

**Creating** Discuss the importance of clear and complete labels on a chart, so that the reader can understand the information that the chart contains. You may want to ask if any students are familiar with European shoe sizes.

# Solving Equations by Adding or Subtracting Fractions

5-7

## What You'll Learn

1. To solve equations by subtracting fractions
2. To solve equations by adding fractions

## ... And Why

To solve equations in real-world situations, such as recycling

## PART 1 Using Subtraction to Solve Equations

You solve equations with fractions the same way you solve equations with integers and decimals, by using inverse operations.

REAL-WORLD  CONNECTION

### EXAMPLE 1

**_Recycling_ In 1995 the average household in the United States recycled about $\frac{1}{4}$ of its solid waste. The Environmental Protection Agency (EPA) has set a goal of recycling about $\frac{1}{3}$ of solid waste. By how much would the average U.S. household need to increase its recycling to meet the EPA goal?**

| | | | | | |
|---|---|---|---|---|---|
| **Words** | fraction U.S. households recycle | plus | the increase | is | EPA goal |
| | Let $n$ = the increase. | | | | |
| **Equation** | $\frac{1}{4}$ | $+$ | $n$ | $=$ | $\frac{1}{3}$ |

$$\frac{1}{4} + n = \frac{1}{3}$$

$$\frac{1}{4} - \frac{1}{4} + n = \frac{1}{3} - \frac{1}{4} \quad \text{Subtract } \tfrac{1}{4} \text{ from each side.}$$

$$n = \frac{4 \cdot 1 - 3 \cdot 1}{3 \cdot 4} \quad \text{Use } 3 \cdot 4 \text{ as the common denominator.}$$

$$n = \frac{4 - 3}{12} \quad \text{Use the Order of Operations.}$$

$$n = \frac{1}{12} \quad \text{Simplify.}$$

To meet the EPA goal, the average U.S. household needs to recycle $\frac{1}{12}$ more of its waste.

**Check** Is the answer reasonable? The present fraction of solid waste that is recycled plus the increase must equal the goal. Since $\frac{1}{4} + \frac{1}{12} = \frac{3}{12} + \frac{1}{12} = \frac{4}{12} = \frac{1}{3}$, the answer is reasonable.

In 1996, people in the United States generated 209.7 million tons of solid waste, or 4.3 lb per person per day. The same year, 57.3 million tons of solid waste were recycled, or 1.2 lb per person per day.

SOURCE: Environmental Protection Agency

**TRY THIS** Solve and check each equation.

1. $y + \frac{8}{9} = \frac{5}{9}$ $-\frac{1}{3}$
2. $\frac{2}{3} = u + \frac{3}{5}$ $\frac{1}{15}$
3. $c + \frac{3}{10} = \frac{11}{15}$ $\frac{13}{30}$



# Tools to Monitor Progress

## BEFORE THE LESSON

**To check prerequisite skills:**

- Solving equations

**Skills You Need,** p. 221

**Skills Handbook,** p. 739

**Skills Intervention Kit,** Pre-Algebra Basics

## DURING THE LESSON

**To check understanding:**

**Try This** exercises on student page

- **Additional Example 1**

One school recycles about $\frac{1}{3}$ of its waste paper. The student council set a goal of recycling $\frac{3}{4}$ of the school's waste paper by the end of the year. By how much does the school need to increase its paper recycling to reach the goal? $\frac{5}{12}$

# 5-7

## Getting Ready

**Resources** A complete list of resources for this lesson is on p. 221H.

## Daily Skills Warm-Up

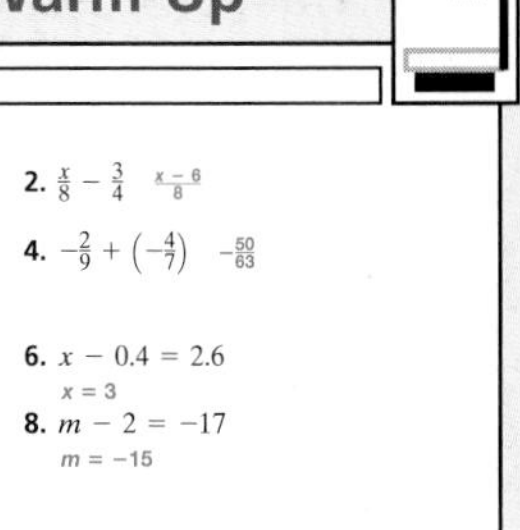

**Lesson 5-7**

Add or subtract.

1. $2\frac{1}{5} + \frac{3}{10}$ $2\frac{1}{2}$
2. $\frac{x}{8} - \frac{3}{4}$ $\frac{x-6}{8}$
3. $1\frac{2}{3} - \frac{5}{6}$ $\frac{5}{6}$
4. $-\frac{2}{9} + \left(-\frac{4}{7}\right)$ $-\frac{50}{63}$

Solve each equation.

5. $x + 9 = 4$ $x = -5$
6. $x - 0.4 = 2.6$ $x = 3$
7. $y + 0.27 = 0.15$ $y = -0.12$
8. $m - 2 = -17$ $m = -15$

## Background for the Lesson

Inverse operations are operations that undo each other. To solve an equation involving addition, such as $x + 5 = 9$, use the inverse operation, subtraction, to isolate the variable and get it alone on one side of the equal sign.

$$x + 5 = 9$$
$$x + 5 - 5 = 9 - 5$$
$$x = 4$$

For equations that have a number subtracted from the variable, add that number to each side of the equation to isolate the variable.

# 1 Focus

## Connecting to Students' Lives

Example 1 in this lesson involves recycling. Ask students about the recycling facilities available in your city. Discuss how students can recycle at home or buy recycled products.

## Connecting to Prior Knowledge

In Lesson 5-3, students learned to add and subtract fractions. In this lesson, students solve equations by adding or subtracting fractions. In Lesson 5-8, they will solve equations by multiplying fractions.

# 2 Teach

## Part 1 Teaching Notes

Have students review the steps they could use to solve the equation $3 + x = 7$. Point out that they can use these same steps when the equation involves fractions.

### Example 1

**Build understanding.** Ask: How can you tell that the value of the variable in this equation will be a proper fraction? The sum is a fraction less than 1.

## Part 2 Teaching Notes

Help students see the pattern in using subtraction to solve equations involving addition and using addition to solve equations involving subtraction.

### Example 2

**Build understanding.** Ask: How would you solve the equation if it were written as $-\frac{3}{4} + n = -\frac{5}{8}$? You would still add $\frac{3}{4}$ to both sides.

### Example 3

**Build understanding.** Explain why you do not need to rewrite the mixed numbers as improper fractions before you add them. You can add mixed numbers by first adding the fractional parts and then adding the whole number parts.

**Extension** When you solve equations containing fractions, will the value of the variable always be a fraction? Explain your reasoning. No; for example, in the equation $x - \frac{1}{3} = \frac{2}{3}$, $x = 1$.

**Error Prevention** When solving equations with fractions, students may lose track of operation signs while they concentrate on finding the LCD. Tell students to make sure they write the operation signs before they find the LCD when they add or subtract the same number from each side of the equation.

## Using Addition to Solve Equations

You can use addition to solve equations involving subtraction.

### Example 2

**Solve $n - \frac{3}{4} = -\frac{5}{8}$.**

| | |
|---|---|
| $n - \frac{3}{4} = -\frac{5}{8}$ | |
| $n - \frac{3}{4} + \frac{3}{4} = -\frac{5}{8} + \frac{3}{4}$ | Add $\frac{3}{4}$ to each side. |
| $n = \frac{-5 \cdot 4 + 8 \cdot 3}{8 \cdot 4}$ | Use $8 \cdot 4$ as the common denominator. |
| $n = \frac{-20 + 24}{32}$ | Use the Order of Operations. |
| $n = \frac{\cancel{4}^{1}}{\cancel{32}_{8}}$ | Divide the common factors. |
| $n = \frac{1}{8}$ | Simplify. |

**Try This** Solve and check each equation.

**4.** $a - \frac{3}{5} = \frac{1}{5}$ $\frac{4}{5}$

**5.** $\frac{6}{7} = x - \frac{2}{7}$ $1\frac{1}{7}$

You can use the same methods for equations with mixed numbers.

### Example 3

**Solve $p - 1\frac{3}{5} = 2\frac{1}{4}$.**

| | |
|---|---|
| $p - 1\frac{3}{5} = 2\frac{1}{4}$ | |
| $p - 1\frac{3}{5} + 1\frac{3}{5} = 2\frac{1}{4} + 1\frac{3}{5}$ | Add $1\frac{3}{5}$ to each side. |
| $p = \frac{9}{4} + \frac{8}{5}$ | Write mixed numbers as improper fractions. |
| $p = \frac{9 \cdot 5 + 4 \cdot 8}{4 \cdot 5}$ | Use $4 \cdot 5$ as the common denominator. |
| $p = \frac{45 + 32}{20}$ | Use the Order of Operations. |
| $p = \frac{77}{20}$ | Simplify. |
| $p = 3\frac{17}{20}$ | Write as a mixed number. |

**Try This** Solve and check each equation.

**6.** $c - 2\frac{1}{6} = 5\frac{1}{4}$ $7\frac{5}{12}$

**7.** $3\frac{7}{18} = z - 1\frac{1}{3}$ $4\frac{13}{18}$



- **Additional Example 2**

Solve $x - \frac{2}{3} = \frac{1}{9}$. $x = \frac{7}{9}$

- **Additional Example 3**

Solve $q - 6\frac{1}{2} = -1\frac{3}{5}$. $q = 4\frac{9}{10}$

## AFTER THE LESSON

**To assess knowledge:**

**Lesson Quiz**

Solve the following equations.

1. $\frac{3}{7} + s = \frac{13}{21}$ $s = \frac{4}{21}$
2. $k + \frac{2}{5} = \frac{7}{9}$ $k = \frac{17}{45}$
3. $u - \frac{1}{12} = \frac{3}{4}$ $u = \frac{5}{6}$
4. $-\frac{5}{11} + g = \frac{19}{22}$ $g = 1\frac{7}{22}$
5. $x - 2\frac{1}{3} = -4\frac{4}{15}$ $x = -1\frac{14}{15}$

- For enrichment and reteaching options see Resources on p. 221H.

# Exercises

## Check Understanding

**Solve each equation.**

**1.** $a - \frac{1}{8} = \frac{5}{8}$ $\frac{3}{4}$

**2.** $t - \frac{2}{3} = \frac{4}{9}$ $1\frac{1}{9}$

**3.** $c - \frac{9}{10} = \frac{1}{3}$ $1\frac{7}{30}$

**4.** $x + 1\frac{1}{4} = 4\frac{3}{4}$ $3\frac{1}{2}$

**5.** $5\frac{1}{4} = w + 2\frac{1}{2}$ $2\frac{3}{4}$

**6.** $y + 4\frac{7}{8} = 2$ $-2\frac{7}{8}$

**7.** *Health* At the end of the school year Jamie's height was $62\frac{1}{2}$ in. During the school year she had grown $1\frac{5}{8}$ inches. What was her height at the beginning of the school year? $60\frac{7}{8}$ in.

## Practice and Problem Solving

*Mental Math* **Solve each equation.**

**8.** $b + \left(-\frac{4}{5}\right) = 6$ $6\frac{4}{5}$

**9.** $z - 7\frac{5}{9} = -7\frac{5}{9}$ 0

**10.** $g - \frac{9}{10} = -\frac{7}{10}$ $\frac{1}{5}$

**11.** $c - 2\frac{1}{12} = 3\frac{1}{12}$ $5\frac{1}{6}$

**12.** $10\frac{1}{2} = x + 1\frac{1}{2}$ 9

**13.** $a + \frac{3}{5} = \frac{4}{5}$ $\frac{1}{5}$

**Solve each equation.**

**14.** $m - \frac{3}{4} = \frac{1}{4}$ 1

**15.** $p - 3\frac{2}{3} = 1\frac{1}{3}$ 5

**16.** $n - \frac{5}{8} = 6\frac{1}{3}$ $6\frac{23}{24}$

**17.** $a - \frac{5}{8} = \frac{7}{12}$ $1\frac{5}{24}$

**18.** $1\frac{3}{8} = b + 2\frac{1}{6}$ $-\frac{19}{24}$

**19.** $y - 4\frac{7}{8} = \frac{3}{4}$ $5\frac{5}{8}$

**20.** $k + 2\frac{1}{9} = 1\frac{1}{3}$ $-\frac{7}{9}$

**21.** $\frac{5}{16} = c + \frac{3}{16}$ $\frac{1}{8}$

**22.** $t + \frac{1}{4} = \frac{5}{9}$ $\frac{11}{36}$

**23.** $f + 4\frac{5}{12} = 5\frac{3}{8}$ $\frac{23}{24}$

**24.** $g + 8\frac{4}{9} = 3\frac{1}{6}$ $-5\frac{5}{18}$

**25.** $n + \frac{5}{8} = -3$ $-3\frac{5}{8}$

**26.** $h + 2\frac{1}{2} = 5\frac{7}{10}$ $3\frac{1}{5}$

**27.** $6\frac{1}{4} = a + \frac{5}{8}$ $5\frac{5}{8}$

**28.** $2\frac{1}{16} = d + 5\frac{7}{16}$ $-3\frac{3}{8}$

*Number Sense* **Without solving each equation, tell whether $x$ is *positive, negative,* or *equal to zero*. Justify your reasoning.** 29–34. Explanations may vary. Sample explanations are given.

✪**29.** $x + \frac{1}{2} = \left(-3\frac{4}{5}\right)$ Negative; otherwise the sum would be positive

✪**30.** $x + 2\frac{9}{11} = 2\frac{9}{11}$ See below.

✪**31.** $x - 5\frac{7}{9} = 6\frac{1}{4}$ See below.

**32.** $x + \frac{9}{10} = \frac{1}{2}$ Negative; the sum is less than $\frac{9}{10}$.

**33.** $x + 4\frac{1}{5} = 5\frac{1}{2}$ Positive; the sum is greater than $4\frac{1}{5}$.

✪**34.** $x + \left(-\frac{3}{4}\right) = -3\frac{3}{4}$ Negative; the sum is less than $-\frac{3}{4}$.

**35.** **TEST PREP** A tree is $10\frac{1}{2}$ ft tall. Which equation can you use to find the height of the tree before last spring's growth of 8 in.? A

**A.** $t + \frac{8}{12} = 10\frac{1}{2}$ **B.** $t - \frac{8}{12} = 10\frac{1}{2}$ **C.** $t + 10\frac{1}{2} = \frac{8}{12}$ **D.** $t - 10\frac{1}{2} = \frac{8}{12}$

30. Zero; the value is unchanged.

31. Positive; otherwise the difference would be negative.



# 3 Practice/Assess

## Assignment Guide

To provide flexible scheduling, this lesson can be divided into parts.

▼ **Part 1**

**Core** 4–6, 8, 12–13, 18, 20–28, 32–33, 35–36, 38

✪ **Extension** 29–30, 39, 40

▼ **Part 2**

**Core** 1–3, 7, 9–11, 14–17, 19, 37, 41

✪ **Extension** 31, 34

Mixed Review can be assigned at any time for maintenance.

## Exercises

**Auditory Learning Exercises 8–13** Mental math may be easier if they think or say "I need to add . . . to each side."

**Test Prep Exercise 35** Notice that there are two different units in this problem, feet and inches.

## ✪ Challenge

Explain why you cannot solve the following equation by adding or subtracting the same number from each side. $\frac{x}{2} = -\frac{3}{4}$; There is no addition or subtraction in this equation to undo with the inverse operation.

## Closure

To solve equations with fractions, use inverse operations to undo addition or subtraction. You can undo multiplication by multiplying each side of the equation by the reciprocal of the variable's coefficient.

## Daily Cumulative Review

**Work backward to solve each problem.** *(Lesson 5-6)*

1. Your family is planning a 6-hour car trip. Along the way, you are planning to make four twenty-minute rest stops and a lunch stop for forty-five minutes. At what time should you leave home to arrive at your destination by 5:00 P.M.? 8:55 A.M.
2. After shopping at the mall you had $6.90 left from your birthday money. You spent $5.80 at the food court, $3.10 at the card shop, and $14.95 on a shirt. How much money did you get for your birthday? $30.75

**Use estimation, mental math, or paper and pencil to convert from one unit to the other.** *(Lesson 5-5)*

**3.** 6 c = 3 pt **4.** 5,000 lb = $2\frac{1}{2}$ t **5.** 80 fl oz = 10 c

**6.** 22 qt = $5\frac{1}{2}$ gal **7.** 2 mi = 10,560 ft **8.** 2 ft 3 in. = 27 in.

**9.** $2\frac{1}{3}$ yd = 84 in. **10.** 20 pt = 40 c **11.** 2 lb = 32 oz

**Mixed Review**

**Solve each equation.**

**12.** (2-6) $5x = 45$ $x = 9$

**13.** (2-6) $-10b = 100$ $b = -10$

**14.** (2-6) $\frac{n}{3} = 12$ $n = 36$

**15.** (2-6) $-6 = \frac{d}{8}$ $-48 = d$

**16.** (2-6) $72 = 9m$ $8 = m$

**17.** (3-6) $0.036s = 0.072$ $s = 2$

**18.** (3-6) $-4.5 = \frac{b}{2.3}$ $-10.35 = b$

**19.** (3-6) $-0.202k = 0.404$ $k = -2$

**20.** (3-6) $0.3w = 9.09$ $w = 30.3$

**In which quadrant or on which axis does each ordered pair lie?**

**21.** (1-10) (21, −56) IV **22.** (1-10) (0, −34) y-axis **23.** (1-10) (|−12|, 5) I

**Compare. Use >, <, or = to complete each statement.**

**24.** (1-2) $(15 - 3) \cdot 3$ > $15 - 3 \cdot 3$ **25.** (1-2) $14 - 2 + 7$ > $14 - (2 + 7)$



## Alternative Assessment

Have students write a comparison of adding or subtracting to solve equations with rational numbers and adding or subtracting to solve equations with integers. Hint: Integers can be written as rational numbers.

## Practice

**Solve each equation.**

1. $m - \left(-\frac{7}{10}\right) = -1\frac{1}{5}$ $-1\frac{9}{10}$
2. $k - \frac{3}{4} = \frac{2}{5}$ $1\frac{3}{20}$
3. $x - \frac{5}{6} = \frac{1}{10}$ $\frac{14}{15}$
4. $t - \left(-3\frac{1}{6}\right) = 7\frac{2}{3}$ $4\frac{1}{2}$
5. $x + \frac{5}{8} = \frac{7}{8}$ $\frac{1}{4}$
6. $k + \frac{4}{5} = 1\frac{3}{5}$ $\frac{4}{5}$
7. $4 = \frac{4}{9} + y$ $3\frac{5}{9}$
8. $h + \left(-\frac{5}{8}\right) = -\frac{5}{12}$ $\frac{5}{24}$
9. $n + \frac{2}{3} = \frac{1}{9}$ $-\frac{5}{9}$
10. $e - \frac{11}{16} = -\frac{7}{8}$ $-\frac{3}{16}$
11. $w - 14\frac{1}{12} = -2\frac{3}{4}$ $11\frac{1}{3}$
12. $v + \left(-4\frac{5}{6}\right) = 2\frac{1}{3}$ $7\frac{1}{6}$
13. $a - 9\frac{1}{6} = -3\frac{19}{24}$ $5\frac{3}{8}$
14. $f + \left|-3\frac{11}{12}\right| = 18$ $14\frac{1}{12}$
15. $z + \left(-3\frac{2}{5}\right) = -4\frac{1}{10}$ $-\frac{7}{10}$
16. $x - \frac{7}{15} = \frac{7}{60}$ $\frac{7}{12}$
17. $h - \left(-6\frac{1}{2}\right) = 14\frac{1}{4}$ $7\frac{3}{4}$
18. $p - 5\frac{3}{8} = -\frac{11}{24}$ $4\frac{11}{12}$

**Solve each equation using mental math.**

19. $x + \frac{3}{7} = \frac{5}{7}$ $\frac{2}{7}$
20. $k - \frac{8}{9} = -\frac{1}{9}$ $\frac{7}{9}$
21. $a + \frac{1}{9} = \frac{3}{9}$ $\frac{2}{9}$
22. $g - \frac{4}{5} = -\frac{2}{5}$ $\frac{2}{5}$

**Write an equation to solve each problem.**

23. Pete's papaya tree grew $3\frac{7}{12}$ ft during the year. If its height at the end of the year was $21\frac{1}{6}$ ft, what was its height at the beginning of the year?
    $h + 3\frac{7}{12} = 21\frac{1}{6}$; $h = 17\frac{7}{12}$ ft
24. Lee is $1\frac{3}{4}$ ft taller than Jay. If Lee is $6\frac{1}{4}$ ft tall, how tall is Jay?
    $h + 1\frac{3}{4} = 6\frac{1}{4}$; $h = 4\frac{1}{2}$ ft



Practice

## Reteaching

Solve $h - 2\frac{3}{4} = -3\frac{1}{6}$.

| | |
|---|---|
| $h - 2\frac{3}{4} = -3\frac{1}{6}$ | |
| $h - 2\frac{3}{4} + 2\frac{3}{4} = -3\frac{1}{6} + 2\frac{3}{4}$ | Add $2\frac{3}{4}$ to each side. |
| $h = -3\frac{2}{12} + 2\frac{9}{12}$ | Use a common denominator. |
| $h = -2\frac{14}{12} + 2\frac{9}{12}$ | Rename $-3\frac{2}{12}$ as $-2\frac{14}{12}$. |
| $h = -\frac{5}{12}$ | Subtract $2\frac{14}{12} - 2\frac{9}{12}$. The sum is negative because $\left\|-3\frac{1}{6}\right\| > \left\|2\frac{3}{4}\right\|$ |

**Solve each equation.**

1. $h + \frac{3}{4} = \frac{7}{8}$ $h = \frac{1}{8}$
2. $e + 1\frac{13}{16} = 2\frac{5}{16}$ $e = \frac{1}{2}$
3. $m + \frac{5}{8} = -\frac{3}{16}$ $m = -\frac{13}{16}$
4. $p - 4\frac{5}{12} = 2\frac{7}{12}$ $p = 7$
5. $x - \frac{5}{9} = \frac{5}{6}$ $x = 1\frac{7}{18}$
6. $y - \frac{7}{8} = -\frac{15}{16}$ $y = -\frac{1}{16}$
7. $h + 2\frac{1}{2} = -1\frac{1}{4}$ $h = -3\frac{3}{4}$
8. $n - 3\frac{2}{5} = -1\frac{7}{10}$ $n = 1\frac{7}{10}$
9. $f + 4\frac{3}{8} = 2\frac{1}{3}$ $f = -2\frac{1}{24}$
10. $b - 1\frac{2}{5} = 1\frac{4}{7}$ $b = 2\frac{34}{35}$



## Enrichment

Mount Everest, at 29,028 ft, is the highest mountain in the world. Mount Everest is 6,194 ft higher than the highest mountain in the Western Hemisphere.

1. Write and solve an equation to find the height $h$ of the highest mountain in the Western Hemisphere.
   $h + 6{,}194 = 29{,}028$; $h = 22{,}834$ ft

   What is the name of this mountain and what country is it in? To find out, solve each equation. Then write the variable on the line above its value below.

2. $R + \frac{7}{12} = \frac{3}{8}$ $R = -\frac{5}{24}$
3. $T - \frac{6}{7} = \frac{1}{2}$ $T = 1\frac{5}{14}$
4. $N - \frac{2}{3} = \frac{2}{5}$ $N = 1\frac{1}{15}$
5. $A + \frac{1}{2} = \frac{1}{7}$ $A = -\frac{5}{14}$
6. $E + 1\frac{2}{3} = -2\frac{1}{6}$ $E = -3\frac{5}{6}$
7. $C - 1\frac{1}{2} = -\frac{7}{8}$ $C = \frac{5}{8}$
8. $G - 3\frac{4}{5} = -4\frac{1}{8}$ $G = -\frac{13}{40}$
9. $I + 2\frac{3}{4} = 1\frac{1}{10}$ $I = -1\frac{13}{20}$
10. $O + 4\frac{1}{6} = 1\frac{2}{9}$ $O = -2\frac{17}{18}$
11. $U - 6\frac{2}{5} = 3\frac{3}{4}$ $U = 10\frac{3}{20}$
12. $A - 2\frac{5}{6} = -1\frac{3}{8}$ $A = 1\frac{11}{24}$
13. $N + 2\frac{4}{7} = 3\frac{1}{6}$ $N = \frac{25}{42}$
14. $C + 3\frac{5}{7} = 2\frac{4}{7}$ $C = -1\frac{1}{7}$
15. $A - \frac{9}{16} = -\frac{5}{12}$ $A = \frac{7}{48}$

| A | C | O | N | C | A | G | U | A |
|---|---|---|---|---|---|---|---|---|
| $\frac{7}{48}$ | $-1\frac{1}{7}$ | $-2\frac{17}{18}$ | $1\frac{1}{15}$ | $\frac{5}{8}$ | $-\frac{5}{14}$ | $-\frac{13}{40}$ | $10\frac{3}{20}$ | $\frac{7}{48}$ |

| A | R | G | E | N | T | I | N | A |
|---|---|---|---|---|---|---|---|---|
| $1\frac{11}{24}$ | $-\frac{5}{24}$ | $-\frac{13}{40}$ | $-3\frac{5}{6}$ | $\frac{25}{42}$ | $1\frac{5}{14}$ | $-1\frac{13}{20}$ | $\frac{25}{42}$ | $1\frac{11}{24}$ |



Enrichment



**Write an equation to solve each problem.**

36. A restaurant chef needs $8\frac{1}{2}$ lb of salmon. To get a good price, she buys more than she needs. She ends up with $4\frac{7}{8}$ lb too much. How much salmon did she buy? $13\frac{3}{8}$ lb

In 1998, the average weight of an Alaskan Coho salmon was about $7\frac{9}{10}$ lb.

SOURCE: ADF&G Commercial Fisheries

37. *Carpentry* A carpenter used $3\frac{3}{16}$ lb of nails for a job. After the job was over, the remaining nails weighed $1\frac{1}{16}$ lb. How many pounds of nails did the carpenter have at the beginning of the job? $4\frac{1}{4}$ lb

38. A cookie recipe calls for $1\frac{1}{4}$ c of oatmeal. You have $\frac{3}{8}$ c of oatmeal. How much more oatmeal do you need? $\frac{7}{8}$ c

39. *Environment* During a recent wet spell, the water level in Jasper's Pond rose $2\frac{3}{4}$ in. The depth of the pond was then 10 ft 3 in. What was the depth of the water in the pond before the wet spell? 10 ft $\frac{1}{4}$ in.

40. *Writing* Write a problem that you could solve with the equation $y + \frac{1}{2} = 7$. Solve the problem. Check students' work; $6\frac{1}{2}$.

41. *Error Analysis* Below is a student's work for solving the equation $x - \left(-\frac{1}{2}\right) = 3$. What is the student's error?

$$x - \left(-\tfrac{1}{2}\right) = 3$$
$$x - \left(-\tfrac{1}{2}\right) + \tfrac{1}{2} = 3 + \tfrac{1}{2}$$
$$x = 3\tfrac{1}{2}$$

The student added $\frac{1}{2}$ instead of $-\frac{1}{2}$ on each side of the equation.

**Journal**

*How is solving an equation with fractions similar to solving one with decimals?*

### MIXED REVIEW

**Complete each statement.** *(Lesson 5-5)*

42. $2\frac{2}{3}$ ft = 32 ■ in.
43. $1\frac{1}{2}$ ■ = 12 fl oz c
44. 9 pt = $4\frac{1}{2}$ ■ qt
45. $\frac{1}{2}$ ■ = $\frac{1}{4}$ qt pt
46. 750 lb = $\frac{3}{8}$ ■ t
47. $1\frac{2}{3}$ ■ = 5 ft yd

**Solve each equation.** *(Lesson 3-6)*

48. $3.5t = 8.75$ 2.5
49. $\frac{b}{4} = -38$ −152
50. $y \div 7.5 = -3.75$ −28.125
51. $1.7x = 8.5$ 5

52. a. *Jobs* Your job is to paint $\frac{1}{4}$ of the lockers in the school. Your friend agrees to share the job equally with you. What fraction of the lockers will each of you paint? $\frac{1}{8}$
    b. If the job of painting all of the lockers in the school pays \$1,100, how much will you earn? *(Lesson 5-4)* \$137.50



See also Extra Practice section.

# Solving Equations by Multiplying Fractions

5-8

## PART 1 Using Multiplication to Solve Equations

You know how to undo multiplication by dividing each side of an equation by the same number. You can also multiply each side of an equation by the same fraction to undo multiplication.

### EXAMPLE 1

**Solve $5a = \frac{1}{7}$.**

$5a = \frac{1}{7}$

$\frac{1}{5} \cdot (5a) = \frac{1}{5} \cdot \frac{1}{7}$ Multiply each side by $\frac{1}{5}$, the reciprocal of 5.

$a = \frac{1}{35}$ Simplify.

**TRY THIS** Solve each equation.

1. $8x = \frac{5}{7}$ $\frac{5}{56}$
2. $2y = \frac{7}{9}$ $\frac{7}{18}$
3. $3a = \frac{4}{5}$ $\frac{4}{15}$

When fractions have common factors, you can simplify before multiplying.

### EXAMPLE 2

**Solve $\frac{4}{5}m = \frac{9}{10}$.**

$\frac{4}{5}m = \frac{9}{10}$

$\frac{5}{4} \cdot \frac{4}{5}m = \frac{5}{4} \cdot \frac{9}{10}$ Multiply each side by $\frac{5}{4}$, the reciprocal of $\frac{4}{5}$.

$m = \frac{^{1}5}{4} \cdot \frac{9}{10_{2}}$ Divide common factors.

$m = \frac{9}{8}$ Simplify.

$m = 1\frac{1}{8}$ Write as a mixed number.

**TRY THIS** Solve each equation.

4. $\frac{2}{9}t = \frac{5}{6}$ $\frac{15}{4}$, or $3\frac{3}{4}$
5. $\frac{3}{4}s = \frac{8}{9}$ $\frac{32}{27}$, or $1\frac{5}{27}$
6. $\frac{5}{4}d = \frac{5}{4}$ 1

### What You'll Learn

1. To solve equations by multiplying fractions
2. To solve equations by multiplying mixed numbers

### ... And Why

To solve equations with fractions in real-world situations, such as carpentry



# Tools to Monitor Progress

## BEFORE THE LESSON

**To check prerequisite skills:**

- Solving equations

**Skills You Need,** p. 221

**Skills Handbook,** p. 740

**Skills Intervention Kit,** Pre-Algebra Basics

## DURING THE LESSON

**To check understanding:**

**Try This** exercises on student page

- **Additional Example 1**
  Solve $\frac{1}{3} = 7y$. $y = \frac{1}{21}$
- **Additional Example 2**
  Solve $\frac{13}{15} = \frac{2}{5}w$. $w = 2\frac{1}{6}$
- **Additional Example 3**
  Solve $-\frac{20}{27}c = \frac{4}{9}$. $c = -\frac{3}{5}$

# 5-8

## Getting Ready

**Resources** A complete list of resources for this lesson is on p. 221H.

### Daily Skills Warm-Up

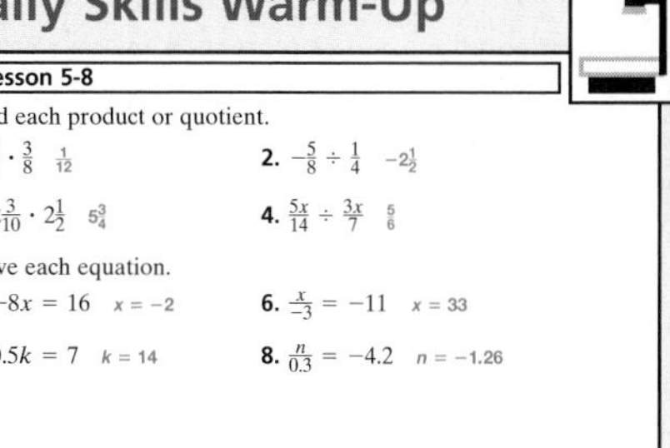

Lesson 5-8

Find each product or quotient.

1. $\frac{2}{9} \cdot \frac{3}{8}$ $\frac{1}{12}$
2. $-\frac{5}{8} \div \frac{1}{4}$ $-2\frac{1}{2}$
3. $2\frac{3}{10} \cdot 2\frac{1}{2}$ $5\frac{3}{4}$
4. $\frac{5x}{14} \div \frac{3x}{7}$ $\frac{5}{6}$

Solve each equation.

5. $-8x = 16$ $x = -2$
6. $\frac{x}{-3} = -11$ $x = 33$
7. $0.5k = 7$ $k = 14$
8. $\frac{n}{0.3} = -4.2$ $n = -1.26$

### Background for the Lesson

In the equation $2x = \frac{1}{3}$, you can ask "What has been done to $x$?" The answer is that $x$ has been multiplied by 2. To isolate the variable and undo what has been done, you can divide by 2 (since multiplication and division are inverse operations). However, dividing by 2 is the same as multiplying by $\frac{1}{2}$.

Two quantities that are reciprocals, such as $\frac{1}{a}$ and $\frac{a}{1}$, multiply to give a product of 1 (when $a \neq 0$). In the equation $2x = \frac{1}{3}$, you can multiply both sides by $\frac{1}{2}$ to undo the multiplication by 2, since $\frac{1}{2}$ is the reciprocal of 2. The result is that $x = \frac{1}{6}$.

## 1 Focus

### Connecting to Prior Knowledge

Students learned that dividing rational numbers is the same as multiplying by reciprocals in Lesson 5-4. In this lesson, students learn that they can use reciprocals to undo multiplication when they solve equations.

# 2 Teach

## Part 1 Teaching Notes

Remind students that dividing by 5 is the same as multiplying by $\frac{1}{5}$.

### Example 1

**Build understanding.** Ask: Why not multiply both sides of the equation by $\frac{1}{a}$? You need to isolate the variable, not the 5.

### Example 2

**Build understanding.** Ask: What does it mean when multiplied fractions have common factors? You can divide the numerator and denominator by any common factor before you multiply.

**Error Prevention** Students tend to use incorrectly the same steps in Example 2 (when they divide the numerator and denominator by 5) when the problem involves addition of fractions. Point out here that you could not divide common factors if the problem were $\frac{5}{4} + \frac{9}{10}$. Make sure students understand that this works in multiplication because you multiply fractions by multiplying the numerators and multiplying the denominators. You do not add fractions in this same way, so in addition you cannot do this division of common factors to simplify.

### Example 3

**Build understanding.** Explain why the reciprocal of a negative fraction must also be negative. The product of reciprocals is 1, which is positive. The product of any two negative numbers is positive.



Remember, the reciprocal of a negative fraction is also negative.

### EXAMPLE 3

**Solve $-\frac{14}{25}k = \frac{8}{15}$.**

$-\frac{14}{25}k = \frac{8}{15}$

$-\frac{25}{14}\left(-\frac{14}{25}k\right) = -\frac{25}{14}\left(\frac{8}{15}\right)$ Multiply each side by $-\frac{25}{14}$, the reciprocal of $-\frac{14}{25}$.

$k = -\frac{{}^{5}\cancel{25} \cdot \cancel{8}^{4}}{{}_{7}\cancel{14} \cdot \cancel{15}_{3}} = -\frac{20}{21}$ Divide common factors and simplify.

**TRY THIS** Solve each equation.

**7.** $-\frac{6}{7}r = \frac{3}{4}$ $-\frac{7}{8}$ **8.** $-\frac{10}{13}b = -\frac{2}{3}$ $\frac{13}{15}$ **9.** $-6n = \frac{3}{7}$ $-\frac{1}{14}$

## Part 2 Solving Equations with Mixed Numbers

To solve equations involving mixed numbers, change them to improper fractions before multiplying.

REAL-WORLD CONNECTION

### EXAMPLE 4

*Carpentry* **Your teacher needs a shelf to hold a set of textbooks each $1\frac{5}{8}$ in. wide. How many books fit on a 26-in.-long shelf?**

| Words | width of each book | times | the number of books | is | width of bookshelf |
|---|---|---|---|---|---|
| | Let $n$ = the number of books. | | | | |
| Equation | $1\frac{5}{8}$ | $\cdot$ | $n$ | $=$ | $26$ |

$1\frac{5}{8} \cdot n = 26$

$\frac{13}{8}n = 26$ Write $1\frac{5}{8}$ as $\frac{13}{8}$.

$\frac{8}{13} \cdot \frac{13}{8}n = \frac{8}{13} \cdot 26$ Multiply each side by $\frac{8}{13}$, the reciprocal of $\frac{13}{8}$.

$n = \frac{8 \cdot \cancel{26}^{2}}{{}_{1}\cancel{13} \cdot 1} = 16$ Divide common factors and simplify.

Your teacher can fit 16 books on the shelf.

**TRY THIS** Solve each equation.

**10.** $3\frac{1}{2}n = 28$ 8 **11.** $1\frac{1}{6}r = -\frac{7}{20}$ $-\frac{3}{10}$ **12.** $-2\frac{3}{4}h = -12\frac{1}{2}$ $4\frac{6}{11}$



- **Additional Example 4**
How many $2\frac{1}{2}$ t trucks can be placed on a rail car that has a carrying capacity of 15 t? 6

## AFTER THE LESSON

**To assess knowledge:**
**Lesson Quiz**

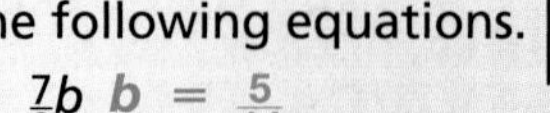

Solve the following equations.

**1.** $\frac{5}{16} = \frac{7}{8}b$ $b = \frac{5}{14}$

**2.** $-\frac{25}{32}g = \frac{5}{8}$ $g = -\frac{4}{5}$

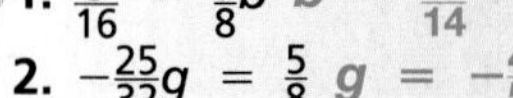

**3.** $15 = -3\frac{6}{13}m$ $m = -4\frac{1}{3}$

- For enrichment and reteaching options see Resources on p. 221H.

# Exercises

## Check Understanding

**Solve each equation.**

1. $\frac{5}{8} = 6p$ $\frac{5}{48}$
2. $\frac{1}{5}x = \frac{2}{3}$ $3\frac{1}{3}$
3. $\frac{2}{3}k = \frac{5}{6}$ $1\frac{1}{4}$
4. $\frac{7}{8}z = 3\frac{1}{2}$ 4
5. $\frac{8}{9} = -6d$ $-\frac{4}{27}$
6. $2\frac{1}{3}m = \frac{7}{12}$ $\frac{1}{4}$
7. $\frac{1}{15} = -1\frac{1}{10}t$ $-\frac{2}{33}$
8. $-1\frac{6}{7}g = -\frac{13}{15}$ $\frac{7}{15}$
9. *Construction* A sheet of plywood is $\frac{3}{4}$ in. thick. Write and solve an equation to find how many sheets of plywood are in a stack 9 in. high. $\frac{3}{4}s = 9$; 12 sheets

## Practice and Problem Solving

*Mental Math* **Solve each equation.**

10. $8d = 16$ 2
11. $\frac{1}{3}y = 2$ 6
12. $\frac{5}{8} = \frac{5}{8}k$ 1
13. $\frac{3}{7}x = 1$ $\frac{7}{3}$ or $2\frac{1}{3}$
14. $-\frac{2}{3}t = -2$ 3
15. $-5s = \frac{5}{7}$ $-\frac{1}{7}$
16. $3 = 1\frac{1}{2}b$ 2
17. $2\frac{1}{2}x = \frac{2}{5}$ $\frac{4}{25}$

**Solve each equation.**

18. $7c = \frac{3}{4}$ $\frac{3}{28}$
19. $9y = \frac{5}{7}$ $\frac{5}{63}$
20. $\frac{5}{9} = \frac{1}{8}h$ $\frac{40}{9}$ or $4\frac{4}{9}$
21. $\frac{1}{7}x = \frac{4}{7}$ 4
22. $\frac{3}{4}d = \frac{3}{8}$ $\frac{1}{2}$
23. $\frac{10}{27} = \frac{5}{9}t$ $\frac{2}{3}$
24. $\frac{2}{7}a = \frac{5}{8}$ $2\frac{3}{16}$
25. $-\frac{1}{9}p = \frac{5}{6}$ $-7\frac{1}{2}$
26. $-\frac{5}{7}x = \frac{9}{10}$ $-1\frac{13}{50}$
27. $\frac{9}{13} = -\frac{6}{11}s$ $-1\frac{7}{26}$
28. $\frac{2}{3}x = -8$ $-12$
29. $-3b = \frac{2}{3}$ $-\frac{2}{9}$
30. $-\frac{12}{13} = -\frac{1}{4}w$ $3\frac{9}{13}$
31. $2\frac{1}{8}k = 7$ $3\frac{5}{17}$
32. $3\frac{1}{9}a = \frac{3}{7}$ $\frac{27}{196}$
33. $1\frac{1}{2}n = 3\frac{4}{9}$ $2\frac{8}{27}$
34. $2\frac{3}{4} = -6\frac{3}{5}y$ $-\frac{5}{12}$
35. $1\frac{1}{2}m = 1\frac{3}{4}$ $1\frac{1}{6}$
36. $-9\frac{1}{3} = -1\frac{1}{4}t$ $7\frac{7}{15}$
37. $3\frac{3}{5}p = -4\frac{4}{9}$ $-1\frac{19}{81}$

*Number Sense* **Without solving each equation, tell whether $x$ is *positive, negative,* or *equal to zero.* Justify your reasoning.** 38–45. See below for explanations.

38. $17x = -\frac{11}{30}$ neg.
39. $\frac{1}{57}x = 2$ pos.
40. $\frac{4}{13}x = 0$ zero
41. $-\frac{3}{4}x = -6$ pos.
42. $\frac{5}{8}x = -1\frac{1}{2}$ neg.
43. $\frac{-5}{-7}x = -\frac{3}{5}$ neg.
44. $3\frac{1}{2}x = -7$ neg.
45. $-6\frac{1}{2}x = 0$ zero
46. *Critical Thinking* By what would you multiply each side of the equation $ax = 27$ to solve for $x$? By what would you multiply each side of the equation $\frac{1}{a}x = 27$ to solve for $x$? $\frac{1}{a}$; $a$

38, 42–44. Product involving different signs is negative.

39, 41. Product involving same sign is positive, e.g. $-6$ and $-\frac{4}{3}$.

40, 45. Product involving zero is zero.



## Part 2 Teaching Notes

Review writing mixed numbers as improper fractions. Remind students that an improper fraction is a fraction with a numerator greater than the denominator. Although this fraction is called *improper*, it is a perfectly *proper* answer to a problem. In algebra, answers are often left as improper fractions instead of being rewritten as mixed numbers.

### Example 4

**Build understanding.** Explain why the improper fraction is *not* the reciprocal of the mixed number. The improper fraction is *equivalent* to the mixed number, not the reciprocal of it.

**Auditory Learning** Have one student read aloud an equation. Have a partner say the reciprocal for multiplying each side to undo the multiplication of the variable.

**Error Prevention** Students may forget to exchange the numerator and denominator when writing reciprocals. Tell students to verify that the reciprocals do have a product of 1.

**Extension** What are the only two numbers that are their own reciprocals? 1 and −1

# 3 Practice/Assess

## Assignment Guide

To provide flexible scheduling, this lesson can be divided into parts.

▼ **Part 1**

**Core** 1–3, 9–15, 18–30, 47–48, 50, 52, 55–56

✪ **Extension** 38–41, 43, 46, 53

▼ **Part 2**

**Core** 4–8, 16–17, 31–37, 49, 54

✪ **Extension** 42, 44–45, 51

Mixed Review can be assigned at any time for maintenance.

## Exercises

**Test Prep Exercise 55** Two answer choices, A and B, can be eliminated immediately because their solutions are negative.

## ✪ Challenge

Solve. Give the answer in the form of a mixed number. $1.35x = 9$. $x = 6\frac{2}{3}$

## Closure

To solve equations with fractions, use inverse operations to undo addition or subtraction. You can undo multiplication by multiplying each side of the equation by the reciprocal of the coefficient of the variable. Change mixed numbers to improper fractions before multiplying.

**Use the article below for Exercises 47 and 48.**

### Paper Recycling on the Rise

During the 1990s, recycling in the United States steadily increased. In 1996, people in the United States recycled about nine twentieths of their paper waste. This amounted to 42.3 million tons of paper, or about 295 lb/person. Only one year earlier, Americans recycled just over two fifths of their paper waste, a total of about 32.7 million tons of paper.

**47.** Solve the equation $\frac{2}{5}p = 32.7$ to find the amount of paper waste produced in the United States in 1995. 81.75 million tons

**48.** Write and solve an equation to find the amount of paper waste produced in the United States in 1996. $\frac{9}{20}p = 42.3$; 94 million tons

**Write an equation to solve each probem.**

**49.** *Biology* In ideal conditions, the kudzu plant can grow at least $1\frac{3}{20}$ ft per week. At this rate, how many weeks would it take a kudzu plant to grow 23 ft? 20 weeks

A native of China and Japan, kudzu was brought to the United States in 1876. Left alone, it grows over trees, telephone poles, and abandoned houses and cars.

**50.** *Weather* Based on annual rainfall, about $\frac{18}{25}$ in. of rain falls each day in Buenaventura, Colombia. At this rate, in how many days does 8 in. of rain fall? about 11 days

✪ **51.** A sailfish can swim about $11\frac{1}{3}$ mi in 10 min. About how many miles can a sailfish swim per minute? At that speed, about how many miles can a sailfish swim per hour? $1\frac{2}{15}$ mi; 68 mi

**52.** *Astronomy* The Chandra satellite telescope views X-rays in space. It orbits as much as 87,000 miles above Earth. This is about $\frac{1}{3}$ of the distance to the moon. About how far away is the moon? 261,000 mi

✪ **53.** A small airplane coming in for a landing descends $\frac{5}{66}$ mi/min. About how long does it take to descend 4,000 ft? (*Hint:* 1 mi = 5,280 ft) 10 min

**54.** *Error Analysis* A student solved the equation $-\frac{7}{10}h = 5\frac{3}{5}$ and found the solution 8. What was the student's error? The student forgot the negative sign.

**55.** **TEST PREP** Which equation has a solution greater than 1? C

A. $-5x = \frac{5}{8}$ B. $-\frac{5}{8}x = 5$ C. $\frac{5}{8}x = 5$ D. $5x = \frac{5}{8}$

**56.** *Writing* Describe how you would solve the equation $\frac{2}{3}x = 3x$. Answers may vary. Sample: Subtract $\frac{2}{3}x$ from each side to get $0 = 2\frac{1}{3}x$. The solution must be 0.



## Alternative Assessment

Ask students to write a jingle or mnemonic device to help them remember the procedures to follow when solving equations by using reciprocals.

## Daily Cumulative Review

**Solve each equation.** *(Lesson 5-7)*

1. $t - \frac{2}{3} = \frac{1}{3}$ $t = 1$
2. $k + \frac{4}{5} = 1\frac{7}{15}$ $k = \frac{2}{3}$
3. $y - 3\frac{6}{7} = \frac{9}{14}$ $y = 4\frac{1}{2}$
4. $\frac{3}{4} = x + \frac{5}{16}$ $\frac{7}{16} = x$
5. $a - \frac{1}{3} = \frac{5}{9}$ $a = \frac{8}{9}$
6. $m + 5\frac{2}{11} = 6\frac{21}{22}$ $m = 1\frac{17}{22}$

**Work backward to solve the problem.** *(Lesson 5-6)*

7. Jamie brought pizzas to the party. There were $1\frac{1}{2}$ pizzas left over. The pizzas were each cut into 8 pieces. Jamie ate 4 pieces, Sarah ate 2 pieces, Mike ate 5 pieces, Mitzi ate 3 pieces, Jake ate 4 pieces, and Mandy ate 2 pieces. How many pizzas did Jamie bring? 4 pizzas

**Mixed Review**

**Complete each equation.**

8. (4-7) $(5^4)^{3} = 5^{12}$
9. (4-7) $(n^{4})^8 = n^{32}$
10. (4-7) $(a^5)^{7} = a^{35}$

**Evaluate each expression.**

11. (4-2) $a^4$, for $a = -3$ 81
12. (4-2) $2s^3$, for $s = 3$ 54
13. (4-2) $(-m)^5$, for $m = 2$ −32

**Simplify each expression.**

14. (4-8) $\frac{13^6}{13^4}$ 169
15. (4-8) $\frac{a^3}{a^6}$ $\frac{1}{a^3}$
16. (4-8) $\frac{35b^7c^8}{7b^6c^2}$ $5bc^6$

**Find the mean, median, and mode. Round to the nearest tenth where necessary. Identify any outliers.**

17. (3-3) 6 5 10 6 4 5 6 6
Mean 6 Median 6 Mode 6 Outliers 10

18. (3-3) 7.8 6.9 7.1 1.1 7 7.1 6.8
Mean 6.3 Median 7 Mode 7.1 Outliers 1.1

## MIXED REVIEW

**Solve each equation or inequality.** ***(Lessons 5-7 and 2-9)***

57. $j + \frac{3}{4} = \frac{7}{8}$ $\frac{1}{8}$
58. $\frac{4}{5} < y - \frac{3}{5}$ $y > 1\frac{2}{5}$
59. $6\frac{1}{2} = m + 2\frac{7}{8}$ $3\frac{5}{8}$
60. $t - 1\frac{1}{2} \geq -\frac{5}{6}$ $t \geq \frac{2}{3}$

**Simplify each expression.** ***(Lessons 4-7 and 4-8)***

61. $3r \cdot r^4$ $3r^5$
62. $\frac{6x^3}{2x}$ $3x^2$
63. $10s^2 \cdot 10s^3$ $100s^5$
64. $\frac{20a^5}{4a^2}$ $5a^3$
65. $x^3 \cdot x^{10}$ $x^{13}$
66. One bag of popcorn holds $1\frac{5}{8}$ oz. Another holds $1\frac{3}{4}$ oz. Which bag holds more popcorn, and how much more? ***(Lesson 5-3)*** The $1\frac{3}{4}$ oz bag holds $\frac{1}{8}$ oz more.

## CHECKPOINT 2 — Lessons 5-4 through 5-8

**Multiply or divide.**

1. $\frac{2}{3}(21)$ 14
2. $\frac{4}{5} \cdot \frac{5}{8}$ $\frac{1}{2}$
3. $-\frac{4}{9}\left(\frac{1}{3}\right)$ $-\frac{4}{27}$
4. $\frac{2}{5} \div \frac{3}{10}$ $1\frac{1}{3}$
5. $-\frac{3}{4} \div \frac{3}{8}$ $-2$
6. $8\frac{1}{2} \div \frac{1}{4}$ 34

**Complete each statement.**

7. ■ t = 4,500 lb $2\frac{1}{4}$
8. $2\frac{1}{2}$ yd = ■ in. 90
9. 24 oz = ■ lb $1\frac{1}{2}$
10. ■ mi = 1,760 ft $\frac{1}{3}$

**Solve each equation.**

11. $y + \frac{2}{5} = \frac{3}{5}$ $\frac{1}{5}$
12. $t - \frac{3}{4} = \frac{7}{8}$ $1\frac{5}{8}$
13. $x - 4\frac{1}{2} = 6\frac{3}{4}$ $11\frac{1}{4}$
14. $5\frac{1}{3} + v = -12$ $-17\frac{1}{3}$
15. $\frac{5}{7}y = \frac{1}{3}$ $\frac{7}{15}$
16. $4t = \frac{24}{35}$ $\frac{6}{35}$
17. $-\frac{8}{9}g = \frac{3}{5}$ $-\frac{27}{40}$
18. $\frac{9}{10} = \frac{1}{4}w$ $3\frac{3}{5}$
19. *Choose a Strategy* You spend $\frac{1}{3}$ of your money on lunch. Your friend then pays back a loan of \$2.50. Later, you spend \$4 on a movie ticket and \$1.25 for a snack. You have \$5.25 left. How much money did you have before lunch? \$12
20. *Open-ended* Describe an object you might measure using the customary system of measurement. Choose a unit of measure and estimate the measurement of the object using that unit. Check students' work.

## ACTIVITY 3 INVESTIGATING

Measure the length of your shoe to the nearest $\frac{1}{4}$ in. Calculate the size of your shoe, using $L$ as the length of your shoe. Compare your calculation to the size on the label of your shoe.

| Finding Shoe Sizes |
|---|
| Women's shoe sizes |
| $3L - 23\frac{3}{4}$ |
| Men's shoe sizes |
| $3L - 24\frac{3}{4}$ |



### Project Activity 3

**Investigating** Students will need rulers or yard sticks for this activity. You may want to have them work in pairs, because some shoes may be too worn to have a legible label. Be aware that some students may be sensitive about their shoe size. Encourage students to compare their measures to the chart and the shoe label rather than among each other.

### Checkpoint

**Multiply or divide.**

1. $-\frac{5}{12} \cdot \frac{6}{7}$ $-\frac{5}{14}$
2. $\frac{4}{7} \div \frac{2}{21}$ 6
3. $6\frac{1}{4} \div \frac{5}{6}$ $7\frac{1}{2}$

**Complete each statement.**

4. 3.75 t = 7,500 lb
5. 15 in. = $1\frac{1}{4}$ ft

**Solve each equation.**

6. $y + \frac{3}{8} = \frac{5}{8}$ $y = \frac{1}{4}$
7. $t - 1\frac{3}{5} = \frac{9}{10}$ $t = 2\frac{1}{2}$
8. $-\frac{2}{3}x = \frac{4}{5}$ $x = -1\frac{1}{5}$
9. $\frac{6}{11} = \frac{3}{4}k$ $k = \frac{8}{11}$
10. You are playing tug-of-war at a class picnic. When the game begins, you move forward 5 ft, then back 12 ft, then forward 4 ft. You end up 14 ft from the center line. Where were you at the start of the game? 11 ft from the center line



### Practice

**Solve each equation.**

1. $\frac{3}{4}x = \frac{9}{16}$ $x = \frac{3}{4}$
2. $-\frac{1}{3}p = \frac{1}{4}$ $p = -\frac{3}{4}$
3. $\frac{-3}{8}k = \frac{1}{2}$ $k = -1\frac{1}{3}$
4. $\frac{1}{8}h = \frac{1}{10}$ $h = \frac{4}{5}$
5. $2\frac{2}{3}e = \frac{1}{18}$ $e = \frac{1}{48}$
6. $-1\frac{2}{7}m = 6$ $m = -4\frac{2}{3}$
7. $-\frac{1}{4}p = \frac{1}{18}$ $p = -\frac{2}{9}$
8. $\frac{11}{-12}w = -1$ $w = 1\frac{1}{11}$
9. $-3\frac{4}{7}x = 0$ $x = 0$
10. $\frac{2}{3}m = 2\frac{2}{9}$ $m = 3\frac{1}{3}$
11. $5c = \frac{2}{3}$ $c = \frac{2}{15}$
12. $-8k = \frac{4}{5}$ $k = -\frac{1}{10}$
13. $\frac{4}{7}y = 4$ $y = 7$
14. $2\frac{1}{4}f = \frac{6}{5}$ $f = \frac{8}{15}$
15. $\frac{10}{11}n = \frac{2}{11}$ $n = \frac{1}{5}$
16. $\frac{7}{8}c = \frac{7}{6}$ $c = 1\frac{1}{3}$

**Solve each equation using mental math.**

17. $7d = 42$ $d = 6$
18. $\frac{1}{4}y = 5$ $y = 20$
19. $-3h = \frac{3}{8}$ $h = -\frac{1}{8}$
20. $\frac{1}{5}k = -\frac{1}{3}$ $k = -1\frac{2}{3}$

**Write an equation to solve each problem.**

21. It takes Nancy $1\frac{2}{3}$ min to read 1 page in her social studies book. It took her $22\frac{1}{2}$ min to complete her reading assignment. How long was the assignment? Let $m$ represent the number of pages she read. $1\frac{2}{3}m = 22\frac{1}{2}$; $m = 13\frac{1}{2}$ pages
22. It takes Gary three hours to drive to Boston. If the trip is 156 miles, what is Gary's average number of miles per hour? Let $x$ represent the miles per hour. $3x = 156$; $x = 52$ mi/h



### Reteaching

Solve $-4\frac{2}{5}x = 1\frac{1}{10}$.

$-4\frac{2}{5}x = 1\frac{1}{10}$

$-\frac{22}{5}x = \frac{11}{10}$ — Write $-4\frac{2}{5}$ as $-\frac{22}{5}$ and $1\frac{1}{10}$ as $\frac{11}{10}$

$-\frac{5}{22} \cdot \frac{-22}{5}x = -\frac{5}{22} \cdot \frac{11}{10}$ — Multiply each side by $-\frac{5}{22}$, the reciprocal of $-\frac{22}{5}$

$x = -\frac{5}{22} \cdot \frac{11}{10} = -\frac{1}{4}$ — Divide common factors and simplify.

**Solve each equation.**

1. $8x = 12$ $x = 1\frac{1}{2}$
2. $\frac{1}{2}x = \frac{3}{4}$ $x = 1\frac{1}{2}$
3. $-\frac{4}{5}y = -\frac{1}{3}$ $y = \frac{5}{12}$
4. $5h = -\frac{10}{11}$ $h = -\frac{2}{11}$
5. $-\frac{3}{14}j = -1\frac{2}{7}$ $j = 6$
6. $\frac{4}{5}p = 2\frac{3}{10}$ $p = 2\frac{7}{8}$
7. $1\frac{3}{7}m = \frac{6}{7}$ $m = \frac{3}{5}$
8. $-\frac{5}{9}n = 2\frac{2}{3}$ $n = -4\frac{4}{5}$
9. $4\frac{1}{2}x = 5\frac{5}{8}$ $x = 1\frac{1}{4}$
10. $-1\frac{2}{3}k = 4\frac{1}{6}$ $k = -2\frac{1}{2}$

Reteaching



### Enrichment

In music notation, the duration of a note (the length of time it is intended to last) is indicated by its shape.

𝅝 = whole  𝅗𝅥 = half note  ♩ = quarter note
♪ = eighth note  𝅘𝅥𝅯 = sixteenth note  𝅘𝅥𝅰 = thirty-second note

The durations of notes are determined relative to one another.

**Example** The duration of the half note is 1 second. Find the durations of the other notes.

**Solution** ♩ = $\frac{1}{2}$𝅗𝅥 = $\frac{1}{2} \cdot 1$ s = $\frac{1}{2}$ s
𝅝 = 2𝅗𝅥 = $2 \cdot 1$ s = 2 s

At the beginning of a piece of music the composer indicates with a symbol the number of one type of note to be played in one minute.

♩ = 180: Play 180 quarter notes in 60 s
Duration of quarter note = $\frac{60}{180} = \frac{1}{3}$ s

**Write the fractional duration of each note, in seconds, in the spaces to the right. Let ♪ = 120.**

1. $\frac{1}{2}$ s  $\frac{1}{2}$ s  1 s  2 s
2. $\frac{1}{4}$ s  $\frac{1}{4}$ s  $\frac{1}{8}$ s  $\frac{1}{8}$ s  $\frac{1}{8}$ s  $\frac{1}{8}$ s  1 s  2 s
3. Suppose that ♩ = 80 appeared at the beginning of the music in Exercises 1 and 2.
   a. Find the duration of a quarter note. $\frac{3}{4}$ s
   b. Find the duration of the music in Exercise 1. 3 s

Placing a dot after a note increases its duration by one-half.

**Example** Let duration of ♩ = $\frac{1}{5}$ s.

**Solution** Duration of ♩. = $\frac{1}{5} + \left(\frac{1}{2} \cdot \frac{1}{5}\right) = \frac{1}{5} + \frac{1}{10} = \frac{3}{10}$ s.

4. ♪ = 240. Find the duration of the note in seconds.

♪ $\frac{1}{4}$ s  ♩ $\frac{1}{2}$ s  ♪. $\frac{3}{8}$ s
𝅗𝅥. $1\frac{1}{2}$ s  𝅘𝅥𝅯. $\frac{3}{32}$ s  ♩. $\frac{3}{4}$ s

## Standardized Test Prep

Standardized tests, such as those administered for state assessment, SAT9, TerraNova™, ITBS, MAT7, or CAT5, may include multiple choice questions, free-response questions, and open-ended questions.

**Multiple Choice Questions** are followed usually by four choices, one of which is correct.

**Exercises 1–6** are multiple choice questions.

**Free-Response Questions** do not give answer choices. Student must provide the one correct answer on their own.

**Exercises 7–8** are free-response questions.

**Open-Ended Questions** allow for more than one solution. Students must construct their own responses instead of choosing from possible answers.

**Exercise 9** is an open-ended question.

### Resources

See p. 221G for a list of assessment options.

### Test-Taking Tip

In Exercise 2, use math reasoning to eliminate all but one of the equations without having to calculate the actual number of water stations.

### Test-Taking Tips on Transparency

Sometimes, it is easiest to compute mentally.

*Example* Find the next number in this pattern.

20, 15, 10, 5, 0, −5, . . .

A. −1 B. −10 C. 0 D. Not Here

To find the pattern, mentally compute how the terms change.

20 15 10 5 0 −5
−5 −5 −5 −5 −5

To find each term, subtract 5 from the previous term.

−5 − 5 = −10

The answer is −10, or choice B

Use mental math to find the answer. Explain your reasoning.

1. What are the next two numbers in this pattern?

$\frac{1}{4}$, 1, 4, 16, . . .

A. 64, 128 B. 28, 50 C. 64, 256 D. Not Here

2. Which of the following number patterns has the rule: divide each number by 2 to obtain the next number?

F. 4, 2, 0, −2, . . . G. 320, 40, 8, $\frac{8}{5}$, . . .

H. 40, 10, $\frac{5}{2}$, $\frac{5}{8}$, . . . J. 20, 10, 5, $\frac{5}{2}$, . . .



# Standardized Test Prep

## Multiple Choice

**Choose the best answer.**

1. Use the line graph below. Which statement is true? A

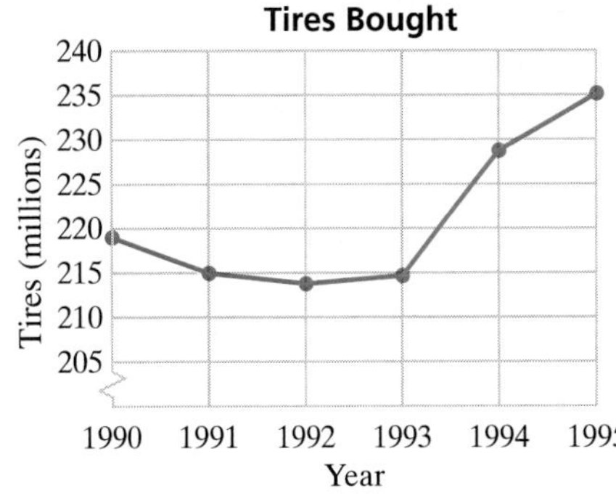


SOURCE: *Statistical Abstract of the United States*

A. The greatest increase was between 1993 and 1994.
B. The least decrease was between 1993 and 1994.
C. The most car tires were bought in 1992.
D. There were fewer tires bought in 1994 than in 1990.

2. Which equation would you use to solve the following problem? J

A walkathon route is 20 mi long. There is a water station every $1\frac{1}{4}$ mi. How many water stations $w$ are along the route?

F. $20w = 1\frac{1}{4}$
G. $w - 1\frac{1}{4} = 20$
H. $1\frac{1}{4} + w = 20$
J. $1\frac{1}{4}w = 20$

3. The price of one share of a stock is $16\frac{3}{8}$. What is the price in decimal form? C

A. 16.38 B. 16.83
C. 16.375 D. 16.335

4. A recipe for soup includes 1 pt of tomato juice. Suppose Martin plans to double the recipe. How many cups of tomato juice does he need? H

F. 1 c G. 2 c H. 4 c J. 8 c

5. Michael drove at 30 mi/h for $\frac{1}{2}$ h, and 50 mi/h for 1 h. Find his mean speed to the nearest mile per hour. B

A. 40 mi/h B. 43 mi/h
C. 45 mi/h D. 47 mi/h

6. Suppose you are building a tree house. You have a board that is 6 ft $5\frac{3}{4}$ in. long, but you need one 5 ft $6\frac{1}{2}$ in. long. How much should you cut off? F

F. $11\frac{1}{4}$ in. G. $11\frac{3}{4}$ in.
H. $12\frac{3}{4}$ in. J. $13\frac{1}{4}$ in.

## Free Response

**For Exercises 7–9, show your work.**

7. Shana had $40 before she went shopping. She bought three books for $7.24 each including tax, and a pair of earrings for $8.99, including tax. How much money did she have left at the end of her shopping trip? $9.29

8. What is the area of the shaded region in the figure below? 36 in.$^2$

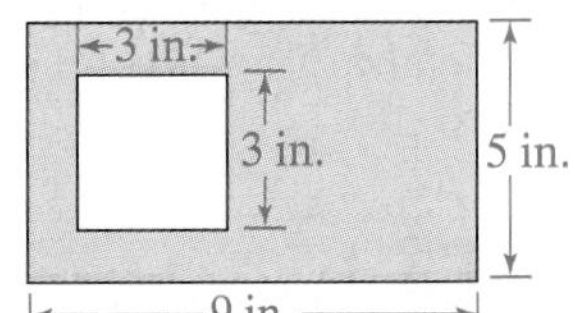


9. *Open-ended* Find two fractions for which the product is greater than 1 and the quotient is less than 1. Answers may vary. Sample: $\frac{1}{2}$, $\frac{5}{2}$

# Powers of Products and Quotients

## Part 1 Finding Powers of Products

You can use the Commutative and Associative Properties of Multiplication to find a pattern in products raised to a power.

| | |
|---|---|
| $(4 \cdot 2)^3 = (4 \cdot 2) \cdot (4 \cdot 2) \cdot (4 \cdot 2)$ | Write the factors. |
| $= 4 \cdot 4 \cdot 4 \cdot 2 \cdot 2 \cdot 2$ | Use the Commutative Property to arrange the factors. |
| $= (4 \cdot 4 \cdot 4) \cdot (2 \cdot 2 \cdot 2)$ | Use the Associative Property to group the factors. |
| $= 4^3 \cdot 2^3$ | Write the powers. |

This result suggests a rule for simplifying products raised to a power.

**Rule for Raising a Product to a Power**

To raise a product to a power, raise each factor to the power.

| Arithmetic | Algebra |
|---|---|
| $(5 \cdot 3)^4 = 5^4 \cdot 3^4$ | $(ab)^m = a^m b^m$, for any positive integer $m$ |

Remember, to simplify an expression, you write it with no like terms or parentheses.

### Example 1

**Simplify $(4x^2)^3$.**

| | |
|---|---|
| $(4x^2)^3 = 4^3 \cdot (x^2)^3$ | Raise each factor to the power 3. |
| $= 4^3 \cdot x^{2 \cdot 3}$ | Use the Rule for Raising a Power to a Power. |
| $= 4^3 \cdot x^6$ | Multiply exponents. |
| $= 64x^6$ | Simplify. |

**Try This** Simplify each expression.

1. $(2(3))^3$ 216
2. $(2p)^4$ $16p^4$
3. $(xy^2)^5$ $x^5y^{10}$
4. $(5x^3)^2$ $25x^6$

5-9

**What You'll Learn**

1. To find powers of products
2. To find powers of quotients

**. . . And Why**

To extend your knowledge of the properties of exponents

**Quick Review**

$2^3 = 2 \cdot 2 \cdot 2$ (2 is the base; 3 is the exponent)

**Quick Review**

$(a^m)^n = a^{m \cdot n}$



# Tools to Monitor Progress

**BEFORE THE LESSON**

**To check prerequisite skills:**

- Using exponents

**Skills Intervention Kit,** Pre-Algebra Basics

**DURING THE LESSON**

**To check understanding:**

**Try This** exercises on student page

- **Additional Example 1**
  Simplify $(3z^5)^4$. $81z^{20}$
- **Additional Example 2**
  a. Simplify $(-3a)^4$. $81a^4$
  b. Simplify $-(3a)^4$. $-81a^4$

# 5-9

## Getting Ready

**Resources** A complete list of resources for this lesson is on p. 221H.

### Daily Skills Warm-Up

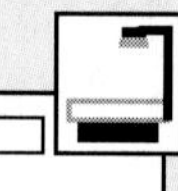

**Lesson 5-9**

Simplify each expression.

1. $x^3 \cdot x^7$ $x^{10}$
2. $\frac{x^8}{x}$ $x^7$
3. $\frac{m^5n^2}{m^2n^4}$ $\frac{m^3}{n^2}$
4. $p^{-7}$ $\frac{1}{p^7}$

Evaluate each expression for $a = -5$ and $b = 2$

5. $a^2b$ 50
6. $4b^2 - 7$ 9
7. $(3b - 7)^8$ 1
8. $-b^2$ $-4$

### Background for the Lesson

You can rewrite the expression $(5x^2)^3$ as $(5x^2)(5x^2)(5x^2)$ which is the same as $5^3x^6$. When you raise a quantity, such as $(5x^2)$, to a power, such as $^3$, each factor in the quantity is affected by the power. In $(ab^3)^5$, you write each factor in $ab^3$ five times and then multiply to find the product. An efficient way to express this relationship is to say that you multiply the powers when you raise a power to a power.

## 1 Focus

### Connecting to Students' Lives

Ask students if they have ever seen exponents used outside of the math classroom. Any situation that involves area (units$^2$) and volume (units$^3$) also involves exponents.

### Connecting to Prior Knowledge

In Lesson 4-2, students learned how to find powers using exponents. In this lesson, students expand their knowledge of exponents by using exponents to find the powers of products and quotients.

# 2 Teach

## Part 1 Teaching Notes

Remind students that they can expand a simple example, such as writing $(5x^2)^3$ as $(5x^2)(5x^2)(5x^2)$ and then as $125x^6$, to verify that they have remembered the rules correctly.

### Example 1

**Build understanding.** Ask: How do you know that $(x^2)^3$ is $x^6$? $(x^2)^3$ means $(x^2)(x^2)(x^2)$, which is $x$ used as a factor 6 times.

### Example 2

**Build understanding.** Ask: Why is $(-5)^2$ positive? $(-5)^2 = (-5)(-5)$ or 25

**Error Prevention** Students may assume from Example 2 that any negative number raised to any power is positive. Help them see with examples that a negative number raised to an even power will be positive, and a negative number raised to an odd power will be negative.

## Part 2 Teaching Notes

Show students that finding the powers of quotients is similar to finding the powers of products. Stress to students the importance of using the exponent for both the numerator and denominator.

### Example 3

**Build understanding.** Ask: What would the area be if the side length were $\frac{3}{b^2}$? $\frac{9}{b^4}$

**Extension** Simplify $\left(a^2\frac{b}{c}\right)^2$. $a^4\frac{b^2}{c^2}$

The location of a negative sign affects the value of an expression.

**EXAMPLE 2**

**a. Simplify $(-5x)^2$.**

$(-5x)^2 = (-5)^2(x)^2$
$= 25x^2$

**b. Simplify $-(5x)^2$.**

$-(5x)^2 = (-1)(5x)^2$
$= (-1)(5)^2(x)^2$
$= -25x^2$

**TRY THIS** Simplify each expression.

**5.** $(-2y)^4$ $16y^4$ **6.** $-(2y)^4$ $-16y^4$ **7.** $(-5a^2b)^3$ $-125a^6b^3$

## PART 2 Finding Powers of Quotients

**Reading Math**

You read $\left(\frac{2}{3}\right)^5$ as "two thirds to the fifth power." You read $\frac{2}{3^5}$ as "two divided by three to the fifth power."

You can use repeated multiplication to write a power of a quotient.

$$\left(\frac{4}{5}\right)^3 = \left(\frac{4}{5}\right)\left(\frac{4}{5}\right)\left(\frac{4}{5}\right) = \frac{4 \cdot 4 \cdot 4}{5 \cdot 5 \cdot 5} = \frac{4^3}{5^3}$$

**Raising a Quotient to a Power**

To raise a quotient to a power, raise both the numerator and denominator to the power.

| Arithmetic | Algebra |
|---|---|
| $\left(\frac{2}{3}\right)^4 = \frac{2^4}{3^4}$ | $\left(\frac{a}{b}\right)^m = \frac{a^m}{b^m}$, for $b \neq 0$ and any positive integer $m$ |

**GEOMETRY CONNECTION**

**EXAMPLE 3**

**Find the area of the square tile.**

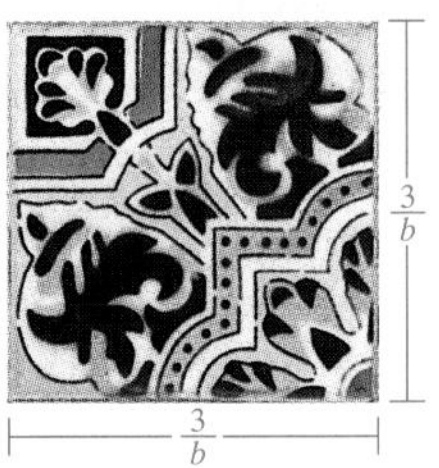


$A = s^2$ $s$ = length of a side

$= \left(\frac{3}{b}\right)^2$

$= \frac{3^2}{b^2} = \frac{9}{b^2}$

The area of the tile is $\frac{9}{b^2}$ square units.

**TRY THIS** Simplify each expression.

**8.** $\left(\frac{1}{2}\right)^3$ $\frac{1}{8}$ **9.** $\left(-\frac{2}{3}\right)^4$ $\frac{16}{81}$ **10.** $\left(\frac{2x^2}{3}\right)^3$ $\frac{8x^6}{27}$



- **Additional Example 3**

  Find the volume of a cube with side length $\frac{x}{4}$. Volume = side³ $\frac{x^3}{64}$

**AFTER THE LESSON**

**To assess knowledge: Lesson Quiz**

Simplify each expression.

1. $(12x^2yz)^2$ $144x^4y^2z^2$
2. $(-4ab^3)^3$ $-64a^3b^9$
3. $-(-2g^2h)^8$ $-256g^{16}h^8$
4. $\left(\frac{u^3}{6}\right)^2$ $\frac{u^6}{36}$
5. $\left(\frac{3q^8r^6}{s^7}\right)^5$ $\frac{243q^{40}r^{30}}{s^{35}}$

- For enrichment and reteaching options see Resources on p. 221H.

# Exercises

## Check Understanding

**Simplify each expression.**

1. $(3 \cdot 5)^2$ 225
2. $(4a^5)^2$ $16a^{10}$
3. $(2c^2)^5$ $32c^{10}$
4. $(-10x^3)^4$ $10{,}000x^{12}$
5. $\left(\frac{2}{5}\right)^2$ $\frac{4}{25}$
6. $\left(-\frac{2}{5}\right)^3$ $-\frac{8}{125}$
7. $\left(\frac{4}{7y}\right)^2$ $\frac{16}{49y^2}$
8. $\left(\frac{3x^2}{10}\right)^4$ $\frac{81x^8}{10{,}000}$

**Complete each equation.**

9. $(5 \cdot 2)^{■} = 25 \cdot 4$ 2
10. $(a^2)^{■} = a^2$ 1
11. $(4m)^{■} = 256m^4$ 4
12. $\left(-\frac{1}{2}\right)^{■} = -\frac{1}{8}$ 3
13. $\left(\frac{b^{■}}{5}\right)^2 = \frac{b^{10}}{25}$ 5
14. $\left(\frac{3}{7}\right)^{■} = \frac{27}{343}$ 3
15. *Geometry* Find the area of a square with side length $4c$. $16c^2$ units$^2$

## Practice and Problem Solving

**Simplify each expression.**

16. $(3 \cdot 4)^3$ 1,728
17. $(-2 \cdot 5)^2$ 100
18. $-(xy)^2$ $-x^2y^2$
19. $(2x^2)^3$ $8x^6$
20. $(-5b)^3$ $-125b^3$
21. $-(3x)^2$ $-9x^2$
22. $(a^2b^4)^3$ $a^6b^{12}$
23. $(5c^3)^2$ $25c^6$
24. $(2ab^3)^2$ $4a^2b^6$
25. $-(x^2y^2)^2$ $-x^4y^4$
26. $(3a^4b)^3$ $27a^{12}b^3$
27. $(m^2 \cdot n)^4$ $m^8n^4$
28. $\left(\frac{4}{9}\right)^2$ $\frac{16}{81}$
29. $\left(-\frac{3}{7}\right)^2$ $\frac{9}{49}$
30. $\left(-\frac{5}{8}\right)^3$ $-\frac{125}{512}$
31. $\left(-\frac{2}{x^3}\right)^5$ $-\frac{32}{x^{15}}$
32. $\left(\frac{2c}{7d}\right)^2$ $\frac{4c^2}{49d^2}$
33. $\left(-\frac{3a}{b^2}\right)^3$ $-\frac{27a^3}{b^6}$
34. $\left(-\frac{2x}{7y}\right)^2$ $\frac{4x^2}{49y^2}$
35. $\left(\frac{2c}{d^2}\right)^4$ $\frac{16c^4}{d^8}$
36. $\left(-\frac{m}{b^3}\right)^6$ $\frac{m^6}{b^{18}}$
37. $\left(-\frac{xy}{2xy^4}\right)^5$ $-\frac{1}{32y^{15}}$
38. $\left(\frac{x^3}{2y^4}\right)^5$ $\frac{x^{15}}{32y^{20}}$
39. $\left(\frac{1}{3x^2}\right)^4$ $\frac{1}{81x^8}$

**Complete each equation.**

40. ✪ $(4 \cdot (-7))^{■} = 64 \cdot (-343)$ 3
41. ✪ $(2b^{■})^2 = 4b^8$ 4
42. ✪ $(gh^2)^{■} = g^3h^6$ 3

**Evaluate for $a = -1$, $b = 3$, and $c = \frac{1}{2}$.**

43. $(2a^5)^3$ $-8$
44. $(-b^2)^2$ 81
45. $(c^3)^2$ $\frac{1}{64}$
46. $\left(\frac{a}{b}\right)^3$ $-\frac{1}{27}$
47. $(2b)^3$ 216
48. $(ac^2)^2$ $\frac{1}{16}$
49. $(4c^2)^2$ 1
50. $(a^2b)^2$ 9
51. *Geometry* A square has sides $3x^2$ units long. Write an expression for the area of the square. Simplify your expression. $(3x^2)^2$; $9x^4$



# 3 Practice/Assess

## Assignment Guide

To provide flexible scheduling, this lesson can be divided into parts.

**Part 1**
**Core** 1–4, 9–11, 15–27, 51–53
✪ **Extension** 40–42

**Part 2**
**Core** 5–8, 12–14, 28–39, 43–50, 54
✪ **Extension** 55–57

Mixed Review can be assigned at any time for maintenance.

## Exercises

**Exercises 16–39** Suggest that students first decide on the sign of the answer.

## ✪ Challenge

Simplify $\left(\frac{1}{6}d\frac{5}{c^2}\right)^3$ $\frac{1}{216}d^3\frac{125}{c^6}$ or $\frac{125d^3}{216c^6}$

## Closure

To raise a product to a power, raise each factor to the power. To raise a quotient to a power, raise both the numerator and the denominator to the power.

## Alternative Assessment

Have students create a poster that explains how to find the powers of products and quotients. However, the posters must not include any words. Suggest that they use as many drawings and symbols as they can think of, as long as they do not include words. Display student posters in the classroom.

## Daily Cumulative Review

**Solve each equation.** *(Lesson 5-8)*

1. $9x = \frac{3}{4}$ $x = \frac{1}{12}$
2. $\frac{5}{7}d = \frac{2}{3}$ $d = \frac{14}{15}$
3. $\frac{4}{13}p = -36$ $p = -117$
4. $-\frac{11}{13} = -\frac{1}{3}h$ $2\frac{7}{13} = h$
5. $-5a = \frac{7}{9}$ $a = -\frac{7}{45}$
6. $3\frac{1}{6}r = 4$ $r = 1\frac{5}{19}$

**Solve each equation.** *(Lesson 5-7)*

7. $g + \frac{3}{4} = \frac{7}{8}$ $g = \frac{1}{8}$
8. $5\frac{7}{72} = x + 4\frac{2}{9}$ $\frac{7}{8} = x$
9. $f - 2\frac{3}{8} = 1\frac{1}{8}$ $f = 3\frac{1}{2}$
10. $n - 3\frac{3}{11} = 1\frac{5}{22}$ $n = 4\frac{1}{2}$
11. $v - \frac{6}{13} = \frac{3}{26}$ $v = \frac{15}{26}$
12. $2\frac{5}{12} = k + 1\frac{7}{8}$ $\frac{13}{24} = k$

**Mixed Review**

**Write in simplest form.**

13. $\frac{15}{25}$ (4-4) $\frac{3}{5}$
14. $\frac{38}{48}$ (4-4) $\frac{19}{24}$
15. $\frac{12}{16}$ (4-4) $\frac{3}{4}$
16. $\frac{24}{60}$ (4-4) $\frac{2}{5}$
17. $\frac{3}{12}$ (4-4) $\frac{1}{4}$
18. $\frac{52}{208}$ (4-4) $\frac{1}{4}$

**Write the coordinates of each point.**

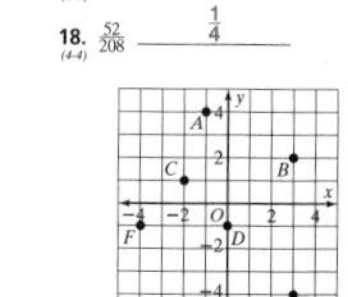


19. $A$ (1-10) $(-1, 4)$
20. $B$ (1-10) $(3, 2)$
21. $C$ (1-10) $(-2, 1)$
22. $D$ (1-10) $(0, -1)$
23. $E$ (1-10) $(3, -4)$
24. $F$ (1-10) $(-4, -1)$

**Write a variable expression for each word phrase.**

25. 234 divided by $g$ (1-1) $234 \div g$
26. twelve subtracted from a number $s$ (1-1) $s - 12$

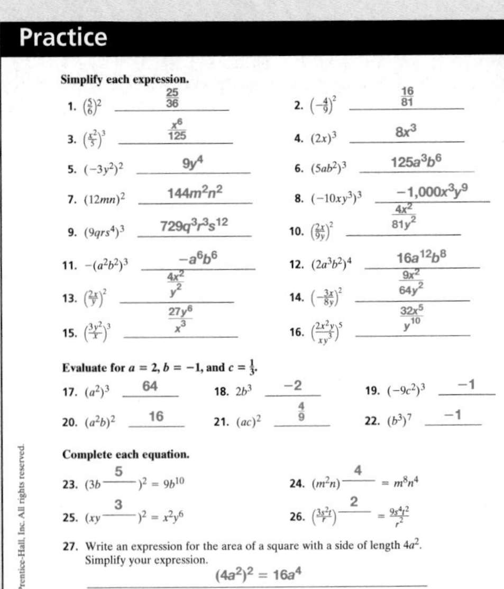

## Practice

**Simplify each expression.**

1. $\left(\frac{5}{6}\right)^2$ $\frac{25}{36}$
2. $\left(-\frac{4}{9}\right)^2$ $\frac{16}{81}$
3. $\left(\frac{x^2}{5}\right)^3$ $\frac{x^6}{125}$
4. $(2x)^3$ $8x^3$
5. $(-3y^2)^2$ $9y^4$
6. $(5ab^2)^3$ $125a^3b^6$
7. $(12mn)^2$ $144m^2n^2$
8. $(-10xy^3)^3$ $-1{,}000x^3y^9$
9. $(9qrs^4)^3$ $729q^3r^3s^{12}$
10. $\left(\frac{2x}{9y}\right)^2$ $\frac{4x^2}{81y^2}$
11. $-(a^2b^2)^3$ $-a^6b^6$
12. $(2a^3b^2)^4$ $16a^{12}b^8$
13. $\left(\frac{2x}{y}\right)^2$ $\frac{4x^2}{y^2}$
14. $\left(-\frac{3x}{8y}\right)^2$ $\frac{9x^2}{64y^2}$
15. $\left(\frac{3y^2}{x}\right)^3$ $\frac{27y^6}{x^3}$
16. $\left(\frac{2x^2y}{xy^3}\right)^5$ $\frac{32x^5}{y^{10}}$

**Evaluate for $a = 2$, $b = -1$, and $c = \frac{1}{3}$.**

17. $(a^2)^3$ 64
18. $2b^3$ $-2$
19. $(-9c^2)^3$ $-1$
20. $(a^2b)^2$ 16
21. $(ac)^2$ $\frac{4}{9}$
22. $(b^3)^7$ $-1$

**Complete each equation.**

23. $(3b^{\underline{5}})^2 = 9b^{10}$
24. $(m^2n)^{\underline{4}} = m^8n^4$
25. $(xy^{\underline{3}})^2 = x^2y^6$
26. $\left(\frac{3s^2t}{r}\right)^{\underline{2}} = \frac{9s^4t^2}{r^2}$
27. Write an expression for the area of a square with a side of length $4a^2$. Simplify your expression. $(4a^2)^2 = 16a^4$
28. Write an expression for the volume of a cube with a side of length $3z^5$. Simplify your expression. $(3z^5)^3 = 27z^{15}$



## Reteaching

Simplify $\left(\frac{x^3}{-y^2}\right)^5$.

$\left(\frac{x^3}{-y^2}\right)^5 = \frac{(x^3)^5}{(-y^2)^5}$ Raise both the numerator and the denominator to the power of 5.

$= \frac{x^{15}}{(-1)^5(y^2)^5}$ Multiply exponents in the numerator. Raise each factor to the power of 5 in the denominator.

$= -\frac{x^{15}}{y^{10}}$ Multiply exponents and simplify.

**Simplify each expression.**

1. $(2 \cdot 5)^4$ 10,000
2. $(-3 \cdot 2)^3$ $-216$
3. $(4x)^2$ $16x^2$
4. $(a^2b)^5$ $a^{10}b^5$
5. $(3ab^3)^2$ $9a^2b^6$
6. $-(5m^2n^3)^3$ $-125m^6n^9$
7. $\left(\frac{2}{9}\right)^2$ $\frac{4}{81}$
8. $\left(-\frac{7}{8}\right)^2$ $\frac{49}{64}$
9. $\left(-\frac{3}{10}\right)^3$ $-\frac{27}{1{,}000}$
10. $\left(\frac{4}{x^4}\right)^2$ $\frac{16}{x^8}$
11. $\left(\frac{3x}{5}\right)^3$ $\frac{27x^3}{125}$
12. $\left(-\frac{a^2}{b^5}\right)^4$ $\frac{a^8}{b^{20}}$
13. $\left(\frac{xy^2}{2z^3}\right)^5$ $\frac{x^5y^{10}}{32z^{15}}$
14. $\left(\frac{-1}{2n^3}\right)^4$ $\frac{1}{16n^{12}}$
15. $\left(\frac{-2r^3s}{3t^2}\right)^2$ $\frac{4r^6s^2}{9t^4}$
16. $\left(\frac{-3}{a^2bc^2}\right)^3$ $-\frac{27}{a^6b^3c^6}$
17. $(p^4q^3r^2)^3$ $p^{12}q^9r^6$
18. $\left(\frac{x^2yz^3}{-2}\right)^4$ $\frac{x^8y^4z^{12}}{16}$
19. $\left(\frac{5}{j^3k}\right)^2$ $\frac{25}{j^6k^2}$
20. $\left(\frac{ac^4}{4b}\right)^3$ $\frac{a^3c^{12}}{64b^3}$



## Enrichment

1. a. Simplify $4^3$. 64
   b. Simplify $2^6$. 64
   c. What do you notice? $4^3 = 2^6$
2. a. Simplify $9^4$. 6,561
   b. Simplify $3^8$. 6,561
   c. What do you notice? $9^4 = 3^8$
3. Substitute $2^2$ for 4 in $4^3$ and simplify to show why the pattern in Exercise 1 holds. $4^3 = (2^2)^3 = 2^6$
4. Substitute $3^2$ for 9 in $9^4$ and simplify to show why the pattern in Exercise 2 holds. $9^4 = (3^2)^4 = 3^8$

You can use this relationship to simplify expressions like $5^4 \cdot 25^3$:
$5^4 \cdot 25^3 = 5^4 \cdot (5^2)^3 = 5^4 \cdot 5^6 = 5^{10}$

**Simplify each expression.**

5. $2^5 \cdot 4^3$ $2^{11}$
6. $3^4 \cdot 9^3$ $3^{10}$
7. $8^2 \cdot 2^6$ $2^{12}$
8. $36^2 \cdot 6^3$ $6^7$
9. $81^2 \cdot 3^5$ $3^{13}$
10. $4^3 \cdot 16^2 \cdot 2^4$ $2^{18}$
11. $32^2 \cdot 16^3$ $2^{22}$
12. $125^2 \cdot 5^4$ $5^{10}$
13. $16^4 \cdot 2^7 \cdot 4^3$ $2^{29}$
14. $27^4 \cdot 3^6$ $3^{18}$
15. $49^5 \cdot 7^3$ $7^{13}$
16. $100^5 \cdot 10^7$ $10^{17}$
17. $81^6 \cdot 3^5 \cdot 27^4$ $3^{41}$
18. $4^7 \cdot 32^3 \cdot 16^5$ $2^{49}$



52. *Error Analysis* What is the error in the following computation? $(3y)^7 = 3y^7$ **3 should be raised to the seventh power also.**

53. *Open-ended* Write $a^{36}$ as a power of the form $(a^m)^n$ in two different ways. **Answers may vary. Sample: $(a^6)^6$, $(a^9)^4$**

54. *Writing* Explain why $\left(-\frac{1}{7}\right)^2 = \left(\frac{1}{7}\right)^2$. **Answers may vary. Sample: The square of a number and the square of its opposite are the same.**

*Geometry* **Use the formula $V = s^3$, where $s$ is the length of a side, to find the volume of each cube.**

55. 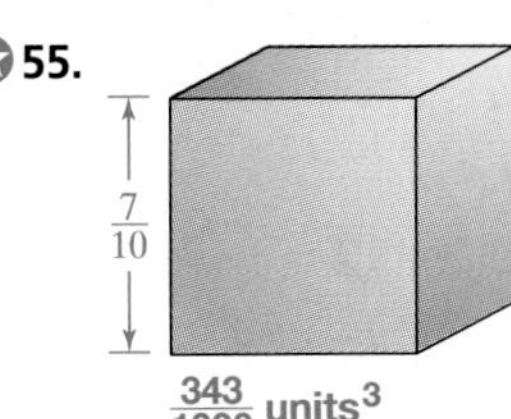

$\frac{343}{1000}$ units$^3$

56. 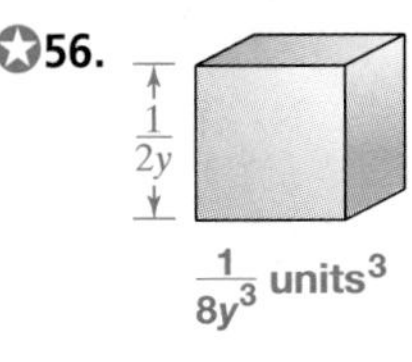

$\frac{1}{8y^3}$ units$^3$

57. 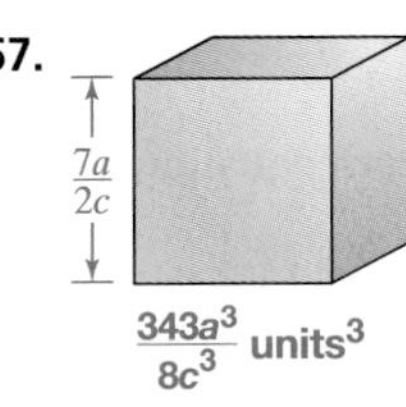

$\frac{343a^3}{8c^3}$ units$^3$

## Mixed Review

**Solve each equation.** *(Lesson 5-8)*

58. $\frac{2}{7}h = \frac{7}{8}$ $3\frac{1}{16}$
59. $6\frac{3}{4}c = 1\frac{5}{9}$ $\frac{56}{243}$
60. $\frac{5}{8} = \frac{10}{12}x$ $\frac{3}{4}$
61. $10\frac{3}{4} = -5\frac{1}{2}y$ $-1\frac{21}{22}$

**Use the coordinate plane at the right. Write the coordinates of each point named below. Write the name of each point with the coordinates given below.** *(Lesson 1-10)*

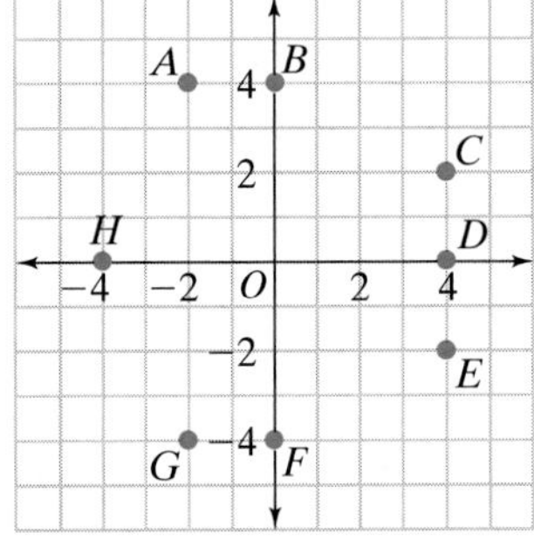


62. $A$ (−2, 4)
63. $(4, -2)$ $E$
64. $C$ (4, 2)
65. $(-4, 0)$ $H$
66. $F$ (0, −4)
67. $(0, 4)$ $B$

68. Delia bought three plants for \$5.99, \$12.99 and $x$ dollars. She paid a total of \$34.97 for the plants. How much did the third plant cost? *(Lesson 3-5)* **\$15.99**

Chapter Project 5

## Activity 4 Calculating

Extend your shoe-size chart by adding a column for shoe length. Calculate the length in inches of each whole and half size. Use the expression in the table at the right, where $s$ is the shoe size. Put the results in your chart.

| Finding Shoe Lengths |
|---|
| Women's shoe lengths: $\frac{s}{3} + 7\frac{11}{12}$ |
| Men's shoe lengths: $\frac{s}{3} + 8\frac{1}{4}$ |

 See also Extra Practice section.

### Project Activity 4

**Calculating** Encourage students to show the steps they use in their calculations so that they can find and correct any errors.

## FINISHING THE CHAPTER PROJECT

**Make a Comparison Chart** The Project Activities on pages 228, 254, 263, and 268 will help you complete your project. Here is a checklist to help you gather the different parts.

- ✔ examples of the duodecimal system in everyday life
- ✔ comparison of calculated size to labeled size
- ✔ calculations of shoe lengths
- ✔ shoe-size comparison chart

Manufacturers often distribute helpful charts to retailers as a form of advertising. Assume that your comparison chart will be distributed to shoe stores. Your chart should be easy to read and simply presented, so that anyone can use it.

***Reflect and Revise***

Ask a friend to review your chart and your calculations. Is your chart accurate? Is it presented attractively? If necessary, make changes to improve your chart.

### *Web Extension*

**Visit Prentice Hall's Web site. You'll find some interesting links and ideas related to sizes. You'll also be able to share information about your project.**

**www.phschool.com**

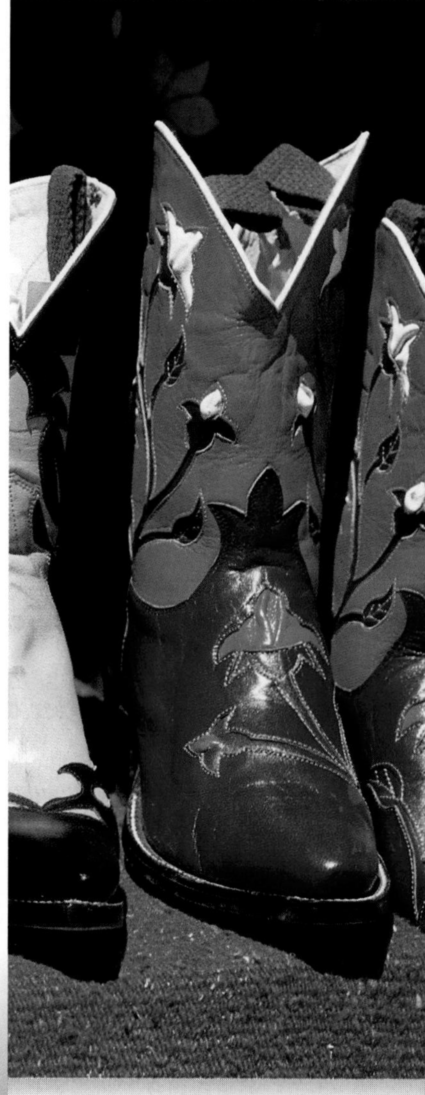

## FINISHING THE PROJECT

**Project Day** You may wish to plan a project day on which students share their completed projects. Encourage students to explain their process as well as their product.

**Block Scheduling** If you have block scheduling or extended periods, you may wish to intersperse the sharing of projects over Days 4 and 5 between the completion of one lesson and the start of a new lesson.

### Project Notebook

Have students review their project work and bring their notebooks up to date. Call attention to the fact that they can share their projects with other students through the Web site **www.phschool.com**.

Be sure students include in their notebooks their completed Project Manager and Scoring Rubric forms.

**Portfolio** Students may wish to include their projects and/or their project notebooks in their portfolios.

### Web Extension

**Tell Us About Your Project**

Students may wish to share their projects with other students on the Web site: **www.phschool.com**.

### Scoring Rubric

3 You calculate all numbers in your chart accurately. You prepare your chart so it is neat, easy to read, simply presented, and eye-pleasing. You organize your calculations so they are easy to follow.

2 You make minor errors when calculating numbers for your chart. Your chart is complete and basically accurate, but it could be neater or easier to read. You present clear calculations, but they could be better organized.

1 You calculate numbers in your chart inaccurately. Your chart could be neater and easier to read. Your calculations are difficult to follow due to lack of organization.

0 Major elements of the project are incomplete or missing.

# Wrap Up

## Resources

Glossary, p. 748
Extra Practice, p. 714

For a complete list of resources for the chapter, see p. 221H.

# 5 Wrap Up

## Key Terms

dimensional analysis (p. 246)
least common denominator (LCD) (p. 226)
least common multiple (LCM) (p. 224)
multiple (p. 224)
repeating decimal (p. 230)
reciprocals (p. 242)
terminating decimal (p. 229)

## Graphic Organizer

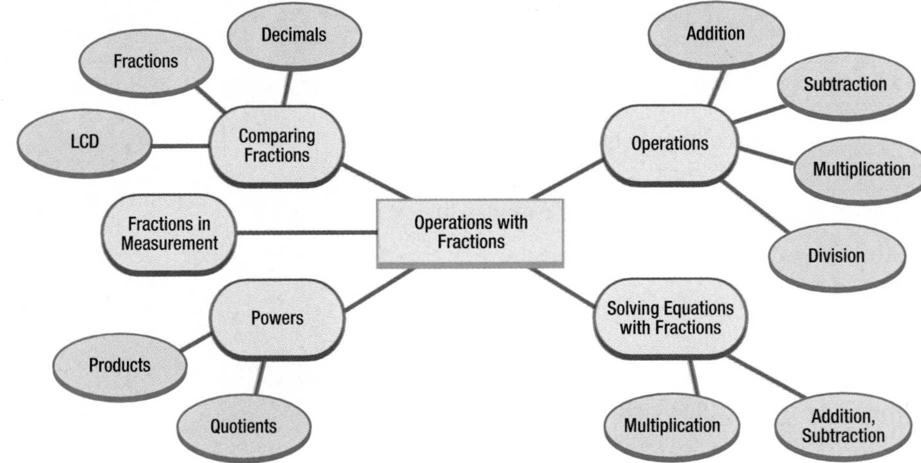


## Comparing and Ordering Fractions 5-1

*Summary* A **multiple** of a number is the product of that number and any whole number. A *common multiple* of any group of numbers is a number that is a multiple of all the numbers. The common multiple with the least value is the **least common multiple (LCM)** of the numbers.

To compare fractions, use the LCM as the **least common denominator (LCD)** and write equivalent fractions.

**Find the LCM of each group of numbers or expressions.**

**1.** 12, 18 36 **2.** $8m^2, 14m$ $56m^2$ **3.** 3, 5, 7 105 **4.** $6x, 15y$ $30xy$

**Compare. Use >, <, or = to complete each statement.**

**5.** $\frac{5}{9} \blacksquare \frac{5}{11}$ > **6.** $\frac{2}{3} \blacksquare \frac{3}{4}$ < **7.** $-\frac{4}{5} \blacksquare -\frac{7}{8}$ > **8.** $\frac{1}{3} \blacksquare \frac{4}{12}$ =

## Fractions and Decimals 5-2

*Summary* To write a fraction as a decimal, divide the numerator by the denominator. If the division has a remainder of zero, the decimal is a **terminating decimal.** If the division produces a repeating block of digits, the decimal is a **repeating decimal.** The repeating part of the decimal is written with an overbar.

Reading a decimal correctly provides one way to write it as a fraction. To write a repeating decimal as a fraction, use algebra to eliminate the repeating part.

**Write each fraction as a decimal.**

**9.** $\frac{3}{5}$ 0.6 **10.** $\frac{1}{6}$ $0.1\overline{6}$ **11.** $\frac{5}{8}$ 0.625 **12.** $\frac{3}{10}$ 0.3 **13.** $\frac{7}{100}$ 0.07

**Write each decimal as a fraction or mixed number.**

**14.** 0.25 $\frac{1}{4}$ **15.** $0.8\overline{3}$ $\frac{5}{6}$ **16.** 5.6 $5\frac{3}{5}$ **17.** $2.\overline{04}$ $2\frac{4}{99}$

## Adding and Subtracting Fractions 5-3

*Summary* To add or subtract fractions and mixed numbers, write them with a common denominator. Then you can add or subtract the numerators. Change a mixed number to an improper fraction before adding or subtracting.

**Add or subtract.**

**18.** $2\frac{1}{3} + \frac{3}{4}$ $3\frac{1}{12}$ **19.** $16\frac{4}{5} - 9\frac{2}{3}$ $7\frac{2}{15}$ **20.** $\frac{6}{x} + \frac{3}{5}$ $\frac{30 + 3x}{5x}$ **21.** $1\frac{1}{2} - \frac{5}{8}$ $\frac{7}{8}$

**22.** An upholsterer cuts a piece of cording $1\frac{2}{3}$ ft long from a piece $2\frac{1}{4}$ ft long. How much cording is left? $\frac{7}{12}$ ft, or 7 in.

## Multiplying and Dividing Fractions 5-4

*Summary* To multiply fractions, multiply their numerators and their denominators. To divide fractions, multiply the first fraction by the **reciprocal** of the second fraction.

To multiply or divide mixed numbers, write them as improper fractions before multiplying or dividing.

**Find each product or quotient.**

**23.** $\frac{1}{4} \cdot \frac{7}{10}$ $\frac{7}{40}$ **24.** $-\frac{2}{3} \div \frac{5}{6}$ $-\frac{4}{5}$ **25.** $1\frac{3}{5} \cdot \frac{3}{4}$ $1\frac{1}{5}$ **26.** $5\frac{1}{4} \div 2\frac{3}{5}$ $2\frac{1}{52}$ **27.** $\frac{3x}{5} \div \frac{6x}{5}$ $\frac{1}{2}$



**Portfolio** Students may wish to include their completed work for the Wrap Up in their portfolios.

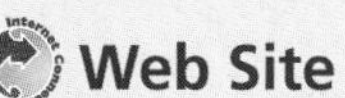

### Web Site

Students can find self-assessment materials on the Web site: **www.phschool.com.**

## Using Customary Units of Measure — 5-5

*Summary* To convert units of measure in the customary system of measurement, use **dimensional analysis.**

**Complete each statement.**

28. 30 in. = ■ ft $2\frac{1}{2}$

29. ■ lb = 54 oz $3\frac{3}{8}$

30. 20 yd = ■ ft 60

31. ■ fl oz = $1\frac{1}{2}$ pt 24

32. 12 gal = ■ pt 96

33. $2\frac{3}{4}$ t = ■ lb 5,500

## Work Backward — 5-6

*Summary* To solve some problems, you have to work backward.

34. Your family is planning a 4-h car trip. Along the way, you are planning to make five $\frac{1}{2}$-h stops. At what time should you leave home to arrive at the destination by 8:00 P.M.? 1:30 P.M.

35. Buses bound for Los Angeles leave the station every hour from 6:00 A.M. to 8:00 P.M. How many buses is that in one day? 15 buses

36. *Writing* Explain how solving a problem by working backward is similar to solving an equation. Check students' work.

## Solving Equations — 5-7 and 5-8

*Summary* To solve equations with fractions, use inverse operations to undo addition or subtraction. You can undo multiplication by multiplying each side of the equation by the same fraction.

**Solve each equation.**

37. $\frac{1}{8} + x = 2\frac{1}{2}$ $2\frac{3}{8}$

38. $x - \frac{1}{3} = \frac{4}{5}$ $1\frac{2}{15}$

39. $x + 4\frac{2}{3} = 6$ $1\frac{1}{3}$

40. $6x = \frac{1}{9}$ $\frac{1}{54}$

41. $-\frac{3}{4}x = \frac{2}{7}$ $-\frac{8}{21}$

42. $2\frac{3}{4}x = \frac{14}{33}$ $\frac{56}{363}$

## Powers of Products and Quotients — 5-9

*Summary* To raise a product to a power, raise each factor to the power. To raise a quotient to a power, raise both the numerator and the denominator to the power.

**Simplify each expression.**

43. $(2d)^4$ $16d^4$

44. $(-3(2))^2$ 36

45. $(a^2b)^5$ $a^{10}b^5$

46. $\left(-\frac{1}{2}\right)^3$ $-\frac{1}{8}$

47. $\left(\frac{x}{3}\right)^2$ $\frac{x^2}{9}$

48. $\left(\frac{2a}{c^2}\right)^4$ $\frac{16a^4}{c^8}$



### Chapter Assessment Form A Page 1

**Circle the letter of the best answer.**

1. Find the LCM of 24 and 32.
   A. 8 B. 768 C. 384 (D.) 96
2. Find the LCM of $14a^2b^3$ and $21ab^4$.
   F. $294a^3b^7$ (G.) $42a^2b^4$ H. $21a^2b^4$ J. $42a^2b^3$
3. Which fraction is less than $\frac{8}{15}$?
   (A.) $\frac{2}{5}$ B. $\frac{2}{3}$ C. $\frac{7}{10}$ D. $\frac{5}{6}$
4. Write $\frac{1}{16}$ as a decimal.
   (F.) 0.0625 G. 0.625 H. 0.00625 J. 0.16
5. Write 0.28 as a fraction.
   A. $\frac{2}{8}$ B. $\frac{9}{25}$ C. $\frac{1}{4}$ (D.) $\frac{7}{25}$
6. $\frac{2}{3} + \frac{7}{8} =$
   F. $1\frac{3}{8}$ (G.) $1\frac{13}{24}$ H. $\frac{7}{10}$ J. $1\frac{1}{2}$
7. $3\frac{3}{5} - 4\frac{1}{2} =$
   A. $1\frac{1}{10}$ B. $\frac{9}{10}$ (C.) $-\frac{9}{10}$ D. $-1\frac{1}{10}$
8. $3\frac{1}{3} \cdot \frac{4}{5} =$
   F. $\frac{4}{5}$ G. $3\frac{4}{15}$ (H.) $2\frac{2}{3}$ J. $4\frac{1}{6}$
9. $-\frac{3}{7} \div \frac{5}{14} =$
   A. $\frac{15}{98}$ B. $-\frac{15}{98}$ C. $1\frac{1}{5}$ (D.) $-1\frac{1}{5}$
10. Which of the following is in order from shortest to longest?
    F. $2\frac{1}{2}$ ft, $\frac{7}{9}$ yd, $2\frac{2}{3}$ ft, 33 in. (G.) $\frac{7}{9}$ yd, $2\frac{1}{2}$ ft, $2\frac{2}{3}$ ft, 33 in.
    H. $\frac{7}{9}$ yd, $2\frac{1}{2}$ ft, 33 in., $2\frac{2}{3}$ ft J. 33 in., $2\frac{1}{2}$ ft, $2\frac{2}{3}$ ft, $\frac{7}{9}$ yd

**Compare. Use >, <, or = to complete each statement.**

11. $\frac{5}{12}$ [<] $\frac{2}{3}$
12. $-1.1875$ [=] $-1\frac{3}{16}$
13. Write $0.\overline{45}$ as a fraction in simplest form. $\frac{5}{11}$
14. Write $\frac{7}{12}$ as a decimal. $0.58\overline{3}$

**Solve each equation.**

15. $x + \frac{3}{7} = -\frac{1}{2}$ $x = -\frac{13}{14}$
16. $t - 5 = 7\frac{1}{8}$ $t = 12\frac{1}{8}$



Assessment

### Chapter Assessment Form A Page 2

17. $-6n = 2\frac{3}{4}$ $n = -\frac{11}{24}$

**Complete each statement.**

18. 5 qt = $1\frac{1}{4}$ gal
19. $1\frac{5}{8}$ lb = 26 oz

**Simplify each expression.**

20. $(-4x)^2$ $16x^2$
21. $\left(\frac{3m}{2n}\right)^3$ $\frac{27m^3}{8n^3}$
22. $-(xy^2)^3$ $-x^3y^6$
23. Write an equation to solve the problem.
    A jar contains 54 pennies, and $\frac{2}{3}$ of the coins in the jar are pennies. How many coins $c$ are in the jar?
    $\frac{2}{3}c = 54$; $c = 81$ coins
24. A guide-dog training center took $\frac{1}{2}$ of the puppies at the dog pound. Steve took $\frac{1}{2}$ of the remaining. Tanya took the 5 that were left. How many puppies were there to begin with?
    20 puppies
25. Write a word problem that could be solved with the equation $x - \frac{3}{4} = 6\frac{3}{4}$.
    Sample answer: A baby lost $\frac{3}{4}$ lb in the week after it was born. At the end of the week it weighed $6\frac{3}{4}$ lb. What was its birth weight?

# Assessment

**Find the LCM of each group of numbers.**

1. 24, 36 72
2. 50, 100 100
3. $3x, 2y$ $6xy$
4. 16, 20 80

**Compare. Use >, <, or = to complete each statement.**

5. $\frac{7}{8}$ ■ $\frac{7}{9}$ >
6. $\frac{2}{3}$ ■ $\frac{10}{15}$ =
7. $\frac{7}{10}$ ■ 0.71 <
8. $2\frac{3}{5}$ ■ $2\frac{2}{3}$ <
9. $-0.87$ ■ $-\frac{7}{8}$ >
10. $\frac{3}{4}$ ■ $\frac{14}{20}$ >

**Order from least to greatest.**

11. $0.5, \frac{1}{10}, 0, -\frac{1}{4}$ $-\frac{1}{4}, 0, \frac{1}{10}, 0.5$
12. $-\frac{3}{5}, -0.\overline{6}, \frac{1}{6}, \frac{2}{3}$ $-0.\overline{6}, -\frac{3}{5}, \frac{1}{6}, \frac{2}{3}$

**Write each decimal as a fraction.**

13. 0.4 $\frac{2}{5}$
14. $0.\overline{7}$ $\frac{7}{9}$
15. $12.\overline{36}$ $\frac{136}{11}$, or $12\frac{4}{11}$
16. 5.2 $\frac{26}{5}$, or $5\frac{1}{5}$
17. 0.002 $\frac{1}{500}$
18. $7.\overline{1}$ $\frac{64}{9}$, or $7\frac{1}{9}$

**Write each fraction as a decimal.**

19. $\frac{4}{15}$ $0.2\overline{6}$
20. $-\frac{2}{3}$ $-0.\overline{6}$
21. $\frac{3}{8}$ 0.375
22. $\frac{1}{2}$ 0.5
23. $\frac{6}{7}$ $0.\overline{857142}$
24. $\frac{5}{9}$ $0.\overline{5}$

**Add or subtract.**

25. $\frac{1}{8} + \frac{3}{4}$ $\frac{7}{8}$
26. $\frac{2}{3} - \frac{1}{9}$ $\frac{5}{9}$
27. $-\frac{1}{6x} + \frac{1}{4}$ $\frac{-2 + 3x}{12x}$
28. $11\frac{5}{6} - 5\frac{3}{8}$ $6\frac{11}{24}$
29. $\frac{2}{3} - \left(-\frac{8y}{9}\right)$ $\frac{6 + 8y}{9}$
30. $2\frac{1}{5} - \frac{3}{4}$ $1\frac{9}{20}$

**Multiply or divide.**

31. $\frac{3}{5} \cdot \frac{1}{2}$ $\frac{3}{10}$
32. $-\frac{3}{4} \cdot \frac{5}{8}$ $-\frac{15}{32}$
33. $\frac{5}{8x} \div \frac{7}{16}$ $\frac{10}{7x}$
34. $\frac{4}{m} \div \frac{5m}{9}$ $\frac{36}{5m^2}$
35. $3\frac{3}{4} \cdot 2\frac{4}{5}$ $10\frac{1}{2}$
36. $-1\frac{1}{3} \div \left(-\frac{5}{9}\right)$ $2\frac{2}{5}$

**Complete each statement.**

37. 10 yd = ■ ft 30
38. 20 oz = ■ lb $1\frac{1}{4}$
39. ■ lb = $1\frac{3}{4}$ t 3,500
40. 6 pt = ■ qt 3
41. $3\frac{1}{2}$ qt = ■ c 14
42. ■ in. = $1\frac{3}{4}$ yd 63

**Solve each equation.**

43. $m - \frac{2}{3} = \frac{1}{4}$ $\frac{11}{12}$
44. $h + \frac{3}{5} = \frac{9}{10}$ $\frac{3}{10}$
45. $x - \frac{5}{6} = -\frac{5}{6}$ 0
46. $\frac{3}{5}a = 9$ 15
47. $n + \frac{7}{8} = \frac{1}{3}$ $-\frac{13}{24}$
48. $2\frac{1}{2}n = 3\frac{3}{4}$ $1\frac{1}{2}$
49. $-5b = 3\frac{1}{3}$ $-\frac{2}{3}$
50. $\frac{3}{8}y = -15$ $-40$

**Simplify each expression.**

51. $(3(4))^2$ 144
52. $(2a)^3$ $8a^3$
53. $\left(\frac{3}{4}\right)^3$ $\frac{27}{64}$
54. $(3x^2)^3$ $27x^6$
55. $-(2x^2y)^4$ $-16x^8y^4$
56. $\left(\frac{2y}{5x}\right)^3$ $\frac{8y^3}{125x^3}$

**Solve.**

57. *Number Sense* Suppose you take a number, subtract 8, multiply by 7, add 10, and divide by 5. The result is 9. What is the original number? 13
58. You spend $\frac{3}{4}$ of your money on clothes and have $21 left. How much did you have before you bought the clothes? $84
59. *Writing* Write a word problem for the equation $x - 1\frac{1}{4} = 5$. Check students' work.
60. Two packages each weigh $1\frac{7}{8}$ lb. How much do they weigh altogether? $3\frac{3}{4}$ lb
61. You rode your bicycle a mile and a half to school. Then you rode to a friend's house. Altogether you rode $2\frac{1}{10}$ mi. Write and solve an equation to find how far it is from school to your friend's house. $1\frac{1}{2} + d = 2\frac{1}{10}$; $\frac{3}{5}$ mi



## Chapter Assessment

**Resources** For a complete list of resources for this chapter, see p. 221H.

### Chapter Assessment Form B Page 1

**Circle the letter of the best answer.**

1. Find the LCM of 14 and 35.
   (A.) 70 B. 490 C. 140 D. 145
2. Find the LCM of $18a^2b^4$ and $27a^3b$.
   (F.) $54a^3b^4$ G. $27a^3b^4$ H. $27a^2b$ J. $54a^2b^4$
3. Which number is greater than $-3\frac{1}{5}$?
   A. $-3\frac{1}{2}$ B. $-3\frac{1}{4}$ (C.) $-3\frac{1}{6}$ D. $-3\frac{2}{5}$
4. Write $\frac{12}{25}$ as a decimal.
   F. 0.5 G. 0.45 (H.) 0.48 J. 0.12
5. Which fraction is equal to 0.375?
   A. $\frac{1}{8}$ B. $\frac{2}{8}$ (C.) $\frac{3}{8}$ D. $\frac{3}{75}$
6. $4\frac{1}{3} + \frac{5}{6} =$
   F. $4\frac{2}{3}$ (G.) $5\frac{1}{6}$ H. $5\frac{1}{3}$ J. $4\frac{1}{6}$
7. $-\frac{1}{4} \div \frac{1}{2} =$
   A. $-\frac{1}{8}$ B. $-2$ C. $-8$ (D.) $-\frac{1}{2}$
8. $\frac{5}{9} - \frac{5}{6} =$
   (F.) $-\frac{5}{18}$ G. $\frac{5}{18}$ H. $\frac{1}{3}$ J. $1\frac{7}{18}$
9. $2\frac{1}{7} \div \frac{5}{7}$
   A. $-3$ (B.) 3 C. $2\frac{4}{5}$ D. $1\frac{26}{49}$
10. Which of the following is in order from lightest to heaviest?
    F. $1\frac{3}{8}$ lb, 20 oz, 25 oz, $1\frac{1}{2}$ lb
    G. $1\frac{3}{8}$ lb, $1\frac{1}{2}$ lb, 20 oz, 25 oz
    H. $1\frac{3}{8}$ lb, 20 oz, $1\frac{1}{2}$ lb, 25 oz
    (J.) 20 oz, $1\frac{3}{8}$ lb, $1\frac{1}{2}$ lb, 25 oz

**Compare. Use >, <, or = to complete each statement.**

11. $-2\frac{1}{8}$ [>] $-2\frac{2}{3}$
12. $\frac{7}{8}$ [>] 0.8
13. Write $0.\overline{8}$ as a fraction in simplest form. $\frac{8}{9}$
14. Write $\frac{7}{15}$ as a decimal. $0.4\overline{6}$

**Solve each equation.**

15. $\frac{2}{3} = x + \frac{1}{5}$ $x = \frac{7}{15}$
16. $-\frac{3}{4} = y - 2$ $y = 1\frac{1}{4}$

Assessment



### Chapter Assessment Form B Page 2

17. $\frac{3}{4}z = -4\frac{1}{8}$ $z = -5\frac{1}{2}$

**Complete each statement.**

18. 9 in. $\frac{3}{4}$ ft
19. $1\frac{1}{2}$ gal 6 qt

**Simplify each expression.**

20. $(-5x)^3$ $-125x^3$
21. $\left(\frac{7m}{9n}\right)^2$ $\frac{49m^2}{81n^2}$
22. $-(x^2y)^5$ $-x^{10}y^5$
23. Write an equation to solve the problem.
    Lethal Yellowing, a disease that kills palm trees, is moving across the Caribbean Islands at a rate of about $1\frac{3}{10}$ miles per month. How many months $m$ will it take for the disease to spread a distance of 195 mi?
    $1\frac{3}{10}m = 195$; $m = 150$ months
24. Suppose you take a number, subtract 7, multiply by 3, add 6, and divide by 7. The result is 3. What is the original number?
    12
25. Write a word problem that could be solved with the equation $\frac{3}{4}d = 6$.
    Sample answer: Thomas runs $\frac{3}{4}$ mi a day. How many days will it take him to run a total of 6 mi?

# Cumulative Review

## Cumulative Review Page 1

**Circle the letter of the best answer.**

1. Find the sum of $\frac{3}{4}$, $\frac{5}{8}$, and $\frac{1}{6}$ in simplest form.
   A. $\frac{11}{8}$ B. $\frac{23}{24}$ C. $1\frac{3}{8}$ (D.) $1\frac{13}{24}$
2. Which expression is equivalent to $4b^6$?
   F. $4b^3 \cdot b^2$ (G.) $(2b^3)^2$ H. $(4b^3)^2$ J. $4(b^3)^3$
3. What is the prime factorization of 72?
   (A.) $3^2 \cdot 2^3$ B. $3^2 \cdot 2 \cdot 4$ C. $9 \cdot 8$ D. $3^2 \cdot 2^4$
4. Write an equation for *one-half the quantity seven less than t equals four.*
   F. $\frac{1}{2} \cdot 7 - t = 4$ G. $\frac{1}{2}(7 - t) = 4$ (H.) $\frac{1}{2}(t - 7) = 4$ J. $t - \frac{1}{2} \cdot 7 = 4$
5. Which group of numbers is in order from least to greatest?
   A. $\frac{4}{9}$, 0.431, $\frac{2}{5}$, 0.452 B. 0.431, $\frac{2}{5}$, $\frac{4}{9}$, 0.452
   C. $\frac{2}{5}$, $\frac{4}{9}$, 0.431, 0.452 (D.) $\frac{2}{5}$, 0.431, $\frac{4}{9}$, 0.452
6. Which statement is *not* true about the expression below?
   $\frac{7}{18}x + \frac{5}{9}y - \frac{7}{9}xy$
   F. The expression has no constant.
   G. The expression has no like terms.
   (H.) The coefficient of $x$ is greater than the coefficient of $y$.
   J. The coefficient of $y$ is greater than the coefficient of $xy$.

**Add or subtract.**

7. $\frac{7}{12} + \frac{5}{8}$ $1\frac{5}{24}$
8. $\frac{5}{9} - \frac{5}{6}$ $-\frac{5}{18}$
9. $\frac{7}{10} + 2\frac{7}{12}$ $3\frac{17}{60}$

**Complete each statement.**

10. $3\frac{1}{2}$ ft = 42 in.
11. 9 qt = $2\frac{1}{4}$ gal

**Write each decimal as a fraction in simplest form.**

12. 0.55 $\frac{11}{20}$
13. $0.1\overline{3}$ $\frac{2}{15}$
14. Evaluate $5d^2 - 7$, for $d = \frac{1}{5}$ $-6\frac{4}{5}$



## Cumulative Review Page 2

**Simplify each expression.**

15. $\frac{4}{5}(6 - 11)^3$ $-100$
16. $\frac{5}{7} \div \left(\frac{2}{3} + \frac{1}{6}\right)$ $\frac{6}{7}$
17. $(6k)^2$ $36k^2$
18. $\left(-\frac{x}{3}\right)^4$ $\frac{x^4}{81}$
19. $\left(\frac{2m}{n^2}\right)^3$ $\frac{8m^3}{n^6}$
20. Write a rule for the pattern below. Find the next three terms.
    $\frac{2}{1}, \frac{2}{3}, \frac{2}{9}, \frac{2}{27}, \frac{2}{81}, \frac{2}{243}, \frac{2}{729}$
    Sample answer: Start with 2 and multiply by $\frac{1}{3}$ repeatedly.



Assessment

# 5 Cumulative Review

Preparing for Algebra

**Choose the best answer.**

1. Which group of numbers is in order from least to greatest? A
   A. 0.583, $\frac{7}{12}$, $\frac{5}{8}$, 0.635
   B. $\frac{7}{12}$, 0.583, $\frac{5}{8}$, 0.635
   C. $\frac{5}{8}$, 0.583, $\frac{7}{12}$, 0.635
   D. $\frac{5}{8}$, 0.583, 0.635, $\frac{7}{12}$
2. Which statement is *not* true about the expression below? J
   $$\frac{5}{16}m + \frac{7}{11}t - mt^2$$
   F. The expression has no constants.
   G. The coefficient of $m$ is less than the coefficient of $t$.
   H. The expression has no like terms.
   J. The coefficient of $m$ is less than the coefficient of $mt^2$.
3. Find the sum of $\frac{2}{5}$, $\frac{3}{10}$, and $\frac{3}{4}$ in simplest form. A
   A. $1\frac{9}{20}$ B. $\frac{30}{20}$ C. $1\frac{23}{30}$ D. $\frac{18}{200}$
4. Which expression is equivalent to $8b^4$? G
   F. $2^3(b^2 + b^2)$
   G. $(4 + 4)(b^2)^2$
   H. $(2 \cdot 2 \cdot 2)(b + b + b + b)$
   J. $(2b)^4$
5. What is the prime factorization of 750? C
   A. $2 \cdot 5^2 \cdot 7$ B. $3 \cdot 5^3 \cdot 7$
   C. $2 \cdot 3 \cdot 5^3$ D. $15 \cdot 50$
6. A student bought 3 pens for $p$ cents each, 4 notebooks for $n$ cents each, and a ruler for $1.29. Which expression models this situation? J
   F. $3p + 4n + 1.29$
   G. $3n + 4p + 129$
   H. $0.3p + 0.4n + 1.29$
   J. $3p + 4n + 129$

**Add or subtract.**

7. $4 - (-7)$ 11
8. $-9 + 3.5$ $-5.5$
9. $\frac{5}{8} + \frac{1}{8}$ $\frac{3}{4}$
10. $\frac{3}{4} + \frac{3}{5}$ $1\frac{7}{20}$
11. $\frac{7}{11} - \frac{2}{5}$ $\frac{13}{55}$
12. $-\frac{6}{7} + \frac{3}{14}$ $-\frac{9}{14}$
13. $1\frac{1}{9} - \frac{3}{4}$ $\frac{13}{36}$
14. $10\frac{4}{5} - 9\frac{1}{2}$ $1\frac{3}{10}$

**Complete each statement.**

15. $5\frac{1}{2}$ yd = ■ ft $16\frac{1}{2}$
16. 3 c = ■ pt $1\frac{1}{2}$
17. 4 fl oz = ■ c $\frac{1}{2}$
18. ■ gal = 3 qt $\frac{3}{4}$
19. ■ ft = $1\frac{1}{2}$ mi 7,920
20. 18 in. = ■ ft $1\frac{1}{2}$

**Write each decimal as a fraction in simplest form.**

21. 0.56 $\frac{14}{25}$
22. $0.\overline{45}$ $\frac{5}{11}$
23. 0.18 $\frac{9}{50}$

**Simplify each expression.**

24. $\frac{2}{3}(8 - 5)^3$ 18
25. $3\left(\frac{6 + 4}{2}\right)^2$ 75
26. $\frac{7}{12} \cdot \frac{6}{21} \div \frac{2}{3}$ $\frac{1}{4}$
27. $\frac{1}{2} \div \left(\frac{3}{4} + \frac{1}{8}\right)$ $\frac{4}{7}$

**Evaluate each expression for $c = -3$ and $d = \frac{1}{4}$.**

28. $4c + 3d$ $-11\frac{1}{4}$
29. $6d^2 - 9$ $-8\frac{5}{8}$
30. $c^2 + 2c^3$ $-45$
31. $5 + 7d - c$ $9\frac{3}{4}$

**Simplify each expression.**

32. $(6 \cdot 3)^3$ 5,832
33. $\left(\frac{4}{5}\right)^2$ $\frac{16}{25}$
34. $\left(\frac{2}{3}\right)^4$ $\frac{16}{81}$
35. $\left(\frac{3x}{y}\right)^3$ $\frac{27x^3}{y^3}$
36. $\left(-\frac{x}{2}\right)^5$ $-\frac{x^5}{32}$
37. $(4y)^2$ $16y^2$
38. *Patterns* Write a rule for the pattern below. Find the next three terms.
    $$\frac{1}{1}, \frac{1}{2}, \frac{1}{4}, \frac{1}{8}, \ldots$$
    Start with $\frac{1}{1}$ and multiply by $\frac{1}{2}$ repeatedly; $\frac{1}{16}$, $\frac{1}{32}$, $\frac{1}{64}$.



| Item | Chapter/ Lesson | Review Topic |
|---|---|---|
| 2, 6–8 | 1-5, 1-6, 1-7 | Algebraic Expressions and Rational Numbers |
| 4, 5, 32–37 | 4-3, 4-7 | Factors and Exponents |
| 1, 3, 9–31, 38 | 5-1, 5-2, 5-3, 5-4, 5-5, 5-8, 5-9 | Operations with Fractions |

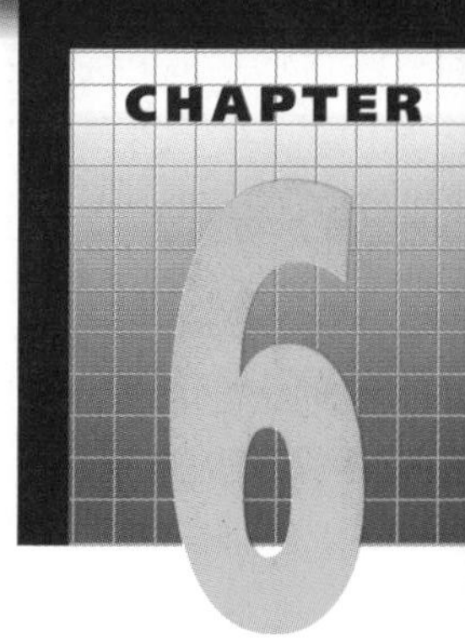


# Ratios, Proportions, and Percents

## Content Overview for Chapter 6

Chapter 6 begins by introducing the terms *ratio, rate,* and *unit rate.* A ratio compares two quantities by division. A rate is a ratio that compares two quantities that have different units. A unit rate is a rate that has a denominator of 1. You can use what you know about writing and simplifying ratios to write and solve proportions. You can then apply proportions to problems involving similar figures and scale drawings.

When outcomes are random (equally likely) you can use formulas that contain ratios to find the probability of an event and the odds in favor of an event.

You can apply your skills of writing and simplifying ratios to write ratios with denominators of 100 as decimals, fractions, and percents. You can solve percent problems by using a proportion and an equation. The percent of change is the ratio of the amount of change to the original amount. Markup is a real-world application of percent of increase. Discount is a real-world application of percent of decrease.

## Making Connections

| Lesson | Interdisciplinary and Real-World Connections | Math Integration |
|---|---|---|
| 6-1 | Science | Data Analysis |
| 6-2 | Navigation | Measurement, Geometry |
| 6-3 | Geography | Geometry, Measurement |
| 6-4 | Statistics | Data Analysis |
| 6-5 | Maps | Data Analysis, Probability |
| 6-6 | Statistics | Data Analysis |
| 6-7 | Statistics | Data Analysis |
| 6-8 | Zoology | Data Analysis |
| 6-9 | Retailing | Data Analysis |
| 6-10 | Biology | Problem Solving, Geometry, Probability |

**SCHOOL/HOME CONNECTION**

English and Spanish versions are available in the *Help at Home* book of copy masters.

**Helper's Page** You will find detailed instruction, more examples, and

**Student Page** Review Exercises for Lessons 6-1 to 6-4

**Find each unit rate.** *(Lesson 6-1)*

1. 108 mi in 3 h ______ 2. $17.91 for 9 gal ______ 3. a fall of 192 ft in 4 s ______

**Solve each proportion. Where necessary, round to the nearest tenth.** *(Lesson 6-2)*

4. $\frac{6}{25} = \frac{x}{40}$ $x =$ ______ 5. $\frac{9}{15} = \frac{11}{x}$ $x \approx$ ______ 6. $\frac{12}{n} = \frac{7}{20}$ $n \approx$ ______

**Each pair of triangles is similar. Find the missing length. Round to the nearest tenth where necessary.** *(Lesson 6-3)*

7. 4.5 ft, $n$, 6 ft; 3 ft, 6 ft, 4 ft $n =$ ______

8. $y$, 4 cm; 7 cm, 10 cm $y =$ ______

**The scale of a map is 2 cm : 9 km. Find the actual distance for each map distance.** *(Lesson 6-3)*

9. 8 cm ______ 10. 11 cm ______ 11. 4.2 cm ______

**A set of 24 flash cards is numbered from 1 to 24. A card is chosen at random. Find each probability.** *(Lesson 6-4)*

12. $P$(a number greater than 20) ______ 13. $P$(a prime number) ______

14. **Test Prep** One cup of salad dressing serves 4 people. How many cups are needed to serve 9 people? *(Lesson 6-2)*

A. 36 c B. 0.4 c C. 2.25 c D. 5 c ______

Helper: ______ Comments: ______

**Helper's Page** You will find detailed instruction, more examples, and

**Student Page** Review Exercises for Lessons 6-5 to 6-9

**Complete the table.** *(Lesson 6-5)*

| | Fraction | Decimal | Percent |
|---|---|---|---|
| 1. | | | 36% |
| 2. | $\frac{7}{8}$ | | |
| 3. | | 0.005 | |

**Write a proportion. Then solve. Where necessary, round to the nearest tenth or tenth of a percent.** *(Lesson 6-6)*

4. Find 35% of 90. proportion: ______
5. What percent of 80 is 42? proportion: ______
6. 158 is 75% of what number? proportion: ______

**Write and solve an equation. Where necessary, round to the nearest tenth or tenth of a percent.** *(Lesson 6-7)*

7. Find 24% of 159. equation: ______
8. What percent of 125 is 56? equation: ______
9. 8 is 85% of what number? equation: ______

**Find each percent of change. Round to the nearest tenth of a percent. Tell whether the change is an increase or a decrease.** *(Lesson 6-8)*

10. from 18 to 25 ______ 11. from 40 to 56 ______ 12. from 72 to 61 ______

13. **Test Prep** Find the selling price for an item costing $65 with a 20% markup. Round to the nearest cent, if necessary. *(Lesson 6-9)*

A. $78 B. $13 C. $52 D. $81.25 ______

Helper: ______ Comments: ______

CHAPTER 6

# Chapter 6 at a Glance

To accommodate flexible scheduling, most lessons are divided into parts. Assignment Options are given in the Teacher's Edition for each lesson.

| Pages | Lesson | NCTM | Parts |
|---|---|---|---|
| 278–281 | **Lesson 6-1** Measurement: Ratios and Unit Rates | 1, 4, 6, 7, 8, 9, 10 | Part 1 Writing Ratios<br>Part 2 Finding Rates and Unit Rates |
| 284–288 | **Lesson 6-2** Proportions | 1, 2, 4, 6, 7, 8, 9, 10 | Part 1 Solving Proportions<br>Part 2 Using Proportions to Solve Problems<br>**Project Activity 1** |
| 289–293 | **Lesson 6-3** Geometry: Similar Figures and Scale Drawings | 1, 4, 6, 8, 9, 10 | Part 1 Using Similar Figures<br>Part 2 Using Scale Drawings<br>**Project Activity 2** |
| 310–313 | **Lesson 6-7** Percents and Equations | 1, 2, 6, 8, 9, 10 | Part 1 Writing and Solving Percent Equations<br>Part 2 Using Equations to Solve Percent Problems |
| 314–317 | **Lesson 6-8** Data Analysis: Percent of Change | 1, 2, 6, 7, 8, 9, 10 | Part 1 Finding Percent of Increase<br>Part 2 Finding Percent of Decrease<br>**Project Activity 4** |
| 318–321 | **Lesson 6-9** Markup and Discount | 1, 2, 6, 8, 9, 10 | Part 1 Finding Markups<br>Part 2 Finding Discounts<br>**Checkpoint 2** |

## Pacing Options

This chart suggests pacing for only the core lessons and their parts, and it is provided merely as a possible guide. It will help you determine how much time you have in your schedule to cover other features, such as the Chapter Project, Math Toolboxes, Standardized Test Prep, Wrap Up, and Assessment.

| | Day 1 | Day 2 | Day 3 | Day 4 | Day 5 | Day 6 | Day 7 | Day 8 | Day 9 | Day 10 | Day 11 |
|---|---|---|---|---|---|---|---|---|---|---|---|
| **Traditional** (40–45 min. class periods) | 6–1 (1) 6–1 (2) | 6–2 (1) 6–2 (2) | 6–3 (1) 6–3 (2) | 6–4 (1) | 6–4 (2) | 6–5 (1) 6–5 (2) | 6–6 (1) | 6–6 (2) | 6–7 (1) 6–7 (2) | 6–8 (1) 6–8 (2) | 6–9 (1) 6–9 (2) |
| **Pre-Algebra Over 2 Years** (40–45 min. class periods) | 6–1 (1) | 6–1 (2) | 6–1 (2) | 6–2 (1) | 6–2 (2) | 6–2 (2) | 6–3 (1) | 6–3 (2) | 6–3 (2) | 6–4 (1) | 6–4 (2) |
| **Block Scheduling** (90 min. class periods) | 6–1 (1) (2) 6–2 (1) (2) | 6–3 (1) (2) 6–4 (1) (2) | 6–5 (1) (2) 6–6 (1) (2) | 6–7 (1) (2) 6–8 (1) (2) | 6–9 (1) 6–9 (2) 6–10 | | | | | | |

| Pages 295–299 | **Lesson 6-4** **Probability** |
|---|---|
| **NCTM** 5, 6, 8, 9 | Part 1 Finding Probability<br>Part 2 Finding Odds<br>**Checkpoint 1** |

| Pages 300–304 | **Lesson 6-5** **Fractions, Decimals, and Percents** |
|---|---|
| **NCTM** 1, 8, 9 | Part 1 Writing Percents as Fractions and Decimals<br>Part 2 Writing Decimals and Fractions as Percents<br>**Project Activity 3** |

| Pages 305–309 | **Lesson 6-6** **Proportions and Percents** |
|---|---|
| **NCTM** 1, 6, 8, 9, 10 | Part 1 Finding Part of a Whole<br>Part 2 Finding a Whole Amount |

| Pages 323–326 | **Lesson 6-10** **Problem Solving Strategy** |
|---|---|
| **NCTM** 1, 2, 6, 8, 9, 10 | Make a Table<br>**Math at Work** |

**NCTM STANDARDS 2000**

1. Number and Operations
2. Algebra
3. Geometry
4. Measurement
5. Data Analysis and Probability
6. Problem Solving
7. Reasoning and Proof
8. Communication
9. Connections
10. Representation

| Day 12 | Day 13 | Day 14 | Day 15 | Day 16 | Day 17 | Day 18 | Day 19 | Day 20 | Day 21 | Day 22 | Day 23 | Day 24 |
|---|---|---|---|---|---|---|---|---|---|---|---|---|
| 6–10 | | | | | | | | | | | | |
| 6–4 2 | 6–5 1 | 6–5 2 | 6–6 1 | 6–6 2 | 6–6 2 | 6–7 1 | 6–7 2 | 6–8 1 | 6–8 2 | 6–9 1 | 6–9 2 6-10 | 6–10 |

**Block Scheduling Notes**

Consider these suggestions:

- **Day 1** Before starting Lesson 6-2, teach Math Toolbox 1, pp. 282–283.
- **Day 2** Before starting Lesson 6-4, teach Math Toolbox 2, p. 294.
- **Day 3** After completing Lesson 6-6, begin presentations for Finish the Project.
- **Day 5** Before starting Lesson 6-10, teach the Standardized Test Prep, p. 322.

# Math Background

## Lessons 6-1 and 6-2

### Ratios, Unit Rates, and Proportions

You compare two numbers by division when you write a *ratio*. In words you might say that the ratio of girls to boys in the class is 15 to 16; in symbols this same ratio can be written 15 : 16, or $\frac{15}{16}$. The order of the numbers in a ratio is important. The ratio of girls to boys in this example is $\frac{15}{16}$, but the ratio of boys to girls is written as $\frac{16}{15}$.

A *rate* is a ratio that compares quantities that have different units. One familiar rate is miles per hour. If you drive 90 miles in 1.5 hours, then your rate is $\frac{90}{1.5}$ mph. A rate with a denominator of 1 is called a *unit rate.* The example of $\frac{90}{1.5}$ mph is more often given in the equivalent unit rate of 60 mph, since $\frac{90}{1.5} = \frac{60}{1}$.

An equality between two ratios is called a *proportion*. For example, $\frac{90}{1.5} = \frac{60}{1}$ is a proportion. Notice that both sides of a proportion can be written as a fraction and that a proportion shows equality between two division expressions.

You can solve a proportion that contains a variable by using the fact that in a proportion the *cross products* are equal. In the following statement the cross products are *ad* and *bc*.

$\frac{a}{b} = \frac{c}{d}$ means that $ad = bc$. For example, you can solve $\frac{x}{2} = \frac{2}{3}$ by writing the equation with the cross products, $3x = 4$, and then dividing both sides by 3 to get $x = 1\frac{1}{3}$.

The following proof shows why cross products are equal.

| | |
|---|---|
| $\frac{a}{b} = \frac{c}{d}$ | Given |
| $bd \bullet \frac{a}{b} = bd \bullet \frac{c}{d}$ | Multiplication Property of Equality |
| $\frac{bd}{1} \bullet \frac{a}{b} = \frac{bd}{1} \bullet \frac{c}{d}$ | $\frac{n}{1} = n$ |
| $\frac{bda}{b} = \frac{bdc}{d}$ | $1n = n$; multiplication of fractions |
| $da = bc$ | $\frac{n}{n} = 1$ |
| $ad = bc$ | Commutative Property of Multiplication |

## Lesson 6-3

### Similar Figures and Scale Drawings

Two geometric figures are *similar* if they have exactly the same shape, though not necessarily the same size. For example, any square is similar to any other square. *Corresponding parts* of two figures are those parts that occur in the same relative position when the two figures have the same orientation. In the following example, side *AC* corresponds to side *EG;* both form the left side of the largest angle in the triangle.

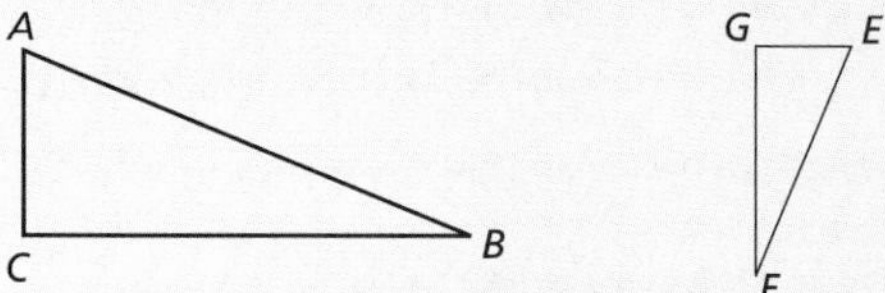


In figures that are similar, the corresponding angles have equal measures and the corresponding sides are proportional. In the similar triangles shown, for example, $\frac{AC}{EG} = \frac{AB}{EF}$.

A map is a scale drawing. On a map, if two inches represents one mile, then the *scale* is two inches to a mile.

## Lesson 6-4

### Probability

A ratio that expresses the chance or likelihood that a certain event will occur is called the *probability* of that event. Theoretical probability is a number that estimates how often an event will occur. Experimental probability, instead of being an estimate, reports how often an event actually did occur.

The probability of an event is always between 0 and 1. If an event is certain to happen, the probability of that event is 1. If an event is impossible, then the probability of that event is 0. The probability of an event is not a very good predictor of what will happen in a small number of cases. The laws of probability predict only what will happen when you survey a very large number of events.

The probability of $A$, as long as all possible outcomes are equally likely, is given by

$P(A) = \frac{\text{number of outcomes of event } A}{\text{number of possible outcomes}}$.

The probability that $A$ does not occur is $P(\text{not } A) = 1 - P(A)$. The event $A$ and the event (not $A$) are *complements.* The sum of $P(A)$ and $P(\text{not } A)$ is always 1.

The probability ratio compares the number of favorable outcomes (event $A$) with the number of all possible outcomes. Another ratio, called the *odds in favor* of an event, compares the number of favorable outcomes with the number of unfavorable outcomes.

odds in favor $= \frac{\text{number of favorable outcomes}}{\text{number of unfavorable outcomes}}$

The *odds against* an event is the ratio of the number of unfavorable outcomes to the number of favorable outcomes.

odds against $= \frac{\text{number of unfavorable outcomes}}{\text{number of favorable outcomes}}$

## LESSONS 6-5 AND 6-6

### Fractions, Decimals, Percents, and Proportions

A ratio that compares a number with 100 is called a *percent.* The word "percent" comes from the Latin phrase "per centum," meaning "divided by one hundred." Recall that one dollar is 100 cents; 5 cents is 5 per hundred, or 5%, of one dollar.

Because percent is a way of expressing a fraction in terms of hundredths, you can change the form of a number among percent, fraction, or decimal. For example,

- $27\% = \frac{27}{100}$, which is 0.27 as a decimal.
- $0.349 = \frac{34.9}{100}$, or 34.9%.
- $\frac{4}{7}$, when divided, is approximately 0.57143, which is $\frac{57.143}{100}$, or 57.143%.
- $1\frac{1}{4} = \frac{5}{4}$. Multiplying $\frac{5}{4}$ by $\frac{25}{25}$ gives $\frac{125}{100}$, or 125%.

A percent greater than 100% converts into an improper fraction or a decimal number greater than 1.

To answer the question "What percent of 7 is 4?" you can rename $\frac{4}{7}$ as a percent by setting up this proportion: $\frac{4}{7} = \frac{x}{100}$.

Writing cross products gives $7x = 400$, and using inverse operations gives $x = \frac{400}{7}$, which again simplifies to 57.143. Since $x$ is a percent, this means that $x \approx 57.143\%$.

## LESSONS 6-7 AND 6-8

### Percents, Equations, and Percent of Change

Another method for solving a percent problem is to write an equation. For example, to answer the question "24 is 150% of what number?" write 150% as a decimal and set up the equation $24 = 1.5 \bullet x$, so $x = \frac{24}{1.5} = 16$.

The percent of change is the percent that a quantity increases or decreases compared with the original quantity.

% of increase $= \frac{\text{amount of increase}}{\text{original amount}}$

% of decrease $= \frac{\text{amount of decrease}}{\text{original amount}}$

## LESSONS 6-9

### Markup and Discount

When a store sells an item, it adds an amount called *markup* to the store's cost. In the case of prices, the percent of increase is called the *percent of markup.*

% of markup $= \frac{\text{amount of markup}}{\text{store's cost}}$

When a store puts an item on sale, the amount subtracted from the original price is the *discount*. The percent of decrease is the *percent of discount*.

% of discount $= \frac{\text{amount of discount}}{\text{original price}}$

For professional development tips visit our Web site **www.phschool.com**.

# Monitoring Progress

## Universal Access

### ▶ *Preventing a Student from Falling Behind*

These resources are particularly helpful in preventing a student from falling behind his or her appropriate math level. For a complete list of resources for this chapter, see page 275H.

#### Skills You Need for Chapter 6

Student Edition, p. 275
Teacher's Edition, p. 275

- Simplifying Fractions
- Solving Equations by Multiplying and Dividing
- Fractions, Decimals, and Percents

#### Skills Handbook

Student Edition, pp. 723–741
Teacher's Edition, pp. 723–741

- Writing Equivalent Fractions, p. 737
- Multiplying Decimals, p. 731

#### Reteaching Worksheets

There is a Reteaching worksheet for every lesson in this chapter.

- Chapter 6 Support File, Teaching Resources box
- See TE p. 275H for a complete list of resources

#### Skills Intervention Kit with CD-ROM

| For | Use |
|---|---|
| Lessons 6-1, 6-4 | Fraction Concepts |
| Lesson 6-2 | Pre-Algebra Basics |
| Lessons 6-3, 6-6, 6-10 | Ratio, Proportion, and Percent |
| Lesson 6-5 | Decimals |

#### Daily Cumulative Review Blackline Masters

There is a Daily Cumulative Review worksheet for every lesson in this chapter.

See TE p. 275H for a complete list of resources.

### ▶ *Accommodating Diverse Learning Styles*

#### Tactile Learning

Draw two lines to form an X to indicate the cross products of a proportion. (Lesson 6-2)

Make posters in groups or do skits that demonstrate the cost, markup, and the price, and then discount the sale of an item. (Lesson 6-9)

#### Advanced Learner

Every lesson has at least one challenge problem.

#### ELL (English Language Learner)

Read aloud the various ways you can write a ratio. (Lesson 6-1)

Compare the meanings of $=$, $\approx$, and $\sim$. (Lesson 6-3)

#### Auditory Learning

Say ratios aloud. (Lesson 6-1)

Read problems aloud. (Lesson 6-4)

Say the definition of percent of change aloud. (Lesson 6-8)

#### Visual Learning

Use a concept map to help you remember that every rate is a ratio and every unit rate is both a rate and a ratio. (Lesson 6-1)

Shade a sketch of a circle or a bar to compare a part and the whole. (Lesson 6-6)

# Aligning Assessment with Instruction

## Assessment Options

| | Chapter Opener | 6-1 | 6-2 | 6-3 | 6-4 | 6-5 | 6-6 | 6-7 | 6-8 | 6-9 | 6-10 | End |
|---|---|---|---|---|---|---|---|---|---|---|---|---|
| Chapter Project | ■ | | | ■ | | | ■ | | | | | ■ |
| Try This Exercises | | ■ | ■ | ■ | ■ | ■ | ■ | ■ | ■ | ■ | ■ | |
| Mixed Reviews | | ■ | ■ | ■ | ■ | ■ | ■ | ■ | ■ | ■ | ■ | |
| Checkpoints | | | | | ■ | | | | | ■ | | |
| Writing | | ■ | ■ | ■ | ■ | ■ | ■ | ■ | ■ | ■ | | ■ |
| Chapter Assessment | | | | | | | | | | | | ■ |
| Cumulative Review | | | | | | | | | | | | ■ |
| Standardized Test Prep | | | ■ | | ■ | ■ | ■ | ■ | ■ | | | |
| | Standardized Test Prep, p. 322 | | | | | | | | | | | |
| Computer Item Generator | Can be used to create custom-made practice pages or assessment pages at any time. | | | | | | | | | | | |

### Test-Taking Tips on Transparencies

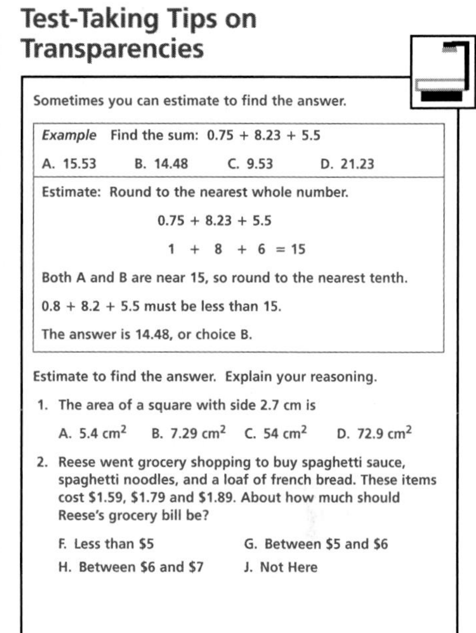
Sometimes you can estimate to find the answer.

*Example* Find the sum: 0.75 + 8.23 + 5.5

A. 15.53 B. 14.48 C. 9.53 D. 21.23

Estimate: Round to the nearest whole number.

0.75 + 8.23 + 5.5

1 + 8 + 6 = 15

Both A and B are near 15, so round to the nearest tenth.

0.8 + 8.2 + 5.5 must be less than 15.

The answer is 14.48, or choice B.

Estimate to find the answer. Explain your reasoning.

1. The area of a square with side 2.7 cm is

   A. 5.4 $cm^2$ B. 7.29 $cm^2$ C. 54 $cm^2$ D. 72.9 $cm^2$

2. Reese went grocery shopping to buy spaghetti sauce, spaghetti noodles, and a loaf of french bread. These items cost $1.59, $1.79 and $1.89. About how much should Reese's grocery bill be?

   F. Less than $5 G. Between $5 and $6
   H. Between $6 and $7 J. Not Here

*Use with Standardized Test Prep and Chapter Assessments.*

## Correlation to Standardized Tests

| Lesson | | CAT5 | CTBS/5 Terra Nova | ITBS | MAT7 | SAT9 | LOCAL OBJECTIVES |
|---|---|---|---|---|---|---|---|
| 6-1 | Ratios and Unit Rates | | | ■ | | ■ | |
| 6-2 | Proportions | | | | ■ | ■ | |
| 6-3 | Similar Figures and Scale Drawings | ■ | ■ | | | ■ | |
| 6-4 | Probability | | | | ■ | ■ | |
| 6-5 | Fractions, Decimals, and Percents | | ■ | ■ | ■ | ■ | |
| 6-6 | Proportions and Percents | ■ | ■ | | ■ | ■ | |
| 6-7 | Percents and Equations | | | | | ■ | |
| 6-8 | Percents of Change | | | | | ■ | |
| 6-9 | Markup and Discount | | | | ■ | ■ | |
| 6-10 | Problem Solving Strategy: Make a Table | | | | | ■ | |

**CAT5** California Achievement Test, 5th edition
**CTBS TerraNova** Comprehensive Test of Basic Skills, 5th edition
**ITBS** Iowa Test of Basic Skills, Form M
**MAT7** Metropolitan Achievement Test, 7th edition
**SAT** Stanford Achievement Test, Advanced 1

For other standardized test correlations, follow the link to your state at **www.phschool.com**.

# Resources for Chapter 6

| | TEACHING RESOURCES BOX: CHAPTER 6 SUPPORT FILE | | | | | | | | TEACHING RESOURCES BOX | | | | | | |
|---|---|---|---|---|---|---|---|---|---|---|---|---|---|---|---|
| | Practice | Reteach | Enrichment | Project Manager | Checkpoints | Cumulative Review | Chapter Assessment | Alternative Assessment | Cumulative Assessment | Lesson Planners Plus | Daily Cum Review | Teaching Transparencies | Warm-Up Transparencies | Help at Home | SE Answers Transparenc |
| Begin Chapter | | | | ■ | | | | | | ■ | | | | | |
| 6-1 | ■ | ■ | ■ | | | | | | | ■ | ■ | | ■ | | ■ |
| 6-2 | ■ | ■ | ■ | | | | | | | ■ | ■ | | ■ | | ■ |
| 6-3 | ■ | ■ | ■ | | | | | | | ■ | ■ | 6, 56 | ■ | | ■ |
| 6-4 | ■ | ■ | ■ | | ■ | | | | | ■ | ■ | 57 | ■ | ■ | ■ |
| 6-5 | ■ | ■ | ■ | | | | | | | ■ | ■ | 58 | ■ | | ■ |
| 6-6 | ■ | ■ | ■ | | | | | | | ■ | ■ | | ■ | | ■ |
| 6-7 | ■ | ■ | ■ | | | | | | | ■ | ■ | 59 | ■ | | ■ |
| 6-8 | ■ | ■ | ■ | | | | | | | ■ | ■ | | ■ | | ■ |
| 6-9 | ■ | ■ | ■ | | ■ | | | | | ■ | ■ | | ■ | ■ | ■ |
| 6-10 | ■ | ■ | ■ | | | | | | | ■ | ■ | 19 | ■ | | ■ |
| End Chapter | | | | | | ■ | ■ (2 forms) | ■ | After Ch. 3, 6, 9, 13 | | | | | | |

**Also available for use with the chapter:**

Solution Key
Computational Practice Skills Booklet
Mathematics Standardized Test Prep, Student Edition and Teacher's Edition
Overhead Manipulatives Kit
Practice Workbook
Algebra Readiness Kit
Student Manipulatives Kit
Test-Taking Tips on Transparencies
Assessment Success Kit
Teaching Aids and Letters
Graphing Calculator Handbook
Spanish Resources
Success-Building Puzzle and Problem Masters

## Technology

**Computer Item Generator with Standardized Test Prep**

CD-ROM with an unlimited supply of questions with varying degrees of difficulty for customized practice sheets, quizzes, and tests.

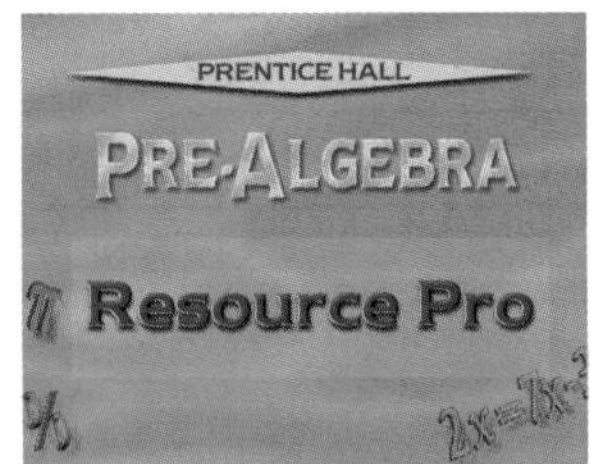


**Resource Pro® with Planning Express®**

CD-ROM with complete classroom planning tool and teaching resources for customizing and planning lessons.

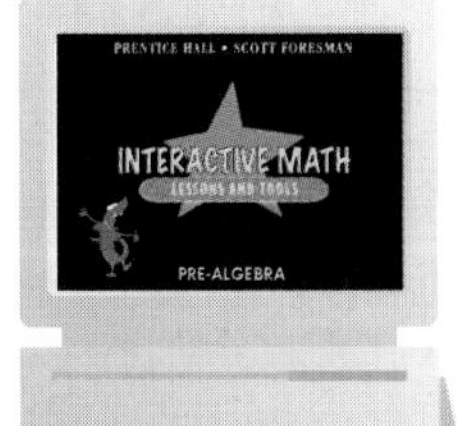


**Interactive Math Lessons and Tools**

CD-ROM with lessons and tools to make abstract concepts visual and accessible.

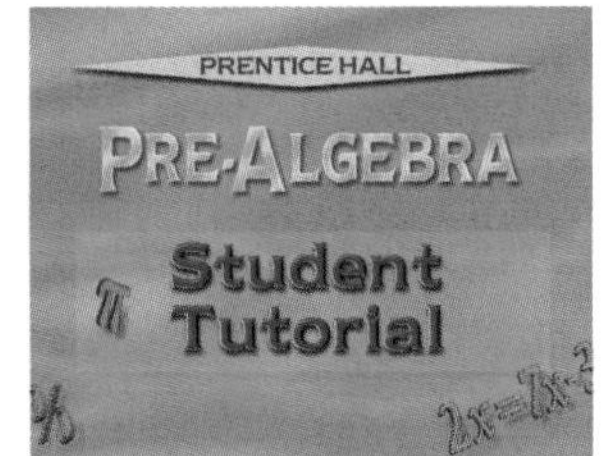


**Student Tutorial**

Test preparation software for students on CD-ROM with management system for teachers; includes Secondary Math Lab Toolkit™.

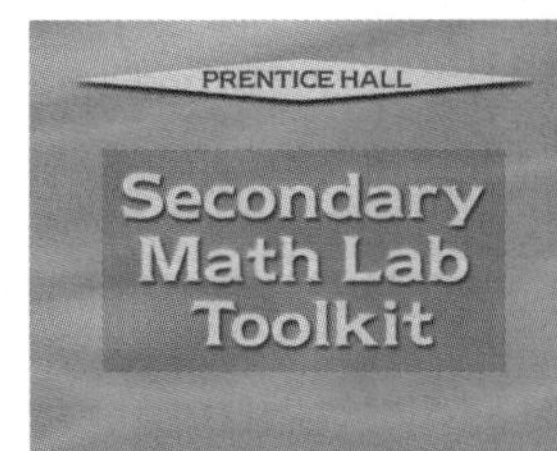


**Secondary Math Lab Toolkit™ with Integrated Math Labs**

Integrated software package with linkable math tools for exploring key concepts.

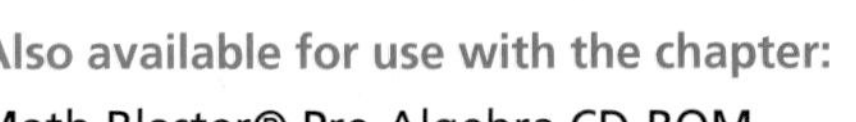
**Also available for use with the chapter:**

Math Blaster® Pre-Algebra CD-ROM
Video Fieldtrips, Vol. I: Algebra Applications
Video Fieldtrips, Vol. II: Geometry Applications
Wide World of Mathematics CD-ROM
Wide World of Mathematics Video

### *Web Extension*

**www.phschool.com**

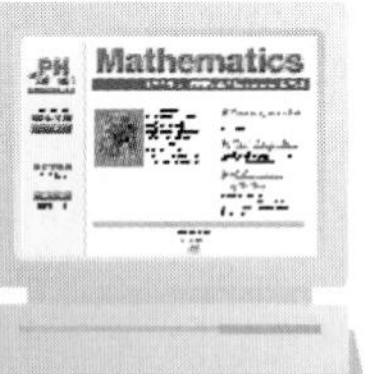


**For Students**
- Chapter Support with Internet Links
- Internet Activities

**For Teachers**
- Curriculum Support
- Professional Development
- Product Information
- Regional Support Information

# Skills You Need for Chapter

## ▶ *Simplifying fractions*

Use before Lessons 6-1, 6-2, and 6-4.

**Write each fraction in simplest form.**

1. $\frac{2}{8}$ $\frac{1}{4}$
2. $\frac{6}{24}$ $\frac{1}{4}$
3. $\frac{12}{15}$ $\frac{4}{5}$
4. $\frac{6}{16}$ $\frac{3}{8}$
5. $\frac{18}{42}$ $\frac{3}{7}$
6. $\frac{25}{200}$ $\frac{1}{8}$
7. $\frac{80}{96}$ $\frac{5}{6}$
8. $\frac{40}{1{,}000}$ $\frac{1}{25}$

## ▶ *Solving equations by multiplying or dividing*

Use before Lessons 6-2, 6-3, and 6-7.

**Solve each equation.**

9. $3x = 48$ 16
10. $94.5 = 7r$ 13.5
11. $\frac{3}{7}t = \frac{3}{8}$ $\frac{7}{8}$
12. $0.5y = 1.25$ 2.5
13. $\frac{4}{5}x = 1$ $1\frac{1}{4}$
14. $38.5 = 1.4m$ 27.5

## ▶ *Writing fractions and decimals*

Use before Lesson 6-5.

**Write each fraction as a decimal. Write each decimal as a fraction or a mixed number in simplest form.**

15. $\frac{7}{20}$ 0.35
16. 0.06 $\frac{3}{50}$
17. $\frac{30}{8}$ 3.75
18. 0.35 $\frac{7}{20}$
19. 0.875 $\frac{7}{8}$
20. $3\frac{3}{5}$ 3.6
21. 1.07 $1\frac{7}{100}$
22. $\frac{12}{18}$ $0.\overline{6}$
23. $11\frac{1}{9}$ $11.\overline{1}$
24. $0.\overline{3}$ $\frac{1}{3}$
25. $\frac{100}{16}$ 6.25
26. 3.98 $3\frac{49}{50}$

## ▶ *Writing percents*

Use before Lessons 6-5, 6-6, 6-7, and 6-8.

**Write each of the following as a percent with the % symbol.**

27. 5 percent 5%
28. 50 percent 50%
29. 5 tenths of a percent 0.5%
30. 17 hundredths percent 0.17%
31. 1 and 7 tenths percent 1.7%
32. 17 percent 17%



# Skills You Need

### Simplifying fractions

**In Lessons 6-1, 6-2, and 6-4** students will simplify fractions in order to simplify ratios.

### Solving equations by multiplying or dividing

**In Lessons 6-2 and 6-7** students will solve proportions and percent equations by multiplying and dividing.

### Writing fractions and decimals

**In Lesson 6-5** students will write percents as fractions and decimals and will write decimals and fractions as percents.

### Writing percents

**In Lessons 6-6, 6-7, and 6-8** students will solve percent problems.

# Skills Trace

| SKILL | INTRODUCED | DEVELOPED IN LESSON(S) | REVIEWED/REINFORCED |
|---|---|---|---|
| Writing and simplifying ratios and solving proportions | 6-1 | 6-2 | pp. 288, 293, 353, 473, 532, 576 |
| Solving problems that involve scale drawings | 6-3 | 6-3 | pp. 299, 373 |
| Finding probability | 6-4 | 6-5 | pp. 304, 326, 339, 408, 425, 625 |
| Writing decimals and fractions as percents | 6-5 | 6-6 | pp. 309, 313, 395, 419, 431, 463, 563 |
| Solving percent problems, including percent of increase and decrease, markups and discounts | 6-8 | 6-9 | pp. 321, 326, 359, 368, 402, 453, 468, 640 |

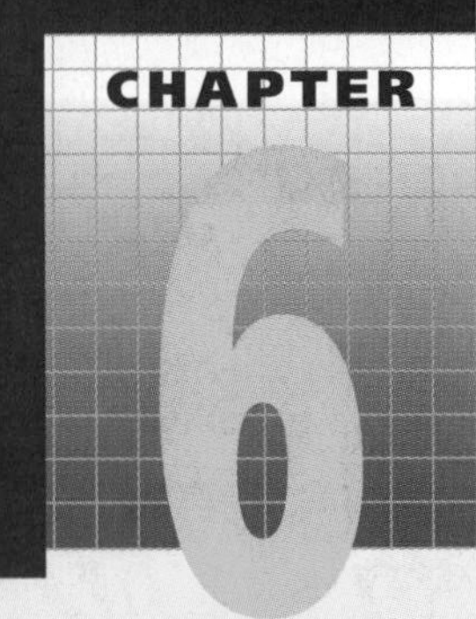

# Ratios, Proportions, and Percents

## Connecting to Students' Lives

Ask students to describe any experiences they have with playing or listening to music made on a stringed instrument.

## Interdisciplinary Connections

The Chapter Project connects math, music, and physics. You may want to display pictures or information about stringed instruments and vibrating strings.

## About the Project

The Chapter Project directs students to apply their knowledge of ratios and proportions to examining the physics of musical vibrations from stringed instruments.

CHAPTER 6

# Ratios, Proportions, and Percents

**What you'll learn in this chapter:**

- How to find and use ratios and unit rates
- How to write and solve proportions
- How to find and use percents

276 Chapter 6

*Web Extension*
**www.phschool.com**

For Students
Chapter Support with Internet links
Interactive Activities

For Teachers
Curriculum Support
Professional Development
Product Information
Regional Support Information

# STRING BAND

Guitars, fiddles, harps . . . people have been enjoying stringed instruments for thousands of years. The music from a stringed instrument follows rules of mathematics that you will learn in this chapter.

***Make a Musical Instrument*** For the chapter project, you will construct and play a simple stringed instrument. You will make measurements that can be applied to a real instrument. Your final project will consist of drawings that show how to play notes on both instruments.

### *Steps to help you complete the project*


**p. 288** Activity: Creating

**p. 293** Activity: Investigating

**p. 304** Activity: Calculating

**p. 317** Activity: Calculating

**p. 327** Finishing the Chapter Project

*Web Extension*
**www.phschool.com**

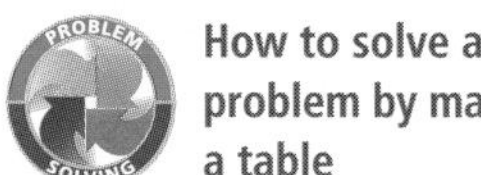

How to solve a problem by making a table

## LAUNCHING THE PROJECT

*The Chapter Project is optional and may be assigned at your discretion.*

Ask students:

- What are the names of some stringed instruments?
- How do stringed instruments make sound and music?
- What about the string in an instrument changes to change the musical note?

Distribute a copy of the Project Manager and Scoring Rubric to help students get an overview of the project.

Review the scoring rubric with students.

###  Project Notebook

Encourage students to keep all project-related materials in a separate folder or notebook. Call attention to the fact that they will find much useful information on the Web site **www.phschool.com**.

**Tracking the Project** Set benchmark deadlines for students to show you their work in progress.

## Scoring Rubric

**3** You calculate all string lengths accurately. You draw the instruments neatly to scale and label them correctly.

**2** You make minor errors in calculating string lengths or in labeling your drawing. Your drawing is neat but not to scale.

**1** You find inaccurate string lengths. Your drawing is incomplete and not to scale.

**0** Major elements of the project are incomplete or missing.

*Available in the Chapter 6 Support File in the Teaching Resources box.*

**Project Manager and Scoring Rubric**

**Getting Started** You will be making a drawing to show how to play notes on a string instrument you construct and on a cello. Read about the project in your textbook. As you work on the project, you will need a 12-inch ruler, a pencil, two rubber bands, materials to make your drawing, and materials to record your data and calculations.

**Checklist and Suggestions**

| | | |
|---|---|---|
| ❑ | Make your instrument and try it. | Play two notes and decide which is higher. |
| ❑ | Measure string lengths for notes in "The Star-Spangled Banner." | Be sure to measure from your finger to the pencil and record your results. |
| ❑ | Calculate the ratios of string lengths. | Write each ratio in simplest form and record the ratios in a table. |
| ❑ | Calculate the location of notes on a cello. | Use a proportion. |
| ❑ | Make your drawing. | Draw the instruments to scale. |
| ❑ | Share your drawing and calculations with a friend. | Make any necessary changes. |

**Scoring Rubric**


**3** You calculate all string lengths accurately. You draw the instruments neatly to scale and label them correctly.

**2** You make minor errors in calculating string lengths or in labeling your drawing. Your drawing is neat but not to scale.

**1** You find inaccurate string lengths. Your drawing is incomplete and not to scale.

**0** Major elements of the project are incomplete or missing.


**Your Evaluation of the Project** Evaluate your work, based on the Scoring Rubric.

**Teacher's Evaluation of the Project**

# 6-1

## Getting Ready

**Key Terms and Symbols** ratio, rate, unit rate

**Resources** A complete list of resources for this lesson is on p. 275H.

### Daily Skills Warm-Up

**Lesson 6-1**

Write each fraction in simplest form.

1. $\frac{30}{35}$ $\frac{6}{7}$
2. $\frac{24}{40}$ $\frac{3}{5}$
3. $\frac{34}{51}$ $\frac{2}{3}$
4. $\frac{54}{60}$ $\frac{9}{10}$

Find each quotient.

5. $120 \div 3$ 40
6. $840 \div 4$ 210
7. $\$4.75 \div 5$ $.95
8. $\$39.48 \div 6$ $6.58

### Background for the Lesson

A *ratio* compares two quantities by division. So, a ratio could say that a team has a 3 to 5 win-loss record. However, saying a team won two more games than they lost is a comparison, not a ratio. A *rate* is a ratio that compares quantities with two different units, such as 30 miles every 2 hours. A unit rate has a denominator of 1, as in 15 miles per (1) hour.

The order of the numbers in a ratio is very important. A team that has lost 5 games and won 3 has a win-loss ratio of 3 to 5. The first number in a ratio always names the quantity mentioned first.

## 1 Focus

### Connecting to Students' Lives

Discuss with students examples of ratios such as a team record for games won and lost or the ratio of girls to boys in a class.

### Connecting to Prior Knowledge

In Lesson 4-4, students learned to write fractions in simplest form by using the GCF. In this lesson, students use that skill when they write ratios as fractions in simplest form. In Lesson 6-2, they will use ratios in proportions.



# 6-1 Ratios and Unit Rates

**What You'll Learn**

1. To write and simplify ratios
2. To find rates and unit rates

**. . . And Why**

To use and compare measures such as unit prices, gas mileage, and speed

## PART 1 Writing Ratios

*Statistics* In the United States, about 10 out of every 15 people eligible to vote are registered to vote. The numbers 10 and 15 form a *ratio.*

**Ratio**

A **ratio** is a comparison of two quantities by division. You can write a ratio in different ways.

| Arithmetic | Algebra |
|---|---|
| 10 to 15   10 : 15   $\frac{10}{15}$ | $a$ to $b$   $a : b$   $\frac{a}{b}$, for $b \neq 0$ |

DATA ANALYSIS CONNECTION

**EXAMPLE 1**

**Students were asked in a survey whether they had after-school jobs. Write each ratio as a fraction in simplest form.**

**After-School Jobs**

| Response | Number |
|---|---|
| Have a Job | 40 |
| Don't Have a Job | 60 |
| Total | 100 |

**a. students with jobs to students without jobs**

$$\frac{\text{students with jobs}}{\text{students without jobs}} = \frac{40}{60} = \frac{2}{3}$$

**b. students without jobs to all students surveyed**

$$\frac{\text{students without jobs}}{\text{all students surveyed}} = \frac{60}{100} = \frac{3}{5}$$

**TRY THIS** Write each ratio as a fraction in simplest form.

1. students with jobs to all students surveyed $\frac{2}{5}$
2. students without jobs to students with jobs $\frac{3}{2}$



## Tools to Monitor Progress

**BEFORE THE LESSON**

**To check prerequisite skills:**

- Simplifying fractions

**Skills You Need,** p. 275

**Skills Handbook,** p. 737

**Skills Intervention Kit,** Number Theory and Fraction Concepts

**DURING THE LESSON**

**To check understanding:**

**Try This** exercises on student page

- **Additional Example 1**

  Use the table in Example 1 to write the ratio of all students surveyed to students without jobs. $\frac{100}{60}$

## Finding Rates and Unit Rates

A **rate** is a ratio that compares quantities in different units. A **unit rate** is a rate that has a denominator of 1. Examples of unit rates include unit prices, gas mileage, and speed.

**DATA ANALYSIS** CONNECTION

### EXAMPLE 2

*Unit Prices* **The table shows prices for different sizes of the same dish detergent. Which size has the lowest unit price?**

Mini: $\frac{\text{price} \rightarrow}{\text{volume} \rightarrow} \frac{\$1.20}{12 \text{ fl oz}} = \$.10/\text{fl oz}$

Family: $\frac{\text{price} \rightarrow}{\text{volume} \rightarrow} \frac{\$2.24}{28 \text{ fl oz}} = \$.08/\text{fl oz}$ — Find the unit prices.

Economy: $\frac{\text{price} \rightarrow}{\text{volume} \rightarrow} \frac{\$3.60}{40 \text{ fl oz}} = \$.09/\text{fl oz}$

The Family size has the lowest unit price.

**Dish Detergent Prices**

| Size | Volume (fl oz) | Price |
|---|---|---|
| Mini | 12 | $1.20 |
| Family | 28 | $2.24 |
| Economy | 40 | $3.60 |

**TRY THIS** Find each unit rate.

3. Two liters of spring water costs $1.98. $.99/L
4. A car goes 425 mi on 12.5 gal of gas. 34 mi/gal

You can use dimensional analysis to choose conversion factors for converting rates.

### EXAMPLE 3

**Convert 10 mi/h to feet per minute.**

$10 \text{ mi/h} = \frac{10 \text{ mi}}{1 \text{ h}} \cdot \frac{5{,}280 \text{ ft}}{1 \text{ mi}} \cdot \frac{1\text{h}}{60 \text{ min}}$ — Use conversion factors that convert miles to feet and hours to minutes.

$= \frac{\overset{1}{\cancel{10}} \cancel{\text{mi}}}{1 \cancel{\text{h}}} \cdot \frac{\overset{880}{\cancel{5{,}280}} \text{ ft}}{1 \cancel{\text{mi}}} \cdot \frac{1\cancel{\text{h}}}{\underset{1}{\cancel{60}} \text{ min}}$ — Divide the common factors and units.

$= \frac{880 \text{ ft}}{\text{min}}$ — Simplify.

10 mi/h equals 880 ft/min.

**TRY THIS** Complete each statement.

5. 3.5 qt/min = ■ gal/h 52.5
6. 12 cm/s = ■ m/h 432



# 2 Teach

## Part 1 Teaching Notes

The order of the words in the problem tells how to order the numbers in the ratio. Make sure students understand that the ratios $\frac{3}{5}$ and $\frac{5}{3}$ are not equivalent.

**ELL** Have students practice reading aloud the various ways you can write a ratio. Explain that all three symbols have the same meaning whether the ratio is written, for example, as 2 to 3, 2 : 3, or $\frac{2}{3}$.

### Example 1

**Build understanding.** Ask: What does the order of the words *students with jobs to students without jobs* tell you about how to write the fraction? **The numerator is the number of students with jobs.**

**Auditory Learning** Saying ratios aloud helps students write the numbers in the same order as the words.

## Part 2 Teaching Notes

**Visual Learning** Use a concept map such as this one to help students remember that every rate is a ratio and every unit rate is both a rate and a ratio.

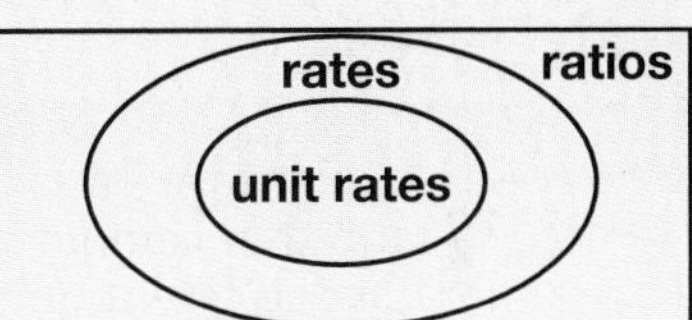


### Example 2

**Build understanding.** Ask: According to the table, how much detergent can you buy for $2.24? **28 fl oz**

- **Additional Example 2**
  You can buy a package of 100 index cards for $2.70 or 50 cards for $1.30, or 25 cards for $.75. Which size has the lowest unit price? **50 card pack; unit price, $.026/index card**
- **Additional Example 3**
  Convert 30 gal/min to c/s. **8 c/s**

## AFTER THE LESSON

**To assess knowledge:**

**Lesson Quiz**

Find the unit rate.

1. 9 pizzas made every 12 min **0.75 pizzas/min**

Write the ratio in three different ways.

2. for a square with a side of 1, the ratio of its side length to its perimeter **$\frac{1}{4}$; 1 : 4; 1 to 4**

- For enrichment and reteaching options see Resources on p. 275H.

# 3 Practice/Assess

## Assignment Guide

To provide flexible scheduling, this lesson can be divided into parts.

**▼ Part 1**
**Core** 1–6, 12–23, 37, 41
✪ **Extension** 36, 38

**▼ Part 2**
**Core** 7–11, 24–35, 40, 42
✪ **Extension** 39

Mixed Review can be assigned at any time for maintenance.

**Connecting to History** The width-to-length ratio of any official United States flag must be 1 : 1.9, according to federal regulations set by President Taft in 1912.

### Exercises

**Math Reasoning Exercise 36** One counterexample disproves the statement. One example does not prove that the statement is true; that requires a general mathematical proof.

### ✪ Challenge

Is the ratio of senators to representatives in Congress greater than or less than $\frac{1}{4}$? Explain. **less than $\frac{1}{4}$; 100 senators to 435 representatives**

### Closure

A ratio compares two quantities by division. A rate is a ratio that compares two quantities that have different units. A unit rate is a rate that has a denominator of 1.

### Daily Cumulative Review

**Simplify each expression.** *(Lesson 5-9)*

1. $\left(\frac{2}{7}\right)^2$ $\frac{4}{49}$
2. $\left(-\frac{4}{5}\right)^2$ $\frac{16}{25}$
3. $(-6x)^3$ $-216x^3$
4. $-(r^2s^2)^2$ $-r^4s^4$
5. $(2s^3t^4)^3$ $8s^9t^{12}$
6. $\left(\frac{3c}{8d}\right)^3$ $\frac{27c^3}{512d^3}$

**Solve each equation.** *(Lesson 5-8)*

7. $-\frac{3}{7}x = \frac{9}{28}$ $x = -\frac{3}{4}$
8. $8a = \frac{6}{11}$ $a = \frac{3}{44}$
9. $3\frac{1}{4}k = \frac{2}{5}$ $k = \frac{8}{65}$
10. $-\frac{25}{26} = -\frac{1}{3}r$ $2\frac{23}{26} = r$
11. $\frac{7}{8} = -\frac{1}{4}m$ $-3\frac{1}{2} = m$
12. $1\frac{3}{4} = -5\frac{3}{5}n$ $-\frac{5}{16} = n$

**Mixed Review**

**Use the Distributive Property to simplify.**

13. 5(82) (2-2) 410
14. (302)6 (2-2) 1,812
15. 8(89) (2-2) 712
16. 6(5) + 6(4) (2-2) 54
17. 9(4) − 9(3) (2-2) 9
18. 8(2) + 3(2) (2-2) 22

**Solve each equation.**

19. $5a = 35$ (2-6) $a = 7$
20. $25x = 325$ (2-6) $x = 13$
21. $45 = 3c$ (2-6) $15 = c$
22. $20 = 4n$ (2-6) $5 = n$
23. $12v = 192$ (2-6) $v = 16$
24. $9r = 162$ (2-6) $r = 18$

**Estimate each product or quotient.**
Answers may vary. Accept any reasonable answer.

25. 3.8 · 19 (3-2) about 80
26. 6.2 ÷ 3.1 (3-2) about 2
27. 1.5 · 2.1 (3-2) about 4
28. 49.5 · 3.7 (3-2) about 200
29. 1.1 · 27 (3-2) about 27
30. 24.1 ÷ 6.3 (3-2) about 4



# Exercises

## CHECK UNDERSTANDING

**Write each ratio as a fraction in simplest form.**

1. 9 : 27 $\frac{1}{3}$
2. 12 to 8 $\frac{3}{2}$
3. 10 out of 16 $\frac{5}{8}$
4. 2 to 18 $\frac{1}{9}$
5. 6 : 50 $\frac{3}{25}$
6. $\frac{1,000}{10,000}$ $\frac{1}{10}$

**Find the unit rate for each situation.**

7. A sprinter runs 200 m in 25 s. 8 m/s
8. A keyboarder types 1,575 words in 25 min. 63 words/min

**Complete each statement.**

9. 720 m/day = ■ m/min $\frac{1}{2}$
10. 1.5 gal/min = ■ qt/h 360
11. $9/h = ■ ¢/min 15

## PRACTICE AND PROBLEM SOLVING

**Write each ratio as a fraction in simplest form.**

12. 3 : 8 $\frac{3}{8}$
13. 7 to 9 $\frac{7}{9}$
14. 8 out of 11 $\frac{8}{11}$
15. $\frac{14}{18}$ $\frac{7}{9}$
16. 15 : 25 $\frac{3}{5}$
17. 36 to 48 $\frac{3}{4}$
18. 60 to 24 $\frac{5}{2}$
19. 16 : 12 $\frac{4}{3}$

**For each situation, write a ratio as a fraction in simplest form.**

20. 3 out of 12 people live in a rural area. $\frac{1}{4}$
21. In one class, there are 6 girls for every 10 boys. $\frac{3}{5}$
22. 98 homes in 100 have a TV. $\frac{49}{50}$
23. 70 homes out of 125 have a personal computer. $\frac{14}{25}$

**Find each unit rate.**

24. 20 mi in 5 h 4 mi/h
25. 42 gal in 7 min 6 gal/min
26. a fall of 144 ft in 3 s 48 ft/s
27. 245 mi in 56 h $4\frac{3}{8}$ mi/h
28. 676 mi in 13 h 52 mi/h
29. 20 gal flowing in 4 min 5 gal/min

**Complete each statement.**

30. $29/kg = ■ ¢/g 2.9
31. 32 yd/min = ■ in./s 19.2
32. 0.85 km/s = ■ m/min 51,000
33. 80 mi/h = ■ ft/s 117.3
34. 20 fl oz/min = ■ qt/day 900
35. $\frac{90 \text{ m}}{4 \text{ s}}$ = ■ km/h 81

✪ 36. *Mathematical Reasoning* A student claims that a ratio remains unchanged if 1 is added to both the numerator and the denominator of the fraction. Does $\frac{a}{b}$ equal $\frac{a+1}{b+1}$? Explain, and give an example or a counterexample. **Answers may vary. Sample: Usually not; adding 1 to both the numerator and the denominator leaves the ratio unchanged only when $a = b$. $\frac{1}{1} = \frac{1+1}{1+1}$, but $\frac{1}{2} \neq \frac{1+1}{2+1}$, or $\frac{2}{3}$**



### Alternative Assessment

Have students write and simplify ratios using facts from the classroom: pencils to pens, cats to dogs for pets, play or not play a musical instrument, and so forth.

37a. class A $\frac{6}{30}$ or $\frac{1}{5}$; class B $\frac{4}{24}$ or $\frac{1}{6}$

37. a. For each class, write the ratio of the number of boys to the total number of students.
    b. Which class has the greater ratio of boys to students? class A

**Boys in Two Classes**

| Class | Number of Boys | Number of Students |
|---|---|---|
| A | 6 | 30 |
| B | 4 | 24 |

38. A bookstore sells hardbacks, paperbacks, and magazines. The store sells 5 magazines for every 3 hardbacks. It sells 20 paperbacks for every 10 magazines. Write a ratio for each pair of sales categories.
    a. hardbacks to magazines $\frac{3}{5}$
    b. magazines to paperbacks $\frac{1}{2}$
    c. hardbacks to all publications (*Hint:* First find the number of hardbacks sold for every 10 magazines.) $\frac{1}{6}$

39. *Science* Density is the ratio of a substance's mass to its volume. A volume of 20 cubic centimeters of gold has a mass of 386 grams. Express the density of gold as a unit rate. 19.3 g/cm$^3$

40. *Error Analysis* A student converts 100 ft/min to 500 in./s. Use dimensional analysis to explain why the student's result is not reasonable. Answers may vary. Sample: $\frac{100 \text{ ft}}{1 \text{ min}} \cdot \frac{12 \text{ in.}}{1 \text{ ft}} \cdot \frac{1 \text{ min}}{60 \text{ s}}$ shows that $100 \div 5$ not $100 \cdot 5$ gives inches per second.

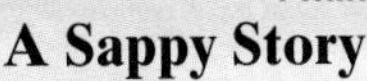

## A Sappy Story

Connecticut has more than 100 farms that produce maple syrup. Sugarers collect sap and boil it down to syrup. In a good year, one small sugarer in Connecticut collects 300 gallons of sap from 200 trees. The sap boils down to just seven gallons of syrup. The syrup is sold for \$4.50 per half pint or \$44 per gallon.

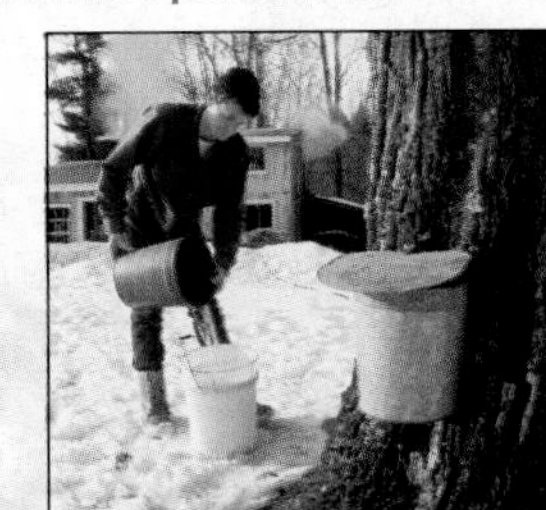

*Math in the Media* **Refer to the article above.**

41. Write the ratio of sap to syrup in three different ways. 300 : 7, 300 to 7, $\frac{300}{7}$

42. Calculate the unit prices for syrup sold by the half-pint and syrup sold by the gallon. Which has the lower unit price? \$9/pint or \$72/gal, \$44/gal; syrup sold by the gallon

## Mixed Review

**Simplify each expression.** *(Lesson 5-9)*

43. $(-3 \cdot 4)^3$ $-1{,}728$

44. $(2x^2y)^4$ $16x^8y^4$

45. $\left(-\frac{ab^3}{a^2b}\right)^3$ $-\frac{b^6}{a^3}$

**Compare. Use >, <, or = to complete each statement.** *(Lesson 5-2)*

46. $\frac{7}{8}$ ■ $\frac{14}{24}$ >

47. $\frac{4}{12}$ ■ $\frac{10}{30}$ =

48. $\frac{13}{20}$ ■ 0.6 >

49. *Choose a Strategy* Three friends shared the driving on a long trip. Marla drove 7 mi more than Guido. Guido drove five times as far as Juanita did. Juanita drove 112 mi. How long was the trip? 1,239 mi

See also Extra Practice section.



## Practice

**Find each unit rate.**

1. 78 mi on 3 gal 26 mi/gal
2. \$52.50 in 7 h \$7.50/h
3. 416 mi in 8 h 52 mi/h
4. 9 bull's eyes in 117 throws 13 throws/bull's eye

**Write each ratio as a fraction in simplest form.**

|  | Boys | Girls |
|---|---|---|
| 7th Grade | 26 | 34 |
| 8th Grade | 30 | 22 |

5. 7th-grade boys to 8th-grade boys $\frac{13}{15}$
6. 7th-grade girls to 7th-grade boys $\frac{17}{13}$
7. 7th graders to 8th graders $\frac{15}{13}$
8. boys to girls $\frac{1}{1}$
9. girls to all students $\frac{1}{2}$

**Write three different ratios for each model.**

10. □□□ ○○○○ $\frac{3}{4}, \frac{3}{7}, \frac{4}{7}$
11. ●●● ○○ $\frac{3}{2}, \frac{3}{5}, \frac{2}{5}$
12. $\frac{2}{4}, \frac{2}{6}, \frac{4}{6}$

**Write each ratio as a fraction is simplest form.**

13. 7 : 12 $\frac{7}{12}$
14. 3 is to 6 $\frac{1}{2}$
15. 10 : 45 $\frac{2}{9}$
16. 32 out of 40 $\frac{4}{5}$
17. 36 is to 60 $\frac{3}{5}$
18. 13 out of 14 $\frac{13}{14}$
19. 9 out of 21 $\frac{3}{7}$
20. 45 : 63 $\frac{5}{7}$
21. 24 is to 18 $\frac{4}{3}$
22. 15 out of 60 $\frac{1}{4}$



Practice

## Reteaching

One store has 6-packs of juice for \$.90. Another store has 8-packs of the same size juice cartons for \$1.12. Which is the better buy?

JUICE JUICE 6-pack \$0.90

JUICE JUICE 8-pack \$1.12

Find the unit rates.

6-pack: $\frac{\text{price} \rightarrow}{\text{number} \rightarrow} \frac{\$.90}{6} = \$.15/\text{carton}$

8-pack: $\frac{\text{price} \rightarrow}{\text{number} \rightarrow} \frac{\$1.12}{8} = \$.14/\text{carton}$

The 8-pack has the lowest unit price.

**Find each unit rate.**

1. \$91 in 14 h \$6.50/h
2. 372 mi in 6 h 62 mi/h
3. \$13.14 for 12 gal \$1.095/gal
4. 570 gal in 60 min 9.5 gal/min
5. 54¢ for 4 oz 13.5¢/oz
6. 592 words in 8 min 74 words/min
7. A 12 fl oz bottle of shampoo costs \$1.08 at Discount Mart. A 20 fl oz bottle of the same shampoo costs \$2.20 at Super Store. Find each unit rate and determine which is the better buy.

   12 fl oz bottle: \$.09/ fl oz

   20 fl oz bottle: \$.11/fl oz

   Better buy: 12 fl oz bottle
8. A school bus travels 53.3 mi on 6.5 gal of gas on its way to a museum for a field trip. On the return trip it takes the freeway and travels 53.2 mi on 5.6 gal of gas. Find the gas mileages of each trip and determine which is greater.

   To the museum: 8.2 mi/gal

   Returning from the museum: 9.5 mi/gal

   Better mileage: returning from the museum



Reteaching

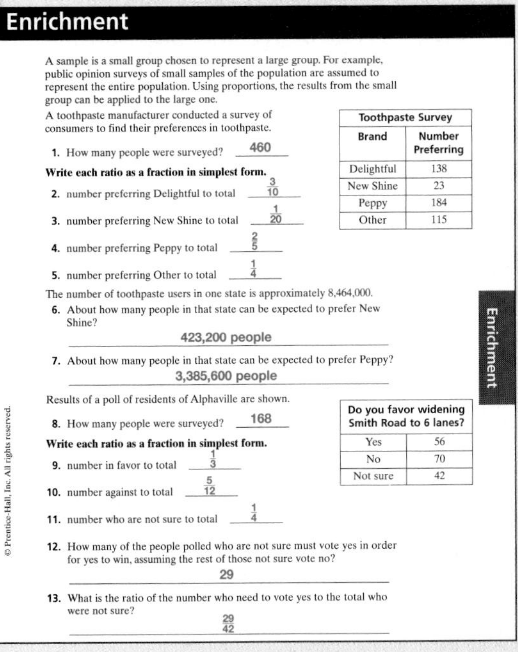

## Enrichment

A sample is a small group chosen to represent a large group. For example, public opinion surveys of small samples of the population are assumed to represent the entire population. Using proportions, the results from the small group can be applied to the large one.

A toothpaste manufacturer conducted a survey of consumers to find their preferences in toothpaste.

| Toothpaste Survey | |
|---|---|
| Brand | Number Preferring |
| Delightful | 138 |
| New Shine | 23 |
| Peppy | 184 |
| Other | 115 |

1. How many people were surveyed? 460

**Write each ratio as a fraction in simplest form.**

2. number preferring Delightful to total $\frac{3}{10}$
3. number preferring New Shine to total $\frac{1}{20}$
4. number preferring Peppy to total $\frac{2}{5}$
5. number preferring Other to total $\frac{1}{4}$

The number of toothpaste users in one state is approximately 8,464,000.

6. About how many people in that state can be expected to prefer New Shine? 423,200 people
7. About how many people in that state can be expected to prefer Peppy? 3,385,600 people

Results of a poll of residents of Alphaville are shown.

| Do you favor widening Smith Road to 6 lanes? | |
|---|---|
| Yes | 56 |
| No | 70 |
| Not sure | 42 |

8. How many people were surveyed? 168

**Write each ratio as a fraction in simplest form.**

9. number in favor to total $\frac{1}{3}$
10. number against to total $\frac{5}{12}$
11. number who are not sure to total $\frac{1}{4}$
12. How many of the people polled who are not sure must vote yes in order for yes to win, assuming the rest of those not sure vote no? 29
13. What is the ratio of the number who need to vote yes to the total who were not sure? $\frac{29}{42}$



Enrichment

## MATH TOOLBOX

### Extension

In Lesson 6-1 students used unit rates, which are rates with denominators of 1. This Math Toolbox shows students how to use a conversion factor, similar to a unit rate, to convert measures.

### Math Background

A conversion factor is a ratio with units that has a value of 1 either in the numerator $\left(\frac{1 \text{ yd}}{36 \text{ in.}}\right)$ or in the denominator $\left(\frac{36 \text{ in.}}{1 \text{ yd}}\right)$. A conversion factor may have both parts of the ratio in the same measurement system $\left(\frac{36 \text{ in.}}{1 \text{ yd}}\right)$ or a conversion factor may have units in different systems $\left(\frac{0.914 \text{ m}}{1 \text{ yd}}\right)$. When you multiply by a conversion factor, the units follow the same rules as numbers. Using a conversion factor to convert between different measurement systems is called *dimensional analysis.*

## Teaching Notes

**Error Prevention** Students may not select the correct conversion factor. Suggest that they actually strike through the units as they divide.

**Monitoring Progress** Example 1 Remind students that a mile is longer than a kilometer. Ask them to estimate whether the number of miles equivalent to 50 km will be greater than or less than 50. $< 50$

**Monitoring Progress** Example 2 Ask students which is greater, an ounce or a gram? ounce; almost 30 times greater

**Monitoring Progress** Example 3 How many quarts are in a gallon? 4 What is a reasonable estimate for the number of liters in 4 qt? about 4 About how many 2-L soda bottles is this? about 2

**Block Scheduling** If you have block scheduling or extended periods, you may wish to insert this Math Toolbox lesson between the completion of Part 2 of Lesson 6-1 and the beginning of Part 1 of Lesson 6-2. Use the Pacing Options on p. 275B to see the possibilities.

## MATH TOOLBOX

*Extension*
*After Lesson 6-1*

# *Converting between Measurement Systems*

You can use conversion factors to convert a unit of measure from one system to another. For example, since 1 mi ≈ 1.61 km, you can use $\frac{1 \text{ mi}}{1.61 \text{ km}}$ and $\frac{1.61 \text{ km}}{1 \text{ mi}}$ as conversion factors.

The table shows some useful conversion factors.

| Customary Units and Metric Units | Conversion Factor |
|---|---|
| 1 in. = 2.54 cm | $\frac{1 \text{ in.}}{2.54 \text{ cm}}$ or $\frac{2.54 \text{ cm}}{1 \text{ in.}}$ |
| 1 mi ≈ 1.61 km | $\frac{1 \text{ mi}}{1.61 \text{ km}}$ or $\frac{1.61 \text{ km}}{1 \text{ mi}}$ |
| 1.06 qt ≈ 1 L | $\frac{1.06 \text{ qt}}{1 \text{ L}}$ or $\frac{1 \text{ L}}{1.06 \text{ qt}}$ |
| 1 oz ≈ 28.4 g | $\frac{1 \text{ oz}}{28.4 \text{ g}}$ or $\frac{28.4 \text{ g}}{1 \text{ oz}}$ |
| 2.20 lb ≈ 1 kg | $\frac{2.20 \text{ lb}}{1 \text{ kg}}$ or $\frac{1 \text{ kg}}{2.20 \text{ lb}}$ |

You can use dimensional analysis to decide which conversion factor to use.

### EXAMPLE 1

**The longest track event at the Olympics is the 50-km walk. How long is the race in miles?**

$50 \text{ km} \approx 50 \text{ km} \cdot \frac{1 \text{ mi}}{1.61 \text{ km}}$ Use a conversion factor that changes kilometers to miles.

$= 50 \text{ km} \cdot \frac{1 \text{ mi}}{1.61 \text{ km}}$ Divide the common units.

$= \frac{50 \text{ mi}}{1.61}$ Multiply.

$\approx 31 \text{ mi}$ Divide.

The 50-km walk is about 31 mi long.

**Convert. Where necessary, round to the nearest tenth.**

1. 16 cm = ■ in. 6.3
2. ■ mi = 20 km 12.4
3. ■ km = 100 mi 161
4. ■ L = 50 qt 47.2
5. ■ g = 15 oz 426
6. 15 L = ■ qt 15.9
7. ■ lb = 14 kg 30.8
8. 44 lb = ■ kg 20



- **Additional Example 1**
  Jenny walks a 3-km trail on Saturday. About how long is her walk in miles? ≈ 1.86 mi, or about 2 mi
- **Additional Example 2**
  About how many ounces are in 45 g? about 1.6 oz
- **Additional Example 3**
  For a weekend trip, the family plans to take about 4 gal of water. How many 1-L bottles should they pack? 15 1-L bottles

You can estimate using conversion factors.

## EXAMPLE 2

**About how many ounces are in 60 grams?**

$60\text{ g} \approx 60\text{ g} \cdot \frac{1\text{ oz}}{28.4\text{ g}}$ Use the conversion factor that changes grams to ounces.

$\approx 60\text{ g} \cdot \frac{1\text{ oz}}{30\text{ g}}$ Round the conversion factor to a number compatible with 60.

$= \overset{2}{\cancel{60}}\text{ g} \cdot \frac{1\text{ oz}}{\underset{1}{\cancel{30}}\text{ g}}$ Divide the common factors and units.

$= 2\text{ oz}$ Simplify.

There are about 2 ounces in 60 grams.

Sometimes you may need to use two or more conversion factors.

## EXAMPLE 3

**A punch recipe calls for a gallon of sparkling water. How many 2-L bottles should you buy?**

$1\text{ gal} \approx 1\text{ gal} \cdot \frac{4\text{ qt}}{1\text{ gal}} \cdot \frac{1\text{ L}}{1.06\text{ qt}}$ Use conversion factors that change gallons to quarts and quarts to liters.

$= 1\text{ }\cancel{\text{gal}} \cdot \frac{4\text{ }\cancel{\text{qt}}}{1\text{ }\cancel{\text{gal}}} \cdot \frac{1\text{ L}}{1.06\text{ }\cancel{\text{qt}}}$ Divide the common units.

$= \frac{4\text{ L}}{1.06}$ Multiply numerators and multiply denominators.

$= 3.8\text{ L}$ Divide.

Now find the number of bottles you need for 3.8 L.

$\frac{3.8}{2} = 1.9$ Divide by 2, since there are 2 L per bottle.

You need about 1.9 bottles. You should buy two bottles.

**Convert. Where necessary, round to the nearest tenth.**

9. 100 oz = ■ kg 2.8
10. ■ L = 212 pt 100
11. 500 g = ■ lb 1.1
12. 1,000 mm = ■ in. 39.4
13. ■ gal = 20 L 5.3
14. ■ km/h = 10 mi/h 16.1
15. *Home Economics* A recipe calls for 8 oz of figs. The figs come in packages of 100 g. How many packages should you buy? 3 packages
16. *Writing* Explain how you would estimate the number of kilometers in 19 miles. Answers may vary. Sample: Estimate the product of 1.61 and 19 as $1.6 \times 20$, or 32.

# 6-2

## Getting Ready

**Key Terms and Symbols** proportion, cross products, Cross Products Property

**Resources** A complete list of resources for this lesson is on p. 275H.

### Daily Skills Warm-Up

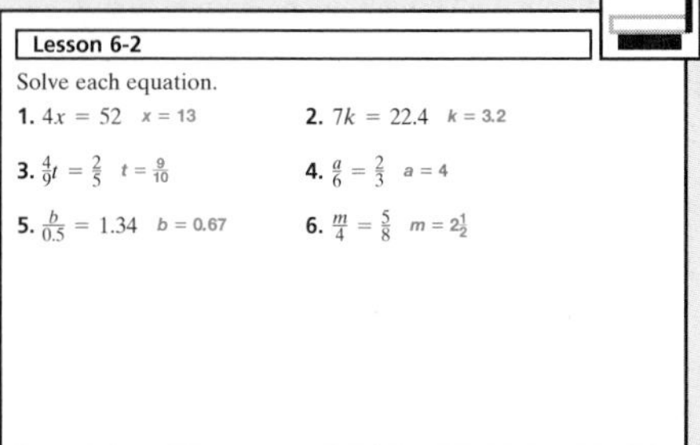

Lesson 6-2

Solve each equation.

1. $4x = 52$ $x = 13$
2. $7k = 22.4$ $k = 3.2$
3. $\frac{4}{9}t = \frac{2}{5}$ $t = \frac{9}{10}$
4. $\frac{a}{6} = \frac{2}{3}$ $a = 4$
5. $\frac{b}{0.5} = 1.34$ $b = 0.67$
6. $\frac{m}{4} = \frac{5}{8}$ $m = 2\frac{1}{2}$

### Background for the Lesson

A mathematical sentence that states that two ratios are equal is a *proportion.* Like any mathematical sentence, a proportion may be true ($\frac{3}{4} = \frac{6}{8}$), or false ($\frac{3}{4} = \frac{4}{3}$), or neither ($\frac{3}{4} = \frac{x}{8}$) because it contains a variable. To solve a proportion with a variable, you find the value of *x* that makes the sentence true: $x = 6$. You can multiply each side of any proportion by the product of the denominators, or by the LCD (least common denominator) to simplify it. Setting the cross products equal to each other is a shortcut for this.

## 1 Focus

### Connecting to Students' Lives

You use proportions when you make a mixture, such as juice or soup from concentrate. If you want to mix half the package, you solve a proportion to find the amount of liquid to use.

### Connecting to Prior Knowledge

In Lesson 6-1, students learned to write ratios and simplify ratios by using the GCF. In this lesson, they use those skills to write and solve proportions. In Lesson 6-3, students will apply proportions to similar figures and scale drawings.

# 6-2 Proportions

**What You'll Learn**

1. To solve proportions
2. To use proportions to solve problems

**. . . And Why**

To solve real-world problems involving science

## PART 1 Solving Proportions

A **proportion** is an equality of two ratios—for example, $\frac{6}{9} = \frac{8}{12}$. You can use the Multiplication Property of Equality to show an important property of all proportions.

If $\frac{a}{b} = \frac{c}{d}$

then $\frac{a}{b} \cdot bd = \frac{c}{d} \cdot bd$ Multiplication Property of Equality

$\frac{ab d}{b} = \frac{cbd}{d}$ $\frac{b}{b} = 1$ and $\frac{d}{d} = 1$

and $ad = cb$, or $ad = bc$.

The products $ad$ and $bc$ are called the **cross products** of the proportion $\frac{a}{b} = \frac{c}{d}$.

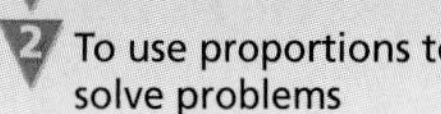

**Reading Math**

Read the proportion $\frac{6}{9} = \frac{8}{12}$ as "the ratio of 6 to 9 equals the ratio of 8 to 12," or as "6 is to 9 as 8 is to 12."

**Cross Products**

In a proportion, the cross products are equal.

| Arithmetic | Algebra |
|---|---|
| $\frac{6}{9} = \frac{8}{12}$ | $\frac{a}{b} = \frac{c}{d}$ |
| $6 \cdot 12 = 9 \cdot 8 = 72$ | $ad = bc$ |

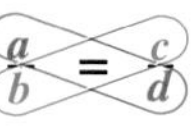

To solve a proportion that contains a variable, you find the value that makes the equation true.

**EXAMPLE 1**

**Solve $\frac{x}{9} = \frac{4}{6}$.**

**Method 1** Multiplication Property of Equality

$\frac{x}{9} = \frac{4}{6}$

$\frac{x}{9} \cdot 9 = \frac{4}{6} \cdot 9$

$x = \frac{36}{6}$

$x = 6$

**Method 2** cross products

$\frac{x}{9} = \frac{4}{6}$

$x \cdot 6 = 9 \cdot 4$

$6x = 36$

$\frac{6x}{6} = \frac{36}{6}$

$x = 6$



## Tools to Monitor Progress

### BEFORE THE LESSON

**To check prerequisite skills:**

- Simplifying fractions
- Solving equations by multiplying or dividing

**Skills You Need,** p. 275

**Skills Handbook,** p. 737

**Skills Intervention Kit,** Pre-Algebra Basics

### DURING THE LESSON

**To check understanding:**

**Try This** exercises on student page

- **Additional Example 1**
  Solve $\frac{2}{7} = \frac{y}{14}$. $y = 4$
- **Additional Example 2**
  Do the ratios $\frac{3}{5}$ and $\frac{21}{35}$ form a proportion? yes

■ **TRY THIS** Solve each proportion

1. $\frac{h}{9} = \frac{2}{3}$ 6
2. $\frac{4}{5} = \frac{t}{55}$ 44
3. $\frac{22}{d} = \frac{6}{21}$ 77

Two ratios form a proportion if their cross products are equal.

### EXAMPLE 2

**Do the ratios $\frac{4}{6}$ and $\frac{10}{14}$ form a proportion?**

| | |
|---|---|
| $\frac{4}{6} \stackrel{?}{=} \frac{10}{14}$ | Test by writing as a proportion. |
| $4 \cdot 14 \stackrel{?}{=} 6 \cdot 10$ | Write cross products. |
| $56 \neq 60$ | Simplify. |

No, the ratios do not form a proportion.

■ **TRY THIS** Tell whether each pair of ratios forms a proportion.

4. $\frac{6}{9}, \frac{4}{6}$ yes
5. $\frac{15}{20}, \frac{5}{7}$ no
6. $\frac{7}{12}, \frac{17.5}{30}$ yes

## PART 2 Using Proportions to Solve Problems

You can write and solve proportions for many real-world problems.

**MEASUREMENT** CONNECTION

### EXAMPLE 3

*Navigation* **One hundred nautical miles equals about 115 standard, or statute, miles. To the nearest mile, how far in statute miles is 156 nautical miles?**

Let $d$ = distance in statute miles.

$$\frac{\text{distance in nautical miles}}{\text{distance in statute miles}} \rightarrow \frac{100}{115} = \frac{156}{d} \leftarrow \frac{\text{distance in nautical miles}}{\text{distance in statute miles}}$$

| | |
|---|---|
| $100d = 115(156)$ | Write cross products. |
| $d = \frac{115(156)}{100}$ | Divide each side by 100. |
| $d \approx 179$ | A calculator may be useful. |

156 nautical miles is about 179 statute miles.

Sailors and astronauts measure distances in *nautical miles.* This photo of the Great Lakes was taken from the space shuttle at an altitude of 156 nautical miles.

■ **TRY THIS**

7. To the nearest mile, how far in nautical miles is 100 statute miles? 87 nautical miles



# 2 Teach

## PART 1 Part 1 Teaching Notes

Walk students carefully through the math reasoning and steps that lead to the conclusion that the cross products of a proportion are equal.

### ■ Example 1

**Build understanding.** Ask: Where do the 9's on the left side of the equation go when you multiply each side by 9? **$\frac{9}{9}$ is 1, the multiplicative identity; the 9's can be omitted on the left side.**

### ■ Example 2

**Build understanding.** Ask: What does the question mark over the equals sign mean? **You don't know whether the two ratios are actually equal to each other.**

**ELL** Explain that you write the question mark (?) over the equals sign (=) until you know that the two sides are either equal or are not equal.

## PART 2 Part 2 Teaching Notes

Sailors call the unit rate of one nautical mile per hour a *knot,* from a time when sailors used a knotted rope to measure how fast they were going. So, 10 *knots* is actually 10 nautical miles per hour.

### ■ Example 3

**Build understanding.** Estimate first. Will 156 statute miles be greater or less than 156 nautical miles? Why? **less than; A statute mile contains less feet than a nautical mile.**

**Error Prevention** Students may change the order of the quantities in the ratios of a proportion. Suggest that they say the units aloud, for example: "nautical over statute equals nautical over statute" to check that both ratios are written in the same order.

**Tactile Learning** Suggest that students draw two lines, forming an X, to indicate the cross products of a proportion.

- **Additional Example 3**
One fathom is 2 yd and 1 rod is 5.5 yd. About how many fathoms is 25 rods? **68.75 fathoms**

## AFTER THE LESSON

**To assess knowledge:**

**Lesson Quiz**

Solve each proportion.

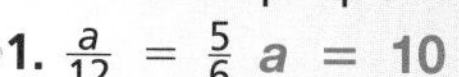

1. $\frac{a}{12} = \frac{5}{6}$ $a = 10$

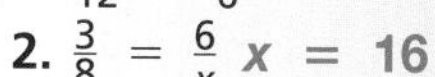

2. $\frac{3}{8} = \frac{6}{x}$ $x = 16$

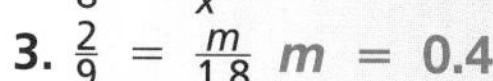

3. $\frac{2}{9} = \frac{m}{1.8}$ $m = 0.4$

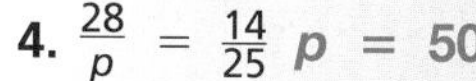

4. $\frac{28}{p} = \frac{14}{25}$ $p = 50$

- For enrichment and reteaching options see Resources on p. 275H.

# 3 Practice/Assess

## Assignment Guide

To provide flexible scheduling, this lesson can be divided into parts.

**Part 1**
**Core** 1–6, 10–47
**Extension** 48–51

**Part 2**
**Core** 7–9, 52–61
**Extension** 62–66

Mixed Review can be assigned at any time for maintenance.

## Exercises

**Math Reasoning Exercise 9** Students can prove this either by using the Multiplicative Property of Equality or by using cross products.

**Test Prep Exercise 58** Think of an actual amount, such as two spoons of red paint to three spoons of blue. Find the total number of spoons of paint for purple.

## Challenge

A pharmacist makes up a solution of boric acid that has 5 parts acid to 95 parts water. She uses 3 fl oz of acid. How many fl oz of water will she use? 57 fl oz

## Closure

A proportion is a statement that two ratios are equal. You can solve a proportion with a variable in it by setting the cross products equal to each other and solving the equation.

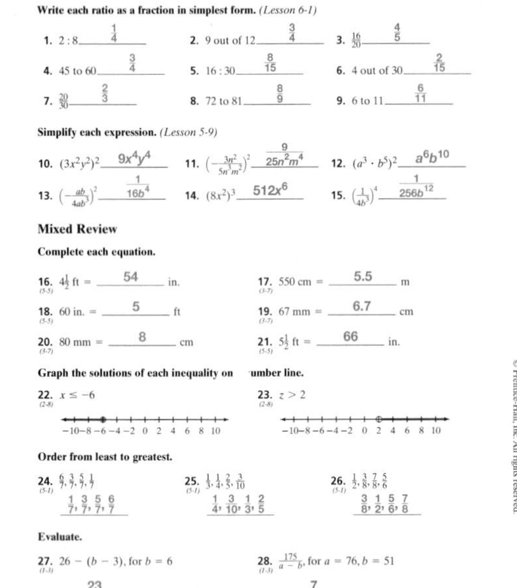

**Daily Cumulative Review**

**Write each ratio as a fraction in simplest form.** *(Lesson 6-1)*

1. 2 : 8 $\frac{1}{4}$
2. 9 out of 12 $\frac{3}{4}$
3. $\frac{16}{20}$ $\frac{4}{5}$
4. 45 to 60 $\frac{3}{4}$
5. 16 : 30 $\frac{8}{15}$
6. 4 out of 30 $\frac{2}{15}$
7. $\frac{20}{30}$ $\frac{2}{3}$
8. 72 to 81 $\frac{8}{9}$
9. 6 to 11 $\frac{6}{11}$

**Simplify each expression.** *(Lesson 5-9)*

10. $(3x^2y^2)^2$ $9x^4y^4$
11. $\left(-\frac{3n^2}{5n^3m^2}\right)^2$ $\frac{9}{25n^2m^4}$
12. $(a^3 \cdot b^5)^2$ $a^6b^{10}$
13. $\left(-\frac{ab}{4ab^3}\right)^2$ $\frac{1}{16b^4}$
14. $(8x^2)^3$ $512x^6$
15. $\left(\frac{1}{4b^3}\right)^4$ $\frac{1}{256b^{12}}$

**Mixed Review**

**Complete each equation.**

16. (5-5) $4\frac{1}{2}$ ft = 54 in.
17. (3-7) 550 cm = 5.5 m
18. (5-5) 60 in. = 5 ft
19. (3-7) 67 mm = 6.7 cm
20. (3-7) 80 mm = 8 cm
21. (5-5) $5\frac{1}{2}$ ft = 66 in.

**Graph the solutions of each inequality on umber line.**

22. (2-8) $x \leq -6$
−10 −8 −6 −4 −2 0 2 4 6 8 10
23. (2-8) $z > 2$
−10 −8 −6 −4 −2 0 2 4 6 8 10

**Order from least to greatest.**

24. (5-1) $\frac{6}{7}, \frac{3}{7}, \frac{5}{7}, \frac{1}{7}$ $\frac{1}{7}, \frac{3}{7}, \frac{5}{7}, \frac{6}{7}$
25. (5-1) $\frac{1}{3}, \frac{1}{4}, \frac{2}{5}, \frac{3}{10}$ $\frac{1}{4}, \frac{3}{10}, \frac{1}{3}, \frac{2}{5}$
26. (5-1) $\frac{1}{2}, \frac{3}{8}, \frac{7}{8}, \frac{5}{6}$ $\frac{3}{8}, \frac{1}{2}, \frac{5}{6}, \frac{7}{8}$

**Evaluate.**

27. (1-3) $26 - (b - 3)$, for $b = 6$ 23
28. (1-3) $\frac{175}{a - b}$, for $a = 76, b = 51$ 7





# Exercises

## CHECK UNDERSTANDING

**Solve each proportion.**

1. $\frac{2}{v} = \frac{1}{8}$ 16
2. $\frac{z}{42} = \frac{25}{70}$ 15
3. $\frac{4}{11} = \frac{x}{16.5}$ 6

**Tell whether each pair of ratios forms a proportion.**

4. $\frac{2}{3}$ and $\frac{10}{20}$ no
5. $\frac{80}{25}$ and $\frac{16}{5}$ yes
6. $\frac{3.9}{5.4}$ and $\frac{13}{18}$ yes

**Write a proportion for each situation. Then solve.**

7. Four ounces of orange juice contain 50 calories. Fourteen ounces contain $c$ calories. $\frac{14}{c} = \frac{4}{50}$; 175 calories
8. A lion has 12 heartbeats in 16 s, and $h$ heartbeats in 60 s. $\frac{12}{16} = \frac{h}{60}$; 45 heartbeats
9. *Mathematical Reasoning* If $\frac{a}{b} = \frac{c}{d}$, will $\frac{a}{c} = \frac{b}{d}$? Assume that $b \neq 0$, $c \neq 0$, and $d \neq 0$. Explain your reasoning. Yes; multiply each side by $\frac{b}{c}$.

## PRACTICE AND PROBLEM SOLVING

*Mental Math* **Solve by mental math.**

10. $\frac{1}{6} = \frac{a}{72}$ 12
11. $\frac{h}{4} = \frac{10}{8}$ 5
12. $\frac{16}{4} = \frac{8}{s}$ 2
13. $\frac{2}{9} = \frac{r}{36}$ 8
14. $\frac{n}{12} = \frac{12}{2}$ 72
15. $\frac{1}{15} = \frac{3}{p}$ 45
16. $\frac{120}{24} = \frac{y}{2}$ 10
17. $\frac{10}{v} = \frac{3}{1.5}$ 5

**Solve each proportion. Where necessary, round to the nearest tenth.**

18. $\frac{4}{15} = \frac{a}{75}$ 20
19. $\frac{4}{3} = \frac{b}{21}$ 28
20. $\frac{13}{c} = \frac{39}{60}$ 20
21. $\frac{3}{6} = \frac{7}{d}$ 14
22. $\frac{6}{25} = \frac{e}{80}$ 19.2
23. $\frac{4}{9} = \frac{f}{15}$ 6.7
24. $\frac{3}{8} = \frac{50}{g}$ 133.3
25. $\frac{24}{17} = \frac{108}{h}$ 76.5
26. $\frac{7}{9} = \frac{j}{22.5}$ 17.5
27. $\frac{11}{18} = \frac{k}{49.5}$ 30.3
28. $\frac{6}{13} = \frac{7.8}{m}$ 16.9
29. $\frac{20}{27} = \frac{1.1}{n}$ 1.5

*Estimation* **Estimate the solution of each proportion.**

30. $\frac{w}{20} = \frac{6}{23}$ 5
31. $\frac{3}{2} = \frac{29}{d}$ 20
32. $\frac{20}{3.9} = \frac{s}{6}$ 30
33. $\frac{1.5}{p} = \frac{2.1}{4.1}$ 3
34. $\frac{f}{4} = \frac{12}{49}$ 1
35. $\frac{60}{g} = \frac{24.1}{8.1}$ 20
36. $\frac{b}{19} = \frac{13}{6}$ 38
37. $\frac{9}{4.4} = \frac{x}{19}$ 38



## Alternative Assessment

Have students work with a partner to each write a proportion, then exchange, and test whether the proportion is true.

**Tell whether each pair of ratios forms a proportion.**

**38.** $\frac{4}{7}$ and $\frac{20}{25}$ no **39.** $\frac{3}{2}$ and $\frac{16}{10}$ no **40.** $\frac{3}{4}$ and $\frac{12}{15}$ no **41.** $\frac{8}{3}$ and $\frac{56}{21}$ yes

**42.** $\frac{9}{24}$ and $\frac{15}{40}$ yes **43.** $\frac{32}{20}$ and $\frac{20}{12}$ no **44.** $\frac{40}{24}$ and $\frac{75}{45}$ yes **45.** $\frac{120}{144}$ and $\frac{145}{75}$ no

**For Exercises 46–51, write a proportion for each phrase. Then solve. Where necessary, round to the nearest hundredth.**

**46.** 3 oz for \$1.65; 5 oz for $x$ dollars $\frac{3}{1.65} = \frac{5}{x}$; \$2.75

**47.** 20 lb for \$27.50; 12 lb for $x$ dollars $\frac{20}{27.50} = \frac{12}{x}$; \$16.50

**48.** 5 km in 18 min 36 s; 8 km in $v$ min See below right.

**49.** 25 yd in $2\frac{1}{2}$ s; 100 yd in $x$ seconds $\frac{25}{2.5} = \frac{100}{x}$; 10 s

**50.** 96 oz for \$2; $y$ pounds for \$10 $\frac{6}{2} = \frac{y}{10}$; 30 lb

**51.** 4 oz for \$1.85; 1 lb for $t$ dollars $\frac{4}{1.85} = \frac{16}{t}$; \$7.40

48. $\frac{5}{18.6} = \frac{8}{v}$; 29.76 min

**52.** Three posters cost \$9.60. At that rate, how many posters can you buy for \$48? 15 posters

**53.** Three tea bags are needed to make a gallon of iced tea. How many tea bags are needed to make four gallons? 12 tea bags

**54.** At the Copy Shoppe, 18 copies cost \$1.08. At that rate, how much will 40 copies cost? \$2.40

**55.** At the rate shown in the cartoon, how much would five potatoes cost? \$36.67

**56.** *Quality Control* A microchip inspector found three defective chips in a batch containing 750 chips. At that rate, how many defective chips would there be in 10,000 chips? 40 defective chips

**57.** *Geometry* A rectangle that is 20 cm long and 28 cm wide is the same shape as one that is 9 cm long and $z$ cm wide. Find $z$. 12.6 cm

**58.** **TEST PREP** An artist makes purple paint by mixing red and blue paint in the ratio of 2 parts red to 3 parts blue. What is the ratio of red paint to purple paint? D

**A.** 3 : 2 **B.** 3 : 5 **C.** 2 : 3 **D.** 2 : 5

REAL LIFE ADVENTURES by Gary Wise and Lance Aldrich

If the people who own the shops at the airport owned other things.

**59.** *Exchange Rates* On a recent day, the exchange rate for U.S. dollars to French francs was 0.16 dollars per franc. On that day, how many francs would you get for 25 dollars? 156 francs

**60.** *Writing* A truck driver estimates that it will take him 12 h to drive 1,160 km. After 5 h, he has driven 484 km. Is he on schedule? Explain. Answers may vary. Sample: Yes; $\frac{1{,}160}{12} = \frac{d}{5}$, so $d \approx 483$, very close to the driver's 484 km.

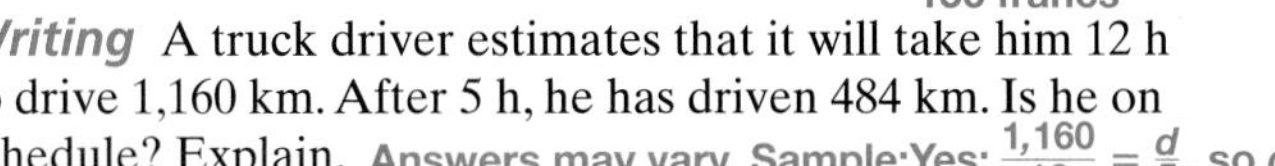

**61.** *Error Analysis* Fancy ribbon costs \$3 for 15 in. Your friend wants to find the cost of 3 ft of ribbon. He uses the proportion $\frac{3}{15} = \frac{x}{3}$ and gets an answer of \$.60. Explain your friend's error. Answers may vary. Sample: the lengths in the proportion, 3 ft and 15 in., have different units. They should use the same unit.

**Use the table for Exercises 62–65.**

**Human Heart Rates**

| Age (years) | Beats per Minute |
|---|---|
| newborn | 140 |
| 1 | 120 |
| 6 | 100 |
| 10 | 90 |
| 12 | 85 |
| adult | 80 |

62. How many times does an adult's heart beat in 270 s? 360 times

63. In how many seconds will a newborn's heart beat 35 times? 15 s

64. In how many seconds will a 12-year-old's heart beat 17 times? 12 s

65. In 45 s, how many more times does a newborn's heart beat than a 6-year-old's heart? 30 more times

66. On Monday, the ratio of Tara's pocket money to her brother Seth's pocket money was $\frac{3}{1}$. On Tuesday, Tara gave \$5 to Seth. Then the ratio of Tara's money to Seth's was $\frac{2}{1}$.

a. Let $3x$ equal the amount Tara had on Monday and $x$ equal the amount Seth had on Monday. Write two ratios that show $\frac{\text{Tara's money on Tuesday}}{\text{Seth's money on Tuesday}}$. $\frac{3x-5}{x+5}$, $\frac{2}{1}$

b. Use the ratios to write a proportion. Solve for $x$. Then find the amount of money each person had on Monday. $\frac{3x-5}{x+5} = \frac{2}{1}$; Tara \$45; Seth \$15

## Mixed Review

**Write each ratio as a fraction in simplest form.** ***(Lesson 6-1)***

67. ten per thousand $\frac{1}{100}$

68. 30 to 55 $\frac{6}{11}$

69. 125 : 70 $\frac{25}{14}$

**Tell whether each equation is true or false.** ***(Lessons 1-3 and 5-3)***

70. $\left|-2\frac{1}{4}\right| - \left|2\frac{1}{4}\right| = 0$ true

71. $\left|-2\frac{1}{4}\right| + \left|2\frac{1}{4}\right| = 0$ false

72. $-\left|-\frac{9}{4}\right| + \left|2\frac{1}{4}\right| = 0$ true

73. *Choose a Strategy* On Saturday afternoon, a student bought two music tapes for \$8.95 each and a sweater for \$24.95. She received \$20 for mowing a lawn. On Saturday night, she had \$45.12. How much money did the student have on Saturday morning? \$67.97

Chapter Project 6

## Activity 1 Creating

Use a 12-in. ruler, a pencil, and two rubber bands to make a simple stringed instrument like the one at the right. Pluck a string and listen to the resulting sound. Then press the string down against the ruler somewhere between 0 and 10. Using your other hand, pluck the string again. Describe how the resulting sound differs from the first sound.

Put pencil at 10-in. mark.

See also Extra Practice section.

### Project Activity 1

**Creating** Suggest that students may want to use descriptive words such as *higher* and *lower* to compare sounds.

## Practice

**Write a proportion for each phrase. Then solve. When necessary, round to the nearest hundredth.**

1. 420 ft² painted in 36 min; $f$ ft² painted in 30 min
$\frac{420}{36} = \frac{f}{30}$, $f = 350$ ft²

2. 75 points scored in 6 games; $p$ points scored in 4 games
$\frac{75}{6} = \frac{p}{4}$, $p = 50$ pts

3. 6 apples for \$1.00; 15 apples for $d$ dollars
$\frac{6}{1.00} = \frac{15}{d}$, $d = \$2.50$

**Tell whether each pair of ratios forms a proportion.**

4. $\frac{3}{4}$ and $\frac{9}{12}$ proportion
5. $\frac{25}{40}$ and $\frac{5}{8}$ proportion
6. $\frac{8}{12}$ and $\frac{14}{21}$ proportion
7. $\frac{13}{15}$ and $\frac{4}{5}$ not a proportion
8. $\frac{4}{5}$ and $\frac{5}{6}$ not a proportion
9. $\frac{49}{21}$ and $\frac{28}{12}$ proportion

**Solve each proportion. Where necessary, round to the nearest tenth.**

10. $\frac{3}{5} = \frac{15}{x}$ $x = 25$
11. $\frac{15}{30} = \frac{n}{34}$ $n = 17$
12. $\frac{h}{36} = \frac{21}{27}$ $h = 28$
13. $\frac{11}{6} = \frac{f}{60}$ $f = 110$
14. $\frac{26}{15} = \frac{130}{m}$ $m = 75$
15. $\frac{36}{j} = \frac{7}{20}$ $j = 102.9$
16. $\frac{r}{23} = \frac{17}{34}$ $r = 11.5$
17. $\frac{77}{93} = \frac{x}{24}$ $x = 19.9$

18. At Discount Copy, 12 copies cost \$0.66. Melissa needs 56 copies. How much should they cost?
\$3.08

19. You estimate that you can do 12 math problems in 45 min. How long should it take you to do 20 math problems?
75 min



## Reteaching

Solve $\frac{x}{6} = \frac{10}{4}$

Method 1: multiplication property of equality

$\frac{x}{6} = \frac{10}{4}$

$\frac{x}{6} \cdot 6 = \frac{10}{4} \cdot 6$ Multiply each side by 6.

$x = \frac{60}{4}$ Simplify.

$x = 15$

Method 2: cross products

$\frac{x}{6} \times \frac{10}{4}$

$4x = 60$ Find the cross products.

$\frac{4x}{4} = \frac{60}{4}$ Divide each side by 4.

$x = 15$ Simplify.

**Solve each proportion. When necessary, round to the nearest hundredth.**

1. $\frac{6}{p} = \frac{18}{42}$ $p = 14$
2. $\frac{12}{21} = \frac{x}{14}$ $x = 8$
3. $\frac{y}{9} = \frac{26}{6}$ $y = 39$
4. $\frac{x}{9} = \frac{7}{12}$ $x = 5.25$
5. $\frac{63}{t} = \frac{14}{16}$ $t = 72$
6. $\frac{28}{15} = \frac{y}{25}$ $y = 46.67$
7. $\frac{7}{20} = \frac{e}{70}$ $e = 24.5$
8. $\frac{8}{3} = \frac{40}{k}$ $k = 15$
9. $\frac{m}{54} = \frac{5}{12}$ $m = 22.5$
10. $\frac{8}{w} = \frac{5}{24}$ $w = 38.4$
11. $\frac{63}{18} = \frac{14}{z}$ $z = 4$
12. $\frac{a}{70} = \frac{2}{5}$ $a = 28$
13. $\frac{5}{13} = \frac{20}{r}$ $r = 52$
14. $\frac{6}{t} = \frac{7}{56}$ $t = 48$
15. $\frac{c}{21} = \frac{6}{20}$ $c = 6.3$
16. $\frac{10}{e} = \frac{15}{27}$ $e = 18$

17. Which method did you use the most?
Answers may vary.



## Enrichment

**Consider the proportion $\frac{3}{5} = \frac{9}{15}$.**

If the ratio of the numerators is set equal to the ratio of the denominators, another true proportion results: $\frac{3}{9} = \frac{5}{15}$.

1. Write a true proportion. Then write the proportion that results when you set the ratio of the numerators equal to the ratio of the denominators. Is this proportion true or false?
Sample answers:
$\frac{4}{5} = \frac{8}{10}$ $\frac{4}{8} = \frac{5}{10}$ (T) or F?

2. If $\frac{A}{B} = \frac{C}{D}$, then it appears that $\frac{A}{C} =$ $\frac{B}{D}$

**Consider the true proportion $\frac{15}{21} = \frac{20}{28}$. Answer true or false.**

3. $\frac{21}{15} = \frac{28}{20}$ true

4. If $\frac{A}{B} = \frac{C}{D}$, then it appears that $\frac{B}{A} =$ $\frac{D}{C}$

**Consider the true proportion $\frac{6}{8} = \frac{3}{4}$. Answer true or false.**

5. $\frac{6}{4} = \frac{3}{8}$ false

6. If $\frac{A}{B} = \frac{C}{D}$, then it appears that $\frac{A}{D} = \frac{C}{B}$. false

**Consider the true proportion $\frac{3}{8} = \frac{9}{24}$. Answer true or false.**

7. $\frac{3+8}{8} = \frac{9+24}{24}$ true

8. $\frac{3-8}{8} = \frac{9-24}{24}$ true

9. If $\frac{A}{B} = \frac{C}{D}$, then it appears that $\frac{A+B}{B} =$ $\frac{C+D}{D}$, and $\frac{A-B}{B} =$ $\frac{C-D}{D}$.

**Use the proportion you wrote in Exercise 1 to explore this theorem:**

**If $\frac{A}{B} = \frac{C}{D}$, then $\frac{A+B}{A-B} = \frac{C+D}{C-D}$.** Sample answers are shown.

10. Test the theorem. Write three new proportions.
$\frac{9}{-1} = \frac{18}{-2}$ $\frac{5}{-1} = \frac{15}{-3}$ $\frac{15}{-1} = \frac{30}{-2}$

11. Does the theorem appear to be true? yes

# Similar Figures and Scale Drawings

6-3

## Using Similar Figures

**Similar figures** have the same shape, but not necessarily the same size. Similar figures have *corresponding angles* and *corresponding sides*.

The symbol ~ means *is similar to.* At the right, $\triangle ABC \sim \triangle XYZ$.

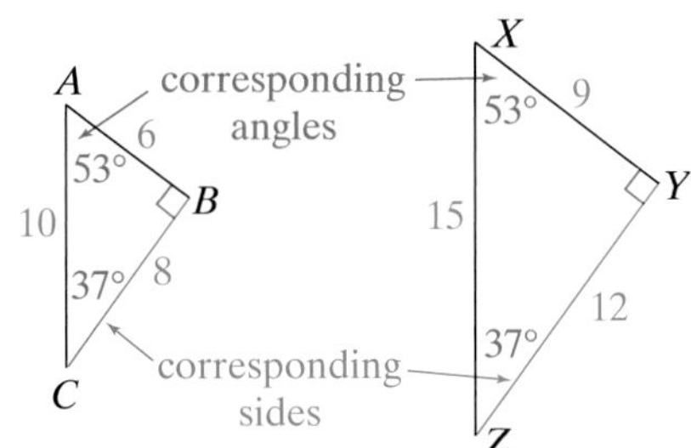


### What You'll Learn

1. To solve problems that involve similar figures
2. To solve problems that involve scale drawings

### . . . And Why

To apply proportions to geometry and measurement

### Similar Figures

Similar figures have two properties.

- The corresponding angles have equal measures.
- The lengths of corresponding sides are in proportion.

GEOMETRY CONNECTION

### Example 1

**Parallelogram *ABCD* ~ parallelogram *EFGH*. Find the value of *x*.**

Write a proportion for corresponding sides.

| | | |
|---|---|---|
| Side *DA* corresponds to side *HE*. | $\frac{x}{18} = \frac{16}{24}$ | Side *AB* corresponds to side *EF*. |
| | $x \cdot 24 = 18 \cdot 16$ | Write cross products. |
| | $\frac{24x}{24} = \frac{18 \cdot 16}{24}$ | Divide each side by 24. |
| | $x = 12$ | Simplify. |

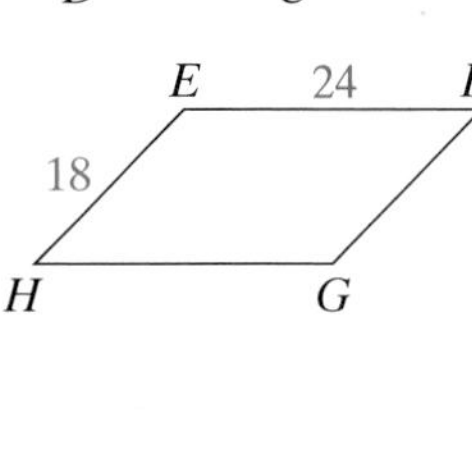


### Try This

1. Parallelogram *KLMN* is similar to parallelogram *ABCD* in Example 1. Find the value of *y*. 15.75

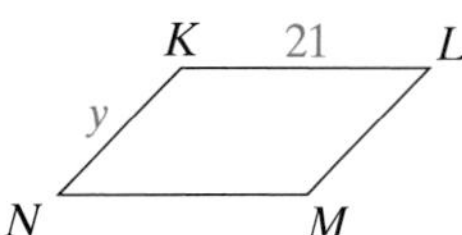


You can use similar figures to compute distances that are difficult to measure directly. This method is called **indirect measurement.**



# 6-3

## Getting Ready

**Key Terms and Symbols** similar figures, indirect measurement, scale drawing

**Resources** A complete list of resources for this lesson is on p. 275H.

### Daily Skills Warm-Up

Lesson 6-3

Solve. Round to the nearest tenth where necessary.

1. $\frac{6}{7} = \frac{3}{n}$ $n = 3.5$
2. $\frac{28}{5} = \frac{m}{2}$ $m = 11.2$
3. $\frac{k}{25} = \frac{5}{12}$ $k = 10.4$
4. $\frac{15}{x} = \frac{6}{16}$ $x = 40$

Does the pair of figures have the same size? Do they have the same shape?

5. not same size; same shape
6. neither

### Background for the Lesson

Geometric figures that are similar have exactly the same shape, but may not be the same size. You can write a true proportion using the corresponding sides of similar figures. Corresponding sides are those sides that are in matching positions in the two figures. Using similar figures to find the measurement of a length that is difficult to measure is called *indirect measurement.*

## 1 Focus

### Connecting to Students' Lives

Discuss whether students have built or seen scale models such as planes or trains. Remind students that when they use a copy machine to make a copy of a drawing similar to the original, they may enlarge or reduce the size of the drawing.

### Connecting to Prior Knowledge

In Lesson 6-2, students learned to write and solve proportions. In this lesson, they use those skills to find the lengths of the sides in geometric figures that are similar. In Lesson 6-6, students will use proportions with percents.

## Tools to Monitor Progress

### BEFORE THE LESSON

**To check prerequisite skills:**

- Writing equivalent fractions

**Skills Handbook,** p. 737

**Skills Intervention Kit,** Ratio, Proportion, and Percent

### DURING THE LESSON

**To check understanding:**

**Try This** exercises on student page

- **Additional Example 1**

These two trapezoids are similar. Find *k*.

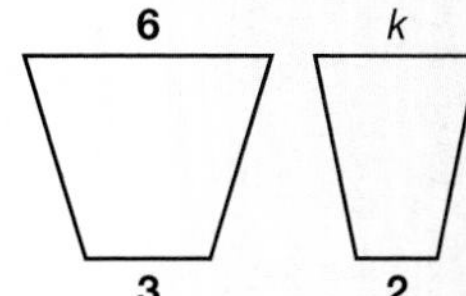


$k = 4$

# 2 Teach

## Part 1 Teaching Notes

Have students point to and name the pairs of corresponding sides in similar figures before they write a proportion.

### Example 1

**Build understanding.** Ask: The numerators in both ratios come from which parallelogram? **parallelogram *ABCD***

**Error Prevention** Students may set up the proportion incorrectly so that the corresponding parts are not in matching order. Remind them that the order in which you name the vertices tells you which parts correspond.

### Example 2

**Build understanding.** Ask: In indirect measurement, why is it important to measure both shadows at approximately the same time? **The length of the shadows will change as the sun moves across the sky.**

**ELL** Ask students to compare the meanings of the math symbols used for equals (=), is approximately equal to (≈), and is similar to (~).

## Part 2 Teaching Notes

You may wish to have some road maps available for students to look at as examples of scale drawings. Have them find the key on the map that tells the scale.

### Example 3

**Build understanding.** Ask: Is the distance that you measure or calculate from the map greater than or less than the distance you would travel if you drove from Atlanta to Athens? Explain. **less than; Roads often do not go in a straight line.**

GEOMETRY CONNECTION

### EXAMPLE 2

*Indirect Measurement* **A tree casts a shadow 10 ft long. A 5-ft woman casts a shadow 4 ft long. The triangle shown for the woman and her shadow is similar to the triangle shown for the tree and its shadow. How tall is the tree?**

5 ft
4 ft
10 ft

| | |
|---|---|
| $\frac{4}{10} = \frac{5}{x}$ | Corresponding sides of similar triangles are in proportion. |
| $4x = 10 \cdot 5$ | Write cross products. |
| $\frac{4x}{4} = \frac{10 \cdot 5}{4}$ | Divide each side by 4. |
| $x = 12.5$ | Simplify. |

The tree is 12.5 ft tall.

### TRY THIS

70 ft
150 ft
Flagpole
60 ft

2. *Indirect Measurement* A building 70 ft high casts a 150-ft shadow. A nearby flagpole casts a 60-ft shadow. Draw a diagram. Use similar triangles to find the height of the flagpole. **28 ft**
**See left for diagram.**

## Part 2 Using Scale Drawings

A **scale drawing** is an enlarged or reduced drawing that is similar to an actual object or place. The ratio of a distance in the drawing to the corresponding actual distance is the *scale* of the drawing.

MEASUREMENT CONNECTION

### EXAMPLE 3

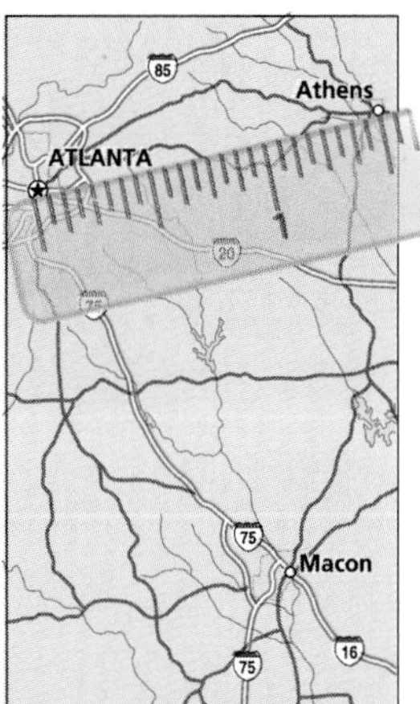


*Maps* **The scale of the map is 1 in. : 40 mi. About how far from Atlanta is Athens?**

| | |
|---|---|
| Map distance $= 1\frac{1}{2}$ in., or 1.5 in. | Measure the map distance. |
| $\frac{\text{map (in.)}}{\text{actual (mi)}} \rightarrow \frac{1}{40} = \frac{1.5}{d} \leftarrow \frac{\text{map (in.)}}{\text{actual (mi)}}$ | Write a proportion. |
| $1 \cdot d = 40 \cdot 1.5$ | Write cross products. |
| $d = 60$ | Simplify. |

Athens is about 60 mi from Atlanta.

### TRY THIS

3. *Maps* Find the approximate distance from Atlanta to Macon. **70 mi**



- **Additional Example 2**
  A flagpole casts a shadow 5 ft long at the same time that a yardstick casts a shadow 1.5 ft long. How tall is the flagpole? **10 ft**
- **Additional Example 3**
  The scale of a map is 1 in. : 24 mi. About how far is it between two cities that are 3 in. apart on the map? **72 mi**

## AFTER THE LESSON

**To assess knowledge:**
**Lesson Quiz**

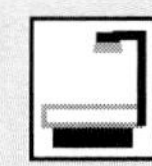

The scale is 3 in. : 100 mi. Find the actual distance.

**1.** 1 in. **$33\frac{1}{3}$ mi** **2.** 9 in. **300 mi**

A scale drawing has a scale of 5 cm : 25 ft. Find the length on the drawing for each actual length.

**3.** 15 ft **3 cm** **4.** 70 ft **14 cm**

- For enrichment and reteaching options see Resources on p. 275H.

# Exercises

## CHECK UNDERSTANDING

**Trapezoid *EFGH* ~ trapezoid *MNOP*. Find each length.**

F, 6 ft, G, 3 ft, E, H; O, 5 ft, N, 2 ft, P, M

1. length *EF* $2\frac{2}{5}$
2. length *OP* $2\frac{1}{2}$
3. A scale drawing has a scale of 1 in. : 10 ft. What is the distance on the drawing for an actual distance of 20 ft? Of 45 ft? 2 in.; 4.5 in.
4. *Critical Thinking* A note at the bottom of a map says "not to scale." Explain why that is important information. Answers may vary. Sample: You cannot assume that map distances are proportional to actual distances.

## PRACTICE AND PROBLEM SOLVING

**Each pair of triangles is similar. Find the missing length. Round to the nearest tenth where necessary.**

5.
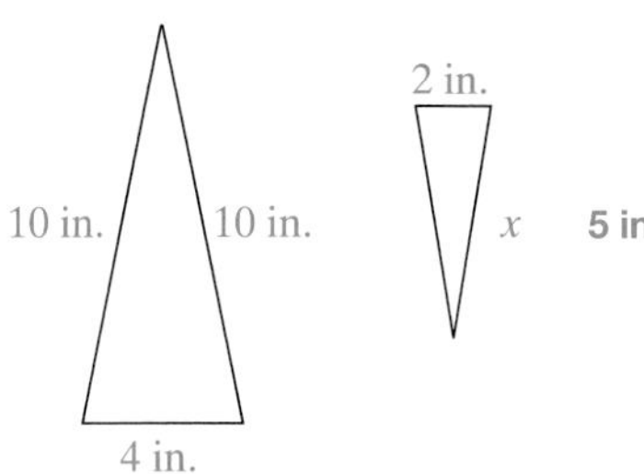

5 in.

6.
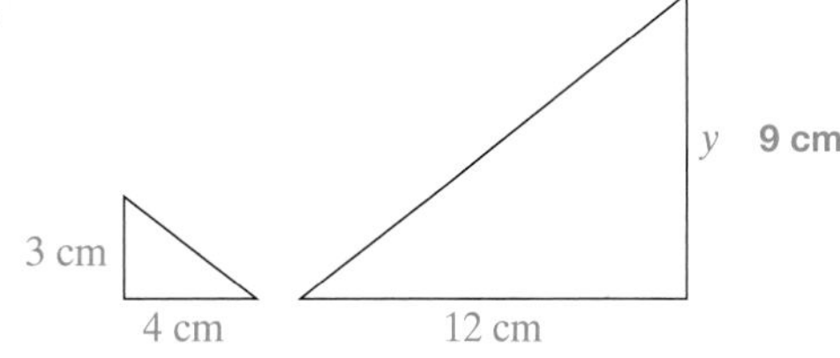

9 cm

7. 8, z, 7, 5 — 5.7

8.
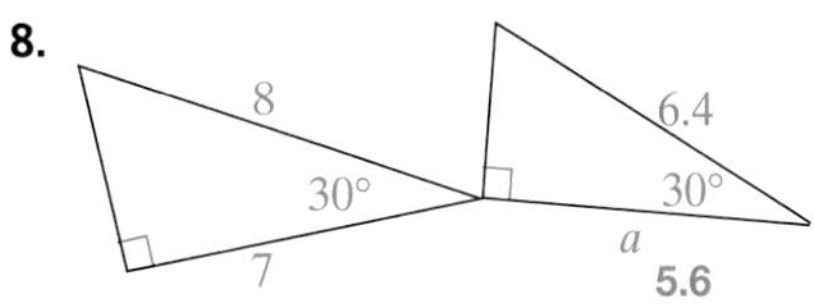

5.6

**The scale of a map is 2 cm : 15 km. Find the actual distance for each map distance.**

9. 6 cm 45 km
10. 2.1 cm 15.75 km
11. 10 mm 7.5 km
12. 17.4 cm 130.5 km

**A scale drawing has a scale of $\frac{1}{2}$ in. : 10 ft. Find the length on the drawing for each actual length.**

13. 40 ft 2 in.
14. 5 ft $\frac{1}{4}$ in.
15. 35 ft $1\frac{3}{4}$ in.
16. $3\frac{1}{2}$ ft $\frac{7}{40}$ in.



# 3 Practice/Assess

## Assignment Guide

To provide flexible scheduling, this lesson can be divided into parts.

**Part 1**
**Core** 1–2, 5–8, 17–19
**Extension** 20

**Part 2**
**Core** 3–4, 9–16, 21–26, 29–31, 34
**Extension** 27–28, 32–33

Mixed Review can be assigned at any time for maintenance.

## Exercises

**Visual Learning Exercises 17–18** Suggest that students draw and label the similar figures before they write a proportion.

**ELL Exercise 30** Explain that the *dimensions* of a figure refer to its length and width.

## Challenge

The scale drawing of a toy has a length of 5 cm. The actual toy has a corresponding length of 15 in. How many cm represent one in. on the toy? $\frac{1}{3}$ cm

## Closure

Similar figures have the same shape but not necessarily the same size. You can use the fact that corresponding sides of similar figures are proportional to find the actual size of an object in a scale drawing.

## Alternative Assessment

Have students make a scale drawing of something in the classroom. Have them include a scale as well as the steps and calculations they used to decide on the various line lengths.

## Daily Cumulative Review

**Solve each proportion. Where necessary, round to the nearest tenth.** *(Lesson 6-2)*

1. $\frac{6}{7} = \frac{b}{42}$ $b = 36$
2. $\frac{3}{2} = \frac{c}{6}$ $c = 9$
3. $\frac{17}{d} = \frac{68}{60}$ $d = 15$
4. $\frac{w}{33.2} = \frac{64}{166}$ $w = 12.8$
5. $\frac{2.5}{a} = \frac{3.5}{9.8}$ $a = 7$
6. $\frac{13}{18} = \frac{x}{25.8}$ $x \approx 18.6$

**For each situation, write a ratio as a fraction in simplest form.** *(Lesson 6-1)*

7. 97 homes in 120 have cable. $\frac{97}{120}$
8. 4 out of 8 people have pets. $\frac{1}{2}$
9. 16 out of 24 boys have on shorts. $\frac{2}{3}$
10. There are 7 oranges for every 10 apples. $\frac{7}{10}$

**Mixed Review**

**Write in simplest form.**

11. (4-4) $\frac{4}{16}$ $\frac{1}{4}$
12. (4-4) $\frac{14}{22}$ $\frac{7}{11}$
13. (4-4) $\frac{9}{33}$ $\frac{3}{11}$
14. (4-4) $\frac{8}{12}$ $\frac{2}{3}$
15. (4-4) $\frac{16}{20}$ $\frac{4}{5}$
16. (4-4) $\frac{13}{15}$ $\frac{13}{15}$

**Write the coordinates of each point.**

17. (1-10) A (0, 3)
18. (1-10) B (1, −2)
19. (1-10) C (−1, −1)
20. (1-10) D (−3, 0)
21. (1-10) E (5, 3)
22. (1-10) F (4, −1)

**Find the LCM of each group of numbers.**

23. (5-1) 3, 8 24
24. (5-1) 2, 7 14
25. (5-1) 6, 8 24
26. (5-1) 5, 8 40
27. (5-1) 2, 3 6
28. (5-1) 10, 15 30

17. An image on a slide is similar to its projected image. A slide is 35 mm wide and 21 mm high. Its projected image is 85 cm wide. To the nearest centimeter, how high is the image? **51 cm**

18. *Indirect Measurement* A tree casts a shadow 8 ft long. A 6-ft man casts a shadow 4 ft long. The triangle formed by the tree and its shadow is similar to the triangle formed by the man and his shadow. How tall is the tree? **12 ft**

19. *Open-ended* Give some examples of similar figures you find in everyday life. **Check students' work.**

20. *Writing* Are all squares similar? Explain. **Yes; all angles have equal measures and the ratios of the lengths of corresponding sides are all equal.**

21. *Architecture* The actual length of a room is 16 ft. The scale of a blueprint is $\frac{1}{2}$ in. : 1 ft. Find the room's length in the blueprint. **8 in.**

22. *Geography* The cities of Jackson, Mississippi, and Carson City Nevada, are 1,750 mi apart.
    a. A map of the United States has a scale of 1 in. : 250 mi. How far apart on the map are the cities? **7 in.**
    b. On another map, the cities are 5 in. apart. What is the scale of the map? **1 in. : 350 mi**

**The length of each piece in a model railroad built on the HO scale is $\frac{1}{87}$ of the actual length. Another popular model is the N scale, for which the scale is $\frac{1}{160}$.**

23. The student in the photograph is holding an HO model and an N model. Which type of model is labeled *A?* Which type of model is labeled *B?* **N model; HO model**

24. Each car on a full-size passenger train is 80 ft long. What is the length in inches of a model passenger car in the HO scale? In the N scale? **$11\frac{1}{29}$ in.; 6 in.**

25. A diesel locomotive is 60 ft long. How long is a model of the locomotive in the N scale? **4.5 in.**

26. In the O scale, the length of a model is $\frac{1}{48}$ of an actual length. An O-scale locomotive is 1.05 ft long. How long is the actual locomotive? **50.4 ft**

27. A boxcar on a freight train is 40 ft long. A model boxcar is 3 in. long. In which scale was the model built? **N scale**

28. You are building a display shelf for your model train. You have 12 cars. Each car is 1.2 ft long. You want 1.2 in. of space between cars. How long must the shelf be? **$15\frac{1}{2}$ ft**

*Architecture* **A 2-in. length in the scale drawing represents an actual length of 20 ft.**

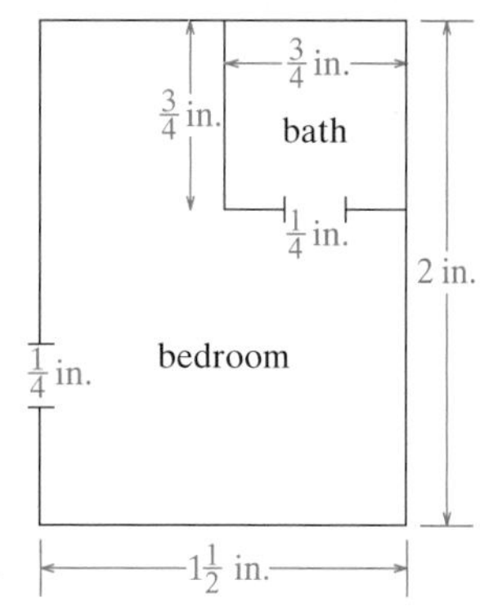


**29.** What is the scale of the drawing? 1 in. : 10 ft

**30.** What are the actual dimensions of the bath? 7.5 ft by 7.5 ft

**31.** Find the actual width of the doorways that lead into the bedroom and the bathroom. 2.5 ft

**32.** Find the actual area of the bedroom. 243.75 ft$^2$

**33.** Can a bed 6 ft long and 3 ft wide fit into the narrow section of the bedroom? Justify your answer. Yes; the narrow section in the drawing is $\frac{3}{4}$ in. by $\frac{3}{4}$ in., representing a space 7.5 ft by 7.5 ft.

**34.** You want to design a rectangular dance floor 90 ft long and 75 ft wide. You want to make a drawing with a scale of 1 in. : 9 ft. Can you fit the drawing on a piece of paper $8\frac{1}{2}$ in. by 11 in.? Justify your answer. Yes; to scale the dance floor will measure $8\frac{1}{3}$ in. by 10 in.

## Mixed Review

**Solve each proportion.** ***(Lesson 6-2)***

**35.** $\frac{x}{5} = \frac{32}{80}$ 2 **36.** $\frac{3}{8} = \frac{r}{15}$ $5\frac{5}{8}$ **37.** $\frac{40}{w} = \frac{50}{3}$ $2\frac{2}{5}$ **38.** $\frac{24}{16} = \frac{204}{c}$ 136

**Find the mean, median, and mode.** ***(Lesson 3-3)***

**39.** 12, 10, 11, 7, 9, 8, 10, 5 9, 9.5, 10 **40.** 4.5, 3.2, 6.3, 5.2, 5, 4.8, 6, 3.9 4.8625, 4.9, no mode

**Write each fraction as a decimal.** ***(Lesson 5-2)***

**41.** $\frac{3}{8}$ 0.375 **42.** $\frac{4}{9}$ $0.\overline{4}$ **43.** $\frac{7}{16}$ 0.4375 **44.** $\frac{5}{12}$ $0.41\overline{6}$

**45.** *Gas Mileage* A car travels 264 mi on 12 gal of gas. Find the unit rate in miles per gallon. ***(Lesson 6-1)*** 22 mi/gal

## ACTIVITY 2 INVESTIGATING

By experimenting with your stringed instrument, learn to play the notes of "The Star Spangled Banner" that correspond to the words *say, can, you,* and *see*. Use the full string length for *say*. For the other notes, press the string down against the ruler. For each note, measure the string length, which is the distance between your finger and the pencil. Record the results.

See also Extra Practice section.



## Project Activity 2

**Investigating** To verify that students record the results accurately, suggest that they have a classmate or an adult try to follow their written instructions to play the first four notes. After this tryout, students may have to clarify or correct their recorded results.

## Practice

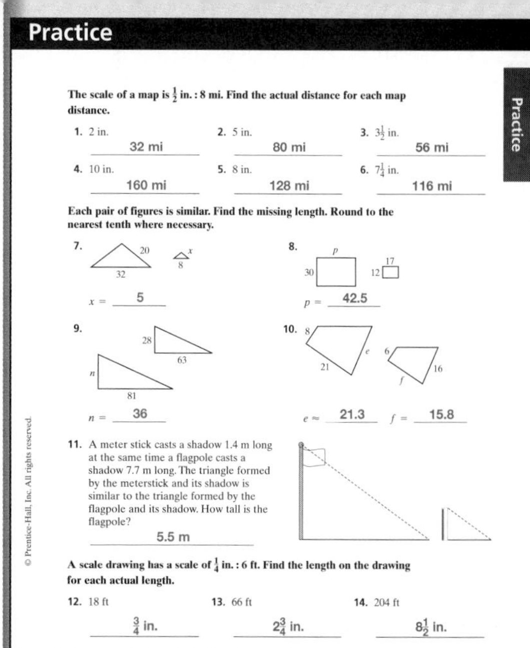
**The scale of a map is $\frac{1}{2}$ in. : 8 mi. Find the actual distance for each map distance.**

1. 2 in. 32 mi
2. 5 in. 80 mi
3. $3\frac{1}{2}$ in. 56 mi
4. 10 in. 160 mi
5. 8 in. 128 mi
6. $7\frac{1}{4}$ in. 116 mi

**Each pair of figures is similar. Find the missing length. Round to the nearest tenth where necessary.**

7. $x =$ 5
8. $p =$ 42.5
9. $n =$ 36
10. $e \approx$ 21.3 $f =$ 15.8
11. A meter stick casts a shadow 1.4 m long at the same time a flagpole casts a shadow 7.7 m long. The triangle formed by the meterstick and its shadow is similar to the triangle formed by the flagpole and its shadow. How tall is the flagpole? 5.5 m

**A scale drawing has a scale of $\frac{1}{4}$ in. : 6 ft. Find the length on the drawing for each actual length.**

12. 18 ft $\frac{3}{4}$ in.
13. 66 ft $2\frac{3}{4}$ in.
14. 204 ft $8\frac{1}{2}$ in.



## Reteaching

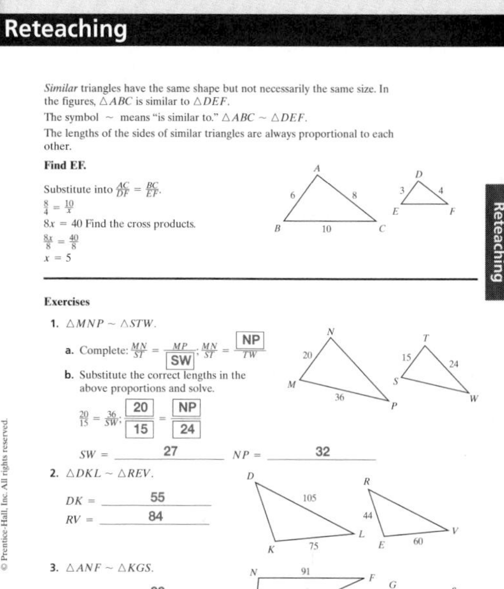
*Similar* triangles have the same shape but not necessarily the same size. In the figures, $\triangle ABC$ is similar to $\triangle DEF$.

The symbol $\sim$ means "is similar to." $\triangle ABC \sim \triangle DEF$.

The lengths of the sides of similar triangles are always proportional to each other.

**Find EF.**

Substitute into $\frac{AC}{DF} = \frac{BC}{EF}$.

$\frac{8}{4} = \frac{10}{x}$

$8x = 40$ Find the cross products.

$\frac{8x}{8} = \frac{40}{8}$

$x = 5$

**Exercises**

1. $\triangle MNP \sim \triangle STW$.
   a. Complete: $\frac{MN}{ST} = \frac{MP}{SW}$; $\frac{MN}{ST} = \frac{NP}{TW}$
   b. Substitute the correct lengths in the above proportions and solve.
   $\frac{20}{15} = \frac{36}{SW}$; $\frac{20}{15} = \frac{NP}{24}$
   $SW =$ 27 $NP =$ 32
2. $\triangle DKL \sim \triangle REV$.
   $DK =$ 55
   $RV =$ 84
3. $\triangle ANF \sim \triangle KGS$.
   $AN =$ 39
   $GS =$ 42



## Enrichment

**Make a scale drawing of the floor plan of your classroom.**

1. Measure carefully and complete the first two columns of the table. The extra rows are for alcoves and other places where the room deviates from a rectangle. Add more rows if necessary.
   Answers may vary.

| Item | Measure | Length in Scale Drawing |
|---|---|---|
| Length of room at greatest point | | |
| Width of room at greatest point | | |
| | | |
| | | |

Check that measures are reasonable and scale lengths are proportional.

2. Decide what scale to use. Make sure your drawing will fit in the space below.
   Scale: ________ = ________ Answers may vary.
3. Complete the last column of the table.
4. Make your scale drawing.

Check student's drawings.

## MATH TOOLBOX

### Dilations

In Lesson 6-3 students found the dimensions for scale drawings and models. This Math Toolbox shows students how to use geometry software to make a scale drawing.

**Materials** geometry software

### Math Background

When you make a dilation of a figure, you first must choose a point to be *the center of dilation* and a *scale factor.*

*Dilate* means"to grow larger," as when the pupil of the eye *dilates.* A math dilation can be enlarging or shrinking. Dilation is one of a number of ways to *change* a figure. Together these are called *transformations,* which includes changing a figure by slides, turns, and flips.

## Teaching Notes

**Error Prevention** Students may choose a scale factor and forget to choose a center of dilation. Emphasize that both are necessary to define a dilation.

**Monitoring Progress Exercise 1** Students may tend to draw a special triangle, such as one that is equilateral or isosceles. Suggest that they draw a triangle with no sides equal so it is easier to tell what has happened in the dilation.

**Block Scheduling** If you have block scheduling or extended periods, you may wish to insert this Math Toolbox lesson between the completion of Part 2 of Lesson 6-3 and the beginning of Part 1 of Lesson 6-4. Use the Pacing Options on p. 275B to see the possibilities.

## MATH TOOLBOX

*Technology*

*After Lesson 6-3*

# *Dilations*

You can use geometry software to make a scale drawing, or *dilation,* of a figure. First choose the Dilate command. Then choose a center of dilation and a scale, which is also known as a *scale factor.*

**EXAMPLE**

**Draw a triangle. Then draw a dilation with scale factor 3.**

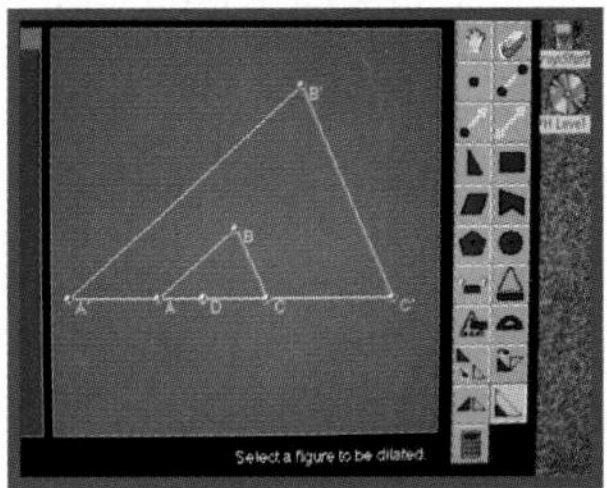

Use geometry software to draw $\triangle ABC$. Draw a point $D$ on one side of the triangle. Choose $D$ as the center of a dilation with scale factor 3. The result is an image like the one at the right. Each side of the dilation is 3 times as long as the corresponding side of $\triangle ABC$.

If you move point $D$, the dilation also will move. If instead you move $A$, $B$, or $C$, the dilation will change as $\triangle ABC$ changes.

**Use geometry software to draw $\triangle PQR$.**

1. a. Draw a point $S$ *outside* $\triangle PQR$. Draw a dilation of $\triangle PQR$ with center $S$ and scale factor 2.5. Label the dilation $\triangle XYZ$. $\triangle XYZ$ is similar to $\triangle PQR$. Angle $X$ corresponds to angle $P$, angle $Y$ corresponds to angle $Q$, and angle $Z$ corresponds to angle $R$. Check students' work.
   b. Compare the location of $\triangle XYZ$ to the location of $\triangle PQR$. Does the dilation lie inside the original triangle? Outside the triangle? Do the triangles overlap? No; the dilation could lie outside or it could overlap the original triangle.
   c. Now move $S$ to be *inside* $\triangle PQR$. Once again, compare the locations of the two triangles. How did moving the center of dilation change the relative locations of the triangles? $\triangle PQR$ lies inside $\triangle XYZ$. Check students' work.
2. Change the location of point $S$ so that $\triangle PQR$ and $\triangle XYZ$ have the given number of points in common. Print an example of each case. 2a–d. Check students' work.
   a. 0 b. 1 c. 2 d. more than 2
3. With $S$ inside $\triangle PQR$, change the scale factor to 0.5. Describe the relative locations of the two triangles. $\triangle XYZ$ lies inside $\triangle PQR$.
4. a. Keep the scale factor of the dilation at 0.5. Use the Area tool to find the area of $\triangle PQR$. Use the Area tool again to find the area of $\triangle XYZ$. Write a ratio to compare the areas. (area $\triangle PQR$) : (area $\triangle XYZ$) = 4 : 1.
   b. Move $P$, $Q$, or $R$ to see how the area of $\triangle XYZ$ changes as the area of $\triangle PQR$ changes. Does the ratio of the areas change? No
   c. *Mathematical Reasoning* What do your results suggest about the areas of similar triangles that have a scale factor of 0.5? They have the ratio 4 : 1 or 1 : 4.

294 Math Toolbox

• **Additional Example**

Draw a fairly large triangle with no equal sides. Then draw a dilation with a scale factor 0.75. Each side of the image is what fraction of the corresponding side in your original figure? $\frac{3}{4}$

# Probability

## 6-4

### What You'll Learn

1. To find probability
2. To find odds

### . . . And Why

To understand the likelihood of everyday events, such as rolling a number on a number cube or being a twin

## *Investigate*

**EXPLORING PROBABILITY**

Many board games involve rolling two number cubes and then adding the numbers on the cubes. Are certain sums more likely than others? The table shows the possible rolls and their sums.

**Sums of 2 Number Cubes**

| | 1 | 2 | 3 | 4 | 5 | 6 |
|---|---|---|---|---|---|---|
| **1** | 2 | 3 | 4 | ■5 | 6 | 7 |
| **2** | 3 | 4 | 5 | 6 | ■7 | 8 |
| **3** | 4 | 5 | ■6 | 7 | 8 | 9 |
| **4** | 5 | ■6 | 7 | 8 | 9 | 10 |
| **5** | 6 | 7 | 8 | 9 | 10 | ■ 11 |
| **6** | ■7 | 8 | 9 | 10 | 11 | 12 |

1. Copy and complete the table.
2. What is the number of times each sum appears in the chart? 2(1), 3(2), 4(3), 5(4), 6(5), 7(6), 8(5), 9(4), 10(3), 11(2), 12(1)
3. Which sum appears most frequently? 7
4. There are a total of 36 sums in the table. Use your answer to Question 3 to write the ratio $\frac{\text{number of times the most frequent sum appears}}{\text{total number of sums}}$. $\frac{6}{36}$

## PART 1 Finding Probability

**Outcomes** are the possible results of an action. There are six outcomes for rolling a single number cube: 1, 2, 3, 4, 5, and 6.

An **event** is any outcome or group of outcomes. In rolling two number cubes, for example, rolling a sum of 4 is an event corresponding to three different outcomes.

Three different outcomes result in the event *a sum of 4.*

The outcomes for rolling two number cubes are *random* and therefore *equally likely* to occur. When outcomes are equally likely, you can use a ratio to find the *probability of an event.*

**probability** of an event $= P(\text{event}) = \frac{\text{number of favorable outcomes}}{\text{number of possible outcomes}}$



# Tools to Monitor Progress

### BEFORE THE LESSON

**To check prerequisite skills:**

- Simplifying fractions

**Skills You Need,** p. 275

**Skills Handbook,** p. 737

**Skills Intervention Kit,** Number Theory and Fraction Concepts

### DURING THE LESSON

**To check understanding:**

**Try This** exercises on student page

- **Additional Example 1**

  Find *P* (prime number) for rolling one number cube. $\frac{3}{6}$ or $\frac{1}{2}$

- **Additional Example 2**

  The probability that a child is an identical twin is 4 in 1,000. Find *P*(not an identical twin). $\frac{996}{1,000}$ or $\frac{249}{250}$

## 6-4

## Getting Ready

**Key Terms and Symbols** outcomes, event, probability, complement, odds

**Resources** A complete list of resources for this lesson is on p. 275H.

### Daily Skills Warm-Up

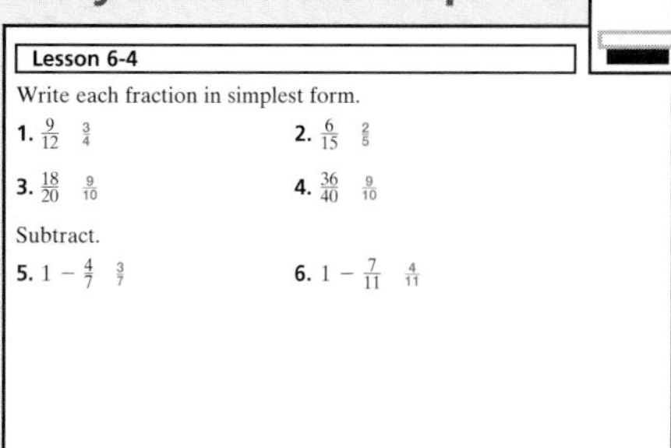

Lesson 6-4

Write each fraction in simplest form.

1. $\frac{9}{12}$ $\frac{3}{4}$
2. $\frac{6}{15}$ $\frac{2}{5}$
3. $\frac{18}{20}$ $\frac{9}{10}$
4. $\frac{36}{40}$ $\frac{9}{10}$

Subtract.

5. $1 - \frac{4}{7}$ $\frac{3}{7}$
6. $1 - \frac{7}{11}$ $\frac{4}{11}$

### Background for the Lesson

The probability that an event will occur is often written as a ratio comparing the number of favorable outcomes to the number of possible outcomes. Probability will always be between 0 (not possible) and 1 (must happen).

Theoretical probability describes the number of outcomes that should occur. Experimental probability describes the number of outcomes that do occur.

## 1 Focus

### Investigate

Help students simplify the ratio that they write to $\frac{1}{6}$. Ask them to hypothesize about why some people may consider 7 to be a "lucky" number.

### Connecting to Students' Lives

When students hear on television that a certain disease strikes one in five, they need to realize that, if their family has five members, this statement of probability does not mean that one of their family will get the disease. Probability is only a description for a very large number of cases; it does not predict for individuals or particular events.

# 2 Teach

## Part 1 Teaching Notes

The mathematical probability of an event is not much good as a predictor of what will happen in a small number of cases. The laws of probability predict only what will happen when you survey a very large number of events.

### Example 1

**Build understanding.** Ask: How do you know the number of faces on a number cube based on the probability? The cube has 6 faces because the number of possible outcomes is 6.

### Example 2

**Build understanding.** Ask: How do you read the math language "*P*(not a twin)" aloud? the probability that a child is not a twin

**Connecting to Science** The rate of identical twins (from a single egg) is about 4 : 1,000. This rate has remained the same throughout history. The rate of fraternal twins (from different eggs) fluctuates with the age of the mother and where she lives.

**Writing Math** Point out that the complement of an event *completes* the probability since an event and its complement add to 1. This association helps students to spell the word correctly and to distinguish it from *compliment,* which means to express admiration.

**Connecting to Geometry** Remind students that complementary angles add to a right angle. In a similar way, the probabilities of complementary events add to a probability of 1.

**Reading Math**

You can read the probability $\frac{3}{6}$ as "three in six" or "three out of six."

### Example 1

**Find *P*(rolling an even number) with one number cube.**

$\frac{\text{number of favorable outcomes}}{\text{number of possible outcomes}} = \frac{3}{6}$ ← 3 even-number outcomes ← 6 possible outcomes

$P(\text{rolling an even number}) = \frac{3}{6}$, or $\frac{1}{2}$

**Try This** Find each probability for rolling one number cube.

**5.** $P(\text{odd number})$ $\frac{1}{2}$ **6.** $P(2)$ $\frac{1}{6}$ **7.** $P(5 \text{ or } 6)$ $\frac{1}{3}$

All probabilities range from 0 to 1.

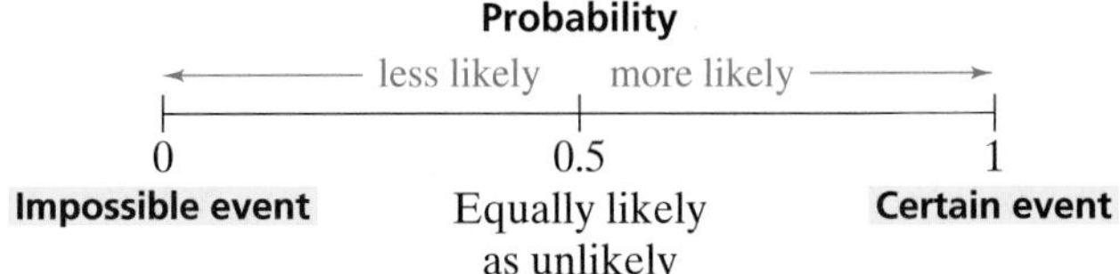


The **complement** of an event is the opposite of that event. The events *no rain* and *rain* are complements of each other. The probability of an event plus the probability of its complement always equals 1.

DATA ANALYSIS CONNECTION

### Example 2

*Vital Statistics* **In the United States, the probability that a child is a twin is 2 in 90, or $\frac{2}{90}$. Find *P*(not a twin).**

$P(\text{twin}) + P(\text{not a twin}) = 1$ Write an equation.

$\frac{2}{90} + P(\text{not a twin}) = 1$ Substitute.

$\frac{2}{90} - \frac{2}{90} + P(\text{not a twin}) = 1 - \frac{2}{90}$ Subtract $\frac{2}{90}$ from each side.

$P(\text{not a twin}) = \frac{88}{90} = \frac{44}{45}$ Simplify.

The probability that a child is not a twin is $\frac{44}{45}$.

**Try This**

**8.** When you roll a number cube, what is $P(\text{not } 2)$? $\frac{5}{6}$

**9.** What is the complement of an impossible event? a certain event



- **Additional Example 3**
You have five different coins in your pocket: a penny, a nickel, a dime, a quarter, and a half-dollar. You pull out one coin at random. What are the odds that the coin you take is worth less than ten cents? $\frac{2}{3}$

## AFTER THE LESSON

### To assess knowledge: Lesson Quiz

A set of ten index cards has a different digit (0–9) written on each card. What are the odds against selecting a card at random that has a number greater than 5? $\frac{3}{2}$

- For enrichment and reteaching options see Resources on p. 275H.

## Part 2 Finding Odds

You can think of probability as a ratio of $\frac{\text{part}}{\text{whole}}$. You can also use a $\frac{\text{part}}{\text{part}}$ ratio, called *odds,* to describe the likelihood of an event.

$$\textbf{odds} \text{ in favor of an event} = \frac{\text{number of } \textit{favorable} \text{ outcomes}}{\text{number of } \textit{unfavorable} \text{ outcomes}}$$

$$\textbf{odds} \text{ against an event} = \frac{\text{number of } \textit{unfavorable} \text{ outcomes}}{\text{number of } \textit{favorable} \text{ outcomes}}$$

REAL-WORLD CONNECTION

### Example 3

**The reverse sides of five quarters are shown below. What are the odds that a quarter chosen at random from these has at least one human figure on its reverse?**

odds in favor $= \frac{3}{2}$ ← 3 have a human figure. ← 2 do not.

The odds are $\frac{3}{2}$, or 3 to 2, in favor.

**Reading Math**

Reads odds of $\frac{3}{2}$ as "three to two."

### Try This

**10.** What are the odds that a quarter chosen at random from the five shows a horse? What are the odds that it shows no horse? 1 to 4; 4 to 1

**11.** Consider the event of randomly choosing a quarter that shows the outline of a state.

**a.** What are the odds in favor of the event? 2 to 3

**b.** What are the odds against the event? 3 to 2

## Part 2 Teaching Notes

Remind students that these definitions for the mathematical probabilities and odds apply only when the event occurs at random. In mathematics, a *random* event is one for which all the outcomes are equally likely.

### Example 3

**Build understanding.** Ask: What would be a favorable outcome in this example? **a quarter that has at least one human figure on its reverse**

**Error Prevention** Students may forget to use the fact that $P(\text{event}) + P(\text{not the event}) = 1$. Remind them to use this relationship as they solve and check problems.

**ELL** Help students remember the definitions of *odds in favor* and *odds against* by associating the words "in favor" with the words "favorable outcome" and associating "against" with "unfavorable outcome."

**Math Reasoning** You roll one number cube. Compare the *odds in favor* of getting a 6 to the *probability* of getting a 6. Which is greater? Justify your answer. **The numerators of the ratios are the same, but the denominator of the probability ratio is larger, because it includes all outcomes. This means that the odds ($\frac{1}{5}$) are greater than the probability ($\frac{1}{6}$).**

# 3 Practice/Assess

## Assignment Guide

To provide flexible scheduling, this lesson can be divided into parts.

▼ Part 1

**Core** 1–3, 5–18, 30

✪ **Extension** 31–32

▼ Part 2

**Core** 4, 19–29, 33

✪ **Extension** 34–35

Mixed Review can be assigned at any time for maintenance.

## Exercises

**ELL Exercises 24–29** Ask a student to explain what flash cards are and what they look like.

**Test Prep Exercise 30** Count the sections in the spinner to find the denominator of the probability ratio.

## ✪ Challenge

A spinner has 12 sections that alternate black and white. What are the odds in favor of the spinner stopping on black? 1 (These are sometimes called *even* odds since they favor neither black nor white.)

## Closure

When outcomes are random (equally likely) you can use formulas to find the probability of an event and the odds in favor of an event.

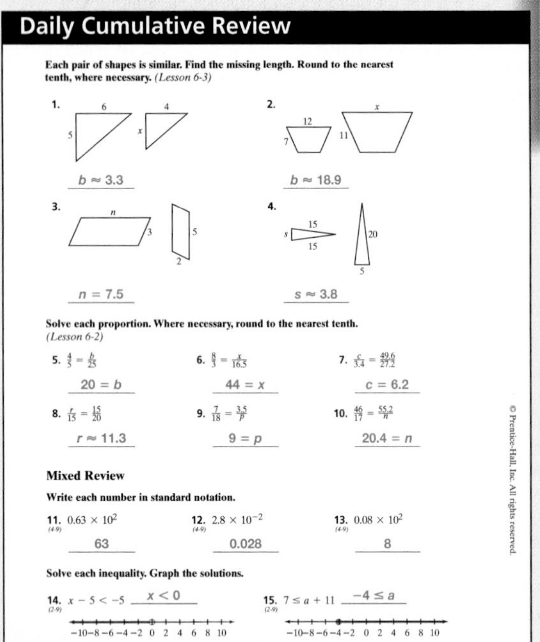

**Daily Cumulative Review**

**Each pair of shapes is similar. Find the missing length. Round to the nearest tenth, where necessary.** *(Lesson 6-3)*

1. $b \approx 3.3$
2. $b \approx 18.9$
3. $n = 7.5$
4. $s \approx 3.8$

**Solve each proportion. Where necessary, round to the nearest tenth.** *(Lesson 6-2)*

5. $\frac{4}{5} = \frac{b}{25}$ $20 = b$
6. $\frac{8}{3} = \frac{x}{16.5}$ $44 = x$
7. $\frac{c}{3.4} = \frac{49.6}{27.2}$ $c = 6.2$
8. $\frac{r}{15} = \frac{15}{20}$ $r \approx 11.3$
9. $\frac{7}{18} = \frac{3.5}{p}$ $9 = p$
10. $\frac{46}{17} = \frac{55.2}{n}$ $20.4 = n$

**Mixed Review**

**Write each number in standard notation.**

11. (4-9) $0.63 \times 10^2$ 63
12. (4-9) $2.8 \times 10^{-2}$ 0.028
13. (4-9) $0.08 \times 10^2$ 8

**Solve each inequality. Graph the solutions.**

14. (2-9) $x - 5 < -5$ $x < 0$
15. (2-9) $7 \le a + 11$ $-4 \le a$



# Exercises

## Check Understanding

**Suppose you select a letter at random from the word ARKANSAS.**

1. What is the probability of selecting the letter A? $\frac{3}{8}$
2. What is the probability of *not* selecting the letter A? $\frac{5}{8}$
3. What is the probability of selecting the letter C? 0
4. What are the odds in favor of selecting a vowel? $\frac{3}{5}$

5a–b. Explanations may vary. Samples are given.

5. a. *Critical Thinking* Can a probability be greater than 1? Explain. No; the number of favorable outcomes is always less than or equal to the number of possible outcomes.
   b. Can a probability be less than 0? Explain. No; the number of favorable outcomes is greater than or equal to 0, and the number of possible outcomes is positive.

## Practice and Problem Solving

**Find each probability for one roll of a number cube.**

6. $P(3)$ $\frac{1}{6}$
7. $P(3 \text{ or } 4)$ $\frac{1}{3}$
8. $P(1, 2, \text{or } 3)$ $\frac{1}{2}$
9. $P(7)$ 0
10. $P(\text{not } 2, 3, \text{or } 6)$ $\frac{1}{2}$
11. $P(\text{greater than } 2)$ $\frac{2}{3}$
12. $P(\text{less than } 3)$ $\frac{1}{3}$
13. $P(\text{not } 1, 3, 4, \text{or } 5)$ $\frac{1}{3}$

**Find each probability for choosing a letter at random from the word MATHEMATICS.**

14. $P(\text{consonant})$ $\frac{7}{11}$
15. $P(\text{M})$ $\frac{2}{11}$
16. $P(\text{not E})$ $\frac{10}{11}$
17. $P(\text{K})$ 0
18. $P(\text{one of the letters that occurs more than once})$ $\frac{6}{11}$

**A student is chosen at random from a class of 10 boys and 15 girls. Find the odds in favor of each event.**

19. A girl is chosen. $\frac{3}{2}$
20. A boy is chosen. $\frac{2}{3}$
21. A boy is not chosen. $\frac{3}{2}$
22. A girl is not chosen. $\frac{2}{3}$
23. Neither a girl nor a boy is chosen. $\frac{0}{25}$

**A set of 36 flash cards is numbered from 1 to 36. A card is chosen at random. Find the odds against each selection.**

24. an even number 1 to 1
25. a number greater than 20 5 to 4
26. a multiple of 3 2 to 1
27. a multiple of both 2 and 3 5 to 1
28. a multiple of 2 or 3 1 to 2
29. a prime number 25 to 11

30. **TEST PREP** Refer to the spinner. Find the probability of the complement of *stopping on red or yellow*. C

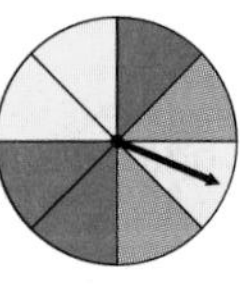

A. $\frac{3}{8}$ B. $\frac{3}{4}$ C. $\frac{1}{4}$ D. Not here



## Alternative Assessment

Have students in groups make a spinner similar to the one in Exercise 30, but with six sections colored any way they choose. Ask them to use the spinner as they write and answer several questions that require finding the probability of an event, the odds against an event, and the probability of the complement of an event.

32. Answers may vary. Sample: getting a number less than 7 on one roll of a number cube; all the numbers on a number cube are less than 7.

31. *Mathematical Reasoning* The table describes the loose socks in Lola's drawer. One morning Lola pulls a sock from the drawer without looking. It is white. She pulls out another sock without looking. Find the probability that it also is white. $\frac{3}{14}$

**Lola's Socks**

| Color | Number of Socks |
|---|---|
| Pink | 6 |
| White | 4 |
| Green | 3 |
| Purple | 2 |

32. *Open-ended* Give an example of an event for which the probability equals 1. Justify your answer. See above.

33. *Number Sense* A number is chosen at random from the whole numbers less than 100. Find the odds in favor of each event.
**a.** It has only one digit. 1 to 9 **b.** It has more than one digit. 9 to 1

34. *Error Analysis* Your friend is flipping a coin. He says that heads and tails are equally likely outcomes, so the probability of getting heads is $\frac{50}{50}$. Explain your friend's error. The friend found odds rather than probability.

35. *Writing* Explain how you can use odds to find probability. Include an example. Answers may vary. Sample: If the odds in favor of an event are $a:b$, then the probability of the event is $\frac{a}{a+b}$. Example: The odds in favor of a number less than 6 on a number cube are 5 to 1. The probability is $\frac{5}{5+1}$, or $\frac{5}{6}$.

## Mixed Review

**The scale of a map is 3 in. : 20 mi. Find the actual distance for each map distance.** *(Lesson 6-3)*

36. 6 in. 40 mi
37. 1 in. $6\frac{2}{3}$ mi
38. 4.2 in. 28 mi
39. $10\frac{1}{2}$ in. 70 mi

**Write each decimal as a fraction or mixed number in simplest form.** *(Lesson 5-2)*

40. 0.25 $\frac{1}{4}$
41. $0.\overline{6}$ $\frac{2}{3}$
42. 0.8125 $\frac{13}{16}$
43. 5.15 $5\frac{3}{20}$

44. Students paid $855 for tickets to a dance. Each ticket cost $5. Write and solve an equation to find the number of tickets the students purchased. *(Lesson 2-6)* $5x = 855$; 171 tickets

## Checkpoint 1 — Lessons 6-1 through 6-4

**Write each phrase as a unit rate.**

1. 20 mi in 5 h 4 mi/h
2. 42 gal in 7 min 6 gal/min
3. a fall of 144 ft in 3 s 48 ft/s

4. *Geometry* The figures are similar. Find the missing length. 4.5

5. A person blinks 112 times in 4 min. At that rate, how many times does the person blink in 1.5 min? 42 times

6. **TEST PREP** Suppose you roll a number cube. Which event has the same probability as $P$(not 1, 2, or 3)? D
A. $P$(3 or 4) B. $P$(less than 5) C. $P$(more than 4)
D. $P$(not an odd number) E. Not here

See also Extra Practice section.



## Practice

**Find each probability for choosing a letter at random from the word PROBABILITY.**

1. $P$(B) $\frac{2}{11}$
2. $P$(P) $\frac{1}{11}$
3. $P$(A or I) $\frac{3}{11}$
4. $P$(not P) $\frac{10}{11}$

**A child is chosen at random from the Erb and Smith families. Find the odds in favor of each of the following being chosen.**

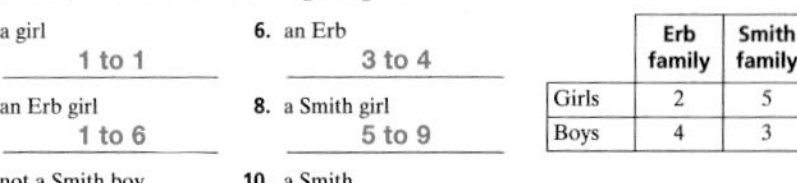

| | Erb family | Smith family |
|---|---|---|
| Girls | 2 | 5 |
| Boys | 4 | 3 |

5. a girl 1 to 1
6. an Erb 3 to 4
7. an Erb girl 1 to 6
8. a Smith girl 5 to 9
9. not a Smith boy 11 to 3
10. a Smith 4 to 3

**A box contains 7 red, 14 yellow, 21 green, 42 blue, and 84 purple marbles. A marble is drawn at random from the box. Find each probability.**

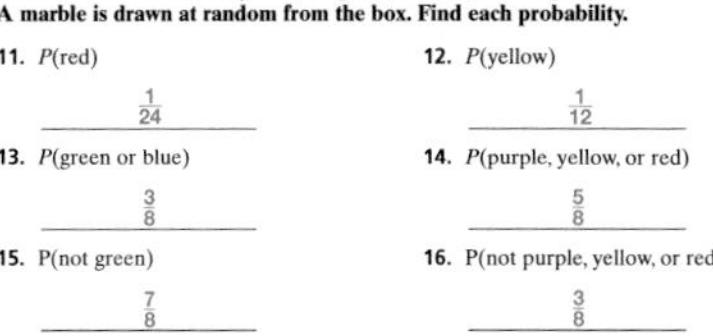

11. $P$(red) $\frac{1}{24}$
12. $P$(yellow) $\frac{1}{12}$
13. $P$(green or blue) $\frac{3}{8}$
14. $P$(purple, yellow, or red) $\frac{5}{8}$
15. P(not green) $\frac{7}{8}$
16. P(not purple, yellow, or red) $\frac{3}{8}$

**Find the odds in favor of each selection when a marble is chosen at random from the box described above.**

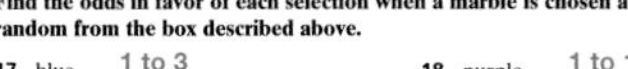

17. blue 1 to 3
18. purple 1 to 1
19. not red 23 to 1
20. not green or blue 5 to 3
21. yellow 1 to 11
22. not purple or yellow 5 to 7



## Reteaching

Suppose you select a letter at random from the words MIDDLE SCHOOL. Find $P$(L) and $P$(not L). First determine the number of possible outcomes. There are 12 letters in the two words, so there are 12 possible outcomes when you select a letter at random. Next determine the number of favorable outcomes for $P$(L). There are two L's.

Thus, $P(\text{L}) = \frac{\text{number of favorable outcomes}}{\text{number of possible outcomes}} = \frac{2}{12} = \frac{1}{6}$

You can find $P$(not L) several ways. Since there are 12 possible outcomes and 2 are L, $12 - 2 = 10$ are not L.

Thus, $P(\text{not L}) = \frac{\text{number of favorable outcomes}}{\text{number of possible outcomes}} = \frac{10}{12} = \frac{5}{6}$

Also $P(\text{not L}) = 1 - P(\text{L})$
$= 1 - \frac{1}{6}$
$= \frac{5}{6}$

**A drawer contains 6 red socks, 4 blue socks, and 14 white socks. A sock is pulled from the drawer at random. Find the probability for each case.**

1. red $\frac{1}{4}$
2. blue $\frac{1}{6}$
3. red or white $\frac{5}{6}$
4. red, white, or blue 1
5. not red $\frac{3}{4}$
6. green 0

**A spinner numbered from 1 to 20 is spun randomly. Find the probability of where the spinner lands for each case.**

7. 17 $\frac{1}{20}$
8. an odd number $\frac{1}{2}$
9. a number divisible by 5 $\frac{1}{5}$
10. 26 0
11. a number with a 1 in it $\frac{11}{20}$
12. a prime number $\frac{2}{5}$
13. a number less than 6 $\frac{1}{4}$
14. a number 1
15. a number that is not less than 17 $\frac{1}{5}$
16. a number divisible by 3 or 4 $\frac{1}{2}$



## Enrichment

**The spinner is spun. Find the probability of each event and the odds in favor of the event.**

| | Outcome Spinner Lands On | Probability | Odds in Favor |
|---|---|---|---|
| 1. | a 5 | $\frac{1}{8}$ | 1 to 7 |
| 2. | an even number | $\frac{1}{2}$ | 1 to 1 |
| 3. | a number not divisible by 3 | $\frac{3}{4}$ | 3 to 1 |
| 4. | a number greater than 5 | $\frac{3}{8}$ | 3 to 5 |

5. Look for a pattern. If the odds in favor of an event are $a$ to $b$, what is the probability the event occurs? $\frac{a}{a+b}$

**Two spinners are spun together. Find the odds:**

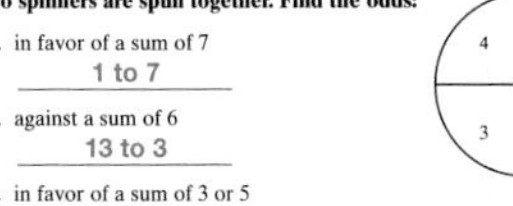

6. in favor of a sum of 7 1 to 7
7. against a sum of 6 13 to 3

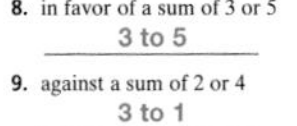

8. in favor of a sum of 3 or 5 3 to 5

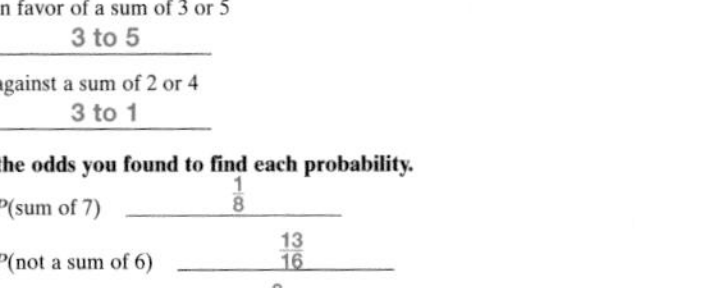

9. against a sum of 2 or 4 3 to 1

**Use the odds you found to find each probability.**

10. $P$(sum of 7) $\frac{1}{8}$
11. $P$(not a sum of 6) $\frac{13}{16}$
12. $P$(sum of 3 or 5) $\frac{3}{8}$
13. $P$(not a sum of 2 or 4) $\frac{3}{4}$



## Checkpoint

**Write each phrase as a unit rate.**

1. 70 mi in 5 h 14 mi/h
2. $9.52 for 8 gal $1.19/gal
3. a fall of 192 ft in 6 s 32 ft/s
4. The figures are similar. Find the missing length. 17.5
5. Patrick drank 64 fl oz of water in 3 days. At this rate, how long will it take him to drink a gallon (128 fl oz)? 6 days
6. Suppose you spin a spinner which is equally likely to land on any one of the numbers from 1 to 8. Which event has the same probability as $P$(not 2 or 3)?
A. $P$(2 or 3) B. $P$(even) C. $P$(more than 6)
(D.) $P$(less than 7) E. Not here

# 6-5

## Getting Ready

**Key Terms and Symbols** percent

**Resources** A complete list of resources for this lesson is on p. 275H.

### Daily Skills Warm-Up

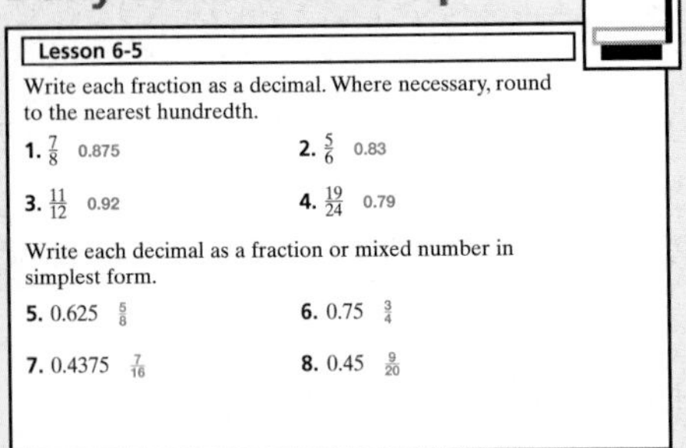

Lesson 6-5

Write each fraction as a decimal. Where necessary, round to the nearest hundredth.

1. $\frac{7}{8}$ 0.875
2. $\frac{5}{6}$ 0.83
3. $\frac{11}{12}$ 0.92
4. $\frac{19}{24}$ 0.79

Write each decimal as a fraction or mixed number in simplest form.

5. 0.625 $\frac{5}{8}$
6. 0.75 $\frac{3}{4}$
7. 0.4375 $\frac{7}{16}$
8. 0.45 $\frac{9}{20}$

### Background for the Lesson

A percent is a ratio that can be written as a fraction with a denominator of 100. The word *percent* comes from the Latin phrase *per centum,* meaning *by the hundred* or per 100. So 28% means 28 out of 100, which you can also write as the fraction $\frac{28}{100}$ or the decimal 0.28. You can replace the % sign with *per one hundred,* or /100, so 115% is 115/100 or $\frac{115}{100}$, which you can also write as 1.15 or the mixed number $1\frac{3}{20}$.

## 1 Focus

### Connecting to Students' Lives

Discuss with students the percents they have seen as grades and as advertised sales (25% off!). Suggest that they examine a daily newspaper to find other common uses for percents.

### Connecting to Prior Knowledge

In Lesson 6-3, students learned to write and simplify ratios by using the GCF (greatest common factor). In this lesson they use those skills to write ratios with denominators of 100 as decimals, fractions, and percents.

# Fractions, Decimals, and Percents

**What You'll Learn**

1. To write percents as fractions and decimals
2. To write decimals and fractions as percents

**. . . And Why**

To use percents to report data such as the number of families who own pets

## PART 1 Writing Percents as Fractions and Decimals

A **percent** is a ratio that compares a number to 100. Therefore, you can write a percent as a fraction with a denominator of 100.

### EXAMPLE 1

**Write each percent as a fraction or a mixed number.**

| a. 5% | | b. 125% |
|---|---|---|
| $\frac{5}{100}$ | ← Write as a fraction with a denominator of 100. → | $\frac{125}{100}$ |
| $\frac{1}{20}$ | ← Simplify. → | $\frac{5}{4}$ |
| | Write as a mixed number. → | $1\frac{1}{4}$ |

**TRY THIS** Write each percent as a fraction or mixed number in simplest form.

1. 58% $\frac{29}{50}$
2. 72% $\frac{18}{25}$
3. 144% $1\frac{11}{25}$

**Reading Math**

Percent means "per hundred." The root *cent* shows up in many other words, such as centimeter, century, and centipede. In money, a cent is $\frac{1}{100}$ of a dollar, or $.01.

To write a percent as a decimal, write the percent as a fraction with a denominator of 100. Then divide to convert the fraction to a decimal.

### EXAMPLE 2

**Write 9.7% as a decimal.**

$9.7\% = \frac{9.7}{100}$ Write as a fraction with a denominator of 100.

$= 009.7$ Divide by moving the decimal point two places to the left. You may need to add one or more zeros.

$= 0.097$

**TRY THIS** Write each percent as a decimal.

4. 16% 0.16
5. 62.5% 0.625
6. 120% 1.2
7. *Biology* About 45% of the people in the United States have type O blood. Express this percent as a decimal and as a fraction in simplest form. 0.45, $\frac{9}{20}$



## Tools to Monitor Progress

**BEFORE THE LESSON**

**To check prerequisite skills:**

- Writing fractions and decimals

**Skills You Need,** p. 275

**Skills Handbook,** p. 727

**Skills Intervention Kit,** Decimals

**DURING THE LESSON**

**To check understanding:**

**Try This** exercises on student page

- **Additional Example 1**

  Write each percent as a fraction or a mixed number.

  a. 30% $\frac{3}{10}$

  b. 175% $1\frac{3}{4}$

- **Additional Example 2**

  Express 7.3% as a decimal. 0.073

## Writing Decimals and Fractions as Percents

To write a decimal as a percent, rewrite the decimal as a fraction with a denominator of 100. Then write the fraction as a percent.

Another way to change a decimal to a percent is to move the decimal point two places to the right and add a percent sign.

### EXAMPLE 3

**Express 0.333 as a percent.**

**Method 1**
Rewrite as a fraction.

$$0.333 = \frac{333}{1{,}000} = \frac{333 \div 10}{1{,}000 \div 10} = \frac{33.3}{100} = 33.3\%$$

**Method 2**
Move the decimal point.

$$0.333 = 33.3\%$$

**TRY THIS** Write each decimal as a percent.

**8.** 0.4 40% **9.** 0.023 2.3% **10.** 1.75 175%

To write a fraction as a percent, divide the numerator by the denominator. Then convert the decimal quotient to a percent.

**DATA ANALYSIS** CONNECTION

### EXAMPLE 4

**Five out of sixteen families in the United States own dogs. What percent of families own dogs?**

| | |
|---|---|
| $\frac{5}{16}$ | Write a fraction. |
| 0.3125 | Divide the numerator by the denominator. |
| 31.25% | Write as a percent. |

About 31% of families own dogs.

There are about 55 million dogs and 61 million cats in the United States. What percent of the total number of dogs and cats are cats? about 53%

**TRY THIS**

**11.** Three out of eleven families in the United States own cats. To the nearest percent, what percent of families own cats? 27%



# 2 Teach

## Part 1 Teaching Notes

Help students think of the percent sign, %, as another way of writing a fraction bar and the two zeros in 100. Show them that they can write 15% as $\frac{15}{100}$.

### Example 1

**Build understanding.** Ask: Based on the examples, answer the following questions. If 5% of a class of 20 students play the piano, how many students in this class play the piano? 1 The class earned $100 at the bake sale last month. This month they earned 125% of last month's sales. How much money did they earn this month? $125

### Example 2

**Build understanding.** Ask: When you write 9.9% as a fraction with a denominator of 100, what will the numerator be? 9.9

**ELL** Review the margin note on Reading Math with the students. Ask them for words in other languages that contain *cent-* and have a meaning related to 100.

## Part 2 Teaching Notes

Encourage students to think of multiplying by 100 as multiplying by 10 and by 10 again, which makes the number greater by two decimal places.

### Example 3

**Build understanding.** You can think of the % in your answer to part a. as dividing by 100. Why do you multiply 0.333 by 100 to write it as a percent? **Dividing by 100 and multiplying by 100 are inverse operations that leave the value of 0.333 unchanged, although the form is different.**

### Example 4

**Build understanding.** Estimate. What percent would 5 out of 15 families be? What percent would 2 out of 10 families be? 33.33%; 20%

- **Additional Example 3**
  Express each decimal as a percent.
  **a.** 0.666 66.6%
  **b.** 0.012 1.2%
  **c.** 5.5 550%
- **Additional Example 4**
  Four out of seven members of the chess club are boys. What percent of the chess club members are boys? about 57% are boys

## AFTER THE LESSON

**To assess knowledge:**
**Lesson Quiz**

Write each percent as a fraction and as a decimal.

**1.** 325% $\frac{13}{4}$; 3.25
**2.** 0.11% $\frac{11}{10{,}000}$; 0.0011

Write each as a percent.

**3.** 2.01 201% **4.** $\frac{3}{5}$ 60%

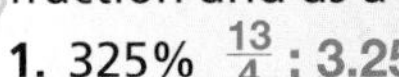

- For enrichment and reteaching options see Resources on p. 275H.

# 3 Practice/Assess

## Assignment Guide

To provide flexible scheduling, this lesson can be divided into parts.

**Part 1**
**Core** 1–4, 14–29, 42–44, 61
**Extension** 62–66

**Part 2**
**Core** 5–13, 30–41, 45–60, 67–70
**Extension** 71–72

Mixed Review can be assigned at any time for maintenance.

### Exercises

**Math Reasoning Exercises 14–21** When is a percent equivalent to a decimal that is less than one? When is a percent equivalent to a decimal that is greater than one? **when the percent is < 100%; when the percent is > 100%**

**Test Prep Exercise 68** One way to compare is to express 30 : 35 and 87% as decimals.

### Challenge

Jon has 8 paperback books and 2 hardback books. His brother has 20 paperbacks and 30 hardbacks. Who has the greater percent of paperbacks in his book collection? **Jon has 80%; his brother has only 40%.**

### Closure

A percent is a ratio that compares a number to 100.

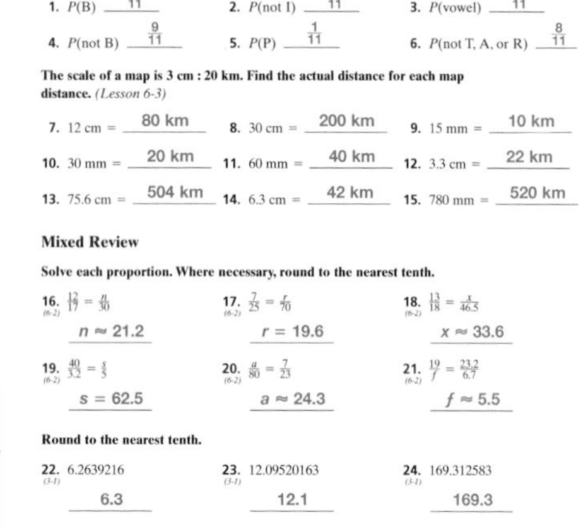

### Daily Cumulative Review

**Find each probability for choosing a letter at random from the word PROBABILITY.** *(Lesson 6-4)*

1. $P(B)$ $\frac{2}{11}$ 2. $P(\text{not I})$ $\frac{9}{11}$ 3. $P(\text{vowel})$ $\frac{4}{11}$
4. $P(\text{not B})$ $\frac{9}{11}$ 5. $P(P)$ $\frac{1}{11}$ 6. $P(\text{not T, A, or R})$ $\frac{8}{11}$

**The scale of a map is 3 cm : 20 km. Find the actual distance for each map distance.** *(Lesson 6-3)*

7. 12 cm = 80 km 8. 30 cm = 200 km 9. 15 mm = 10 km
10. 30 mm = 20 km 11. 60 mm = 40 km 12. 3.3 cm = 22 km
13. 75.6 cm = 504 km 14. 6.3 cm = 42 km 15. 780 mm = 520 km

**Mixed Review**

**Solve each proportion. Where necessary, round to the nearest tenth.**

16. (6-2) $\frac{12}{17} = \frac{n}{30}$ $n \approx 21.2$
17. (6-2) $\frac{7}{25} = \frac{r}{70}$ $r = 19.6$
18. (6-2) $\frac{13}{18} = \frac{x}{46.5}$ $x \approx 33.6$
19. (6-2) $\frac{40}{3.2} = \frac{s}{5}$ $s = 62.5$
20. (6-2) $\frac{a}{80} = \frac{7}{23}$ $a \approx 24.3$
21. (6-2) $\frac{19}{f} = \frac{23.2}{6.7}$ $f \approx 5.5$

**Round to the nearest tenth.**

22. (3-1) 6.2639216 6.3
23. (3-1) 12.09520163 12.1
24. (3-1) 169.312583 169.3

**Insert grouping symbols to make each number sentence true.**

25. (1-2) $(6 + 12) \cdot 5 = 90$
26. (1-2) $(10 - 7) \cdot (8 + 4) = 36$

**Mental Math. Evaluate each expression.**

27. (2-1) $a(b)(-c)$, for $a = 6, b = -5, c = 2$ 60
28. (2-1) $s + t + r$, for $s = 10, t = -6, r = 4$ 8



# Exercises

## CHECK UNDERSTANDING

**Write each percent as a fraction in simplest form and as a decimal.**

1. 40% $\frac{2}{5}$, 0.4
2. 28% $\frac{7}{25}$, 0.28
3. 39% $\frac{39}{100}$, 0.39
4. 55% $\frac{11}{20}$, 0.55

**Write each decimal or fraction as a percent.**

5. 1.68 168%
6. 0.36 36%
7. 0.70 70%
8. 0.002 0.2%
9. $\frac{23}{100}$ 23%
10. $\frac{1}{4}$ 25%
11. $\frac{11}{20}$ 55%
12. $\frac{1}{6}$ $16.\overline{6}$%

13. *Critical Thinking* Explain why 0.25 is different from 0.25%. Explanations may vary. Sample: 0.25 is 25%.

## PRACTICE AND PROBLEM SOLVING

**Write each percent as a fraction or mixed number in simplest form.**

14. 20% $\frac{1}{5}$
15. 6% $\frac{3}{50}$
16. 45% $\frac{9}{20}$
17. 98% $\frac{49}{50}$
18. 65% $\frac{13}{20}$
19. 36% $\frac{9}{25}$
20. 220% $2\frac{1}{5}$
21. 0.4% $\frac{1}{250}$

**Write each percent as a decimal.**

22. 1% 0.01
23. 19.25% 0.1925
24. 0.06% 0.0006
25. 6.3% 0.063
26. 133% 1.33
27. 79.7% 0.797
28. 350.5% 3.505
29. $4\frac{1}{2}$% 0.045

**Write each decimal or fraction as a percent. Round to the nearest tenth of a percent where necessary.**

30. 0.33 33%
31. 0.85 85%
32. 0.06 6%
33. 0.0075 0.75%
34. 1.88 188%
35. 2.59 259%
36. $\frac{79}{100}$ 79%
37. $\frac{26}{50}$ 52%
38. $\frac{7}{20}$ 35%
39. $\frac{2}{9}$ 22.2%
40. $\frac{5}{6}$ 83.3%
41. $\frac{111}{100}$ 111%

*Estimation* **About what percent of each flag is red?** 42–44. Answers may vary. Samples are given.

42. about 80%

Tennessee

43. about 25%

Arizona

44. about 33%

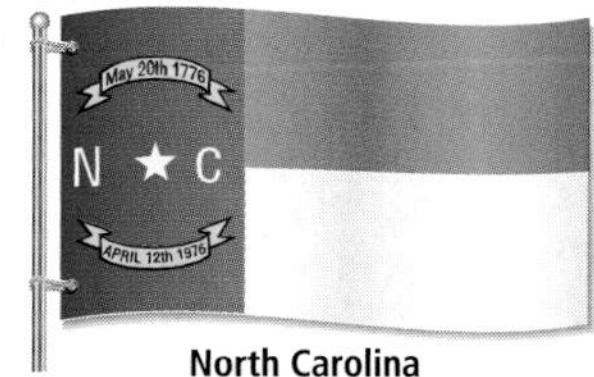


North Carolina



### Alternative Assessment

Have students use graph paper to shade a block of 100 squares to show 60% and then write the equivalent fraction and decimal.

*Probability* **Find each probability for one roll of a number cube. Write the probability as a percent. Where necessary, round to the nearest tenth of a percent.**

45. $P(6)$ 16.7%
46. $P(\text{even})$ 50%
47. $P(1 \text{ or } 2)$ 33.3%
48. $P(\text{not } 1)$ 83.3%

**Copy and complete the table.**

| | Fraction | Decimal | Percent |
|---|---|---|---|
| 49. | $\frac{4}{5}$ | ■ 0.8 | ■ 80 |
| 50. | ■ $\frac{1}{10}$ | 0.10 | ■ 10 |
| 51. | ■ $\frac{1}{2}$ | 0.5 | ■ 50 |
| 52. | $\frac{3}{4}$ | ■ 0.75 | ■ 75 |
| 53. | ■ $\frac{67}{100}$ | ■ 0.67 | 67 |
| 54. | ■ $\frac{1}{4}$ | ■ 0.25 | 25 |

**Compare. Use >, <, or = to complete each statement.**

55. 0.05% ■ 50% <
56. $\frac{7}{12}$ ■ 60% <
57. 0.0325 ■ 32.5% <
58. $\frac{7}{8}$ ■ 68% >
59. 0.1756 ■ 176% <
60. $\frac{140}{130}$ ■ 104% >

61. *Maps* A map has a scale of 0.01%. Express the scale as a fraction. $\frac{1}{10,000}$

*Critical Thinking* **For Exercises 62–65, does each sentence make sense? Explain.** 62–65. Explanations may vary. Samples are given.

62. About 17% of Americans go camping. That means about 83% do not go camping. Yes; 100% − 17% = 83%

63. A student correctly answered 200% of the items on a test. No; it is not possible to answer more items than are on the test.

64. Today a runner ran 150% of the distance she ran yesterday. Yes; the runner ran $1\frac{1}{2}$ times as far as she ran yesterday.

65. On a test, a student missed 12 items and correctly answered 96% of all items. Yes; the test had 300 items and the student answered 288 of them correctly.

66. *Open-ended* Use a percent to describe an everyday event. Then write the percent as a fraction and as a decimal. Check students' work.

67. *Statistics* In the United States, about one person in eight lives in California. Complete: About ■% of the people in the United States live in California. 12.5

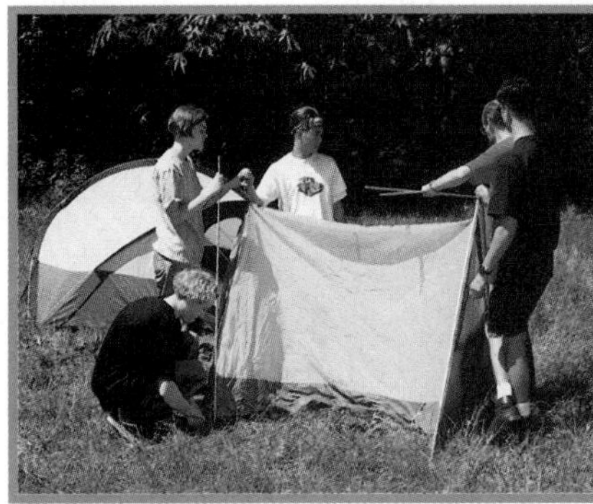

Each year, about 45 million Americans go camping. How many do not go camping? about 220 million

## Practice

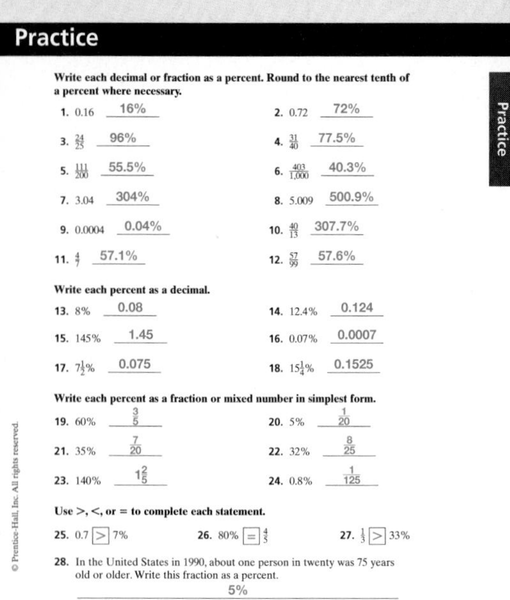

Write each decimal or fraction as a percent. Round to the nearest tenth of a percent where necessary.

1. 0.16 16%
2. 0.72 72%
3. $\frac{24}{25}$ 96%
4. $\frac{31}{40}$ 77.5%
5. $\frac{111}{200}$ 55.5%
6. $\frac{403}{1,000}$ 40.3%
7. 3.04 304%
8. 5.009 500.9%
9. 0.0004 0.04%
10. $\frac{40}{13}$ 307.7%
11. $\frac{4}{7}$ 57.1%
12. $\frac{57}{99}$ 57.6%

Write each percent as a decimal.

13. 8% 0.08
14. 12.4% 0.124
15. 145% 1.45
16. 0.07% 0.0007
17. $7\frac{1}{2}$% 0.075
18. $15\frac{1}{4}$% 0.1525

Write each percent as a fraction or mixed number in simplest form.

19. 60% $\frac{3}{5}$
20. 5% $\frac{1}{20}$
21. 35% $\frac{7}{20}$
22. 32% $\frac{8}{25}$
23. 140% $1\frac{2}{5}$
24. 0.8% $\frac{1}{125}$

Use >, <, or = to complete each statement.

25. 0.7 > 7%
26. 80% = $\frac{4}{5}$
27. $\frac{1}{3}$ > 33%
28. In the United States in 1990, about one person in twenty was 75 years old or older. Write this fraction as a percent. 5%



Practice

## Reteaching

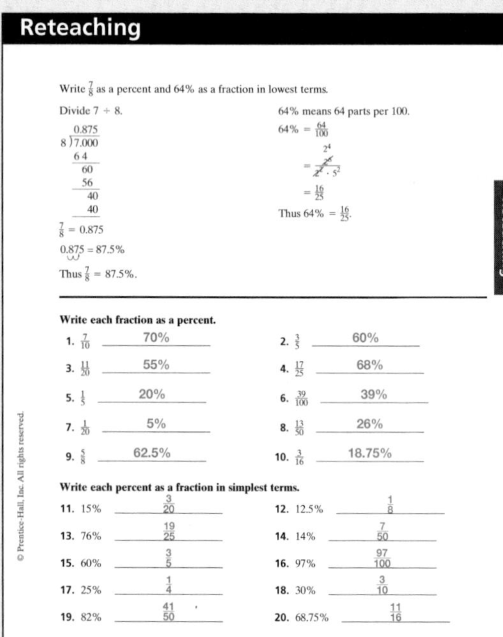

Write $\frac{7}{8}$ as a percent and 64% as a fraction in lowest terms.

Divide 7 ÷ 8.

$8\overline{)7.000}$ = 0.875 (64, 60, 56, 40, 40)

$\frac{7}{8}$ = 0.875

0.875 = 87.5%

Thus $\frac{7}{8}$ = 87.5%.

64% means 64 parts per 100.

$64\% = \frac{64}{100} = \frac{2^4 \cdot 2^2}{2^2 \cdot 5^2} = \frac{16}{25}$

Thus $64\% = \frac{16}{25}$.

Write each fraction as a percent.

1. $\frac{7}{10}$ 70%
2. $\frac{3}{5}$ 60%
3. $\frac{11}{20}$ 55%
4. $\frac{17}{25}$ 68%
5. $\frac{1}{5}$ 20%
6. $\frac{39}{100}$ 39%
7. $\frac{1}{20}$ 5%
8. $\frac{13}{50}$ 26%
9. $\frac{5}{8}$ 62.5%
10. $\frac{3}{16}$ 18.75%

Write each percent as a fraction in simplest terms.

11. 15% $\frac{3}{20}$
12. 12.5% $\frac{1}{8}$
13. 76% $\frac{19}{25}$
14. 14% $\frac{7}{50}$
15. 60% $\frac{3}{5}$
16. 97% $\frac{97}{100}$
17. 25% $\frac{1}{4}$
18. 30% $\frac{3}{10}$
19. 82% $\frac{41}{50}$
20. 68.75% $\frac{11}{16}$



Reteaching

## Enrichment

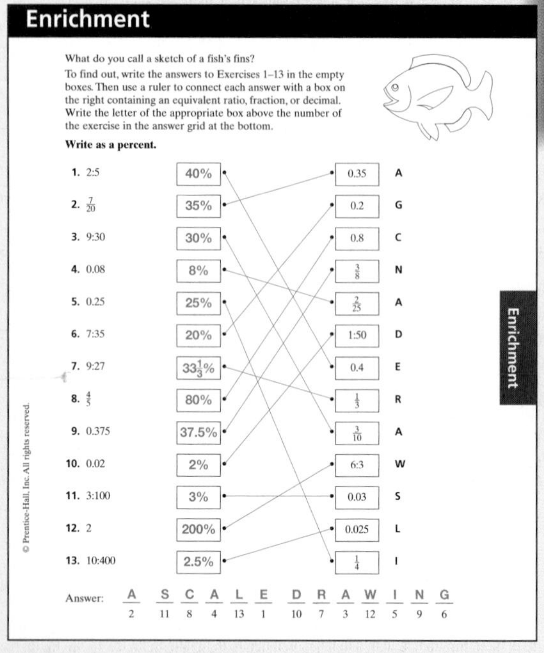

What do you call a sketch of a fish's fins?

To find out, write the answers to Exercises 1–13 in the empty boxes. Then use a ruler to connect each answer with a box on the right containing an equivalent ratio, fraction, or decimal. Write the letter of the appropriate box above the number of the exercise in the answer grid at the bottom.

Write as a percent.

| Exercise | Answer | Box | Letter |
|---|---|---|---|
| 1. 2:5 | 40% | 0.35 | A |
| 2. $\frac{7}{20}$ | 35% | 0.2 | G |
| 3. 9:30 | 30% | 0.8 | C |
| 4. 0.08 | 8% | $\frac{3}{8}$ | N |
| 5. 0.25 | 25% | $\frac{2}{25}$ | A |
| 6. 7:35 | 20% | 1:50 | D |
| 7. 9:27 | $33\frac{1}{3}$% | 0.4 | E |
| 8. $\frac{4}{5}$ | 80% | $\frac{1}{3}$ | R |
| 9. 0.375 | 37.5% | $\frac{3}{10}$ | A |
| 10. 0.02 | 2% | 6:3 | W |
| 11. 3:100 | 3% | 0.03 | S |
| 12. 2 | 200% | 0.025 | L |
| 13. 10:400 | 2.5% | $\frac{1}{4}$ | I |

Answer:

| A | S | C | A | L | E | D | R | A | W | I | N | G |
|---|---|---|---|---|---|---|---|---|---|---|---|---|
| 2 | 11 | 8 | 4 | 13 | 1 | 10 | 7 | 3 | 12 | 5 | 9 | 6 |



Enrichment



68. **TEST PREP** In a free-throw contest, three players take the same number of shots. Player A makes 30 of 35 shots. Player B makes 0.84 of his shots. Player C makes 87% of her shots. Who wins?
**A.** Player A **B.** Player B **C.** Player C **D.** A and C tie. C

69. Jeanette answered 32 questions correctly on a 45-question test. The passing grade was 70%. Did Jeanette pass? Justify your answer. See below right.

70. *Scale Drawings* A scale drawing has a scale of 1.12. Express the scale as a percent. 112%

71. A crowd filled the 8,000 seats in a stadium. There were 1,400 children and 4,800 men present. Write a ratio and a percent to describe how many seats were filled by each group.
a. men $\frac{3}{5}$, 60% b. children $\frac{7}{40}$, 17.5% c. women $\frac{9}{40}$, 22.5%

72. *Writing* Explain how to write a decimal as a percent. Give examples. Answers may vary. Sample: Move the decimal point two places to the right and add a percent sign; 0.25 = 25%, 1.35 = 135%.

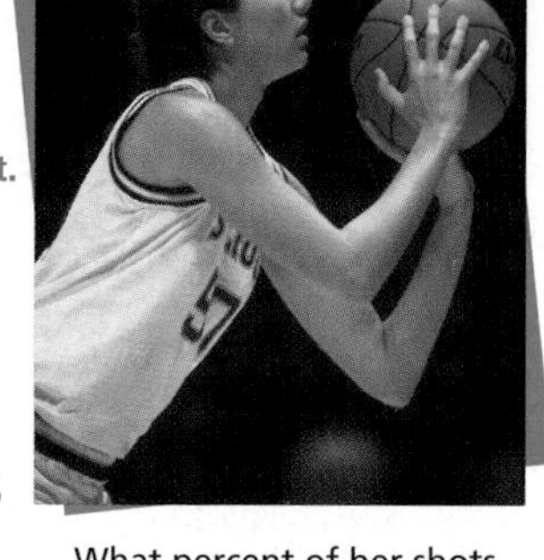

What percent of her shots did Player A make? about 86

69. Yes; $\frac{32}{45} \approx 71\%$.

## Mixed Review

**Find each probability for choosing a letter at random from the word PROBABLE.** *(Lesson 6-4)*

73. $P(\text{B})$ $\frac{1}{4}$
74. $P(\text{vowel})$ $\frac{3}{8}$
75. $P(\text{R})$ $\frac{1}{8}$
76. $P(\text{not L or R})$ $\frac{3}{4}$

**Solve each equation.** *(Lesson 3-6)*

77. $0.85x = 39.95$ 47
78. $4.8y = -0.84$ −0.175
79. $100 = \frac{a}{13.2}$ 1,320
80. $\frac{b}{-25} = 1.8$ −45

81. *Choose a Strategy* The average of three test scores is 85. One test score is 90. Another is 72. What is the third? 93

## Chapter Project 6 — Activity 3 Calculating

Use your results from Activity 2. For each note, calculate the ratio of the string length to 10 in., the string length for the note *say*. Put your results in a table like the one at the right.

| Note | String Length (in.) | Ratio to *say*'s Length |
|---|---|---|
| *can* | ■ | $\frac{■}{10}$ |
| *you* | ■ | $\frac{■}{10}$ |
| *see* | ■ | $\frac{■}{10}$ |



See also Extra Practice section.

### Project Activity 3

**Calculating** Discuss the advantages of writing the string lengths for the various notes as percentages rather than as actual lengths. Suggest that students may want to test their results by using a 20-in. string.

# Proportions and Percents



## PART 1 Finding Part of a Whole

You can solve a percent problem by writing and solving a proportion.

A model can help you write a proportion. This model shows that 30 is 75% of 40.

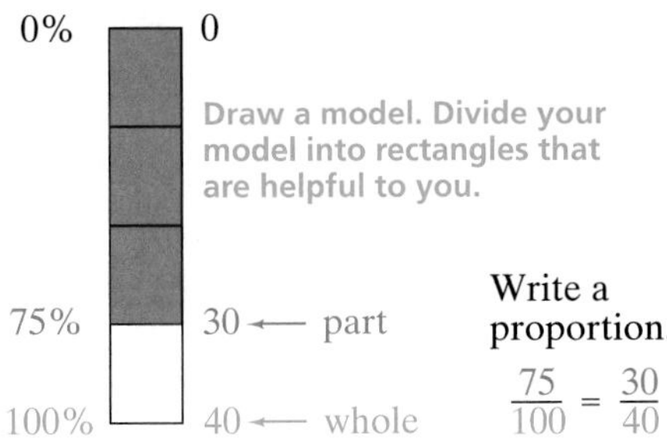


Write a proportion.

$\frac{75}{100} = \frac{30}{40}$

**What You'll Learn**

1. To find a percent and a part of a whole
2. To find a whole amount

**. . . And Why**

To compare numbers, including drive-in movie data

**EXAMPLE 1**

**Find 65% of 245.**

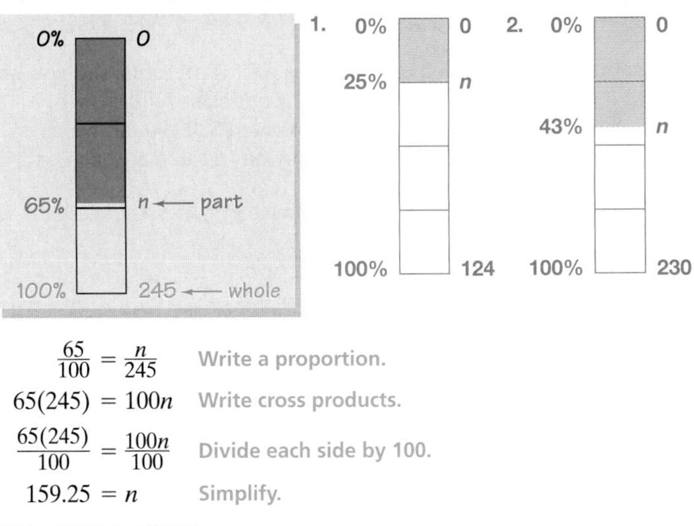


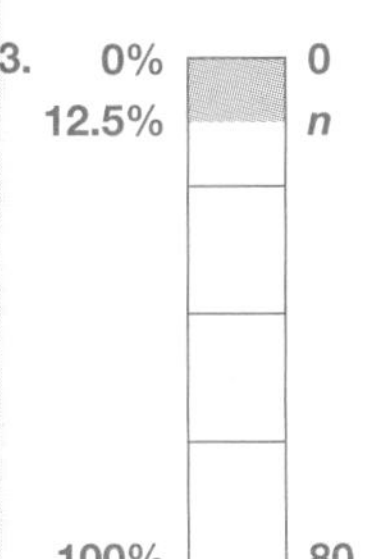


$\frac{65}{100} = \frac{n}{245}$ Write a proportion.

$65(245) = 100n$ Write cross products.

$\frac{65(245)}{100} = \frac{100n}{100}$ Divide each side by 100.

$159.25 = n$ Simplify.

65% of 245 is 159.25.

**TRY THIS** Draw a model and write a proportion. Then solve.

1–3. For models, see above.

1. 25% of 124 is ■. $\frac{25}{100} = \frac{n}{124}$; 31
2. 43% of 230 is ■. $\frac{43}{100} = \frac{n}{230}$; 98.9
3. 12.5% of 80 is ■. $\frac{12.5}{100} = \frac{n}{80}$; 10



# 6-6

## Getting Ready

**Resources** A complete list of resources for this lesson is on p. 275H.

### Daily Skills Warm-Up

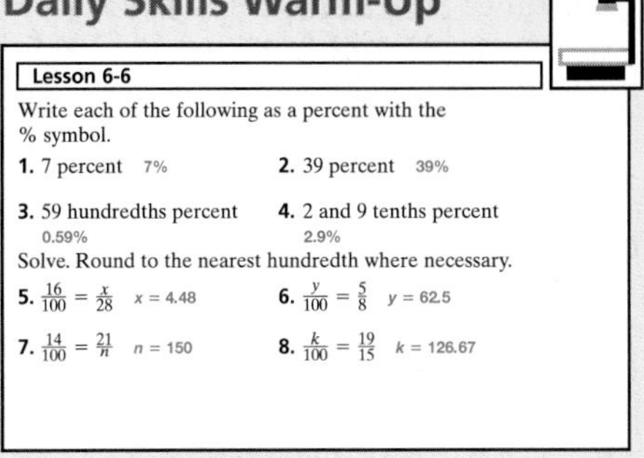

Lesson 6-6

Write each of the following as a percent with the % symbol.

1. 7 percent 7%
2. 39 percent 39%
3. 59 hundredths percent 0.59%
4. 2 and 9 tenths percent 2.9%

Solve. Round to the nearest hundredth where necessary.

5. $\frac{16}{100} = \frac{x}{28}$ $x = 4.48$
6. $\frac{y}{100} = \frac{5}{8}$ $y = 62.5$
7. $\frac{14}{100} = \frac{21}{n}$ $n = 150$
8. $\frac{k}{100} = \frac{19}{15}$ $k = 126.67$

### Background for the Lesson

You can use a proportion to solve a percent problem. Be careful to set up the proportion so that the parts of the ratios correspond to the parts of the problem. In general, a percent problem has a part over the whole equal to another part over another whole. To find 35% of 623, begin by making a rough estimate: will 35% be greater or less than roughly half of 623? Since 35% is less than 50% (or half), you can expect to get an answer that is less than 300. Then set up the proportion: 35 is to 100 as the part of 623 is to the whole of 623: $\frac{35}{100} = \frac{x}{623}$. Set the cross products equal and solve by dividing each side of the equation by 100 to get $x = 218.05$. Then compare the solution to the estimate.

## Tools to Monitor Progress

### BEFORE THE LESSON

**To check prerequisite skills:**

- Writing percents

**Skills You Need,** p. 275

**Skills Handbook,** p. 731

**Skills Intervention Kit,** Ratio, Proportion, and Percent

### DURING THE LESSON

**To check understanding:**

**Try This** exercises on student page

- **Additional Example 1**
  Find 23% of 158. 36.34
- **Additional Example 2**
  What percent of 34 is 28? Round to the nearest tenth of a percent. 82.4%

## 1 Focus

### Connecting to Students' Lives

Discuss where students have seen percents: for example, interest paid on savings accounts and investments is usually quoted as a percent. Sales tax is also usually quoted as a percent.

### Connecting to Prior Knowledge

In Lesson 6-5, students learned to write percents as decimals and as fractions. In Lesson 6-2, students learned to solve proportions. In this lesson, they use both these skills to solve percent problems using proportions.

# 2 Teach

## Part 1 Teaching Notes

You can solve most percent problems by a number of different methods. Encourage students to begin with a rough estimate and to set up the problem in a way that makes sense to them.

### Example 1

**Build understanding.** Ask: Will 65% of 245 be greater or less than half of 245? Why? greater than half, because 50% is one-half and 65 > 50

### Example 2

**Build understanding.** Ask: What number is 100% of 60? What percent would you estimate that 52 is of 60? 60; sample answer: close to 100%

**ELL** Discuss the fact that "What percent of 60 is 52?" means the same as "What percent is 52 of 60?" Show students that the *of* is a signal that the next number is the whole of which 52 is the part.

## Part 2 Teaching Notes

Remind students that the whole is not necessarily larger than the part in a percent problem. In the question "What percent is \$50 of last year's price of \$20?" the \$50 is the part (or numerator) and the \$20 is the whole (or denominator), so \$50 is 250% of \$20.

### Example 3

**Build understanding.** Estimate. Will the number be greater than or less than 2 • 207, or 414? Since 207 would be 50% of 414, but 207 is only 46% of the answer, the answer must be a little greater than 414.

**Extension** 72 is 200% of what number? 36

### EXAMPLE 2

**What percent of 60 is 52? Round to the nearest tenth of a percent.**

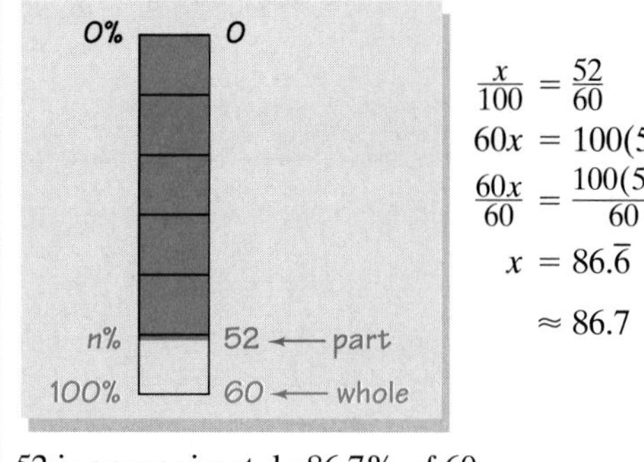


$\frac{x}{100} = \frac{52}{60}$ Write a proportion.

$60x = 100(52)$ Write cross products.

$\frac{60x}{60} = \frac{100(52)}{60}$ Divide each side by 60.

$x = 86.\overline{6}$ Simplify.

$\approx 86.7$ Round.

52 is approximately 86.7% of 60.

**TRY THIS** Round to the nearest tenth of a percent.

4. What percent of 250 is 138? 55.2%
5. 14 is what percent of 15? 93.3%

## PART 2 Finding a Whole Amount

Sometimes you know the percent that a part represents, and you want to find the whole amount. For example, your class fundraising committee might announce, "We've collected \$207 so far, which is 46% of our goal!" You can use a proportion to calculate the goal.

### EXAMPLE 3

**207 is 46% of what number?**

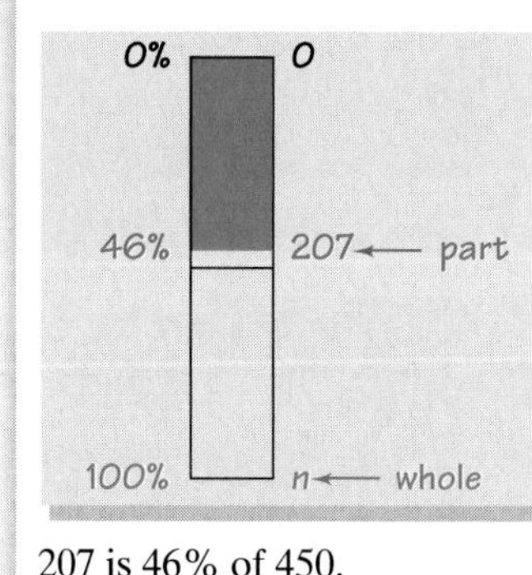


$\frac{46}{100} = \frac{207}{n}$ Write a proportion.

$46n = 100(207)$ Write cross products.

$\frac{46n}{46} = \frac{100(207)}{46}$ Divide each side by 46.

$n = 450$ Simplify.

207 is 46% of 450.



- **Additional Example 3**
  216 is 72% of what number? 300
- **Additional Example 4**
  The floor has 90 blue tiles, or 15% of all the tiles in the floor. How many total tiles are there in the floor? 600

## AFTER THE LESSON

**To assess knowledge: Lesson Quiz**

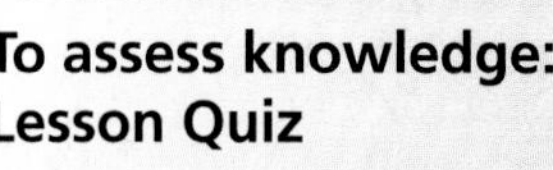

1. Find 47% of 2,400. 1,128
2. 6 is 3% of what number? 200
3. What is 214% of 700? 1,498
4. Find 7.3% of 500. 36.5
5. What is $66\frac{2}{3}$% of 168? 112

- For enrichment and reteaching options see Resources on p. 275H.

**TRY THIS** Round to the nearest tenth.

6. 19 is 75% of what number? 25.3
7. 310 is 99% of what number? 313.1

**DATA ANALYSIS** CONNECTION

## EXAMPLE 4

**In 1998, the number of drive-in movie screens in the United States was only about 21% of the number in 1980. About how many drive-in screens were there in 1980?**

**Drive-In Movies**

| Year | Number of Screens |
|---|---|
| 1980 | ■ |
| 1990 | 915 |
| 1998 | 748 |

SOURCE: Motion Picture Association of America

$\frac{21}{100} = \frac{748}{n}$ Write a proportion.

$21n = 100(748)$ Write cross products.

$\frac{21n}{21} = \frac{100(748)}{21}$ Divide each side by 21.

$s \approx 3{,}560$ Estimate.

There were about 3,560 screens in 1980.

**Check** Is the answer reasonable? The original problem says that the number of screens in 1998 was 21% of the number in 1980. Check by estimating:
21% of 3,560 $\approx 0.2 \times 3{,}600 = 720$, which is close to 748, the number for 1998. So the answer is reasonable.

**TRY THIS**

8. Refer to the table in Example 4. In 1990, the number of drive-in movie screens was about 32.4% of the number in 1985. Find the number of drive-in screens in 1985. about 2,824 screens

The table below summarizes how to use proportions to solve percent problems.

**Percents and Proportions**

| Finding the Percent | Finding the Part | Finding the Whole |
|---|---|---|
| What percent of 40 is 6? | What number is 15% of 40? | 6 is 15% of what number? |
| $\frac{n}{100} = \frac{6}{40}$ ← part ← whole | $\frac{15}{100} = \frac{n}{40}$ ← part ← whole | $\frac{15}{100} = \frac{6}{n}$ ← part ← whole |



## Example 4

**Build understanding.** Only about 20% of the screens from 1980 still remain. Since 20% is $\frac{20}{100}$ or $\frac{1}{5}$, a rough estimate might be 700 times what number? 5; an estimate of 5 • 700, or 3,500

**Connecting to History** Ask a student to explain (perhaps after some research) what drive-in movie screens are, when they were most popular, and what happened to most of them.

**Visual Learning** Students can shade a sketch of a circle or a bar, divided into parts, to help them compare a part and the whole.

**Math Reasoning** The price of a car this year is higher than last year's price for the same car. When you find what percent of last year's cost is this year's cost, what can you predict about the size of the answer? It will most likely be >100%.

**Reading Math** Explain that the number that follows the *of* in a problem is almost always the whole that will be the denominator of the fraction or ratio.

**Error Prevention** To check calculations, you may want to estimate using a fraction that is approximately equal to the percent in the problem.

# 3 Practice/Assess

## Assignment Guide

To provide flexible scheduling, this lesson can be divided into parts.

**Part 1**
**Core** 1–6, 10–23, 32–33, 35
✪ **Extension** 24, 34, 36

**Part 2**
**Core** 7–9, 25–29, 37–40
✪ **Extension** 30–31, 41

Mixed Review can be assigned at any time for maintenance.

## Exercises

**Test Prep Exercise 37** Read the statement in the reverse order: "60% of $n$ is 42" and then compare the words to the math sentences.

## ✪ Challenge

Is a percent of a number always less than the number? Justify your answer. No; sample answer: 200% of $x$ is $2x$. When $x$ is positive, $2x > x$.

## Closure

You can solve percent problems by using a proportion.

# Exercises

## Check Understanding

**Write a proportion. Then solve. Where necessary, round to the nearest tenth or tenth of a percent.**

1. Find 80% of 20. 16
2. Find 300% of 50. 150
3. What percent of 40 is 30? 75%
4. What percent of 20 is 40? 200%
5. What is 40% of 60? 24
6. What is 53% of 70? 37.1
7. 25% of what number is 8? 32
8. 18% of ■ is 14.4. 80
9. 250% of $t$ is 50. What is $t$? 20
10. *Mathematical Reasoning* Do $a$% of $b$ and $b$% of $a$ represent the same amount? Justify your answer. Explanations may vary. Sample: Yes; for $a$% of $b$, solve $\frac{a}{100} = \frac{n}{b}$ to get $n = \frac{ab}{100}$. For $b$% of $a$, solve $\frac{b}{100} = \frac{n}{a}$ to get $n = \frac{ab}{100}$.

## Practice and Problem Solving

**Write and solve a proportion.**

11. $\frac{n}{100} = \frac{16}{20}$; 80
12. $\frac{n}{100} = \frac{18}{75}$; 24
13. $\frac{75}{100} = \frac{420}{n}$; 560

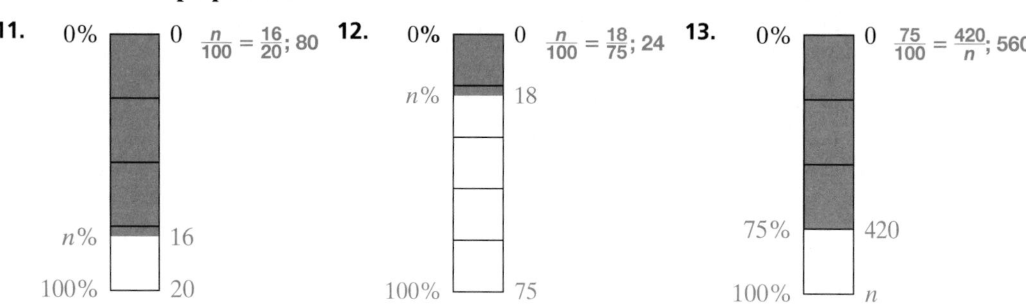


**Write a proportion. Then solve. Where necessary, round to the nearest tenth or tenth of a percent.** 14–31. For proportions see margin.

14. What percent of 25 is 13? 52%
15. Find 18% of 150. 27
16. Find 116% of 75. 87
17. Find 60% of 15. 9
18. 75 is ■ percent of 250. 30
19. Find 92% of 625. 575
20. Find 53% of 76,550. 40,571.5
21. What percent of 92 is 17? 18.5%
22. Find 9.3% of 47.89. 4.5
23. Find 98% of 6.1. 6.0
24. ✪ Find $33\frac{1}{3}$% of 54. 18
25. 14 is 35% of ■. 40
26. 1 is 2% of what number? 50
27. 35% of ■ is 52.5. 150
28. 49% of ■ is 31.85. 65
29. 2.5% of ■ is 912.5. 36,500
30. ✪ $12\frac{1}{2}$% of ■ is 6. 48
31. ✪ 116% of $a$ is 125. What is $a$? 107.8
32. A bicycle cost $250 last year. The same bike costs $200 this year. What percent of last year's cost is this year's cost? 80%



## Daily Cumulative Review

**Write each percent as a decimal.** *(Lesson 6-5)*

1. 48% 0.48
2. 65.8% 0.658
3. 129% 1.29
4. 30% 0.3
5. 2% 0.02
6. 75% 0.75

**A fish is chosen at random from a group of 15 black fish and 20 orange fish. Find the odds in favor of each event.** *(Lesson 6-4)*

7. A black fish is chosen. 3 to 4
8. An orange fish is chosen. 4 to 3
9. A black fish is not chosen. 4 to 3
10. A black or orange fish is chosen. 1 to 0

**Mixed Review**

**Solve each equation.**

11. (3-6) $3.96 = 1.8r$ $2.2 = r$
12. (3-5) $x + 2.9 = 35$ $x = 32.1$
13. (5-8) $7b = \frac{3}{4}$ $b = \frac{3}{28}$
14. (5-8) $3\frac{1}{3}k = \frac{4}{5}$ $k = \frac{6}{25}$
15. (3-5) $17.4 = n + 13.9$ $3.5 = n$
16. (3-6) $\frac{m}{0.81} = 2{,}452$ $m = 1{,}986.12$

**Simplify each expression.**

17. (2-3) $6(5x - 3) - x$ $29x - 18$
18. (5-9) $(r^2 \cdot s^3)^3$ $r^6s^9$
19. (4-2) $6(8 - 4)^2$ 96
20. (5-9) $(2b^6c^4)^8$ $256b^{48}c^{32}$
21. (2-3) $9a - 10c + 4a$ $13a - 10c$
22. (4-2) $5^2 - 2^4$ 9

**Write a rule for the pattern. Find the next three numbers in the pattern.**

23. (1-8) 4, 14, 5, 15, 6, 16, 7, 17, 8
Rule: Start with 4. Add 10, then subtract 9 repeatedly.



## Alternative Assessment

Have students find an advertisement containing a percent discount for an item they would like to buy. Ask them to write and solve a percent problem using the information in the advertisement.

14. $\frac{n}{100} = \frac{13}{25}$
15. $\frac{18}{100} = \frac{n}{150}$
16. $\frac{116}{100} = \frac{n}{75}$
17. $\frac{60}{100} = \frac{n}{15}$
18. $\frac{n}{100} = \frac{75}{250}$
19. $\frac{92}{100} = \frac{n}{625}$
20. $\frac{53}{100} = \frac{n}{76{,}550}$

33. *Statistics* The population of Alaska was about 129,000 in 1950. The population was about 614,000 in 1998. The 1950 population was about what percent of the 1998 population? 21%

34. *Sales Tax* The table shows sales tax rates for different states.
a. For each state, find the amount of sales tax on a $15,000 car.
b. For each state, find the car's total cost. 34a–b. See below right.

| State | Sales Tax Rate |
|---|---|
| Georgia | 7% |
| Kansas | 4.9% |
| Pennsylvania | 6% |
| South Carolina | 5% |

35. *Writing* At Pineapples, all books and posters are marked 30% off. At Avocados, the same items are marked $\frac{1}{3}$ off. Which store offers the greater discount rate? Explain. Avocados; $\frac{1}{3} = 33.\overline{3}\%$

36. A student pole-vaulted 5 ft yesterday. Today she vaulted 20% higher. How high was her vault today? 6 ft

37. **TEST PREP** Which proportion would you use to solve *42 is 60% of n?* A

A. $\frac{60}{100} = \frac{42}{n}$ B. $\frac{42}{100} = \frac{60}{n}$ C. $\frac{n}{100} = \frac{60}{42}$ D. $\frac{60}{100} = \frac{n}{42}$

38. *Profit* You invested some money and made a profit of $55. Your profit was 11% of your investment. How much did you invest? $500

34a. Georgia $1,050; Kansas $735; Pennsylvania $900; South Carolina $750

b. Georgia $16,050; Kansas $15,735; Pennsylvania $15,900; South Carolina $15,750

39. Nineteen members, or 38%, of the ski club are going on a ski trip. Find the total number of members in the club. 50 members

40. *Error Analysis* Your class has 26 students, which represents 5% of your school's enrollment. Your friend uses the proportion $\frac{5}{100} = \frac{n}{26}$ to find the number of students in your school. Explain your friend's error. The friend should have used the ratio $\frac{26}{n}$, comparing class enrollment, 26, to school enrollment, *n*.

41. *Open-ended* Write and solve a word problem involving percents. Check students' work.

## Mixed Review

**Write each number as a percent.** *(Lesson 6-5)*

42. 0.08 8% 43. 0.523 52.3% 44. $\frac{7}{12}$ $58.\overline{3}\%$ 45. 4.56 456%

**Order from least to greatest.** *(Lesson 4-9)*

46. $10^3, 10^{-2}, 10^{-1}, 10^0$
$10^{-2}, 10^{-1}, 10^0, 10^3$

47. $2.3 \times 10^4, 2.03 \times 10^5, 2.03 \times 10^4, 2.4 \times 10^3$
$2.4 \times 10^3, 2.03 \times 10^4, 2.3 \times 10^4, 2.03 \times 10^5$

48. Peter has four cousins. Paul has *c* cousins fewer than Peter. Write an expression for the number of Paul's cousins. $4 - c$ *(Lesson 1-1)*

See also Extra Practice section.



21. $\frac{n}{100} = \frac{17}{92}$

22. $\frac{9.3}{100} = \frac{n}{47.89}$

23. $\frac{98}{100} = \frac{n}{6.1}$

24. $\frac{33\frac{1}{3}}{100} = \frac{n}{54}$

25. $\frac{35}{100} = \frac{14}{n}$

26. $\frac{2}{100} = \frac{1}{n}$

27. $\frac{35}{100} = \frac{52.5}{n}$

28. $\frac{49}{100} = \frac{31.85}{n}$

29. $\frac{2.5}{100} = \frac{912.5}{n}$

30. $\frac{12\frac{1}{2}}{100} = \frac{6}{n}$

31. $\frac{116}{100} = \frac{125}{a}$

## Practice

**Write a proportion. Then solve. Where necessary, round to the nearest tenth or tenth of a percent.**

1. $62\frac{1}{2}\%$ of *t* is 35. What is *t*? 56
2. 38% of *n* is 33.44. What is *n*? 88
3. 120% of *y* is 42. What is *y*? 35
4. 300% of *m* is 600. What is *m*? 200
5. 1.5% of *h* is 12. What is *h*? 800
6. What percent of 40 is 12? 30%
7. What percent of 48 is 18? 37.5%
8. What percent is 54 of 60? 90%
9. What percent is 39 of 50? 78%
10. Find 80% of 25. 20
11. Find 150% of 74. 111
12. Find 44% of 375. 165
13. Find 65% of 180. 117
14. The Eagles won 70% of the 40 games that they played. How many games did they win? 28 games
15. Thirty-five of 40 students surveyed said that they favored recycling. What percent of those surveyed favored recycling? 87.5%
16. Candidate Carson received 2,310 votes, 55% of the total. How many total votes were cast? 4,200 votes



## Reteaching

What percent of 98 is 24.5?

You can solve percent problems by writing and solving a proportion.

Any percent problem of the form *x*% of *a* is *b* can be written as:

$\frac{x}{100} = \frac{b}{a}$

so $\frac{x}{100} = \frac{24.5}{98}$ Write a proportion.

$98x = 2{,}450$ Write cross products.

$\frac{98x}{98} = \frac{2{,}450}{98}$ Divide each side by 98.

$x = 25$ Simplify.

24.5 is 25% of 98.

**Write a proportion. Then solve. Where necessary, round to the nearest tenth or tenth of a percent.**

1. What percent of 75 is 60? 80%
2. What percent of 68 is 51? 75%
3. What percent is 17 of 25? 68%
4. What percent of 51 is 65? 127.5%
5. What percent of 144 is 126? 87.5%
6. What percent of 95 is 25? 26.3%
7. Find 24% of 120. 28.8
8. Find 75% of 76. 57
9. Find 260% of 30. 78
10. Find $27\frac{1}{2}\%$ of 96. 26.4
11. Find 38% of 32. 12.2
12. Find 17% of 85. 14.5
13. 40% of *x* is 28. What is *x*? 70
14. 9% of *k* is 27. What is *k*? 300
15. 75% of *p* is 12. What is *p*? 16
16. 0.9% of *h* is 276. What is *h*? 30,666.7
17. 13% of *r* is 209. What is *r*? 1,607.7
18. 68% of *j* is 44. What is *j*? 64.7



## Enrichment

A survey of recreation preferences was conducted. The table lists the results by gender and age categories.

| Respondent Summary | |
|---|---|
| Male | 160 |
| Female | 240 |
| Under 20 | 80 |
| 20–39 | 152 |
| 40–59 | 140 |
| 60 and over | 28 |

1. How many people were polled? 400
2. What percent of those polled were:
   female? 60%
   aged 40–59? 35%
   aged 60 and over 7%
3. Which group listed in the table contains 38% of those polled? age 20–39
4. Seventy-five percent of the males polled said that they participate in a sport. How many males participate in a sport? 120 males
5. Thirty females said that tennis is their favorite sport. What percent of all females prefer tennis to other sports? 12.5%
6. In a more extensive poll, 768 of the females questioned (or 12%) said that they prefer tennis. How many females were questioned in the larger survey? 6,400 females
7. Twenty-five percent of those 40 and over who were questioned named bowling as their favorite sport. Twelve were in the 60 and over category. How many were in the 40–59 category? 30 respondents
8. Twenty-eight of those under 20 named basketball as their favorite sport.
   a. What percent in this category prefer basketball? 35%
   b. Of those in this category who do not prefer basketball, 26.9% (to the nearest tenth of a percent) prefer baseball. How many named baseball as their favorite sport? 14 respondents

# 6-7

## Getting Ready

**Key Terms and Symbols** commission

**Resources** A complete list of resources for this lesson is on p. 275H.

### Daily Skills Warm-Up

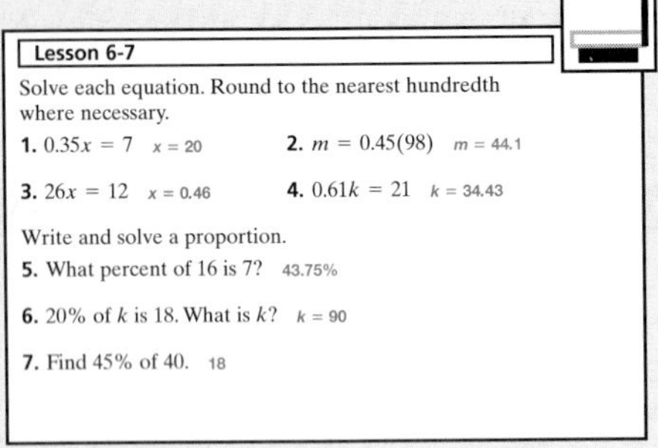

Lesson 6-7

Solve each equation. Round to the nearest hundredth where necessary.

1. $0.35x = 7$ $x = 20$
2. $m = 0.45(98)$ $m = 44.1$
3. $26x = 12$ $x = 0.46$
4. $0.61k = 21$ $k = 34.43$

Write and solve a proportion.

5. What percent of 16 is 7? 43.75%
6. 20% of $k$ is 18. What is $k$? $k = 90$
7. Find 45% of 40. 18

### Background for the Lesson

You can write and solve an equation in order to solve a percent problem. You can often rewrite the words almost directly into an equation:
What percent of 100 is 18? becomes
$x \bullet 100 = 18$.
In mathematics, the word *of* most often means *multiply* and *is* almost always means *equals.*

## 1 Focus

### Connecting to Students' Lives

Ask students if they have ever heard a news program or read a news article that claims that a certain percentage of people prefer one item to another. Explain that claims such as these result from a poll in which people are surveyed to find their preferences. The results of polls are usually presented in percentage terms. In this lesson, students will learn how to solve problems involving percents.

### Connecting to Prior Knowledge

In Lesson 6-6, students solved percent problems by writing proportions. In this lesson, students learn to solve percent problems by writing and solving equations.

# 6-7 Percents and Equations

**What You'll Learn**

1. To write and solve percent equations
2. To use equations in solving percent problems

**. . . And Why**

To solve problems involving surveys and earnings from commissions

## Part 1 Writing and Solving Percent Equations

You can solve a percent problem by writing and solving an equation. When you use a percent in an equation, write it as a decimal.

**Percent Equations**

| Finding the Percent | Finding the Part | Finding the Whole |
|---|---|---|
| What percent of 40 is 6? | What is 15% of 40? | 6 is 15% of what? |
| $n \cdot 40 = 6$ | $n = 0.15 \cdot 40$ | $6 = 0.15 \cdot n$ |

**EXAMPLE 1**

**What is 85% of 62?**

$n = 0.85 \cdot 62$ Write an equation. Write the percent as a decimal.
$n = 52.7$ Simplify.

85% of 62 is 52.7.

You can write and solve an equation to find a percent greater than 100%.

**EXAMPLE 2**

**What percent of 48 is 54?**

$n \cdot 48 = 54$ Write an equation.
$\frac{48n}{48} = \frac{54}{48}$ Divide each side by 48.
$n = 1.125$ Simplify.
$= 112.5\%$ Change the decimal to a percent.

54 is 112.5% of 48.

**TRY THIS** Write and solve an equation.

1. What is 45.5% of 20? $n = 0.455 \cdot 20$; 9.1
2. 380 is 125% of what number? $380 = 1.25n$; 304



## Tools to Monitor Progress

**BEFORE THE LESSON**

**To check prerequisite skills:**

- Solving equations by multiplying or dividing
- Writing percents

**Skills You Need,** p. 275

**Skills Handbook,** p. 731, 735

**Skills Intervention Kit,** Ratio, Proportion, and Percent

**DURING THE LESSON**

**To check understanding:**

**Try This** exercises on student page

- **Additional Example 1**
  What is 35% of 84? 29.4
- **Additional Example 2**
  What percent of 26 is 65? 250%

## PART 2 Using Equations to Solve Percent Problems

Some sales jobs pay an amount based on how much you sell. This amount is called a **commission.**

**REAL-WORLD**  CONNECTION

### EXAMPLE 3

*Commission* **A real estate agent makes a 4.5% commission on property she sells. How much does she make on the sale of a house for $132,500?**

| | | | | | |
|---|---|---|---|---|---|
| **Words** | amount of commission | is | 4.5% | of | $132,500 |
| | Let $c$ = amount of commission. | | | | |
| **Equation** | $c$ | = | 0.045 | · | 132,500 |

$c = 0.045 \cdot 132{,}500$
$= 5{,}962.50$

The broker's commission is $5,962.50.

### TRY THIS

3. *Royalties* A singer receives a 5% royalty on each CD sale. To the nearest cent, find his royalty for a CD that sells for $16.99. $.85

**DATA ANALYSIS** CONNECTION

### EXAMPLE 4

**The graph shows the results of a survey. There were 1,023 people who answered yes. How many people were surveyed?**

| | | | | | |
|---|---|---|---|---|---|
| **Words** | 1,023 | is | 93% | of | number surveyed |
| | Let $n$ = number surveyed. | | | | |
| **Equation** | 1,023 | = | 0.93 | · | $n$ |

$0.93n = 1{,}023$

$\frac{0.93n}{0.93} = \frac{1{,}023}{0.93}$

$n = 1{,}100$

1,100 people were surveyed.

**Responses to the question "Do you feel good about your life overall?"**

100%
75%
50%
25%
0%
93%
7%
Yes
No

### TRY THIS

4. In a survey, 922 people, or about 68.6%, preferred smooth peanut butter to chunky. How many people were surveyed? 1,344 people



# 2 Teach

## PART 1 Part 1 Teaching Notes

After students learn several ways to solve percent problems, they can choose the method they understand best.

### Example 1

**Build understanding.** Estimate. Will 85% of 62 be greater than or less than one-half of 62? **greater than, since 85% is greater than 50%**

### Example 2

**Build understanding.** Ask: Since 54 is greater than 48, what kind of answer do you estimate you will get? **a percent greater than 100%**

**Reading Math** Remind students that they can usually interpret the word *of* as multiplication in an expression or equation.

##  Part 2 Teaching Notes

Discuss with students that commissions and royalties are both ways of paying people for their labor.

### Example 3

**Build understanding.** Ask: What work does a real estate agent do to earn this commission? **sample answer: finding houses, showing them, arranging financing**

### Example 4

**Build understanding.** Ask: According to the graph, what percent answered yes? **93%**

**Extension** In Example 4, why must the answer to the question be a whole number? **You can't survey part of a person.**

**Math Reasoning** The first-period class has a higher percentage of girls than the second-period class. What can you conclude about the number of girls in the first class compared with the number of girls in the second class? **nothing; A higher percent does not necessarily mean a higher number.**

- **Additional Example 3**
  A car salesman makes a 6.5% commission on each car he sells. How much does he make on the sale of a car for $35,000? **$2,275**
- **Additional Example 4**
  On a telephone survey, 414 people, or 46% of those called, said that they were watching station RFGT at the time of the call. How many people were called? **900**

## AFTER THE LESSON

**To assess knowledge:**
**Lesson Quiz** 

1. What percent of 9 is 3? $33\frac{1}{3}\%$
2. What percent of 3 is 9? 300%
3. Find 9% of 30. 2.7
4. Find 25% of 312. 78
5. 90% of $a$ is 63. What is $a$? 70

- For enrichment and reteaching options see Resources on p. 275H.

# 3 Practice/Assess

## Assignment Guide

To provide flexible scheduling, this lesson can be divided into parts.

**▼ Part 1**
**Core** 1–4, 7–30
✪ **Extension** 31–34

**▼ Part 2**
**Core** 5–6, 35–38
✪ **Extension** 39–41

Mixed Review can be assigned at any time for maintenance.

## Exercises

**Tactile Learning** **Exercises 7, 13, 18** Students can use counters to model these problems as part of estimating before they calculate.

**Exercises 31–34** One technique is to estimate 10% and then add that amount to half of that amount.

**Test Prep** **Exercise 38** Ask a student to explain what a VCR (videocassette recorder) is.

## ✪ Challenge

Martin received a 6% commission on sales of $500 and Dana received a 4% commission on sales of $700. Who made the most money? Martin

## Closure

You can solve percent problems by using an equation.

## Daily Cumulative Review

**Write a proportion. Then solve. Where necessary, round to the nearest tenth or tenth of a percent.** *(Lesson 6-6)*

1. Find 80% of 12. $\frac{80}{100} = \frac{x}{12}$; $x = 9.6$
2. 5 is 2% of what number? $\frac{2}{100} = \frac{5}{x}$; $x = 250$
3. 5.5% of what number is 62.5? $\frac{5.5}{100} = \frac{62.5}{x}$; $x \approx 1{,}136.4$
4. What percent of 86 is 12? $\frac{x}{100} = \frac{12}{86}$; $x \approx 14.0\%$

**Write each fraction as a percent.** *(Lesson 6-5)*

5. $\frac{4}{5}$ 80%
6. $\frac{3}{4}$ 75%
7. $\frac{5}{20}$ 25%
8. $\frac{19}{27}$ $70.\overline{370}\%$
9. $\frac{7}{18}$ $38.\overline{8}\%$
10. $\frac{9}{15}$ 60%
11. $\frac{75}{81}$ $92.\overline{592}\%$
12. $\frac{16}{25}$ 64%
13. $\frac{1}{5}$ 20%

**Mixed Review**

**Name the point with the given coordinates.**

14. (0, 3) *(1-10)* E
15. (5, −2) *(1-10)* C
16. (−1, −4) *(1-10)* B
17. (−3, 4) *(1-10)* A
18. (−2, 3) *(1-10)* D
19. (5, 0) *(1-10)* F

**Write an equation for each sentence. Is the equation true, false, or an open sentence?**

20. *(2-4)* The product of negative seventeen and a number $x$ is negative twenty-two.
$-17x = -22$; open sentence

21. *(2-4)* The sum of forty and negative twenty-six is negative fourteen.
$40 + (-26) = -14$; false equation

**Complete each statement.**

22. *(3-7)* 0.36 m = 36 cm
23. *(3-7)* 676 g = 0.676 kg
24. *(3-7)* 2,100 mL = 2.1 L



# Exercises

## Check Understanding

**Write and solve an equation.**

1. Find 30% of 30. $n = 0.3 \cdot 30$; 9
2. What percent of 40 is 25? $25 = n \cdot 40$; 62.5%
3. 120 is 15% of what number? $120 = 0.15n$; 800
4. Find 150% of 90. $n = 1.5 \cdot 90$; 135
5. *Commission* A real estate agent received a $7,000 commission for a sale of $175,000. Find the percent of commission. 4%
6. *Critical Thinking* Describe a situation in which you would use a percent greater than 100%. Check students' work.

## Practice and Problem Solving

**Write and solve an equation. Where necessary, round to the nearest tenth or tenth of a percent.**

7. What percent of 20 is 11? $n \cdot 20 = 11$; 55%
8. Find 56% of 75. $n = 0.56 \cdot 75$; 42
9. 135% of $t$ is 63. What is $t$? $1.35t = 63$; 46.7
10. What percent of 25 is 17? $n \cdot 25 = 17$; 68%
11. Find 500% of 12. $n = 5 \cdot 12$; 60
12. 85% of $z$ is 106,250. What is $z$? $0.85z = 106{,}250$; 125,000
13. What percent of 4 is 9? $n \cdot 4 = 9$; 225%
14. Find 5.5% of 44. $n = 0.055 \cdot 44$; 2.4
15. What percent of 150 is 96? $n \cdot 150 = 96$; 64%
16. What percent of 45 is 24? $n \cdot 45 = 24$; 53.3%
17. Find 15% of 150. $n = 0.15 \cdot 150$; 22.5
18. What percent of 8 is 20? $n \cdot 8 = 20$; 250%
19. Find 225% of 3.6. $n = 2.25 \cdot 3.6$; 8.1
20. 3.5% of $d$ is 0.105. What is $d$? $0.035d = 0.105$; 3

*Mental Math* **Use mental math.**

21. What percent of 60 is 30? 50%
22. Find 20% of 20. 4
23. 100% of $t$ is 100. What is $t$? 100
24. What percent of 3 is 30? 1,000%
25. What percent of 55 is 11? 20%
26. Find 5% of 10. 0.5
27. Find 15% of 12. 1.8
28. What percent of 70 is 140? 200%
29. Find 150% of 200. 300
30. 50% of $g$ is 24. What is $g$? 48

*Estimation* **For each restaurant bill, estimate a 15% tip for the server.**

✪ 31. $3.52 about $.50
✪ 32. $9.95 about $1.50
✪ 33. $20.14 about $3
✪ 34. $13.88 about $2.10



## Alternative Assessment

Ask students to write a percent problem in words, and then show at least two different ways to solve it.

35. In 1985, daily newspaper circulation in the United States was about 63 million. In 1995, it was about 58 million. About what percent of the 1985 circulation was the 1995 circulation? 92%

36. *Commission* A salesperson receives 5.4% commission. On one sale, she received $6.48. What was the amount of the sale? $120

**Use the table at the right for Exercises 37–39.**

**United States Households with VCRs**

| Year | Households (millions) |
|---|---|
| 1980 | 1 |
| 1985 | 18 |
| 1990 | 63 |
| 1995 | ■ |

SOURCE: *Statistical Abstract of the United States*

37. a. The number of households with VCRs in 1985 was about 23.4% of the number with VCRs in 1995. About how many households had VCRs in 1995? 76.9 million households
    b. The number of households with VCRs in 1991 was about 106% of the number with VCRs in 1990. About how many households had VCRs in 1991? 66.8 million households

38. **TEST PREP** There were about 92 million households in the United States in 1990. About what percent of them had VCRs? A
    A. 68% B. 146% C. 92% D. 63%

39. *Critical Thinking* Is each statement true or false? Explain.
    a. The number of households with VCRs in 1985 was less than 10% of the number of households with VCRs in 1990. False; 18 is not less than 10% of 63, or 6.3.
    b. The number of households with VCRs in 1985 was more than 1,000% of the number in 1980. True; 18 is more than 1,000% of 1, or 10.

40. *Writing* Explain why someone taking a survey might be more interested in the percent than in the actual number of people who responded in each category. See below.

41. Polly got a 20% discount on a computer that regularly cost $x$ dollars. She paid sales tax of 5%. Later she sold the computer for 70% of what she paid for it. Write an expression for the amount Polly received for the computer. $0.588x$

40. Answers may vary. Sample: A percent is a ratio that could be used to find a proportional result for a group of any size.

**Journal**

*Which approach do you prefer to use in solving percent problems—the approach you learned in this lesson, or the one you learned in Lesson 6-6? Explain.*

## MIXED REVIEW

**Write a proportion. Then solve.** *(Lesson 6-6)*

42. ■% of 360 is 45. $\frac{n}{100} = \frac{45}{360}$; 12.5

43. 35% of 60 is ■. $\frac{35}{100} = \frac{n}{60}$; 21

44. 45 is 1.5% of ■. $\frac{1.5}{100} = \frac{45}{n}$; 3,000

**Simplify each expression.** *(Lesson 4-7)*

45. $10^2 \cdot 10^4$ 1,000,000

46. $9y^4 \cdot y^5$ $9y^9$

47. $(x^3)^7$ $x^{21}$

48. *Choose a Strategy* Ernest started writing a story on a Friday. He worked on the story for $\frac{1}{2}$ h each day. He took 7 h to finish it. On what day did Ernest finish his story? Thursday, 13 days later

See also Extra Practice section.



## Practice

**Write and solve an equation. Where necessary, round to the nearest tenth or tenth of a percent.**

1. What percent of 25 is 17? 68%
2. What percent is 10 of 8? 125%
3. What percent is 63 of 84? 75%
4. What percent is 3 of 600? 0.5%
5. Find 45% of 60. 27
6. Find 325% of 52. 169
7. Find $66\frac{2}{3}$% of 87. 58
8. Find 1% of 3,620. 36.2
9. $62\frac{1}{2}$% of $x$ is 5. What is $x$? 8
10. 300% of $k$ is 42. What is $k$? 14
11. $33\frac{1}{3}$% of $p$ is 19. What is $p$? 57
12. 70% of $c$ is 49. What is $c$? 70
13. 15% of $n$ is 1,050. What is $n$? 7,000
14. 38% of $y$ is 494. What is $y$? 1,300
15. A camera regularly priced at $295 was placed on sale at $236. What percent of the regular price was the sale price? 80%
16. Nine hundred thirty-six students, 65% of the entire student body, attended the football game. Find the size of the student body. 1,440 students



Practice

## Reteaching

8 is 16% of what?

You can solve percent problems by writing and solving an equation.

8 is 16% of what?

$8 = 0.16 \cdot n$ Write an equation. Write the percent as a decimal.

$\frac{8}{0.16} = \frac{0.16n}{0.16}$ Divide each side by 0.16.

$50 = n$ Simplify

8 is 16% of 50.

**Write and solve an equation. Where necessary, round to the nearest tenth or tenth of a percent.**

1. What percent is 84 of 60? 140%
2. What percent of 40 is 26? 65%
3. What percent is 22 of 33? 66.7%
4. What percent of 32 is 28? 87.5%
5. What percent is 18 of 48? 37.5%
6. What percent of 81 is 18? 22.2%
7. Find 37.5% of 104. 39
8. Find 0.4% of 25. 0.1
9. Find 68% of 150. 102
10. Find 180% of 65. 117
11. Find 12.5% of 56. 7
12. Find 86% of 55. 47.3
13. 95% of $h$ is 60. What is $h$? 63.2
14. 24% of $m$ is 17. What is $m$? 70.8
15. 30% of $n$ is 42. What is $n$? 140
16. 28% of $b$ is 49. What is $b$? 175
17. 25% of $y$ is 96. What is $y$? 384
18. 72% of $k$ is 234. What is $k$? 325



Reteaching

## Enrichment

You can use compatible numbers to estimate percents mentally.

**Example** Of the 88 members of the school orchestra, 68.2% practice at least 1 hour a day. Mentally estimate the numbers of players who practice at least 1 hour.

**Solution**
1. Choose a simple fraction close to the given percent. $\frac{2}{3} = 66\frac{2}{3}\%$
2. Choose an appropriate base close to the given base. Ninety is close to 88 and is divisible by 3.
3. Solve mentally. Think: $\frac{2}{3} \times 90 = 60$

About 60 members practice at lease 1 hour per day.

1. To use this method, you must know some basic percent-fraction equivalents. Complete the table of equivalents.

**Percent-Fraction Equivalents**

| 10% | $12\frac{1}{2}$% | 20% | 25% | 30% | $33\frac{1}{3}$% | 40% | 50% | 60% | 70% | 75% | 80% | $83\frac{1}{3}$% | 90% |
|---|---|---|---|---|---|---|---|---|---|---|---|---|---|
| $\frac{1}{10}$ | $\frac{1}{8}$ | $\frac{1}{5}$ | $\frac{1}{4}$ | $\frac{3}{10}$ | $\frac{1}{3}$ | $\frac{2}{5}$ | $\frac{1}{2}$ | $\frac{3}{5}$ | $\frac{7}{10}$ | $\frac{3}{4}$ | $\frac{4}{5}$ | $\frac{5}{6}$ | $\frac{9}{10}$ |

**Estimate each percent mentally.**

2. 41.7% of 26 10
3. 73.9% of 43.1 33
4. $82\frac{1}{2}$% of 37 30
5. 59% of 198 120
6. 34% of 61 20
7. 48.7% of 498.7 250
8. 91% of 68.7 63
9. 11.7% of 7,977 1,000
10. The sizes of the four sections of the school orchestra are given. Estimate how many of the 88 members are in each.

    string, 48.9% 44 woodwind, 17% 15

    brass, 23.9% 22 percussion, 10.2% 9
11. Of the 26 eighth graders in the orchestra, 15 play stringed instruments. Estimate the percent who play strings. 60%



Enrichment

# 6-8

## Getting Ready

**Key Terms and Symbols** percent of change

**Resources** A complete list of resources for this lesson is on p. 275H.

### Daily Skills Warm-Up

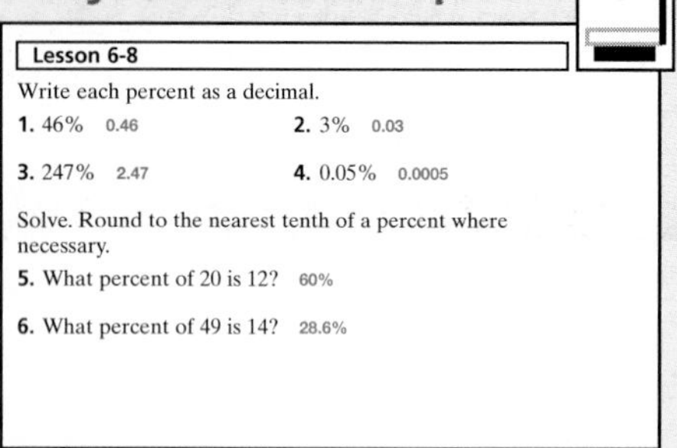
Lesson 6-8

Write each percent as a decimal.

1. 46% 0.46
2. 3% 0.03
3. 247% 2.47
4. 0.05% 0.0005

Solve. Round to the nearest tenth of a percent where necessary.

5. What percent of 20 is 12? 60%
6. What percent of 49 is 14? 28.6%

### Background for the Lesson

When sales go from 100 units in April to 110 units in May, the sales in May are 110% of those in April. This ratio, $\frac{110}{100}$, compares the new amount to the old amount. You can also write a ratio that compares *the amount of the change* to the old amount: $\frac{10}{100}$ or 10%. This ratio is the *percent of change*. When the amount of change is positive, you have a percent of increase. When the amount of change is negative, you have a percent of decrease. To find the percent of change, evaluate this ratio: $\frac{\textit{amount of change}}{\textit{original amount}}$.

## 1 Focus

### Investigate

Students may have difficulty understanding how Nevada can have a greater percent change, when it had such a smaller change in population. Explain that the percent change is compared to the original amount.

### Connecting to Students' Lives

When students try to increase their personal best in athletics, they often report their progress in terms of the percent of change: My time in the 400-m race was 10% better this week.



# 6-8 Percent of Change

**What You'll Learn**

1. To find percent of increase
2. To find percent of decrease

**. . . And Why**

To use percent of change in real-world applications, such as environmental management

## Investigate

EXPLORING PERCENT OF CHANGE

**Populations of Two States**

| State | 1980 | 1990 |
|---|---|---|
| California | 23,668,000 | 29,786,000 |
| Nevada | 800,000 | 1,202,000 |

1. Find the change in population from 1980 to 1990 for each state. California 6,118,000; Nevada 402,000
2. Which state had the greater change in population? California
3. Write the ratio $\frac{\text{change in population}}{\text{1980 population}}$ for each state. Then write each ratio as a percent. California $\frac{6{,}118{,}000}{23{,}668{,}000} \approx 25.8\%$; Nevada $\frac{402{,}000}{800{,}000} \approx 50.3\%$
4. Compare the two percents. Which state had the greater population change in terms of percent? Nevada

## PART 1 Finding Percent of Increase

The percent a quantity increases or decreases from its original amount is the **percent of change.**

$$\text{percent of change} = \frac{\text{amount of change}}{\text{original amount}}$$

### EXAMPLE 1

**Find the percent of increase from 4 to 7.5.**

$$\text{amount of increase} = 7.5 - 4 = 3.5$$

$$\text{percent of increase} = \frac{\text{amount of increase}}{\text{original amount}} = \frac{3.5}{4} = 0.875 = 87.5\%$$

The percent of increase from 4 to 7.5 is 87.5%.

**TRY THIS** Find each percent of increase.

5. from 100 to 114 14%
6. from 2.0 to 3.2 60%
7. from 4,000 to 8,500 112.5%



# Tools to Monitor Progress

### BEFORE THE LESSON

**To check prerequisite skills:**

- Writing percents

**Skills You Need,** p. 275

**Skills Handbook,** p. 727

**Skills Intervention Kit,** Ratio, Proportion, and Percent

### DURING THE LESSON

**To check understanding:**

**Try This** exercises on student page

- **Additional Example 1**

  Find the percent of increase from 8 to 9.6. 20%

DATA ANALYSIS CONNECTION

## EXAMPLE 2

*Environmental Management* **The annual production of municipal solid waste in the United States has more than doubled since 1960. Find the percent of increase from 1960 to 1990.**

amount of increase = 205 − 88 = 117

$$\text{percent of increase} = \frac{\text{amount of increase}}{\text{original amount}} = \frac{117}{88} = 1.32\overline{954} \approx 133\%$$

The percent of increase from 1960 to 1990 was about 133%.

SOURCE: Environmental Protection Agency

### TRY THIS

8. *Environmental Management* Find the percent of increase in solid waste production from 1970 to 1980. Round to the nearest percent. 9%

## PART 2 Finding Percent of Decrease

You can also find percent of decrease.

## EXAMPLE 3

**Find the percent of decrease from 1,500 to 1,416.**

amount of decrease = 1,500 − 1,416 = 84

$$\text{percent of decrease} = \frac{\text{amount of decrease}}{\text{original amount}} = \frac{84}{1{,}500} = 0.056 = 5.6\%$$

**TRY THIS** Find each percent of decrease. Where necessary, round to the nearest tenth of a percent.

9. from 9.6 to 4.8 50%
10. from 202 to 192 5%
11. from 854.5 to 60.6 92.9%
12. A computer that cost $1,099 last year costs $999 this year. Find the percent of decrease to the nearest percent. 9%



# 2 Teach

## PART 1 Part 1 Teaching Notes

A large percent of change may not necessarily mean large numbers. To add 2 (in an increase from 2 to 4) is a percent of change of 100% while to add 100 to 400 (in an increase from 400 to 500) is only a 25% percent change. Help students understand that percent of change compares the amount of the increase to the original, not the size of the numbers in the increase.

### Example 1

**Build understanding.** Ask: Is the amount of increase a number that is close to the original or much less than the original? fairly close to the original So what do you expect the percent of increase to be close to? 100%

### Example 2

**Build understanding.** Ask: According to the chart, how many tons were produced in 1990? 205 million tons

## PART 2 Part 2 Teaching Notes

Discuss with students how they can tell whether the change is an increase or a decrease.

### Example 3

**Build understanding.** Ask: What is the result when you write 0.056 as a fraction and then divide the numerator and denominator by 10? $\frac{56}{1{,}000}$ or $\frac{5.6}{100}$, which is 5.6%

**Extension** When will a percent of increase be more than 100%? when the amount of increase is greater than the original amount

**Error Prevention** To prevent incorrectly writing the ratio, begin by writing the formula: percent of change = amount of change : original amount. Then substitute numbers in the formula.

**Auditory Learning** Suggest that students say the definition of percent of change aloud as they work.

- **Additional Example 2**
  In a given year, Hillsboro had a total of 7.5 in. of rain by March 1 and a total of 22.5 in. by May 1. Find the percent of increase in the total amount of rainfall from March 1 to May 1. 200%
- **Additional Example 3**
  Find the percent of decrease from 1,250 to 1,120. 10.4%

## AFTER THE LESSON

### To assess knowledge:

**Lesson Quiz**

Find each percent of change. Round to the nearest tenth of a percent. Tell whether the change is an increase or a decrease.

1. from 6.3 to 2.2 65.1% decrease
2. from 63 to 22 65.1% decrease
3. from 0.22 to 0.63 186.4% increase

- For enrichment and reteaching options see Resources on p. 275H.

# 3 Practice/Assess

## Assignment Guide

To provide flexible scheduling, this lesson can be divided into parts.

▼ **Part 1**
**Core** 1–3, 7–13, 29–30
✪ **Extension** 32

▼ **Part 2**
**Core** 4–6, 14–28, 31
✪ **Extension** 33–34

Mixed Review can be assigned at any time for maintenance.

## Exercises

**Exercise 33** Suggest that students work in cooperative groups to solve problems such as this one.

## ✪ Challenge

Describe a situation when a percent of decrease is greater than 100%. sample answer: When a person goes from having \$5 to owing \$2, the amount of decrease is 140%.

## Closure

The percent of change is the ratio of the amount of change to the original amount.

# Exercises

## Check Understanding

**Find each percent of change. Tell whether the change is an increase or a decrease.**

1. from 30 to 39 30% increase
2. from 55 to 176 220% increase
3. from 48 to 60 25% increase
4. from 60 to 48 20% decrease
5. from 96 to 78 18.75% decrease
6. from 240 to 90 62.5% decrease

7. *Error Analysis* Eva's first step in finding the percent of change from 7 to 8 was to write $\frac{8-7}{8} = \frac{1}{8}$. Explain Eva's error. Eva should compare 8 – 7 to 7, not 8.

## Practice and Problem Solving

**Find each percent of change. Round to the nearest tenth of a percent. Tell whether the change is an increase or a decrease.**

8. from 50 to 66 32% increase
9. from 80 to 95 18.8% increase
10. from 32 to 76 137.5% increase
11. from 45 to 105 133.3% increase
12. from 38 to 95 150% increase
13. from 27 to 72 166.7% increase
14. from 90 to 75 16.7% decrease
15. from 64 to 24 62.5% decrease
16. from 120 to 95 20.8% decrease
17. from 280 to 126 55% decrease
18. from 111 to 74 33.3% decrease
19. from 180 to 54 70% decrease

*Choose* **Use mental math or pencil and paper to find each percent of change. Round to the nearest tenth of a percent. Tell whether the change is an increase or a decrease.**

20. from 25 to 30 20% increase
21. from 40 to 45 12.5% increase
22. from 50 to 45 10% decrease
23. from 87 to 108 24.1% increase
24. from 59 to 127 115.3% increase
25. from 77 to 13 83.1% decrease
26. from 132 to 46.2 65% decrease
27. from 1,800 to 1,000 44.4% decrease
28. from 100 to 101.1 1.1% increase

29. *Statistics* In the United States in the 20th century, average life expectancy increased from about 47 years to about 77 years. Find the percent of increase to the nearest percent. 64%

30. **TEST PREP** Percent of sales tax is an example of percent of increase. The retail price of an item is \$5.99. With sales tax, the total cost of the item is \$6.35. Find the percent of sales tax. D
    **A.** 3% **B.** 4% **C.** 5% **D.** 6%

31. *Economics* The average cost of a gallon of gasoline was \$1.29 in 1997 and \$1.12 in 1998. Find the percent of decrease to the nearest percent. 13%



## Daily Cumulative Review

**Write and solve an equation. Where necessary, round to the nearest tenth or tenth of a percent.** *(Lesson 6-7)*

1. Find 300% of 20. $n = 3.00 \cdot 20; n = 60$
2. 70% of *n* is 20,320. What is *n*? $n \cdot 0.70 = 20{,}320; n \approx 29{,}028.6$
3. What percent of 37 is 11? $n \cdot 37 = 11; n \approx 29.7\%$
4. Find 0.325% of 16. $n = 0.00325 \cdot 16; n \approx 0.1$

**Write a proportion. Then solve. Where necessary, round to the nearest tenth or tenth of a percent.** *(Lesson 6-6)*

5. Find 66.5% of 34. $\frac{66.5}{100} = \frac{x}{34}; x \approx 22.6$
6. 65 is what percent of 360% $\frac{x}{100} = \frac{65}{360}; x \approx 18.1\%$
7. What percent of 19 is 2? $\frac{x}{100} = \frac{2}{19}; x \approx 10.5\%$
8. 3 is 4% of what number? $\frac{4}{100} = \frac{3}{x}; x = 75$

**Mixed Review**

**Find each unit rate.**

9. (6-1) 360 mi in 15 h 24 mi/h
10. (6-1) 12 gal in 3 min 4 gal/min
11. (6-1) 36 ft in 9 days 4 ft/day

**A set of 24 flash cards is numbered from 1 to 24. A card is chosen at random. Find the odds against each selection.**

12. (6-4) an odd number 1 to 1
13. (6-4) a multiple of 4 or 5 5 to 3
14. (6-4) a number greater than 22 11 to 1

**Solve each equation.**

15. (3-6) $\frac{x}{1.8} = 0.36$ $x = 0.648$
16. (3-6) $\frac{r}{3.12} = 0.08$ $r = 0.2496$
17. (3-6) $150 = \frac{s}{4.5}$ $675 = s$



## Alternative Assessment

Have students write and solve two example problems, one to find the percent of increase and one to find the percent of decrease.

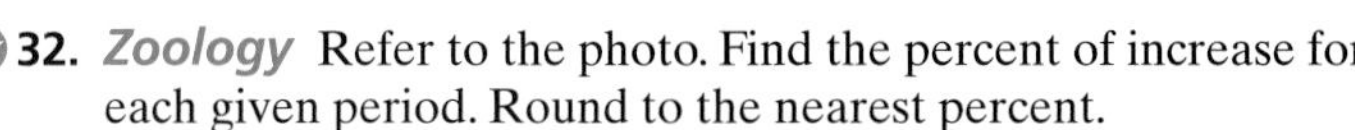

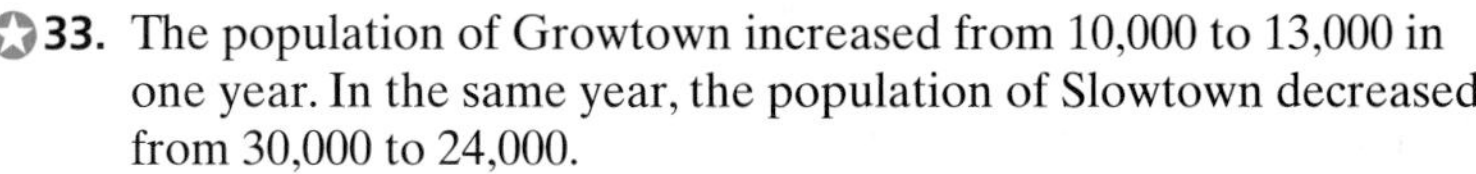

32. *Zoology* Refer to the photo. Find the percent of increase for each given period. Round to the nearest percent.
   a. After one month, Ganesh weighed 300 lb. 41%
   b. After one year, Ganesh weighed 1,061 lb. 398%

33. The population of Growtown increased from 10,000 to 13,000 in one year. In the same year, the population of Slowtown decreased from 30,000 to 24,000.
   a. Find each town's percent of increase or decrease in population. Growtown 30% increase; Slowtown 20% decrease
   b. If each town maintains the same rate of change, within how many years will the population of Growtown exceed that of Slowtown? 3 years

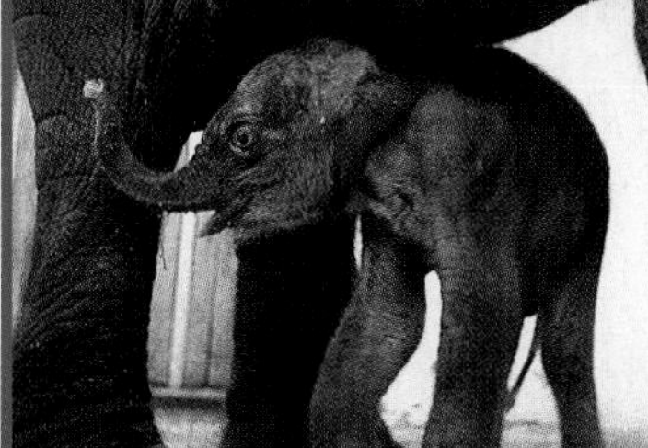

Ganesh was the first baby elephant born at the Cincinnati Zoo. At birth, he weighed 213 lb.

34. a. *Mathematical Reasoning* 100 is increased by 10%. The result is decreased by 10%. Is the final result 100? Explain. No; the decrease is 10% of a greater amount.
   b. Compare the final result in part (a) to 100, the original number. Find the percent of change. 1% decrease

## Mixed Review

**Evaluate each expression.** ***(Lesson 4-2)***

35. $3x^2$ for $x = -5$ 75

36. $[(3 + 12)(8 \div 2)]^2$ 3,600

37. $(7 + 4y)^2$ for $y = -2$ 1

**Find each sum or difference.** ***(Lesson 5-3)***

38. $5\frac{3}{4} - 2\frac{5}{8}$ $3\frac{1}{8}$

39. $-4\frac{1}{3} + 2\frac{1}{2}$ $-1\frac{5}{6}$

40. $-6\frac{1}{3} - 6\frac{1}{3}$ $-12\frac{2}{3}$

41. *Astronomy* The Space Surveillance Center in Colorado tracks about 8,500 objects in orbit around Earth. All but about 500 objects are junk from past space missions. What percent are junk? Round to the nearest percent. ***(Lesson 6-7)*** 94%

## Chapter Project 6 — Activity 4 Calculating

Suppose you want to play your notes on a real cello. A cello string is about 24 in. long from the bridge to the nut. Using a full string length for *say,* how far from the bridge should you press down the string to play the notes for *can, you,* and *see*?

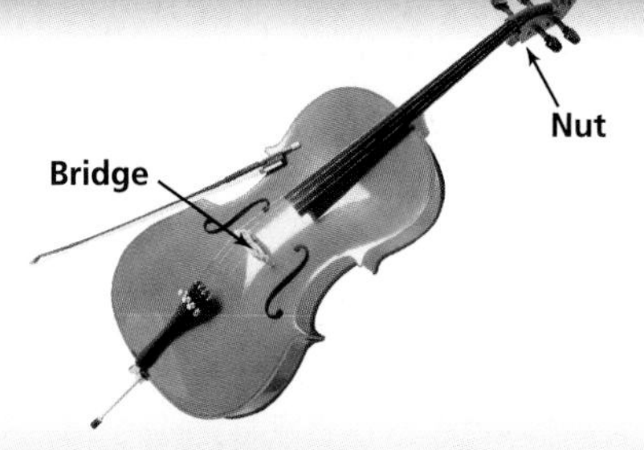


See also Extra Practice section.



## Project Activity 4

**Calculating** If any students play a stringed instrument, such as a guitar, ukulele, or violin, encourage them to measure a string on an actual instrument, calculate the distances using their ratios, and then try playing the notes according to their calculations.

## Practice

**Find each percent of change. Round to the nearest tenth of a percent. Tell whether the change is an increase or a decrease.**

1. 24 to 21 12.5%; decrease
2. 64 to 80 25%; increase
3. 100 to 113 13%; increase
4. 50 to 41 18%; decrease
5. 63 to 105 66.7%; increase
6. 42 to 168 300%; increase
7. 80 to 24 70%; decrease
8. 200 to 158 21%; decrease
9. 56 to 71 26.8%; increase
10. 127 to 84 33.9%; decrease
11. 20 to 24 20%; increase
12. 44 to 22 50%; decrease
13. 16 to 12 25%; decrease
14. 10 to 100 900%; increase
15. 20 to 40 100%; increase
16. 10 to 50 400%; increase
17. 12 to 16 33.3%; increase
18. 80 to 100 25%; increase
19. 69 to 117 69.6%; increase
20. 19 to 9 52.6%; decrease
21. 95 to 145 52.6%; increase
22. 88 to 26 70.5%; decrease
23. Mark weighed 110 pounds last year. He weighs 119 pounds this year. What is the percent of increase in his weight, to the nearest tenth of a percent? 8.2%
24. Susan had $140 in her savings account last month. She added $20 this month and earned $.50 interest. What is the percent of increase in the amount in her savings account to the nearest tenth of a percent? 14.6%
25. The population density of California was 151.4 people per square mile in 1980. By 1990 it had increased to 190.8 people per square mile. Find the percent increase to the nearest percent. 26%



## Reteaching

Find the percent of decrease from 85 to 60.

Find the amount of decrease.

$85 - 60 = 25$

$$\text{percent of decrease} = \frac{\text{amount of decrease}}{\text{original amount}} = \frac{25}{85} \approx 0.294 = 29.4\%$$

The percent of decrease is about 29.4%

**Find each percent of increase. Where necessary, round to the nearest tenth of a percent.**

1. 40 is increased to 45. 12.5%
2. 33 is increased to 55. 66.7%
3. 15 is increased to 34. 126.7%
4. 11 is increased to 88. 700%
5. 72 is increased to 117. 62.5%
6. 28 is increased to 49. 75%
7. 35 is increased to 49. 40%
8. 48 is increased to 132. 175%

**Find each percent of decrease. Where necessary, round to the nearest tenth of a percent.**

9. 60 is decreased to 15. 75%
10. 56 is decreased to 35. 37.5%
11. 140 is decreased to 77. 45%
12. 96 is decreased to 64. 33.3%
13. 99 is decreased to 69. 30.3%
14. 50 is decreased to 44. 12%
15. 83 is decreased to 0. 100%
16. 475 is decreased to 152. 68%



## Enrichment

Each month, the United States Bureau of Labor Statistics publishes cost-of-living figures called the Consumer Price Index (CPI). The CPI measures how the prices of goods and services change over time. Current prices are given relative to 1982–1984 prices, which are arbitrarily set at 100.

**Example** The CPI for dairy products in 1996 was 142.1. Find the 1996 cost of a quart of milk which cost $.80 in 1983.

**Solution** $\text{Cost} = \frac{\text{CPI}}{100} \times 1983 \text{ price} = \frac{142.1}{100} \times 0.8 \approx 1.14$

The cost of a quart of milk in 1996 was about $1.14

**The table shows the Consumer Price Index for several items in 1990 and 1996. Use the table to find the 1996 cost for each of the following.**

| Item | 1990 CPI | 1996 CPI |
|---|---|---|
| Footwear | 117.4 | 126.6 |
| Gasoline | 101.0 | 105.9 |
| Cereals and bakery products | 140.0 | 174.0 |

1. A pair of shoes that cost $35 in 1983. $44.31
2. A donut that cost $.20 in 1983. $.35
3. A gallon of gasoline that cost $.95 in 1983. $1.01

*Inflation* measures the increase in prices. You can find inflation by calculating the percent of increase in the CPI.

**Example** The CPI for public transportation rose from 142.6 in 1990 to 181.9 in 1996. Find the inflation in the cost of public transportation for the period.

**Solution** $181.9 - 142.6 = 39.3$

$39.3 \div 142.6 \approx 0.276$

Inflation was about 27.6% for this period.

**Find the inflation from 1990 to 1996 to the nearest tenth of a percent.**

4. on cost of footwear 7.8%
5. on cost of gasoline 4.9%
6. on cost of cereal 24.3%

# 6-9

## Getting Ready

**Key Terms and Symbols** markup, discount

**Resources** A complete list of resources for this lesson is on p. 275H.

### Daily Skills Warm-Up

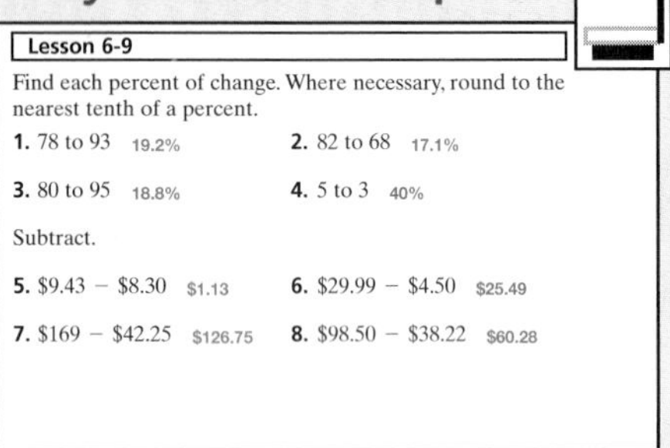

Lesson 6-9

Find each percent of change. Where necessary, round to the nearest tenth of a percent.

| | |
|---|---|
| **1.** 78 to 93 19.2% | **2.** 82 to 68 17.1% |
| **3.** 80 to 95 18.8% | **4.** 5 to 3 40% |

Subtract.

| | |
|---|---|
| **5.** \$9.43 − \$8.30 \$1.13 | **6.** \$29.99 − \$4.50 \$25.49 |
| **7.** \$169 − \$42.25 \$126.75 | **8.** \$98.50 − \$38.22 \$60.28 |

### Background for the Lesson

One example of percent of increase is the increase, or *markup,* that stores use to find the selling price for their merchandise. You can define percent of increase as $\frac{\text{amount of change}}{\text{original amount}}$. You can define, in a similar way, the percent of markup as $\frac{\text{markup (or amount of change)}}{\text{original cost to the store}}$ to the store. If the school store buys a notebook for \$2 and sells it for \$2.25, then the markup is \$.25 and the percent of markup is $\frac{25}{200}$ or 12.5%.

## 1 Focus

### Connecting to Students' Lives

Students may have participated in a sale of candy bars or other items to earn money for the band or some other organization. Usually the organization pays a certain amount for the items and then adds a markup to get the selling price.

### Connecting to Prior Knowledge

In Lesson 6-8, students learned how to calculate percent of change by using a ratio. In this lesson, students use their knowledge in calculating percent of change to find percent markup and discount.

# 6-9 Markup and Discount

**What You'll Learn**

1. To find markups
2. To find discounts

**. . . And Why**

To understand how markups and discounts are used in pricing consumer products

## PART 1 Finding Markups

To make a profit, stores charge more for merchandise than they pay for it. The amount of increase is called the **markup.** The percent of increase is the *percent of markup*.

REAL-WORLD CONNECTION

### EXAMPLE 1

**A music store's percent of markup is 67%. A CD costs the store \$10.15. Find the markup.**

$$\begin{aligned}\text{markup} &= \text{percent of markup} \cdot \text{store's cost}\\ &= 0.67 \cdot 10.15\\ &\approx 6.80\end{aligned}$$
Simplify. Round to the nearest cent.

The markup is \$6.80.

**TRY THIS**

1. A clothing store pays \$56 for a jacket. The store's percent of markup is 75%. Find the markup for the jacket. \$42

The store's cost plus the markup equals the *selling price*.

REAL-WORLD CONNECTION

### EXAMPLE 2

*Retailing* **A computer store pays \$6 for a computer mouse. The percent of markup is 75%. Find the mouse's selling price.**

$0.75 \cdot 6 = 4.50$ Multiply to find the markup.

$6.00 + 4.50 = 10.50$ store's cost + markup = selling price

The selling price is \$10.50.

**TRY THIS**

2. A store pays \$5 for a baseball cap. The percent of markup is 70%. Find the selling price of the cap. \$8.50



## Tools to Monitor Progress

### BEFORE THE LESSON

**To check prerequisite skills:**

- Writing percents

**Skills Handbook,** p. 727

**Skills Intervention Kit,** Ratio, Proportion, and Percent

### DURING THE LESSON

**To check understanding:**

**Try This** exercises on student page

- **Additional Example 1**
  A grocery store has a 20% markup on a can of soup. The can costs the store \$1.25. Find the markup. \$.25

## Finding Discounts

When an item goes on sale, the amount of the price decrease is called the **discount.** The percent of decrease is the *percent of discount*. The original price minus the discount is the *sale price*.

Here are two ways to use percent of discount to find a sale price.

## Different Ways to Solve a Problem

**A video game that regularly sells for $39.95 is on sale for 20% off. What is the sale price?**

**Method 1**

Find the discount. Then find the sale price.

discount = percent of discount · original price
= 0.20 · 39.95
= 7.99

sale price = original price − discount
= 39.95 − 7.99
= 31.96

The sale price is $31.96.

**Method 2**

Find the sale price directly. The sale price equals 100% of the original price minus 20% of the original price.

sale price = (100% − 20%) · original price
= 80% · original price
= 0.80(39.95)
= 31.96

The sale price is $31.96.

**Choose a Method**

1. Which method do you prefer? Explain. 1. Answers may vary. Sample: Method 2; the subtraction is done earlier with simpler numbers.
2. Find the sale price if the percent of discount is 25%. Round to the nearest cent. $29.96

**Reading Math**

*20% off* means a discount of 20%.



# 2 Teach

### Part 1 Teaching Notes

Help students distinguish between *markup* (the amount of the increase) and *percent of markup* (the ratio of the increase to the cost).

#### Example 1

**Build understanding.** Ask: What is the ratio of $6.80 to $10.15? Use this to check your work. ≈ 67%

**Extension** What is the selling price for the CD? $16.95

#### Example 2

**Build understanding.** Ask: What ratio can you write (with the information in the problem) that will equal 75%? 4.50 : 6.00

### Part 2 Teaching Notes

Show students that percent of discount is the ratio $\frac{\text{discount (or amount of change)}}{\text{original selling price}}$. The original selling price minus the discount is the sale price.

#### Different Ways to Solve a Problem

**Build understanding.** Ask: What is the percent of discount on the video game? 20%

**ELL** Help students distinguish between the original *selling price* and the *sale price,* which you find by subtracting the discount from the selling price.

**Error Prevention** Students may incorrectly compare the discount to the cost rather than to the original price. Remind them to write a statement in words first and then substitute values and solve.

**Tactile Learning** Have students in groups make posters or do skits that demonstrate the cost, marking up, pricing, and then discounting the sale of an item.

**Reading Math** Call attention to the margin note about the meaning of 20% off.

**Additional Example 2**

A newsstand pays $2 for a magazine. The percent of markup is 45%. Find the selling price of the magazine. $2.90

**AFTER THE LESSON**

**To assess knowledge: Lesson Quiz**

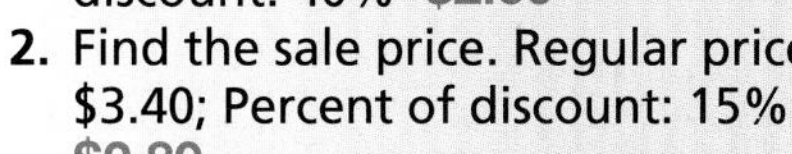

1. Find the discount. Regular price: $6.50; Percent of discount: 40% $2.60
2. Find the sale price. Regular price: $3.40; Percent of discount: 15%. $2.89

- For enrichment and reteaching options see Resources on p. 275H.

# 3 Practice/Assess

## Assignment Guide

To provide flexible scheduling, this lesson can be divided into parts.

▼ Part 1
**Core** 1–3, 7–9, 13–14
✪ **Extension** 17

▼ Part 2
**Core** 4–6, 10–12, 15–16, 18–19
✪ **Extension** 20–21

Mixed Review can be assigned at any time for maintenance.

## Exercises

**Visual Learning Exercise 15** Have students prepare a large price tag that shows the regular price, the percent of decrease, the discount, and the sale price for the shoes.

## ✪ Challenge

A store wants to get rid of some old CDs. The cost to the store was $10 and the original selling price was $16. The sale price is $5. What is the percent of discount on each CD? 68.75% What would the sale price be if the percent of discount were greater than 100%? The discount cannot be greater than the original price, so this is impossible.

## Closure

Markup is a real-world application of percent of increase. Discount is a real-world application of percent of decrease.

### Daily Cumulative Review

**Find each percent of change. Round to the nearest tenth of a percent. Tell whether the change is an increase or a decrease.** *(Lesson 6-8)*

1. from 55 to 95 — 72.7%; increase
2. from 39 to 96 — 146.2%; increase
3. from 130 to 85 — 34.6%; decrease
4. from 380 to 226 — 40.5%; decrease
5. from 190 to 84 — 55.8%; decrease
6. from 66 to 166 — 151.5%; increase

**Write and solve an equation. Where necessary, round to the nearest tenth or tenth of a percent.** *(Lesson 6-7)*

7. What percent of 40 is 12? — $n \cdot 40 = 12; n = 30\%$
8. Find 42% of 80. — $n = 0.42 \cdot 80; n = 33.6$
9. 125% of $n$ is 40. What is $n$? — $1.25 \cdot n = 40; n = 32$
10. What percent of 9 is 30? — $n \cdot 9 = 30; n \approx 333.3\%$

**Mixed Review**

**Solve using any strategy.**

11. (3-6) Jason is going to a baseball game. The game begins at 2:00 P.M. He has a 20-minute walk to the bus from his house and a 2-minute walk from the bus stop to the ballpark. The bus ride takes 47 minutes. What is the latest bus he can take to reach the game on time?

| Bus Departure Times | |
|---|---|
| 9:55 A.M. | 12:45 P.M. |
| 10:35 A.M. | 1:30 P.M. |
| 11:15 A.M. | 2:00 P.M. |

12:45 P.M.

12. (3-8) In a bowling tournament, each bowler bowls one game against each of the other bowlers. There are 8 bowlers scheduled to bowl in the tournament. How many games will be bowled?

28 games

**Compare. Use >, <, or = to complete each statement.**

13. (5-1) $\frac{3}{7} < \frac{5}{9}$
14. (5-1) $-\frac{6}{13} < -\frac{5}{11}$
15. (5-1) $\frac{12}{31} > \frac{4}{11}$



# Exercises

## CHECK UNDERSTANDING

**Find each markup.**

1. cost: $1.50
percent of markup: 70% $1.05
2. cost: $38
percent of markup: 58% $22.04
3. cost: $111.00
percent of markup: 50% $55.50

**Find each discount.**

4. regular price: $100
percent of discount: 27% $27
5. regular price: $24.50
percent of discount: 20% $4.90
6. regular price: $700
percent of discount: 30% $210

## PRACTICE AND PROBLEM SOLVING

**Find each selling price. Round to the nearest cent where necessary.**

7. cost: $6
percent of markup: 75% $10.50
8. cost: $2.66
percent of markup: 50% $3.99
9. cost: $149.99
percent of markup: 100% $299.98

**Find each sale price. Round to the nearest cent where necessary.**

10. regular price: $180
percent of discount: 40% $108
11. regular price: $14.99
percent of discount: 15% $12.74
12. regular price: $180
percent of discount: 75% $45

13. A beach store pays $11.40 for each beach umbrella. The store's percent of markup is 75%. Find the markup. $8.55

14. A record store buys a CD for $9.99 and marks it up by 60%. Find the markup and the selling price. $5.99, $15.98

15. A pair of shoes regularly sells for $49 at the shop in the photo.
   a. Find the discount. $9.80
   b. Find the sale price. $39.20

SALE... 20% OFF ENTIRE STOCK
SHOE SALE
SALE 20% OFF ENTIRE STOCK

16. Software that regularly sells for $60 is on sale for 15% off. Find the sale price. $51

✪ 17. *Mathematical Reasoning* A store buys an item for $$x$ and sells it for $$y$.
   a. Write an expression for the markup. a. $y - x$
   b. Write an expression for the percent of markup. b. $\frac{y - x}{x}(100)$

18. *Choose a Method* An $11 shirt is on sale for 10% off.
   a. Describe two different methods of finding the sale price. 18a. Find 10% of $11 to get the discount and subtract the result from $11; or find 90% of $11.
   b. Use one of the methods to calculate the sale price. $9.90



## Alternative Assessment

Have students write one or two questions they would like to have answered about percent of change and related topics.

19. Store A is selling a video for 20% off the store's regular price of \$25.95. Store B is selling the same video for 30% off the store's regular price of \$29.50. Which store's sale price is lower? How much lower is it? store B; \$.11

20. *Estimation* Suppose you want to buy the three books shown in the table. The bookstore is having a $\frac{1}{4}$-off sale. Your state charges sales tax of 5% of an item's final price. You have \$20. Do you have enough money? Justify your answer. No; the sale price (before sales tax) is about \$21.

| Title | Regular Price |
|---|---|
| *Variable Blues* | \$6.95 |
| *Math Moments* | \$9.95 |
| *City of Angles* | \$10.95 |

21. *Writing* Identical sweaters are on sale in two different stores. In the first store, the sale price is 30% off the regular price of \$25. In the second store, the sale price is 40% off the regular price of \$30. Which sweater is the better buy? Explain. The sweater at the first store; its sale price (\$17.50) is less (by \$.50).

## Mixed Review

**Find each percent of decrease. Round to the nearest tenth of a percent.** *(Lesson 6-8)*

22. from 90 to 70 22.2%
23. from 44.4 to 14.8 66.7%
24. from 1,750 to 1,125 35.7%

**Draw a coordinate plane. Graph each point.** *(Lesson 1-10)* 25–27. See margin.

25. $A(1, 0)$
26. $B(-2, 3)$
27. $C(-1, 2)$

28. *Recipes* A bread recipe calls for $6\frac{1}{2}$ cups of flour. You have $4\frac{3}{4}$ cups. How much more flour do you need? *(Lesson 5-3)* $1\frac{3}{4}$ c

## Checkpoint 2

Lessons 6-5 through 6-9

**Compare. Use >, <, or = to complete each statement.**

1. $\frac{14}{25}$ ■ 56% =
2. 1.1% ■ 0.11 <
3. $\frac{3}{11}$ ■ 27% >

**Write and solve an equation.**

4. Find 33% of 120. $0.33 \cdot 120 = n$; 39.6
5. Find 125% of 42. $1.25 \cdot 42 = n$; 52.5
6. What percent of 5.6 is 1.4? $n \cdot 5.6 = 1.4$; 25%
7. 15% of $q$ is 9.75. What is $q$? $0.15q = 9.75$; 65
8. What percent of 500 is 1,375? $n \cdot 500 = 1{,}375$; 275%
9. 80% of $w$ is 120. What is $w$? $0.8w = 120$; 150
10. A car originally priced at \$12,000 is sold at a 20% discount. Find the sale price. \$9,600
11. *Open-ended* Choose an item you buy that has changed in price. Give the original and new prices. Find the percent of change. Check students' work.

See also Extra Practice section.



25–27.

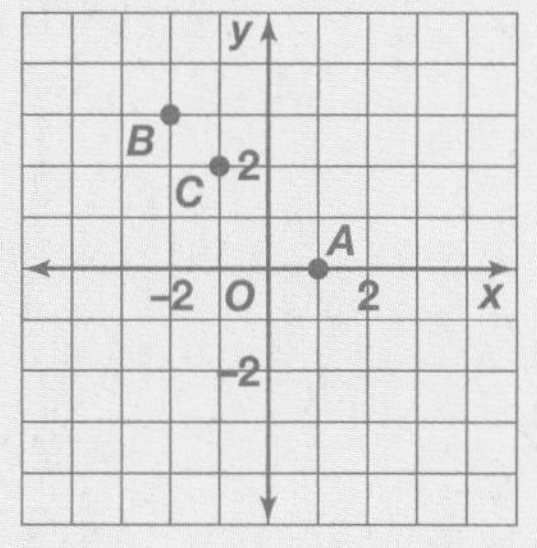


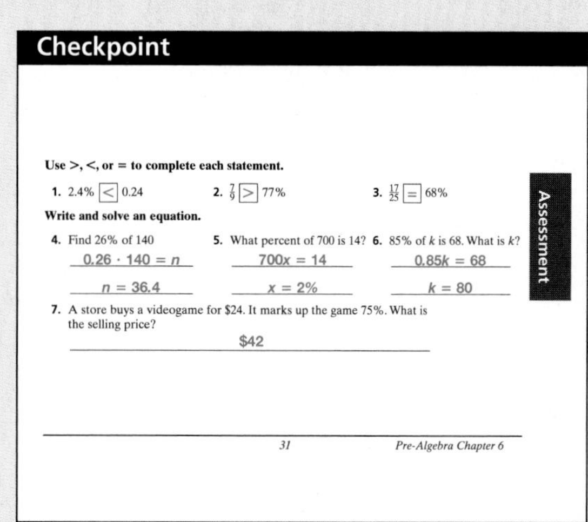

## Checkpoint

**Use >, <, or = to complete each statement.**

1. 2.4% [<] 0.24
2. $\frac{7}{9}$ [>] 77%
3. $\frac{17}{25}$ [=] 68%

**Write and solve an equation.**

4. Find 26% of 140
   $0.26 \cdot 140 = n$
   $n = 36.4$
5. What percent of 700 is 14?
   $700x = 14$
   $x = 2\%$
6. 85% of $k$ is 68. What is $k$?
   $0.85k = 68$
   $k = 80$
7. A store buys a videogame for \$24. It marks up the game 75%. What is the selling price?
   \$42

31 *Pre-Algebra Chapter 6*

Assessment

## Practice

**Find each sale price. Round to the nearest cent where necessary.**

| | Regular price | Percent of discount | Sale price |
|---|---|---|---|
| 1. | \$46 | 25% | \$34.50 |
| 2. | \$35.45 | 15% | \$30.13 |
| 3. | \$174 | 40% | \$104.40 |
| 4. | \$1.40 | 30% | \$.98 |
| 5. | \$87 | 50% | \$43.50 |
| 6. | \$675 | 20% | \$540.00 |

**Find each selling price. Round to the nearest cent where necessary.**

| | Cost | Percent markup | Selling price |
|---|---|---|---|
| 7. | \$5.50 | 75% | \$9.63 |
| 8. | \$25 | 50% | \$37.50 |
| 9. | \$170 | 85% | \$314.50 |
| 10. | \$159.99 | 70% | \$271.98 |
| 11. | \$12.65 | 90% | \$24.04 |
| 12. | \$739 | 20% | \$886.80 |

13. A company buys a sweater for \$14 and marks it up 90%. It later discounts the sweater 25%.
    a. Find the original selling price of the sweater. \$26.60
    b. How much was the discount? \$6.65
    c. Find the sale price after the discount. \$19.95
    d. The company's profit on the sweater can be found by subtracting the final selling price minus the cost. What was the company's profit on the sweater? \$5.95
    e. The profit was what percent of the cost? 42.5%



Practice

## Reteaching

A store pays \$8 for a basketball. The markup is 60%. Later, they discount the basketball 25%. Find the original selling price and the sale price of the basketball.

**Method 1**

The markup is 60% of the cost.
Find 60% of \$8.
0.6(8) = \$4.80
Store's cost + markup = selling price
8 + 4.80 = \$12.80
The original selling price is \$12.80.
The discount is 25% of the original selling price.
Find 25% of \$12.80
0.25(12.80) = 3.20
original price − discount = sale price
12.80 − 3.20 − 9.60
The sale price is \$9.60

**Method 2**

The selling price equals 100% of the cost plus 60% (the markup) of the cost, or 160%.
Find 160% of \$8.
1.60(8) = \$12.80
The original selling price is \$12.80.
The sale price is 100% of the original price minus 25% of the original price, or 75%.
Find 75% of \$12.80
0.75(12.80) = \$9.60
The sale price is \$9.60

**Complete each table. Where necessary, round to the nearest cent.**

| | Cost | Markup | Selling Price |
|---|---|---|---|
| 1. | \$17 | 50% | \$25.50 |
| 2. | \$48 | 70% | \$81.60 |
| 3. | \$110 | 85% | \$203.50 |
| 4. | \$87 | 65% | \$143.55 |
| 5. | \$335 | 35% | \$452.25 |

| | Original Selling Price | Discount | Sale Price |
|---|---|---|---|
| 6. | \$19 | 25% | \$14.25 |
| 7. | \$136 | 15% | \$115.60 |
| 8. | \$849 | 30% | \$594.30 |
| 9. | \$29.99 | 40% | \$17.99 |
| 10. | \$2.59 | 35% | \$1.68 |



Reteaching

## Enrichment

The Shirt Shack is having a 25% markdown sale the first week of the month. This means that the sale price is 25% less than the original price. In the middle of the month Shirt Shack marked down the sale shirts another 15%.

1. Do you think a markdown of 25% followed by another markdown of 15% is the same as a single markdown of 40%? Explain.
   Sample answer: No; a single markdown of 40% is better because it is taken off the total price.
2. For question 1, which do you think is the better buy and why?
   Sample answer is given in question 1.
3. What is the sale price of a \$25 shirt first marked down 25% and then marked down another 15% (to the nearest cent)?
   \$15.94
4. What is the sale price of a \$25 shirt marked down 40%?
   \$15
5. Compare your answer to question 1 and 2 with your results for questions 3 and 4. How would you now answer questions 1 and 2?
   The single markdown is a better buy. By taking 15% off the already reduced price, you are taking 15% off a lesser amount.
6. Successive markdowns of 25% on a \$25 shirt and then 15% are equal to a single markdown of what percent? Explain how you would solve the problem using a calculator. Then solve.
   $1 - (0.75 \times 0.85) = 0.3625$
   It is equal to a single markdown of 36.25%
7. The Shirt Shack is giving a 50% markdown on sweatshirts. The store, Terrific Tops, has marked the same sweatshirt down three times: 25%, 20%, and 15%. If the shirt originally sold for \$35, which store has the better buy? What was the final price at each store.
   The final price at Shirt Shack is \$17.50. The final price at Terrific Tops is \$17.85. Shirt Shack has the better buy.



Enrichment

# Standardized Test Prep

Standardized tests, such as those administered for state assessment, SAT9, TerraNova™, ITBS, MAT7, or CAT5, may include multiple choice questions, free-response questions, and open-ended questions.

**Multiple Choice Questions** are followed usually by four choices, one of which is correct.

**Exercises 1–8** are multiple choice questions.

**Free-Response Questions** do not give answer choices. Student must provide the one correct answer on their own.

**Exercises 9–15** are free-response questions.

## Resources

See p. 275G for a list of assessment options.

## Test-Taking Tip

Read the problem twice before you start to calculate. Notice the key words in the problem, particularly what is asked in the question.

### Test-Taking Tips on Transparency

Sometimes you can estimate to find the answer.

*Example* Find the sum: 0.75 + 8.23 + 5.5

A. 15.53 B. 14.48 C. 9.53 D. 21.23

Estimate: Round to the nearest whole number.

0.75 + 8.23 + 5.5

1 + 8 + 6 = 15

Both A and B are near 15, so round to the nearest tenth.

0.8 + 8.2 + 5.5 must be less than 15.

The answer is 14.48, or choice B.

Estimate to find the answer. Explain your reasoning.

1. The area of a square with side 2.7 cm is
   A. 5.4 $cm^2$ B. 7.29 $cm^2$ C. 54 $cm^2$ D. 72.9 $cm^2$
2. Reese went grocery shopping to buy spaghetti sauce, spaghetti noodles, and a loaf of french bread. These items cost $1.59, $1.79 and $1.89. About how much should Reese's grocery bill be?
   F. Less than $5 G. Between $5 and $6
   H. Between $6 and $7 J. Not Here

# Standardized Test Prep

## Multiple Choice

**Choose the best answer.**

1. Suppose you pick one of the chips below at random. What is the probability of picking an even-numbered chip? B

   ① ❷ ❷ ③ ❹ ❹ ⑤ ❻ ⑦ ❽ ⑨ ❿

   A. $\frac{7}{10}$ B. $\frac{7}{12}$ C. $\frac{1}{2}$ D. $\frac{5}{12}$

2. Only 12% of an iceberg's mass is above water. If the mass above water is 9,000,000 kg, what is the mass of the entire iceberg? H
   F. 108,000 kg
   G. 1,080,000 kg
   H. 75,000,000 kg
   J. 120,000,000 kg

3. The scale drawing below is for a billboard 21 ft wide and 10.5 ft high. Measure the drawing. What is its scale? D

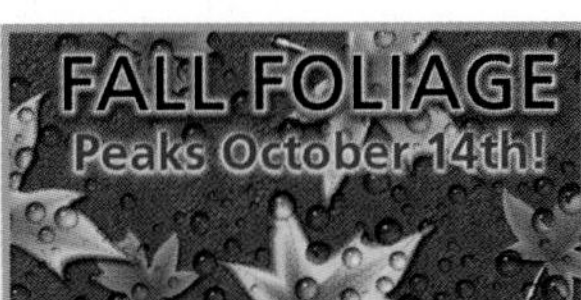
FALL FOLIAGE
Peaks October 14th!

   A. 1 in. : 21 ft B. 1.5 in. : 21 ft
   C. 2 ft : 1 in. D. 1 in. : 10.5 ft

4. A 50-lb bag of Glossy Coat Horse Feed costs $23.50. A 25-lb bag costs $15.50. How much money per pound would you save by buying the bag with the lower unit price? J
   F. $.47 G. $.62
   H. $.32 J. $.15

5. Diego paid $1.25 in sales tax for an item he purchased. The sales tax rate was 5%. What was the price of the item before tax? A
   A. $25.00 B. $26.25
   C. $2.50 D. $6.25

6. Last week $\frac{9}{10}$ of the students in a class had perfect attendance. Three students were absent. How many students had perfect attendance? G
   F. 30 G. 27 H. 18 J. 33

7. A $59.50 coat is on sale for $36.50. Find the percent of discount. A
   A. about 39%
   B. $23.00
   C. more than half off
   D. about 63%

8. Karla and her dad were nailing up plywood. They started at 10:00. Karla drove 30 nails in 10 min, the time it took her dad to drive 50 nails. At that rate, when did they finish driving 392 nails? J
   F. 10:30 G. 10:39
   H. 10:45 J. 10:49

9. Chan's; 70% of 20 = 14, which is greater than 80% of 15 = 12.

## Free Response

**For each exercise, show all your work.**

9. Chan's team won 70% of the 20 games it played. Latisha's team played 15 games and won 80% of them. Whose team won the greater number of games? Explain. See above.

10. Twenty-five students voted for Tim, 25% voted for Gina, $\frac{2}{5}$ voted for Lee, and the remaining 45 students voted for Ronnie. Who won? Explain, including the number of votes each person received. See below.

**Copy and complete the table.**

| | Sale | Percent of Commission | Amount of Commission |
|---|---|---|---|
| 11. | $270.00 | 8% | ■$21.60 |
| 12. | $566.50 | 10% | ■$56.65 |
| 13. | ■$815.50 | 12% | $97.86 |
| 14. | ■$2,735 | 15% | $410.25 |
| 15. | $12,348.00 | ■19% | $2,346.12 |

10. Lee; Gina's 25% and Lee's $\frac{2}{5}$ (40%) equal 65%, so Tim's and Ronnie's 70 votes form the other 35% of what had to be 200 votes. Votes: Tim 25, Gina 50, Lee 80, Ronnie 45

# Make a Table

6-10

*Math Strategies in Action*

Have you ever watched a baseball game at a field that doesn't have a scoreboard? It's hard to keep track of the score!

A scoreboard is a type of table. You can use tables to organize information. Tables are particularly helpful in solving problems that require several steps.

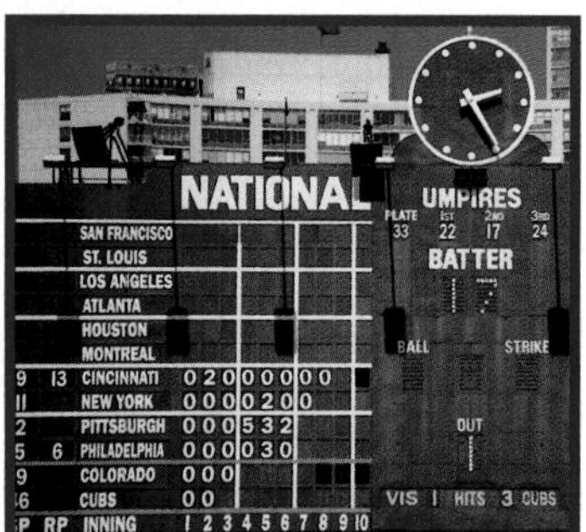


## Sample Problem

*Population Prediction* At the beginning of the year 2000, the population of the United States was about 273.5 million. The rate of population growth was about 0.85% per year. If that rate continues, what will the population be at the beginning of 2010?

### Read

Read the problem carefully.

1. What information are you asked to find? the population at the beginning of 2010
2. What information will you need to use to solve the problem? the population in 2000 and the growth rate

### Plan

Decide on a strategy. You can use the percent of increase to predict the population increase for each year from 2000 to 2010. You can make a table to organize your predictions for each year.

3. How can you find the increase in population from the beginning of 2000 to the end of that year? Answers may vary. Sample: Multiply 273.5 million by 0.0085.
4. How can you find the population at the beginning of 2001? Answers may vary. Sample: Add the population increase during 2000 to the population at the beginning of 2000.
5. The percent of increase is the same each year. Does that mean that the increase in population also will be the same each year? Explain your reasoning. No; each year the increase is the same percent of an increasing amount.

**Problem Solving Strategies**

- Account for All Possibilities
- Draw a Diagram
- Look for a Pattern
- Make a Model
- Make a Table
- Simplify a Problem
- Simulate a Problem
- Solve by Graphing
- Try, Test, Revise
- Use Multiple Strategies
- Work Backward
- Write an Equation
- Write a Proportion



# Tools to Monitor Progress

## BEFORE THE LESSON

**To check prerequisite skills:**

- Multiplying decimals

**Skills Handbook,** p. 731

**Skills Intervention Kit,** Ratio, Proportion, and Percent

## DURING THE LESSON

- **Additional Sample Problem**

  Martin started his orchard by planting 100 apple trees the first year. Each year after that he planted trees at a rate of increase of about 10% each year. He now has 161 trees. For how many years has Martin had his orchard? 6

# 6-10

## Getting Ready

**Resources** A complete list of resources for this lesson is on p. 275H.

### Daily Skills Warm-Up

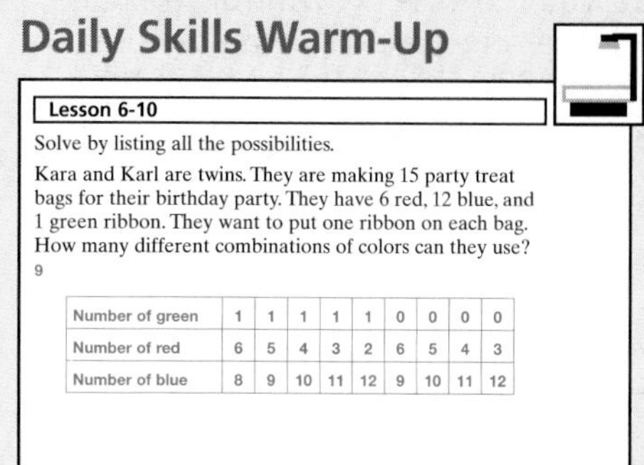

Lesson 6-10

Solve by listing all the possibilities.

Kara and Karl are twins. They are making 15 party treat bags for their birthday party. They have 6 red, 12 blue, and 1 green ribbon. They want to put one ribbon on each bag. How many different combinations of colors can they use?

9

| Number of green | 1 | 1 | 1 | 1 | 1 | 0 | 0 | 0 | 0 |
|---|---|---|---|---|---|---|---|---|---|
| Number of red | 6 | 5 | 4 | 3 | 2 | 6 | 5 | 4 | 3 |
| Number of blue | 8 | 9 | 10 | 11 | 12 | 9 | 10 | 11 | 12 |

### Background for the Lesson

You can use a table to help solve problems that describe relationships that occur over and over again in a regular sequence. With a table, you can organize and present many related facts in a way that makes the information clear. Label the parts of a table to tell a reader exactly the meaning of the numbers in the parts of the table.

## 1 Focus

### Connecting to Students' Lives

Students often see data presented in the form of a table. Statistics for sports teams, weather forecasts, and perhaps the weekly school cafeteria menu are all often presented in the form of a table.

### Connecting to Prior Knowledge

In Lesson 6-8, students learned to solve problems using the percent of increase. In this lesson, they use those skills to make a table as a problem solving strategy.

## 2 Teach

### Part 1 Teaching Notes

Discuss the labels on the tables in the lesson and make sure students understand what they mean, and what the units are for each column.

### Sample Problem

**Build understanding.** Ask: As an estimate, what would be the growth for the first year if the rate were 1%? The rate is actually 0.85%. Would you expect the first-year growth to be greater than or less than this estimate?
≈ 2.735 million; less than

**ELL** Help students relate the word *population* to the word *people* to help them understand its meaning.

**Error Prevention** Students may not read the problem carefully enough to see that the rate is *per year* and that the question is asking for a number that will occur 10 years later. Point out the table in Step 7 to correct this error.

**Visual Learning** Suggest that students fill in the table for each year as they find it so that they can see how they are working toward the final answer to the question.

**Extension** The population of India is growing at about 6% per year. The current population of India is about one billion people. What will the population be after one year? 1.06 billion

**Technology Option** You may want to have the students solve the sample problem by using a computer spreadsheet.

### Solve

Copy and complete the table below.

6. Find the numbers for Column 4 by multiplying the numbers in Columns 2 and 3. Round to the nearest tenth of a million. See table.
7. Find the numbers for Column 5 by adding the numbers in Columns 2 and 4. See table.

| 1 | 2 | 3 | 4 | 5 |
|---|---|---|---|---|
| Year | Population at Beginning of Year (millions) | Rate of Increase (0.85%) | Increase in Population (millions) | Population at End of Year (millions) |
| 2000 | 273.5 | 0.0085 | 2.3 | 275.8 |
| 2001 | 275.8 | 0.0085 | 2.3 | 278.1 |
| 2002 | 278.1 | 0.0085 | 2.4 | 280.5 |
| 2003 | 280.5 | 0.0085 | 2.4 | 282.9 |
| 2004 | 282.9 | 0.0085 | 2.4 | 285.3 |
| 2005 | 285.3 | 0.0085 | 2.4 | 287.7 |
| 2006 | 287.7 | 0.0085 | 2.4 | 290.1 |
| 2007 | 290.1 | 0.0085 | ■ 2.5 | ■ 292.6 |
| 2008 | ■ 292.6 | 0.0085 | ■ 2.5 | ■ 295.1 |
| 2009 | ■ 295.1 | 0.0085 | ■ 2.5 | ■ 297.6 |
| 2010 | ■ 297.6 | | | |

8. Answers may vary. Sample: It changes when the increase rounds to the next greatest tenth.

8. Sometimes the number in Column 4 changes from one year to the next, and sometimes it does not change. Explain.
9. What is your prediction for population at the beginning of 2010? 297.6 million

### Look Back

10. Answers may vary. Sample: No; the increase is slightly greater each year. So your friend's answer will be low.

10. Your friend says that she knows a quicker way to find the answer. Simply multiply 273.5 · 0.0085 · 10 to find the increase for the ten-year period 2000 to 2010. Do you agree with your friend's approach? Explain your reasoning.
11. Suppose the annual percent of increase in population is 0.9%. At that rate, what will the population be at the beginning of 2010? about 299 million



- **Additional Sample Problem**
At a used book sale, paperback books were priced at $.60 each and hardcover books at $1.00 each. Steve spent $4.40. How many of each kind of book did he buy? 4 paperback and 2 hardcover books

### AFTER THE LESSON

**To assess knowledge: Lesson Quiz**

1. Kaleb uses his initials, KWT, for his password. How many different passwords can he make? 6
2. At an auction, one bid starts at $100 and increases 50% every minute. After how many minutes is the bid over $2,000? 8

- For enrichment and reteaching options, see Resources on p. 275H.

# Exercises

## Check Understanding

**Make a table to solve each problem.**

1. *Biology* A microbe population increases 100% every 10 min. If you start with 1 microbe, how many will you have at the end of 1 h? 64 microbes
2. Cher has forgotten the combination to her locker. She knows it consists of three numbers—3, 5, and 9—but she can't remember the order. She decides to try every possible order until she gets the right one. How many possible orders are there? 6 orders
3. In how many ways can you make 40¢ in change without using pennies? 7 ways

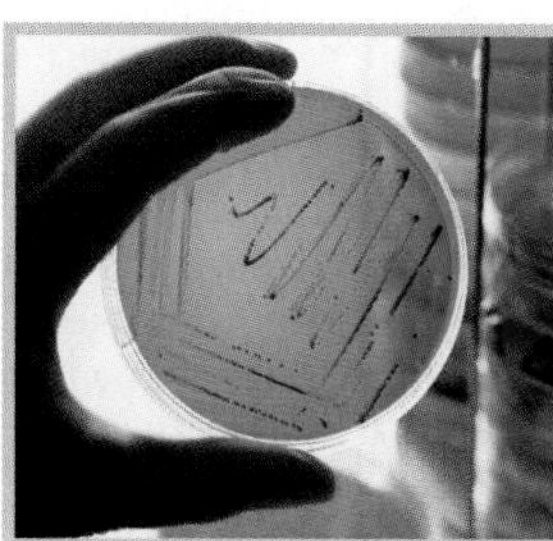

Scientists grow microbe cultures on agar gel in petri dishes.

## Practice and Problem Solving

**Make a table to solve each problem.**

4. *Population* The population of a town increases at the rate of 1% each year. Today the town's population is 8,500. What will the population be in five years? Round to the nearest person. 8,934
5. Paco has four pairs of jeans and four T-shirts. How many outfits of a T-shirt and a pair of jeans can Paco make? 16 outfits
6. *Related Rates* A train leaves a station at noon and averages 45 mi/h. Another train leaves the same station an hour after the first and averages 60 mi/h in the same direction. At what time will the second train catch up with the first? How far from the station will the trains be? 4 P.M.; 180 mi
7. A family went to the movies. Tickets cost $4 for each child and $6 for each adult. The total admission charge for the family was $26. List all the possible numbers of adults and children in the family. 1 adult, 5 children; 3 adults, 2 children

**Use any strategy to solve each problem.**

8. A class sold tickets for a pancake breakfast. One hundred twenty people came. They accounted for 60% of the tickets sold. How many tickets were sold? 200 tickets
9. *Geometry* The length of a rectangle is twice the width. The perimeter of the rectangle is 42 cm. Find the length and width. 14 cm, 7 cm



# 3 Practice/Assess

## Assignment Guide

**Core** 1–13

**✪ Extension** 14

Mixed Review can be assigned at any time for maintenance.

### Exercises

**Tactile Learning** **Exercises 1–7** Have students in groups choose one problem and prepare a poster to show their work and solution.

**Exercises 1–14** These problems are suitable for cooperative group work.

### ✪ Challenge

If the rate of U.S. population growth stays the same, at the start of what year will the population first be greater than 300 million? 2011

### Closure

You can make a table to organize information or to solve problems that have several steps.

### Alternative Assessment

Have students research information on the enrollment at their school and prepare a table showing past growth and predicting future growth.

### Daily Cumulative Review

**Find each selling price. Round to the nearest cent where necessary.** *(Lesson 6-9)*

1. cost: $8; percent of markup: 60% — $12.80
2. cost: $3.15; percent of markup: 85% — $5.83
3. cost: $236.29; percent of markup: 37% — $323.72
4. cost: $75.24; percent of markup: 55% — $116.62

**Find each percent of change. Round to the nearest tenth of a percent. Tell whether the change is an increase or a decrease.** *(Lesson 6-8)*

5. from 28 to 36 — 28.6%; increase
6. from 110 to 95 — 13.6%; decrease
7. from 112 to 99 — 11.6%; decrease
8. from 20 to 50 — 150%; increase
9. from 250 to 260 — 4%; increase
10. from 17 to 27 — 58.8%; increase

**Mixed Review**

**Solve each equation.**

11. (2-5) $47 = n + 16$ — $31 = n$
12. (2-5) $x - 14 = 9$ — $x = 23$
13. (2-6) $-64 = 2r$ — $-32 = r$
14. (2-6) $\frac{s}{6} = -8$ — $s = -48$
15. (2-5) $652 = a + 398$ — $254 = a$
16. (2-6) $4t = 60$ — $t = 15$

**Simplify each expression.**

17. (2-1) $43 + 19 + (-6)$ — 56
18. (2-1) $4 \cdot (-6) \cdot 2$ — $-48$
19. (2-1) $15 + (-8) + (-2)$ — 5

**Write each decimal as a percent.**

20. (6-5) 0.653 — 65.3%
21. (6-5) 2.5 — 250%
22. (6-5) 0.009 — 0.9%

## Practice

**Make a table to solve each problem.**

1. A car was worth $12,500 in 1998. It's value depreciates, or decreases, 15% per year. Find its value in 2002.

| Year | 1998 | 1999 | 2000 | 2001 | 2002 |
|---|---|---|---|---|---|
| Car's value | $12,500 | $10,625 | $9,031.25 | $7,676.56 | $6,525.08 |

2. Marcus spent $105 on 6 items at a sale. Videotapes were on sale for $15 each and music CD's were on sale for $20 each. How many of each item did Marcus buy?

| Number of videotapes | 1 | 2 | 3 | 4 | 5 |
|---|---|---|---|---|---|
| Number of CD's | 5 | 4 | 3 | 2 | 1 |
| Total cost | $115 | $110 | $105 | $100 | $95 |

Marcus bought 3 videotapes and 3 CD's.

3. Karina likes to mix either apple, orange, or grape juice with either lemon lime soft drink or sparkling water to make a fizz. How many different fizzes can she make?

6 fizzes

4. How many ways can you have 25 cents in change?

13 ways

5. The deer population of a state park has increased 8% a year for the last 4 years. If there are 308 deer in the park this year, find how large the population was 4 years ago by completing the table.

| Year | | 1 | 2 | 3 | 4 |
|---|---|---|---|---|---|
| Deer population | 226 | 244 | 264 | 285 | 308 |

6. How many different sandwiches can you make from 3 types of bread, 2 types of cheese, and 2 types of meat? Assume that only one type of each item is used per sandwich.

12 different sandwiches

7. A bus leaves a station at 8:00 A.M. and averages 30 mi/h. Another bus leaves the same station following the same route two hours after the first and averages 50 mi/h. When will the second bus catch up with the first bus?

1:00 P.M.



## Reteaching

A saving account pays 4% interest per year. You deposit $1,000 and then do not deposit or withdraw any money. How much will be in the account at the end of 5 years?

A table can help you solve the problem.

| Year | Beginning Balance | Interest | Ending Balance |
|---|---|---|---|
| 1 | $1,000 | $40 | $1,040 |
| 2 | $1,040 | $41.60 | $1,081.60 |
| 3 | $1,081.60 | $43.26 | $1,124.86 |
| 4 | $1,124.86 | $44.99 | $1,169.85 |
| 5 | $1,169.85 | $46.79 | $1,216.64 |

The first year, your interest is 4% of $1,000 or $40. At the end of the first year and the beginning of the second year, you have $1,040. The second year, your interest is 4% of $1,040 or $41.60. If you finish the table, you find you have $1,216.64 at the end of 5 years.

A savings account pays 5% interest per year. You deposit $1800 and then do not deposit or withdraw any money. Complete the table to find out how much will be in the account at the end of 10 years.

| Year | Beginning Balance | Interest | Ending Balance |
|---|---|---|---|
| 1 | $1,800 | $90 | $1,890 |
| 2 | $1,890 | $94.50 | $1,984.50 |
| 3 | $1,984.50 | $99.23 | $2,083.73 |
| 4 | $2,083.73 | $104.19 | $2,187.92 |
| 5 | $2,187.92 | $109.40 | $2,297.32 |
| 6 | $2,297.32 | $114.87 | $2,412.19 |
| 7 | $2,412.19 | $120.61 | $2,532.80 |
| 8 | $2,532.80 | $126.64 | $2,659.44 |
| 9 | $2,659.44 | $132.97 | $2,792.41 |
| 10 | $2,792.41 | $139.62 | $2,932.03 |

Amount: $2,932.03



## Enrichment

You borrow $12,000 to buy a car. You are charged 9% interest. Your payments are $300 a month. How much do you owe at the end of a year? Interest can be found with the formula $I = Prt$ where $I$ is the interest you pay, $P$ is the principal or money you owe, $r$ is the interest rate, and $t$ is the time. Interest rates are usually given as a percent that is charged per year.

1. Find the interest charged on a $12,000 loan at 9% for 1 year.

$1,080

2. Add the interest to the $12,000 and then subtract your payments for one year. Using this method, how much would you owe at the end of a year?

$9,480

Because this method is easy to understand, many loan companies use it to compute a loan balance. However, this method charges the borrower interest on the whole $12,000 for the year, even after some of the loan is paid off. The table shows a more appropriate way to compute a loan balance. The interest is computed each month on the "declining balance." In the interest formula, $t = \frac{1}{12}$ of a year.

3. Complete the table. The first two months are done for you.

| Month | Beginning Balance | Interest | Ending Balance |
|---|---|---|---|
| 1 | $12,000 | $90 | $11,790 |
| 2 | $11,790 | $88.43 | $11,578.43 |
| 3 | $11,578.43 | $86.84 | $11,365.27 |
| 4 | $11,365.27 | $85.24 | $11,150.51 |
| 5 | $11,150.51 | $83.63 | $10,934.14 |
| 6 | $10,934.14 | $82.01 | $10,716.15 |
| 7 | $10,716.15 | $80.37 | $10,496.52 |
| 8 | $10,496.52 | $78.72 | $10,275.24 |
| 9 | $10,275.24 | $77.06 | $10,052.30 |
| 10 | $10,052.30 | $75.39 | $9,827.69 |
| 11 | $9,827.69 | $73.71 | $9,601.40 |
| 12 | $9,601.40 | $72.01 | $9,373.41 |

4. How much more do you owe at the end of one year with the straight method than with the declining balance method?

$106.59



10. *Number Sense* The difference of two numbers is 18. The sum of the two numbers is 34. What are the two numbers? 8, 26

11. *Capacity* You fill a container $\frac{3}{4}$ full of water. The amount of water now in the container is 6 quarts. How much can the container hold? 8 qt

12. *Number Sense* A number $n$ is multiplied by $\frac{5}{8}$. The product is subtracted from $\frac{2}{3}$. The result is $\frac{7}{12}$. What is $n$? $\frac{2}{15}$

13. At a local high school, 60% of the students are girls. Of these girls, 75% own cassette players. What percent of all students are girls who do *not* own cassette players? 15%

14. *Water Resources* Water for irrigation is measured in *acre-feet*. One acre-foot is the volume of water that would cover one acre of land to a depth of one foot. How many acre-feet of water would it take to cover 600 acres to a depth of one inch? 50 acre-feet

### Journal

Describe how you could use indirect measurement to estimate the height of your school.

## Mixed Review

**Find each sale price.** *(Lesson 6-9)*

15. regular price: $5
percent of discount: 34% $3.30

16. regular price: $39
percent of discount: 30% $27.30

17. regular price: $159.95
percent of discount: 20% $127.96

**Write in simplest form.** *(Lesson 4-4)*

18. $\frac{16}{36}$ $\frac{4}{9}$

19. $\frac{10x}{65x}$ $\frac{2}{13}$

20. $\frac{8ab}{2bc}$ $\frac{4a}{c}$

21. *Probability* What is the probability that a digit selected at random from the number 364,892 is a multiple of 3? *(Lesson 6-4)* $\frac{1}{2}$

## Math at Work

### Caterer

A caterer provides food for parties, weddings, and other events. Caterers plan the menu, buy the ingredients, and cook the food. Often they provide seating and music. For each event, a caterer determines the cost per guest.

The catering business requires a thorough knowledge of ratios, proportions, and percents.

For more information about careers in catering, visit the Prentice Hall Web site.
**www.phschool.com**

### Math at Work

If you have block scheduling or extended class periods, have small groups of students research the math of catering by talking to individuals at one or more catering businesses. Have them display information of what they have learned about how math is used to track costs, amounts, and portions.

Students can find additional information on the Web site **www.phschool.com**.

**Make a Musical Instrument** The Project Activities on pages 288, 293, 304, and 317 will help you complete your project. Here is a checklist to help you gather the different parts.

- ✔ your stringed instrument
- ✔ measurements of string lengths for different notes
- ✔ table of ratios of string lengths
- ✔ calculations of locations of notes on a cello

Make a drawing of the stringed instrument you constructed. On the drawing, label the locations of the points that correspond to the notes for *can, you,* and *see*. Make and label a similar drawing of a cello.

***Reflect and Revise***

Ask a friend to review your drawings and your calculations. Are they accurate? Are they clearly drawn and labeled? If necessary, make changes to improve your drawings.

### *Web Extension*

**Visit Prentice Hall's Web site. You'll find some interesting links and ideas related to musical instruments. You'll also be able to share information about your project.**
**www.phschool.com**

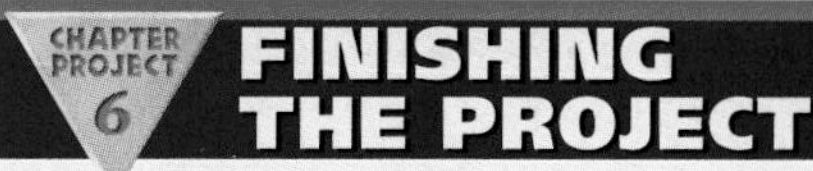


**Project Day** You may wish to plan a project day on which students share their completed projects. Encourage students to explain their process as well as their product.

**Block Scheduling** If you have block scheduling or extended periods, you may wish to intersperse the sharing of projects over Days 3, 4, 5 between the completion of one lesson and the start of a new lesson.

 **Project Notebook**

Have students review their project work and bring their notebooks up to date. Call attention to the fact that they can share their projects with other students through the Web site **www.phschool.com**.

Be sure students include in their notebooks their completed Project Manager and Scoring Rubric forms.

**Portfolio** Students may wish to include their projects and/or their project notebooks in their portfolios.

## Web Extension

**Tell Us About Your Project**

Students may wish to share their projects with other students on the Web site: **www.phschool.com**.

## Scoring Rubric

**3** You calculate all string lengths accurately. You draw the instruments neatly to scale and label them correctly.

**2** You make minor errors in calculating string lengths or in labeling your drawing. Your drawing is neat but not to scale.

**1** You find inaccurate string lengths. Your drawing is incomplete and not to scale.

**0** Major elements of the project are incomplete or missing.

# Wrap Up

## Resources

Glossary, p. 748
Extra Practice, p. 715

For a complete list of resources for the chapter, see p. 275H.

### Quarterly Assessment Form A Page 1

**Circle the letter of the best answer.**

1. Which of the following is the best estimate of $3\frac{3}{4} + 2\frac{1}{5}$?
   A. 4 B. 5 **C. 6** D. 7
2. Evaluate the expression $a^2 + b^2$, for $a = -2$ and $b = -3$.
   F. 25 **G. 13** H. −13 J. −25
3. Write 3,400,000 in scientific notation.
   A. $3.4 \times 10^4$ B. $34 \times 10^5$ **C. $3.4 \times 10^6$** D. $3.4 \times 10^5$
4. State the prime factorization of 84.
   F. $2 \cdot 42$ **G. $2^2 \cdot 3 \cdot 7$** H. $4 \cdot 3 \cdot 7$ J. $2 \cdot 3 \cdot 7$
5. Find the GCF of 18 and 32.
   A. 8 B. 4 **C. 2** D. 6
6. Find the LCM of $15a^3b^2$ and $18ab^4$.
   F. $3ab^2$ G. $90ab^2$ **H. $90a^3b^4$** J. $3a^3b^4$
7. $1\frac{2}{5} \cdot \frac{2}{3} =$
   **A. $\frac{14}{15}$** B. $1\frac{4}{15}$ C. $1\frac{1}{8}$ D. $2\frac{1}{10}$
8. Solve $7 = y - 2\frac{3}{7}$.
   **F. $y = 9\frac{3}{7}$** G. $y = 4\frac{4}{7}$ H. $y = \frac{17}{39}$ J. $y = 4\frac{2}{7}$
9. Find the probability that a spinner with numbers 1 to 10 lands on a number greater than 6 when spun.
   A. $\frac{3}{10}$ B. $\frac{1}{2}$ C. $\frac{3}{5}$ **D. $\frac{2}{5}$**
10. Which of the following is *not* true?
    F. $\frac{5}{8} = 62.5\%$ G. $35\% = \frac{7}{20}$ H. $\frac{9}{2} = 4.5$ **J. $0.05\% = 5$**
11. Which of following is *not* true?
    A. $\frac{7}{9} > 77\%$
    **B. $4.38 \times 10^{-3} > 2.65 \times 10^{-2}$**
    C. 15 oz < 1 lb
    D. $\frac{4}{7} < \frac{4}{5}$

**Simplify.**

12. $6(8 - 6)^3$ 48
13. $\frac{(x^3 \cdot y^4)^2}{x^5y^4}$ $xy^4$
14. $\frac{35mn}{14m}$ $\frac{5n}{2}$



### Quarterly Assessment Form A Page 2

15. Multiply $(2.7 \times 10^{-5})(3.1 \times 10^{-4})$. Write your answer in scientific notation. $8.37 \times 10^{-9}$
16. State whether 285,432 is divisible by 2, 3, 5, 9, or 10. 2 and 3
17. List all factors of 40. 1, 2, 4, 5, 8, 10, 20, 40
18. Evaluate $\frac{a+b}{3b}$, for $a = -2$ and $b = 5$. $\frac{1}{5}$
19. Write $0.\overline{18}$ as a fraction in simplest form. $\frac{2}{11}$
20. Complete: 10 qt = $2\frac{1}{2}$ gal
21. Write as a unit rate: An airplane travels 2,250 km in 3 h. 750 km/h
22. 35% of $k$ is 7. What is $k$? $k = 20$
23. Find the percent of change from 40 to 45. 12.5%
24. The figures are similar. Find the value of $x$. 4.8

25. In a scale drawing of a house, the dining room is 0.75 in. long. The actual length of the dining room is 24 ft. The living room is 32 ft long. Find the length of the living room on the drawing. 1 in.
26. A store bought frozen pizzas for $3 and marked them up 45%. What is the selling price of the pizzas? $4.35
27. There are 12 seats in the front row of a theatre. Each row has 4 more seats than the row in front of it. How many seats are there in the first 8 rows? 208 seats
28. Explain why $(x^3)^2 = x^6$. Sample answer is shown.
    $(x^3)^2 = x^3 \cdot x^3 = x^{3+3} = x^6$



# 6 Wrap Up

## Key Terms

| | | | |
|---|---|---|---|
| commission (p. 311) | indirect measurement (p. 289) | percent (p. 300) | rate (p. 279) |
| complement (p. 296) | markup (p. 318) | percent of change (p. 314) | ratio (p. 278) |
| cross products (p. 284) | odds (p. 297) | probability (p. 295) | scale drawing (p. 290) |
| discount (p. 319) | outcome (p. 295) | proportion (p. 284) | similar figures (p. 289) |
| event (p. 295) | | | unit rate (p. 279) |

## Graphic Organizer

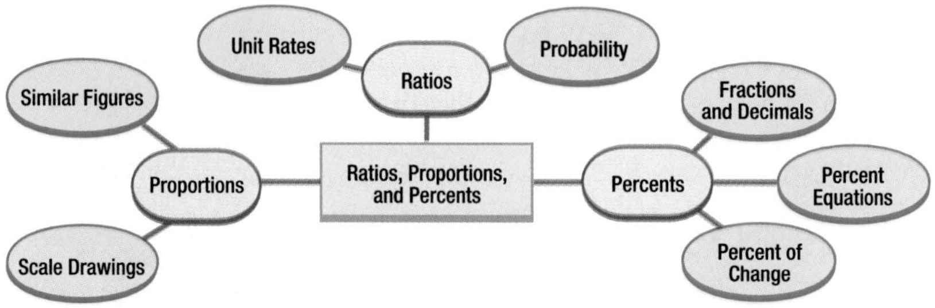


## Ratios and Unit Rates 6-1

**Summary** A **ratio** is a comparison of two quantities by division. A **rate** is a ratio that compares quantities in different units. A **unit rate** is a rate that has a denominator of 1.

**Write each ratio as a fraction in simplest form.**

1. 9 : 24 $\frac{3}{8}$
2. 20 : 35 $\frac{4}{7}$
3. 15 : 20 $\frac{3}{4}$
4. 100 : 130 $\frac{10}{13}$

**Write each ratio as a unit rate.**

5. 150 mi in 3 h 50 mi/h
6. 270 words in 3 min 90 words/min
7. $9.45 for 5 lb $1.89/lb

## Proportions 6-2

**Summary** A **proportion** is an equality of ratios. To solve a proportion, write the cross products, and then solve.

**Solve. Round to the nearest tenth where necessary.**

8. $\frac{5}{6} = \frac{n}{42}$ 35
9. $\frac{53}{2} = \frac{18}{x}$ 0.7
10. $\frac{15}{a} = \frac{30}{98}$ 49
11. $\frac{m}{150} = \frac{21}{25}$ 126

## Similar Figures and Scale Drawings 6-3

**Summary** **Similar figures** have the same shape, but not necessarily the same size. In similar figures, the corresponding angles have equal measures and the corresponding sides are proportional.

A **scale drawing** is an enlarged or reduced drawing of an object.

**Each pair of figures is similar. Find $x$.**

**12.**

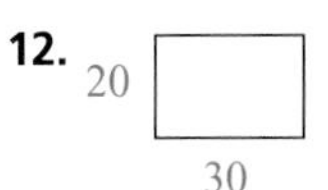


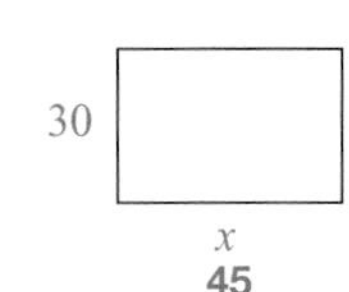


**13.**

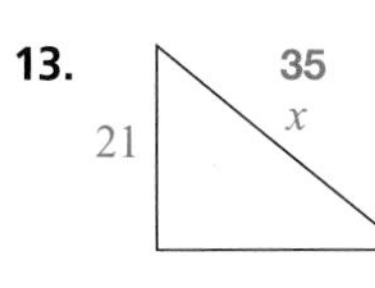


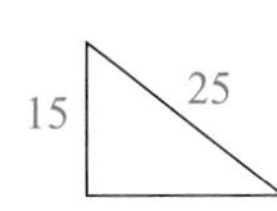


**14.** A map has a scale of 1 cm : 75 km. What is the distance on the map for an actual distance of 37.5 km? 0.5 cm

## Probability 6-4

**Summary** **Outcomes** are the possible results of an action. An **event** is any outcome or group of outcomes. When outcomes are equally likely, you can use formulas to find the **probability** of an event and the **odds** in favor of an event.

$$\text{probability} = \frac{\text{number of favorable outcomes}}{\text{number of possible outcomes}} \qquad \text{odds} = \frac{\text{number of favorable outcomes}}{\text{number of unfavorable outcomes}}$$

**Suppose you select a letter at random from the word EXPONENT. Find the probability of each event. Then find the odds in favor of the event.**

**15.** selecting P $\frac{1}{8}$; 1 to 7

**16.** selecting N $\frac{1}{4}$; 1 to 3

**17.** selecting a vowel $\frac{3}{8}$; 3 to 5

## Fractions, Decimals, and Percents 6-5

**Summary** A **percent** is a ratio that compares a number to 100.

**Write each percent as a fraction in simplest form and as a decimal.**

**18.** 24% $\frac{6}{25}$; 0.24

**19.** 72% $\frac{18}{25}$; 0.72

**20.** 8% $\frac{2}{25}$; 0.08

**21.** 0.5% $\frac{1}{200}$; 0.005

**Write each number as a percent. Round to the nearest tenth of a percent.**

**22.** 0.3 30%

**23.** 0.33 33%

**24.** $\frac{1}{3}$ 33.3%

**25.** 0.35 35%

**26.** $\frac{16}{18}$ 88.9%

**27.** 0.021 2.1%

**28.** $\frac{120}{50}$ 240%

**29.** 0.0064 0.6%



**Portfolio** Students may wish to include their completed work for the Wrap Up in their portfolios.

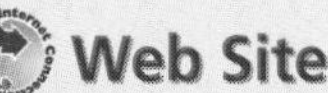

**Web Site**

Students can find self-assessment materials on the Web site: **www.phschool.com.**

### Quarterly Assessment Form B Page 1

**Circle the letter of the best answer.**

**1.** Which of the following is the best estimate of $6\frac{1}{9} - 2\frac{2}{3}$?
A. 1 B. 2 (C.) 3 D. 4

**2.** Evaluate the expression $2(m^2 + n^2)$, when $m = 1$ and $n = 3$.
F. 32 (G.) 20 H. 11 J. 10

**3.** Write $2.5 \times 10^6$ in standard notation.
A. 2,500 B. 25,000 C. 250,000 (D.) 2,500,000

**4.** State the prime factorization of 135.
F. $2^2 \cdot 4 \cdot 7$ G. $1 \cdot 135$ (H.) $3^3 \cdot 5$ J. $3^2 \cdot 5$

**5.** Find the LCM of 42 and 35.
(A.) 210 B. 245 C. 294 D. 1,470

**6.** Find the GCF of $30x$ and $36x^2y$.
F. 6 (G.) $6x$ H. $6xy$ J. $30x$

**7.** $\frac{3}{4} + \frac{5}{12} =$
A. $\frac{1}{2}$ (B.) $1\frac{1}{6}$ C. $\frac{15}{16}$ D. $\frac{1}{3}$

**8.** Solve $2\frac{2}{5} = -4y$.
F. $y = 3$ G. $y = -\frac{3}{4}$ (H.) $y = -\frac{3}{5}$ J. $y = -\frac{5}{3}$

**9.** Find the probability that a digit selected at random from the number 345,602 is odd.
A. $\frac{1}{2}$ B. $\frac{2}{3}$ (C.) $\frac{1}{3}$ D. $\frac{2}{7}$

**10.** Which of the following is *not* true?
(F.) $\frac{7}{2} = 35\%$ G. $0.4\% = 0.004$ H. $45\% = \frac{9}{20}$ J. $\frac{4}{5} = 80\%$

**11.** Which of the following is *not* true?
A. $6.79 \times 10^{-4} < 3.58 \times 10^{-3}$
B. $\frac{3}{8} > \frac{3}{11}$
C. $\frac{5}{11} > 45\%$
(D.) 1.2 ft > 15 in.

**Simplify.**

**12.** $9(4 - 5)^7$ $-9$

**13.** $\frac{(a^5b^2)^3}{a^7b^3}$ $a^8b^3$

**14.** $\frac{28xy}{49y}$ $\frac{4x}{7}$



### Quarterly Assessment Form B Page 2

**15.** Multiply $(1.8 \times 10^{-6})(4.1 \times 10^{-4})$. Write your answer in scientific notation. $7.38 \times 10^{-10}$

**16.** State whether 1,487,630 is divisible by 2, 3, 5, 9, or 10. 2, 5, and 10

**17.** List all of the factors of 32. 1, 2, 4, 8, 16, 32

**18.** Evaluate $\frac{a - b}{2b}$, for $a = -7$ and $b = 3$ $-1\frac{2}{3}$

**19.** Write $0.\overline{54}$ as a fraction in simplest form. $\frac{6}{11}$

**20.** Complete 24 oz = 1.5 lb

**21.** Write as a unit rate:
A car travels 256 mi on 8 gal of gas. 32 mi/gal

**22.** 44% of $k$ is 11. What is $k$? $k = 25$

**23.** Find the percent of change from 20 to 18. −10%

**24.** The figures are similar. Find the value of $x$. 10.5

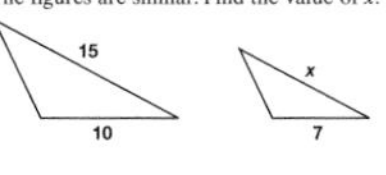


**25.** Clarissa can make 6 paper roses in 45 minutes. How long will it take her to make 32 for the school dance? 240 min

**26.** A store bought boxes of cereal for $1.30 each and marked them up 60%. What is the selling price for a box of cereal? $2.08

**27.** Marcus ran 1 mile on Monday. He ran 0.25 mi further each day. How many miles did he run in all from Monday to Friday? 7.5 mi

**28.** Explain why $x^3 \cdot x^2 = x^5$. Sample answer is shown.
$x^3 \cdot x^2 = (x \cdot x \cdot x) \cdot (x \cdot x) = (x \cdot x \cdot x \cdot x \cdot x) = x^5$

## Finding Percents — 6-6 and 6-7

**Summary** Solve percent problems by using a proportion or an equation.

**Write and solve a proportion.**

**30.** Find 15% of 48. $\frac{15}{100} = \frac{n}{48}$; 7.2

**31.** 20% of $x$ is 30. What is $x$? $\frac{20}{100} = \frac{30}{x}$; 150

**32.** What percent of 300 is 90? $\frac{n}{100} = \frac{90}{300}$; 30

**33.** 125% of $y$ is 100. What is $y$? $\frac{125}{100} = \frac{100}{y}$; 80

**Write and solve an equation.**

**34.** 35% of $a$ is 70. What is $a$? $0.35a = 70$; 200

**35.** Find 68% of 300. $n = 0.68 \cdot 300$; 204

**36.** What percent of 180 is 9? $n \cdot 180 = 9$; 5%

**37.** What percent of 56 is 3.5? $n \cdot 56 = 3.5$; 6.25%

## Percent of Change, Markup, and Discount — 6-8 and 6-9

**Summary** percent of change $= \frac{\text{amount of change}}{\text{original amount}}$

**Markup** is a real-world application of percent of increase. **Discount** is a real-world application of percent of decrease.

**Find each percent of change. Tell whether the change is an increase or decrease.**

**38.** 120 to 90 25% decrease

**39.** 148 to 37 75% decrease

**40.** 285 to 342 20% increase

**41.** 1,000 to 250 75% decrease

**42.** A cap that cost a retailer $5 was marked up by 75%. Find the selling price. $8.75

**43.** Peaches that are usually priced at $2/lb are on sale for 15% off. Find the sale price. $1.70/lb

## Make a Table — 6-10

**Summary** Make a table to organize information or to solve problems that have several steps.

**44.** Alicia bikes 25% of a 100-mi trip on the first day. She bikes $\frac{1}{3}$ of the remaining distance on the second day. On the third day, she bikes 40% of the remaining distance. Make a table to find the number of miles left in Alicia's trip. 30 mi

**45.** *Writing* Describe how you could use the strategy *Make a Table* together with another problem solving strategy that you have studied. Justify your answer with an example. Check students' work.



### Chapter Assessment Form A Page 1

**Circle the letter of the best answer.**

1. Write the ratio of *270 mi in 5 h* as a unit rate.
   (A.) 54 mi/h  B. 52 mi/h  C. 56 mi/h  D. 1,350 mi/h
2. Two cases of cans weigh 32 lb. How much do 7 cases weigh?
   F. 23 lb  (G.) 112 lb  H. 102 lb  J. 224 lb

**Suppose you select a marble at random from a jar containing 3 green, 2 red, and 5 blue marbles. Find each probability.**

3. selecting a green marble
   A. $\frac{3}{7}$  B. $\frac{4}{7}$  C. $\frac{1}{3}$  (D.) $\frac{3}{10}$
4. not selecting a red marble
   F. $\frac{1}{4}$  G. $\frac{4}{7}$  (H.) $\frac{4}{5}$  J. $\frac{1}{5}$
5. Write 0.065 as a percent.
   (A.) 6.5%  B. 65%  C. 0.65%  D. 0.00065%
6. Write $\frac{37}{50}$ as a percent.
   F. 37%  (G.) 74%  H. 64%  J. 50%
7. What percent of 20 is 13?
   A. 52%  (B.) 65%  C. 153.8%  D. 13%
8. Find 12.5% of 80.
   F. 100  G. 1,000  (H.) 10  J. 640
9. Find the percent of change from 65 to 143.
   A. 78%  (B.) 120%  C. 54.5%  D. 83.3%
10. Find the percent of change from 60 to 42.
   F. 3%  G. 70%  H. 27.5%  (J.) 30%

**Solve. Use the data below.**

Student's Television Watching Habits

| Hours of TV watched per day | Number of students |
|---|---|
| 0 | 8,000 |
| 1 h or less | 4,000 |
| 1–2 h | 3,120 |
| 2–5 h | 4,800 |
| More than 5 h | 80 |



### Chapter Assessment Form A Page 2

11. What percent of the students watch 1–2 h of television per day?
   A. 40%  B. 20%  (C.) 15.6%  D. 18.5%
12. What percent of the students watch 2 h or less per day?
   (F.) 75.6%  G. 53.5%  H. 60%  J. 70%
13. Which number is *not* equal to $\frac{18}{8}$?
   A. $2\frac{1}{4}$  B. 225%  C. $\frac{9}{4}$  (D.) 2.25%
14. Write a proportion and solve: A student types 120 words in 3 min and $x$ words in 5 min. Find $x$.
   $\frac{120}{3} = \frac{x}{5}$; $x = 200$ words
15. Write = or ≠ to complete the statement.
   $\frac{15}{20}$ [≠] $\frac{12}{15}$

**In a scale drawing of a house, the living room is 1 in. long. The actual length is 24 ft. Solve.**

16. The actual width of the living room is 18 ft. Find the width on the drawing.
   $\frac{3}{4}$ in.
17. On the drawing, a hallway is $\frac{1}{4}$ in. wide. Find the actual width.
   6 ft
18. A videogame player that usually sells for $189 is on sale for 25% off. Find the saleprice.
   $141.75
19. How many ways can you make change for a dollar using no pennies and at most 1 nickel?
   5 ways
20. Explain how you can tell a proportion is true.
   Sample answer: A proportion is true if the cross products are equal. Thus, $\frac{a}{b} = \frac{c}{d}$ is true if $ad = bc$.



Assessment

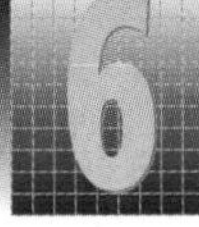

# Assessment

## Find each unit rate.

1. A car travels 84 mi on 3 gal of gas. 28 mi/gal
2. A car travels 220 mi in 4 h. 55 mi/h

## Write = or ≠ to complete each statement.

3. $\frac{7}{8}$ ■ $\frac{42}{40}$ ≠
4. $\frac{3}{5}$ ■ $\frac{45}{75}$ =
5. $\frac{12}{18}$ ■ $\frac{18}{12}$ ≠
6. $\frac{5}{9}$ ■ $\frac{25}{81}$ ≠

## Solve each proportion.

7. $\frac{x}{8} = \frac{90}{120}$ 6
8. $\frac{0.8}{90} = \frac{5.6}{y}$ 630

## Write a proportion to describe each situation. Then solve.

9. Three cans of dog food sell for 99¢. Find the cost of 15 cans. $\frac{3}{0.99} = \frac{15}{x}$; $4.95
10. A photo that measures 5 in. by 7 in. is enlarged to 7.5 in. by $b$ in. $\frac{5}{7} = \frac{7.5}{b}$; 10.5 in.
11. A student reads 45 pages in 2 h and $x$ pages in 3 h. $\frac{45}{2} = \frac{x}{3}$; 67.5 pages

## The length of the kitchen in the drawing below is $1\frac{1}{4}$ in. The actual length is 20 ft. Use the drawing for Exercises 12–14.

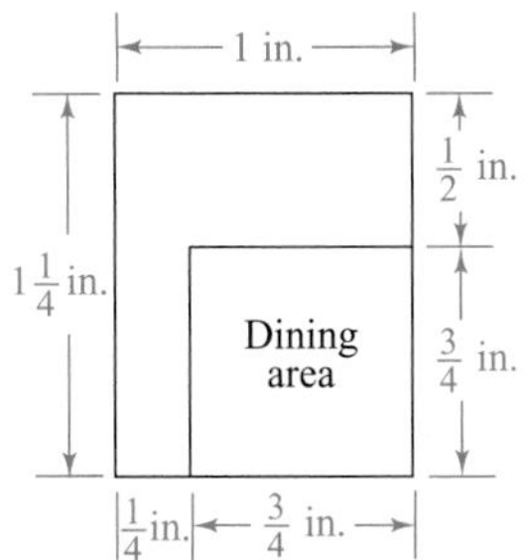


12. What is the scale of the drawing? 1 in. : 16 ft
13. What is the actual width of the kitchen? 16 ft
14. What are the actual length and width of the dining area? 12 ft, 12 ft

## Find each probability for one roll of a number cube.

15. $P(1)$ $\frac{1}{6}$
16. $P(1 \text{ or } 2)$ $\frac{1}{3}$
17. $P(\text{not } 2 \text{ or } 6)$ $\frac{2}{3}$
18. $P(\text{greater than } 1)$ $\frac{5}{6}$

## Write each decimal as a percent.

19. 0.37 37%
20. 0.005 0.5%
21. 1.02 102%

## Write each fraction as a percent.

22. $\frac{5}{8}$ 62.5%
23. $\frac{7}{16}$ 43.75%
24. $\frac{5}{4}$ 125%

## Solve.

25. What percent of 400 is 20? 5%
26. Find 45% of 12. 5.4
27. 20% of $c$ is 24. What is $c$? 120
28. What percent of 3 is 15? 500%
29. Find 125% of 50. 62.5
30. 60% of $y$ is 75. 125

## Find each percent of change. Tell whether the change is an increase or decrease. Round to the nearest tenth of a percent.

31. from 60 to 36 40% decrease
32. from 18 to 24 33.3% increase
33. from 15 to 25 66.7% increase
34. from 85 to 50 41.2% decrease
35. from 8.8 to 30 240.9% increase
36. from 1.2 to 0.2 83.3% decrease
37. A salesperson made a $128 commission selling merchandise. His commission rate was 5%. Find the dollar amount of his sales. $2,560
38. A bicycle that usually sells for $230 is on sale for 15% off. Find the sale price. $195.50
39. *Writing* Explain the difference between a markup and a discount. See below left.
40. In how many ways can you make change for $.35 without using pennies? 6 ways

39. Answers may vary. Sample: A markup is an amount added to get a selling price. A discount is an amount subtracted from the regular selling price.



# Chapter Assessment

**Resources** For a complete list of resources for this chapter, see p. 275H.

## Chapter Assessment Form B Page 1

**Circle the letter of the best answer.**

1. Write the ratio of *$1,568 in 28 days* as a unit rate.
   (A.) $56/day B. $46/day C. $36/day D. $28/day
2. A dressmaker can sew 5 collars in 60 min. How many minutes will it take to sew 20 collars?
   F. 175 G. 300 H. 250 (J.) 240

**Suppose you select a marble at random from a jar containing 3 green, 2 red, and 5 blue marbles. Find each probability.**

3. Selecting a blue marble
   A. $\frac{1}{5}$ (B.) $\frac{1}{2}$ C. $\frac{1}{1}$ D. $\frac{1}{10}$
4. not selecting a green marble
   F. $\frac{3}{10}$ G. $\frac{3}{7}$ H. $\frac{1}{7}$ (J.) $\frac{7}{10}$
5. Write 3.25 as a percent.
   A. 3.25% B. 32.5% (C.) 325% D. 0.0325%
6. Write $\frac{45}{20}$ as a percent
   F. 2.25% (G.) 225% H. 22.5% J. 0.0225%
7. What percent of 30 is 6?
   (A.) 20% B. 2% C. 5% D. 50%
8. Find 37.5% of 160.
   F. 6,000 G. 4.3 H. 426.7 (J.) 60
9. Find the percent of change from 50 to 85.
   A. 41.2% B. 58.8% (C.) 70% D. 35%
10. Find the percent of change from 80 to 65.
   F. 23.1% (G.) 18.75% H. 81.25% J. 133.3%

**Solve. Use the data below.**

| Favorite subject | Percent |
|---|---|
| Math | 45 |
| Science | 6 |
| English | 6 |
| Reading | 2 |
| Other | 41 |



## Chapter Assessment Form B Page 2

11. If 500 people were surveyed, how many chose English as their favorite subject?
   (A.) 30 B. 300 C. 10 D. 12
12. If 270 people chose math as their favorite subject, how many people were surveyed?
   F. 800 G. 500 (H.) 600 J. 122
13. Which number is *not* equal to $\frac{30}{12}$?
   A. $2\frac{1}{2}$ B. 250% C. $\frac{5}{2}$ (D.) 25%
14. Write a proportion and solve: A letter 8.5 in. by 11 in. is reduced to $n$ in. by 8.25 in. Find $n$.
   $\frac{8.5}{11} = \frac{n}{8.25}$; $n = 6.375$ in.
15. Write = or ≠ to complete the statement.
   $\frac{42}{35}$ [=] $\frac{36}{30}$

**In a scale drawing of a playground, the total length is 5 inches. The actual length is 45 feet. Solve.**

16. The actual width of the playground is 30 ft. Find the width on the drawing.
   $3\frac{1}{3}$ in.
17. On the drawing, the swings are $\frac{2}{3}$ in. long. Find the actual length.
   6 ft
18. A soccer jersey that usually sells for $35 is on sale for 30% off. Find the sale price.
   $24.50
19. Manuella likes pepperoni, mushrooms, and extra cheese on her pizza. How many different pizzas can she order with one, two, or all three of these toppings?
   7 pizzas
20. Explain how to solve a proportion.
   Sample answer: Find the cross products and then solve the resulting equation for the missing value.



Assessment

# Cumulative Review

## Cumulative Review Page 1

**Circle the letter of the best answer.**

1. Evaluate $5n + 11$ for $n = -2$.
   A. 21 (B.) 1 C. 16 D. $-1$
2. $-5$ is a solution of which equation?
   F. $7x = 35$ G. $\frac{-40}{x} = -8$ (H.) $x - 3 = -8$ J. $x + 4 = 1$
3. Simplify $(-2)^3 \cdot (-6)^0$.
   A. 48 B. $-48$ C. 8 (D.) $-8$
4. Solve $-6n = -31.26$.
   F. $n = -37.26$ G. $n = -25.26$ H. $n = -5.21$ (J.) $n = 5.21$
5. Express $6.11 \times 10^5$ in standard notation.
   (A.) 611,000 B. 61,100,000 C. 610,000 D. 61,100
6. Solve $-4\frac{1}{6}x = 25$.
   (F.) $x = -6$ G. $x = 20\frac{5}{6}$ H. $x = 29\frac{1}{6}$ J. $x = -104\frac{1}{6}$
7. Which number is less than $-\frac{3}{4}$?
   A. $-\frac{3}{5}$ B. $-\frac{2}{3}$ C. $-0.74$ (D.) $-\frac{7}{9}$
8. Write 360 mi in 8 h as a unit rate.
   (F.) 45 mi/h G. 50 mi/h H. 55 mi/h J. 90 mi/h
9. What percent of 50 is 20.7?
   A. 50% B. 24.2% (C.) 41.4% D. 20.7%
10. Find 70% of 60.
    F. 420 G. 4.2 (H.) 42 J. 1.17
11. Which has the lowest unit price?
    A. \$9.52 for 8 gal (B.) \$12.84 for 12 gal
    C. 11 gal for \$11.99 D. 9 gal for \$10.08
12. The figures are similar. Write a proportion. Then solve for $x$.
    $\frac{x}{120} = \frac{114}{144}$
    $x =$ 95



13. Find the sale price of an item with a regular price of \$29.99 marked 30% off.
    \$20.99



Assessment

## Cumulative Review Page 2

**Write each number as a percent. Round to the nearest tenth of a percent where necessary.**

14. 0.039 3.9% 15. $\frac{14}{25}$ 56% 16. $\frac{8}{33}$ 24.2%

**Find each probability for one spin of a spinner numbered 1 to 9.**

17. $P(1 \text{ or } 2)$ $\frac{2}{9}$ 18. $P(\text{less than } 7)$ $\frac{2}{3}$

**The scale on a map is 1 in. = 8 mi. Find the actual distance for each map distance.**

19. 4.5 in. 36 mi 20. 10.75 in. 86 mi

**Solve each proportion. Where necessary, round to the nearest tenth.**

21. $\frac{6}{10} = \frac{9}{x}$ $x =$ 15 22. $\frac{n}{14} = \frac{5}{3}$ $n =$ 23.3

**Write each ratio as a fraction in simplest form.**

23. 24 : 56 $\frac{3}{7}$ 24. 40 : 75 $\frac{8}{15}$
25. Explain how to find selling price given cost and markup.
    Sample answer: Multiply the percent of markup in decimal form by the cost. Add the result to the cost.



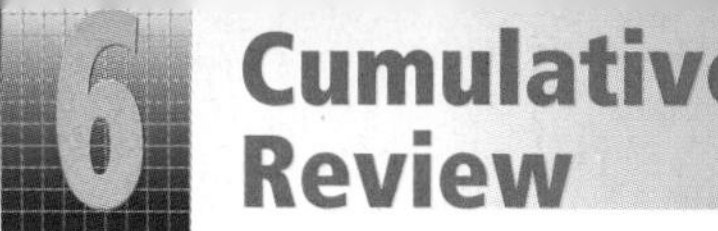

# Cumulative Review

**Preparing for Algebra**

**Choose the best answer.**

1. Evaluate $6x - 9$ for $x = -11$. C
   A. 57 B. $-59$
   C. $-75$ D. 75
2. $-4$ is a solution of which equation? H
   F. $9z = 36$ G. $\frac{-36}{z} = -9$
   H. $z + 9 = 5$ J. $z - 9 = -5$
3. Simplify $(-1)^7 \cdot (-2)^0$. B
   A. 2 B. $-1$
   C. $-14$ D. 14
4. Solve $y + 0.5 = 3$. F
   F. 2.5 G. 1.5
   H. 3.5 J. $-2.5$
5. Write 56,500,000,000 in scientific notation. C
   A. $5.65 \cdot 10^8$ B. $56.5 \cdot 10^{10}$
   C. $5.65 \cdot 10^{10}$ D. $565 \cdot 10^9$
6. Solve $\frac{2}{3}x = 2\frac{2}{9}$. J
   F. $\frac{3}{10}$ G. $7\frac{2}{3}$ H. $2\frac{5}{8}$ J. $3\frac{1}{3}$
7. Complete $\left|2\frac{4}{5}\right| \blacksquare \left|-\frac{9}{4}\right|$. A
   A. $>$ B. $<$ C. $=$ D. $\leq$
8. What is the unit rate for a ball moving 252 ft in 4 s? G
   F. 252 : 4 G. 63 ft/s
   H. 252 ft/s J. 1,008 ft/s
9. What percent of 63 is 41? C
   A. about 41% B. about 82%
   C. about 65% D. about 0.65%
10. Find 40% of 40. J
    F. 20 G. 15 H. 4 J. 16
11. Which has the lowest unit price? C
    A. 30 oz for \$.87
    B. 10 oz for \$.30
    C. \$.56 for 20 oz
    D. \$1.16 for 40 oz

**For Exercises 12–33, show your work.**

12. The figures below are similar. Write a proportion. Then solve for $x$. $\frac{80}{x} = \frac{180}{270}$; 120



**Find the sale price. Round to the nearest cent where necessary.**

13. regular price: \$58
    percent of discount: 45% \$31.90
14. regular price: \$15.98
    percent of discount: 80% \$3.20

**Write each number as a percent.**

15. 0.84 84% 16. $\frac{16}{20}$ 80% 17. $\frac{33}{55}$ 60%
18. $\frac{6}{22}$ $27.\overline{27}$% 19. $\frac{524}{200}$ 262% 20. 0.045 4.5%

**Find each probability for one roll of a number cube.**

21. $P(5 \text{ or } 6)$ $\frac{1}{3}$ 22. $P(\text{less than } 4)$ $\frac{1}{2}$

**The scale on a map is 1 in. = 5 mi. Find the actual distance for each map distance.**

23. 5.5 in. 27.5 mi 24. 12 in. 60 mi 25. 9.75 in. 48.75 mi

**Solve each proportion.**

26. $\frac{5}{8} = \frac{15}{n}$ 24 27. $\frac{28}{x} = \frac{14}{2.5}$ 5
28. $\frac{n}{9} = \frac{40}{12}$ 30 29. $\frac{6}{21} = \frac{s}{70}$ 20

**Write each ratio as a fraction in simplest form.**

30. 20 : 45 $\frac{4}{9}$ 31. 8 : 96 $\frac{1}{12}$
32. 30 : 36 $\frac{5}{6}$ 33. 120 : 80 $\frac{3}{2}$



| Item | Chapter/ Lesson | Review Topic |
|---|---|---|
| 1, 7 | 1-3 | Algebraic Expressions and Integers |
| 2 | 2-5 | Solving One-Step Equations and Inequalities |
| 4 | 3-5 | Decimals and Equations |
| 3, 5 | 4-7 | Factors, Fractions, and Exponents |
| 6 | 5-4, 5-8 | Operations with Fractions |
| 8–33 | 6-1, 6-2, 6-3, 6-4, 6-5, 6-6, 6-9 | Ratios, Proportions, and Percents |

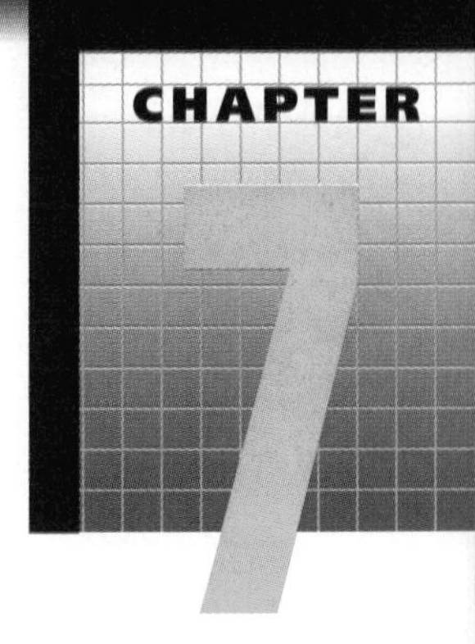


# Solving Equations and Inequalities

## Content Overview for Chapter 7

Chapter 7 builds on the skills learned in Chapter 2 for solving one-step equations. To solve two-step equations, undo addition and subtraction first and then undo multiplication and addition. To solve multi-step equations, remove grouping symbols and combine like terms first. Then follow the steps for solving two-step equations. Also, multiply by either reciprocals or powers of 10 to simplify the equations before solving multi-step equations. When variables are on both sides of an equation, first simplify both sides of the equation. Then use the properties of equality to get the variable alone on one side of the equation.

Solving two-step inequalities involves the same steps as solving two-step equations. Reverse the direction of the inequality symbol when you multiply or divide by a negative number.

You can apply the skills of solving multi-step equations to transforming formulas. Use the properties of equality to transform a formula to represent one quantity in terms of the others. You can transform interest formulas to calculate interest and account balances. Simple interest is the product of the principal amount, the annual interest rate, and the time in years. Compound interest is paid on both the principal and the previous interest.

## Making Connections

| Lesson | Interdisciplinary and Real-World Connections | Math Integration |
|---|---|---|
| 7-1 | Health | Algebra |
| 7-2 | Construction | Geometry |
| 7-3 | Consumer Issues | Geometry |
| 7-4 | Physics | Problem Solving, Geometry |
| 7-5 | Economics | Algebra |
| 7-6 | Economics | Data Analysis |
| 7-7 | Science | Geometry |
| 7-8 | Banking | Data Analysis |

**SCHOOL/HOME CONNECTION**
English and Spanish versions are available in the *Help at Home* book of copy masters.

**Helper's Page** You will find detailed instruction, more examples, and

**Student Page** **Review Exercises for Lessons 7-1 to 7-4**

**Solve each equation.** *(Lessons 7-1, 7-2, and 7-3)*

1. $5n - 12 = 18$ $n =$ ______
2. $9 + \frac{a}{3} = 11$ $a =$ ______
3. $15 = 6 + \frac{m}{2}$ $m =$ ______
4. $8 - 4b = 36$ $b =$ ______
5. $x + (3x - 5) = -13$ $x =$ ______
6. $2(5y - 7) = 16$ $y =$ ______
7. $3(2k - 9) - k = 8$ $k =$ ______
8. $4(3v - 5) - 8v = 12$ $v =$ ______
9. $\frac{3}{4}w + 6 = -15$ $w =$ ______
10. $0.25p - 5 = 9$ $p =$ ______
11. $-\frac{7}{8}c + \frac{1}{4} = \frac{3}{4}$ $c =$ ______
12. $0.3x + 0.4x = 2.8$ $x =$ ______

**Write an equation. Then solve.** *(Lesson 7-4)*

13. Jai earns \$407 per week plus 2% commission on her sales. If she earned \$2,907 last week by selling a house, how much was the selling price of the house?

______ ______

14. **Test Prep** The sum of three consecutive integers is 177. Which equation can be used to find the integers? *(Lesson 7-2)*
    A. $3n + 2 = 177$
    B. $3n + 3 = 177$
    C. $n + (n + 1) = 177$
    D. $n + (n + 2) + (n + 4) = 177$ ______

Helper: ______ Comments: ______

**Helper's Page** You will find detailed instruction, more examples, and

**Student Page** **Review Exercises for Lessons 7-5 to 7-7**

**Solve each equation.** *(Lesson 7-5)*

1. $5x - 9 = 3x + 7$ $x =$ ______
2. $9y = y + 72$ $y =$ ______
3. $3n - 5 = 7n + 11$ $n =$ ______
4. $6a = 4(a - 2)$ $a =$ ______
5. $4 - (6m - 10) = m$ $m =$ ______
6. $\frac{1}{3}(6k + 27) = 15$ $k =$ ______

**Solve each inequality. Graph the solutions on a number line.** *(Lesson 7-6)*

7. $3y + 4 \geq 1$
   −5 −4 −3 −2 −1 0 1 2 3 4 5 ______
8. $6 - 4n > -2$
   −5 −4 −3 −2 −1 0 1 2 3 4 5 ______
9. $-\frac{x}{3} + 3 < 4$
   −5 −4 −3 −2 −1 0 1 2 3 4 5 ______

**Solve for the indicated variable.** *(Lesson 7-7)*

10. $y = \frac{2}{3}x - 4$ for $x$ $x =$ ______
11. $S = ph + B$ for $p$ $p =$ ______
12. $P = 6s$ for $s$ $s =$ ______
13. **Test Prep** Solve the inequality $9 - 3m > 27$. *(Lesson 7-6)*
    A. $m < 12$ B. $m > 12$ C. $m > -6$ D. $m < -6$ ______

Helper: ______ Comments: ______

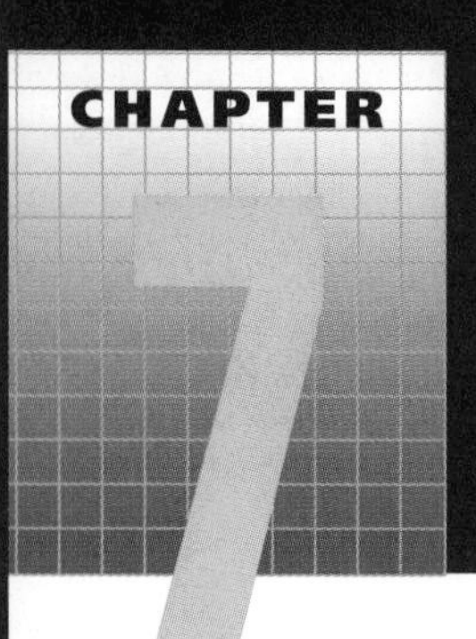

# Chapter 7 at a Glance

To accommodate flexible scheduling, most lessons are divided into parts. Assignment Options are given in the Teacher's Edition for each lesson.

### Lesson 7-1 Solving Two-Step Equations
**Pages 336–339**

**NCTM 1, 2, 6, 8, 9, 10**

- Part 1 Using Properties to Solve Two-Step Equations
- Part 2 Solving Problems with Two-Step Equations

### Lesson 7-2 Solving Multi-Step Equations
**Pages 340–344**

**NCTM 1, 2, 6, 8, 9, 10**

- Part 1 Combining Like Terms in Equations
- Part 2 Using the Distributive Property
- **Project Activity 1**

### Lesson 7-3 Multi-Step Equations with Fractions and Decimals
**Pages 345–349**

**NCTM 1, 2, 6, 8, 9, 10**

- Part 1 Solving Multi-Step Equations with Fractions
- Part 2 Solving Multi-Step Equations with Decimals

### Lesson 7-7 Transforming Formulas
**Pages 365–368**

**NCTM 1, 2, 3, 4, 6, 8, 9, 10**

- Part 1 Solving Formulas for a Given Variable
- Part 2 Using Formulas to Solve Problems
- **Checkpoint 2**

### Lesson 7-8 Simple and Compound Interest
**Pages 369–373**

**NCTM 1, 2, 6, 8, 9, 10**

- Part 1 Simple Interest
- Part 2 Compound Interest
- **Project Activity 3**

## Pacing Options

This chart suggests pacing for only the core lessons and their parts, and it is provided merely as a possible guide. It will help you determine how much time you have in your schedule to cover other features, such as the Chapter Project, Math Toolboxes, Standardized Test Prep, Wrap Up, and Assessment.

| | Day 1 | Day 2 | Day 3 | Day 4 | Day 5 | Day 6 | Day 7 | Day 8 | Day 9 | Day 10 | Day 11 |
|---|---|---|---|---|---|---|---|---|---|---|---|
| **Traditional** (40–45 min. class periods) | 7–1 (1), 7–1 (2) | 7–2 (1) | 7–2 (2) | 7–3 (1) | 7–3 (2) | 7–4 | 7–5 (1), 7–5 (2) | 7–6 (1), 7–6 (2) | 7–7 (1), 7–7 (2) | 7–8 (1) | 7–8 (2) |
| **Pre-Algebra Over 2 Years** (40–45 min. class periods) | 7–1 (1) | 7–1 (1) | 7–1 (2) | 7–2 (1) | 7–2 (1) | 7–2 (2) | 7–2 (2) | 7–3 (1) | 7–3 (1) | 7–3 (2) | 7–3 (2) |
| **Block Scheduling** (90 min. class periods) | 7–1 (1) (2), 7–2 (1) (2) | 7–3 (1) (2), 7–4 | 7–5 (1) (2), 7–6 (1) (2) | 7–7 (1) (2), 7–8 (1) (2) | | | | | | | |

| Pages 350–353 | **Lesson 7-4** **Problem Solving Strategy** |
|---|---|
| NCTM **1, 2, 6, 8, 9, 10** | Write an Equation<br>**Checkpoint 1** |

| Pages 355–359 | **Lesson 7-5** **Solving Equations with Variables on Both Sides** |
|---|---|
| NCTM **1, 2, 6, 8, 9, 10** | Part 1 Solving Equations with Variables on Both Sides<br>Part 2 Using Equations with Variables on Both Sides<br>**Math At Work** |

| Pages 360–363 | **Lesson 7-6** **Solving Two-Step Inequalities** |
|---|---|
| NCTM **1, 2, 6, 8, 9, 10** | Part 1 Solving Two-Step Inequalities<br>Part 2 Using Two-Step Inequalities<br>**Project Activity 2** |

**NCTM STANDARDS 2000**

1 Number and Operations
2 Algebra
3 Geometry
4 Measurement
5 Data Analysis and Probability
6 Problem Solving
7 Reasoning and Proof
8 Communication
9 Connections
10 Representation

| Day 12 | Day 13 | Day 14 | Day 15 | Day 16 | Day 17 | Day 18 | Day 19 | Day 20 | Day 21 | Day 22 | Day 23 | Day 24 |
|---|---|---|---|---|---|---|---|---|---|---|---|---|
| 7–4 | 7–4 | 7–5 1 | 7–5 1 | 7–5 2 | 7–6 1 | 7–6 1 | 7–6 2 | 7–7 1 | 7–7 1 | 7–7 2 | 7–8 1 | 7–8 2 |

**Block Scheduling Notes**

Consider these suggestions:

- **Day 3** Before starting Lesson 7-5, teach the Standardized Test Prep, p. 354.
- **Day 3** After completing Lesson 7-5, begin presentations for Finish the Project.
- **Day 4** Before starting Lesson 7-7, teach Math Toolbox 1, p. 364.
- **Day 4** After finishing Lesson 7-8, teach Math Toolbox 2, p. 374.

# Math Background

## Lesson 7-1

### Solving Two-Step Equations

You can use algebra tiles to provide a model for the process of solving two-step equations. A set of algebra tiles consists of three kinds of tiles. The smallest tile represents a unit; it measures 1 by 1. The green tile measures 1 unit by $x$. Notice that the length ($x$) of this tile is not exactly a certain number of units. This is because the length of the tile represents an unknown variable and not a multiple of the unit tile. For all the tiles, the red tile represents a negative quantity. You can use algebra tiles to make a concrete model of an equation such as $3x - 5 = 1$.

When you solve an equation such as this, whether modeling with tiles or using algebraic properties, you get the variable alone on one side of the equation by *reversing* the order of operations. To isolate the variable, you first add or subtract the same quantity from both sides.

$3x - 5 = 1$

$3x - 5 + 5 = 1 + 5$

$3x = 6$

In the second step, you use inverse operations to undo the multiplication.

$\frac{3x}{3} = \frac{6}{3}$, so $x = 2$.

To model with algebra tiles, divide both sides into 3 groups of tiles, modeling $x = 2$.

## Lessons 7-2 and 7-3

### Solving Multi-Step Equations

When solving a multi-step equation, combine like terms to simplify the expressions on each side of the equation before you begin to solve. You may also need to use the Distributive Property to simplify the equation.

When you perform the same operation (other than multiplying or dividing by zero) on both sides of an equation, the result is an *equivalent equation.* This means that the solution of the resulting equation is the same as the solution of the original equation.

When an equation has a fraction as the coefficient of the variable, for example, $\frac{2}{3}(x + 5) = 6$, you may choose to simplify by multiplying both sides of the equation by the reciprocal of the coefficient instead of using the Distributive Property first.

$\frac{2}{3}(x + 5) = 6$

$\frac{3}{2} \bullet \frac{2}{3}(x + 5) = 6 \bullet \frac{3}{2}$

$x + 5 = 9$

$x = 4$

When an equation has decimal coefficients, you can either calculate with the decimal numbers or multiply both sides by the multiple of ten that will enable you to rewrite all the decimals as integers, as shown here.

$0.4x = 0.6$

$10(0.4x) = 10(0.6)$

$4x = 6$

$x = 1.5$

## Lesson 7-4

### Write an Equation

This lesson begins with the very famous formula of Einstein's, $E = mc^2$. Albert Einstein, a German-born American citizen who died in 1955, discovered that the amount of energy, $E$, released when matter is changed into energy is a product of the mass, $m$, and the square of $c$, the constant velocity of light. This velocity of light is about 186,281 miles per second.

## Lessons 7-5 and 7-6

### Solving Equations and Inequalities

To collect terms when an equation has the variable on both sides, you apply the same procedures as before. For example, using the Distributive Property and the Commutative Property of Addition, $14 - 2(x - 1) = 3x + 4 - 2x$ becomes$14 - 2x + 2 = 3x - 2x + 4$.

Collecting terms and constants on each side gives $-2x + 16 = x + 4$. You can collect the terms with variables on either the right or left side of the equation. The variable on the right side ($x$) has a positive coefficient (1), and the variable on the left side has a negative coefficient ($-2$), so you might choose to collect the $x$ terms on the right and the constants on the left, as shown in the following:

$$-2x + 16 + 2x - 4 = x + 4 + 2x - 4$$
$$12 = 3x$$

Then divide both sides by 3 to get $x = 4$.

Solving inequalities involves the same steps as solving equations, but there are a few important differences between equations and inequalities.

First, a variable equation of the type in this chapter usually has a single solution; there is just one value for the variable that makes the equation true. For example, the solution for $4 + x = 2$ is $x = -2$. An inequality usually has more than one solution. For example, the solution for $x < -2$ is all the numbers on the number line to the left of $-2$.

Second, the rules for doing inverse operations to both sides of an inequality differ in one important way from the rules for equations. Multiplying or dividing an inequality by a negative number *reverses* the direction of the inequality symbol.

## Lessons 7-7 and 7-8

### Formulas

You may wish to change the form of a formula so the variable whose value you are seeking is isolated on the left side of the equation. For example, if you are solving $d = rt$ for $d$ (distance), you would use the formula in the given form. However, if you are solving for $r$ (rate) or $t$ (time), another version of the formula may be more useful. The proof that follows shows this transformation.

| | |
|---|---|
| $d = rt$ | Given |
| $\frac{d}{t} = \frac{rt}{t}$ | Division Property of Equality |
| $\frac{d}{t} = \frac{rt}{1t}$ | One is the multiplicative identity. |
| $\frac{d}{t} = \frac{r}{1} \bullet \frac{t}{t}$ | multiplication of fractions |
| $\frac{d}{t} = r \bullet 1$ | One is the identity for multiplication and division. |
| $\frac{d}{t} = r$ | |
| $r = \frac{d}{t}$ | If $a = b$ then $b = a$. (Symmetric Property of Equality) |

A similar transformation leads to $t = \frac{d}{r}$.

The formula for simple interest is $I = prt$, where $I$ is the interest on the principal, $p$, at the yearly rate, $r$, for a time period of $t$ years. Simple interest is computed only on the original deposit or principal.

Compound interest is interest that is computed on the original principal and also on any accumulated interest. If the rates and the principal invested are the same, an investment earning compound interest will grow faster than an investment earning simple interest.

The complete formula for compound interest follows.

$B = p(1 + \frac{r}{n})^{nt}$

where $B$ is the final balance accumulated,
$p$ is the principal amount invested,
$r$ is the rate per year written as a decimal,
$t$ is the time in years, and
$n$ the number of interest periods, which tells how many times per year the interest is compounded.

Note that if the interest is compounded yearly, then $n = 1$, and the formula simplifies to $B = p(1 + r)^t$.

For professional development tips visit our Web site **www.phschool.com**.

# Monitoring Progress

## Universal Access

### ▶ Preventing a Student from Falling Behind

These resources are particularly helpful in preventing a student from falling behind his or her appropriate math level. For a complete list of resources for this chapter, see page 333H.

#### Skills You Need for Chapter 7

Student Edition, p. 333
Teacher's Edition, p. 333

- Solving Equations
- Simplifying Expressions
- Writing Variable Expressions
- Solving Inequalities

#### Skills Handbook

Student Edition, pp. 723–741
Teacher's Edition, pp. 723–741

#### Reteaching Worksheets

There is a Reteaching worksheet for every lesson in this chapter.

- Chapter 7 Support File, Teaching Resources box
- See TE p. 333H for a complete list of resources

####  Skills Intervention Kit with CD-ROM

| For | Use |
|---|---|
| Lesson 7-1 | Pre-Algebra Basics |
| Lesson 7-8 | Ratio, Proportion, Percent |

#### Daily Cumulative Review Blackline Masters

There is a Daily Cumulative Review worksheet for every lesson in this chapter.

See TE p. 333H for a complete list of resources.

### ▶ Accommodating Diverse Learning Styles

#### Tactile Learning

Use algebra tiles to model a problem. (Lesson 7-1, 7-5)

#### Advanced Learner

Every lesson has at least one challenge problem.

Explain how an equation can be solved without using the Distributive Property. (Lesson 7-2)

#### ELL (English Language Learner)

Understand that *consecutive* means "one after the other." (Lesson 7-2)

Make a table to show the symbols and words for *at least, greater than,* and *less than.* (Lesson 7-6)

#### Auditory Learning

Explain to a partner which method they would use to solve an equation. (Lesson 7-3)

Say solutions aloud to remind them to use closed circles for "or equal to" inequalities. (Lesson 7-6)

#### Visual Learning

Draw sketches or diagrams to picture the situations in word problems. (Lesson 7-1)

Draw figures to help write equations to solve perimeter problems. (Lesson 7-4)

# Aligning Assessment with Instruction

## Assessment Options

| | Chapter Opener | 7-1 | 7-2 | 7-3 | 7-4 | 7-5 | 7-6 | 7-7 | 7-8 | End |
|---|---|---|---|---|---|---|---|---|---|---|
| Chapter Project | ■ | | | ■ | | | ■ | | | ■ |
| Try This Exercises | | ■ | ■ | ■ | ■ | ■ | ■ | ■ | ■ | |
| Mixed Reviews | | ■ | ■ | ■ | ■ | ■ | ■ | ■ | ■ | |
| Checkpoints | | | | | ■ | | | ■ | | |
| Writing | | ■ | ■ | ■ | | ■ | ■ | ■ | ■ | ■ |
| Chapter Assessment | | | | | | | | | | ■ |
| Cumulative Review | | | | | | | | | | ■ |
| Standardized Test Prep | | ■ | | ■ | | | ■ | | ■ | |
| | Standardized Test Prep, p. 354 | | | | | | | | | |
| Computer Item Generator | Can be used to create custom-made practice pages or assessment pages at any time. | | | | | | | | | |

### Test-Taking Tips on Transparencies

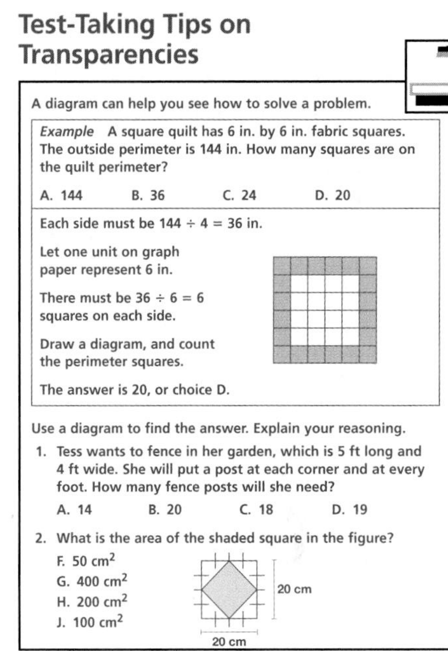
A diagram can help you see how to solve a problem.

*Example* A square quilt has 6 in. by 6 in. fabric squares. The outside perimeter is 144 in. How many squares are on the quilt perimeter?

A. 144 B. 36 C. 24 D. 20

Each side must be 144 ÷ 4 = 36 in.

Let one unit on graph paper represent 6 in.

There must be 36 ÷ 6 = 6 squares on each side.

Draw a diagram, and count the perimeter squares.

The answer is 20, or choice D.

Use a diagram to find the answer. Explain your reasoning.

1. Tess wants to fence in her garden, which is 5 ft long and 4 ft wide. She will put a post at each corner and at every foot. How many fence posts will she need?
   A. 14 B. 20 C. 18 D. 19
2. What is the area of the shaded square in the figure?
   F. 50 $cm^2$
   G. 400 $cm^2$
   H. 200 $cm^2$
   J. 100 $cm^2$



*Use with Standardized Test Prep and Chapter Assessments.*

## Correlation to Standardized Tests

**LOCAL OBJECTIVES**

| Lesson | | CAT5 | CTBS/5 TerraNova™ | ITBS | MAT7 | SAT9 | Local Objectives |
|---|---|---|---|---|---|---|---|
| 7-1 | Solving Two-Step Equations | | | ■ | ■ | ■ | |
| 7-2 | Solving Multi-Step Equations | | | | | ■ | |
| 7-3 | Multi-Step Equations with Fractions and Decimals | | | | | ■ | |
| 7-4 | Problem Solving Strategy: Write an Equation | ■ | | | ■ | ■ | |
| 7-5 | Solving Equations with Variables on Both Sides | | | | ■ | ■ | |
| 7-6 | Solving Two-Step Inequalities | | | | | ■ | |
| 7-7 | Transforming Formulas | | | | | ■ | |
| 7-8 | Simple and Compound Interest | ■ | | | | ■ | |

**CAT5** California Achievement Test, 5th Edition
**CTBS TerraNova** Comprehensive Test of Basic Skills, 5th Edition
**ITBS** Iowa Test of Basic Skills, Form M
**MAT7** Metropolitan Achievement Test, 7th Edition
**SAT** Stanford Achievement Test, Advanced 1

For other standardized test correlations, follow the link to your state at **www.phschool.com**.

# Resources for Chapter 7

| | TEACHING RESOURCES BOX | | | | | | | | | | | | | | |
|---|---|---|---|---|---|---|---|---|---|---|---|---|---|---|---|
| | CHAPTER 7 SUPPORT FILE | | | | | | | | | | | | | | |
| | Practice | Reteach | Enrichment | Project Manager | Checkpoints | Cumulative Review | Chapter Assessment | Alternative Assessment | Cumulative Assessment | Lesson Planners Plus | Daily Cum Review | Teaching Transparencies | Warm-Up Transparencies | Help at Home | SE Answers Transparencies |
| Begin Chapter | | | | ■ | | | | | | ■ | | | | | |
| 7-1 | ■ | ■ | ■ | | | | | | | ■ | ■ | 16, 60 | ■ | | ■ |
| 7-2 | ■ | ■ | ■ | | | | | | | ■ | ■ | | ■ | | ■ |
| 7-3 | ■ | ■ | ■ | | | | | | | ■ | ■ | | ■ | | ■ |
| 7-4 | ■ | ■ | ■ | | ■ | | | | | ■ | ■ | 61 | ■ | ■ | ■ |
| 7-5 | ■ | ■ | ■ | | | | | | | ■ | ■ | | ■ | | ■ |
| 7-6 | ■ | ■ | ■ | | | | | | | ■ | ■ | | ■ | | ■ |
| 7-7 | ■ | ■ | ■ | | ■ | | | | | ■ | ■ | 3 | ■ | ■ | ■ |
| 7-8 | ■ | ■ | ■ | | | | | | | ■ | ■ | 62 | ■ | | ■ |
| End Chapter | | | | | | ■ | ■ (2 forms) | ■ | After Ch. 3, 6, 9, 13 | | | | | | |

Also available for use with the chapter:

Solution Key
Computational Practice Skills Booklet
Mathematics Standardized Test Prep, Student Edition and Teacher's Edition
Overhead Manipulatives Kit
Practice Workbook
Algebra Readiness Kit
Student Manipulatives Kit
Test-Taking Tips on Transparencies
Assessment Success Kit
Teaching Aids and Letters
Graphing Calculator Handbook
Spanish Resources
Success-Building Puzzle and Problem Masters

## TECHNOLOGY

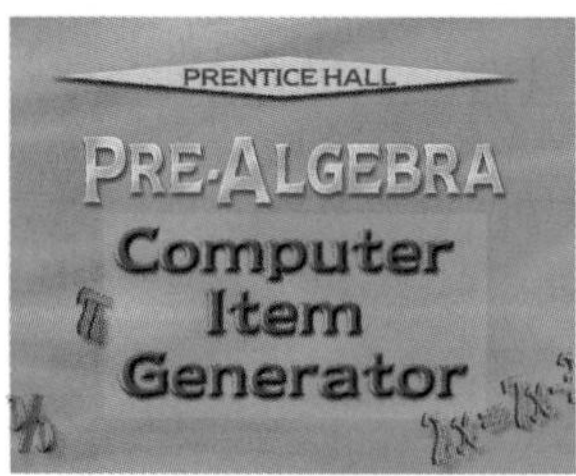


**Computer Item Generator with Standardized Test Prep**

CD-ROM with an unlimited supply of questions with varying degrees of difficulty for customized practice sheets, quizzes, and tests.

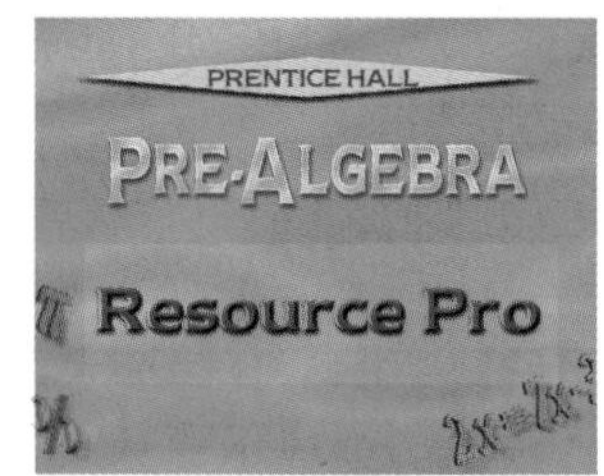


**Resource Pro® with Planning Express®**

CD-ROM with complete classroom planning tool and teaching resources for customizing and planning lessons.

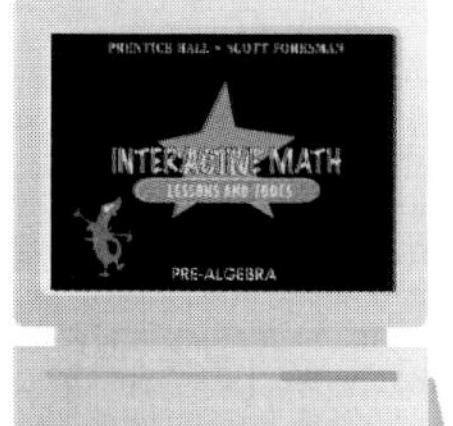


**Interactive Math Lessons and Tools**

CD-ROM with lessons and tools to make abstract concepts visual and accessible.

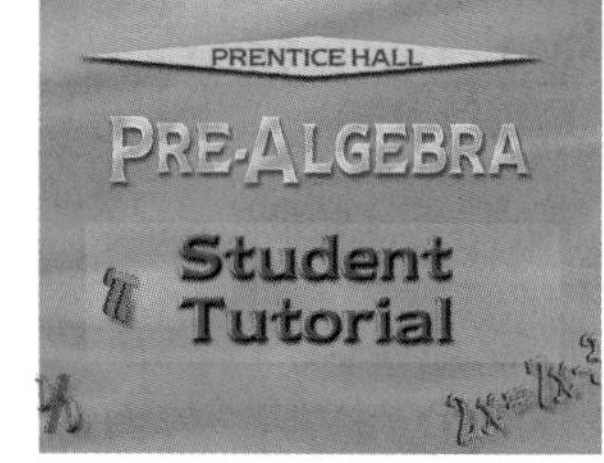


**Student Tutorial**

Test preparation software for students on CD-ROM with management system for teachers; includes Secondary Math Lab Toolkit™.

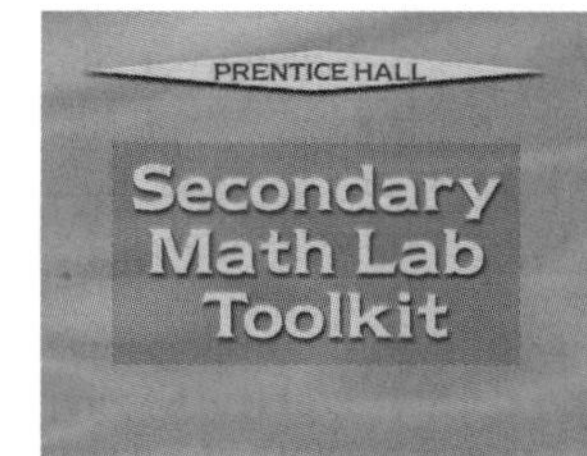


**Secondary Math Lab Toolkit™ with Integrated Math Labs**

Integrated software package with linkable math tools for exploring key concepts.

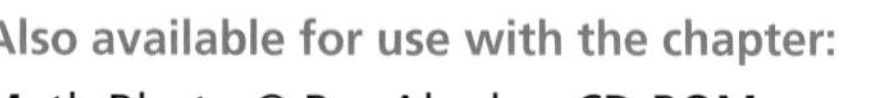

Also available for use with the chapter:

Math Blaster® Pre-Algebra CD-ROM
Video Fieldtrips, Vol. I: Algebra Applications
Video Fieldtrips, Vol. II: Geometry Applications
Wide World of Mathematics CD-ROM
Wide World of Mathematics Video

### *Web Extension*

**www.phschool.com**

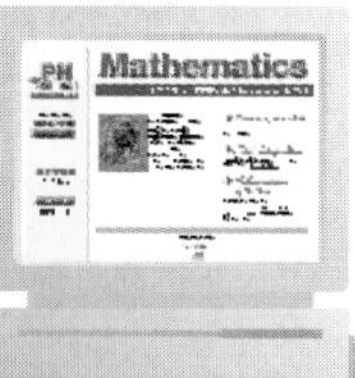


**For Students**
- Chapter Support with Internet Links
- Internet Activities

**For Teachers**
- Curriculum Support
- Professional Development
- Product Information
- Regional Support Information

# Skills You Need for Chapter 7

### ▶ *Solving equations* — Use before Lesson 7-1.

**Solve each equation.**

1. $a - 3 = 8$ 11
2. $-9 = 12 + x$ −21
3. $\frac{m}{7} = -14$ −98
4. $-10 = -2b$ 5
5. $y \div 2 = 4$ 8
6. $6.8 = c - 2.2$ 9.0
7. $\frac{x}{-4} = 8$ −32
8. $-40 = 5a$ −8
9. $x + 16 = 4$ −12

### ▶ *Simplifying expressions* — Use before Lessons 7-2, 7-3, 7-4, and 7-5.

**Simplify each expression.**

10. $3n + n$ $4n$
11. $5b + 10 - 8b$ $-3b + 10$
12. $6x + x - 4x + 5x$ $8x$
13. $12c + 9 + 7c + 4$ $19c + 13$
14. $3x + 2y - 7y - 10x$ $-7x - 5y$
15. $2(a + 3)$ $2a + 6$
16. $9(6 - 4b)$ $-36b + 54$
17. $5(m - 7) + 4m$ $9m - 35$
18. $-5y + 2(x + y)$ $2x - 3y$

### ▶ *Writing variable expressions* — Use before Lesson 7-3.

**Write a variable expression for each situation.**

19. three more than $p$ points $p + 3$
20. six fewer than $q$ questions $q - 6$
21. the number of months in $y$ years $12y$
22. the value in cents of $d$ dimes $10d$
23. twice as many as $b$ baskets $2b$
24. eight fewer than $n$ nickels $n - 8$

### ▶ *Solving inequalities* — Use before Lesson 7-5.

**Solve and graph each inequality.** For graphs, see back of book.

25. $c + 6 \ge 7$ $c \ge 1$
26. $y - 8 < -6$ $y < 2$
27. $\frac{a}{2} < 5$ $a < 10$
28. $5b < 20$ $b < 4$
29. $-3x < 0$ $x > 0$
30. $12 \le x + 18$ $x \ge -6$
31. $-m > 17$ $m < -17$
32. $-\frac{x}{3} \ge -5$ $x \le 15$
33. $b - 15 \le 4$ $b \le 19$
34. $24 > -8a$ $a > -3$
35. $\frac{m}{4} \ge 20$ $m \ge 80$
36. $16y \ge -16$ $y \ge -1$



# Skills You Need

## Solving equations

**In Lesson 7-1** students will use mathematical properties to solve two-step equations.

## Simplifying expressions

**In Lesson 7-2** students will simplify expressions to solve multi-step equations.

**In Lesson 7-3** students will solve multi-step equations with fractions and decimals by simplifying expressions.

**In Lesson 7-4** students will write equations and then solve them by simplifying expressions.

**In Lesson 7-5** students will solve equations with variables on both sides by simplifying expressions.

## Writing variable expressions

**In Lesson 7-3** students will write variable expressions and solve multi-step equations with fractions and decimals.

## Solving inequalities

**In Lesson 7-6** students will solve two-step inequalities.

# Skills Trace

| SKILL | INTRODUCED | DEVELOPED IN LESSON(S) | REVIEWED/REINFORCED |
|---|---|---|---|
| Solving multi-step equations | 7-1 | 7-2, 7-3 | pp. 390, 419, 458, 513 |
| Writing equations | 7-4 | 7-5 | pp. 359, 368, 581 |
| Solving equations with variables on both sides | 7-5 | 7-5 | pp. 458, 550 |
| Solving two-step inequalities | 7-6 | 7-6 | pp. 368, 402, 425 |
| Transforming formulas | 7-7 | 7-7 | pp. 373, 414, 478 |
| Finding simple and compound interest | 7-8 | Math Toolbox, p. 374 | pp. 390, 478 |

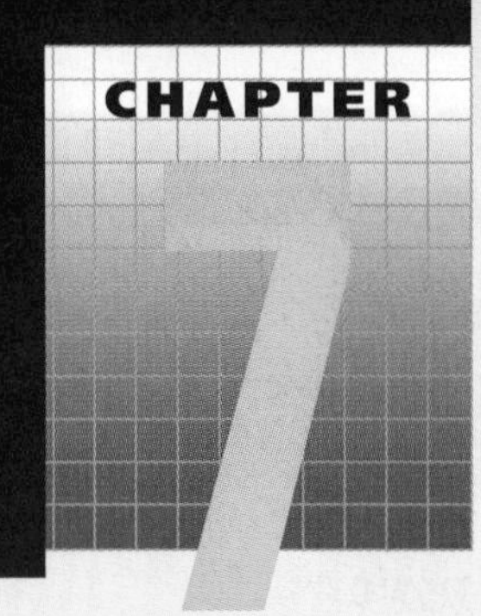

# Solving Equations and Inequalities

## Connecting to Students' Lives

Ask students to describe any experiences they have with cooking in which they used water, vinegar, vegetable oil, or corn syrup.

## Interdisciplinary Connections

The Chapter Project connects math, chemistry, and physics. You may want to display pictures or information about recipes and foods that contain the four liquids involved.

## About the Project

The Chapter Project directs students to apply their knowledge of measurement and solving equations to calculating the density of four liquids.

CHAPTER 7

# Solving Equations and Inequalities

**What you'll learn in this chapter:**

- How to write and solve multi-step equations
- How to write and solve two-step inequalities
- How to find simple interest and compound interest

334 Chapter 7

*Web Extension*
**www.phschool.com**

For Students
Chapter Support with Internet links
Interactive Activities

For Teachers
Curriculum Support
Professional Development
Product Information
Regional Support Information

Have you ever wondered why some objects sink while others float? People float in the salt water of the Dead Sea. Pebbles sink when tossed into a river. The densities of a liquid and an object influence whether the object sinks or floats in the liquid. Similarly, the densities of two liquids influence whether they combine or separate.

***Find the Densities of Liquids*** For the chapter project, you will measure the masses and volumes of several liquids. You will use your measurements and an equation to calculate the density of each liquid.

### *Steps to help you complete the project*


**p. 344** ACTIVITY: MEASURING

**p. 363** ACTIVITY: CALCULATING

**p. 373** ACTIVITY: CALCULATING

**p. 375** FINISHING THE CHAPTER PROJECT

***Web Extension***
**www.phschool.com**

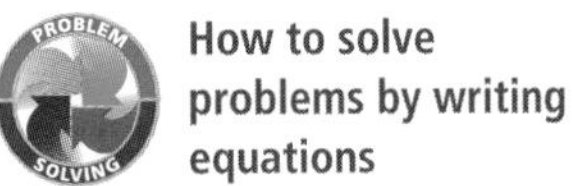


How to solve problems by writing equations

*The Chapter Project is optional and may be assigned at your discretion.*

Ask students:

- Have you used a measuring cup to measure amounts of water, vinegar, vegetable oil, or corn syrup?
- Which of these four liquids is easiest to pour? Which is most difficult to pour?
- What liquids might be even more difficult to pour than vegetable oil or corn syrup?

Distribute a copy of the Project Manager and Scoring Rubric to help students get an overview of the project.

Review the scoring rubric with students.

### Project Notebook

Encourage students to keep all project-related materials in a separate folder or notebook. Call attention to the fact that they will find much useful information on the Web site **www.phschool.com**.

**Tracking the Project** Set benchmark deadlines for students to show you their work in progress.

*Available in the Chapter 7 Support File in the Teaching Resources box.*

### Project Manager and Scoring Rubric

**Getting Started** You will be writing a report on the densities of several liquids. Read about the project in your textbook. As you work on the project, you will need a container marked in milliliters, a scale that measures mass, at least 250 mL of each liquid including water, vinegar, vegetable oil, and corn syrup, materials to make your report and materials to record your measurements.

**Checklist and Suggestions**

| | | |
|---|---|---|
| ❑ | Measure the mass of your container and of the container and water together. | Measure carefully. |
| ❑ | Write and solve an equation for the density of the water. | The volume of the water is 250 mL. |
| ❑ | Measure the mass of the other liquids and calculate the density of each. | Write and solve an equation for each liquid. |
| ❑ | Compare the density of each liquid to water. | Decide which liquids are more dense than water and which are less dense. |
| ❑ | Write your report. | Summarize your activities and present your results clearly. |
| ❑ | Share your report with a friend. | Make any necessary changes. |

**Scoring Rubric**

**3** You accurately measure the mass of each liquid and calculate each density correctly. You explain your procedures thoroughly and clearly. You report is complete, accurate, and easy to read.

**2** You make minor errors in your measurements or calculations. Your report is thorough and accurate, but it could be clearer or easier to read.

**1** You measure the masses, and calculate the densities incorrectly. Your report is incomplete and unclear.

**0** Major elements of the project are incomplete or missing.

**Your Evaluation of the Project** Evaluate your work, based on the Scoring Rubric.

**Teacher's Evaluation of the Project**



## Scoring Rubric

**3** You accurately measure the mass of each liquid and calculate each density correctly. You explain your procedures thoroughly and clearly. Your report is complete, accurate, and easy to read.

**2** You make minor errors in your measurements or calculations. Your report is thorough and accurate, but it could be clearer or easier to read.

**1** You measure the masses and calculate the densities incorrectly. Your report is incomplete and unclear.

**0** Major elements of the project are incomplete or missing.

# 7-1

## Getting Ready

**Materials** algebra tiles

**Resources** A complete list of resources for this lesson is on p. 333H.

### Daily Skills Warm-Up

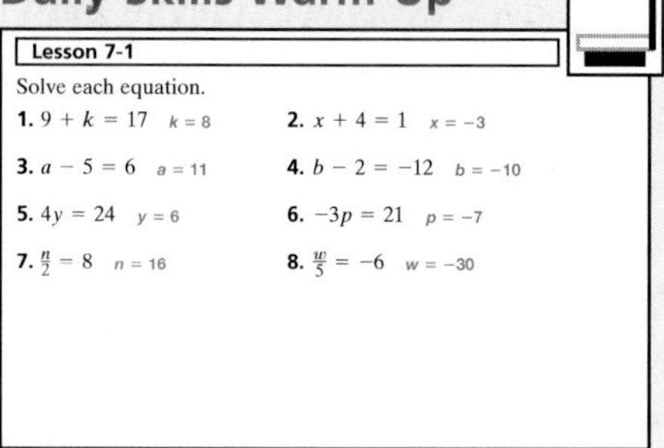
Lesson 7-1

Solve each equation.

1. $9 + k = 17$ $k = 8$
2. $x + 4 = 1$ $x = -3$
3. $a - 5 = 6$ $a = 11$
4. $b - 2 = -12$ $b = -10$
5. $4y = 24$ $y = 6$
6. $-3p = 21$ $p = -7$
7. $\frac{n}{2} = 8$ $n = 16$
8. $\frac{w}{5} = -6$ $w = -30$

### Background for the Lesson

To solve a single-step equation, you perform one operation on each side of the equation in order to isolate the variable. To solve two-step equations, you perform one operation to isolate the term with the variable, and then you perform a second operation to isolate the variable itself. So, in the equation $4x + 13 = 25$, you first subtract 13 from both sides to isolate $4x$. Then divide both sides by 4 to isolate $x$. In solving two-step equations, you are undoing the order of operations, so you first undo addition and subtraction, and then you undo multiplication and division.

## 1 Focus

### Connecting to Students' Lives

Discuss with students any processes, such as baking cookies or building a fence, done with several steps in sequence.

### Connecting to Prior Knowledge

Students learned how to solve single-step equations by adding and subtracting in Lesson 2-5 and how to solve single-step equations by multiplying and dividing in Lesson 2-6. In this lesson, students learn to add and subtract and then multiply and divide to solve two-step equations. In Lesson 7-2, students will apply these skills to solving multi-step equations.

# 7-1 Solving Two-Step Equations

**What You'll Learn**

1. To solve two-step equations
2. To use two-step equations to solve problems

**. . . And Why**

To solve problems involving savings

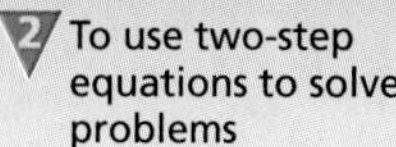

### Part 1 Using Properties to Solve Two-Step Equations

Algebra tiles can help you understand the algebra behind solving the equation $2x + 1 = 5$.

$2x + 1 = 5$

Model the equation.

$2x + 1 - 1 = 5 - 1$
$2x = 4$

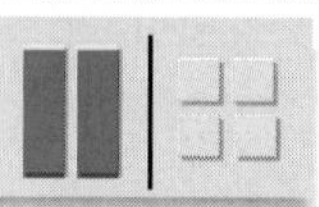

Remove 1 tile from each side.

$\frac{2x}{2} = \frac{4}{2}$

Divide each side into two equal groups.

$x = 2$

Simplify.

To solve a two-step equation, first undo addition or subtraction. Then undo multiplication or division.

#### Example 1

**Solve $3n - 6 = 15$.**

$3n - 6 = 15$
$3n - 6 + 6 = 15 + 6$ Add 6 to each side.
$3n = 21$ Simplify.
$\frac{3n}{3} = \frac{21}{3}$ Divide each side by 3.
$n = 7$ Simplify.

**Check** $3n - 6 = 15$
$3(7) - 6 \stackrel{?}{=} 15$ Replace $n$ with 7.
$21 - 6 \stackrel{?}{=} 15$ Multiply.
$15 = 15$ ✔ Subtract.



## Tools to Monitor Progress

**BEFORE THE LESSON**

**To check prerequisite skills:**

- Solving equations

**Skills You Need,** p. 333

**Skills Intervention Kit,** Pre-Algebra Basics

**DURING THE LESSON**

**To check understanding:**

**Try This** exercises on student page

- **Additional Example 1**
  Solve $5v - 12 = 8$. $v = 4$
- **Additional Example 2**
  Solve $7 - 3b = 1$. $b = 2$

**TRY THIS** Solve each equation. Explain each step.

1. $15x + 3 = 48$ 3; subtract 3, divide by 15.
2. $\frac{t}{4} - 10 = -6$ 16; add 10, multiply by 4.
3. $9g + 11 = 2$ −1; subtract 11, divide by 9.

**EXAMPLE 2**

**Solve $5 - x = 17$.**

| | |
|---|---|
| $5 - x = 17$ | |
| $-5 + 5 - x = -5 + 17$ | Add −5 to each side. |
| $0 - x = 12$ | Simplify. |
| $-x = 12$ | $0 - x = -x$ |
| $-1(-x) = -1(12)$ | Multiply each side by −1. |
| $x = -12$ | Simplify. |

**TRY THIS** Solve each equation.

4. $-a + 6 = 8$ −2
5. $-9 - \frac{y}{7} = -12$ 21
6. $13 - 6f = 31$ −3

## PART 2 Solving Problems with Two-Step Equations

You can use two-step equations to model real-world situations.

REAL-WORLD  CONNECTION

**EXAMPLE 3**

**Lynne saves \$45 each week. She now has \$180. She plans to save for a trip to Puerto Rico. To find how many weeks *w* she will take to save \$900, solve $180 + 45w = 900$.**

| | |
|---|---|
| $180 + 45w = 900$ | |
| $180 + 45w - 180 = 900 - 180$ | Subtract 180 from each side. |
| $45w = 720$ | Simplify. |
| $\frac{45w}{45} = \frac{720}{45}$ | Divide each side by 45. |
| $w = 16$ | Simplify. |

Lynne will take 16 weeks to save \$900.

If you flew to San Juan, Puerto Rico, in December 1999, it could have cost you \$186 to leave from New York City, \$590 to leave from San Francisco, \$914 to leave from Reno, Nevada, or \$1,392 to leave from Dallas, Texas.

**TRY THIS**

7. Jacob bought four begonias in 6-in. pots and a \$19 fern at a fund-raiser. He spent a total of \$83. Solve the equation $4p + 19 = 83$ to find the price *p* of each begonia. \$16



# 2 Teach

## PART 1 Part 1 Teaching Notes

Remind students that solving an equation means isolating the variable on one side of the equation. First you isolate the term that contains the variable and then you isolate the variable itself.

### Example 1

**Build understanding.** Explain why you could replace dividing each side by 3 with multiplying each side by $\frac{1}{3}$. **Dividing by 3 is the same as multiplying by the reciprocal of 3; $\frac{1}{3}$ is the reciprocal of 3.**

**Error Prevention** In solving a two-step equation, students may try to multiply or divide before they add or subtract, making the calculations more complicated. Encourage students to isolate the variable term by undoing the addition or subtraction first.

### Example 2

**Build understanding.** Explain how you could solve this another way by adding *x* to each side. **You then subtract 17 from each side.**

## PART 2 Part 2 Teaching Notes

### Example 3

**Build understanding.** Explain why the equation is $180 + 45w = 900$ instead of $45w = 900$. **Lynne already has \$180; she wants to know how many *more* weeks it will take her to save \$900.**

**Extension** Explain how it would be possible, but more complicated, to solve $3x + 4 = 10$ by dividing first, then subtracting. **By dividing first, you get $\frac{(3x + 4)}{3} = \frac{10}{3}$, which simplifies to $x + \frac{4}{3} = \frac{10}{3}$, or $x = 2$.**

• **Additional Example 3**

You borrow \$350 to buy a bicycle. You agree to pay \$100 the first week, then \$25 each week until the balance is paid off. After the first payment, how long will it take you to repay the loan? 10 wk

**AFTER THE LESSON**

**To assess knowledge: Lesson Quiz**

Solve each equation.

1. $12x - 14 = 10$ $x = 2$
2. $\frac{r}{3} + 7 = -4$ $r = -33$
3. $9 - w = 13$ $w = -4$
4. $-22 - \frac{q}{5} = -15$ $q = -35$
5. $4d - 57 = 7$ $d = 16$

• For enrichment and reteaching options see Resources on p. 333H.

# 3 Practice/Assess

## Assignment Guide

To provide flexible scheduling, this lesson can be divided into parts.

**Part 1**
**Core** 1–9, 11–29, 32
**Extension** 36, 38

**Part 2**
**Core** 10, 30–31, 33–34, 37
**Extension** 35

Mixed Review can be assigned at any time for maintenance.

## Exercises

**Visual Learning Exercises 30–35** Suggest that students draw sketches or diagrams to picture the situations in these word problems. These representations often help students make a connection between the words and the equations.

**Test Prep Exercise 32** Round the numbers in the equation to estimate.

## Challenge

Solve $5z + 7 = 0$. $-1\frac{2}{5}$

## Closure

To solve two-step equations, undo addition and subtraction first and then undo multiplication and addition.

# Exercises

## Check Understanding

**State the first step in solving each equation.**

1. $2b + 9 = 3$ Subtract 9 from each side.
2. $\frac{a}{3} - 4 = 9$ Add 4 to each side.
3. $-6t + (-3) = 14$ Subtract −3 from each side.

**Solve each equation.**

4. $\frac{h}{6} + 9 = 21$ 72
5. $4b - 6 = -18$ −3
6. $5 = -\frac{x}{3} + 10$ 15
7. $-8c + 1 = -3$ $\frac{1}{2}$
8. $2d - 8 = -10$ −1
9. $12 - 11a = 45$ −3

10. Thomas, Ardell, and Nichole baked muffins, which they shared equally. Nichole ate a muffin on the way home. She then had 14 muffins left. Solve the equation $\frac{m}{3} - 1 = 14$ to find the number of muffins $m$ that Thomas, Ardell, and Nichole baked. 45 muffins

## Practice and Problem Solving

**Solve and check each equation.**

11. $9x - 15 = 39$ 6
12. $10 = 3 + \frac{b}{2}$ 14
13. $-35 = 4h + 1$ −9
14. $\frac{x}{3} + 2 = 0$ −6
15. $18 = -a + 2$ −16
16. $4 - \frac{m}{5} = 18$ −70
17. $-75 - k = -95$ 20
18. $4 - \frac{z}{3} = -17$ 63
19. $3n - 5 = -23$ −6
20. $\frac{b}{2} - 8 = -10$ −4
21. $15 = -11b + 4$ −1
22. $9 - 3p = -27$ 12
23. $21 = 6 - \frac{t}{5}$ −75
24. $12y - 6 = 138$ 12
25. $-\frac{d}{7} + 14 = 0$ 98

*Mental Math* **Solve each equation.**

26. $2x + 3 = 15$ 6
27. $\frac{n}{6} + 2 = -8$ −60
28. $4a - 1 = 27$ 7
29. $\frac{n}{6} + 3 = 6$ 18

30. You bought a CD for \$16.95 and eight blank video tapes. The total cost was \$52.55 before the sales tax was added. Solve the equation $8t + 16.95 = 52.55$ to find the cost of each blank video tape. \$4.45

31. You had \$235 in your savings account nine weeks ago. You withdrew the same amount each week for eight weeks. Your balance was then \$75. Solve the equation $235 - 8m = 75$ to find how much money $m$ you withdrew each week. \$20



## Alternative Assessment

Ask students to model the two-step equation, $3x - 2 = 4$, with algebra tiles. Have students use the tiles to solve the equation. Ask them to draw tiles to show the steps they use.

## Daily Cumulative Review

**Make a table to solve each problem.** *(Lesson 6-10)*

1. John can read 15 pages in 10 minutes. He has 1 hour and 10 minutes before football practice. How many pages can he read before practice?

| Minutes | 10 min | 20 min | 30 min | 40 min | 50 min | 60 min | 70 min |
|---|---|---|---|---|---|---|---|
| Pages | 15 | 30 | 45 | 60 | 75 | 90 | 105 |

105 pages

2. In how many ways can you make \$.80 in change without using pennies or half-dollars?

| Quarters | 3 | 2 | 2 | 2 | 2 | 1 | 1 | 1 | 1 | 1 | 1 | 0 | 0 | 0 | 0 | 0 | 0 | 0 | 0 | 0 |
|---|---|---|---|---|---|---|---|---|---|---|---|---|---|---|---|---|---|---|---|---|
| Dimes | 0 | 3 | 2 | 1 | 0 | 5 | 4 | 3 | 2 | 1 | 0 | 8 | 7 | 6 | 5 | 4 | 3 | 2 | 1 | 0 |
| Nickels | 1 | 0 | 2 | 4 | 6 | 1 | 3 | 5 | 7 | 9 | 11 | 0 | 2 | 4 | 6 | 8 | 10 | 12 | 14 | 16 |

20 different ways

**Find each sale price. Round to the nearest cent where necessary.** *(Lesson 6-9)*

3. regular price: \$17.80
percent of discount: 30%
\$12.46

4. regular price: \$280
percent of discount: 40%
\$168

5. regular price: \$15.99
percent of discount: 25%
\$11.99

6. regular price: \$27.35
percent of discount: 15%
\$23.25

7. regular price: \$45.50
percent of discount: 75%
\$11.38

8. regular price: \$2.85
percent of discount: 35%
\$1.85

**Mixed Review**

**Multiply each expression.**

9. (2-2) $6(c + 4)$ $6c + 24$
10. (2-2) $(6 - r)(-8)$ $8r - 48$
11. (2-2) $-2(-k + 5)$ $2k - 10$

**Simplify each expression.**

12. (2-3) $8 + 2y - 6y$ $-4y + 8$
13. (2-3) $a + 6 - 4a + a$ $-2a + 6$
14. (2-3) $2(x + 3) + 5x$ $7x + 6$

32. **TEST PREP** A reasonable estimate of the solution to the equation $28x + 52 = 183$ would be ■. A

A. 6 B. 10 C. 25 D. 100

33. *Construction* A building contractor buys 525 metal bars. Because he is buying more than 500 bars, the wholesaler gives him a discount of \$420. The total price is \$3,780. Solve the equation $525b - 420 = 3{,}780$ to find the cost of each metal bar. \$8

34. Carmela wants to buy a digital camera for \$249. She has \$24 and is saving \$15 each week. Solve the equation $15w + 24 = 249$ to find how many weeks $w$ she will take to save enough to buy the digital camera. 15 weeks

35. *Nutrition* A soccer player wants to eat 700 calories at a meal that includes a Reuben sandwich and pickles. The sandwich has 464 calories, and the pickles have 7 calories each.
   a. Solve the equation $464 + 7f = 700$ to find the number of pickles the soccer player can eat. 34 pickles
   b. Suppose the soccer player drinks a 200-calorie sports drink with the meal. Solve the equation $664 + 7f = 700$ to find the number of pickles the soccer player can eat now. 5 pickles

36. *Error Analysis* A student solved the equation $\frac{x}{4} + 5 = 1$ without showing all the work. The student's solution is incorrect. What error did the student make? See above right.

$$\frac{x}{4} + 5 = 1$$
$$\frac{x}{4} = -4$$
$$x = -1$$

36. The student divided by 4 instead of multiplying by 4.

37. *Open-ended* Write a word problem for which you could use the equation $3g + 4 = 16$. Check students' work.

**Journal**

Explain how to solve the equation $2x - 5 = 19$.

38. *Writing* Explain how the process of solving $\frac{x}{4} - 2 = 8$ is different from the process of solving $\frac{x}{4} = 8$.
The first problem requires an initial step of adding 2 to each side.

## Mixed Review

**Find each percent of markup.** *(Lesson 6-9)*

39. wholesale price: \$12.00 selling price: \$18.00 50%
40. wholesale price: \$34 selling price: \$42.50 25%
41. wholesale price: \$45.95 selling price: \$82.71 80%

**Simplify each expression.** *(Lesson 2-3)*

42. $3x + 8 - 5x$ $-2x + 8$
43. $a + 3b + 9a$ $10a + 3b$
44. $2(c + 4) - 5c$ $-3c + 8$

45. *Probability* A student is chosen at random from a class of 20 boys and 15 girls. Find the odds that a girl is chosen. *(Lesson 6-4)* 3 to 4

See also Extra Practice section.



## Practice

**Solve each equation.**

1. $4x - 17 = 31$ $x = 12$
2. $15 = 2m + 3$ $m = 6$
3. $\frac{k}{3} + 3 = 8$ $k = 15$
4. $7 = 3 + \frac{h}{6}$ $h = 24$
5. $9n + 18 = 81$ $n = 7$
6. $5 = \frac{y}{3} - 9$ $y = 42$
7. $14 = 5k - 31$ $k = 9$
8. $\frac{t}{9} - 7 = -5$ $t = 18$
9. $\frac{v}{8} - 9 = -13$ $v = -32$
10. $25 - 13f = -14$ $f = 3$

**Solve each equation using mental math.**

11. $3p + 5 = 14$ $p = 3$
12. $\frac{k}{2} - 5 = 1$ $k = 12$
13. $\frac{m}{7} - 3 = 0$ $m = 21$
14. $10v - 6 = 24$ $v = 3$
15. $8 + \frac{x}{2} = -7$ $x = -30$
16. $7 = 6r - 17$ $r = 4$

**Choose the correct equation. Solve.**

17. Tehira has read 110 pages of a 290-page book. She reads 20 pages each day. How many days will it take to finish?
   A. $20 + 110p = 290$
   B. $20p + 290 = 110$
   (C.) $110 + 20p = 290$
   D. $290 = 110 - 20p$

   $p = 9$; It will take her 9 days.

**Write an equation to describe the situation. Solve.**

18. A waitress earned \$73 for 6 hours of work. The total included \$46 in tips. What was her hourly wage?

   $6w + 46 = 73$

   $w = 4.5$; She earned \$4.50 an hour.

19. You used $6\frac{3}{4}$ c of sugar while baking muffins and nutbread for a class party. You used a total of $1\frac{1}{2}$ c of sugar for the muffins. Your nutbread recipe calls for $1\frac{3}{4}$ c of sugar per loaf. How many loaves of nutbread did you make?

   $b \cdot 1\frac{3}{4} + 1\frac{1}{2} = 6\frac{3}{4}$

   $b = 3$; You made 3 batches of nutbread.



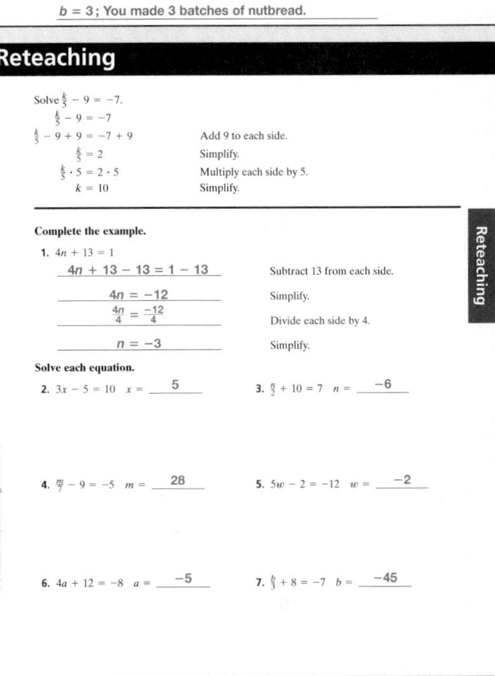

## Reteaching

Solve $\frac{k}{5} - 9 = -7$.

| | |
|---|---|
| $\frac{k}{5} - 9 = -7$ | |
| $\frac{k}{5} - 9 + 9 = -7 + 9$ | Add 9 to each side. |
| $\frac{k}{5} = 2$ | Simplify. |
| $\frac{k}{5} \cdot 5 = 2 \cdot 5$ | Multiply each side by 5. |
| $k = 10$ | Simplify. |

**Complete the example.**

1. $4n + 13 = 1$

| | |
|---|---|
| $4n + 13 - 13 = 1 - 13$ | Subtract 13 from each side. |
| $4n = -12$ | Simplify. |
| $\frac{4n}{4} = \frac{-12}{4}$ | Divide each side by 4. |
| $n = -3$ | Simplify. |

**Solve each equation.**

2. $3x - 5 = 10$ $x =$ 5
3. $\frac{n}{2} + 10 = 7$ $n =$ −6
4. $\frac{m}{7} - 9 = -5$ $m =$ 28
5. $5w - 2 = -12$ $w =$ −2
6. $4a + 12 = -8$ $a =$ −5
7. $\frac{b}{3} + 8 = -7$ $b =$ −45



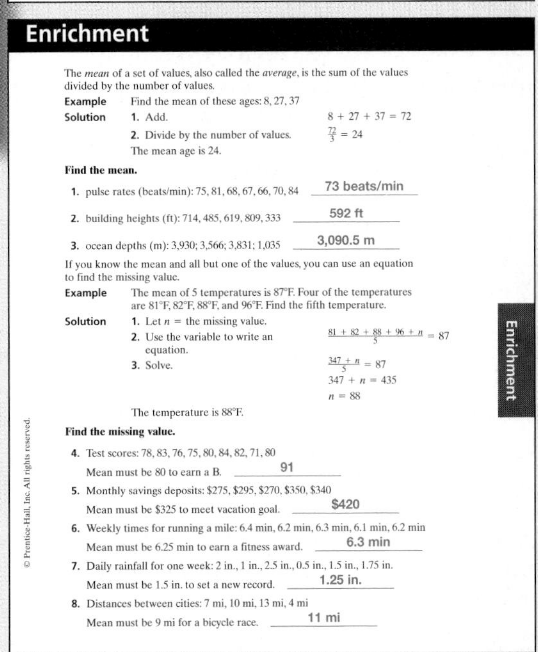

## Enrichment

The *mean* of a set of values, also called the *average*, is the sum of the values divided by the number of values.

**Example** Find the mean of these ages: 8, 27, 37

**Solution**
1. Add. $8 + 27 + 37 = 72$
2. Divide by the number of values. $\frac{72}{3} = 24$

The mean age is 24.

**Find the mean.**

1. pulse rates (beats/min): 75, 81, 68, 67, 66, 70, 84 73 beats/min
2. building heights (ft): 714, 485, 619, 809, 333 592 ft
3. ocean depths (m): 3,930; 3,566; 3,831; 1,035 3,090.5 m

If you know the mean and all but one of the values, you can use an equation to find the missing value.

**Example** The mean of 5 temperatures is 87°F. Four of the temperatures are 81°F, 82°F, 88°F, and 96°F. Find the fifth temperature.

**Solution**
1. Let $n =$ the missing value.
2. Use the variable to write an equation. $\frac{81 + 82 + 88 + 96 + n}{5} = 87$
3. Solve. $\frac{347 + n}{5} = 87$
   $347 + n = 435$
   $n = 88$

The temperature is 88°F.

**Find the missing value.**

4. Test scores: 78, 83, 76, 75, 80, 84, 82, 71, 80
   Mean must be 80 to earn a B. 91
5. Monthly savings deposits: \$275, \$295, \$270, \$350, \$340
   Mean must be \$325 to meet vacation goal. \$420
6. Weekly times for running a mile: 6.4 min, 6.2 min, 6.3 min, 6.1 min, 6.2 min
   Mean must be 6.25 min to earn a fitness award. 6.3 min
7. Daily rainfall for one week: 2 in., 1 in., 2.5 in., 0.5 in., 1.5 in., 1.75 in.
   Mean must be 1.5 in. to set a new record. 1.25 in.
8. Distances between cities: 7 mi, 10 mi, 13 mi, 4 mi
   Mean must be 9 mi for a bicycle race. 11 mi

# 7-2

## Getting Ready

**Key Terms and Symbols** consecutive integers

**Materials** algebra tiles

**Resources** A complete list of resources for this lesson is on p. 333H.

### Daily Skills Warm-Up

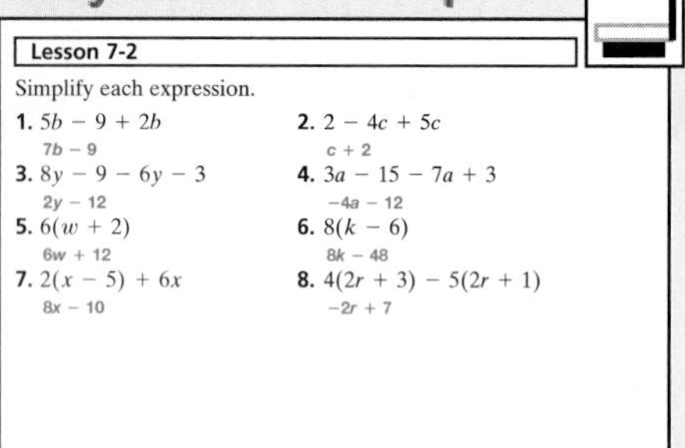
Lesson 7-2

Simplify each expression.

1. $5b - 9 + 2b$   $7b - 9$
2. $2 - 4c + 5c$   $c + 2$
3. $8y - 9 - 6y - 3$   $2y - 12$
4. $3a - 15 - 7a + 3$   $-4a - 12$
5. $6(w + 2)$   $6w + 12$
6. $8(k - 6)$   $8k - 48$
7. $2(x - 5) + 6x$   $8x - 10$
8. $4(2r + 3) - 5(2r + 1)$   $-2r + 7$

### Background for the Lesson

To solve multi-step equations, first apply the Distributive Property if necessary, then combine all like terms on each side. Then undo addition and subtraction and, finally, undo multiplication and division.

## 1 Focus

### Investigate

When students model the equation with tiles, they can see that the $x$ tiles can be rearranged so that they are together. Help students understand how the model translates into the algebraic steps: adding the coefficients of the terms with the variable $x$ is the same as putting the $x$ tiles together.

### Connecting to Prior Knowledge

Students learned in Lesson 7-1 how to solve two-step equations by undoing addition and subtraction first and then multiplication and division. In this lesson, students learn the additional step of using the Distributive Property as they solve multi-step equations with integral coefficients. In Lesson 7-3, they will learn how to solve multi-step equations with fraction and decimal coefficients.



# 7-2 Solving Multi-Step Equations

**What You'll Learn**

1. To combine like terms to simplify an equation
2. To use the distributive property to simplify an equation

**. . . And Why**

To solve problems involving consecutive integers

## Investigate

USING PROPERTIES TO SIMPLIFY EQUATIONS

The tiles model the equation $2x + 7 + x = 16$.

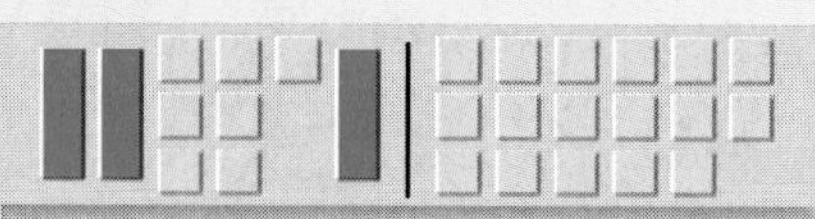

1. How does this equation differ from others you have seen? There are two variable terms instead of one.
2. a. Group the tiles so that all the $x$ tiles are together. This is the same as combining like terms. Write an equation to represent the tiles once the $x$ tiles are grouped together. $3x + 7 = 16$
   b. Solve your equation. Check your solution. 3

## PART 1 Combining Like Terms

Combine like terms to simplify an equation before you solve it.

REAL-WORLD CONNECTION

### EXAMPLE 1

**Jake and Suki collect model airplanes. Suki has four fewer than twice as many model airplanes as Jake. Together they have 14 models. Solve the equation $m + 2m - 4 = 14$. Find the number of models each person has.**

| | |
|---|---|
| $m + 2m - 4 = 14$ | |
| $3m - 4 = 14$ | Combine like terms. |
| $3m - 4 + 4 = 14 + 4$ | Add 4 to each side. |
| $3m = 18$ | Simplify. |
| $\frac{3m}{3} = \frac{18}{3}$ | Divide each side by 3. |
| $m = 6$ | Simplify. |

Jake has 6 models. Suki has $2(6) - 4 = 8$ models.

**Check** Is the solution reasonable? Jake and Suki have a total of 14 models. Since $6 + 8 = 14$, the solution is reasonable.



## Tools to Monitor Progress

### BEFORE THE LESSON

**To check prerequisite skills:**

- Simplifying expressions

**Skills You Need,** p. 333

### DURING THE LESSON

**To check understanding:**

**Try This** exercises on student page

- **Additional Example 1**

  In his stamp collection, Jorge has five more than three times as many stamps as Helen. Together they have 41 stamps. Solve the equation $s + (3s + 5) = 41$. Find the number of stamps each one has. **$s = 9$; Helen has 9 stamps and Jorge has 32.**

## Try This

3. One basketball team defeated another by 13 points. The total number of points scored by both teams was 171. Solve the equation $p + p - 13 = 171$ to find the number of points $p$ scored by the winning team. 92 points

When you count by ones from any integer, you are counting **consecutive integers.**

| two consecutive integers | three consecutive integers |
|---|---|
| 120, 121 | −5, −4, −3 |

## Example 2

*Number Sense* **The sum of three consecutive integers is 96. Find the integers.**

**Words** sum of three consecutive integers is  96

Let $n$ = the least integer.
Then $n + 1$ = the second integer,
and $n + 2$ = the third integer.

**Equation** $n + (n + 1) + (n + 2) = 96$

$$n + (n + 1) + (n + 2) = 96$$

$$(n + n + n) + (1 + 2) = 96$$ Use the Commutative and Associative Properties of Addition to group like terms together.

$$3n + 3 = 96$$ Combine like terms.

$$3n + 3 - 3 = 96 - 3$$ Subtract 3 from each side.

$$3n = 93$$ Simplify.

$$\frac{3n}{3} = \frac{93}{3}$$ Divide each side by 3.

$$n = 31$$ Simplify.

If $n = 31$, then $n + 1 = 32$, and $n + 2 = 33$. The three integers are 31, 32, and 33.

**Check** Is the solution reasonable? Yes, because $31 + 32 + 33 = 96$.

## Try This

4. *Number Sense* Find four consecutive integers with a sum of 358. 88, 89, 90, 91

5. For *consecutive even integers,* the first is $n$, and the second is $n + 2$. Find two consecutive even integers with a sum of 66. 32, 34



# 2 Teach

## Part 1 Teaching Notes

Ask students to explain how they would solve the equation $2 + 7 = x$ by writing $9 = x$. Point out that this step of adding the numbers on the left side of the equation is called *combining like terms.* Show students how to combine like terms to write $2x + 7x = 18$ as $9x = 18$ and then $x = 2$.

### Example 1

**Build understanding.** Ask: Why are $m$ and $2m$ considered to be *like* terms? **They have the same variable, *m*.**

**Tactile Learning** When students solve problems like Example 1, provide tiles so they can model the problem and check their solution.

**ELL** Make sure students understand that *consecutive* means "one after the other." Have students give examples of consecutive objects such as desks in a row. Then ask for examples of consecutive numbers and, finally, consecutive integers.

### Example 2

**Build understanding.** Do consecutive integers have to be positive? Explain and give an example. **no; Integers can be negative, such as −8, −7, −6.**

**Math Reasoning** The sum of the consecutive integers 1, 2, and 3 is 6. If you increase each by one, you get 2, 3, and 4. The sum of the consecutive integers 2, 3, and 4 is 9. Generalize what happens to the sum when you increase each of a set of three consecutive integers by one. **You add 1 three times to increase the sum by 3.**

- **Additional Example 2**
  The sum of three consecutive integers is 42. Find the integers.
  13, 14, 15
- **Additional Example 3**
  Solve each equation.
  a. $4(2q - 7) = -4$ $q = 3$
  b. $44 = 5(4 - r) - r$ $r = -4$

### AFTER THE LESSON

**To assess knowledge: Lesson Quiz**

Solve each equation.

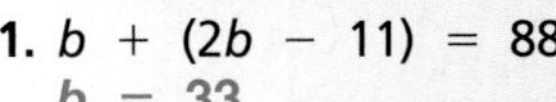

1. $b + (2b - 11) = 88$ $b = 33$

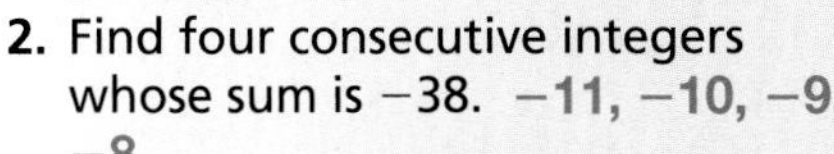

2. Find four consecutive integers whose sum is −38. −11, −10, −9, −8
3. $6(2n - 5) = -90$ $n = -5$

- For enrichment and reteaching options see Resources on p. 333H.

## Part 2 Teaching Notes

Ask a volunteer to go to the board and give an example of how the Distributive Property works: $a(b + c) = ab + ac$. Explain that using the Distributive Property to distribute a factor to each term inside a set of parentheses is often the first step in solving an equation.

### Example 3

**Build understanding.** In part b., why was the + 2 inside the parentheses rewritten as − 6 when you removed the parentheses? **Each term in the parentheses, including the + 2, was multiplied by −3.**

**Error Prevention** There are two common errors students could make when they use the Distributive Property to solve an equation such as $2(x + 1) + x = 7$. They may forget to distribute the 2 to all of the terms in the parentheses, or they may distribute the 2 to the terms in the parentheses and also to the $x$ that is outside of the parentheses. Remind students that the Distributive Property multiplies *each* term inside the parentheses by the factor, and does *not* include terms that are not inside the parentheses.

**Advanced Learners** Have students explain how an equation such as $3(t + 7) = 12$ can be solved without using the Distributive Property. **You can divide each side of this equation by 3, leaving $t + 7 = 4$. Then subtract 7 from both sides to get $t = -3$.**



**Quick Review**

The Distributive Property
$5(a + 4) = 5a + 20$
$3(6b - 2) = 18b - 6$

## PART 2 Using the Distributive Property

Sometimes you may need to use the Distributive Property when you solve a multi-step equation.

### EXAMPLE 3

**Solve each equation.**

**a. $2(5x - 3) = 14$**

| | |
|---|---|
| $2(5x - 3) = 14$ | |
| $10x - 6 = 14$ | Use the Distributive Property. |
| $10x - 6 + 6 = 14 + 6$ | Add 6 to each side. |
| $10x = 20$ | Simplify. |
| $\frac{10x}{10} = \frac{20}{10}$ | Divide each side by 10. |
| $x = 2$ | Simplify. |

**b. $38 = -3(4y + 2) + y$**

| | |
|---|---|
| $38 = -3(4y + 2) + y$ | |
| $38 = -12y - 6 + y$ | Use the Distributive Property. |
| $38 = -12y + y - 6$ | Use the Commutative and Associative Properties of Addition to group like terms together. |
| $38 = -11y - 6$ | Combine like terms. |
| $38 + 6 = -11y - 6 + 6$ | Add 6 to each side. |
| $44 = -11y$ | Simplify. |
| $\frac{44}{-11} = \frac{-11y}{-11}$ | Divide each side by −11. |
| $-4 = y$ | Simplify. |

**TRY THIS** Solve each equation.

6. $-3(m - 6) = 4$ $\frac{14}{3}$
7. $3(x + 12) - x = 8$ $-14$

**Useful Steps for Solving a Multi-Step Equation**

**Step 1** Use the Distributive Property, if necessary.
**Step 2** Combine like terms.
**Step 3** Undo addition or subtraction.
**Step 4** Undo multiplication or division.

# Exercises

## CHECK UNDERSTANDING

**Simplify the left side of each equation. (Do not solve.)**

**1.** $8a + 4a = 144$ $12a$  **2.** $5b + 11 - 2b = 50$ $3b + 11$  **3.** $-2(x - 7) = 8$ $-2x + 14$

**Solve each equation.**

**4.** $9x - 2x = -42$ $-6$  **5.** $4a + 1 - a = 19$ $6$  **6.** $18 = b - 7b$ $-3$

**7.** $3(n - 2) = 36$ $14$  **8.** $-3(2y + 7) = -18$ $-\frac{1}{2}$  **9.** $-2(a + 3) - a = 0$ $-2$

**10.** *Number Sense* Which equation can you use to find four consecutive integers with a sum of 50? D

A. $n + n + n + n = 50$  B. $n + 2n + 3n + 4n = 50$

C. $50 = n + 4$  D. $n + (n + 1) + (n + 2) + (n + 3) = 50$

## PRACTICE AND PROBLEM SOLVING

**Solve and check each equation.**

**11.** $d + 3d = 20$ $5$  **12.** $5x - x = -12$ $-3$  **13.** $-6 = a + a + 4$ $-5$

**14.** $y + 2 - 3y = -8$ $5$  **15.** $-9 - b + 8b = -23$ $-2$  **16.** $36 = y - 5y - 12$ $-12$

**17.** $7 = 2(a + 6)$ $-\frac{5}{2}$  **18.** $4(y - 1) = 36$ $10$  **19.** $16 = 2(x - 1) - x$ $18$

**20.** $9(2c + 5) + 3c = -75$ $-\frac{40}{7}$  **21.** $21 = 2(4a + 2)$ $\frac{17}{8}$  **22.** $8 - 3(x - 4) = 4$ $\frac{16}{3}$

**23.** $15 = -8(b - 1) + 9$ $\frac{1}{4}$  **24.** $\frac{1}{3}(x - 12) = 8$ $36$  **25.** $3 = \frac{1}{4}(m - 4) + \frac{1}{4}m$ $8$

**26.** *Error Analysis* A student solved the equation $7x - 5 - 5x = 15$ and found $x = 5$. What might be the student's error? See below.

*Number Sense* **Write and solve an equation for each situation.**

**27.** Two consecutive integers sum to 33. 16, 17

**28.** Four consecutive even integers sum to −92. −20, −22, −24, −26

**29.** *Construction* A carpenter is building a fence around a swimming pool. One side of the pool is next to the house and does not need fencing. The carpenter has 120 feet of fencing and plans to use it all. Solve the equation $w + 76 + w = 120$ to find the unknown dimension of the enclosed rectangular area. 22 ft

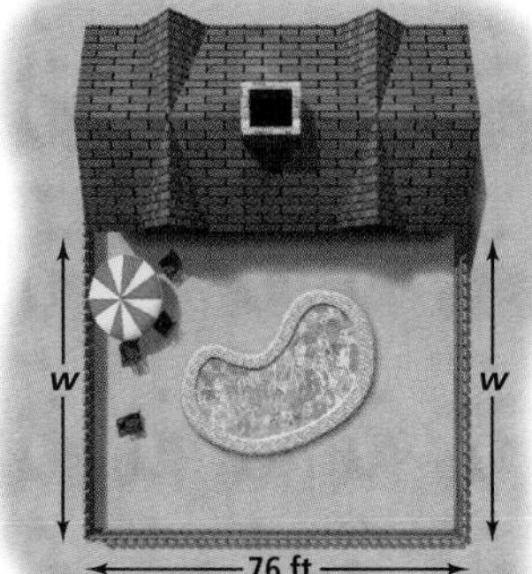


26. The student subtracted 5 from the right side of the equation instead of adding 5.



# 3 Practice/Assess

## Assignment Guide

To provide flexible scheduling, this lesson can be divided into parts.

**Part 1**

**Core** 1, 2, 4–6, 10–16, 27–29, 31

**Extension** 26, 30, 33

**Part 2**

**Core** 3, 7–9, 17–25, 32

**Extension** 34–35

Mixed Review can be assigned at any time for maintenance.

## Exercises

**Exercises 24–25** Dividing by a number is the same as multiplying by its reciprocal.

**Advanced Learners Exercise 24–25** Multiplying each side by 3 (Exercise 24) or by 4 (Exercise 25) is an efficient way to simplify these equations.

**Connecting to Geometry Exercises 34–35** Recall that the area $A$ of a rectangle is $A = lw$ where $l$ is the length and $w$ is the width.

## Challenge

Find three consecutive integers whose sum is zero. **−1, 0, 1**

## Closure

To solve multi-step equations, use the Distributive Property to remove grouping symbols and combine like terms first. Then follow the steps for solving two-step equations.

## Daily Cumulative Review

**Solve each equation.** *(Lesson 7-1)*

**1.** $14 = 5 - \frac{n}{6}$ $-54 = n$  **2.** $\frac{x}{6} + 3 = 0$ $x = -18$  **3.** $15 = -6a - 3$ $-3 = a$

**4.** $6r - 25 = 35$ $r = 10$  **5.** $\frac{-b}{8} + 20 = 1$ $b = 152$  **6.** $-36 - 5s = -26$ $s = -2$

**Make a table to solve the problem.** *(Lesson 6-10)*

**7.** The bus carrying the football team leaves Stillwater at 10:00 A.M. Their bus averages 50 mi/h. The van carrying the cheerleaders leaves at 11:00 A.M. Their van averages 60 mi/h. Both vehicles are going the same direction. At what time will the van catch up with the bus? How far from Stillwater will the vehicles be?

| | 10 A.M. | 11 A.M. | 12 P.M. | 1 P.M. | 2 P.M. | 3 P.M. | 4 P.M. |
|---|---|---|---|---|---|---|---|
| Bus | 0 | 50 mi | 100 mi | 150 mi | 200 mi | 250 mi | 300 mi |
| Van | 0 | 0 | 60 mi | 120 mi | 180 mi | 240 mi | 300 mi |

4:00 P.M.; 300 miles from Stillwater

**Mixed Review**

**Solve each equation.**

**8.** (5-7) $a - \frac{3}{5} = \frac{1}{5}$ $a = \frac{4}{5}$  **9.** (3-5) $k + 8.3 = 12.1$ $k = 3.8$  **10.** (3-6) $0.003n = 0.12$ $n = 40$

**11.** (5-8) $\frac{7}{9}t = \frac{5}{6}$ $t = 1\frac{1}{14}$  **12.** (5-7) $r + \frac{2}{7} = \frac{9}{14}$ $r = \frac{5}{14}$  **13.** (3-6) $13.5 = 1.5f$ $9 = f$

**Use mental math to simplify each expression.**

**14.** (5-4) $\frac{5}{8} \cdot 4$ $2\frac{1}{2}$  **15.** (5-4) $\frac{2}{3}(-3)$ $-2$  **16.** (5-4) $\frac{5}{7}(21)$ $15$



## Alternative Assessment

Ask students to write several multi-step equations and then to provide steps and solutions for each equation they create.

## Practice

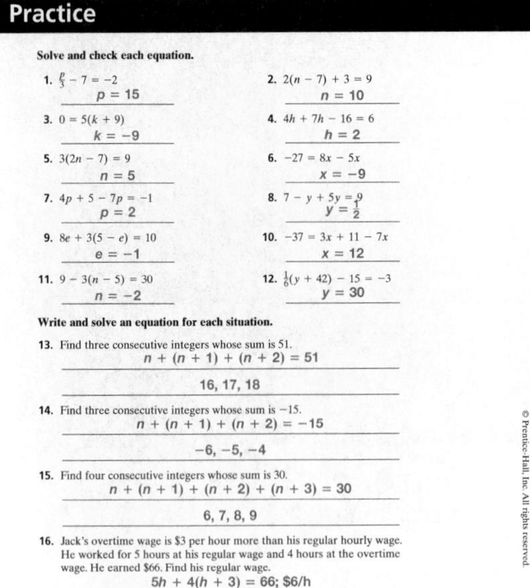

**Solve and check each equation.**

1. $\frac{p}{3} - 7 = -2$ $p = 15$
2. $2(n - 7) + 3 = 9$ $n = 10$
3. $0 = 5(k + 9)$ $k = -9$
4. $4h + 7h - 16 = 6$ $h = 2$
5. $3(2n - 7) = 9$ $n = 5$
6. $-27 = 8x - 5x$ $x = -9$
7. $4p + 5 - 7p = -1$ $p = 2$
8. $7 - y + 5y = 9$ $y = \frac{1}{2}$
9. $8e + 3(5 - e) = 10$ $e = -1$
10. $-37 = 3x + 11 - 7x$ $x = 12$
11. $9 - 3(n - 5) = 30$ $n = -2$
12. $\frac{1}{6}(y + 42) - 15 = -3$ $y = 30$

**Write and solve an equation for each situation.**

13. Find three consecutive integers whose sum is 51.
$n + (n + 1) + (n + 2) = 51$
16, 17, 18
14. Find three consecutive integers whose sum is −15.
$n + (n + 1) + (n + 2) = -15$
−6, −5, −4
15. Find four consecutive integers whose sum is 30.
$n + (n + 1) + (n + 2) + (n + 3) = 30$
6, 7, 8, 9
16. Jack's overtime wage is $3 per hour more than his regular hourly wage. He worked for 5 hours at his regular wage and 4 hours at the overtime wage. He earned $66. Find his regular wage.
$5h + 4(h + 3) = 66$; $6/h



## Reteaching

Solve $6 - 2(x + 5) = 8$

| | |
|---|---|
| $6 - 2(x + 5) = 8$ | |
| $6 - 2x - 10 = 8$ | Distribute. |
| $-2x - 4 = 8$ | Simplify. Think of $6 - 2x$ as $6 + (-2x)$. Then subtract $6 - 10$. |
| $-2x - 4 + 4 = 8 + 4$ | Add 4 to each side. |
| $-2x = 12$ | Simplify. |
| $\frac{-2x}{-2} = \frac{12}{-2}$ | Divide each side by −2. |
| $x = -6$ | Simplify. |

**Solve each equation.**

1. $3(a - 4) = 9$

| | |
|---|---|
| $3a - 12 = 9$ | Distribute. |
| $3a - 12 + 12 = 9 + 12$ | Add 12 to each side. |
| $3a = 21$ | Simplify. |
| $\frac{3a}{3} = \frac{21}{3}$ | Divide each side by 3. |
| $a = 7$ | Simplify. |

**Solve each equation.**

2. $n + 5n = 30$ $n =$ 5
3. $y - 4y = 33$ $y =$ −11
4. $12 = 4(b - 2)$ $b =$ 5
5. $-3(k - 4) = -6$ $k =$ 6
6. $m - 3m + 3 = 11$ $m =$ −4
7. $2(x - 9) + 5 = 1$ $x =$ 7



## Enrichment

You can use two-step equations to solve problems involving odd and even numbers and multiples of whole numbers.

**The sum of three consecutive odd numbers is 99. Answer these questions to learn a method for finding the numbers.**

1. Let $n$ be the first number. Write an expression for each of the other two numbers in terms of $n$.
$n + 2$, $n + 4$
2. Write and solve an equation to find the three numbers.
$n + (n + 2) + (n + 4) = 99$; $3n + 6 = 99$;
$n = 31$; 31, 33, 35

**Find the numbers described.**

3. three consecutive odd numbers with a sum of 261
85, 87, 89
4. two consecutive even numbers with a sum of 894
446, 448
5. an odd number which when multiplied by 4 and added to the next odd number produces a sum of 177
35

**Use the same principle to solve problems involving multiples of whole numbers.**

6. $m$ is a multiple of 6. Write the next two multiples of 6 in terms of $m$.
$m + 6$, $m + 12$

**Write and solve an equation for each situation.**

7. The sum of three consecutive multiples of 5 is 90. Find the numbers.
$n + (n + 5) + (n + 10) = 90$; 25, 30, 35
8. The sum of four consecutive multiples of 7 is 378. Find the numbers.
$n + (n + 7) + (n + 14) + (n + 21) = 378$; 84, 91, 98, 105
9. The sum of three times a multiple of 4 and the next two multiples of 4 is 272. Find the numbers.
$3m + (m + 4) + (m + 8) = 272$; 52, 56, 60





30. Bill and his younger sister Jasmine collect glass marbles. Together, they have 94 marbles. Bill calculated he has 4 more than twice as many marbles as Jasmine. If Jasmine has $m$ marbles, then Bill has $(2m + 4)$ marbles. Solve the equation $m + (2m + 4) = 94$. Find how many glass marbles each has. **Jasmine 30 marbles, Bill 64 marbles**

31. *Number Sense* Two numbers are $w$ and $3w - 5$. Their sum is 23. Solve the equation $w + 3w - 5 = 23$. Find the numbers. **7, 16**

32. *Writing* Explain how to solve $3(9 + 4a) - 19 = 32$. **See below.**

33. Together, Donal, Yolanda, and Iris made 28 birdhouses for a school fair. Yolanda made $n$ birdhouses. Donal made one more birdhouse than Yolanda, and Iris made one more than Donal. Solve the equation $n + (n + 1) + (n + 1 + 1) = 27$. Find the number of birdhouses each one made. **8, 9, and 10 birdhouses**

*Geometry* **For each rectangle, the area is 20 cm². Find the value of $x$.**

34. **2**

35. **3**

32. **First, use the Distributive Property and combine like terms. Next, subtract 8 from each side. Finally, divide each side by 12.**

## Mixed Review

**Solve each equation.** *(Lesson 7-1)*

36. $10a - 32 = -28$ **$\frac{2}{5}$**
37. $5 - 2d = 15$ **−5**
38. $\frac{c}{4} - 7 = 5$ **48**

**Solve each equation.** *(Lessons 3-5 and 5-8)*

39. $\frac{7}{10}a = \frac{3}{5}$ **$\frac{6}{7}$**
40. $\frac{4}{5}x = 8$ **10**
41. $5.3 + k = 23.9$ **18.6**
42. $z - 3.2 = 7$ **10.2**

43. *Measurement* If you take $\frac{2}{3}$ c of flour from a bowl containing $2\frac{1}{2}$ c of flour, how much flour is left in the bowl? *(Lesson 5-5)* **$1\frac{5}{6}$ c**

## Chapter Project 7 — Activity 1 Measuring

You'll need a beaker or measuring cup marked in milliliters and a scale that measures mass. Measure and record the mass of the empty beaker. Add 250 mL of water to the beaker. Measure and record the total mass of the beaker and water. Find the mass of the water.

 See also Extra Practice section.

### Project Activity 1

**Modeling** you can use the equation $Mass_{total} - Mass_{beaker} = Mass_{liquid}$ or $M_t - M_b = M_l$ to model the mathematics of the activity.

# Multi-Step Equations with Fractions and Decimals

# 7-3

## PART 1 Solving Multi-Step Equations with Fractions

Remember, when the coefficient of a variable in an equation is a fraction, you can use reciprocals to solve the equation.

$$\frac{4}{5}x = 12$$

$$\frac{5}{4} \cdot \frac{4}{5}x = \frac{5}{4} \cdot 12 \quad \text{Multiply each side by } \frac{5}{4}\text{, because } \frac{5}{4} \cdot \frac{4}{5} = 1.$$

$$x = 3$$

When you have a multi-step equation and the coefficient of the variable is a fraction, gather the variables on one side of the equation and the constants on the other before multiplying by the reciprocal.

### EXAMPLE 1

**Solve $\frac{2}{3}n - 6 = 22$.**

$\frac{2}{3}n - 6 = 22$

$\frac{2}{3}n - 6 + 6 = 22 + 6$ — Add 6 to each side.

$\frac{2}{3}n = 28$ — Simplify.

$\frac{3}{2} \cdot \frac{2}{3}n = \frac{3}{2} \cdot 28$ — Multiply each side by $\frac{3}{2}$, the reciprocal of $\frac{2}{3}$.

$1n = \frac{3 \cdot \cancel{28}^{14}}{{}_{1}\cancel{2}}$ — Divide common factors.

$n = 42$ — Simplify.

**Check** $\frac{2}{3}n - 6 = 22$

$\frac{2}{3}(42) - 6 \stackrel{?}{=} 22$ — Replace $n$ with 42.

$\frac{2 \cdot \cancel{42}^{14}}{{}_{1}\cancel{3}} - 6 \stackrel{?}{=} 22$ — Divide common factors.

$28 - 6 \stackrel{?}{=} 22$ — Multiply.

$22 = 22$ ✔

**TRY THIS** Solve each equation.

1. $-\frac{7}{10}k + 14 = -21$ 50
2. $\frac{2}{3}(m - 6) = 3$ $\frac{21}{2}$, or $10\frac{1}{2}$

### What You'll Learn

1 To solve multi-step equations with fractions

2 To solve multi-step equations with decimals

### . . . And Why

To solve problems involving cost of phone service

*Need Help?* For more help with fractions and reciprocals, see Skills Handbook, page 740.



# Tools to Monitor Progress

### BEFORE THE LESSON

**To check prerequisite skills:**

- Simplifying expressions
- Writing variable expressions

**Skills You Need,** p. 333

### DURING THE LESSON

**To check understanding:**

**Try This** exercises on student page

- **Additional Example 1**
$\frac{3}{4}p - 7 = 11$ $p = 24$

# 7-3

## Getting Ready

**Resources** A complete list of resources for this lesson is on p. 333H.

### Daily Skills Warm-Up

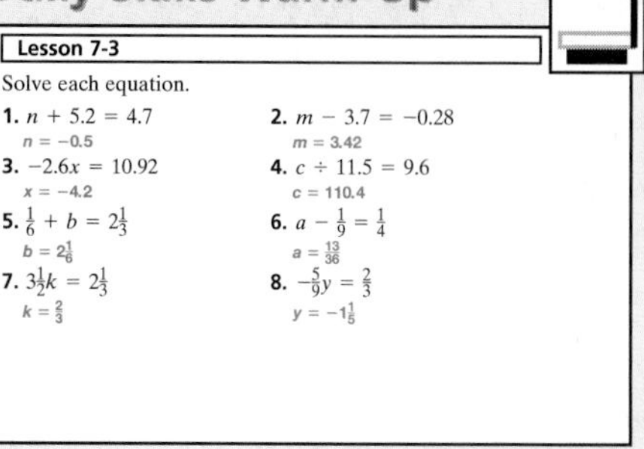

Lesson 7-3

Solve each equation.

1. $n + 5.2 = 4.7$ $n = -0.5$
2. $m - 3.7 = -0.28$ $m = 3.42$
3. $-2.6x = 10.92$ $x = -4.2$
4. $c \div 11.5 = 9.6$ $c = 110.4$
5. $\frac{1}{6} + b = 2\frac{1}{3}$ $b = 2\frac{1}{6}$
6. $a - \frac{1}{9} = \frac{1}{4}$ $a = \frac{13}{36}$
7. $3\frac{1}{2}k = 2\frac{1}{3}$ $k = \frac{2}{3}$
8. $-\frac{5}{9}y = \frac{2}{3}$ $y = -1\frac{1}{5}$

### Background for the Lesson

You solve multi-step equations with fractions or decimals just as you solve multi-step equations with integers. You undo addition and subtraction and then multiplication and division to isolate the variable. When the coefficient of a variable is a fraction, multiply each side by the reciprocal of the fraction. When the numerator of a fraction contains a variable, multiply each side by the denominator to eliminate the fraction. You can simplify decimals by multiplying each side of the equation by a multiple of 10.

## 1 Focus

### Connecting to Students' Lives

Discuss situations where students might have to find a fractional part of an unknown quantity such as "I give one-tenth of what I earn to charity," or "I get to keep two-thirds of the apples I pick," or "Pete makes one-third of his free throws."

### Connecting to Prior Knowledge

In Lesson 7-2, students learned to solve multi-step equations by using the Distributive Property and by combining like terms. In this lesson, students use the same methods to solve equations with fractions or decimals. In Lesson 7-4, students will apply these skills to an equation they write to solve a problem.

# 2 Teach

## Part 1 Teaching Notes

It is usually easier to solve equations with fractions if you first rewrite them so as to replace fractions with integers. You can do this by multiplying each side by the denominator of the fraction.

### Example 1

**Build understanding.** Ask: Why is the product of $\frac{3}{2}$ and $\frac{2}{3}$ equal to 1? **The product $\frac{6}{6}$ equals 1.**

### Example 2

**Build understanding.** Ask: How does multiplying the left side of the equation by 3 clear the denominator? **$\frac{93 + 80 + t}{3}$ is the same as $\frac{1}{3}(93 + 80 + t)$. So, $3 \cdot \frac{1}{3}(93 + 80 + t) = (93 + 80 + t)$.**

### Example 3

**Build understanding.** Ask: What are the denominators in this example? **5, 4** What number will you use to multiply each side to clear the denominators? **20**

**Error Prevention** When solving an equation such as $\frac{1}{4}x + 3 = \frac{3}{4}$, students may multiply both sides of the equation by 4 to clear the denominators and forget to multiply the 3. Remind students to multiply *each* term of the equation, both $\frac{1}{4}x$ and 3, as well as the $\frac{3}{4}$ on the other side.

You can use the Multiplication Property of Equality to make equations involving fractions easier to solve. Use the LCM of the denominators to clear the equation of fractions.

**REAL-WORLD**  **CONNECTION**

### Example 2

**A student has two test scores of 93 and 80. Solve the equation $\frac{93 + 80 + t}{3} = 90$ to find what the student would have to score on a third test to average 90.**

| | |
|---|---|
| $\frac{93 + 80 + t}{3} = 90$ | |
| $3\left(\frac{93 + 80 + t}{3}\right) = 3(90)$ | Multiply each side by 3. |
| $93 + 80 + t = 270$ | Simplify each side of the equation. |
| $173 + t = 270$ | Add. |
| $173 - 173 + t = 270 - 173$ | Subtract 173 from each side. |
| $t = 97$ | Simplify. |

The student would have to score 97 on a third test to average 90.

**Try This** Solve each equation.

3. $-\frac{12 + x}{2} = 13$ **−38**

4. $\frac{4}{7}(a + 6) = 2$ **$-\frac{5}{2}$, or $-2\frac{1}{2}$**

### Example 3

**Solve $\frac{2}{5}x + 2 = \frac{3}{4}$.**

| | |
|---|---|
| $\frac{2}{5}x + 2 = \frac{3}{4}$ | |
| $20\left(\frac{2}{5}x + 2\right) = 20\left(\frac{3}{4}\right)$ | Multiply each side by 20, the LCM of 5 and 4. |
| $20 \cdot \frac{2}{5}x + 20 \cdot 2 = 20\left(\frac{3}{4}\right)$ | Use the Distributive Property. |
| $8x + 40 = 15$ | Simplify. |
| $8x + 40 - 40 = 15 - 40$ | Subtract 40 from each side. |
| $8x = -25$ | Simplify. |
| $\frac{8x}{8} = \frac{-25}{8}$ | Divide each side by 8. |
| $x = -3\frac{1}{8}$ | Simplify. |

**Try This** Solve each equation.

5. $-\frac{5}{8}y + y = \frac{1}{8}$ **$\frac{1}{3}$**

6. $\frac{1}{3}b - 1 = \frac{5}{6}$ **$\frac{11}{2}$, or $5\frac{1}{2}$**



- **Additional Example 2**
  The teacher told three math classes that if they had an average grade of 85 on the final exam, they could have a party. The first two classes had averages of 81 and 83. Solve the equation $\frac{81 + 83 + c}{3} = 85$ to find out what average the third class must have to get the party. **91**
- **Additional Example 3**
  Solve $\frac{5}{7}y + 4 = \frac{3}{7}$. **$y = -5$**

## AFTER THE LESSON

### To assess knowledge:

### Lesson Quiz

Solve each equation.

1. $\frac{1}{6}d + 13 = 20$ **$d = 42$**
2. $\frac{3}{5}(s - 8) = 9$ **$s = 23$**
3. $\frac{w + 25 + 12}{8} = 7$ **$w = 19$**
4. $5 + \frac{12 + 2c}{4} = 14$ **$c = 12$**
5. $\frac{1}{8}y - 2 = \frac{7}{8}$ **$y = 23$**

- For enrichment and reteaching options see Resources on p. 333H.

## Solving Multi-Step Equations with Decimals

You can solve multi-step equations containing decimals by calculating with the decimals or by multiplying by a power of 10 to clear the equation of decimals.

### Different Ways to Solve a Problem

**For local telephone service, the McNeils pay $9.95/month plus $.035/min for local calls. Last month, they paid $12.75 for local service. To find the minutes $m$ of local calls, solve the equation $0.035m + 9.95 = 12.75$.**

**Method 1**

You can work with decimals as you have before.

$$0.035m + 9.95 = 12.75$$
$$0.035m + 9.95 - 9.95 = 12.75 - 9.95$$
$$0.035m = 2.8$$
$$\frac{0.035m}{0.035} = \frac{2.8}{0.035}$$
$$m = 80$$

The McNeils made 80 min of local calls.

**Method 2**

Use multiplication to clear the decimals. Use the decimal with the greatest number of decimal places to decide what power of 10 to use.

$$0.035m + 9.95 = 12.75$$
$$1{,}000(0.035m + 9.95) = 1{,}000(12.75)$$
$$35m + 9{,}950 = 12{,}750$$
$$35m + 9{,}950 - 9{,}950 = 12{,}750 - 9{,}950$$
$$35m = 2{,}800$$
$$\frac{35m}{35} = \frac{2{,}800}{35}$$
$$m = 80$$

The McNeils made 80 min of local calls.

**Choose a Method**

1. For the problem above, which method do you prefer? Explain. 1. Answers may vary. Sample: Method 2 because it is easier to work with whole numbers than decimals.
2. In Method 2, why was 1,000 used to multiply each side of the equation? 2. The number with the greatest number of decimal places had 3, so the 3rd power of 10, or 1,000, was used to clear the equation of decimals.

The telephone company also offers monthly rate of $32.95 for unlimited local calls. How many minutes of local calls can the McNeils make before the monthly rate of $32.95 becomes the better deal? 658 min, or 10 h 58 min

## Part 2 Teaching Notes

Ask students which of the following equations is easier to solve: $0.07z = 0.21$ or $7z = 21$. Lead students to see that these equations are equivalent.

### Different Ways to Solve a Problem

**Build understanding.** In Method 1, use estimation to explain why it is reasonable for the expression $\frac{2.8}{0.035}$ to equal 80. 2.8 is about 3; The decimal is close to 0.03. You can simplify $\frac{3}{0.03}$ by multiplying by $\frac{100}{100}$ to get $\frac{300}{3}$, which is 100. So, 80 is a reasonable answer.

**Auditory Learning** Have students look at exercises that involve decimals. Ask students to explain to a partner which method they would use to solve the equation, and why they would choose that method.

**Extension** Use a third method to solve $0.035m + 9.95 = 12.75$. Write each of the decimals as a fraction before you multiply each side by 1,000.

# 3 Practice/Assess

## Assignment Guide

To provide flexible scheduling, this lesson can be divided into parts.

**▼ Part 1**

**Core** 1, 3–6, 10–12, 14–22, 32

✪ **Extension** 36, 38

**▼ Part 2**

**Core** 2, 7–9, 13, 23–31, 35, 37

✪ **Extension** 33, 34

Mixed Review can be assigned at any time for maintenance.

## Exercises

**Exercises 14–31** Be sure to multiply every term on each side of the equation when multiplying to clear denominators or decimals.

**Test Prep Exercise 32** You can either solve the equation or test each answer by substituting the value for the variable.

## ✪ Challenge

Solve $\frac{15}{22}n + 0.75 = \frac{3}{4}$. $n = 0$

## Closure

To solve two-step equations, undo addition and subtraction, then multiplication and division. You can multiply by either reciprocals or powers of 10 to simplify the equations before you start to solve.

## Daily Cumulative Review

**Solve each equation.** *(Lesson 7-2)*

1. $-8 = x + 6 + x$ — $-7 = x$
2. $-r - 8 + 6r = -13$ — $r = -1$
3. $45 = 3(t + 5)$ — $10 = t$
4. $\frac{1}{4}(s - 24) = 34$ — $s = 160$
5. $k + 8 - 5k = -8$ — $k = 4$
6. $4 = \frac{1}{3}(p - 6) + \frac{1}{3}p$ — $9 = p$

**Solve each equation.** *(Lesson 7-1)*

7. $8y - 5 = 163$ — $y = 21$
8. $-29 = 3r + 4$ — $-11 = r$
9. $22 = -12b - 26$ — $-4 = b$
10. $\frac{f}{6} - 8 = 40$ — $f = 288$
11. $2 - \frac{t}{5} = 27$ — $t = -125$
12. $-43 - 8m = -67$ — $m = 3$

**Mixed Review**

**Write an equation for each sentence. Is each equation true, false, or an open sentence?**

13. (2-4) Twenty-eight equals a number $a$ plus four.
$28 = a + 4$; open sentence

14. (2-4) Sixty-four divided by eight is seven.
$64 \div 8 = 7$; false equation

**Write an equation for the sentence. Solve for the variable.**

15. (3-6) The product of some number $n$ and $-4.6$ equals $-10.58$.
$-4.6n = -10.58$; $n = 2.3$

**Write an equation to solve the problem.**

16. (3-7) A cupcake recipe calls for $2\frac{1}{3}$ c of flour. You have $\frac{3}{4}$ c of flour. Find how much more flour you need.
$\frac{3}{4} + x = 2\frac{1}{3}$; $x = 1\frac{7}{12}$ more cups



# Exercises

## Check Understanding

**State the first step in solving each equation. (Do not solve.)**

1. $\frac{1}{4}x + 3 = 2$ Subtract 3 from each side.
2. $16 = 2.8y - 1.5$ Add 1.5 to each side.
3. $\frac{7}{9}w - w = \frac{1}{9}$ Combine like terms.

**Solve each equation.**

4. $\frac{3}{4}b + 5 = 14$ 12
5. $\frac{7}{10}c - 10 = \frac{2}{5}$ $14\frac{6}{7}$
6. $-\frac{1}{3}(x - 9) = -1$ 12
7. $2.25x - 6.1 = 14.15$ 9
8. $1.2n + 3.4 = 10$ 5.5
9. $-0.8k - 3.1 = -8.3$ 6.5

10. *Weather* On three days in August 1999, the high temperatures in Jackson, Mississippi, were 96°F, 96°F, and $x$°F. The average high temperature for the three days was 97°F. Solve the equation $\frac{96 + 96 + x}{3} = 97$ to find the high temperature on the third day. 99°F

## Practice and Problem Solving

**By what number would you multiply each equation to get an equation without denominators or decimals? Do not solve.**

11. $\frac{1}{8}h - 1 = \frac{3}{8}$ 8
12. $\frac{1}{5}y + 3 = \frac{2}{3}$ 15
13. $6.25f - 3.5 = 24.5$ 100

**Solve and check each equation.**

14. $\frac{1}{4}c + 2 = \frac{3}{4}$ $-5$
15. $\frac{2}{3}(a - 3) = -\frac{1}{3}$ $\frac{5}{2}$
16. $\frac{5}{8}(p - 4) = 2$ $\frac{36}{5}$
17. $\frac{2}{7}n + n = \frac{5}{9}$ $\frac{35}{81}$
18. $8 - \frac{w}{10} = \frac{3}{5}$ 74
19. $p + \frac{1}{3}p = \frac{2}{3}$ $\frac{1}{2}$
20. $-\frac{3}{4}y + \frac{1}{4} = \frac{1}{2}$ $-\frac{1}{3}$
21. $\frac{x}{4} - \frac{3x}{2} = -\frac{1}{2}$ $\frac{2}{5}$
22. $\frac{2}{7}k - \frac{1}{14}k = -3$ $-14$
23. $2.4b + 5.6 = -11.2$ $-7$
24. $4x + 2 = -28.4$ $-7.6$
25. $0.07x + 9.95 = 12.47$ 36
26. $0.9x + 2.3x = -6.4$ $-2$
27. $-0.5x + 4 + 2x = 9$ $3.\overline{3}$ or $3\frac{1}{3}$
28. $0.4(a + 2) = 2$ 3
29. $1.2c + 2.6c = 4.56$ 1.2
30. $12p - 6.5p + 7 = -15$ $-4$
31. $5(t - 0.4) + 6t = 0$ $\frac{2}{11}$

32. **TEST PREP** What is the solution of $\frac{1}{2}(x - 1) = \frac{1}{2}$? D

A. $-1$  B. 0  C. 1  D. 2



## Alternative Assessment

Have students demonstrate several methods for solving the equation $0.7y - 0.3 = 1.1$ and write the steps for their various methods. $y = 2$

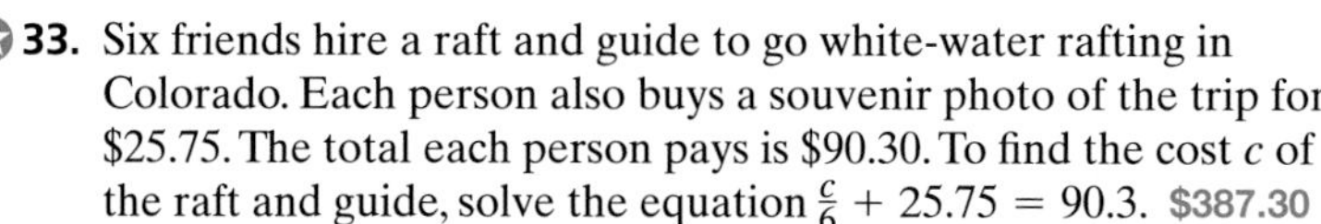

33. Six friends hire a raft and guide to go white-water rafting in Colorado. Each person also buys a souvenir photo of the trip for \$25.75. The total each person pays is \$90.30. To find the cost $c$ of the raft and guide, solve the equation $\frac{c}{6} + 25.75 = 90.3$. \$387.30

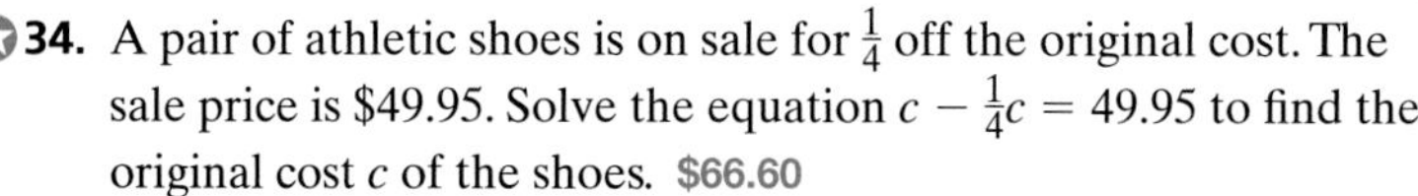

34. A pair of athletic shoes is on sale for $\frac{1}{4}$ off the original cost. The sale price is \$49.95. Solve the equation $c - \frac{1}{4}c = 49.95$ to find the original cost $c$ of the shoes. \$66.60

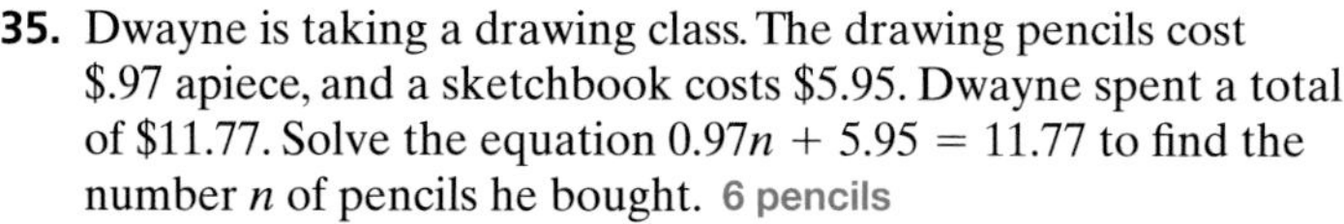

35. Dwayne is taking a drawing class. The drawing pencils cost \$.97 apiece, and a sketchbook costs \$5.95. Dwayne spent a total of \$11.77. Solve the equation $0.97n + 5.95 = 11.77$ to find the number $n$ of pencils he bought. 6 pencils

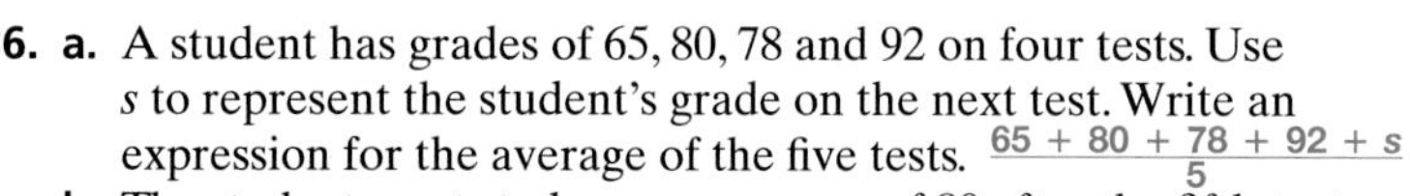

36. a. A student has grades of 65, 80, 78 and 92 on four tests. Use $s$ to represent the student's grade on the next test. Write an expression for the average of the five tests. $\frac{65 + 80 + 78 + 92 + s}{5}$
b. The student wants to have an average of 80 after the fifth test. Use the expression you wrote in part (a) to write an equation. $\frac{65 + 80 + 78 + 92 + s}{5} = 80$
c. Solve the equation to find the grade the student must earn on the fifth test to have an average of 80 for the class. 85

White-water rafting trips can be as short as two hours or as long as several days. If the trip in Exercise 33 takes 4 hours, about how much is each person's cost per hour? about \$22.58

37. *Writing* At a 15%-off sale, a customer pays \$11.01 for a video. Explain how to solve the equation $p - 0.15p = 11.01$ to find the original price $p$ of the video. Answers may vary. Sample: First, combine like terms. Then divide each side by 0.85.

38. *Geometry* Use the rectangle at the right.
a. Find the value of $x$ if the area is 15 square units. 4
b. Find the value of $x$ if the perimeter is 24 units. 12

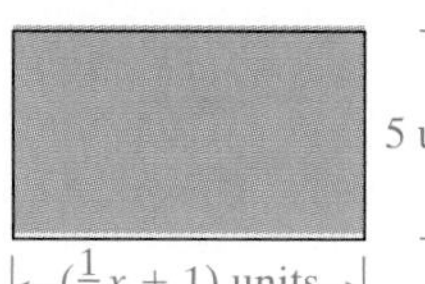


## Mixed Review

**Solve each equation.** *(Lesson 7-2)*

39. $-9 = 3(y + 4)$ −7
40. $5(t - 8) = 10$ 10
41. $x + 7 - 3x = 7$ 0

**Write using exponents.** *(Lesson 4-2)*

42. $4 \cdot 4 \cdot 4$ $4^3$
43. $(-7) \cdot (-7)$ $(-7)^2$
44. $c \cdot c \cdot c \cdot c \cdot d$ $c^4d$
45. $9 \cdot a \cdot a \cdot 2$ $18a^2$

46. *Choose a Strategy* Mrs. Milton travels 60 mi round-trip to work. She works five days a week. Her car gets about 25 mi/gal of gasoline. About how many gallons of gasoline does Mrs. Milton's car use during her weekly commute? 12 gal

See also Extra Practice section.



## Practice

**Solve and check each equation.**

1. $0.7n - 1.5 + 7.3n = 14.5$ $n = 2$
2. $18p - 45 = 0$ $p = 2.5$
3. $16.3k + 19.2 + 7.5k = -64.1$ $k = -3.5$
4. $h + 3h + 4h = 100$ $h = 12\frac{1}{2}$
5. $40 - 5n = -2$ $n = 8.4$
6. $14 = \frac{2}{3}(9y - 15)$ $y = 4$
7. $\frac{2}{3}y - 6 = 2$ $y = 12$
8. $1.2m + 7.5m + 2.1 = 63$ $m = 7$
9. $\frac{7}{8}h - \frac{5}{8} = 2$ $h = 3$
10. $93.96 = 4.7p + 8.7p - 2.6p$ $p = 8.7$
11. $9w - 16.3 = 5.3$ $w = 2.4$
12. $88.1 - 2.3f = 72.46$ $f = 6.8$
13. $-15.3 = -7.5k + 55.2$ $k = 9.4$
14. $26e + 891 = -71$ $e = -37$
15. $2.3(x + 1.4) = -9.66$ $x = -5.6$
16. $(x - 17.7) + 19.6 = 27.8$ $x = 25.9$

**Write an equation to describe each situation. Solve.**

17. Jolene bought three blouses at one price and 2 blouses priced \$3 below the others. The total cost was \$91.50. Find the prices of the blouses. $3x + 2(x - 3) = 91.50$; \$19.50 and \$16.50
18. A car rented for \$29 per day plus \$.08 per mile. Julia paid \$46.12 for a one-day rental. How far did she drive? $29 + 0.08m = 46.12$; $m = 214$ miles

**By what number would you multiply each equation to clear denominators or decimals? Do not solve.**

19. $\frac{1}{3}z + \frac{1}{6} = 5\frac{1}{6}$ 6
20. $3.7 + 2.75k = 27.35$ 100



## Reteaching

Solve $0.25x - 0.4 = 1.6$

You can clear the decimals first. Since 0.25 is the decimal with the greatest number of decimal places and $0.25 = \frac{25}{100}$, multiply each side by 100.

| | |
|---|---|
| $0.25x - 0.4 = 1.6$ | |
| $100(0.25x - 0.4) = 100(1.6)$ | Multiply each side by 100. |
| $25x - 40 = 160$ | Distribute and simplify. |
| $25x - 40 + 40 = 160 + 40$ | Add 40 to each side. |
| $25x = 200$ | Simplify. |
| $\frac{25x}{25} = \frac{200}{25}$ | Divide each side by 25. |
| $x = 8$ | Simplify. |

**Solve each equation.**

1. $0.8x + 2.1 = 5.3$ $x =$ 4
2. $0.5k - 3.4 = 0.1$ $k =$ 7
3. $2.7n + 4.1 = 36.5$ $n =$ 12
4. $0.96m - 1.8m = -12.6$ $m =$ 15
5. $0.7b + 6 - 0.3b = 6.8$ $b =$ 2
6. $1.4a + 3.5a - 4.3 = 44.7$ $a =$ 10



## Enrichment

You can use a shortcut to solve equations containing fractions.

**Example** Solve $\frac{2}{3}x - \frac{7}{6} = \frac{7}{2}$

**First, use the normal method to solve. Complete.**

1. $\frac{2}{3}x - \frac{7}{6} + \boxed{\frac{7}{6}} = \frac{7}{2} + \boxed{\frac{7}{6}}$
2. $\frac{2}{3}x = \boxed{\frac{28}{6}}$
3. $\frac{2}{3}x \cdot \boxed{\frac{3}{2}} = \boxed{\frac{28}{6}} \cdot \boxed{\frac{3}{2}}$
4. $x = \boxed{7}$

**To use the shortcut, first find the LCM of all the denominators appearing in the equation.**

5. LCM of 3, 6, and 2 = 6
6. Multiply both sides of the equation by the LCM.
$\boxed{6}\left(\frac{2}{3}x - \frac{7}{6}\right) = \boxed{6}\frac{7}{2}$
7. Apply the distributive property.
$\boxed{6}\left(\frac{2}{3}x\right) - \boxed{6}\left(\frac{7}{6}\right) = \boxed{21}$
8. Multiply. $\boxed{4x} - \boxed{7} = \boxed{21}$
9. Solve. $x = \boxed{7}$

**Solve using the shortcut.**

10. $\frac{3}{5}k - \frac{7}{10} = \frac{1}{2}$ $k =$ 2
11. $\frac{1}{3}m + \frac{1}{6} = \frac{4}{9}$ $m = \frac{5}{6}$
12. $\frac{5}{8}y - \frac{1}{2} = \frac{3}{4}$ $y =$ 2
13. $\frac{5}{7}n - \frac{3}{14} = \frac{1}{2}$ $n =$ 1
14. $\frac{3}{8}h + \frac{7}{12} = \frac{3}{4}$ $h = \frac{4}{9}$
15. $\frac{13}{30}e - \frac{7}{10} = \frac{3}{5}$ $e =$ 3

# 7-4

## Getting Ready

**Resources** A complete list of resources for this lesson is on p. 333F.

### Daily Skills Warm-Up

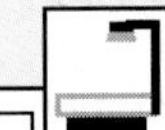

**Lesson 7-4**

Write and solve an equation.

1. Pierre bought a puppy for $48, which was $21 less than the original price. What was the original price of the puppy?
   $p - 21 = 48$, $p = 69$; The original price was $69.
2. For an experiment, Ms. Ortiz's class left a measuring cup of water in the sun to evaporate. After 6 days, $\frac{3}{4}$ of a cup had evaporated. How much water evaporated each day?
   $6e = \frac{3}{4}$; $e = \frac{1}{8}$, $\frac{1}{8}$ cup evaporated each day.

### Background for the Lesson

When you solve problems outside of the classroom, those problems are nearly always stated in words. When you rewrite those words into the form of an equation, you are stating the relationships in a clear and unambiguous way to help you solve the problem. When you rewrite words into an equation, organize what you know and what you want to find into a mathematical sentence. Write what you want to find as the variable. Write the relationships (such as *is*), with math operation symbols.

## 1 Focus

### Connecting to Students' Lives

Discuss collections students may have, such as comic books or stuffed animals. Suppose they had a certain amount of money to spend on their collection. How would they know the number of items they could add? Writing an equation can help to solve this problem.

### Connecting to Prior Knowledge

In Lesson 7-1, students solved problems for which the equation was given to them. In this lesson, students will learn how to write (and solve) their own equations from problems stated in words. In Lesson 7-5 they will continue to practice this skill in more complex problem situations.

# Write an Equation

**Problem Solving Strategies**

Account for All Possibilities
Draw a Diagram
Look for a Pattern
Make a Model
Make a Table
Simplify a Problem
Simulate a Problem
Solve by Graphing
Try, Test, Revise
Use Multiple Strategies
Work Backward
Write an Equation
Write a Proportion

*Math Strategies in Action* You probably recognize Albert Einstein's famous formula, $E = mc^2$. Many scientists write and use equations and formulas every day. Banks use equations to calculate interest and loan information. Statisticians use equations to find sports and population statistics. Doctors use equations to calculate correct doses of medicines.

You have written one-step equations for word problems. Now you will extend your skills to more complex situations.

**Sample Problem**

A moving van rents for $29.95 a day plus $.12/mi. Ms. Smith's bill for a two-day rental was $70.46. How many miles did she drive?

### Read

1. What is the goal of this problem? to find how many miles Ms. Smith drove
2. For how long did Ms. Smith rent the van? 2 days
3. What does the van cost without mileage? $29.95 per day
4. What is the mileage charge? $.12/mi



## Tools to Monitor Progress

**BEFORE THE LESSON**

**To check prerequisite skills:**

- Simplifying expressions

**Skills You Need,** p. 333

**DURING THE LESSON**

**To check understanding:**

- **Additional Sample Problem**
  Ms. Smith rented the van to help a friend of hers move to the city. They spent $137.80 and drove the van 150 mi. The daily rental rate was $29.95 plus $.12/mi. How many days did they keep the van? 4 days

### Plan

Write an equation.

**Words** $\boxed{\text{two days}} \cdot \$29.95/\text{d} + \$.12/\text{mi} \cdot \boxed{\text{number of miles}} = \boxed{\$70.46}$

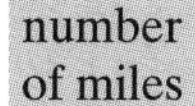

Let $\boxed{m}$ = the number of miles Ms. Smith drove the van.

**Equation** $\boxed{2} \cdot 29.95 + 0.12 \cdot \boxed{m} = \boxed{70.46}$

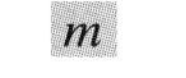

### Solve

Solve the equation.

$2 \cdot 29.95 + 0.12 \cdot m = 70.46$

$59.9 + 0.12m = 70.46$ — Multiply 2 and 29.95.

$59.9 - 59.9 + 0.12m = 70.46 - 59.9$ — Subtract 59.9 from each side.

$0.12m = 10.56$ — Simplify.

$\frac{0.12m}{0.12} = \frac{10.56}{0.12}$ — Divide each side by 0.12.

$m = 88$ — Simplify.

Ms. Smith drove the van 88 mi.

### Look Back

**5.** A student suggested that another way to solve the gas mileage problem was to use the strategy *Try, Test, Revise.* Suppose that Ms. Smith's bill for the two-day rental was \$76.34. How many miles did she drive the van? See part (b).

**a.** Copy and complete the table below to keep track of your trials.

| Miles | Cost | High/Low? |
|---|---|---|
| 75 | 75 · 0.12 = ■ (9) | low |
| 100 | ■ (100) · 0.12 = ■ (12) | ■ low |

**b.** Extend the table to find the solution to the problem. 137 miles

**c.** Check your solution by writing and solving an equation.

5c. Answers may vary. Sample:

$2 \cdot 29.95 + 0.12m = 76.34$

$59.9 + 0.12m = 76.34$

$59.9 - 59.9 + 0.12m = 76.34 - 59.9$

$0.12m = 16.44$

$m = \frac{16.44}{0.12}$

$m = 137$

**6.** *Reasoning* Which method do you prefer for solving this type of problem? Explain. Answers may vary. Sample: Write and solve an equation because it is faster.



# 2 Teach

## Teaching Notes

Help students find the words in problems that are keys to math operations. For example, words like *per* or *each* often mean multiplication. The words *and* or *plus* may mean addition. Words like *less* mean subtraction. You often write the verb as an equal sign.

In the Sample Problem, two pieces of information (the daily rate and the mileage charge) determine the total price of the rental. These two factors combine in a two-step equation.

### ■ Sample Problem

**Build understanding.** List the facts you know from the problem. daily cost, rate per mile, the fact that it was a two-day rental, and total amount of the bill

**Math Reasoning** Suppose that Mr. Ramirez rented the same moving van that Ms. Smith did, but his total bill was \$389.75. What can you conjecture about how many days he rented the van and how many miles he drove? He rented it for more days or drove more miles.

**Error Prevention** Suggest that students write words above the numbers, similar to those in the Plan for the Sample Problem, to label the quantities in their equations. This helps them see how the equation is related to the words in the problem.

### Additional Sample Problem

Linda made a phone call that cost \$.35 for the first minute and \$.15 for each additional minute. She spoke for 14 minutes. How much did the call cost her? \$2.30

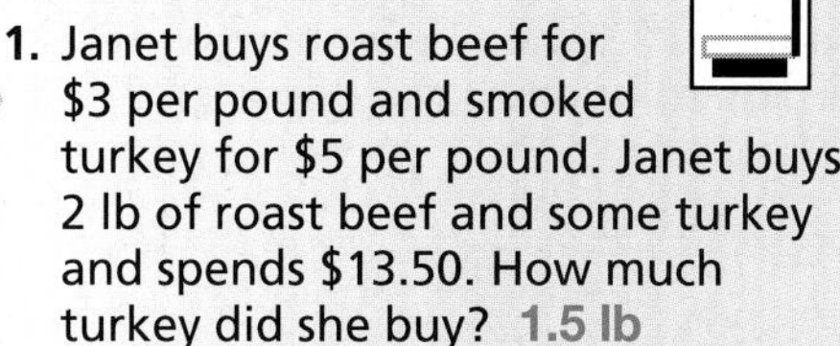

### AFTER THE LESSON

**To assess knowledge: Lesson Quiz**

1. Janet buys roast beef for \$3 per pound and smoked turkey for \$5 per pound. Janet buys 2 lb of roast beef and some turkey and spends \$13.50. How much turkey did she buy? 1.5 lb

- For enrichment and reteaching options see Resources on p. 333H.

# 3 Practice/Assess

## Assignment Guide

**Core** 1–7, 9

✪ **Extension** 8, 10–11

Mixed Review can be assigned at any time for maintenance.

### Exercises

**Visual Learning** **Exercises 3, 7** Draw these figures on a piece of paper to help write equations and solve the problems.

**Connecting to Science** **Exercise 8** An object's weight is different on each planet because weight depends on the force of gravity. Each planet has a different gravitational force because of its size. Although the weight differs, the *mass* of an object remains the same on each planet because the amount and makeup of matter in the object remains constant.

### ✪ Challenge

Axel measured two screws with a tape measure. Together, they measured $4\frac{1}{4}$ in. in length. One screw is $\frac{1}{2}$ in. more than twice the length of the first screw. How long is each screw? $1\frac{1}{4}$ in. and 3 in.

### Closure

One strategy for solving problems is to write and solve an equation. Use the problem-solving steps: Read, Plan, Solve, Look Back.

### Daily Cumulative Review

**Solve each equation.** *(Lesson 7-3)*

1. $41.68 = 4.7 - 8.6a$ $\quad -4.3 = a$
2. $f + \frac{1}{4}f = 10$ $\quad f = 8$
3. $\frac{4}{9}m - \frac{1}{18}m = -7$ $\quad m = -18$
4. $-\frac{1}{2}b + 3 = 1$ $\quad b = 4$
5. $5c + 6 = -24.75$ $\quad c = -6.15$
6. $0.6(s + 4) = 3$ $\quad s = 1$

**Solve each equation.** *(Lesson 7-2)*

7. $9(c - 2) = 45$ $\quad c = 7$
8. $8u - u = -21$ $\quad u = -3$
9. $2(5w + 4) + 2w = -76$ $\quad w = -7$
10. $22 = 4(s - 8) - 2s$ $\quad 27 = f$
11. $24 = x - 6x + 4$ $\quad -4 = x$
12. $12 - 4(d - 3) = 20$ $\quad d = 1$

**Mixed Review**

**Solve and check each equation.**

13. (7-1) $3x + 4 = 13$ $\quad x = 3$
14. (7-1) $45 - a = 13$ $\quad a = 32$
15. (7-1) $4s + 8 = -20$ $\quad s = -7$
16. (7-1) $2r - 100 = 44$ $\quad r = 72$
17. (7-1) $2 = 5 - \frac{b}{6}$ $\quad 18 = b$
18. (7-1) $-4 = 2f + 10$ $\quad -7 = f$

**Find the mean, median, and mode. Round to the nearest tenth, where necessary. Identify any outliers.**

19. (3-3) 37 46 47 53 99 33 46

Mean 51.6 Median 46 Mode 46 Outlier 99

20. (3-3) 2.6 3.8 0.2 2.5 3.9 2.5 3.0

Mean 2.6 Median 2.6 Mode 2.5 Outlier 0.2

**Write three fractions equivalent to each fraction.** Answers may vary.

21. (4-6) $\frac{3}{5}$ $\quad \frac{6}{10}, \frac{9}{15}, \frac{12}{20}$
22. (4-6) $\frac{7}{22}$ $\quad \frac{14}{44}, \frac{21}{66}, \frac{28}{88}$
23. (4-6) $\frac{16}{20}$ $\quad \frac{4}{5}, \frac{8}{10}, \frac{32}{40}$
24. (4-6) $\frac{1}{3}$ $\quad \frac{2}{6}, \frac{3}{9}, \frac{4}{12}$
25. (4-6) $\frac{2}{6}$ $\quad \frac{1}{3}, \frac{4}{12}, \frac{6}{18}$
26. (4-6) $\frac{1}{10}$ $\quad \frac{2}{20}, \frac{3}{30}, \frac{4}{40}$



# Exercises

## Check Understanding

**Write an equation. Then solve.**

1. The sale price of a sweater is \$48. The price is 20% less than the original price. What was the original price? \$60

2. *Budgeting* Elena has \$240 in the bank. She withdraws \$15 each week to pay for piano lessons. How many lessons can she afford with her savings? 16 lessons

3. *Geometry* The perimeter of a rectangle is 64 cm. The length is 4 cm less than twice the width. Find the length and width. 20 cm, 12 cm

## Practice and Problem Solving

**Solve using any strategy.**

4. Lamar's summer job is mowing lawns for a landscaper. His pay is \$7.50/h. Lamar also makes \$11.25/h for any time over 40 h that he works in one week. He worked 40 h last week plus $n$ overtime hours and made \$339.38. How many hours overtime did he work? 3.5 h

5. Cathy has a collection of dimes and quarters. The number of dimes equals the number of quarters. She has a total of \$2.80. How many of each coin does Cathy have? (*Hint:* Let $n =$ the number of dimes. Since each dime has a value of 10¢, the value of $n$ dimes is $10n$. Since the number of quarters is also $n$, the value of $n$ quarters is $25n$. Also change the value of \$2.80 to its value in cents.) 8 of each coin

6. *Number Sense* Find two whole numbers with a sum of 15 and a product of 54. 9 and 6

7. A farmer is building a square pen 21 ft on each side. He puts one post at each corner and one post every 3 ft in between. How many posts will he use? 28 posts

8. ✪ *Physics* The weight of an object on Venus is about $\frac{9}{10}$ of its weight on Earth. The weight of an object on Jupiter is about $\frac{13}{5}$ times its weight on Earth.
   a. If a rock weighs 23 lb on Venus, how much would it weigh on Earth? 25.6 lb
   b. If the same rock were on Jupiter, how much would it weigh? 66.4 lb



### Alternative Assessment

Suggest that students take one of the problems from the Exercises section and rewrite it to reflect a situation in their own life. Students may change both the wording and numbers to make the problem represent an event in their life. Then have them write and explain the solution to their problem.

9. a. It takes 8 painters 6 hours to paint the walls of a gymnasium. How many person-hours does this job require? 48 person-hours
b. How many hours will 12 painters take to paint the gymnasium? 4 h

10. Ladonna and Jane are renting an apartment. They pay the landlord the amount of the first month's rent, the same amount for the last month's rent, and half of a month's rent for a security deposit. The total is \$1,625. What is the monthly rent? \$650

11. Jackson, Petra, and Tyrone went to the beach and collected seashells over the weekend. Jackson collected $s$ seashells. Petra and Tyrone each collected thirteen less than twice the number of seashells Jackson collected. At the end of the weekend, they had 94 seashells. How many seashells did each person collect?
Jackson: 24 seashells; Petra and Tyrone: 35 seashells apiece

## Mixed Review

**Solve each equation.** *(Lesson 7-3)*

12. $\frac{3}{5}k + \frac{1}{5}k = 4$ 5
13. $1.4x + 8.8 = 92.8$ 60
14. $\frac{1 + x + 7}{5} = 7$ 27

**Write each percent as a fraction in simplest form and as a decimal.** *(Lesson 6-5)*

15. 52% $\frac{13}{25}$, 0.52
16. 20.5% $\frac{41}{200}$, 0.205
17. 0.5% $\frac{1}{200}$, 0.005
18. 205% $\frac{41}{20}$, 2.05

19. You can buy 12 pencils for \$.80. At this rate, how much will you pay for 27 pencils? *(Lesson 6-1)* \$1.80

## Checkpoint 1 — Lessons 7-1 through 7-4

**Solve each equation.**

1. $12n + 60 = 300$ 20
2. $5y - 9 - 3y = 13$ 11
3. $-44 = 3x + 10$ −18
4. $\frac{a}{4} - \frac{3}{4} = \frac{1}{4}$ 4
5. $\frac{4}{7}x - 3 = 13$ 28
6. $-\frac{x}{6} - 7 = 0$ −42
7. $0.6x + 1.9x = 5$ 2
8. $10(5 + m) = 63$ 1.3
9. $2c + 4 + 3c = -26$ −6
10. $\frac{1}{5}(x + 10) = 2$ 0
11. $7(2y - 1) = 7$ 1
12. $3a + 9 = 27$ 6

**Write an equation for each situation. Solve.**

13. Wendy bought a drill at a 10%-off sale. The sale price was \$75.60. Find the original price $p$. \$84

14. *Number Sense* Three consecutive integers have a sum of 132. Find the integers. 43, 44, 45



## Checkpoint

**Solve each equation.**

1. $8x + 73 = 1$ — $x = -9$
2. $-\frac{n}{3} - 10 = 0$ — $n = -30$
3. $15y - 7 - 13y = 17$ — $y = 12$
4. $3(2m + 8) = 6$ — $m = -3$
5. $\frac{2}{3}k - 1 = \frac{5}{6}$ — $k = 2\frac{3}{4}$
6. $0.4x + 2.6 = 0.2$ — $x = -6$

**Write an equation for the situation. Solve.**

7. Find the three consecutive integers whose sum is 99.
$n + (n + 1) + (n + 2) = 99$
$n = 32$; 32, 33, 34

Name ______________ Class ______________ Date ______________

## Practice

**Write an equation. Then solve.**

1. Bill purchased 4 pens for \$3.32, including \$.16 sales tax. Find the cost of 1 pen.
$4p + 0.16 = 3.32$
$p = 0.79$; One pen costs \$.79.

2. Arnold had \$1.70 in dimes and quarters. He had 3 more dimes than quarters. How many of each coin did he have?
$0.10(n + 3) + 0.25n = \$1.70$
$n = 4$; Arnold had 7 dimes and 4 quarters.

3. A baby weighed 3.2 kg at birth. She gained 0.17 kg per week. How old was she when she weighed 5.75 kg?
$3.2 + 0.17w = 5.75$
$w = 15$; She was 15 weeks old.

4. In the parking lot at a truck stop there were 6 more cars than 18-wheel trucks. There were 134 wheels in the parking lot. How many cars and trucks were there?
$4(v + 6) + 18v = 134$
$v = 5$; There were 11 cars and 5 trucks.

5. The product of 6 and 3 more than $k$ is 48.
$6(k + 3) = 48$
$k = 5$

6. A bottle and a cap together cost \$1.10. The bottle costs \$1 more than the cap. How much does each cost?
$c + (c + 1) = 1.10$
$c = 0.05$; The bottle costs \$1.05 and the cap cost \$.05

7. The perimeter of a rectangular garden is 40 ft. The width is 2 ft more than one half the length. Find the length and width.
$2\left(2 + \frac{1}{2}l + l\right) = 40$
$l = 12$; The length is 12 and the width is 8.



## Reteaching

**Write an equation. Then solve.**

Orlando worked for \$6/h one week and \$7/h the next week. He worked 5 more hours the second week than the first and earned \$347 for the 2 weeks of work. How many hours did he work each week.

Let $h$ be the number of hours Orlando worked the first week.

Then he worked $h + 5$ hours the second week. He earned $6h$ dollars the first week.

| Earnings week 1 | + | Earnings week 2 | = | Total earnings |
|---|---|---|---|---|
| $6h$ | + | $7(h + 5)$ | = | 347 |

Now solve.

| | |
|---|---|
| $6h + 7(h + 5) = 347$ | |
| $6h + 7h + 35 = 347$ | Distribute. |
| $13h + 35 = 347$ | Simplify. |
| $13h + 35 - 35 = 347 - 35$ | Subtract 35 from each side. |
| $13h = 312$ | Simplify. |
| $\frac{13h}{13} = \frac{312}{13}$ | Divide each side by 13. |
| $h = 24$ | |

Orlando worked 24 hours the first week. He worked $h + 5 = 24 + 5 = 29$ hours the second week.

Check: $24 \cdot 6 + 29 \cdot 7 = 144 + 203 = 347$.

**Write an equation. Then solve.**

1. The sum of half of a number and 8 less than the number is 25.
$\frac{1}{2}n + (n - 8) = 25$
$n = 22$; The number is 22.

2. A triangle has two sides equal in length and a third side 5 in. longer than half the length of each of the other two sides. If the perimeter of the triangle is 50 in., how long is each side?
$s + s + \frac{1}{2}s + 5 = 50$
$s = 18$; $\frac{1}{2}s + 5 = 14$
The sides are 18 in., 18 in., and 14 in.



## Enrichment

You can use equations to solve work problems.

Marie can clean a garage in 3 h. Megan can clean it in 4 h. How long would it take them to clean the garage if they worked together?

The key to solving work problems is to look at what happens in 1 h.

| | Amount Marie does in 1 h | + | Amount Megan does in 1 h | = | Amount they do together in 1 h |
|---|---|---|---|---|---|
| | $\frac{1}{3}$ | + | $\frac{1}{4}$ | = | $\frac{1}{h}$ |
| Add the fractions. | | | $\frac{7}{12}$ | = | $\frac{1}{h}$ |
| Find the cross product | | | $7h$ | = | 12 |
| Solve. | | | $h$ | = | $\frac{12}{7}$ or $1\frac{5}{7}$ |

Cleaning the garage will take them $1\frac{5}{7}$ h if they work together.

**Write an equation. Then solve.**

1. Marjorie can wash the car in 2 h. Brad can wash it in 4 h. How long will the job take if they work together?
$\frac{1}{2} + \frac{1}{4} = \frac{1}{h}$; $h = 1\frac{1}{3}$ h

2. Joe can wax the gym in 3 h. Steve can wax it in 2 h. How long will the job take if they work together?
$\frac{1}{3} + \frac{1}{2} = \frac{1}{h}$; $h = 1\frac{1}{5}$ h

3. Jessie can paint a barn in 8 h. Jerome needs 10 h to do the same job. How long will it take them working together?
$\frac{1}{8} + \frac{1}{10} = \frac{1}{h}$; $h = 4\frac{4}{9}$ h

4. Lucy can mow the golf course in 6 h. Stan needs 8 h to do the same job, and Yolanda needs 12 h. How long will it take them to mow the course if they work together?
$\frac{1}{6} + \frac{1}{8} + \frac{1}{12} = \frac{1}{h}$; $h = 2\frac{2}{3}$ h

5. A swimming pool has 3 drains. One can drain the pool in 5 h, one can drain it in 8 h, and one can drain it in 10 h. How long would it take to drain the pool if all three were open at once?
$\frac{1}{5} + \frac{1}{8} + \frac{1}{10} = \frac{1}{h}$; $h = 2\frac{6}{17}$ h

# Standardized Test Prep

Standardized tests, such as those administered for state assessment, SAT9, TerraNova™, ITBS, MAT7, or CAT5, may include multiple choice questions, free-response questions, and open-ended questions.

**Multiple Choice Questions** are followed usually by four choices, one of which is correct.

**Exercises 1–8** are multiple choice questions.

**Free-Response Questions** do not give answer choices. Student must provide the one correct answer on their own.

**Exercises 9–12** are free-response questions.

**Open-Ended Questions** allow for more than one solution. Students must construct their own responses instead of choosing from possible answers.

**Exercise 12** is an open-ended question.

## Resources

See page 333G for a list of assessment options.

## Test-Taking Tip

If you have time, solve a problem before you look at the answer choices. Otherwise the answer choices may lead you to choose an answer that seems correct but is not.

### Test-Taking Tips on Transparency

A diagram can help you see how to solve a problem.

*Example* A square quilt has 6 in. by 6 in. fabric squares. The outside perimeter is 144 in. How many squares are on the quilt perimeter?

A. 144 B. 36 C. 24 D. 20

Each side must be 144 ÷ 4 = 36 in.

Let one unit on graph paper represent 6 in.

There must be 36 ÷ 6 = 6 squares on each side.

Draw a diagram, and count the perimeter squares.

The answer is 20, or choice D.

Use a diagram to find the answer. Explain your reasoning.

1. Tess wants to fence in her garden, which is 5 ft long and 4 ft wide. She will put a post at each corner and at every foot. How many fence posts will she need?

   A. 14 B. 20 C. 18 D. 19

2. What is the area of the shaded square in the figure?

   F. 50 $cm^2$
   G. 400 $cm^2$
   H. 200 $cm^2$
   J. 100 $cm^2$

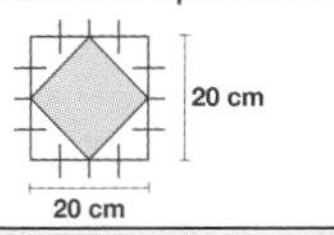

# Standardized Test Prep

## Multiple Choice

**Choose the best answer.**

1. At Store A, a $5\frac{1}{2}$-lb bag of carrots costs \$4.40. Store B charges the same price for an 84-oz bag of carrots. Which expression will help you find the number of ounces in a $5\frac{1}{2}$-lb bag of carrots? A

   A. $\frac{11}{2}\text{lb} \cdot \frac{16\text{ oz}}{1\text{ lb}}$ B. $\$4.40 \div \frac{16\text{ oz}}{1\text{ lb}}$
   C. $84\text{ oz} - \frac{16\text{ oz}}{2\text{ lb}}$ D. $\frac{11}{2}\text{ lb} \div 16\text{ oz}$

2. The sides of square W are three times the sides of square Z. How many times the area of square Z is the area of square W? J

   F. 2 times G. 4 times
   H. 6 times J. 9 times

3. The Sullivans rented a large truck for \$49.95 plus \$.60/mi. Before returning the truck, they filled the gas tank, which cost \$9.00. The total cost for renting the truck, including gasoline, was \$93.23. Find the number of miles the truck was driven to the nearest mile. B

   A. 20 mi B. 57 mi
   C. 72 mi D. 155 mi

4. One third of the businesses bordering the Fir River donated money for its cleanup. One half of the businesses that donated money supplied volunteers as well. About what percent of the businesses supplied volunteers? H

   F. 6% G. 13%
   H. 17% J. 50%

5. Which of the following equals $2 \cdot 2 \cdot 2 \cdot a \cdot a$? C

   A. $2a2^3$ B. $6a^2$
   C. $2^3a^2$ D. $8a^3$

6. A video rental company rents movies for \$3.95 for the first day. Each additional day costs \$1.25. Sara paid a total of \$7.70 for renting a movie. For how many additional days did Sara keep the movie? J

   F. 6 days G. 5 days
   H. 4 days J. 3 days

7. The area of a rectangle is 64 in.$^2$. If the area is increased by 25%, which of these could be the dimensions of the new rectangle? A

   A. 10 in. by 8 in. B. 8 in. by 8 in.
   C. 6 in. by 8 in. D. 10 in. by 10 in.

8. Suppose you drop a ball from the ledge of a third-story window. Each bounce of the ball reaches one half the height of the previous bounce. On the third bounce the ball reaches a height of 3 ft and is caught. The total vertical distance traveled by the ball is 63 ft. What is the height of the window ledge? H

   F. 22 ft G. 11 ft
   H. 24 ft J. 48 ft

## Free Response

**For Exercises 9–12, show all your work.**

9. Solve $-\frac{x}{7} + 3 = -2$. 35

10. The sum of three consecutive integers is 57. What are the integers? 18, 19, 20

11. You eat three meals a day for seven days each week. About how many meals will you eat in 25 years? 27,300 meals

12. *Open-ended* Write an equation involving one variable and two or more consecutive integers. Solve your equation. Check students' work.

# Solving Equations with Variables on Both Sides

7-5

## *Investigate*

**USING MODELS TO SOLVE EQUATIONS**

Work in pairs.

1. Write an equation for the model at the right. $5x - 8 = 3x$

2. a. You must do the same thing to each side of the model. What can you do to get all of the green tiles on only one side?
   b. Show what the model will look like when green tiles are on only one side. Write the new equation. 2a–b. See below right.
   c. Solve your new equation. 4

### What You'll Learn

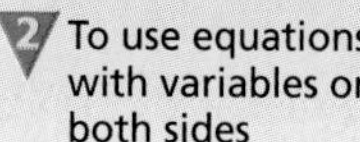

1. To solve equations with variables on both sides
2. To use equations with variables on both sides

### . . . And Why

To solve problems that involve time and distance

2a. Remove 3 green tiles from each side.

2b.

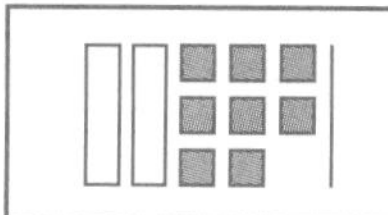

$2x - 8 = 0$

## PART 1 Solving Equations with Variables on Both Sides

To solve an equation with variables on both sides, use addition or subtraction to get the variable on only one side of the equation.

### EXAMPLE 1

**Solve $9a + 2 = 4a - 18$.**

| | |
|---|---|
| $9a + 2 = 4a - 18$ | |
| $9a - 4a + 2 = 4a - 4a - 18$ | Subtract $4a$ from each side. |
| $5a + 2 = -18$ | Combine like terms. |
| $5a + 2 - 2 = -18 - 2$ | Subtract 2 from each side. |
| $5a = -20$ | Simplify. |
| $\frac{5a}{5} = \frac{-20}{5}$ | Divide each side by 5. |
| $a = -4$ | Simplify. |

**Check**

| | |
|---|---|
| $9a + 2 = 4a - 18$ | |
| $9(-4) + 2 \stackrel{?}{=} 4(-4) - 18$ | Substitute $-4$ for $a$. |
| $-36 + 2 \stackrel{?}{=} -16 - 18$ | Multiply. |
| $-34 = -34$ ✔ | |



# 7-5

## Getting Ready

**Materials** algebra tiles

**Resources** A complete list of resources for this lesson is on p. 333H.

### Daily Skills Warm-Up

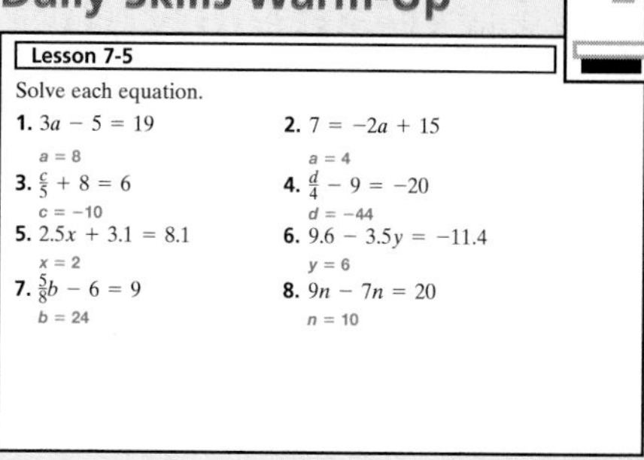

Lesson 7-5

Solve each equation.

1. $3a - 5 = 19$ $a = 8$
2. $7 = -2a + 15$ $a = 4$
3. $\frac{c}{5} + 8 = 6$ $c = -10$
4. $\frac{d}{4} - 9 = -20$ $d = -44$
5. $2.5x + 3.1 = 8.1$ $x = 2$
6. $9.6 - 3.5y = -11.4$ $y = 6$
7. $\frac{5}{8}b - 6 = 9$ $b = 24$
8. $9n - 7n = 20$ $n = 10$

### Background for the Lesson

When you solve equations with variables on both sides, you again will isolate the variable. First gather like terms so that the variable is only on one side of the equation. To move either constants or variables from one side to the other, you use inverse operations. For example, in $x + 2 = 5$, subtract 2 from each side to get $x = 3$. Similarly, in $2y = y - 8$, subtract $y$ from both sides to get $y = -8$.

## 1 Focus

### Investigate

Remind students that a green tile represents one variable, such as $x$, and a red tile represents the number $-1$.

### Connecting to Prior Knowledge

In Lesson 7-2, students learned how to solve equations for multi-step problems. In this lesson, students learn how to solve multi-step equations with the variable on both sides of the equation. In Lesson 7-7, student will use these skills to transform formulas.

# Tools to Monitor Progress

### BEFORE THE LESSON

**To check prerequisite skills:**

- Simplifying expressions

**Skills You Need,** p. 333

### DURING THE LESSON

**To check understanding:**

**Try This** exercises on student page

- **Additional Example 1**

  Solve $4c + 3 = 15 - 2c$. $c = 2$

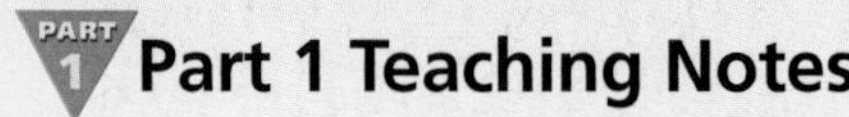

# 2 Teach

## Part 1 Teaching Notes

Suggest that students ask themselves this question: "Which side of the equation has more of the variable?" The math is a little easier if they decide to collect all the variable terms on the side that already has the greater coefficient on the variable.

### Example 1

**Build understanding.** Ask: Are the variable expressions $9a$ and $4a$ like terms? Explain. Yes, both contain the variable $a$.

**Advanced Learners** Ask students how they might get the variable on only one side of this equation $3b + 4 + 2b = 8 - 7b + 4b$. sample answer: Combine like terms, and then add $3b$ to both sides.

**ELL** Verify that students understand that using properties to get the variable terms gathered together on only one side of the equation means writing equivalent equations with all of the variable terms collected on one side of the equation and all the constants collected on the other side.

## Part 2 Teaching Notes

Review how to use the Distributive Property as part of solving an equation.

### Example 2

**Build understanding.** Ask: In this equation, $x$ represents time. How do you know the units for the time in this problem? Ted's time is $x - \frac{1}{2}$, where the $\frac{1}{2}$ represents one half of an hour.

**Extension** What would you change in the problem in Example 2 for Ted's time to be $x + \frac{1}{2}$? Ted would have to leave $\frac{1}{2}$ hour before Beth.



---

**TRY THIS** Solve and check each equation.

3. $4x + 4 = 2x + 36$ 16
4. $-15 + 6b = -8b + 13$ 2

## Part 2 Using Equations with Variables on Both Sides

You may need to use the Distributive Property to simplify one or both sides of an equation before you can get the variable alone on one side.

REAL-WORLD  CONNECTION

### EXAMPLE 2

**Beth leaves home on her bicycle, riding at a steady rate of 8 mi/h. Her brother Ted leaves home on his bicycle half an hour later, following Beth's route. He rides at a steady rate of 12 mi/h. How long after Beth leaves home will Ted catch up?**

distance Beth travels = distance Ted travels

**Words** 8 mi/h · Beth's time = 12 mi/h · Ted's time

Let $x$ = Beth's time.

Then $x - \frac{1}{2}$ = Ted's time.

**Equation** $8 \cdot x = 12 \cdot \left(x - \frac{1}{2}\right)$

$$8x = 12\left(x - \tfrac{1}{2}\right)$$

$$8x = 12x - 6 \quad \text{Use the Distributive Property.}$$

$$8x - 12x = 12x - 12x - 6 \quad \text{Subtract } 12x \text{ from each side.}$$

$$-4x = -6 \quad \text{Combine like terms.}$$

$$\frac{-4x}{-4} = \frac{-6}{-4} \quad \text{Divide each side by } -4.$$

$$x = \tfrac{6}{4} \text{ or } 1\tfrac{1}{2} \quad \text{Simplify.}$$

Ted will catch up with Beth $1\frac{1}{2}$ h after she leaves home.

**Check** Test the solution. At 8 mi/h, Beth will ride 12 mi in $1\frac{1}{2}$ h. Ted's time is $\frac{1}{2}$ h less than Beth's. He rides for 1 h. At 12 mi/h, he travels 12 mi in all. Since Beth and Ted each travel 12 mi, the answer checks.

An estimated 80.6 million people in the United States ride bicycles. About 14.5% of the nation's bicycle riders live in California.
SOURCE: Bicycle Market Research Institute

**TRY THIS**

5. Car A leaves Eastown traveling at a steady rate of 50 mi/h. Car B leaves Eastown 1 h later following Car A. It travels at a steady rate of 60 mi/h. How long after Car A leaves Eastown will Car B catch up? 6 h



---

- **Additional Example 2**
  Steve types at a rate of 15 words/min and Jenny types at a rate of 20 words/min. If Steve and Jenny are both typing the same document, but Steve starts 5 min before Jenny, how long will Jenny have typed when she catches up with Steve? 15 min

## AFTER THE LESSON

**To assess knowledge:**
**Lesson Quiz**
Solve each equation.

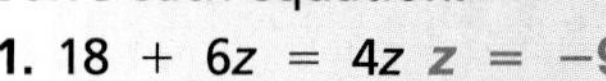
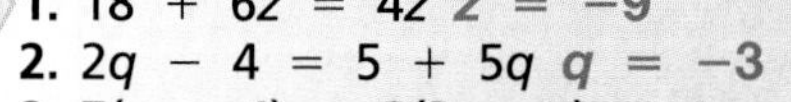

1. $18 + 6z = 4z$ $z = -9$
2. $2q - 4 = 5 + 5q$ $q = -3$
3. $7(v - 4) = 3(3 + v) - 1$ $v = 9$

- For enrichment and reteaching options see Resources on p. 333H.

# Exercises

## Check Understanding

**Copy and complete the steps to solve each equation.**

1. $-2a + 7 = a - 8$
   $-2a + 7 - a = a - 8 - ■$ a
   $-3a ■ + 7 = -8$
   $-3a ■ + 7 - 7 = -8 - 7$
   $-3a ■ = -15$
   $\frac{-3a}{-3} ■ = \frac{-15}{-3}$
   $a = ■$ 5

2. $2(x + 8) = -x - 5$
   $2x + ■ = -x - 5$ 16
   $2x + 16 + ■ = -x - 5 + ■$ x, x
   $3x ■ + 16 = -5$
   $3x + 16 - ■ = -5 - ■$ 16, 16
   $3x ■ = -21$
   $\frac{3x ■}{3} = \frac{-21}{3}$
   $x = ■$ −7

**Solve each equation.**

3. $3y - 20 = 8y$ −4
4. $x - 7 = 2x - 6$ −1
5. $2(x - 4) = 3x$ −8

6. A jet airplane leaves an airport traveling at a steady rate of 600 km/h. Another jet leaves the same airport $\frac{3}{4}$ h later traveling at 800 km/h in the same direction. How long will the second jet take to overtake the first? $2\frac{1}{4}$ h

## Practice and Problem Solving

**Solve each equation.**

7. $5x + 8 = 7x$ 4
8. $3a = a + 22$ 11
9. $20.6 + 2.1x = -8.2x$ −2
10. $2a + 6 = -a - 8$ $-\frac{14}{3}$
11. $4w + 8 = 6w - 4$ 6
12. $7a = 2(a - 10)$ −4
13. $5(n - 3) = 2n - 6$ 3
14. $4(8 - y) = 2y + 16$ $\frac{8}{3}$
15. $-2(y + 6) = y + 3 + 2y$ −3
16. $b + b + 18 = 4b$ 9
17. $q + q + q = q + 6$ 3
18. $\frac{1}{2}(4d - 2) = d + 5$ 6
19. $m - 14 = 3m + 18 + 2m$ −8
20. $6(g + 3) = -2(g + 31)$ −10
21. ✪ $7a - 4 + 2a = 3a - 2$ $\frac{1}{3}$
22. ✪ $3(2y - 0.3) = 19.4 - y$ 2.9
23. ✪ $9 - (2k - 3) = k$ 4
24. ✪ $2\left(2a + \frac{1}{2}\right) = 3\left(a - \frac{2}{3}\right)$ −3

# 3 Practice/Assess

## Assignment Guide

To provide flexible scheduling, this lesson can be divided into parts.

**Part 1**

**Core** 1–5, 7–20, 31–32, 34–35

**Extension** 21–25, 33

**Part 2**

**Core** 6, 26–29

**Extension** 30

Mixed Review can be assigned at any time for maintenance.

## Exercises

**Error Prevention** **Exercises 7–24** Remind students that they may have to use the Distributive Property to simplify one or both sides of the equation before isolating the variable on one side.

**Tactile Learning** **Exercise 27** Students may want to use algebra tiles to model this problem.

## Challenge

$4a(12 - \frac{2}{a}) = a(4 + \frac{3}{a}),\ a \neq 0$ $a = \frac{1}{4}$

## Closure

You can solve equations with variables on both sides by first simplifying both sides of the equation. Then use properties of equality to get the variable alone on one side of the equation.

## Daily Cumulative Review

**Write an equation. Then solve.** *(Lesson 7-4)*

1. The perimeter of a rectangle is 310 ft. The width is 35 ft less than the length. Find the width and length of the rectangle.
   $310 = 2L + 2(L - 35)$; length = 95 ft, width = 60 ft
2. Mike and Rob each purchased a bicycle for a total of \$469. Mike paid \$56 more for his bike than Rob did. How much did each boy pay?
   $468 = x + (x + 56)$; Mike paid \$262. Rob paid \$206.

**Solve each equation.** *(Lesson 7-3)*

3. $16.3 - 7.2y = -8.18$ — $y = 3.4$
4. $3.3c + 1.5c = 7.68$ — $c = 1.6$
5. $\frac{1}{5}r + 10 = \frac{2}{5}$ — $r = -48$
6. $\frac{5}{6}(d - 24) = 5$ — $d = 30$
7. $\frac{a}{4} - \frac{2a}{4} = \frac{1}{4}$ — $a = -1$
8. $-1.5t + 5 + 3t = 6$ — $t = 0.\overline{6}$

**Mixed Review**

**Solve each inequality.**

9. (2-10) $\frac{x}{4} \geq 2$ — $x \geq 8$
10. (2-9) $5 < a + 2.8$ — $2.2 < a$
11. (2-10) $6s > 48$ — $s > 8$
12. (2-9) $b - 8 < -6$ — $b < 2$
13. (2-10) $15 \leq -3t$ — $-5 \geq t$
14. (2-9) $8.4 + p < 2.4$ — $p < -6$

**Graph each solution on the number line.**

15. (2-8) $s \geq -2$
    −5 −4 −3 −2 −1 0 1 2 3 4 5
16. (2-9) $r - 6 < -3$
    −5 −4 −3 −2 −1 0 1 2 3 4 5

**Simplify each expression.**

17. (4-2) $0.6^2$ — 0.36
18. (4-2) $-5^2$ — −25
19. (4-2) $3(2 + 3)^2$ — 75



25. *Mental Math* Is the solution to $5b = 2b - 42 - 3b$ positive or negative? Explain. Explanations may vary. Sample: Negative; when the variable is on only one side of the equation, its coefficient is positive while the constant on the other side of the equation is negative.
26. *Open-ended* Write a problem that you can represent with an equation with variables on both sides. Write and solve the equation. Check students' work.

**Write an equation for each situation. Solve.**

27. *Number Sense* If a number $n$ is subtracted from 18, the result is four less than $n$. What is the value of $n$? 11
28. A cellular phone company charges a \$27.95 monthly fee and \$.12/min for local calls. Another company charges \$12.95 a month and \$.32/min for local calls. For what number of minutes of local calls is the cost of the plans the same? 75 min
29. A group of campers and one group leader left a campsite in a canoe traveling at a steady 8 km/h. One hour later, the other group leader left the campsite in a motorboat with all of the supplies. The motorboat followed the canoe at a steady 20 km/h. How long after the canoe left the campsite did the motorboat overtake it? $1\frac{2}{3}$ h
30. A video store offers two types of rental cards. Each rental card is good for six months. The gold rental card costs \$25 plus \$1.75/rental. The silver rental card costs \$10 plus \$3.25/rental. For what number of videos is the total cost of the rental cards the same? 10 videos

*Math in the Media* **Use the article below for Exercises 31 and 32.**

### The Father of Algebra

Diophantus was a Greek mathematician who lived in the third century. He was one of the first mathematicians to use algebraic symbols.

Most of what is known about Diophantus's life comes from an algebraic riddle from around the early sixth century. The riddle states, "Diophantus's youth lasted one sixth of his life. He grew a beard after one twelfth more. After one seventh more of his life he married. Five years later he and his wife had a son. The son lived exactly one half as long as his father, and Diophantus died four years after his son. All of this adds up to the years Diophantus lived." The riddle, the "facts" of which may or may not be true, results in the following equation:

$$\frac{1}{6}a + \frac{1}{12}a + \frac{1}{7}a + 5 + \frac{1}{2}a + 4 = a$$

where $a$ is Diophantus's age at the time of his death.

31. Solve the equation in the article to determine how many years Diophantus lived. 84 years
32. How old was Diophantus when he married? 34 years



## Alternative Assessment

Select one equation from Practice Exercises 7–24 and write a word problem that can be solved by using the equation you select.

33a. Explanations may vary. Sample: No; multiplying by $\frac{8}{5}$ will leave $\frac{8}{5}b$ on the right side.

33. a. *Reasoning* Would you solve the equation $\frac{5}{8}b = 10 - b$ by multiplying each side by $\frac{8}{5}$ as your first step? Why or why not?
b. Solve the equation. $\frac{80}{13}$

34. *Writing* Describe the steps you would use to solve the equation $5(2a - 3) = 20 + a$. See below.

35. *Error Analysis* The student who solved the equation at the right made an error. Find the error. State the correct solution.
The student subtracted 4x from each side of the equation instead of adding 4x. The solution is $-\frac{2}{3}$.

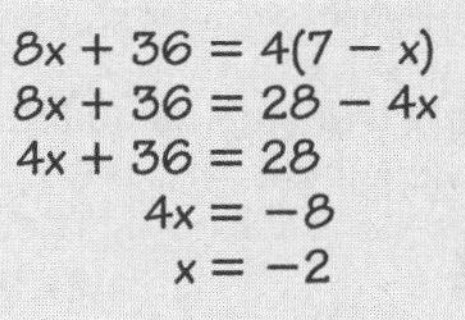

$$8x + 36 = 4(7 - x)$$
$$8x + 36 = 28 - 4x$$
$$4x + 36 = 28$$
$$4x = -8$$
$$x = -2$$

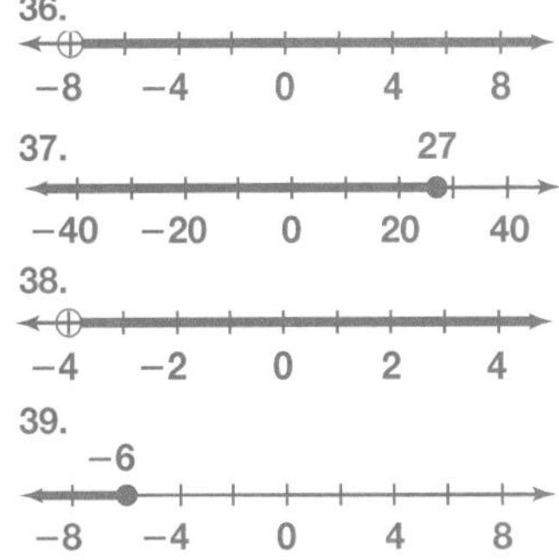


34. First, use the Distributive Property on the left side. Next, get the variable on the left side only and the constants on the right side. Finally, divide each side by the coefficient of *a*.

## Mixed Review

**Solve and graph each inequality.** ***(Lesson 2-10)*** 36–39. For graphs, see above.

36. $-4x < 32$ $x > -8$
37. $\frac{a}{-9} \geq -3$ $a \leq 27$
38. $-12 < 3y$ $y > -4$
39. $12 \leq -2y$ $y \leq -6$

**Find each discount or markup.** ***(Lesson 6-9)***

40. \$15; 25% discount \$3.75
41. \$88; 32% markup \$28.16
42. \$24; 72% markup \$17.28
43. \$110; 75% discount \$82.50

44. *Choose a Strategy* In a collection of dimes and quarters, there are seven more quarters than there are dimes. How many dimes and quarters are there if the collection is worth \$3.50? 5 dimes, 12 quarters

## Math at Work

### City Planner

City planners, also called urban planners or regional planners, determine the best use of a community's land and resources for homes, businesses, and recreation. They also work on community problems such as traffic congestion and air pollution. They study the effects of proposed changes in a community, such as the addition of a bus line or a new highway. Planners use mathematical analysis to evaluate different courses of action and to predict the impact of each course on a community.

For more information about city planners, visit the Prentice Hall Web site. **www.phschool.com**

See also Extra Practice section.



### Math at Work

If you have block scheduling or extended class periods, have a group of students write a set of questions about how city planners use math. Then help the group interview your local city planner to ask him or her for specifics about using math on the job. Have students report their findings to the class.

Students can find additional information on the Web site **www.phschool.com**.

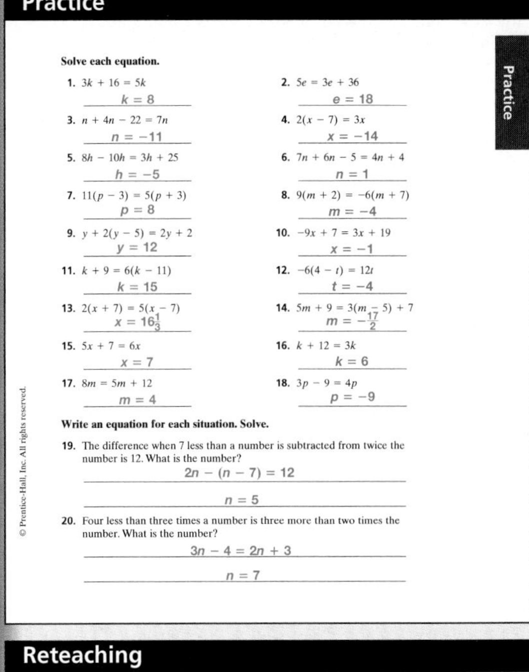

## Practice

**Solve each equation.**

1. $3k + 16 = 5k$   $k = 8$
2. $5e = 3e + 36$   $e = 18$
3. $n + 4n - 22 = 7n$   $n = -11$
4. $2(x - 7) = 3x$   $x = -14$
5. $8h - 10h = 3h + 25$   $h = -5$
6. $7n + 6n - 5 = 4n + 4$   $n = 1$
7. $11(p - 3) = 5(p + 3)$   $p = 8$
8. $9(m + 2) = -6(m + 7)$   $m = -4$
9. $y + 2(y - 5) = 2y + 2$   $y = 12$
10. $-9x + 7 = 3x + 19$   $x = -1$
11. $k + 9 = 6(k - 11)$   $k = 15$
12. $-6(4 - t) = 12t$   $t = -4$
13. $2(x + 7) = 5(x - 7)$   $x = 16\frac{1}{3}$
14. $5m + 9 = 3(m - 5) + 7$   $m = -\frac{17}{2}$
15. $5x + 7 = 6x$   $x = 7$
16. $k + 12 = 3k$   $k = 6$
17. $8m = 5m + 12$   $m = 4$
18. $3p - 9 = 4p$   $p = -9$

**Write an equation for each situation. Solve.**

19. The difference when 7 less than a number is subtracted from twice the number is 12. What is the number?
$2n - (n - 7) = 12$
$n = 5$

20. Four less than three times a number is three more than two times the number. What is the number?
$3n - 4 = 2n + 3$
$n = 7$



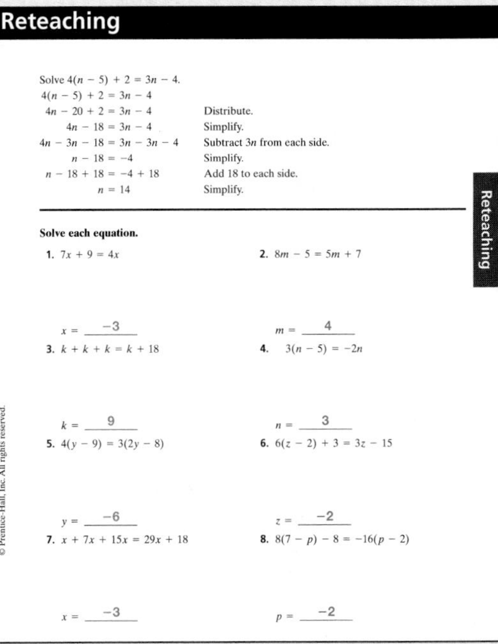

## Reteaching

Solve $4(n - 5) + 2 = 3n - 4$.

| | |
|---|---|
| $4(n - 5) + 2 = 3n - 4$ | |
| $4n - 20 + 2 = 3n - 4$ | Distribute. |
| $4n - 18 = 3n - 4$ | Simplify. |
| $4n - 3n - 18 = 3n - 3n - 4$ | Subtract 3*n* from each side. |
| $n - 18 = -4$ | Simplify. |
| $n - 18 + 18 = -4 + 18$ | Add 18 to each side. |
| $n = 14$ | Simplify. |

**Solve each equation.**

1. $7x + 9 = 4x$   $x =$ −3
2. $8m - 5 = 5m + 7$   $m =$ 4
3. $k + k + k = k + 18$   $k =$ 9
4. $3(n - 5) = -2n$   $n =$ 3
5. $4(y - 9) = 3(2y - 8)$   $y =$ −6
6. $6(z - 2) + 3 = 3z - 15$   $z =$ −2
7. $x + 7x + 15x = 29x + 18$   $x =$ −3
8. $8(7 - p) - 8 = -16(p - 2)$   $p =$ −2



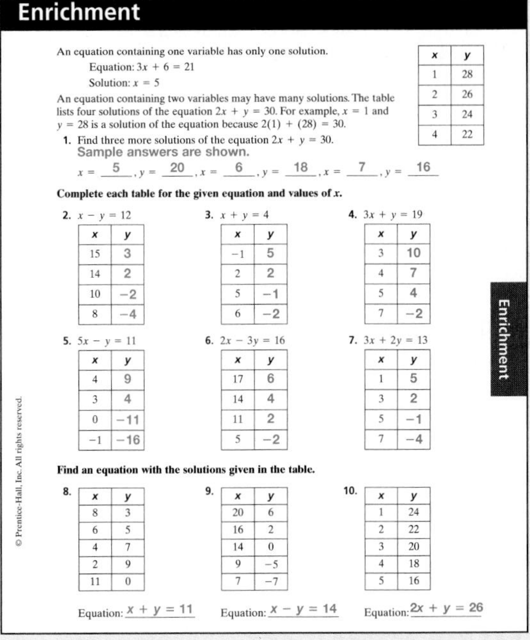

## Enrichment

An equation containing one variable has only one solution.
Equation: $3x + 6 = 21$
Solution: $x = 5$

An equation containing two variables may have many solutions. The table lists four solutions of the equation $2x + y = 30$. For example, $x = 1$ and $y = 28$ is a solution of the equation because $2(1) + (28) = 30$.

| x | y |
|---|---|
| 1 | 28 |
| 2 | 26 |
| 3 | 24 |
| 4 | 22 |

1. Find three more solutions of the equation $2x + y = 30$.
Sample answers are shown.
$x =$ 5, $y =$ 20, $x =$ 6, $y =$ 18, $x =$ 7, $y =$ 16

**Complete each table for the given equation and values of *x*.**

2. $x - y = 12$

| x | y |
|---|---|
| 15 | 3 |
| 14 | 2 |
| 10 | −2 |
| 8 | −4 |

3. $x + y = 4$

| x | y |
|---|---|
| −1 | 5 |
| 2 | 2 |
| 5 | −1 |
| 6 | −2 |

4. $3x + y = 19$

| x | y |
|---|---|
| 3 | 10 |
| 4 | 7 |
| 5 | 4 |
| 7 | −2 |

5. $5x - y = 11$

| x | y |
|---|---|
| 4 | 9 |
| 3 | 4 |
| 0 | −11 |
| −1 | −16 |

6. $2x - 3y = 16$

| x | y |
|---|---|
| 17 | 6 |
| 14 | 4 |
| 11 | 2 |
| 5 | −2 |

7. $3x + 2y = 13$

| x | y |
|---|---|
| 1 | 5 |
| 3 | 2 |
| 5 | −1 |
| 7 | −4 |

**Find an equation with the solutions given in the table.**

8.

| x | y |
|---|---|
| 8 | 3 |
| 6 | 5 |
| 4 | 7 |
| 2 | 9 |
| 11 | 0 |

Equation: $x + y = 11$

9.

| x | y |
|---|---|
| 20 | 6 |
| 16 | 2 |
| 14 | 0 |
| 9 | −5 |
| 7 | −7 |

Equation: $x - y = 14$

10.

| x | y |
|---|---|
| 1 | 24 |
| 2 | 22 |
| 3 | 20 |
| 4 | 18 |
| 5 | 16 |

Equation: $2x + y = 26$

# 7-6

## Getting Ready

**Resources** A complete list of resources for this lesson is on p. 333H.

### Daily Skills Warm-Up

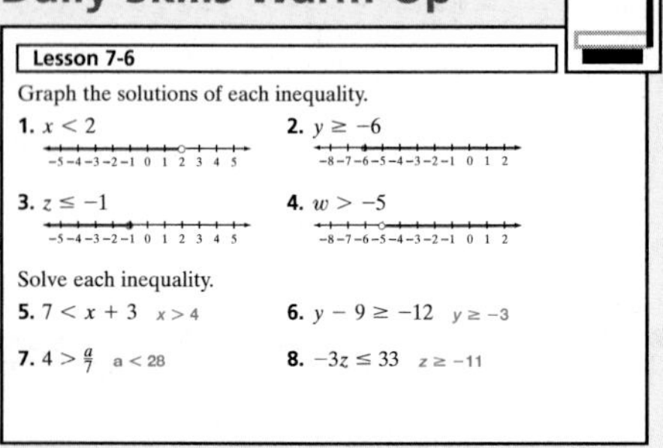
Lesson 7-6

Graph the solutions of each inequality.

1. $x < 2$
2. $y \geq -6$
3. $z \leq -1$
4. $w > -5$

Solve each inequality.

5. $7 < x + 3$ $x > 4$
6. $y - 9 \geq -12$ $y \geq -3$
7. $4 > \frac{a}{7}$ $a < 28$
8. $-3z \leq 33$ $z \geq -11$

### Background for the Lesson

You solve two-step inequalities just as you solve two-step equations by using inverse operations to isolate the variable. First add or subtract to get the term containing the variable alone on one side of the inequality. Then divide or multiply each side of the inequality to isolate the variable. Multiplying or dividing by a negative number reverses the sign of the inequality.

## 1 Focus

### Connecting to Students' Lives

Ask students what they know about the weight limits airlines put on luggage. Often this weight limit is expressed as an inequality.

### Connecting to Prior Knowledge

In Lesson 7-1, students learned how to solve two-step equations. Students use the same procedures in this lesson to solve two-step inequalities. In the Math Toolbox that follows this lesson, students will apply what they learned to solving compound inequalities.

# 7-6 Solving Two-Step Inequalities

**What You'll Learn**

1. To solve two-step inequalities
2. To use two-step inequalities to solve problems

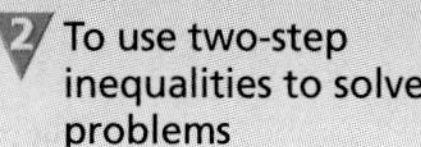

**. . . And Why**

To solve problems involving camping and jobs

## PART 1 Solving Two-Step Inequalities

Solving two-step inequalities involves the same steps as solving two-step equations.

### EXAMPLE 1

**Solve and graph $2y - 3 \leq -5$.**

$2y - 3 \leq -5$

$2y - 3 + 3 \leq -5 + 3$ Add 3 to each side.

$2y \leq -2$ Simplify.

$\frac{2y}{2} \leq \frac{-2}{2}$ Divide each side by 2.

$y \leq -1$ Simplify.

−6 −4 −2 0 2 4 6

**TRY THIS** Solve and graph each inequality.

1. $5a - 9 > 11$ $a > 4$
2. $-10 \geq 2x - 6$ $x \leq -2$
3. $17 + \frac{1}{2}c < 14$ $c < -6$

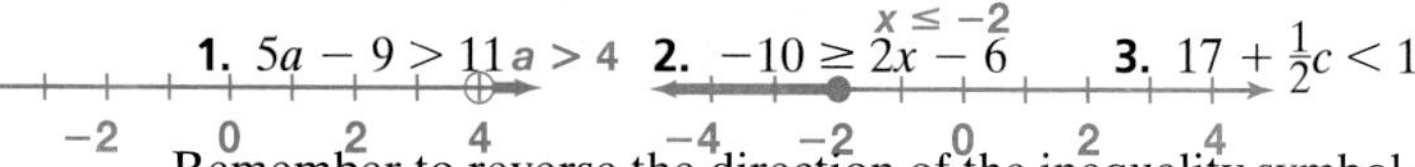

Remember to reverse the direction of the inequality symbol when you multiply or divide by a negative number.

**Quick Review**

If $a > b$, then $a + c > b + c$.

If $a > b$, then $a - c > b - c$.

If $a > b$ and $c > 0$, then $ac > bc$.

If $a > b$ and $c > 0$, then $\frac{a}{c} > \frac{b}{c}$.

If $a > b$ and $c < 0$, then $ac < bc$.

If $a > b$ and $c < 0$, then $\frac{a}{c} < \frac{b}{c}$.

### EXAMPLE 2

**Solve $-9 > -\frac{1}{3}x + 6$.**

$-9 > -\frac{1}{3}x + 6$

$-9 - 6 > -\frac{1}{3}x + 6 - 6$ Subtract 6 from each side.

$-15 > -\frac{1}{3}x$ Simplify.

$-3(-15) < -3\left(-\frac{1}{3}x\right)$ Multiply each side by −3. Reverse the direction of the inequality symbol.

$45 < x$ or $x > 45$ Simplify.



## Tools to Monitor Progress

**BEFORE THE LESSON**

**To check prerequisite skills:**

- Solving inequalities

**Skills You Need,** p. 333

**DURING THE LESSON**

**To check understanding:**

**Try This** exercises on student page

- **Additional Example 1**
  Solve $7g + 11 > 67$. $g > 8$
- **Additional Example 2**
  Solve $6 \leq -\frac{2}{3}r - 6$. $-18 \geq r$, or $r \leq -18$

**TRY THIS** Solve each inequality.

4. $\frac{m}{-5} + 4 \le 7$ $m \ge -15$ 5. $6 - x > 3$ $x < 3$ 6. $8.3 < -0.5b - 2.7$ $b < -22$

## PART 2 Using Two-Step Inequalities

Now that you know how to solve two-step inequalities, you can use them to solve real-world problems.

REAL-WORLD CONNECTION

### EXAMPLE 3

**An expedition leader estimates that a group of hikers can carry less than 550 lb of food and equipment. The group must carry 336 lb of equipment as well as 25 lb of food for each climber. What is the greatest possible number of people in the expedition?**

| **Words** | 336 lb of equipment | + | 25 lb of food/person | times | number of people | is less than | 550 lb |
|---|---|---|---|---|---|---|---|

Let $p$ = number of people in the expedition.

| **Inequality** | 336 | + | 25 | · | $p$ | < | 550 |
|---|---|---|---|---|---|---|---|

$336 + 25p < 550$

$336 + 25p - 336 < 550 - 336$ Subtract 336 from each side.

$25p < 214$ Simplify.

$\frac{25p}{25} < \frac{214}{25}$ Divide each side by 25.

$p < 8.56$ Simplify.

Since $p$ is the number of people, $p$ must be a whole number. The greatest number of people in the expedition is 8.

**Check** Is the answer reasonable? The original problem states that the total of the equipment plus 25 lb of food per person is less than 550 lb. Since $336 + 25(8) = 536$, the equipment plus the food is less than 550 lb. The answer is reasonable.

A pint of water weighs 1 lb. You need about a gallon of water per person per day. About how much does water weigh for eight people for four days? 256 lb

**TRY THIS**

7. *Commissions* A stereo salesperson earns a salary of \$1,200 per month, plus a commission of 4% of sales. The salesperson wants to maintain a monthly income of at least \$1,500. How much must the salesperson sell each month? at least \$7,500



# 2 Teach

## PART 1 Part 1 Teaching Notes

Review the key difference between solving inequalities and equations by asking students to multiply each side of $-3 < 2$ by $-5$. The result, $15 > -10$, is only true if you reverse the direction of the inequality symbol because you multiplied each side by a negative number.

### Example 1

**Build understanding.** Ask: Why is the solution to this inequality graphed with a closed circle rather than an open circle? Since −1 makes the sentence true, you can show that it is part of the solution with a closed circle.

**Error Prevention** Students may forget that they are solving inequalities and use an equals sign. Remind students that each step must result in an inequality equivalent to the original one.

### Example 2

**Build understanding.** Ask: Why must you reverse the direction of the inequality symbol? You multiplied by a negative number.

## PART 2 Part 2 Teaching Notes

Encourage students to write a plan, like the one opposite Words in Example 3, before they write their inequality.

**ELL** Help students make a table of examples to show the symbols and words for *at least*, *at most*, *greater than*, and *less than*. Start with "$x$ is at least 10 means $x \ge 10$," and so on.

### Example 3

**Build understanding.** Ask: Why would it not be possible for the total weight of food and equipment to equal 550 lb? The problem says *less than*, not *less than or equal to*.

**Math Reasoning** When might the answer to the question asked in a problem be different from the solution to the equation? sample answer: when the problem situation restricts answers to positive or whole numbers

### Additional Example 3

Dale has \$25 to spend at a carnival. If admission to the carnival is \$4 and the rides cost \$1.50 each, what is the greatest number of rides Dale can go on? 14 rides

## AFTER THE LESSON

**To assess knowledge: Lesson Quiz**

Solve each inequality.

1. $14 > 4d - 10$ $6 > d$
2. $\frac{-3}{k} + 8 \le 7$ $3 \ge k$
3. $32 - 12g < 176$ $g > -12$

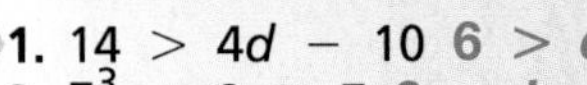

- For enrichment and reteaching options see Resources on p. 333H.

# 3 Practice/Assess

## Assignment Guide

To provide flexible scheduling, this lesson can be divided into parts.

▼ Part 1

**Core** 1–7, 9–28, 30–31

✪ **Extension** 29

▼ Part 2

**Core** 8, 32–34

✪ **Extension** 35

Mixed Review can be assigned at any time for maintenance.

## Exercises

**Auditory Learning Exercises 9–16** Students may want to say the solutions aloud to themselves as a reminder to use a closed circle on the graph when the inequality symbol contains "or equal to."

**Test Prep Exercise 30** Solve the inequality before looking at the graphs.

## ✪ Challenge

Solve $-\frac{14}{23}y + 82 \le 82$. $y \ge 0$

## Closure

Solving two-step inequalities involves the same steps as solving two-step equations. Remember to reverse the direction of the inequality symbol when you multiply or divide by a negative number.

# Exercises

## Check Understanding

**Tell what you can do to the first inequality in order to get the second. Be sure to list *all* the steps.**

1. $4x - 2 \le 6; x \le 2$ — Add 2 to each side, simplify, divide each side by 4, and simplify.
2. $\frac{1}{2}a - 1 < 3; a < 8$ — Add 1 to each side, simplify, multiply each side by 2, and simplify.
3. $2 - 3y > 20; y < -6$ — Subtract 2 from each side, simplify, divide each side by −3, reverse the inequality sign, and simplify.

**Solve each inequality.**

4. $-2x - 1 < 11$ $x > -6$
5. $10 + 4a < -6$ $a < -4$
6. $-\frac{b}{7} + 7 \le 6$ $b \ge 7$
7. $2.1 - 0.6y \ge 0.9$ $y \le 2$
8. ***Number Sense*** You divide a number $x$ by −3. Then you subtract 1 from the quotient. The result is at most 5. Write and solve an inequality to find all possible solutions. $\frac{x}{-3} - 1 \le 5; x \ge -18$

## Practice and Problem Solving

**Solve and graph each inequality.** For graphs, see margin.

9. $2m + 8 > 0$ $m > -4$
10. $-\frac{x}{5} + 2 > 3$ $x < -5$
11. $-9c + 3 \ge 21$ $c \le -2$
12. $6 + 3y > 5$ $y > -\frac{1}{3}$
13. $-2a + 18 < 0$ $a > 9$
14. $4x - 9 > -7$ $x > \frac{1}{2}$
15. $11 - 3b > 5$ $b < 2$
16. $\frac{1}{3}a - 4 \ge -1$ $a \ge 9$

**Solve each inequality.**

17. $10 \le -8x - 6$ $x \le -2$
18. $-5y + 3 \ge 28$ $y \le -5$
19. $3.4 < 1 + 0.8p$ $p > 3$
20. $4 + 7a \ge 32$ $a \ge 4$
21. $1.6 - 0.4b > -6.4$ $b < 20$
22. $-\frac{1}{9}c + 13 \ge 5$ $c \le 72$
23. $-21 - 3m < 0$ $m > -7$
24. $\frac{x}{3} + 11 < 31$ $x < 60$
25. $-\frac{x}{6} - 2 < 4$ $x > -36$
26. $6y - 10 - y > 14$ $y > \frac{24}{5}$
27. $-4(2a + 7) \le -12$ $a \ge -2$
28. $\frac{1}{2}c - \frac{1}{4} < -\frac{3}{4}$ $c < -1$

✪29. ***Error Analysis*** A student solved and graphed the inequality $-12x + 40 > 4$. What error did the student make? The student simplified $\frac{-36}{-12}$ to −3 instead of 3.

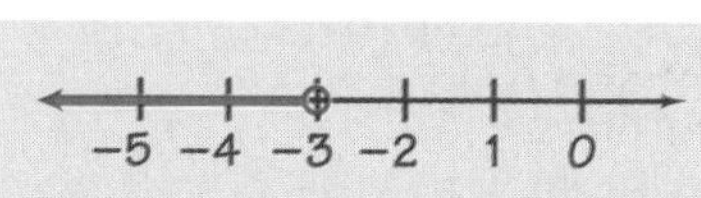


30. **TEST PREP** Which graph shows the solution of $-15 < -2x - 7$? C

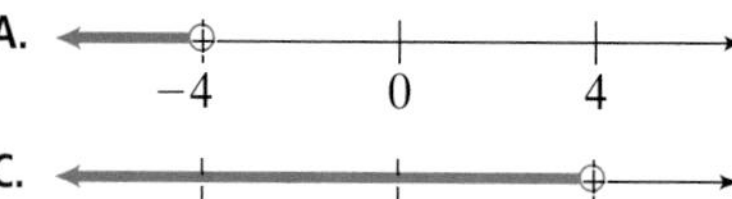


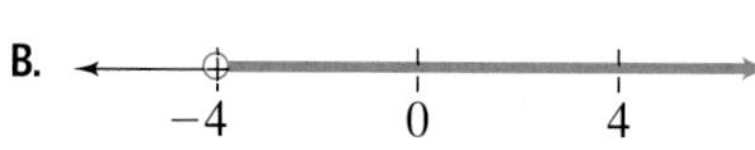


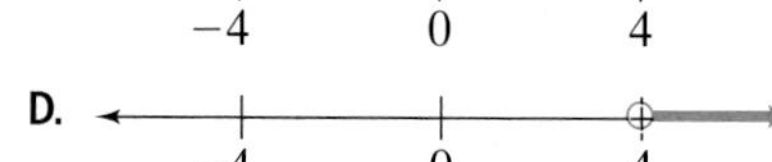




## Daily Cumulative Review

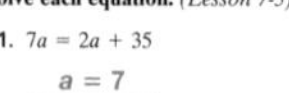

**Solve each equation.** *(Lesson 7-5)*

1. $7a = 2a + 35$ $a = 7$
2. $6b = 3(b - 33)$ $b = -33$
3. $d + 26 + d = 4d$ $13 = d$
4. $f + f + f + f + f = 2f + 36$ $f = 12$
5. $4(m - 0.6) = 36.8 - m$ $m = 7.84$
6. $3\left(3n + \frac{2}{3}\right) = 4\left(n - \frac{3}{4}\right)$ $n = -1$

**Write an equation. Then solve.** *(Lesson 7-4)*

7. A 215-in. piece of yarn is cut into three pieces. The second piece is 5 in. longer than the first. The third piece is 6 in. shorter than the first. How long is each piece?
   $m + (m + 5) + (m - 6) = 215$;
   1st is 72 in., 2nd is 77 in., 3rd is 66 in.

**Mixed Review**

**Use the formula $P = 2l + 2w$. Find $P$, $l$, or $w$.**

8. (3-4) $P = 14$ in., $l = 4$ in. $w = 3$ in.
9. (3-4) $P = 28$ ft, $w = 5$ ft $l = 9$ ft

**Is the given number a solution of the equation?**

10. (2-4) $5 + d = 7; 3$ no
11. (2-4) $10 = 3a + 1; 3$ yes
12. (2-4) $3f = f + 12; 6$ yes

**Is each number prime or composite? If composite write the prime factorization.**

13. (4-3) 45 composite; $3^2 \cdot 5$
14. (4-3) 28 composite; $2^2 \cdot 7$
15. (4-3) 31 prime
16. (4-3) 125 composite; $5^3$



## Alternative Assessment

Have students in pairs draw a graph that represents an inequality and then write a two-step inequality for which the graph shows the solution.

9.
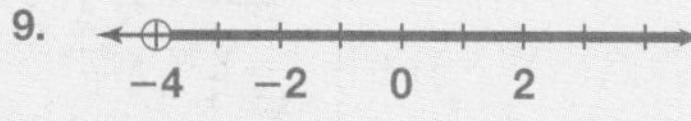


10.
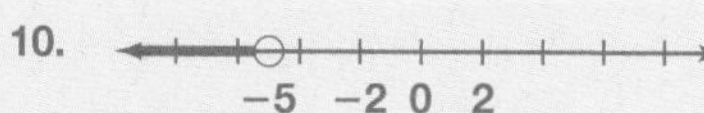


11.
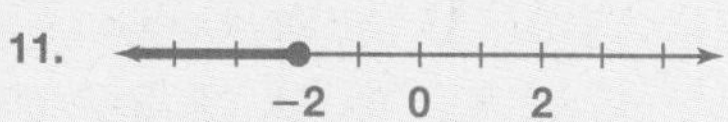


12.
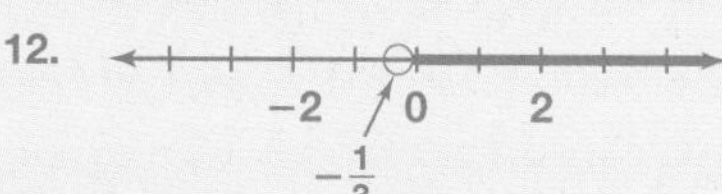


13.
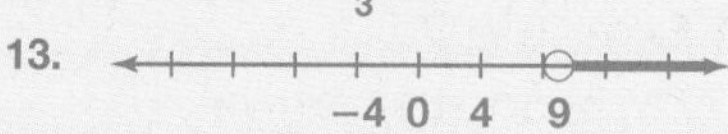


14. −2 0 $\frac{1}{2}$ 2

15. −2 0 2

16.
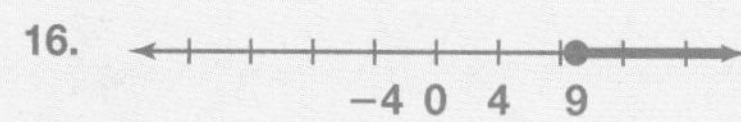

31. Letter excerpt. First undo addition and subtraction, and then undo division and multiplication. Remember to reverse the inequality sign when multiplying or dividing by a negative number.

31. *Writing* A friend was absent from class today. Write a letter to your friend telling how to solve two-step inequalities.

**Photo Price List**

| Size | Price |
|---|---|
| 3 in. x 5 in. | \$.40 |
| 4 in. x 6 in. | \$.45 |
| 5 in. x 7 in. | \$1.95 |
| 8 in. x 10 in. | \$4.95 |
| 8 in. x 12 in. | \$6.45 |
| 11 in. x 14 in. | \$7.00 |
| 16 in. x 20 in. | \$13.95 |
| 20 in. x 30 in. | \$16.95 |

**Write an inequality for each situation. Then solve the inequality.**

32. *Data Analysis* Maureen is ordering photographic reprints and enlargements. She can spend at most \$11. She wants to order an 11-in. × 14-in. enlargement and some 3-in. × 5-in. reprints. How many reprints can she order using the price list at the right? at most 10

33. You want to spend at most \$10 for a taxi ride. Before you go anywhere, the taxi driver sets the meter at the initial charge of \$2. The meter then adds \$1.25 for every mile driven. If you plan on a \$1 tip, what is the farthest you can go? 5 mi

34. Students in a math class need an average of at least 90 points to earn an A. One student's test scores are 88, 91, and 85. What must the student score on the next test to earn an A? 96 or above

35. Corey wants to go on a school music trip to Florida in the spring. His parents agree to lend him \$162 if Corey will pay them back at least \$18 per month. How long will it take Corey to pay the money he owes to his parents? at most 9 months

## MIXED REVIEW

**Solve each equation.** *(Lesson 7-2)*

36. $a - 81 = 9a + 7$ −11

37. $8x - 15 + 4x = 5x + 6$ 3

38. $4(5m - 7) = 10m + 2$ 3

**Use the distance formula, $d = rt$. Find each missing value.** *(Lesson 3-4)*

39. $r = 45$ mi/h, $t = 3.25$ h 146.25 mi

40. $d = 351$ mi, $r = 54$ mi/h 6.5 h

41. $d = 12$ cm, $t = 0.25$ h 48 cm/h

42. *Sales Tax* A stereo costs \$262.99. The sales tax rate is 5%. What is the total cost of the stereo? *(Lesson 6-6)* \$276.14

## ACTIVITY 2 CALCULATING

You can use the formula $D = \frac{M}{V}$ to find the density of a liquid, where $D$ is density, $M$ is the mass of the liquid, and $V$ is the volume of the liquid. Substitute your values from Activity 1 for $M$ and $V$ to find the density of water.

See also Extra Practice section.



## Project Activity 2

**Calculating** The formula Density = Mass / Volume or $D = M/V$, is the standard science formula for calculating density. Another formula for density, which incorporates the subtraction done in Project Activity 1, is $D = (M_t - M_b)/V$.

## Practice

**Solve each inequality. Graph the solutions on a number line.**

1. $5x + 2 \le 17$ $x \le 3$
2. $7x + 2x \ge 21 - 3$ $x \ge 2$
3. $9 - x > 10$ $x < -1$
4. $19 + 8 \le 6 + 7x$ $x \ge 3$
5. $-6x < 12$ $x > -2$
6. $\frac{x}{-4} > 0$ $x < 0$

**Solve each inequality.**

7. $2x - 5 > 1$ $x > 3$
8. $9x - 7 \le 38$ $x \le 5$
9. $3 < \frac{1}{4}x + 1$ $x > 4$
10. $-12 < -12x$ $x < 1$
11. $-8x + 18 > -22$ $x < 5$
12. $50 < 8 - 6x$ $x < -7$
13. $\frac{1}{5}x + 6 > -3$ $x > -45$
14. $30 \ge -6(5 - x)$ $x \le 10$

**Write an inequality for each situation. Then solve the inequality.**

15. Nine more than half the number $n$ is no more than −8. Find $n$.
$\frac{1}{2}n + 9 \le -8$
$n \le -34$

16. Judith drove $h$ hours at a rate of 55 mi/hr. She did not reach her goal of driving 385 miles for the day. How long did she drive?
$55h < 385$
$h < 7$; She drove less than 7 h.



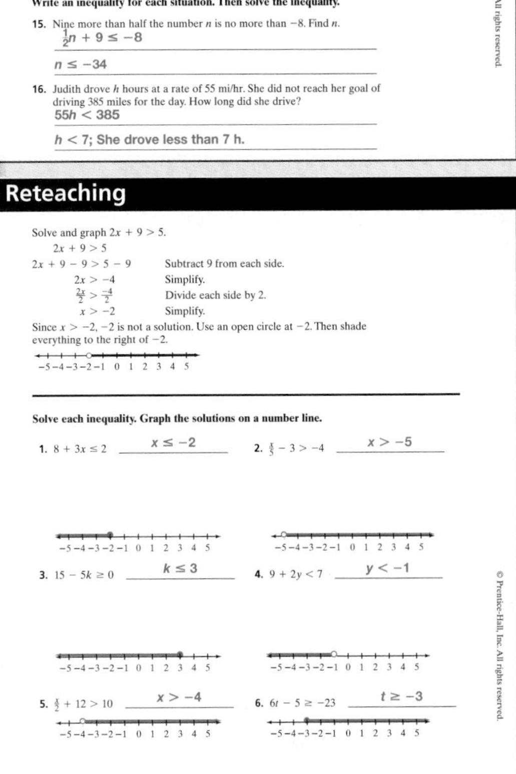

## Reteaching

Solve and graph $2x + 9 > 5$.

$2x + 9 > 5$

$2x + 9 - 9 > 5 - 9$ Subtract 9 from each side.

$2x > -4$ Simplify.

$\frac{2x}{2} > \frac{-4}{2}$ Divide each side by 2.

$x > -2$ Simplify.

Since $x > -2$, −2 is not a solution. Use an open circle at −2. Then shade everything to the right of −2.

**Solve each inequality. Graph the solutions on a number line.**

1. $8 + 3x \le 2$ $x \le -2$
2. $\frac{x}{5} - 3 > -4$ $x > -5$
3. $15 - 5k \ge 0$ $k \le 3$
4. $9 + 2y < 7$ $y < -1$
5. $\frac{x}{2} + 12 > 10$ $x > -4$
6. $6t - 5 \ge -23$ $t \ge -3$



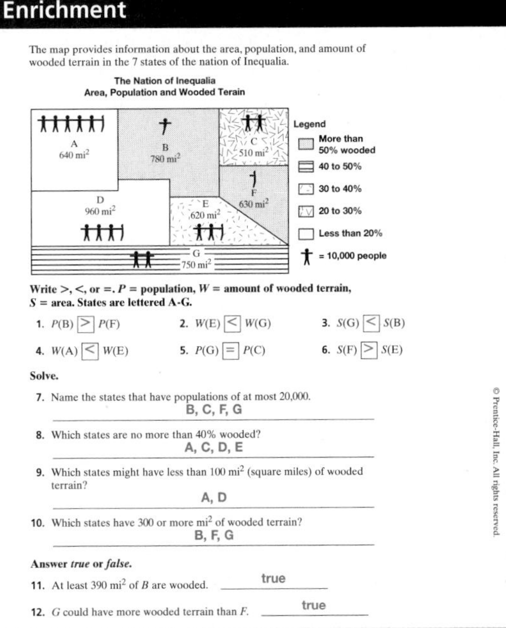

## Enrichment

The map provides information about the area, population, and amount of wooded terrain in the 7 states of the nation of Inequalia.



**Write >, <, or =. $P$ = population, $W$ = amount of wooded terrain, $S$ = area. States are lettered A-G.**

1. $P(B)$ > $P(F)$
2. $W(E)$ < $W(G)$
3. $S(G)$ < $S(B)$
4. $W(A)$ < $W(E)$
5. $P(G)$ = $P(C)$
6. $S(F)$ > $S(E)$

**Solve.**

7. Name the states that have populations of at most 20,000. B, C, F, G
8. Which states are no more than 40% wooded? A, C, D, E
9. Which states might have less than 100 mi² (square miles) of wooded terrain? A, D
10. Which states have 300 or more mi² of wooded terrain? B, F, G

**Answer *true* or *false*.**

11. At least 390 mi² of $B$ are wooded. true
12. $G$ could have more wooded terrain than $F$. true

## MATH TOOLBOX

### Compound Inequalities

In Lesson 7-6, students learned how to solve two-step inequalities. This Math Toolbox shows students how to solve compound inequalities.

### Math Background

The solution to a compound inequality joined by *and* must make both of the inequalities true. The solution to a compound inequality joined by *or* must make either one (but not necessarily both) of the inequalities true. The graph of the compound inequality ($x > 2$ and $x < 4$) is

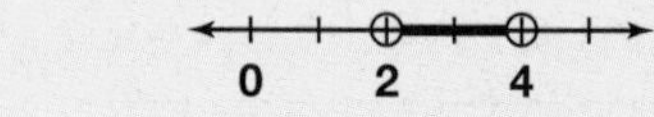


For ($x > 2$ or $x < 4$), the graph is

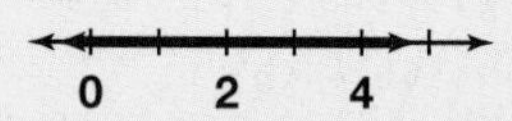


For ($x < 2$ or $x > 4$), the graph is

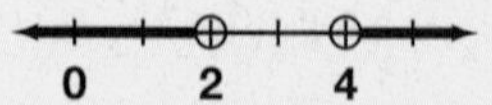


The compound inequality ($x < 2$ and $x > 4$) has no solution, because no number makes both inequalities true.

## Teaching Notes

**Error Prevention** Students may not pay close attention to the word that joins a compound inequality. Point out that the word is important and may make a great difference in the graph.

**Monitoring Progress Exercises 1–9** Students must name a number that is part of the solution shown on the graph. This means selecting a number shaded on their graph and checking that it does indeed make the compound inequality true.

**Block Scheduling** If you have block scheduling or extended periods, you may wish to insert this Math Toolbox lesson between the completion of Part 2 of Lesson 7-6 and the beginning of Part 1 of Lesson 7-7. Use the Pacing Options on page 333B to see the possibilities.

---

## MATH TOOLBOX

*Extension*

*After Lesson 7-6*

# *Compound Inequalities*

*Compound inequalities* are two inequalities joined by the word *and* or the word *or.*

$x > 4$ and $x \leq 6$

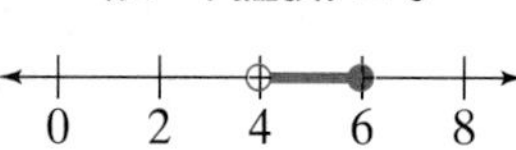


A solution of a compound inequality joined by *and* is any number that makes both inequalities true.

$x \leq -2$ or $x > 3$

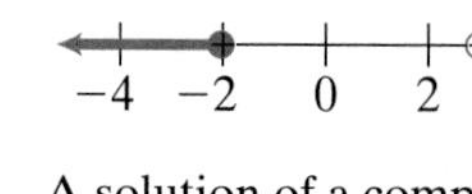


A solution of a compound inequality joined by *or* is any number that makes at least one of the inequalities true.

### EXAMPLE

**Graph each compound inequality on a number line.**

**a.** $2 \leq x$ and $x < 6$

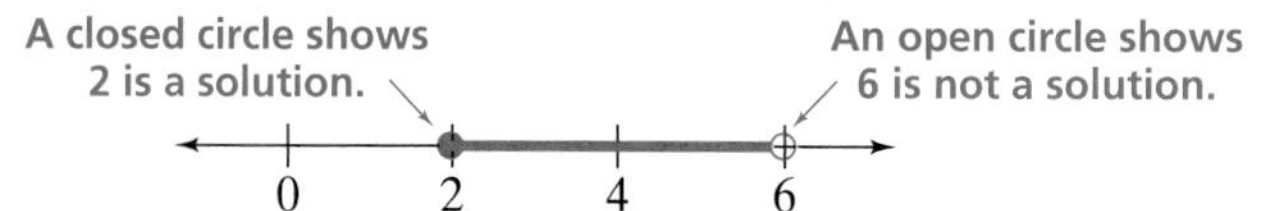
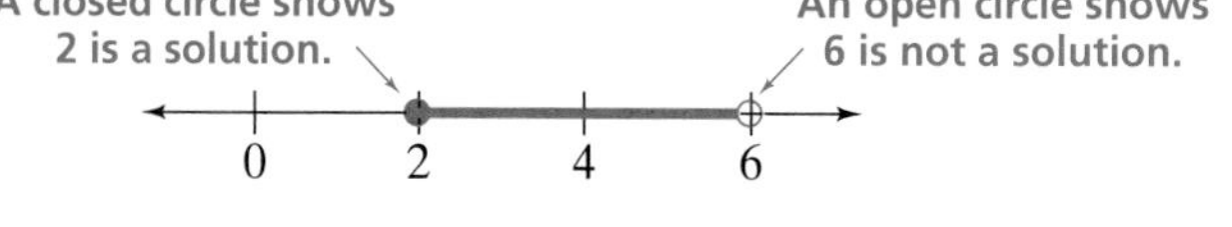


**b.** $z > 4$ or $z \leq 1$

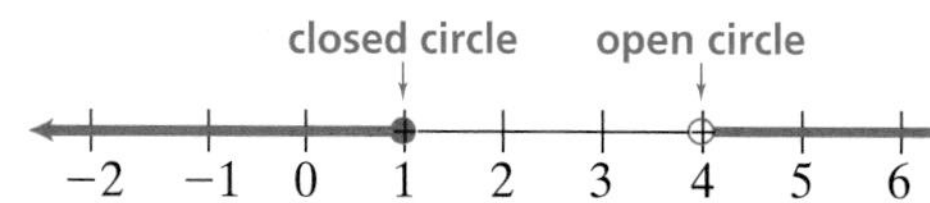


**Graph each compound inequality.** 1–9. See graphs above.

1. $x \geq 0$ and $x \leq 7$
2. $z < -2$ and $z \geq -4$
3. $5 > a$ and $a \geq -6$
4. $b < -1$ or $b > 4$
5. $c < 2$ or $c > 3.5$
6. $y \geq 1$ or $y < -3$
7. $x \leq 4$ and $x \geq 3$
8. $n \leq -5$ or $n > 0$
9. $3 > m$ and $m > -3$
10. *Writing* Explain why there are no solutions of the compound inequality $x > 2$ and $x \leq -2$.
Answers may vary. Sample: There is no number that is both less than or equal to −2 and greater than 2.

1.–2.

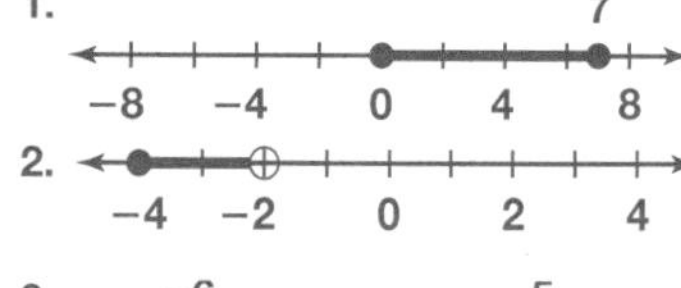


3.–4.

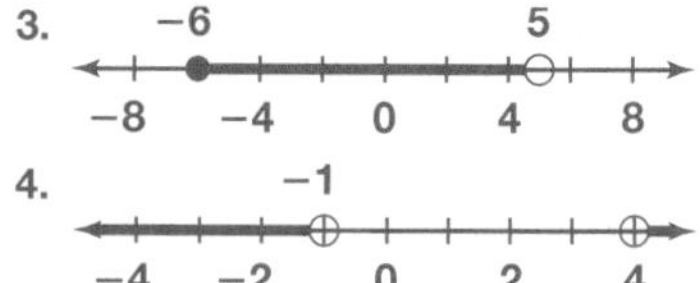


5. 3.5

6.

7.–8.

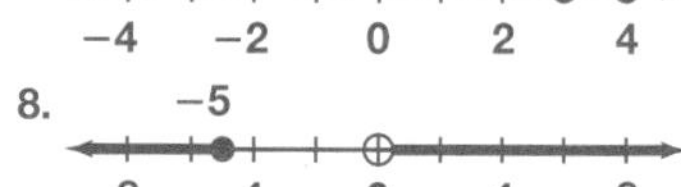


9.

• **Additional Example**

Graph the compound inequality on a number line. Identify one solution.
$-5 \geq y$ and $y > -8$ sample answer: −6

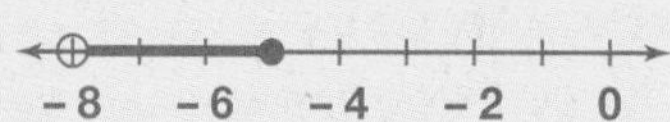

# 7-7

# Transforming Formulas

## Part 1 Solving Formulas for a Given Variable

### What You'll Learn

1. To solve a formula for a given variable
2. To use formulas to solve problems

### . . . And Why

To find distance or area in real-world situations

Remember that a formula shows the relationship between two or more quantities. You can use the properties of equality to transform a formula to represent one quantity in terms of another.

**GEOMETRY** CONNECTION

### Example 1

**Solve the area formula $A = \ell w$ for $\ell$.**

$A = \ell w$

$\frac{A}{w} = \frac{\ell w}{w}$ Use the Division Property of Equality.

$\frac{A}{w} = \ell$ or $\ell = \frac{A}{w}$ Simplify.

**Try This** Solve for the variable indicated in red.

1. $p = s - c$ $s = p + c$
2. $h = \frac{k}{j}$ $k = hj$
3. $I = prt$ $p = \frac{I}{rt}$

Sometimes you may need to use more than one step.

**GEOMETRY** CONNECTION

### Example 2

**Solve the perimeter formula $P = 2\ell + 2w$ for $\ell$.**

$P = 2\ell + 2w$

$P - 2w = 2\ell + 2w - 2w$ Subtract $2w$ from each side.

$P - 2w = 2\ell$ Simplify.

$\frac{P - 2w}{2} = \frac{2\ell}{2}$ Divide each side by 2.

$\ell = \frac{P - 2w}{2}$ Simplify.

**Try This** Solve for the variable indicated in red.

4. $5a + 7 = b$ $a = \frac{b - 7}{5}$
5. $P = 2\ell + 2w$ $w = \frac{P - 2\ell}{2}$
6. $y = \frac{x}{3} + 8$ $x = 3(y - 8)$



# Tools to Monitor Progress

### BEFORE THE LESSON

**To check prerequisite skills:**

- Solving Equations

**Skills Intervention Kit,** Pre-Algebra Basics

### DURING THE LESSON

**To check understanding:**

**Try This** exercises on student page

- **Additional Example 1**
  Solve the formula for the circumference of a circle $C = 2\pi r$ for $r$, the radius of a circle. $r = \frac{C}{2\pi}$
- **Additional Example 2**
  Solve the perimeter formula $P = 2l + 2w$ for $w$. $w = \frac{P - 2l}{2}$

# 7-7

## Getting Ready

**Resources** A complete list of resources for this lesson is on p. 333H.

### Daily Skills Warm-Up

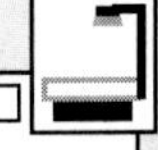

Lesson 7-7

Evaluate each formula for the values given.

1. distance: $d = rt$, when $r = 80$ km/hr, $t = 4$ hr
   $d = 320$ km
2. perimeter of a rectangle: $P = 2l + 2w$, when $l = 9$ m and $w = 7$ m
   $P = 32$ m
3. area of a triangle: $A = \frac{1}{2}bh$, when $b = 12$ ft and $h = 8$ ft
   $A = 48$ sq ft
4. sale price: $c = 0.75p$, when $p = \$95$
   $c = \$71.25$

### Background for the Lesson

You can transform formulas to solve for any variable in the formula. For example, you can transform the formula $d = rt$ (distance equals the product of rate and time) to solve for the rate, $r = \frac{d}{t}$, or to solve for the time, $t = \frac{d}{r}$.

To transform a formula, use the procedures for solving equations. First, identify the variable in the formula that you wish to isolate. Then use inverse operations on each side to isolate it.

## 1 Focus

### Connecting to Students' Lives

Discuss the fact that distances in track and field events are often measured in the metric system. You can use formulas to convert such metric measurements to customary units.

### Connecting to Prior Knowledge

In Lessons 7-2 and 7-3, students learned how to solve multi-step variable equations. In this lesson, students apply these skills to the task of transforming formulas.

# 2 Teach

## Part 1 Teaching Notes

Transforming formulas is an application of the skills already learned for solving variable equations. Review these skills: combining like terms, adding or subtracting from each side of the equation, factoring, and multiplying or dividing each side of an equation.

### Example 1

**Build understanding.** Ask: Why is there no step to add or subtract anything from each side of this equation? **The equation involves only multiplication, which you undo by dividing each side by *w*.**

**Reading Math** Geometry problems often use specific letters consistently to represent certain measures, such as *A* for area, $\ell$ and *w* for length and width, and *P* for perimeter.

### Example 2

**Build understanding.** Why do you subtract 2*w* from each side of the equation?.
**You need to get $2\ell$ alone on one side of the equation.**

## Part 2 Teaching Notes

**ELL** Explain that *substitute* means to replace some of the variables in a formula with quantities or numbers you know.

### Example 3

**Build understanding.** Ask: What do the variables *d*, *r*, and *t* stand for in this formula? **$d$ = distance, $r$ = rate, and $t$ = time**

### Example 4

**Build understanding.** Ask: Why do you multiply both sides of the equation by $\frac{5}{9}$ to isolate *C*? **$\frac{5}{9}$ is the inverse of $\frac{9}{5}$, so $\frac{9}{5}C \cdot \frac{5}{9} = C$.**

## Using Formulas to Solve Problems

You can transform formulas to solve real-world problems.

REAL-WORLD CONNECTION

### Example 3

**You plan a 425-mi trip to Bryce Canyon National Park. You estimate you will average 50 mi/h. To find about how long the trip will take, solve the distance formula $d = rt$ for $t$. Then substitute to find the time.**

$d = rt$

$\frac{d}{r} = \frac{rt}{r}$    Divide each side by *r*.

$\frac{d}{r} = t$ or $t = \frac{d}{r}$    Simplify.

$t = \frac{425}{50} = 8.5$    Replace *d* with 425 and *r* with 50. Simplify.

It will take you about 8.5 h to complete the trip.

Wind and water, rushing along stone plateaus, erode the stone and create shapes called "fins" and "hoodoos" in Bryce Canyon, Utah. Each year, more than 1.5 million people visit the national park.

### Try This

**7.** Solve the distance formula in Example 3 for *r*. $r = \frac{d}{t}$

REAL-WORLD CONNECTION

### Example 4

*Temperature* **An exchange student in your class wants to know the Celsius equivalent of 77°F. First solve the formula $F = \frac{9}{5}C + 32$ for $C$. Then substitute to find the temperature.**

$F = \frac{9}{5}C + 32$

$F - 32 = \frac{9}{5}C + 32 - 32$    Subtract 32 from each side.

$F - 32 = \frac{9}{5}C$    Simplify.

$\frac{5}{9}(F - 32) = \frac{5}{9} \cdot \frac{9}{5}C$    Multiply each side by $\frac{5}{9}$.

$\frac{5}{9}(F - 32) = C$ or $C = \frac{5}{9}(F - 32)$    Simplify and rewrite.

$C = \frac{5}{9}(77 - 32) = 25$    Replace *F* with 77. Simplify.

77°F is 25°C.

### Try This

**8.** Solve the batting average formula, $a = \frac{h}{n}$, for *h*. Find the number of hits *h* a batter needs in 40 times at bat *n* to have an average of 0.275. $h = an$; 11 hits



- **Additional Examples 3–4**
The high temperature for the day in San Diego will be 32°C. Will you wear a sweater or a T-shirt? Solve the formula $C = \frac{5}{9}(F - 32)$ for *F*. Then substitute to find the temperature in degrees Fahrenheit. **89.6°F; You can wear a T-shirt.**

### AFTER THE LESSON

**To assess knowledge: Lesson Quiz**

Solve for the given variable.

1. The area of a triangle with base *b* and height *h* is $A = \frac{1}{2}bh$. Solve for *b*. $b = \frac{2A}{h}$
2. Solve $3y + 2 = z$ for *y*. $y = \frac{z - 2}{3}$

- For enrichment and reteaching options see Resources on p. 333H.

# Exercises

## Check Understanding

**Complete the steps to solve each equation for the variable indicated in red.**

1. $a = 6c + 3$
   $a - ■ = 6c + 3 - 3$ 3
   $a - ■ = 6c$ 3
   $\frac{a-3}{■} = \frac{6c}{■}$ 6 6
   $\frac{a-3}{■} = ■$ 6 c

2. $g = \frac{h}{j}$
   $j■g = j\left(\frac{h}{j}\right)$
   $jg = ■$ h
   $\frac{jg}{■} = \frac{h}{g}$ g
   $j■ = \frac{h}{g}$

**Choose the correct transformation for the variable indicated in red.**

3. $z = xy$ A — A. $x = \frac{z}{y}$ B. $x = \frac{y}{z}$ C. $x = yz$
4. $r = 2s - 8$ C — A. $s = \frac{r+2}{8}$ B. $s = r + 4$ C. $s = \frac{r+8}{2}$
5. $\frac{2}{3}m - 5 = n$ B — A. $m = \frac{2}{3}(n + 5)$ B. $m = \frac{3}{2}(n + 5)$ C. $m = \frac{3}{2}n + 5$

## Practice and Problem Solving

**Solve for the variable indicated in red.**

6. $V = \ell wh$ $w = \frac{V}{\ell h}$
7. $P = 4s$ $s = \frac{P}{4}$
8. $V = \frac{1}{3}\ell wh$ $h = \frac{3V}{\ell w}$
9. $m = \frac{a+b}{2}$ $a = 2m - b$
10. $q = \frac{p}{d}$ $p = qd$
11. $A = \frac{1}{2}bh$ $b = \frac{2A}{h}$
12. ✪ $d^2 = \frac{3}{2}h$ $h = \frac{2}{3}d^2$
13. ✪ $T = 2h + 3k$ $k = \frac{T - 2h}{3}$

14. *Commission* LaTanya sells business suits and gets a 4% commission on her sales. Last week, she received a paycheck that included \$19.60 in commissions. Solve the formula $C = 0.04s$ for $s$, where $C$ is the amount of commission and $s$ is the amount of sales. Substitute to find LaTanya's sales. \$490

15. a. *Geometry* You can use the formula $C = \pi d$ to find the circumference $C$ of a circle when you know the diameter. Solve the formula for $d$. $d = \frac{C}{\pi}$
    b. The circumference of a circle is 15.7 in. Use 3.14 for $\pi$. Find the diameter. 5.0 in.

16. *Writing* The formula for the perimeter of a rectangle is $P = 2\ell + 2w$. Explain how you would find the width of the rectangle if you knew the perimeter and the length. Answers may vary. Sample: Solve the equation for $w$ and substitute the known values.



# 3 Practice/Assess

## Assignment Guide

To provide flexible scheduling, this lesson can be divided into parts.

**Part 1**
**Core** 1–11
✪ **Extension** 12–13

**Part 2**
**Core** 14–17
✪ **Extension** 18

Mixed Review can be assigned at any time for maintenance.

## Exercises

**Math Reasoning Exercise 14** Explain how you can estimate whether sales, $s$, will be greater or less than $C$, which is \$19.60. **The commission is a percentage of sales that is less than 100 percent, so $s$ will be greater than $C$.**

**Visual Learning Exercise 15** Draw a circle and label its parts to help solve this problem.

## ✪ Challenge

Use $d = rt$ to show how much time you might save by driving 70 mi/h on a 30-mi trip instead of driving 60 mi/h. Round times to the nearest minute. You save about 4 min.

## Closure

You use the properties of equality to transform a formula to represent one quantity in terms of the others.

## Daily Cumulative Review

**Solve each inequality.** *(Lesson 7-6)*

1. $4x - 2 > 18$ — $x > 5$
2. $4 + 3a \le 31$ — $a \le 9$
3. $\frac{-x}{3} - 6 > 12$ — $x < -54$
4. $\frac{1}{3}c - \frac{1}{6} > -\frac{5}{6}$ — $c > -2$
5. $6 - 5b < 31$ — $b > -5$
6. $-4m + 16 + 2m < 30$ — $m > -7$

**Solve each equation.** *(Lesson 7-5)*

7. $5(a + 4) = 3(a - 2)$ — $a = -13$
8. $2.1m + 45.2 = 3.2 - 8.4m$ — $m = -4$
9. $9s + 13 = 8s$ — $s = -13$
10. $16.8 + 3.2t = -13.6t$ — $t = -1$

**Mixed Review**

**Write and solve an equation. Where necessary, round to the nearest tenth.**

11. (6-7) Find 65% of 83. — $n = 0.65(83); n \approx 54.0$
12. (6-7) Find 7% of 570. — $n = 0.07(570); n = 39.9$
13. (6-7) Find 15% of 200. — $n = 0.15(200); n = 30$
14. (6-7) Find 120% of 630. — $n = 1.2(630); n = 756$

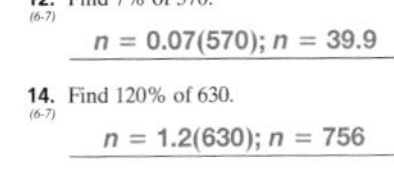

**Find each selling price.**

15. (6-9) cost: \$650, percent of markup: 30% — \$845
16. (6-9) cost: \$320, percent of markup: 55% — \$496

**Compare. Use <, >, or = to complete each statement.**

17. (5-2) $\frac{5}{6}$ [<] 0.84
18. (5-1) $\frac{6}{11}$ [>] $\frac{3}{8}$
19. (4-7) $(3^2)^3$ [>] $3^5$
20. (1-2) $7 + 21 \div 7$ [>] $(7 + 21) \div 7$
21. (1-9) $-36 \div (-3)$ [>] $72 \div -6$

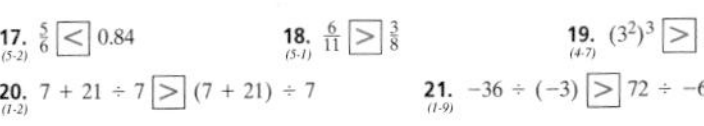



## Alternative Assessment

Ask students to bring formula problems from other classes such as health, science, shop, or home economics. Have them share these with the class and demonstrate how to solve problems by transforming these formulas.

17. a. *Construction* Bricklayers use the formula $N = 7LH$ to estimate the number $N$ of bricks needed in a wall. $L$ is the length of the wall and $H$ is the height. Solve the formula for $H$. $H = \frac{N}{7L}$

b. If 1,134 bricks are used to build a wall that is 18 ft long, how high is the wall? 9 ft

18. a. *Economics* Joe uses the formula $p = wh + 1.5wv$ to figure his weekly pay. In the formula, $p$ is the weekly pay, $w$ is the hourly wage, $h$ is the number of regular hours, and $v$ is the number of overtime hours. Solve the formula for $v$. $v = \frac{p - wh}{1.5w}$

b. Joe's hourly wage is \$6.25/h. If he earned \$282.81 last week working 40 regular hours plus overtime, how many hours overtime did he work? 3.5 h

## Mixed Review

**Solve each inequality.** *(Lesson 7-5)*

19. $3x - 12 > -6$ $x > 2$

20. $17 \leq -4a + 5$ $a \leq -3$

21. $-\frac{b}{2} + 9 < -3$ $b > 24$

22. $\frac{1}{3}y - 7 \geq 2$ $y \geq 27$

**Write and solve an equation. Where necessary, round to the nearest tenth or tenth of a percent.** *(Lesson 6-7)*

23. What percent of 20 is 15? 75%

24. Find 35% of 45. 15.8

25. 80% of what number is 25? 31.3

26. *Budgeting* Audrey wants to buy a dress for \$54. She has \$6 already and plans to save \$8 each week. In how many weeks will she be able to buy the dress? *(Lesson 7-1)* 6 weeks

## Checkpoint 2 — Lessons 7-5 through 7-7

**Solve each equation or inequality.**

1. $-8a - 6 = 10$ $-2$

2. $9b + 42 = -12$ $-6$

3. $2c + 6 + 7c = 8$ $\frac{2}{9}$

4. $18y = 12y + 24$ 4

5. $2x + 5 = 9x - 16$ 3

6. $12(m - 4) = 3m - 3$ 5

7. $15 - 10y < 24$ $y > -\frac{9}{10}$

8. $23 > -\frac{x}{2} - 5$ $x > -56$

9. $1.8x - 3.4 > 5.6$ $x > 5$

**Solve for the variable indicated in red.**

10. $s = g + h$ $h = s - g$

11. $3r + 4 = kr$ $r = \frac{k - 4}{3}$

12. $I = prt$ $t = \frac{I}{pr}$

13. $M = \frac{4h}{1.5}$ $h = 0.375M$

14. **TEST PREP** A school car wash charged \$5 per car. Supplies for the car wash cost \$23. The total of extra donations was \$35. The treasurer says at least \$150 was made at the car wash. What was the least possible number of cars washed? D

A. 18 cars B. 19 cars C. 27 cars D. 28 cars



See also Extra Practice section.

## Practice

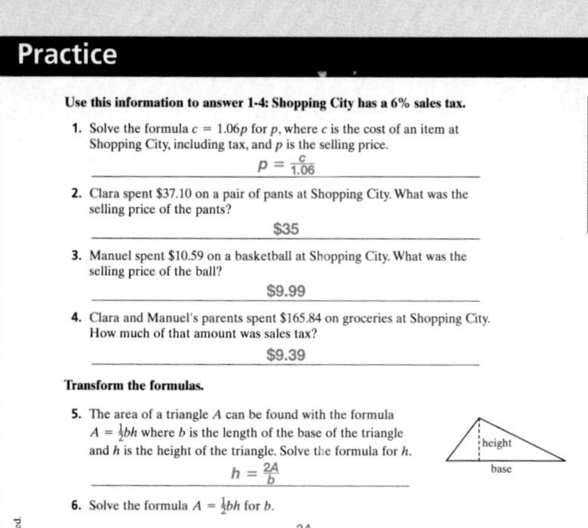

**Use this information to answer 1-4: Shopping City has a 6% sales tax.**

1. Solve the formula $c = 1.06p$ for $p$, where $c$ is the cost of an item at Shopping City, including tax, and $p$ is the selling price. $p = \frac{c}{1.06}$

2. Clara spent \$37.10 on a pair of pants at Shopping City. What was the selling price of the pants? \$35

3. Manuel spent \$10.59 on a basketball at Shopping City. What was the selling price of the ball? \$9.99

4. Clara and Manuel's parents spent \$165.84 on groceries at Shopping City. How much of that amount was sales tax? \$9.39

**Transform the formulas.**

5. The area of a triangle $A$ can be found with the formula $A = \frac{1}{2}bh$ where $b$ is the length of the base of the triangle and $h$ is the height of the triangle. Solve the formula for $h$. $h = \frac{2A}{b}$

6. Solve the formula $A = \frac{1}{2}bh$ for $b$. $b = \frac{2A}{h}$

**Find the missing part of each triangle.**

7. $A = 27$ cm² $h =$ 6 cm

8. $A = 18$ ft² $b =$ 9 ft

**Solve for the variable indicated.**

9. $V = \frac{1}{3}lwh$, for $w$ $w = \frac{3V}{lh}$

10. $\frac{1}{a} + \frac{1}{b} = \frac{1}{c}$, for $c$ $c = \frac{ab}{a + b}$



## Reteaching

Solve the surface area formula $s = 2\pi r^2 + 2\pi rh$ for $h$.

| | |
|---|---|
| $s = 2\pi r^2 + 2\pi rh$ | |
| $s - 2\pi r^2 = 2\pi r^2 - 2\pi r^2 + 2\pi rh$ | Subtract $2\pi r^2$ from each side. |
| $s - 2\pi r^2 = 2\pi rh$ | Simplify. |
| $\frac{s - 2\pi r^2}{2\pi r} = \frac{2\pi rh}{2\pi r}$ | Divide each side by $2\pi r$. |
| $\frac{s - 2\pi r^2}{2\pi r} = h$ | Simplify. |

**Solve for the indicated variable.**

1. $y = mx + b$, for $x$ $x = \frac{y - b}{m}$

2. $y = mx + b$, for $m$ $m = \frac{y - b}{x}$

3. $p = 6s$, for $s$ $s = \frac{p}{6}$

4. $A = \frac{1}{2}h(B + b)$, for $h$ $h = \frac{2A}{B + b}$

5. $I = Prt$, for $P$ $P = \frac{I}{rt}$

6. $y = \frac{3}{4}x - 5$, for $x$ $x = \frac{3(y + 5)}{2}$

7. $t = 0.05p$, for $p$ $p = \frac{t}{0.05}$

8. $V = lwh$, for $w$ $w = \frac{V}{lh}$

9. $k = \frac{1}{2}mv^2$, for $m$ $m = \frac{2k}{v^2}$

10. $W = p(V - L)$, for $V$ $V = \frac{W + pL}{p}$

11. $F = \frac{Gm_1m_2}{r^2}$, for $G$ $G = \frac{Fr^2}{m_1m_2}$

12. $W = p(V - L)$, for $L$ $L = \frac{pV - W}{p}$

13. $V = \frac{h}{e}v - \frac{E}{e}$, for $e$ $e = \frac{hv - E}{V}$

14. $mv = (m + M)u$, for $m$ $m = \frac{Mu}{v - u}$



## Enrichment

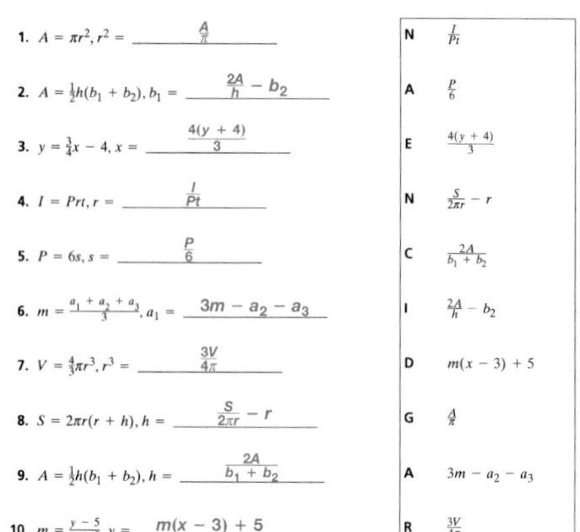

What are two-step equations?
To find the answer, solve each formula for the indicated variable. Then write the letter corresponding to the answer above the problem number below.

1. $A = \pi r^2$, $r^2 =$ $\frac{A}{\pi}$
2. $A = \frac{1}{2}h(b_1 + b_2)$, $b_1 =$ $\frac{2A}{h} - b_2$
3. $y = \frac{3}{4}x - 4$, $x =$ $\frac{4(y + 4)}{3}$
4. $I = Prt$, $r =$ $\frac{I}{Pt}$
5. $P = 6s$, $s =$ $\frac{P}{6}$
6. $m = \frac{a_1 + a_2 + a_3}{3}$, $a_1 =$ $3m - a_2 - a_3$
7. $V = \frac{4}{3}\pi r^3$, $r^3 =$ $\frac{3V}{4\pi}$
8. $S = 2\pi r(r + h)$, $h =$ $\frac{S}{2\pi r} - r$
9. $A = \frac{1}{2}h(b_1 + b_2)$, $h =$ $\frac{2A}{b_1 + b_2}$
10. $m = \frac{y - 5}{x - 3}$, $y =$ $m(x - 3) + 5$

| | |
|---|---|
| N | $\frac{I}{Pt}$ |
| A | $\frac{P}{6}$ |
| E | $\frac{4(y + 4)}{3}$ |
| N | $\frac{S}{2\pi r} - r$ |
| C | $\frac{2A}{b_1 + b_2}$ |
| I | $\frac{2A}{h} - b_2$ |
| D | $m(x - 3) + 5$ |
| G | $\frac{A}{\pi}$ |
| A | $3m - a_2 - a_3$ |
| R | $\frac{3V}{4\pi}$ |

Answer: Equations that

| A | R | E | D | A | N | C | I | N | G |
|---|---|---|---|---|---|---|---|---|---|
| 6 | 7 | 3 | 10 | 5 | 8 | 9 | 2 | 4 | 1 |



## Checkpoint

**Solve each equation or inequality.**

1. $9y = 5y - 36$ $y = -9$

2. $20x - 7 = 18x - 3$ $x = 2$

3. $4(m - 3) = 12 - 2m$ $m = 4$

4. $3k + 5 > 17$ $k > 4$

5. $\frac{n}{7} - 1 \leq 4$ $n \leq 35$

6. $8 - 5a \geq -12$ $a \leq 4$

7. Solve $y = \frac{3}{4}x - 6$ for $x$ $x = \frac{4}{3}(y + 6)$

8. At a bake sale, students charged \$.25 per cookie, brownie, or cupcake. Some parents donated money rather than baked goods. Donations totaled \$18. The students earned at least \$46. What was the least number of desserts sold?

A. 110 (B.) 112 C. 120 D. 125

# Simple and Compound Interest

7-8

## Part 1 Simple Interest

When you first deposit money in a savings account, your deposit is called **principal.** The bank takes the money and invests it. In return, the bank pays you **interest** based on the **interest rate.** **Simple interest** is interest paid only on the principal.

**Simple Interest Formula**

$I = prt$,
where $I$ is the interest, $p$ is the principal,
$r$ is the interest rate per year, and $t$ is the time in years.

REAL-WORLD CONNECTION

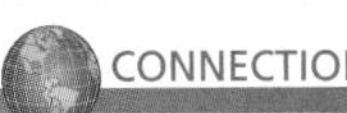

**EXAMPLE 1**

*Banking* **Suppose you deposit $400 in a savings account. The interest rate is 5% per year.**

**a. Find the interest earned in six years. Find the total of principal plus interest.**

$I = prt$ Use the simple interest formula.
$I = 400 \cdot 0.05 \cdot 6$ Replace $p$ with 400, $r$ with 0.05, and $t$ with 6.
$I = 120$ Simplify.
total $= 400 + 120 = 520$ Find the total.

The account will earn $120 in six years. There will be $520 in the account at the end of six years.

**b. Find the interest earned in three months. Find the total of principal plus interest.**

$t = \frac{3}{12} = \frac{1}{4} = 0.25$ Write the months as part of a year.
$I = prt$ Use the simple interest formula.
$I = 400 \cdot 0.05 \cdot 0.25$ Replace $p$ with 400, $r$ with 0.05, and $t$ with 0.25.
$I = 5$ Simplify.
total $= 400 + 5 = 405$ Find the total.

The account will earn $5 in three months. The balance at the end of three months will be $405.

### What You'll Learn

1. To solve simple interest problems
2. To solve compound interest problems

### . . . And Why

To find interest paid on investments using simple and compound interest



# Tools to Monitor Progress

## BEFORE THE LESSON

**To check prerequisite skills:**

- Finding percents

**Skills Intervention Kit,** Ratio, Proportion, and Percent

## DURING THE LESSON

**To check understanding:**

**Try This** exercises on student page

- **Additional Example 1**

Suppose you deposit $1,000 in a savings account that earns 6% per year. Find the interest earned in 2 years. Find the total of the principal plus interest. $120; $1,120

# 7-8

## Getting Ready

**Key Terms and Symbols** principal, interest, interest rate, simple interest, compound interest, balance

**Resources** A complete list of resources for this lesson is on p. 333F.

### Daily Skills Warm-Up

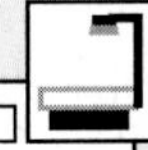

Lesson 7-8

1. Find 6% of $400. $24
2. Find 5% of $2,000. $100
3. Find 4.5% of $700. $31.50
4. Find $5\frac{1}{2}$% of $325. $17.88
5. A store buys a skateboard for $20.52 and marks it up about 45%. What is the selling price of the skateboard? $29.75

### Background for the Lesson

The rate for simple interest is the *annual* percentage rate, or the amount of interest that is paid in one year. In simple interest calculations with the formula $I = prt$, $t$ is a fraction if the time period is less than a year. In the compound interest formula, $B = p(1 + r)^n$, $r$ is the interest rate for each of the $n$ interest periods. If you know the annual rate, you can find $r$ by dividing the annual percentage rate by $n$, the number of interest periods, or the number of times the interest is compounded in a year.

## 1 Focus

### Connecting to Students' Lives

Discuss saving money in an account where you earn interest compared to borrowing money where you have to pay interest. Ask for the advantages of a savings account over saving money at home.

### Connecting to Prior Knowledge

In Lesson 7-7, students learned how to transform formulas. In this lesson, students use interest formulas to calculate interest and account balances. In Lesson 10-1, students will use these skills as they work with formulas again to find measures for geometric figures.

# 2 Teach

## Part 1 Teaching Notes

To use the simple interest formula, students will have to solve equations involving fractions and decimals. Ask volunteers to review the procedures for solving equations with fractions and decimals to clear up any questions.

### Example 1

**Build understanding.** Ask: The problem states that the interest rate is 5%, so why are the principal and time multiplied by 0.05? **5% means $\frac{5}{100}$ or 0.05**

**Connecting to Economics** Banks pay interest on savings accounts as a fee for letting the banks use this money. Banks use the money to make loans on which they charge interest. Banks collect interest on loans at a higher rate than they pay their savings customers. This difference forms part of the banks' profit.

## Part 2 Teaching Notes

Savings institutions show the amount of the compound interest earned by a savings account on a monthly statement they send to the customer.

**ELL** Make sure students understand that the *balance* of an account is the *principal*, which was the initial deposit, plus any interest earned since the initial deposit was made.

### Example 2

**Build understanding.** Ask: Why do you have to make five interest calculations, instead of multiplying a single interest calculation by 5? **You must recalculate the interest each year based on the new balance.**

**TRY THIS** Find the simple interest.

1. principal = $250
   interest rate = 4%
   time = 3 years **$30**

2. principal = $250
   interest rate = 3.5%
   time = 6 months **$4.38**

## Part 2 Compound Interest

When a bank pays interest on the principal *and* on the interest an account has earned, the bank is paying **compound interest.** The principal plus the interest is the **balance,** which becomes the principal on which the bank figures the next interest payment.

REAL-WORLD  CONNECTION

### EXAMPLE 2

*Banking* **You deposit $400 in an account that earns 5% interest compounded annually (once per year). What is the balance in your account after 4 years? In your last calculation, round to the nearest cent.**

| Principal at Beginning of Year | Interest | Balance |
|---|---|---|
| Year 1: $400.00 | 400.00 · 0.05 = 20.00 | 400 + 20 = 420.00 |
| Year 2: $420.00 | 420.00 · 0.05 = 21.00 | 420 + 21 = 441.00 |
| Year 3: $441.00 | 441.00 · 0.05 = 22.05 | 441 + 22.05 = 463.05 |
| Year 4: $463.05 | 463.05 · 0.05 = 23.1525 | 463.05 + 23.1525 ≈ 486.20 |

After four years, the balance is $486.20.

**TRY THIS** Make a table and find the balance. The interest is compounded annually.

3. principal = $500
   interest rate = 3%
   time = 2 years **See left.**

4. principal = $625
   interest rate = 2%
   time = 4 years **See left.**

3.

| Bal. at Yr Start | Interest | Bal. at Yr End |
|---|---|---|
| $500.00 | $15.00 | $515.00 |
| $515.00 | $15.45 | $530.45 |

4.

| Bal. at Yr Start | Interest | Bal. at Yr End |
|---|---|---|
| $625.00 | $12.50 | $637.50 |
| $637.50 | $12.75 | $650.25 |
| $650.25 | $13.01 | $663.26 |
| $663.26 | $13.27 | $676.53 |

You can find a balance using compound interest in one step with the compound interest formula and a calculator. An *interest period* is the length of time over which interest is calculated. The interest period can be a year or less than a year.



- **Additional Example 2**
  What is your account balance if you leave the money in the account for another four years, for a total of 8 years? Round your answer to the nearest cent in your last calculation. **$590.98**
- **Additional Example 3**
  Find the balance on a deposit of $2,500 earning 3% interest compounded monthly, after 4 years. **$2,818.32**

### AFTER THE LESSON

**To assess knowledge:**
**Lesson Quiz**
Find the simple interest.

1. $1,200 at 5.5% for 2 years **$132**
2. $2,500 at 8% for 6 months **$100**

Find the balance.

3. $12,000 at 9.5% compounded semi-annually for 10 years **$30,357.21**

- For enrichment and reteaching options see Resources on p. 333H.

### Compound Interest Formula

$B = p(1 + r)^n$,
where $B$ is the final balance, $p$ is the principal,
$r$ is the interest rate for each interest period, and
$n$ is the number of interest periods.

You can use this formula to solve Example 2.

$B = p(1 + r)^n$

$B = 400(1 + 0.05)^4$ Replace $p$ with 400, $r$ with 0.05, and $n$ with 4.

$B \approx 486.20$ Use a calculator. Round to the nearest cent.

The balance is $486.20. Using the formula means there are fewer calculations and fewer chances for mistakes.

*Calculator HINT*

Remember to use the parentheses on your calculator when evaluating the compound interest formula.

When interest is compounded semiannually (twice per year), you must *divide* the interest rate by the number of interest periods, which is 2.

6% annual interest rate ÷ 2 interest periods = 3% semiannual interest rate

To find the number of payment periods, *multiply* the number of years by the number of interest periods per year.

REAL-WORLD CONNECTION

## Example 3

*Banking* **Find the balance on a deposit of $1,000, earning 6% interest compounded semiannually for 5 years.**

The interest rate $r$ for compounding semiannually is $0.06 \div 2$, or 0.03. The number of payment periods $n$ is 5 years × 2 interest periods per year, or 10.

$B = p(1 + r)^n$ Use the compound interest formula.

$B = 1{,}000(1 + 0.03)^{10}$ Replace $p$ with 1,000, $r$ with 0.03, and $n$ with 10.

$B \approx 1{,}343.92$ Use a calculator. Round to the nearest cent.

The balance is $1,343.92.

**Try This** Find the balance for each account.

Amount deposited: $900, annual interest rate: 2%, time: 3 years

5. compounding annually $955.09
6. compounding semiannually $955.37



### Example 3

**Build understanding.** Ask: How would the value of $r$ and $n$ in this problem change if the interest was compounded monthly but everything else stayed the same? $r = 0.005$; $n = 60$

**Error Prevention** Ask students to check whether the number of interest periods in their formula matches the problem. If a balance is compounded semi-annually for 4 years, there will be 8 interest periods. Students may forget to divide the rate (which is an annual rate) by the number of interest periods per year.

**Technology Option** You may wish to have students use spreadsheet software and the formulas in this lesson to create a spreadsheet that calculates simple and compound interest. Encourage students to use the formulas from the textbook rather than using pre-programmed formulas in the spreadsheet software. Have students share and explain their spreadsheets.

**Math Reasoning** Explain why the balance of $1,000 at 10% compounded annually for 5 years is slightly less than the balance of $1,000 at 10% compounded semi-annually for 5 years. **The account compounded annually earns interest on a single balance each year; The balance of the semi-annual account increases every 6 months.**

# 3 Practice/Assess

## Assignment Guide

To provide flexible scheduling, this lesson can be divided into parts.

**Part 1**
Core 1–2, 7–10
Extension 18

**Part 2**
Core 3–6, 11–16, 19–20
Extension 17, 21

Mixed Review can be assigned at any time for maintenance.

## Exercises

**Exercises 11–12** Check the final balance in the tables by using the compound interest formula.

**Test Prep Exercise 18** Read problems carefully. This problem is looking for the interest earned, not the final balance. To find the correct answer, you must subtract the initial investment from the ending balance.

## Challenge

Find the balance of $5,000 at 12% compounded weekly for 2 years. $6,354.49

## Closure

Simple interest is the product of the principal amount, the annual interest rate, and the time in years. Compound interest is paid on both the principal and the previous interest.

## Daily Cumulative Review

**Solve for the variable indicated in bold.** *(Lesson 7-7)*

1. $A = \frac{1}{2}bh$ — $h = \frac{2A}{b}$
2. $V = lwh$ — $h = \frac{V}{lw}$
3. $E = mc^2$ — $m = \frac{E}{c^2}$
4. $x = 7c + 5$ — $c = \frac{x - 5}{7}$
5. $\frac{4}{5}r - 6 = s$ — $r = \frac{5}{4}(s + 6)$
6. $p = mn$ — $m = \frac{p}{n}$

**Solve each inequality.** *(Lesson 7-6)*

7. $5 + 9a \geq 23$ — $a \geq 2$
8. $7.5 < 1.2 + 0.9s$ — $7 < s$
9. $2p + 3 < 27$ — $p < 12$
10. $-3(3r + 4) \geq 69$ — $r \leq -9$
11. $-\frac{2}{7}t + 17 \leq 39$ — $t \geq -77$
12. $2.3 - 0.2x < -5.1$ — $x > 37$

**Mixed Review**

**Write the coordinates of each point.**

13. *A* (1-10) (−3, 2)
14. *B* (1-10) (−3, −2)
15. *C* (1-10) (3, −2)
16. *D* (1-10) (3, 2)
17. *E* (1-10) (−2, −4)
18. *F* (1-10) (2, 4)

**Write each number in standard notation.**

19. (4-9) $9.67 \times 10^8$ — 967,000,000
20. (4-9) $3.29 \times 10^{-6}$ — 0.00000329
21. (4-9) $4 \times 10^{-5}$ — 0.00004

**Find the GCF and the LCM.**

22. 16, 54
    a. (4-3) GCF 2
    b. (5-1) LCM 432
23. 80, 800
    a. (4-3) GCF 80
    b. (5-1) LCM 800
24. $6a, 14a^2$
    a. (4-3) GCF $2a$
    b. (5-1) LCM $42a^2$



# Exercises

## Check Understanding

**Find the simple interest.**

1. $200 deposited at an interest rate of 7% for 2 years $28
2. $870 deposited at an interest rate of 6% for 9 months $39.15

**Find the balance.**

3. $495 at 8% compounded annually for 2 years $577.37
4. $1,280 at 13% compounded annually for 3 years $1,846.91
5. $2,000 at 5% compounded semiannually for 2 years $2,207.63
6. $15,600 at 10% compounded semiannually for 3 years $20,905.49
7. *Mental Math* Calculate the amount of simple interest on $9,000 deposited at an interest rate of 5% for 2 years. $900

## Practice and Problem Solving

**Find the simple interest.**

8. $500 deposited at an interest rate of 3% for 4 years $60
9. $35 deposited at an interest rate of 2.5% for 1 year $.88
10. $900 deposited at an interest rate of 8% for 3 months $18

**Complete each table. Compound the interest annually.**

11. $3,000 at 4% for 3 years

| Principal at Beginning of Year | Interest | Balance |
|---|---|---|
| Year 1: $3,000 | ■ | ■ |
| Year 2: ■ | ■ | ■ |
| Year 3: ■ | ■ | ■ |

$3,120.00, $3,244.80 — $120.00, $124.80, $129.79 — $3,120.00, $3,244 .80, $3,374.59

12. $10,000 at 6% for 3 years

| Principal at Beginning of Year | Interest | Balance |
|---|---|---|
| Year 1: $10,000 | ■ | ■ |
| Year 2: ■ | ■ | ■ |
| Year 3: ■ | ■ | ■ |

$10,600.00, $11,236.00 — $600.00, $636.00, $674.16 — $10,600.00, $11,236.00, $11,910.16

**Find each balance.**

13. $3,000 at 14% compounded annually for 4 years $5,066.88
14. $8,900 at 9% compounded semiannually for 5 years $13,821.43
15. $54,500 at 3% compounded semiannually for 9 years $71,250.06
16. *Banking* You deposit $600 in a savings account for 3 years. The account pays 8% annual interest compounded quarterly.
    a. What is the quarterly interest rate? 2%
    b. What is the number of payment periods? 12 periods
    c. Find the final balance in the account. $760.95



## Alternative Assessment

Have students find the interest rates paid locally by banks for savings accounts and certificates of deposit. Using these rates and the formulas in this lesson, have students find out what account would earn the most for investing $10,000 for 5 years.

17. *Banking* Leroy borrows $800 at 10% annual interest compounded semiannually. He makes no payments.
a. How much will he owe after four years? $1,181.96
b. How much interest will he owe in four years? $381.96

26–29.

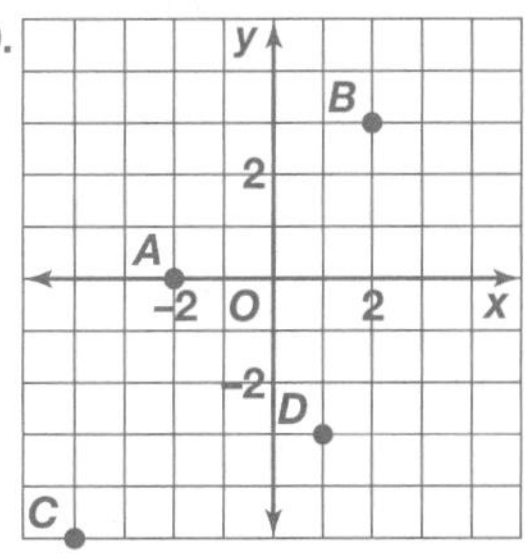


18. **TEST PREP** Matthew invests $5,000 at 14% simple interest. About how much interest will he earn in eight months? A
A. $467 B. $700 C. $1,050 D. $5,467

19. *Open-ended* Choose an amount of money to be invested and an interest rate. Find the value of the investment after 5 years if the interest is simple interest; if the interest is compounded annually. 19. Answers may vary. Sample: $10,000 at 6%; $13,000; $13,382.26

20. *Writing* Explain the difference between simple interest and compound interest. See below.

21. *Banking* Ling invests $1,000 in an account paying 8% interest.
a. Compare the account balances after 5 years of simple interest and after 5 years of interest compounded annually. $1,400 and $1,469.33
b. After how many years of compounded interest will the account balance be about twice Ling's initial investment? 9
c. *Critical Thinking* What would the simple interest rate on Ling's investment have to be for the investment to double in the same amount of time? about 11.1%

**Journal**

*Many banks compound interest on a daily basis. Explain what it would mean to compound interest daily.*

20. Answers may vary. Sample: Simple interest is computed only on the original principal. Compound interest is computed on both the principal and the previous interest.

## Mixed Review

**Solve for the variable indicated in red.** *(Lesson 7-6)*

22. $f = \frac{15m}{a}$ $m = \frac{fa}{15}$
23. $E = mc^2$ $m = \frac{E}{c^2}$
24. $y = 4x - 9$ $x = \frac{y + 9}{4}$
25. $d = \frac{5}{8}k + 1$ $k = \frac{8}{5}(d - 1)$

**Graph each point on a coordinate plane.** *(Lesson 1-10)* 26–29. See above.

26. $A(-2, 0)$
27. $B(2, 3)$
28. $C(-4, -5)$
29. $D(1, -3)$

30. *Architecture* A floor plan has a scale of $\frac{1}{4}$ in. : 5 ft. Find the length on the drawing for an actual length of 60 ft. *(Lesson 6-3)* 3 in.

CHAPTER PROJECT 7

## Activity 3 Calculating

Measure and record the mass of 250 mL of each of these liquids: vinegar, vegetable oil, and corn syrup. Use the formula from Activity 2 to calculate the density of each liquid. Compare the density of each liquid to the density of water.

See also Extra Practice section.



## Project Activity 3

**Calculating** Have students make a prediction of the relative densities by arranging the 4 liquids (water, vinegar, oil, and syrup) in order (from least to most dense) of the results they predict.

## Practice

**Find each balance.**

| | Principal | Interest rate | Compounded | Time (years) | Balance |
|---|---|---|---|---|---|
| 1. | $400 | 7% | annually | 3 | $490.02 |
| 2. | $8,000 | 5% | annually | 9 | $12,410.63 |
| 3. | $1,200 | 4% | semi-annually | 2 | $1,298.92 |
| 4. | $50,000 | 6% | semi-annually | 6 | $71,288.04 |

**Find the simple interest.**

5. $900 deposited at an interest rate of 3% for 5 years $135

6. $1,348 deposited at an interest rate of 2.5% for 18 months $50.55

**Complete each table. Compound the interest annually.**

7. $5,000 at 6% for 4 years

| Principal at beginning of year | Interest | Balance |
|---|---|---|
| Year 1: $5,000 | $300 | $5,300 |
| Year 2: $5,300 | $318 | $5,618 |
| Year 3: $5,618 | $337.08 | $5,955.08 |
| Year 4: $5,955.08 | $357.30 | $6,312.38 |

8. $7,200 at 3% for 4 years

| Principal at beginning of year | Interest | Balance |
|---|---|---|
| Year 1: $7,200 | $216 | $7,416 |
| Year 2: $7,416 | $222.48 | $7,638.48 |
| Year 3: $7,638.48 | $229.15 | $7,867.63 |
| Year 4: $7,867.63 | $236.03 | $8,103.66 |



## Reteaching

Find the balance in an account when $500 is deposited at 4% interest compounded semi-annually for 2 years.
The table shows the interest and balance for each half year.

| Principal at beginning of period | Interest | Balance |
|---|---|---|
| $\frac{1}{2}$ year: $500 | $10 | $510 |
| 1 year: $510 | $10.20 | $520.20 |
| $1\frac{1}{2}$ year: $520.20 | $10.40 | $530.60 |
| 2 year: $530.60 | $10.61 | $541.21 |

The balance after 2 years is $541.21.
You can also find the balance with the formula $B = p(1 + r)^n$, where $B$ is the ending balance. The principal $p$ is 500. The rate is for a half year; 4% annual interest equals 2% per half year. Thus $r$ is 0.02. The number of compounding periods $n$ is 4, because there are 4 half years in 2 years.

$B = p(1 + r)^n$
$B = 500(1 + 0.02)^4$ Substitute
$B = \$541.22$ Use a calculator. Round to the nearest cent.

With the formula, the ending balance is $541.22. The difference is due to rounding error.

**Find the ending balance when $1,500 is deposited at 6% interest compounded semi-annually for 2 years.**

1. Use a table.

| Principal at beginning of period | Interest | Balance |
|---|---|---|
| $\frac{1}{2}$ year: $1,500 | $45 | $1,545 |
| 1 year: $1,545 | $46.35 | $1,591.35 |
| $1\frac{1}{2}$ year: $1,591.35 | $47.74 | $1,639.09 |
| 2 year: $1,639.09 | $49.17 | $1,688.26 |

2. Use the formula: $B = p(1 + r)^n$ = $1{,}500(1 + 0.03)^4$ = $1,688.26



## Enrichment

Do you earn more interest when it is compounded more often than when it is compounded less often?

**Find the balance and interest on a deposit of $2,000, earning 4% interest, after 3 years, for each compounding period.**

1. annually
balance: $2,249.73 interest: $249.73
2. semi-annually
balance: $2,252.32 interest: $252.32

The interest rate $r$ for compounding quarterly (four times a year) is $0.04 \div 4 = 0.01$. The number of payment periods $n$ is 4 per year × 3 years, or 12.

3. quarterly
balance: $2,253.65 interest: $253.65
4. Which compounding period earned the most interest? quarterly

**Find the balance and interest on a deposit of $500, earning 6% interest, after 4 years, for each compounding period.**

5. annually
balance: $631.24 interest: $131.24
6. semi-annually
balance: $633.39 interest: $133.39
7. quarterly
balance: $634.49 interest: $134.49
8. bi-monthly
balance: $634.87 interest: $134.87
9. monthly
balance: $635.24 interest: $135.24
10. Which compounding period earned the most interest? monthly
11. What do you notice about how the amount of interest increases each time interest is compounded twice as often? There is a smaller increase each time.

## MATH TOOLBOX

### Credit Card Interest

In Lesson 7-8, students learned how to calculate simple and compound interest This Math Toolbox shows students how to use a spreadsheet program to calculate credit card interest.

### Math Background

The example in this lesson shows how you can use a credit card to pay for a large purchase over a period of time by paying interest. You can use a spreadsheet to calculate how long it will take to pay off the balance and the amount of interest that you will pay. Credit card companies charge interest on the monthly balance of the account at a monthly rate. The monthly rate is the annual percentage rate of the card divided by 12. In this example, the monthly rate is 1.8%, which means the annual percentage rate of the card is 21.6%.

## Teaching Notes

**Error Prevention** If the spreadsheet has the same values on each row, students may have copied and pasted the formulas in each column instead of using the spreadsheet's fill down function.

**Monitoring Progress** Exercises 2–3
As students make changes to the values in their spreadsheets, they need to check to make sure the changes are reflected down to the other rows in the spreadsheet.

**Block Scheduling** If you have block scheduling or extended periods, you may wish to insert this Math Toolbox lesson between the completion of Part 2 of Lesson 7-8 and the beginning of the chapter Wrap Up and Assessment.

## MATH TOOLBOX

*Technology*
*After Lesson 7-8*

# *Credit Card Interest*

When you use a credit card, you are charged interest each month on the balance in your account. You can use a spreadsheet to investigate the interest charged on a credit card account.

You use a credit card to buy a \$450 airline ticket. You are charged 1.8% monthly interest on your account balance, and you make a \$40 payment each month. Using a spreadsheet program, create a spreadsheet with the formulas shown in red.

| | A | B | C | D | E | F |
|---|---|---|---|---|---|---|
| 1 | Month | Balance | Planned Monthly Payment | Interest | New Balance | Total Interest |
| 2 | 1 | 450 | 40 | =B2*0.018 | =B2+D2−C2 | =D2 |
| 3 | =A2+1 | =E2 | | | | =F2+D3 |
| 4 | ↓ | ↓ | ↓ | ↓ | ↓ | ↓ |
| | ⋮ | ⋮ | ⋮ | ⋮ | ⋮ | ⋮ |

The arrows indicate you should use the Fill Down feature of your spreadsheet program. This will calculate successive months for you.

**Use your spreadsheet. Round any totals to the nearest cent.**

1. a. In which month is the balance less than the monthly payment? 13
   b. Your last payment is the balance plus the interest in the month you found in part (a). What is the amount of the last payment? \$27.41
   c. What is the total interest paid on this account? \$57.42
2. a. Change the monthly payment to \$60 a month. In which month is the balance less than the monthly payment? 9
   b. What is the total interest paid on this account? \$37.82
3. a. Create a new spreadsheet using a beginning balance of \$1,200, 2.1% monthly interest, and a monthly payment of \$100. What is the total interest paid on this account in 5 months? \$109.96
   b. Change the monthly payment to \$200. What is the total interest paid on this account in 5 months? \$88.51
   c. *Critical Thinking* What can you conclude about the relationship between the amount of monthly payments and the amount of interest charges? If you increase the monthly payments, the interest charges will be less.



- **Additional Example**
  Create a spreadsheet to calculate how long it would take you to have a balance of \$450 in a savings account if you saved \$40 each month at an annual rate of interest of 5% compounded monthly. Since you are adding \$40 each month, do not use the formula for compound interest. **After the 11th month interest is added, you have a little more than \$450.**

CHAPTER PROJECT 7

# FINISHING THE CHAPTER PROJECT

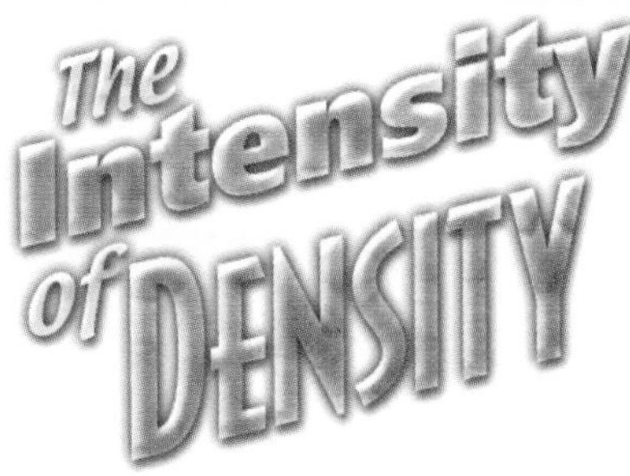

**Find the Densities of Liquids** The Project Activities on pages 344, 363, and 373 will help you complete your project. Here is a checklist to help you gather the different parts.

- ✔ your measurements of the mass and volume of water
- ✔ your calculation of the density of water
- ✔ your measurements and calculations for the densities of other liquids

Write a report that summarizes your activities and presents your results. Which liquid has the greatest density? Make a prediction about what would happen if you poured two of the liquids into one jar or beaker. Use diagrams and tables as needed to illustrate the report.

***Reflect and Revise***

Ask a friend or someone at home to review your calculations and your report. Are they accurate and clear? If necessary, make changes to improve them.

## *Web Extension*

**Visit Prentice Hall's Web site. You'll find some interesting links and ideas related to density. You'll also be able to share information about your project.**

**www.phschool.com**



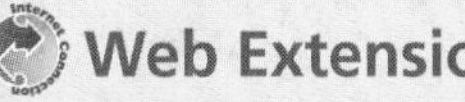

## Web Extension

### Tell Us About Your Project

Students may wish to share their projects with other students on the Web site: **www.phschool.com**.

### Scoring Rubric

**3** You accurately measure the mass of each liquid and calculate each density correctly. You explain your procedures thoroughly and clearly. Your report is complete, accurate, and easy to read.

**2** You make minor errors in your measurements or calculations. Your report is thorough and accurate, but it could be clearer or easier to read.

**1** You measure the masses and calculate the densities incorrectly. Your report is incomplete and unclear.

**0** Major elements of the project are incomplete or missing.

# FINISHING THE PROJECT

**Project Day** You may wish to plan a project day on which students share their completed projects. Encourage students to explain their process as well as their product.

**Block Scheduling** If you have block scheduling or extended periods, you may wish to intersperse the sharing of projects over Days 3, 4, 5 between the completion of one lesson and the start of a new lesson.

## Project Notebook

Have students review their project work and bring their notebooks up to date. Call attention to the fact that they can share their projects with other students through the Web site **www.phschool.com**.

Be sure students include in their notebooks their completed Project Manager and Scoring Rubric forms.

**Portfolio** Students may wish to include their projects and/or their project notebooks in their portfolios.

# Wrap Up

## Resources

Glossary, p. 748
Extra Practice, p. 716

For a complete list of resources for the chapter, see p. 333H.

# 7 Wrap Up

## Key Terms

balance (p. 370)
compound interest (p. 370)
consecutive integers (p. 341)
interest (p. 369)
interest rate (p. 369)
principal (p. 369)
simple interest (p. 369)

## Graphic Organizer

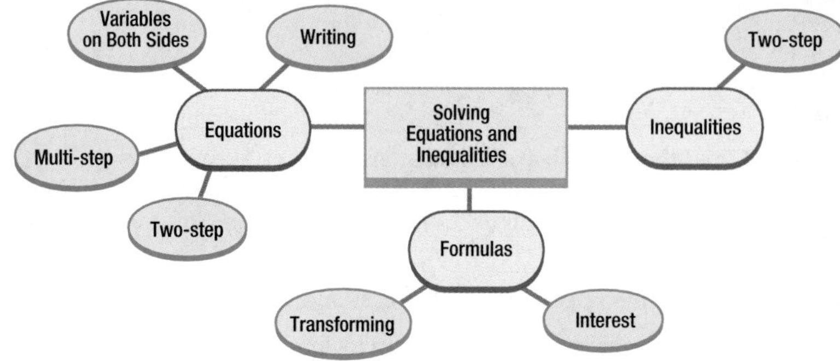


## Two-Step Equations 7-1

*Summary* To solve two-step equations, undo addition and subtraction, then undo multiplication and division.

**Solve each equation.**

1. $2a - 7 = -15$ −4
2. $3 = -6x + 15$ 2
3. $\frac{c}{4} + 10 = 22$ 48
4. $1.5y + 3.4 = 7.9$ 3
5. $\frac{2}{3}y - 9 = 5$ 21
6. $8 = 9x - 7$ $\frac{5}{3}$

## Multi-Step Equations 7-2 and 7-3

*Summary* To solve multi-step equations, remove grouping symbols and combine like terms first. Then follow the steps for solving two-step equations.

**Solve each equation.**

7. $8m - 3m = 4$ $\frac{4}{5}$
8. $6 - 2y - y = 12$ −2
9. $\frac{2}{3}q + 5 = \frac{3}{4}$ $-6\frac{3}{8}$
10. $\frac{1}{4}(b - 7) = 8$ 39
11. $3(2x + 5) = -39$ −9
12. $-2(5 + 6c) + 16 = -90$ 8
13. *Number Sense* Find four consecutive integers with a sum of −66. −18, −17, −16, −15

## Write an Equation 7-4

*Summary* One strategy for solving problems is to write an equation and then solve the equation.

**Write an equation. Solve.**

**14.** A pair of jeans is on sale for 15% off the original price. The sale price of the jeans is \$29.74. What was the original price? \$34.99

**15.** A bank teller is counting his money and notices that he has an equal number of tens and twenties. He also has \$147 in other bills. If the total value of the bills he has is \$1,167, how many tens and twenties does he have? 34 tens, 34 twenties

**16.** *Finance* Jalisha invested some money and made an 8% profit. The current value of her investment is \$1,308. How much did she invest initially? \$1,211.11

## Equations with Variables on Both Sides 7-5

*Summary* To solve equations with variables on both sides, first simplify both sides of the equation. Then use properties of equality to get the variable alone on one side of the equation.

**Solve each equation.**

**17.** $7x = 33 - 4x$ 3 **18.** $2a - 24 - 3a = 5a$ −4 **19.** $5x + 7 = -5x + 19$ $\frac{6}{5}$

**20.** $4x - 26 = 5(2 - x)$ 4 **21.** $8(b + 3) = 4b - 4$ −7 **22.** $2x - (9 - 3x) = 8x - 11$ $\frac{2}{3}$

**23.** A refrigerated truck leaves a rest stop traveling at a steady rate of 56 mi/h. A car leaves the same rest stop $\frac{1}{4}$ h later following the truck at a steady rate of 64 mi/h. How long after the truck leaves the rest stop will the car overtake the truck? 2 h

## Two-Step Inequalities 7-6

*Summary* Solving two-step inequalities involves the same steps as solving two-step equations. Reverse the direction of the inequality symbol when you multiply or divide by a negative number.

**Solve and graph each inequality.** See margin for graphs.

**24.** $2a - 3 > 11$ $a > 7$ **25.** $9y + 13 \leq -14$ $y \leq -3$ **26.** $-6c + 12 \geq 8$ $c \leq \frac{2}{3}$ **27.** $23 < 7 - 4x$ $x < -4$

**28.** $\frac{8}{9}x + 5 < -3$ $x < -9$ **29.** $-\frac{b}{2} + 14 > 13$ $b < 2$ **30.** $-17 > \frac{x}{3} - 19$ $x < 6$ **31.** $x + 4x + 9 \geq 6$ $x \geq -\frac{3}{5}$



24.
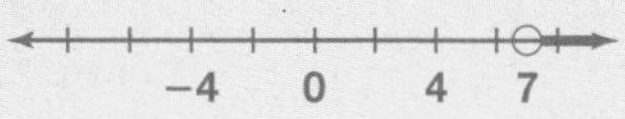


25.
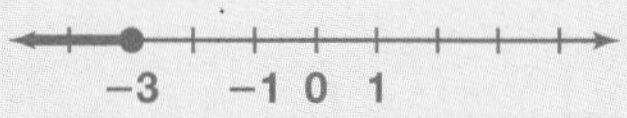


26.
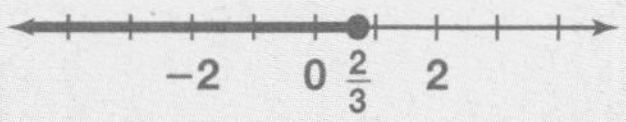


27.
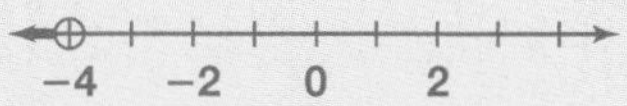


28.
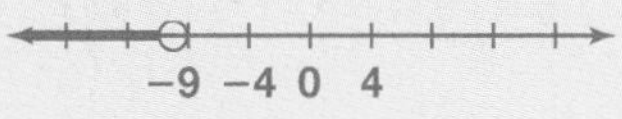


29.
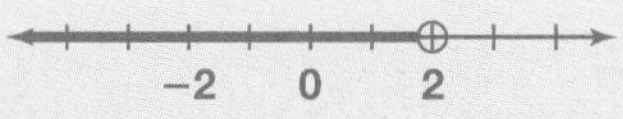


30.
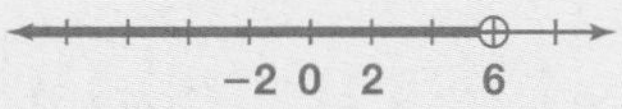


31.
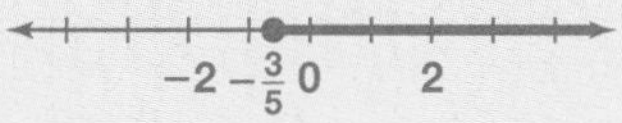


**Portfolio** Students may wish to include their completed work for the Wrap Up in their portfolios.

### Web Site

Students can find self-assessment materials on the Web site: **www.phschool.com.**

32. Last year's personal computer model is on sale for \$799. You can add more memory to the computer. Each chip of 8 megabytes of memory costs \$25. How many megabytes of memory can you add if you have at most \$1,000 to spend? Write and solve an inequality. **64 megabytes**

## Transforming Formulas 7-7

*Summary* Use the properties of equality to transform a formula.

**Solve for the variable indicated in red.**

33. $r = 6km$ $m = \frac{r}{6k}$
34. $8x = 6y$ $y = \frac{4}{3}x$
35. $Q = gp$ $g = \frac{Q}{p}$
36. $a = b - 2c$ $b = a + 2c$
37. $w = 3a + 5n$ $a = \frac{w - 5n}{3}$
38. $e = \frac{h}{6} + 11$ $h = 6(e - 11)$

## Simple and Compound Interest 7-8

*Summary* You can calculate **simple interest** using the formula $I = prt$, where $I$ is the interest, $p$ is the **principal** (original amount deposited), $r$ is the **interest rate** per year, and $t$ is the time in years.

**Compound interest** is interest paid on both the principal and interest. It is found using the formula $B = p(1 + r)^n$, where $B$ is the final **balance**, $p$ is the principal, $r$ is the interest rate for each interest period, and $n$ is the number of interest periods.

**Find the simple interest.**

39. \$150 deposited at an interest rate of 9% for 2 years **\$27**
40. \$2,525 deposited at an interest rate of 2.5% for 4 years **\$252.50**
41. \$6,500 deposited at an interest rate of 3% for 6 months **\$97.50**

**Find each balance.**

42. \$8,000 at 12% compounded annually for 3 years **\$11,239.42**
43. \$17,500 at 17% compounded annually for 6 years **\$44,890.37**
44. \$22,000 at 6% compounded semiannually for 8 years **\$35,303.54**
45. \$33,800 at 18% compounded semiannually for 5 years **\$80,016.89**

46. *Writing* The more interest periods there are, the more interest you make on an investment. Do you agree with this statement? Explain why or why not. **Answers may vary. Sample: No; you would earn more interest at 5% compounded annually than at 4% compounded quarterly.**



## Chapter Assessment Form A Page 1

**Circle the letter of the best answer.**

1. Solve $\frac{1}{3}(b - 4) = 1$.
   A. $b = 5$  B. $b = -1$  (C.) $b = 7$  D. $b = 1\frac{3}{4}$
2. Solve $3w - 4 = w + 8$.
   F. $w = 30$  G. $w = -20$  H. $w = -6$  (J.) $w = 6$
3. Solve $2.4(n - 1) = 12$.
   (A.) $n = 6$  B. $n = 1.5$  C. $n = 5$  D. $n = -5$
4. Solve $5t + 1 > 3t - 13$.
   F. $t > -6$  (G.) $t > -7$  H. $t > 6$  J. $t < 7$
5. Solve $3n - 16 \leq 8n + 29$.
   A. $-n \leq -9$  B. $n \geq 9$  (C.) $n \geq -9$  D. $n \leq -9$
6. Find the simple interest on \$750 deposited at an interest rate of 3.5% for 3 years.
   F. \$828.75  G. \$262.50  H. \$67.50  (J.) \$78.75
7. Find the balance on \$1,800 deposited at 5% compounded annually for 4 years.
   A. \$1,986.86  (B.) 2,187.91  C. \$186.86  D. \$387.91
8. Find the balance on \$6,000 deposited at 6% compounded semi-annually for 3 years.
   (F.) \$7,164.31  G. \$7,146.10  H. \$8,511.11  J. \$6,556.36
9. Which equation does *not* represent the problem? Sebastian's school bus averages 28 mi/h, including stops. One day Sebastian forgot his backpack. His mom left home 15 minutes (0.25 h) after Sebastian and traveled at an average speed of 42 mi/h. How long did it take Sebastian's mom to catch the bus?
   A. $42t = 28(t + 0.25)$  (B.) $42t = 28t + 0.25$
   C. $14t = 7$  D. $42t = 28t + 7$

**Solve each equation.**

10. $5 - 2y = 7$ $y = -1$
11. $\frac{3}{4}x + 8 = 5$ $x = -4$
12. $5(x - 3) = 2x + 6$ $x = 7$
13. $-12 + 4n = 6(n - 2)$ $n = 0$



## Chapter Assessment Form A Page 2

14. Solve $P = 2l + 2w$ for $w$ $w = \frac{P - 2l}{2}$

**Solve each inequality. Graph the solutions on a number line.**

15. $-4k - 5 \leq 3$ $k \geq -2$
    −5 −4 −3 −2 −1 0 1 2 3 4 5
16. $7t + 15 > 3t - 13$ $t > -7$
    −8 −7 −6 −5 −4 −3 −2 −1 0 1 2

**Write an equation. Solve.**

17. Find the three consecutive integers whose sum is 156.
    $n + (n + 1) + (n + 2) = 156$
    $n = 51$; 51, 52, 53
18. At Kara and Karl's favorite pizza restaurant, a large pizza costs \$9.99 plus \$.35 per topping. They paid \$11.74 for a pizza. How many toppings did they get?
    $9.99 + 0.35t = 11.74$
    $t = 5$, 5 toppings

**Solve.**

19. The average age of the four Berger children is at least 15. The ages of three of the children are 19, 14, and 12. What is the age of the fourth child?
    at least 15
20. Which do you think pays more: 4.25% simple interest for 3 years or 4% interest compounded semi-annually for the same amount of time? Explain. Sample answer is shown:
    The higher interest rate pays more. For example, \$1,000 would pay \$127.50 at 4.25% simple interest, whereas the same amount would pay only \$126.16 at 4%, even with compounding.



Assessment

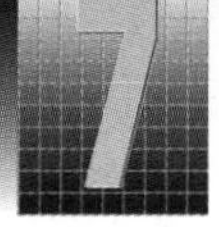

# Assessment

**Solve each equation.**

1. $3x + 4 = 19$ 5
2. $5 + \frac{c}{9} = -31$ −324
3. $2y - 15 = 11$ 13
4. $8a + 3 = -12.2$ −1.9
5. $\frac{3}{5}b - 8 = 4$ 20
6. $\frac{m}{2} - 5 = 7$ 24
7. $-83 = 9x - 2$ −9
8. $18 - \frac{a}{4} = -5$ 92
9. $\frac{3}{5}y + \frac{2}{5} = \frac{4}{5}$ $\frac{2}{3}$
10. $-23 - c = -19$ −4
11. $3x + 4x = 21$ 3
12. $\frac{1}{2}(10y + 4) = 17$ 3
13. $2(7b - 6) - 4 = 12$ 2
14. $2m - 6 = m$ 6
15. $\frac{2}{3}a - 5 + \frac{8}{9}a = -19$ −9
16. $0.015x + 3.45 = 4.65$ 80
17. $12y + 3 = 9y - 15$ −6
18. $3(2b + 6) = 2(4b - 8)$ 17

**Write an equation. Solve.**

19. *Number Sense* Find three consecutive integers with a sum of 267. 88, 89, 90
20. A rental car company charges \$35 a day plus \$.15/mi for a mid-size car. A customer owes \$117.25 for a three-day rental. How many miles did the customer drive? $81\frac{2}{3}$ mi
21. A moving truck leaves a house and travels at a steady rate of 40 mi/h. The family leaves the house 1 h later following the same route in a car. They travel at a steady rate of 60 mi/h. How long after the moving truck leaves the house will the car catch up with the truck? 3 h
22. The Jaspers have a jar where they collect nickels, dimes, and quarters. When they count the change in the jar, there are twice as many nickels as there are quarters. If there is \$15.30 in dimes and \$74.80 in all, how many quarters are there? 170 quarters

**Solve and graph each inequality.** See margin for graphs.

23. $7m - 8 > 6$ $m > 2$
24. $2x - 6 \geq -9$ $x \geq -\frac{3}{2}$
25. $-9a - 1 \leq 26$ $a \geq -3$
26. $22 < 6c + 4$ $c > 3$
27. $\frac{b}{3} + 12 > -3$ $b > -45$
28. $-\frac{2}{3}x + 8 \leq 2$ $x \geq 9$
29. $11 > -3y + 2$ $y > -3$
30. $16 - 4a \geq 18$ $a \leq -\frac{1}{2}$
31. *Commissions* An insurance salesperson earns a salary of \$1,200 per month plus a commission of 3% of sales. How much must the salesperson sell to have a monthly income of at least \$1,500? \$10,000
32. *Writing* How is solving a two-step inequality different from solving a two-step equation?

32. Answers may vary. Sample: You must reverse the direction of the inequality when multiplying or dividing by a negative number.

**Solve for the variable indicated in red.**

33. $H = 3w$ $w = \frac{H}{3}$
34. $g = cst$ $s = \frac{g}{ct}$
35. $R = 6n + 4p$ $p = \frac{R - 6n}{4}$
36. $y = \frac{x}{5} - 4$ $x = 5(y + 4)$

**Find the simple interest.**

37. \$800 deposited at an interest rate of 1.5% for 3 years \$36
38. \$1,050 deposited at an interest rate of 2% for 9 months \$15.75
39. \$2,500 deposited at an interest rate of 8% for 5 years \$1,000

**Find each balance.**

40. \$12,000 at 8% compounded annually for 4 years \$16,325.87
41. \$1,950 at 5% compounded annually for 2 years \$2,149.88
42. \$18,500 at 9% compounded semiannually for 5 years \$28,729.93
43. \$75,000 at 15% compounded semiannually for 8 years \$238,559.49



23.
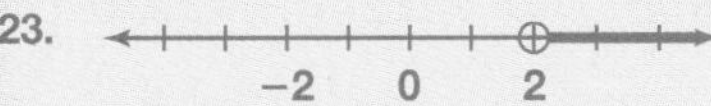


24.
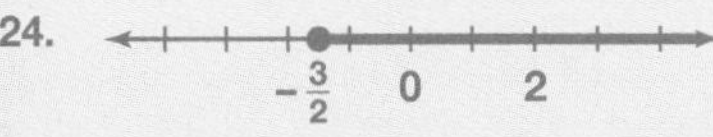


25.
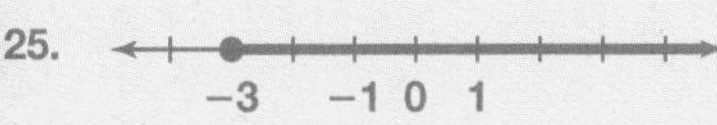


26. −1 0 1 3

27. −45 −20 0 20

28. −4 0 4 9

29.
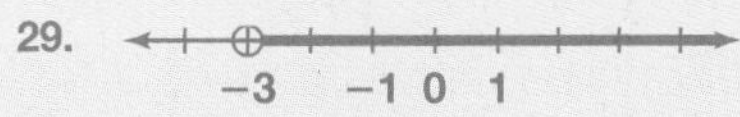


30. −2 $-\frac{1}{2}$ 0 1

# Chapter Assessment

**Resources** For a complete list of resources for this chapter, see p. 333H.

## Chapter Assessment Form B Page 1

**Circle the letter of the best answer.**

1. Solve $\frac{1}{2}(k - 5) = 3$.
   (A.) $k = 11$ B. $k = 1$ C. $k = -11$ D. $k = -1$
2. Solve $7n - 3 = 2n + 12$.
   F. $n = -3$ G. $n = 1$ (H.) $n = 3$ J. $n = -1$
3. Solve $3(x - 9) > -18$.
   A. $x > -3$ B. $x < -3$ C. $x < 3$ (D.) $x > 3$
4. Solve $2m - 7 > 9m + 35$.
   F. $m > -6$ (G.) $m < -6$ H. $m > -4$ J. $m < -4$
5. Solve $5d + 3 \leq -3d + 7$.
   A. $d \leq 2$ (B.) $d \leq \frac{1}{2}$ C. $d \leq 5$ D. $d \leq -2$
6. Find the simple interest on \$840 deposited at an interest rate of 4.5% for 4 years.
   F. \$161.72 G. \$134.40 H. \$142.68 (J.) \$151.20
7. Find the balance on \$2,500 deposited at 3% compounded annually for 3 years.
   (A.) \$2,731.82 B. \$2,725.00 C. \$2,614.20 D. \$2,733.61
8. Find the balance on \$7,000 deposited at 4% compounded semi-annually for 2 years.
   F. \$7,572.80 G. \$7,560.00 (H.) \$7,577.03 J. \$7,571.20
9. Which equation does *not* represent the problem? There are 5 more girls than boys in a class. There are 23 students in the class. How many boys and how many girls are in the class?
   A. $2s = 18$ B. $2s + 5 = 23$
   C. $s + (s + 5) = 23$ (D.) $s + 5 = 23$

**Solve each equation.**

10. $8 - 5y = 33$ $y = -5$
11. $\frac{2}{3}x + 7 = 3$ $x = -6$
12. $3(x - 5) = 2x + 11$ $x = 26$
13. $-17 + 3n = 7(n - 2)$ $n = -\frac{3}{4}$
14. Solve $m = \frac{y - 5}{-4}$ for $y$ $y = -4m + 5$



## Chapter Assessment Form B Page 2

**Solve each inequality. Graph the solutions on a number line.**

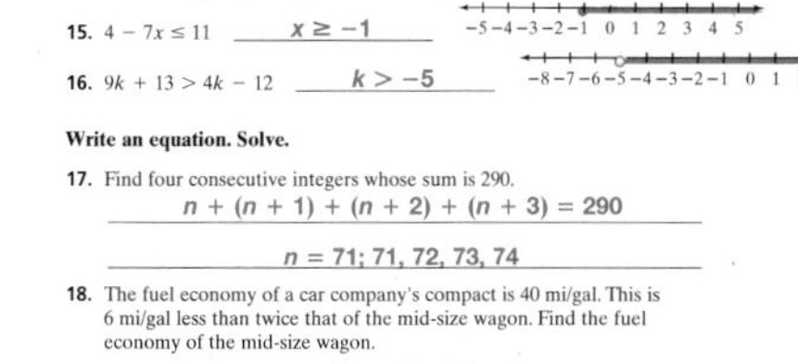

15. $4 - 7x \leq 11$ $x \geq -1$ (number line −5 −4 −3 −2 −1 0 1 2 3 4 5)
16. $9k + 13 > 4k - 12$ $k > -5$ (number line −8 −7 −6 −5 −4 −3 −2 −1 0 1 2)

**Write an equation. Solve.**

17. Find four consecutive integers whose sum is 290.
    $n + (n + 1) + (n + 2) + (n + 3) = 290$
    $n = 71$; 71, 72, 73, 74
18. The fuel economy of a car company's compact is 40 mi/gal. This is 6 mi/gal less than twice that of the mid-size wagon. Find the fuel economy of the mid-size wagon.
    $2w - 6 = 40$
    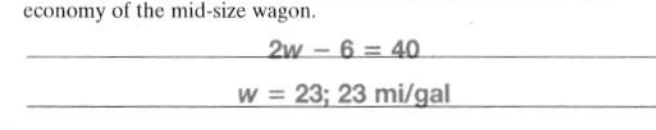
    $w = 23$; 23 mi/gal

**Solve.**

19. Five less than three times the number $k$ is neither less than nor equal to 19. Find $k$.
    $k > 8$
20. Which do you think pays more 5.5% simple interest for 4 years or 5% interest compounded annually for the same amount of time? Explain.
    Sample answer is shown:
    The higher interest rate pays more. For example, \$1,000 would pay \$220 at 5.5% simple interest, whereas the same amount would pay only \$215.51 at 5%, even with compounding.



Assessment

# Cumulative Review

## Cumulative Review Page 1

**Circle the letter of the best answer.**

1. Simplify $5z + 3y - (z + y)$.
   (A.) $4z + 2y$ B. $4z + 4y$ C. $8z - 2y$ D. $6z + 4y$
2. Use the formula $t = \frac{d}{r}$ for $t = 3.5$ h and $r = 60$ mi/h. Find the distance driven, $d$.
   F. 17 mi G. 180 mi H. 200 mi (J.) 210 mi
3. Find the GCF of $5a^3b^2$ and $15ab^4$.
   A. $5ab$ (B.) $5ab^2$ C. $15ab^2$ D. $15a^3b^4$
4. Teresa is training for a 10,000-meter race. Her goal is to be able to run $6\frac{1}{5}$ miles, which is very close to 10,000 meters. Yesterday she ran $5\frac{7}{10}$ miles. How far is she from her goal?
   F. $\frac{2}{5}$ mi G. $\frac{3}{5}$ mi (H.) $\frac{1}{2}$ mi J. $1\frac{1}{2}$ mi
5. Twenty-one of the 25 members of the Science club had an entry in the science fair. What percent of the club had an entry.
   (A.) 84% B. 80% C. 21% D. 16%
6. Which is the graph of the solution of $-9 > 4x - 1$?
   F. −5 −4 −3 −2 −1 0 1 2 3 4 5 G. −5 −4 −3 −2 −1 0 1 2 3 4 5
   (H.) −5 −4 −3 −2 −1 0 1 2 3 4 5 J. −5 −4 −3 −2 −1 0 1 2 3 4 5
7. Ali's little sister takes 5 steps to cover the same distance that Ali covers in 3 steps. If Ali takes 82 steps walking home from school, how many steps does his sister take?.
   A. about 123 steps B. about 75 steps
   C. about 49 steps (D.) about 137 steps
8. A car costs $29 a day plus $.25 a mile to rent. The rental company uses the formula $c = 29 + 0.25m$ to find the daily cost $c$ for $m$ miles. Solve the formula for $m$.
   F. $m = c - 29$ (G.) $m = \frac{c - 29}{0.25}$ H. $m = 4c + 29$ J. $m = \frac{c}{0.25} - 29$
9. Use the formula you found in the previous exercise to find the number of miles driven in a day for a total cost of $60.25.
   A. about 31 mi B. 212 mi (C.) 125 mi D. 270 mi
10. Which expression is equal to $2\frac{1}{3}$?
    (F.) $4\frac{1}{b} - 1\frac{5}{b}, b = 6$ G. $\frac{2 - a}{a - 2.5}, a = 5.5$ H. $3\frac{1}{3} - 1\frac{2}{3}$ J. $\frac{-7}{-3} - \frac{1}{3}$
11. Which statement is *not* true?
    A. $\frac{4}{9} > 44\%$ B. $0.25\% < \frac{1}{4}$ C. $150\% = 1.5$ (D.) $0.375 > 40\%$



Assessment

## Cumulative Review Page 2

12. Solve $3y - 9 = 6$.
    F. $y = -5$ (G.) $y = 5$ H. $y = 9$ J. $y = -9$

**Solve each equation.**

13. $3(x + 7) + 2(x - 5) = x - 5$ $x =$ −4
14. $\frac{2}{3}p + 12 = \frac{1}{3}p + 10$ $p =$ −6
15. $0.2n + 13 = 1.3n - 14.5$ $n =$ 25
16. $\frac{1}{2}(e - 6) = \frac{1}{4}(e + 8)$ $e =$ 20
17. Use >, <, or = to complete the statement.
    $18(4) - (-5)$ [>] $-40 + (-3)11$.
18. The rate of interest on a savings account is 7%. What is the simple interest for three years on $352?
    $73.92
19. a. Parth deposits $600 into a savings account that earns 4% interest compounded yearly. What is Parth's balance after three years?
    $674.92
    b. How much interest did Parth's account earn?
    $74.92
20. Write and solve a word problem to describe $2x - 4 = 8$.
    Sample answer is shown: Olga earns $2 each day she delivers newspapers, but she pays her mother $4 a week for gas. How many days does she deliver newspapers to clear $8?
    $x = 6$; 6 days



# 7 Cumulative Review

Preparing for Algebra

**Choose the best answer.**

1. Complete $43(2) - (-3)$ ■ $-58 + (-4)12$. A
   A. > B. < C. = D. ≤
2. Simplify $3(a + 2b) - 3a$. J
   F. $-6a + 6b$ G. $3a + 6b$
   H. $2b$ J. $6b$
3. Use the batting average formula $a = \frac{h}{n}$ for $a = 0.254$ and $n = 25$. Find the number of hits $h$. Round to the nearest integer. C
   A. 98 B. 7 C. 6 D. 0
4. Find the GCF of $4a^3b^2$ and $12ab^3$. F
   F. $4ab^2$ G. $12a^3b^3$ H. $3a^2b$ J. $16a^2b^4$
5. Which expression is equal to $1\frac{1}{2}$? C
   A. $2\frac{5}{8} - 1\frac{1}{4}$ B. $\frac{-3}{-2} - \frac{1}{2}$
   C. $3\frac{1}{s} - 1\frac{3}{s}, s = 4$ D. $\frac{b - 1.5}{3.5 - b}, b = \frac{1}{2}$
6. Scott jumped 15 ft $6\frac{3}{8}$ in. The school record for the long jump is 15 ft $8\frac{7}{8}$ in. How much shorter was Scott's jump? F
   F. $2\frac{1}{2}$ in. G. $1\frac{1}{2}$ in. H. $2\frac{1}{8}$ in. J. $2\frac{1}{4}$ in.
7. Which statement is *not* true? D
   A. $\frac{5}{8} > 40\%$ B. $0.09\% < \frac{1}{10}$
   C. $100\% = 1$ D. $0.125 > 20\%$
8. Sixteen of the 50 members of the rock climbing club are going climbing today. What percent of the club is going? G
   F. 33% G. 32% H. 3.125% J. 0.32
9. Which graph shows the solutions of $-15 > 7x + 20$? B

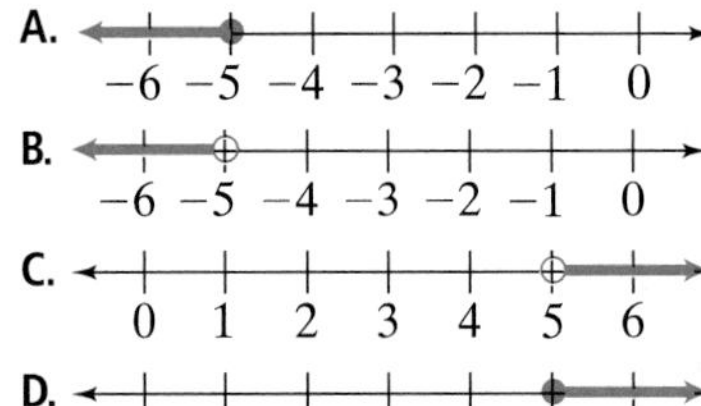


10. A recipe requires 2.5 cups of juice concentrate for every 4 cups of water. How much juice concentrate is required to fill a 20-cup punch bowl? F
    F. 12.5 cups G. 10 cups
    H. 50 cups J. 8 cups
11. A magazine telemarketer receives a weekly salary of $240 plus $3.00 for each magazine subscription she sells. She uses the formula $p = 240 + 3n$ where $p$ is total pay and $n$ is the number of subscriptions sold. Solve the formula for $n$. D
    A. $n = p + 240$ B. $n = \frac{240 + p}{3}$
    C. $n = 240 + 3p$ D. $n = \frac{p - 240}{3}$
12. Use the formula you found for Exercise 11 to find the number of subscriptions for total pay $p$ of $360. G
    F. 30 G. 40 H. 90 J. 120

**For Exercises 13–22, show your work.**

13. A savings account earns 10% simple interest. How much interest does an $800 deposit earn in four years? $320
14. a. Greg deposits $800 into a savings account that earns 10% interest compounded annually. What is Greg's balance after four years? $1,171.28
    b. How much interest did Greg's account earn? $371.28

**Solve each equation.**

15. $4x - 2 = 18$ 5
16. $3(n - 5) = 12$ 9
17. $\frac{1}{2}(4a + 16) = 5$ $-\frac{3}{2}$
18. $5.2 = 3.8h + 7.1$ $-\frac{1}{2}$
19. $\frac{2}{5}m + 4 = -\frac{3}{5}$ $-\frac{23}{2}$
20. $14 - \frac{m}{3} = \frac{7}{9}$ $39\frac{2}{3}$
21. $14n + 12 = 5n - 6$ −2
22. $6(k - 2) = 3k - 6$ 2



| Item | Chapter/ Lesson | Review Topic |
|---|---|---|
| 1, 2 | 1-9 | Expressions and Integers |
| 3 | 3-4 | Decimals and Equations |
| 4 | 4-3 | Factors, Fractions, and Exponents |
| 5, 6 | 5-3, 5-5 | Operations with Fractions |
| 7, 8, 10 | 6-2, 6-5, 6-6 | Ratios, Proportions, and Percents |
| 9, 11–22 | 7-1, 7-2, 7-3, 7-5, 7-6, 7-7, 7-8 | Solving Equations and Inequalities |

CHAPTER 8

# Linear Functions and Graphing

## Content Overview for Chapter 8

Chapter 8 introduces graphing with a section on relating graphs to events. Any set of ordered pairs is a relation. A function is a relation in which no two different ordered pairs have the same first coordinate. Graphing a relation on a coordinate plane gives you a visual way to tell whether the relation is a function.

A solution to an equation with two variables forms a function. Any ordered pair that makes the equation true is a solution. The set of ordered pairs forms a graph of the equation. Slope is a measure describing the tilt of a line. The slope-intercept form of a linear equation is $y = mx + b$, where $m$ is the slope and $b$ is the $y$-intercept. You can write linear equations from graphs. You can write linear equations in function notation and also write function rules from tables or graphs.

A scatter plot is a graph that shows the relationship between two sets of data. A scatter plot can help you find trends between sets of data. A trend line is a line that fits the data points in a scatter plot. You can use a trend line to make predictions about the relationship between the two sets of data on the scatter plot.

Two or more linear equations with the same variables form a system of linear equations. A solution of the system is any ordered pair that is a solution of each equation. You can solve a system by graphing. Two or more linear inequalities with the same variables form a system of linear inequalities. A solution of the system is any ordered pair that is a solution of each inequality in the system. You can solve a system by graphing.

## Making Connections

| Lesson | Interdisciplinary and Real-World Connections | Math Integration |
|---|---|---|
| 8-1 | Home Economics | Geometry |
| 8-2 | Meteorology, Language | Algebra |
| 8-3 | Engineering | Algebra |
| 8-4 | Science, Physics | Measurement, Geometry, Data Analysis |
| 8-5 | Nutrition, Sports | Data Analysis |
| 8-6 | Engineering, Physics | Problem Solving, Statistics |
| 8-7 | Industrial Arts | Geometry |
| 8-8 | Consumer Issues | Data Analysis |

**SCHOOL/HOME CONNECTION**

English and Spanish versions are available in the *Help at Home* book of copy masters.

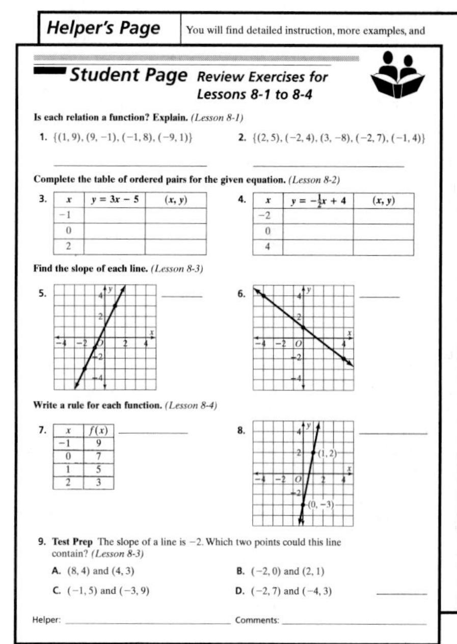

**Helper's Page** You will find detailed instruction, more examples, and

**Student Page** Review Exercises for Lessons 8-1 to 8-4

**Is each relation a function? Explain.** *(Lesson 8-1)*

1. $\{(1, 9), (9, -1), (-1, 8), (-9, 1)\}$ ______

2. $\{(2, 5), (-2, 4), (3, -8), (-2, 7), (-1, 4)\}$ ______

**Complete the table of ordered pairs for the given equation.** *(Lesson 8-2)*

3.

| $x$ | $y = 3x - 5$ | $(x, y)$ |
|---|---|---|
| −1 | | |
| 0 | | |
| 2 | | |

4.

| $x$ | $y = -\frac{1}{2}x + 4$ | $(x, y)$ |
|---|---|---|
| −2 | | |
| 0 | | |
| 4 | | |

**Find the slope of each line.** *(Lesson 8-3)*

5. ______

6. ______

**Write a rule for each function.** *(Lesson 8-4)*

7.

| $x$ | $f(x)$ |
|---|---|
| −1 | 9 |
| 0 | 7 |
| 1 | 5 |
| 2 | 3 |

______

8. ______



9. **Test Prep** The slope of a line is −2. Which two points could this line contain? *(Lesson 8-3)*

A. (8, 4) and (4, 3)
B. (−2, 0) and (2, 1)
C. (−1, 5) and (−3, 9)
D. (−2, 7) and (−4, 3) ______

Helper: ______ Comments: ______

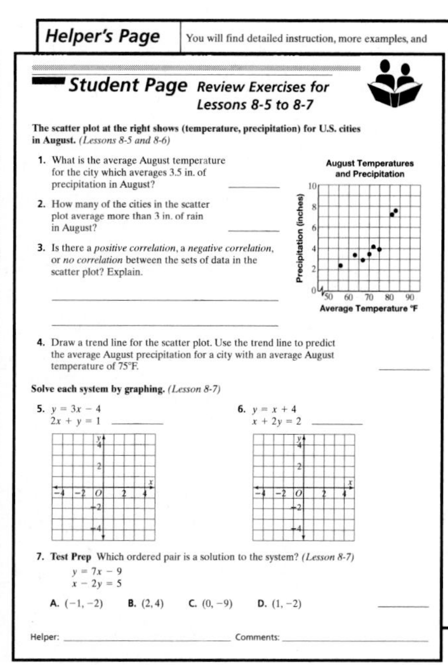

**Helper's Page** You will find detailed instruction, more examples, and

**Student Page** Review Exercises for Lessons 8-5 to 8-7

**The scatter plot at the right shows (temperature, precipitation) for U.S. cities in August.** *(Lessons 8-5 and 8-6)*

1. What is the average August temperature for the city which averages 3.5 in. of precipitation in August? ______

2. How many of the cities in the scatter plot average more than 3 in. of rain in August? ______

3. Is there a *positive correlation*, a *negative correlation*, or *no correlation* between the sets of data in the scatter plot? Explain.

______



4. Draw a trend line for the scatter plot. Use the trend line to predict the average August precipitation for a city with an average August temperature of 75°F. ______

**Solve each system by graphing.** *(Lesson 8-7)*

5. $y = 3x - 4$
$2x + y = 1$ ______

6. $y = x + 4$
$x + 2y = 2$ ______

7. **Test Prep** Which ordered pair is a solution to the system? *(Lesson 8-7)*
$y = 7x - 9$
$x - 2y = 5$

A. (−1, −2) B. (2, 4) C. (0, −9) D. (1, −2) ______

Helper: ______ Comments: ______

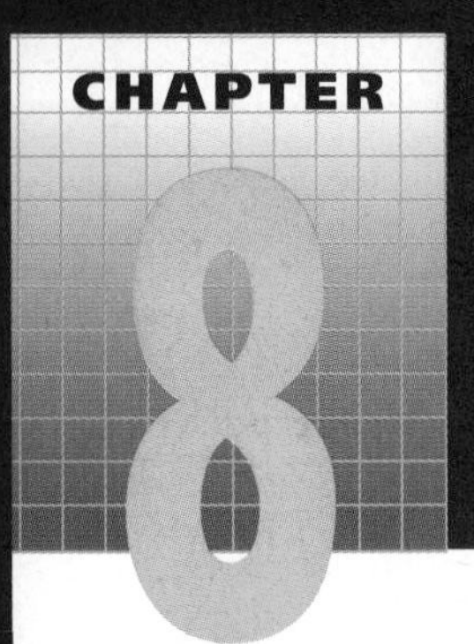


# Chapter 8 at a Glance

To accommodate flexible scheduling, most lessons are divided into parts. Assignment Options are given in the Teacher's Edition for each lesson.

## Lesson 8-1 Relations and Functions

Pages 386–390

NCTM 2, 6, 7, 8, 9, 10

- Part 1 Identifying Relations and Functions
- Part 2 Graphing Relations and Functions

## Lesson 8-2 Equations with Two Variables

Pages 391–395

NCTM 2, 6, 7, 8, 9, 10

- Part 1 Finding Solutions
- Part 2 Graphing Equations with Two Variables

**Project Activity 1**

## Lesson 8-3 Slope and *y*-intercept

Pages 397–402

NCTM 2, 8, 9, 10

- Part 1 Finding the Slope of a Line
- Part 2 Using Slope to Graph Linear Equations

**Math at Work**

## Lesson 8-7 Solving Systems of Linear Equations

Pages 420–425

NCTM 2, 6, 8, 9, 10

- Part 1 Graphing Systems of Linear Equations
- Part 2 Writing Systems of Linear Equations

**Checkpoint 2**

## Lesson 8-8 Graphing Linear Inequalities

Pages 426–431

NCTM 2, 8, 9, 10

- Part 1 Graphing Linear Inequalities
- Part 2 Graphing Systems of Linear Inequalities

**Project Activity 3**

# Pacing Options

This chart suggests pacing for only the core lessons and their parts, and it is provided merely as a possible guide. It will help you determine how much time you have in your schedule to cover other features, such as the Chapter Project, Math Toolboxes, Standardized Test Prep, Wrap Up, and Assessment.

| | Day 1 | Day 2 | Day 3 | Day 4 | Day 5 | Day 6 | Day 7 | Day 8 | Day 9 | Day 10 | Day 11 |
|---|---|---|---|---|---|---|---|---|---|---|---|
| **Traditional** (40–45 min. class periods) | 8–1 1, 8–1 2 | 8–2 1 | 8–2 2 | 8–3 1 | 8–3 2 | 8–4 1, 8–4 2 | 8–5 1, 8–5 2 | 8–6 | 8–7 1 | 8–7 2 | 8–8 1, 8–8 2 |
| **Pre-Algebra Over 2 Years** (40–45 min. class periods) | 8–1 1 | 8–1 1 | 8–1 2 | 8–2 1 | 8–2 1 | 8–2 2 | 8–2 2 | 8–3 1 | 8–3 1 | 8–3 2 | 8–3 2 |
| **Block Scheduling** (90 min. class periods) | 8–1 1 2, 8–2 1 2 | 8–3 1 2, 8–4 1 2 | 8–5 1 2, 8–6 | 8–7 1 2, 8–8 1 2 | | | | | | | |

| Pages 404–408 | Lesson 8-4 Writing Rules for Linear Functions |
|---|---|
| NCTM 2, 7, 8, 9, 10 | Part 1 Writing Rules from Words<br>Part 2 Writing Rules from Tables or Graphs<br>**Checkpoint 1** |

| Pages 409–414 | Lesson 8-5 Data Analysis: Scatter Plots |
|---|---|
| NCTM 2, 5, 6, 8, 9, 10 | Part 1 Interpreting and Drawing Scatter Plots<br>Part 2 Using Scatter Plots to Find Trends |

| Pages 416–419 | Lesson 8-6 Problem Solving Strategy |
|---|---|
| NCTM 2, 5, 6, 8, 9, 10 | Solve by Graphing<br>**Project Activity 2** |

**NCTM STANDARDS 2000**

1 Number and Operations
2 Algebra
3 Geometry
4 Measurement
5 Data Analysis and Probability
6 Problem Solving
7 Reasoning and Proof
8 Communication
9 Connections
10 Representation

| Day 12 | Day 13 | Day 14 | Day 15 | Day 16 | Day 17 | Day 18 | Day 19 | Day 20 | Day 21 | Day 22 | Day 23 | Day 24 |
|---|---|---|---|---|---|---|---|---|---|---|---|---|
| 8-4 1 | 8-4 2 | 8-4 2 | 8-5 1 | 8-5 1 | 8-5 2 | 8-6 | 8-6 | 8-7 1 | 8-7 1 | 8-7 2 | 8-7 2 | 8-8 1, 8-8 2 |

**Block Scheduling Notes**

Consider these suggestions:

- **Day 1** Before starting Lesson 8-1, teach Math Toolbox 1, p. 384.
- **Day 2** Before starting Lesson 8-3, teach Math Toolbox 2, p. 396.
- **Day 2** Before starting Lesson 8-4, teach Math Toolbox 3, p. 403.
- **Day 3** Before starting Lesson 8-6, teach the Standardized Test Prep, p. 415.
- **Day 4** After completing Lesson 8-8, teach Math Toolbox 4, p. 432.

# Math Background

## LESSON 8-1
### Relations and Functions

Consider this set of ordered pairs as an example:

(2, 4), (3 ,6), (5, 10).

These pairs of numbers are called *ordered* pairs because the order of the numbers makes a difference; the pair (2, 4) is not the same as the pair (4, 2). A *relation* is a set of ordered pairs such as this. The first numbers, or coordinates, in a relation form the *domain* of the relation, and the second coordinates form the *range* of the relation.

You can also express this relation in the form of an equation: $y = 2x$. The relation defined by the equation $y = 2x$ contains an infinite number of ordered pairs, unless you restrict the domain to the numbers 2, 3, and 5.

Another way to write the relation (2, 4), (3, 6), (5, 10) is to graph the points on a coordinate plane.

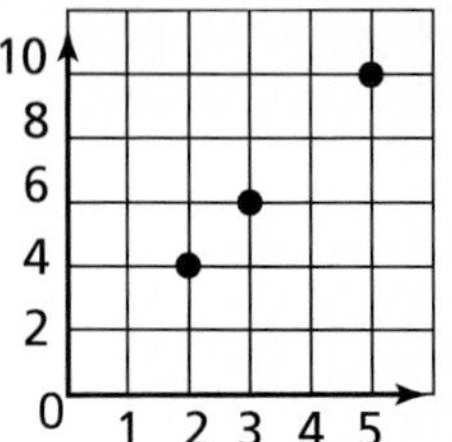


One special kind of relation is called a *function.* A function is a relation in which one element in the domain is paired with *exactly one* element in the range. (In mathematics, the words *exactly one* mean that there is always one, neither more nor less.) The relation (2, 4), (3, 6), (5, 10) is a function because each number in the domain (2, 3, and 5) has exactly one partner, or match, in the range.

However, the relation: (2, 4), (3, 6), (5, 10), (3, 9) is not a function because 3 is matched with two numbers, both 6 and 9.

It may not be obvious that the relation (2, 4), (3, 6), (5, 10), (2, $\frac{20}{5}$) is also a function. The last ordered pair is merely a repeat of the first ordered pair, with the number in the range renamed, so 2 has only one corresponding point in the range, and the given relation is a function.

When you graph a relation, you can use the *vertical-line test* to tell whether or not the relation is a function. If a relation is a function, no two points of the graph will be on the same vertical line.

## LESSON 8-2
### Equations with Two Variables

A linear function (whose graph is always a straight line) can be written as an equation with two variables, such as $y = 3x - 2$. An equation with two variables can have many solutions. One way to show these solutions is to graph them.

A linear equation is a function unless it is of the form $x = b$. Notice that $x = b$ has no $y$-term and its graph will always be a vertical line $b$ units from the $y$-axis.

## LESSON 8-3
### Slope and *y*-intercept

When you write a linear equation with the $y$ isolated on the left (with no coefficient other than 1) and the $x$ term with its coefficient and the constant on the right, the form of the equation looks like this: $y = mx + b$. This is called the *slope-intercept form* of the equation. In this form, $m$ is the slope of the line (the ratio $\frac{\text{change in } y}{\text{change in } x}$ between any two points on the graph of the line) and $b$ is the *y-intercept* (where the graph crosses the $y$-axis).

The graph of the line $y = x$ extends upward from left to right through the origin and bisects Quadrants I and III. The graph of the line $y = -x$ extends downward from left to right through the origin and bisects Quadrants II and IV. The graphs of lines with slopes greater than 1 or less than $-1$ are more steep than $y = x$ and $y = -x$. Every horizontal line has a slope of zero because it has no steepness at all. Every vertical line has a slope that it is undefined.

When the equation of a line is written in slope-intercept form ($y = mx + b$), if $m > 0$, then the right end of the line is higher than the left end and the line has a positive slope. If you think of this as climbing a hill from left to right, you are climbing up.

On the other hand, when the equation of a line is written in slope-intercept form and $m < 0$, then the left end of the line is higher than the right end and the line has a negative slope. If you think of this as a hill, from left to right you are sliding down.

## LESSON 8-4

### Writing Rules for Linear Functions

When the value of $y$ depends of the value of $x$ (as in $y = 5x - 2$), then you can say that $y$ is a function of $x$. To say that $y$ is a function of $x$ means, informally, "You tell me what a value of $x$ is and I'll tell you what the resulting $y$-value is."

For many students, the idea of function may be new. The notation may also be confusing. The statement "$y$ is a function of $x$" is written as $y = f(x)$. This does not mean that $f$ is a variable, nor that it is multiplied by $x$. The letter $f$ and the parentheses have a special meaning in this notation, so you say $f(x) = 5x - 2$ as "$f$ of $x$ is five $x$ minus two" or "the function of $x$ is $5x - 2$." In this case, the equation $y = 5x - 2$ is a function rule that can be written as the function $f(x) = 5x - 2$.

## LESSONS 8-5 AND 8-6

### Scatter Plots and Solve by Graphing

When a relation is a set of ordered pairs, or of data, that consists of separate points (called *discrete values*), rather than every point on a line (called *continuous values*), then the graph of the relation is a collection of points called a *scatter plot.*

The points on a scatter plot show a *positive correlation* when an increase in $x$ shows a corresponding increase in $y$. When an increase in $x$ shows a corresponding decrease in $y$, there is a *negative correlation* in the data. Some sets of data will show neither trend; they have *no correlation*. To find whether a correlation exists and what kind it is, you can plot pairs of data points on a scatter plot. If there is a correlation, you can draw a *trend line* that closely fits the data points in the scatter plot. A trend line with a positive slope (right end higher) indicates a positive correlation in the data.

## LESSONS 8-7 AND 8-8

### Solving Systems of Linear Equations and Graphing Linear Inequalities

You can graph the relation $y = 5x - 2$ as a straight line. Every solution of $y = 5x - 2$ (an ordered pair that makes the equation true) is a point on the graph. Every point on the graph represents an ordered pair that makes the equation true.

You can find the common solution of two or more linear equations by graphing. The point where the graphs cross (if there is one) is a solution for both equations. This is called the *solution of the system* of the two equations. When the graphs are parallel lines, the system has no solution. When the graphs of two equations are the same line, the system has infinitely many solutions.

If you replace the equal sign (=) in a linear equation with an inequality sign ($<, \leq, >, \geq$) the result is called a *linear inequality.* When the sign shows that the border is included (as with $\leq$ or $\geq$), then the graph is a region (or half-plane) with a solid line on the border. When the border is excluded ($<$ or $>$), you use a dotted line at the edge of the region that contains the solutions to the inequality.

You can find the common solution to a system of linear inequalities by graphing the inequalities on the same coordinate plane.

For professional development tips visit our Web site **www.phschool.com**.

# Monitoring Progress

## Universal Access

### ▶ Preventing a Student from Falling Behind

These resources are particularly helpful in preventing a student from falling behind his or her appropriate math level. For a complete list of resources for this chapter, see page 381H.

#### Skills You Need for Chapter 8

Student Edition, p. 381
Teacher's Edition, p. 381

- Transforming equations
- Graphing points
- Simplifying ratios
- Describing number patterns

#### Skills Handbook

Student Edition, pp. 723–741
Teacher's Edition, pp. 723–741

#### Reteaching Worksheets

There is a Reteaching worksheet for every lesson in this chapter.

- Chapter 8 Support File, Teaching Resources box
- See TE p. 381H for a complete list of resources

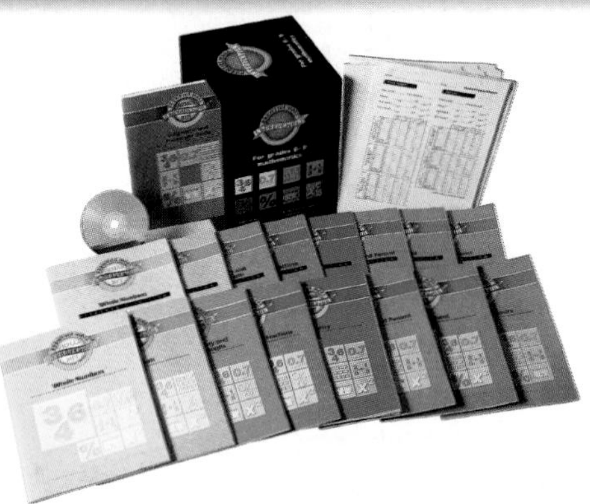

#### Skills Intervention Kit with CD-ROM

| For | Use |
|---|---|
| Lessons 8-1, 8-8 | Pre-Algebra Basics |

#### Daily Cumulative Review Blackline Masters

There is a Daily Cumulative Review worksheet for every lesson in this chapter.

See TE p. 381H for a complete list of resources.

### ▶ Accommodating Diverse Learning Styles

#### Tactile Learning

Construct ramps with positive and negative slopes. (Lesson 8-3)

Create a coordinate plane on a classroom bulletin board to practice graphing systems of linear inequalities. (Lesson 8-8)

#### Advanced Learner

Every lesson has at least one challenge problem.

Examine the relationship between daily mean temperature and latitude from a scatter plot. (Lesson 8-5)

#### ELL (English Language Learner)

Recognize a straight line as the solution t the graph of a linear equation. (Lesson 8-

Understand that the graph of a linear inequality is a *region*. (Lesson 8-8)

#### Auditory Learning

Say the slope and *y*-intercept aloud when reading equations. (Lesson 8-3)

Translate spoken words into equations. (Lesson 8-7)

#### Visual Learning

Graph points to use the vertical line test. (Lesson 8-1)

Check ordered pairs if graph is not a straight line. (Lesson 8-2)

Draw trend lines on scatter plots. (Lesson 8-6)

# Aligning Assessment with Instruction

## Assessment Options

| | Chapter Opener | 8-1 | 8-2 | 8-3 | 8-4 | 8-5 | 8-6 | 8-7 | 8-8 | End |
|---|---|---|---|---|---|---|---|---|---|---|
| Chapter Project | ■ | | | ■ | | | ■ | | | ■ |
| Try This Exercises | | ■ | ■ | ■ | ■ | ■ | ■ | ■ | ■ | |
| Mixed Reviews | | ■ | ■ | ■ | ■ | ■ | ■ | ■ | ■ | |
| Checkpoints | | | | | ■ | | | ■ | | |
| Writing | | ■ | ■ | ■ | ■ | | | ■ | ■ | ■ |
| Chapter Assessment | | | | | | | | | | ■ |
| Cumulative Review | | | | | | | | | | ■ |
| Standardized Test Prep | | | ■ | ■ | ■ | ■ | | ■ | ■ | |
| | Standardized Test Prep, p. 415 | | | | | | | | | |
| Computer Item Generator | Can be used to create custom-made practice pages or assessment pages at any time. | | | | | | | | | |

### Test-Taking Tips on Transparencies

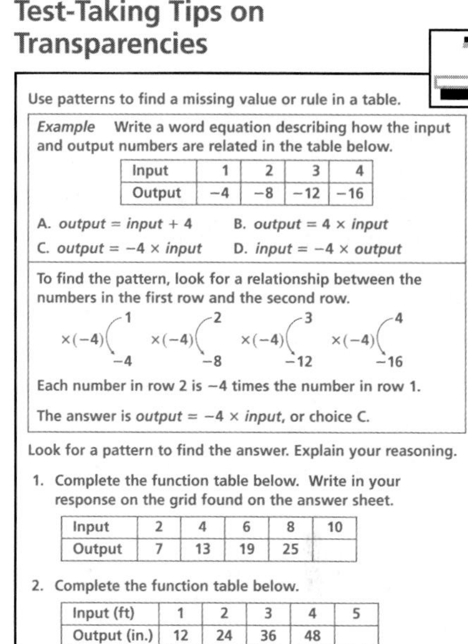

Use patterns to find a missing value or rule in a table.

*Example* Write a word equation describing how the input and output numbers are related in the table below.

| Input | 1 | 2 | 3 | 4 |
|---|---|---|---|---|
| Output | −4 | −8 | −12 | −16 |

A. *output* = *input* + 4 B. *output* = 4 × *input*
C. *output* = −4 × *input* D. *input* = −4 × *output*

To find the pattern, look for a relationship between the numbers in the first row and the second row.

×(−4): 1 → −4; 2 → −8; 3 → −12; 4 → −16

Each number in row 2 is −4 times the number in row 1.

The answer is *output* = −4 × *input*, or choice C.

Look for a pattern to find the answer. Explain your reasoning.

1. Complete the function table below. Write in your response on the grid found on the answer sheet.

| Input | 2 | 4 | 6 | 8 | 10 |
|---|---|---|---|---|---|
| Output | 7 | 13 | 19 | 25 | |

2. Complete the function table below.

| Input (ft) | 1 | 2 | 3 | 4 | 5 |
|---|---|---|---|---|---|
| Output (in.) | 12 | 24 | 36 | 48 | |

A. 5 B. 60 C. 48 D. Not Here

*Use with Standardized Test Prep and Chapter Assessments.*

## Correlation to Standardized Tests

| Lesson | | CAT5 | CTBS/5 TerraNova™ | ITBS | MAT7 | SAT9 | LOCAL OBJECTIVES |
|---|---|---|---|---|---|---|---|
| 8-1 | Relations and Functions | | | | | ■ | |
| 8-2 | Equations with Two Variables | | | | | ■ | |
| 8-3 | Slope and *y*-intercept | | | | | ■ | |
| 8-4 | Writing Rules for Linear Functions | | | | | ■ | |
| 8-5 | Scatter Plots | | | | | ■ | |
| 8-6 | Problem Solving Strategy: Solve by Graphing | | | | | ■ | |
| 8-7 | Solving Systems of Linear Equations | | | | | ■ | |
| 8-8 | Graphing Linear Inequalities | | ■ | ■ | | ■ | |

**CAT5** California Achievement Test, 5th edition
**CTBS TerraNova** Comprehensive Test of Basic Skills, 5th edition
**ITBS** Iowa Test of Basic Skills, Form M
**MAT7** Metropolitan Achievement Test, 7th edition
**SAT** Stanford Achievement Test, Advanced 1

For other standardized test correlations, follow the link to your state at **www.phschool.com**.

# Resources for Chapter 8

| | TEACHING RESOURCES BOX | | | | | | | | | | | | | | |
|---|---|---|---|---|---|---|---|---|---|---|---|---|---|---|---|
| | CHAPTER 8 SUPPORT FILE | | | | | | | | | | | | | | |
| | Practice | Reteach | Enrichment | Project Manager | Checkpoints | Cumulative Review | Chapter Assessment | Alternative Assessment | Cumulative Assessment | Lesson Planners Plus | Daily Cum Review | Teaching Transparencies | Warm-Up Transparencies | Help at Home | SE Answers Transparenc |
| Begin Chapter | | | | ■ | | | | | | ■ | | | | | |
| 8-1 | ■ | ■ | ■ | | | | | | | ■ | ■ | | ■ | | ■ |
| 8-2 | ■ | ■ | ■ | | | | | | | ■ | ■ | 63 | ■ | | ■ |
| 8-3 | ■ | ■ | ■ | | | | | | | ■ | ■ | 25, 64 | ■ | | ■ |
| 8-4 | ■ | ■ | ■ | | ■ | | | | | ■ | ■ | 26, 65 | ■ | ■ | ■ |
| 8-5 | ■ | ■ | ■ | | | | | | | ■ | ■ | 66, 67 | ■ | | ■ |
| 8-6 | ■ | ■ | ■ | | | | | | | ■ | ■ | | ■ | | ■ |
| 8-7 | ■ | ■ | ■ | | ■ | | | | | ■ | ■ | | ■ | ■ | ■ |
| 8-8 | ■ | ■ | ■ | | | | | | | ■ | ■ | 68 | ■ | | ■ |
| End Chapter | | | | | | ■ | ■ (2 forms) | ■ | After Ch. 3, 6, 9, 13 | | | | | | |

Also available for use with the chapter:

Solution Key
Computational Practice Skills Booklet
Mathematics Standardized Test Prep, Student Edition and Teacher's Edition
Overhead Manipulatives Kit
Practice Workbook
Algebra Readiness Kit
Student Manipulatives Kit
Test-Taking Tips on Transparencies
Assessment Success Kit
Teaching Aids and Letters
Graphing Calculator Handbook
Spanish Resources
Success-Building Puzzle and Problem Masters

## TECHNOLOGY

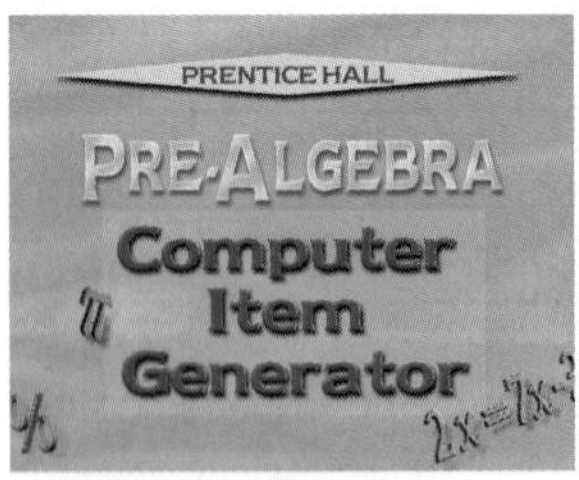


**Computer Item Generator with Standardized Test Prep**

CD-ROM with an unlimited supply of questions with varying degrees of difficulty for customized practice sheets, quizzes, and tests.

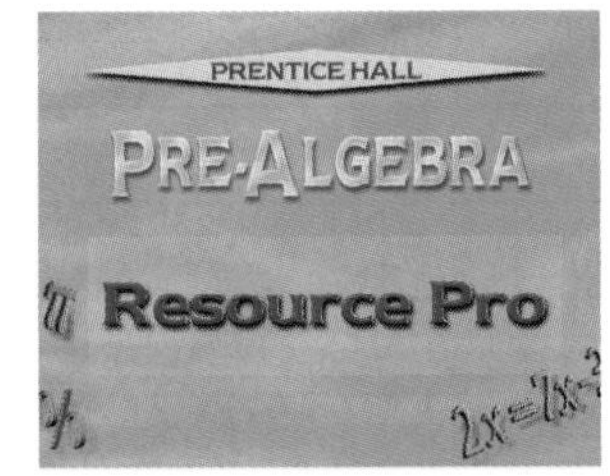


**Resource Pro® with Planning Express®**

CD-ROM with complete classroom planning tool and teaching resources for customizing and planning lessons.

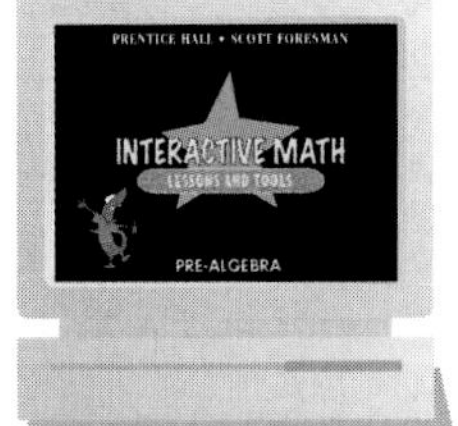


**Interactive Math Lessons and Tools**

CD-ROM with lessons and tools to make abstract concepts visual and accessible.

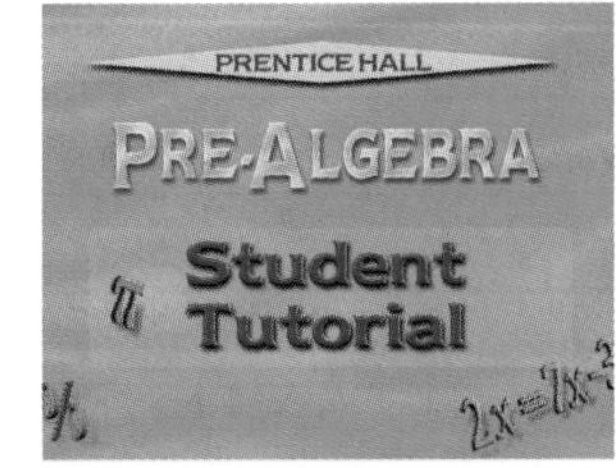


**Student Tutorial**

Test preparation software for students on CD-ROM with management system for teachers; includes Secondary Math Lab Toolkit™.

**Secondary Math Lab Toolkit™ with Integrated Math Labs**

Integrated software package with linkable math tools for exploring key concepts.

Also available for use with the chapter:

Math Blaster® Pre-Algebra CD-ROM
Video Fieldtrips, Vol. I: Algebra Applications
Video Fieldtrips, Vol. II: Geometry Applications
Wide World of Mathematics CD-ROM
Wide World of Mathematics Video

### *Web Extension*

**www.phschool.com**

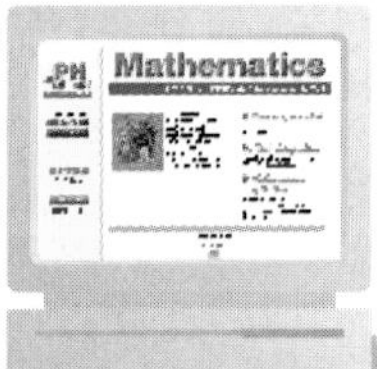


**For Students**
- Chapter Support with Internet Links
- Internet Activities

**For Teachers**
- Curriculum Support
- Professional Development
- Product Information
- Regional Support Information

# Skills You Need for Chapter

## ▶ *Transforming equations*

Use before Lesson 8-2.

**Solve each equation for $y$.**

1. $4x + y = 3$ $y = -4x + 3$
2. $y - 4 = -2x$ $y = -2x + 4$
3. $8x - 4y = 24$ $y = 2x - 6$
4. $8 + y + 6x = 0$ $y = -6x - 8$
5. $12 - y = x$ $y = -x + 12$
6. $2y + x = 5$ $y = -\frac{1}{2}x + \frac{5}{2}$
7. $5y - 20 = x$ $y = \frac{1}{5}x + 4$
8. $3x + 4y = 12$ $y = -\frac{3}{4}x + 3$

## ▶ *Graphing points*

Use before Lessons 8-2, 8-3, 8-4, and 8-7.

**Write the coordinates of each point.**

9. $A$ (5, 2)
10. $B$ (−3, 4)
11. $C$ (4, 0)
12. $D$ (6, −3)
13. $E$ (−4, −3)
14. $F$ (0, 3)

**Draw a coordinate plane. Graph each point.** 15–20. See margin.

15. $G(3, 0)$
16. $H(-2, 4)$
17. $J(6, 1)$
18. $K(5, -3)$
19. $L(-4, -3)$
20. $M(0, -2)$

## ▶ *Simplifying ratios*

Use before Lesson 8-3.

**Write each ratio in simplest form.**

21. $\frac{6-2}{3-1}$ 2
22. $\frac{8-5}{4-2}$ $1\frac{1}{2}$
23. $\frac{7-(-1)}{10-2}$ 1
24. $\frac{-3-5}{4-0}$ −2
25. $\frac{-5-(-4)}{12-(-6)}$ $-\frac{1}{18}$
26. $\frac{15-(-12)}{17-8}$ 3
27. $\frac{-4-1}{-7-(-2)}$ 1
28. $\frac{4.3-3.5}{7.1-4.7}$ $\frac{1}{3}$

## ▶ *Describing number patterns*

Use before Lesson 8-6.

**Write the next two numbers in each pattern.**

29. −3, −5, −7, −9, . . . −11, −13
30. 7, 12, 17, 22, . . . 27, 32
31. 8, 5, 2, −1, . . . −4, −7
32. 43, 37, 31, 25, . . . 19, 13
33. 4.5, 6, 7.5, 9, . . . 10.5, 12
34. 27, 41, 55, 69, . . . 83, 97



# Skills You Need

## Transforming equations

**In Lesson 8-2** students will transform linear equations into the slope-intercept form.

## Graphing points

**In Lesson 8-2** students will graph points to graph linear equations.

**In Lesson 8-3** students will graph points in order to graph linear equations using the slope and $y$-intercept.

**In Lesson 8-4** students will graph points to check the linear functions they write.

**In Lesson 8-7** students will graph points to solve systems of linear equations.

## Simplifying ratios

**In Lesson 8-3** students will simplify ratios to find slope.

## Describing number patterns

**In Lesson 8-6** students will describe number patterns to solve problems.

15–20.

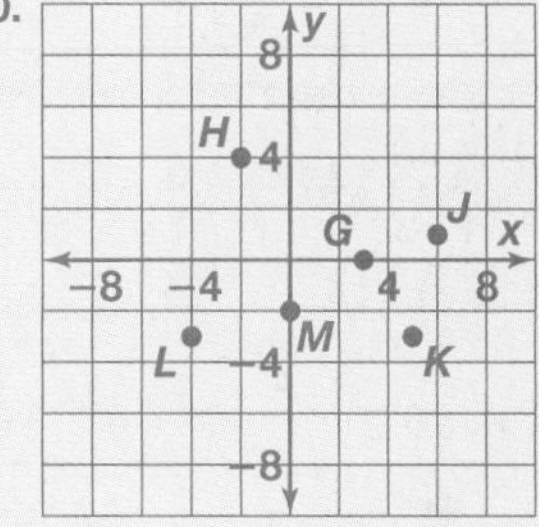


# Skills Trace

| SKILL | INTRODUCED | DEVELOPED IN LESSON(S) | REVIEWED/REINFORCED |
|---|---|---|---|
| Identifying relations and functions | 8-1 | 8-4 | pp. 395, 414, 473, 586 |
| Solving and graphing linear equalities and inequalities | 8-2 | 8-3 | Math Toolboxes pp. 396, 403, 432; pp. 488, 525, 545, 592 |
| Writing function rules from tables or graphs | 8-4 | 8-6 | p. 414 |
| Interpreting graphs and scatter plots | Math Toolbox p. 384 | 8-5 | p. 425 |
| Solving and graphing systems of linear equations and inequalities | 8-7 | 8-8 | pp. 431, 447, 463, 478 |

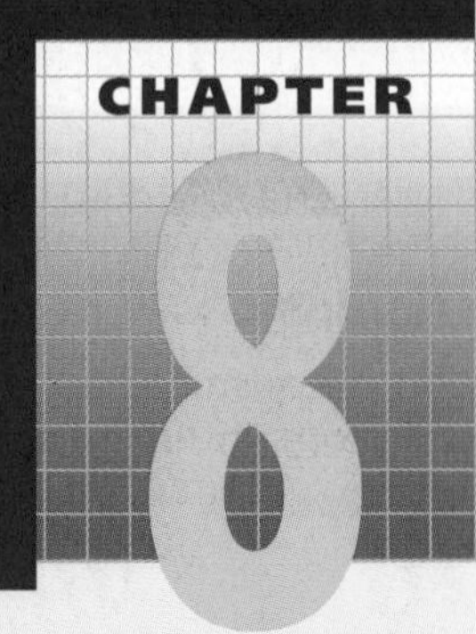


# Linear Functions and Graphing

## Connecting to Students' Lives

Ask students to describe any events they might know about that involved planning the seating and refreshments for large numbers of people.

## Interdisciplinary Connections

The Chapter Project connects math and business. You may want to display graphs from the business pages and ads of newspapers and newsmagazines showing a comparison of costs.

## About the Project

The Chapter Project directs students to apply their knowledge of writing equations and graphing them to compare the cost of renting chairs from several different companies.

CHAPTER 8 Linear Functions and Graphing

**What you'll learn in this chapter:**

- How to determine whether a relation is a function
- How to solve linear equations
- How to solve systems of linear equations and inequalities

382 Chapter 8

*Web Extension*

**www.phschool.com**

**For Students**
Chapter Support with Internet links
Interactive Activities

**For Teachers**
Curriculum Support
Professional Development
Product Information
Regional Support Information

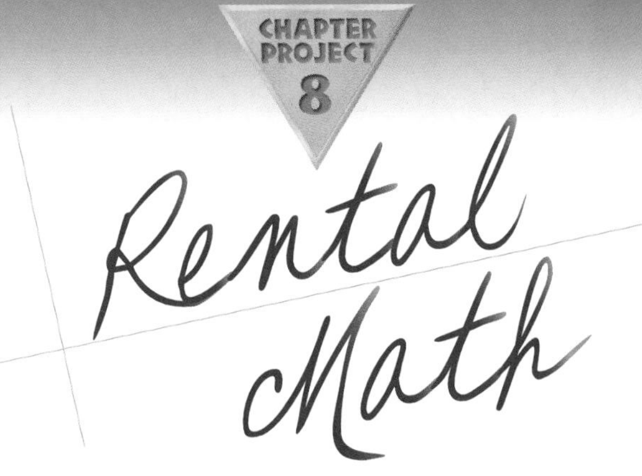

Your school is planning its graduation ceremony. Hundreds of people will be coming, and they need a place to sit. Your school has some chairs, but not enough for this crowd! Better call a rental company.

***Compare Prices*** For the chapter project, you will research the cost of renting folding chairs. You do not yet know how many chairs you will need, so you will investigate the price per chair, as well as delivery charges. For your report to the graduation committee, you will write and graph equations to show the total costs of renting chairs from different companies.

### *Steps to help you complete the project*

**p. 395** ACTIVITY 1: RESEARCHING
**p. 419** ACTIVITY 2: GRAPHING
**p. 431** ACTIVITY 3: ANALYZING
**p. 433** FINISHING THE CHAPTER PROJECT

***Web Extension***
**www.phschool.com**

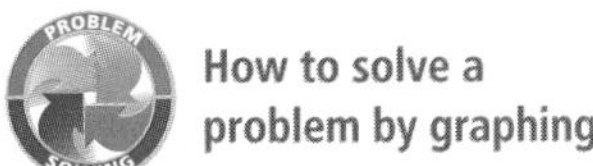


How to solve a problem by graphing

*The Chapter Project is optional and may be assigned at your discretion.*

Ask students:

- Have you ever telephoned a company to ask about the prices of their products or services?
- What information will you need to provide when you inquire about the products and services of a company?
- What questions will you ask, and how will you make a record of the answers?

Distribute a copy of the Project Manager and Scoring Rubric to help students get an overview of the project.

Review the scoring rubric with students.

## Project Notebook

Encourage students to keep all project-related materials in a separate folder or notebook. Call attention to the fact that they will find much useful information on the Web site **www.phschool.com**.

**Tracking the Project** Set benchmark deadlines for students to show you their work in progress.

*Available in the Chapter 8 Support File in the Teaching Resources box.*

### Project Manager and Scoring Rubric

**Getting Started** You will be writing a report comparing different companies' costs of renting folding chairs for graduation. Read about the project in your textbook. As you work on the project, you will need graph paper and materials to make your report.

**Checklist and Suggestions**

| | | |
|---|---|---|
| ❑ | Research the cost of renting plastic folding chairs. | Organize your information in a table. |
| ❑ | Write and graph an equation for each rental company. | Find the range of y values before drawing your scale. |
| ❑ | Analyze your graph. | Compare the slope and y-intercept of each line to your original data. |
| ❑ | Prepare your report. | Justify your recommendations. |
| ❑ | Share your report with a friend. | Make any necessary changes. |

**Scoring Rubric**

3 You write and analyze your equations correctly. Your graph has an appropriate scale and is drawn correctly and neatly. You justify your recommendations clearly and thoroughly.

2 You make minor errors in your equations, graphs, or analysis. You justify your recommendations, but the justification could be clearer or more thorough.

1 You either write or graph your equations incorrectly. Your report is incomplete, lacks organization, and does not provide adequate justification for your recommendations.

0 Major elements of the project are incomplete or missing.

**Your Evaluation of the Project** Evaluate your work, based on the Scoring Rubric.

**Teacher's Evaluation of the Project**



## Scoring Rubric

**3** You write and analyze your equations correctly. Your graph has an appropriate scale and is drawn correctly and neatly. You justify your recommendations clearly and thoroughly.

**2** You make minor errors in your equations, graphs, or analysis. You justify your recommendations, but the justification could be clearer or more thorough.

**1** You either write or graph your equations incorrectly. Your report is incomplete, lacks organization, and does not provide adequate justification for your recommendations.

**0** Major elements of the project are incomplete or missing.

## MATH TOOLBOX

### Relating Graphs to Events

This Math Toolbox shows how a graph expresses the relationship between two variables. Students sketch a graph to describe a situation.

### Math Background

A graph can show the relationship between two variables, one of which may be time. When time is one of the variables for a graph, you often represent it on the *x*-axis, increasing from left to right on the graph. Represent the other variable on the *y*-axis, increasing from bottom to top on the graph. The origin of the graph usually represents a zero value for both variables. The graph itself shows the relationship between the two variables at any given point.

## Teaching Notes

**Error Prevention** Students frequently fail to label their graphs correctly. Suggest that students begin a graph by labeling both axes and giving the graph a title. Remind them that time is often represented along the *x*-axis.

**Monitoring Progress** Exercise 5
The low temperature on this graph could conceivably be below zero. Ask students where the graph would start if this is the case and the origin represents zero. The graph would start below the *x*-axis.

**Block Scheduling** If you have block scheduling or extended periods, you may wish to insert this Math Toolbox lesson between the completion of Part 1 of Lesson 8-1 and the beginning of Part 2 of Lesson 8-1.

## MATH TOOLBOX

*Modeling*
*Before Lesson 8-1*

# *Relating Graphs to Events*

You can use graphs to show real-world relationships visually. Labels can help explain the parts of a graph.

### EXAMPLE 1

*Transportation* **The graph at the right shows one trip from home to school and back. The trip combines walking and getting a ride from a neighbor. Tell what the graph shows by labeling each part.**

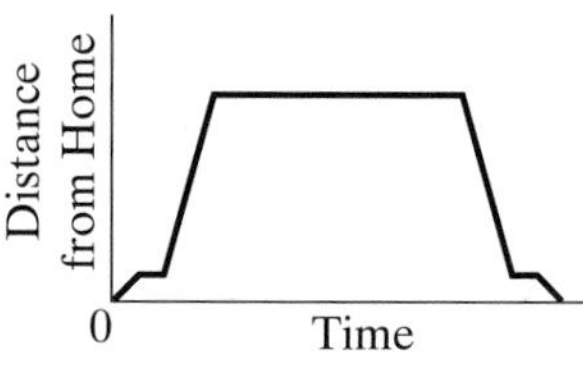


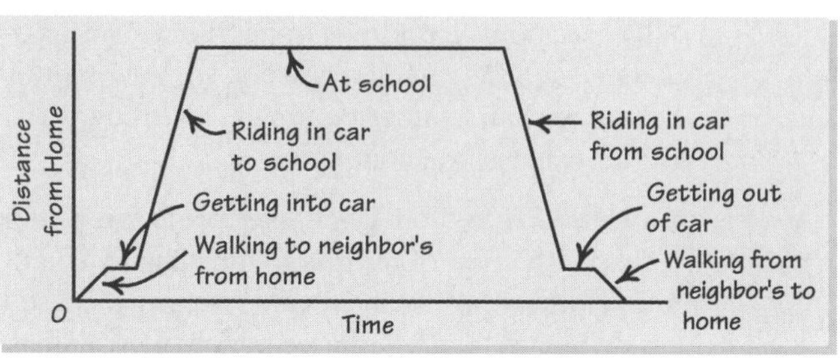


**Label the parts of each graph.** 1–2. Answers may vary. Samples are given. See margin, p. 385.

**1.**

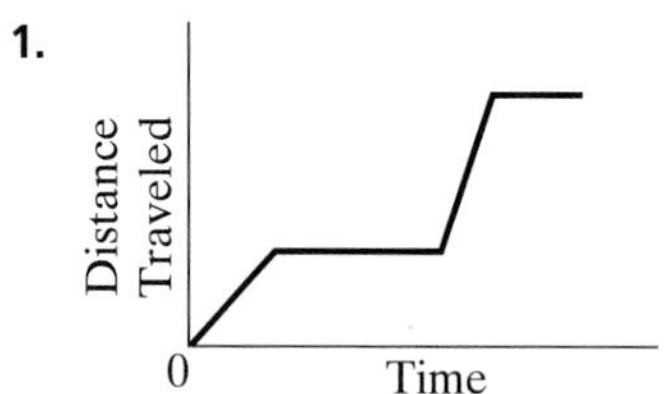


**2.**

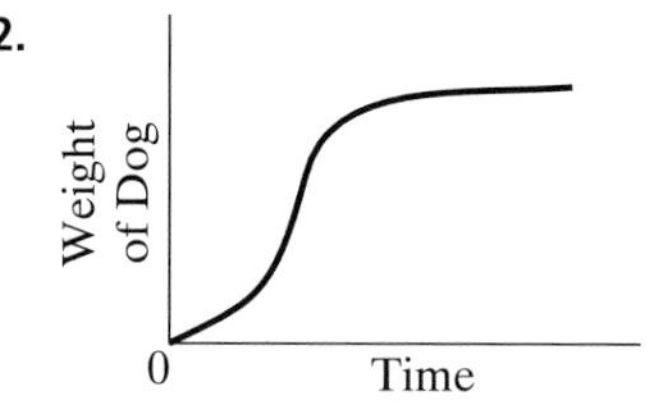


**3.** The graph at the right is a *step graph*. It shows the prices at a parking garage. $2
   **a.** How much does parking cost for an hour or less?
   **b.** How much does parking cost for 4 hours and 20 minutes? $6
   **c.** A receipt from the parking garage is for $7. What is the greatest length of time the car could have been in the garage? 6 h

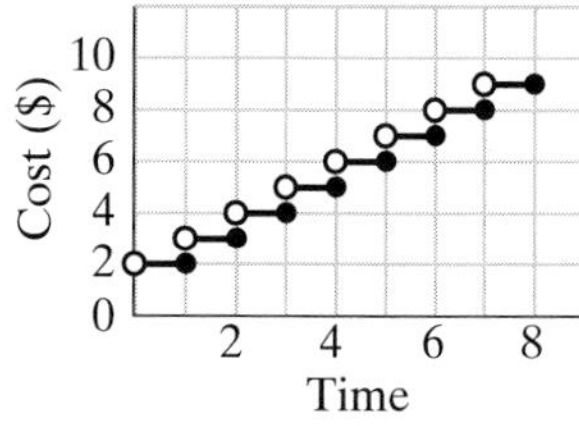




- **Additional Example 1**
Suppose the graph in this example showed one trip from home to school and back, but related the distance from school (instead of from home) to time. How would the graph be different? It would be upside down. The distance from school would be greatest before the trip began and would be zero while you were at school.

- **Additional Example 2**
Suppose you took an airplane to get to your summer vacation destination. Sketch a graph to show your height above the ground while you are on the plane. Identify your axes and include labels for each part.

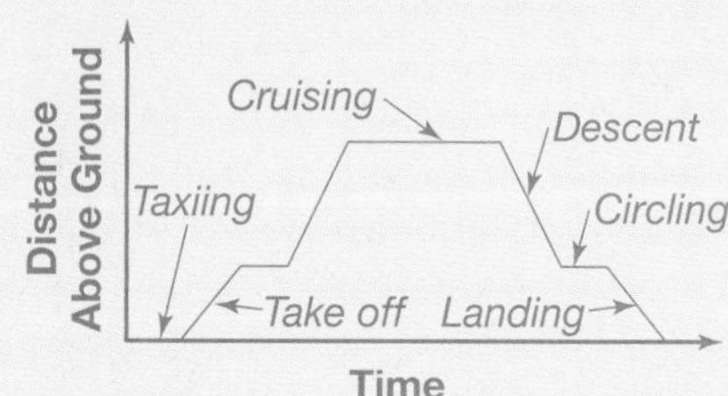

4. *Critical Thinking* Use the graph below. Jolene and Tamika were sprinting. Which girl ran faster? Explain. Tamika; Tamika took less time to run the same distance as Jolene ran.

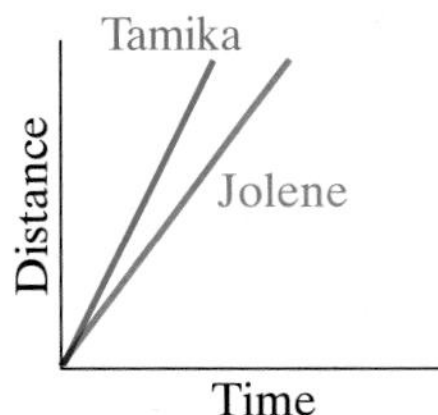


When you draw a graph without actual data, you are making a sketch. A sketch can help you visualize relationships.

## Example 2

**You go to an amusement park and ride a moving horse on a carousel. Sketch a graph to show your height above the ground. Identify your axes and include labels for each part.**

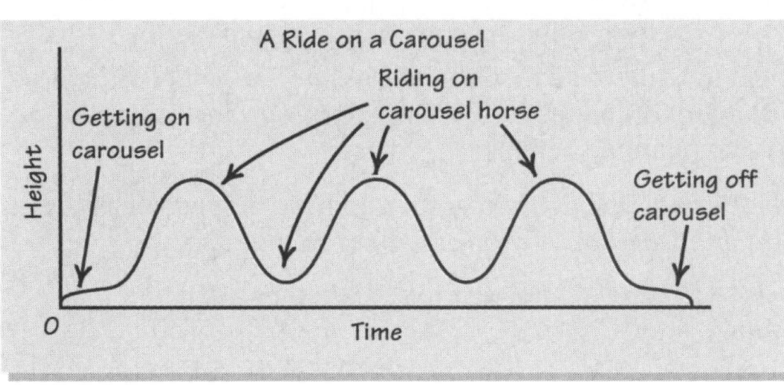


**Sketch a graph for each situation. Identify your axes and include labels for each part.** 5–7. Graphs may vary. Samples are given. See above right.

5. the temperature outside during one 24-hour period
6. your speed as you take a trip on a train
7. the total distance you travel as you go to a concert and return home
8. the distance above ground of a pole vaulter's feet at a track meet 8–9. See margin.
9. You pour water at a constant rate into the container shown at the right. Sketch a graph of the water level as you fill the container.

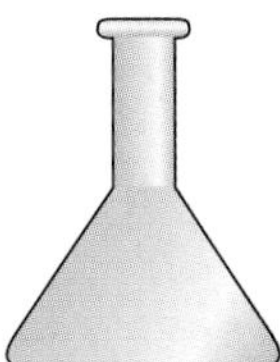

5. mid-day heat; pre-dawn; evening cool; Temperature; Time (24 h)

6.

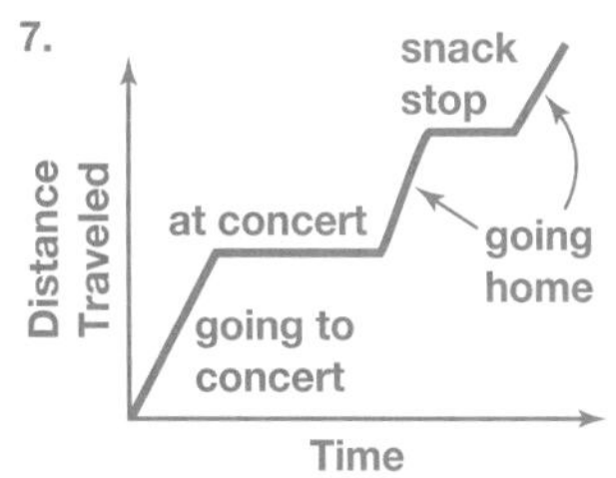


7. snack stop; at concert; going home; going to concert; Distance Traveled; Time



8.

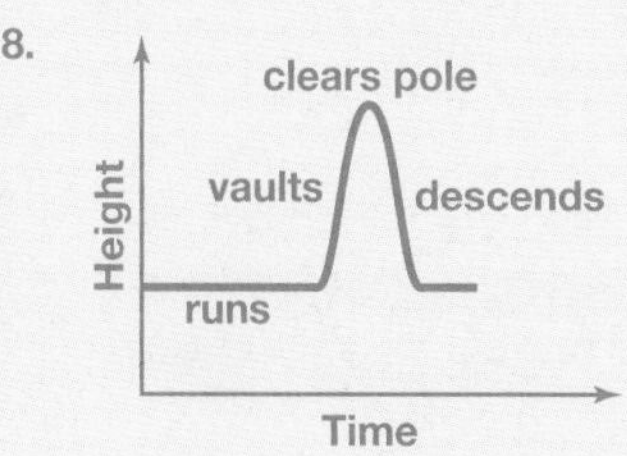


9.

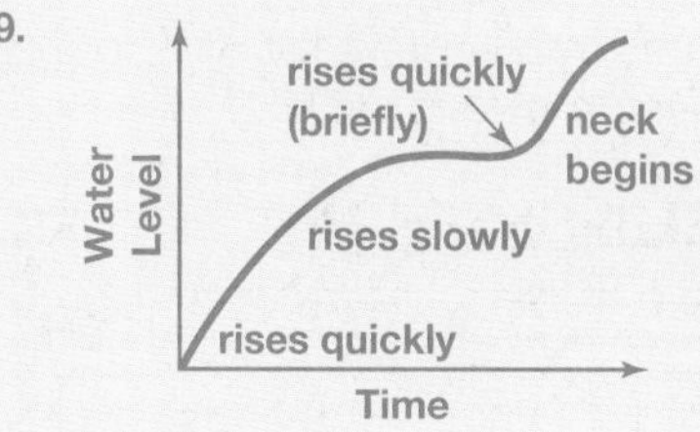


1.

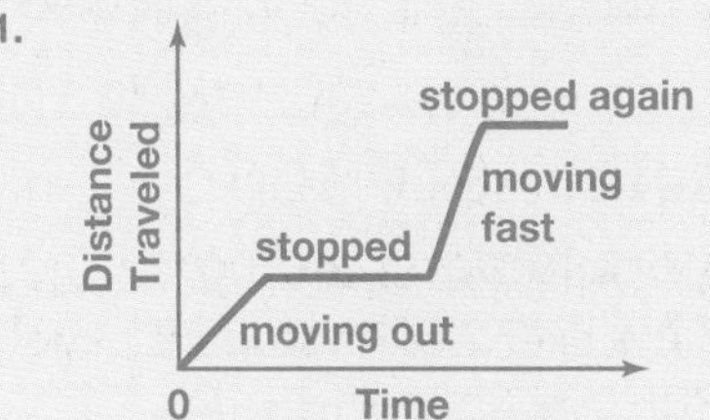


2.

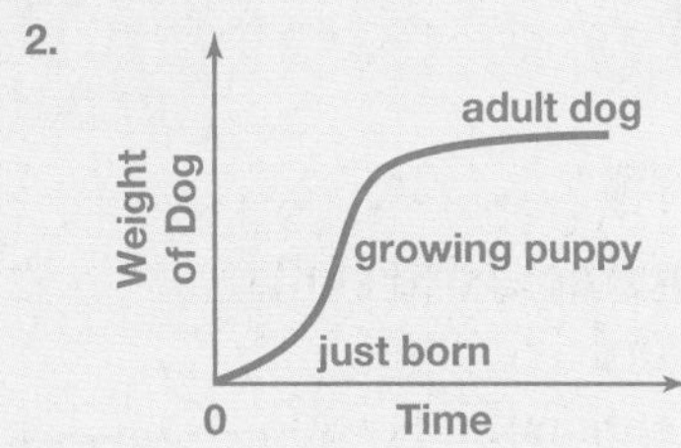

# 8-1

## Getting Ready

**Key Terms and Symbols** relation, domain, range, function, vertical-line test

**Resources** A complete list of resources for this lesson is on p. 381H.

### Daily Skills Warm-Up

**Lesson 8-1**

Graph each point.

1. $A(3, 4)$
2. $B(-3, 1)$
3. $C(-4, -3)$
4. $D(2, -2)$
5. $E(0, -4)$

### Background for the Lesson

In math, you call a collection of one or more pairs of ordered numbers, such as (2, 3), a relation. The pair (2, 3) is not the same as the pair (3, 2) because the order of the numbers makes a difference. You can think of a relation as a number generator. If you input one number (such as 2), the relation outputs, or specifies, a second number (such as 3). The first coordinate in each ordered pair is the input number, a member of the domain of the relation. The second coordinate in each ordered pair is the output number, a member of the range of the relation. Some relations are functions. A function has only a single value for a specific member of the domain. So (2, 3), (2, −3) is a relation but it is not a function, since 2 is paired with both 3 and −3.

## 1 Focus

### Connecting to Students' Lives

Ask students to imagine how confusing using the phone would be if the number you dialed (the input) rang in more than one house (two different outputs).

# 8-1 Relations and Functions

### What You'll Learn

1. To determine whether a relation is a function
2. To graph relations and functions

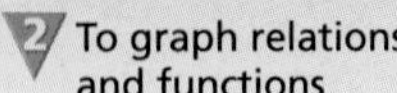

### . . . And Why

To model everyday activities in which one quantity depends on another, such as cooking a turkey

## PART 1 Identifying Relations and Functions

The table shows the results of a canned food drive.

**Food for Life Canned Food Drive**

| Homeroom | Number of Students | Number of Cans |
|---|---|---|
| 101 | 25 | 133 |
| 102 | 22 | 216 |
| 103 | 24 | 148 |
| 104 | 22 | 195 |
| 105 | 20 | 74 |
| 106 | 21 | 150 |

You can write the data in the table as a **relation,** a set of ordered pairs. The first coordinate of each ordered pair is the number of students in a homeroom. The second coordinate is the number of cans the students in that homeroom collected.

Here is the relation represented by the table: {(25, 133), (22, 216), (24, 148), (22, 195), (20, 74), (21, 150)}. The braces, {}, indicate that these are all the ordered pairs in this relation. The first coordinates are the **domain** of the relation. The second coordinates are the **range** of the relation.

Some relations are functions. In a **function,** each member of the domain is paired with exactly one member of the range.

You can draw a *mapping diagram* to see whether a relation is a function.

### EXAMPLE 1

**Is each relation a function? Explain.**

**a. {(0, 1), (1, 2), (1, 3), (2, 4)}**

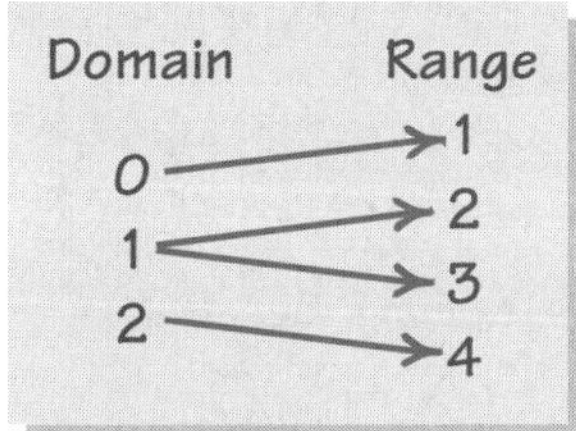


List the domain values and the range values in order.

Draw arrows from the domain values to their range values.

There are two range values for the domain value 1. This relation is not a function.



## Tools to Monitor Progress

### BEFORE THE LESSON

**To check prerequisite skills:**

- Graphing ordered pairs

**Skills Intervention Kit,** Pre-Algebra Basics

### DURING THE LESSON

**To check understanding:**

**Try This** exercises on student page

- **Additional Example 1**

  Is each relation a function? Explain.

  **a.** {(0, 5), (1, 6), (2, 5), (3, 7)} Yes, there is one range value for each domain value.

  **b.** {(0, 5), (1, 5), (2, 6), (3, 7)} Yes, there is one range value for each domain value.

**b.** $\{(0, 1), (1, 2), (2, 2), (3, 4)\}$

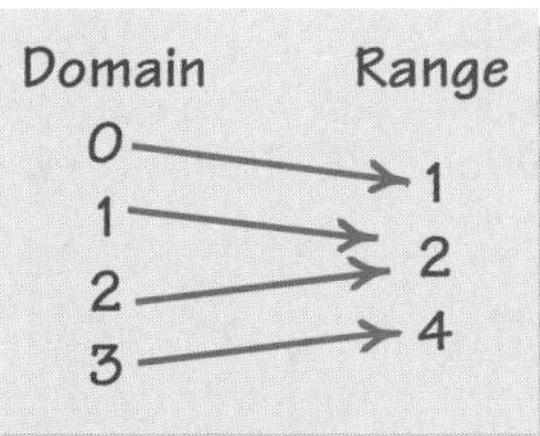


There is one range value for each domain value. This relation is a function.

**c.** $\{(0, 1), (1, 3), (2, 2), (3, 4)\}$

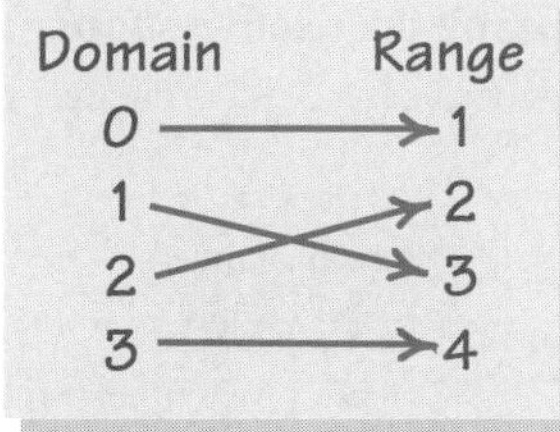


There is one range value for each domain value. This relation is a function.

■ **TRY THIS** Is each relation a function? Explain.

1. $\{(-2, 3), (2, 2), (2, -2)\}$ 1. No; there are two range values for the domain value 2.
2. $\{(-5, -4), (0, -4), (5, -4)\}$ 2. Yes; there is one range value for each domain value.

Functions can model many everyday situations when one quantity depends on another. One quantity *is a function of* the other.

REAL-WORLD  CONNECTION

■ **EXAMPLE 2**

*Cooking* **Is the time needed to cook a turkey a function of the weight of the turkey? Explain.**

The time the turkey cooks (range value) is determined by the weight of the turkey (domain value). This relation is a function.

You can estimate the cooking time of a turkey: 20 minutes per pound unstuffed, or 30 minutes per pound stuffed.

■ **TRY THIS**

3. For the United States Postal Service, is package weight a function of the postage paid to mail the package? Explain. 3. No; a specific postage cost (domain value) can mail packages of different weights (range values).
4. Is the cost of postage a function of package weight? Explain. Yes; For each package weight (domain value) there is one postage cost to the same zip code (range value).

## PART 2 Graphing Relations and Functions

Graphing a relation on a coordinate plane gives you a visual way to tell whether the relation is a function. If the relation is a function, then any vertical line can pass through only one point on the graph. If you can find a vertical line that passes through two points on the graph, then the relation is *not* a function. This is the **vertical-line test.**



# 2 Teach

## PART 1 Part 1 Teaching Notes

You can also test a relation to see if it is a function by using two ordered pairs. If the two ordered pairs have the same domain value and a different range value, then the relation is not a function.

### ■ Example 1

**Build understanding.** Ask: What on a mapping diagram tells you that a relation is not a function? when two arrows come from the same domain value and point to different range values

**Error Prevention** Remind students to look at mapping diagrams carefully. If a domain value has two range values, then the relation is not a function. However, in a function, two different domain values can have the same range value.

### ■ Example 2

**Build understanding.** Ask: What proves that a relation is not a function? naming two different values in the range that pair with the same value in the domain

**Advanced Learners** Some long distance service providers charge a flat fee for calls up to 20 minutes. Then they charge a per-minute rate for any additional time. Is this type of rate plan a function? Explain. Yes, because although a 10-min call and a 2-min call have the same price, a call of *m* minutes will never have two different prices.

## PART 2 Part 2 Teaching Notes

Remind students that a negative *x*-value means the point will be to the *left* of the *y*-axis, just as a negative number is to the *left* of zero on a number line. Similarly, a negative *y*-value means the point will be *below* the *x*-axis.

**ELL** Make sure students understand the difference between *vertical* and *horizontal*. Suggest that they think of the horizon to remember *horizontal*.

**Tactile Learning** To reinforce the concept of a vertical line, have students stand beside their desks and form a vertical line with their arms. Then, have them form a horizontal line for contrast.

**c.** $\{(0, 5), (0, 6), (1, 6), (2, 7)\}$ No, there are two range values for the domain value 0.

• **Additional Example 3**

Graph the relation. Use the vertical-line test. Is the relation a function? Explain. $\{(-3, 5), (-5, 3), (3, 5), (5, 3)\}$ The vertical pencil does not pass through any two points, so the relation is a function.

## AFTER THE LESSON

**To assess knowledge:**

**Lesson Quiz**

Is each relation a function? Explain.

1. $\{(-2, -1), (4, 2), (-8, -4), (6, 3)\}$ yes, no repeated first coordinates
2. $\{(5, 0), (7, 2), (9, 4), (5, 1)\}$ No, 5 is repeated.
3. $\{(-1, 7), (0, 7), (1, 7), (2, 7)\}$ yes, no repeated first coordinates

• For enrichment and reteaching options see Resources on page 381H.

## ■ Example 3

**Build understanding.** Ask: When you use the vertical-line test, how do you hold the pencil in relation to the $y$-axis and the $x$-axis? parallel to the $y$-axis, perpendicular to the $x$-axis

**Math Reasoning** Use math reasoning and what you know about relations to explain why the vertical-line test can determine that a relation is not a function. A relation is not a function if a single member of the domain is paired with more than one member of the range. If a vertical line passes through more than one point on the graph, there is one $x$-value paired with two $y$-values. The single $x$-value occurs where the vertical line intersects the $x$-axis and the two $y$-values occur at the two points where the vertical line intersects the graph.

5.

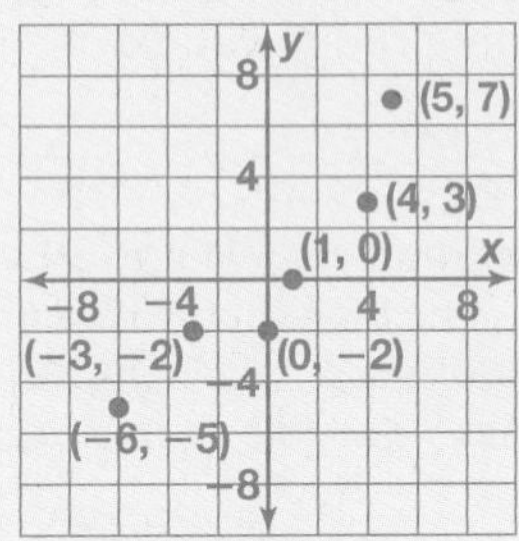


6.

(-2, 6)
(-7, 4)
(0, 5)
(1, 5)
(-1, 3)
(-1, -1)

7.

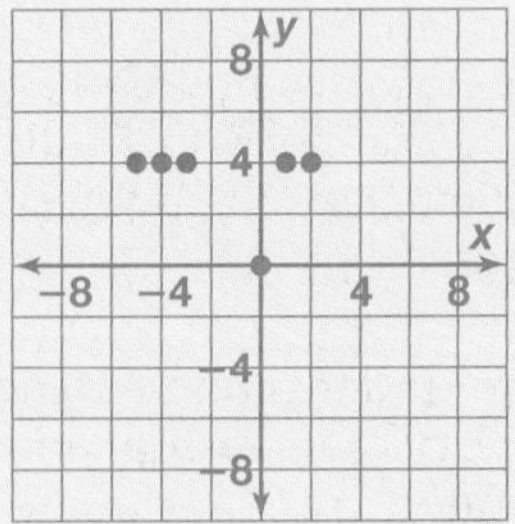


**Quick Review**

The first value in an ordered pair is the $x$-coordinate, which shows horizontal position.

The second value in an ordered pair is the $y$-coordinate, which shows vertical position.

## ■ EXAMPLE 3

**a. Graph the relation shown in the table.**

$x$-coordinates $y$-coordinates

| Domain Value | Range Value |
|---|---|
| −4 | −3 |
| 2 | 0 |
| 2 | 3 |
| 4 | 3 |
| 5 | −4 |

Graph the ordered pairs (−4, −3), (2, 0), (2, 3), (4, 3), and (5, −4).

**b. Use the vertical-line test. Is the relation a function? Explain.**

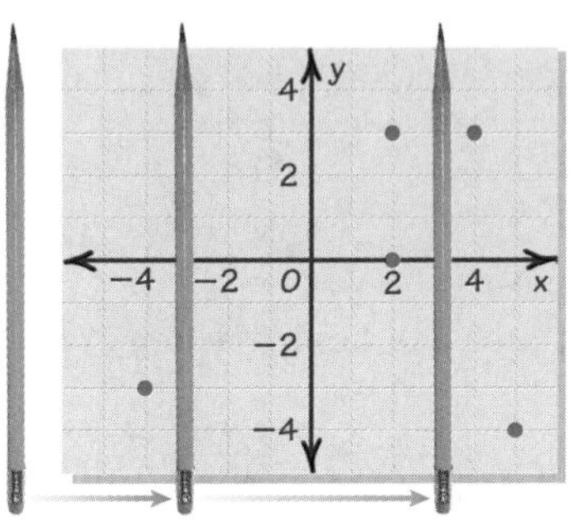

Pass a pencil across the graph as shown. Keep the pencil vertical (parallel to the $y$-axis) to represent a vertical line.

The pencil held vertically would pass through both (2, 0) and (2, 3), so the relation is *not* a function.

■ **TRY THIS** Graph each relation. Use the vertical-line test to tell whether the relation is a function. 5–7. See margin for graphs.

5. a function

| $x$ | $y$ |
|---|---|
| −6 | −5 |
| −3 | −2 |
| 0 | −2 |
| 1 | 0 |
| 4 | 3 |
| 5 | 7 |

6. not a function

| $x$ | $y$ |
|---|---|
| −7 | 4 |
| −2 | 6 |
| −1 | −1 |
| −1 | 3 |
| 0 | 5 |
| 1 | 5 |

7. a function

| $x$ | $y$ |
|---|---|
| −5 | 4 |
| −4 | 4 |
| −3 | 4 |
| 0 | 0 |
| 1 | 4 |
| 2 | 4 |



### Check Understanding

3. No; there are three range values for the domain value 3.
4. Yes; there is one range value for each domain value.
5. Yes; there is one range value for each domain value.
6. No; there are, for example, two range values for the domain value –4.
7. Yes; no vertical line passes through two graphed points (vertical-line test).
8. Yes; not vertical line passes through two graphed points (vertical-line test).
12. No; there are two range values for the domain value –1.
13. Yes; there is one range value for each domain value.
14. No; there are, for example, two range values for the domain value 4.
15. Yes; there is one range value for each domain value.

# Exercises

## CHECK UNDERSTANDING

**For each relation, list the members of the domain. Then list the members of the range.**

**1.** $\{(0, 1), (3, 5), (2, 2), \left(-\frac{1}{2}, \frac{4}{5}\right)\}$ $-\frac{1}{2}$, 0, 2, 3; $\frac{4}{5}$, 1, 2, 5 **2.** $\{(-1, 2), (-2, 2), (-2, 3), (0, 2)\}$ −2, −1, 0; 2, 3

**Is each relation a function? Explain.** 3–8. See margin for explanations.

**3.** $\{(3, -1), (3, 0), (-3, 4), (3, 8), (-2, 8)\}$ no

**4.** $\{(-3, -2), (-1, 0), (1, 0), (5, -2), (6, 4)\}$ yes

**5.** Domain Range
yes

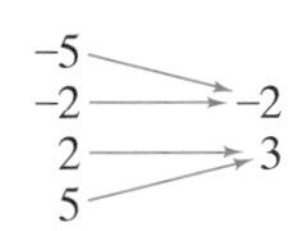


**6.** Domain Range
no

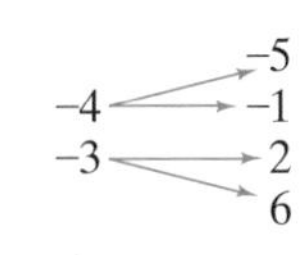


**7.** yes

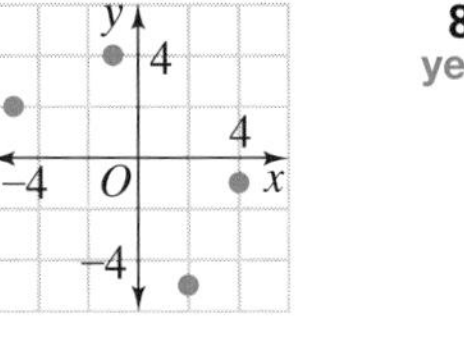


**8.** yes

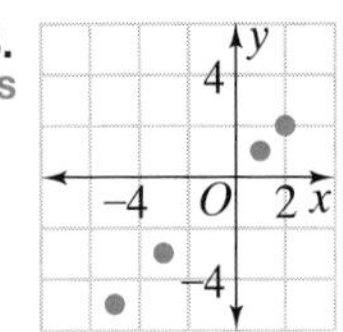


**9.** Is age a function of height? no

**10.** Is the time you take to walk to the library a function of the distance to the library? yes

**11.** Is the price of a piece of cloth a function of the length of the cloth? yes

## PRACTICE AND PROBLEM SOLVING

**Is each relation a function? Explain.** 12–19. See margin for explanations.

**12.** $\{(-1, 9), (0, -1), (-1, 4), (4, 9)\}$ no

**13.** $\{(-12, 7), (-3, -6), (0, -6), (8, 7)\}$ yes

**14.** $\{(4, -8), (4, -6), (1, 2), (1, 5), (1, -6)\}$ no

**15.** $\{(-1.2, 1.5), (1.5, -1.2), (0.37, -0.37)\}$ yes

**16.** Domain Range
no

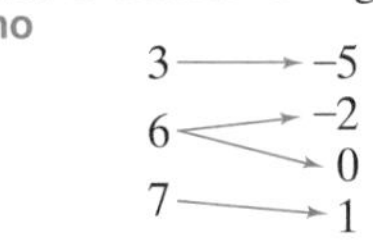


**17.** yes

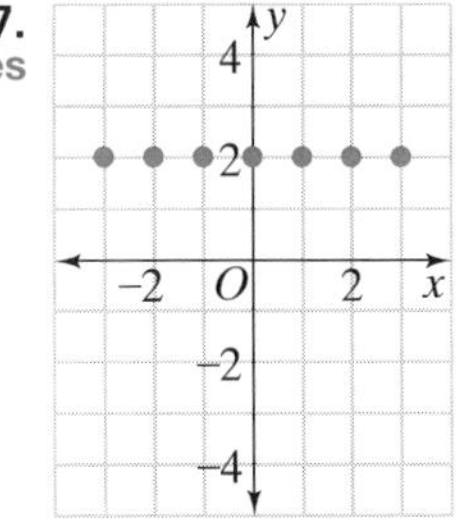


**18.** no

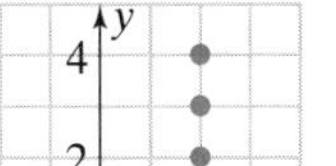

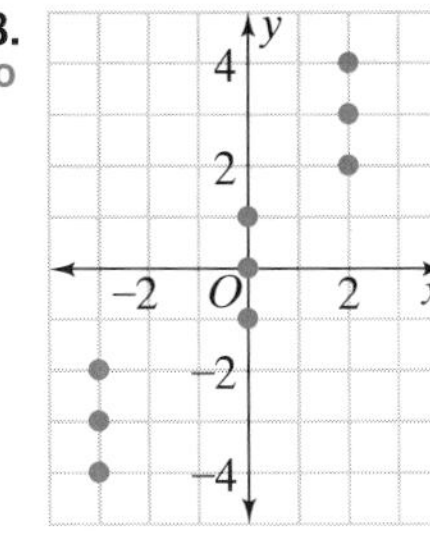


**19.** yes

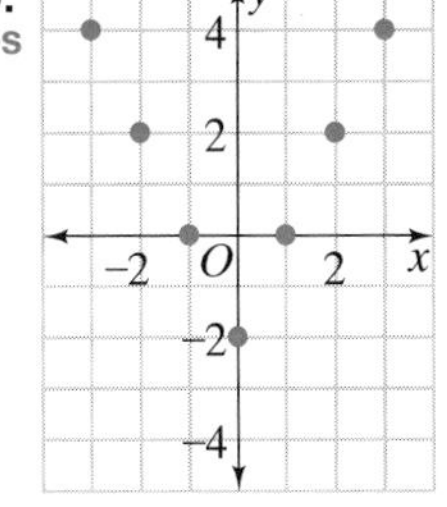




# 3 Practice/Assess

## Assignment Guide

To provide flexible scheduling, this lesson can be divided into parts.

**Part 1**

**Core** 1–6, 9–16, 28–31, 33

**Extension** 24–27

**Part 2**

**Core** 7, 8, 17–23

**Extension** 32

Mixed Review can be assigned at any time for maintenance.

## Exercises

**Visual Learning** **Exercises 12–15** Visual learners can graph these points (without, however, joining them) and use the vertical-line test to determine whether the relations are functions.

**Math Reasoning** **Exercises 24–27** Use words or write an equation in terms of *x* and *y* to describe the patterns.

## Challenge

Is the relation $\{(0, -2)\}$ a function? Explain. Yes; There is no repeated domain value, and it passes the vertical-line test.

## Closure

Any set of ordered pairs is a relation. A function is a relation in which no two different ordered pairs have the same first coordinate.

## Alternative Assessment

Have students write in their math journals some if . . . then statements to summarize how they can determine whether a relation is a function.

16. Yes; no vertical line passes through two graphed points (vertical-line test).

17. Yes; no vertical line passes through two graphed points (vertical-line test).

18. No; a vertical line passes through two graphed points (vertical line-test).

19. Yes; no vertical line passes through two graphed points (vertical line test).

## Daily Cumulative Review

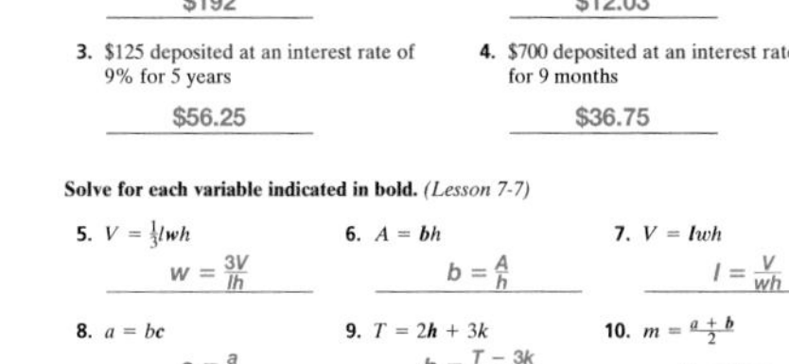

**Find the simple interest.** *(Lesson 7-8)*

1. \$600 deposited at an interest rate of 8% for 4 years — \$192
2. \$875 deposited at an interest rate of 5.5% for 3 months — \$12.03
3. \$125 deposited at an interest rate of 9% for 5 years — \$56.25
4. \$700 deposited at an interest rate of 7% for 9 months — \$36.75

**Solve for each variable indicated in bold.** *(Lesson 7-7)*

5. $V = \frac{1}{3}lwh$ — $w = \frac{3V}{lh}$
6. $A = bh$ — $b = \frac{A}{h}$
7. $V = lwh$ — $l = \frac{V}{wh}$
8. $a = bc$ — $c = \frac{a}{b}$
9. $T = 2h + 3k$ — $h = \frac{T - 3k}{2}$
10. $m = \frac{a + b}{2}$ — $b = 2m - a$

**Mixed Review**

**Evaluate. Write in simplest form.**

11. (1-2) $x - 8$, for $x = 20$ — 12
12. (1-2) $3a + 4$, for $a = 2$ — 10
13. (1-2) $6p - 15$, for $p = 4$ — 9
14. (4-6) $\frac{a - b}{-2}$, for $a = 15, b = 5$ — −5
15. (4-6) $\frac{x}{y}$, for $x = 125, y = 5$ — 25
16. (4-6) $\frac{25}{-m + n}$, for $m = -2, n = 3$ — 5

**Simplify each expression.**

17. (5-9) $(-3b)^4$ — $81b^4$
18. (5-9) $\left(\frac{3}{4}\right)^3$ — $\frac{27}{64}$
19. (5-9) $\left(\frac{2c}{d^2}\right)^5$ — $\frac{32c^5}{d^{10}}$
20. (2-3) $5 + 6b + 7$ — $6b + 12$
21. (2-3) $-3(d + 4) - 2d$ — $-5d - 12$
22. (2-3) $c - 3d + 4c + 8$ — $5c - 3d + 8$

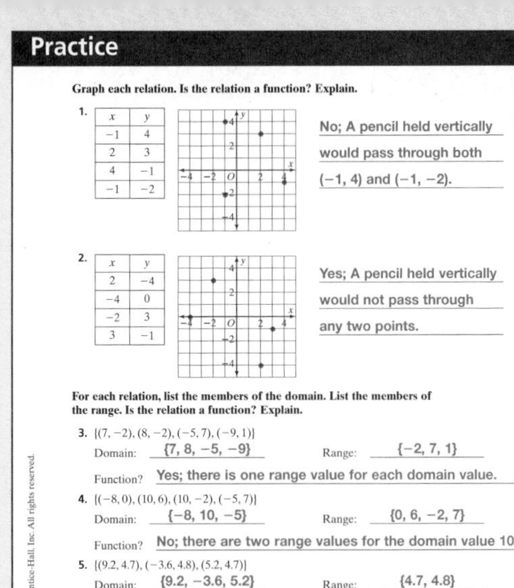
## Practice

**Graph each relation. Is the relation a function? Explain.**

1.

| x | y |
|---|---|
| −1 | 4 |
| 2 | 3 |
| 4 | −1 |
| −1 | −2 |

No; A pencil held vertically would pass through both (−1, 4) and (−1, −2).

2.

| x | y |
|---|---|
| 2 | −4 |
| −4 | 0 |
| −2 | 3 |
| 3 | −1 |

Yes; A pencil held vertically would not pass through any two points.

**For each relation, list the members of the domain. List the members of the range. Is the relation a function? Explain.**

3. {(7, −2), (8, −2), (−5, 7), (−9, 1)}
Domain: {7, 8, −5, −9} Range: {−2, 7, 1}
Function? Yes; there is one range value for each domain value.

4. {(−8, 0), (10, 6), (10, −2), (−5, 7)}
Domain: {−8, 10, −5} Range: {0, 6, −2, 7}
Function? No; there are two range values for the domain value 10.

5. {(9.2, 4.7), (−3.6, 4.8), (5.2, 4.7)}
Domain: {9.2, −3.6, 5.2} Range: {4.7, 4.8}
Function? Yes; there is one range value for each domain value.

6. Is the time is takes you to run a 100-meter race a function of the speed you run? Explain.
Yes; there is one time for each speed.



## Reteaching

Graph the relation. Is the relation a function? Explain.

| x | y |
|---|---|
| 3 | 4 |
| −1 | 2 |
| 4 | −3 |
| −4 | −2 |

x-axis → origin y-axis

First, plot the point (3, 4). Start at the origin, where the x-axis and the y-axis cross. Go right 3 units and up 4 units.
To plot (−1, 2), from the origin go left one unit and up 2 units.
To plot (4, −3), from the origin, go right 4 units and down 3 units.
To plot (−4, −2), from the origin, go left 4 units and down 2 units.
Next, use the vertical line test. Hold a pencil vertically to the left of the graph. Slowly move it to the right. If you can find a vertical line that passes through two graphed points, then the relation is not a function. If you cannot find such a line, the relation *is* a function. This relation is a function because the vertical pencil does not pass through two points anywhere on the graph.

**Graph the relation. Is the relation a function? Explain.**

| x | y |
|---|---|
| −4 | 1 |
| 1 | 3 |
| 4 | 0 |
| 1 | −2 |

No; a pencil held vertically would pass through both (1, 3) and (1, −2).



## Enrichment

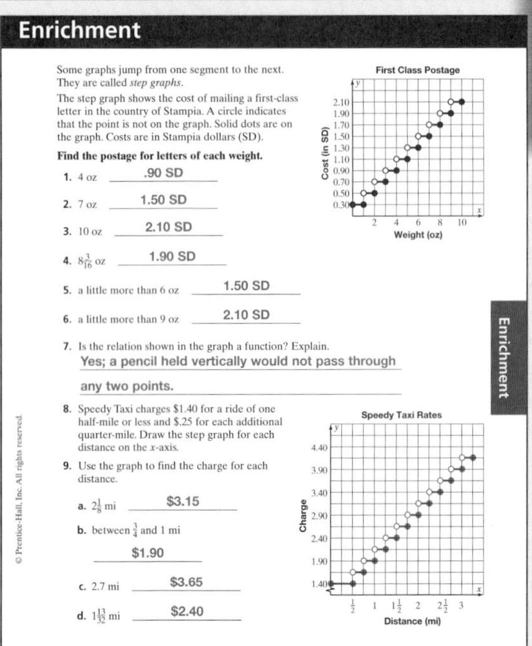
Some graphs jump from one segment to the next. They are called *step graphs*.
The step graph shows the cost of mailing a first-class letter in the country of Stampia. A circle indicates that the point is not on the graph. Solid dots are on the graph. Costs are in Stampia dollars (SD).



**Find the postage for letters of each weight.**

1. 4 oz .90 SD
2. 7 oz 1.50 SD
3. 10 oz 2.10 SD
4. $8\frac{3}{16}$ oz 1.90 SD
5. a little more than 6 oz 1.50 SD
6. a little more than 9 oz 2.10 SD
7. Is the relation shown in the graph a function? Explain.
Yes; a pencil held vertically would not pass through any two points.
8. Speedy Taxi charges $1.40 for a ride of one half-mile or less and $.25 for each additional quarter-mile. Draw the step graph for each distance on the x-axis.
9. Use the graph to find the charge for each distance.
a. $2\frac{5}{8}$ mi $3.15
b. between $\frac{3}{4}$ and 1 mi $1.90
c. 2.7 mi $3.65
d. $1\frac{13}{32}$ mi $2.40







---

20–22. See margin for graphs
23. See back of book for graph.

**Graph each relation. Is the relation a function? Explain.**

20.

| x | y |
|---|---|
| −5 | 6 |
| −2 | 3 |
| 3 | 3 |
| 4 | 6 |

A function; no vertical line passes through two points on the graph.

21.

| x | y |
|---|---|
| 6 | −2 |
| 1 | −1 |
| 0 | −2 |
| −1 | −3 |

A function; no vertical line passes through two points on the graph.

22.

| x | y |
|---|---|
| −7 | 3 |
| −5 | 1 |
| −5 | −1 |
| −7 | −3 |

Not a function; a vertical line passes through two points on the graph.

23.

| x | y |
|---|---|
| 1 | −3 |
| 2 | −3 |
| 3 | −3 |
| 4 | −3 |

A function; no vertical line passes through two points on the graph.

***Patterns*** **In each function below, there is a pattern to how the range values relate to the domain values. Describe the pattern.**

24. $\{(-7, -5), (-2, 0), (0, 2), (3, 5), (8, 10)\}$ Each range value is two greater than its domain value.

25. $\{(-5, 5), (-1, 1), (0, 0), (3, 3), (9, 9)\}$ Each range value is the absolute value of its domain value.

26. $\{(-4, -2), (-1, -0.5), (2, 1), (7, 3.5)\}$ Each range value is $\frac{1}{2}$ its domain value.

27. $\{(1, 1), (2, 4), (3, 9), (4, 16), (5, 25)\}$ Each range value is the square of its domain value.

28. Is the number of students on a field trip a function of the number of buses used? Explain. No; a specific number of buses (domain value) can carry different numbers of students (range values).

29. Is the number of buses used for a field trip a function of the number of students on the field trip? Explain. Yes; a specific number of students (domain value) requires a particular number of buses (range value).

30. ***Writing*** Is every relation a function? Is every function a relation? Explain. No; yes; a relation can have more than one range value for a domain value and thereby not be a function. A function is a relation by definition.

31. ***Geometry*** Explain why the area of a square is a function of the length of a side of the square. For each side length, there is one and only one area of the square.

32. a. ***Open-ended*** Write two different relations for which the domain is $\{-1, 0, 1\}$ and the range is $\{1, 2\}$. Answers may vary. Sample: {(−1, 1), (0, 2), (1, 2)}, {(−1, 1), (0, 1), (0, 2), (1, 1)}
b. Graph your relations. Use the vertical-line test to tell whether each relation is a function. See back of book for sample graphs.

33. ***Error Analysis*** Your friend says that a relation is not a function when two ordered pairs have the same *y*-coordinate. Explain your friend's error. A function can have the same *y*-coordinate with different *x*-coordinates.

## Mixed Review

**Solve each equation.** ***(Lessons 7-1 and 7-3)***

34. $-42 + 3c = -6$ 12
35. $\frac{3}{2}t - 4 = \frac{1}{2}$ 3
36. $2m - 4.9 = -3.6$ 0.65
37. $-4x + 7 = -5$ 3

38. ***Banking*** Suppose you invest $1,200 in an account that earns 3.5% interest compounded annually. Find the account balance after four years. ***(Lesson 7-8)*** $1,377.03



See also Extra Practice section.

20.
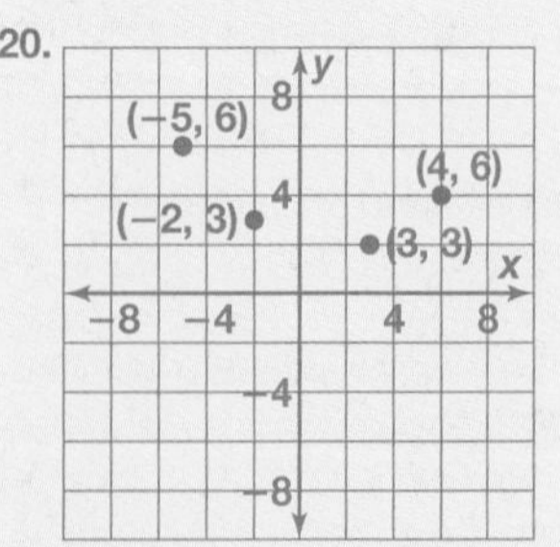


21.
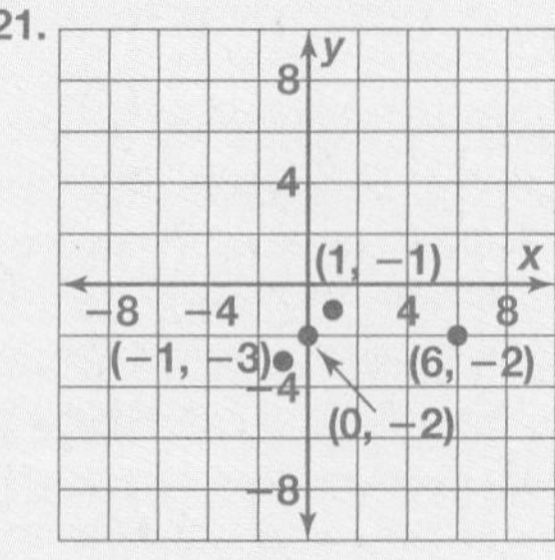


22.
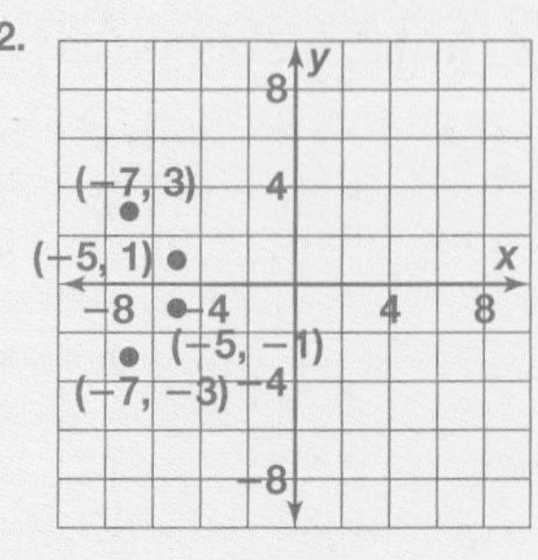

# Equations with Two Variables

8-2

## Part 1 Finding Solutions

In previous chapters you solved equations like $2x + 5 = 7x$, which has only one variable. In this chapter, you will find solutions of equations like $y = 3x + 4$, which has two variables. An ordered pair that makes an equation in two variables a true statement is a **solution** of the equation.

### Example 1

**Find the solution of $y = 3x + 4$ for $x = -1$.**

$y = 3x + 4$
$y = 3(-1) + 4$ Replace $x$ with $-1$.
$y = -3 + 4$ Multiply.
$y = 1$ Add.

A solution of the equation is $(-1, 1)$.

**Try This** Find the solution of each equation for $x = -3$.

1. $y = 2x + 1$ $(-3, -5)$
2. $y = -4x + 3$ $(-3, 15)$
3. $y = 0x - 4$ $(-3, -4)$

You can use two-variable equations to model real-world situations.

REAL-WORLD CONNECTION

### Example 2

*Meteorology* **The equation $t = 21 - 0.01n$ models the normal low July temperature in degrees Celsius at Mt. Rushmore, South Dakota. In the equation, $t$ is the temperature at $n$ meters above the base of the mountain. Find the normal low July temperature at 300 m above the base.**

$t = 21 - 0.01n$
$t = 21 - 0.01(300)$ Replace $n$ with 300.
$t = 21 - 3$ Multiply.
$t = 18$ Subtract.

A solution of the equation is (300, 18). The normal low July temperature at 300 m above the base of the mountain is 18°C.

**What You'll Learn**

1. To find solutions of linear equations with two variables
2. To graph linear equations with two variables

**... And Why**

To investigate relationships in meteorology and oceanography

Mt. Rushmore is 1,745 meters tall.



# Tools to Monitor Progress

## BEFORE THE LESSON

**To check prerequisite skills:**

- Transforming equations
- Graphing points

**Skills You Need,** p. 381

## DURING THE LESSON

**To check understanding:**

**Try This** exercises on student page

- **Additional Example 1–2**

The equation $a = 5 + 3p$ gives the price for admission $a$ to a park for one car with $p$ people in it. Find the price of admission for a car with four people in it. $17

8-2

## Getting Ready

**Key Terms and Symbols** solution, linear equation

**Resources** A complete list of resources for this lesson is on p. 381H.

### Daily Skills Warm-Up

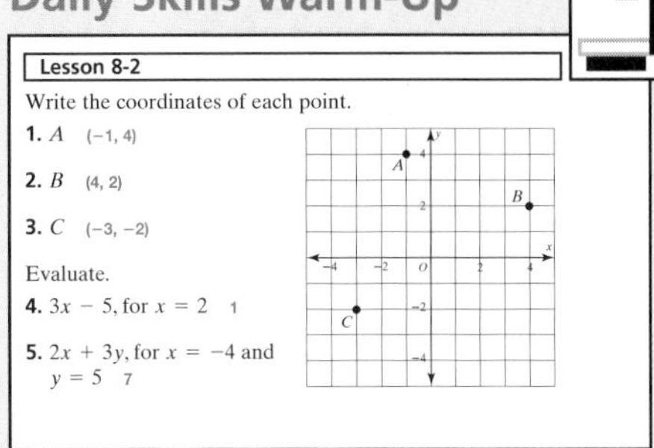
Lesson 8-2

Write the coordinates of each point.

1. $A$ (−1, 4)
2. $B$ (4, 2)
3. $C$ (−3, −2)

Evaluate.

4. $3x - 5$, for $x = 2$ 1
5. $2x + 3y$, for $x = -4$ and $y = 5$ 7

### Background for the Lesson

You can represent a function by an equation with two variables. Any ordered pair that makes the equation true is a solution for the equation. Any equation of the general form $y = mx + b$ is a linear function whose graph is a straight line. So $y = 3$ is a function (where $m = 0$ and $b = 3$). However, $x = 3$ is not a function. The equation of any vertical line is not a function.

## 1 Focus

### Connecting to Students' Lives

Students may know that in a video arcade some premium games cost more to play than standard games. Students could find out what combination of standard and premium games they could play with a set amount of money by using an equation with two variables.

### Connecting to Prior Knowledge

In Lesson 8-1, students learned that a set of ordered pairs can be a function. In this lesson students learn that the solutions to an equation with two variables form a function. In Lesson 8-4, students will learn to use functional notation to write equations.

# 2 Teach

## Part 1 Teaching Notes

Students have already substituted values into single-variable equations to check whether the value is a solution. With two-variable equations, students substitute a value for one of the variables, and then they solve the equation to find a corresponding value for the other variable.

### Example 1

**Build understanding.** Ask: Why does the last line of the example say "A solution of the equation . . ." instead of "The solution . . . "? **The ordered pair (−1, 1) is not the only solution. For example, (0, 4) is another solution.**

### Example 2

**Build understanding.** In the solution (300, 18), explain which value is *t* and which is *n*. ***n* is 300 m and *t* is 18°C.**

**Extension** In Example 2, as the distance above the base increases, would you expect the low temperature to increase or decrease? Explain. **The low temperature would decrease because as *n* increases, 0.01*n* also increases. This means that the amount subtracted from 21 increases and the result of 21 − 0.01*n* decreases.**

## Part 2 Teaching Notes

The coordinates of every point on the graph of the line make the equation of the line true. Any ordered pair that makes the equation true lies on the line that is the graph of the equation.

**ELL** Anything that is described by the adjective *linear* is related to a straight line. All of the solutions to the equation lie on the line that is the graph of the equation.

### Example 3

**Build understanding.** Ask: How can you find out where the line crosses the *y*-axis? **Every point on the *y*-axis has an *x*-coordinate of 0. Substitute 0 for *x* in the equation to find the solution (0, 3).**

---

**Try This**

4. Find the normal low July temperature at 700 m above the base of Mt. Rushmore. **14°C**

5.
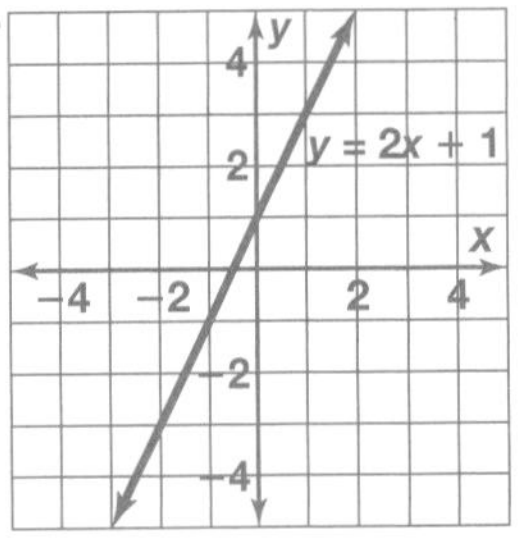


**Quick Review**

The expression $-\frac{1}{2}x$ means "the opposite of $\frac{1}{2}x$." So when the value of *x* is −2, the expression $-\frac{1}{2}x$ represents the opposite of one half of −2, which is 1.

6.
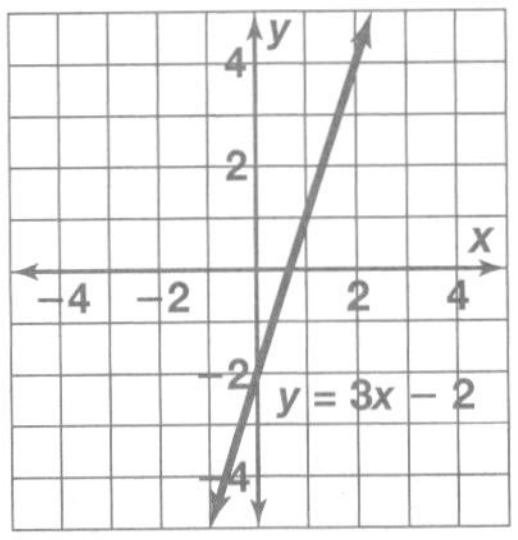


7.
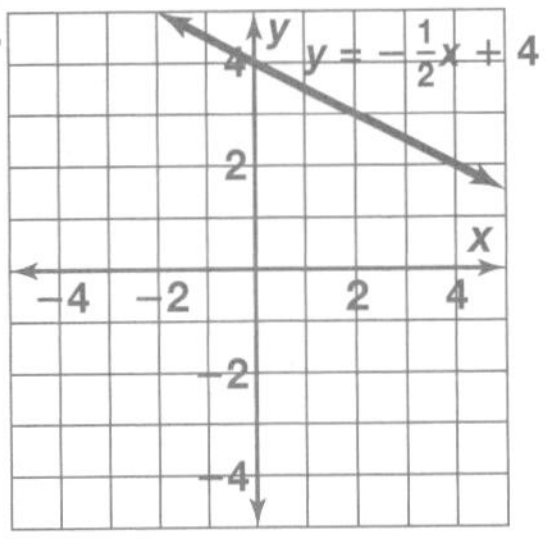


## Part 2 Graphing Equations with Two Variables

An equation with two variables can have many solutions. One way to show these solutions is to graph them, which also gives a graph of the equation. A **linear equation** is any equation whose graph is a line. All the equations in this lesson are linear equations.

### Example 3

**Graph $y = -\frac{1}{2}x + 3$.**

Make a table of values to show ordered-pair solutions.

| $x$ | $-\frac{1}{2}x + 3$ | $(x, y)$ |
|---|---|---|
| −2 | $-\frac{1}{2}(-2) + 3 = 1 + 3 = 4$ | (−2, 4) |
| 0 | $-\frac{1}{2}(0) + 3 = 0 + 3 = 3$ | (0, 3) |
| 4 | $-\frac{1}{2}(4) + 3 = -2 + 3 = 1$ | (4, 1) |

Graph the ordered pairs. Draw a line through the points.

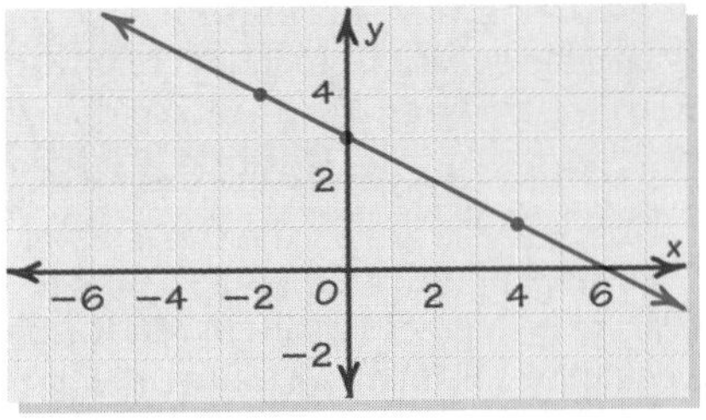


**Try This** Graph each linear equation. **5–7. See left.**

5. $y = 2x + 1$  6. $y = 3x - 2$  7. $y = -\frac{1}{2}x + 4$

If you use the vertical-line test on the graph in Example 3, you see that every *x*-value has exactly one *y*-value. This means that the relation $y = -\frac{1}{2}x + 3$ is a function. A linear equation is a function *unless* its graph is a vertical line.



---

**• Additional Example 3**

Graph $y = 4x - 2$.

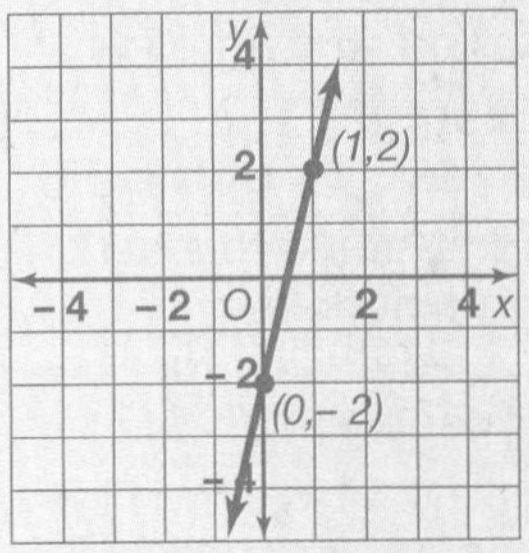


**• Additional Example 4**

Graph each equation. Is the equation a function?

**a.** $y = 7$ **yes**  **b.** $x = 4$ **no**

## EXAMPLE 4

**Graph each equation. Is the equation a function?**

**a.** $y = 2$

For every value of $x$, $y = 2$.

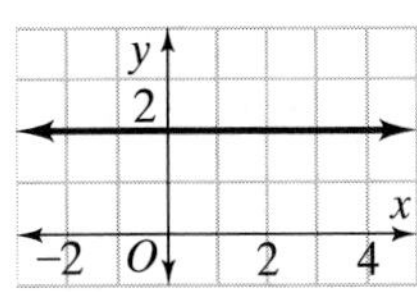

This is a horizontal line.

The graph of $y = 2$ is a function.

**b.** $x = 2$

For every value of $y$, $x = 2$.

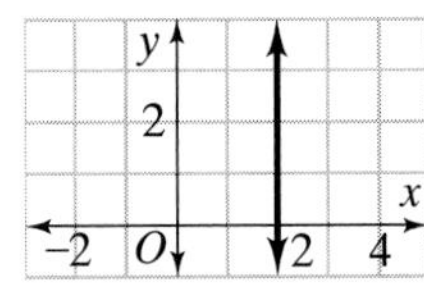

This is a vertical line.

The graph of $x = 2$ is *not* a function.

**TRY THIS** Graph each equation. Is the equation a function?

8–10. See right for graphs.

**8.** $x = 1$ no **9.** $y = -4$ yes **10.** $x = 0$ no

You may find it helpful to solve an equation for $y$ before you find solutions and graph the equation.

## EXAMPLE 5

**Solve $3x + y = -5$ for $y$. Then graph the equation.**

Solve the equation for $y$.

$$3x + y = -5$$

$$3x + y - 3x = -5 - 3x \quad \text{Subtract } 3x \text{ from each side.}$$

$$y = -3x - 5 \quad \text{Simplify.}$$

Make a table of values.

| $x$ | $-3x - 5$ | $(x, y)$ |
|---|---|---|
| $-2$ | $-3(-2) - 5 = 1$ | $(-2, 1)$ |
| $-1$ | $-3(-1) - 5 = -2$ | $(-1, -2)$ |
| $0$ | $-3(0) - 5 = -5$ | $(0, -5)$ |

Graph.

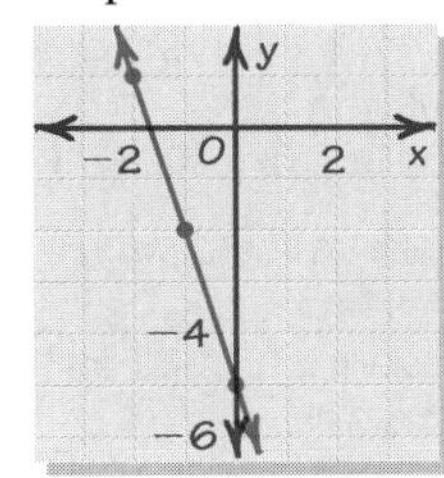

**TRY THIS** Solve each equation for $y$. Then graph the equation.

**11.** $2x + y = 3$
$y = -2x + 3$
See right for graph.

**12.** $y - x = 5$
$y = x + 5$
See right for graph.

**13.** $-3x + 2y = 6$
$y = \frac{3}{2}x + 3$
See margin for graph.

8.

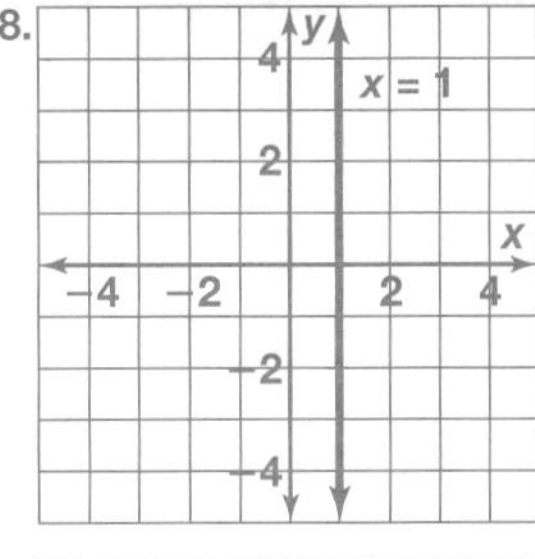


9.

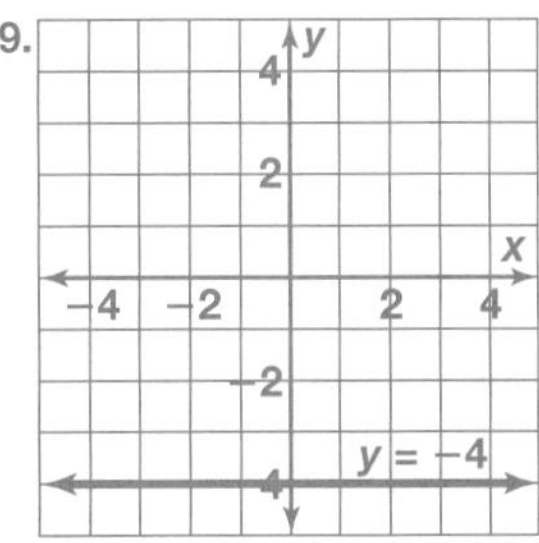


10.

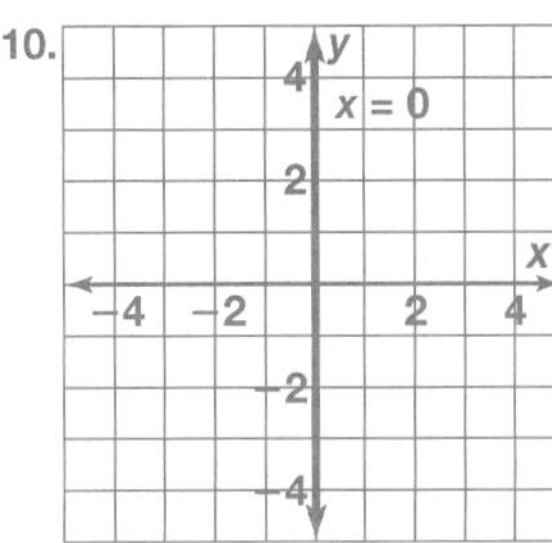


11.

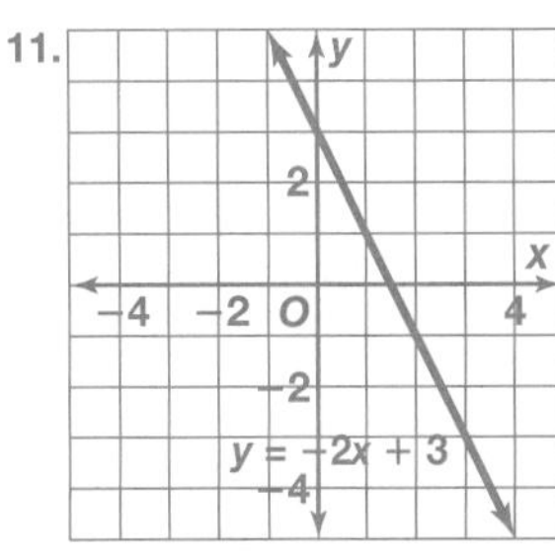


12.

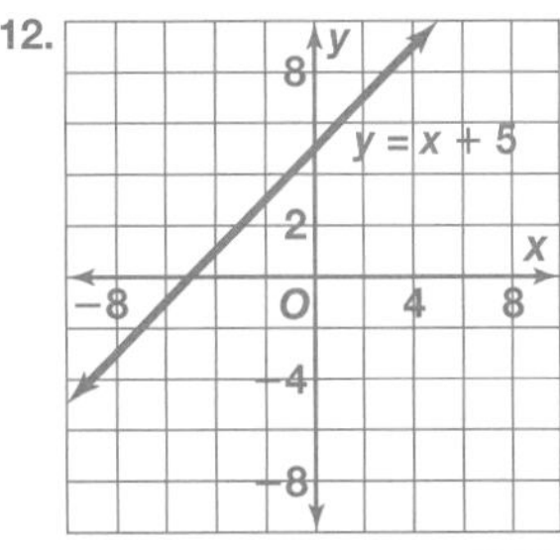




### Example 4

**Build understanding.** Ask: In this example, what is the difference between the equation that is a function and the one that is not? **The equation that is not a function has no $y$-variable.**

**Error Prevention** Students may assume that all linear equations are functions. Remind students that linear equations whose graphs are vertical lines are not functions. They do not pass the vertical-line test.

### Example 5

**Build understanding.** Ask: Which property do you use to subtract $3x$ from both sides of the equation? **Subtraction Property of Equality**

13.

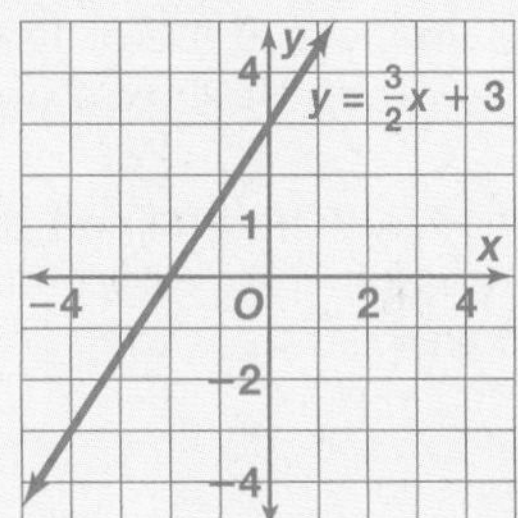


- **Additional Example 5**

Solve $y - \frac{1}{2}x = 3$ for $y$. Then graph the function.
$y = \frac{1}{2}x + 3$

The line will pass through the $y$-axis at 3 and have a slope of $\frac{1}{2}$.

## AFTER THE LESSON

**To assess knowledge:**

**Lesson Quiz**

Write each equation in "$y = \ldots$" form.

1. $12x + y = 15$ $y = -12x + 15$
2. $y - 7x = 0$ $y = 7x$
3. $9x + 3y = 27$ $y = -3x + 9$
4. $11 = y - 4x$ $y = 4x + 11$
5. $\frac{y}{4} = 5x + 2$ $y = 20x + 8$

- For enrichment and reteaching options see Resources on p. 381H.

# 3 Practice/Assess

## Assignment Guide

To provide flexible scheduling, this lesson can be divided into parts.

**Part 1**
**Core** 1–5, 12–19, 32
✪ **Extension** 33, 36

**Part 2**
**Core** 6–11, 20–29, 34, 35
✪ **Extension** 30, 31, 37

Mixed Review can be assigned at any time for maintenance.

## Exercises

**Visual Learning** **Exercises 20–31** If any of your graphs for these linear equations is not a straight line, check the ordered pairs you used to graph the equation.

**Test Prep** **Exercise 32** The first coordinate in each ordered pair is the *x*-coordinate, and the second coordinate is the *y*-coordinate.

## ✪ Challenge

Graph $y = |x| + 1$. Make sure you find points with both positive and negative *x*-values. Is this a linear equation? Is it a function? Explain. It is not a linear equation, but it is a function that passes the vertical-line test.

## Closure

A solution of an equation with two variables is any ordered pair that makes the equation true.

### Daily Cumulative Review

**Is each relation a function? Explain.** *(Lesson 8-1)*

1. $\{(-3, 2), (4, 2), (-3, 3), (-4, 3), (4, 1)\}$
There are two range values for each of the domain values −3 and 4. This relation is not a function.

2. $\{(1, 2), (2, 1), (3, 6), (4, 2), (-1, 2)\}$
There is one range value for each domain value. This relation is a function.

3. $\{(6, 2), (4, -2), (2, -2), (6, -2), (3, 4)\}$
There are two range values for the domain value 6. This relation is not a function.

**Find each balance.** *(Lesson 7-8)*

4. \$375 at 6% compounded semi-annually for 3 years — \$447.77
5. \$4,000 at 7% compounded annually for 7 years — \$6,423.13
6. \$2,650 at 12% compounded semi-annually for 5 years — \$4,745.75
7. \$12,600 at 18% compounded semi-annually for 2 years — \$17,785.93

**Mixed Review**

**Solve for *y* in each equation.**

8. (7-7) $4x + y = 3$ — $y = -4x + 3$
9. (7-7) $-b = mx - y$ — $y = mx + b$
10. (7-7) $3y + 5x = 15$ — $y = -\frac{5}{3}x + 5$

**Write each ratio as a fraction in simplest form.**

11. (6-1) 7 : 9 — $\frac{7}{9}$
12. (6-1) 8 to 10 — $\frac{4}{5}$
13. (6-1) 14 out of 18 — $\frac{7}{9}$



# Exercises

## Check Understanding

**Is each ordered pair a solution of $4x - 3y = 6$?**

**1.** $(3, 2)$ yes  **2.** $(-3, -2)$ no  **3.** $(0, 2)$ no  **4.** $(2, 0)$ no  **5.** $(1.5, 0)$ yes

**Solve each equation for *y*.**

**6.** $-4x + y = 16$ $y = 4x + 16$  **7.** $-3y = 3x - 9$ $y = -x + 3$  **8.** $2x - 4y = 12$ $y = \frac{1}{2}x - 3$

**Graph each equation.** 9–11. See back of book.

**9.** $y = x - 3$  **10.** $-1 = y$  **11.** $4x + y = -3$

## Practice and Problem Solving

**Find the solutions of each equation for $x = -2, 1,$ and $4$.**

**12.** $y = 4x - 5$ (−2, −13), (1, −1), (4, 11)
**13.** $y = -2x$ (−2, 4), (1, −2), (4, −8)
**14.** $y = 2x - 1$ (−2, −5), (1, 1), (4, 7)
**15.** $y = 7 - 3x$ (−2, 13), (1, 4), (4, −5)
**16.** $y = x + 4$ (−2, 2), (1, 5), (4, 8)
**17.** $y = -x + 32$ (−2, 34), (1, 31), (4, 28)
**18.** $y = \frac{1}{4}x + 6$ $\left(-2, 5\frac{1}{2}\right), \left(1, 6\frac{1}{4}\right), (4, 7)$
**19.** $y = \frac{3}{5}x - 6$ $\left(-2, -7\frac{1}{5}\right), \left(1, -5\frac{2}{5}\right), (4, -3$

**Graph each equation.** 20. See margin. 21–31. See back of book.

**20.** $y = x + 3$  **21.** $y = x - 10$  **22.** $y = 2x - 1$  **23.** $y = 0.5x - 6$

**24.** $y = -3x + 7$  **25.** $y = -6$  **26.** $y = -x - 2$  **27.** $-3x = 2y$

**28.** $x = 7$  **29.** $y = \frac{3}{2}x + 5$  ✪**30.** $x - 2y = 8$  ✪**31.** $x - 2y = -2$

**32.** **TEST PREP** Which ordered pair is *not* a solution of $-4y = 3x - 1$? A

A. $(0, -1)$  B. $\left(\frac{2}{3}, -\frac{1}{4}\right)$  C. $(-1.5, 1.375)$  D. $(0.\overline{3}, 0)$

✪ **33.** **a.** For the equation $y = 3x - 2$, make a table of values for $x = 1, 2, 3, 4,$ and $5$. See right.

33a.

| *x* | (*x*, *y*) |
|---|---|
| 1 | (1, 1) |
| 2 | (2, 4) |
| 3 | (3, 7) |
| 4 | (4, 10) |
| 5 | (5, 13) |

**b.** *Patterns* Describe the number pattern formed by the *y*-coordinates. Begin with 1 and add 3 repeatedly.

**34.** *Error Analysis* A student solved $3x + 4y = 12$ for *y*. Her work is at the right. What error did the student make?
The student forgot to divide −3x by 4.

$$3x + 4y = 12$$
$$4y = 12 - 3x$$
$$y = 3 - 3x$$

**35.** *Writing* Explain how you can determine from a linear equation whether the solutions of the equation form a function.
Answers may vary. Sample: Check whether the range values vary.



## Alternative Assessment

Show the graphs of $y = x$, $y = -4$, and $x = 4$ on the board or overhead projector, but do not give the students the equation or any solutions. From what they have learned, have students write the equation of each line as well as several points in the solution of each equation.

20.

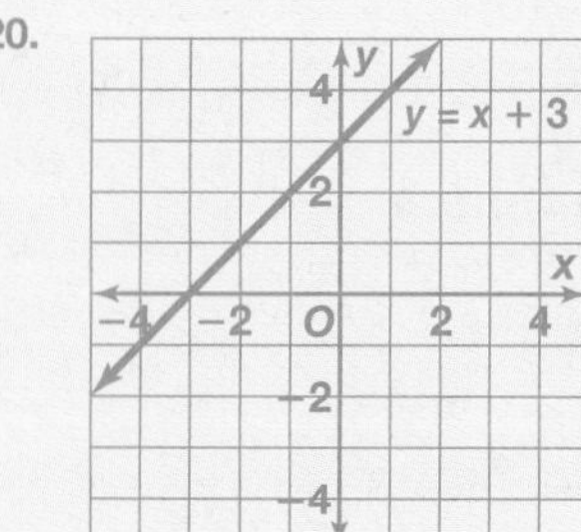

36a. Answers may vary. Sample: (0, 14.7), (10, 19.1), (100, 58.7), (10,000, 4.414.7)

*Math in the Media* **Use the article for Exercise 36.**

**36.** The equation $y = 14.7 + 0.44x$ gives the pressure $y$ in pounds per square inch at a depth of $x$ feet below sea level.

**a.** *Open-ended* Find four solutions of this equation.

**b.** Find the pressure at the depth of the record dive. about 15,773 lb/in.$^2$

**Mountains Under the Sea**

There is a mountain range in the Pacific Ocean far beneath the surface. Jacques Piccard and Donald Walsh made a record dive in these mountains in a submersible. Piccard and Walsh descended to 35,814 ft.

The depth of the dive is remarkable because of the tremendous of pressure at these depths. The pressure of the air at sea level is 14.7 lb/in.$^2$, and the pressure increases about 0.44 lb/in.$^2$ for every foot an object descends below sea level.

**37.** If you swim the backstroke, you burn 9 cal/min (calories per minute). If you swim the butterfly stroke, you burn 12 cal/min. The equation $9x + 12y = 360$ models how you can burn 360 cal by swimming the backstroke for $x$ min and the butterfly for $y$ min.

**a.** Find the solutions of the equation for $x = 0$ and $y = 0$. Explain what your solutions mean. See below right.

**b.** Graph the solutions you found in part (a). Draw a line through the two points. See margin.

**c.** *Language* The solutions you found in part (a) are the *y-intercept* and the *x-intercept* of the graph. Explain why these names are appropriate. See below right.

**d.** Use your graph from part (b). If you swim the butterfly stroke for 10 min, how long should you swim the backstroke to burn a total of 360 calories? about 27 min

37a. (0, 30) and (40, 0); You burn 360 cal by swimming only the butterfly stroke for 30 min and only the backstroke for 40 min.

37c. (0, 30) is the point at which the graph and the $y$-axis intercept each other. (40, 0) is the point at which the graph and the $x$-axis intercept each other.

## Mixed Review

**Is each relation a function? Explain.** ***(Lesson 8-1)*** 39. Yes; there is one range value for each domain value.

**38.** $\{(2, 4), (3, 6), (-3, 6), (1, 2)\}$ **39.** $\{(0, 3), (2, 1), (-7, 2), (1, 1)\}$ **40.** $\{(3, 4), (2.3, 6), (3, -7)\}$

38. Yes; there is one range value for each domain value.

40. No; there are two range values for the domain value 3.

**Write each decimal or fraction as a percent.** ***(Lesson 6-5)***

**41.** 0.62 62% **42.** $\frac{3}{8}$ 37.5% **43.** 1.2 120% **44.** 3.507 350.7% **45.** $\frac{17}{20}$ 85% **46.** $\frac{11}{10}$ 110%

**47.** *Astronomy* The sun orbits the Milky Way galaxy at about 135 mi/s. How far does the sun travel in an hour? In a week? Write your answers in scientific notation. ***(Lessons 4-9 and 5-5)*** about $4.86 \times 10^5$ mi; about $8.16 \times 10^7$ mi

CHAPTER PROJECT 8

## Activity 1 Researching

Contact two or three rental companies in your area. Find out the price per chair for renting plastic folding chairs. Also find out the delivery charge. Organize the information in a table like the one at the right.

| Company | Price per Chair | Delivery Charge |
|---|---|---|
| ■ | ■ | ■ |
| ■ | ■ | ■ |

See also Extra Practice section.



### Project Activity 1

**Researching** Before students actually begin to do their research, look over the list of questions the students plan to ask and their table for organizing the answers.

37b.

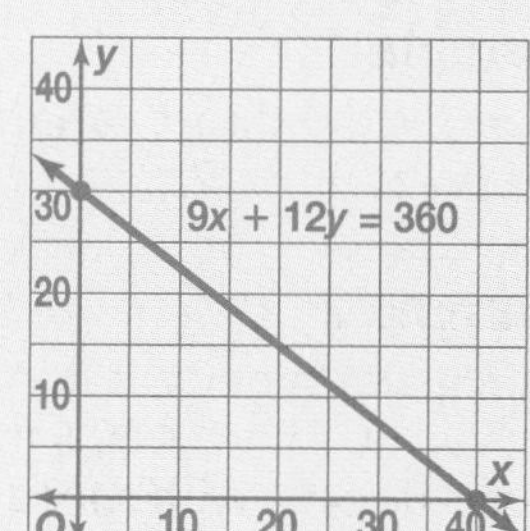


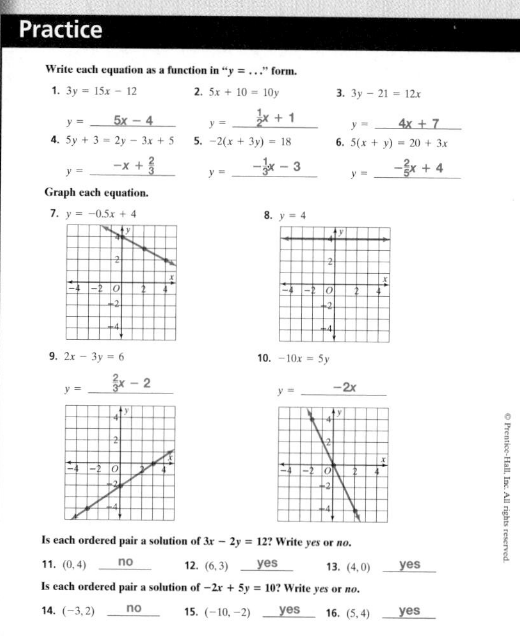

## Practice

**Write each equation as a function in "y = . . ." form.**

1. $3y = 15x - 12$ $y =$ $5x - 4$
2. $5x + 10 = 10y$ $y =$ $\frac{1}{2}x + 1$
3. $3y - 21 = 12x$ $y =$ $4x + 7$
4. $5y + 3 = 2y - 3x + 5$ $y =$ $-x + \frac{2}{3}$
5. $-2(x + 3y) = 18$ $y =$ $-\frac{1}{3}x - 3$
6. $5(x + y) = 20 + 3x$ $y =$ $-\frac{2}{5}x + 4$

**Graph each equation.**

7. $y = -0.5x + 4$
8. $y = 4$
9. $2x - 3y = 6$ $y =$ $\frac{2}{3}x - 2$
10. $-10x = 5y$ $y =$ $-2x$

**Is each ordered pair a solution of $3x - 2y = 12$? Write *yes* or *no*.**

11. (0, 4) no
12. (6, 3) yes
13. (4, 0) yes

**Is each ordered pair a solution of $-2x + 5y = 10$? Write *yes* or *no*.**

14. (−3, 2) no
15. (−10, −2) yes
16. (5, 4) yes



## Reteaching

Graph $y = \frac{1}{4}x - 2$.

Make a table of ordered pairs. Then graph the ordered pairs and draw a line through the points. Choose values that make computations easy.

| $x$ | Substitute and Simplify $y = \frac{1}{4}x - 2$ | $(x, y)$ |
|---|---|---|
| 0 | $y = \frac{1}{4}(0) - 2 = 0 - 2 = -2$ | (0, −2) |
| 4 | $y = \frac{1}{4}(4) - 2 = 1 - 2 = -1$ | (4, −1) |
| −4 | $y = \frac{1}{4}(-4) - 2 = -1 - 2 = -3$ | (−4, −3) |

**Graph each equation.**

1. $y = \frac{3}{2}x - 1$

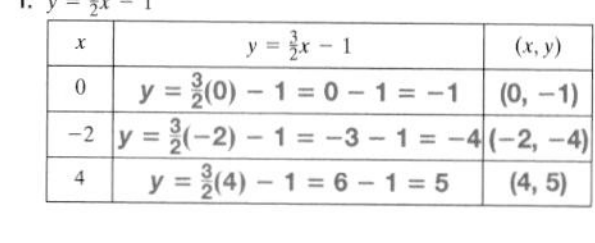

| $x$ | $y = \frac{3}{2}x - 1$ | $(x, y)$ |
|---|---|---|
| 0 | $y = \frac{3}{2}(0) - 1 = 0 - 1 = -1$ | (0, −1) |
| −2 | $y = \frac{3}{2}(-2) - 1 = -3 - 1 = -4$ | (−2, −4) |
| 4 | $y = \frac{3}{2}(4) - 1 = 6 - 1 = 5$ | (4, 5) |

2. $y = x - 3$

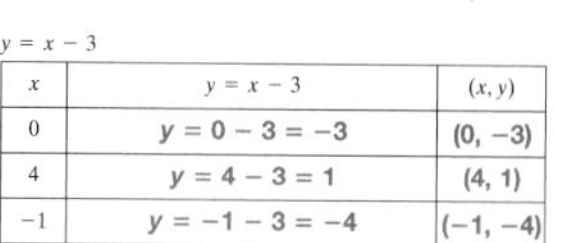

| $x$ | $y = x - 3$ | $(x, y)$ |
|---|---|---|
| 0 | $y = 0 - 3 = -3$ | (0, −3) |
| 4 | $y = 4 - 3 = 1$ | (4, 1) |
| −1 | $y = -1 - 3 = -4$ | (−1, −4) |

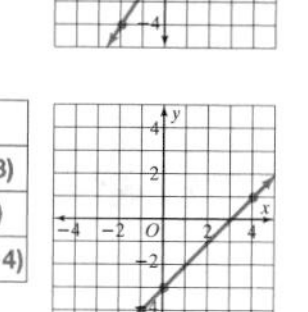



## Enrichment

What did the mathematician do when the waiter informed her that the restaurant had no more peaches for dessert?

**To find the answer, decide which of the two given ordered pairs is a solution of the equation. Circle the ordered pair. Write the letter of the correct pair above the number of the exercise in the answer grid at the bottom of the page.**

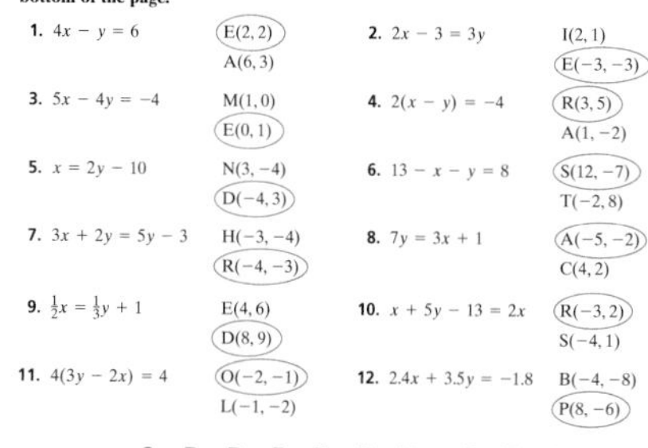

1. $4x - y = 6$ E(2, 2) A(6, 3)
2. $2x - 3 = 3y$ I(2, 1) E(−3, −3)
3. $5x - 4y = -4$ M(1, 0) E(0, 1)
4. $2(x - y) = -4$ R(3, 5) A(1, −2)
5. $x = 2y - 10$ N(3, −4) D(−4, 3)
6. $13 - x - y = 8$ S(12, −7) T(−2, 8)
7. $3x + 2y = 5y - 3$ H(−3, −4) R(−4, −3)
8. $7y = 3x + 1$ A(−5, −2) C(4, 2)
9. $\frac{1}{2}x = \frac{1}{3}y + 1$ E(4, 6) D(8, 9)
10. $x + 5y - 13 = 2x$ R(−3, 2) S(−4, 1)
11. $4(3y - 2x) = 4$ O(−2, −1) L(−1, −2)
12. $2.4x + 3.5y = -1.8$ B(−4, −8) P(8, −6)

Answer: She O R D E R E D P E A R S.

| O | R | D | E | R | E | D | P | E | A | R | S |
|---|---|---|---|---|---|---|---|---|---|---|---|
| 11 | 4 | 9 | 1 | 7 | 3 | 5 | 12 | 2 | 8 | 10 | 6 |

MATH TOOLBOX

## Direct Variation

In Lesson 8-2, students learned that a solution to a linear equation is any ordered pair that makes the equation true. In this Math Toolbox, students learn how to write the equation for a direct variation from a single set of coordinates.

## Math Background

The equations for direct variations are a special subset of linear equations of the general form $y = mx - b$. In direct variations, the $b$ term disappears. Direct variations have equations of the form $y = kx$. The coefficient $k$ is called the *constant of variation.* The value of $k$ is also the slope of the line represented by the equation $y = kx$. You can think of a direct variation as finding a $y$-value by multiplying the $x$-value by a constant of variation. The conversion from pounds to ounces is an example of a direct variation. So, $y$ oz $= 16(x$ lb$)$. The constant of variation is 16 because there are 16 oz in every pound.

## Teaching Notes

**Error Prevention** Help students carry through both parts of the two-step process: first, substituting the coordinates to solve for $k$, and, second, putting $k$ in the equation along with an $x$-value to find the corresponding $y$-value.

**Monitoring Progress** Exercises 1–4
Compare the value of the constant of variation for each of the four equations you wrote. For 1. and 4., $k = \frac{3}{4}$; for 2. and 3., $k = -\frac{3}{4}$.

**Block Scheduling** If you have block scheduling or extended periods, you may wish to insert this Math Toolbox lesson between the completion of Part 2 of Lesson 8-2 and Part 1 of Lesson 8-3.

MATH TOOLBOX

*Extension*
*After Lesson 8-2*

# *Direct Variation*

A *direct variation* is a linear function modeled by the equation $y = kx$, where $k \neq 0$. The coefficient $k$ is the slope, or the *constant of variation.* In a direct variation, you can find $k$ from one ordered pair $(x, y)$. The graph of a direct variation always includes the origin.

### Example 1

**Write an equation for the direct variation that includes $A(-3, 5)$.**

**Step 1** First find the value of $k$.

| | |
|---|---|
| $y = kx$ | Use the equation for a direct variation. |
| $5 = k(-3)$ | Replace $y$ with 5 and $x$ with $-3$. |
| $k = -\frac{5}{3}$ | Solve for $k$. |

**Step 2** Write the equation using the value of $k$.

| | |
|---|---|
| $y = kx$ | Use the equation for a direct variation. |
| $y = -\frac{5}{3}x$ | Replace $k$ with $-\frac{5}{3}$. |

**Write an equation for a direct variation that includes each point.**

**1.** $(4, 3)$ $y = \frac{3}{4}x$ **2.** $(4, -3)$ $y = -\frac{3}{4}x$ **3.** $(-4, 3)$ $y = -\frac{3}{4}x$ **4.** $(-4, -3)$ $y = \frac{3}{4}x$

You can write a direct variation to find the conversion factor between two measurement systems.

### Example 2

*Measurement* **A segment measures 5 in. or 12.7 cm. Let $x$ represent inches and let $y$ represent centimeters. Write a direct variation to convert inches to centimeters. Then convert 24 in. to centimeters.**

| | |
|---|---|
| $y = kx$ | Use the equation for a direct variation. |
| $12.7 = k(5)$ | Replace $x$ with 5 and $y$ with 12.2. |
| $2.54 = k$ | Solve for $k$. |
| $y = 2.54x$ | Replace $k$ with 2.54 to write a direct variation. |
| $y = 2.54(24)$ | Solve for $x = 24$. |
| $y = 60.96$ | Multiply. |

A length that measures 24 in. is 60.96 cm.

**5.** *Measurement* A carton indicates that it contains 2 qt of juice or 1.89 L of juice. Write a direct variation for the relationship between quarts and liters. Find the number of liters in 8 quarts.

5. $y = 0.945x$ ($y$ is the number of liters and $x$ is the number of quarts) or $y = 1.058x$ ($y$ is the number of quarts and $x$ is the number of liters); 7.56 L.



- **Additional Example 1**
Write an equation for the direct variation that includes the point $(6, -12)$.
$y = -2x$

- **Additional Example 2**
The speed limit on major highways in Austria is 130 km/h, which is the same as 80.6 mi/h. Speed in mi/h varies directly with speed in km/h. Let $x$ represent km/h and $y$ represent mi/h. Write a direct variation equation to convert km/h to mi/h. The speed limit on smaller highways in Austria is 80 km/h. Use your equation to convert 80 km/h to mi/h.
$y = 0.62x$; 80 km/h $=$ 49.6 mi/h

# Slope and y-intercept

8-3

## Investigate

UNDERSTANDING SLOPE

1a–c. See below right.

1. a. Graph $y = x$, $y = 2x$, and $y = 3x$ on one coordinate plane.
   b. *Writing* How do the graphs change as the coefficient of $x$ increases? They become steeper.
   c. Graph $y = -x$ on the same coordinate plane.
   d. How are the graphs of $y = x$ and $y = -x$ alike? Different? Answers may vary. Sample: They both are lines through the origin. From left to right, one rises while the other falls.

**What You'll Learn**

1 To find the slope of a line

2 To use slope-intercept form in graphing a linear equation

**. . . And Why**

To describe features of common objects, such as the incline of a ramp or the slant of a roof

1a–c.

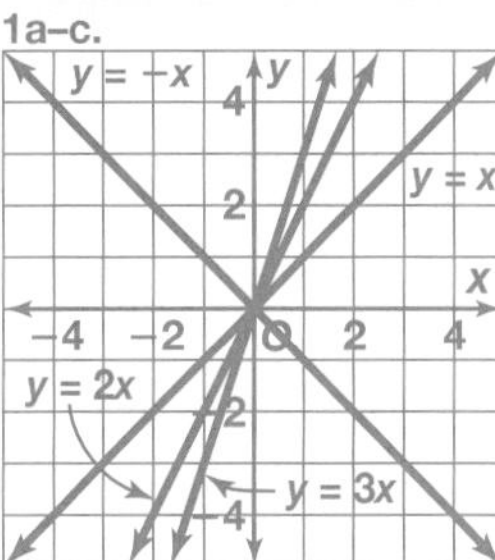


## PART 1 Finding the Slope of a Line

The ratio that describes the tilt of a line is its slope. If a line slants upward from left to right, it has positive slope. If it slants downward, it has negative slope. To calculate slope, you use this ratio.

$$\textbf{slope} = \frac{\text{vertical change}}{\text{horizontal change}} = \frac{\text{rise}}{\text{run}}$$

Rise shows vertical change. Up is positive; down is negative. Run shows horizontal change. Right is positive; left is negative.

### EXAMPLE 1

**Find the slope of each line.**

**a.**

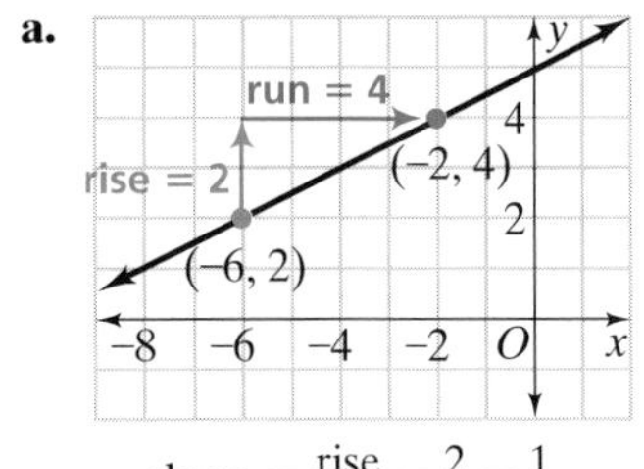

slope $= \frac{\text{rise}}{\text{run}} = \frac{2}{4} = \frac{1}{2}$

**b.**

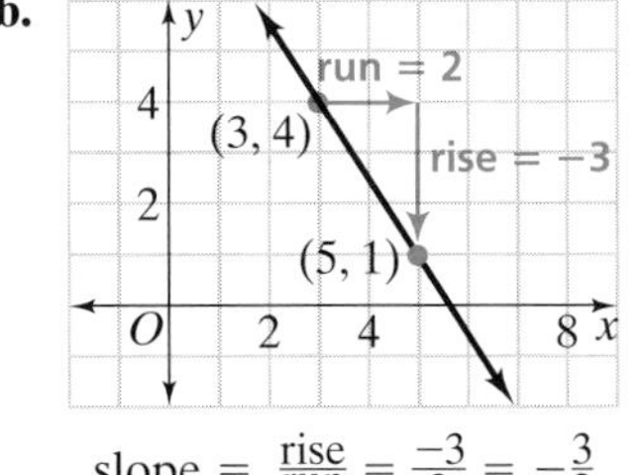


slope $= \frac{\text{rise}}{\text{run}} = \frac{-3}{2} = -\frac{3}{2}$

### TRY THIS

2. What is the slope of the ski trail at the right? $-\frac{3}{4}$

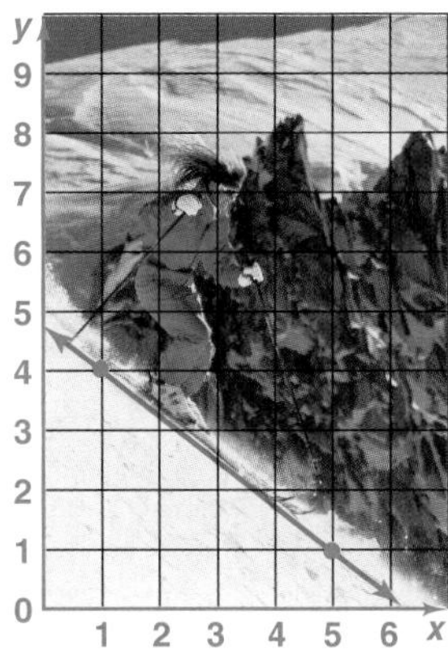



# 8-3

## Getting Ready

**Key Terms and Symbols** slope, y-intercept, slope-intercept form

**Resources** A complete list of resources for this lesson is on p. 381H.

### Daily Skills Warm-Up

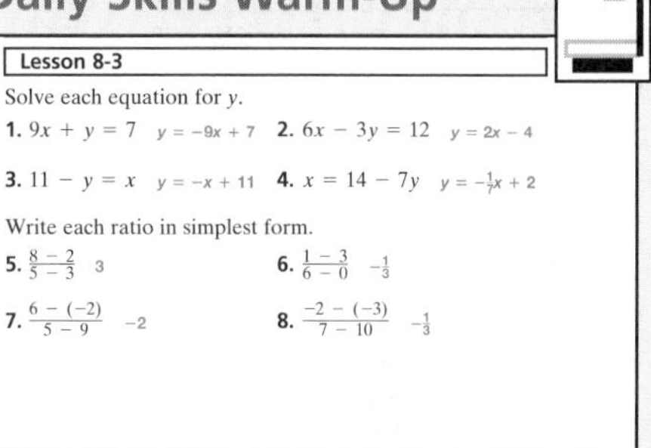

Lesson 8-3

Solve each equation for $y$.

1. $9x + y = 7$ $\quad y = -9x + 7$
2. $6x - 3y = 12$ $\quad y = 2x - 4$
3. $11 - y = x$ $\quad y = -x + 11$
4. $x = 14 - 7y$ $\quad y = -\frac{1}{7}x + 2$

Write each ratio in simplest form.

5. $\frac{8-2}{5-3}$ $\quad 3$
6. $\frac{1-3}{6-0}$ $\quad -\frac{1}{3}$
7. $\frac{6-(-2)}{5-9}$ $\quad -2$
8. $\frac{-2-(-3)}{7-10}$ $\quad -\frac{1}{3}$

### Background for the Lesson

If you know two points on a line, you can find the slope of the line by finding the change in $y$ divided by the change in $x$ as you move from one point to the other. When you write a linear equation in slope-intercept form, $y = mx + b$, the slope is $m$ and the $y$-intercept (the point where the line crosses the $y$-axis) is $b$. You can also use the slope-intercept form to write a linear equation from a graph by finding the slope of the line and the $y$-intercept and putting them in the $y = mx + b$ form of the equation.

## 1 Focus

### Investigate

The coefficient of $x$ in a linear equation affects the steepness of the graph of the equation. Remind students that $x$ by itself in the equation has an understood coefficient of 1.

### Connecting to Prior Knowledge

In Lesson 8-2, students used the solutions of a linear equation to graph the equation. In this lesson, students relate a graph to its slope and $y$-intercept. In Lesson 8-4, students will use these properties to write function rules from graphs.

## Tools to Monitor Progress

**BEFORE THE LESSON**

**To check prerequisite skills:**

- Graphing points

**Skills You Need,** p. 381

**DURING THE LESSON**

**To check understanding:**

**Try This** exercises on student page

- **Additional Example 1**

Find the slope of this line. 4

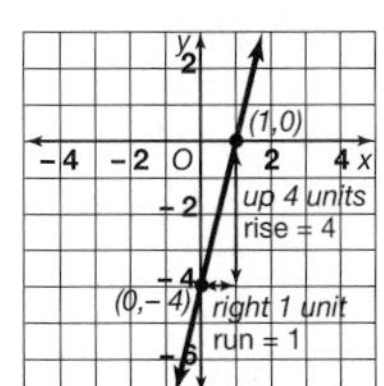

# 2 Teach

## Part 1 Teaching Notes

Have students develop mnemonic devices to help them remember the formula for slope, $\frac{\text{rise}}{\text{run}}$. For example, "Before you go skiing, you must *rise* from bed and then *run* to the ski lift."

### Example 1

**Build understanding.** Ask: If you walked the line in graph b. from left to right, would you be walking up or down this slope? What does this tell you about the slope? **down; The slope is negative.**

**Tactile Learning** Place students in groups and give each group several wood blocks and a board that is approximately 3 ft in length. Have each group construct a ramp that has a positive slope (from left to right) and then walk across the ramp from left to right. Next have students build a ramp that has a negative slope, then walk across it from left to right.

### Example 2

**Build understanding.** Ask: In addition to having an undefined slope, what else do you know about a vertical line? **Its equation is not a function.**

**Connecting to Geography** The steepest railroad in the world is the Mt. Pilatus Railway in Lucerne, Switzerland. This railroad has a grade of 38%, which means that for every 100 ft of run, the slope rises 38 ft. In order to travel up and down the steep track, the locomotive is driven by a cog that fits into a toothed rail in the middle of the track.

### Example 3

**Build understanding.** Explain why it does not matter which point you use first when finding the differences in the *x*- and *y*-coordinates, as long as you begin with the same point for both *x* and *y*. **The distance between the two *x*-coordinates and the two *y*-coordinates is the same, no matter which one is subtracted from the other.**

Horizontal and vertical lines are special cases for slope.

**Test Prep TIP**

You may say that a vertical line has *no slope*. But be sure that you do not confuse *no slope* with *slope 0*.

### EXAMPLE 2

**Find the slope of each line.**

**a.**

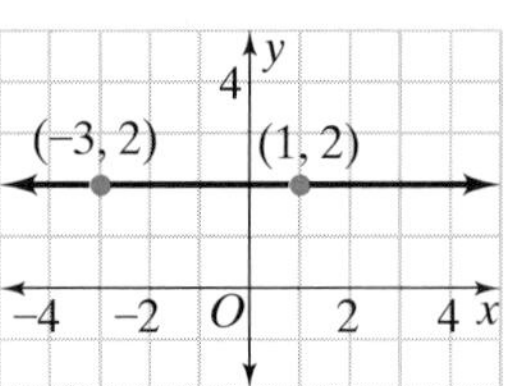


slope $= \frac{2-2}{1-(-3)} = \frac{0}{4} = 0$

Slope is 0 for a horizontal line.

**b.**

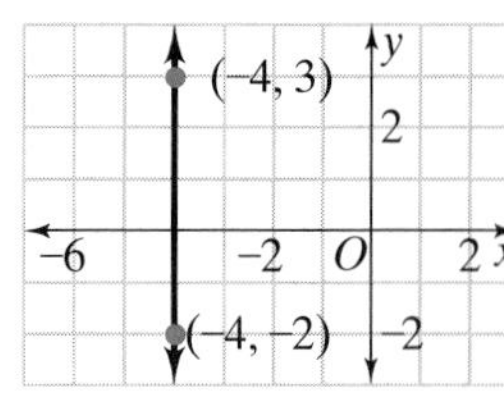


slope $= \frac{-2-3}{-4-(-4)} = \frac{-5}{0}$

Division by zero is undefined. Slope is *undefined* for a vertical line.

**TRY THIS** Find the slope of each line.

**3.** no slope

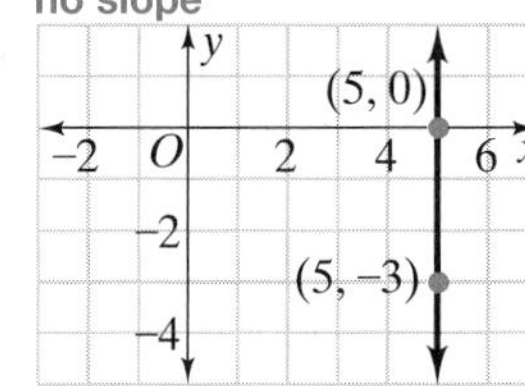


**4.** 0

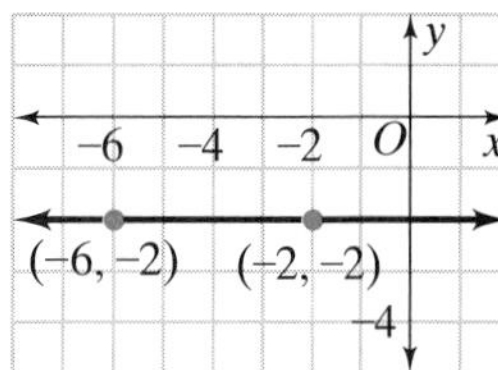


If you know two points of a line, you can find the slope of the line using the following formula.

$$\text{slope} = \frac{\text{difference in } y\text{-coordinates}}{\text{difference in } x\text{-coordinates}}$$

The *y*-coordinate you use first in the numerator must correspond to the *x*-coordinate you use first in the denominator.

### EXAMPLE 3

**Find the slope of the line through $C(-2, 6)$ and $D(4, 3)$.**

$$\text{slope} = \frac{\text{difference in } y\text{-coordinates}}{\text{difference in } x\text{-coordinates}} = \frac{3-6}{4-(-2)} = \frac{-3}{6} = \frac{-1}{2}$$

**TRY THIS** Find the slope of the line through each pair of points.

**5.** $V(8, -1), Q(0, -7)$ $\frac{3}{4}$

**6.** $S(-4, 3), R(-10, 9)$ $-1$



- **Additional Example 2**
  Which line has a slope of 0? **line *A***

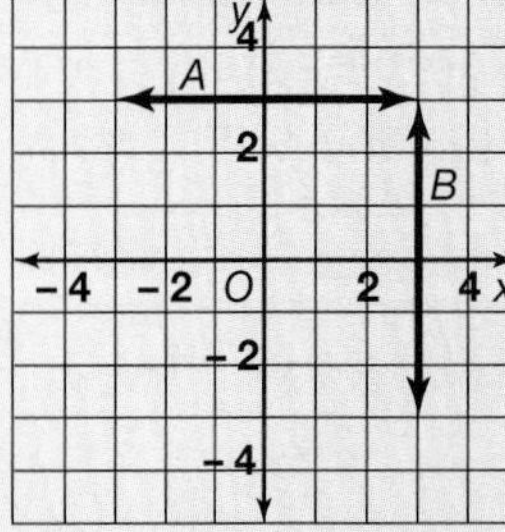


- **Additional Example 3**
  Find the slope of the line through $E(7, 5)$ and $F(-2, 0)$. $\frac{5}{9}$

## Using Slope to Graph Linear Equations

Here is the graph of $y = -\frac{1}{2}x + 3$.

The slope of the line is $\frac{-2}{4}$ or $-\frac{1}{2}$.

The **y-intercept** of the line is the point where the line crosses the $y$-axis. The constant in the equation is the same as the $y$-intercept.

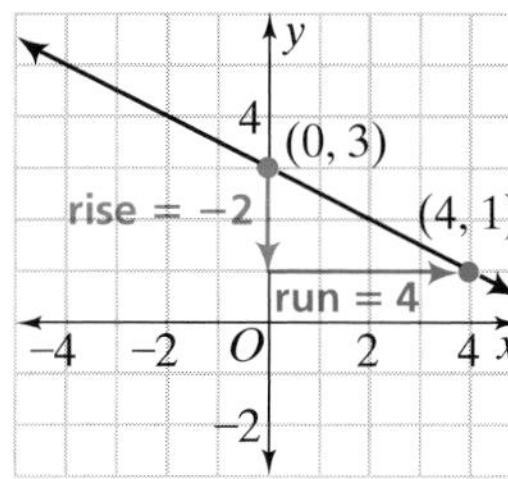


$$y = -\frac{1}{2}x + 3$$

slope ↑ y-intercept ↑

**Slope-Intercept Form**

The equation $y = mx + b$ is the slope-intercept form. In this form, $m$ is the slope of the line, and $b$ is the $y$-intercept.

You can use slope-intercept form to help you graph a function.

REAL-WORLD CONNECTION

### EXAMPLE 4

*Engineering* **A ramp slopes from a warehouse door down to a street. The function $y = -\frac{1}{3}x + 2$ models the ramp, where $x$ is the distance in feet from the door and $y$ is the height in feet above the street. Graph the function.**

**Step 1** Since the $y$-intercept is 2, graph (0, 2).

**Step 2** Since the slope is $-\frac{1}{3}$ or $\frac{-1}{3}$, move 1 unit down from (0, 2). Then move 3 units right to graph a second point.

**Step 3** Draw a line through the points.

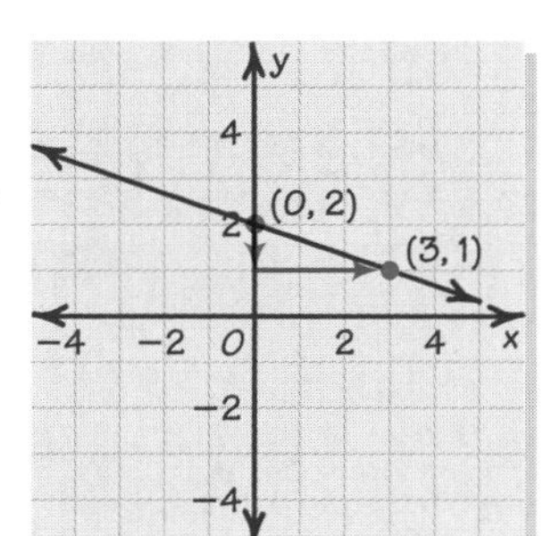


**TRY THIS** Graph each equation. See right.

**7.** $y = 2x - 3$ **8.** $y = -x + 4$

7.

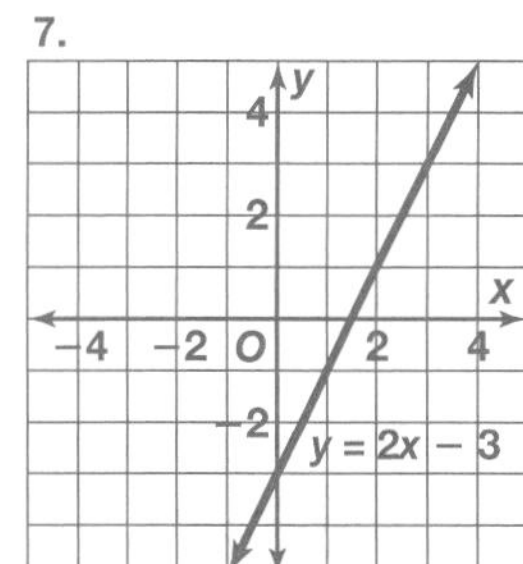


8.

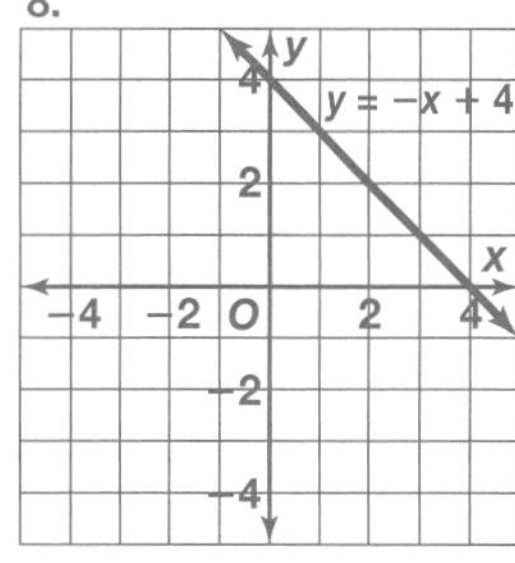




## Part 2 Teaching Notes

Once you know one point, the $y$-intercept, and the slope, you can begin at the point you know and use the slope (written as a fraction) to move up and over (rise over run) to find a second point.

**ELL** If *intercept* is an unfamiliar term, suggest thinking of the $y$-intercept as the *y-crossing,* or the place where the graph *crosses* the $y$-axis.

### Example 4

**Build understanding.** Ask: What does the $y$-intercept of 2 tell you about the ramp? **It starts 2 ft above the street.**

**Error Prevention** Suggest that students check their graphs by substituting a point from the graph back into the function. The graph is correct if the coordinates of the point make the function true.

**Math Reasoning** Use math reasoning to explain how you know where the $y$-intercept of $y = \frac{1}{2}x$ is. **Since there is no $b$-value in the equation, you can think of the equation as $y = \frac{1}{2}x + 0$, which would make the $y$-intercept 0, or the origin. When you substitute 0 for $y$ in the equation, $x$ also equals 0, which confirms that the $y$-intercept is at the origin, or (0, 0).**

### Additional Example 4

The function $y = -\frac{1}{5}x + b$ models a ramp sloping from a warehouse door down to the street, where $x$ is the feet from the door, and $y$ is the height in feet above the street. What is $b$ if the door is 4 ft above the street? Is the left end of the ramp higher or lower than the right end? **4; higher**

### AFTER THE LESSON

**To assess knowledge:**

**Lesson Quiz**

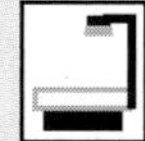

Find the slope of the line through each pair of points.

**1.** $A(2, 4)$, $B(-2, -4)$ **2**

**2.** $F(-5, 1)$, $G(0, -9)$ **−2**

Find the slope and $y$-intercept.

**3.** $y = -\frac{4}{3}x - 7$ **$-\frac{4}{3}$; −7**

- For enrichment and reteaching options see Resources on p. 381H.

# 3 Practice/Assess

## Assignment Guide

To provide flexible scheduling, this lesson can be divided into parts.

**Part 1**
**Core** 1–6, 10–21, 41, 42, 45
**Extension** 44, 47

**Part 2**
**Core** 7–9, 22–35
**Extension** 36–40, 43, 46

Mixed Review can be assigned at any time for maintenance.

### Exercises

**Auditory Learning Exercises 7–9** Quietly say the slope and *y*-intercept aloud to yourself as you read the equations.

**Test Prep Exercise 45** When all answer choices are similar, double-check your arithmetic before making an answer choice. Pay close attention to negative signs.

### Challenge

Find the slope and *y*-intercept of the equation $14x + 21y = 63$.
$-\frac{2}{3}$; 3

### Closure

Slope is a measure describing the tilt of a line, which you can calculate using the ratio of $\frac{\text{vertical change}}{\text{horizontal change}}$. The slope-intercept form of a linear equation is $y = mx + b$, where $m$ is the slope and $b$ is the $y$-intercept.

### Daily Cumulative Review

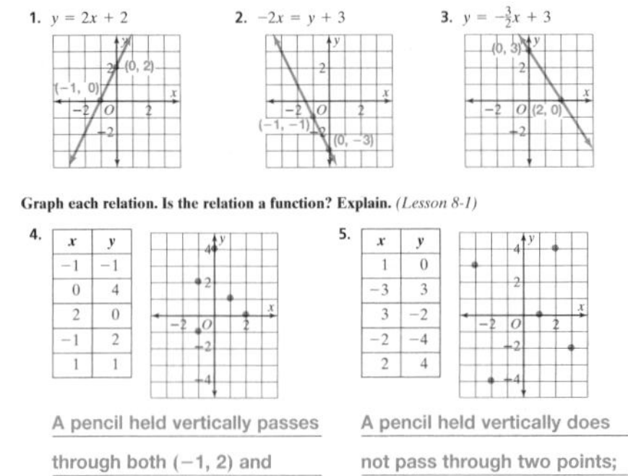

Graph each equation. *(Lesson 8-2)*

1. $y = 2x + 2$
2. $-2x = y + 3$
3. $y = -\frac{3}{2}x + 3$



Graph each relation. Is the relation a function? Explain. *(Lesson 8-1)*

4.

| x | y |
|---|---|
| −1 | −1 |
| 0 | 4 |
| 2 | 0 |
| −1 | 2 |
| 1 | 1 |

A pencil held vertically passes through both (−1, 2) and (−1, −1); not a function

5.

| x | y |
|---|---|
| 1 | 0 |
| −3 | 3 |
| 3 | −2 |
| −2 | −4 |
| 2 | 4 |

A pencil held vertically does not pass through two points; a function

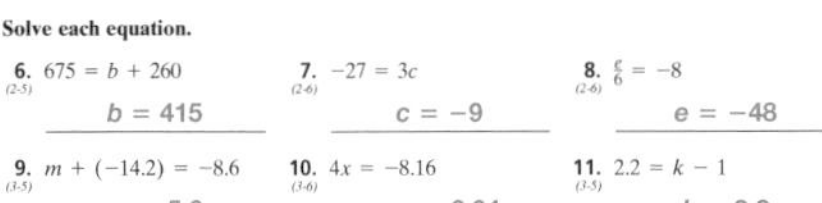

Mixed Review

Solve each equation.

6. $675 = b + 260$ (2-5) $b = 415$
7. $-27 = 3c$ (2-6) $c = -9$
8. $\frac{e}{6} = -8$ (2-6) $e = -48$
9. $m + (-14.2) = -8.6$ (3-5) $m = 5.6$
10. $4x = -8.16$ (3-6) $x = -2.04$
11. $2.2 = k - 1$ (3-5) $k = 3.2$

List all the factors of each number.

12. 56 (4-1) 1, 2, 4, 7, 8, 14, 28, 56
13. 64 (4-1) 1, 2, 4, 8, 16, 32, 64



# Exercises

## Check Understanding

**Find the slope of each line.**

1. $\frac{3}{4}$

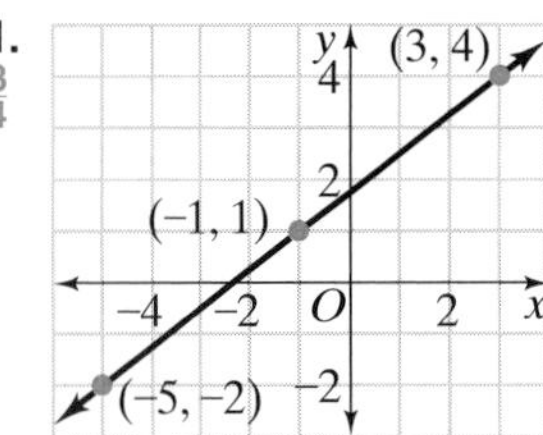


2. −1

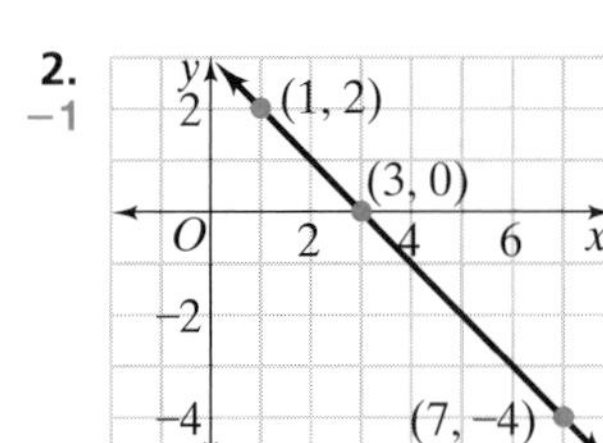


3. no slope

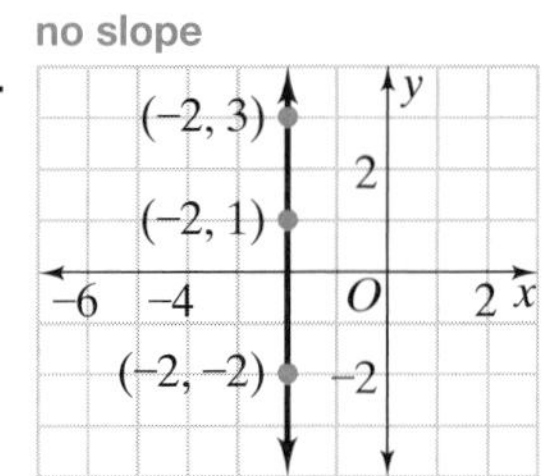


**Find the slope of the line through each pair of points.**

4. $A(2, 6), B(8, 1)$ $-\frac{5}{6}$
5. $R(-4, 5), S(-1, 5)$ 0
6. $W(-10, -2), Z(2, -10)$ $-\frac{2}{3}$

**Identify the slope and the *y*-intercept of the graph of each equation. Then graph each equation.** See back of book for graphs.

7. $y = 7x + 3$ 7, 3
8. $y = -x - 4$ −1, −4
9. $y = \frac{1}{2}x - 8$ $\frac{1}{2}$, −8

## Practice and Problem Solving

**Find the slope of each line.**

10. $-\frac{1}{4}$

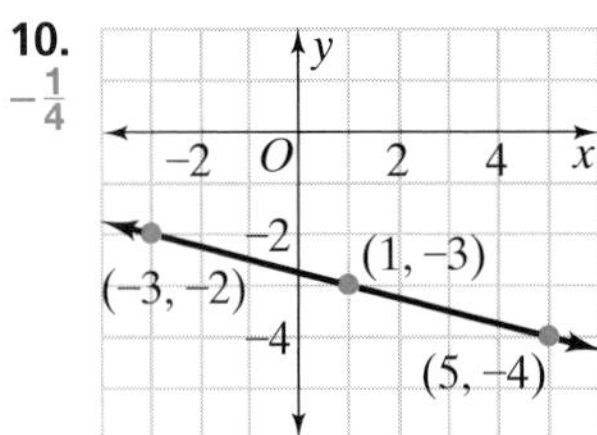


11. 0

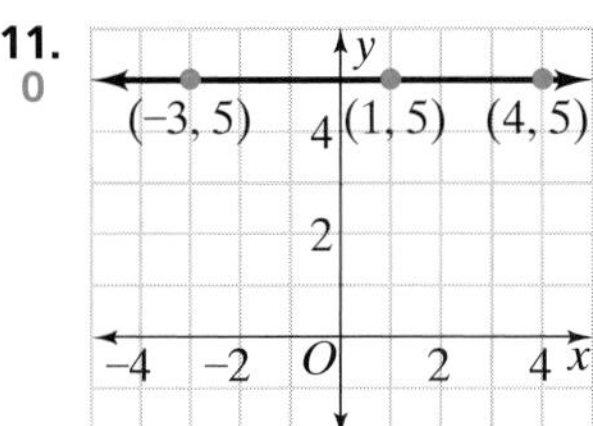


12. 1

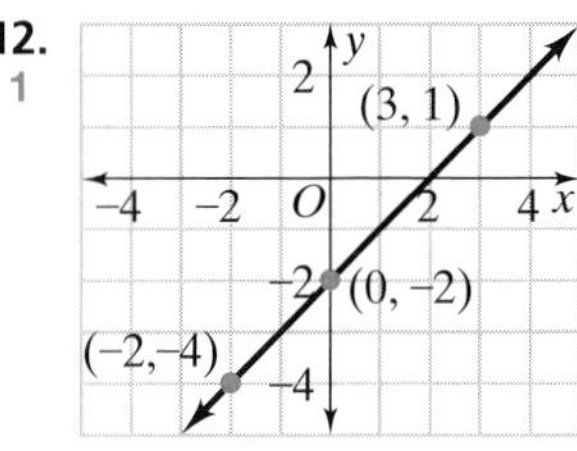


13. $-\frac{1}{3}$

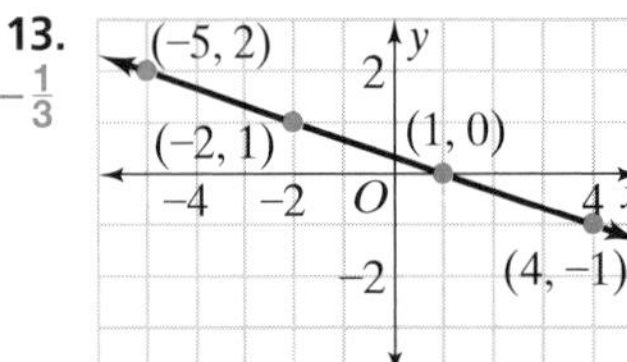


14. 0

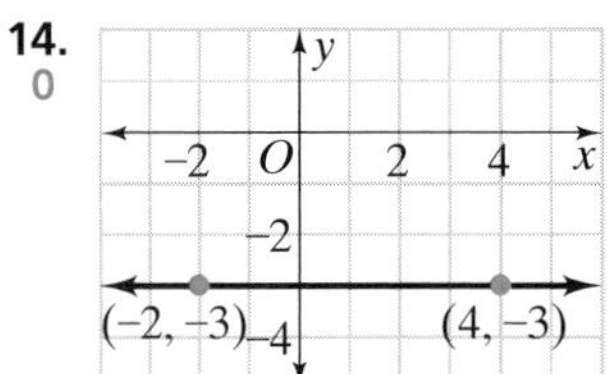


15. $-\frac{3}{5}$

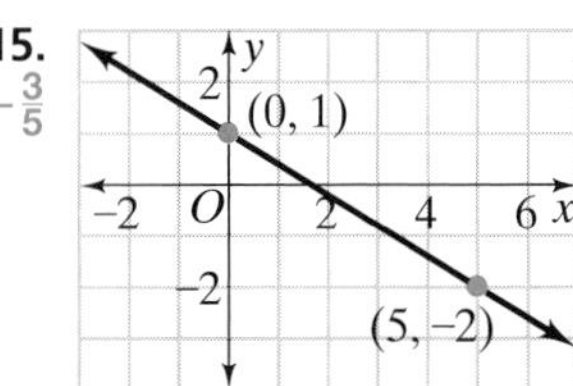




### Alternative Assessment

Have students in pairs write and exchange a word problem that describes a real-world situation involving slope that is solved by writing an equation in slope-intercept form. Have them verify their partner's solution.

30.

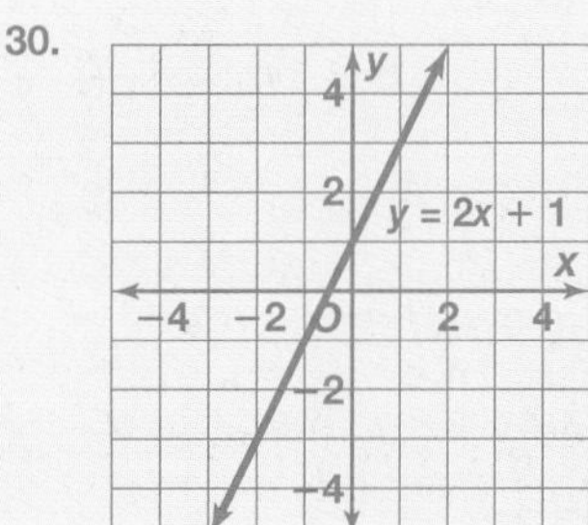

**Find the slope of the line through each pair of points.**

**16.** $C(2, 1), D(3, 1)$ 0
**17.** $J(-2, 5), K(-2, -1)$ no slope
**18.** $G(3, 4), H(6, 10)$ 2
**19.** $N(-5, 2), Q(1, -4)$ −1
**20.** $E(1, -2), F(4, -8)$ −2
**21.** $L(-1, 15), M(3, 5)$ $-\frac{5}{2}$

**Identify the slope and the *y*-intercept of the graph of each equation.**

**22.** $y = 2x + 4$ 2, 4
**23.** $y = 5x - 3$ 5, −3
**24.** $y = -x + 1$ −1, 1
**25.** $y = -\frac{2}{3}x + 1$ $-\frac{2}{3}$, 1
**26.** $y = x - \frac{3}{4}$ 1, $-\frac{3}{4}$
**27.** $y = -\frac{2}{5}x - 2$ $-\frac{2}{5}$, −2
**28.** $y = \frac{1}{2}x$ $\frac{1}{2}$, 0
**29.** $y = -3$ 0, −3

**Graph each equation.** See margin.

**30.** $y = 2x + 1$
**31.** $y = -x$
**32.** $y = -3x - 1$
**33.** $y = -\frac{1}{4}x - 12$
**34.** $y = 4$
**35.** $y = \frac{2}{3}x + 5$
**36.** $3x + y = 3$
**37.** $2y + 3x = 12$

**Graph each line.** 38. See margin. 39–40. See back of book.

**38.** slope 5, through $(-4, -5)$
**39.** no slope, through $(4, -2)$
**40.** slope $\frac{2}{3}$, through $(0, -4)$

**41.** *Construction* The slope of a roof is its *pitch*. You indicate the pitch of a roof by a ratio $a : b$, where $a$ is the number of feet of rise for every $b$ feet of run. In the photos at the right, which house has a roof with steeper pitch? Explain. The upper roof has the steeper pitch because it has the greater slope.

**42.** *Error Analysis* A student said that the slope of the line through (8, 4) and (2, 2) is 3. What error could this student have made? See below right.

**43. a.** Graph the three groups of equations on three coordinate planes. See back of book.

| Group 1 | Group 2 | Group 3 |
|---|---|---|
| $y = 2x - 5$ | $y = -3x - 1$ | $y = -6$ |
| $y = 2x$ | $y = -3x$ | $y = 1$ |
| $y = 2x + 3$ | $y = -3x + 4$ | $y = 4.5$ |

**b.** *Writing* How are the lines in each group related to each other? Explain. See margin.

**c.** *Critical Thinking* What is the coefficient of $x$ in the equation of a graph that has slope 0? 0

**44.** *Construction* The slope of a road is its *grade*. What do you think it means for the grade of a road to be 4%? (*Hint:* Write the percent as a fraction.) $\frac{\text{rise}}{\text{run}} = \frac{4}{100}$. As you "run" 100 ft horizontally you rise 4 ft vertically.

**45.** **TEST PREP** The slope of a line is −1. Which two points could this line contain? B

A. $(0, 1), (0, -1)$ B. $(0, 1), (1, 0)$ C. $(0, 1), (-1, 0)$ D. Not here

42. The student could have calculated $\frac{\text{difference in } x\text{-coordinates}}{\text{difference in } y\text{-coordinates}}$.



31.
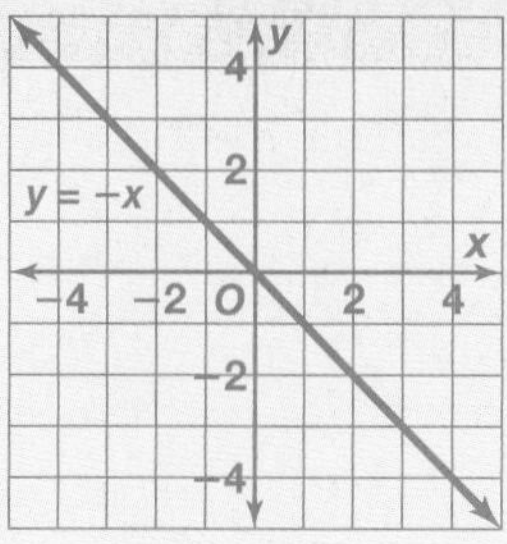


32.
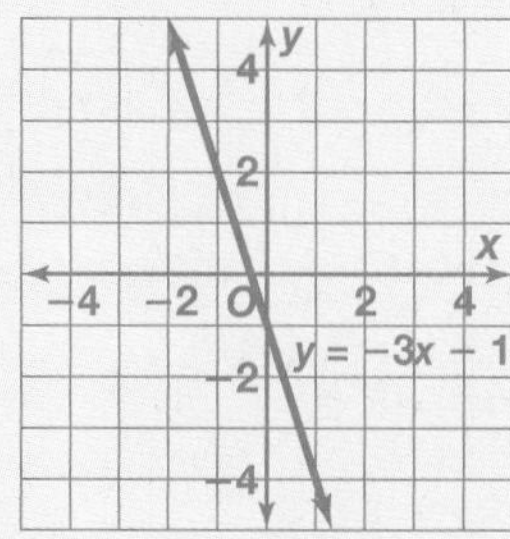


33.
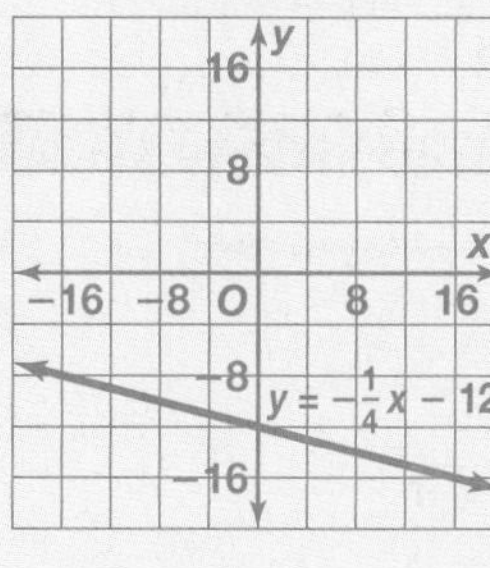


34.
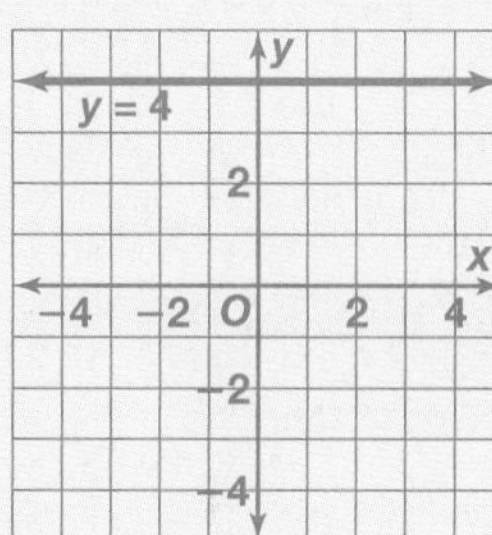


35.
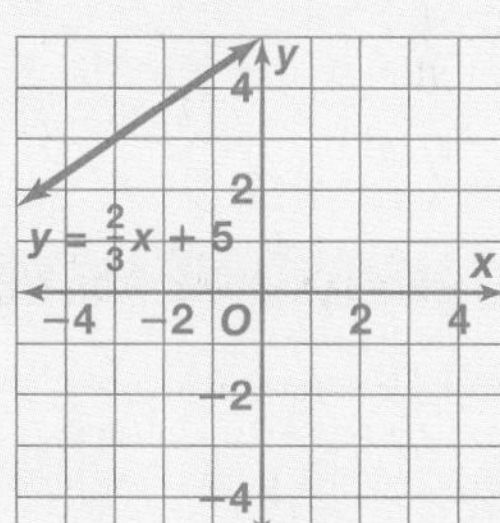


36.
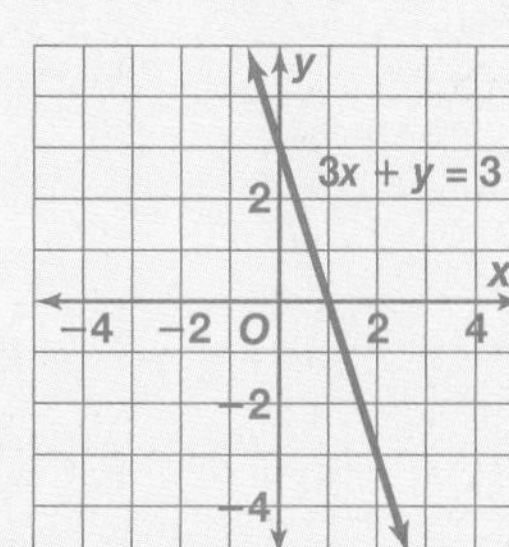

37.
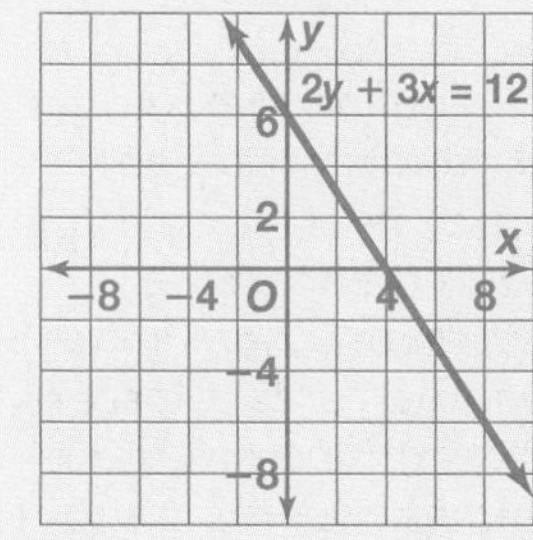


38.
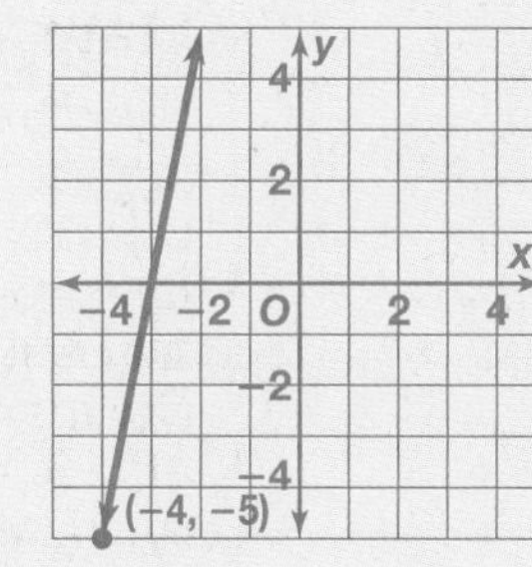


43.b. The lines are parallel. Explanations may vary. Sample: Their slopes are the same, so they never meet.

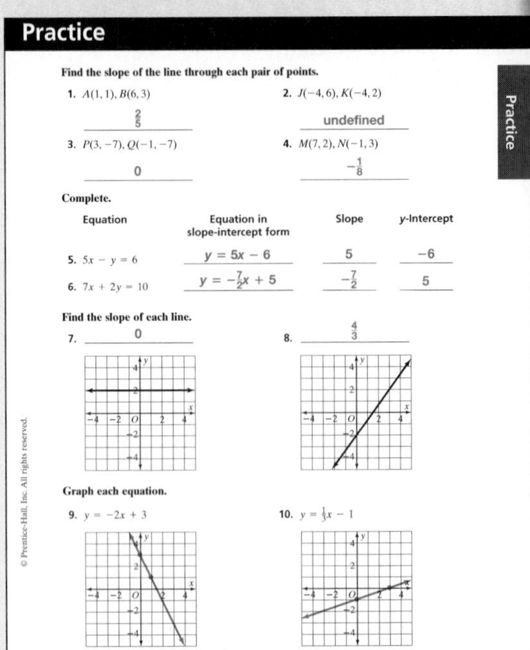

## Practice

**Find the slope of the line through each pair of points.**

1. $A(1, 1), B(6, 3)$ — $\frac{2}{5}$
2. $J(-4, 6), K(-4, 2)$ — undefined
3. $P(3, -7), Q(-1, -7)$ — 0
4. $M(7, 2), N(-1, 3)$ — $-\frac{1}{8}$

**Complete.**

| | Equation | Equation in slope-intercept form | Slope | y-Intercept |
|---|---|---|---|---|
| 5. | $5x - y = 6$ | $y = 5x - 6$ | 5 | −6 |
| 6. | $7x + 2y = 10$ | $y = -\frac{7}{2}x + 5$ | $-\frac{7}{2}$ | 5 |

**Find the slope of each line.**

7. 0
8. $\frac{4}{3}$

**Graph each equation.**

9. $y = -2x + 3$
10. $y = \frac{1}{3}x - 1$



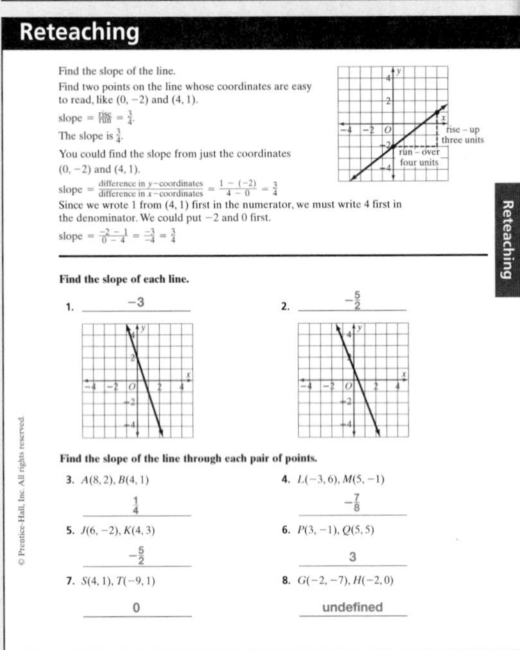

## Reteaching

Find the slope of the line.

Find two points on the line whose coordinates are easy to read, like (0, −2) and (4, 1).

slope $= \frac{\text{rise}}{\text{run}} = \frac{3}{4}$.

The slope is $\frac{3}{4}$.

You could find the slope from just the coordinates (0, −2) and (4, 1).

slope $= \frac{\text{difference in } y\text{-coordinates}}{\text{difference in } x\text{-coordinates}} = \frac{1 - (-2)}{4 - 0} = \frac{3}{4}$

Since we wrote 1 from (4, 1) first in the numerator, we must write 4 first in the denominator. We could put −2 and 0 first.

slope $= \frac{-2 - 1}{0 - 4} = \frac{-3}{-4} = \frac{3}{4}$



**Find the slope of each line.**

1. −3
2. $-\frac{5}{2}$

**Find the slope of the line through each pair of points.**

3. $A(8, 2), B(4, 1)$ — $\frac{1}{4}$
4. $L(-3, 6), M(5, -1)$ — $-\frac{7}{8}$
5. $J(6, -2), K(4, 3)$ — $-\frac{5}{2}$
6. $P(3, -1), Q(5, 5)$ — 3
7. $S(4, 1), T(-9, 1)$ — 0
8. $G(-2, -7), H(-2, 0)$ — undefined



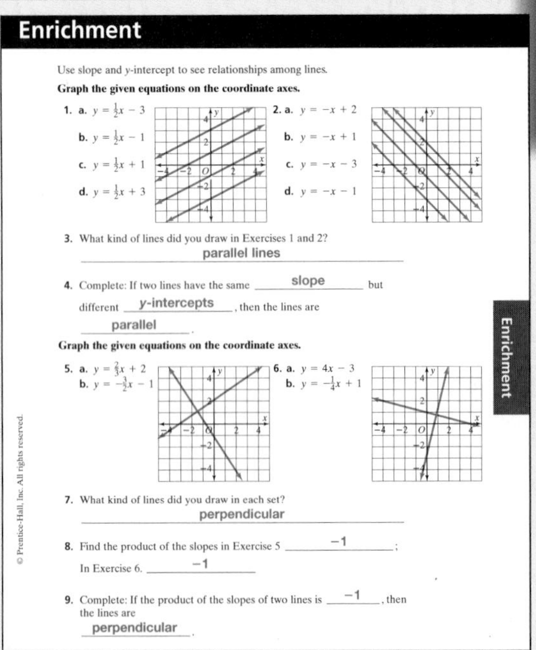

## Enrichment

Use slope and y-intercept to see relationships among lines.

**Graph the given equations on the coordinate axes.**

1. a. $y = \frac{1}{2}x - 3$
   b. $y = \frac{1}{2}x - 1$
   c. $y = \frac{1}{2}x + 1$
   d. $y = \frac{1}{2}x + 3$
2. a. $y = -x + 2$
   b. $y = -x + 1$
   c. $y = -x - 3$
   d. $y = -x - 1$
3. What kind of lines did you draw in Exercises 1 and 2? parallel lines
4. Complete: If two lines have the same slope but different y-intercepts, then the lines are parallel.

**Graph the given equations on the coordinate axes.**

5. a. $y = \frac{2}{3}x + 2$
   b. $y = -\frac{3}{2}x - 1$
6. a. $y = 4x - 3$
   b. $y = -\frac{1}{4}x + 1$
7. What kind of lines did you draw in each set? perpendicular
8. Find the product of the slopes in Exercise 5 −1; In Exercise 6. −1
9. Complete: If the product of the slopes of two lines is −1, then the lines are perpendicular.





46. *Critical Thinking* Find the slope of the line at the right using two points. Then find the slope using two other points. Are the slopes the same? Explain. Answers may vary. Sample: Yes; the slope of the line is the same all along it.

47. *Open-ended* Write equations for five different lines that intersect at (0, 3). Answers may vary. Sample: $y = 3$, $y = \frac{1}{2}x + 3, y = x + 3, y = 2x + 3, y = 4x + 3$

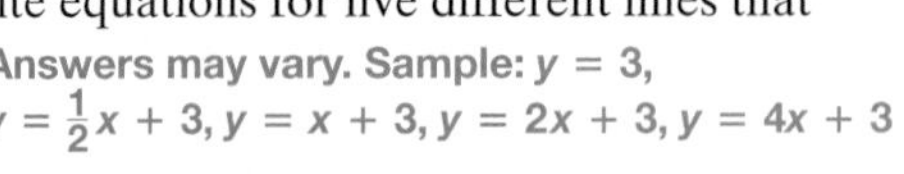

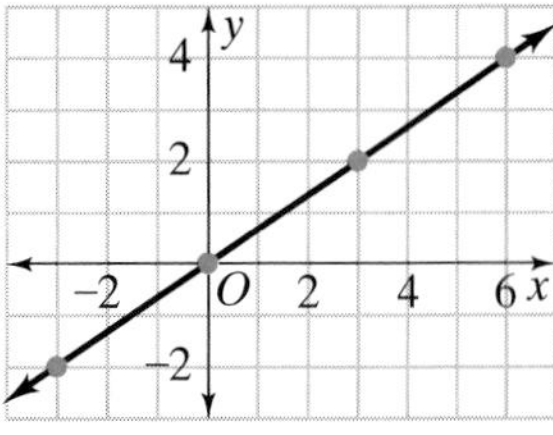

## Mixed Review

**Find each percent of change. Tell whether the change is an increase or a decrease.** ***(Lesson 6-8)***

48. from 12 to 15 — 25% increase
49. from 10 to 9 — 10% decrease
50. from 20 to 30 — 50% increase
51. from 52 to 39 — 25% decrease

**Solve and graph each inequality.** ***(Lesson 7-6)*** See margin for graphs.

52. $4x + 5 < 17$ — $x < 3$
53. $18 \le 5 - 2x$ — $x \le -6.5$
54. $-x + 6 > 31$ — $x < -25$
55. $9 + \frac{1}{2}x \ge -3$ — $x \ge -24$

56. a. During the 1998–1999 season, New York theatergoers bought 11.7 million tickets for \$588.5 million. To the nearest dollar, what was the mean price for a theater ticket in New York? ***(Lesson 3-6)*** \$50
    b. The box office receipts for New York shows were up 5.5% from the year before. What were the New York receipts for the 1997–1998 season? ***(Lesson 6-7)*** about \$557.8 million

## Math at Work

### Movie Camera Operator

Lights . . . camera . . . action! These are familiar words for movie camera operators. When the action begins, movie camera operators are responsible for capturing the action on film. One scene in a movie can cost hundreds of thousands of dollars, so a scene has to be filmed correctly in as few tries as possible. Camera operators are trained in the effective use of lighting, lens filters, and camera angles. The operators determine the precise movements of the camera and its platform and the camera angles in advance of the actual shooting. It takes a good understanding of algebra and coordinate geometry to do that!

For more information about movie camera operators, see the Prentice Hall Web site. **www.phschool.com**



See also Extra Practice section.

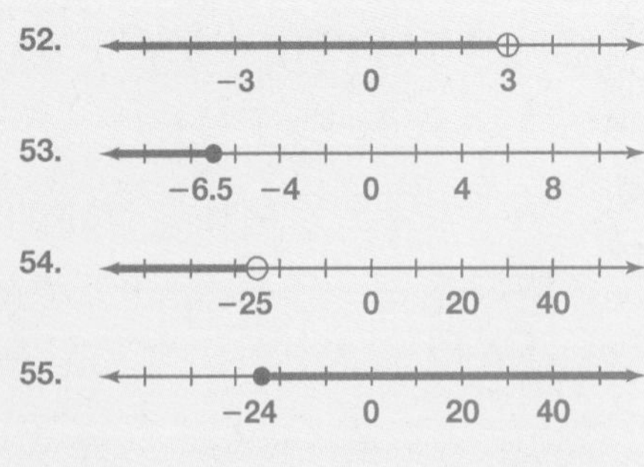



### Math at Work

If you have block scheduling or extended class periods, have small groups of students research the math used by a movie camera operator by finding reference materials on film making in the local or school library. Groups may also want to contact local film production companies to find out if they could interview a camera operator about using math on the job.

Students can find additional information on the Web site **www.phschool.com**.

Technology
After Lesson 8-3

# Graphing Lines

You can use a graphing calculator to graph equations in slope-intercept form and find solutions.

## EXAMPLE

**Graph $y = 3x - 2$.**

**Step 1** Press the Y= key. Enter $3x - 2$.

**Step 2** Press ZOOM 6 to graph your equation with the standard viewing window.

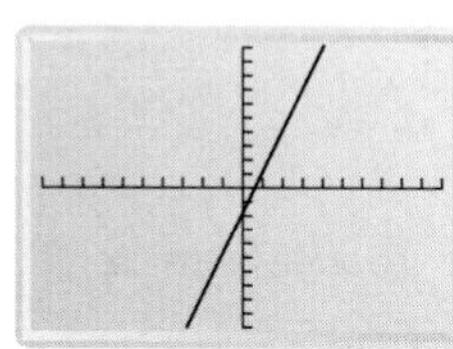

**Step 3** Press TABLE to see solutions.

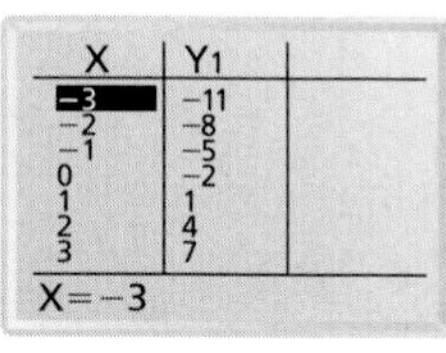


**Step 4** Sketch your graph and copy the table of solutions.

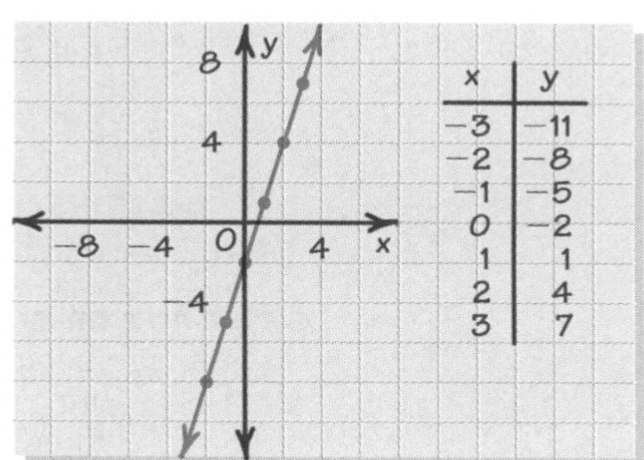


| x | y |
|---|---|
| −3 | −11 |
| −2 | −8 |
| −1 | −5 |
| 0 | −2 |
| 1 | 1 |
| 2 | 4 |
| 3 | 7 |

**Graph each equation.** 1–2. See margin. 3–9. See back of book.

1. $y = 2x + 1$
2. $y = x - 4$
3. $y = 3x + 2$
4. $y = -x$
5. $y = -x + 4$
6. $y = 4x - 3$
7. $y = -3x - 2$
8. $y = \frac{1}{2}x - 5$
9. $y = -\frac{1}{2}x + 2$



MATH TOOLBOX

## Graphing Lines

In Lessons 8-2 and 8-3, students learned how to graph linear equations by first finding ordered-pair solutions and then graphing the line. In this Math Toolbox, students learn how to graph linear equations and find solutions with a graphing calculator.

## Math Background

Graphing linear equations is an important skill in algebra as well as in other advanced mathematics courses. Using a graphing calculator to graph linear equations develops an understanding of the relationship between equations and their graphs, because graphing with the calculator is both rapid and accurate, and changes to the equation are reflected immediately in the graph. Ability to use the graphing calculator is required for many standardized tests as well as for higher math courses and many work situations.

# Teaching Notes

**Error Prevention** Enter keystrokes carefully, following the procedures in the example. Check work by sketching a graph quickly using estimation techniques.

**Monitoring Progress Exercises 1–9** Ask: Does the slope and *y*-intercept of the graph on the screen agree with the slope and *y*-intercept that you identified from reading the equations?

**Block Scheduling** If you have block scheduling or extended periods, you may wish to insert this Math Toolbox lesson between the completion of Part 2 of Lesson 8-3 and Part 1 of Lesson 8-4.

1.

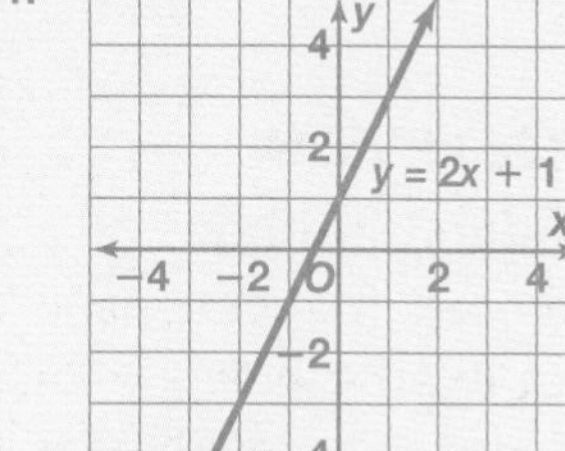


**• Additional Example**

Graph $y = -2x + 4$.

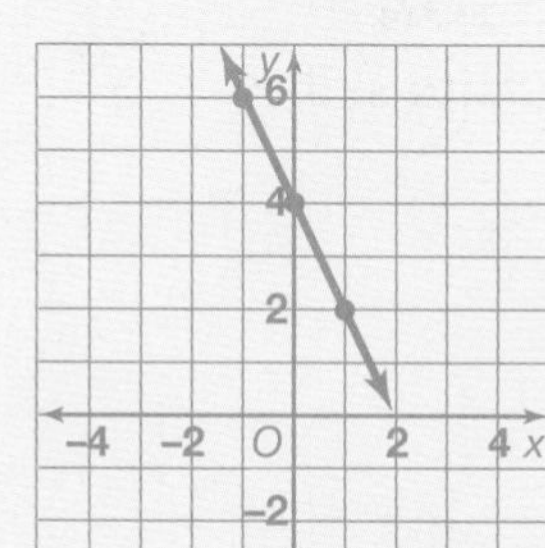


| x | y |
|---|---|
| −1 | 6 |
| 0 | 4 |
| 1 | 2 |
| 2 | 0 |
| 3 | −2 |

2.

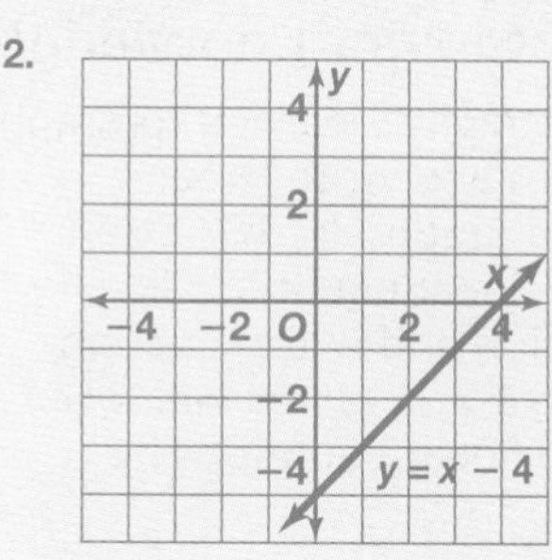

# 8-4

## Getting Ready

**Key Terms and Symbols** function notation, function rule

**Resources** A complete list of resources for this lesson is on p. 381H.

### Daily Skills Warm-Up

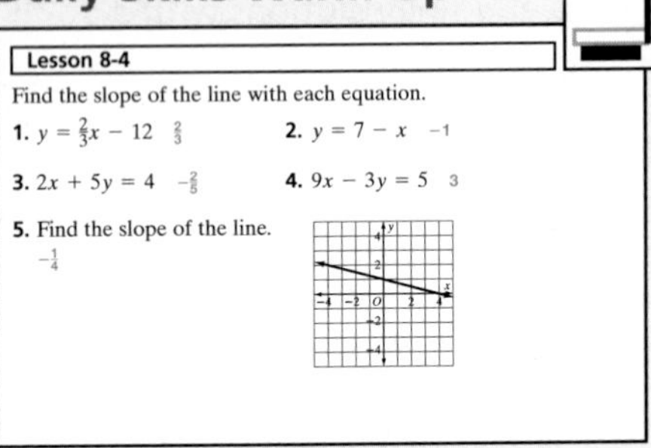

Lesson 8-4

Find the slope of the line with each equation.

1. $y = \frac{2}{3}x - 12$ $\frac{2}{3}$
2. $y = 7 - x$ $-1$
3. $2x + 5y = 4$ $-\frac{2}{5}$
4. $9x - 3y = 5$ $3$
5. Find the slope of the line. $-\frac{1}{4}$

### Background for the Lesson

When you say that *y* is a function of *x*, this means that the value of *y* depends on the value of *x*. When you write an equation using function notation, you replace the *y* with *f*(*x*), which you read by saying either "*f* of *x*" or "function of *x*." For the function $f(x) = 2x + 1$, you can find $f(-2)$ by substituting the value $-2$ for *x*: $f(-2) = 2(-2) + 1$ which is $-3$. You can then say that $f(-2) = -3$.

## 1 Focus

### Connecting to Students' Lives

Ask students if they have ever seen a souvenir coin press. You place a penny in these machines and they press it into a different shape and imprint a name or picture. A coin press is like a function in that you put in a penny (*x*), and you get out a changed version which is *y* or *f*(*x*).

### Connecting to Prior Knowledge

In Lesson 8-3, students learned to graph linear equations and write linear equations from graphs. In this lesson, students write linear equations in function notation and write function rules. In Lesson 8-7, students will solve systems of two linear equations by graphing.



# 8-4 Writing Rules for Linear Functions

**What You'll Learn**

1. To write a function rule for a word relationship
2. To write a function rule by analyzing a table or graph

**. . . And Why**

To model everyday tasks such as converting measurements or finding the cost of a mail order

## Part 1 Writing Rules from Words

You can write a function using **function notation,** where you use $f(x)$ instead of *y*. You read $f(x)$ as "*f* of *x*." You can think of a domain value as an *input* and the resulting range value as the *output*. A **function rule** is an equation that describes a function.

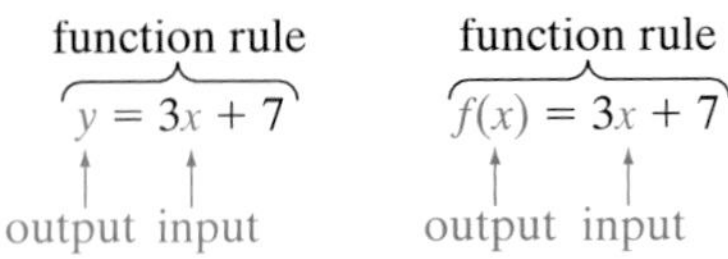

### Example 1

*Sales Commissions* **Paulo works at a local store. Each week he earns a $300 salary plus a 3% commission on his sales.**

**a. Write a function rule that relates total earnings to sales.**

**Words** total earnings are $300 plus 3% of sales

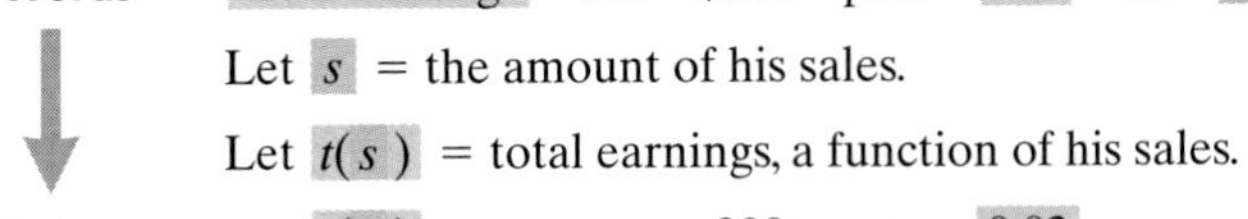

Let $s$ = the amount of his sales.

Let $t(s)$ = total earnings, a function of his sales.

**Rule** $t(s) = 300 + 0.03 \cdot s$

A rule for the function is $t(s) = 300 + 0.03s$.

**b. Find his earnings for one week if his sales are $2,500.**

| | |
|---|---|
| $t(s) = 300 + 0.03s$ | |
| $t(2{,}500) = 300 + 0.03(2{,}500)$ | Replace *s* with 2,500. |
| $t(2{,}500) = 300 + 75$ | Multiply. |
| $t(2{,}500) = 375$ | Add. |

Paul earns $375 if his sales are $2,500.

**Try This** $c(p) = 3p + 4$; $19

1. Scrumptious Snack Mix is sold by mail order. It costs $3/lb, plus $4 for shipping and handling. Write a function rule for the total cost $c(p)$ based on the number of pounds *p* bought. Use your function to find the total cost of 5 lb of snack mix.



## Tools to Monitor Progress

**BEFORE THE LESSON**

**To check prerequisite skills:**

- Graphing points

**Skills You Need,** p. 381

**DURING THE LESSON**

**To check understanding:**

**Try This** exercises on student page

- **Additional Example 1**
  A long distance company charges its customers a monthly fee of $4.95 plus 9¢ for each minute of a long distance call. Write a function rule that relates the total monthly bill to the number of minutes the customer spent on long distance calls.
  $t(m) = 4.95 + 0.09m$

## Writing Rules from Tables or Graphs

To write a function rule from a table, look for a pattern. The formula $y = mx + b$ in function notation is $f(x) = mx + b$. The slope $m$ is $\frac{\text{difference in } f(x)\text{-values}}{\text{difference in } x\text{-values}}$, and $b$ is the value of $f(x)$ when $x = 0$.

### EXAMPLE 2

**Write a rule for the linear function in the table below.**

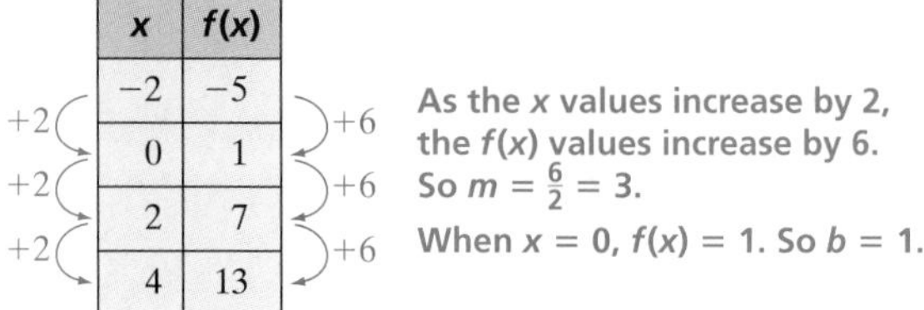

| $x$ | $f(x)$ |
|---|---|
| −2 | −5 |
| 0 | 1 |
| 2 | 7 |
| 4 | 13 |



As the $x$ values increase by 2, the $f(x)$ values increase by 6. So $m = \frac{6}{2} = 3$.
When $x = 0$, $f(x) = 1$. So $b = 1$.

A rule for the function is $f(x) = 3x + 1$.

**TRY THIS** Write a rule for each linear function.

**2.**

| $x$ | $f(x)$ |
|---|---|
| −1 | −2 |
| 0 | 0 |
| 1 | 2 |
| 2 | 4 |

$f(x) = 2x$

**3.**

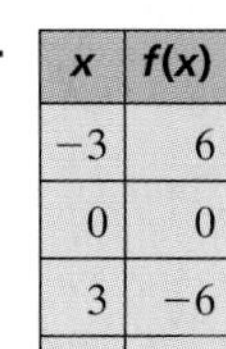

| $x$ | $f(x)$ |
|---|---|
| −3 | 6 |
| 0 | 0 |
| 3 | −6 |
| 6 | −12 |

$f(x) = -2x$

**4.**

| $x$ | $y$ |
|---|---|
| −6 | −11 |
| −4 | −7 |
| −2 | −3 |
| 0 | 1 |

$y = 2x + 1$

You can use slope-intercept form, $f(x) = mx + b$ or $y = mx + b$, when you write a rule for a linear function.

### EXAMPLE 3

**Write a rule for the linear function graphed below.**

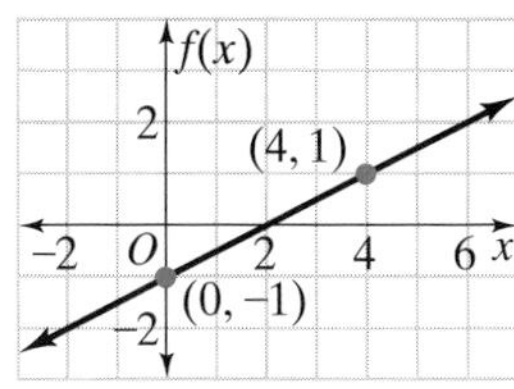


$\text{slope} = \frac{1 - (-1)}{4 - 0} = \frac{2}{4} = \frac{1}{2}$

$y\text{-intercept} = -1$

A rule for the function is $f(x) = \frac{1}{2}x - 1$.

**TRY THIS** $y = -x + 2$

**5.** Write a rule for the function graphed at the right.

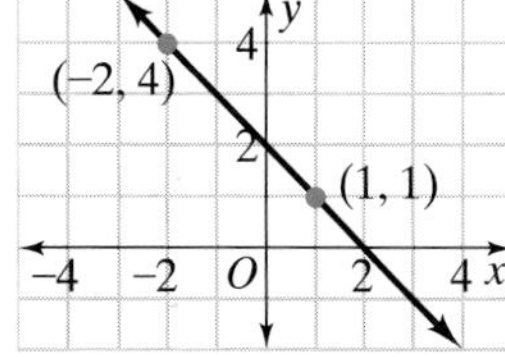




## 2 Teach

### Part 1 Teaching Notes

Make sure students understand that the equation $f(x) = mx + b$ is the same as the equation $y = mx + b$. Write several linear equations on the board and ask volunteers to change them into function notation.

#### Example 1

**Build understanding.** Ask: How does 3% of sales end up as 0.03*s* in the function rule? **3% is the same as 0.03, and the word *of* tells you that 3% is multiplied by his sales, *s*.**

#### Example 2

**Build understanding.** Ask: What does each ordered pair in the table represent? **a solution of the function**

#### Example 3

**Build understanding.** Ask: What do you know about the sign of the slope of this function from looking at the graph? **It is positive.**

**Visual Learning** Emphasize the value of the information students can gain about a function by simply looking at its graph, such as the $y$-intercept and whether the slope is positive or negative. If a line is steeper than the line $y = x$, the absolute value of its slope is greater than 1.

**Error Prevention** Remind students to check their functions by substituting a solution from the table or graph to find out if the solution makes the function true.

**Math Reasoning** Use math reasoning to explain why $f(x) = 1$ is or is not a function. **The equation $f(x) = 1$ is a function because the graph of $f(x) = 1$, or $y = 1$, is a horizontal line.**

### Additional Examples 2–3

Write a rule for the linear function in the table below. Then graph the function.

| $x$ | $f(x)$ |
|---|---|
| 2 | 3 |
| 0 | −5 |

**$f(x) = 4x - 5$; The graph has a slope of 4 and a $y$-intercept of −5.**

### AFTER THE LESSON

**To assess knowledge: Lesson Quiz**

Write a rule for each function.

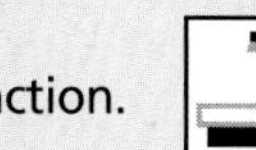

**1.**

| $x$ | $f(x)$ |
|---|---|
| 6 | 7 |
| 2 | −9 |

$f(x) = 4x - 17$

**2.**

| $x$ | $f(x)$ |
|---|---|
| 0 | 0 |
| 1 | 1 |
| 2 | 2 |

$f(x) = x$

- For enrichment and reteaching options see Resources on p. 381H.

# 3 Practice/Assess

## Assignment Guide

To provide flexible scheduling, this lesson can be divided into parts.

**Part 1**
**Core** 1, 5–7, 10
**Extension** 8, 9

**Part 2**
**Core** 2–4, 11–21
**Extension** 22–25

Mixed Review can be assigned at any time for maintenance.

## Exercises

**Test Prep Exercise 10** Notice that *m* stands here for a number of *millimeters.* Recall that millimeters are much smaller than centimeters, so there will be many of them in 1 centimeter. Ask yourself: what would I do to 1 millimeter to change it into centimeters?

## Challenge

Write a rule to find the difference between any two temperatures.
$d(t) = |t_1 - t_2|$

## Closure

You can write a function rule from a verbal description, from a table of values, or from a graph.

# Exercises

## Check Understanding

1. *Money* Suppose you give a salesperson \$20 for a purchase. Write a function rule to express the amount of change $a(c)$ that you receive as a function of the cost $c$. $a(c) = 20 - c$

**Write a rule for each linear function.**

2.

| $x$ | $f(x)$ |
|---|---|
| −9 | −18 |
| 0 | −9 |
| 9 | 0 |
| 18 | 9 |

$f(x) = x - 9$

3.

| $x$ | $f(x)$ |
|---|---|
| −4 | 4 |
| −2 | 2 |
| 0 | 0 |
| 2 | −2 |

$f(x) = -x$

4.

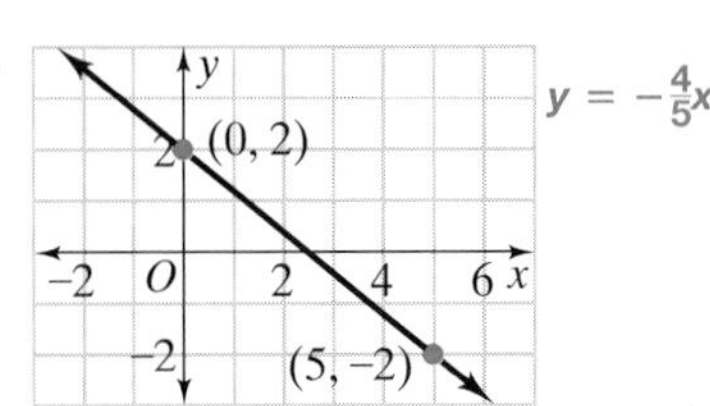


$y = -\frac{4}{5}x + 2$

## Practice and Problem Solving

**Write a function rule for each situation.**

5. *Science* The temperature $k$ in degrees *Kelvin* is 273.15 less than the temperature $c$ in degrees *Celsius.* $k(c) = c - 273.15$

6. *Physics* The force of gravity is less on Mars than it is on Earth. As a result, the weight of an object on Mars $m$ is 40% of its weight on Earth $w$. $m(w) = 0.4w$

7. *Measurement* Write a rule that expresses the number of quarts $q$ of a liquid as a function of each of the following. See above right.
   a. the number of pints $p$
   b. the number of fluid ounces $f$

7a. $q(p) = \frac{1}{2}p$
b. $q(f) = \frac{f}{32}$

**Quick Review**

8 fluid ounces = 1 cup
2 cups = 1 pint
2 pints = 1 quart
4 quarts = 1 gallon

8. a. *Measurement* Express the number of inches $n(d)$ as a function of the number of yards $d$. $n(d) = 36d$
   b. Use your function to find the number of inches in 4 yards. $n(4) = 36(4) = 144$ There are 144 inches in 4 yards.

9. a. *Geometry* Write a rule that expresses the perimeter $p(s)$ of a square as a function of the length $s$ of one side. $p(s) = 4s$
   b. Use your function to find the perimeter of a square with side length 7 cm. $p(7) = 4(7) = 28$. The perimeter is 28 in.

10. **TEST PREP** Which function rule describes the number of centimeters $c(m)$ as a function of a number of millimeters $m$? B
    A. $c(m) = 10m$ B. $c(m) = 0.1m$ C. $c(m) = 100m$ D. $c(m) = 0.01m$



## Alternative Assessment

Have students pick a standard measurement, such as gallons, and write a function that can be used to convert the measurement into its metric equivalent, such as liters. Ask students to include a graph with their function.

## Daily Cumulative Review

**Find the slope of each line.** *(Lesson 8-3)*

1. Graph through (−1, 2) and (1, −2). slope = −2
2. Graph through (−3, −2), (−1, −1) and (3, 1). slope = $\frac{1}{2}$
3. Graph through (−3, 3), (−1, 3) and (2, 3). slope = 0

**Find the solutions of each equation for $x = -3, 2,$ and $5$.** *(Lesson 8-2)*

4. $y = 2x + 2$ (−3, −4), (2, 6), (5, 12)
5. $y = -3x + 1$ (−3, 10), (2, −5), (5, −14)
6. $y = -2x - 4$ (−3, 2), (2, −8), (5, −14)

**Mixed Review**

**Complete each statement.**

7. (3-7) 8,630 mg = 8.63 g
8. (3-7) 6.32 m = 632 cm
9. (5-5) 40 c = 10 qt
10. (5-5) 2 ft 5 in. = 29 in.
11. (5-5) 6 lb = 96 oz
12. (3-7) 6,000 mL = 6 L

**Find each product or quotient.**

13. (5-4) $\frac{5}{6} \cdot \frac{3}{4}$ $\frac{5}{8}$
14. (5-4) $\frac{3}{4} \div \frac{1}{2}$ $1\frac{1}{2}$
15. (5-4) $\frac{1}{a} \div \frac{4}{a}$ $\frac{1}{4}$

**Write and solve an equation.**

16. (6-7) 180 is 20% of what number? $180 = 0.20 \cdot n$; $n = 900$
17. (6-7) What percent of 80 is 54? $n \cdot 80 = 54$; $n = 67.5\%$

**Write in simplest form.**

18. (4-4) $\frac{4}{12}$ $\frac{1}{3}$
19. (4-4) $\frac{6b}{8b^2}$ $\frac{3}{4b}$
20. (4-4) $\frac{18}{22}$ $\frac{9}{11}$

**Write a rule for each function.**

**11.**

| $x$ | $f(x)$ |
|---|---|
| 2 | −2.4 |
| 4 | −4.8 |
| 6 | −7.2 |
| 8 | −9.6 |

$f(x) = -1.2x$

**12.**

| $x$ | $y$ |
|---|---|
| −3 | 2 |
| 0 | 2 |
| 3 | 2 |
| 6 | 2 |

$y = 2$

**13.**

| $x$ | $f(x)$ |
|---|---|
| −5 | −7 |
| −1 | −3 |
| 0 | −2 |
| 8 | 6 |

$f(x) = x - 2$

**14.**

| $x$ | $f(x)$ |
|---|---|
| −6 | −15 |
| 1 | −1 |
| 7 | 11 |
| 11 | 19 |

$f(x) = 2x - 3$

**15.**

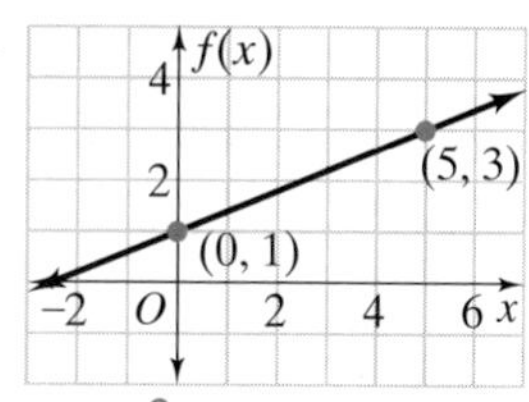


$f(x) = \frac{2}{5}x + 1$

**16.**

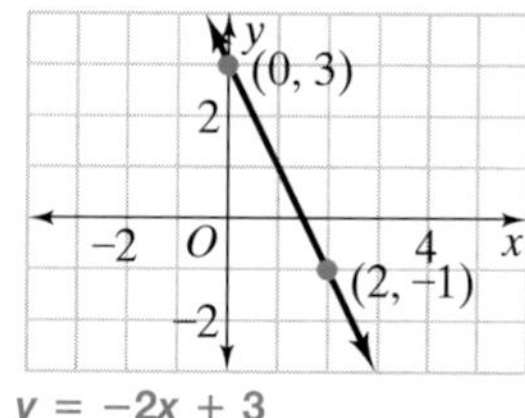


$y = -2x + 3$

**17.**

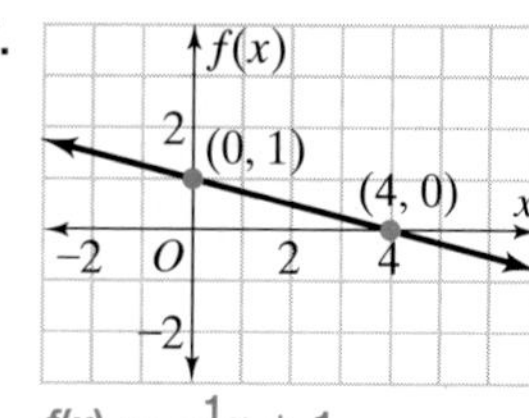


$f(x) = -\frac{1}{4}x + 1$

**18.**

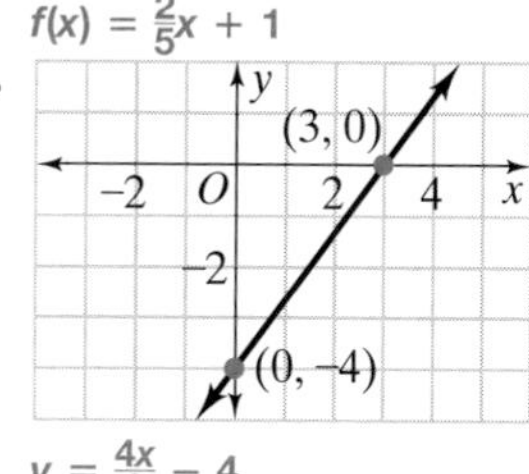


$y = \frac{4x}{3} - 4$

**19.**

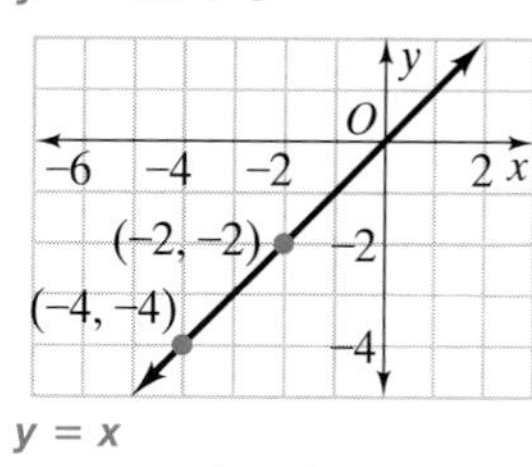


$y = x$

**20.**

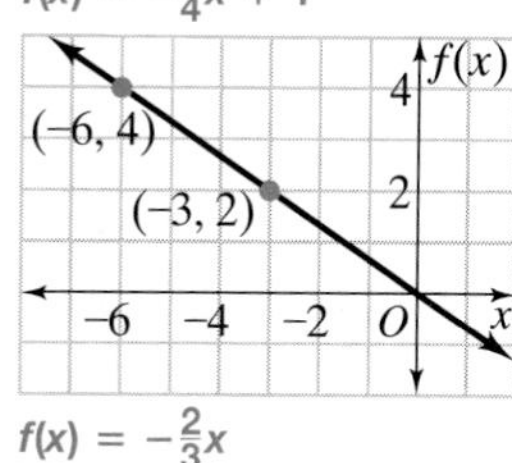


$f(x) = -\frac{2}{3}x$

**21.** *Writing* Describe the advantages you see in using a rule for a function rather than listing function values in a table. Describe the disadvantages. Check students' work

*Data Analysis* **Use the data at the right for Exercises 22–24.**

22. $c(k) = 0.05691k + 7.77$

**22.** Write a function rule for the total monthly charge to a customer who has electric space heating. (*Hint:* Remember to write the rule either in dollars or in cents.)

23a. $c(k) = 0.04968k + 6.87$

**23. a.** Write a function rule for the total monthly charge to a residential customer.

**b.** Suppose a residential customer received a monthly bill for \$22.52. How many kilowatt-hours did the customer use that month? 315 kwh

**24.** *Critical Thinking* Write a rule to describe how much a customer saves by being a residential customer rather than a customer who uses electricity for space heating. $S(k) = 0.00723k + 0.9$

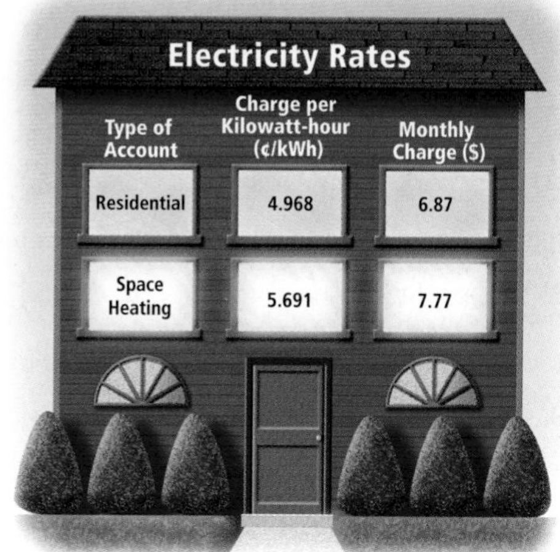

**Electricity Rates**

| Type of Account | Charge per Kilowatt-hour (¢/kWh) | Monthly Charge (\$) |
|---|---|---|
| Residential | 4.968 | 6.87 |
| Space Heating | 5.691 | 7.77 |

25. *Patterns* The rule for a function is $y = \frac{3}{2}x$.

a. Use the domain $\{-6, -4, -2, 0, 2, 4\}$ to make a function table. See below right.

b. Complete this statement: As the domain values in the table in part (a) increase by 2, the corresponding range values __?__. increase by 3

c. How is the pattern from part (b) related to the slope of the line with equation $y = \frac{3}{2}x$? $\frac{\text{increase in range values}}{\text{increase in domain values}} = \frac{3}{2}$, which is the slope of the line.

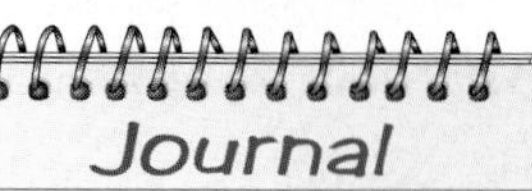

**Journal**

*Summarize the different ways you can represent a function.*

## MIXED REVIEW

**Find the slope of the line through each pair of points. *(Lesson 8-3)***

26. $C(0, -2), D(2, 1)$ $\frac{3}{2}$

27. $J(-3, 1), K(-6, -1)$ $\frac{2}{3}$

28. $G(12, 8), H(6, 2)$ 1

**Find each probability for choosing a letter at random from the word FUNCTION. *(Lesson 6-4)***

29. $P(\text{N or C})$ $\frac{3}{8}$

30. $P(\text{consonant})$ $\frac{5}{8}$

31. $P(\text{not T})$ $\frac{7}{8}$

32. *Sports* In 1999, Hicham El Guerrouj of Morocco broke the former world record for running the mile by 1.26 seconds. The previous record was 3 min, 44.39 sec, set in 1993. Write and solve an equation to find the 1999 record time. ***(Lesson 3-5)*** $r + 1.26 = 44.39$; $r = 43.13$ for a 1999 record time of 3 min 43.13 s

25a.

| $x$ | $f(x)$ |
|---|---|
| −6 | −9 |
| −4 | −6 |
| −2 | −3 |
| 0 | 0 |
| 2 | 3 |
| 4 | 6 |

## CHECKPOINT 1

**Lessons 8-1 through 8-4**

1. Find three solutions of $9x - 2y = 18$. Answers may vary. Sample: (0, −9), (2, 0), (1, −4.5)

2. Graph $3x - y = 5$ on a coordinate plane.

3. Is $\{(-2, 0), (-1, 3), (0, -2), (3, -1)\}$ a function? Explain. Yes; there is one range value for each domain value.

4. *Writing* Explain how to use the vertical-line test to determine whether a relation is a function. Answers may vary. Sample: If every vertical line passes through at most one graphed point, then the relation is a function.

2. [graph of $3x - y = 5$; axes labeled $x$, $y$; ticks −4, −2, O, 2, 4]

**Find the slope of the line through the given points.**

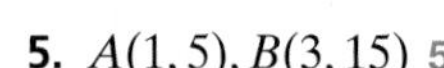

5. $A(1, 5), B(3, 15)$ 5

6. $D(-2, -4), F(0, -6)$ −1

7. $G(-3, 4), H(-3, -6)$ no slope

8. What are the slope and the $y$-intercept of $y = -2x + 5$? −2, 5

9. *Measurement* Write a rule to describe the number of pounds $p(t)$ as a function of a number of tons $t$. $p(t) = 2{,}000t$

10. **TEST PREP** Which rule is the same function as $x + y = 6$? C

A. $y = x + 6$ B. $y = x - 6$ C. $y = 6 - x$ D. Not here



See also Extra Practice section.

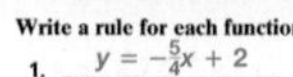

## Practice

**Write a rule for each function.**

1. $y = -\frac{5}{4}x + 2$

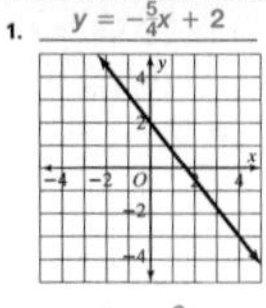

2. $y = 2x - 4$

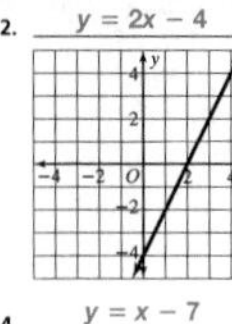

3. $y = -6x$

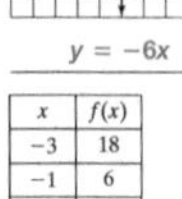

| $x$ | $f(x)$ |
|---|---|
| −3 | 18 |
| −1 | 6 |
| 1 | −6 |
| 3 | −18 |

4. $y = x - 7$

| $x$ | $f(x)$ |
|---|---|
| 5 | −2 |
| 7 | 0 |
| 9 | 2 |
| 11 | 4 |

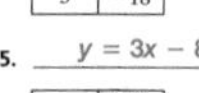

5. $y = 3x - 8$

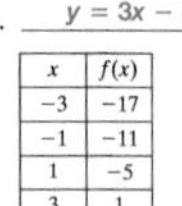

| $x$ | $f(x)$ |
|---|---|
| −3 | −17 |
| −1 | −11 |
| 1 | −5 |
| 3 | 1 |

6. $y = \frac{1}{2}x + 6$

| $x$ | $f(x)$ |
|---|---|
| −4 | 4 |
| 0 | 6 |
| 2 | 7 |
| 4 | 8 |

**Write a function rule to describe each situation.**

7. The number of pounds $p(z)$ as a function of the number of ounces $z$. $p(z) = \frac{z}{16}$

8. The selling price $s(c)$ after a 45% markup of an item as a function of the stores' cost $c$. $s(c) = 1.45c$

9. The total number of miles $m(r)$ covered when you walk 7 miles before lunch, and you walk for 2 hours at $r$ mi/hr after lunch. $m(r) = 2r + 7$



## Reteaching

Write a rule for the function.

| $x$ | $f(x)$ |
|---|---|
| −2 | −12 |
| 0 | −2 |
| 2 | 8 |
| 4 | 18 |

As the $x$ values increase by 2, the $f(x)$ values increase by 10. So $m = \frac{10}{2} = 5$. When $x = 0$, $f(x) = -2$. So $b = -2$. Substitute $m = 5$ and $b = -2$ into $f(x) = mx + b$.
$f(x) = 5x + (-2)$
$f(x) = 5x - 2$

**Write a rule for each function.**

1. $y = 7x$

| $x$ | $f(x)$ |
|---|---|
| −1 | −7 |
| 0 | 0 |
| 1 | 7 |
| 2 | 14 |

2. $y = x - 8$

| $x$ | $f(x)$ |
|---|---|
| −9 | −17 |
| 0 | −8 |
| 9 | 1 |
| 18 | 10 |

3. $y = -2x + 9$

| $x$ | $f(x)$ |
|---|---|
| 0 | 9 |
| 2 | 5 |
| 4 | 1 |
| 6 | −3 |

4. $y = \frac{1}{3}x + 9$

| $x$ | $f(x)$ |
|---|---|
| −6 | 7 |
| −3 | 8 |
| 0 | 9 |
| 3 | 10 |

5. $y = -\frac{1}{4}x - 7$

| $x$ | $f(x)$ |
|---|---|
| −4 | −6 |
| 0 | −7 |
| 4 | −8 |
| 8 | −9 |

6. $y = 6x - 11$

| $x$ | $f(x)$ |
|---|---|
| −12 | −83 |
| −6 | −47 |
| 0 | −11 |
| 6 | 25 |



## Enrichment

A pair of brackets ([ ]) indicates the *greatest integer relationship*.
$y = [x]$ means "$y$ is the greatest integer that is less than or equal to $x$."
**Examples** If $x = 3.7, y = 3$; If $x = -2, y = -2$; If $x = -6.2, y = -7$

1. $y = [x]$. Complete the table of ordered pairs.

| $x$ | 3.5 | 0 | $-3\frac{1}{2}$ | $2\frac{3}{5}$ | −4 | −0.1 | 2 | $-2\frac{6}{19}$ |
|---|---|---|---|---|---|---|---|---|
| $y$ | 3 | 0 | −4 | 2 | −4 | −1 | 2 | −3 |

2. The graph of the greatest integer relationship is a step graph. Complete the graph below, using solid dots to indicate points that are on the graph and circles to indicate points that are not on the graph.

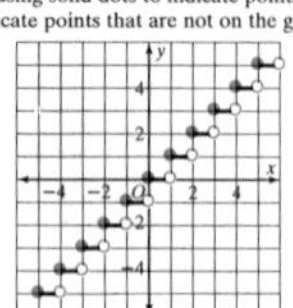

**Write a rule for each function.**

3. $y = [x + 1]$

| $x$ | 3.5 | 0 | $-3\frac{1}{2}$ | $2\frac{3}{5}$ | −4 | −0.1 | 2 | $-2\frac{6}{19}$ |
|---|---|---|---|---|---|---|---|---|
| $y$ | 4 | 1 | −3 | 3 | −3 | 0 | 3 | −2 |

4. $y = [2x]$

| $x$ | 3.5 | 0 | $-3\frac{1}{2}$ | $2\frac{3}{5}$ | −4 | −0.1 | 2 | $-2\frac{6}{19}$ |
|---|---|---|---|---|---|---|---|---|
| $y$ | 7 | 0 | −7 | 5 | −8 | −1 | 4 | −5 |



## Checkpoint

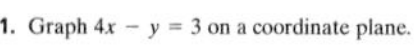

1. Graph $4x - y = 3$ on a coordinate plane.

2. Is $\{(-3, 6), (-2, 5), (-3, -1), (4, -3)\}$ a function? Explain. No. There are two range values for the domain value −3.

3. Find the slope of the line through the points $A(8, 7)$ and $B(5, -2)$. 3

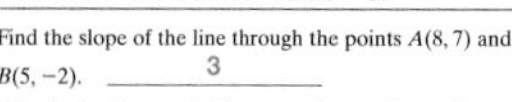

4. What is the slope and $y$-intercept of $y = -8x + 1$?
slope: −8 $y$-intercept: 1

5. Write a rule to describe the cost $c(p)$ of an item on sale for 25% off as a function of its original price $p$. $c(p) = 0.75p$

6. Which rule is the same function as $9x + y = 4$.
A. $y = 9x - 4$ B. $y = 9x + 4$ (C.) $y = -9x + 4$ D. $y = -9x - 4$

Name ______ Class ______ Date ______

# 8-5 Scatter Plots

## Investigate

MAKING SCATTER PLOTS

1–3a. Check students' work.

1. *Data Collection* For each person in your group, measure the height and *hand span,* the greatest distance possible between the tips of the thumb and little finger on one hand.
2. Graph the lengths as ordered pairs (height, hand span).
3. a. Share your data with the class. Make a graph of the class data.
   b. *Critical Thinking* Compare the two graphs you made. Does one graph show a relationship between height and hand span more clearly than the other? Explain.
   The class data should show a clearer relationship because more points are plotted, making unusual points less important.

**What You'll Learn**

1. To interpret and draw scatter plots
2. To use scatter plots for finding trends

**. . . And Why**

To investigate trends in income, climate, and sports

## PART 1 Interpreting and Drawing Scatter Plots

A **scatter plot** is a graph that shows the relationship between two sets of data. To make a scatter plot, graph the data as ordered pairs.

REAL-WORLD  CONNECTION

### EXAMPLE 1

*Income* **The scatter plot shows education and income data.**

**a. Describe the person represented by point *A*.**
This person has 12 years of education and earns \$20,000 each year.

**b. How many years of education did the person who earns \$100,000 finish?**
The point (16, 100) has income coordinate 100. The person earning \$100,000 each year has 16 years of education.

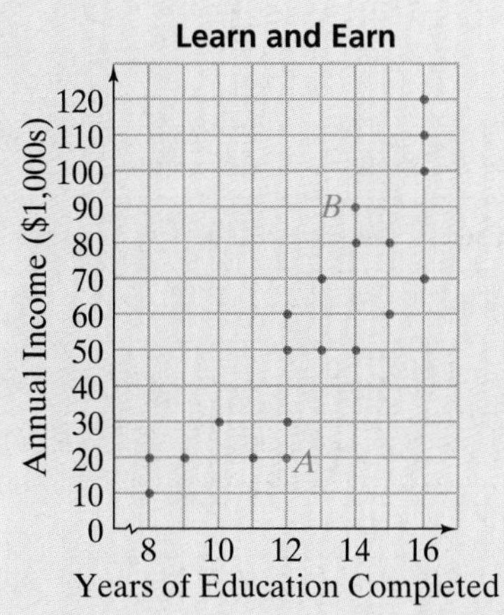


**TRY THIS** Use the scatter plot in Example 1.

4. Describe the person represented by point *B*. has 14 years of education and annual income of \$90,000
5. How many people have exactly 12 years of education? 4 people



# 8-5

## Getting Ready

**Key Terms and Symbols** scatter plot, positive correlation, negative correlation, no correlation

**Resources** A complete list of resources for this lesson is on p. 381H.

### Daily Skills Warm-Up

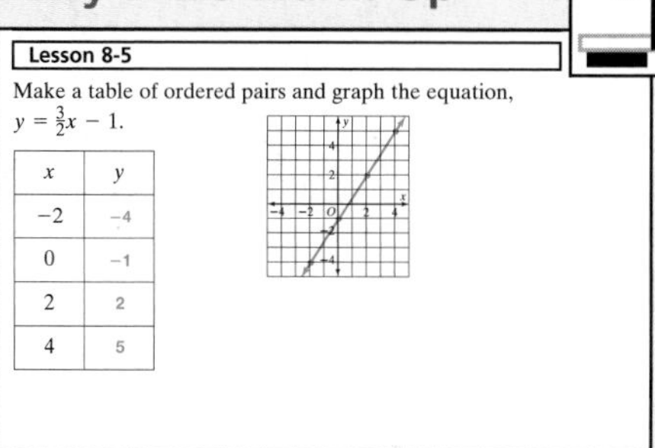
Lesson 8-5

Make a table of ordered pairs and graph the equation, $y = \frac{3}{2}x - 1$.

| $x$ | $y$ |
|---|---|
| −2 | −4 |
| 0 | −1 |
| 2 | 2 |
| 4 | 5 |

### Background for the Lesson

The graph of a linear equation contains all the points that are solutions of the equation. A scatter plot has separate points, unconnected by a line, that show the relationship between two sets of data. For example, the electric utility company might relate the daily high temperatures in August to the megawatts of electricity used. Each day it could graph an ordered pair with temperature as the *x*-coordinate and the megawatts as the *y*-coordinate. This scatter plot would show that as the temperature increases so does the number of megawatts used. This repeated relationship between the two sets of data is a trend in the data.

## 1 Focus

### Investigate

Help students see that separate points can show a relationship even though all the points are not on one straight line.

### Connecting to Students' Lives

Discuss how representing data on a graph in a newspaper article or with a television news report often communicates more and is more convincing than just reading or hearing about the data.

## Tools to Monitor Progress

**BEFORE THE LESSON**

**To check prerequisite skills:**

**Skills You Need,** p. 381

**DURING THE LESSON**

**To check understanding:**

**Try This** exercises on student page

- **Additional Example 1**
  Use the scatter plot from Example 1 to answer these questions.
  **a.** Describe the person represented by point *B*. 14 yr of education, annual salary of \$90,000
  **b.** How many people have 14 years of education? What are their incomes? 3; \$90,000, \$80,000, \$50,000

# 2 Teach

## Part 1 Teaching Notes

Show students that graphing points on a scatter plot uses the same steps as graphing points on a coordinate plane. When the values in a scatter plot are all positive, the graph is in Quadrant I of the coordinate plane, and you do not have to show the rest of the coordinate plane.

### Example 1

**Build understanding.** Ask: What is represented by the *x*-coordinate? by the *y*-coordinate? **years of education; annual income**

### Example 2

**Build understanding.** Ask: Based on the scatter plot, about what would you expect the daily mean temperature to be for a city at 40° north latitude? **about 50°F**

**Connecting to Geography** Latitude, measured in degrees north or south, is the distance from the equator. The greater the latitude, the greater the distance from the equator. Longitude, measured in degrees east or west, is the distance from the prime meridian.

**Error Prevention** Remind students to label the axes and to plot points carefully when making scatter plots. Errors could cause students to draw the wrong conclusions about the relationship between the two sets of data.

**Technology Option** Have students use available math software or a graphing calculator to create the scatter plots in this lesson.

6.

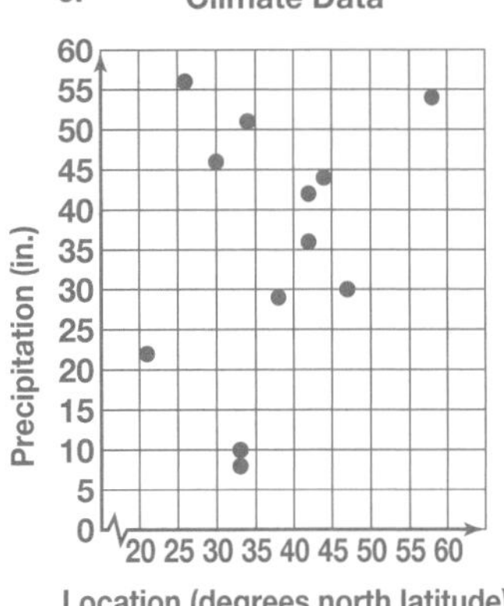


7.

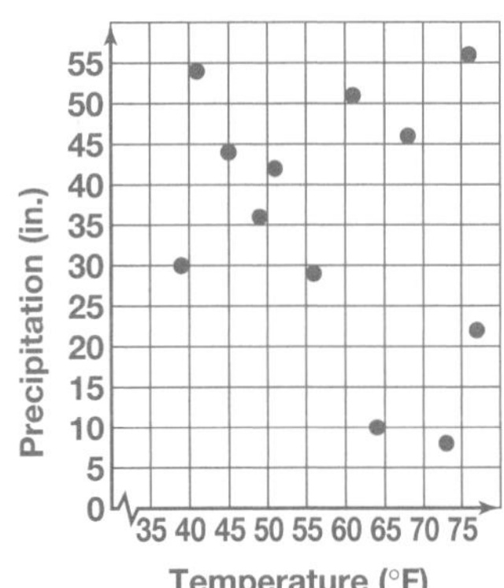


REAL-WORLD CONNECTION

### EXAMPLE 2

*Climate* **Use the table to make a scatter plot of the latitude and temperature data.**

**Climate Data**

| City | Location (degrees north latitude) | Daily Mean Temperature (°F) | Mean Annual Precipitation (inches) |
|---|---|---|---|
| Atlanta, GA | 34 | 61 | 51 |
| Boston, MA | 42 | 51 | 42 |
| Chicago, IL | 42 | 49 | 36 |
| Duluth, MN | 47 | 39 | 30 |
| Honolulu, HI | 21 | 77 | 22 |
| Houston, TX | 30 | 68 | 46 |
| Juneau, AK | 58 | 41 | 54 |
| Miami, FL | 26 | 76 | 56 |
| Phoenix, AZ | 33 | 73 | 8 |
| Portland, ME | 44 | 45 | 44 |
| San Diego, CA | 33 | 64 | 10 |
| Wichita, KS | 38 | 56 | 29 |

SOURCES: *The World Almanac* and *Statistical Abstract of the United States*

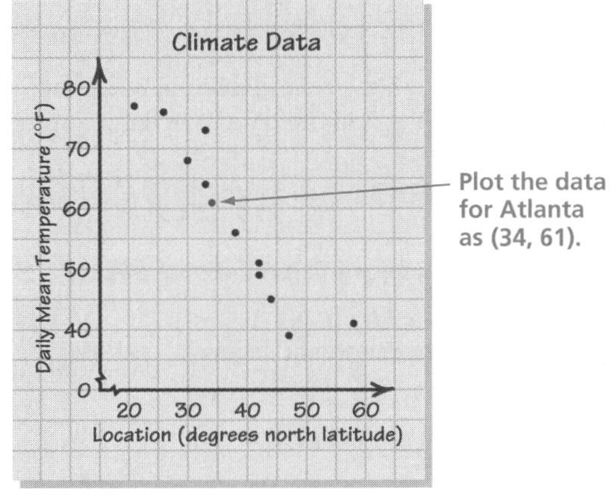


### TRY THIS

6. Use the table in Example 2. Make a scatter plot of the latitude and precipitation data.
7. Use the table in Example 2. Make a scatter plot of the temperature and precipitation data. Plot temperature along the horizontal axis of the graph.



- **Additional Example 2**
  What does the scatter plot in Example 2 show you about the relationship between daily mean temperature and latitude? **The higher the latitude is, the lower the daily mean temperature.**

- **Additional Example 3**
  Use the scatter plot you created in Exercise 7. Describe the correlation between daily mean temperature and mean annual precipitation. **no correlation**

## Using Scatter Plots to Find Trends

You can use scatter plots to look for trends. The next three scatter plots show the types of relationships two sets of data may have.

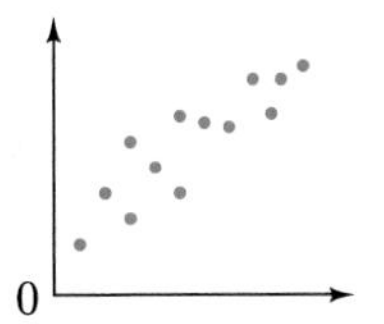

0

**Positive correlation**
As one set of values increases, the other set tends to increase.

0

**Negative correlation**
As one set of values increases, the other set tends to decrease.

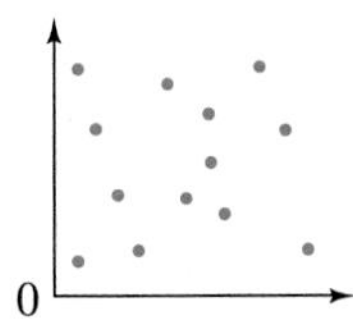

0

**No correlation**
The values show no relationship.

**REAL-WORLD**  CONNECTION

### EXAMPLE 3

*Sports* **Use the scatter plot below. Is there a *positive correlation*, a *negative correlation*, or *no correlation* between the year and the winning time? Explain.**

**Olympic Games: Men's 110-Meter Hurdles**

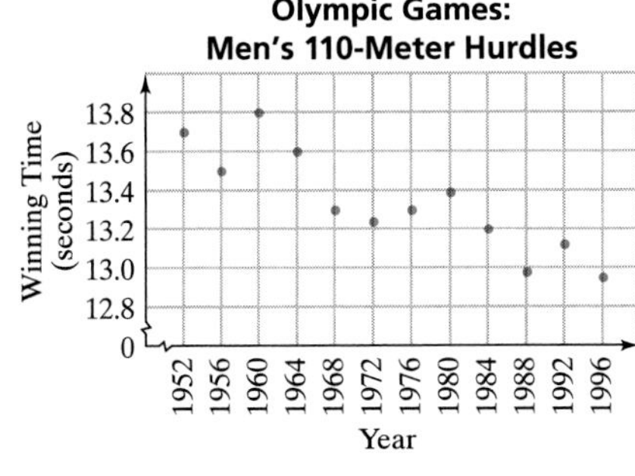


Since 1952, the winning time has generally decreased. There is a negative correlation.

### TRY THIS

8. *Sports* Use the scatter plot at the right. Is there a *positive correlation*, a *negative correlation*, or *no correlation* between the year and the winning distance? Explain.
Positive correlation; as time goes by, the winning distance has tended to increase.

**Olympic Games: Women's Long Jump**

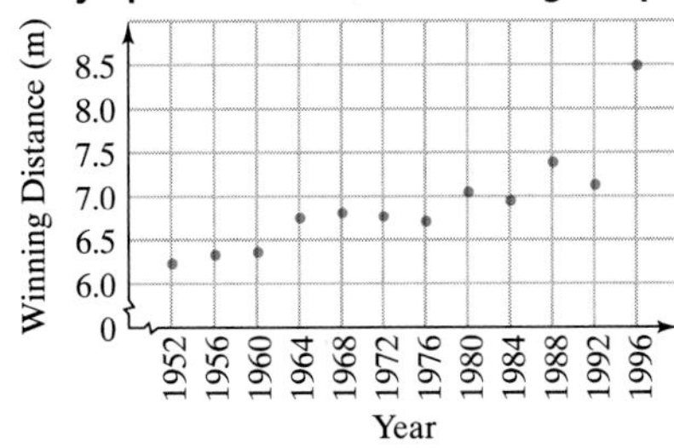




## Part 2 Teaching Notes

Point out to students that the individual points in scatter plots with a positive correlation tend to fall along a line with a positive slope. Similarly, points in scatter plots with a negative correlation tend to fall along a line that has a negative slope.

**Auditory Learning** Have students work with a partner and have one describe a scatter plot from the text while the other identifies it as having a positive correlation, a negative correlation, or no correlation.

### Example 3

**Build understanding.** Ask: If the scatter plot had a positive correlation, what would have happened to the winning times since 1952? They would have increased.

**Math Reasoning** Use math reasoning to explain what kind of correlation a trend would have if the *y*-values stay approximately the same as the *x*-values increase. To have either a positive correlation or a negative correlation, one set of values has to increase or decrease as the other increases. Since the *y*-value neither increases nor decreases as the *x*-values increase, the trend must have no correlation.

**AFTER THE LESSON**
**To assess knowledge:**
**Lesson Quiz**

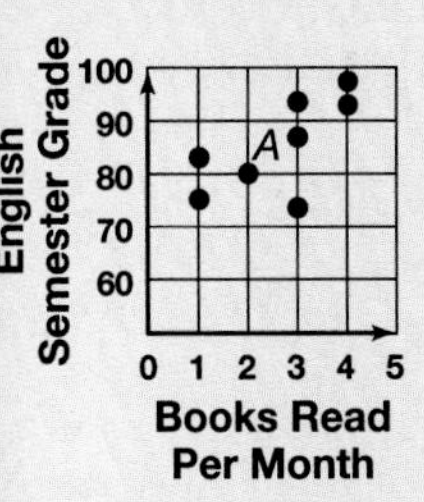


1. What do you know about the student at point *A*? read 2 books, grade: 80
2. How many students read 3 books per month? 3
3. What correlation exists for the number of books read and the grade? a positive correlation

- For enrichment and reteaching options see Resources on p. 381H.

# 3 Practice/Assess

## Assignment Guide

To provide flexible scheduling, this lesson can be divided into parts.

**Part 1**
**Core** 1–3, 7–9, 17–19
✪ **Extension** 10

**Part 2**
**Core** 4–6, 11–16, 20, 21
✪ **Extension** 22

Mixed Review can be assigned at any time for maintenance.

## Exercises

**Test Prep Exercise 21** Think about whether the correct scatter plot will have a positive correlation, a negative correlation, or no correlation before you look at the answer choices.

## ✪ Challenge

If there is a positive correlation between two sets of data, does it matter which data set is represented on the *x*- and *y*-axes of a scatter plot? Explain. In a positive correlation, as one value increases, the other also increases. So, no matter which value goes on which axis, the plot will still show the positive correlation.

## Closure

A scatter plot is a graph that shows the relationship between two sets of data. A scatter plot can help you find trends between sets of data.

### Daily Cumulative Review

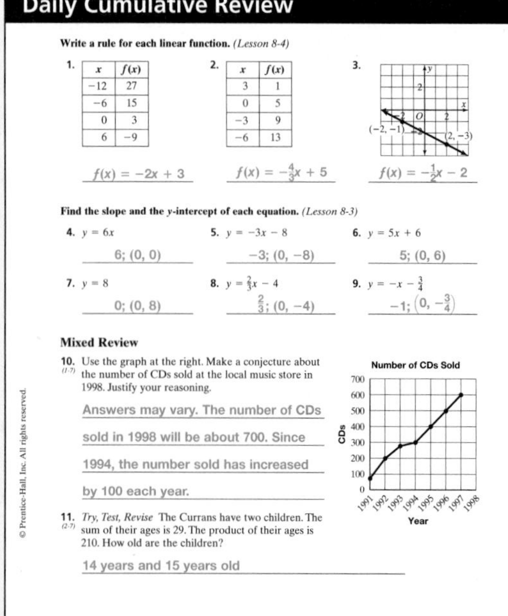

**Write a rule for each linear function.** *(Lesson 8-4)*

1.

| $x$ | $f(x)$ |
|---|---|
| −12 | 27 |
| −6 | 15 |
| 0 | 3 |
| 6 | −9 |

$f(x) = -2x + 3$

2.

| $x$ | $f(x)$ |
|---|---|
| 3 | 1 |
| 0 | 5 |
| −3 | 9 |
| −6 | 13 |

$f(x) = -\frac{4}{3}x + 5$

3. 

$f(x) = -\frac{1}{2}x - 2$

**Find the slope and the *y*-intercept of each equation.** *(Lesson 8-3)*

4. $y = 6x$ — 6; (0, 0)
5. $y = -3x - 8$ — −3; (0, −8)
6. $y = 5x + 6$ — 5; (0, 6)
7. $y = 8$ — 0; (0, 8)
8. $y = \frac{2}{3}x - 4$ — $\frac{2}{3}$; (0, −4)
9. $y = -x - \frac{3}{4}$ — −1; $\left(0, -\frac{3}{4}\right)$

**Mixed Review**

10. (1-7) Use the graph at the right. Make a conjecture about the number of CDs sold at the local music store in 1998. Justify your reasoning.
Answers may vary. The number of CDs sold in 1998 will be about 700. Since 1994, the number sold has increased by 100 each year.



11. (2-7) *Try, Test, Revise* The Currans have two children. The sum of their ages is 29. The product of their ages is 210. How old are the children?
14 years and 15 years old



# Exercises

## Check Understanding

*Statistics* **The scatter plot at the right shows the average time fifteen students spent watching television and the average time they spent on physical activity in a day.** averaged 4 h watching television and 2 h of physical activity daily

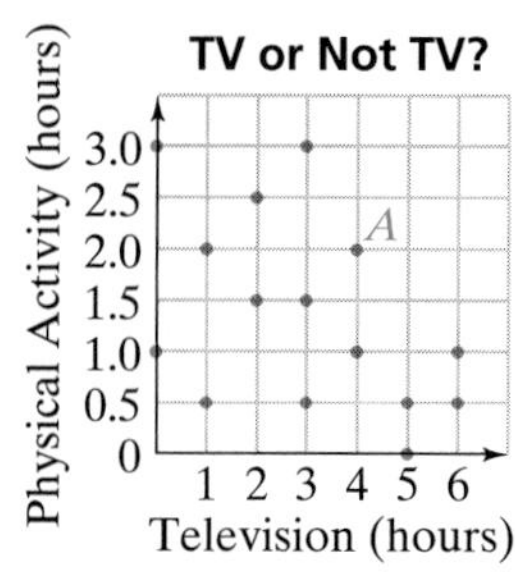


1. Describe the student represented by point $A$.
2. How many students had one hour of physical activity or less? 8 students
3. How many students spent four or more hours watching television? 6 students

4. No correlation; there is no apparent relationship.
5. Positive correlation; as one set of values increases, the other tends to increase.
6. Negative correlation; as one set of values increases, the other tends to decrease.

**Is there a *positive correlation*, a *negative correlation*, or *no correlation* between the sets of data in each scatter plot? Explain.** 4–6. See above right.

4. 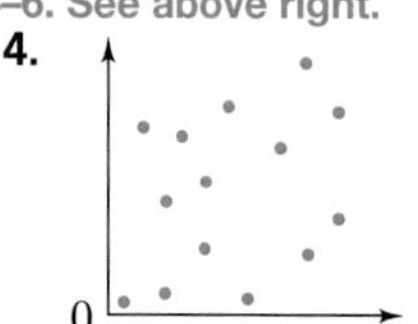


5. 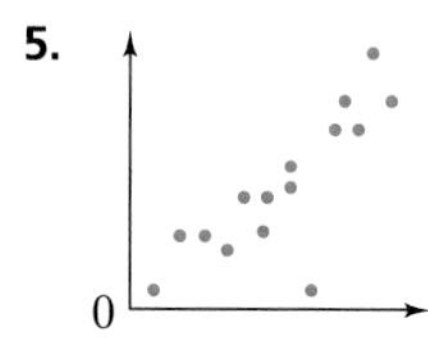


6. 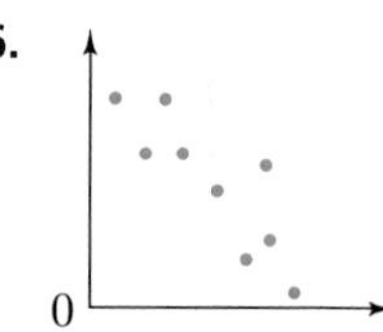


## Practice and Problem Solving

*Data Analysis* **The scatter plot at the right shows the relationship between distance from school and the time it takes to get to school for the students in one class.**

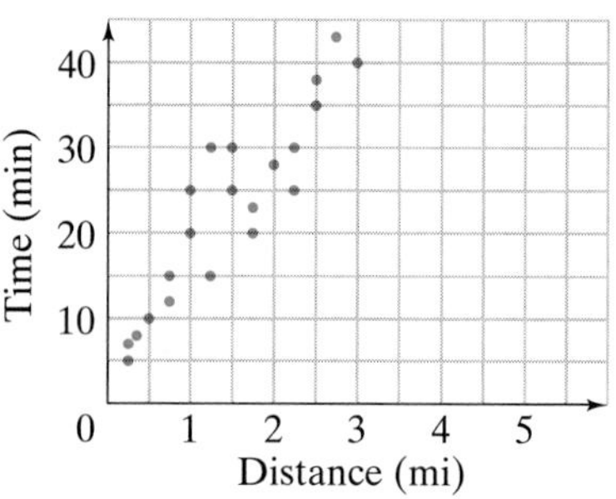


7. How long does the student who lives 0.5 mi from school take to get to school? 10 min
8. How many students live closer than 1 mi from school? 6 students
9. How many students take longer than 35 min to get to school? 3 students

✪ 10. *Open-ended* Describe two data sets for which a scatter plot would be an appropriate way to look for a correlation. Check students' work.



## Alternative Assessment

Ask students to check newspapers and magazines for articles where two sets of data are compared. Have students use the data from the articles that they find to create scatter plots that illustrate the relationship between the data sets.

18.

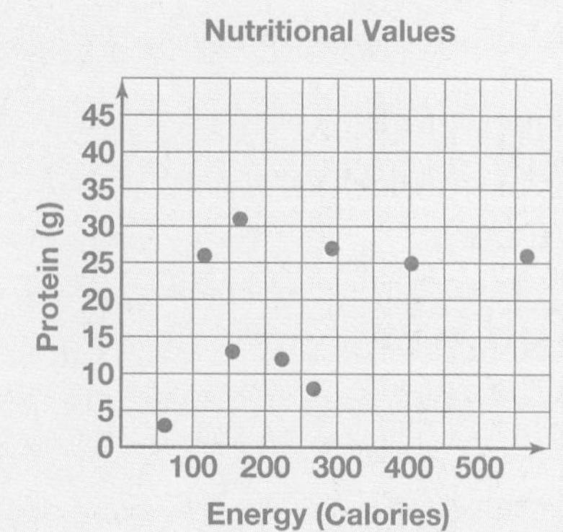

**Is there a *positive correlation*, a *negative correlation*, or *no correlation* between the two data sets in each scatter plot? Explain.** 11–13. See margin for explanations.

**11.**

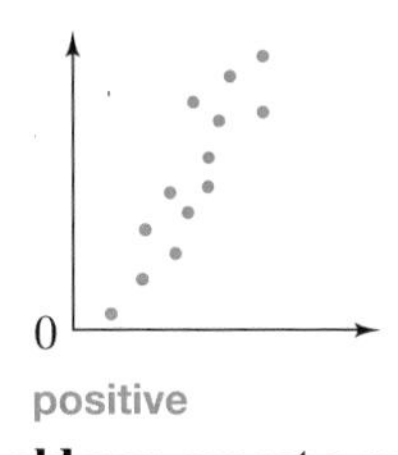


positive

**12.**

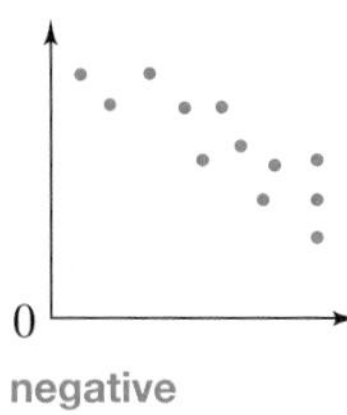


negative

**13.**

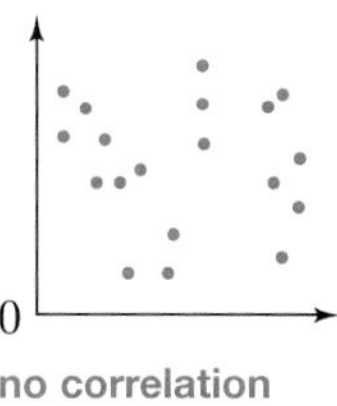


no correlation

**Would you expect a *positive correlation*, a *negative correlation*, or *no correlation* between the two sets of data? Explain.**
14–16. See margin for explanations.

**14.** the shoe sizes and the shirt sizes for men positive

**15.** the time candles take to burn and their original height positive

**16.** the number of students in a school and the number of stores near a school no correlation

*Nutrition* **Use the data in the table for Exercises 17–20.**

**Nutritional Values for 100 Grams of Food**

| Food | Fat (grams) | Protein (grams) | Carbohydrate (grams) | Energy (calories) |
|---|---|---|---|---|
| Bread | 4 | 8 | 50 | 267 |
| Cheese | 33 | 25 | 1 | 403 |
| Chicken | 4 | 31 | 0 | 165 |
| Eggs | 11 | 13 | 1 | 155 |
| Ground beef | 19 | 27 | 0 | 292 |
| Milk | 3 | 3 | 5 | 61 |
| Peanuts | 49 | 26 | 16 | 567 |
| Pizza | 5 | 12 | 33 | 223 |
| Tuna | 1 | 26 | 0 | 116 |

SOURCE: U. S. Department of Agriculture Nutrient Database for Standard Reference

**17.** Make a scatter plot of the data for calories and grams of fat. Graph the calories on the horizontal axis.

**18.** Make a scatter plot of the data for calories and grams of protein. Graph the calories on the horizontal axis. See margin.

**19.** Make a scatter plot of the data for calories and grams of carbohydrates. Graph the calories on the horizontal axis. See margin.

**20.** *Data Analysis* Use your graphs for Exercises 17–19. Is there a *positive correlation*, a *negative correlation*, or *no correlation* between the numbers of calories and grams of each nutrient?

**a.** fat positive correlation **b.** protein no correlation **c.** carbohydrate no correlation

17.

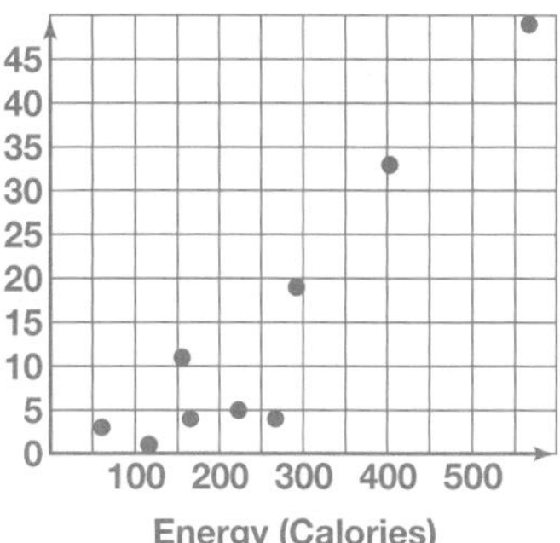




11. As one set of values increases, the other set tends to increase.

12. As one set of values increases, the other set tends to decrease.

13. There is no apparent relationship.

14. As shoe size increases, shirt size is likely to increase also.

15. Candles with longer burning times are likely to have greater original heights.

16. Schools are often located in residential areas where stores are not allowed, no matter how many students are at the school.

19.

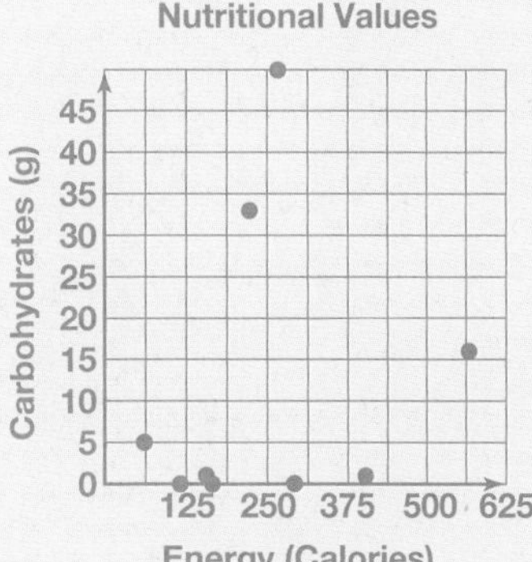

## Practice

**Use the data in the table.**

1. Make a (year, units of CD's) scatter plot.

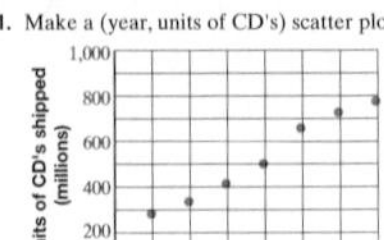


| Sales of Recorded Music | | | |
|---|---|---|---|
| Year | Millions of Units Shipped | | |
| | CD's | Cassettes | LP's |
| 1990 | 287 | 442 | 12 |
| 1991 | 333 | 360 | 5 |
| 1992 | 408 | 366 | 2 |
| 1993 | 495 | 340 | 1 |
| 1994 | 662 | 345 | 2 |
| 1995 | 723 | 273 | 2 |
| 1996 | 779 | 225 | 3 |

2. Make a (year, units of cassettes) scatter plot.

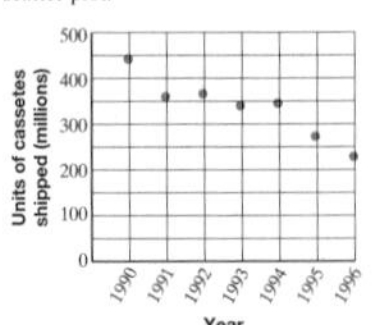


3. Make a (year, units of LP's) scatter plot.

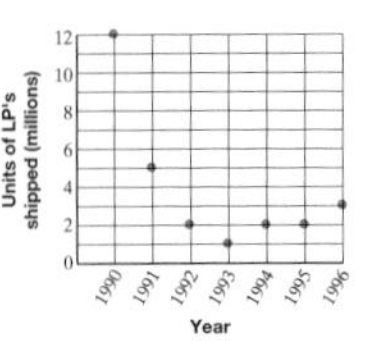


**Is there a *positive correlation*, a *negative correlation*, or *no correlation* between the data sets in each scatter plot?**

4. (year, units of CD's) scatterplot positive correlation
5. (year, units of cassettes) scatterplot negative correlation
6. (year, units of LP's) scatterplot no correlation



Practice

## Reteaching

Make a (U.S. Open wins, Wimbledon wins) scatter plot of the data in the table. Is there a *positive correlation*, a *negative correlation*, or *no correlation* between the two sets of data?

| Player | U.S. Open | Wimble-don | French Open | Aust. Open |
|---|---|---|---|---|
| Andre Agassi | 1 | 1 | 0 | 1 |
| Jimmy Conners | 5 | 2 | 0 | 1 |
| Chris Evert | 6 | 3 | 7 | 2 |
| Steffie Graf | 5 | 7 | 5 | 4 |
| John McEnroe | 4 | 3 | 0 | 0 |
| Martina Navratilova | 4 | 9 | 2 | 3 |
| Pete Sampras | 4 | 4 | 0 | 2 |
| Monica Seles | 2 | 0 | 3 | 4 |

Plot each (U.S. Open wins, Wimbledon wins) ordered pair.

There does not seem to be a trend in the data. As the number of U.S. Open wins increase, the number of Wimbledon wins does not seem to increase or decrease. Thus, there is no correlation.

1. Make a (U.S. Open wins, French Open wins) scatter plot using the data in the table above.

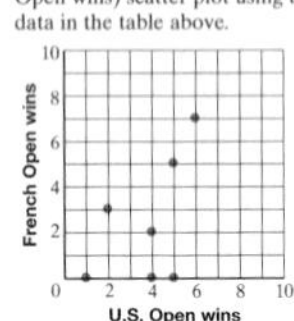


2. Make a (Wimbledon wins, Australian Open wins) scatter plot using the data in the table above.

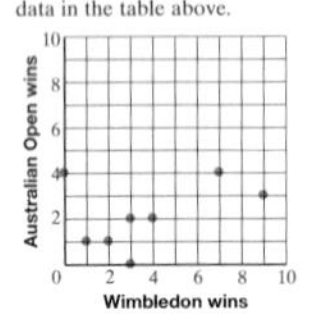


**Is there a *positive correlation*, a *negative correlation*, or *no correlation* between the data sets in each scatter plot?**

3. (U.S. Open wins, French Open wins) no correlation
4. (Wimbledon wins, Australian Open wins) positive correlation



Reteaching

## Enrichment

The figure in Quadrant II is the *reflection* of the figure in Quadrant I. The $y$-axis acts like a mirror, creating a reflected image of $ABCDE$.

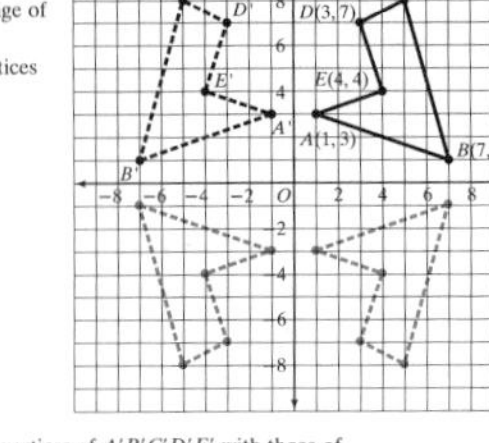


1. Write the coordinates of the vertices of $A'B'C'D'E'$.

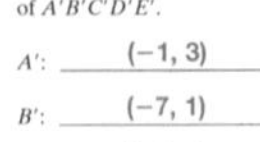

$A'$: (−1, 3)

$B'$: (−7, 1)

$C'$: (−5, 8)

$D'$: (−3, 7)

$E'$: (−4, 4)

2. Compare the coordinates of the vertices of $A'B'C'D'E'$ with those of the vertices of $ABCDE$. Then give the coordinates of the point $(m, n)$ after it is reflected across the $y$-axis. $(-m, n)$
3. Draw the reflection of $ABCDE$ across the $x$-axis in Quadrant IV.
4. Compare the coordinates of the points you have drawn with those of the vertices of $ABCDE$. Then give the coordinates of the point $(m, n)$ after it is reflected across the $x$-axis. $(m, -n)$
5. Draw the reflection of the figure $A'B'C'D'E'$ across the $x$-axis in Quadrant III.
6. Compare the coordinates of the points you have drawn in Quadrant III with those of the vertices of $ABCDE$. Then give the coordinates of the point $(m, n)$ after it is reflected across both the $x$-axis and the $y$-axis. $(-m, -n)$



Enrichment



21. **TEST PREP** Which scatter plot shows that as the number of pages in a magazine increases, the weight of the magazine increases? A

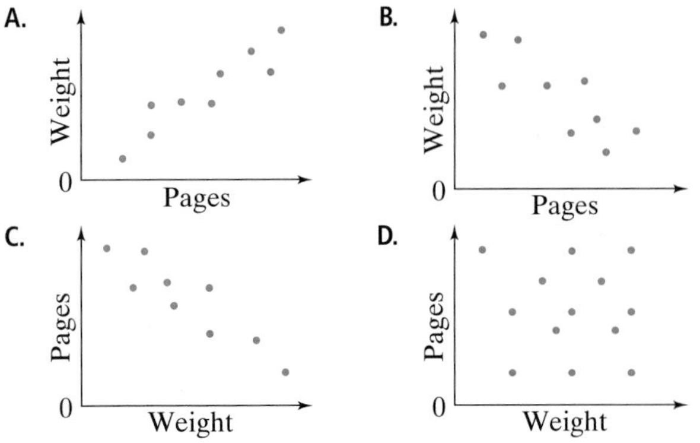

A.

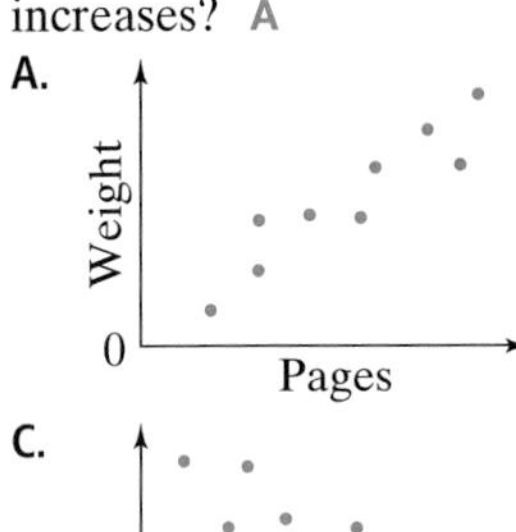


B.

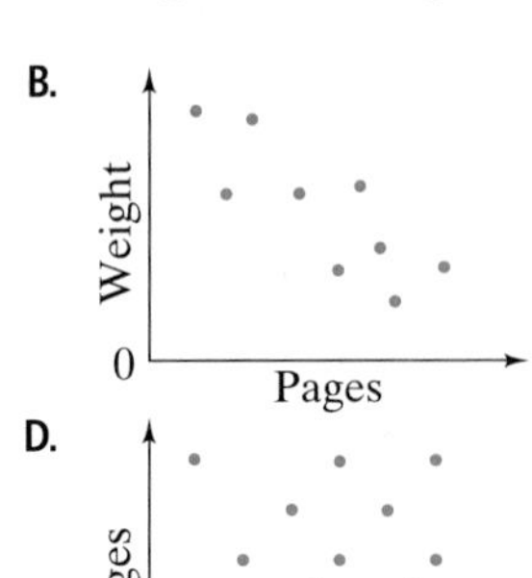


C. (Pages vs. Weight scatter plot)

D. (Pages vs. Weight scatter plot)

22a.

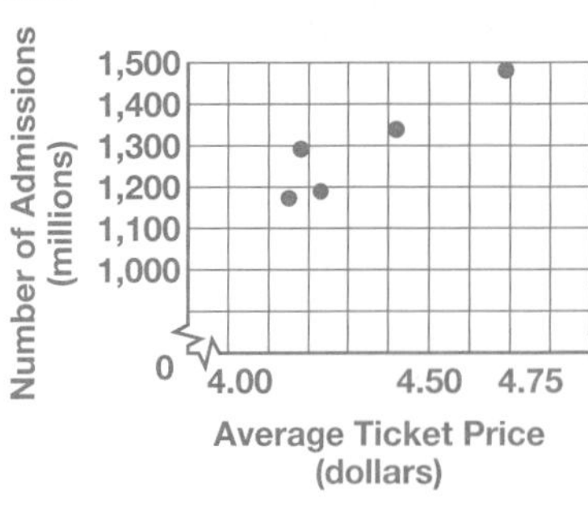


22. The table at the right shows the average price of a movie ticket and the number of movie admissions.

 a. Make a scatter plot of the data in the table. Graph the price of a movie ticket on the horizontal axis. See above right.

 b. *Data Analysis* Is there a *positive correlation*, a *negative correlation*, or *no correlation* between the number of admissions and the price of a ticket? positive correlation

 c. *Critical Thinking* Would your answer to part (b) be the same or different if you graphed the price of a movie ticket on the vertical axis instead? Explain. Same; interchanging the axes doesn't affect the relationship between the variables.

| Year | Number of Admissions (millions) | Average Ticket Price |
|---|---|---|
| 1990 | 1,189 | \$4.23 |
| 1992 | 1,173 | \$4.15 |
| 1994 | 1,292 | \$4.18 |
| 1996 | 1,339 | \$4.42 |
| 1998 | 1,481 | \$4.69 |

SOURCE: Motion Picture Association of America

## MIXED REVIEW

**Write a rule for each function.** ***(Lesson 8-5)***

23. $y = \frac{5}{2}x$

| $x$ | $y$ |
|---|---|
| −4 | −10 |
| −2 | −5 |
| 0 | 0 |
| 2 | 5 |

24. $y = -\frac{2}{3}x + 1$

| $x$ | $y$ |
|---|---|
| −6 | 5 |
| −3 | 3 |
| 0 | 1 |
| 3 | −1 |

25. $f(x) = -x + 7$

| $x$ | $f(x)$ |
|---|---|
| −2 | 9 |
| 1 | 6 |
| 4 | 3 |
| 7 | 0 |

26. $f(x) = 2x + 12$

| $x$ | $f(x)$ |
|---|---|
| −5 | 2 |
| −4 | 4 |
| −3 | 6 |
| −2 | 8 |

**Solve each formula for the variable indicated in red.** ***(Lesson 7-7)***

27. $A = \frac{1}{2}(b + c)h$ $h = \frac{2A}{b + c}$

28. $V = \frac{1}{3}Bh$ $B = \frac{3V}{h}$

29. $S = \frac{a}{1 - r}$ $a = S(1 - r)$

30. $c = \frac{p}{h}$ $h = \frac{p}{c}$

31. *Choose a Strategy* Ms. Jimenez earns \$27,000 per year. She is paid weekly. She puts 8% of her salary in a retirement fund. How much money goes into this fund each week? \$41.54



See also Extra Practice section.

# Standardized Test Prep

## Multiple Choice

**Choose the best answer.**

1. Which ordered pair names the coordinates of a point on the line at the right? A

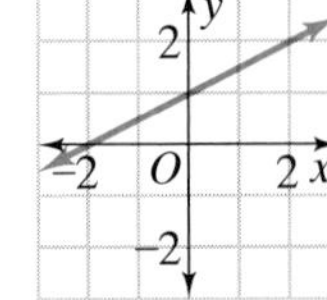

A. (0, 1)
B. (2, −2)
C. (−2, −2)
D. (1, −1)

2. A ball is dropped from different heights. The height of the bounce is measured each time the ball is dropped. Which statement describes the data in the graph? J

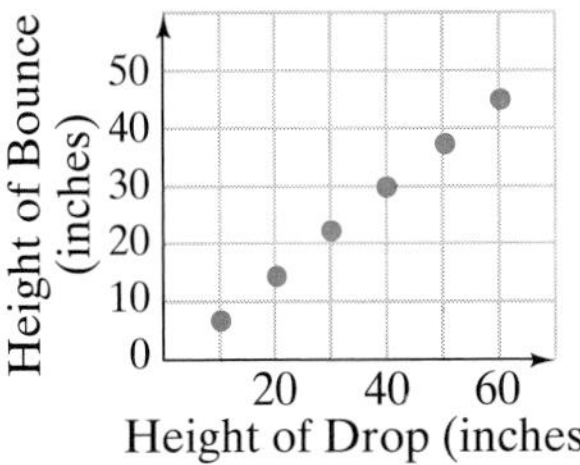


F. The height of a bounce is about $1\frac{1}{3}$ of the height from which the ball is dropped.
G. The height of a bounce is about 6 inches less than the height from which the ball is dropped.
H. The height of a bounce is about 6 inches greater than the height from which the ball is dropped.
J. The height of a bounce is about $\frac{3}{4}$ of the height from which the ball is dropped.

3. The ordered pair (4, 6) is *not* a solution of which equation? D
A. $x - y = -2$
B. $-10 = -x - y$
C. $y - x = 2$
D. $x - y = 2$

4. Classify the slope of the line below. F

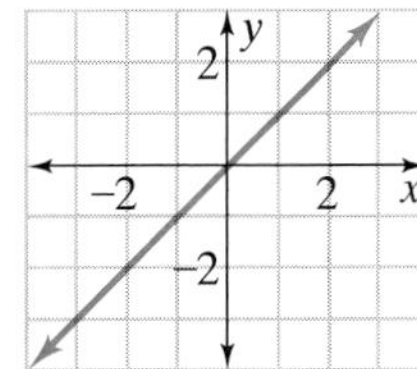

F. positive
G. negative
H. zero
J. undefined

8. negative $x$-coordinate and positive $y$-coordinate; negative $x$-coordinate and negative $y$-coordinate; positive $x$-coordinate and negative $y$-coordinate

5. What is the slope of a line through the points (−2, 4) and (6, 3)? A
A. $-\frac{1}{8}$ B. $\frac{4}{7}$ C. $\frac{7}{4}$ D. −8

6. The slope of a line is −1. Through which two points could this line pass? G
F. (0, 3) and (0, −3)
G. (0, 3) and (3, 0)
H. (0, 3) and (−3, 0)
J. (−3, 0) and (3, 0)

7. Which rule describes the function in the table? B
A. $f(x) = x + 8$
B. $f(x) = 4x + 8$
C. $f(x) = x - 1$
D. $f(x) = x + 17$

| $x$ | $f(x)$ |
|---|---|
| −3 | −4 |
| 0 | 8 |
| 3 | 20 |
| 6 | 32 |

## Free Response

**For Exercises 8–10, show your work.**

8. Each point in Quadrant I has a positive $x$-coordinate and a positive $y$-coordinate. Describe the signs of the coordinates for points in Quadrants II, III, and IV. See above right.

9. Find the value of $n$ that makes (−3, 3) a solution of the equation $x + ny = 6$. 3

10. Is the relation {(3, 4), (−3, 2), (5, 1), (2, 2)} a function? Explain.
Yes; there is one range value for each domain value.



## Standardized Test Prep

Standardized tests, such as those administered for state assessment, SAT9, TerraNova™, ITBS, MAT7, or CAT5, may include multiple choice questions, free-response questions, and open-ended questions.

**Multiple Choice Questions** are followed usually by four choices, one of which is correct.

**Exercises 1–7** are multiple choice questions.

**Free-Response Questions** do not give answer choices. Student must provide the one correct answer on their own.

**Exercises 8–10** are free-response questions.

### Resources

See p. 381G for a list of assessment options.

### Test-Taking Tip

When answering problems such as those in Exercises 5 and 7, it is often a good idea to sketch a graph of the lines to double-check your answers.

### Test-Taking Tips on Transparency

Use patterns to find a missing value or rule in a table.

*Example* Write a word equation describing how the input and output numbers are related in the table below.

| Input | 1 | 2 | 3 | 4 |
|---|---|---|---|---|
| Output | −4 | −8 | −12 | −16 |

A. *output* = *input* + 4 B. *output* = 4 × *input*
C. *output* = −4 × *input* D. *input* = −4 × *output*

To find the pattern, look for a relationship between the numbers in the first row and the second row.

×(−4): 1 → −4; 2 → −8; 3 → −12; 4 → −16

Each number in row 2 is −4 times the number in row 1.

The answer is *output* = −4 × *input*, or choice C.

Look for a pattern to find the answer. Explain your reasoning.

1. Complete the function table below. Write in your response on the grid found on the answer sheet.

| Input | 2 | 4 | 6 | 8 | 10 |
|---|---|---|---|---|---|
| Output | 7 | 13 | 19 | 25 | |

2. Complete the function table below.

| Input (ft) | 1 | 2 | 3 | 4 | 5 |
|---|---|---|---|---|---|
| Output (in.) | 12 | 24 | 36 | 48 | |

A. 5 B. 60 C. 48 D. Not Here

# 8-6

## Getting Ready

**Key Terms and Symbols** trend line

**Resources** A complete list of resources for this lesson is on p. 381H.

### Daily Skills Warm-Up

Lesson 8-6

Write a rule for each function.

1.

| $x$ | $y$ |
|---|---|
| −1 | −12 |
| 0 | −7 |
| 1 | −2 |
| 2 | 3 |
| 3 | 8 |

$y = 5x - 7$

2. $y = 3x - 2$

### Background for the Lesson

Scatter plots can show trends in the relationship between two sets of data. When a scatter plot shows a trend, you can draw a line on the graph to approximate the trend. This line is called a *trend line.* You use a trend line to predict the relationship between points that are between or beyond existing points on the graph. You can also write an equation for the trend line to predict new data points on the graph.

## 1 Focus

### Connecting to Students' Lives

Before you plan a vacation, you might find out what the weather is going to be. While no one can predict the weather exactly, you can find out what the weather is usually like at that time for your destination.

### Connecting to Prior Knowledge

In Lesson 8-5, students learned how to make a scatter plot. In this lesson, students learn how to use a scatter plot and a trend line to make predictions about data. In Lesson 8-7, students extend what they know about graphing and solving equations to solving systems of linear equations.



# 8-6

## Solve by Graphing

**Problem Solving Strategies**

Account for All Possibilities
Draw a Diagram
Look for a Pattern
Make a Model
Make a Table
Simplify a Problem
Simulate a Problem
Solve by Graphing
Try, Test, Revise
Use Multiple Strategies
Work Backward
Write an Equation
Write a Proportion

*Math Strategies in Action*

Businesses and government agencies use scatter plots to look for trends and make predictions. For example, the park service at Isle Royale, Michigan, surveys the moose and wolf populations each spring. They use a scatter plot to show the relationship between them. Then they draw a **trend line** that closely fits the data points in the scatter plot. Using the trend line, they can predict the size of one population from the size of the other.

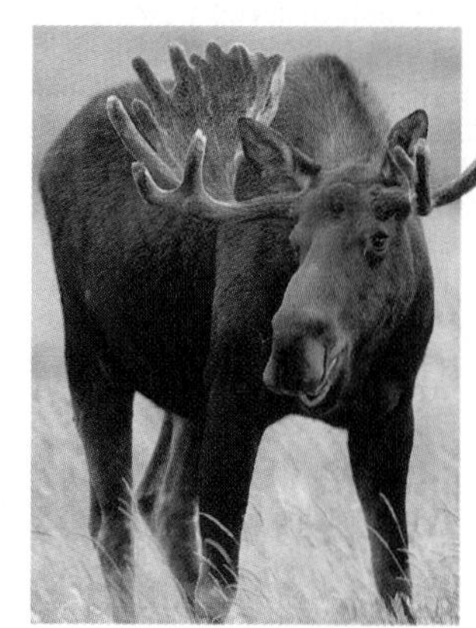

### Sample Problem

*Wildlife* Use the data in the table below. Suppose there were 18 wolves one year. About how many moose would you expect to be on the island that year?

**Isle Royale Populations**

| Year | Wolf | Moose | Year | Wolf | Moose | Year | Wolf | Moose |
|---|---|---|---|---|---|---|---|---|
| 1982 | 14 | 700 | 1988 | 12 | 1,653 | 1994 | 15 | 1,800 |
| 1983 | 23 | 900 | 1989 | 11 | 1,397 | 1995 | 16 | 2,400 |
| 1984 | 24 | 811 | 1990 | 15 | 1,216 | 1996 | 22 | 1,200 |
| 1985 | 22 | 1,062 | 1991 | 12 | 1,313 | 1997 | 24 | 500 |
| 1986 | 20 | 1,025 | 1992 | 12 | 1,600 | 1998 | 14 | 700 |
| 1987 | 16 | 1,380 | 1993 | 13 | 1,880 | 1999 | 25 | 750 |

Source: Isle Royale National Park Service

### Read

1. What are the two variables? the number of wolves and the number of moose
2. What are you trying to predict? the number of moose when there are 18 wolves.



## Tools to Monitor Progress

### BEFORE THE LESSON

**To check prerequisite skills:**

- Describing number patterns

**Skills You Need,** p. 381

### DURING THE LESSON

**To check understanding:**

- **Additional Sample Problem**
  Use the data and scatter plot for the Sample Problem to answer this question. Suppose in the year 2000 there are 28 wolves on the island. Predict how many moose would be on the island that year. a little more than 600

## Plan

You can graph the data in a scatter plot. If the points show a correlation, you can draw a trend line. You can then use the line to predict other data values.

## Solve

**Step 1** Make a scatter plot by graphing the (wolf, moose) ordered pairs. Use the $x$-axis for wolves and the $y$-axis for moose.

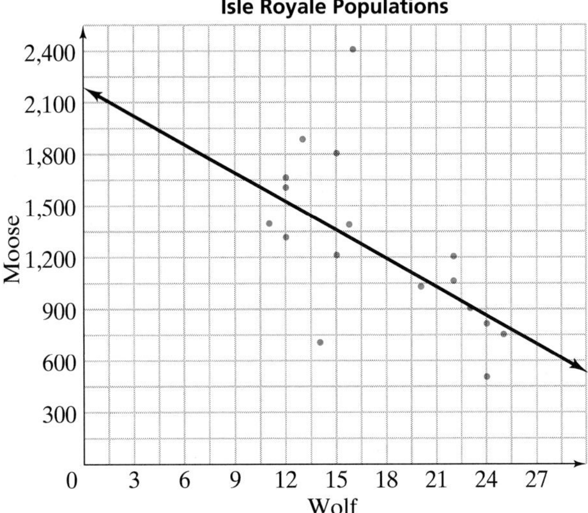


**Step 2** Sketch a trend line. The line should be as close as possible to each data point. There should be about as many points above the trend line as below it.

**Step 3** To predict the number of moose when there are 18 wolves, find 18 along the horizontal axis. Look up to find the point on the trend line that corresponds to 18 wolves. Then look across to the value on the vertical axis, which is 1,200.

There will be about 1,200 moose when there are 18 wolves.

## Look Back

You can write an equation for a trend line. You can use the equation to make predictions.

3. Answers may vary. Samples are given.

**3. a.** What is the $y$-intercept of the trend line above? about 2,175

**b.** Locate one other point on the trend line. Then find the slope of the trend line. about −55

**c.** Write an equation for the trend line in slope-intercept form. $y = -55x + 2,175$

**d.** Use the equation you wrote in part (c). Find the solution of the equation when $x = 18$. 1,185



# 2 Teach

## Teaching Notes

Point out that a trend line is only approximate. The line may not pass through many (or even any) of the points on the scatter plot; instead the points cluster around the line. The trend line passes through the *middle* of the data points. About half of the points that are not on the line should be above it, and half should be below it.

**Visual Learning** Where you draw a trend line on a scatter plot affects the predictions you make about the data. Have students draw several scatter plots on the board, then draw trend lines on the plots. Discuss the possibilities for the placement of the trend lines.

**Error Prevention** Students may think they need to *connect the dots* when they draw a trend line. Explain that trend lines are straight lines, and they do not go through all of the points on a scatter plot.

### Sample Problem

**Build understanding.** Ask: Why is it important to say that there will be *about* 1,200 moose when there are 19 wolves? Why not just say that there will be 1,200 moose? The solution to this problem is a prediction based on a trend line. You can make a reasonable estimate that the number of moose will be approximately 1,200 based on the data, but you cannot know the exact number.

**Math Reasoning** Use the data and scatter plot from the Sample Problem to answer these questions: Suppose the wolf population suddenly dropped to 6 in the year 2000. Use the trend line to predict the moose population for that year. Explain why you might expect the actual moose population for 2000 to be lower than that predicted by the trend line. about 1,950; The population might not grow that fast from 750 in 1999.

### Additional Sample Problem

Suppose in the year 2003 there are 16 wolves on the island. Predict how many moose would be on the island that year.
about 1,300
Why is there such a difference among 1987, 1995, and 2003?
Sample answer: a trend line gives an estimate and not an exact answer.

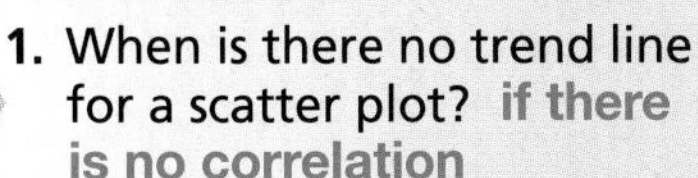

### AFTER THE LESSON

**To assess knowledge: Lesson Quiz**

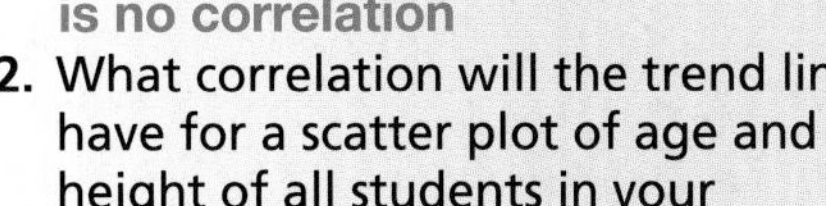

1. When is there no trend line for a scatter plot? if there is no correlation
2. What correlation will the trend line have for a scatter plot of age and height of all students in your school? positive

- For enrichment and reteaching options see Resources on p. 381H.

# 3 Practice/Assess

## Assignment Guide

**Core** 1–5, 7–9
**Extension** 6

Mixed Review can be assigned at any time for maintenance.

### Exercises

**Exercise 1** These predictions are approximate and should be worded accordingly.

### Challenge

Which scatter plot would make a more accurate prediction, one with 4 points, or one with 12 points? Explain. 12 points, because more data points enable you to draw a more accurate trend line

### Closure

A trend line is a line that fits the data points in a scatter plot. You can use a trend line to make predictions about the relationship between the two sets of data on the scatter plot.

### Daily Cumulative Review

**Is there a *positive correlation*, a *negative correlation*, or *no correlation* between the sets of data in each scatter plot?** *(Lesson 8-5)*

1. no correlation
2. negative correlation
3. positive correlation

**Write a function rule to describe each situation.** *(Lesson 8-4)*

4. Juana sells computers at a local store. Each week she earns $375 salary plus 5% of her sales. $t(s) = 375 + 0.05s$
5. Express the number of ounces $n(s)$ as a function of the number of pounds $s$. $n(s) = 16s$
6. Large pizzas cost $15 each, plus a $2 delivery fee for each order. Write a rule to describe total cost of one order $c(p)$ as a function of the number of large pizzas $p$. $c(p) = 15p + 2$

**Mixed Review**

**Graph each equation.**

7. $-4x = 6y$ (8-2)
8. $y = -x + 1$ (8-2)
9. $y = 2x - 1$ (8-2)



# Exercises

## Check Understanding

*Statistics* **The table shows the populations of some states and the numbers of cars registered in those states. Use the data for Exercises 1 and 2.** 1a–b. See below right.

1. a. Use the data to make a scatter plot of the data. Use the population data for the horizontal axis.
   b. Draw a trend line.
   c. Predict how many cars are registered by the 32.2 million people in California. about 13 million cars
   d. Write an equation for your trend line. Predict the number of cars registered by the 7.3 million people in North Carolina. $y = 0.4x + 0.4$; about 3 million cars

**State Populations and Cars**

| State | Population (millions) | Registered Cars (millions) | State | Population (millions) | Registered Cars (millions) |
|---|---|---|---|---|---|
| FL | 14.4 | 7.2 | NY | 18.1 | 7.9 |
| GA | 7.3 | 3.8 | OH | 11.2 | 6.6 |
| IL | 11.8 | 6.2 | PA | 12.0 | 5.9 |
| KS | 2.6 | 1.2 | SC | 3.7 | 1.8 |
| ME | 1.2 | 0.6 | TN | 5.3 | 3.0 |
| MS | 2.7 | 1.3 | TX | 19.1 | 7.4 |
| NV | 1.6 | 0.6 | WA | 5.5 | 2.6 |

SOURCE: *Statistical Abstract of the United States*

2. Describe the correlation between the two sets of data. positive correlation

## Practice and Problem Solving

**Solve using any strategy.**

3. A delivery van travels 240.8 mi on the highway using 10.6 gal of gasoline. Its gas tank holds 13.6 gal. How many highway miles can the driver expect the van to travel on a full tank of gasoline? Round your answer to the nearest mile. 309 mi

4. *Data Analysis* Use the data in the table below. Predict the number of gallons bought for $12. 9 gal

**Gasoline Purchases**

| Dollars Spent | 10 | 11 | 9 | 10 | 8 | 5 | 8 | 6 |
|---|---|---|---|---|---|---|---|---|
| Gallons Bought | 8.3 | 8.7 | 6.5 | 7.1 | 6.7 | 3.6 | 5.6 | 4.1 |

5. Four candidates are running for president of the student council. Three other candidates are running for vice-president. How many different ways can the two offices be filled? 12 ways

1a–b. Trend lines may vary. Sample is given.

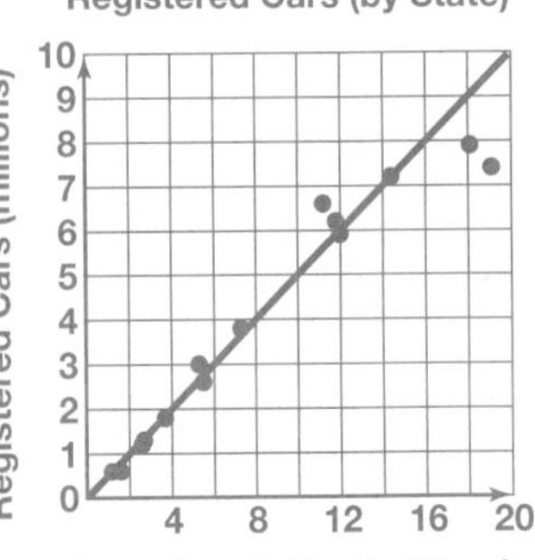




### Alternative Assessment

Have students search for census data on the population of the United States for the past century. Have them create a scatter plot with the data and draw a trend line on the plot. Finally, have students use their trend line to predict the population of the United States in 2010 and in 2050.

6. *Physics* As the weight held by a spring increases, the length of the spring also increases proportionally. Suppose a 2-lb weight stretches a spring to 15 in., and a 12-lb weight stretches the same spring to 20 in. What is the length of the spring with no weight attached? 14 in.

7. *Engineering* To provide wheelchair access, a ramp with a slope of $\frac{1}{15}$ is being built to a door of a building. Suppose that the bottom of the door is 3 ft above street level. How far will the ramp extend from the building? 45 ft

8. A plumber charges $45 for a service call, plus $70/h for her time.
   a. Find the cost of a two-hour service call. $185
   b. How long was a service call that cost $150? 1.5 h

9. *Business* A supermarket charges $1.19 for a 12-oz jar of salsa and $1.89 for a 20-oz jar. Now the producer is introducing a 16-oz jar of the same salsa. What do you think would be a fair price for this new size? Justify your answer. Answers may vary. Sample: $1.54; (16, 1.54) is on the line through the two points (12, 1.19) and (20, 1.89).

## Mixed Review

**Find the solutions of each equation for $x = -3, 0,$ and $2$.** ***(Lesson 8-2)***

10. $y = 2x - 1$ $-7, -1, 3$
11. $y = -3x$ $9, 0, -6$
12. $y = \frac{1}{3}x + 4$ $3, 4, 4\frac{2}{3}$
13. $y = 0.5x - 2$ $-3\frac{1}{2}, -2, -1$

**Solve each equation.** ***(Lessons 7-2 and 7-5)***

14. $3x + 7 = 4x - 12$ 19
15. $7t + 3 - 4t = -6$ −3
16. $8(2 - c) - 12 = -3c$ $\frac{4}{5}$

17. About 150 million of the 20 billion hot dogs that are eaten in the United States each year are eaten during the Fourth of July weekend. What percent of the hot dogs are eaten during the Fourth of July weekend? ***(Lesson 6-6)*** about 0.75%

## Activity 2 Graphing

Refer to your results from Activity 1. For each rental company, write an equation in the form $y = Px + D$, where $y$ is the total cost of the chairs, $P$ is the price per chair, $x$ is the number of chairs, and $D$ is the delivery charge. Graph the equations on the same coordinate plane for values of $x$ from 0 to 500.

See also Extra Practice section.



### Project Activity 2

**Graphing** Students may want to use a different color (or pattern, such as dots or dashes) for each rental company. Remind students to label their graphs clearly.

## Practice

A giraffe was 1 ft tall at birth. 7 ft tall at the age of 4, and $11\frac{1}{2}$ ft tall at the age of 7.

1. Use the data to make a (age, height) scatter plot.
2. Draw a trend line.
3. Write an equation for your trend line in slope-intercept form.
   $y = \frac{3}{2}x + 1$
4. Use your equation to find the following information.
   a. the giraffe's height at the age of 5
   $8\frac{1}{2}$ ft
   b. the age at which the giraffe was 16 ft tall

   10 yr

Giraffe Height — Height (ft), Age (yrs)

A hippopotamus weighed 700 lb at the age of 1 and 1,900 lb at the age of 3, and 2,500 lb at the age of 4.

5. Use the data to make a (age, weight) scatter plot.
6. Draw a trend line.
7. Write an equation for your trend line.
   $y = 600x + 100$
8. Use the equation to predict the following information.
   a. the hippo's weight at the age of 8
   4,900 lb
   b. the age at which the hippo weighed 7,900 lb
   13 yr
9. Can this equation be used to predict the hippo's weight at any age? Explain.
   Sample answer is shown: No; the hippo will not continue to gain weight indefinitely.

Hippopotamus Weight — Weight (lb), Age (yrs)



## Reteaching

The driver of a car slowed to a stop. After 3 seconds the car was traveling 41 mi/h. After 5 seconds it was traveling 30 mi/h and after 8 seconds it was traveling 12 mi/h.

a. Make a scatter plot of the data and draw a trend line. Plot the points (3, 41), (5, 30) and (8, 12). Draw a line through (5, 30) and (8, 12).
b. About how fast was the car moving when the driver first applied the brakes?
   When the time was 0, the speed was 60. So the driver was moving 60 mi/h.
c. Write an equation for your trend line. The $y$-intercept, $b$, is 60. You can use the points (5, 30) and (8, 12) to find the slope.
   $m = \frac{\text{difference in } y\text{-values}}{\text{difference in } x\text{-values}} = \frac{12 - 30}{8 - 5} = \frac{-18}{3} = -6$
   Substitute $m = -6$ and $b = 60$ into $y = mx + b$.
   $y = mx + b$
   $y = -6x + 60$
d. Use your equation to find about how long it took for the car to stop.
   When the car stops, the speed, $y$, is zero.
   $y = -6x + 60$
   $0 = -6x + 60$
   $6x = 60$
   $x = 10$
   It took the car 10 seconds to stop.

Braking Rates — Speed (mph), Time (seconds)

**The water pressure at a depth of 100 ft in the ocean is 45 lb/in.$^2$. At a depth of 500 ft the pressure is 225 lb/in.$^2$.**

1. Make a (pressure, depth) scatter plot of the data.
2. Draw a trend line.
3. Write an equation for your trend line.
   $y = \frac{20}{9}x$
4. Use your equation to find the approximate depth where the pressure is 180 lb/in.$^2$

   400 ft
5. Use you equation to find the approximate pressure at a depth of 800 ft.
   360 lb/in.$^2$

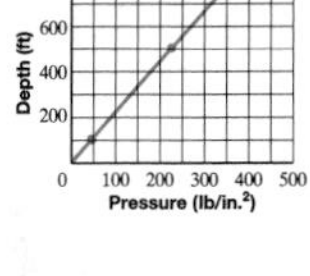




## Enrichment

**The table shows the percentage of U.S. households owning a computer and having cable TV in several years.**

1. Use the data to make a (computer, cable) scatter plot.

| Percentage of U.S. Households | | |
|---|---|---|
| Year | Owning a Computer | Having Cable TV |
| 1990 | 22% | 59% |
| 1991 | 25% | 61% |
| 1992 | 27% | 62% |
| 1993 | 30% | 63% |
| 1994 | 33% | 63% |
| 1995 | 37% | 66% |
| 1996 | 40% | 67% |

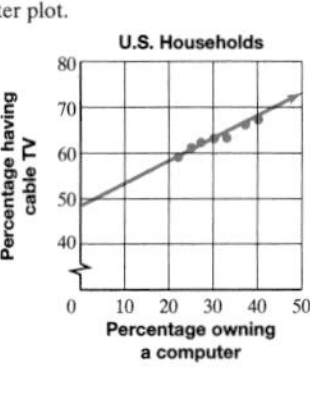


2. Draw a trend line through the data for 1990 and 1993.
3. Predict the percentage of households that will have cable TV when 45% of U.S. households own a computer.
   70%
4. Find the slope of your trend line. $m =$ $\frac{1}{2}$
5. Find the $y$-intercept by substituting the slope you found and the point (22, 59) into the equation $y = mx + b$. Solve for $b$.
   $b =$ 48
6. Write an equation for your trend line.
   $y = \frac{1}{2}x + 48$
7. Use the equation to predict the percentage of households with cable TV when 50% of households own a computer.
   73%
8. Use the equation to predict the percentage of households owning a computer when 80% of households have cable TV.
   64%

# 8-7

## Getting Ready

**Key Terms and Symbols** system of linear equations

**Resources** A complete list of resources for this lesson is on p. 381H.

### Daily Skills Warm-Up

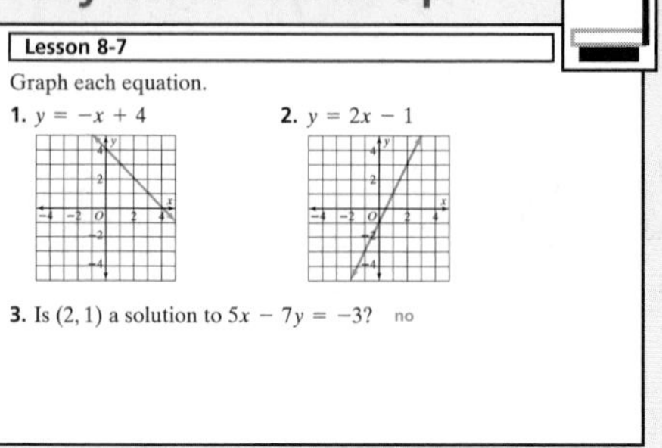

Lesson 8-7

Graph each equation.

1. $y = -x + 4$  2. $y = 2x - 1$

3. Is (2, 1) a solution to $5x - 7y = -3$? no

### Background for the Lesson

The coordinates of every point on the graph of a line satisfy the equation of the line. So when two lines cross, the point of intersection, which is on both lines, is a solution of both the equations. You call two (or more) linear equations taken together a *system of equations*. The point at which the lines intersect is the solution of the system. One way to find the solution to a system of linear equations is to graph the lines and read from the graph the coordinates of the point where the lines intersect.

## 1 Focus

### Connecting to Students' Lives

Discuss the intersection of two streets at a corner. The intersection contains a point on both streets. The intersection is the point the two have in common.

### Connecting to Prior Knowledge

In Lesson 8-2, students learned that a solution is any point on the line that is the graph of the equation. In this lesson, students learn that the solution to a system of linear equations is the point where the lines intersect. In Lesson 8-8, students will learn how to solve a system of linear inequalities.

# 8-7 Solving Systems of Linear Equations

**What You'll Learn**

1. To solve systems of linear equations by graphing
2. To solve problems by solving systems of linear equations

**. . . And Why**

To model real-world problems involving carpentry

## PART 1 Graphing Systems of Linear Equations

Two or more linear equations form a **system of linear equations.** A *solution of the system* is any ordered pair that is a solution of each equation in the system.

You can solve some systems of equations by graphing the equations on a coordinate plane and identifying the point(s) of intersection.

### EXAMPLE 1

**Solve the system $y = -x + 1$ and $y = 2x + 4$ by graphing.**

**Step 1** Graph each line.

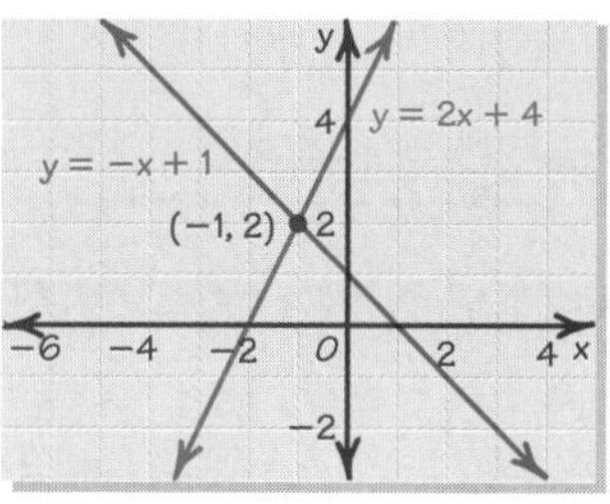


**Step 2** Find the point of intersection.

The lines intersect at one point, $(-1, 2)$. The solution is $(-1, 2)$.

**Check** See whether $(-1, 2)$ makes both equations true.

$y = -x + 1$  $y = 2x + 4$

$2 \stackrel{?}{=} -(-1) + 1$ ← Replace $x$ with $-1$ and $y$ with 2. → $2 \stackrel{?}{=} 2(-1) + 4$

$2 = 2$ ✔ The solution checks. $2 = 2$ ✔

**TRY THIS** Solve each system of equations by graphing.

1. $y = x - 6$ See above left.
   $y = -2x$
2. $y = 3x - 3$ See left.
   $x + y = 1$

1. (2, −4)

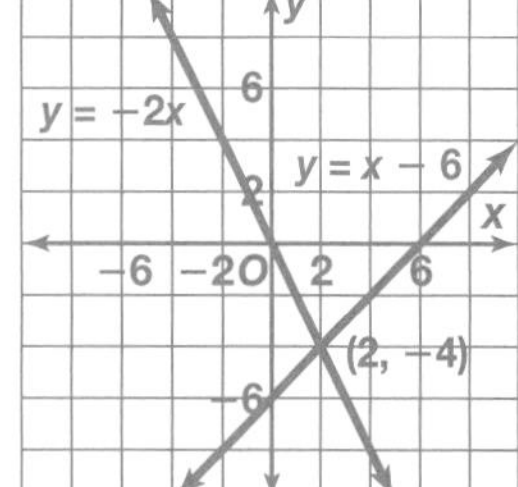


2. (1, 0)

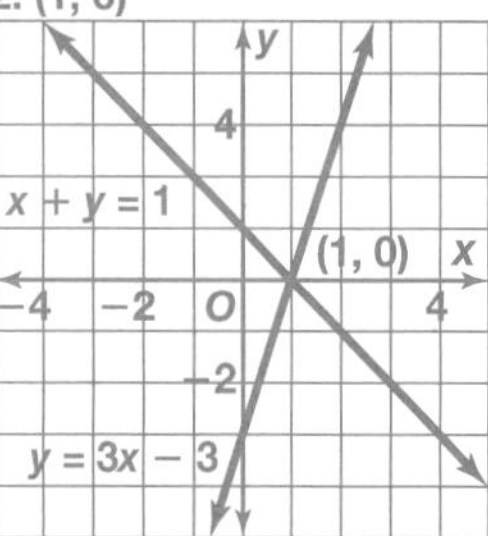


When the graphs of two equations are parallel, there is no point of intersection. The system has *no solution*.

When the graphs of two equations are the same line, all the points on the line are solutions. The system has *infinitely many solutions*.



## Tools to Monitor Progress

**BEFORE THE LESSON**

**To check prerequisite skills:**

- Graphing points

**Skills You Need,** p. 381

**DURING THE LESSON**

**To check understanding:**

**Try This** exercises on student page

- **Additional Example 1**
  Solve the system $y = x - 7$ and $y = 4x + 2$ by graphing. $(-3, -10)$

## Example 2

**Solve each system by graphing.**

**a.** $x + y = 1; y = -x + 3$

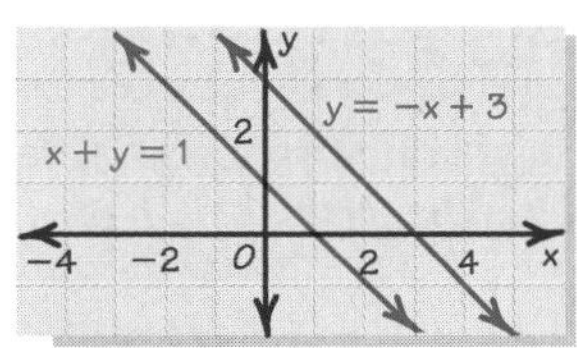


The lines are parallel. They do not intersect. There is no solution.

**b.** $x - 2y = 4; 2x - 4y = 8$

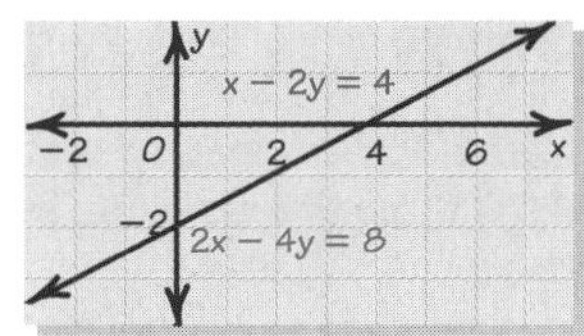


The graphs are the same line. There are infinitely many solutions.

### Graphing Calculator HINT

You can use a graphing calculator to check your solution of a system. Write the equations in slope-intercept form, press Y=, and enter them as Y1 and Y2. Then use the CALC menu to find the coordinates of the intersection point.

**Try This** Solve each system by graphing.

**3.** $y = x - 6; x - y = 6$
See right.

**4.** $y = x + 4; y = 2x$
See below right.

3. infinitely many solutions

4. (4, 8)

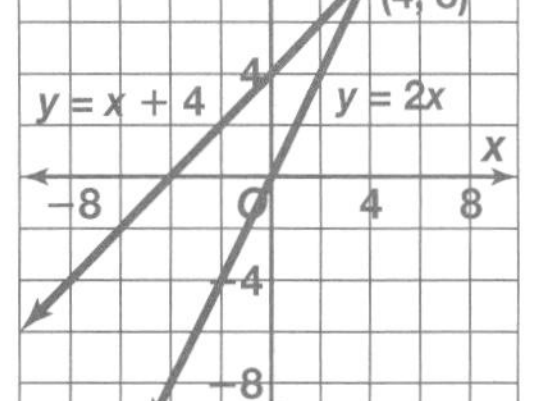


## Part 2 Writing Systems of Linear Equations

You can write and graph systems of equations to solve problems.

## Example 3

**Find two numbers with a sum of 6 and a difference of 4.**

**Step 1** Write equations.

Let $x$ = the greater number.
Let $y$ = the lesser number.

*Equation 1* Sum is 6.
$x + y = 6$

*Equation 2* Difference is 4.
$x - y = 4$

**Step 2** Graph the equations.

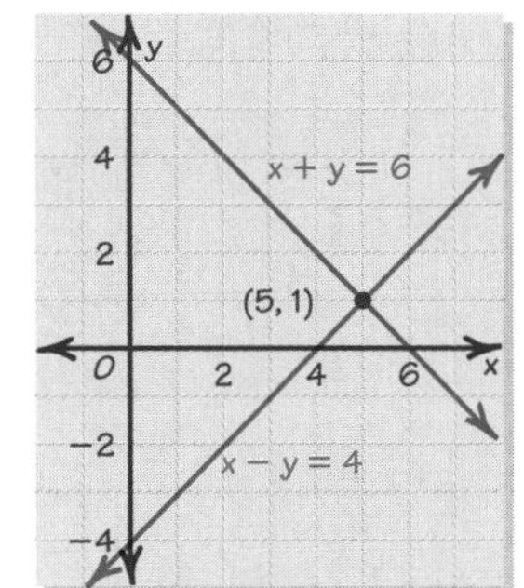


The lines intersect at (5, 1).
The numbers are 5 and 1.

**Check** Since the sum of 5 and 1 is 6 and the difference of 5 and 1 is 4, the answer is correct.

**Try This**

**5.** Find two numbers with a difference of 2 and a sum of −8.
−3, −5



# 2 Teach

## Part 1 Teaching Notes

Help students see that any two lines, unless they are parallel, will eventually intersect. Have students draw two lines on a coordinate plane on the board and extend the lines until they intersect.

### Example 1

**Build understanding.** Ask: Is (−1, 2) the only solution to the first equation in this system? Explain. No, any point along the graphs of each equation is a solution to that equation. The solution (−1, 2) is the only solution that satisfies both equations.

**Tactile Learning** Have students place two pencils on a desk to represent a system of two linear equations with no solution, with one solution, and with infinitely many solutions.

### Example 2

**Build understanding.** Ask: Explain why you do not have to graph the system of equations in part b. to know the solution. When you put the equations into $y = mx + b$ form, you see they are the same line, so there are infinitely many solutions.

**Extension** How can you tell that a system of equations has no solution by looking at the equations in slope-intercept form? A system of equations that has no solution consists of parallel lines. Parallel lines have the same slope. If the equations in a system have the same slope but different $y$-intercepts, then the system has no solution.

- **Additional Example 2**
  Solve each system by graphing.
  **a.** $27x + 9y = 36$
  $y = 4 - 3x$
  infinitely many solutions
  **b.** $8 = 4x + 2y$
  $2x + y = 5$ no solution
- **Additional Example 3**
  Find two numbers with a sum of 10 and a difference of 2. (6, 4)

## After the Lesson

**To assess knowledge:**

**Lesson Quiz**

Solve each system by graphing.

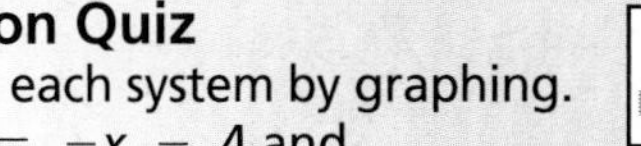

1. $y = -x - 4$ and $y = 4x + 1$ (−1, −3)
2. $y = -3x + 12$ and $18x + 6y = 42$ no solution

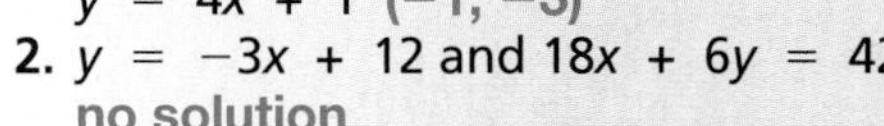

3. Find two numbers with a sum of 15 and a difference of 1. (8, 7)

- For enrichment and reteaching options see Resources on p. 381H.

## Part 2 Teaching Notes

Solving problems by using a system of two equations with two variables is a strategy that is often more efficient than Try, Test, and Revise.

### Example 3

**Build understanding.** Explain why you could not write Equation 2 as $y - x = 4$. **The variable $x$ is defined as the greater number, so to get a difference of 4, you must subtract the lesser number ($y$) from the greater ($x$) and not the other way around.**

**Error Prevention** The two numbers in Example 3 are 5 and 1. Remind students that they defined $x$ as the greater number, so the solution is (5, 1) and not (1, 5).

**Auditory Learning** Problems such as Example 3 provide students with an excellent opportunity to practice translating words into equations. You may want to read several of these types of problems aloud to students while they write the equations and then solve the system by graphing.

### Different Ways to Solve a Problem

**Build understanding.** Ask: What is one important difference between Method 1 and Method 2? **Method 2 does not involve graphing.**

**Advanced Learners** You can solve the equations in Method 1 without graphing. Try substituting $3y$ for $x$ (since they are equal) in Equation 2.



You can solve some problems involving two variables by writing and graphing a system of equations, or you may be able to use one variable to write and solve an equation.

## Different Ways to Solve a Problem

*Carpenter* **A carpenter cuts an 8-ft board into two pieces. One piece is three times as long as the other. What is the length of each piece?**

**Method 1**

Write and graph a system of equations.
Let $x$ = length of longer piece; $y$ = length of shorter piece.

Equation 1 Longer piece is three times shorter piece.
$x = 3 \cdot y$

Equation 2 Sum of lengths is eight.
$x + y = 8$

Graph the equations.

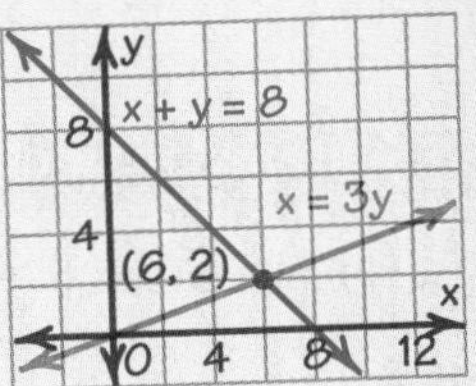


The lines intersect at (6, 2). The lengths are 6 ft and 2 ft.

**Method 2**

Write a one-variable equation.
Let $x$ = length of shorter piece; $3x$ = length of longer piece.

Equation Shorter piece plus longer piece is 8 feet.

$$x + 3x = 8$$
$$4x = 8$$
$$x = 2$$

The shorter piece is 2 ft, and the longer piece is $3(2) = 6$ ft.

**Choose a Method** 1–2. See left.

1. Which method would you use to find the lengths? Explain.
2. In Method 1, suppose $x$ = length of shorter piece. What difference would this make in the equations and the graph?

1. Answers may vary. Sample: Method 2; it is faster.
2. The first equation would be $y = 3x$. Its graph is steeper than the graph of $x = 3y$ and the graphs would intersect at (2, 6).

# Exercises

## Check Understanding

**Use the graph to find the solution of each system. Check each solution.**

1. $y = x + 1$
   $y = 3x - 7$
   (4, 5)

2. $y = x + 1$
   $x + y = -3$
   (−2, −1)

3. $-3x + y = 5$
   $y = 3x - 7$
   no solution

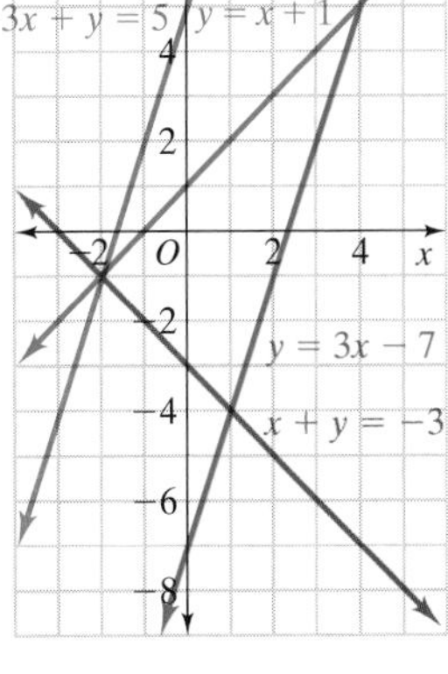


**Is (−1, 5) a solution of each system? Show your work.**

4. $x + y = 4$ no
   $x - y = 6$

5. $y = -2x + 3$ no
   $y = x - 4$

6. $2x = y - 7$ yes
   $2y = -x + 9$

**Solve each system by graphing.** 7. See margin 8–9. See back of book for graphs.

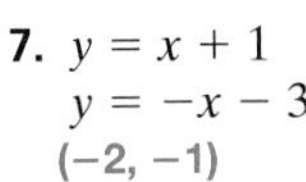

7. $y = x + 1$
   $y = -x - 3$
   (−2, −1)

8. $y = -x - 3$
   $y = -x + 2$
   no solution

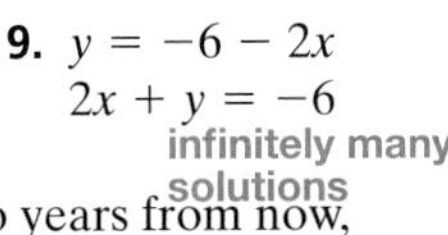

9. $y = -6 - 2x$
   $2x + y = -6$
   infinitely many solutions

10. Cliff is six years older than his sister Claire. Two years from now, Cliff's age will be twice Claire's age.
    a. Let $x$ = Cliff's present age, and let $y$ = Claire's present age. Write an equation relating their ages now, and another equation relating their ages two years from now. $x = y + 6$; $x + 2 = 2(y + 2)$
    b. Graph the system of equations you wrote in part (a). See back of book.
    c. What are Cliff's and Claire's present ages? Cliff: 10 years; Claire: 4 years

## Practice and Problem Solving

**Is each ordered pair a solution of the given system? Show your work.**

11. $y = x + 2$ yes
    $x - 3y = 4$; $(-5, -3)$

12. $x + y = 2$ no
    $-x + y = -4$; $(3, 1)$

13. $2x + 5y = 3$ no
    $y = 7.5x$; $(1.5, 0.2)$

**Solve each system by graphing. Check your solution.** 14–25. See back of book for graphs.

14. $y = x + 5$
    $y = -2x + 8$
    (1, 6)

15. $y = x - 4$
    $y = 3x$
    (−2, −6)

16. $y = 2x - 2$
    $y = 6$
    (4, 6)

17. $y = -x + 1$
    $y = 2x - 5$
    (2, −1)

18. $x = -2$
    $y = -0.5x + 7$
    (−2, 8)

19. $y = x$
    $y = 4x - 9$
    (3, 3)

20. $x + y = 3$
    $2x = 10 - 2y$
    no solution

21. $x - y = -4$
    $x + y = 6$
    (1, 5)

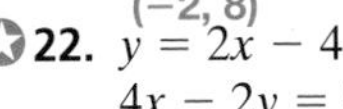

22. $y = 2x - 4$
    $4x - 2y = 8$
    infinitely many solutions

23. $2x - 4y = 4$
    $y = 0.5x - 1$
    infinitely many solutions

24. $y = x - 2$
    $x + 3y = 6$
    (3, 1)

25. $3y - 2x = 3$
    $6y = 4x + 6$
    infinitely many solutions

*Open-ended* **Write a system of equations with the given solutions.**
26–28. Check students' work.

26. no solutions
27. one solution
28. infinitely many solutions



# 3 Practice/Assess

## Assignment Guide

To provide flexible scheduling, this lesson can be divided into parts.

**Part 1**
**Core** 1–9, 11–21, 35–37
**Extension** 22–25, 38

**Part 2**
**Core** 10, 29–34
**Extension** 26–28, 39

Mixed Review can be assigned at any time for maintenance.

## Exercises

**Exercises 14–25** Equations with the same slope and different *y*-intercepts have no solution, and equations that are equivalent have infinitely many solutions.

**Test Prep Exercise 36** Solve this system of equations by sketching a graph before you select an answer choice.

## Challenge

Solve the system $y = x$ and $y = -x$ by graphing. (0, 0)

## Closure

Two or more linear equations with the same variables form a system of linear equations. A solution of the system is any ordered pair that is a solution of each equation. You can solve a system by graphing.

## Alternative Assessment

ive students the graphs of $y = 2x$ and $= 2$ (without showing the equations) and ave them write the system of linear quations for the lines and the solution to the ystem.

7.

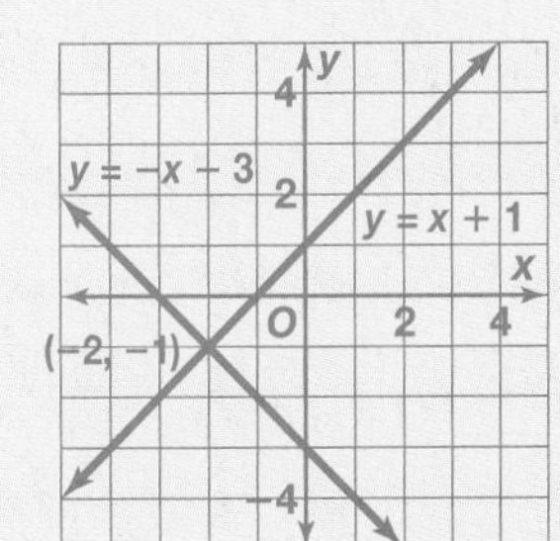


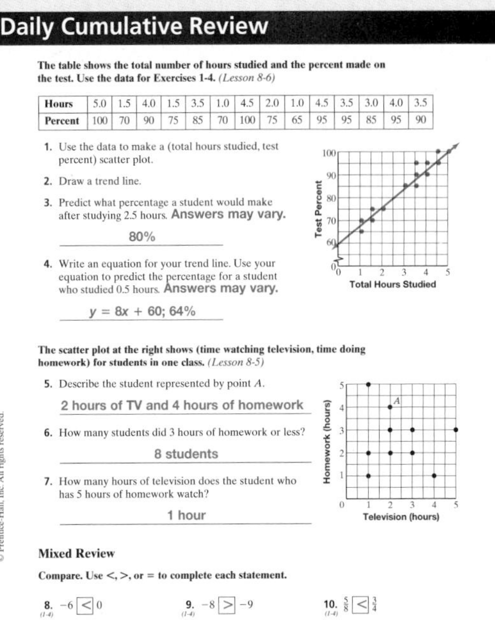

## Daily Cumulative Review

**The table shows the total number of hours studied and the percent made on the test. Use the data for Exercises 1-4.** *(Lesson 8-6)*

| Hours | 5.0 | 1.5 | 4.0 | 1.5 | 3.5 | 1.0 | 4.5 | 2.0 | 1.0 | 4.5 | 3.5 | 3.0 | 4.0 | 3.5 |
|---|---|---|---|---|---|---|---|---|---|---|---|---|---|---|
| Percent | 100 | 70 | 90 | 75 | 85 | 70 | 100 | 75 | 65 | 95 | 95 | 85 | 95 | 90 |

1. Use the data to make a (total hours studied, test percent) scatter plot.
2. Draw a trend line.
3. Predict what percentage a student would make after studying 2.5 hours. Answers may vary.
   80%
4. Write an equation for your trend line. Use your equation to predict the percentage for a student who studied 0.5 hours. Answers may vary.
   $y = 8x + 60$; 64%



**The scatter plot at the right shows (time watching television, time doing homework) for students in one class.** *(Lesson 8-5)*

5. Describe the student represented by point *A*.
   2 hours of TV and 4 hours of homework
6. How many students did 3 hours of homework or less?
   8 students
7. How many hours of television does the student who has 5 hours of homework watch?
   1 hour





**Mixed Review**

**Compare. Use <, >, or = to complete each statement.**

8. (1-4) $-6 \; \boxed{<} \; 0$
9. (1-4) $-8 \; \boxed{>} \; -9$
10. (1-4) $\frac{5}{8} \; \boxed{<} \; \frac{3}{4}$

35a.

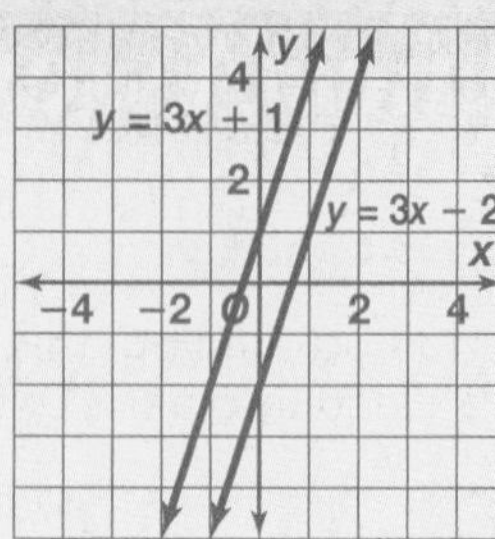


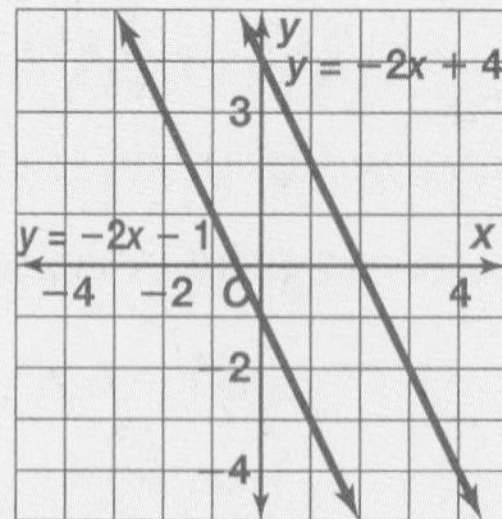


**29.** There are 16 questions on a test. Each question is worth either 5 points or 10 points. The total is 100 points.

**a.** Let $x$ = the number of 5-point questions. $x + y = 16$
Let $y$ = the number of 10-point questions. $5x + 10y = 100$
Write a system of equations to find the number of each type of question.

**b.** Solve the system by graphing. See below right.

**c.** How many questions of each type are on the test?
12 five-point questions, 4 ten-point questions

**30.** *Geometry* A four-foot-long wooden rod is cut into two pieces to make a kite. One piece is three times as long as the other.

**a.** Let $x$ = the length of the longer piece. $x + y = 4$
Let $y$ = the length of the shorter piece. $x = 3y$
Write a system of equations to find the length of each piece.

**b.** Solve the system by graphing. See below right.

**c.** What are the lengths of the pieces? 3 ft, 1 ft

**Solve each problem using a system of linear equations.**

**31.** Find two numbers with a sum of $-8$ and a difference of 4. Let $x$ be the greater number and $y$ be the lesser number. $-2, -6$

**32.** The difference of two numbers is 5. The result when the greater number is decreased by twice the lesser is 9. Let $x$ be the greater number and $y$ be the lesser number. Find the numbers. $1, -4$

**33.** *Geometry* The perimeter of a rectangle is 24 ft. Its length is five times its width. Let $x$ be the length and $y$ be the width. What is the area of the rectangle? 20 ft$^2$

**34.** There are eleven animals in a barnyard. Some are chickens and some are cows. There are 38 legs in all. Let $x$ be the number of chickens and $y$ be the number of cows. How many of each animal are in the barnyard? 3 chickens, 8 cows

**35. a.** *Mathematical Reasoning* Graph each system of equations on a separate coordinate plane. See margin.

$y = 3x + 1$ $\qquad$ $y = -2x - 1$
$y = 3x - 2$ $\qquad$ $y = -2x + 4$

**b.** *Writing* Use the graphs of systems of equations with the same slope. Make a conjecture about the number of solutions of these systems. Conjectures may vary. Sample: A system of equations with the same slope has 0 solutions.

**36.** **TEST PREP** Use the system $x + y = -6$, and $x - y = 2$. What is the relationship of the $x$-coordinate and the $y$-coordinate of the solution of the system? A

**A.** $x > y$ **B.** $x < y$ **C.** $x = y$ **D.** cannot be determined

29b. (12, 4)

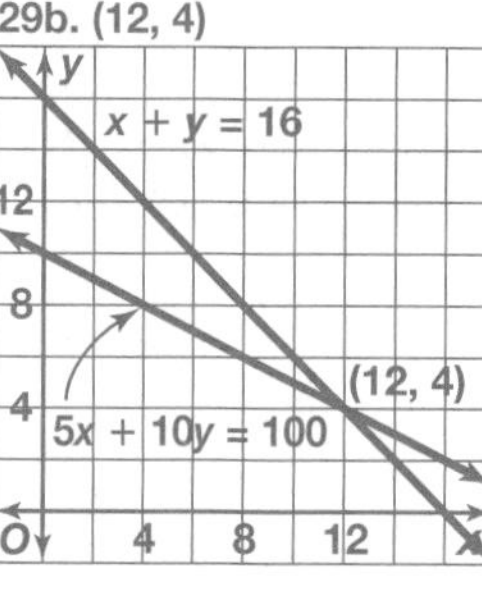


30b. (3, 1)

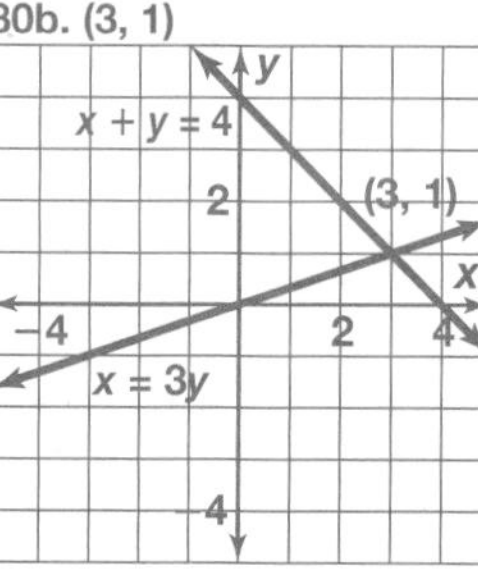




Checkpoint

2.

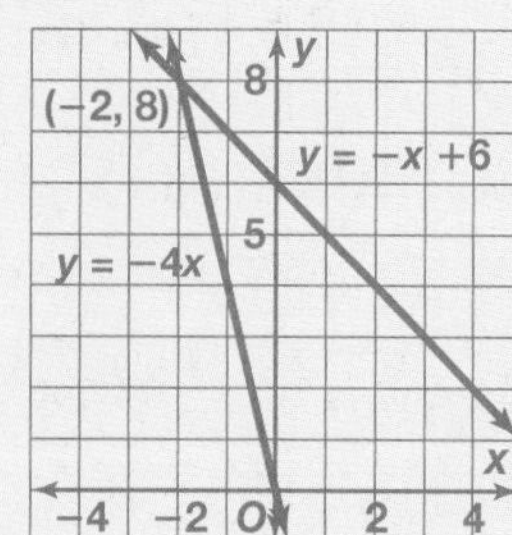


3.

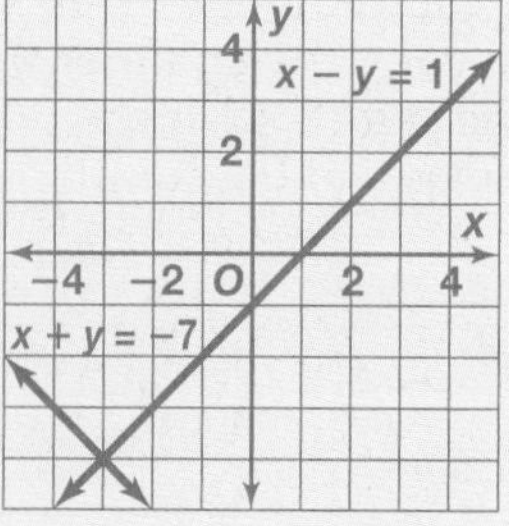

37. Solve the system $y = x + 2$, $y = 4x + 11$, and $y = -2x - 7$. $(-3, -1)$

38. *Geometry* The graphs of $y = 3$, $y = 7$, $x = 2$, and $x = 5$ contain the sides of a rectangle. Find the area of the rectangle. 12 units$^2$

39. *Open-ended* Write a system of two linear equations that has $(-2, 8)$ as its solution. Answers may vary. Sample: $y = x + 10$, $y = -x + 6$

## MIXED REVIEW

40. *Schoolwork* Use the scatter plot at the right. *(Lesson 8-5)*
    a. How many hours did the person who saw four movies spend? 5 h
    b. How many people saw more than three movies? 3 people
    c. How many people spent less than three hours watching movies? 2 people

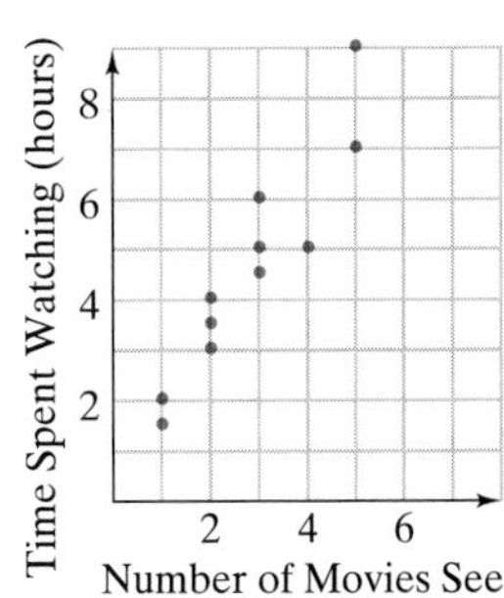


**Solve each inequality.** *(Lessons 2-9, 2-10, 7-6)*

41. $6x < -12$ $x < -2$
42. $m + 4 > -10$ $m > -14$
43. $3t - 1 \leq 17$ $t \leq 6$
44. $-2c + 5 \geq 3$ $c \leq 1$

**Find each probability for one roll of a number cube.** *(Lesson 6-4)*

45. $P(2)$ $\frac{1}{6}$
46. $P(6 \text{ or } 5)$ $\frac{1}{3}$
47. $P(-1)$ 0
48. $P(4, 2, \text{or } 5)$ $\frac{1}{2}$

## CHECKPOINT 2

**Lessons 8-5 through 8-7**

1a., 1c. See back of book.

1. a. *Statistics* Use the table at the right. Make a scatter plot relating newspaper circulation and television sets.
   b. Is there a *positive correlation*, a *negative correlation*, or *no correlation* between daily newspaper circulation and the number of television sets in homes? Explain. See below.
   c. *Data Analysis* Draw a trend line on your scatter plot. Use the trend line to predict the number of television sets when newspaper circulation is 55 million.

1b. Negative correlation; as the number of television sets increases, the newspaper circulation decreases.

**Media in the United States**

| Year | Daily Newspaper Circulation (millions) | Television Sets in Homes (millions) |
|---|---|---|
| 1980 | 62 | 128 |
| 1985 | 63 | 155 |
| 1990 | 62 | 193 |
| 1991 | 61 | 193 |
| 1992 | 60 | 192 |
| 1993 | 60 | 201 |
| 1994 | 59 | 211 |
| 1995 | 57 | 217 |
| 1996 | 57 | 223 |

SOURCE: *Statistical Abstract of the United States*

**Solve each system by graphing.**

2–4. See margin for graphs.

2. $y = -4x$
   $y = -x + 6$
   $(-2, 8)$
3. $x - y = 1$
   $x + y = -7$
   $(-3, -4)$
4. $6x + 2y = 12$
   $y = 3x$
   $(1, 3)$

5. *Measurement* One gallon of liquid occupies 231 cubic inches. Write a rule that expresses the number of gallons $g(c)$ as a function of the number of cubic inches $c$. $g(c) = \frac{c}{231}$

6. Find two numbers with a sum of $-4$ and a difference of 10. Let $x$ be the greater number and $y$ be the lesser number. 3, $-7$

See also Extra Practice section.



4.

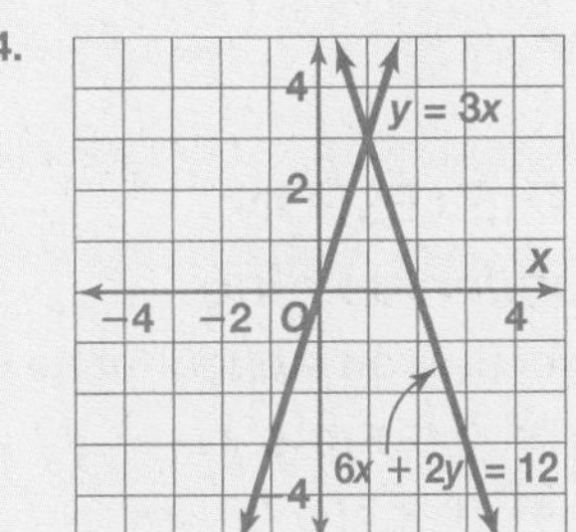


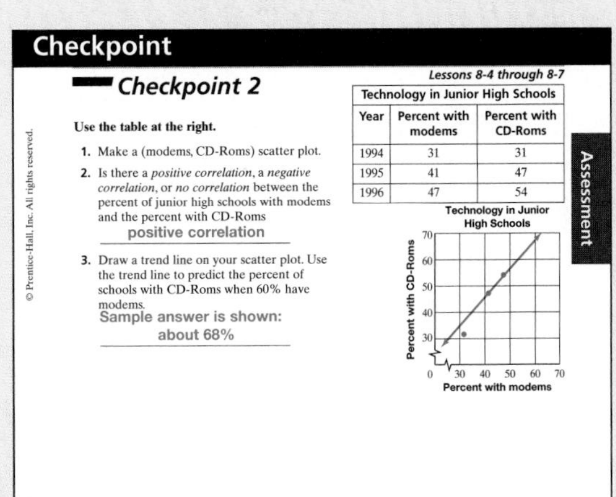

## Checkpoint

### Checkpoint 2

*Lessons 8-4 through 8-7*

**Use the table at the right.**

1. Make a (modems, CD-Roms) scatter plot.
2. Is there a *positive correlation*, a *negative correlation*, or *no correlation* between the percent of junior high schools with modems and the percent with CD-Roms
   positive correlation
3. Draw a trend line on your scatter plot. Use the trend line to predict the percent of schools with CD-Roms when 60% have modems.
   Sample answer is shown: about 68%

**Technology in Junior High Schools**

| Year | Percent with modems | Percent with CD-Roms |
|---|---|---|
| 1994 | 31 | 31 |
| 1995 | 41 | 47 |
| 1996 | 47 | 54 |





## Practice

**Is each ordered pair a solution of the given system? Write *yes* or *no*.**

1. $y = 6x + 12$
   $2x - y = 4$
   $(-4, -12)$ yes
2. $y = -3x$
   $x = 4y + \frac{1}{2}$
   $\left(-\frac{1}{2}, \frac{3}{2}\right)$ no
3. $x + 2y = 2$
   $2x + 5y = 2$
   $(6, -2)$ yes

**Solve each system by graphing. Check your solution.**

4. $x + y = 3$
   $x - y = -1$
   Solution: $(1, 2)$
5. $2x + y = 1$
   $x - 2y = 3$
   Solution: $(1, -1)$
6. $y + 2 = 0$
   $2x + y = 0$
   Solution: $(1, -2)$
7. $3x + 2y = -6$
   $x + 3y = -2$
   Solution: $(-2, 0)$

**Write a system of linear equations. Solve by graphing.**

8. The sum of two numbers is 3. Their difference is 1. Find the numbers.
   $x + y = 3$
   $x - y = 1$
   (2, 1); 2 and 1



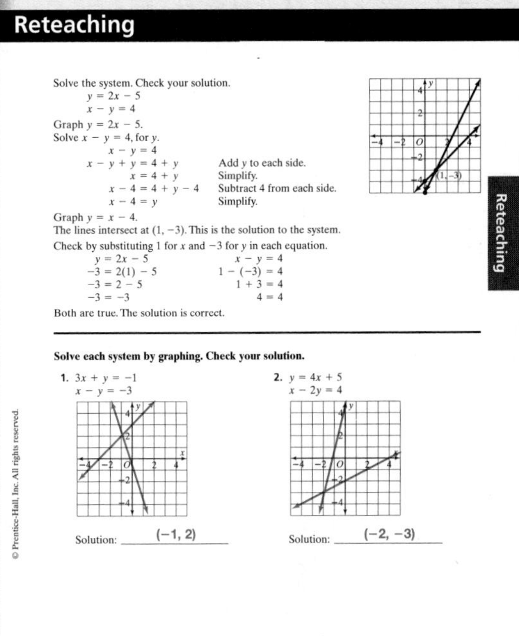

## Reteaching

Solve the system. Check your solution.

$y = 2x - 5$
$x - y = 4$

Graph $y = 2x - 5$.
Solve $x - y = 4$, for $y$.

$x - y = 4$
$x - y + y = 4 + y$ Add $y$ to each side.
$x = 4 + y$ Simplify.
$x - 4 = 4 + y - 4$ Subtract 4 from each side.
$x - 4 = y$ Simplify.

Graph $y = x - 4$.
The lines intersect at $(1, -3)$. This is the solution to the system.
Check by substituting 1 for $x$ and $-3$ for $y$ in each equation.

$y = 2x - 5$ | $x - y = 4$
$-3 = 2(1) - 5$ | $1 - (-3) = 4$
$-3 = 2 - 5$ | $1 + 3 = 4$
$-3 = -3$ | $4 = 4$

Both are true. The solution is correct.

**Solve each system by graphing. Check your solution.**

1. $3x + y = -1$
   $x - y = -3$
   Solution: $(-1, 2)$
2. $y = 4x + 5$
   $x - 2y = 4$
   Solution: $(-2, -3)$



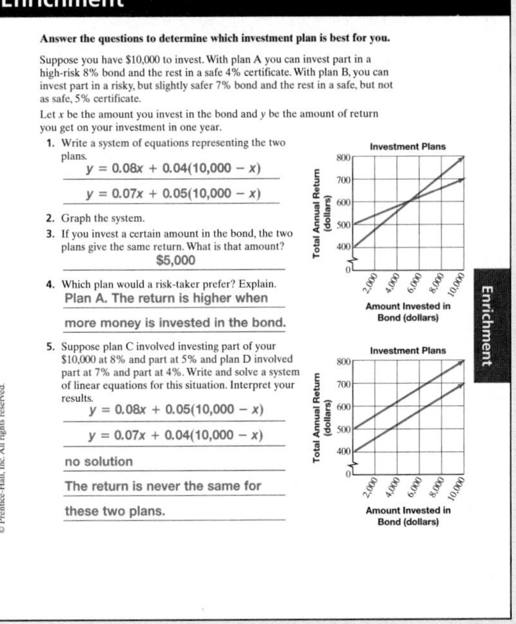

## Enrichment

**Answer the questions to determine which investment plan is best for you.**

Suppose you have \$10,000 to invest. With plan A you can invest part in a high-risk 8% bond and the rest in a safe 4% certificate. With plan B, you can invest part in a risky, but slightly safer 7% bond and the rest in a safe, but not as safe, 5% certificate.

Let $x$ be the amount you invest in the bond and $y$ be the amount of return you get on your investment in one year.

1. Write a system of equations representing the two plans.
   $y = 0.08x + 0.04(10{,}000 - x)$
   $y = 0.07x + 0.05(10{,}000 - x)$
2. Graph the system.
3. If you invest a certain amount in the bond, the two plans give the same return. What is that amount?
   \$5,000
4. Which plan would a risk-taker prefer? Explain.
   Plan A. The return is higher when more money is invested in the bond.
5. Suppose plan C involved investing part of your \$10,000 at 8% and part at 5% and plan D involved part at 7% and part at 4%. Write and solve a system of linear equations for this situation. Interpret your results.
   $y = 0.08x + 0.05(10{,}000 - x)$
   $y = 0.07x + 0.04(10{,}000 - x)$
   no solution
   The return is never the same for these two plans.

# 8-8

## Getting Ready

**Key Terms and Symbols** linear inequality, system of linear inequalities

**Resources** A complete list of resources for this lesson is on p. 381H.

### Daily Skills Warm-Up

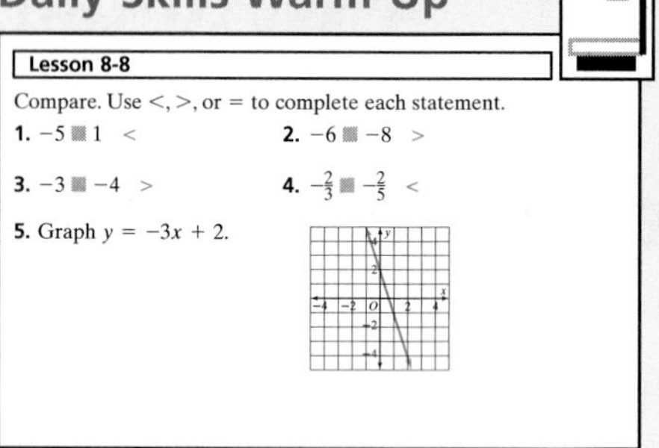
Lesson 8-8

Compare. Use <, >, or = to complete each statement.

1. $-5 \,\blacksquare\, 1$ <
2. $-6 \,\blacksquare\, -8$ >
3. $-3 \,\blacksquare\, -4$ >
4. $-\frac{2}{3} \,\blacksquare\, -\frac{2}{5}$ <
5. Graph $y = -3x + 2$.

### Background for the Lesson

The solutions to a linear inequality in two variables, such as $y \geq x - 3$, is a region containing all the points on the coordinate plane that make the inequality true. This region is bounded by the line that is the graph of the corresponding equality, such as $y = x - 3$. The points on the boundary line are included in the solution region if the inequality sign is *or equal to,* and the boundary line is solid. A dashed boundary line shows that the inequality was *less than* or *greater than.*

## 1 Focus

### Connecting to Students' Lives

The barricades that block off a sidewalk because of construction are similar to the boundary line that defines the solution region for an inequality in two variables.

### Connecting to Prior Knowledge

In Lesson 8-7 students learned how to solve systems of linear equations. In this lesson, students learn how to graph and solve systems of linear equations. In Lesson 9-8, students will apply these graphing skills to transformations.

# 8-8 Graphing Linear Inequalities

### What You'll Learn

1. To graph linear inequalities
2. To graph systems of linear inequalities

### . . . And Why

To model real-world situations such as grocery shopping and earnings from jobs

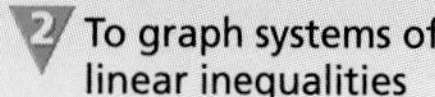


- < is less than
- > is greater than
- ≤ is less than or equal to
- ≥ is greater than or equal to

## PART 1 Graphing Linear Inequalities

If you replace the equal sign in a linear equation with >, <, ≥, or ≤, the result is a **linear inequality.** The graph of a linear inequality is a region of the coordinate plane bounded by a line. Every point in the region is a solution of the inequality.

### Example 1

**Graph each inequality on a coordinate plane.**

**a.** $y \leq x + 2$ **b.** $y < -2x$

**Step 1** Graph the boundary line.

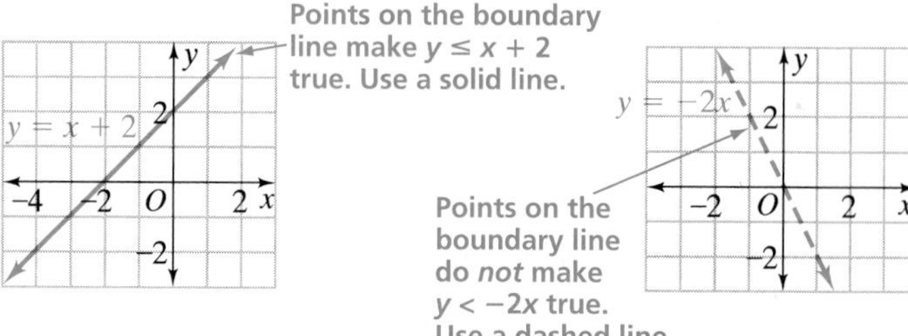


**Step 2** Test a point not on the boundary line.

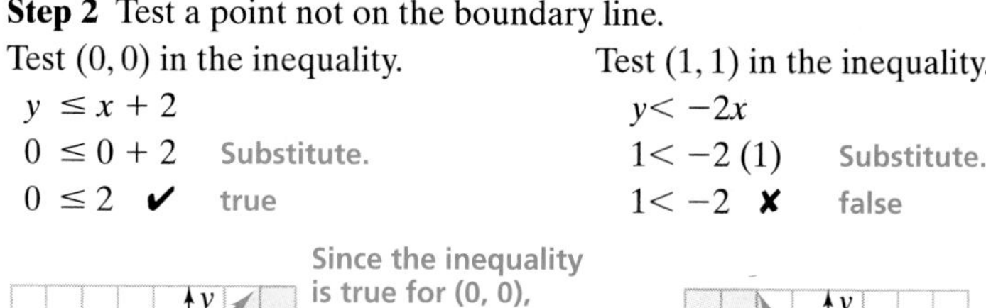

Test (0, 0) in the inequality.

$y \leq x + 2$

$0 \leq 0 + 2$ Substitute.

$0 \leq 2$ ✔ true

Test (1, 1) in the inequality.

$y < -2x$

$1 < -2(1)$ Substitute.

$1 < -2$ ✘ false

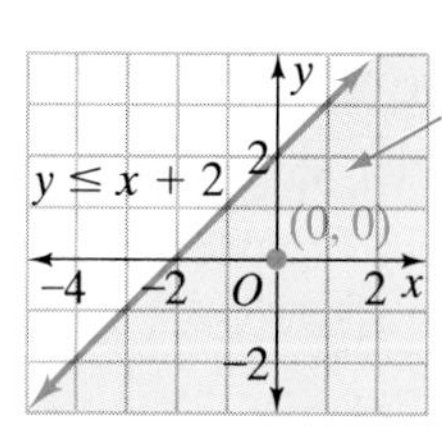


Since the inequality is true for (0, 0), shade the region containing (0, 0).

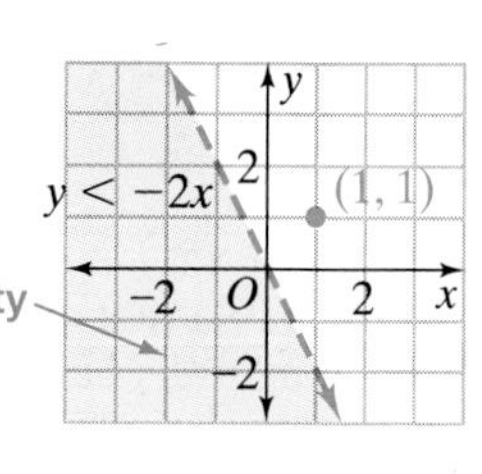


Since the inequality is false for (1, 1), shade the region that does not contain (1, 1).



## Tools to Monitor Progress

### BEFORE THE LESSON

**To check prerequisite skills:**

- Graphing equations

**Skills Intervention Kit,** Pre-Algebra Basics

### DURING THE LESSON

**To check understanding:**

**Try This** exercises on student page

- **Additional Example 1**

Compare these graphs:
$y > 2x + 1$ and
$y \leq 2x + 1$. **The first has a dashed boundary line; the second has a solid boundary line.**

■ **TRY THIS** Graph each inequality on a separate coordinate plane.

**1.** $y \geq 3x - 1$ **2.** $y > -x + 3$ **3.** $y < 2x - 4$ 1–3. See below right.

REAL-WORLD CONNECTION

■ **EXAMPLE 2**

**Apricots cost \$3/lb. Tomatoes cost \$1/lb. You plan to spend no more than \$10. How many pounds of each can you buy?**

**Step 1** Write an inequality.

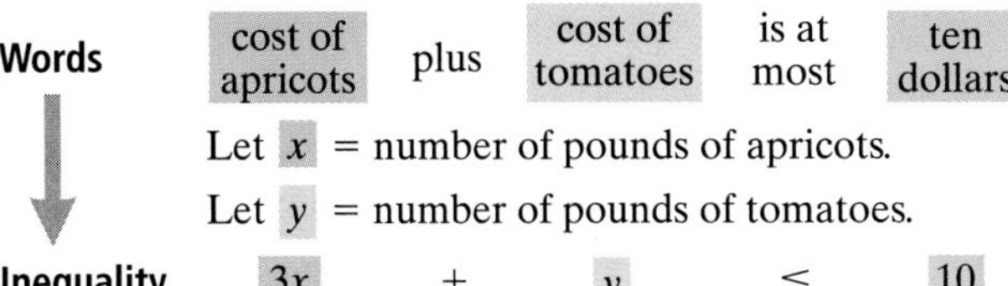

| Words | cost of apricots | plus | cost of tomatoes | is at most | ten dollars |
|---|---|---|---|---|---|

Let $x$ = number of pounds of apricots.

Let $y$ = number of pounds of tomatoes.

| Inequality | $3x$ | $+$ | $y$ | $\leq$ | $10$ |
|---|---|---|---|---|---|

**Step 2** Write the equation of the boundary line in slope-intercept form.

$3x + y = 10$

$\rightarrow y = -3x + 10$

**Step 3** Graph $y = -3x + 10$ in Quadrant I since weight is not negative.

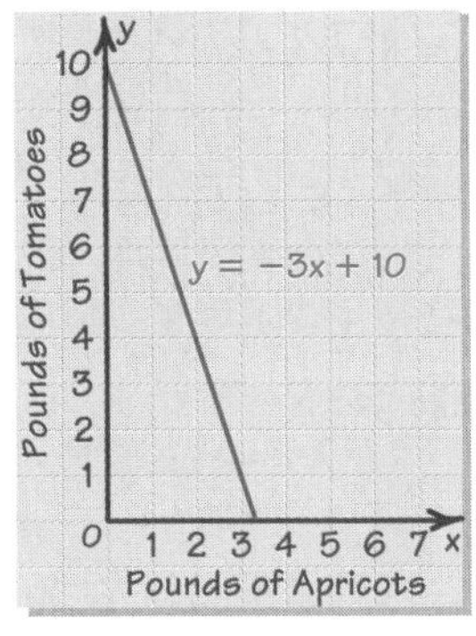


**Step 4** Test (1, 1).

$y \leq -3x + 10$

$1 \leq -3(1) + 10$

$1 \leq 7$ ✔

The inequality is true. (1, 1) is a solution.

**Step 5** Shade the region containing (1, 1).

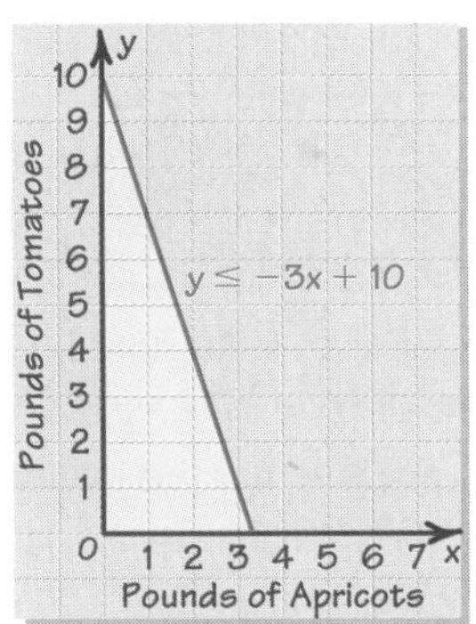


The graph shows the possible solutions. For example, you could buy 1 pound of apricots and 5 pounds of tomatoes.

1\.

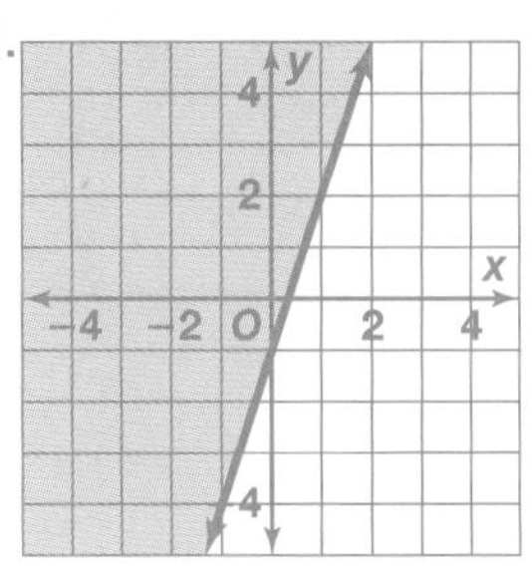

2\.

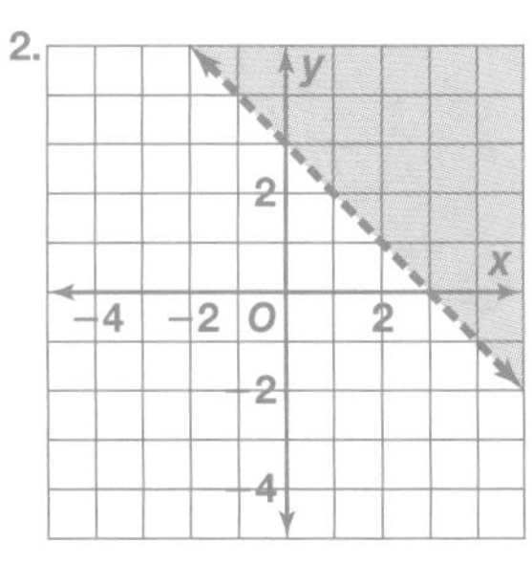

3\.

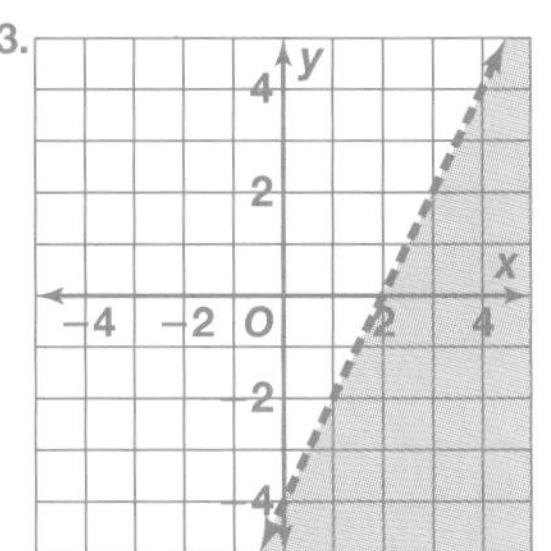



# 2 Teach

## PART 1 Part 1 Teaching Notes

To find the boundary line, think first of the inequality as an equation (with an equal sign) and graph the equation. To see if this boundary line is solid or dashed, test a point on the boundary line. Then test a point not on the boundary line to find out which side of the line is shaded to indicate the region of solutions to the inequality.

**ELL** Make sure students understand that the graph of a linear inequality is a *region* of the coordinate plane. A region is an area or part of the coordinate plane.

### ■ Example 1

**Build understanding.** Ask: Why is the boundary line for $y < -2x$ dashed? Since the inequality is <, and not ≤, points on the boundary line are not solutions to the inequality. The dashed line shows this.

**Error Prevention** It is generally true that for an inequality with $y$ on the left and the > or ≥ symbol, the area *above* the boundary should be shaded to indicate the region of solutions. Similarly, the area *below* an inequality with < or ≤ should be shaded to indicate solutions. However, as lines become increasingly vertical, it may be difficult to tell what is *above* and *below* the line. Therefore, it is always best to test a point on either side of the line to decide which side is the region of solutions.

### ■ Example 2

**Build understanding.** Ask: Why is the inequality for this problem written with ≤ instead of <? you could spend the whole \$10

- **Additional Example 3**

Solve the system $y \geq x + 1$ and $y < 2x + 3$ by graphing. Graph shows solid boundary with $y$-intercept of 1 and slope of 1, plus dashed boundary with $y$-intercept of 3 and slope of 2. Area shaded between the lines, above and to the right of the intersection.

## AFTER THE LESSON

### To assess knowledge: Lesson Quiz

Tell whether the point is in the graph of the solution.

1. $y < 4x$ (3, 0) solution
2. $y > -x - 1$ (2, −3) not a solution
3. $y \leq 4x - 2$ (−1, 1) not a solution
4. $y \leq 3x + 1$ and $y > 2x + 2$ (6, 1) not a solution

- For enrichment and reteaching options see Resources on p. 381H.

# Part 2 Teaching Notes

Compare and contrast systems of linear equations with systems of linear inequalities. While there is often only one solution to a system of linear equations (unless they coincide or are parallel), there are many solutions to a system of linear inequalities.

**Tactile Learning** Create a coordinate plane on a classroom bulletin board. Have students use string, thumbtacks, and construction paper to practice graphing systems of linear inequalities.

## Example 3

**Build understanding.** Ask: Is the point where the boundary lines intersect a solution to this system of inequalities? Explain. No, the point (1, 1) does not make the inequality $y > x$ true.

**Extension** Explain why the point where the boundary lines of a system of linear inequalities intersect may or may not be a solution to the system. If either of the inequalities is $<$ or $>$, then the boundary line for that inequality does not contain solutions to the inequality. Therefore, the point at which boundary lines intersect is not a solution.

### Try This

4. Adult tickets to the school play cost \$4. Children's tickets cost \$2. Your goal is to sell tickets worth at least \$30. Let $x$ be the number of children's tickets and $y$ be the number of adult tickets. Graph a linear inequality to show how many of each type of ticket you must sell to reach your goal. See margin for graph of $2x + 4y \geq 30$.

## Part 2 Graphing Systems of Linear Inequalities

Two or more linear inequalities form a **system of linear inequalities.** A *solution of a system of linear inequalities* is any ordered pair that makes each inequality in the system true. To solve a system, graph the inequalities on one coordinate plane.

### Example 3

**Solve the system $y > x$ and $y \leq -x + 2$ by graphing.**

**Step 1** Graph $y > x$ on a coordinate plane.

**Step 2** Graph $y \leq -x + 2$ on the same coordinate plane.

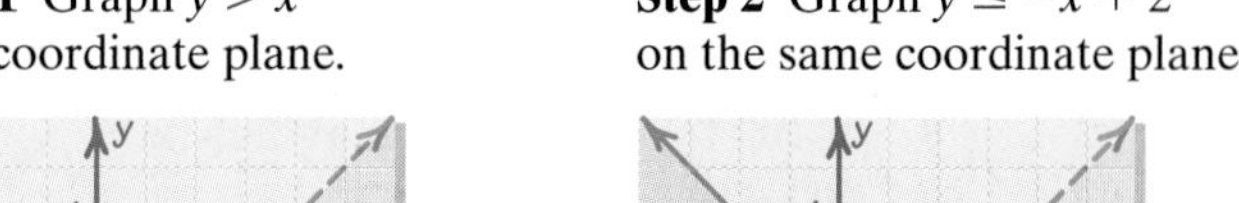

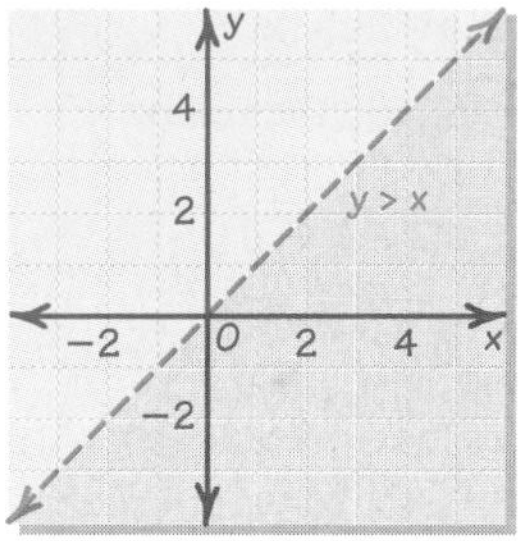


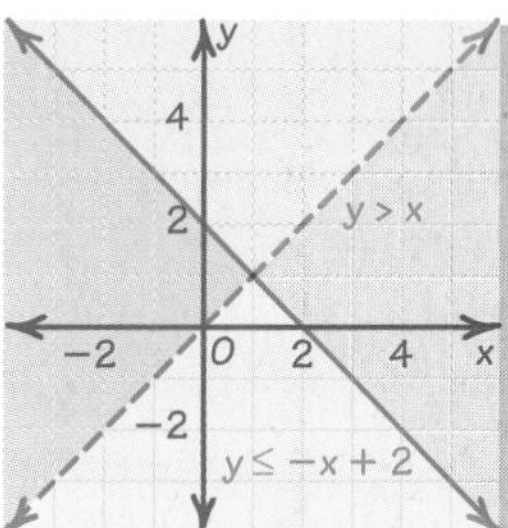


The solutions are the coordinates of all the points in the region that is shaded in both colors.

**Check** See whether the solution $(-1, 0)$ makes both of the inequalities true.

| | | |
|---|---|---|
| $y > x$ | | $y \leq -x + 2$ |
| $0 > -1$ | Replace $x$ with $-1$ and $y$ with 0. | $0 \leq -(-1) + 2$ |
| $0 > -1$ ✔ | The solutions check. | $0 \leq 3$ ✔ |

### Try This Solve each system by graphing. 5–6. See left.

5. $y \leq -2x - 5$
$y < \frac{1}{2}x$

6. $y > x - 1$
$y < 3x + 4$



5\.

6\.

4\.

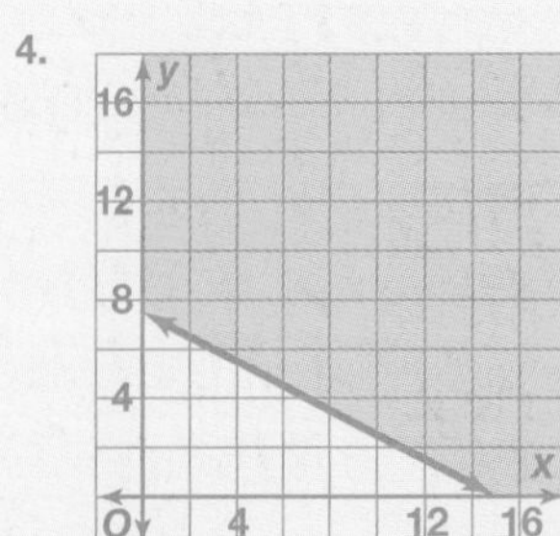

# Exercises

## Check Understanding

**Solve each inequality for y.**

1. $4x + y < -3$ $y < -4x - 3$
2. $-y \le 2x$ $y \ge -2x$
3. $2x + 3y \le 7$ $y \le -\frac{2}{3}x + \frac{7}{3}$

**Graph each inequality on a separate coordinate plane.** 4–5. See margin. 6. See back of book.

4. $y \ge 3x - 1$
5. $x - y > 10$
6. $y \le 5$

**Solve each system by graphing.** 7–9. See back of book.

7. $y > -x$ <br> $y < x + 6$
8. $2x + y \le 4$ <br> $y + 1 \ge -2x$
9. $x + y > -3$ <br> $x - y < 5$

10. a. *Income* You can earn \$6/h mowing lawns and \$3/h baby-sitting. You want to earn at least \$45. Let $x$ = number of hours mowing lawns and $y$ = number of hours baby-sitting. Write a linear inequality to model this situation. $6x + 3y \ge 45$
    b. Graph the linear inequality.
    c. If you baby-sit for 6 hours, what is the number of hours you will need to mow lawns to earn \$45? $4\frac{1}{2}$ h

10b.

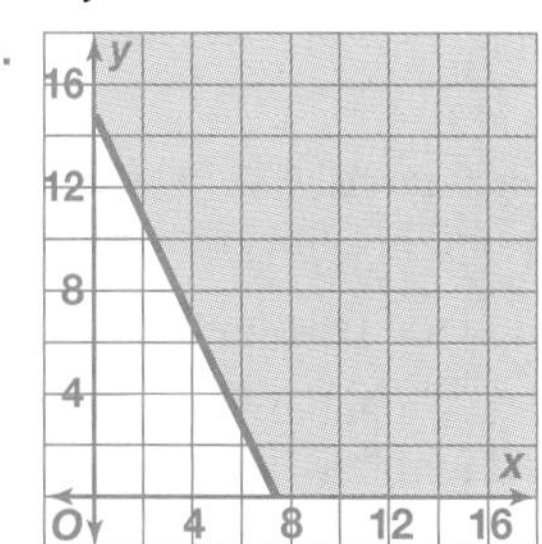

## Practice and Problem Solving

**TEST PREP** **Choose a linear inequality to match each graph.**

11. C

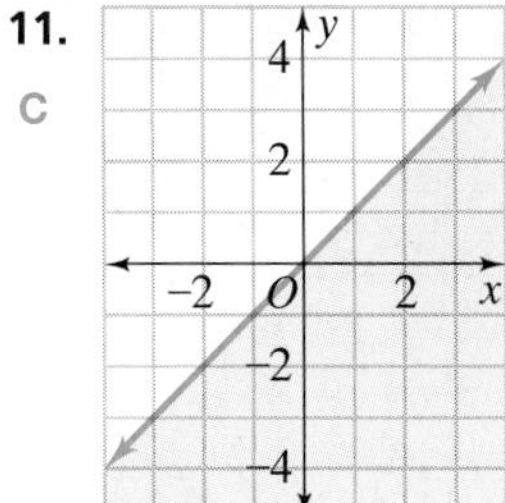

A. $-y \ge x$
B. $-y \le x$
C. $-y \ge -x$
D. $-y \le -x$

12. B

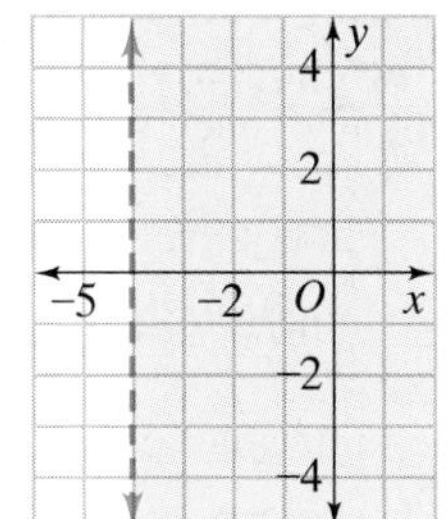

A. $x < -4$
B. $x > -4$
C. $-x < -4$
D. $-x > -4$

13. A

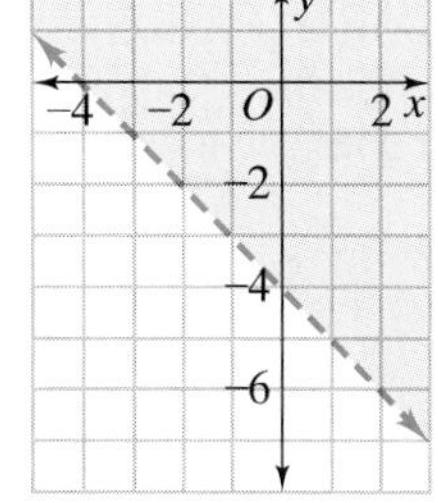

A. $x + y > -4$
B. $x - y > 4$
C. $x + y < 4$
D. $x - y < -4$



# 3 Practice/Assess

## Assignment Guide

To provide flexible scheduling, this lesson can be divided into parts.

**Part 1**
**Core** 1–6, 10–27, 38–43
**Extension** 28–29

**Part 2**
**Core** 7–9, 30–35
**Extension** 36, 37, 44, 45

Mixed Review can be assigned at any time for maintenance.

## Exercises

**Test Prep Exercise 43** If one inequality has the same solutions as another, then the inequalities are equivalent. Write the inequalities in slope-intercept form to see which choice is equivalent to the one in the question.

## Challenge

Describe the solutions of the system of inequalities $y < x + 1$ and $y > x + 1$. Solutions can be found everywhere on the coordinate plane, except for on the boundary line.

## Closure

Two or more linear inequalities with the same variables form a system of linear inequalities. A solution of the system is any ordered pair that is a solution of each inequality in the system. You can solve a system by graphing.

## Alternative Assessment

Tell students to write an inequality in which half of the coordinate plane is a solution to the inequality. Tell them to start by graphing this problem, then write an inequality that describes the graph.

4.

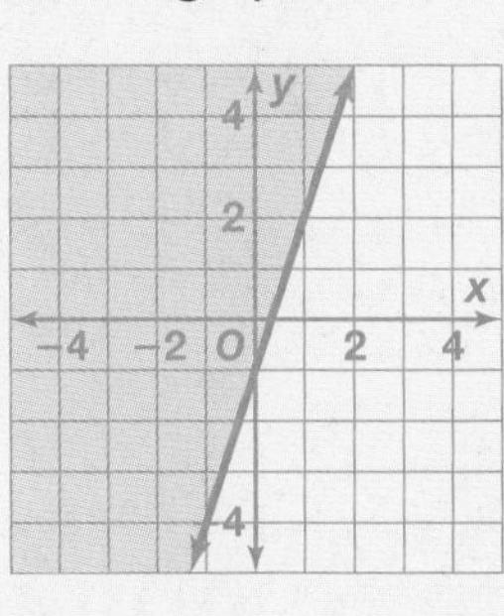

5.

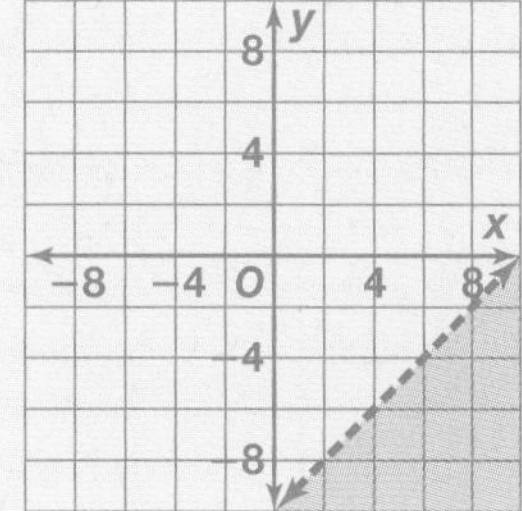

## Daily Cumulative Review

**Solve each problem using a system of linear equations.** *(Lesson 8-7)*

1. The difference of two numbers is 8. The result when the greater number is decreased by half of the smaller number is 10. Let $x$ be the greater number and $y$ be the lesser number. Find the numbers. $x = 12$ and $y = 4$
2. There are fifteen bikes in the bike store. Some are bicycles and some are tricycles. There are 36 wheels in all. Let $x$ be the number of tricycles and $y$ be the number of bicycles. How many of each bike are in the store? $y = 9$ bicycles and $x = 6$ tricycles

**Solve using any strategy.** *(Lesson 8-6)*

3. Shelly is making sugar cookies. She has 5 different cookie cutters. She also has 4 different colors of icing. In how many different ways can she make the cookies? 20 different ways
4. A fruit inspector found twelve rotten apples in a box containing 150 apples. At that rate, how many rotten apples would there be in 2,100 apples? 168 rotten apples

**Mixed Review**

**Solve each inequality. Graph the solutions.**

5. $6 \ge x - 10$ (2-9) $16 \ge x$
6. $x - 7 < -15$ (2-9) $x < -8$

**Order from least to greatest.**

7. $45 \times 10^4, 321 \times 10^3, 3.624 \times 10^4$ (4-9) $3.624 \times 10^4, 321 \times 10^3, 45 \times 10^4$
8. $\frac{1}{3}, 0.3, \frac{4}{3}, \frac{2}{3}$ (5-2) $0.3, \frac{1}{3}, \frac{2}{3}, \frac{4}{3}$

22.

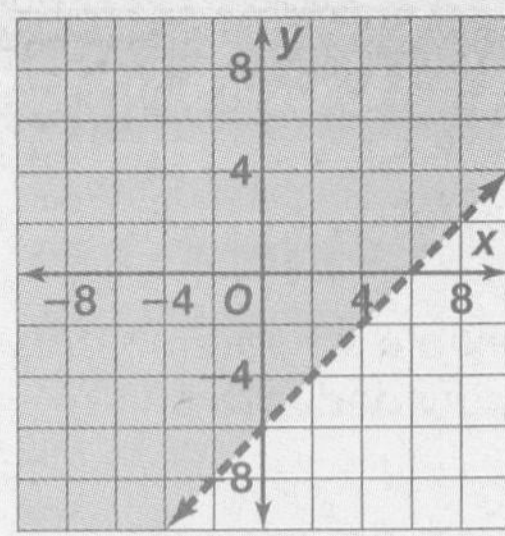


23.

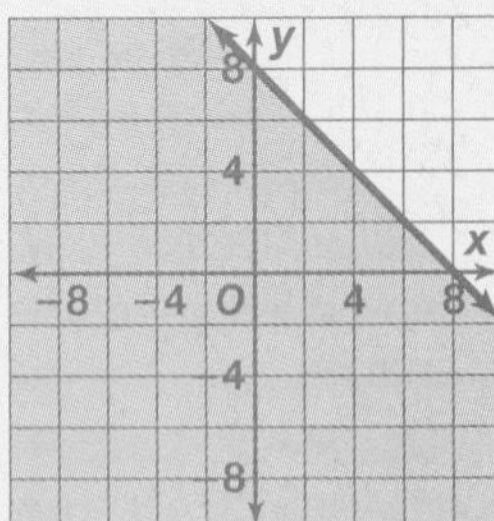


24.

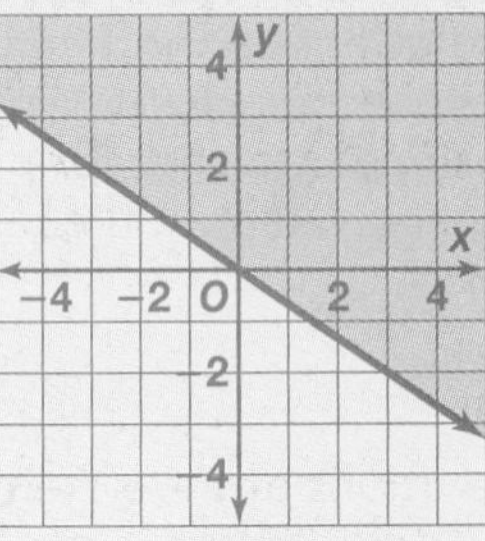


25.

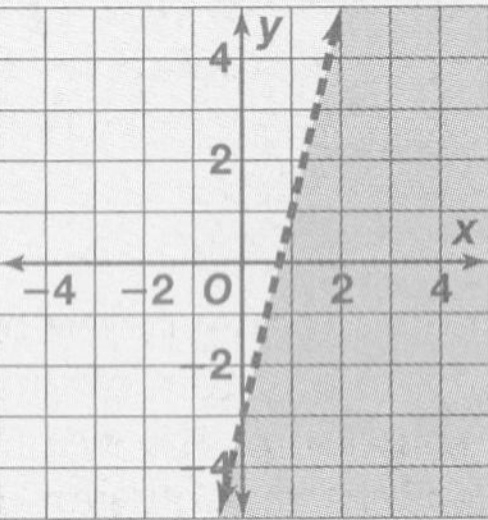


26.

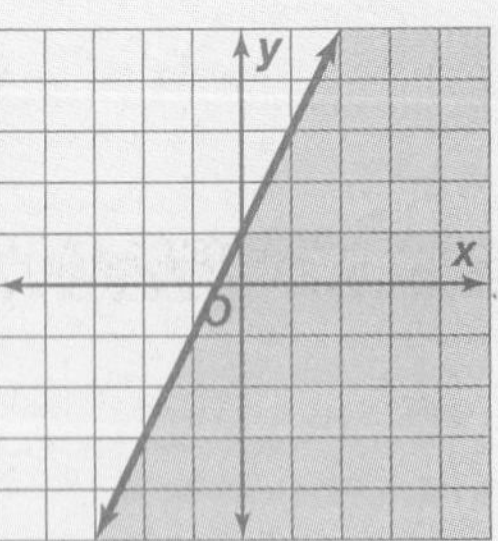


**Write the equation of each boundary line in slope-intercept form. Tell whether the boundary line is solid or dashed.**

14. $2x + y \geq 3$ $y = -2x + 3$; solid
15. $y - 2 < 3x$ $y = 3x + 2$; dashed
16. $-y > 4x$ $y = -4x$; dashed
17. $-y \leq -\frac{1}{2}x$ $y = \frac{1}{2}x$; solid
18. $x + y < -3$ $y = -x - 3$; dashed
19. $x - y \geq 7$ $y = x - 7$; solid
20. $5x + 3y \leq 9$ $y = -\frac{5}{3}x + 3$; solid
21. $4x - 2y > 10$ $y = 2x - 5$; dashed

**Graph each inequality on a separate coordinate plane.** See margin.

22. $y > x - 6$
23. $y \leq -x + 8$
24. $y \geq -\frac{2}{3}x$
25. $y < 4x - 3$
26. $y \leq 2x + 1$
27. $y > x + 2$
28. $9x + 3y < 3$
29. $x - 2y \geq -12$

**Solve each system by graphing. Use a separate coordinate plane for each system.** See back of book.

30. $y \leq x$
$y \geq -x - 4$
31. $y > -x$
$y > 2x + 3$
32. $x < 6$
$y \leq 2x$
33. $y < 4$
$x > -5$
34. $y \leq -x + 1$
$y > x - 5$
35. $y > x - 4$
$y \leq x + 2$
36. $-2x + y > 1$
$x + 2y < 2$
37. $3x + y > 5$
$y \geq -2$

**For Exercises 38–41 show all the solutions of each problem by graphing a linear inequality.** 38–41. See back of book for graphs.

38. Find two numbers with a sum greater than three. $x + y > 3$
39. A number is greater than or equal to three times another number. What are the numbers? $y \geq 3x$
40. Use the prices shown in the photo at the right. Let $x$ be the number of medium drinks sold and $y$ be the number of large drinks sold. How many drinks must the vendor sell to have at least \$60 in sales? $2x + 3y \geq 60$
41. Melissa has a collection of dimes and nickels with a total face value of less than one dollar. Let $x$ be the number of dimes and $y$ be the number of nickels. How many of each type of coin does she have? $10x + 5y < 100$

MEDIUM \$2
LARGE \$3

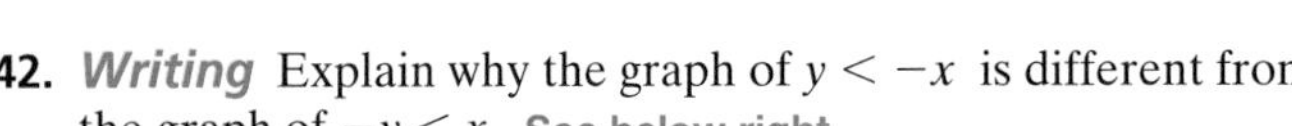

42. *Writing* Explain why the graph of $y < -x$ is different from the graph of $-y < x$. See below right.
43. **TEST PREP** Which inequality has the same solutions as $y \geq -2x + 1$? B
A. $2x + y \leq 1$
B. $2x + y \geq 1$
C. $2x - y \leq 1$
D. $2x - y \geq 1$
44. *Open-ended* Write a system of inequalities that has no solutions.
Answers may vary. Sample: $y > x + 5, y < x + 3$.

42. Multiply both sides of $-y < x$ by $-1$ to get $y > -x$. The graph of $y < -x$ are the points below the graph of $y = -x$. The graph of $y > -x$ are the points above the graph of $y = -x$



27.

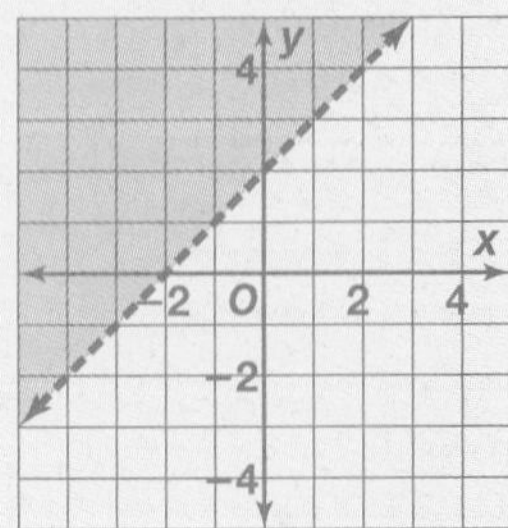


28.

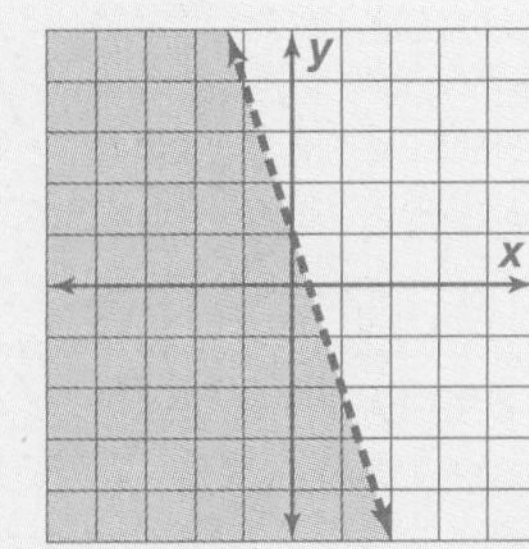


29.

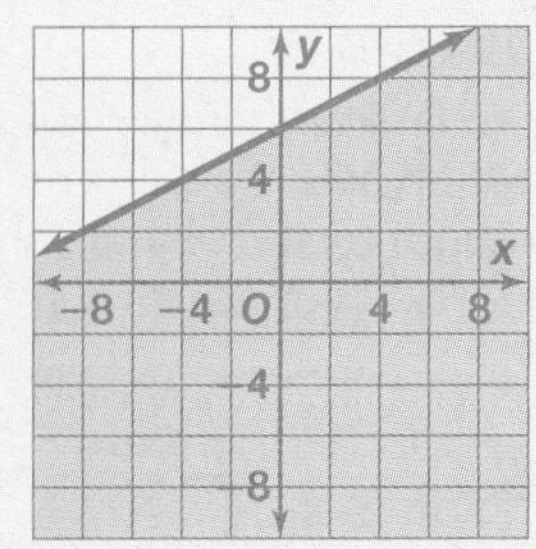

**45.** *Critical Thinking* Write a system of linear inequalities to describe each graph. 45a. $y > -6$; $x < 2$

**a.** **b.**

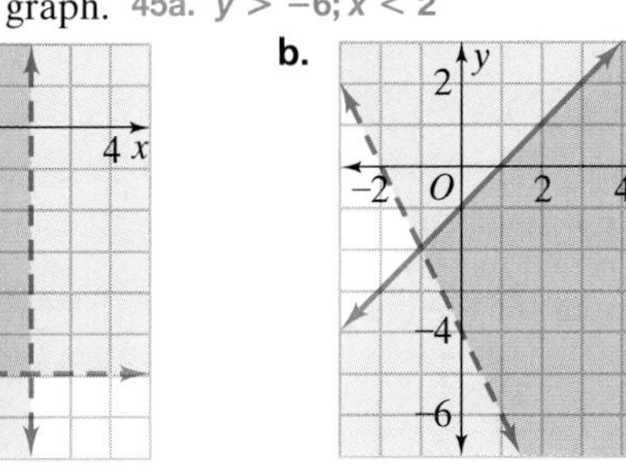

45b. $y \le x - 1$
$y > -2x - 4$

### Journal

*How is graphing an inequality on a coordinate plane similar to graphing an inequality on a number line? How is it different?*

## MIXED REVIEW

**Solve each system of equations by graphing.** ***(Lesson 8-7)*** 46–49. See back of book for graphs.

**46.** $y = x + 3$
$y = -2x - 3$
(−2, 1)

**47.** $x + y = 8$
$x - y = -2$
(3, 5)

**48.** $y = 2x - 1$
$2x - y = 3$
no solution

**49.** $3y = -2x - 3$
$3y = x - 12$
(3, −3)

**Solve each equation.** ***(Lessons 5-7, 5-8)***

**50.** $m - \frac{2}{3} = \frac{1}{6}$ $\frac{5}{6}$

**51.** $\frac{5}{4}c = \frac{3}{2}$ $1\frac{1}{5}$

**52.** $\frac{3}{4} + w = \frac{9}{10}$ $\frac{3}{20}$

**53.** $\frac{5}{9}p = \frac{5}{12}$ $\frac{3}{4}$

**Evaluate each expression for $c = 4$ and $m = -3$.** ***(Lesson 4-6)***

**54.** $\frac{c + m}{5}$ $\frac{1}{5}$

**55.** $\frac{m - c}{2}$ $-\frac{7}{2}$

**56.** $\frac{2c - m}{-4}$ $-\frac{11}{4}$

**57.** $\frac{4m}{2 - c}$ 6

**58.** *Animals* In 1999, there were 162 California condors. Of these birds, 113 were in captivity, 29 were living free in California, and 20 were living free in Arizona. ***(Lesson 6-6)***

**a.** What percent of the condors were living free in Arizona? Round your answer to the nearest tenth of a percent. 12.3%

**b.** What percent of the condors were living free in all? Round your answer to the nearest tenth of a percent. 30.2%

CHAPTER PROJECT 8

## ACTIVITY 3 ANALYZING

Analyze your graph from Activity 2. What does the slope of each line represent? What does the *y*-intercept of each line represent? Do the lines intersect at any point? Explain the significance of such an intersection. Which company will charge the least? Will the number of chairs you rent affect your answer? Explain.

See also Extra Practice section.



## Project Activity 3

**Analyzing** You may want to have students work in pairs to name the slopes and explain to each other the meanings of the various points of intersection.

## Practice

**Graph each inequality.**

**1.** $y < x$

**2.** $x + y \le 2$

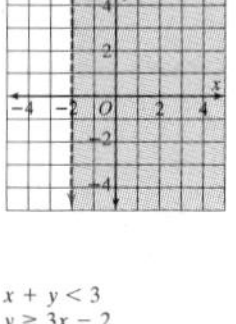

**3.** $x + 2y \ge 4$

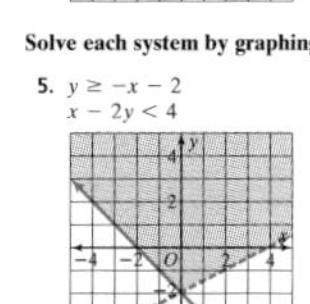

**4.** $x > -2$

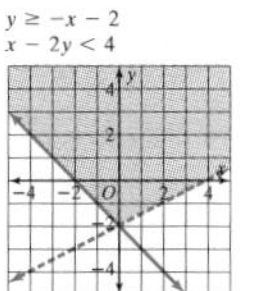

**Solve each system by graphing.**

**5.** $y \ge -x - 2$
$x - 2y < 4$

**6.** $x + y < 3$
$y \ge 3x - 2$

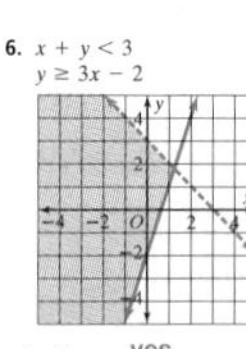

**7.** Is the origin a solution to the system in Exercise 5? yes

**8.** Is (4, 0) a solution to the system in Exercise 5? no

**9.** Is (1, 0) a solution to the system in Exercise 6? no

**10.** Is (−1, 0) a solution to the system in Exercise 6? yes



## Reteaching

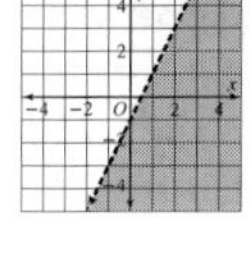

Graph $y < 2x - 1$.

Graph the bounding line $y = 2x - 1$. The *y*-intercept is −1 and the slope is 2. Since the inequality is <, the boundary line should be dashed.

Try a test point. The origin (0, 0) is usually easy to use.

$y < 2x - 1$
$0 \overset{?}{<} 2(0) - 1$
$0 \overset{?}{<} -1$ No

(0, 0) is not in the solution of $y < 2x - 1$. Shade the side of the boundary line *not* containing the origin.

**Tell whether the boundary line of the graph of each inequality is *solid* or *dashed*.**

**1.** $4x - 5y \ge 3$ solid

**2.** $y < \frac{2}{3}x + 2$ dashed

**3.** $2x > 3 - 2y$ dashed

**4.** $y \le -5$ solid

**5.** $-x + 2y > -3$ dashed

**6.** $8 \le 5y - 3x$ solid

**Tell whether the region containing the origin would be shaded in the graph of each inequality. Write *yes* or *no*.**

**7.** $4x - 5y \ge 3$ no

**8.** $y < \frac{2}{3}x + 2$ yes

**9.** $2x > 3 - 2y$ no

**10.** $y \le -5$ no

**11.** $-x + 2y > -3$ yes

**12.** $8 \le 5y - 3x$ no

**13.** $4x < y$ no

**14.** $\frac{3}{4}x > 2y$ no



## Enrichment

London's Great Fire of 1666 changed a professor of mathematics and physics into a world-renowned architect. This learned man oversaw the rebuilding of much of London, including St. Paul's Cathedral. The name of this mathematician/architect is Sir Christopher Wren.

**To find the answer, decide which of the two inequalities has the given ordered pair as a solution. Circle the inequality. Then write the letter of the inequality above the number of the exercise in the answer grid at the bottom of the page.**

**1.** (1, 6) (R:) $y < 2x + 5$ A: $y > 2x + 5$

**2.** (−3, −11) (E:) $y \ge 3x - 2$ N: $y > 3x - 2$

**3.** (−10, 0) (C:) $y \le \frac{1}{2}x + 5$ I: $y < \frac{1}{2}x + 5$

**4.** (3, −20) (W:) $y > 8 - 12x$ O: $y < 8 - 12x$

**5.** (−1, 0) M: $5 + 4x < y$ (S:) $5 + 4x > y$

**6.** (−8, −7) (I:) $x \le y$ G: $x \ge y$

**7.** (6, −5) (O:) $x > -3$ C: $x < -3$

**8.** (−2, 2) S: $y - 4 > x$ (T:) $y - 4 \ge x$

**9.** (−3, 3) R: $x + y > y$ (H:) $x + y > x$

**10.** $(-\frac{4}{5}, \frac{1}{5})$ (H:) $-x > 0$ P: $-x < 0$

**11.** (2, 1.2) E: $x < 3y - 2$ (R:) $x > 3y - 2$

**12.** (4.5, 3.4) (R:) $3x < 4y$ T: $3x > 4y$

**13.** (−5, 3) M: $2x + 3y > 0$ (I:) $2x + 3y < 0$

**14.** (2.7, 4.8) (S:) $-3x + 5y < 16$ R: $-3x + 5y > 16$

**15.** (0.8, 0.2) W: $8 - 8x > 9y$ (E:) $8 - 8x < 9y$

**16.** (−3.9, −6.5) S: $7x - 4y < -2$ (R:) $7x - 4y > -2$

**17.** (5, 8) (P:) $x \le 5$ A: $x > 5$

**18.** (−3, −10) (N:) $y \le x + 7$ P: $y \ge x - 5$

| S | I | R | C | H | R | I | S | T | O | P | H | E | R | W | R | E | N |
|---|---|---|---|---|---|---|---|---|---|---|---|---|---|---|---|---|---|
| 14 | 6 | 12 | 3 | 9 | 1 | 13 | 5 | 8 | 7 | 17 | 10 | 2 | 16 | 4 | 11 | 15 | 18 |

## Graphing Inequalities

In Lessons 8-8, students learned how to graph and solve linear inequalities and systems of linear inequalities. In this Math Toolbox, students learn how to graph linear inequalities using a graphing calculator.

## Math Background

Graphing linear inequalities with a graphing calculator is almost exactly like graphing linear equations. Begin by setting the viewing window. Enter the equation and press the key to graph the equation. With inequalities, pay particular attention to the boundary line and whether or not it is included in the solution region.

## Teaching Notes

**Error Prevention** Remind students that their calculator may not graph boundaries with dashed lines. Suggest that students check a point on the boundary to see whether it makes the inequality true.

**Monitoring Progress Exercise 9** The solution to the system of inequalities is the region that contains points that make both inequalities true.

**Block Scheduling** If you have block scheduling or extended periods, you may wish to insert this Math Toolbox lesson between the completion of Part 2 and the beginning of the Wrap Up.

MATH TOOLBOX

Technology
After Lesson 8-8

# Graphing Inequalities

Graphing an inequality on a calculator is similar to graphing an equation. If your calculator does not graph dashed lines, you have to remember the type of boundary line you need for the inequality.

### Example

**Graph $y > -x + 4$.**

**Step 1** Press the Y= key. Enter $-x + 4$.

**Step 2** Press ◄ to move to the left of Y1. Press ENTER twice when $y$ is greater than the right side of the equation, or press ENTER three times when $y$ is less than the right side of the equation.

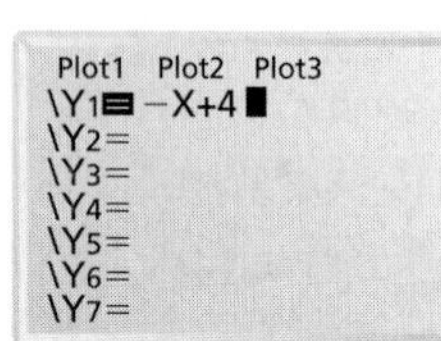


**Step 3** Press ZOOM 6 to graph the inequality using the standard viewing window. Then sketch the inequality.

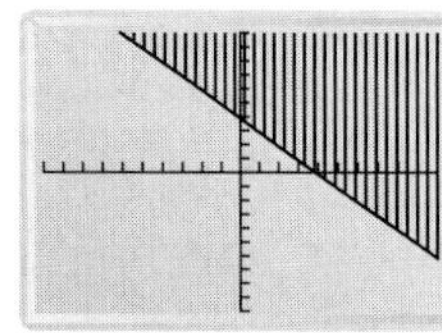
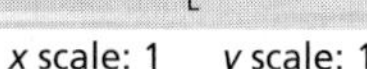




1.
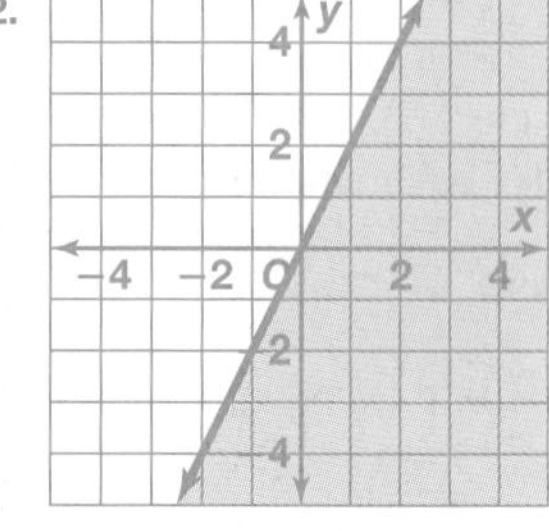

2.
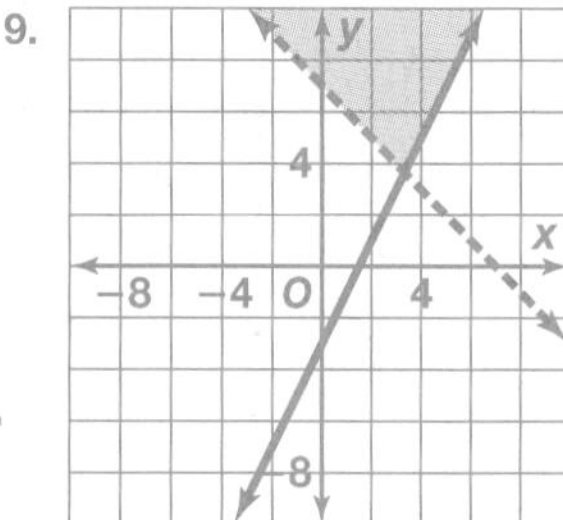

9.

**Graph each inequality. Be sure to graph the boundary line appropriately.** 1–2. See above right. 3. See margin. 4–8. See back of book.

1. $y > 3x + 1$
2. $y \leq 2x$
3. $y < -x - 5$
4. $y \geq 4x + 6$
5. $y \leq -2x - 4$
6. $y < x + 7$
7. $y > -3x + 4$
8. $y \geq -\frac{2}{5}x + 1$
9. Graph the inequalities $y > -x + 7$ and $y \geq 2x - 3$. Sketch the system of inequalities. See above right.

432 Math Toolbox

• **Additional Example**

Graph $y < x - 2$.

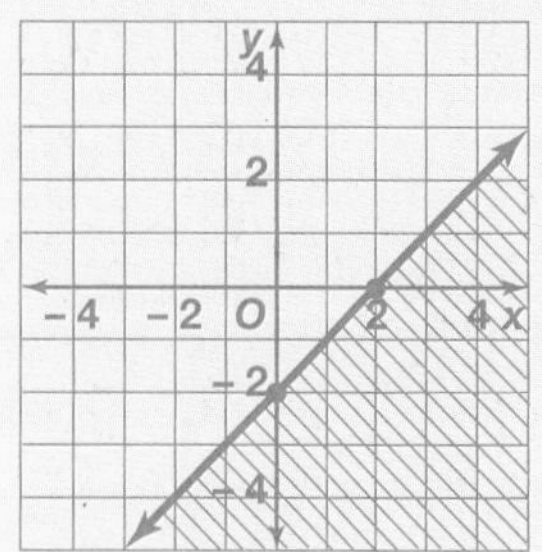

3.
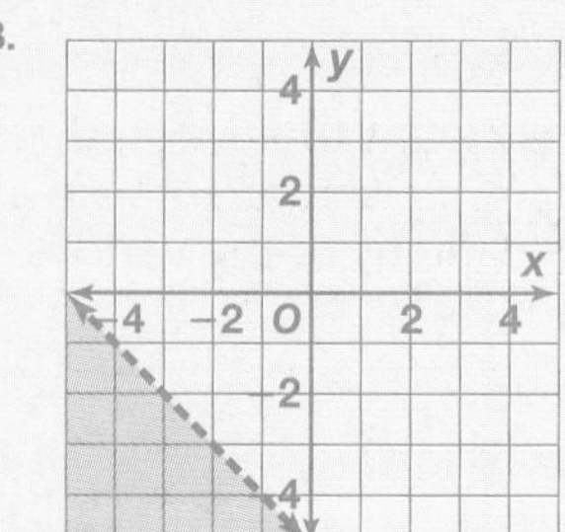

# FINISHING THE CHAPTER PROJECT

Chapter Project 8

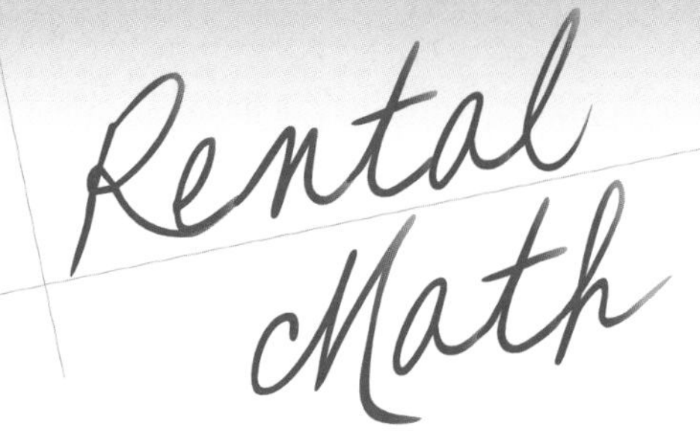


**Compare Prices** The Project Activities on pages 395, 419, and 431 will help you complete your project. Here is a checklist to help you gather the different parts.

- ✔ your table of prices
- ✔ your equations and graphs
- ✔ your analysis of the graphs

Write a report that presents your results. Make a recommendation to the graduation committee about which rental company to hire.

*Reflect and Revise*

Ask a friend or someone at home to review your report. Are your equations and graphs correct? Do they support your recommendation? If necessary, make changes to improve your report.

## *Web Extension*

**Visit Prentice Hall's Web site. You'll find some links related to renting furniture and equipment for celebrations. You'll also be able to share information about your project.**
**www.phschool.com**

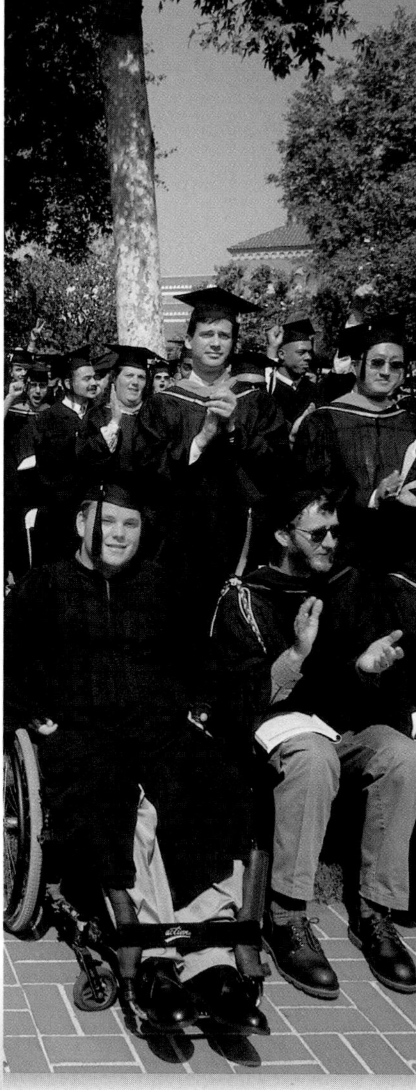

## FINISHING THE PROJECT

**Project Day** You may wish to plan a project day on which students share their completed projects. Encourage students to explain their process as well as their product.

**Block Scheduling** If you have block scheduling or extended periods, you may wish to intersperse the sharing of projects over Days 3 and 4 between the completion of one lesson and the start of a new lesson.

### Project Notebook

Have students review their project work and bring their notebooks up to date. Call attention to the fact that they can share their projects with other students through the Web site **www.phschool.com**.

Be sure students include in their notebooks their completed Project Manager and Scoring Rubric forms.

**Portfolio** Students may wish to include their projects and/or their project notebooks in their portfolios.

### Web Extension

**Tell Us About Your Project**

Students may wish to share their projects with other students on the Web site: **www.phschool.com**.

### Scoring Rubric

**3** You write and analyze your equations correctly. Your graph has an appropriate scale and is drawn correctly and neatly. You justify your recommendations clearly and thoroughly.

**2** You make minor errors in your equations, graphs, or analysis. You justify your recommendations, but the justification could be clearer or more thorough.

**1** You either write or graph your equations incorrectly. Your report is incomplete, lacks organization, and does not provide adequate justification for your recommendations.

**0** Major elements of the project are incomplete or missing.

## Resources

Glossary, p. 748
Extra Practice, p. 717

For a complete list of resources for the chapter, see p. 381H.

9.
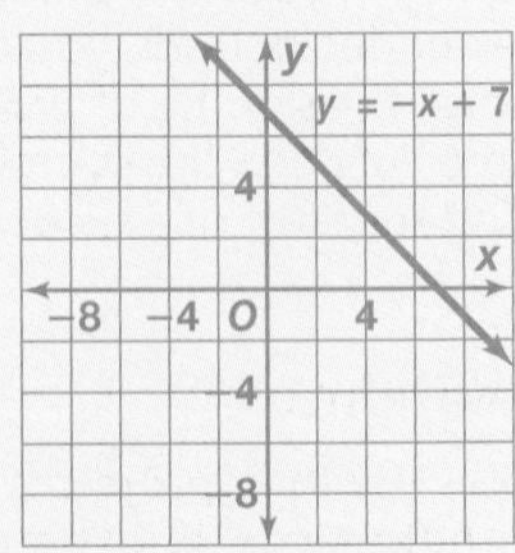


10.
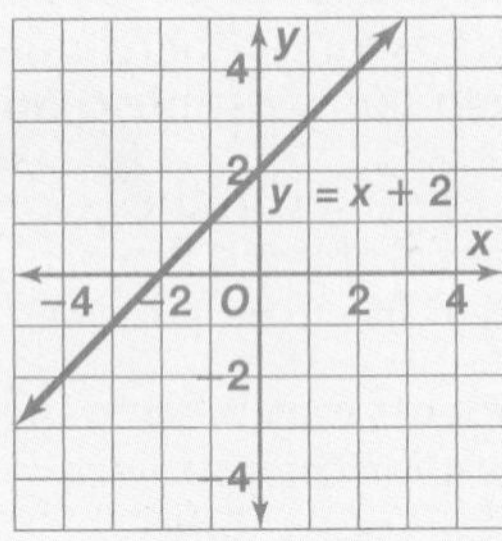


11.
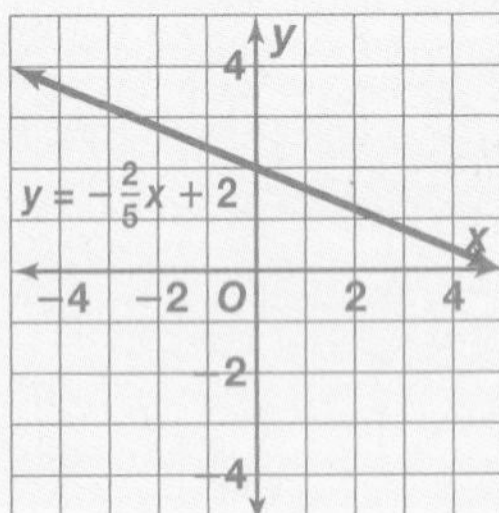


12.
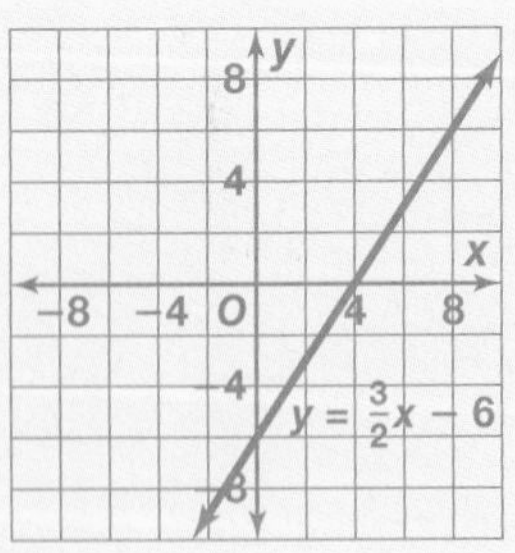


23a.
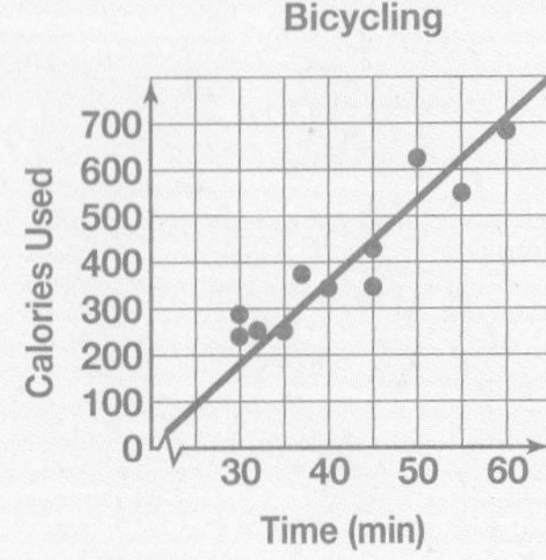

# Wrap Up

## Key Terms

domain (p. 386)
function (p. 386)
function notation (p. 404)
function rule (p. 404)
linear equation (p. 392)
linear inequality (p. 426)
negative correlation (p. 411)
no correlation (p. 411)
positive correlation (p. 411)
range (p. 386)
relation (p. 386)
scatter plot (p. 409)
slope (p. 397)
slope-intercept form (p. 399)
solution (p. 391)
system of linear equations (p. 420)
system of linear inequalities (p. 428)
trend line (p. 416)
vertical-line test (p. 387)
*y*-intercept (p. 399)

## Graphic Organizer

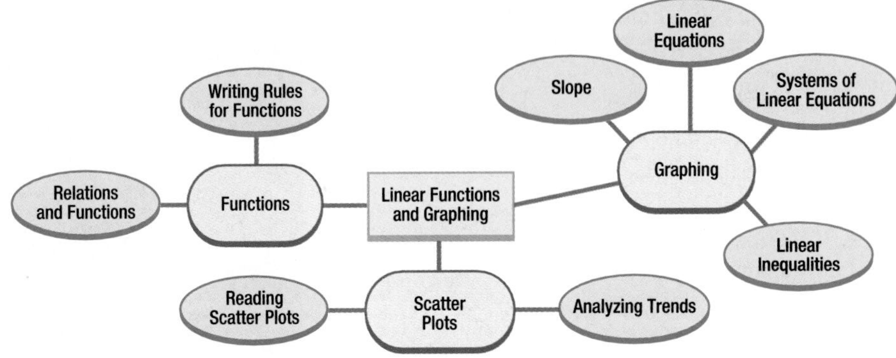


## Relations and Functions 8-1

*Summary* Any set of ordered pairs is a **relation**. The **domain** of a relation is the set of first coordinates of the ordered pairs. The **range** is the set of second coordinates. A **function** is a relation in which no two ordered pairs have the same first coordinate.

**Is each relation a function? Explain.**

1. $\{(2, 3), (4, 3), (0, 1), (-2, 3)\}$
Yes; there is one range value for each domain value.

2.

| *x* | −3 | 4 | −1 | −4 |
|---|---|---|---|---|
| *y* | 0 | 2 | 0 | 1 |

Yes; there is one range value for each domain value.

3. Domain Range

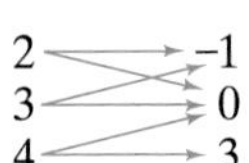


3. No; there are domain values for which there is more than one range value.

4. *Writing* Is the amount of a long-distance telephone bill a function of time spent talking on the telephone? Explain. No; one length of time (for different distances) could result in different costs.



24.
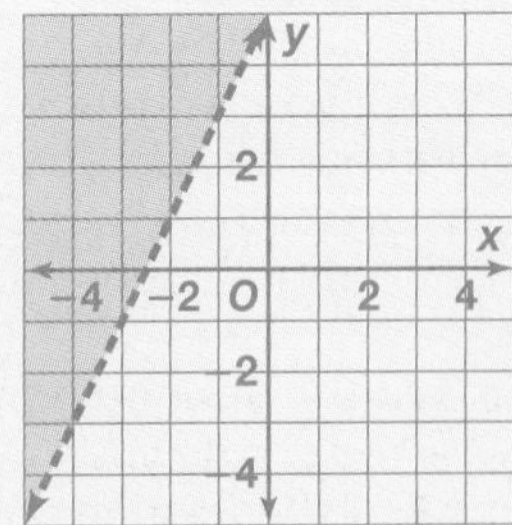

25.
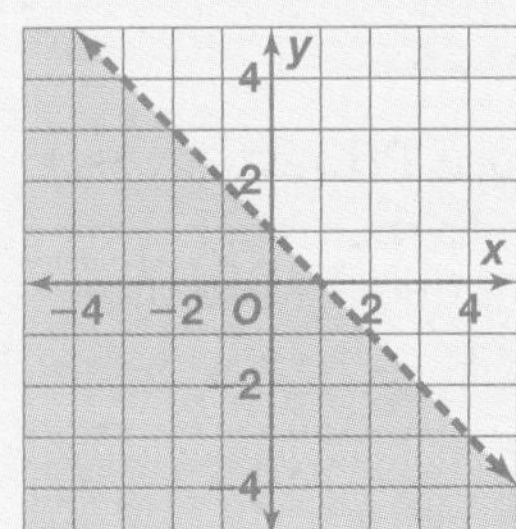

## ■ Equations with Two Variables 8-2

*Summary* A solution of an equation with two variables is any ordered pair that makes the equation true. The graph of a **linear equation** is a line.

**Find the solutions of each equation for $x = -3, 0$, and 2.**

5. $y = x + 5$ (−3, 2), (0, 5), (2, 7)
6. $y = -4x$ (−3, 12), (0, 0), (2, −8)
7. $y = \frac{1}{2}x + 3$ $\left(-3, 1\frac{1}{2}\right)$, (0, 3), (2, 4)
8. $y = 6 - 2x$ (−3, 12), (0, 6), (2, 2)

## ■ Slope and y-intercept 8-3

*Summary* **Slope** is a measure describing the tilt of a line, which you can calculate using the ratio $\frac{\text{vertical change}}{\text{horizontal change}}$, or $\frac{\text{difference in } y\text{-coordinates}}{\text{difference in } x\text{-coordinates}}$. One form of a linear equation is the slope-intercept form, $y = mx + b$, where $m$ is the slope and $b$ is the $y$-intercept.

**Identify the slope and $y$-intercept of each equation. Then graph each equation.** 9–12. See margin for graphs.

9. $x + y = 7$ −1, 7
10. $x - y = -2$ 1, 2
11. $2x + 5y = 10$ $-\frac{2}{5}$, 2
12. $3x - 2y = 12$ $\frac{3}{2}$, −6

**Write the slope of each line.**

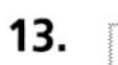

13.

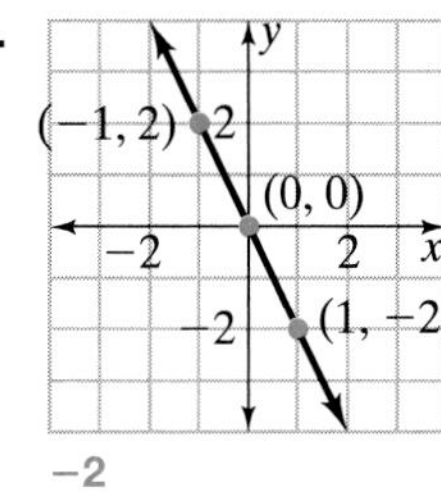


−2

14.

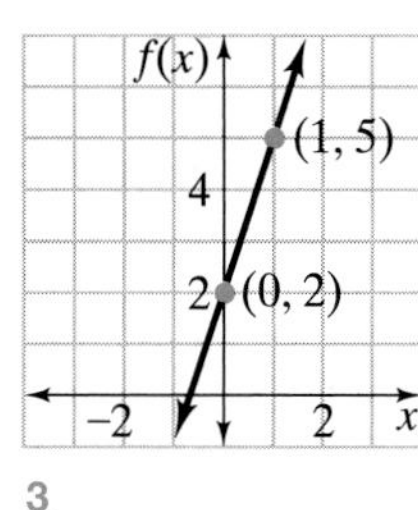


3

15.

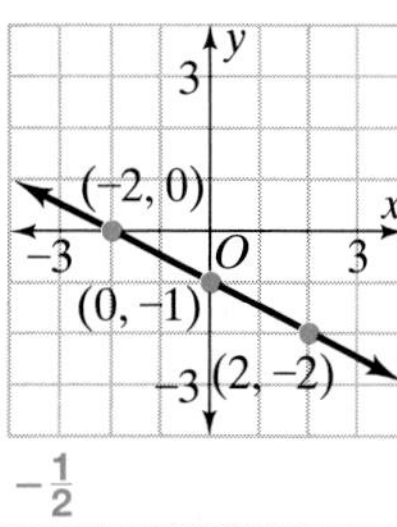


$-\frac{1}{2}$

## ■ Writing Rules for Linear Functions 8-4

*Summary* You can write a **function rule** from a verbal description, from a table of values, or from a graph.

**Write a rule for each function.**

16.

| x | f(x) |
|---|---|
| −2 | 2 |
| −1 | 1 |
| 0 | 0 |
| 1 | −1 |

$f(x) = -x$

17.

| x | y |
|---|---|
| −3 | −5 |
| −2 | −3 |
| −1 | −1 |
| 0 | 1 |

$y = 2x + 1$

18.

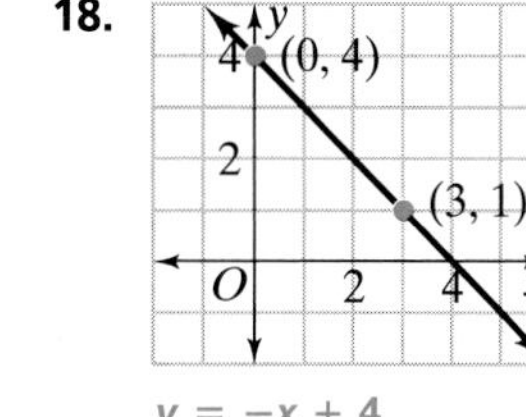


$y = -x + 4$



**Portfolio** Students may wish to include their completed work for the Wrap Up in their portfolios.

### Web Site

Students can find self-assessment materials on the Web site: **www.phschool.com.**

28.

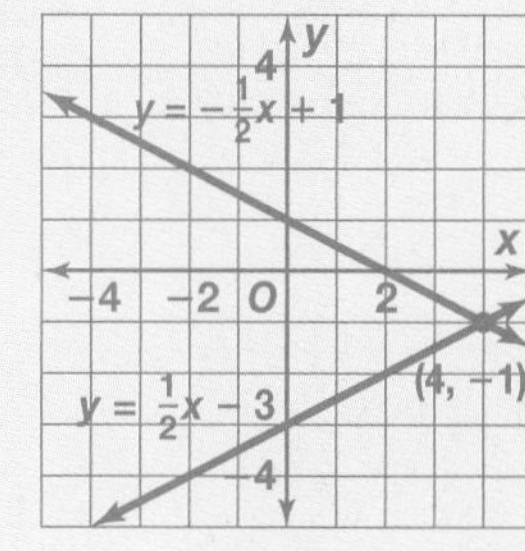


29.

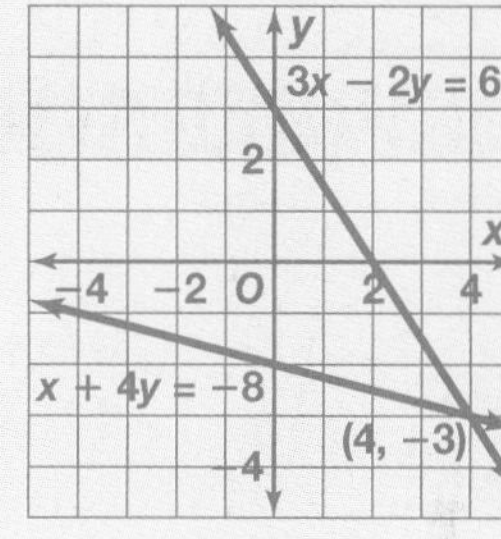


30.

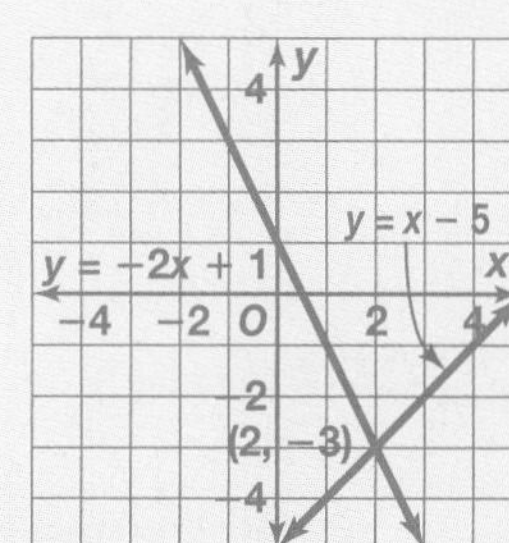


31.

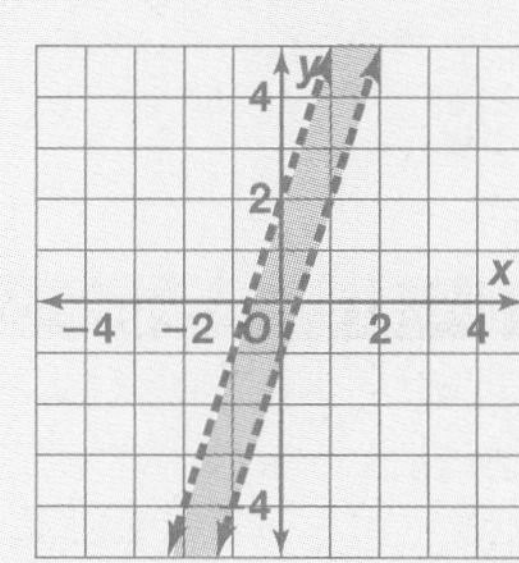


26.

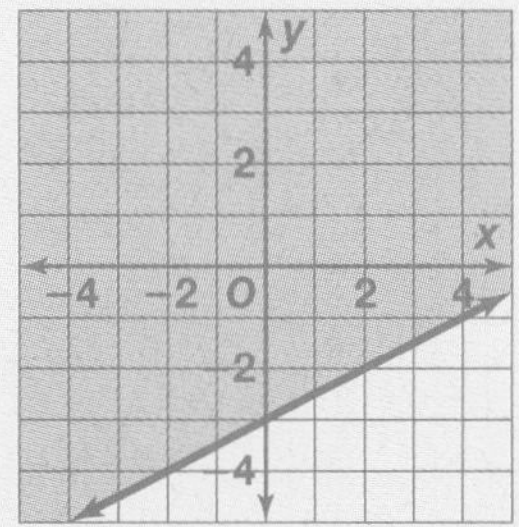


27.

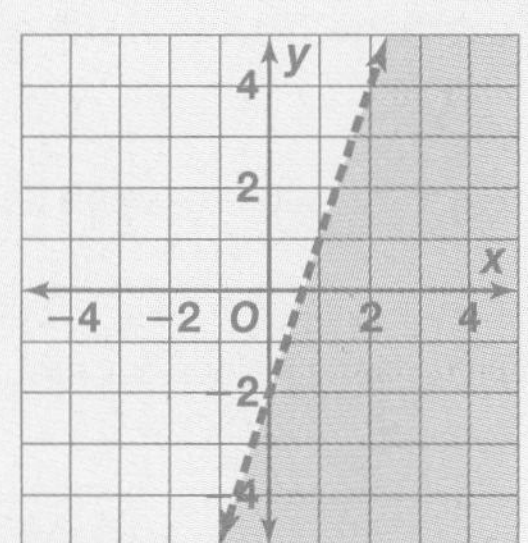

19. Tickets to a play cost \$14 each by mail, plus a \$2 processing fee for each order of one or more tickets. Write a rule to describe total cost $c(t)$ as a function of the number of tickets $t$. $c(t) = 14t + 2$

## ■ Scatter Plots and Trend Lines 8-5 and 8-6

*Summary* A **scatter plot** is a graph that shows the relationship between two sets of data. A scatter plot can help you find trends between sets of data.

**Use the scatter plot at the right.**

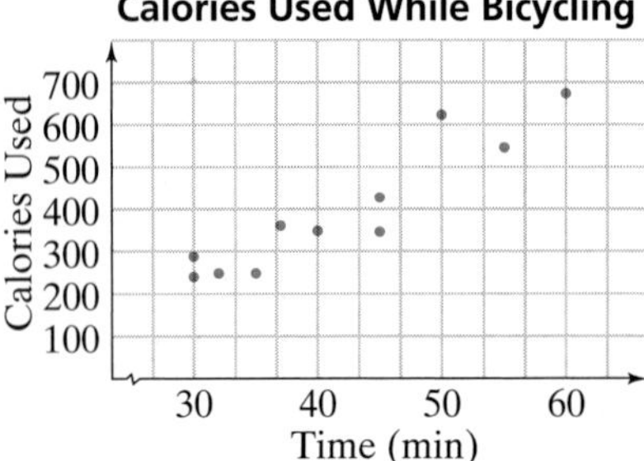


20. How long did the person who used 240 calories ride a bicycle? 30 min

21. How many calories did the person who bicycled 50 minutes use? about 620 calories

22. *Data Analysis* Is there a positive correlation, a negative correlation, or no correlation between the time spent bicycling and the calories used? Explain. See right.

22. Positive correlation; as the time riding increases, the calories used increases.

23. a. *Data Analysis* Copy the scatter plot and draw a trend line. See margin.
b. A person went for a 70-min bicycle ride. Use the trend line to predict how many calories the person used. Answers may vary. Sample: 900 calories

## ■ Solving Systems of Linear Equations and Inequalities 8-7 and 8-8

*Summary* Two or more linear equations with the same variables form a **system of linear equations**. A solution of a system of equations is any ordered pair that makes each equation true.

Two or more linear inequalities with the same variables form a **system of linear inequalities**. A solution of a system of inequalities is any ordered pair that makes both inequalities true. You can solve a system by graphing.

**Graph each inequality.** 24–27. See margin pp. 434–435.

24. $y > 2x + 5$ 25. $y \leq -x + 1$ 26. $y \geq \frac{1}{2}x - 3$ 27. $y < 3x - 2$

**Solve each system by graphing.** 28–31. See margin p. 435 for graphs.

28. $y = \frac{1}{2}x - 3$
$y = -\frac{1}{2}x + 1$
(4, −1)

29. $3x + 2y = 6$
$x + 4y = -8$
(4, −3)

30. $y = x - 5$
$y = -2x + 1$
(2, −3)

31. $y < 3x + 2$
$y > 3x - 1$
infinitely many solutions

32. *Writing* Explain why it is possible for a system of linear equations to have no solutions. The graphs could be parallel lines, so there is no common solution.

436 Chapter 8 Wrap Up

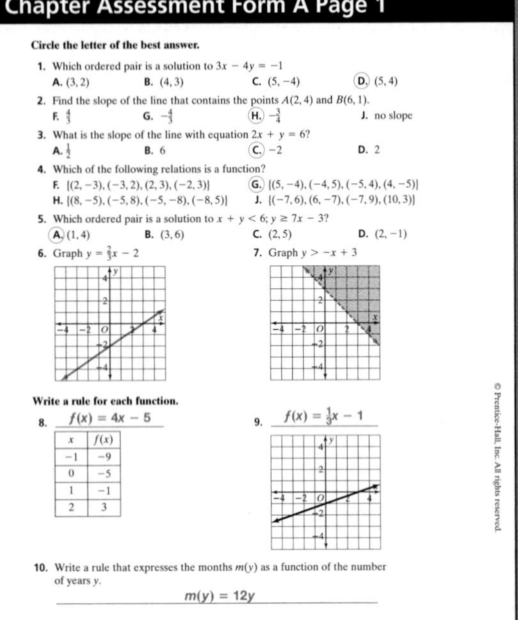

## Chapter Assessment Form A Page 1

**Circle the letter of the best answer.**

1. Which ordered pair is a solution to $3x - 4y = -1$
A. (3, 2) B. (4, 3) C. (5, −4) D. (5, 4)

2. Find the slope of the line that contains the points $A(2, 4)$ and $B(6, 1)$.
F. $\frac{4}{3}$ G. $-\frac{4}{3}$ H. $-\frac{3}{4}$ J. no slope

3. What is the slope of the line with equation $2x + y = 6$?
A. $\frac{1}{2}$ B. 6 C. −2 D. 2

4. Which of the following relations is a function?
F. {(2, −3), (−3, 2), (2, 3), (−2, 3)} G. {(5, −4), (−4, 5), (−5, 4), (4, −5)}
H. {(8, −5), (−5, 8), (−5, −8), (−8, 5)} J. {(−7, 6), (6, −7), (−7, 9), (10, 3)}

5. Which ordered pair is a solution to $x + y < 6$; $y \geq 7x - 3$?
A. (1, 4) B. (3, 6) C. (2, 5) D. (2, −1)

6. Graph $y = \frac{2}{3}x - 2$

7. Graph $y > -x + 3$

**Write a rule for each function.**

8. $f(x) = 4x - 5$

| $x$ | $f(x)$ |
|---|---|
| −1 | −9 |
| 0 | −5 |
| 1 | −1 |
| 2 | 3 |

9. $f(x) = \frac{1}{3}x - 1$

10. Write a rule that expresses the months $m(y)$ as a function of the number of years $y$.
$m(y) = 12y$



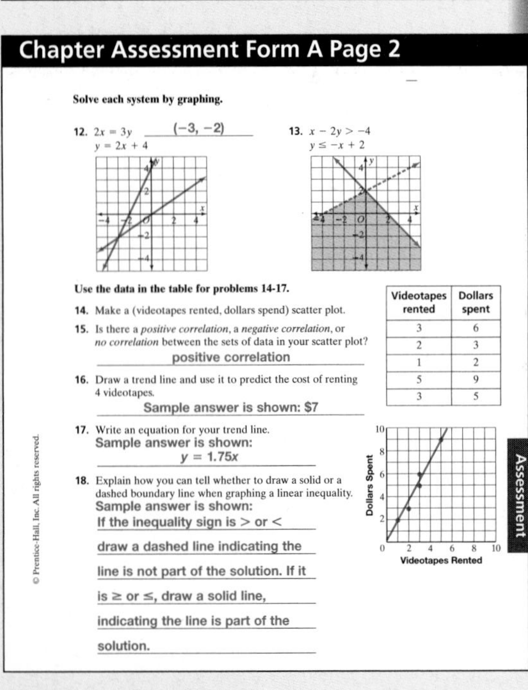

## Chapter Assessment Form A Page 2

**Solve each system by graphing.**

12. $2x = 3y$
$y = 2x + 4$
(−3, −2)

13. $x - 2y > -4$
$y \leq -x + 2$

**Use the data in the table for problems 14-17.**

| Videotapes rented | Dollars spent |
|---|---|
| 3 | 6 |
| 2 | 3 |
| 1 | 2 |
| 5 | 9 |
| 3 | 5 |

14. Make a (videotapes rented, dollars spend) scatter plot.

15. Is there a *positive correlation*, a *negative correlation*, or *no correlation* between the sets of data in your scatter plot?
positive correlation

16. Draw a trend line and use it to predict the cost of renting 4 videotapes.
Sample answer is shown: \$7

17. Write an equation for your trend line.
Sample answer is shown:
$y = 1.75x$

18. Explain how you can tell whether to draw a solid or a dashed boundary line when graphing a linear inequality.
Sample answer is shown:
If the inequality sign is > or < draw a dashed line indicating the line is not part of the solution. If it is ≥ or ≤, draw a solid line, indicating the line is part of the solution.

Dollars Spent / Videotapes Rented



Assessment

1. No; there are four range values for the domain value −2.

2. Yes; there is one range value for each domain value.

3. No; there are three range values for the domain value 1.

4. No; there are, for example, two range values for the domain value 0.

5.

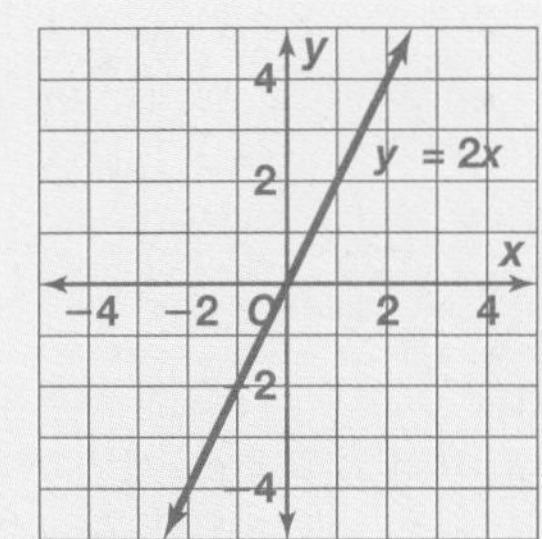

# Assessment

## Is each relation a function? Explain.
1–4. See margin for explanations.

1. $\{(-2,-12),(-2,0),(-2,4),(-2,11)\}$ no
2. $\{(8,1),(4,1),(0,1),(-15,1)\}$ yes
3. $\{(-4,-6),(-3,-2),(1,-2),(1,0),(1,3)\}$ no
4. $\{(0,1),(0,2),(1,2),(1,3),(3,1),(4,2)\}$ no

## Graph each equation. 5–8. See margin.

5. $y = 2x$
6. $y = -x - 2$
7. $2x - y = 4$
8. $3y = x - 6$

## Find the slope of the line through each pair of points.

9. $C(0,1)$ and $D(-5,1)$ 0
10. $M(-4,1)$ and $N(6,3)$ $\frac{1}{5}$
11. $J(-1,-2)$ and $K(2,7)$ 3
12. $P(4,9)$ and $Q(-6,12)$ $-\frac{3}{10}$

## Write a rule for each function.

13. 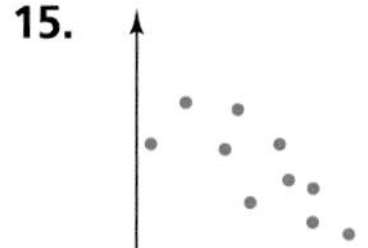

| x | f(x) |
|---|---|
| −2 | −3 |
| −1 | −5 |
| 0 | −7 |
| 1 | −9 |

$f(x) = -2x - 7$

14. 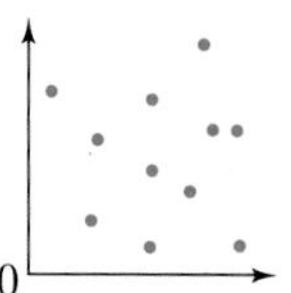

| x | f(x) |
|---|---|
| −3 | 4 |
| 0 | 1 |
| 3 | −2 |
| 6 | −5 |

$f(x) = -x + 1$

## Is there a *positive correlation*, a *negative correlation*, or *no correlation* between the sets of data in each scatter plot? Explain.

15. 16.

15. Negative correlation; as one value increases the other decreases.

16. No correlation; there is no apparent relationship.

## Graph each inequality. 17–18. See back of book.

17. $y \geq 3x - 1$
18. $y < -x + 5$

## Solve each system by graphing. 19–22. See back of book for graphs.

19. $y = x - 1$
$x = 2y$
(2, 1)

20. $x + y = 4$
$2x + 2y = 8$
infinitely many solutions

21. $x + y = 3$
$y = x - 5$
(4, −1)

22. $y \leq 3x - 2$
$y > x + 4$

23. *Writing* Is the amount of sales tax paid a function of the labeled price of a taxable item? Explain. Yes; for each labeled price there is one amount of sales tax.

24. *Writing* Is a person's age a function of his or her height? Explain. No; for each height, there are people of different ages.

25. Use the data in the table below.

**New York Thruway Tolls**

| Distance (miles) | Toll (dollars) | Distance (miles) | Toll (dollars) |
|---|---|---|---|
| 112 | 3.50 | 125 | 3.90 |
| 137 | 3.75 | 100 | 3.10 |
| 112 | 3.40 | 22 | 0.70 |
| 69 | 1.65 | 58 | 1.80 |
| 69 | 2.15 | 137 | 4.25 |
| 169 | 5.70 | 43 | 1.80 |
| 90 | 2.80 | 84 | 3.05 |
| 188 | 5.85 | 164 | 5.10 |

25a–b. See back of book.

a. Make a (distance, toll) scatter plot.
b. Draw a trend line. Predict the toll if a car travels 200 mi on the toll road.
c. Use your trend line to predict how far a car traveled on the toll road if there was a \$4.50 toll. Predictions may vary. Sample: 145 mi
d. Write an equation of your trend line. See below.

26. *Open-ended* The slope of a line through the origin is $-\frac{2}{3}$. Find the coordinates of two points on the line. Answers may vary. Sample: (3, −2), (−3, 2)

25d. Equations may vary. Sample: $t = 3d + 20$ where $t$ is the toll in cents and $d$ is the distance in miles.



6. 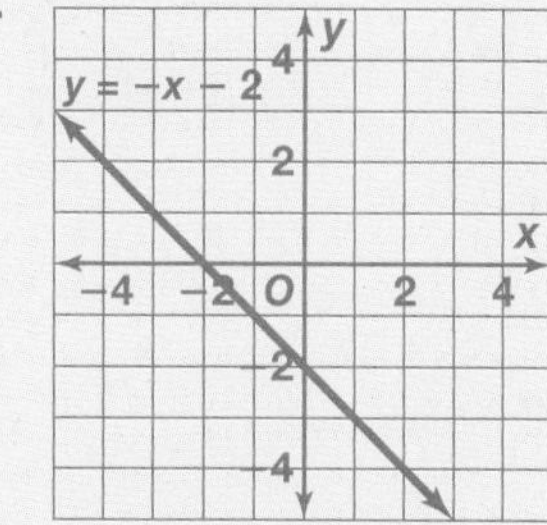


7. 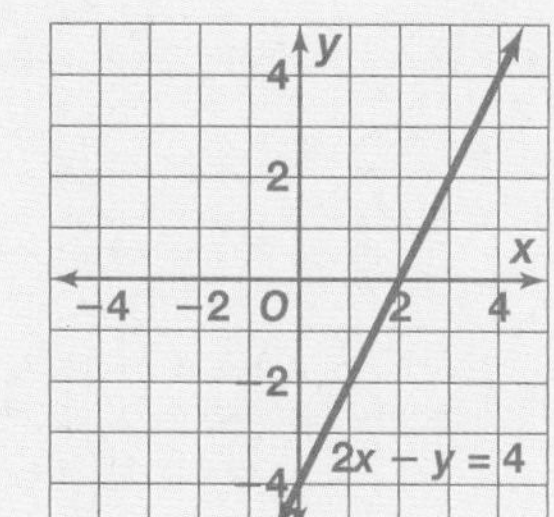


8. 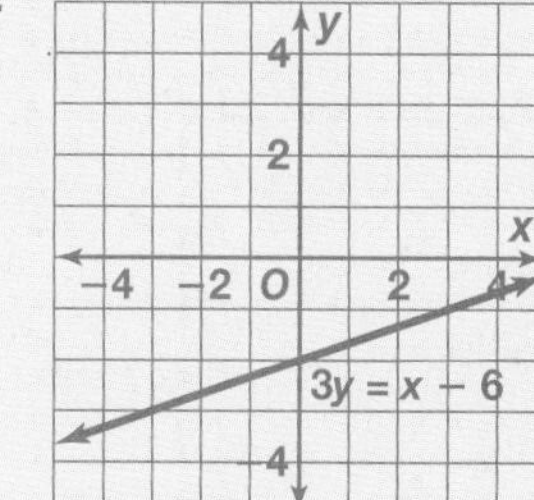


# Chapter Assessment

**Resources** For a complete list of resources for this chapter, see p. 381H.

### Chapter Assessment Form B Page 1

**Circle the letter of the best answer.**

1. Which ordered pair is a solution to $5x - 6y = -4$?
A. (3, −3) B. (3, 3) C. (4, 4) D. (4, −4)
2. Find the slope of the line that contains the points $A(8, 1)$ and $B(3, -1)$.
F. 0 G. no slope H. $-\frac{2}{5}$ J. $\frac{2}{5}$
3. What is the slope of the line with equation $5x + y = 10$?
A. 5 B. −5 C. $\frac{1}{5}$ D. $-\frac{1}{5}$
4. Which of the following relations is a function?
F. {(2, 3), (−2, 3), (3, 2), (−3, −2)} G. {(8, −4), (−4, 8), (−4, −8), (−8, 4)}
H. {(9, −1), (−1, 9), (9, 2), (2, −1)} J. {(5, −7), (4, 6), (−3, 8), (5, 9)}
5. Which ordered pair is a solution to $x + y < 9$; $y \geq 5x - 2$?
A. (2, −1) B. (−1, 10) C. (3, 5) D. (1, 7)
6. Graph $y = \frac{3}{4}x - 2$
7. Graph $y < -x + 2$

**Write a rule for each function.**

8. $f(x) = 6x - 5$

| x | f(x) |
|---|---|
| −1 | −11 |
| 0 | −5 |
| 1 | 1 |
| 2 | 7 |

9. $f(x) = \frac{1}{2}x - 1$

10. Write a rule that expresses the minutes $m(h)$ as a function of the number of hours $h$.
$m(h) = 60h$



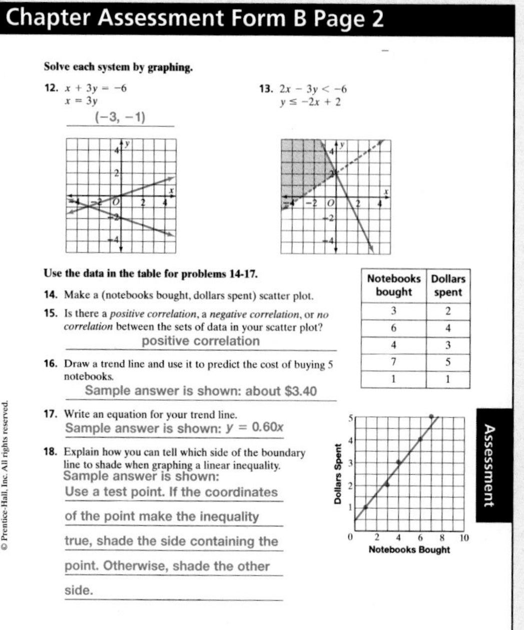

### Chapter Assessment Form B Page 2

**Solve each system by graphing.**

12. $x + 3y = -6$
$x = 3y$
(−3, −1)

13. $2x - 3y < -6$
$y \leq -2x + 2$

**Use the data in the table for problems 14-17.**

| Notebooks bought | Dollars spent |
|---|---|
| 3 | 2 |
| 6 | 4 |
| 4 | 3 |
| 7 | 5 |
| 1 | 1 |

14. Make a (notebooks bought, dollars spent) scatter plot.
15. Is there a *positive correlation*, a *negative correlation*, or *no correlation* between the sets of data in your scatter plot?
positive correlation
16. Draw a trend line and use it to predict the cost of buying 5 notebooks.
Sample answer is shown: about \$3.40
17. Write an equation for your trend line.
Sample answer is shown: $y = 0.60x$
18. Explain how you can tell which side of the boundary line to shade when graphing a linear inequality.
Sample answer is shown:
Use a test point. If the coordinates of the point make the inequality true, shade the side containing the point. Otherwise, shade the other side.





Assessment

# Cumulative Review

## Cumulative Review Page 1

**Circle the letter of the best answer.**

1. Tracie is 59 inches tall. How tall is she in feet and inches?
   A. 4 ft 9 in. (B.) 4 ft 11 in. C. 5 ft 2 in. D. 5 ft 9 in.
2. The probability that Steven gets a hit playing baseball is 1 in 4 times at bat. About how many hits would you expect him to get in 29 times at bat?
   F. 5 hits G. 8 hits H. 6 hits (J.) 7 hits
3. When a number is multiplied by $\frac{1}{2}$, the result is the same as when 5 is subtracted from 3 times the number. Which equation describes the situation?
   A. $\frac{1}{2}n = 3(n - 5)$ B. $\frac{1}{2}n - 5 = 3n$ (C.) $\frac{1}{2}n = 3n - 5$ D. $\frac{1}{2}(3n - 5)$
4. $3\frac{1}{2} + 2\frac{1}{3} =$
   (F.) $5\frac{5}{6}$ G. $5\frac{2}{5}$ H. $5\frac{1}{6}$ J. 6
5. Which ordered pair is *not* a solution of $6x + 3y = 18$?
   A. $(4, -2)$ (B.) $(3, -1)$ C. $(-1, 8)$ D. $(2, 2)$
6. Find the slope of the line through $(3, -2)$ and $(1, 4)$.
   F. $-1$ G. 3 (H.) $-3$ J. $\frac{1}{3}$
7. Which point is a solution of the system $4x - y = 9$ and $y = 2x - 7$?
   A. $(2, -1)$ B. $(3, -1)$ C. $(-1, -8)$ (D.) $(1, -5)$
8. Solve $-3n + 1 \le -8$.
   F. $n \le 3$ G. $n \le -3$ (H.) $n \ge 3$ J. $n \ge -3$
9. Express the equation $3x = 2y - 8$ in slope-intercept form.
   A. $3x - 2y = -8$ B. $2y = 3x + 8$ (C.) $y = \frac{3}{2}x + 4$ D. $y = \frac{3}{2}x - 4$
10. Find the slope of the line with equation $3x - 4y = 24$.
    F. $-\frac{4}{3}$ (G.) $\frac{3}{4}$ H. $\frac{4}{3}$ J. $-\frac{3}{4}$
11. Which equation has a solution of 5?
    (A.) $7 - 2x = -3$ B. $2x - 9 = -1$ C. $4 - x = 1$ D. $x - 8 = 3$
12. Write a function rule to describe the amount of sales tax $t(p)$ as a function of the price $p$ of an item purchased if sales tax is 6%.
    $t(p) = 0.06p$



Assessment

## Cumulative Review Page 2

13. Complete the table of ordered pairs

| $x$ | $y$ |
|---|---|
| 0 | −4 |
| 2 | 0 |
| 3 | 2 |

14. Graph the equation.

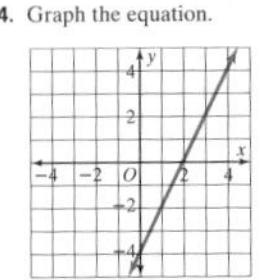


**The table has data on Ayla's height at certain ages. Use the data for problems 15-17.**

15. Use the data to make a (age, height) scatter plot. Draw a trend line.

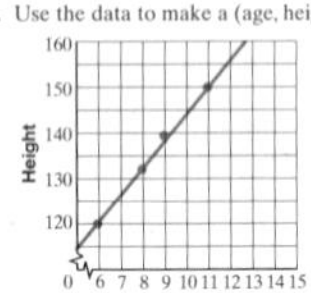


| Age | Height (cm) |
|---|---|
| 6 | 120 |
| 8 | 132 |
| 9 | 139 |
| 11 | 150 |

16. At what age was Ayla about 125 centimeters tall?
    7 years
17. About how tall should Ayla be when she is 12 years old?
    about 156 cm
18. Is height a function of age? Explain.
    Yes. For each age there is only one height.



# 8 Cumulative Review

Preparing for Algebra

**Choose the best answer.**

1. An empty pot weighs 1 lb 11 oz. With oatmeal in it, the pot weighs 3 lb 7 oz. How much does the oatmeal weigh? C
   A. 5 lb 2 oz B. 2 lb 3 oz
   C. 1 lb 12 oz D. 1 lb 4 oz
2. *Probability* The probability that a couple will give birth to a pair of twins is 1 in 90. About how many pairs of twins would you expect to find in 250,000 births? G
   F. 280 G. 2,778 H. 1,316 J. 22,500
3. Which equation has a solution of 8? D
   A. $8x + 8 = 64$ B. $\frac{b}{2} + 7 = 10$
   C. $2z + 5 = 11$ D. $5n - 13 = 27$
4. Four friends split the cost of renting a car for a snorkeling trip. Each person also rents a snorkel for $2. Each person pays a total of $15. Which equation will help find the cost $c$ of renting the car? F
   F. $\frac{c}{4} + 2 = 15$ G. $15 - 2^4 = c$
   H. $15 - 4c = 2$ J. $\frac{c}{2} + 4 = 15$
5. Sara and Juan collect soccer cards. Sara has 6 fewer than three times the number of cards Juan has. Together they have 42 cards. Solve $c + (3c - 6) = 42$ to find the number of cards each student has. D
   A. Sara has 9 cards; Juan has 33 cards.
   B. Sara has 33 cards; Juan has 9 cards.
   C. Sara has 12 cards; Juan has 30 cards.
   D. Sara has 30 cards; Juan has 12 cards.
6. Which ordered pair is *not* a solution of $4x + 2y = 16$? H
   F. $(-2, 12)$ G. $(5, -2)$
   H. $(2, 5)$ J. $(1, 6)$
7. Which function represents the number of kilograms $k(g)$ as a function of the number of grams $g$? D
   A. $k(g) = 100g$ B. $k(g) = 0.01g$
   C. $k(g) = 1{,}000g$ D. $k(g) = 0.001g$
8. Find the slope of the line through $(3, 2)$ and $(1, -2)$. G
   F. $-2$ G. 2 H. 1 J. 3
9. *Data Analysis* In the scatter plot below, each point represents an athlete who ran in the 100-m race. Greg won the race. How old is Greg? B

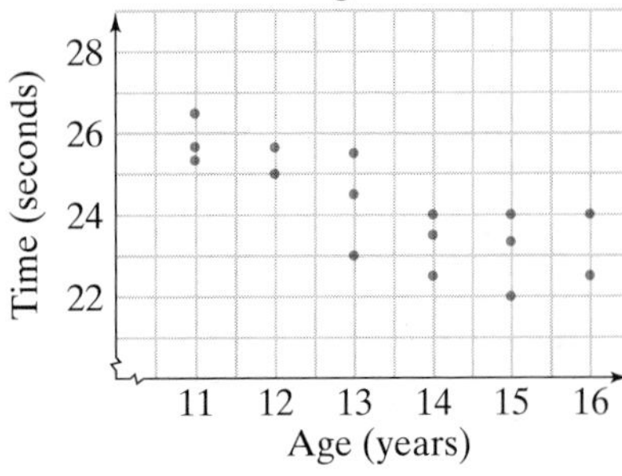


   A. 13 years old B. 15 years old
   C. 14 years old D. 16 years old
10. Which point is a solution of the system $y = x + 2$ and $y = 2x - 2$? H
    F. $(6, 4)$ G. $(1, 3)$
    H. $(4, 6)$ J. no solution
11. Solve $-2(x - 1) \le -6$. D
    A. $x \le 3$ B. $x \le -3$
    C. $x \ge 3$ D. Not here

**Find the solutions of each equation for $x = -3, 0,$ and $2$.**

12. $y = x + 12$
    $(-3, 9), (0, 12), (2, 14)$
13. $4x - 4y = 8$
    $(-3, -5), (0, -2), (2, 0)$

**Write each equation in slope-intercept form. Then find the slope and $y$-intercept of each equation.**

14. $x + \frac{1}{2}y = 4$
    $y = -2x + 8, -2, 8$
15. $6x - 3y = 6$
    $y = 2x - 2; 2, -2$
16. Are the earnings in dollars for an hourly worker a function of the number of hours worked? Explain.
    Yes; for each number of hours worked, there is one amount of earnings.



| Item | Chapter/Lesson | Review Topic |
|---|---|---|
| 1 | 5-5 | Operations with Fractions |
| 2 | 6-4 | Ratios, Proportions, and Percents |
| 3, 4, 5, 11 | 7-1, 7-2, 7-3, 7-6 | Solving Equations and Inequalities |
| 6–10, 12–16 | 8-1, 8-2, 8-3, 8-5, 8-7 | Linear Functions and Graphing |

CHAPTER 9

# Spatial Thinking

## Content Overview for Chapter 9

Chapter 9 introduces basic geometric figures: point, line, plane, line segment, and ray. A point is a position in space. All geometric figures are made up of points. A line is a series of points that extends in two directions without end. A segment is a part of a line and has two endpoints. A ray is a part of a line with exactly one endpoint. An angle is two rays that intersect at their endpoints.

Adjacent angles share a vertex and a side but no points in their interiors. Vertical angles are formed by intersecting lines and are congruent. If parallel lines are crossed by a transversal, their corresponding angles are congruent. Alternate interior angles of parallel lines are also congruent.

A polygon is a closed figure with at least three sides. A triangle can be classified by its angles and sides. You can classify some quadrilaterals as parallelograms, rectangles, squares, rhombuses, and trapezoids. Polygons with the same size and shape are congruent. You can show two triangles are congruent by using the **S**ide-**S**ide-**S**ide, **S**ide-**A**ngle-**S**ide, or **A**ngle-**S**ide-**A**ngle methods.

You can use the formulas $C = \pi d$ and $C = 2\pi r$ to find the circumference of a circle. There are 360° in a circle. An angle whose vertex is the center of a circle is a central angle.

You can use a compass and a straightedge to construct congruent segments, congruent angles, segment bisectors, and angle bisectors. A transformation is a change of position, shape, or size of a figure. The figure after the transformation is called the image. You can transform figures in a plane by translation, reflection, and rotation.

## Making Connections

| Lesson | Interdisciplinary and Real-World Connections | Math Integration |
|---|---|---|
| 9-1 | Architecture | Algebra |
| 9-2 | City Planning | Algebra |
| 9-3 | Construction | Algebra |
| 9-4 | Sports | Problem Solving, Measurement |
| 9-5 | Art and Design | Measurement |
| 9-6 | Accounting | Data Analysis |
| 9-7 | Design | Geometry |
| 9-8 | Art | Geometry |
| 9-9 | Biology | Geometry |
| 9-10 | Botany | Geometry |

**SCHOOL/HOME CONNECTION**

English and Spanish versions are available in the *Help at Home* book of copy masters.

*Helper's Page* You will find detailed instruction, more examples, and

*Student Page* Review Exercises for Lessons 9-1 to 9-5

**Name all of each of the following shown.** *(Lesson 9-1)*

1. Points ______
2. Segments ______
3. Rays ______

J K M

**Find the measure of each angle. $l \parallel m$.** *(Lesson 9-2)*

4. $m\angle 1$ ______ 5. $m\angle 2$ ______
6. $m\angle 3$ ______

1 85° l 2 3 m

**Judging by appearances, classify each triangle by its sides and by its angles.** *(Lesson 9-3)*

7. 8.

**Solve by drawing a diagram.** *(Lesson 9-4)*

9. There are 20 rabbits in a pen. Twelve of the 20 rabbits are brown. Ten of the 20 rabbits are female. Four of the 20 rabbits are both. How many of the rabbits are neither brown nor female? ______

**Explain why the pair of triangles is congruent.** *(Lesson 9-5)*

10. ______

R V T S U

11. **Test Prep** Which quadrilateral does not have opposite angles congruent? *(Lesson 9-1)*
    A. rectangle B. square C. trapezoid D. parallelogram ______

Helper: ______ Comments: ______

*Helper's Page* You will find detailed instruction, more examples, and

*Student Page* Review Exercises for Lessons 9-6 to 9-8

**Find the circumference of each circle with the given radius or diameter.** *(Lesson 9-6)*

1. radius = 32 in. 2. diameter = 40 m 3. radius = 6.8 cm

**Find the measures of the central angles you would draw to represent each percent in a circle graph. Round to the nearest degree, where necessary.** *(Lesson 9-6)*

4. 15% ______ 5. 30% ______ 6. 42% ______

**Construct a segment twice the length of $AB$.** *(Lesson 9-7)*

7. A B

**Write a rule to describe each translation.** *(Lesson 9-8)*

8. 9.

10. **Test Prep** The graph of $y = 6x - 9$ is translated up 3 units and left 5 units. Find the slope of the graph of the image. *(Lesson 9-8)*
    A. 6 B. $-\frac{5}{3}$ C. $\frac{3}{5}$ D. $-\frac{3}{5}$ ______

Helper: ______ Comments: ______

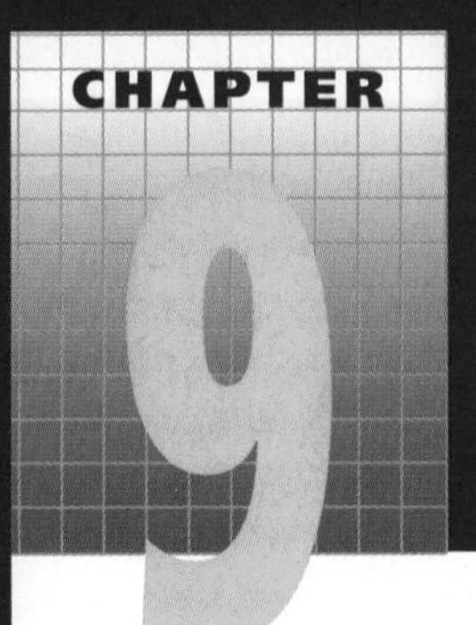


# Chapter 9 at a Glance

To accommodate flexible scheduling, most lessons are divided into parts. Assignment Options are given in the Teacher's Edition for each lesson.

| Pages 442–447 | **Lesson 9-1** Introduction to Geometry: Points, Lines, and Planes |
|---|---|
| NCTM 3, 6, 7, 8, 9, 10 | Part 1 Points, Lines, and Planes<br>Part 2 Intersecting, Parallel, and Skew Lines<br>**Math at Work** |

| Pages 449–453 | **Lesson 9-2** Angle Relationships and Parallel Lines |
|---|---|
| NCTM 3, 4, 7, 8, 10 | Part 1 Adjacent and Vertical Angles<br>Part 2 Relating Angles and Parallel Lines |

| Pages 454–458 | **Lesson 9-3** Classifying Polygons |
|---|---|
| NCTM 3, 4, 7, 8, 9, 10 | Part 1 Classifying Triangles<br>Part 2 Classifying Quadrilaterals<br>▼ **Project Activity 1** |

| Pages 474–478 | **Lesson 9-7** Constructions |
|---|---|
| NCTM 3, 4, 8, 10 | Part 1 Congruent Segments and Angles<br>Part 2 Constructing Bisectors<br>▼ **Project Activity 2** |

| Pages 479–483 | **Lesson 9-8** Translations |
|---|---|
| NCTM 3, 8, 9, 10 | Part 1 Graphing Translations<br>Part 2 Describing Translations<br>**Checkpoint 2** |

| Pages 485–488 | **Lesson 9-9** Symmetry and Reflections |
|---|---|
| NCTM 3, 8, 10 | Part 1 Identifying Lines of Symmetry<br>Part 2 Graphing Reflections |

## Pacing Options

This chart suggests pacing for only the core lessons and their parts, and it is provided merely as a possible guide. It will help you determine how much time you have in your schedule to cover other features, such as the Chapter Project, Math Toolboxes, Standardized Test Prep, Wrap Up, and Assessment.

| | Day 1 | Day 2 | Day 3 | Day 4 | Day 5 | Day 6 | Day 7 | Day 8 | Day 9 | Day 10 | Day 11 |
|---|---|---|---|---|---|---|---|---|---|---|---|
| **Traditional** (40–45 min. class periods) | 9–1 ▼1 | 9–1 ▼2 | 9–2 ▼1, 9–2 ▼2 | 9–3 ▼1 | 9–3 ▼2 | 9–4 | 9–5 ▼1, 9–5 ▼2 | 9–6 ▼1, 9–6 ▼2 | 9–7 ▼1 | 9–7 ▼2 | 9–8 ▼1, 9–8 ▼2 |
| **Pre-Algebra Over 2 Years** (40–45 min. class periods) | 9–1 ▼1 | 9–1 ▼2 | 9–1 ▼2 | 9–2 ▼1 | 9–2 ▼2 | 9–2 ▼2 | 9–3 ▼1 | 9–3 ▼2 | 9–3 ▼2 | 9–4 | 9–4 |
| **Block Scheduling** (90 min. class periods) | 9–1 ▼1 ▼2, 9–2 ▼1 ▼2 | 9–3 ▼1 ▼2, 9–4, 9–5 ▼1 ▼2 | 9–6 ▼1 ▼2, 9–7 ▼1 ▼2, 9–8 ▼1 | 9–8 ▼2, 9–9 ▼1 ▼2, 9–10 ▼1 ▼2 | | | | | | | |

| Pages 460–463 | Lesson 9-4 Problem Solving Strategy |
|---|---|
| NCTM 3, 4, 6, 7, 8, 9, 10 | Draw a Diagram |

| Pages 464–468 | Lesson 9-5 Congruence |
|---|---|
| NCTM 3, 4, 6, 7, 8, 9, 10 | Part 1 Identifying Corresponding Parts<br>Part 2 Identifying Congruent Triangles<br>**Checkpoint 1** |

| Pages 469–473 | Lesson 9-6 Data Analysis: Circles |
|---|---|
| NCTM 3, 4, 6, 8, 9, 10 | Part 1 Finding Circumference<br>Part 2 Making Circle Graphs |

| Pages 490–493 | Lesson 9-10 Rotations |
|---|---|
| NCTM 3, 7, 8, 9, 10 | Part 1 Graphing Rotations<br>Part 2 Identifying Rotational Symmetry<br>**Project Activity 3** |

**NCTM STANDARDS 2000**

1 Number and Operations
2 Algebra
3 Geometry
4 Measurement
5 Data Analysis and Probability
6 Problem Solving
7 Reasoning and Proof
8 Communication
9 Connections
10 Representation

| Day 12 | Day 13 | Day 14 | Day 15 | Day 16 | Day 17 | Day 18 | Day 19 | Day 20 | Day 21 | Day 22 | Day 23 | Day 24 |
|---|---|---|---|---|---|---|---|---|---|---|---|---|
| 9–9 1, 9–9 2 | 9–10 1, 9–10 2 | | | | | | | | | | | |
| 9–5 1 | 9–5 2 | 9–6 1 | 9–6 2 | 9–6 2 | 9–7 1 | 9–7 2 | 9–7 2 | 9–8 1 | 9–8 2 | 9–9 1, 9–9 2 | 9–10 1, 9–10 2 | |

**Block Scheduling Notes**

Consider these suggestions:

- **Day 1** Before starting Lesson 9-2, teach Math Toolbox 1, p. 448.
- **Day 2** Before starting Lesson 9-4, teach Math Toolbox 2, p. 459.
- **Day 4** Before starting Lesson 9-9, teach Math Toolbox 3, p. 484.
- **Day 4** Before starting Lesson 9-10, teach the Standardized Test Prep, p. 489.
- **Day 4** After completing Lesson 9-10, teach Math Toolbox 4, p. 494.

# Math Background

## LESSON 9-1

### Introduction to Geometry: Points, Lines, and Planes

*Geometry* comes from two Greek words that mean "measure the earth." Geometry deals with figures and space and such properties of figures as size and shape. The picture that follows shows the basic figures in geometry:

a *point, A,* which has no size

a *line,* $\overleftrightarrow{BC}$, a series of points that extends in two directions without end

a *plane, DEFG,* a flat surface with no thickness that extends in all directions without end

a *line segment,* $\overline{JK}$, part of a line with two endpoints and length *JK*

a *ray,* $\overrightarrow{RS}$, part of a line that has exactly one endpoint, *R.*

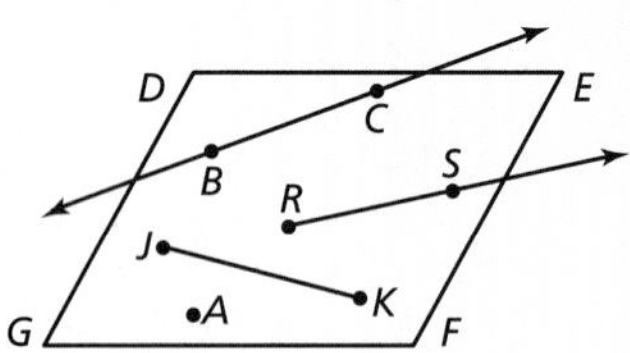


Two lines *intersect* if they have just one point in common. Two lines in the same plane that do not intersect are *parallel. Skew* lines do not lie in the same plane; they are not parallel and they do not intersect.

## LESSON 9-2

### Angle Relationships and Parallel Lines

An *angle* is formed by two rays with a common endpoint. The rays form the *sides* of the angle; the common endpoint is the *vertex.* You name angles with the vertex in the middle, as in $\angle ABC$. In the following picture, $\angle ABC$ is an *acute* angle (less than 90°); $\angle ABD$ is a *right* angle (equal to 90°); $\angle CBE$ is an *obtuse* angle (between 90° and 180°); and $\angle ABE$ is a *straight* angle (equal to 180°).

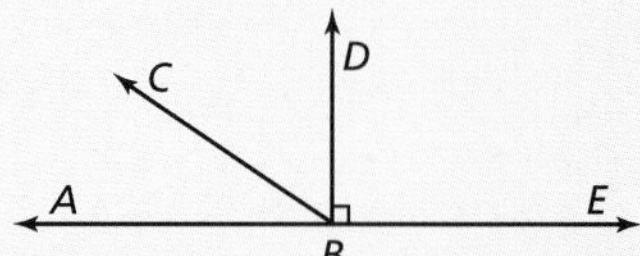


In this picture, $\angle ABC$ and $\angle CBD$ are *adjacent angles* that share a vertex and a side but no points in their interiors. These two adjacent angles are also *complementary* since the sum of their measures is 90°. The two adjacent angles $\angle ABC$ and $\angle CBE$ are *supplementary* since the sum of their measures is 180°.

In the following figure, lines *m* and *n* are parallel. Line *p* is a transversal, a line that intersects two other lines (which may or may not be parallel).

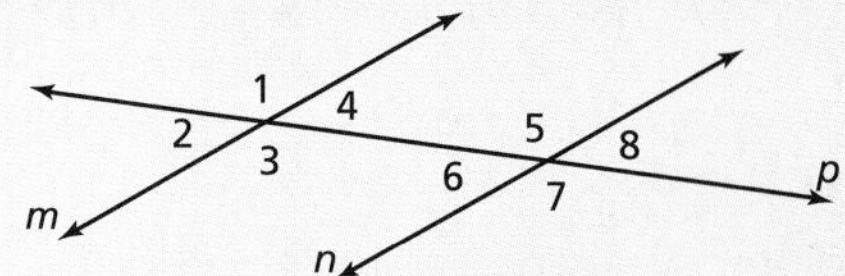


Two intersecting lines form pairs of *vertical angles* that have the same measure: one pair is $\angle 1$ and $\angle 3$; another pair is $\angle 2$ and $\angle 4$. A transversal also forms corresponding angles. Pairs of *corresponding angles* in the preceding figure are $\angle 1$ and $\angle 5$; $\angle 2$ and $\angle 6$; $\angle 3$ and $\angle 7$; $\angle 4$ and $\angle 8$.

Because lines *m* and *n* are parallel in this example, these pairs of corresponding angles are congruent. In this figure, $\angle 3$ and $\angle 5$ are alternate interior angles. Because lines *m* and *n* are parallel, each pair of alternate interior angles is also congruent.

## LESSON 9-3

### Classifying Polygons

A *polygon* is a closed plane figure with at least three sides. The sides meet only at the endpoints. A polygon with three sides is called a *triangle.* You can name a triangle by its angles: a right triangle has one right angle; an obtuse triangle has one obtuse angle; an acute triangle has three acute angles. You can also name a triangle by its sides: an equilateral triangle has three congruent sides; an isosceles triangle has at least two congruent sides; a scalene triangle has no congruent sides.

## Lesson 9-5

### Congruence

*Congruent* polygons have the same size and shape. If you move them so that one superimposes the other, both coincide exactly. The corresponding parts of congruent polygons have the same measure.

You can be sure that two triangles are congruent if these corresponding parts are congruent.
Side-Side-Side (SSS $\cong$ SSS)
Side-Angle-Side (SAS $\cong$ SAS)
Angle-Side-Angle (ASA $\cong$ ASA)
Notice that the angle in SAS must be the angle *included* between the two congruent sides, and the side in ASA must be the side included between the two congruent angles.

## Lesson 9-6

### Circles

All points of a *circle* are the same distance from a point called the *center* of the circle. This distance of each point in the circle from the center is the *radius* of the circle. A line segment with its endpoints on the circle is called a *chord* of the circle. The longest chord in any given circle is the *diameter*, which passes through the center of the circle and is twice the radius.

The *circumference* is the distance around the circle. You can also think of this as the perimeter of the circle. The ratio of the distance around a circle (circumference, or *C*) to the distance across the same circle (diameter, or *d*) is always equal to the same number. This constant ratio of $\frac{C}{d}$ is a number called *pi,* written with the Greek letter $\pi$. The number $\pi$ is irrational and is equal to a decimal that never ends, never repeats, and never shows a pattern. Today, $\pi$ has been calculated to over a million places, but it is usually approximated by 3.14. Although $\pi$ is an irrational number, it is also sometimes approximated by the rational number $\frac{22}{7}$. The following formulas apply to all circles.

$d = 2r \qquad C = \pi d \qquad C = 2\pi r$

## Lesson 9-7

### Constructions

A geometric construction is a figure that is made using only two tools, an unmarked straightedge and a compass. When you make a construction, the arcs that you draw are left in place rather than erased because they show the steps you use in the construction. Make constructions with a fine pencil to approach the theoretical idea of lines and points without thickness.

## Lessons 9-8, 9-9, and 9-10

### Translations; Symmetry and Reflections; Rotations

A *transformation* is a change in the position or size of a figure. One kind of transformation is a *translation,* or slide. The figure that results after a translation is called the *image* of the original figure. Another kind of transformation is a *rotation,* or turn. A third transformation is a *reflection,* or flip.

A translation must specify how far and in what direction(s) the figure is moved. A rotation specifies a fixed point, called *the center of rotation,* about which the figure rotates, and an *angle of rotation* (understood in this text to be a counterclockwise rotation). A reflection must specify a *line of symmetry* around which the original figure is flipped.

For professional development tips visit our Web site **www.phschool.com**.

# Monitoring Progress

## Universal Access

### ▶ Preventing a Student from Falling Behind

These resources are particularly helpful in preventing a student from falling behind his or her appropriate math level. For a complete list of resources for this chapter, see page 439H.

#### Skills You Need for Chapter 9

Student Edition, p. 439
Teacher's Edition, p. 439

- Naming polygons
- Identifying radius and diameter
- Graphing on the coordinate plane

#### Skills Handbook

Student Edition, pp. 723–741
Teacher's Edition, pp. 723–741

#### Reteaching Worksheets

There is a Reteaching worksheet for every lesson in this chapter.

- Chapter 9 Support File, Teaching Resources box
- See TE p. 439H for a complete list of resources.

#### Skills Intervention Kit with CD-ROM

| For | Use |
|---|---|
| Lessons 9-1, 9-10 | Geometry |

#### Daily Cumulative Review Blackline Masters

There is a Daily Cumulative Review worksheet for every lesson in this chapter.

See TE p. 439H for a complete list of resources.

### ▶ Accommodating Diverse Learning Styles

#### Tactile Learning

Model skew lines with pencils. (Lesson 9-1)

Measure to verify that vertical angles are equal. (Lesson 9-2)

Draw figures on tracing paper or transparencies to be able to rotate them and plot the new points. (Lesson 9-10)

#### Advanced Learner

Every lesson has at least one challenge problem.

Explain how a ray on the same line as an angle bisector bisects the same angle. (Lesson 9-7)

#### ELL (English Language Learner)

Understand the difference between *line* and *line segment.* (Lesson 9-1)

Understand the two meanings of the wor *compass.* (Lesson 9-7)

#### Auditory Learning

Name basic figures while a partner draws them. (Lesson 9-1)

Describe aloud angle bisecting constructions. (Lesson 9-7)

Read translation rules aloud while a partner draws them. (Lesson 9-8)

#### Visual Learning

Draw polygons to verify the pattern of increasing sides and diagonals. (Lesson 9-4)

Cut out photos of objects and draw the lines of symmetry. (Lesson 9-9)

# Aligning Assessment with Instruction

## Assessment Options

| | Chapter Opener | 9-1 | 9-2 | 9-3 | 9-4 | 9-5 | 9-6 | 9-7 | 9-8 | 9-9 | 9-10 | End |
|---|---|---|---|---|---|---|---|---|---|---|---|---|
| Chapter Project | ■ | | | ■ | | | ■ | | | | | ■ |
| Try This Exercises | | ■ | ■ | ■ | ■ | ■ | ■ | ■ | ■ | ■ | ■ | |
| Mixed Reviews | | ■ | ■ | ■ | ■ | ■ | ■ | ■ | ■ | ■ | ■ | |
| Checkpoints | | | | | | ■ | | | ■ | | | |
| Writing | | ■ | ■ | | ■ | ■ | ■ | ■ | ■ | ■ | ■ | ■ |
| Chapter Assessment | | | | | | | | | | | | ■ |
| Cumulative Review | | | | | | | | | | | | ■ |
| Standardized Test Prep | | | | | ■ | ■ | ■ | | ■ | ■ | | |
| | Standardized Test Prep, p. 489 | | | | | | | | | | | |
| Computer Item Generator | Can be used to create custom-made practice pages or assessment pages at any time. | | | | | | | | | | | |

### Test-Taking Tips on Transparencies

1. Draw two rectangles of different lengths and widths, with a perimeter of 20 units.

Scoring Guide

3 Draws 2 rectangles of different lengths and widths, with perimeter 20 units indicated by labels on sides.

2 Draws 2 identical rectangles, with perimeter 20 units, OR draws 2 rectangles of different widths and lengths, only 1 with perimeter 20 units.

1 Draws 1 or 2 rectangles, whose perimeters are not 20 units, OR draws 1 or 2 non-rectangles.

0 Answers inappropriately or not at all.

2. The Athletic Council is hosting a sports banquet. It costs $300 to rent a hall, plus $8 per person for food. Between 50 and 90 people will attend. What are the least and greatest amounts of money the banquet could cost? Explain.

Scoring Guide

3 Correctly computes least and greatest costs, AND explains adequately.

2 Computes least cost incorrectly, OR computes greatest cost incorrectly, OR explains inadequately.

1 Computes both costs incorrectly, OR computes one cost correctly, but explains inadequately.

0 Answers inappropriately or not at all.

*Use with Standardized Test Prep and Chapter Assessments.*

## Correlation to Standardized Tests

| Lesson | | CAT5 | CTBS/5 TerraNova™ | ITBS | MAT7 | SAT9 | LOCAL OBJECTIVES |
|---|---|---|---|---|---|---|---|
| 9-1 | Introduction to Geometry: Points, Lines, and Planes | | | | | ■ | |
| 9-2 | Angle Relationships and Parallel Lines | | | | | ■ | |
| 9-3 | Classifying Polygons | | | ■ | | ■ | |
| 9-4 | Problem Solving Strategy: Draw a Diagram | ■ | | | | ■ | |
| 9-5 | Congruence | ■ | ■ | | | ■ | |
| 9-6 | Circles | | ■ | | ■ | ■ | |
| 9-7 | Constructions | | | | | ■ | |
| 9-8 | Translations | ■ | ■ | | ■ | ■ | |
| 9-9 | Symmetry and Reflections | | | | | ■ | |
| 9-10 | Rotations | ■ | ■ | ■ | | ■ | |

**CAT5** California Achievement Test, 5th edition
**CTBS TerraNova** Comprehensive Test of Basic Skills, 5th edition
**ITBS** Iowa Test of Basic Skills, Form M
**MAT7** Metropolitan Achievement Test, 7th edition
**SAT** Stanford Achievement Test, Advanced 1

For other standardized test correlations, follow the link to your state at **www.phschool.com**.

# Resources for Chapter 9

| | TEACHING RESOURCES BOX | | | | | | | | | | | | | | |
|---|---|---|---|---|---|---|---|---|---|---|---|---|---|---|---|
| | CHAPTER 9 SUPPORT FILE | | | | | | | | Cumulative Assessment | Lesson Planners Plus | Daily Cum Review | Teaching Transparencies | Warm-Up Transparencies | Help at Home | SE Answers Transparenci |
| | Practice | Reteach | Enrichment | Project Manager | Checkpoints | Cumulative Review | Chapter Assessment | Alternative Assessment | | | | | | | |
| Begin Chapter | | | | ■ | | | | | | ■ | | | | | |
| 9-1 | ■ | ■ | ■ | | | | | | | ■ | ■ | 12, 13 | ■ | | ■ |
| 9-2 | ■ | ■ | ■ | | | | | | | ■ | ■ | 4, 27, 69 | ■ | | ■ |
| 9-3 | ■ | ■ | ■ | | | | | | | ■ | ■ | 70 | ■ | | ■ |
| 9-4 | ■ | ■ | ■ | | | | | | | ■ | ■ | | ■ | | ■ |
| 9-5 | ■ | ■ | ■ | | ■ | | | | | ■ | ■ | 71 | ■ | ■ | ■ |
| 9-6 | ■ | ■ | ■ | | | | | | | ■ | ■ | 72 | ■ | | ■ |
| 9-7 | ■ | ■ | ■ | | | | | | | ■ | ■ | | ■ | | ■ |
| 9-8 | ■ | ■ | ■ | | ■ | | | | | ■ | ■ | 73 | ■ | ■ | ■ |
| 9-9 | ■ | ■ | ■ | | | | | | | ■ | ■ | 73 | ■ | | ■ |
| 9-10 | ■ | ■ | ■ | | | | | | | ■ | ■ | 73 | ■ | | ■ |
| End Chapter | | | | | | ■ | ■ (2 forms) | ■ | After Ch. 3, 6, 9, 13 | | | | | | |

**Also available for use with the chapter:**

Solution Key
Computational Practice Skills Booklet
Mathematics Standardized Test Prep, Student Edition and Teacher's Edition
Overhead Manipulatives Kit
Practice Workbook
Algebra Readiness Kit
Student Manipulatives Kit
Test-Taking Tips on Transparencies
Assessment Success Kit
Teaching Aids and Letters
Graphing Calculator Handbook
Spanish Resources
Success-Building Puzzle and Problem Masters

## TECHNOLOGY

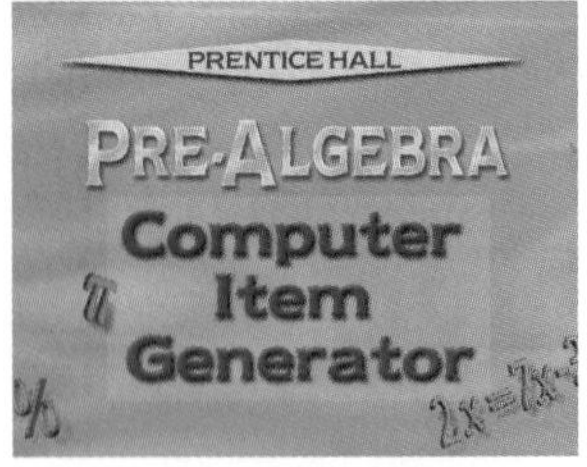


**Computer Item Generator with Standardized Test Prep**
CD-ROM with an unlimited supply of questions with varying degrees of difficulty for customized practice sheets, quizzes, and tests.

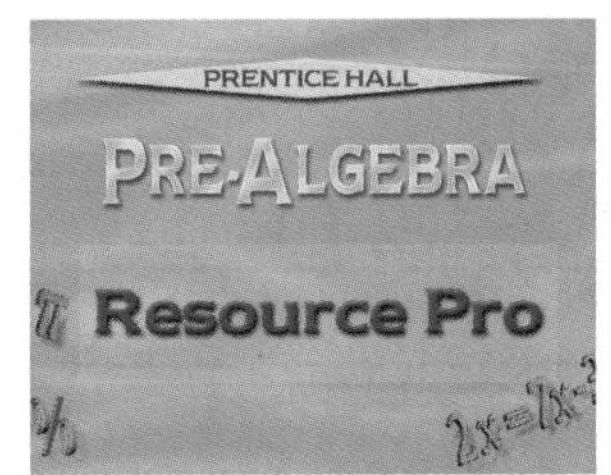


**Resource Pro® with Planning Express®**
CD-ROM with complete classroom planning tool and teaching resources for customizing and planning lessons.

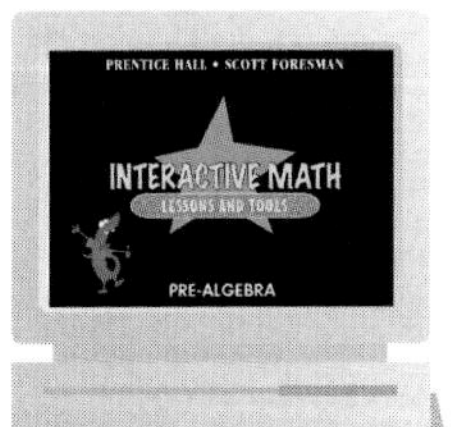


**Interactive Math Lessons and Tools**
CD-ROM with lessons and tools to make abstract concepts visual and accessible.

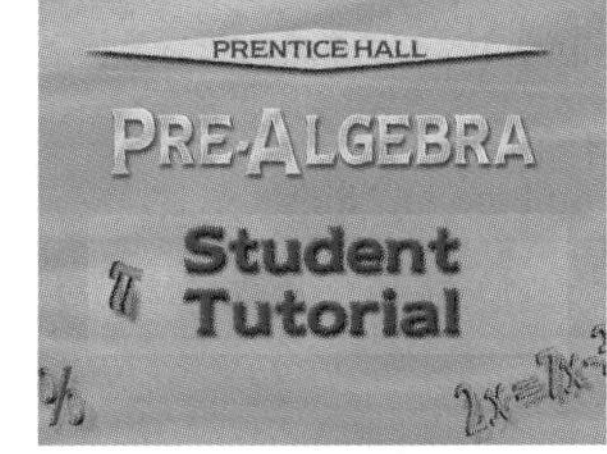


**Student Tutorial**
Test preparation software for students on CD-ROM with management system for teachers; includes Secondary Math Lab Toolkit™.

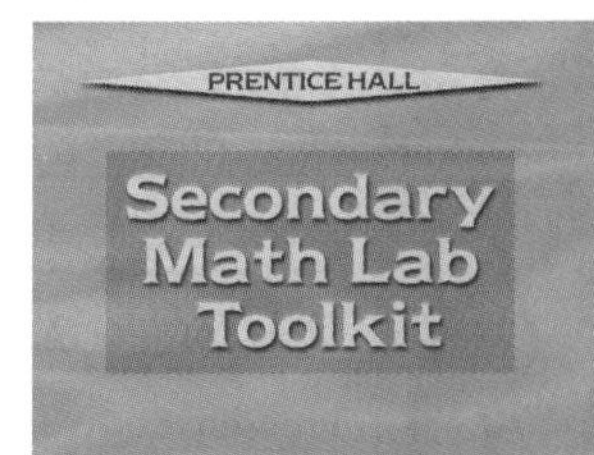


**Secondary Math Lab Toolkit™ with Integrated Math Labs**
Integrated software package with linkable math tools for exploring key concepts.

**Also available for use with the chapter:**

Math Blaster® Pre-Algebra CD-ROM
Video Fieldtrips, Vol. I: Algebra Applications
Video Fieldtrips, Vol. II: Geometry Applications
Wide World of Mathematics CD-ROM
Wide World of Mathematics Video

### *Web Extension*

**www.phschool.com**

**For Students**
- Chapter Support with Internet Links
- Internet Activities

**For Teachers**
- Curriculum Support
- Professional Development
- Product Information
- Regional Support Information

# Skills You Need for Chapter 9

## ▶ *Naming polygons*

Use before Lesson 9-3.

**Match each polygon to its name.**

1. D

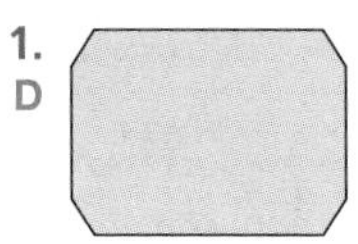

2. B

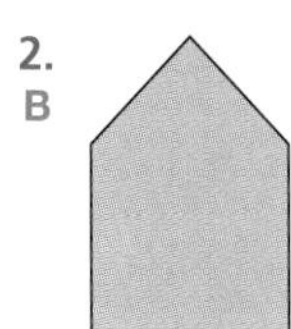

3. A

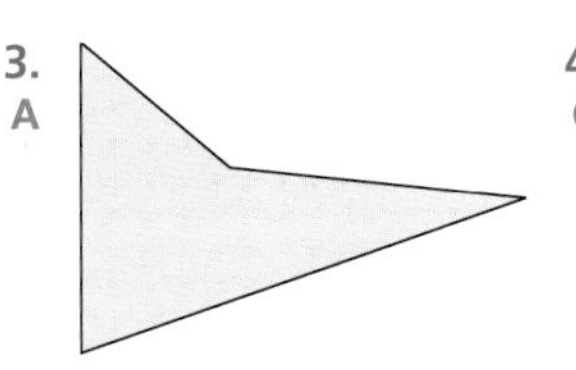

4. C

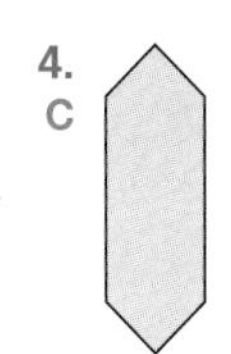

**A.** quadrilateral  **B.** pentagon  **C.** hexagon  **D.** octagon

## ▶ *Identifying radius and diameter*

Use before Lesson 9-6.

**Give the radius of each circle.**

5. 6 cm

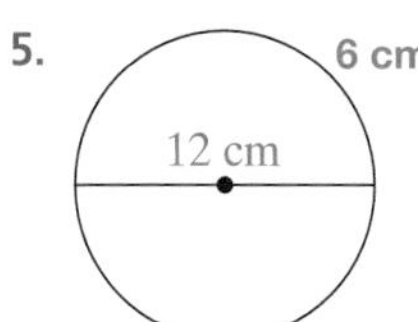


6. $\frac{1}{2}$ in.

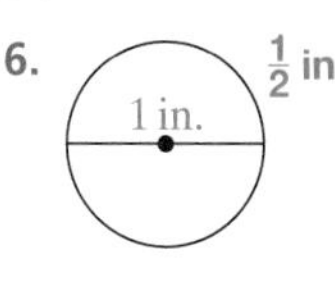


7. 2.8 cm

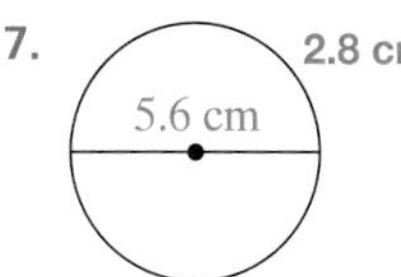


8. 7.5 ft

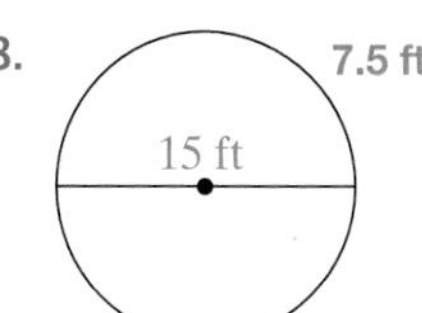


**Give the diameter of each circle.**

9. 6 in.

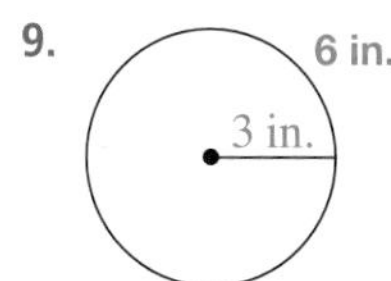


10. 2 in.

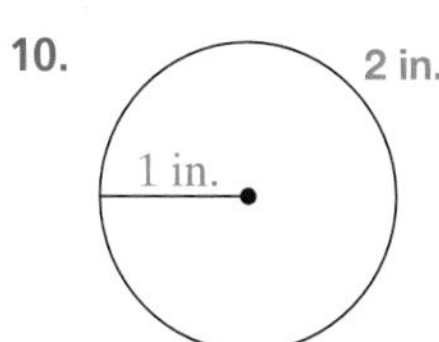


11. 7 m

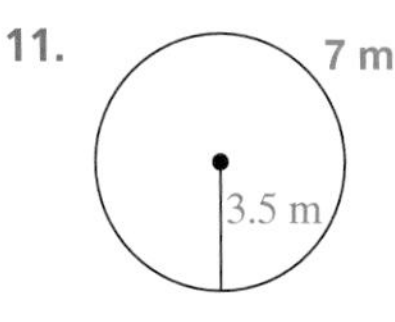


12. $3\frac{1}{2}$ ft

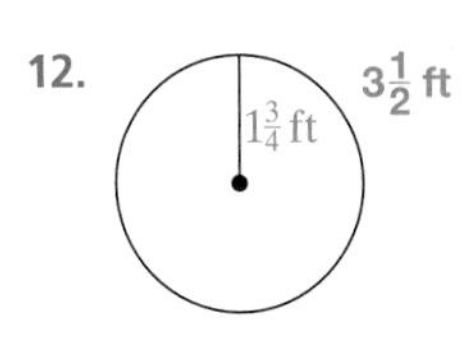


## ▶ *Graphing on the coordinate plane*

Use before Lesson 9-8.

**Graph each point on the same coordinate plane.** 13–22. See margin.

13. $A(0, 7)$  14. $B(-2, 5)$  15. $C(-3, -1)$  16. $D(2, -4)$  17. $E(4, 0)$

18. $F(1\frac{1}{2}, -3)$  19. $G(0, 0)$  20. $H(-5, -5)$  21. $I(-4, -5)$  22. $J(0, -1)$



# Skills You Need

### Naming polygons

**In Lesson 9-4** students will draw polygons as they learn the problem solving strategy of Draw a Diagram.

### Identifying radius and diameter

**In Lesson 9-6** students will find the radius, diameter, and circumference of circles.

### Graphing on the coordinate plane

**In Lesson 9-8** students will graph the effects of the specific transformation called a translation on the coordinate plane.

13–22.

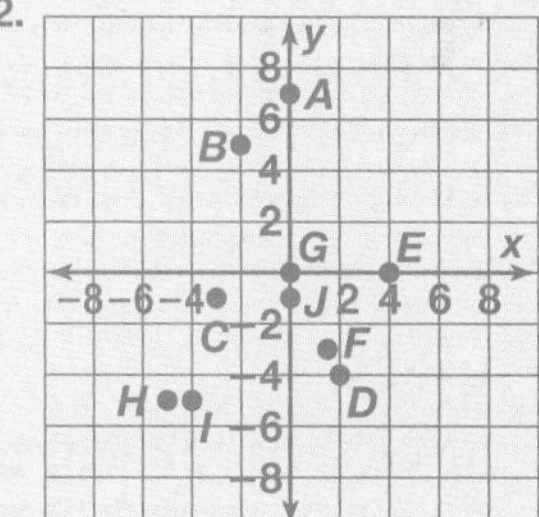


# Skills Trace

| SKILL | INTRODUCED | DEVELOPED IN LESSON(S) | REVIEWED/REINFORCED |
|---|---|---|---|
| Relating lines and angles | 9-1 | 9-2 | Math Toolbox p. 448; pp. 453, 458, 541, 672 |
| Learning about polygons | 9-3 | 9-4, 9-5 | Math Toolbox p. 459; pp. 463, 468, 473, 581, 611, 668 |
| Learning about circles | 9-6 | 9-6 | pp. 478, 483, 545, 586, 668 |
| Making transformations | 9-8 | 9-9, 9-10 | Math Toolboxes pp. 484, 494; pp. 488, 493, 508, 532, 645 |

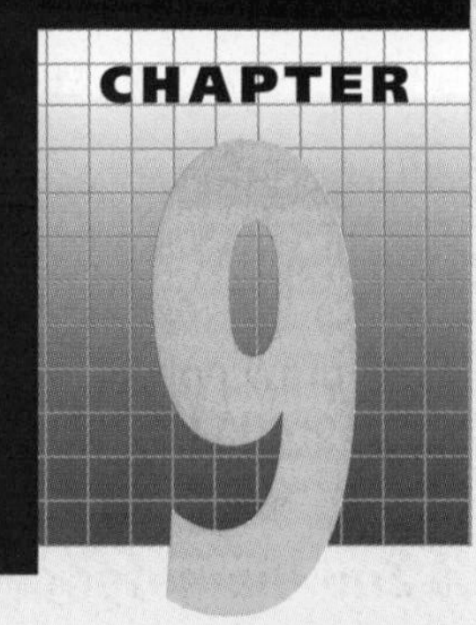

# Spatial Thinking

## Connecting to Students' Lives

Ask students to describe situations in which they use maps. Ask if anyone has used a map to find a town, plan a trip, or find the distance between two points.

## Interdisciplinary Connections

The Chapter Project connects math and geography. You may want to give a short refresher lesson on how to read maps, to use the key, and how to find North and other directions before students begin work on the project activities.

## About the Project

The Chapter Project directs students to apply their knowledge of drawing and measuring angles, and measuring distances to find a point on a map where a hidden treasure is buried.

CHAPTER 9

# Spatial Thinking

Savannah
Wilmington I.
Skidaway I.
Hinesville
Baxley
Ossabaw I.
St. Catherines I.
GEORGIA
Sapelo I.
Everett
Darien
Wolf I.
SEA ISLANDS
St. Simons I.
Brunswick
0 10 20 30 40
Scale (miles)
Jekyll I.
Cumberland I.
Amelia I.
N
ATLANTIC OCEAN
Jacksonville

**What you'll learn in this chapter:**

- How to use properties of figures to solve problems
- How to classify geometric figures
- How to construct figures

440 Chapter 9

**Internet Connection**

*Web Extension*
**www.phschool.com**

**For Students**
Chapter Support with Internet links
Interactive Activities

**For Teachers**
Curriculum Support
Professional Development
Product Information
Regional Support Information

A mysterious map has come into your possession. The map shows the Sea Islands off the coast of Georgia. But that's not all! The map also contains three clues that tell where a treasure is supposedly buried.

***Draw a Treasure Map*** Your project for this chapter will be to find the location of the treasure. Trace the map on the page at the left. Then follow the clues in the activities.

### *Steps to help you complete the project*

*Web Extension*
**www.phschool.com**

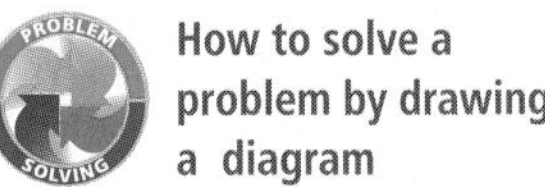


How to solve a problem by drawing a diagram

## LAUNCHING THE PROJECT

*The Chapter Project is optional and may be assigned at your discretion.*

Ask students:

- Have you ever use a map to find the location of a place you've never been?
- What tools will you need to use in order to complete this project?
- What is it that you are trying to locate on the map? Where do you expect to find it?

Distribute a copy of the Project Manager and Scoring Rubric to help students get an overview of the project.

Review the scoring rubric with students.

###  Project Notebook

Encourage students to keep all project-related materials in a separate folder or notebook. Call attention to the fact that they will find much useful information on the Web site **www.phschool.com**.

**Tracking the Project** Set benchmark deadlines for students to show you their work in progress.

### Scoring Rubric

**3** You draw all figures and find the treasure correctly. Your poster is complete, neat, well-organized, and easy to read. Your reasoning is appropriate and explained well.

**2** You make minor errors in your figures or your reasoning. Your poster is complete and descriptive, but it could be better organized or neater.

**1** You draw figures or reason incorrectly. Your poster is incomplete and lacks organization.

**0** Major elements of the project are incomplete or missing.

*Available in the Chapter 9 Support File in the Teaching Resources box.*

### Project Manager and Scoring Rubric

**Getting Started** You will be creating a poster showing how you used clues and a map to locate a treasure. Read about the project in your textbook. As you work on the project, you will need tracing paper, a straightedge, a compass, a protractor, and materials to make your poster.

**Checklist and Suggestions**

| | | |
|---|---|---|
| ❑ | Draw the figures given in the first clue. | Make sure your second line goes southwesterly from Savannah. |
| ❑ | Draw the figures given in the second clue. | Think about what kind of figure contains all the points that are the same distance from a given point. |
| ❑ | Apply the third clue. | Check each possible island to see which one forms an obtuse triangle with Savannah and Everett. |
| ❑ | Make your poster. | Include answers to the questions and explanations of your reasoning. |
| ❑ | Share your poster with a friend. | Make any necessary changes. |

**Scoring Rubric**

**3** You draw all figures and find the treasure correctly. Your poster is complete, neat, well-organized, and easy to read. Your reasoning is appropriate and explained well.

**2** You make minor errors in your figures or your reasoning. Your poster is complete and descriptive, but it could be better organized or neater.

**1** You draw figures or reason incorrectly. Your poster is incomplete and lacks organization.

**0** Major elements of the project are incomplete or missing.

**Your Evaluation of the Project** Evaluate your work, based on the Scoring Rubric.

**Teacher's Evaluation of the Project**

# 9-1

## Getting Ready

**Key Terms and Symbols** point, line, plane, segment, ray, parallel, skew

**Resources** A complete list of resources for this lesson is on p. 439H.

### Daily Skills Warm-Up

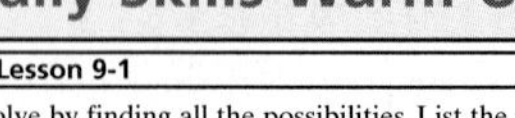

Lesson 9-1

Solve by finding all the possibilities. List the possibilities.

The letters, A, B, C, and D are each listed on a piece of paper and placed in a bag. Juan draws out two letters. How many different combinations of letters could he get?

6 combinations
AB
AC BC
AD BD CD

### Background for the Lesson

The basic geometric figures are the plane, point, line, segment, and ray. You use these to construct many other geometric figures. Point, line, and plane are basic concepts that do not have formal definitions. A point has no dimensions. A line is one-dimensional and has length, but no width or thickness. However, you cannot measure the length of an entire line, only the length of a line segment. A mathematical line is not a thing but an idea, modeled by a drawing. Put an arrow on each end of a line to show that it extends in two directions without end. A line segment, part of a line, has two definite endpoints. A ray is a half-line that starts from one endpoint and goes on forever. You draw a ray with an arrow at one end.

## 1 Focus

### Connecting to Students' Lives

Ask students to point out geometric figures that they can see in the classroom and to write a list of figures they see on their way to school.

**Writing Math** Discuss the differences in the meaning and spelling of *plane* (as in geometry and *airplane*) and *plain* (or ordinary).

# 9-1 Introduction to Geometry: Points, Lines, and Planes

**What You'll Learn**

1. To name basic geometric figures
2. To recognize intersecting lines, parallel lines, and skew lines

**. . . And Why**

To build a basic vocabulary in geometry and to solve problems in architecture

## PART 1 Points, Lines, and Planes

Geometric shapes are evident in many man-made and natural structures. Notice the hexagonal shape of each cell of the honeycomb in the photo below. Two other examples of geometry in nature are the spiral structure of a snail's shell and the shape of a snowflake.

**Basic Geometric Figures**

| Name | Sample | Symbolic Name | Description |
|---|---|---|---|
| Point | • *A* | Point *A* | A **point** is a location in space. It has no size. |
| Line | *A*, *B*, *n* | $\overleftrightarrow{AB}$, $\overleftrightarrow{BA}$, or *n* | A **line** is a series of points that extends in two directions without end. A line can be named with a lower case letter. |
| Plane | *A*, *B*, *C*, *D*, *M* | *ABCD* or *M* | A **plane** is a flat surface. It has no thickness. It continues without end in all directions. |
| Line segment or segment | *P*, *Q* | $\overline{PQ}$, or $\overline{QP}$ | A **segment** is a part of a line. It has two endpoints. The length of $\overline{PQ}$ is written as *PQ*. |
| Ray | *C*, *R* | $\overrightarrow{CR}$ | A **ray** is a part of a line. It has exactly one endpoint. Name its endpoint first. |



## Tools to Monitor Progress

**BEFORE THE LESSON**

**To check prerequisite skills:**

- Identifying polygons

**Skills Intervention Kit,** Geometry

**DURING THE LESSON**

**To check understanding:**

**Try This** exercises on student page

- **Additional Examples 1–3**

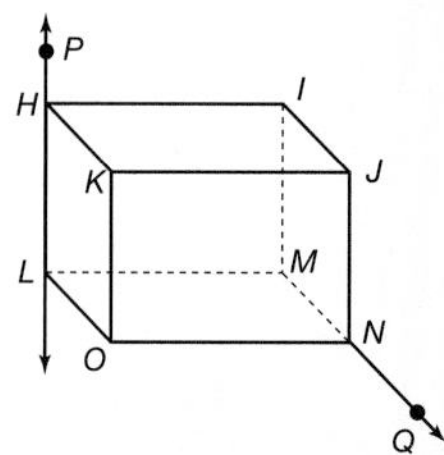

You can combine the basic geometric figures to create many other geometric figures.

## EXAMPLE 1

**Name each figure in the diagram.**

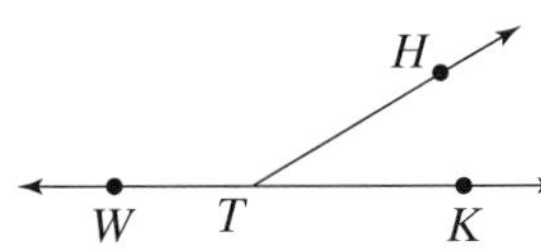


a. **Name four points.** H, K, T, and W — Name a point with a capital letter.

b. **Name four different segments.** $\overline{HT}, \overline{WT}, \overline{TK}$, and $\overline{WK}$ — Name a segment by its endpoints.

c. **Write five other names for $\overleftrightarrow{WT}$.** $\overleftrightarrow{WK}, \overleftrightarrow{TK}, \overleftrightarrow{KT}, \overleftrightarrow{KW}$, or $\overleftrightarrow{TW}$ — There is one line pictured. It has several names.

d. **Name five different rays.** $\overrightarrow{TH}, \overrightarrow{TW}, \overrightarrow{TK}, \overrightarrow{WK}$, or $\overrightarrow{KW}$. — The first letter names the endpoint of the ray.

**TRY THIS** Name each figure in the diagram.

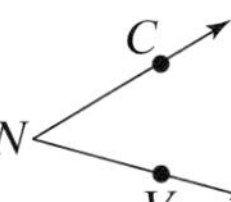


1. three points C, N, V
2. two segments $\overline{NC}, \overline{NV}$
3. two rays $\overrightarrow{NC}, \overrightarrow{NV}$

## PART 2 Intersecting, Parallel, and Skew Lines

Two lines *intersect* if they have exactly one point in common. Two lines that lie in the same plane and do not intersect are **parallel.** You use the symbol ∥ to indicate "is parallel to." Segments and rays are parallel if they lie in parallel lines.

**Skew** lines are lines that do not lie in the same plane. They are not parallel and they do not intersect. Skew segments must be parts of skew lines.

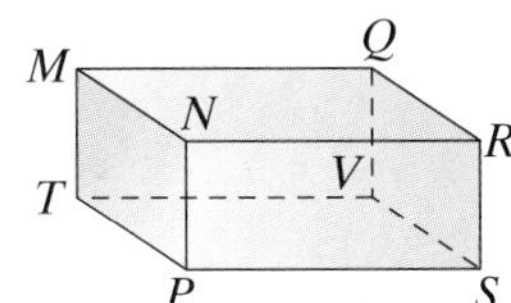


$\overline{MN}$ intersects $\overline{NP}$.
$\overline{MN} \parallel \overline{QR}$
$\overline{MN}$ is skew to $\overline{RS}$.



# 2 Teach

## PART 1 Part 1 Teaching Notes

Explore the basic geometric figures with students by having them give explanations of each figure in their own words. For example, some students might envision a plane as a gym floor. The marks on a basketball court are made up of geometric figures. Point out that *line* in this lesson means a straight line, not a curve.

**ELL** It is common in English to say the word *line* for the geometric figure that is really a *line segment.* Help students understand the difference between these two concepts.

### Example 1

**Build understanding.** Ask: How can $\overleftrightarrow{WT}$ have so many different names? You can name a line using any two points on the line.

**Auditory Learning** Group students in pairs. Using the list of names and symbols for the basic figures, have one student read the name while the other draws the corresponding figure. Then have partners compare and check.

## PART 2 Part 2 Teaching Notes

Emphasize that parallel and intersecting lines always lie in the same plane, and that *skew* lines *do not* lie in the same plane.

**Tactile Learning** To assess students' understanding, have them hold two pencils in position to show skew lines.

a. Name four points. sample answer: H, I, J, K
b. Name four different segments. sample answer: $\overline{HL}, \overline{HK}, \overline{KJ}, \overline{KO}$
c. Write another name for $\overleftrightarrow{LH}$. sample answer: $\overleftrightarrow{LP}$
d. Name three different rays. sample answer: $\overrightarrow{HP}, \overrightarrow{HL}, \overrightarrow{NQ}$
e. Name a segment that is parallel to $\overline{ON}$. sample answer: $\overline{KJ}$

### AFTER THE LESSON

**To assess knowledge:**
**Lesson Quiz**

Draw each figure named.

1. $\overleftrightarrow{ST}$ line with points S and T; arrows on each end
2. $\overrightarrow{EF}$ ray with end point E through point F with arrow on the end past point F

- For enrichment and reteaching options see Resources on p. 439H.

## Example 2

**Build understanding.** Explain what you know must be true about $\overleftrightarrow{DH}$ and $\overleftrightarrow{AE}$. Since segments that are parallel lie in parallel lines, then $\overleftrightarrow{DH}$ and $\overleftrightarrow{AE}$ must be parallel.

**Error Prevention** Students may classify two lines in the same plane as skew if the lines are not shown as intersecting. Suggest that students visualize a cube when thinking of skew lines. The segments in a cube that are not parallel and do not intersect are skew.

**Advanced Learners** Explain why two straight lines that are not parallel can only intersect once. Lines extend in two directions without end. If they intersected again, they would have to curve or change direction, and they would no longer be straight lines.

## Example 3

**Build understanding.** Ask: How do you know the line that intersects the parallel lines is only a segment? Explain. It has no arrows on its ends.

**Math Reasoning** Use math reasoning to explain why two lines that are not skew and are not parallel must intersect. If the lines are not skew, then they must lie in the same plane. Then, if they are not parallel, they must intersect at some point because they lie in the same plane.

## EXAMPLE 2

*Architecture* **This structure is the frame of a room. Name each of the following.**

**a. four segments that intersect $\overline{DH}$**
$\overline{AD}, \overline{CD}, \overline{EH}, \overline{GH}$

**b. three segments parallel to $\overline{DH}$**
$\overline{AE}, \overline{BF}, \overline{CG}$

**c. four segments skew to $\overline{DH}$**
$\overline{AB}, \overline{BC}, \overline{EF}, \overline{FG}$

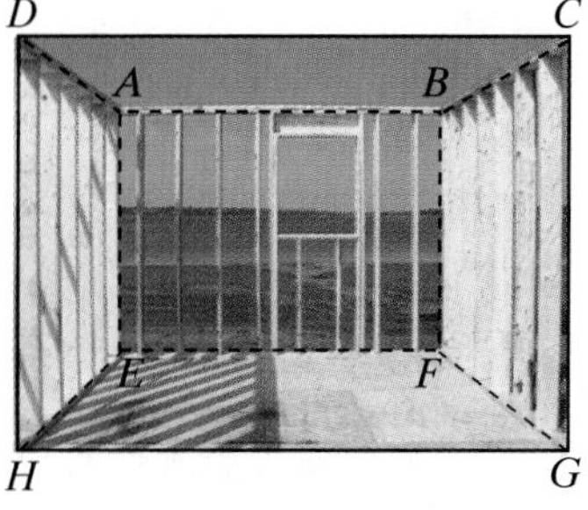


**TRY THIS** Use the diagram in Example 2. Name each of the following.

4. four segments that intersect $\overline{EF}$ $\overline{EH}, \overline{FG}, \overline{AE}, \overline{BF}$
5. three segments parallel to $\overline{EF}$ $\overline{HG}, \overline{DC}, \overline{AB}$
6. four segments skew to $\overline{EF}$ $\overline{DH}, \overline{CG}, \overline{AD}, \overline{BC}$

## EXAMPLE 3

**Draw a figure containing two parallel lines. Then draw a segment that intersects the parallel lines.**

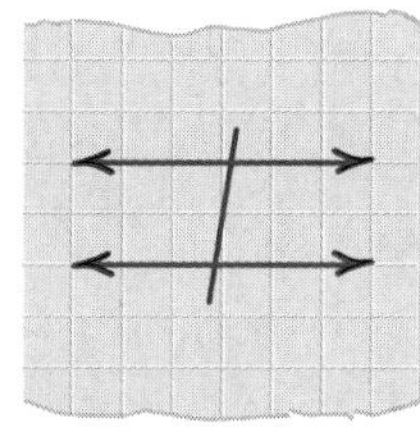

Use the lines on a piece of notebook paper or graph paper to create parallel lines. Then draw a segment that intersects the other two lines.

**TRY THIS**

7. Use notebook paper or graph paper. Draw a figure containing three segments that are parallel to each other. Draw a ray that intersects the parallel segments. See margin.



7. Answers may vary. Sample:

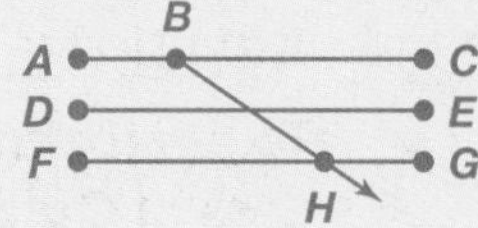

# Exercises

## Check Understanding

**Use the figure at the right.**

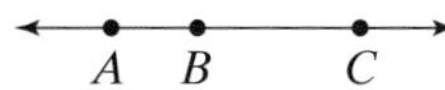


1. Name the line in three ways. Answers may vary. Sample: $\overleftrightarrow{AB}$, $\overleftrightarrow{BC}$, $\overleftrightarrow{AC}$
2. Name three different segments. $\overline{AB}$, $\overline{BC}$, $\overline{AC}$
3. Name four different rays. $\overrightarrow{AC}$, $\overrightarrow{BC}$, $\overrightarrow{BA}$, $\overrightarrow{CA}$

**Use the figure at the right. Find each of the following.**

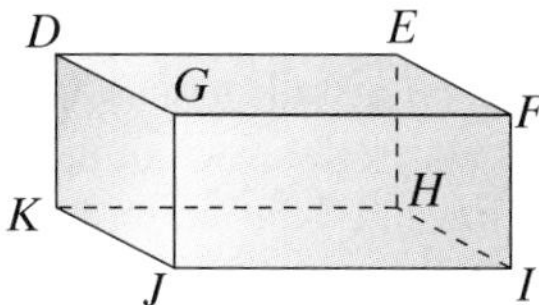


4. all segments that intersect $\overline{DE}$ $\overline{KD}$, $\overline{DG}$, $\overline{EH}$, $\overline{EF}$
5. all segments parallel to $\overline{DE}$ $\overline{GF}$, $\overline{JI}$, $\overline{KH}$
6. all segments skew to $\overline{DE}$ $\overline{GJ}$, $\overline{FI}$, $\overline{KJ}$, $\overline{HI}$

## Practice and Problem Solving

**Name all points, segments, lines, and rays shown.**

7. 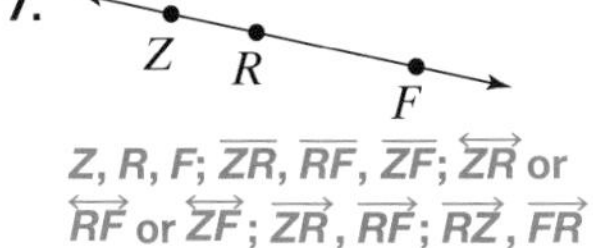


Z, R, F; $\overline{ZR}$, $\overline{RF}$, $\overline{ZF}$; $\overleftrightarrow{ZR}$ or $\overleftrightarrow{RF}$ or $\overleftrightarrow{ZF}$; $\overrightarrow{ZR}$, $\overrightarrow{RF}$; $\overrightarrow{RZ}$, $\overrightarrow{FR}$

8. 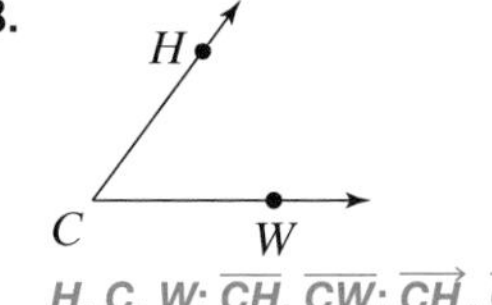


H, C, W; $\overline{CH}$, $\overline{CW}$; $\overrightarrow{CH}$, $\overrightarrow{CW}$

9. 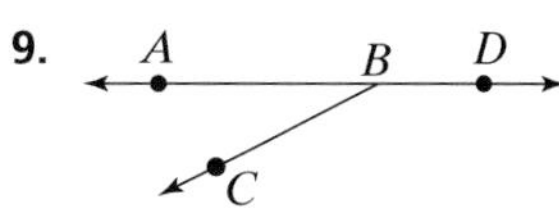


A, B, C, D; $\overline{AB}$, $\overline{AD}$, $\overline{BD}$, $\overline{BC}$; $\overleftrightarrow{DA}$; $\overrightarrow{BA}$, $\overrightarrow{BC}$, $\overrightarrow{BD}$, $\overrightarrow{AD}$, $\overrightarrow{DA}$

10. 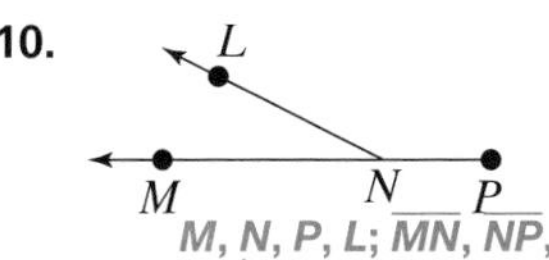


M, N, P, L; $\overline{MN}$, $\overline{NP}$, $\overline{MP}$, $\overline{NL}$; $\overleftrightarrow{NM}$, $\overrightarrow{NL}$, $\overrightarrow{PM}$

11. 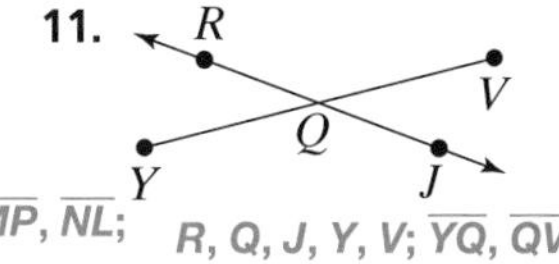


R, Q, J, Y, V; $\overline{YQ}$, $\overline{QV}$, $\overline{YV}$, $\overline{RQ}$, $\overline{QJ}$, $\overline{RJ}$; $\overleftrightarrow{QJ}$; $\overrightarrow{QR}$, $\overrightarrow{QJ}$, $\overrightarrow{JR}$, $\overrightarrow{RJ}$

12. G, W, P, H, Q; $\overline{GW}$, $\overline{WP}$, $\overline{GP}$, $\overline{QW}$, $\overline{WH}$, $\overline{QH}$; $\overleftrightarrow{GP}$, $\overleftrightarrow{HQ}$; $\overrightarrow{GP}$, $\overrightarrow{WP}$, $\overrightarrow{WG}$, $\overrightarrow{PG}$, $\overrightarrow{WH}$, $\overrightarrow{QH}$, $\overrightarrow{HQ}$, $\overrightarrow{WQ}$

Modeling **Draw each figure named.**

13. $\overline{NS}$ 

14. $\overleftrightarrow{VB}$ 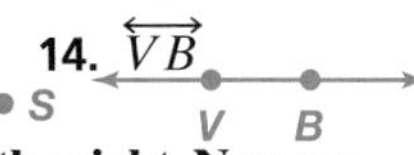


15. $\overrightarrow{KE}$ 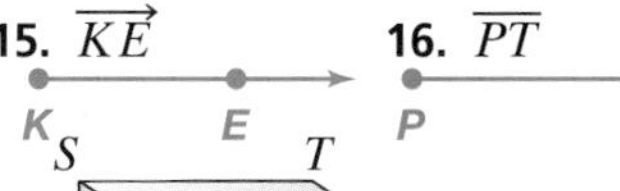


16. $\overline{PT}$ 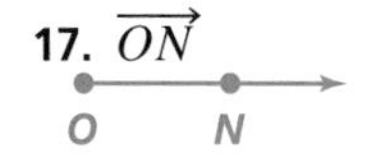


17. $\overrightarrow{ON}$
O N

**Use the figure at the right. Name a segment to make each statement true.**

18–21. Answers may vary. Samples are given.

18. ■ $\parallel \overline{XY}$ $\overline{WZ}$
19. ■ $\parallel \overline{YZ}$ $\overline{WX}$
20. ■ $\parallel \overline{WX}$ $\overline{ST}$
21. ■ $\parallel \overline{SV}$ $\overline{TU}$



# 3 Practice/Assess

## Assignment Guide

To provide flexible scheduling, this lesson can be divided into parts.

**Part 1**
**Core** 1–3, 7–17, 30–37, 40–41
**Extension** 29

**Part 2**
**Core** 4–6, 18–21, 26–28, 38–39, 43
**Extension** 22–25, 42

Mixed Review can be assigned at any time for maintenance.

## Exercises

**Exercises 7–12** Check that you have named *all* of the points, segments, lines, and rays in each figure.

## Challenge

Explain why you cannot draw two truly skew lines on a piece of paper. A piece of paper is a plane, and two skew lines cannot exist in the same plane.

## Closure

A point is a position in space. All geometric figures are made up of points. A line is a series of points that extend in two directions without end. A segment is a part of a line and has two end points. A ray is a part of a line with exactly one endpoint. An angle is two rays that intersect at their endpoints.

## Alternative Assessment

Have students cut pictures that contain geometric figures from old magazines or newspapers. Ask them to outline a figure with a wide black pen and then trace the geometric figures onto a piece of paper. Then have them write labels to identify points, lines, segments, rays, parallel lines, and skew lines.

### Daily Cumulative Review

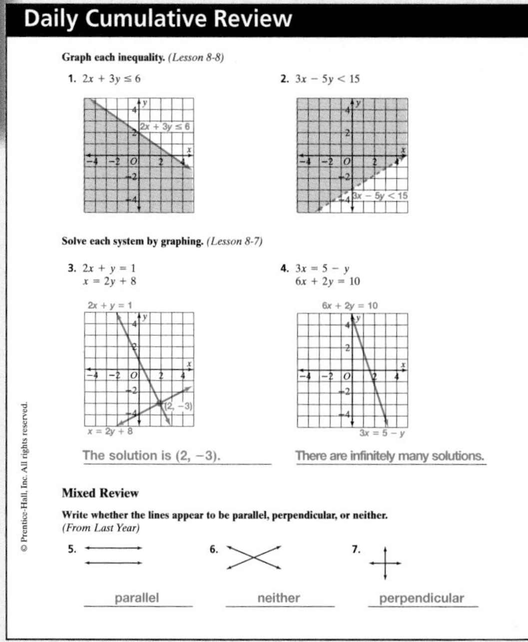
**Graph each inequality.** *(Lesson 8-8)*

1. $2x + 3y \le 6$
2. $3x - 5y < 15$

**Solve each system by graphing.** *(Lesson 8-7)*

3. $2x + y = 1$; $x = 2y + 8$ — The solution is (2, −3).
4. $3x = 5 - y$; $6x + 2y = 10$ — There are infinitely many solutions.

**Mixed Review**

**Write whether the lines appear to be parallel, perpendicular, or neither.** *(From Last Year)*

5. parallel
6. neither
7. perpendicular

Decide whether each pair of objects are usually *intersecting, parallel,* or *skew.* **Justify your answer.** 22–25. Answers may vary. Samples are given.

22. stop sign pole, street curb
23. two rungs of a ladder
24. fence post, fence wire
25. sidewalk, telephone pole

22. Intersecting; the base of the pole can be on the curb.
23. Parallel; they are in the same plane and do not intersect.
24. Intersecting; the wire is attached to the post.
25. Skew; they are not in the same plane.

**Use the figure at the right. Name each of the following.**

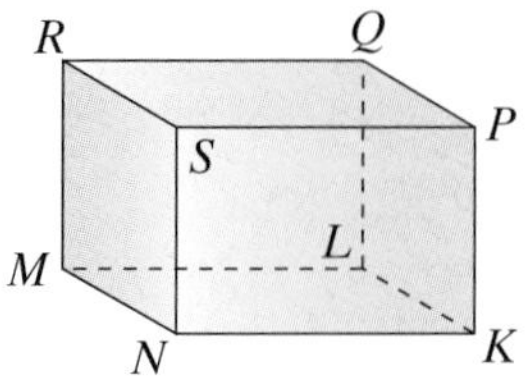

R Q P S L M N K

26. four segments that intersect $\overline{MN}$ $\overline{ML}$, $\overline{NK}$, $\overline{MR}$, $\overline{NS}$
27. three segments parallel to $\overline{MN}$ $\overline{RS}$, $\overline{QP}$, $\overline{LK}$
28. three segments skew to $\overline{MN}$ $\overline{PS}$, $\overline{RQ}$, $\overline{PK}$, (or $\overline{QL}$)

29. a. Suppose a town installs a mailbox at point $P$. How many straight roads can the town build leading to $P$? infinitely many
    b. Suppose a town installs mailboxes at points $P$ and $R$. How many straight roads might the town build that pass by both mailboxes? one

30. Draw $\overleftrightarrow{CD}$ so that it intersects two segments, $\overline{FG}$ and $\overline{HJ}$. Answers may vary. Sample:

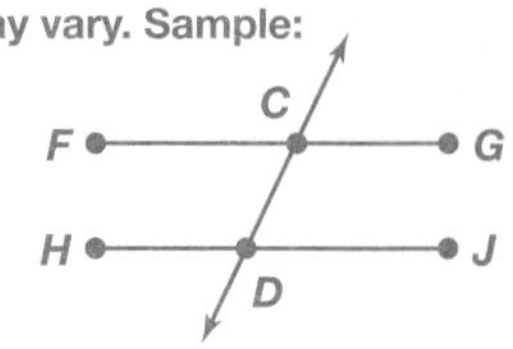

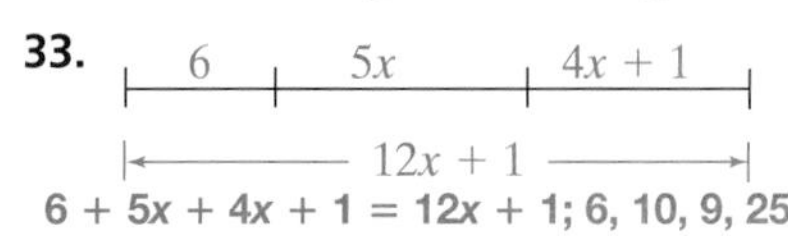


31. Draw two parallel rays. See margin.

*Algebra* **Write an equation, and then find the length of each segment.**

32. 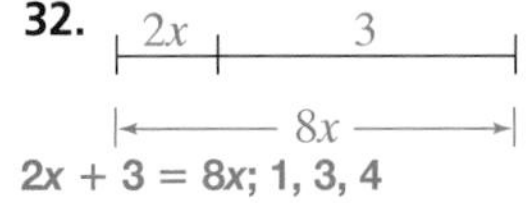

$2x + 3 = 8x$; 1, 3, 4

33. 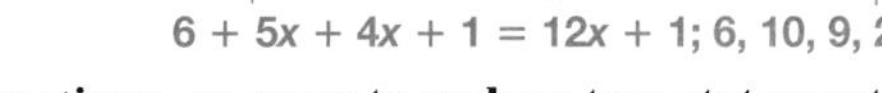

$6 + 5x + 4x + 1 = 12x + 1$; 6, 10, 9, 25

**Complete with *always, sometimes,* or *never* to make a true statement.**

34. $\overrightarrow{AB}$ and $\overrightarrow{BC}$ are _?_ on the same line. sometimes
35. $\overrightarrow{AB}$ and $\overrightarrow{AC}$ are _?_ the same ray. sometimes
36. $\overline{AX}$ and $\overline{XA}$ are _?_ the same segment. always
37. $\overleftrightarrow{TQ}$ and $\overleftrightarrow{QT}$ are _?_ the same line. always
38. Skew lines are _?_ in the same plane. never
39. Two lines in the same plane are _?_ parallel. sometimes
40. *Error Analysis* A student says that $\overrightarrow{AB}$ is the same ray as $\overrightarrow{BA}$. Explain the student's error. Answers may vary. Sample: $\overrightarrow{AB}$ and $\overrightarrow{BA}$ have different endpoints.
41. *Writing* Explain what the symbols $\overline{AB}$ and $AB$ represent. Use an example. $\overline{AB}$ is the segment from $A$ to $B$. $AB$ is a number, the length of $\overline{AB}$.



31. Answers may vary. Sample:

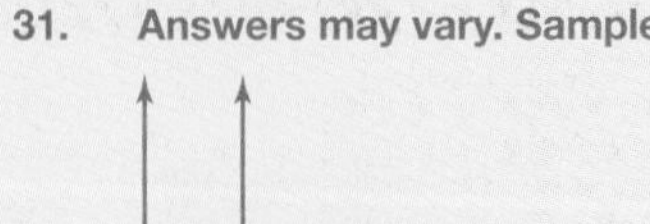

42a.

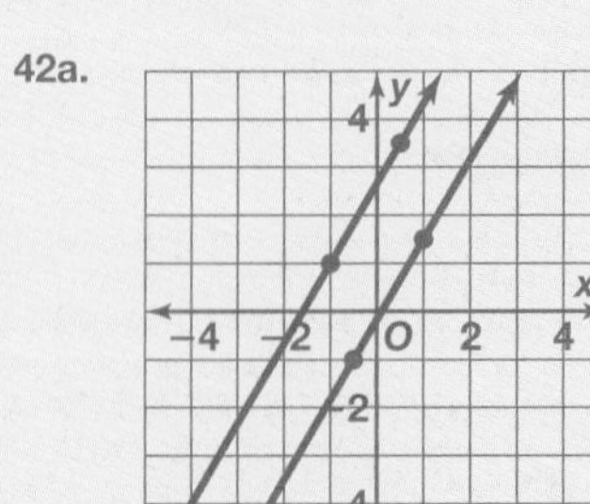

44.

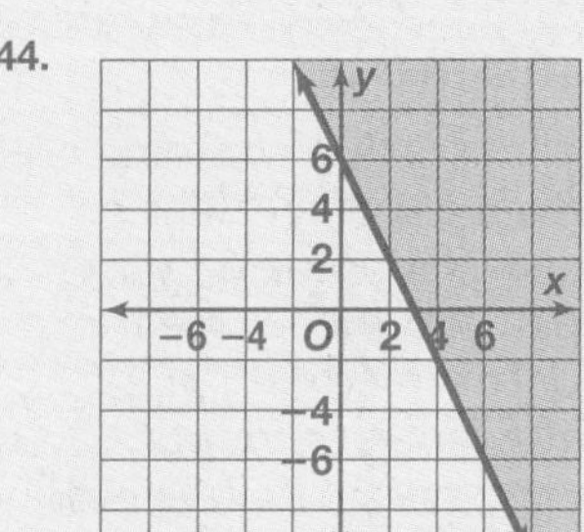

45.

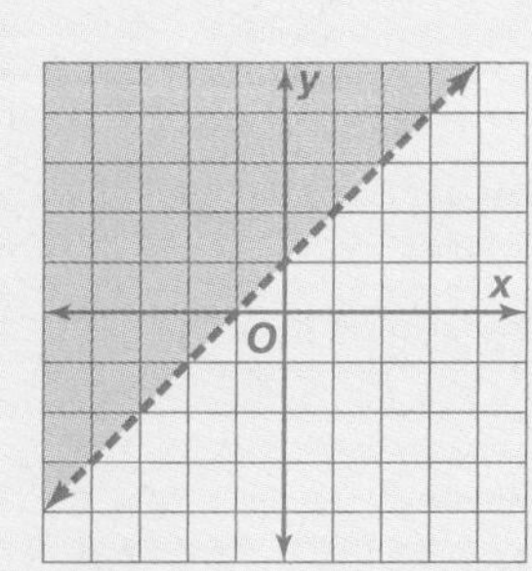

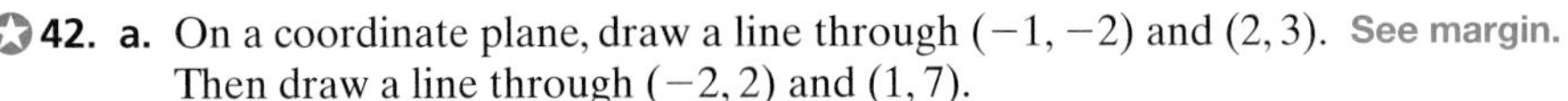

**42.** **a.** On a coordinate plane, draw a line through $(-1, -2)$ and $(2, 3)$. See margin. Then draw a line through $(-2, 2)$ and $(1, 7)$.
**b.** What appears to be true of the two lines that you drew in part (a)? parallel
**c.** Find the slope of each line. $\frac{5}{3}, \frac{5}{3}$
**d.** *Inductive Reasoning* Make a conjecture based on your answer to parts (b) and (c). If the slopes are equal, the lines are parallel.

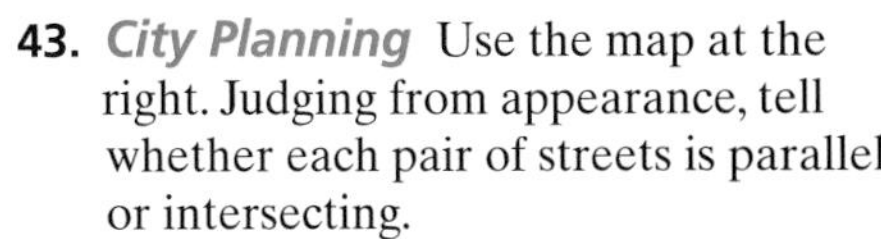

**43.** *City Planning* Use the map at the right. Judging from appearance, tell whether each pair of streets is parallel or intersecting.
**a.** N.W. Highway and Fifth Avenue
**b.** C Street and A Street parallel
**c.** B Street and C Street parallel
**d.** N.W. Highway and B Street
**e.** C Street and Main Street

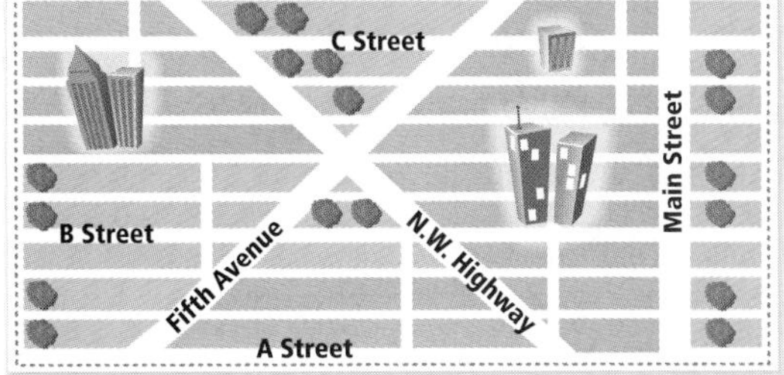


43a. intersecting 43d. intersecting 43e. intersecting

## MIXED REVIEW

**Graph each inequality. Use different coordinate planes.** *(Lesson 8-8)*

**44.** $y \geq -2x + 6$ See margin. **45.** $y > x + 1$ See margin. **46.** $x \leq -4$ See margin.

**Simplify each expression.** *(Lessons 5-3 and 5-4)*

**47.** $\frac{3}{8} + \frac{7}{12}$ $\frac{23}{24}$ **48.** $2\frac{3}{4} - 1\frac{5}{6}$ $\frac{11}{12}$ **49.** $\frac{5}{8} \cdot \frac{3}{4}$ $\frac{15}{32}$ **50.** $2\frac{2}{3} \div \frac{3}{8}$ $7\frac{1}{9}$

## Math at Work

### Choreographer

Choreographers are usually experienced dancers whose hard work and dedication have earned them the opportunity to create original dances. Choreographers have an excellent sense of timing and spatial positioning.

Many choreographed dance numbers reflect geometric shapes such as triangles and quadrilaterals. Next time you see a dance group perform, be on the lookout for geometry—it will help you think like a choreographer!

For more information about choreographers, visit the Prentice Hall Web site. **www.phschool.com**

See also Extra Practice section.



46.

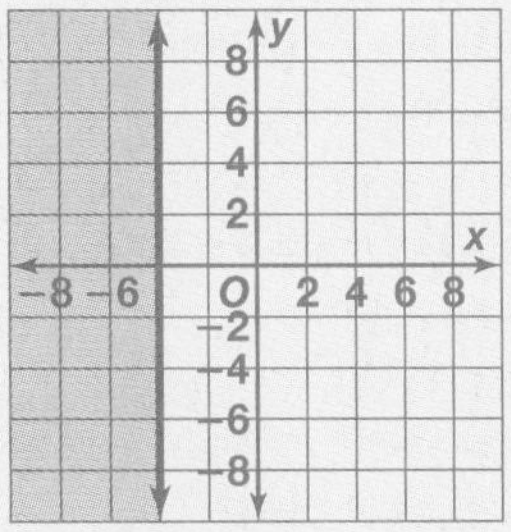

## Math at Work

If you have block scheduling or extended class periods, have small groups of students research the geometry that a choreographer might use. Groups may wish to use reference sources such as books on dance, or watch dance performances, rehearsals, or videos, or talk to a choreographer for their research. Have students present their findings to the class.

Students can find additional information on the Web site **www.phschool.com**.

## Practice

**Use the figures at the right. Name each of the following.**

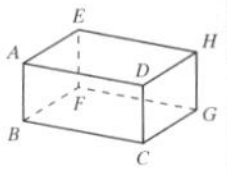

1. Four segments that intersect $\overline{AB}$.
   $\overline{BC}, \overline{BF}, \overline{AE}, \overline{AD}$
2. Three segments parallel to $\overline{AB}$.
   $\overline{DC}, \overline{EF}, \overline{GH}$
3. Four segments skew to $\overline{AB}$.
   $\overline{DH}, \overline{FG}, \overline{EH}, \overline{CG}$

**Use the figure at the right. Find each of the following.**

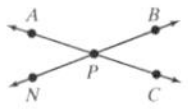

4. all points shown
   A, B, C, P, N
5. all segments shown
   $\overline{AP}, \overline{PC}, \overline{AC}, \overline{NP}, \overline{PB}, \overline{NB}$
6. five different rays Sample answer is shown.
   $\overrightarrow{PA}, \overrightarrow{PC}, \overrightarrow{PB}, \overrightarrow{PN}, \overrightarrow{NB}$
7. all lines shown
   $\overleftrightarrow{AC}, \overleftrightarrow{NB}$
8. all names for $\overleftrightarrow{NB}$
   $\overleftrightarrow{NB}, \overleftrightarrow{BN}, \overleftrightarrow{PN}, \overleftrightarrow{NP}, \overleftrightarrow{BP}, \overleftrightarrow{PB}$

**Write an equation. Then find the length of each segment.**

9. (A, B, C; $AB = 3n$, $BC = 5$, $AC = 5n - 3$)
   equation: $3n + 5 = 5n - 3$
   $n =$ 4
   $AB =$ 12 $AC =$ 17

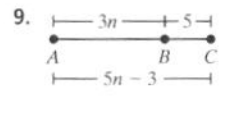

10. (K, L, M, N; $KL = 6x + 7$, $LM = 4$, $MN = 2x + 5$, $KN = 3x + 11$)
   equation: $6x + 7 + 4 + 2x + 5 = 3x + 11$
   $x =$ $-1$
   $MN =$ 3 $KN =$ 8

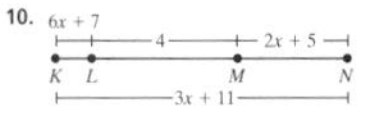

## Reteaching

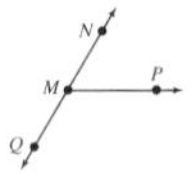

Name all points, segments, lines, and rays shown.

Points are represented with a single capital letter. The points shown are $M, N, Q$, and $P$.

A segment has two endpoints. We write the segment with endpoints $M$ and $N$ as either $\overline{MN}$ or $\overline{NM}$. One way to list the segments shown is: $\overline{MN}, \overline{MP}, \overline{MQ}, \overline{NQ}$.

Lines are infinite. We can name them with any two points. One line in the figure is $\overleftrightarrow{MN}$. The arrows indicate the line extends in each direction without end. Other names for the same line are $\overleftrightarrow{NM}, \overleftrightarrow{NQ}, \overleftrightarrow{QN}, \overleftrightarrow{MQ}$, and $\overleftrightarrow{QM}$.

A ray has one endpoint and extends without end in one direction. The endpoint is named first. Thus, $\overrightarrow{MQ}$ and $\overrightarrow{QM}$ are not the same ray. However, $\overrightarrow{QM}$ and $\overrightarrow{QN}$ are the same ray. After the endpoint, we can use any other point on the line to name the ray. The rays shown are: $\overrightarrow{MQ}, \overrightarrow{MN}, \overrightarrow{MP}, \overrightarrow{NM}, \overrightarrow{QM}$.

**Use the figure below. Name each of the following.**

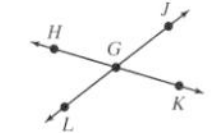


1. all points shown
   G, H, J, K, L
2. all rays shown
   $\overrightarrow{GJ}, \overrightarrow{GK}, \overrightarrow{GL}, \overrightarrow{GH}, \overrightarrow{LG}, \overrightarrow{KG}, \overrightarrow{JG}, \overrightarrow{HG}$
3. all names for $\overleftrightarrow{JL}$
   $\overleftrightarrow{JL}, \overleftrightarrow{LJ}, \overleftrightarrow{JG}, \overleftrightarrow{GJ}, \overleftrightarrow{LG}, \overleftrightarrow{GL}$
4. all segments on $\overleftrightarrow{HK}$
   $\overline{HG}, \overline{HK}, \overline{GK}$



## Enrichment

You can use straight lines to produce the illusion of curves. To see how, connect each pair of identical letters, using a ruler.

1. 2.

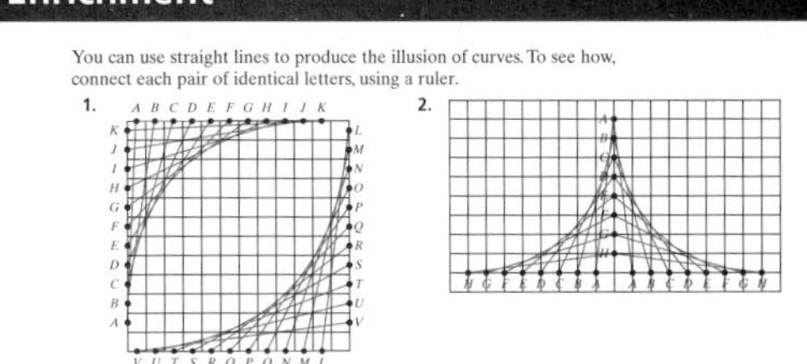

3.

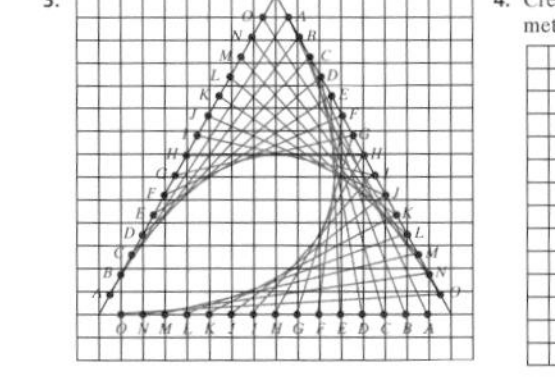

4. Create your own design using the method shown above.

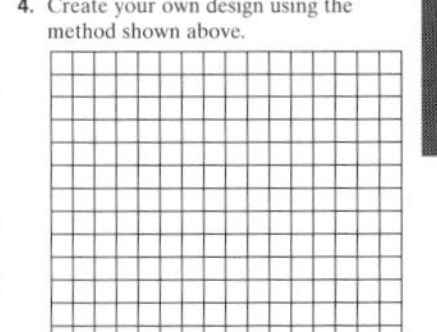

## MATH TOOLBOX

### Drawing and Measuring Angles

This Math Toolbox defines an angle and its parts and tells how to classify angles by their measure. Students use a protractor to draw and measure angles.

### Math Background

Two rays, called the *sides*, with a common end point, called the *vertex*, form an angle. You can name an angle with a single letter or number at its vertex or by naming three points on the angle, with the vertex at the center. The measure of the angle is the amount of opening between the two rays. A straight angle has two rays that are part of the same straight line, and measures 180°. A right angle is one-half of a straight angle and has sides that are perpendicular. An angle that measures more than 180° but less than 360° is called a reflex angle. This Toolbox does not use reflex angles.

**Error Prevention** Encourage students to have a mental picture of the angle they are going to draw and whether it will be acute or obtuse. This estimate will help them choose the correct scale on the protractor.

## Teaching Notes

**Monitoring Progress** **Exercises 1–6** Suggest that students write the word *acute* or *obtuse* by the number of the exercise before they draw the angle.

**Block Scheduling** If you have block scheduling or extended periods, you may wish to insert this Math Toolbox lesson between the completion of Part 1 of Lesson 9-1 and the beginning of Part 2 of Lesson 9-1.

1.

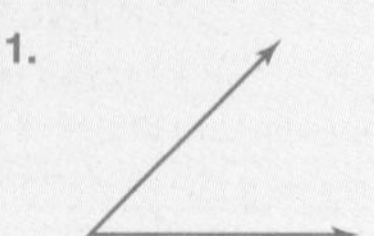

## MATH TOOLBOX

Review

Before Lesson 9-2

# *Drawing and Measuring Angles*

An *angle* is formed by two rays with a common endpoint. The rays are the *sides* of the angle. The common endpoint is the *vertex*. You can name the angle at the right $\angle ABC$, $\angle CBA$, $\angle B$, or $\angle 1$.

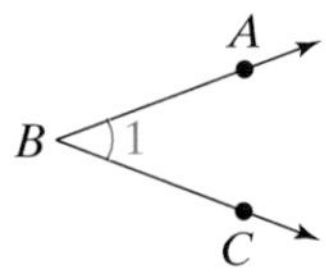


You can classify angles using their measures.

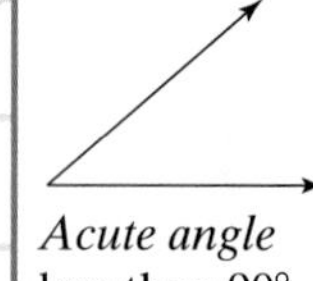

*Acute angle*
less than 90°

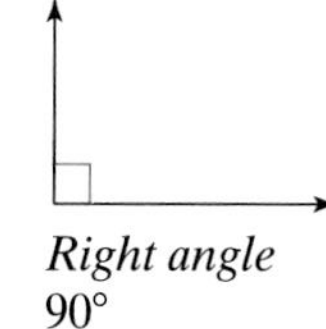

*Right angle*
90°

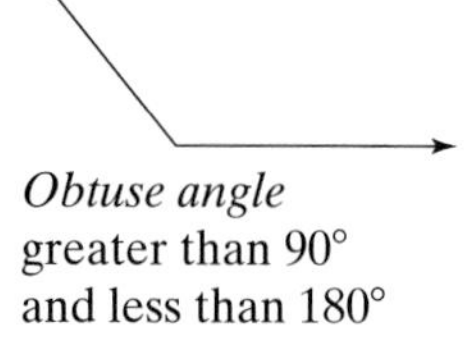

*Obtuse angle*
greater than 90° and less than 180°

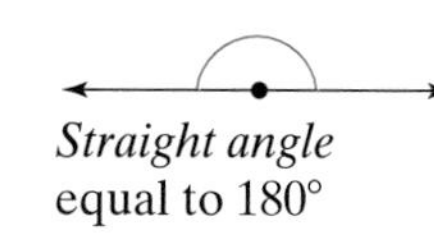

*Straight angle*
equal to 180°

You can use a protractor to draw and to measure angles.

### EXAMPLE

**Draw a 120° angle.**

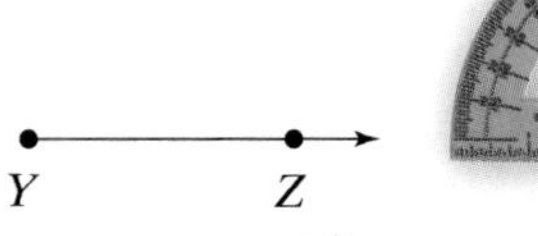


**Step 1** Draw $\overline{YZ}$.

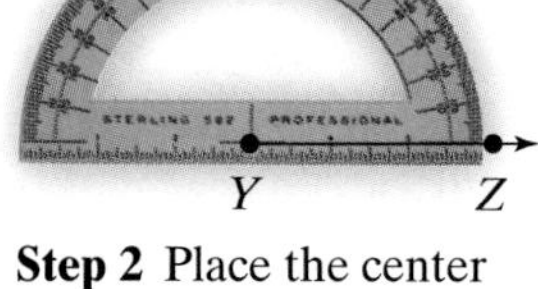


**Step 2** Place the center of the protractor over $Y$. Make sure $\overrightarrow{YZ}$ passes through zero on the protractor scale.

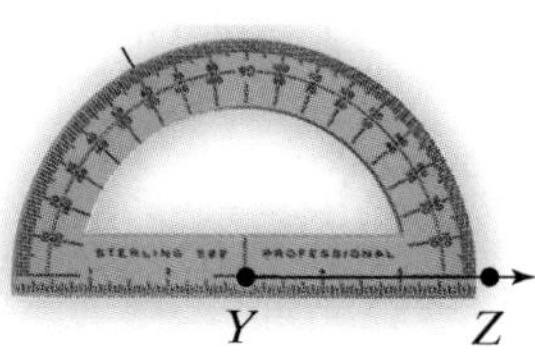


**Step 3** Place a mark on your paper at 120° such that $\angle XYZ$ will be obtuse.

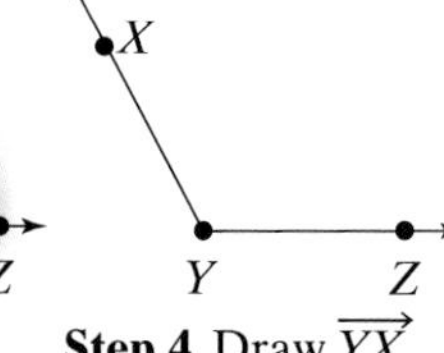


**Step 4** Draw $\overrightarrow{YX}$. The measure of $\angle XYZ$ is 120°.

**Draw an angle with the given measure.** 1–6. See margin.

**1.** 45° **2.** 110° **3.** 80° **4.** 60° **5.** 30° **6.** 150°

**Measure each angle. Then, classify it as *acute*, *right*, or *obtuse*.**

**7.**

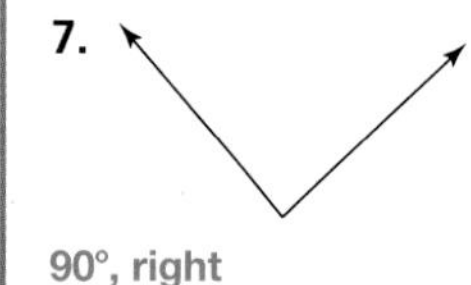

90°, right

**8.** 70°, acute

**9.** 120°, obtuse

**10.** 45°, acute



- **Additional Example**

Draw a 75° angle. Check students' drawings.

2.

3.

4.

5.

6.

# Angle Relationships and Parallel Lines

9-2

## Adjacent and Vertical Angles

In this lesson you will learn to identify special pairs of angles.

**Adjacent angles** share a vertex and a side but no points in their interiors.

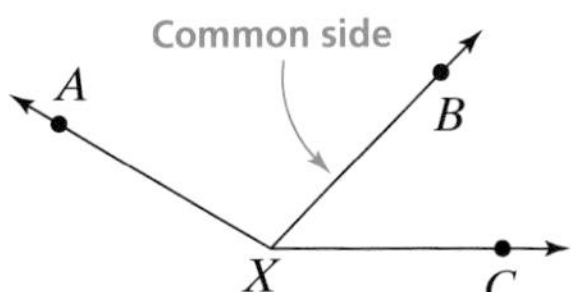


$\angle AXB$ and $\angle BXC$ are adjacent angles.

$\angle AXC$ and $\angle BXC$ not adjacent angles.

**Vertical angles** are formed by two intersecting lines and are opposite each other. Vertical angles have the same measure.

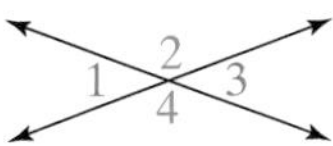


$\angle 1$ and $\angle 3$ are vertical angles.
$\angle 2$ and $\angle 4$ are vertical angles.

Angles that have the same measure are **congruent angles.** In the diagram $\angle 1$ is congruent to $\angle 3$. You can write this as $\angle 1 \cong \angle 3$. You can write *the measure of* $\angle 1$ as $m\angle 1$. Since $\angle 1 \cong \angle 3$, $m\angle 1 = m\angle 3$.

If the sum of the measures of two angles is 180°, the angles are **supplementary.**

If the sum of the measures of two angles is 90°, the angles are **complementary.**

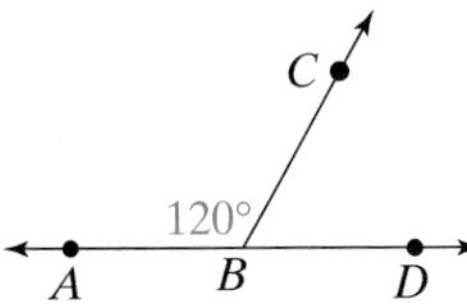


$\angle ABC$ and $\angle CBD$ are supplementary.

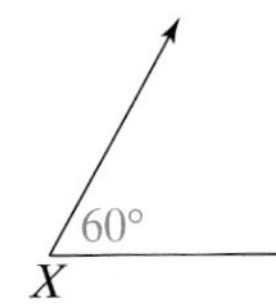


$\angle X$ and $\angle ABC$ are supplementary.
$\angle X$ and $\angle RQS$ are complementary.

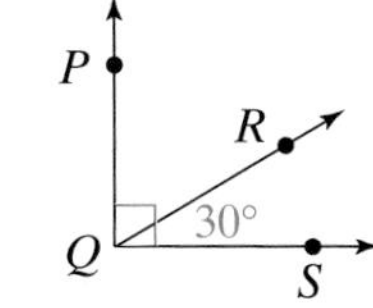


$\angle RQS$ and $\angle PQR$ are complementary.

### What You'll Learn

1. To identify adjacent and vertical angles
2. To find the relationships of angles formed by parallel lines

### . . . And Why

To use the relationships of angles formed by parallel lines in real-world situations, such as setting leaded window panes



# 9-2

## Getting Ready

**Key Terms and Symbols** adjacent angles, vertical angles, congruent angles, complementary, supplementary, transversal, corresponding angles, alternate interior angles

**Resources** A complete list of resources for this lesson is on p. 439H.

### Daily Skills Warm-Up

Lesson 9-2

Classify each angle as acute, right, or obtuse.

1. obtuse
2. right
3. acute

Classify each pair of lines as parallel, perpendicular, or neither.

4. perpendicular
5. parallel
6. neither

### Background for the Lesson

Special relationships exist between certain types of angles. The sum of the measures of two supplementary angles is 180°. Complementary angles have measures that sum to 90°. Vertical angles, formed by intersecting lines, are congruent. When a straight line, or transversal, crosses two parallel lines, the pairs of corresponding and alternate interior angles formed are also congruent.

## 1 Focus

### Connecting to Prior Knowledge

In the Math Toolbox on p. 448, students learned that two rays with a common endpoint form an angle. In this lesson, students learn that there are special pairs of angles with congruent angle measures.

## Tools to Monitor Progress

### BEFORE THE LESSON

**To check prerequisite skills:**

- Measuring angles

**Skills Intervention Kit**, Geometry

### DURING THE LESSON

**To check understanding:**

**Try This** exercises on student page

- **Additional Example 1**

  Find the measure of $\angle 3$ if $m\angle 4 = 110°$. 70°

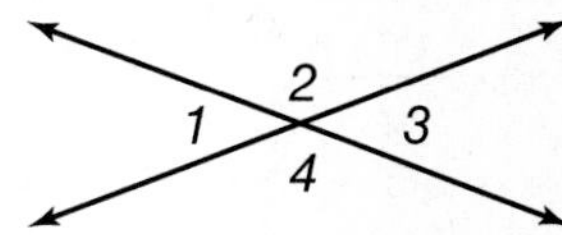

# 2 Teach

## Part 1 Teaching Notes

Point out to students that the special relationships between certain types of angles will help them solve problems involving angles. Suggest that students make a list to summarize the vocabulary and facts about the special angles in this lesson so they can refer to it later.

**ELL** Students learn many new key terms in this lesson, some of which they may never have heard before. Have students record the terms in their math journals, along with a definition and a sketch to describe each term or fact.

**Writing Math** Discuss the fact that you can write that angles are congruent but you write that their measures are equal.

### Example 1

**Build understanding.** Ask: What are the measures of $\angle 2$ and $\angle 3$?
$m\angle 2 = 135°; m\angle 3 = 45°$

**Tactile Learning** Have students draw two intersecting lines and then measure the four angles to verify that vertical angles are indeed congruent.

## Part 2 Teaching Notes

Emphasize that the special relationship between pairs of corresponding angles and alternate interior angles only holds when the transversal intersects two lines that are parallel.

### Example 2

**Build understanding.** Ask: What is the piece of information that tells you certain pairs of angles are congruent? $\ell \parallel m$

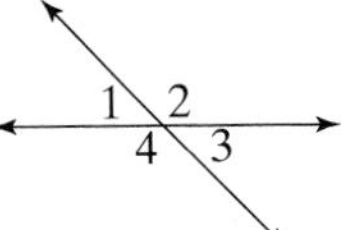

### Example 1

**Find the measure of $\angle 1$ if $m\angle 4 = 135°$.**

| | |
|---|---|
| $m\angle 1 + m\angle 4 = 180°$ | $\angle 1$ and $\angle 4$ are supplementary. |
| $m\angle 1 + 135° = 180°$ | Replace $m\angle 4$ with 135°. |
| $m\angle 1 + 135° - 135° = 180° - 135°$ | Solve for $m\angle 1$. |
| $m\angle 1 = 45°$ | |

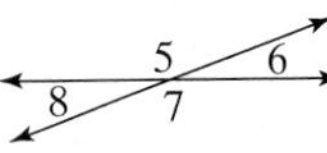

### Try This

1. If $m\angle 8 = 20°$, find the measures of $\angle 5$, $\angle 6$, and $\angle 7$.
160°, 20°, 160°

## Relating Angles and Parallel Lines

A line that intersects two other lines in different points is a **transversal.** Some pairs of angles formed by transversals and two lines have special names.

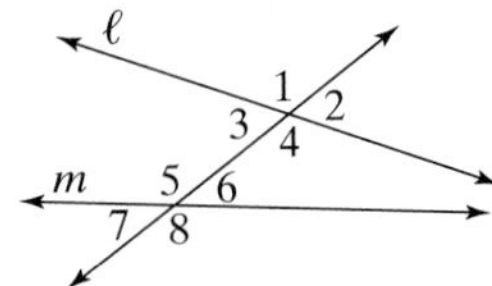

**Corresponding angles** lie on the same side of the transversal and in corresponding positions. $\angle 1$ and $\angle 5$, $\angle 3$ and $\angle 7$, $\angle 2$ and $\angle 6$, and $\angle 4$ and $\angle 8$ are corresponding angles.

**Alternate interior angles** are in the interior of a pair of lines and on opposite sides of the transversal. $\angle 3$ and $\angle 6$, and $\angle 4$ and $\angle 5$ are alternate interior angles.

When a transversal intersects two parallel lines, each pair of corresponding angles is congruent. Each pair of alternate interior angles is also congruent.

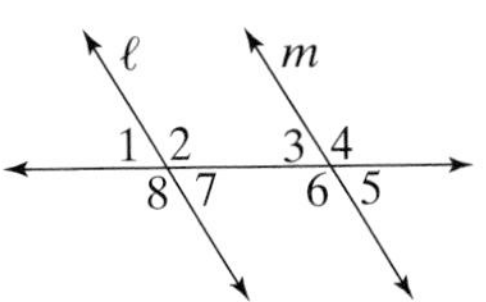

### Example 2

**In the diagram, $\ell \parallel m$. Identify each of the following.**

**a. congruent corresponding angles**
$\angle 1 \cong \angle 3, \angle 2 \cong \angle 4, \angle 8 \cong \angle 6, \angle 7 \cong \angle 5$

**b. congruent alternate interior angles**
$\angle 3 \cong \angle 7, \angle 2 \cong \angle 6$



• **Additional Example 2**

Identify each of the following. In the diagram, $p \parallel q$.

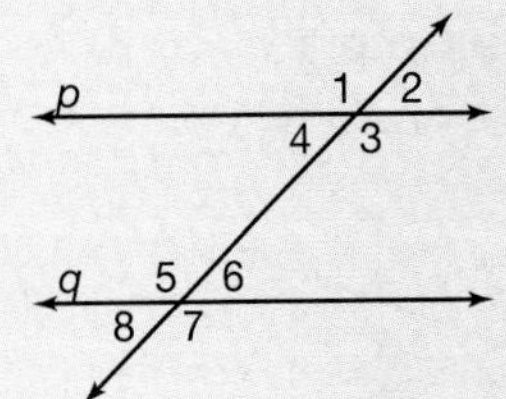

a. congruent corresponding angles
$\angle 1 \cong \angle 5, \angle 4 \cong \angle 8, \angle 2 \cong \angle 6, \angle 3 \cong \angle 7$

b. congruent alternate interior angles
$\angle 4 \cong \angle 6, \angle 3 \cong \angle 5$

■ **Try This**

2. In the diagram $a \parallel b$. Name four pairs of congruent corresponding angles and two pairs of congruent alternate interior angles. $\angle 1 \cong \angle 5$, $\angle 4 \cong \angle 8$, $\angle 2 \cong \angle 6$, $\angle 3 \cong \angle 7$; $\angle 4 \cong \angle 6$, $\angle 3 \cong \angle 5$

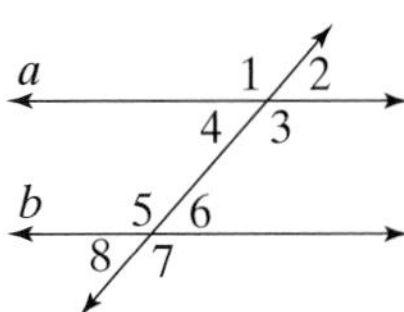


When solving a problem that involves parallel lines, you can often choose whether to use corresponding angles or alternate interior angles.

## ■ Different Ways to Solve a Problem

**The windowpanes at the right are held in place by parallel strips of lead. Lines $q$, $r$, and $s$ indicate lead stripping; $s \parallel r$. If $m\angle 1 = 65°$, what is $m\angle 4$?**

**Method 1**

Use corresponding angles.

$\angle 1 \cong \angle 3$ because they are corresponding angles. So $m\angle 3 = 65°$. $\angle 3$ and $\angle 4$ are supplementary. So $m\angle 3 + m\angle 4 = 180°$.

$$m\angle 3 + m\angle 4 = 180°$$
$$65° + m\angle 4 = 180°$$
$$65° + m\angle 4 - 65° = 180° - 65°$$
$$m\angle 4 = 115°$$

**Method 2**

Use alternate interior angles.

$\angle 1$ and $\angle 2$ are supplementary.

$$m\angle 1 + m\angle 2 = 180°$$
$$65° + m\angle 2 = 180°$$
$$65° + m\angle 2 - 65° = 180° - 65°$$
$$m\angle 2 = 115°$$

Since $\angle 2$ and $\angle 4$ are alternate interior angles, they are congruent. If $m\angle 2 = 115°$, then $m\angle 4 = 115°$.

**Choose a Method**

1. Which method do you prefer? Explain why. 1. Answers may vary. Sample: Method 1; shorter
2. What is another way to solve the problem? Answers may vary. Sample: $\angle 1$ and $\angle 2$ are supplementary. If $m\angle 1 = 65°$, $m\angle 2 = 115°$. $\angle 2$ and $\angle 4$ are alternate interior angles. If $m\angle 2 = 115°$, then $m\angle 4 = 115°$.



**Error Prevention** A common error is for students to assume that all lines intersected by transversals are parallel. Remind students to look for information in the problem or on the diagram that states two lines are parallel before assuming that they are parallel.

### ■ Different Ways to Solve a Problem

**Build understanding.** Ask: Are there any angles formed by the intersection of the transversal $q$ with lines $p$ and $r$ that do not measure either 65° or 115°? Explain. **No, both intersections form vertical angles, which means that the opposite angles are congruent. This makes 65° and 115° the only possible angle measurements.**

**Extension** There are eight angles formed when a transversal intersects two parallel lines. Explain how knowing the measure of any one of those angles will allow you to find the measure of the other seven. **By using corresponding angles, alternate interior angles, vertical angles, and supplementary angles you could find the measure of all eight angles.**

**Connecting to Geometry**

A parallelogram is formed by two sets of intersecting parallel lines. Based on what you learned about angles in this lesson, explain how the interior angles of a parallelogram are related. **The opposite angles are congruent; the adjacent angles are supplementary.**

## AFTER THE LESSON

**To assess knowledge:**

**Lesson Quiz**

Use the figure below to answer the question. In the diagram $d \parallel e$.

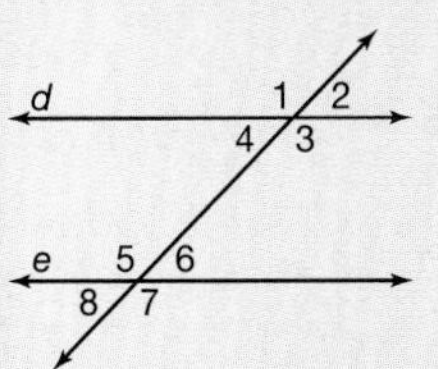


Explain why $\angle 1$ is congruent to $\angle 7$. **sample answer: $\angle 1$ and $\angle 3$ are vertical angles, therefore congruent. $\angle 3$ and $\angle 7$ are corresponding angles, and congruent. So, $\angle 1$ is congruent to $\angle 7$.**

- For enrichment and reteaching options see Resources on p. 439H.

# 3 Practice/Assess

## Assignment Guide

To provide flexible scheduling, this lesson can be divided into parts.

**Part 1**
**Core** 1–5, 11–12
**Extension** 9

**Part 2**
**Core** 6–8, 10, 16–17
**Extension** 13–15, 18

Mixed Review can be assigned at any time for maintenance.

## Exercises

**Exercise 9** You use a variable for an angle measure to write an equation. Then, solve for $x$ to find the measures.

## Challenge

Suppose you are given a pair of vertical angles and asked to duplicate the angles, without using a protractor. How could you do it? Draw a line that is parallel to one of the lines that forms the pair of vertical angles and extend it until it crosses the other line in the original pair.

## Closure

Adjacent angles share a vertex and a side but no points in their interior. Vertical angles are formed by intersecting lines and are congruent. If parallel lines are crossed by a transversal their corresponding angles are congruent. Alternate interior angles of parallel lines are also congruent.

### Daily Cumulative Review

**Use the figure at the right for Exercises 1-4.** *(Lesson 9-1)*

1. Name all the points. $S$, $T$, $U$, and $V$
2. Name all the line segments. $\overline{TV}$, $\overline{ST}$, $\overline{TU}$, $\overline{SU}$
3. Name all the lines. $\overleftrightarrow{ST}$, $\overleftrightarrow{SU}$, $\overleftrightarrow{TU}$ (all denote the same line)
4. Name all the rays. $\overrightarrow{TV}$, $\overrightarrow{TS}$, $\overrightarrow{TU}$, $\overrightarrow{SU}$, $\overrightarrow{US}$

V, S, T, U

**Write the equation of each boundary line in slope-intercept form. Tell whether the boundary line is solid or dashed.** *(Lesson 8-8)*

5. $3x + y \le 4$ $y = -3x + 4$; solid
6. $x + y < -8$ $y = -x - 8$; dashed
7. $5x + 4y \ge 8$ $y = -\frac{5}{4}x + 2$; solid
8. $-y \le -\frac{3}{4}x$ $y = \frac{3}{4}x$; solid
9. $x - y \le 6$ $y = x - 6$; solid
10. $6x + y > 4$ $y = -6x + 4$; dashed

**Mixed Review**

**Use the formula $P = 2l + 2w$. Find the perimeter of each rectangle.**

11. (3-4) 5 ft, $1\frac{1}{2}$ ft 13 ft
12. (3-4) 4 cm, 2 cm 12 cm
13. (3-4) 3.25 mi, 0.75 mi 8 mi

**Multiply each expression.**

14. (2-2) $(r - 4)6$ $6r - 24$
15. (2-2) $6(5 - 3s)$ $-18s + 30$



# Exercises

## Check Understanding

1. Find the sum of the measures of $\angle 1$, $\angle 2$, and $\angle 3$ in the figure at the right. 180°

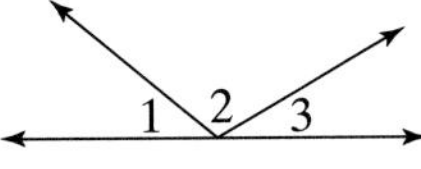


2. Fill in the blank. The sum of the measures of two angles is 90°. The angles are __?__ angles. complementary

**Name the angle vertical to $\angle 1$. Name each angle adjacent to $\angle 1$. Then find $m\angle 1$.**

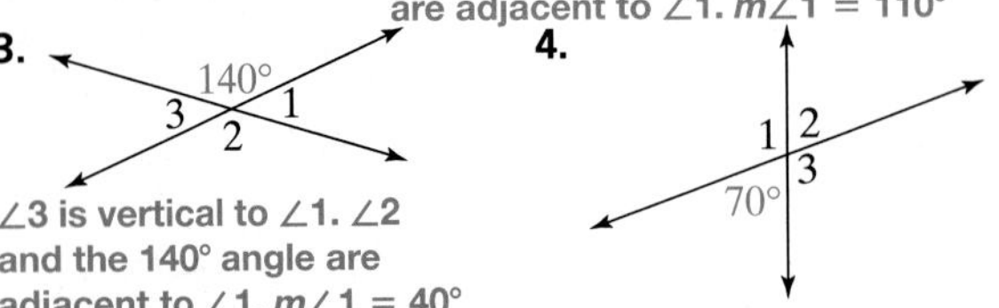


3. $\angle 3$ is vertical to $\angle 1$. $\angle 2$ and the 140° angle are adjacent to $\angle 1$. $m\angle 1 = 40°$
4. $\angle 3$ is vertical to $\angle 1$. $\angle 2$ and the 70° angle are adjacent to $\angle 1$. $m\angle 1 = 110°$
5. $\angle KPL$ is vertical to $\angle 1$. $\angle JPI$ and $\angle HPM$ are adjacent to $\angle 1$. $m\angle 1 = 34°$

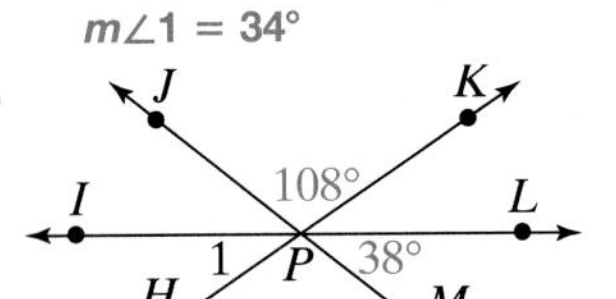


**Use the figure at the right for Exercises 6–8.**

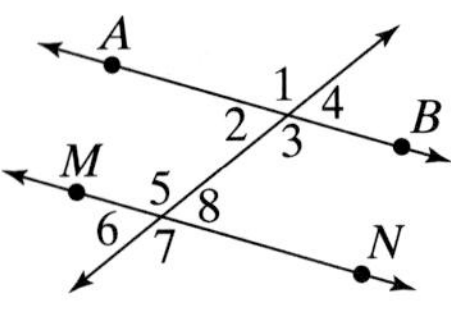


6. Name four pairs of corresponding angles. $\angle 1$ and $\angle 5$, $\angle 2$ and $\angle 6$, $\angle 3$ and $\angle 7$, $\angle 4$ and $\angle 8$
7. Name the alternate interior angles. $\angle 2$ and $\angle 8$, $\angle 3$ and $\angle 5$
8. Suppose $\overleftrightarrow{AB} \parallel \overleftrightarrow{MN}$. Name all angles congruent to $\angle 8$. $\angle 6$, $\angle 2$, $\angle 4$

## Practice and Problem Solving

9. a. *Algebra* Write an equation and find the value of $x$.
   b. Find $m\angle KQB$.
   c. Find $m\angle KQR$.

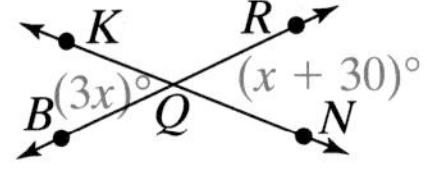


9a. $3x = x + 30$, $x = 15$
9b. 45°
9c. 135°

10. a. In the figure at the right, $x \parallel y$. List all angles that are congruent to $\angle 1$. $\angle 5$, $\angle 3$, $\angle 7$
    b. If $m\angle 5 = 45°$, what are the measures of other angles? See below right.

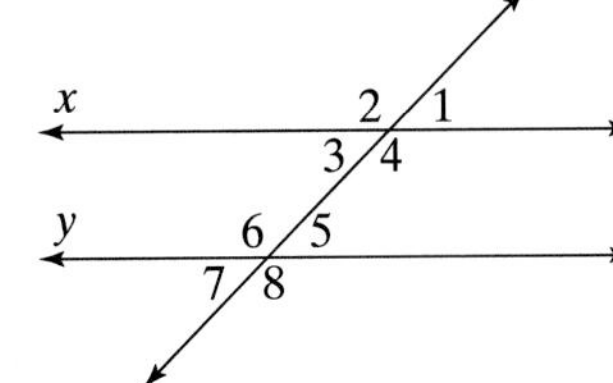


11. Find the measures of $\angle 1$, $\angle 2$, and $\angle 3$ if $m\angle 4 = 100°$. $m\angle 1 = 80°$, $m\angle 2 = 100°$, $m\angle 3 = 80°$

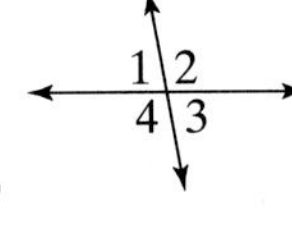


10b. $m\angle 6 = 135°$, $m\angle 7 = 45°$, $m\angle 8 = 135°$, $m\angle 3 = 45°$, $m\angle 2 = 135°$, $m\angle 1 = 45°$, $m\angle 4 = 135°$



## Alternative Assessment

Ask students to write a real-world word problem that can be solved by one of the angle relationships that they learned in this lesson. Have students record the word problems in their math journals.

12. *Writing* Describe how you will keep from confusing the definitions of supplementary angles and complementary angles. Check students' work

*Algebra* **In each figure find the measures of ∠1 and ∠2.**

13. Given: $a \parallel b$ — $m\angle 1 = 60°$, $m\angle 2 = 60°$

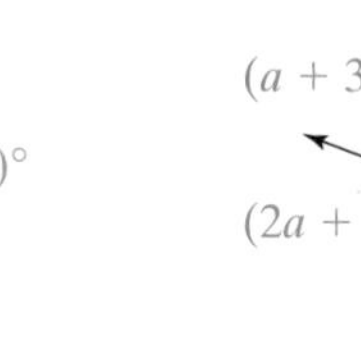


14. Given: $p \parallel q$ — $m\angle 1 = 70°$, $m\angle 2 = 110°$

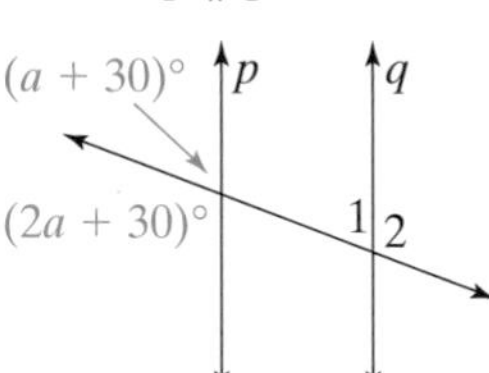


15. Given: $r \parallel s$ — $m\angle 1 = 55°$, $m\angle 2 = 125°$

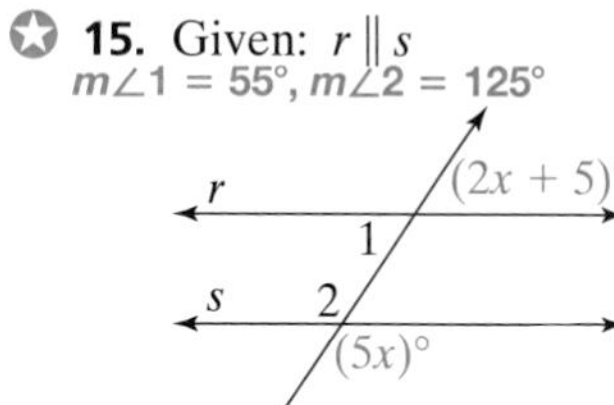


*Math in the Media* **Use the article below and the map for Exercises 16 and 17.**

## New Road Approved

The Middleton City Board approved the proposal for a new road parallel to Highway 10. This new road, to be called Leeway Road, will help ease traffic flow in downtown Middleton during rush hour. Leeway Road will intersect both Sand Avenue and Piper Street.

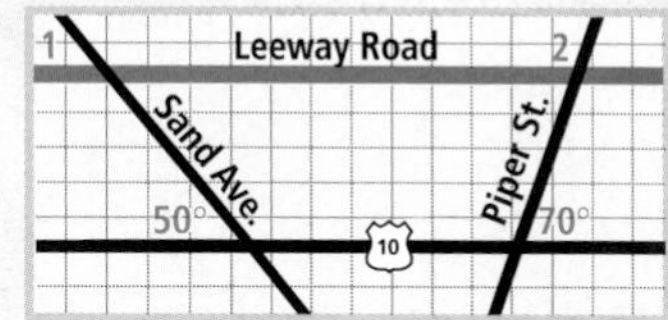


16. When Leeway Road is built, what should be $m\angle 1$? 50°

17. *Error Analysis* A surveyor stated that $m\angle 2$ should be 130°. Explain the surveyor's error. 17. Answers may vary. Sample: The surveyor mistook the angle between Leeway Road and Piper St. as an alternate interior angle to the 50° angle. Then ∠2 would be the supplement of a 50° angle, so it would measure 130°.

18. *Mathematical Reasoning* Angles on the "outside" of two lines and on opposite sides of a transversal are called *alternate exterior angles*. The transversal $q$ intersects two parallel lines $m$ and $n$. If $m\angle 1 = 85°$, what is the measure of ∠5? Explain your reasoning. Answers may vary. Sample: ∠1 ≅ ∠3 because they are corresponding angles. So $m\angle 3 = 85°$. ∠5 ≅ ∠3, so $m\angle 5 = 85°$

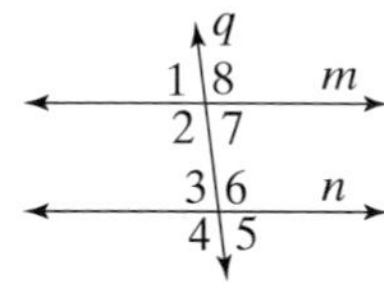


## Mixed Review

**Draw each figure.** ***(Lesson 9-1)***

19. $\overline{AB}$ 20. $\overrightarrow{CD}$ 21. $\overrightarrow{DC}$ 22. $\overleftrightarrow{EF}$ 23. ∠GHI

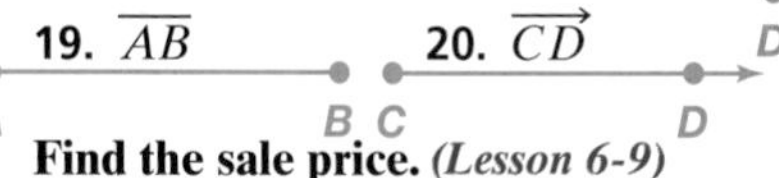


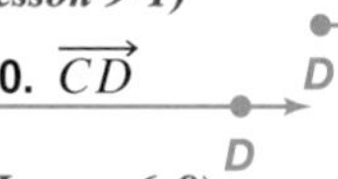


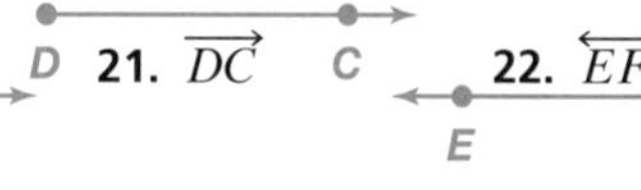


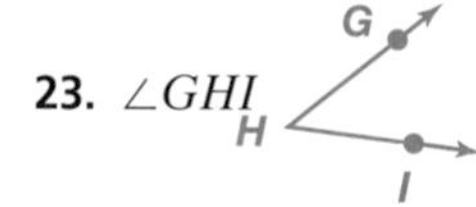


**Find the sale price.** ***(Lesson 6-9)***

24. \$25 at 10% discount \$22.50 25. \$55 at 5% discount \$52.25 26. \$324 at 20% discount \$259.20

27. *Choose a Strategy* In a single elimination tournament a team plays until it loses. Eight teams play in a tournament. How many games must be played? seven

See also Extra Practice section.



## Practice

**Find the measure of each angle in the figure at the right.**

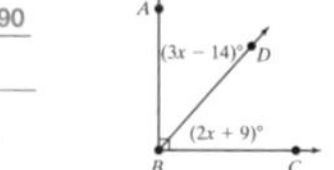


1. $m\angle 1$ 34° 2. $m\angle 2$ 56°
3. $m\angle 3$ 56° 4. $m\angle VWR$ 146°

**Use the figure at the right for Exercises 5-8.**

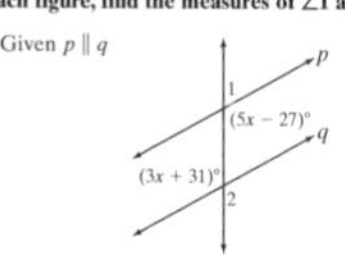


5. Write an equation. (3x − 14) + (2x + 9) = 90
6. Find the value of x. x = 19
7. Find $m\angle ABD$. 43°
8. Find $m\angle DBC$. 47°

**Use the figure at the right for Exercises 9-12.**

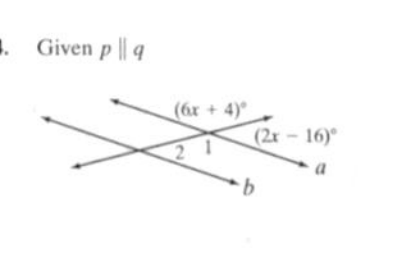


9. Write an equation. 5x − 18 = 4x + 7
10. Find the value of x. x = 25
11. Find $m\angle MNQ$. 107°
12. Find $m\angle MNR$. 73°

**In each figure, find the measures of ∠1 and ∠2.**

13. Given $p \parallel q$

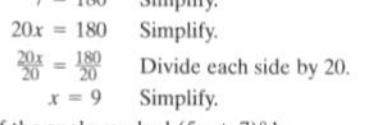


$m\angle 1 =$ 62° $m\angle 2 =$ 118°

14. Given $p \parallel q$

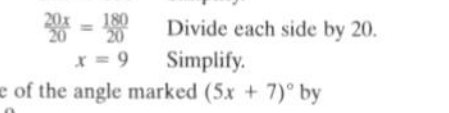


$m\angle 1 =$ 148° $m\angle 2 =$ 32°

15. Find a pair of complementary angles such that the difference of their measures is 12°.
51° and 39°



## Reteaching

Find the measures of ∠1 and ∠2. Given: $r \parallel s$.
Write an equation and solve for $x$.

| | |
|---|---|
| $(5x + 7) + (15x - 7) = 180$ | These angles are supplementary. |
| $5x + 15x + 7 - 7 = 180$ | Simplify. |
| $20x = 180$ | Simplify. |
| $\frac{20x}{20} = \frac{180}{20}$ | Divide each side by 20. |
| $x = 9$ | Simplify. |

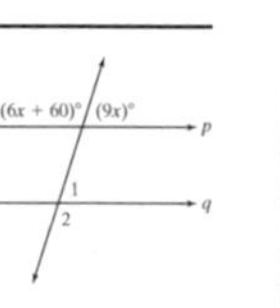


Find the measure of the angle marked $(5x + 7)°$ by substituting $x = 9$.

$$5x + 7 = 5(9) + 7 = 45 + 7 = 52$$

Since this angle and ∠1 are vertical, they have the same measure.
Thus, $m\angle 1 = 52°$.

We can find the measure of ∠2 several ways. The angle marked $(15x - 7)°$ and ∠2 are corresponding angles, so they have the same measure. We can find this measure by substituting $x = 9$ into $15x - 7$ or by realizing that this angle and ∠1 are supplementary.

$180 - 52 = 128$

$15x - 7 = 15(9) - 7 = 135 - 7 = 128$

Either way, $m\angle 2 = 128°$.

**Use the figure at the right.**

Given: $p \parallel q$.

1. Write an equation.
(6x + 60) + 9x = 180
2. Find the value of x.
$x =$ 8
3. Find $m\angle 1$.
$m\angle 1 =$ 72°
4. Find $m\angle 2$.
$m\angle 2 =$ 108°



## Enrichment

**Complete.**

The minute hand of a clock rotates through:

1. 90 degrees in 15 minutes
2. 6 degrees in 1 minute

The hour hand of a clock rotates through:

3. 30 degrees in 1 hour
4. $\frac{1}{2}$ degrees in 1 minute

**Find how long it takes the minute hand to rotate through these angles.**

5. 18° 3 min 6. 78° 13 min 7. 135° $22\frac{1}{2}$ min

**Find how long it takes the hour hand to rotate through these angles.**

8. 24° 48 min 9. 63° 126 min 10. $155\frac{1}{2}$° 311 min

**Find the measure of the angle formed by the hour and minute hands.**

11. 120° 12. 150° 13. 132°

14. 57° 15. 145° 16. 62°

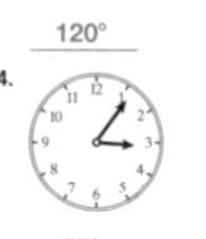

# 9-3

## Getting Ready

**Key Terms and Symbols** polygon, regular polygon, quadrilateral, parallelogram, trapezoid, rectangle, rhombus, square

**Resources** A complete list of resources for this lesson is on p. 439H.

### Daily Skills Warm-Up

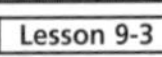

Lesson 9-3

Evaluate each formula for the values given.

1. $P = 2l + 2w$, for $l = 5$ and $w = 2$ 14
2. $P = 2l + 2w$, for $l = 25$ and $w = 12$ 74
3. $P = 2l + 2w$, for $l = 7.5$ and $w = 3.4$ 21.8
4. $P = 4s$, for $s = 19$ 76
5. $P = 4s$, for $s = 3.2$ 12.8

### Background for the Lesson

Many familiar geometric figures—triangles, squares, rectangles, and pentagons—are polygons. Polygons with four sides are quadrilaterals. Quadrilaterals that have exactly one pair of parallel sides are called trapezoids. Quadrilaterals that have two pairs of parallel sides are called parallelograms. A rhombus (a diamond shape) is a parallelogram with four equal sides. Rectangles are parallelograms with four right angles, and squares are rectangles (and rhombuses) with four equal sides and four equal angles.

## 1 Focus

### Connecting to Students' Lives

Have students write a short paragraph, accompanied by a sketch, to describe their favorite geometric shape and to explain why it is their favorite.

### Connecting to Prior Knowledge

In Lesson 9-1, students learned that a line segment is a part of a line. In this lesson, students learn that line segments are the sides of polygons. In Lesson 9-4, students will solve problems involving polygons.

# 9-3 Classifying Polygons

**What You'll Learn**

1 To classify triangles

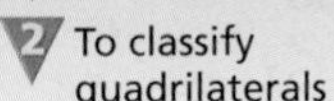

2 To classify quadrilaterals

**. . . And Why**

To use polygons in real-world situations involving design and construction

## PART 1 Classifying Triangles

A **polygon** is a *closed* plane figure with at least three *sides*. The sides meet only at their endpoints.

A triangle is a polygon with three sides. You can classify triangles by angle measures. In the Math Toolbox on page 448 you reviewed how to classify angles. You can also classify triangles by side lengths. Tick marks are used to indicate congruent sides of a figure.

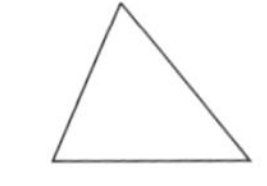

**Acute triangle** three acute angles

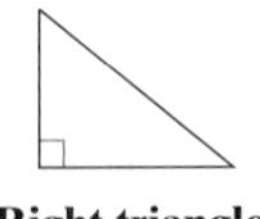

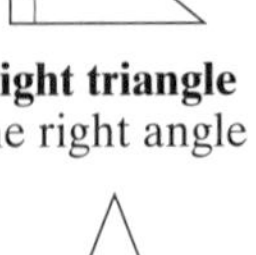

**Right triangle** one right angle

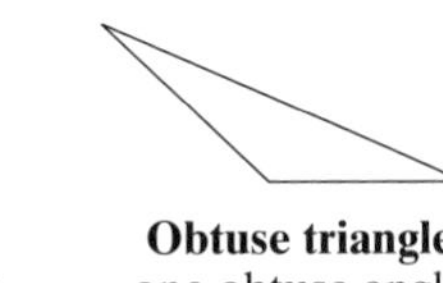

**Obtuse triangle** one obtuse angle

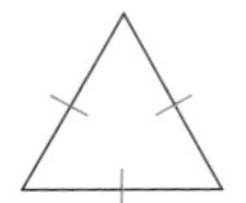

**Equilateral triangle** three congruent sides

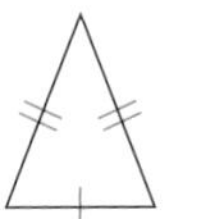

**Isosceles triangle** at least two congruent sides

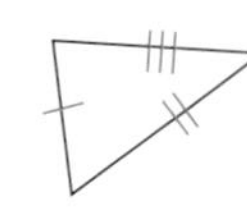

**Scalene triangle** no congruent sides

**EXAMPLE 1**

**Classify the triangle by its sides and angles.**

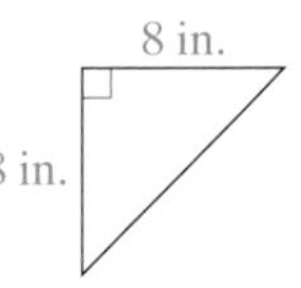


The triangle has two congruent sides and one right angle.

The triangle is an isosceles right triangle.

The piano lid and its support shown here determine a scalene triangle.

**TRY THIS** Judging by appearance, classify each triangle by its sides and angles.

1. scalene right triangle
2. isosceles obtuse triangle
3. scalene obtuse triangle



## Tools to Monitor Progress

**BEFORE THE LESSON**

**To check prerequisite skills:**

- Identifying polygons

**Skills Intervention Kit,** Geometry

**DURING THE LESSON**

**To check understanding:**

**Try This** exercises on student page

- **Additional Example 1**
  Classify by its sides and angles a triangle that has one obtuse angle and no congruent sides. a scalene obtuse triangle
- **Additional Example 2**
  Name the types of quadrilaterals that have at least one pair of

## Part 2 Classifying Quadrilaterals

You can also classify quadrilaterals by their sides and angles.

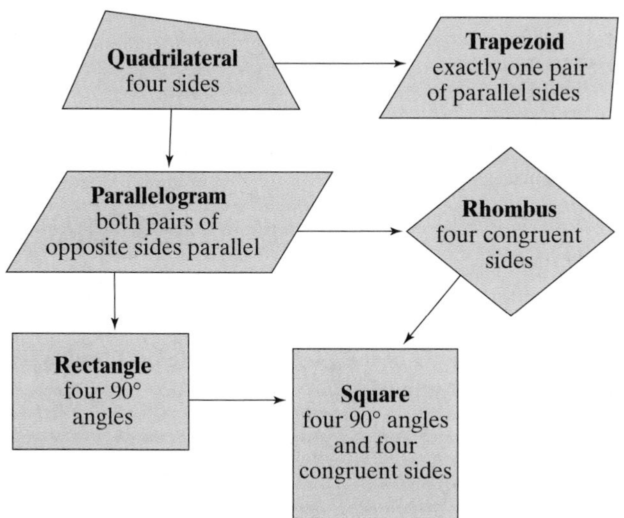


### Example 2

**Name the types of quadrilaterals that have both pairs of opposite sides parallel.**

All parallelograms have opposite sides parallel. Parallelograms include rectangles, rhombuses, and squares.

### Try This

4. Name the types of quadrilaterals that have four right angles. rectangles and squares

In later math courses, you will prove that a parallelogram has opposite sides congruent and opposite angles congruent.

Polygons are named using their vertices. Start at one vertex and list them in consecutive order.

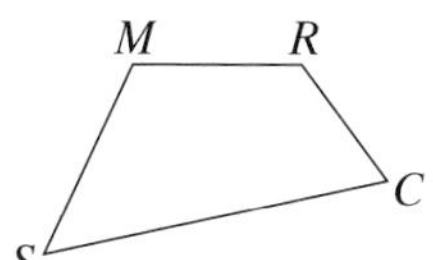


**Starting from *M*, the name of this figure is quadrilateral *MRCS* or quadrilateral *MSCR*.**

**Reading Math**

The plural of *vertex* is *vertices*.



# 2 Teach

## Part 1 Teaching Notes

Point out to students that a closed plane figure is one that has no openings in its sides. The end point for each side is the beginning of another side. Have students draw examples of closed figures on the board.

### Example 1

**Build understanding.** Ask: Suppose the triangle in this example had no congruent sides. Could it still be a right triangle? Explain. Yes, it would be a scalene triangle.

**Error Prevention** Identifying the types of angles in the triangle by appearance may be less challenging than determining whether the sides are congruent. Suggest that students use a ruler to verify that sides are the same length before they decide the sides are congruent.

## Part 2 Teaching Notes

Students may be less familiar with the parallelogram, rhombus, and trapezoid than they are with the rectangle and square. Suggest that students copy the diagram on p. 455 into their math journals as a reference for identifying quadrilaterals.

**ELL** Explain to students that the word *quadrilateral* literally means *four sides.* Suggest that students use the connection between the terms *quad* and *four* and *lateral* and *side* to remember that a quadrilateral is a figure with four sides.

parallel sides. rectangle, square, rhombus, trapezoid, parallelogram

**• Additional Example 3**

The contractor who built the gazebo has also been hired to build a wood deck in the shape of a regular dodecagon (12 sides). Write a formula to find the perimeter of the deck and evaluate the perimeter for a side length of 36 in. $P = 12x$; 432 in.

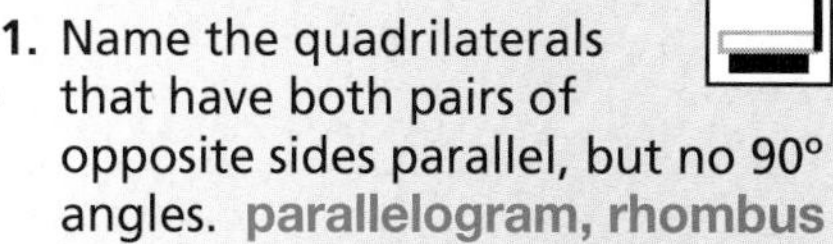

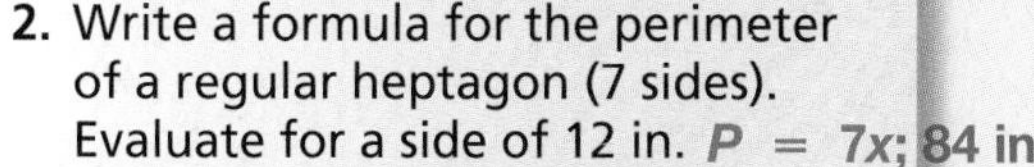

### AFTER THE LESSON

**To assess knowledge: Lesson Quiz**

1. Name the quadrilaterals that have both pairs of opposite sides parallel, but no 90° angles. parallelogram, rhombus
2. Write a formula for the perimeter of a regular heptagon (7 sides). Evaluate for a side of 12 in. $P = 7x$; 84 in.

• For enrichment and reteaching options see Resources on p. 439H.

## Example 2

**Build understanding.** Ask: Which parallelogram has only one pair of parallel sides? **trapezoid**

## Example 3

**Build understanding.** Ask: How would the formula be different if the gazebo were hexagonal instead of octagonal? What would be the perimeter? $P = 6x$; $P = 24$ ft

### Connecting to Language Arts

The prefixes *penta-*, meaning five, *hexa-*, meaning six, and *octo-*, meaning eight, come from the Greek language. In fact, the term *polygon* also has Greek roots. *Poly* is a term that is based on the Greek word *polys*, meaning *many*. *Gon* is based on the Greek term *gonia*, meaning *angle*.

**Math Reasoning** Use math reasoning to explain why not all triangles are regular polygons. **A regular polygon must have congruent sides and congruent angles. The only triangle that fits this description is an equilateral triangle.**

A **regular polygon** has all sides congruent and all angles congruent. Some regular polygons are shown below.

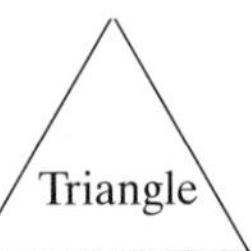

You can use algebra to write a formula for the perimeter of a regular polygon.

REAL-WORLD  CONNECTION

## Example 3

*Construction* **A contractor is framing a regular octagonal gazebo. Write a formula to find the perimeter of the gazebo. Evaluate the formula for a side length of 4 ft.**

Most gazebos are regular hexagons or regular octagons.

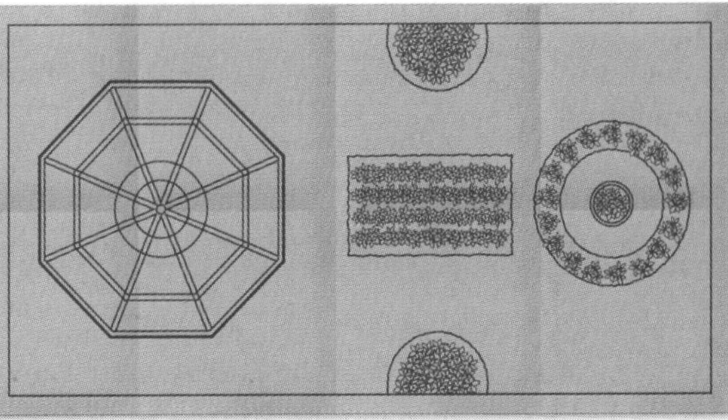

To write a formula, let $x$ = the length of each side. The perimeter of the regular octagon is $x + x + x + x + x + x + x + x$. Therefore the formula for the perimeter is $P = 8x$.

| | |
|---|---|
| $P = 8x$ | Write the formula. |
| $= 8(4)$ | Substitute 4 for $x$. |
| $= 32$ | Simplify. |

For a side length of 4 ft, the perimeter is 32 ft.

## Try This

5. Write a formula to find the perimeter of a regular pentagon. Use the formula to find the perimeter if one side is 16 cm. **$P = 5x$; 80 cm**



1. **Answers may vary. Sample:**

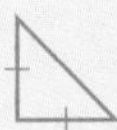

2. **Answers may vary. Sample:**

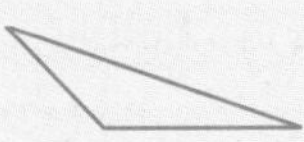

3. **Answers may vary. Sample:**

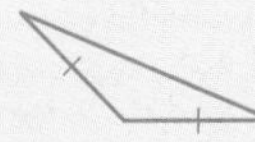

# Exercises

## CHECK UNDERSTANDING

*Open-ended* **Sketch each figure.** 1–3. See margin.

1. an isosceles right triangle
2. a scalene obtuse triangle
3. an isosceles obtuse triangle

**Find the perimeter of each figure.**

4. 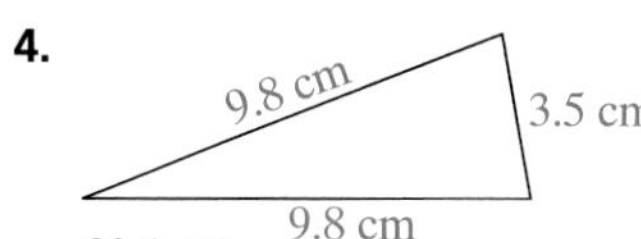

23.1 cm

5. an equilateral triangle that has a side of 36 yd 108 yd

6. a square that has a side of 5.1 cm 20.4 cm

7. Draw a parallelogram without a right angle but with four congruent sides. What is another name for this figure?  rhombus

8. Draw a regular quadrilateral.

## PRACTICE AND PROBLEM SOLVING

**Judging by appearance, classify each triangle by its sides and angles.**

9. 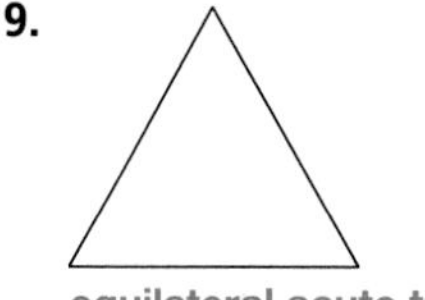
equilateral acute triangle

10. 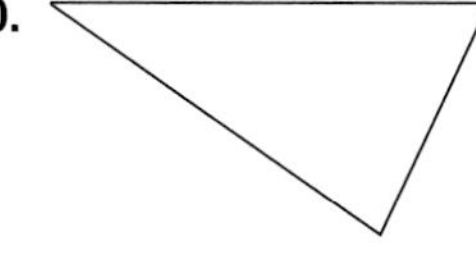
scalene acute triangle

11. 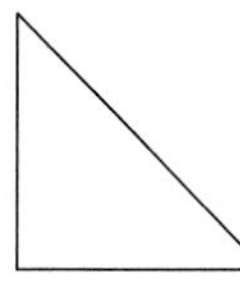
isosceles right triangle

**Write a formula to find the perimeter of each figure. Use the formula to find the perimeter.**

12. an equilateral triangle with one side 3.5 cm $P = 3x$; 10.5 cm
13. a square with one side 12.5 in. $P = 4x$; 50 in.
14. a regular hexagon with one side $\frac{5}{8}$ in. $P = 6x$; $3\frac{3}{4}$ in.
15. a regular pentagon with one side $1\frac{2}{3}$ yd $P = 5x$; $8\frac{1}{3}$ yd

**Name three different figures in each flag.**

16. 
Flag of Antigua

Answers may vary. Sample: trapezoid, scalene right triangle, equilateral triangle

17. 
Flag of Philippines

Answers may vary. Sample: trapezoid, equilateral triangle, rectangle



# 3 Practice/Assess

## Assignment Guide

To provide flexible scheduling, this lesson can be divided into parts.

**Part 1**
**Core** 1–3, 9–11, 18–20

**Part 2**
**Core** 4–8, 12–17, 21–26
**Extension** 27–28

Mixed Review can be assigned at any time for maintenance.

## Exercises

**Exercises 9–11** Classify these triangles by observation; you do not need to measure for these exercises.

## Challenge

To find the perimeter of a decagon (10-sided polygon) that has one side with a length of 7 in., you write the formula $P = 10x$ and use it to find the perimeter. However, when you measure the sides, you get a total of 62 in. for the perimeter. What could be the problem? The decagon is not a regular decagon.

## Closure

A polygon is a closed figure with at least three sides. A triangle can be classified by its angles and sides. You can classify some quadrilaterals as parallelograms, rectangles, squares, rhombuses, and trapezoids.

## Alternative Assessment

Write a letter to a friend that shows a collection of sketched polygons. In the letter, explain various ways to classify the polygons, including why some belong to more than one classification.

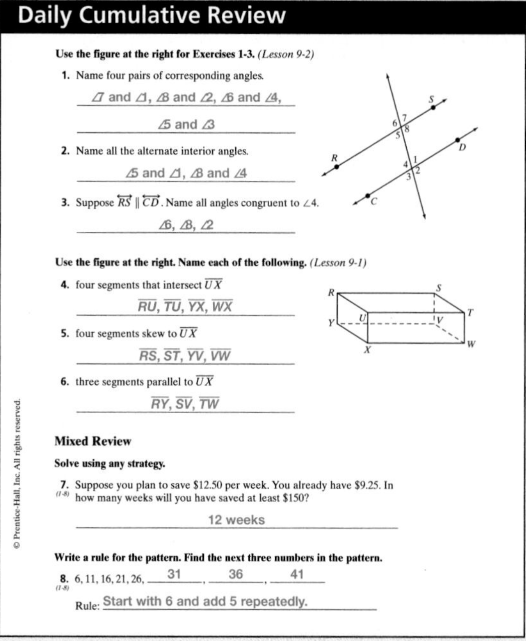
### Daily Cumulative Review

**Use the figure at the right for Exercises 1-3.** *(Lesson 9-2)*

1. Name four pairs of corresponding angles.
∠7 and ∠1, ∠8 and ∠2, ∠6 and ∠4, ∠5 and ∠3
2. Name all the alternate interior angles.
∠5 and ∠1, ∠8 and ∠4
3. Suppose $\overleftrightarrow{RS} \parallel \overleftrightarrow{CD}$. Name all angles congruent to ∠4.
∠6, ∠8, ∠2



**Use the figure at the right. Name each of the following.** *(Lesson 9-1)*

4. four segments that intersect $\overline{UX}$
$\overline{RU}$, $\overline{TU}$, $\overline{YX}$, $\overline{WX}$
5. four segments skew to $\overline{UX}$
$\overline{RS}$, $\overline{ST}$, $\overline{YV}$, $\overline{VW}$
6. three segments parallel to $\overline{UX}$
$\overline{RY}$, $\overline{SV}$, $\overline{TW}$



**Mixed Review**

**Solve using any strategy.**

7. (1-8) Suppose you plan to save $12.50 per week. You already have $9.25. In how many weeks will you have saved at least $150?
12 weeks

**Write a rule for the pattern. Find the next three numbers in the pattern.**

8. (1-8) 6, 11, 16, 21, 26, 31, 36, 41
Rule: Start with 6 and add 5 repeatedly.

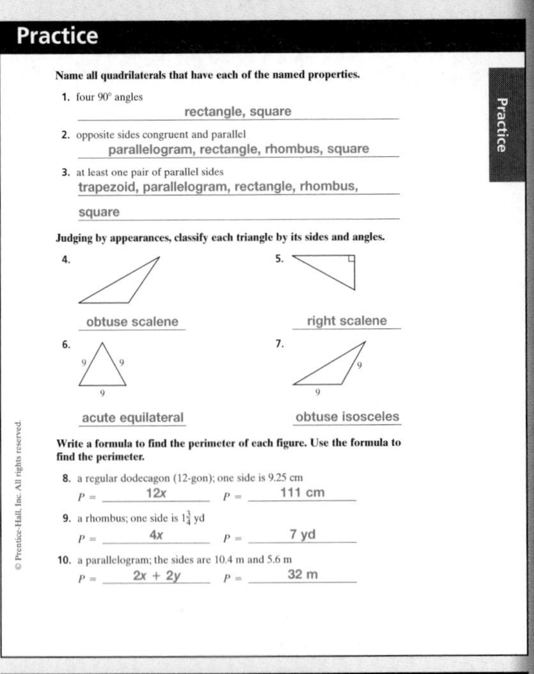

## Practice

**Name all quadrilaterals that have each of the named properties.**

1. four 90° angles rectangle, square
2. opposite sides congruent and parallel parallelogram, rectangle, rhombus, square
3. at least one pair of parallel sides trapezoid, parallelogram, rectangle, rhombus, square

**Judging by appearances, classify each triangle by its sides and angles.**

4. obtuse scalene
5. right scalene
6. acute equilateral
7. obtuse isosceles

**Write a formula to find the perimeter of each figure. Use the formula to find the perimeter.**

8. a regular dodecagon (12-gon); one side is 9.25 cm $P =$ 12x $P =$ 111 cm
9. a rhombus; one side is $1\frac{3}{4}$ yd $P =$ 4x $P =$ 7 yd
10. a parallelogram; the sides are 10.4 m and 5.6 m $P =$ 2x + 2y $P =$ 32 m



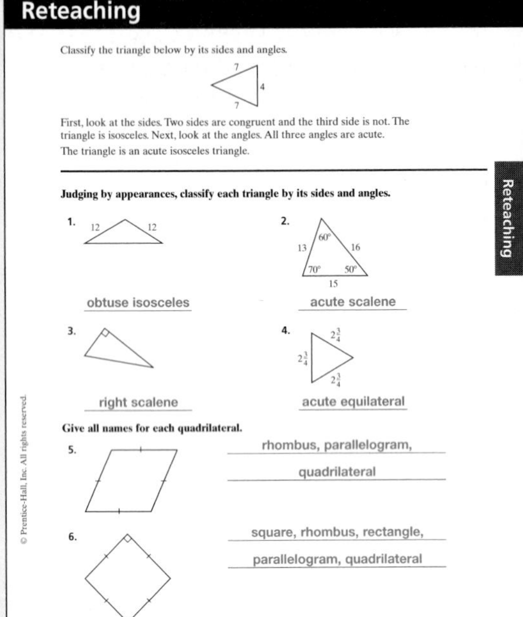

## Reteaching

Classify the triangle below by its sides and angles.

First, look at the sides. Two sides are congruent and the third side is not. The triangle is isosceles. Next, look at the angles. All three angles are acute. The triangle is an acute isosceles triangle.

**Judging by appearances, classify each triangle by its sides and angles.**

1. obtuse isosceles
2. acute scalene
3. right scalene
4. acute equilateral

**Give all names for each quadrilateral.**

5. rhombus, parallelogram, quadrilateral
6. square, rhombus, rectangle, parallelogram, quadrilateral



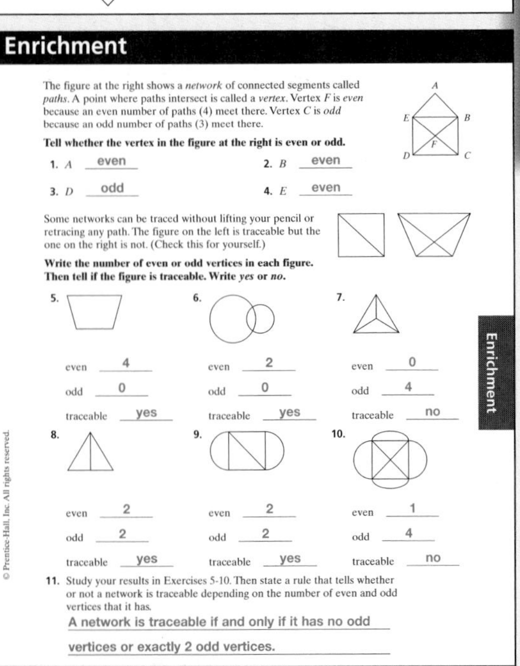

## Enrichment

The figure at the right shows a *network* of connected segments called *paths*. A point where paths intersect is called a *vertex*. Vertex *F* is *even* because an even number of paths (4) meet there. Vertex *C* is *odd* because an odd number of paths (3) meet there.

**Tell whether the vertex in the figure at the right is even or odd.**

1. *A* even 2. *B* even
3. *D* odd 4. *E* even

Some networks can be traced without lifting your pencil or retracing any path. The figure on the left is traceable but the one on the right is not. (Check this for yourself.)

**Write the number of even or odd vertices in each figure. Then tell if the figure is traceable. Write *yes* or *no*.**

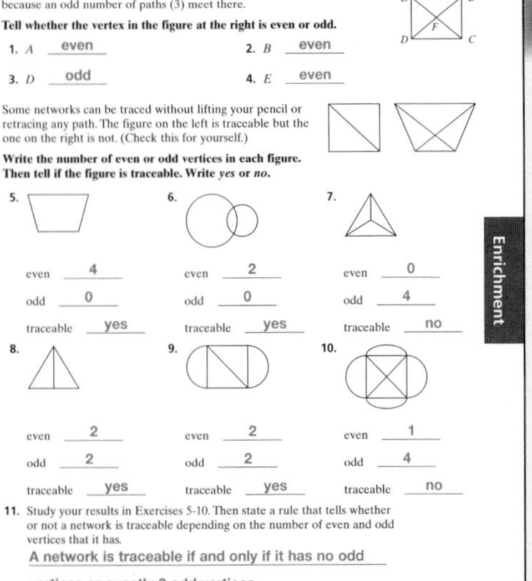

5. even 4, odd 0, traceable yes
6. even 2, odd 0, traceable yes
7. even 0, odd 4, traceable no
8. even 2, odd 2, traceable yes
9. even 2, odd 2, traceable yes
10. even 1, odd 4, traceable no
11. Study your results in Exercises 5-10. Then state a rule that tells whether or not a network is traceable depending on the number of even and odd vertices that it has. A network is traceable if and only if it has no odd vertices or exactly 2 odd vertices.



*Open-ended* **Sketch each figure.** 18–20. See margin.

18. an isosceles acute triangle 19. a scalene right triangle 20. an equilateral triangle

**Name all quadrilaterals that have each of the named properties.**

21. exactly one pair of parallel sides trapezoid
22. four congruent sides square, rhombus
23. two pairs of parallel sides parallelogram, rhombus, square, rectangle
24. opposite sides congruent rectangle, square, rhombus, parallelogram
25. supplementary angles parallelogram, rectangle, rhombus, square, trapezoid
26. opposite angles congruent rectangle, parallelogram, square, rhombus

27. *Mathematical Reasoning* Two sides of an isosceles triangle are 10 cm and 12 cm. Explain why the perimeter could be either 32 cm or 34 cm. See below.

**Journal**

*Are all equilateral triangles isosceles? Are all isosceles triangles equilateral? Explain.*

28. a. A decagon is a polygon with 10 sides. Write a formula for the perimeter of a regular decagon. $P = 10x$
    b. Find the perimeter of a regular decagon that has a side 14.5 m long. 145 m
    c. Find the length of a side of a regular decagon that has a perimeter of 22 ft. 2.2 ft

27. If the congruent sides are 10 cm long, the perimeter is 10 + 10 + 12, or 32 cm. If the congruent sides are 12 cm long, the perimeter is 12 + 12 + 10, or 34 cm.

## Mixed Review

29. A transversal intersects two parallel lines, forming eight angles. One angle measures 60°. Sketch a diagram showing the measures of all eight angles. *(Lesson 9-2)*

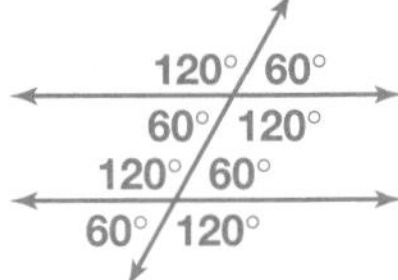


**Solve each equation.** *(Lessons 7-2 and Lesson 7-5)*

30. $x + 20 + 2x = 41$ 7
31. $53 - 6x = 13 - 2x$ 10
32. $3y - 10 + 5y = 6$ 2

33. *Choose a Strategy* A town parade included modern and antique cycles. The modern cycles had two wheels and the antique cycles had three wheels. Altogether there were 64 wheels on the 28 cycles. How many of the cycles had three wheels? 8

CHAPTER PROJECT 9

## ACTIVITY 1 DRAWING

Here is the first clue: *Draw a line from Baxley to Savannah. From Savannah, draw a southwesterly line that forms a 60° angle with the first line. The treasure is on an island that lies along the second line.* On which islands could the treasure be buried?

Sapelo Island, Wolf Island, St. Simons Island, or Cumberland Island



See also Extra Practice section.

18.

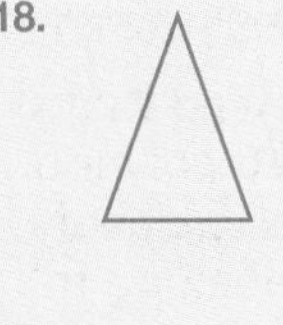

19.

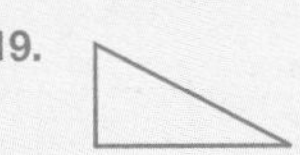

20.

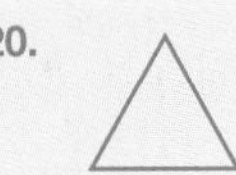

### Project Activity 1

**Drawing** Before students actually begin to draw on their maps to find the treasure, make sure students accurately traced the map from the text. If the map is not correctly traced, students may identify the wrong location.

*Extension*
*After Lesson 9-3*

# Angles of a Polygon

In previous courses, you learned that the sum of the measures of the angles of a triangle is 180°. Now you have the tools to prove that this is true with deductive reasoning.

In the figure, $\overleftrightarrow{AC} \parallel \overleftrightarrow{DE}$. If two parallel lines are cut by a transversal, then alternate interior angles are congruent. Therefore, $\angle 1 \cong \angle 4$, or $m\angle 1 = m\angle 4$. Similarly, $m\angle 3 = m\angle 5$. $\angle ABC$ is a straight angle. So $m\angle 1 + m\angle 2 + m\angle 3 = 180°$. When you substitute $m\angle 4$ for $m\angle 1$ and $m\angle 5$ for $m\angle 3$, you get $m\angle 4 + m\angle 2 + m\angle 5 = 180°$. These are the angles of $\triangle BDE$.

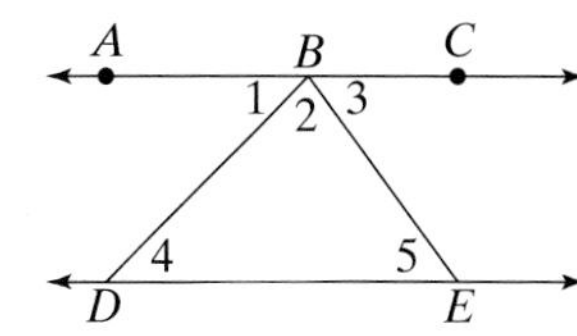


You can use triangles to find the sum of the measures of the angles of any polygon.

## EXAMPLE

**Find the sum of the measures of the angles of a hexagon.**

The hexagon has **6** vertices.
From vertex $A$, there are **5** segments to the other vertices.
The segments determine **4** triangles.

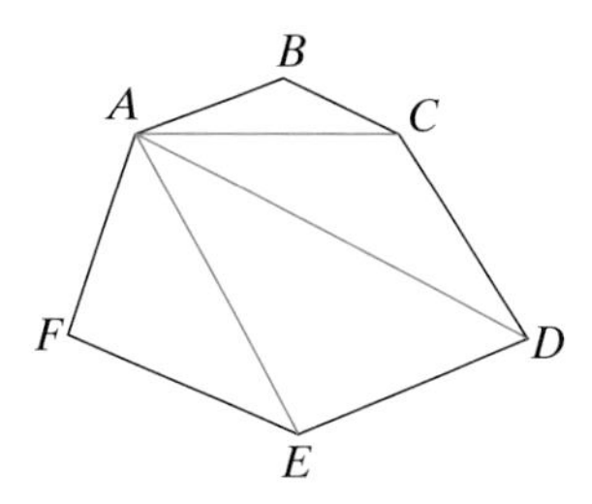


| sum of measures of angles of hexagon | = | number of triangles | · | number of degrees in a triangle |
|---|---|---|---|---|
| 720° | = | 4 | · | 180° |

**Find the sum of the measures of the angles of each polygon.**

1. a quadrilateral 360°
2. a decagon (10 sides) 1440°
3. an octagon 1080°
4. a dodecagon (12 sides) 1800°
5. *Mathematical Reasoning* Write a formula for the sum of the measures of the angles of an $n$-gon ($n$ sides). $s = 180(n - 2)$
6. Find the value of $x$ in the figure at the right. 105°
7. *Writing* The sum of the measures of the angles of a polygon is 1,260°. Explain how you can find the number of sides of the polygon. See above.

7. Answers may vary. Sample: Use the formula $s = 180(n - 2)$. Substitute 1,260 for $s$ and solve. There are 9 sides.

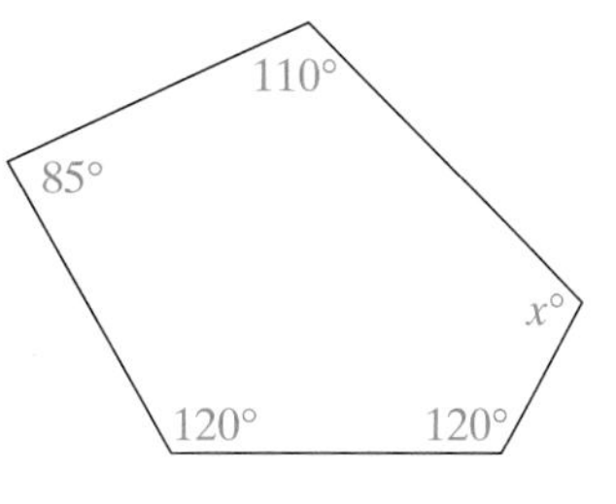




**• Additional Example**

Find the sum of the measures of the angles of a polygon with 15 sides. 2,340°

## MATH TOOLBOX

### Angles of a Polygon

In this Math Toolbox, students use what they know about drawing diagonals of a polygon and the sum of the angles of a triangle to write a formula for the sum of the measures of the (interior) angles of an $n$-gon (a polygon with $n$ sides).

### Math Background

By drawing all the diagonals for polygons with 4, 6, 8, 10, and 12 sides, you can see that any polygon (whether or not it is a regular polygon) can be divided into a certain number of triangles. The pattern for the number of sides and the number of triangles shows that the number of triangles for a polygon of $n$ sides is always $n - 2$. The sum of the measures of the angles of the triangles gives the sum of the measures of the angles of the polygon. This means that you can find the sum of the measures of the angles of a polygon with $n$ sides by finding $180(n - 2)$.

## Teaching Notes

**Error Prevention** Help students discover and verify the pattern with examples before they try to generalize the pattern into an abstract formula.

**Monitoring Progress** **Exercise 7** Explain that mathematicians always want to know if a process works both backward and forward.

**Block Scheduling** If you have block scheduling or extended periods, you may wish to use this Math Toolbox just after using Lesson 9-3 in the same class period.

# 9-4

## Getting Ready

**Resources** A complete list of resources for this lesson is on p. 439H.

### Daily Skills Warm-Up

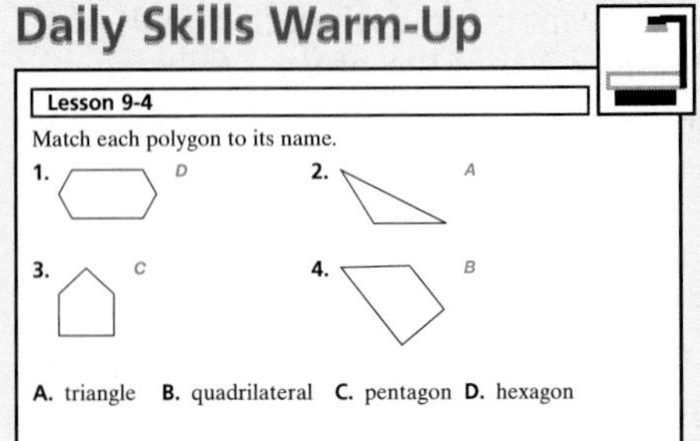
Lesson 9-4

Match each polygon to its name.

1. D
2. A
3. C
4. B

**A.** triangle **B.** quadrilateral **C.** pentagon **D.** hexagon

### Background for the Lesson

Drawing a diagram often helps you model relationships or understand a situation more clearly than just reading the words of a problem. A diagram also acts as a written record of your thought processes to help you see the steps of the problem. After organizing and analyzing the data you collect from the words into your diagram, you may want to write an algebraic equation to use in solving your problem. You can also use diagrams to make clear what the patterns are in a problem.

## 1 Focus

### Connecting to Students' Lives

Ask students if they have drawn plans for something they wanted to build. Architects draw blueprints as diagrams of buildings. The blueprints record details about the construction of the building. Workers use them to answer planning and construction questions.

### Connecting to Prior Knowledge

In Lesson 9-3, students learned that a regular polygon has all sides congruent and all angles congruent. In this lesson, students draw diagrams of regular polygons to solve problems. In Lesson 9-5, students will learn to identify congruent polygons.

**Problem Solving Strategies**

Account for All Possibilities
Draw a Diagram
Look for a Pattern
Make a Model
Make a Table
Simplify a Problem
Simulate a Problem
Solve by Graphing
Try, Test, Revise
Use Multiple Strategies
Work Backward
Write an Equation
Write a Proportion

# Draw a Diagram

*Math Strategies in Action*
Car designers rely on computer design programs to create, test, and modify their plans. The process of drawing a diagram helps them to discover any problems they may have and to see possible solutions.

Drawing a diagram is an important problem solving tool.

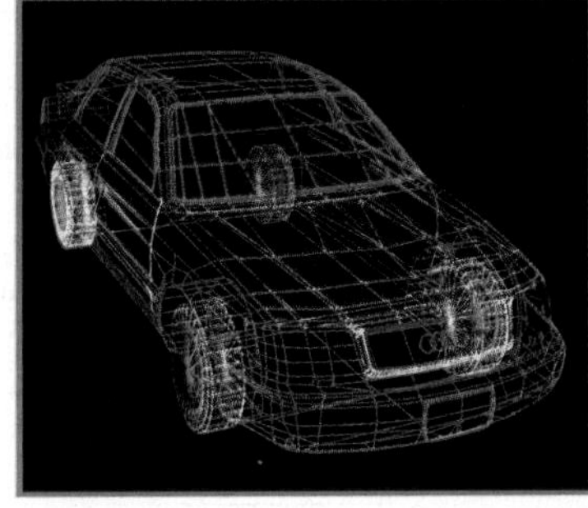

**SAMPLE PROBLEM**

How many diagonals does an octagon have?

### Read

In reading the problem, make sure you understand the meanings of all of the terms.

1. What is an octagon? a polygon with 8 sides
2. What is a diagonal? a line segment that connects two non-consecutive vertices

### Plan

One strategy for solving this problem is to draw a diagram and count the diagonals. An octagon has eight sides. You can draw five diagonals from one vertex of an octagon.

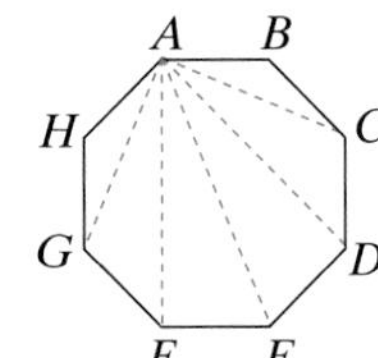


$\overline{AG}$, $\overline{AF}$, $\overline{AE}$, $\overline{AD}$, and $\overline{AC}$ are some of the diagonals.



## Tools to Monitor Progress

**BEFORE THE LESSON**

**To check prerequisite skills:**

- Naming polygons

**Skills You Need,** p. 439

**Skills Intervention Kit,** Geometry

**DURING THE LESSON**

**To check understanding:**

- **Additional Sample Problem**
  How many diagonals does a decagon have? 35

Start at one vertex, draw all diagonals from that vertex, and count them.

**3.** There are 5 diagonals drawn from vertex $A$. Copy the diagram on the previous page. Now find the number of diagonals you can draw from vertex $B$. 5

**4.** How many new diagonals can you draw from vertex $C$? 4

### Solve

It may be helpful to organize your results as you count the diagonals. Make a table similar to the one below and fill in the number of diagonals from each vertex. Do not count a diagonal twice. (The segment from $A$ to $C$ is the same segment as the one from $C$ to $A$.) Then find the sum of the diagonals.

| Vertex | Number of Diagonals |
|---|---|
| $A$ | 5 |
| $B$ | 5 |
| $C$ | 4 |
| $D$ | ■ 3 |
| $E$ | ■ 2 |
| $F$ | ■ 1 |
| $G$ | ■ 0 |
| $H$ | ■ 0 |
| Total | ■ 20 |

### Look Back

Recounting the diagonals after they have all been drawn is not an easy task. To check your results, you may want to try a different approach. Start with figures with fewer sides and see whether there is a pattern of diagonals as you increase the number of sides.

| Figure | Number of Sides | Number of Diagonals |
|---|---|---|
| Triangle | 3 | 0 |
| Quadrilateral | 4 | 2 |
| Pentagon | 5 | 5 |
| Hexagon | 6 | 9 |

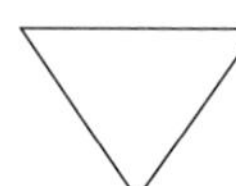

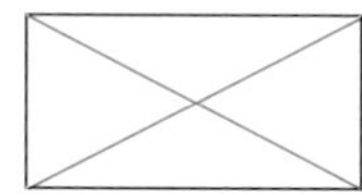

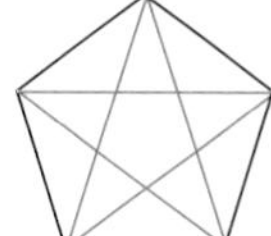

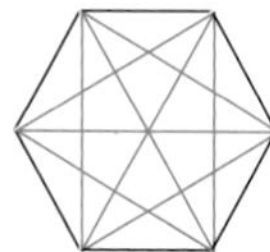

Notice that the number of diagonals increases as you increase the number of sides of the polygon. First the number increases by 2, then by 3, and then by 4. Continue this pattern to check your results.



## 2 Teach

### Teaching Notes

Explain to students that they used a diagram when they drew a map or picture to explain an idea or to give directions. Suggest that they read the problem carefully to help them create an appropriate diagram for solving the problem.

### Sample Problem

**Build understanding.** Ask: Why can you draw fewer diagonals as you make your way around the octagon? Some of the diagonals have already been drawn from previous vertices.

**Error Prevention** To prevent students from counting diagonals twice in their diagrams, suggest that students put a small tick mark on each one as they count it.

**Visual Learning** Have students draw the polygons in the second chart to confirm the given number of diagonals and to verify the pattern of increasing sides and diagonals.

**Extension** Draw diagrams to find out whether the pattern of diagonals and vertices works for non-regular convex (no interior angle more than 180°) polygons. The pattern holds even for irregular polygons.

### • Additional Sample Problem

Jack climbed a set of stairs and stopped at the middle step. He then walked down 2 steps, up 4 steps, down 3 steps, and up 6 steps, and he was at the top of the stairs. How many steps are in the set of stairs? 11 steps

### AFTER THE LESSON

**To assess knowledge:**

**Lesson Quiz**

Solve by drawing a diagram. Cut along each diagonal of a polygon.

1. For a quadrilateral, how many pieces do you have? 4
2. How many pieces for a pentagon? 11
3. How many pieces for a hexagon? 24

- For enrichment and reteaching options see Resources on p. 439H.

# 3 Practice/Assess

## Assignment Guide

**Core** 1–6, 8, 11, 13–16
✪ **Extension** 7, 9–10, 12

Mixed Review can be assigned at any time for maintenance.

## Exercises

**Tactile Learning Exercises 7–15** Solve these problems using any strategy, but drawing a diagram or sketch may help you understand the situation.

**Test Prep Exercise 16** Use $x$ to represent the number he had a year ago.

## ✪ Challenge

Write an equation that relates the number of diagonals $d$ to the number of vertices $n$ of a regular polygon.
$d = n(\frac{n-3}{2})$, or $d = \frac{n^2 - 3n}{2}$

## Closure

Drawing a diagram helps you visualize a problem, which makes the solution easier to find. You need to draw diagrams to solve some problems, but they can help you with any problem.

# Exercises

## Check Understanding

**Solve by drawing a diagram.**

1. A furniture delivery truck leaves the store at 8 A.M. It travels 6 miles east, then 4 miles south, then 2 miles west, and then 4 miles north. At the end of this route, how far is the truck from the store? 4 mi

2. Bill is older than Jim and younger than Jose. Jose is older than Chris and younger than Tandala. Chris is older than Jim. Bill is younger than Tandala. Chris is older than Bill. Who is youngest? Jim

3. *Geometry* How many triangles can you form in a hexagon if you draw all of the diagonals from only one vertex? 4

## Practice and Problem Solving

**Solve by drawing a diagram.**

4. Eight soccer teams are to play each other two times in a season. How many games will be played? 56 games

5. There are 25 students in a math class. Ten students are members of the math club. Twelve students are in the band. Five students are in both. How many students in the math class are members of neither club? 8

6. *Coordinate Geometry* Snoozles are always born as twins, and each snoozle always moves in the opposite direction from its twin. Twin snoozles are at the origin. One follows the path $(0, 0)$ to $(1, 3)$ to $(2, 2)$ to $(4, 7)$. What path will its twin travel? $(0, 0)$ to $(-1, -3)$ to $(-2, -2)$ to $(-4, -7)$

**Solve using any strategy.**

✪ 7. Container A has twice the capacity of container B. Container A is full of sand and container B is empty. Suppose $\frac{1}{8}$ of the sand in container A is poured into container B. What fractional part of container B will contain sand? $\frac{1}{4}$

8. A student was standing in the middle of a line. Twenty-three students were ahead of her. How many students were in the line? 47

✪ 9. *Writing* Suppose you want to find the thickness of one sheet of paper. Describe the problem solving method you would use.
Answers may vary. Sample: Count out a substantial number of sheets, perhaps 200. Then measure the thickness of that stack and divide the measurement by 200.



## Alternative Assessment

Write a problem that you solve by drawing a diagram. Include the diagram and the answer to the problem.

## Daily Cumulative Review

**Judging by appearances, classify each polygon by its sides and angles.** *(Lesson 9-3)*

1. rectangle
2. trapezoid
3. parallelogram
4. hexagon
5. triangle
6. pentagon

**In each figure find the measures of ∠1 and ∠2.** *(Lesson 9-2)*

7. Given: $m \parallel n$
$m\angle 1 = 130°$; $m\angle 2 = 130°$

8. Given: $a \parallel b$
$m\angle 1 = 128°$; $m\angle 2 = 52°$

9. Given: $s \parallel t$
$m\angle 1 = 35°$; $m\angle 2 = 145°$

**Mixed Review**

**Solve each equation.**

10. (7-1) $25 = -9x - 2$ — $-3 = x$
11. (7-1) $\frac{r}{4} + 9 = -3$ — $r = -48$
12. (7-1) $-7 - t + 9t = 49$ — $t = 7$
13. (7-2) $24 = 4(s - 2) + 8$ — $6 = s$
14. (7-2) $k + \frac{3}{4}k = 7$ — $k = 4$
15. (7-2) $7m + 4 = -24.28$ — $m = -4.04$

10. Points $P, Q, R$, and $S$ appear in that order on a line. The ratio $PQ : QR$ is $3 : 4$, and the ratio $QR : RS$ is $2 : 5$. The length $PQ$ is 6 in. Find the length $PS$. 34 in.

11. Shana has three pets, a dog, a cat, and a bird. One of them is named Sammy. Noodles is younger than both the bird and the dog. Fluffy is green. Which pet has the name Sammy? the dog

12. *Geometry* You can draw one segment to connect two points and three distinct segments to connect three named points. How many segments can you draw to connect five points if no three of the points lie on the same line? 10

13. *Writing* What are the next three numbers in the sequence 1, 3, 6, 10, 15, 21, . . . ? Describe the pattern. 28, 36, 45; each increase is one greater than the increase before it.

14. Two friends rented a canoe for 10 days. One friend used the canoe for 6 days. The other friend used the canoe for 4 days. How much of the $150 rental fee should each friend pay? $90, $60

15. *Measurement* Maureen cut a 20-cm ribbon into exactly three pieces. The first piece is 3 cm shorter than the second piece. The third piece is 4 cm shorter than the second piece. Find the length of the shortest piece. 5 cm

16. **TEST PREP** A coin collector has 53 rare coins. This is 12 fewer than 5 times the number he had a year ago. Choose the equation that you could use to find how many coins the collector had a year ago. D

A. $12 - 5x = 53$
B. $53 - 5x = 12$
C. $53 - 12 = 5x$
D. $53 = 5x - 12$

## Mixed Review

**Classify each triangle by its sides and angles.** *(Lesson 9-3)*

17. no congruent sides and one right angle scalene right triangle
18. three congruent sides equilateral triangle
19. one obtuse angle and no congruent sides scalene obtuse triangle
20. a 90° angle and two congruent sides isosceles right triangle

**Write each decimal as a fraction in simplest form and as a percent.** *(Lesson 6-5)*

21. 0.14 $\frac{7}{50}$, 14%
22. 4.5 $4\frac{1}{2}$, 450%
23. 0.11 $\frac{11}{100}$, 11%
24. 0.02 $\frac{1}{50}$, 2%
25. 0.125 $\frac{1}{8}$, 12.5%

26. Adult tickets for the school musical sell for $8 and student tickets sell for $5 each. Let $x$ be the number of adult tickets sold and $y$ be the number of student tickets sold. The school hopes to make at least $1,000. Write a linear inequality to model the situation. Show all of the solutions by graphing the linear inequality. *(Lesson 8-8)* $8x + 5y \geq 1000$; see margin for graph.



26. $8x + 5y \geq 1000$

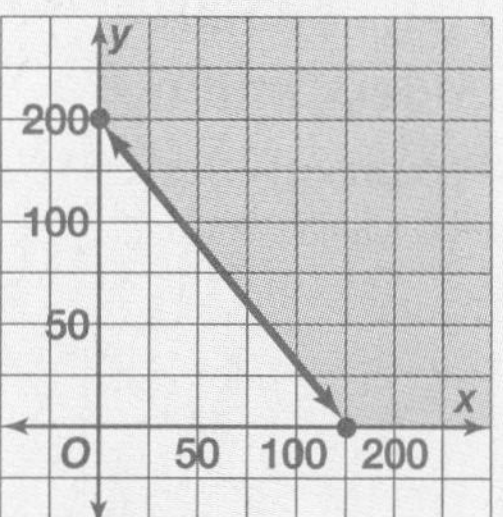


## Practice

**Solve by drawing a diagram.**

1. How many diagonals does a quadrilateral have? 2

2. Which quadrilaterals always have congruent diagonals? square, rectangle, isosceles trapezoid

3. Find a formula for the number of diagonals $d$ in a polygon with $n$ sides. Complete the table to help you. Look for a pattern.

| Figure | Number of sides | Number of vertices | Number of diagonals from each vertex | Total number of diagonals |
|---|---|---|---|---|
| triangle | 3 | 3 | 0 | 0 |
| quadrilateral | 4 | 4 | 1 | 2 |
| pentagon | 5 | 5 | 2 | 5 |
| hexagon | 6 | 6 | 3 | 9 |
| octagon | 8 | 8 | 5 | 20 |
| $n$-gon | $n$ | $n$ | $n - 3$ | $\frac{n(n-3)}{2}$ |

$d = \frac{n(n-3)}{2}$

4. One day in the lunch line, Maurice was ahead of Aquia and behind Rochelle. Rochelle was ahead of Shequille and behind Whitney. Shequille was ahead of Maurice. Who was last? Aquia

5. A mail carrier leaves the post office at 10:00 A.M. and travels 4 miles south, then 7 miles east, then 5 miles south, then 10 miles west, and 9 miles north. At the end of her route, how far and in which direction is the mail carrier from the post office? She is 3 miles west of the post office.



## Reteaching

Solve by drawing a diagram.

Kara and Karl are twins with the same tastes. They like pizza more than tacos, but less than steak. They like mashed potatoes more than tacos, but less than hamburgers. They like hamburgers more than pizza, but less than steak. Which of these foods do they like the most?

Let $p$ = pizza, $t$ = tacos, $s$ = steak, $m$ = mashed potatoes, and $h$ = hamburgers.

Draw a diagram with 5 blanks. Since Kara and Karl like pizza more than tacos, but less than steak, start by putting $s$, $p$, and $t$ in the first 3 blanks.

$s$ $p$ $t$ ___ ___

They like mashed potatoes more than tacos, but less than hamburgers. This moves tacos down. Tentatively, we have:

$s$ $p$ $h$ $m$ $t$

They like hamburgers more than pizza but less than steak.

$s$ $h$ $p$ $m$ $t$

We still cannot be sure if they like pizza more or less than mashed potatoes, but that is not important for answering the question. Kara and Karl like steak the most.

**Solve by drawing a diagram.**

1. Mindy is taller than Olga, but shorter than Thomas. Thomas is taller than Sven, but shorter than Parth. Sven is taller than Olga, but shorter than Mindy. Who's the tallest? Parth

2. How many segments can you draw between pairs of points in the figure at the right. 10

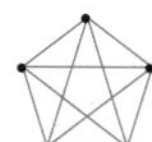



## Enrichment

In a regular polygon, all sides are congruent and all angles are congruent. Each interior angle of any regular $n$-gon has a certain measure. You can write a formula to find this measure based on the number of sides $n$.

1. An equilateral triangle is regular. What is the measure of each interior angle of an equilateral triangle? Explain how you know. 60°; The sum of the measures of the angles of a triangle is 180°. An equilateral triangle has 3 angles that are all the same size, so each is $180 \div 3 = 60°$.

A quadrilateral can be divided into two triangles by a diagonal from a single vertex. The sum of the angles of any quadrilateral is $2(180) = 360°$.

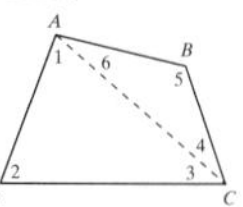


**Complete the table. Look for a pattern. Use diagrams if necessary.**

| | Polygon | $n$ | Number of triangles | Sum of interior angles | Measure of one angle in regular n-gon |
|---|---|---|---|---|---|
| 2. | Triangle | 3 | 1 | 180° | 60° |
| 3. | Quadrilateral | 4 | 2 | $2(180) = 360°$ | 90° |
| 4. | Pentagon | 5 | 3 | $3(180) = 540°$ | 108° |
| 5. | Hexagon | 6 | 4 | $4(180) = 720°$ | 120° |
| 6. | Octagon | 8 | 6 | $6(180) = 1,080°$ | 135° |
| 7. | Decagon | 10 | 8 | $8(180) = 1,440°$ | 144° |
| 8. | Dodecagon | 12 | 10 | $10(180) = 1,800°$ | 150° |
| 9. | $n$-gon | $n$ | $n - 2$ | $(n - 2)(180)$ | $\frac{180(n-2)}{n}$ |

10. Complete the conjecture:
The measure of an interior angle of a regular $n$-gon is $\frac{180(n-2)}{n}$.

# 9-5

## Getting Ready

**Key Terms and Symbols** SSS, SAS, ASA

**Materials** plastic straws, scissors, string

**Resources** A complete list of resources for this lesson is on p. 439H.

### Daily Skills Warm-Up

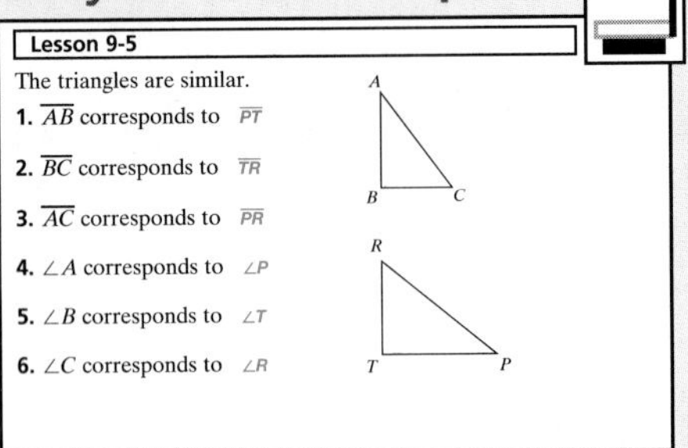
Lesson 9-5

The triangles are similar.

1. $\overline{AB}$ corresponds to $\overline{PT}$
2. $\overline{BC}$ corresponds to $\overline{TR}$
3. $\overline{AC}$ corresponds to $\overline{PR}$
4. $\angle A$ corresponds to $\angle P$
5. $\angle B$ corresponds to $\angle T$
6. $\angle C$ corresponds to $\angle R$



### Background for the Lesson

Two angles are congruent when they have the same measure. When two triangles are congruent, each side of the first triangle has the same measure as the corresponding sides of the second triangle, and each angle of the first triangle has the same measure as the corresponding sides of the second triangle. When two figures are congruent, you can make one fit over, or coincide with, the other by sliding, rotating, or flipping the figure.

## 1 Focus

### Investigate

Point out that these are approximate models of the triangles, so students can overlook small differences caused by differences in how tightly the string is tied and other mechanical considerations.

### Connecting to Prior Knowledge

In Lesson 9-2, students learned that congruent angles have the same measure. In this lesson, students learn that congruent polygons have congruent sides and angles. In Lesson 9-7, students will learn how to construct congruent segments and angles.



# 9-5 Congruence

**What You'll Learn**

1. To identify corresponding parts of congruent triangles
2. To determine whether triangles are congruent

**. . . And Why**

To use congruent figures for finding distance

## *Investigate*

EXPLORING CONGRUENCE

1. Have each member of your group cut plastic straws 3 cm, 6 cm, and 7 cm long. String an 18-cm string through the three straws. Tie the string just tight enough to form a strong triangle without bending any straws. Check students' work.
2. Hold the triangles up to one another to compare. Are they the same size and shape? Describe how the angle measures compare. Yes, all the triangles have sides of the same three lengths and angles with the same three measures.

## Identifying Corresponding Parts

When two polygons are congruent, their corresponding parts have the same measure. The triangles at the left are congruent. You can use tick marks to indicate congruent segments and arcs to indicate congruent angles. You can write a congruence statement by listing the corresponding angles in the same order.

$\triangle ABC \cong \triangle EDF$

| | |
|---|---|
| $\angle A \cong \angle E$ | $\overline{AB} \cong \overline{ED}$ |
| $\angle B \cong \angle D$ | $\overline{BC} \cong \overline{DF}$ |
| $\angle C \cong \angle F$ | $\overline{AC} \cong \overline{EF}$ |

You can use corresponding parts of congruent polygons to find distances.

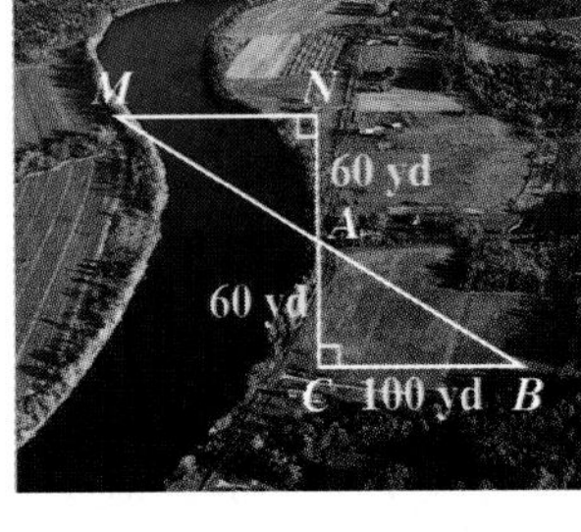


### EXAMPLE 1

*Measurement* **In the figure at the left, $\triangle AMN \cong \triangle ABC$.**

**a. Name the corresponding congruent angles.**
$\angle M \cong \angle B$, $\angle N \cong \angle C$, $\angle MAN \cong \angle BAC$

**b. Name the corresponding congruent sides.**
$\overline{MN} \cong \overline{BC}$, $\overline{NA} \cong \overline{CA}$, $\overline{MA} \cong \overline{BA}$

**c. Find the distance across the river from $M$ to $N$.**
Since $\overline{MN} \cong \overline{BC}$ and $BC = 100$ yd, $MN = 100$ yd.



# Tools to Monitor Progress

**BEFORE THE LESSON**

**To check prerequisite skills:**
- Identifying polygons

**Skills Intervention Kit,** Geometry

**DURING THE LESSON**

**To check understanding:**

**Try This** exercises on student page

Use this figure for Additional Examples 1–2.

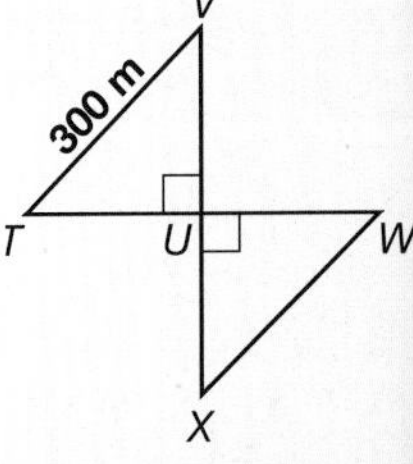

## ■ Try This

3. $\triangle ABC \cong \triangle DEC$. List all pairs of congruent corresponding sides and angles. Then find $AC$. $\overline{AB} \cong \overline{DE}$, $\overline{BC} \cong \overline{EC}$, $\overline{AC} \cong \overline{DC}$, $\angle A \cong \angle D$, $\angle B \cong \angle E$, $\angle BCA \cong \angle ECD$, $AC = 50$ m

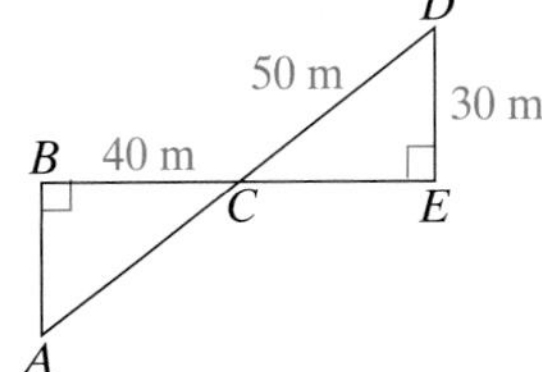

## Identifying Congruent Triangles

You use corresponding parts of triangles to identify congruent triangles. Below are three of the ways to show that two triangles are congruent.

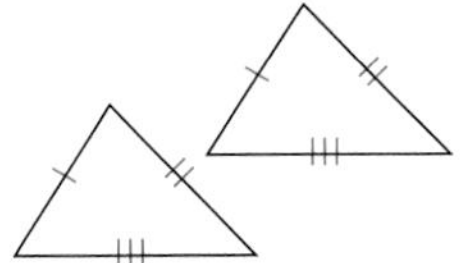

Side–Side–Side (SSS)

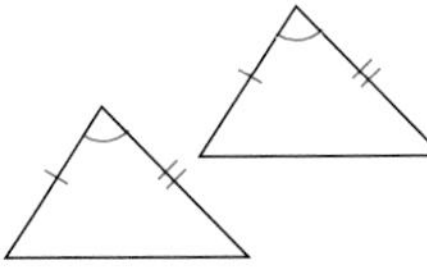

Side–Angle–Side (SAS)

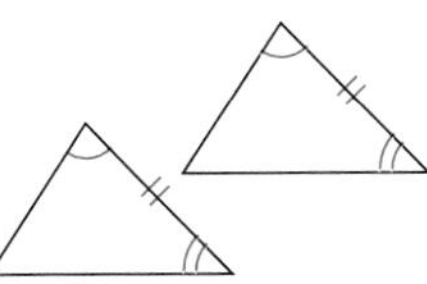

Angle–Side–Angle (ASA)

### Example 2

**List the congruent corresponding parts of each pair of triangles. Write a congruence statement for the triangles.**

**a.**

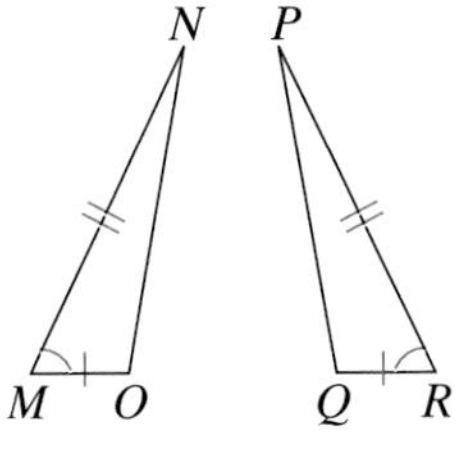


$\overline{MO} \cong \overline{RQ}$ Side
$\angle M \cong \angle R$ Angle
$\overline{MN} \cong \overline{RP}$ Side
$\triangle MNO \cong \triangle RPQ$ by **SAS**

**b.**

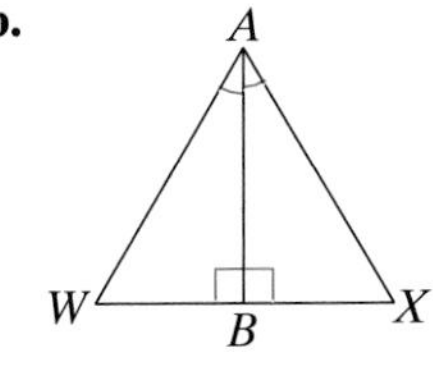


$\angle WAB \cong \angle XAB$ Angle
$\overline{AB} \cong \overline{AB}$ Side
$\angle ABW \cong \angle ABX$ Angle
$\triangle WAB \cong \triangle XAB$ by **ASA**

## ■ Try This

4. List the congruent corresponding parts of the pair of triangles. Write a congruence statement for the triangles. $\overline{FJ} \cong \overline{FG}$, $\overline{JI} \cong \overline{GH}$, $\overline{FI} \cong \overline{FH}$, $\triangle JFI \cong \triangle GFH$ by SSS

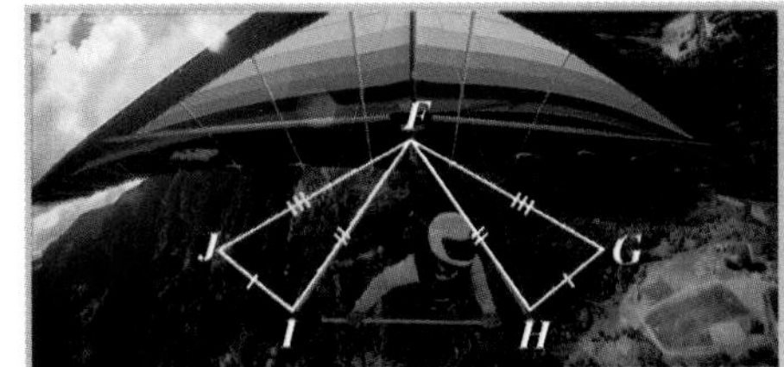




# 2 Teach

## Part 1 Teaching Notes

Emphasize that two polygons need not have the same orientation on the page to be congruent. Students will decide whether two polygons are congruent on the basis of information given about their corresponding sides and angles.

### ■ Example 1

**Build understanding.** Ask: What do you know about the measurement of segments $\overline{MA}$ and $\overline{BA}$? What do you not know? You know they are congruent, but you do not know the exact measurement.

**Error Prevention** Remind students to write the names of triangles with the letters in the proper order when they write congruence statements. The statement $\triangle ABC \cong \triangle DEF$ means that $\angle A \cong \angle D$, $\angle B \cong \angle E$, and $\angle C \cong \angle F$.

## Part 2 Teaching Notes

Explain to students that Side-Side-Side, Side-Angle-Side, and Angle-Side-Angle can prove congruence when you do not know whether all sides or angles are congruent.

### ■ Example 2

**Build understanding.** Ask: How do you know $\angle ABW \cong \angle ABX$? They are both right angles.

**Math Reasoning** Suppose you know that two triangles are congruent by SAS. This means that you know that one pair of angles is congruent. Use math reasoning to explain how you know that the other two pairs of angles are also congruent. If two polygons are congruent, then all of their corresponding sides and angles are congruent.

- **Additional Examples 1–2**

$\triangle TUV \cong \triangle WUX$

a. Name the corresponding congruent angles. $\angle V \cong \angle X$, $\angle T \cong \angle W$, $\angle TUV \cong \angle WUX$

b. Name the corresponding congruent sides. $\overline{TV} \cong \overline{WX}$, $\overline{TU} \cong \overline{WU}$, $\overline{VU} \cong \overline{XU}$

c. Find the length of $\overline{XW}$ 300 m

## AFTER THE LESSON

### To assess knowledge: Lesson Quiz

Given that $\triangle JKL \cong \triangle MNO$, complete the following.

1. $\angle L \cong \angle O$
2. $\overline{JK} \cong \overline{MN}$
3. $\overline{JL} \cong \overline{MO}$
4. $\angle K \cong \angle N$

- For enrichment and reteaching options see Resources on p. 439H.

# Exercises

## Check Understanding

1. Assume that $\triangle ABC \cong \triangle XYZ$. Write six congruence statements involving corresponding sides and angles. $\overline{AB} \cong \overline{XY}$, $\overline{BC} \cong \overline{YZ}$, $\overline{AC} \cong \overline{XZ}$, $\angle A \cong \angle X$, $\angle B \cong \angle Y$, $\angle C \cong \angle Z$

**List the congruent corresponding parts of each pair of triangles. Write a congruence statement for the triangles.**

2. 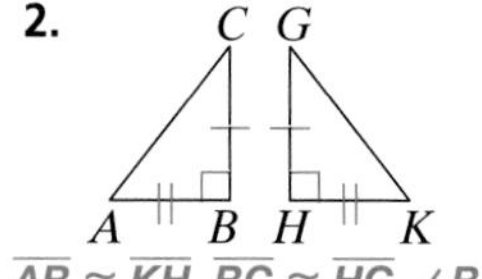

$\overline{AB} \cong \overline{KH}$, $\overline{BC} \cong \overline{HG}$, $\angle B \cong \angle H$, $\triangle ABC \cong \triangle KHG$ by SAS

3. 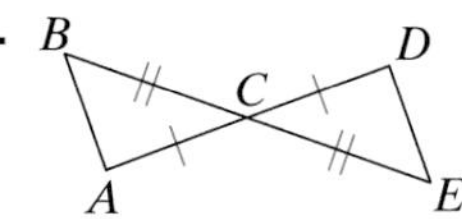

$\overline{BC} \cong \overline{EC}$, $\overline{AC} \cong \overline{DC}$, $\angle BCA \cong \angle ECD$, $\triangle ABC \cong \triangle DEC$ by SAS

4. 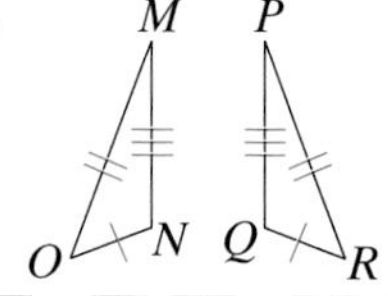

$\overline{OM} \cong \overline{RP}$, $\overline{ON} \cong \overline{RQ}$, $\overline{NM} \cong \overline{QP}$, $\triangle ONM \cong \triangle RQP$ by SSS

## Practice and Problem Solving

**Given that $\triangle ABC \cong \triangle DEF$, complete the following.**

5. $\angle A \cong$ ■ $\angle D$
6. $\angle B \cong$ ■ $\angle E$
7. $\angle C \cong$ ■ $\angle F$
8. $m\angle C =$ ■ $m\angle F$
9. $m\angle B =$ ■ $m\angle E$, or 90°
10. $m\angle A =$ ■ $m\angle D$, or 53°
11. $\overline{AC} \cong$ ■ $\overline{DF}$
12. $\overline{EF} \cong$ ■ $\overline{BC}$
13. $\overline{BA} \cong$ ■ $\overline{ED}$
14. $AB =$ ■ $DE$, or 3 mm
15. $AC =$ ■ $DF$, or 5 mm
16. $FE =$ ■ $CB$, or 4 mm
17. $\triangle CBA \cong$ ■ $\triangle FED$

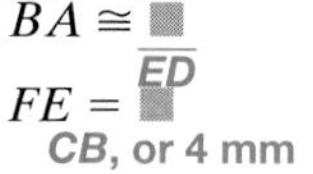


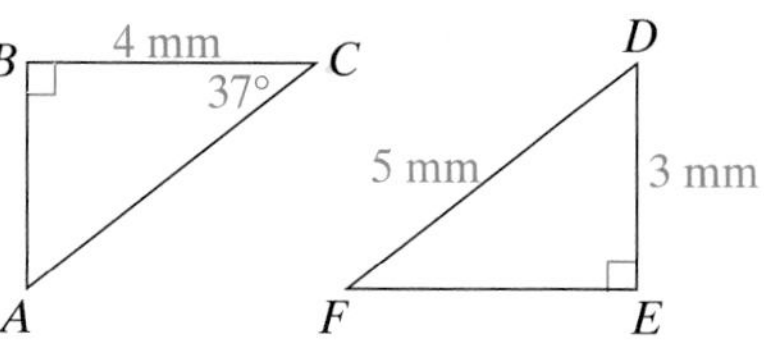


**List the congruent corresponding parts of each pair of triangles. Write a congruence statement for the triangles.**

18. 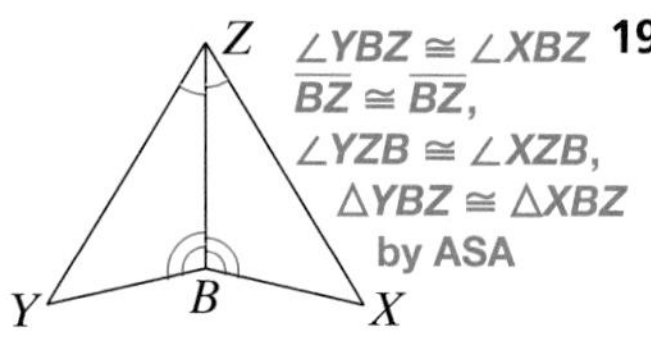

$\angle YBZ \cong \angle XBZ$, $\overline{BZ} \cong \overline{BZ}$, $\angle YZB \cong \angle XZB$, $\triangle YBZ \cong \triangle XBZ$ by ASA

19. 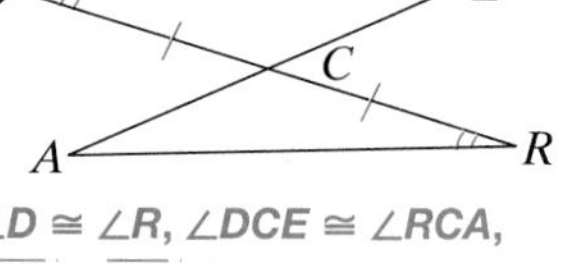

$\angle D \cong \angle R$, $\angle DCE \cong \angle RCA$, $\overline{CD} \cong \overline{CR}$, $\triangle ACR \cong \triangle ECD$ by ASA

20. See margin.

L

K M J

21. 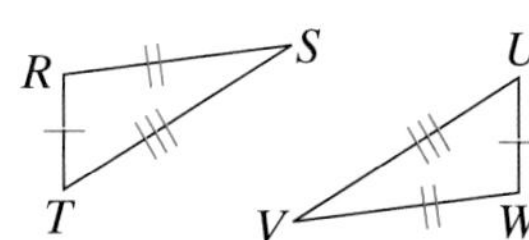

$\overline{RT} \cong \overline{WU}$, $\overline{RS} \cong \overline{WV}$, $\overline{TS} \cong \overline{UV}$, $\triangle RST \cong \triangle WVU$ by SSS

22. 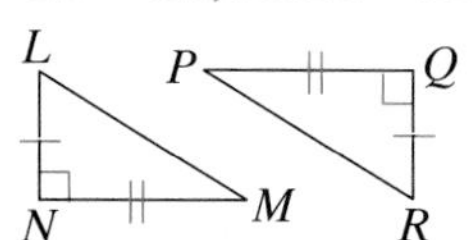

$\overline{NL} \cong \overline{QR}$, $\overline{NM} \cong \overline{QP}$, $\angle N \cong \angle Q$, $\triangle LNM \cong \triangle RQP$ by SAS

23. 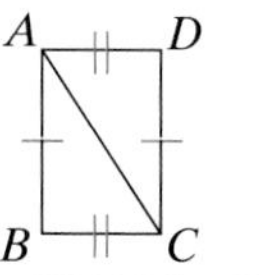

$\overline{AC} \cong \overline{CA}$, $\overline{AB} \cong \overline{CD}$, $\overline{BC} \cong \overline{DA}$, $\triangle ABC \cong \triangle CDA$ by SSS



20. $\overline{KM} \cong \overline{JM}$, , $\overline{ML} \cong \overline{ML}$, $\angle KML \cong \angle JML$, $\triangle KML \cong \triangle JML$ by SAS

33. 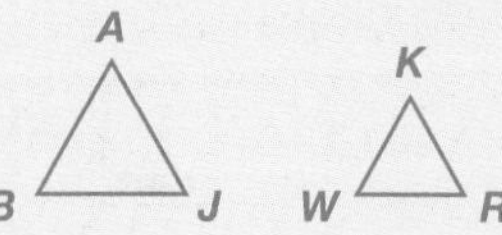

**Explain why each pair of triangles is congruent. Then find the missing measures in each diagram.**

**24.**

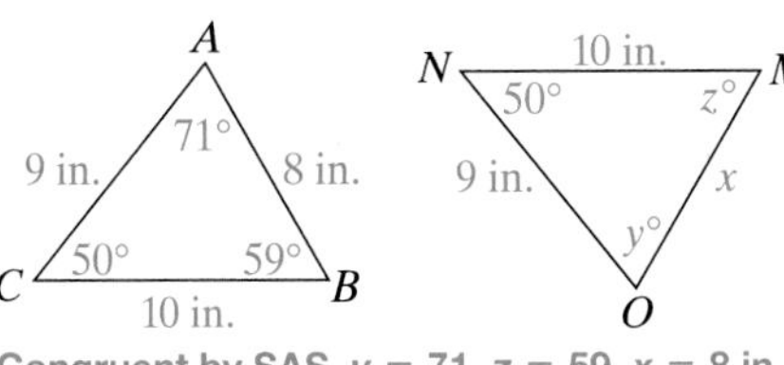


Congruent by SAS, $y = 71$, $z = 59$, $x = 8$ in.

**25.**

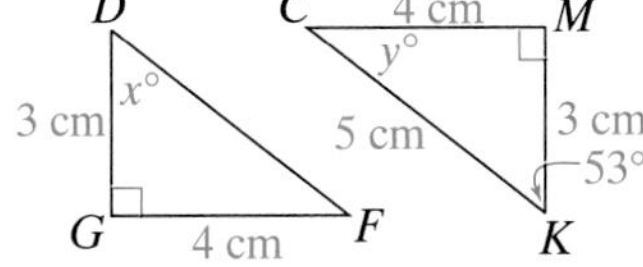


Congruent by SAS. $\angle D \cong \angle K$, so $x = 53°$. Because the sum of the angle measures in a triangle is 180°, $y = 37°$.

*Error Analysis* **The two figures in the diagram are congruent. Explain why each congruence statement in Exercises 26–31 is or is not correct.** 26–27. See below right.

**26.** $RAVK \cong NLUC$ **27.** $RKVA \cong UNLC$

**28.** $AKRV \cong CULN$ Incorrect; $\angle A$ does not correspond with $\angle C$.

**29.** $\overline{NL} \cong \overline{KV}$ See below.

**30.** $\angle V \cong \angle C$ Incorrect; $\angle V$ and $\angle C$ are not corresponding angles.

**31.** $\angle VAR \cong \angle LUC$ See below.

26. Incorrect; $\angle R$ does not correspond with $\angle N$.

27. Incorrect; $\angle R$ does not correspond with $\angle U$.

**32.** **TEST PREP** If $\triangle MFQ \cong \triangle DRW$, which of the following is *not necessarily* true? A

**A.** $\angle M \cong \angle W$ **B.** $\overline{MQ} \cong \overline{DW}$ **C.** $\angle MFQ \cong \angle DRW$ **D.** $m\angle F = m\angle R$

**33.** *Mathematical Reasoning* $\triangle KWR$ is *equiangular* (all angles are congruent). $\triangle ABJ$ is also equiangular. Can you use **A**ngle-**A**ngle-**A**ngle (**AAA**) to show that two triangles are congruent? Use diagrams to justify your conclusion. See margin for diagram. No; $\triangle ABJ$ and $\triangle KWR$ are both equiangular but the sides are not congruent.

**34.** *Writing* $\triangle ABC \cong \triangle XYZ$. What can you conclude about the perimeters of the triangles? Explain. The perimeters are equal.

**35.** *Geometric Patterns* In the quilt design below name the triangles that appear to be congruent. $\triangle AEB$, $\triangle CDH$, $\triangle MIL$, and $\triangle KJF$ appear to be congruent. $\triangle BDE$, $\triangle HID$, $\triangle LJI$, and $\triangle FEJ$ appear to be congruent. $\triangle CDB$, $\triangle MIH$, $\triangle JKL$, $\triangle AEF$, $\triangle DEG$, $\triangle IDG$, $\triangle IJG$, and $\triangle EJG$ appear to be congruent.

29. Correct; these are corresponding sides.

31. Correct; these are corresponding angles.



# 3 Practice/Assess

## Assignment Guide

To provide flexible scheduling, this lesson can be divided into parts.

**Part 1**
**Core** 1, 5–17

**Part 2**
**Core** 2–4, 18–32, 35–36
**Extension** 33–34

Mixed Review can be assigned at any time for maintenance.

## Exercises

**Exercise 10** The sum of the angles of a triangle is 180°.

**Test Prep Exercise 32** Choose the answer that is true sometimes but not always.

## Challenge

Draw an isosceles triangle. Fold the triangle so that the equal angles overlap. Are the two triangles formed congruent? How do you know? Yes, they are congruent by SAS.

## Closure

Polygons with the same size and shape are congruent. You can show two triangles are congruent by using the **Side-Side-Side**, **Side-Angle-Side**, or **Angle-Side-Angle** methods.

## Alternative Assessment

Give students a protractor and have them draw congruent triangles using the Side-Side-Side, Side-Angle-Side, or Angle-Side-Angle methods. Have students mark the congruent parts of their triangles and write congruence statements.

## Daily Cumulative Review

**Solve by drawing a diagram.** *(Lesson 9-4)*

1. How many triangles can you form in an octagon if you draw all of the diagonals from only one vertex? 6 triangles

2. There are 6 students in line at the school store. Julie is third in line. April is somewhere behind Julie. Mike is directly in front of Julie. There is one person between Mike and Francie. There is one person between Francie and Dillon. Eric is somewhere in front of Julie. Where is April? April is between Francie and Dillon.

**Write a formula to find the perimeter of each figure. Use the formula to find the perimeter.** *(Lesson 9-3)*

3. a square that has a side of 1.2 cm $P = 4s$; $P = 4.8$ cm

4. an equilateral triangle that has a side of 15 ft $P = 3s$; $P = 45$ ft

5. a regular pentagon that has a side of $\frac{3}{4}$ in. $P = 5s$; $P = 3\frac{3}{4}$ in.

6. a regular hexagon that has a side of $1\frac{1}{3}$ m $P = 6s$; $P = 7\frac{1}{2}$ m

**Mixed Review**

**Find the simple interest.**

7. (7-8) \$800 deposited at an interest rate of 12% for 8 months \$64

8. (7-8) \$1,200 deposited at an interest rate of 7% for 10 years \$840

**The scale of a map is 3 cm : 15 km. Find the actual distance for each map distance.**

9. (6-3) 5 cm 25 km

10. (6-3) 20 cm 100 km

11. (6-3) 90 cm 450 km

36. The end of the packing crate at the right is rectangular. The diagonals are congruent and intersect at point $H$. $\overline{HB} \cong \overline{HD}$ and $\overline{AH} \cong \overline{CH}$. $\triangle CDH$; congruent SSS or by SAS

a. Which triangle is congruent to $\triangle ABH$? How can you show that the triangles are congruent?

b. Which triangle is congruent to $\triangle ADC$? How can you show that the triangles are congruent? $\triangle BCD$, $\triangle CBA$, and $\triangle DAB$ by either SSS or by SAS

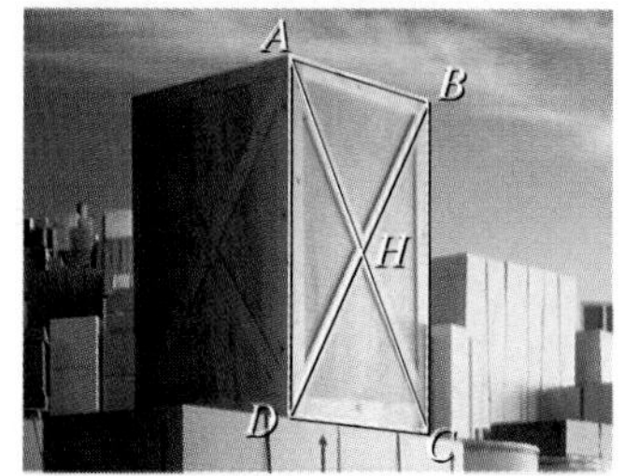


## Mixed Review

**Order from least to greatest.** *(Lesson 5-1)*

37. $\frac{1}{2}, \frac{5}{6}, \frac{3}{8}, \frac{2}{3}$ $\frac{3}{8}, \frac{1}{2}, \frac{2}{3}, \frac{5}{6}$

38. $\frac{3}{8}, \frac{2}{3}, \frac{3}{4}, \frac{4}{5}$ $\frac{3}{8}, \frac{2}{3}, \frac{3}{4}, \frac{4}{5}$

39. $\frac{1}{6}, \frac{1}{5}, \frac{1}{7}, \frac{1}{4}$ $\frac{1}{7}, \frac{1}{6}, \frac{1}{5}, \frac{1}{4}$

**Write and solve an equation.** *(Lesson 6-7)*

40. What percent of 50 is 20? $x \cdot 50 = 20$, 40%

41. 15% of what number is 12? $0.15x = 12$, 80

42. Find 125% of 200. $1.25\,(200) = x$, 250

43. Students are evenly spaced as they sit around a round table. The fourth student is directly across from the 11th student. How many students are seated at the table? *(Lesson 9-4)* 14 students

## Checkpoint 1

Lessons 9-1 through 9-5

**Name the figure that has the properties described.**

1. a part of a line with one endpoint ray
2. a series of points that extends in two directions without end line
3. a location in space point
4. two rays with a common endpoint angle
5. *Algebra* In the diagram at the right, $a \parallel b$.
   a. Write an equation to find $x$. See below.
   b. Find $m\angle TAV$. 50°
   c. Find $m\angle TAN$. 130°
   d. Find $m\angle DNK$. 130°

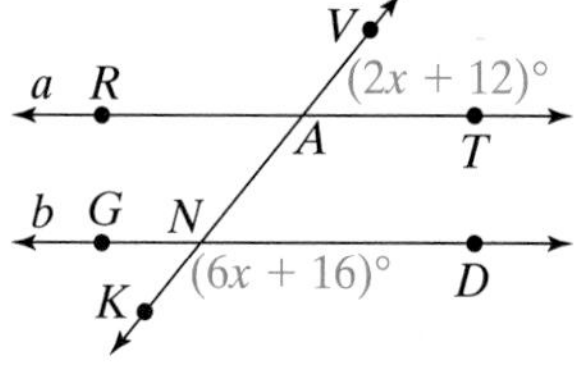


5a. $6x + 16 + 2x + 12 = 180$, $x = 19$

6. *Open-ended* Draw a triangle that is scalene and has a right angle. See margin.
7. **TEST PREP** Which of the following must be true if $\triangle AND \cong \triangle PCK$? C
   A. $\overline{AN} \cong \overline{PK}$
   B. $\angle AND \cong \angle PKC$
   C. $\angle N \cong \angle C$
   D. $\overline{ND} \cong \overline{PC}$



See also Extra Practice section.

6.

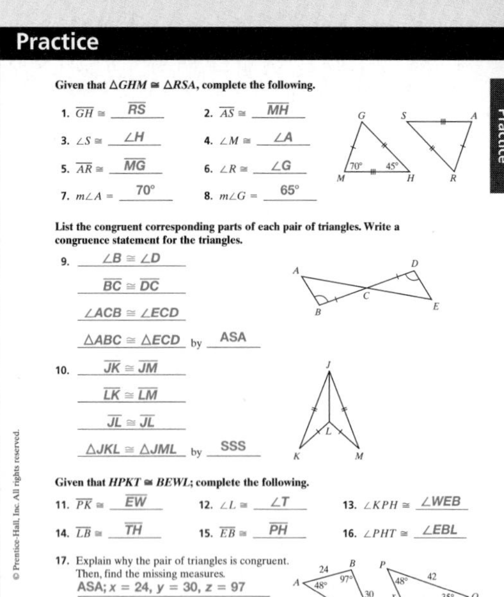
Practice

Given that $\triangle GHM \cong \triangle RSA$, complete the following.

1. $\overline{GH} \cong$ $\overline{RS}$ 2. $\overline{AS} \cong$ $\overline{MH}$
3. $\angle S \cong$ $\angle H$ 4. $\angle M \cong$ $\angle A$
5. $\overline{AR} \cong$ $\overline{MG}$ 6. $\angle R \cong$ $\angle G$
7. $m\angle A =$ 70° 8. $m\angle G =$ 65°

List the congruent corresponding parts of each pair of triangles. Write a congruence statement for the triangles.

9. $\angle B \cong \angle D$; $\overline{BC} \cong \overline{DC}$; $\angle ACB \cong \angle ECD$; $\triangle ABC \cong \triangle ECD$ by ASA

10. $\overline{JK} \cong \overline{JM}$; $\overline{LK} \cong \overline{LM}$; $\overline{JL} \cong \overline{JL}$; $\triangle JKL \cong \triangle JML$ by SSS

Given that $HPKT \cong BEWL$, complete the following.

11. $\overline{PK} \cong$ $\overline{EW}$ 12. $\angle L \cong$ $\angle T$ 13. $\angle KPH \cong$ $\angle WEB$
14. $\overline{LB} \cong$ $\overline{TH}$ 15. $\overline{EB} \cong$ $\overline{PH}$ 16. $\angle PHT \cong$ $\angle EBL$

17. Explain why the pair of triangles is congruent. Then, find the missing measures. ASA; $x = 24$, $y = 30$, $z = 97$



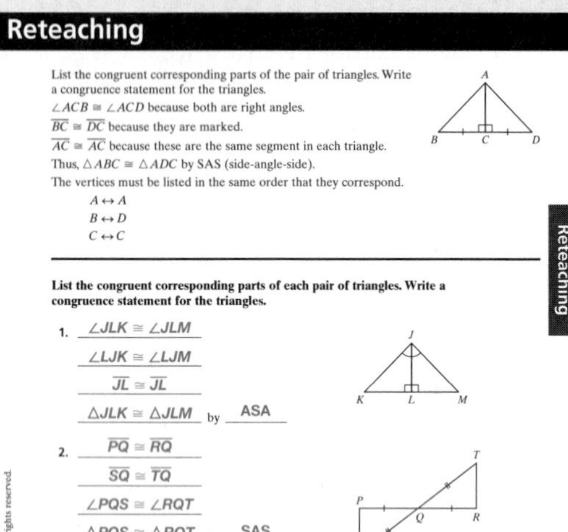
Reteaching

List the congruent corresponding parts of the pair of triangles. Write a congruence statement for the triangles.
$\angle ACB \cong \angle ACD$ because both are right angles.
$\overline{BC} \cong \overline{DC}$ because they are marked.
$\overline{AC} \cong \overline{AC}$ because these are the same segment in each triangle.
Thus, $\triangle ABC \cong \triangle ADC$ by SAS (side-angle-side).
The vertices must be listed in the same order that they correspond.
$A \leftrightarrow A$
$B \leftrightarrow D$
$C \leftrightarrow C$

List the congruent corresponding parts of each pair of triangles. Write a congruence statement for the triangles.

1. $\angle JLK \cong \angle JLM$; $\angle LJK \cong \angle LJM$; $\overline{JL} \cong \overline{JL}$; $\triangle JLK \cong \triangle JLM$ by ASA
2. $\overline{PQ} \cong \overline{RQ}$; $\overline{SQ} \cong \overline{TQ}$; $\angle PQS \cong \angle RQT$; $\triangle PQS \cong \triangle RQT$ by SAS
3. $\angle ZWY \cong \angle XWY$; $\angle ZYW \cong \angle XYW$; $\overline{WY} \cong \overline{WY}$; $\triangle ZWY \cong \triangle XWY$ by ASA



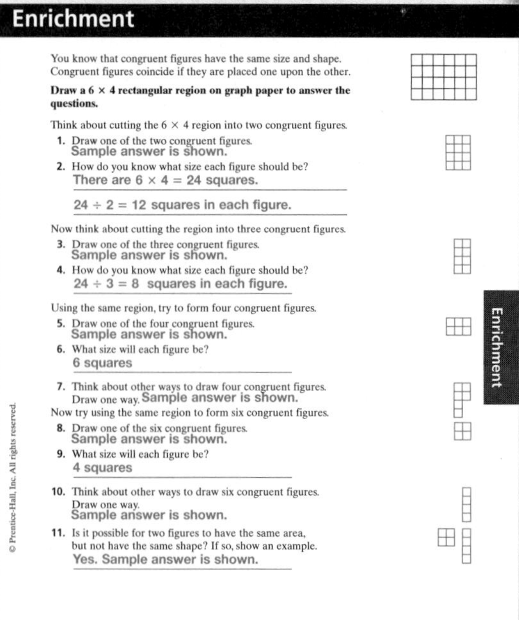
Enrichment

You know that congruent figures have the same size and shape. Congruent figures coincide if they are placed one upon the other.

**Draw a 6 × 4 rectangular region on graph paper to answer the questions.**

Think about cutting the 6 × 4 region into two congruent figures.
1. Draw one of the two congruent figures. Sample answer is shown.
2. How do you know what size each figure should be? There are 6 × 4 = 24 squares. 24 ÷ 2 = 12 squares in each figure.

Now think about cutting the region into three congruent figures.
3. Draw one of the three congruent figures. Sample answer is shown.
4. How do you know what size each figure should be? 24 ÷ 3 = 8 squares in each figure.

Using the same region, try to form four congruent figures.
5. Draw one of the four congruent figures. Sample answer is shown.
6. What size will each figure be? 6 squares
7. Think about other ways to draw four congruent figures. Draw one way. Sample answer is shown.

Now try using the same region to form six congruent figures.
8. Draw one of the six congruent figures. Sample answer is shown.
9. What size will each figure be? 4 squares
10. Think about other ways to draw six congruent figures. Draw one way. Sample answer is shown.
11. Is it possible for two figures to have the same area, but not have the same shape? If so, show an example. Yes. Sample answer is shown.



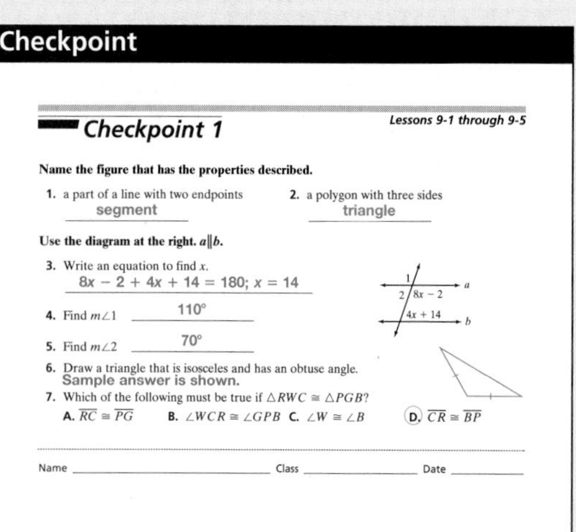
Checkpoint

Checkpoint 1 — Lessons 9-1 through 9-5

Name the figure that has the properties described.
1. a part of a line with two endpoints segment
2. a polygon with three sides triangle

Use the diagram at the right. $a \parallel b$.
3. Write an equation to find $x$. $8x - 2 + 4x + 14 = 180$; $x = 14$
4. Find $m\angle 1$ 110°
5. Find $m\angle 2$ 70°
6. Draw a triangle that is isosceles and has an obtuse angle. Sample answer is shown.
7. Which of the following must be true if $\triangle RWC \cong \triangle PGB$?
A. $\overline{RC} \cong \overline{PG}$ B. $\angle WCR \cong \angle GPB$ C. $\angle W \cong \angle B$ (D.) $\overline{CR} \cong \overline{BP}$

Name ______ Class ______ Date ______

# 9-6 Circles

### What You'll Learn

1. To find circumferences
2. To find central angles and to make circle graphs

### . . . And Why

To display statistics using circle graphs

## Investigate

**EXPLORING PI**

1. Work in groups. Each member of your group should have a ruler, string, and several circular objects, such as jar lids. Make a chart similar to the chart below. Record your results.

| Object | Diameter | Circumference | Ratio $\frac{\text{Circumference}}{\text{Diameter}}$ |
|---|---|---|---|
| ■ | ■ | ■ | ■ |
| ■ | ■ | ■ | ■ |

1–3. Check students' work.

2. Measure the diameter of each circle to the nearest millimeter.
3. Find the circumference of each circle by wrapping a string around the outside of the circle. Then straighten the string and measure its length to the nearest millimeter.
4. Calculate the ratio $\frac{\text{circumference}}{\text{diameter}}$ to the nearest tenth. $\approx 3.1$
5. Make a conjecture about the relationship between the circumference of a circle and its diameter. The ratio is approximately 3.1.

## PART 1 Finding Circumference

A **circle** is the set of all points that are the same distance from a given point, called the center of the circle.

*Radius* is a segment that has one endpoint at the center and the other point on the circle.

*Diameter* is a chord that passes through the center of a circle.

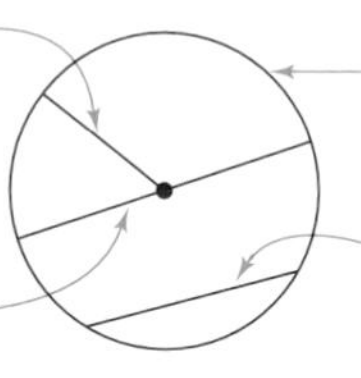

*Circumference* is the distance around the circle.

*Chord* is a segment whose endpoints are on the circle.



# 9-6

## Getting Ready

**Key Terms and Symbols** circle circumference of a circle, central angle

**Materials** ruler, string, circular objects

**Resources** A complete list of resources for this lesson is on p. 439H.

### Daily Skills Warm-Up

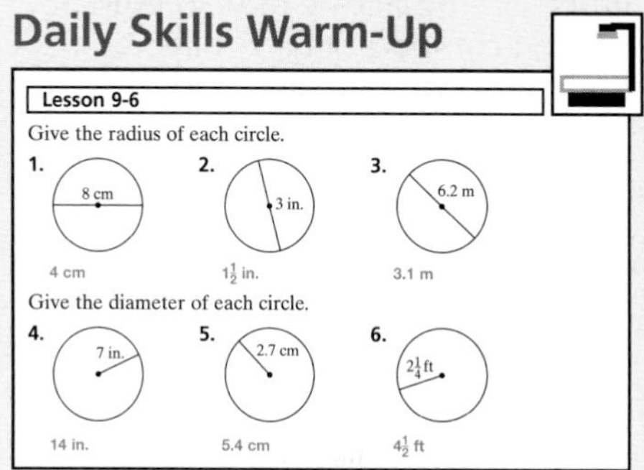
Lesson 9-6

Give the radius of each circle.

1. 8 cm — 4 cm
2. 3 in. — $1\frac{1}{2}$ in.
3. 6.2 m — 3.1 m

Give the diameter of each circle.

4. 7 in. — 14 in.
5. 2.7 cm — 5.4 cm
6. $2\frac{1}{4}$ ft — $4\frac{1}{2}$ ft

### Background for the Lesson

The ratio of a circle's circumference to its diameter is exactly equal to the irrational number $\pi$. This ratio, $\pi$, of distance around a circle to distance across the same circle is irrational; it can never be written as exactly equal to the ratio of two integers. You often use a fraction ($\frac{22}{7}$) or a decimal (3.14) as an approximation of $\pi$. Strictly speaking, calculations using these two rational approximations of $\pi$ are written with $\approx$. This means that for a circle with a diameter of 3, $C \approx 3(3.14)$ but $C = 3\pi$.

## 1 Focus

### Investigate

Measuring with the string is accurate enough to suggest a conjecture.

# Tools to Monitor Progress

### BEFORE THE LESSON

**To check prerequisite skills:**

- Identifying radius and diameter

**Skills You Need,** p. 439

### DURING THE LESSON

**To check understanding:**

**Try This** exercises on student page

- **Additional Example 1**

  Find the circumference of a circle that has a radius of 6 in. $\approx 37.68$ in.

# 2 Teach

## PART 1 Part 1 Teaching Notes

Explain that $\pi$ is only approximately 3.14 or $\frac{22}{7}$ because it is an irrational number. Remind students that irrational numbers cannot be expressed as fractions or as decimals that end or repeat a group of digits.

**Technology Option** You may want to have students use a scientific calculator to compare 3.14, $\frac{22}{7}$, and the calculator's approximation of $\pi$. Suggest that students use these different approximations to calculate the circumference of a circle of diameter 100 cm and compare their results.

### Example 1

**Build understanding.** Ask: What distance would a point on a wheel with a 6-ft diameter travel in one revolution? 18.84 ft

**Connecting to History** Historians have found evidence that $\pi$ was known in very ancient times, though it was approximated as 3. The ancient Greek mathematician Archimedes seems to have been the first person to write about calculating $\pi$, which he approximated as 3.14 in the third century B.C. In the twentieth century, scientists have used computers to calculate $\pi$ to more than 100,000,000 decimal places.

**ELL** The symbol $\pi$ is a letter from the Greek alphabet called pi. When scientists and mathematicians use $\pi$, it represents the irrational number that is the ratio of a circle's circumference to its diameter.

The ratio of every circle's circumference $C$ to its diameter $d$ is the same. It has a special symbol, $\pi$, which is pronounced "pie." Both 3.14 and $\frac{22}{7}$ are good approximations for this ratio. Use $\frac{22}{7}$ for $\pi$ when calculations involve fractions, and use 3.14 when they do not.

If you multiply both sides of the equation $\frac{C}{d} = \pi$ by $d$, you get $C = \pi d$, which is a formula for the circumference of a circle.

**Circumference of a Circle**

The circumference of a circle is $\pi$ times the diameter.

$C = \pi d \qquad C = 2\pi r$

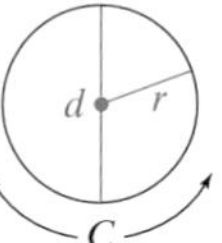


### EXAMPLE 1

**Find the circumference of the circle at the right.**

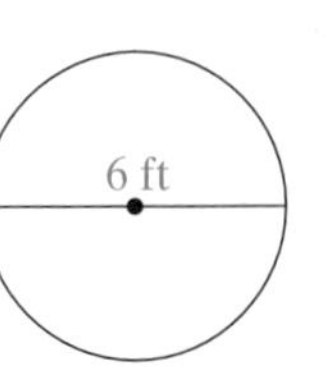


$C = \pi d$ Write the formula.

$C \approx (3.14)6$ Substitute 3.14 for $\pi$ and 6 for $d$.

$= 18.84$ Simplify.

The circumference of the circle is about 18.84 ft.

**TRY THIS** Find the circumference of each circle.

6. diameter = 200 mi about 628 mi
7. radius = 30 mm about 188.4 mm
8. diameter = $2\frac{4}{5}$ in. about $8\frac{4}{5}$ in.

## PART 2 Making Circle Graphs

To make a circle graph, you find the measure of each *central angle*. A **central angle** is an angle whose vertex is the center of a circle. There are 360° in a circle.

### EXAMPLE 2

*Budget* **Make a graph for Juan's weekly budget shown at the left.**

**Juan's Weekly Budget**

| Lunch ($\ell$) | 25% |
|---|---|
| Recreation ($r$) | 20% |
| Clothes ($c$) | 15% |
| Savings ($s$) | 40% |

Use proportions to find the measures of the central angles.

$\frac{25}{100} = \frac{\ell}{360}$ $\quad \frac{20}{100} = \frac{r}{360}$ $\quad \frac{15}{100} = \frac{c}{360}$ $\quad \frac{40}{100} = \frac{s}{360}$

$\ell = 90°$ $\quad r = 72°$ $\quad c = 54°$ $\quad s = 144°$



**• Additional Example 2**

Each week, Jacquie spends 20% of her allowance on entertainment, 20% on food, 10% on transportation, and she saves 50%. Make a circle graph for her budget.

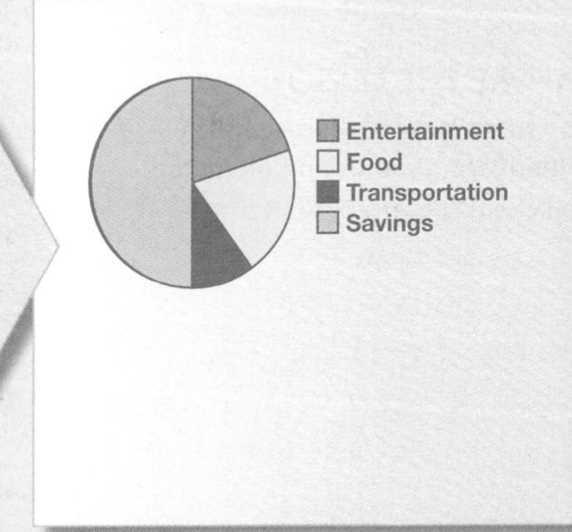

Use a compass to draw a circle. Draw the central angles with a protractor. Label each section. Add a title and necessary information.

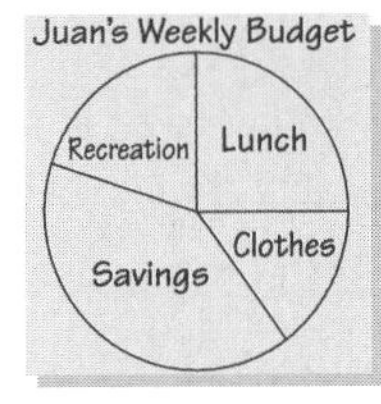


### ■ TRY THIS

9. Draw a circle graph for the data. Round the measure of each central angle to the nearest degree. See margin.

**Blood Types of Population**

| Type A | Type B | Type AB | Type O |
|---|---|---|---|
| 40% | 12% | 5% | 43% |

REAL-WORLD CONNECTION

### ■ EXAMPLE 3

*National Parks* **Draw a circle graph of the data at the right.**

First add to find the total number of visits (in millions).

$0.3 + 0.4 + 1.3 + 1.8 = 3.8$

Use proportions to find the measures of the central angles.

$\frac{0.3}{3.8} = \frac{a}{360°}$ $\frac{0.4}{3.8} = \frac{b}{360°}$ $\frac{1.3}{3.8} = \frac{c}{360°}$ $\frac{1.8}{3.8} = \frac{d}{360°}$

$a \approx 28°$ $b \approx 38°$ $c \approx 123°$ $d \approx 171°$

Use a compass to draw a circle. Draw the central angles with a protractor. Label each section. Add a title and necessary information.

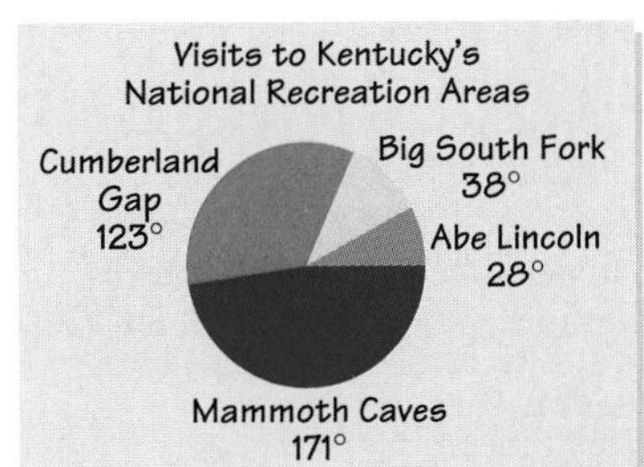


**Visits to Kentucky's National Recreation Areas**

| Site | Visits (millions) |
|---|---|
| Abraham Lincoln's Birthplace | 0.3 |
| Big South Fork | 0.4 |
| Cumberland Gap | 1.3 |
| Mammoth Caves | 1.8 |

### ■ TRY THIS

10. Students at Western High School work in the following places: restaurants, 140; library, 15; auto shop, 60; retail stores, 75; and other places, 30. Draw a circle graph to show where students at Western High School work. Round the measures of the central angles to the nearest degree. See margin.



## Part 2 Teaching Notes

A circle graph is often called a pie graph because the sections look like pieces of pie. A circle can have many different central angles of various measures.

### ■ Example 2

**Build understanding.** Ask: Which part of Juan's budget is easiest to draw on the circle graph? **Lunch takes up about 25%, and 25% = $\frac{1}{4}$, so one fourth of the circle graph is Lunch.**

**Error Prevention** Students may write the percentages the same as the degrees, for example, 50% as 50°. Remind students that in this example they need the number of degrees that equals 50% of the circle, or 50% of 360°, which is 180°.

### ■ Example 3

**Build understanding.** Look at the graph to see which location received close to half of the visitors. How do you know? **Mammoth Caves; its central angle is close to 180°.**

**Tactile Learning** Have students make a puzzle by cutting out the sections of one of their circle graphs and exchanging the pieces with a partner to reassemble into a circle.

**Extension** Have students gather data from their classmates about, for example, everyone's favorite school subject. Have students draw a circle graph to represent their data.

9. Blood Types of Population

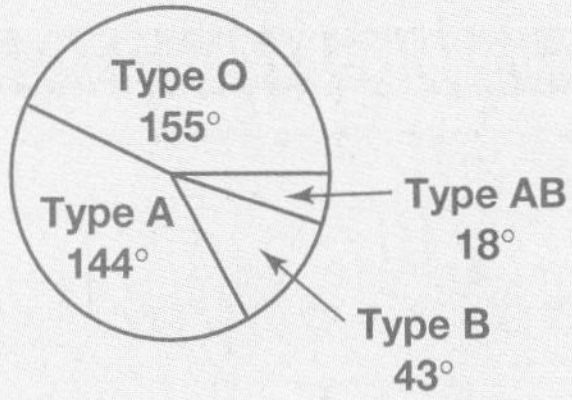


10. Student Jobs at Western High School

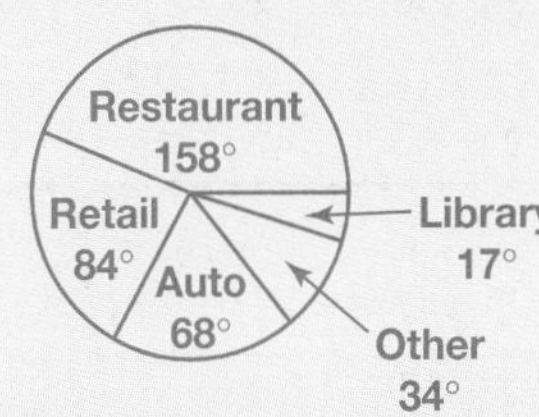


### • Additional Example 3

At the spring dance, there were 120 freshmen, 82 sophomores, 137 juniors, and 101 seniors. Draw a circle graph of the data.

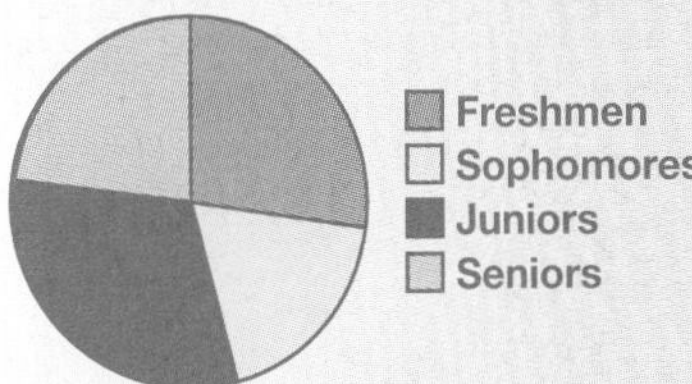


### AFTER THE LESSON

**To assess knowledge:**
**Lesson Quiz**

Find the circumference of each circle.

1. radius = 21 cm $C \approx$ 131.88 cm
2. diameter = 0.25 in. $C \approx$ 0.785 in.

Find the central angle for the given data.

3. Fourteen out of 22 students surveyed preferred milk with their lunch. ≈ 229°

• For enrichment and reteaching options see Resources on p. 439H.

# 3 Practice/Assess

## Assignment Guide

To provide flexible scheduling, this lesson can be divided into parts.

▼ Part 1
**Core** 1–7, 12–17, 23
✪ **Extension** 22, 24

▼ Part 2
**Core** 8–11, 18, 20–21
✪ **Extension** 19

Mixed Review can be assigned at any time for maintenance.

## Exercises

**Test Prep Exercise 23** Calculate (leaving answers in terms of $\pi$) the radius and circumference of both circles.

## ✪ Challenge

Ming's bicycle has 26-in. diameter wheels. How many times do her wheels turn as she rides 1.2 mi from home to school? Round your answer to the nearest whole number. 931 times

## Closure

You can use the formulas $C = \pi d$ and $C = 2\pi r$ to find the circumference of a circle. There are 360° in a circle. An angle whose vertex is the center of a circle is a central angle.

# Exercises

## Check Understanding

**Use the graph at the right.**

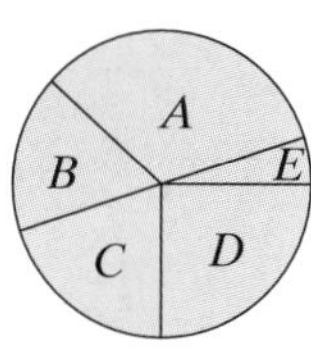


1. *Personal Finance* Nancy spends a third of her salary on rent, a fifth on utilities, a fourth on food, 5% on transportation, and she saves a sixth. Which section of the graph represents rent? Utilities? Food? Transportation? Savings? *A, C, D, E, B*

**Find the circumference of each circle with the given radius or diameter.**

2. radius = 3.5 cm about 21.98 cm
3. diameter = 100 in. about 314 in.
4. radius = $4\frac{2}{3}$ m about $29\frac{1}{3}$ m
5. diameter = 0.1 m about 0.314 m
6. radius = 18 in. about 113.04 in.
7. diameter = 2 mi about 6.28 mi

**Find the measures of the central angles that you would draw to represent each percent in a circle graph. Round to the nearest degree.**

8. 35% 126°
9. 50% 180°
10. 30% 108°
11. 1% 4°

## Practice and Problem Solving

**Find the circumference of each circle with the given radius or diameter.**

12. radius = 25 m about 157 m
13. diameter = 46 yd about 144.44 yd
14. radius = 1,000 mi about 6,280 mi
15. diameter = 6.3 cm about 19.782 cm
16. radius = 90 ft about 565.2 ft
17. diameter = $\frac{1}{2}$ m about $1\frac{4}{7}$ m
18. Find the measures of the central angles that you would draw to represent each percent in a circle graph. no job, 119°; less than \$200, 50°; \$200 to \$399, 90°; \$400 or over, 101°

**What College Students Earn**

| Monthly Income from Jobs | No job | Less than \$200 | \$200 to \$399 | \$400 or over |
|---|---|---|---|---|
| Percent of Total Students | 33% | 14% | 25% | 28% |

✪19. If the total number of college students surveyed in the table above was 10,000, how many students responded "no job"? 3,300

20. *Writing* Write a paragraph to a student who was not in class describing how to make a circle graph. Check students' work



## Daily Cumulative Review

**Given that $\triangle ABC \cong \triangle ZXY$, complete the following.** *(Lesson 9-5)*

1. $\angle A \cong$ $\angle Z$
2. $\angle C \cong$ $\angle Y$
3. $m\angle B =$ $m\angle X$
4. $m\angle C =$ $m\angle Y$
5. $\overline{AB} \cong$ $\overline{ZX}$
6. $\overline{XY} \cong$ $\overline{BC}$
7. $\overline{CA} \cong$ $\overline{YZ}$
8. $\triangle BAC \cong$ $\triangle XZY$

**Solve by drawing a diagram.** *(Lesson 9-4)*

9. Heather walked 3 blocks west to Erin's house. They walked 2 blocks north to the park. Then they walked 8 blocks east to the ice cream parlor. Heather wanted to rent a video, so they walked 4 blocks south to the video store. By the time they picked out a video it was too late to walk home. How many blocks did Heather's mom have to drive to pick them up?
   7 blocks

**Mixed Review**

**Find each percent of change. Tell whether the change is an increase or decrease.**

10. (6-8) from 40 to 63 57.5%; increase
11. (6-8) from 50 to 20 60%; decrease
12. (6-8) from 300 to 900 200%; increase

**Solve each equation.**

13. (7-5) $a + a + a = a + 16$ $a = 8$
14. (7-5) $5(x - 6) = -7(x + 6)$ $x = -1$

**Is the following relation a function? Explain.**

15. (8-1) $\{(-6, 4), (5, 3), (4, -6), (-6, 0), (2, 3)\}$
    There are two range values for the domain value −6.
    This relation is not a function.



## Alternative Assessment

Have students compute the central angles for a set of data. Then have students calculate the length of the circumference for each section of the circle graph with a radius of 10 cm.

21. How Students Travel to School

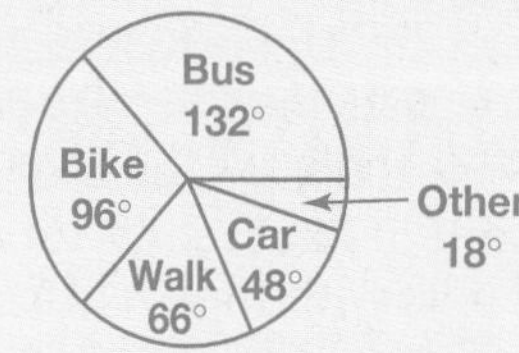


24.

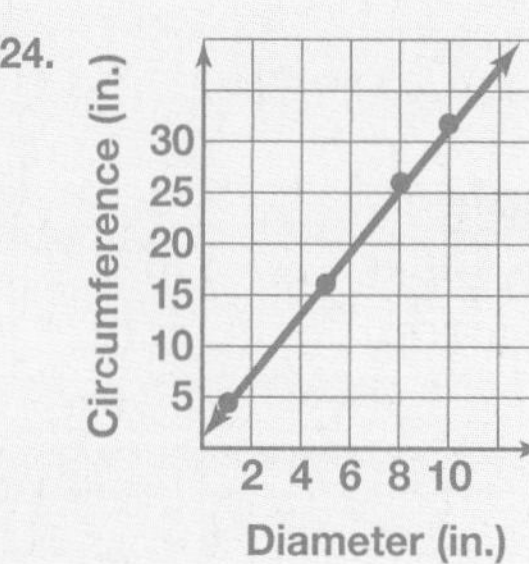

21. The data below show how a group of students travel to school each day. Draw a circle graph for the data. See margin.

**How Students Travel to School**

| Transportation | Walk | Bicycle | Bus | Car | Other |
|---|---|---|---|---|---|
| Number of Students | 55 | 80 | 110 | 40 | 15 |

22. A *tangent* to a circle is a line, segment, or ray in the same plane as the circle and that intersects the circle in exactly one point. A *secant* is a line, segment, or ray that intersects a circle in two points. Use the diagram to identify the following.

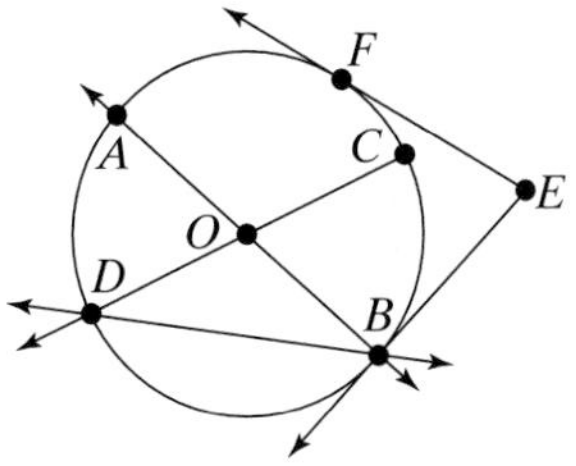


Answers may vary. Sample:

a. one diameter $\overline{DC}$ b. four radii c. two secants $\overleftrightarrow{DB}, \overleftrightarrow{AB}$

d. three chords e. two tangents $\overrightarrow{EF}, \overrightarrow{EB}$ 22d. $\overline{DB}, \overline{AB}, \overline{CD}$

22b. $\overline{OC}, \overline{OD}, \overline{OB}, \overline{OA}$

23. **TEST PREP** The radius of one circle is 7 m. A second circle has a radius twice the length of the radius of the first circle. How many times the circumference of the first circle is the circumference of the second circle? A

A. 2 B. 4 C. 7 D. 14

24. The data at the right represent the circumference and the diameter of four circles of different sizes.

| Diameter | Circumference |
|---|---|
| 1 in. | 3.14 in. |
| 5 in. | 15.7 in. |
| 8 in. | 25.1 in. |
| 10 in. | 31.4 in. |

a. Graph the points on a coordinate plane. Use the diameter as the *x*-coordinate and the circumference as the *y*-coordinate. See margin.

b. Connect the points with a line. See margin.

c. Find the slope of the line. 3.14

d. *Mathematical Reasoning* Explain the meaning of slope in this situation. The slope is the value of $\pi$. For every increase of 1 in. in diameter, the circumference increases by about 3.14 in.

## MIXED REVIEW

**List the congruent corresponding parts of each pair of triangles. Write a congruence statement for the triangles.** ***(Lesson 9-5)***

25.

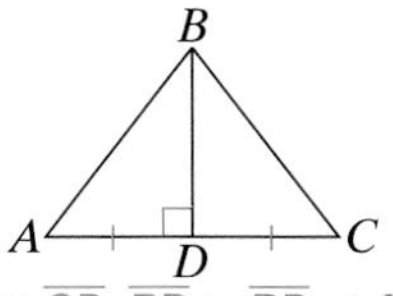


$\overline{AD} \cong \overline{CD}$, $\overline{BD} \cong \overline{BD}$, $\angle ADB \cong \angle CDB$, $\triangle ADB \cong \triangle CDB$ by SAS

26.

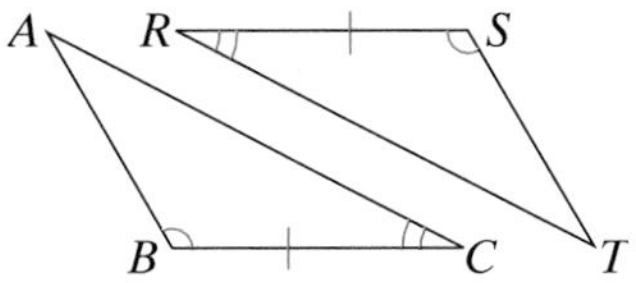


$\angle B \cong \angle S$, $\angle C \cong \angle R$, $\overline{BC} \cong \overline{SR}$, $\triangle ABC \cong \triangle TSR$ by ASA

27.

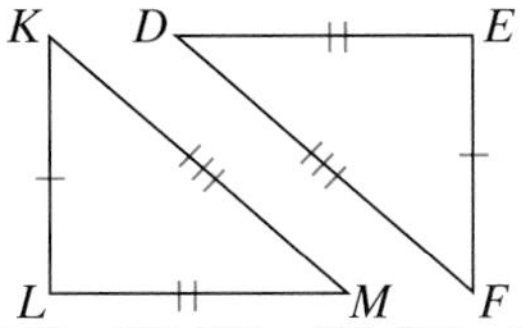


$\overline{KL} \cong \overline{FE}$, $\overline{KM} \cong \overline{FD}$, $\overline{LM} \cong \overline{ED}$, $\triangle KLM \cong \triangle FED$ by SSS

**Is each relation a function? Explain.** ***(Lesson 8-1)***

28. $\{(4, \frac{1}{2}), (6, \frac{1}{2}), (-2, \frac{1}{2})\}$ See below.

29. $\{(1, 0), (1, 5), (1, 3\frac{1}{4})\}$ 29. No; 1 is paired with more than one second element.

30. $\{(3, 7), (5, 11), (8, 17)\}$ Yes; each first element is paired with only one second element.

31. While exercising, your heart beats 32 times in 15 sec. At this rate, how many times will it beat in 2 min? ***(Lesson 6-2)*** 256 times

28. Yes; each first element is paired with only one second element.

See also Extra Practice section.



## Practice

**Find the measures of the central angles that you would draw to represent each percent in a circle graph. Round to the nearest degree.**

| | Voter Preference for Senator | | Central Angle |
|---|---|---|---|
| 1. | Peterson | 40% | 144° |
| 2. | Washington | 30% | 108° |
| 3. | Gomez | 15% | 54° |
| 4. | Thomson | 10% | 36° |
| 5. | Miller | 5% | 18° |

6. Draw a circle graph for the data on voter preference.

Voter Preference for Senator

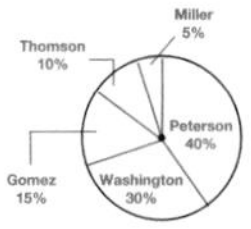


7. The total number of voters surveyed was 5,000. How many voters preferred Gomez? 750

**Find the circumference of each circle with the given radius or diameter. Use 3.14 for $\pi$.**

8. $d = 25.8$ m; $C =$ 81.012 m

9. $r = 9.1$ cm; $C =$ 57.148 cm

10. $r = 0.28$ km; $C =$ 1.7584 km

11. $d = 14$ ft; $C =$ 43.96 ft

12. $d = 5$ in.; $C =$ 15.7 in.

13. $r = \frac{7}{8}$ in.; $C =$ 5.495 in.



## Reteaching

Find the measures of the central angles that you would draw to represent each percent in a circle graph. Round to the nearest degree.

| Employment Distribution in California | | | | |
|---|---|---|---|---|
| Service | Trade | Manufacturing | Government | Other |
| 31% | 23% | 15% | 17% | 14% |

You can use proportions to find the measures of the central angles. You also can use equations.

What is 31% of 360?
$n = (0.31)(360)$
$n = 112°$

What is 23% of 360?
$n = (0.23)(360)$
$n = 83°$

What is 15% of 360?
$n = (0.15)(360)$
$n = 54°$

What is 17% of 360?
$n = (0.17)(360)$
$n = 61°$

What is 14% of 360?
$n = (0.14)(360)$
$n = 50°$

**Find the measures of the central angle that you would draw to represent each percent in a circle graph. Round to the nearest degree.**

| | Employment Distribution in Texas | | Measure of central angle |
|---|---|---|---|
| 1. | Service | 27% | 97° |
| 2. | Trade | 24% | 86° |
| 3. | Manufacturing | 13% | 47° |
| 4. | Government | 18% | 65° |
| 5. | Other | 18% | 65° |



## Enrichment

Mercury, the planet nearest the sun, orbits the sun at an average distance of $3.6 \times 10^7$ mi. Its average speed in orbit is $1.07 \times 10^5$ mi/h.

**Solve. Use 3.14 for $\pi$. Give answers in scientific notation rounded to three decimal places unless otherwise instructed.**

1. Find the circumference of Mercury's orbit. $2.261 \times 10^8$ mi

2. Find the number of hours it takes Mercury to complete one orbit of the sun. $2.113 \times 10^3$ h

3. Convert the above answer to days. Round to the nearest day and express your answer in standard form. 88 days

A "year" on a planet is the length of time it takes the planet to travel once around the sun. One Earth year is about 365 days.

4. About how many Mercury years are there in one Earth year? Round to the nearest year. 4 yr

5. Find your age in Mercury years. Student's age × 4

Pluto, the planet farthest from the sun, orbits the sun at an average distance of $3.67 \times 10^9$ mi. Its average speed in orbit is $1.06 \times 10^4$ mi/h.

6. What is the circumference of Pluto's orbit? $2.305 \times 10^{10}$ mi

7. What is the length of a year on Pluto in days, rounded to the nearest day? 90,596 days

8. What is the number of Earth years in one Pluto year, rounded to the nearest year? 248 yr

9. What is your age in Pluto years? Student's age ÷ 248

# 9-7

## Getting Ready

**Key Terms and Symbols**
segment bisector, perpendicular lines, perpendicular bisector, angle bisector

**Resources** A complete list of resources for this lesson is on p. 439H.

### Daily Skills Warm-Up

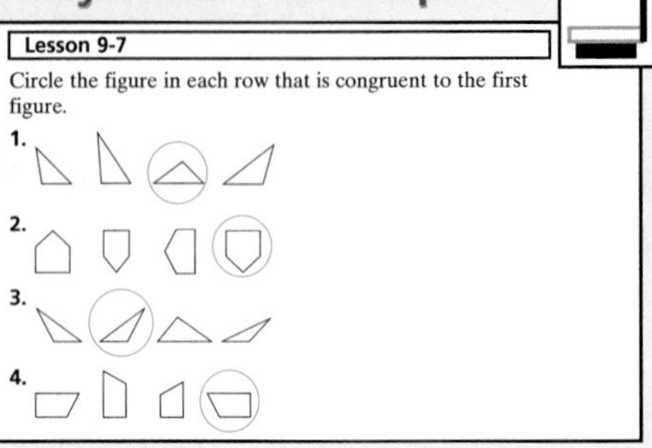

Lesson 9-7
Circle the figure in each row that is congruent to the first figure.
1.
2.
3.
4.


### Background for the Lesson

When you do geometric construction, you draft a figure using only two tools, a compass and an unmarked straightedge (which cannot be used for measuring). Euclid stated these limitations on a construction in his book *Elements* about 300 B.C. With the compass, you can compare two lengths, though you cannot measure them in units. Draw a construction carefully with a fine pencil to approach the ideal of lines and points without width and to find the points of intersection accurately.

## 1 Focus

### Connecting to Students' Lives

Ask students to describe situations where they have had to repeat a certain measurement, but they did not have a ruler or tape measure. How were they able to repeat the measurement?

### Connecting to Prior Knowledge

In Lesson 9-5, students learned the definition of congruent geometric figures. In this lesson, they learn how to construct congruent segments and angles. In Lesson 9-8, they will apply their knowledge of congruent lines and angles to translations.



# 9-7 Constructions

**What You'll Learn**

1. To construct a segment or angle congruent to a given segment or angle
2. To construct segment bisectors and angle bisectors

**. . . And Why**

To construct precise drawings such as those that architects use

## Part 1 Congruent Segments and Angles

In constructions, you use only a *compass* and *straightedge* (an unmarked ruler) to accurately copy a segment or an angle. A compass is a tool used to draw circles or parts of circles. An *arc* is part of a circle.

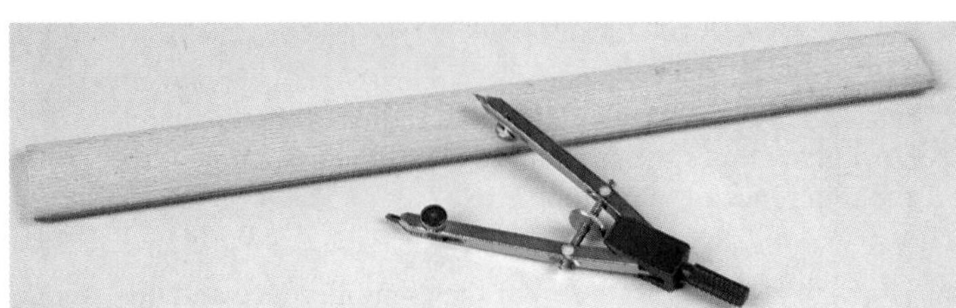

To work with a compass easily, here is one way of holding it.

### Example 1

**Construct a segment congruent to $\overline{AB}$.**

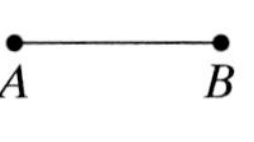


**Step 1** Draw a ray with endpoint $C$.

**Step 2** Open the compass to the length of $\overline{AB}$.

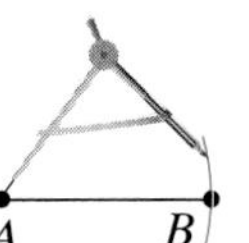


**Step 3** With the *same* compass setting, put the compass tip on $C$. Draw an arc that intersects the ray. Label the intersection $D$.

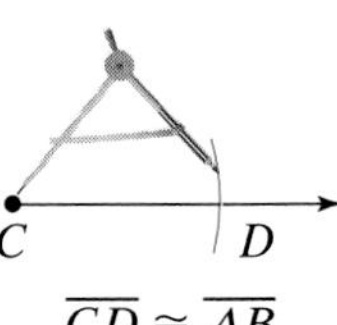


$\overline{CD} \cong \overline{AB}$

### Try This

1. Draw a segment. Construct a segment twice the length of the segment you drew. See margin.



# Tools to Monitor Progress

**BEFORE THE LESSON**

**To check prerequisite skills:**

- Constructing angles

**Skills Intervention Kit,** Geometry

**DURING THE LESSON**

**To check understanding:**

**Try This** exercises on student page

- **Additional Examples 1–4**

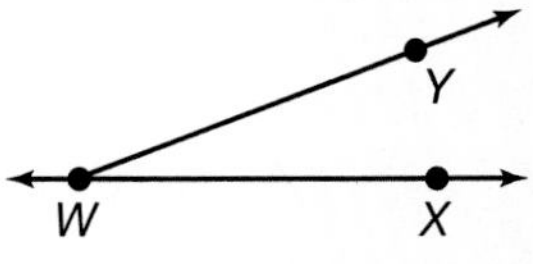


Draw a diagram similar to this one. Then construct each figure.

## Example 2

**Construct an angle congruent to $\angle E$.**

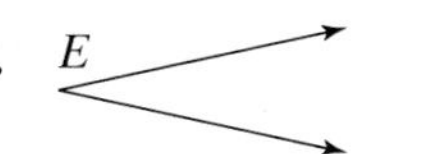


**Step 1** Draw a ray with endpoint $Q$.

**Step 2** With the compass point at $E$, draw an arc that intersects the sides of $\angle E$. Label the intersection points $F$ and $G$.

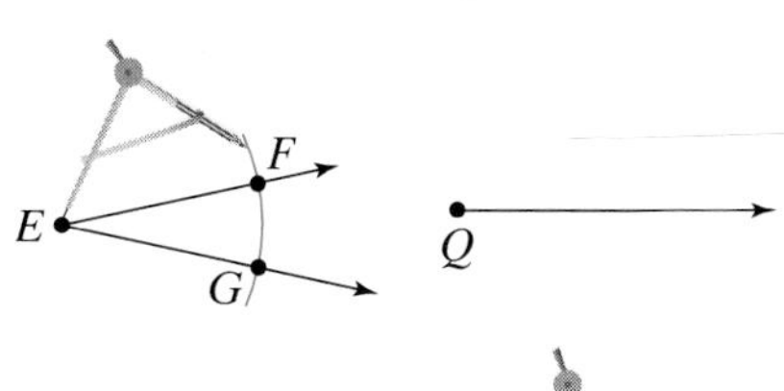


**Step 3** With the *same* compass setting, put the compass tip at $Q$. Draw an arc intersecting the ray at point $P$.

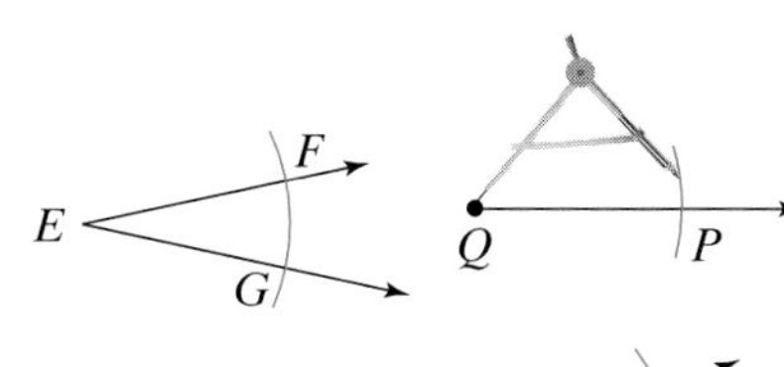


**Step 4** Open the compass to the length of $\overline{FG}$. Using this setting, put the compass tip at $P$. Draw an arc to determine the point $R$. Draw $\overrightarrow{QR}$.

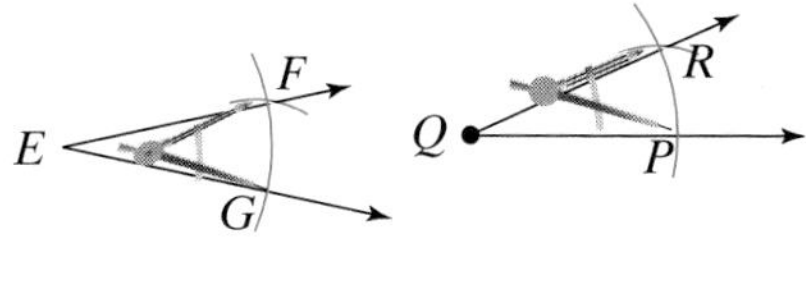


$\angle Q \cong \angle E$

## Try This

2. Draw an obtuse angle. Construct an angle congruent to the angle you drew. See margin.

## Constructing Bisectors

The figures below show some special relationships intersecting lines may have.

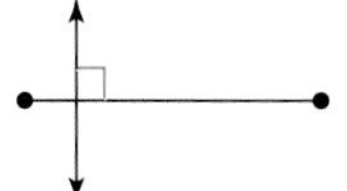

**Perpendicular lines**, segments, or rays intersect to form right angles.

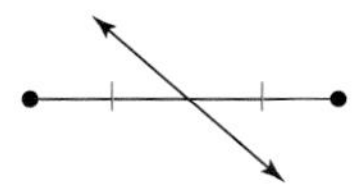

A **segment bisector** is a line, segment, or ray that divides a segment into two congruent segments.

A **perpendicular bisector** is a line, segment, or ray that is perpendicular to the segment it bisects.

**Reading Math**

To *bisect* means to divide into two equal parts. Therefore a segment bisector divides a segment into two congruent parts.



# 2 Teach

## Part 1 Teaching Notes

Review with students the proper use of a compass.

### Example 1

**Build understanding.** Ask: How far is every point on the circumference of a circle from its center? the length of the radius

**Reading Math** An arc is a curve or part of a circle. When you use a compass to mark distances, you do so by making an arc with the compass.

**ELL** The word *compass* has two very different meanings. One is used to draw circles and the other to indicate direction. If possible, show a magnetic compass that points north so that students can see both instruments.

### Example 2

**Build understanding.** Ask: After you mark points $F$ and $G$, what do you know about $\overline{EF}$ and $\overline{EG}$? Why? They are congruent because each is a radius of the same circle.

**Math Reasoning** When constructing a congruent angle, you start by placing the compass point on the vertex of the original angle, then you draw an arc that intersects both sides of the angle. Explain why you can choose any size opening for the compass in this step. You need to mark two equal segments on the sides of the angle; how long they are doesn't matter as long as they are equal.

1.

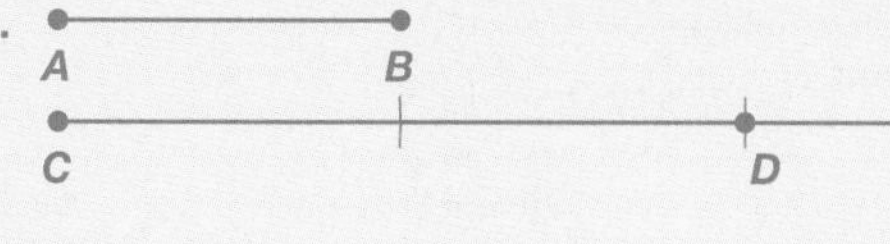


2.

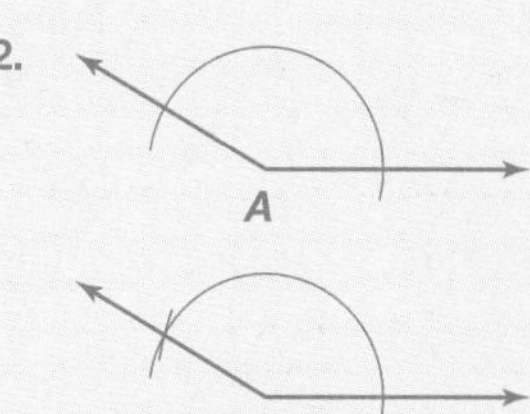


a. $\overline{GH}$ congruent to $\overline{WX}$.
b. $\angle BAC$ congruent to $\angle YWX$
c. the perpendicular bisector of $\overline{WY}$
d. the bisector of $\angle YWX$
a–d. Check students' work.

### AFTER THE LESSON

**To assess knowledge: Lesson Quiz**

Draw and construct the figures.

1. Draw $\overline{QR}$; then construct $\overline{ST} \cong \overline{QR}$.
2. Draw $\angle LMN$; then construct $\angle UVW \cong \angle LMN$.
3. Construct the bisectors of $\overline{ST}$ and $\angle UVW$. 1–3. Check students' work.

- For enrichment and reteaching options see Resources on 439H.

## Part 2 Teaching Notes

A bisector divides a segment or an angle in half, forming two congruent segments or angles. Discuss why constructing a bisector might be useful.

### Example 3

**Build understanding.** Ask: Why do you think it is important to choose a compass opening to more than half the length of $\overline{PQ}$? so the arcs will overlap to form a point of intersection

**Auditory Learning** Read aloud a statement such as "ray *FG* bisects angle *DFH*" and ask students to construct the bisector. Ask students to describe aloud the constructions they make.

### Example 4

**Build understanding.** Write a statement of congruence for the two angles formed by the bisector. $\angle CAD \cong \angle BAD$

**Advanced Learners** Suppose that in Example 4 you use the same compass setting you use to mark point *D* from points *B* and *C* to also make intersecting arcs from points *B* and *C* at a point *E* on the other side of *A*, outside the angle. Would $\overrightarrow{EA}$ be a bisector of $\angle BAC$? Explain. Yes, because point *E* would be on the same line that contains $\overrightarrow{AD}$.

### Example 3

**Construct the perpendicular bisector of $\overline{PQ}$ at the left.**

**Step 1** Open the compass to more than half of the length of $\overline{PQ}$. Put the compass tip at *P*. Draw an arc above and below $\overline{PQ}$. With the same compass setting, repeat from point *Q*.

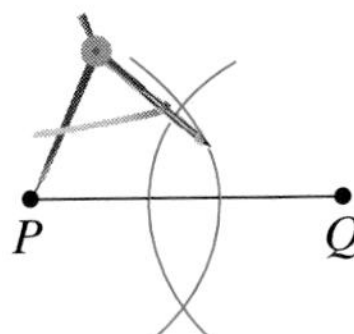


**Step 2** Label the points of intersection *S* and *T*. Draw $\overleftrightarrow{ST}$. Label the intersection of $\overleftrightarrow{ST}$ and $\overline{PQ}$ point *M*.

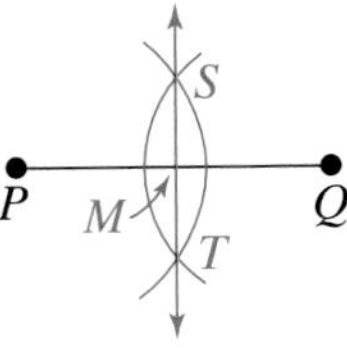


$\overleftrightarrow{ST}$ bisects $\overline{PQ}$.

### Try This

3. Draw a segment. Construct its perpendicular bisector. See margin.

An **angle bisector** is a ray that divides an angle into two congruent angles.

### Example 4

**Construct the bisector of $\angle A$ at the left.**

**Step 1** Put the compass tip at *A*. Draw an arc that intersects the sides of $\angle A$. Label the points of intersection *B* and *C*.

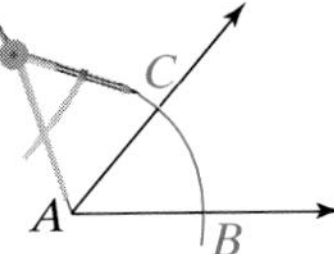


**Step 2** Put the compass tip at *B*. Draw an arc. With the same compass setting, repeat with the compass tip at *C*. Make sure the arcs intersect. Label the intersection of the arcs *D*. Draw $\overrightarrow{AD}$.

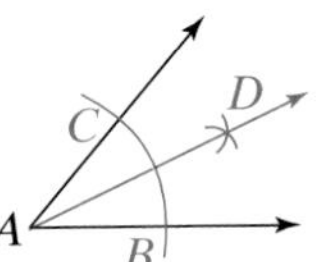


$\overrightarrow{AD}$ bisects $\angle BAC$.

### Try This

4. Draw an obtuse angle. Construct its angle bisector. See margin.



3.

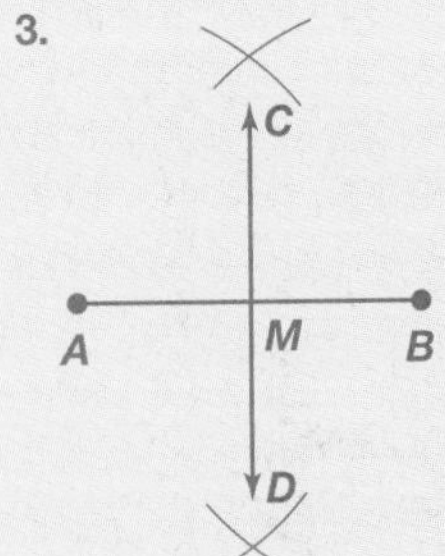


4.

# Exercises

## Check Understanding

**Draw a diagram similar to the one at the right. Then construct each figure.** 1–2. See margin. 3–4. See back of book.

1. $\overline{EF}$ congruent to $\overline{XY}$
2. $\overline{GH}$ half the length of $\overline{XY}$
3. $\angle D$ congruent to $\angle A$
4. $\angle I$ so that $m\angle I = 2m\angle A$
5. $\triangle RST$ with two sides congruent to $\overline{XY}$ and an angle formed by the two sides congruent to $\angle A$. See right.

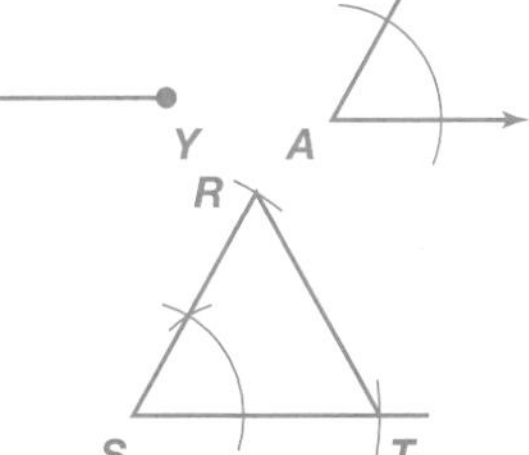


6. Draw $\overline{DE}$ at least 4 in. long. Then construct its perpendicular bisector. See back of book.

## Practice and Problem Solving

**For Exercises 7–11, draw a figure like the ones at the right. Then construct each figure.**

7. $\overline{PQ}$ congruent to $\overline{CD}$ See below right.
8. $\overline{MN}$ three times the length of $\overline{CD}$ See below right.
9. $\angle Y$ congruent to $\angle X$ 9–13. See back of book.
10. $\angle T$ half the measure of $\angle X$
11. $\triangle ABF$ with two angles congruent to $\angle X$
12. Construct a 90° angle.
13. Construct a 45° angle.
14. *Writing* How are constructing a segment bisector and constructing an angle bisector alike? 14. Put the compass on the edges of the segment or angle and open the compass more than half of the distance between the points.
15. The bisector of $\angle XYZ$ is $\overrightarrow{YN}$. If the measure of $\angle XYN$ is 55°, what is the measure of $\angle XYZ$? 110°
16. $\overleftrightarrow{BC}$ is the perpendicular bisector of $\overline{RP}$ at point $N$. Name two congruent segments. $\overline{RN}, \overline{NP}$
17. $\overrightarrow{DB}$ is the bisector of $\angle CDE$. Name two congruent angles. $\angle CDB, \angle BDE$
18. *Open-ended* Use your compass to create a design. Decorate your design. Check students' work



# 3 Practice/Assess

## Assignment Guide

To provide flexible scheduling, this lesson can be divided into parts.

**Part 1**
**Core** 1–5, 7–11

**Part 2**
**Core** 6, 14–18
**Extension** 12–13, 19, 20

Mixed Review can be assigned at any time for maintenance.

## Exercises

**Exercises 12–13** A perpendicular bisector intersects a line to form right angles. A 45° angle is half of a 90° angle.

## Challenge

Explain how you could use constructions to construct a triangle congruent to $\triangle ABC$. First, construct $\angle DEF$ congruent to $\angle ABC$. Then, construct $\overline{EG}$ congruent to $\overline{AB}$ on $\overrightarrow{ED}$. Next, construct $\overline{EH}$ congruent to $\overline{BC}$ on $\overrightarrow{EF}$. Finally, draw $\overline{GH}$ to complete $\triangle GEH$.

## Closure

You can use a compass and a straightedge to construct congruent segments, congruent angles, segment bisectors, and angle bisectors.

## Alternative Assessment

Give students a sketch of a rectangle. Tell them to use what they know about constructions to construct a rectangle with exactly half the area of the given rectangle.

2.

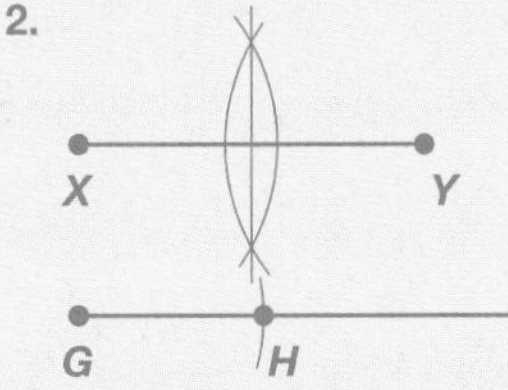


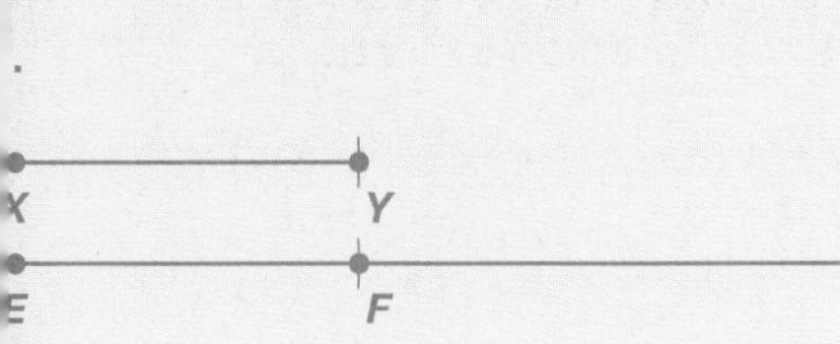


## Daily Cumulative Review

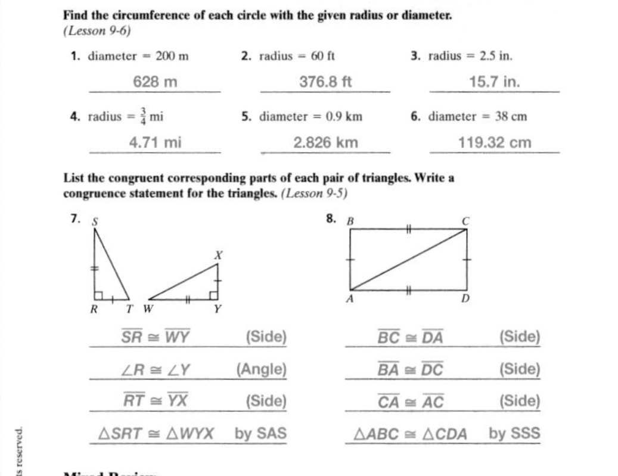

**Find the circumference of each circle with the given radius or diameter.** *(Lesson 9-6)*

1. diameter = 200 m 628 m
2. radius = 60 ft 376.8 ft
3. radius = 2.5 in. 15.7 in.
4. radius = $\frac{3}{4}$ mi 4.71 mi
5. diameter = 0.9 km 2.826 km
6. diameter = 38 cm 119.32 cm

**List the congruent corresponding parts of each pair of triangles. Write a congruence statement for the triangles.** *(Lesson 9-5)*

7.
$\overline{SR} \cong \overline{WY}$ (Side)
$\angle R \cong \angle Y$ (Angle)
$\overline{RT} \cong \overline{YX}$ (Side)
$\triangle SRT \cong \triangle WYX$ by SAS

8.
$\overline{BC} \cong \overline{DA}$ (Side)
$\overline{BA} \cong \overline{DC}$ (Side)
$\overline{CA} \cong \overline{AC}$ (Side)
$\triangle ABC \cong \triangle CDA$ by SSS

**Mixed Review**

**Graph each point.**

9. $K(2, -3)$
10. $L(5, 0)$
11. $M(0, -5)$
12. $P(-2, -1)$
13. $R(-3, 4)$
14. $S(3, 5)$
15. $T(4, 4)$
16. $U(1, -3)$

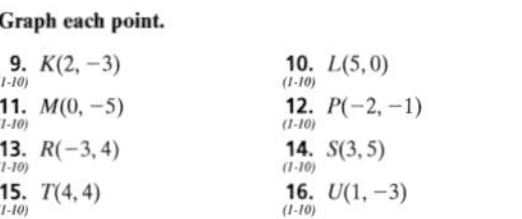

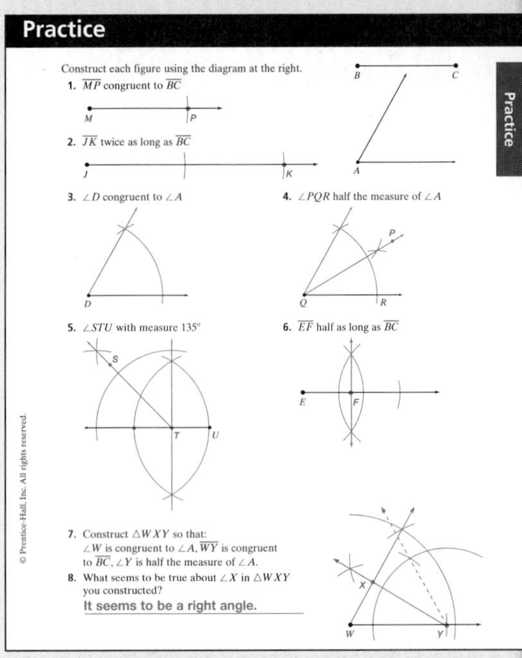

## Practice

Construct each figure using the diagram at the right.

1. $\overline{MP}$ congruent to $\overline{BC}$
2. $\overline{JK}$ twice as long as $\overline{BC}$
3. $\angle D$ congruent to $\angle A$
4. $\angle PQR$ half the measure of $\angle A$
5. $\angle STU$ with measure 135°
6. $\overline{EF}$ half as long as $\overline{BC}$
7. Construct $\triangle WXY$ so that: $\angle W$ is congruent to $\angle A$, $\overline{WY}$ is congruent to $\overline{BC}$, $\angle Y$ is half the measure of $\angle A$.
8. What seems to be true about $\angle X$ in $\triangle WXY$ you constructed? It seems to be a right angle.





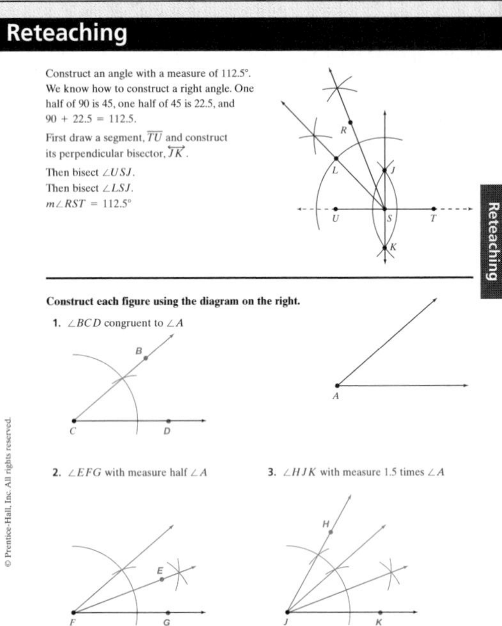

## Reteaching

Construct an angle with a measure of 112.5°. We know how to construct a right angle. One half of 90 is 45, one half of 45 is 22.5, and 90 + 22.5 = 112.5.

First draw a segment, $\overline{TU}$ and construct its perpendicular bisector, $\overleftrightarrow{JK}$.

Then bisect $\angle USJ$.
Then bisect $\angle LSJ$.
$m\angle RST = 112.5°$

**Construct each figure using the diagram on the right.**

1. $\angle BCD$ congruent to $\angle A$
2. $\angle EFG$ with measure half $\angle A$
3. $\angle HJK$ with measure 1.5 times $\angle A$





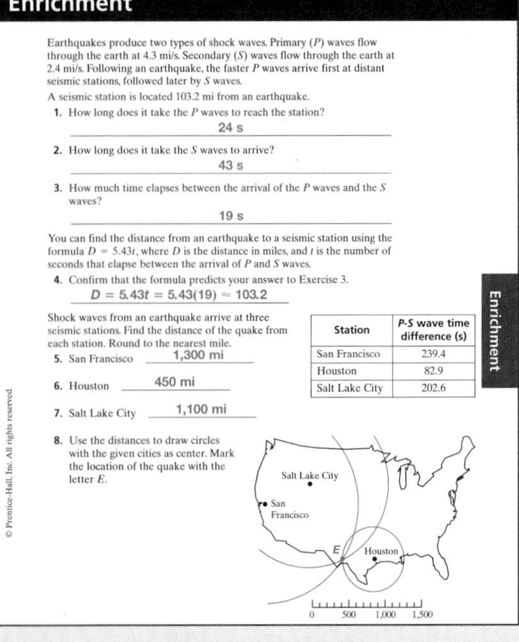

## Enrichment

Earthquakes produce two types of shock waves. Primary ($P$) waves flow through the earth at 4.3 mi/s. Secondary ($S$) waves flow through the earth at 2.4 mi/s. Following an earthquake, the faster $P$ waves arrive first at distant seismic stations, followed later by $S$ waves.

A seismic station is located 103.2 mi from an earthquake.

1. How long does it take the $P$ waves to reach the station? 24 s
2. How long does it take the $S$ waves to arrive? 43 s
3. How much time elapses between the arrival of the $P$ waves and the $S$ waves? 19 s

You can find the distance from an earthquake to a seismic station using the formula $D = 5.43t$, where $D$ is the distance in miles, and $t$ is the number of seconds that elapse between the arrival of $P$ and $S$ waves.

4. Confirm that the formula predicts your answer to Exercise 3. $D = 5.43t = 5.43(19) \approx 103.2$

Shock waves from an earthquake arrive at three seismic stations. Find the distance of the quake from each station. Round to the nearest mile.

5. San Francisco 1,300 mi
6. Houston 450 mi
7. Salt Lake City 1,100 mi

| Station | P-S wave time difference (s) |
|---|---|
| San Francisco | 239.4 |
| Houston | 82.9 |
| Salt Lake City | 202.6 |

8. Use the distances to draw circles with the given cities as center. Mark the location of the quake with the letter $E$.







19. To construct a perpendicular line (or segment) from a point to a line, start by placing your compass tip at the point. Open your compass far enough to draw an arc that intersects the line in two points. Construct the perpendicular bisector of the segment between the two arcs.
    a. Draw a point and a line. Construct the perpendicular segment from the point to the line. See margin.
    b. An *altitude* of a triangle is a perpendicular segment from a vertex to a line containing the side opposite the vertex. Draw a large acute triangle. Construct the three altitudes of the triangle. Check students' work

20. Draw $\triangle PQR$. To construct $\triangle ABC$ congruent to $\triangle PQR$, first construct $\overline{AB}$ congruent to $\overline{PQ}$. Use a compass setting the length of $\overline{PR}$. Draw an arc with the compass tip at $A$. Then use a compass setting the length of $\overline{QR}$. With the compass tip at $B$ draw an arc that intersects the first arc. Label the intersection $C$. Draw $\overline{AC}$ and $\overline{BC}$. See back of book.

## Mixed Review

**Find the measure of the central angle that would represent each percent in a circle graph. Round your answer to the nearest degree. *(Lesson 9-6)***

21. 12% 43°
22. 45% 162°
23. 5% 18°
24. 25% 90°

**Find the simple interest. *(Lesson 7-8)***

25. \$1,000 deposited at an interest rate of 2% for 3 years \$60
26. \$150 deposited at an interest rate of 4% for 6 months \$3

27. Find two numbers with a sum of 25 and with a difference of 15. ***(Lesson 8-7)*** 5 and 20

## Chapter Project 9 — Activity 2 Constructing

Here is the second clue: *The treasure is on an island 22 miles from Everett.* Construct a figure that contains all the points 22 miles from Everett. According to the first two clues, on which islands could the treasure be buried? Explain. Sapelo Island or St. Simons Island; a circle with radius 22 miles passed through these two.

 See also Extra Practice section.

19a.

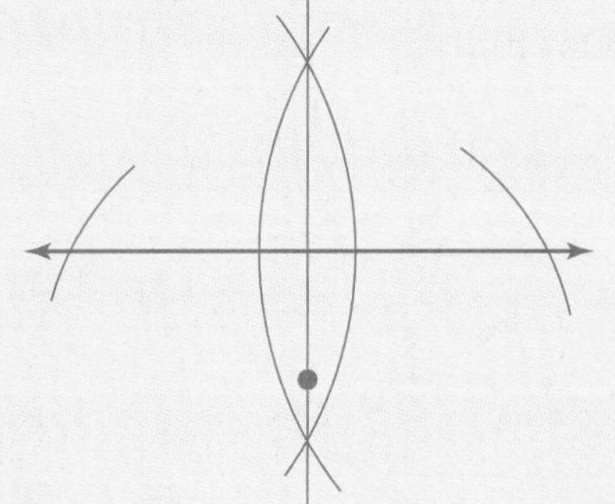

### Project Activity 2

**Constructing** Tell students that the only tool they need to construct the figure for this activity is a compass. Students should measure a distance of 21 miles on the map's key with their compass, then draw a circle with a radius of 21 miles centered on Everett.

# Translations

## PART 1 Graphing Translations

You can move pattern blocks by sliding them, flipping them, or turning them. Each of these moves is a type of transformation. A **transformation** is a change of position or size of a figure.

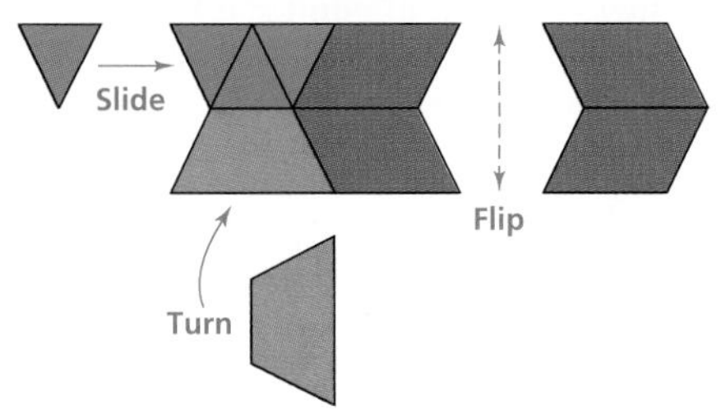


A **translation** is a transformation that moves points the same distance and in the same direction. A figure and its translated image are congruent. You can see examples of translations or slides in wallpaper, fabric, and wrapping paper.

The figure you get after a transformation is called the **image.** To name the image of a point, you use prime notation. The figure at the right shows the translation of $A$ to its image $A'$.

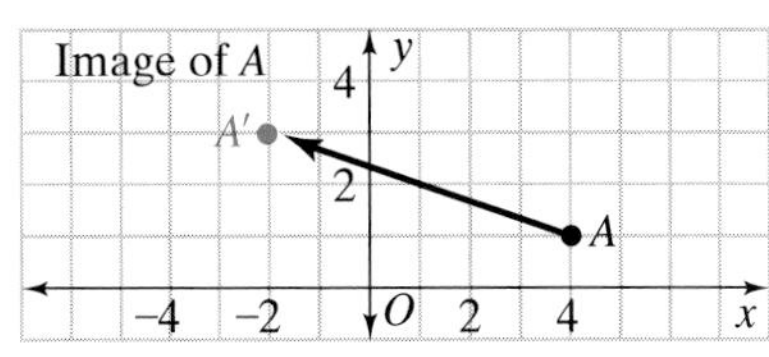


### EXAMPLE 1

**Graph the image of $\triangle KRT$ after a translation 5 units to the right and 3 units down.**

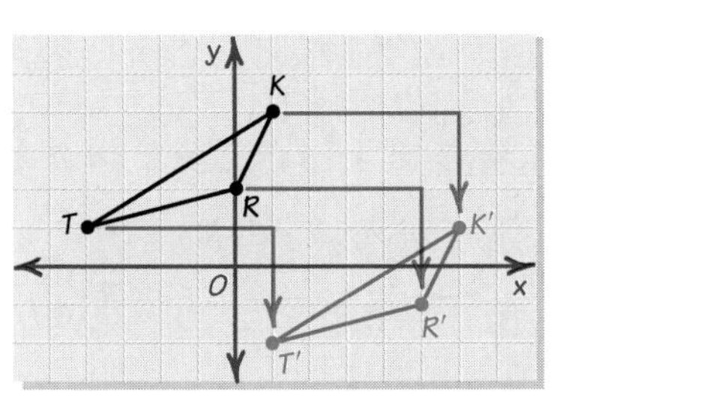


### TRY THIS

1. On a coordinate plane, draw $\triangle KRT$. Graph the image of $\triangle KRT$ after a translation 4 units to the left and 5 units down. See back of book.

# 9-8

### What You'll Learn

1 To graph translations

2 To describe translations

### . . . And Why

To use translations in describing real-world situations, such as moves in a chess game



# Tools to Monitor Progress

## BEFORE THE LESSON

**To check prerequisite skills:**

- Graphing on the coordinate plane

**Skills You Need,** p. 439

## DURING THE LESSON

**To check understanding:**

**Try This** exercises on student page

- **Additional Examples 1–3**

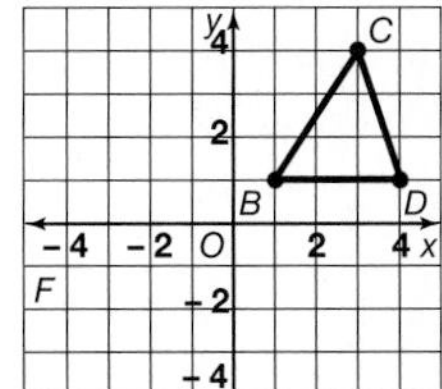


See p. 480 for questions.

# 9-8

## Getting Ready

### Key Terms and Symbols

transformation, translation, image

**Materials** pattern blocks

**Resources** A complete list of resources for this lesson is on p. 439H.

### Daily Skills Warm-Up

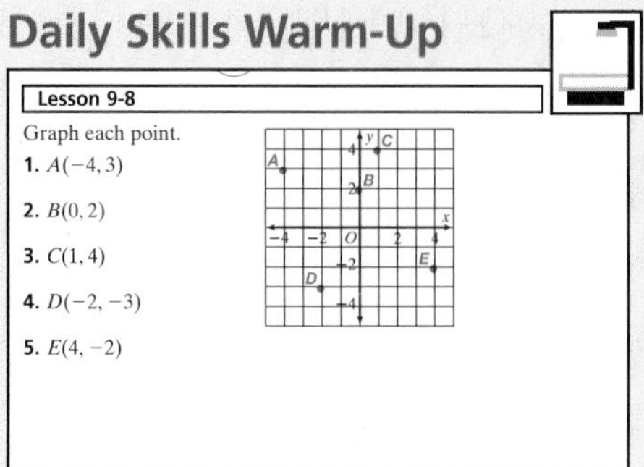

Lesson 9-8

Graph each point.

1. $A(-4, 3)$
2. $B(0, 2)$
3. $C(1, 4)$
4. $D(-2, -3)$
5. $E(4, -2)$

### Background for the Lesson

Transformation geometry is the study of changes in a figure. Three kinds of transformation, called the *rigid motions*: translation (or slides), rotation (or turns), and reflection (or flips) do not change either the shape or the size of the figure. In a translation, the figure moves from one position to another on the coordinate plane without changing size or shape. All points in the figure move the same distance in the same direction.

## 1 Focus

### Connecting to Students' Lives

Ask any students who play chess to describe the moves made by the different chess pieces. These moves are similar to the translation of figures on a plane.

### Connecting to Prior Knowledge

In Lesson 9-7, students learned how to construct congruent geometric figures. In this lesson, students learn how to move figures with translations. In Lessons 9-9 and 9-10, students will learn how to rotate and reflect figures.

# 2 Teach

## Part 1 Teaching Notes

Because all points on a figure move the same distance and direction in a translation, the figure retains its shape and size.

### Example 1

**Build understanding.** Suppose you wanted to translate $\Delta K'R'T'$ to an image that is in Quadrant IV (or on the axis) of the coordinate plane. What is the direction and distance of the smallest move that would do this? down one unit

**Error Prevention** When students translate figures, they may not move all points in the figure the same distance and direction. Suggest that students move each named point independently before drawing the image.

## Part 2 Teaching Notes

When you read ordered pairs, the first coordinate is the *x*-coordinate and the second coordinate is the *y*-coordinate.

### Example 2

**Build understanding.** Ask: Describe in words, using "maps onto," the action represented by the arrow in $A(2, 1) \rightarrow A'(3, -1)$. Explain. The point (2, 1) maps onto the point (3, −1). The point *A* translates, or moves, to the point *A'*.

### Example 3

**Build understanding.** Ask: Which coordinate does the horizontal translation affect? Which coordinate does the vertical translation affect? The horizontal translation affects the *x*-coordinate, and the vertical translation affects the *y*-coordinate.

## Part 2 Describing Translations

You can describe a transformation using arrow (→) notation, which describes the *mapping* of a figure onto its image.

### Example 2

**The movement of point *P* is both horizontal and vertical. Use arrow notation to describe this translation.**

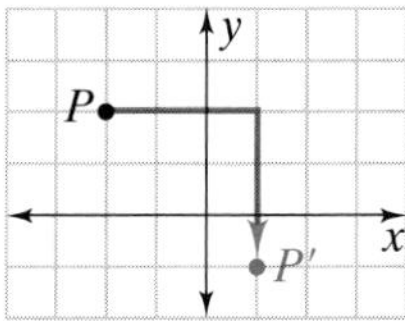


The point moves from $P(-2, 2)$ to $P'(1, -1)$, so the translation is $P(-2, 2) \rightarrow P'(1, -1)$.

### Try This

2. Use arrow notation to describe a translation of $B(-1, 5)$ to $B'(3, 1)$. $B(-1, 5) \rightarrow B'(3, 1)$

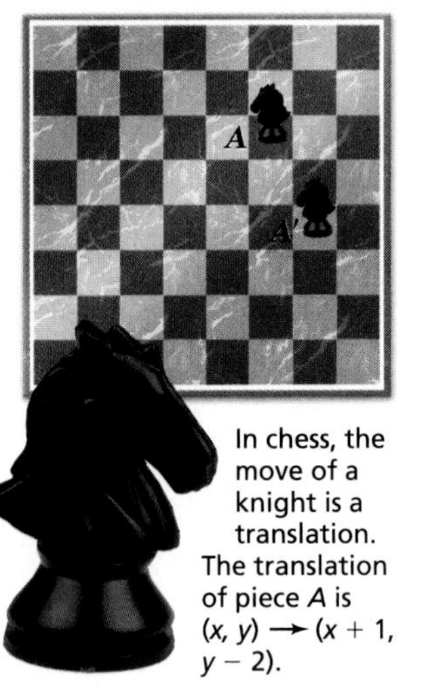


In chess, the move of a knight is a translation. The translation of piece *A* is $(x, y) \rightarrow (x + 1, y - 2)$.

You can also use arrow notation to write a general rule that describes a transformation. To write a rule for a translation, choose corresponding points on a figure and its image. Subtract the coordinates of the preimage from the coodinates of the image.

### Example 3

**Write a rule to describe the translation of $\Delta PQR$ to $\Delta P'Q'R'$.**

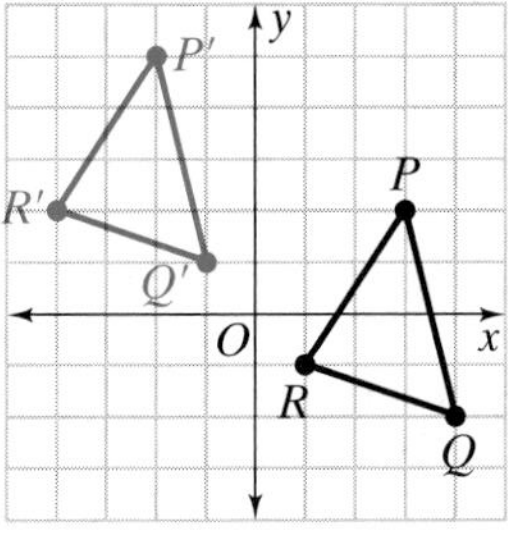


Use $P(3, 2)$ and its image $P'(-2, 5)$ to find the horizontal and vertical translations.

Horizontal translation: $-2 - 3 = -5$

Vertical translation: $5 - 2 = 3$

The rule is $(x, y) \rightarrow (x - 5, y + 3)$.

### Try This

3. Write a rule to describe the translation of quadrilateral $ABCD$ to quadrilateral $A'B'C'D'$. $(x, y) \rightarrow (x + 5, y - 1)$

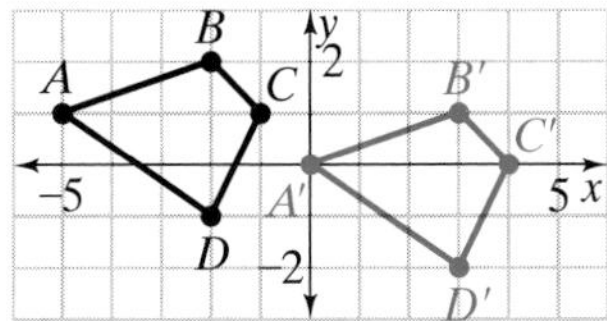




a. Graph the image of $\Delta BCD$ that is left 3 units and down 4 units. $B'(-2, -3)$; $C'(0, 0)$; $D'(1, -3)$

b. Use arrow notation to describe the above translation of *C* to *C'*. $C(3, 4) \rightarrow C'(0, 0)$

c. Write a rule to describe the translation of $\Delta BCD$ to $\Delta B'C'D'$. $(x, y) \rightarrow (x - 3, y - 4)$

## AFTER THE LESSON

**To assess knowledge:**

**Lesson Quiz**

The endpoints of a segment and a translation are given. Graph the segment and its image.

1. $Q(-2, 1)$, $R(1, -1)$; 2 units up and 3 units right $Q'(1, 3)$; $R'(4, 1)$
2. Write a rule for the translation. $(x, y) \rightarrow (x + 3, y + 2)$

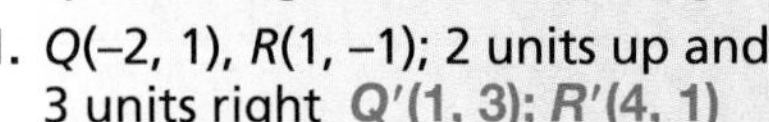

- For enrichment and reteaching options see Resources on p. 439H.

# Exercises

## CHECK UNDERSTANDING

**Complete with *horizontal* or *vertical* to make a true statement.**

1. In a _?_ translation, the $y$-coordinate changes and the $x$-coordinate stays the same. vertical
2. In a _?_ translation, the $x$-coordinate changes and the $y$-coordinate stays the same. horizontal

**The endpoints of a segment and a translation are given. Graph each segment and its image.** 3. See margin. 4–8. See back of book.

3. $A(0, 0), B(0, 5)$; 2 units left
4. $C(0, 0), D(0, 2)$; 2 units up
5. $E(0, 0), F(2, 0)$; 4 units down
6. $G(0, 0), H(-4, 0)$; 4 units up
7. $J(0, 0), K(5, 5)$; 1 unit right
8. $L(-1, 3), M(2, 1)$; 5 units left

**Write a rule to describe each translation.**

9.
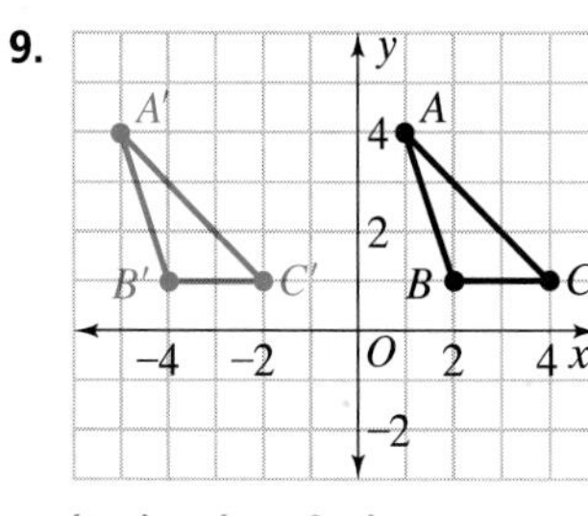


$(x, y) \rightarrow (x - 6, y)$

10.
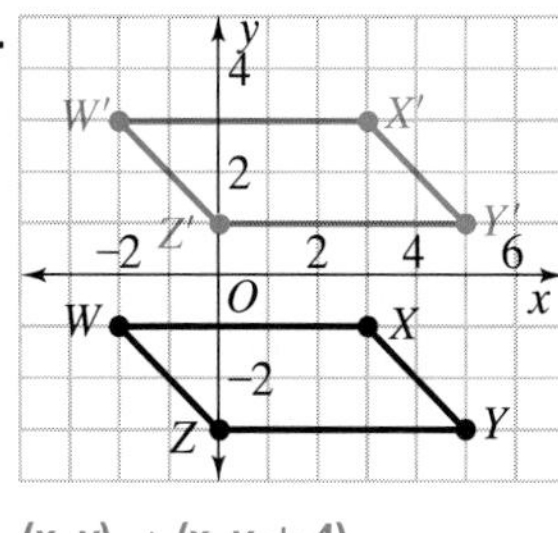


$(x, y) \rightarrow (x, y + 4)$

11.
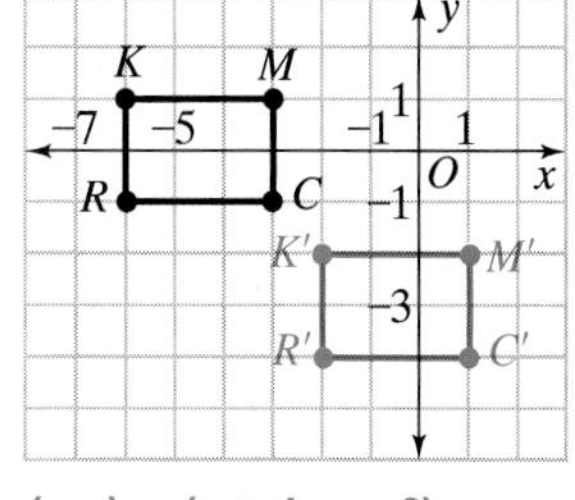


$(x, y) \rightarrow (x + 4, y - 3)$

## PRACTICE AND PROBLEM SOLVING

**The endpoints of a segment and a translation are given. Graph each segment and its image.** 12–15. See margin p. 482.

12. $N(3, 3), P(-3, 4)$; 2 units down
13. $Q(2, -1), R(-2, 1)$; 2 units right
14. $S(4, 3), T(1, -5)$; 4 units left
15. $U(-4, -5), V(2, 1)$; 3 units right, 2 units down
16. The vertices of $\triangle HIJ$ are $H(0, 5), I(-2, 4)$ and $J(-1, -3)$. Graph the triangle and its translation of 3 units to the right and 2 units down. See margin p. 482.
17. You translated a figure to the right 5 units and down 7 units. Complete the general rule to show how to find the image: $(x, y) \rightarrow (x + \blacksquare, y - \blacksquare)$. 5, 7



3.
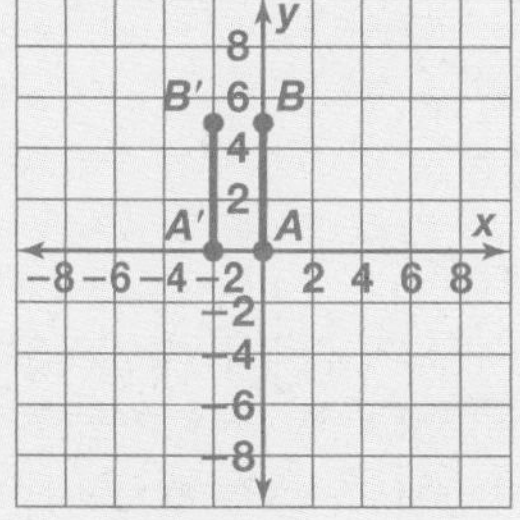


## Alternative Assessment

Have students make a map of the classroom on the coordinate plane. Then ask them to describe a move from their desk to another desk in terms of a translation of a point.

# 3 Practice/Assess

## Assignment Guide

To provide flexible scheduling, this lesson can be divided into parts.

**Part 1**
**Core** 1–8, 12–16
**Extension** 36

**Part 2**
**Core** 9–11, 17–30, 33, 35
**Extension** 31–32, 34

Mixed Review can be assigned at any time for maintenance.

## Exercises

**Test Prep Exercise 35** A translation of a line will always be parallel to the original, so the slope stays the same.

## Challenge

Suppose you have a circle with a radius of 3 units with a center $C(-2, -2)$. You translate that circle 4 units right and 2 units down. What is the greatest possible $y$-value for a point on the image of the circle? The greatest possible $y$-value is −1.

## Closure

A transformation is a change of position, shape, or size of a figure. The figure after the transformation is called the image. You can transform figures in a plane by translation.

## Daily Cumulative Review

**Draw each construction described.** *(Lesson 9-7)*

1. Construct an angle congruent to $\angle R$.
2. Construct the perpendicular bisector of $\overline{HC}$.
3. Construct an angle bisector for $\angle T$.
4. Construct a segment three times the length of $\overline{JC}$.

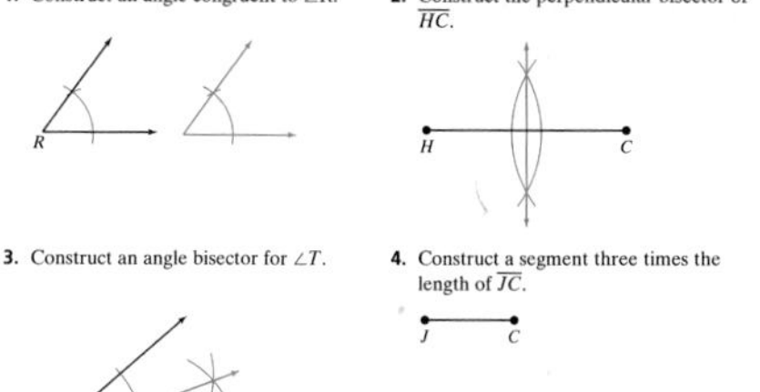


**Find the measure of the central angles that you would draw to represent each percent in a circle graph.** *(Lesson 9-6)*

5. 40% 144°
6. 70% 252°
7. 55% 198°
8. 5% 18°
9. 85% 306°
10. 15% 54°

**Mixed Review**

**Graph each equation.**

11. $x = 3$ (8-2)
12. $y = -2$ (8-2)

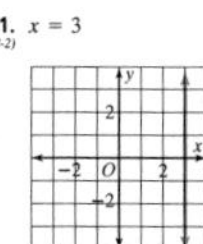
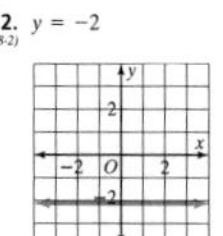

**A point and its image after a translation are given. Write a rule to describe each translation.**

$(x, y) \rightarrow (x - 11, y + 4)$
**18.** $A(7, -3), A'(-4, 1)$

$(x, y) \rightarrow (x + 11, y - 2)$
**19.** $A(-7, 3), A'(4, 1)$

$(x, y) \rightarrow (x - 11, y - 4)$
**20.** $A(7, 3), A'(-4, -1)$

**21.** $A(-7, -3), A'(-4, 1)$
$(x, y) \rightarrow (x + 3, y + 4)$

**22.** $A(7, 3), A'(4, 1)$
$(x, y) \rightarrow (x - 3, y - 2)$

**23.** $A(-7, -3), A'(-4, -1)$
$(x, y) \rightarrow (x + 3, y + 2)$

**Write a rule to describe each translation.**

**24.**

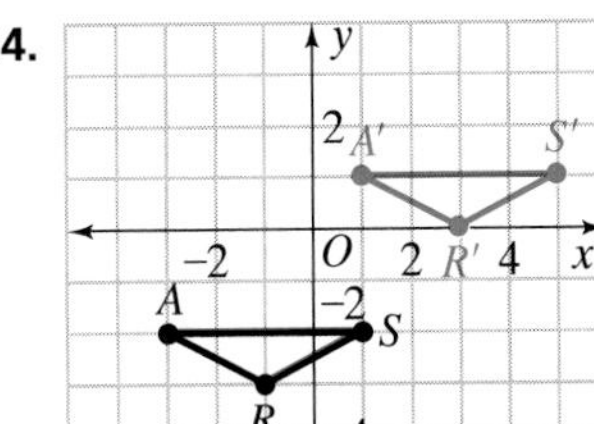


$(x, y) \rightarrow (x + 4, y + 3)$

**25.**

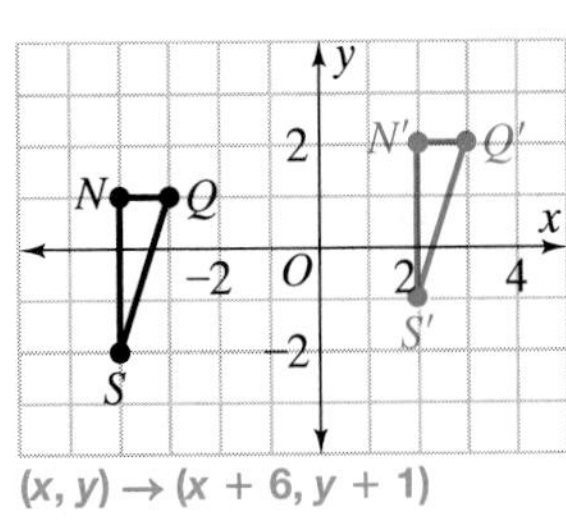


$(x, y) \rightarrow (x + 6, y + 1)$

**26.**

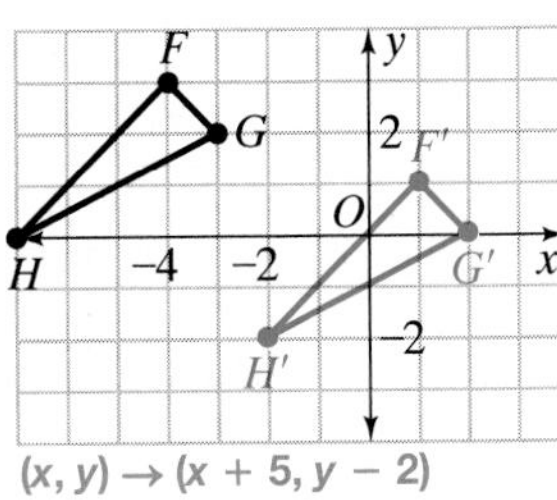


$(x, y) \rightarrow (x + 5, y - 2)$

**27.**

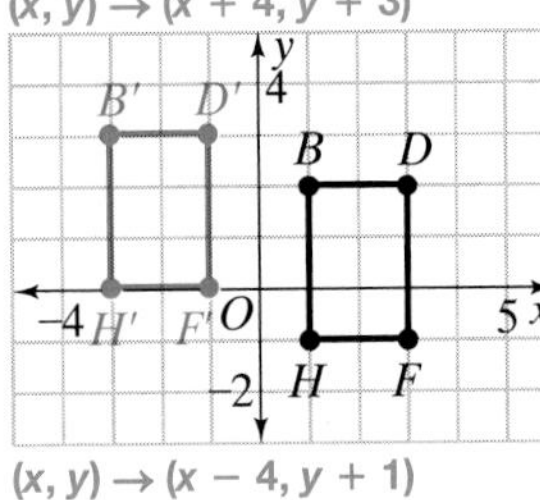


$(x, y) \rightarrow (x - 4, y + 1)$

**28.**

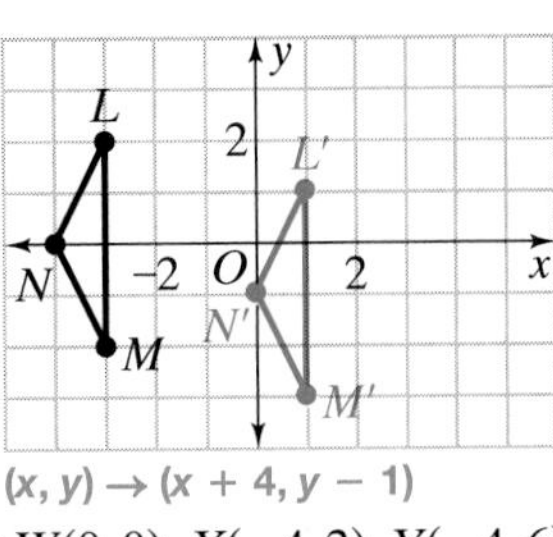


$(x, y) \rightarrow (x + 4, y - 1)$

**29.**

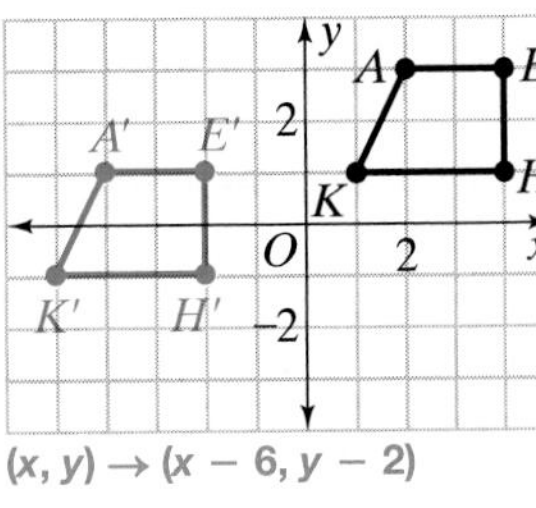


$(x, y) \rightarrow (x - 6, y - 2)$

**30.** Quadrilateral $WXYZ$ has vertices $W(0, 0)$, $X(-4, 2)$, $Y(-4, 6)$, and $Z(0, 4)$. Quadrilateral $W'X'Y'Z'$ has vertices $W'(2, -3)$, $X'(-2, -1)$, $Y'(-2, 3)$, and $Z'(2, 1)$. Write a rule to describe the translation. $(x, y) \rightarrow (x + 2, y - 3)$

**31.** Translate point $T(2, 5)$ 2 units to the right and 6 units up. Translate its image, point $T'$, 4 units to the left and 1 unit down. What are the coordinates of the image of point $T'$? (0, 10)

**32.** $\triangle CDE$ has coordinates $C(0, 2)$, $D(3, 4)$, and $E(5, 1)$. A translation maps $C$ to $(-2, -2)$. What are the coordinates of $D'$ and $E'$? (1, 0), (3, −3)

**33.** *Error Analysis* The image of $D(3, 4)$ is $D'(5, 4)$. A student described the translation as 2 units down. What error did the student make? What should the student have done? The student subtracted $x$-coordinates, which gives the horizontal translation. The student should have answered 2 units right.

**34.** *Writing* Explain why moving a figure $a$ units horizontally and then $-a$ units horizontally results in the original position of the figure. Moving a figure $-a$ units moves the figure just as far as moving it $a$ units, but in the opposite direction.

**35.** **TEST PREP** The graph of $y = 2x + 4$ is translated 3 units down and 4 units right. Find the slope of the graph of the image. D

**A.** $\frac{3}{4}$ **B.** $\frac{4}{3}$ **C.** $-2$ **D.** $2$



12.

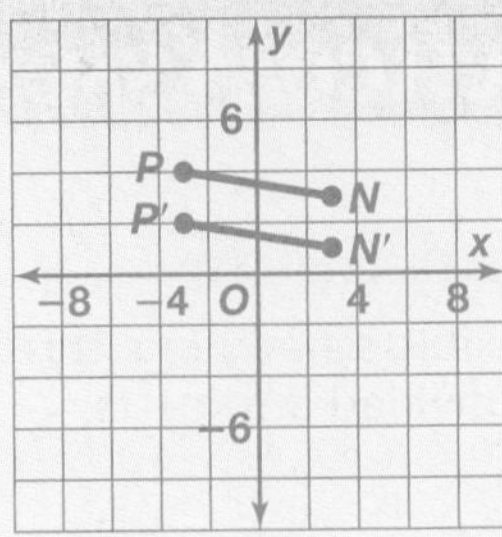


13.

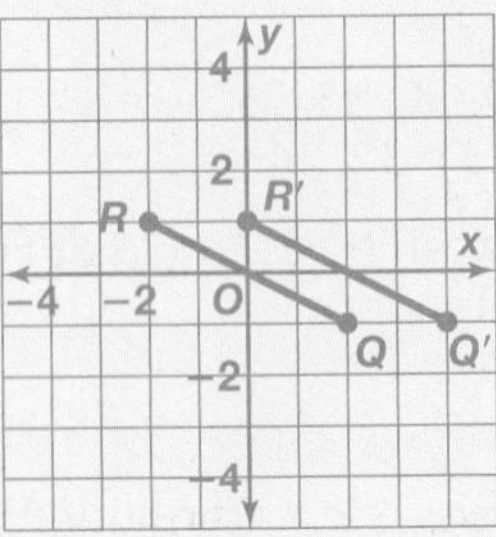


14.

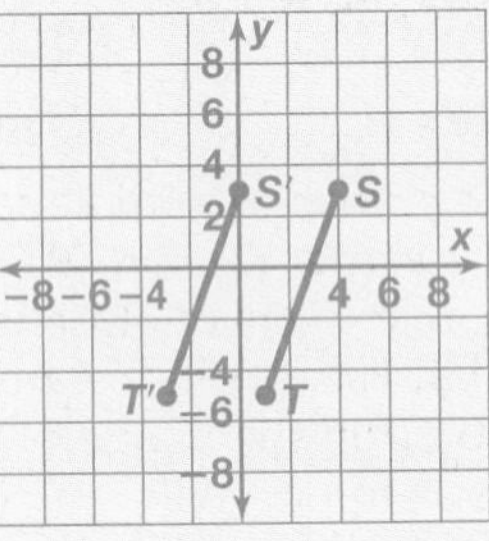


15.

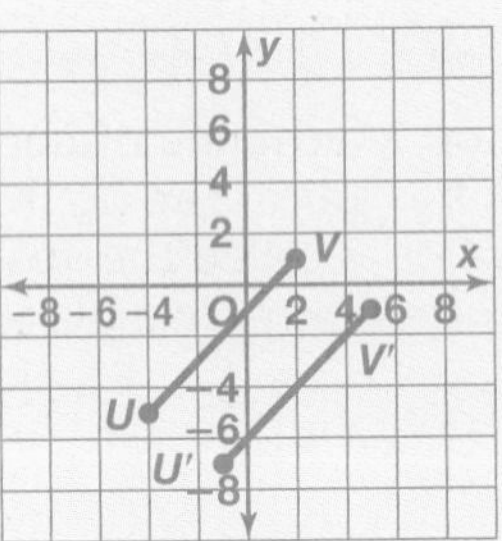


16.

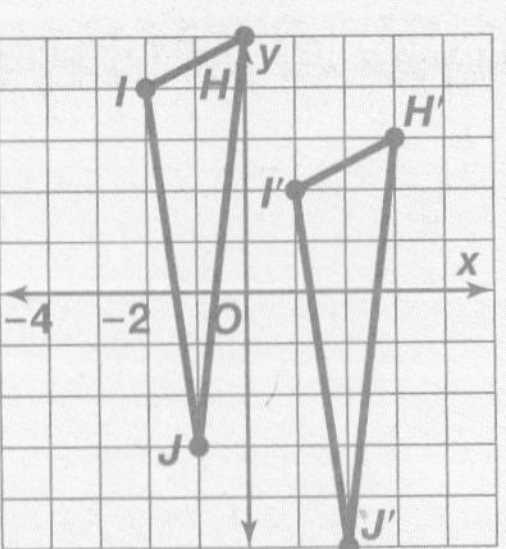


36a.

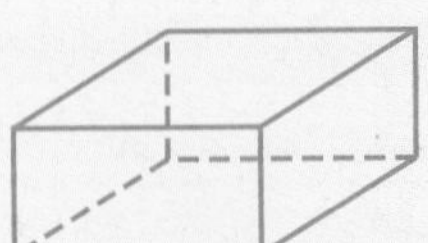

b.

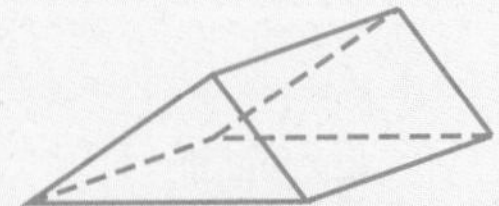

37.

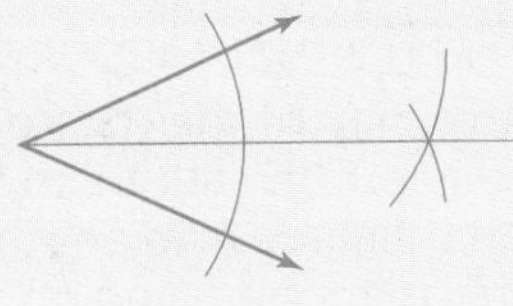

Checkpoint

3.

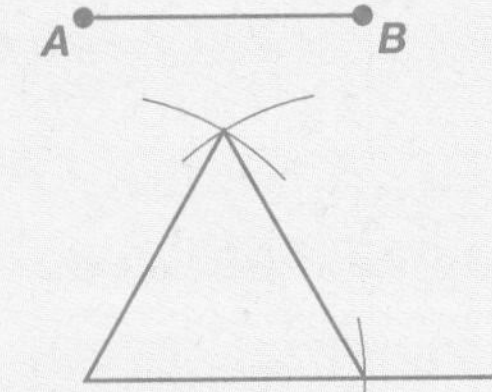

36. *Art* You can use translations to draw three-dimensional figures. Design a figure on graph paper using the following steps.

SAMPLE

| Step 1 | Step 2 | Step 3 | Step 4 |
|---|---|---|---|
| Draw a figure on graph paper. | Translate the figure. | Connect each vertex with its image. | Use dashes for sides that are not visible |

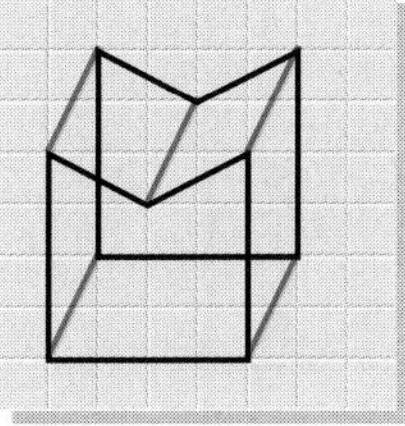
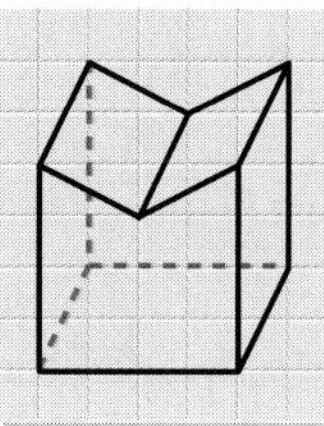

a. Start with a rectangle. Draw a three-dimensional figure. See margin.
b. Start with a triangle. Draw a three-dimensional figure. See margin.

## Mixed Review

37. Draw an acute angle and construct its bisector. *(Lesson 9-7)* See margin.

**Simplify each product.** *(Lesson 5-4)*

38. $\frac{3}{7} \cdot \frac{7}{9}$ $\frac{1}{3}$

39. $\frac{1}{2} \cdot \frac{8}{11}$ $\frac{4}{11}$

40. $\frac{1}{2} \cdot \frac{1}{8}$ $\frac{1}{16}$

41. *Choose a Strategy* Amanda, Adam, and Antoine ate salad, chicken, or tofu for lunch. Amanda did not eat chicken or tofu. Antoine did not eat chicken. Each one had a different meal. What did each person eat? Amanda had salad, Adam had chicken, and Antoine had tofu.

## Checkpoint 2

Lessons 9-6 through 9-8

**Use the circle graph at the right.**

1. Eighty people attended a catered meal. Twenty-eight people ordered fish, half ordered chicken, and twelve ordered the vegetarian meal. Which section represents each of the meals? A is chicken, B is fish, and C is vegetarian.
2. Determine the measure of the central angle of each section in the circle graph. The central angle for A is 180°, B is 126°, and C is 54°.

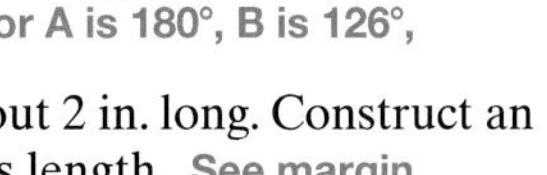
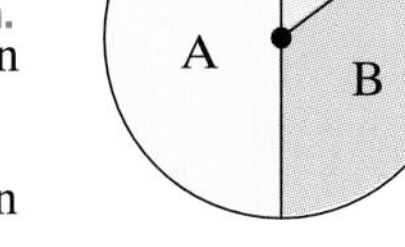


3. *Open-ended* Draw a segment about 2 in. long. Construct an equilateral triangle with sides of this length. See margin.
4. Graph $\overline{NR}$ with endpoints $N(2, 7)$ and $R(-4, 0)$. Then graph its image after a translation 4 units right and 3 units down. See margin.

See also Extra Practice section.

4.
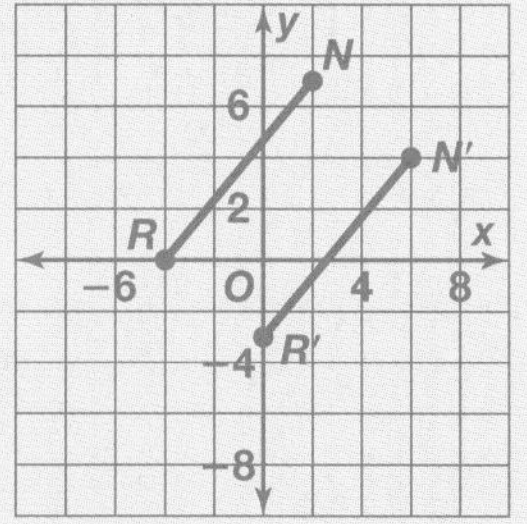


## Practice

Write a rule to describe each translation.

1. $(x, y) \rightarrow$ $(x + 4, y - 3)$
2. $(x, y) \rightarrow$ $(x - 2, y - 2)$
3. $(x, y) \rightarrow$ $(x + 3, y + 1)$
4. $(x, y) \rightarrow$ $(x, y + 2)$

The vertices of a triangle and a translation are given. Graph each triangle and its image.

5. $G(-4, 4), H(-2, 3), J(-3, 0)$; right 5 and down 2
6. $K(0, -1), L(4, 2), M(3, -3)$; left 4 units and up 3 units

A point and its image after a translation are given. Write a rule to describe the translation.

7. $A(9, -4), A'(2, -1)$ $(x, y) \rightarrow$ $(x - 7, y + 3)$
8. $B(-3, 5), B'(-5, -3)$ $(x, y) \rightarrow$ $(x - 2, y - 8)$



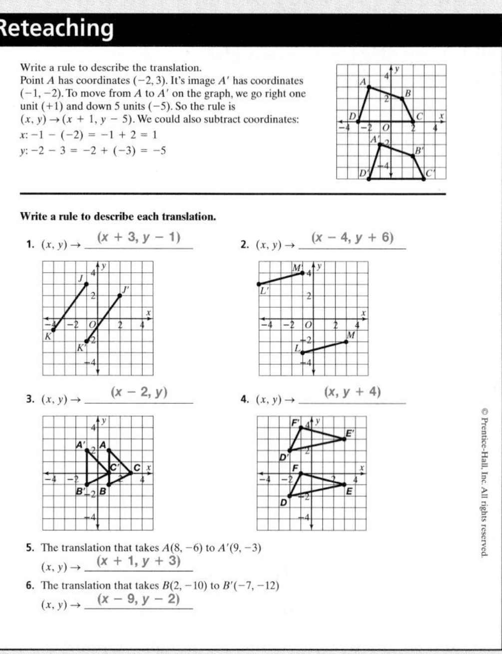

## Reteaching

Write a rule to describe the translation.

Point $A$ has coordinates $(-2, 3)$. It's image $A'$ has coordinates $(-1, -2)$. To move from $A$ to $A'$ on the graph, we go right one unit $(+1)$ and down 5 units $(-5)$. So the rule is $(x, y) \rightarrow (x + 1, y - 5)$. We could also subtract coordinates:

$x: -1 - (-2) = -1 + 2 = 1$

$y: -2 - 3 = -2 + (-3) = -5$

Write a rule to describe each translation.

1. $(x, y) \rightarrow$ $(x + 3, y - 1)$
2. $(x, y) \rightarrow$ $(x - 4, y + 6)$
3. $(x, y) \rightarrow$ $(x - 2, y)$
4. $(x, y) \rightarrow$ $(x, y + 4)$
5. The translation that takes $A(8, -6)$ to $A'(9, -3)$ $(x, y) \rightarrow$ $(x + 1, y + 3)$
6. The translation that takes $B(2, -10)$ to $B'(-7, -12)$ $(x, y) \rightarrow$ $(x - 9, y - 2)$



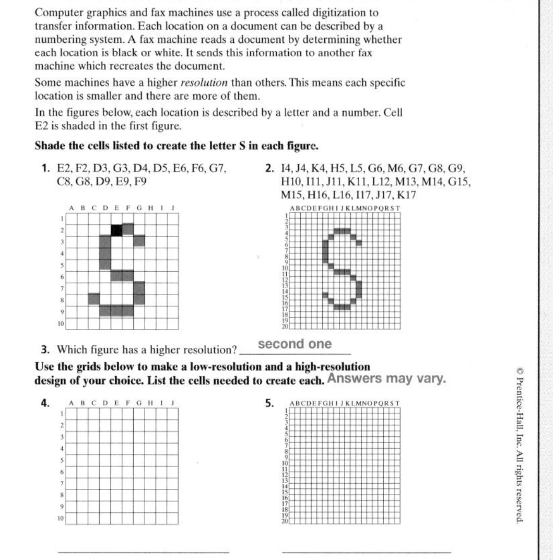

## Enrichment

Computer graphics and fax machines use a process called digitization to transfer information. Each location on a document can be described by a numbering system. A fax machine reads a document by determining whether each location is black or white. It sends this information to another fax machine which recreates the document.

Some machines have a higher *resolution* than others. This means each specific location is smaller and there are more of them.

In the figures below, each location is described by a letter and a number. Cell E2 is shaded in the first figure.

**Shade the cells listed to create the letter S in each figure.**

1. E2, F2, D3, G3, D4, D5, E6, F6, G7, C8, G8, D9, E9, F9
2. I4, J4, K4, H5, L5, G6, M6, G7, G8, G9, H10, I11, J11, K11, L12, M13, M14, G15, M15, H16, L16, I17, J17, K17

3. Which figure has a higher resolution? second one

**Use the grids below to make a low-resolution and a high-resolution design of your choice. List the cells needed to create each.** Answers may vary.

4.
5.



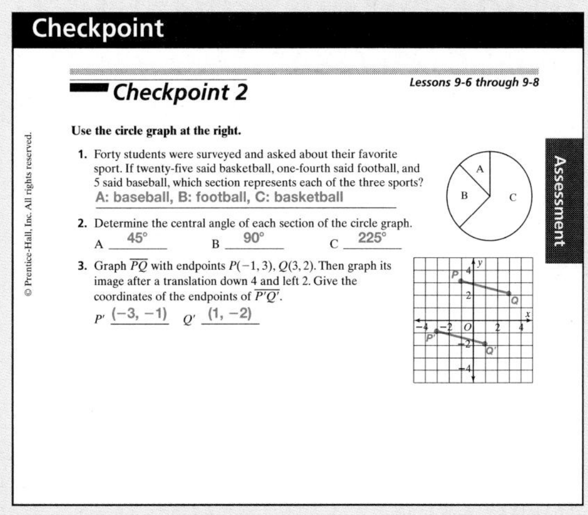

## Checkpoint

### Checkpoint 2

Lessons 9-6 through 9-8

**Use the circle graph at the right.**

1. Forty students were surveyed and asked about their favorite sport. If twenty-five said basketball, one-fourth said football, and 5 said baseball, which section represents each of the three sports? A: baseball, B: football, C: basketball
2. Determine the central angle of each section of the circle graph.
A 45° B 90° C 225°
3. Graph $\overline{PQ}$ with endpoints $P(-1, 3)$, $Q(3, 2)$. Then graph its image after a translation down 4 and left 2. Give the coordinates of the endpoints of $\overline{P'Q'}$.
$P'$ $(-3, -1)$ $Q'$ $(1, -2)$

Assessment

## MATH TOOLBOX

### Matrices and Translations

In Lesson 9-8, students learned about translations. In this Math Toolbox, students will learn what a matrix is and how to use a matrix to transform the vertices of a geometric figure.

### Math Background

A matrix is a rectangular array of numbers. The study of matrices is part of the branch of mathematics called discrete mathematics, because the numbers in a matrix are separate, or discontinuous, entries. Discrete mathematics underlies the way computers solve math problems. Other topics in discrete mathematics involve the study of sequences and series.

## Teaching Notes

**Error Prevention** Students may find that they make errors in reading and writing matrices until they become accustomed to this new way of writing coordinates. Suggest that they verify the entries in the matrix before they do the translation.

**Monitoring Progress** Exercises 1–5
Check your work by using a sketch on graph paper.

**Block Scheduling** If you have block scheduling or extended periods, you may wish to use this Math Toolbox lesson in combination with Lesson 9-8.

# MATH TOOLBOX

Extension
After Lesson 9-8

## Matrices and Translations

A matrix is a rectangular arrangement of numbers. Each number is a matrix entry. You can write the coordinates of the vertices of a figure as a matrix.

$$\begin{matrix} & A & B & C \\ x\text{-coordinate} & \\ y\text{-coordinate} & \end{matrix} \begin{bmatrix} 0 & -1 & -4 \\ 0 & 4 & 0 \end{bmatrix}$$

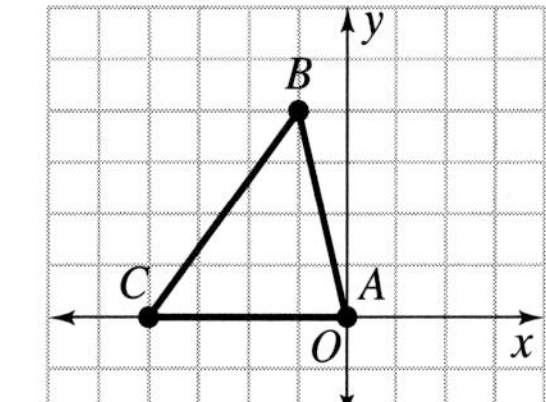


You can use matrices to translate figures.

### EXAMPLE

*Geometry* **Use a matrix to find the vertices of the image of quadrilateral *ABCD* using the rule $(x, y) \rightarrow (x + 3, y - 2)$.**

vertices of quadrilateral + translation matrix = vertices of image

Add 3 to each $x$-coordinate.
Add −2 to each $y$-coordinate.

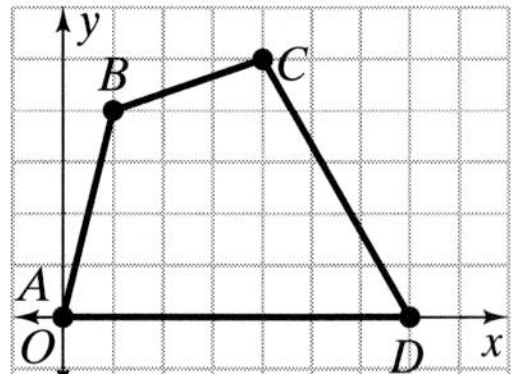


$$\overset{A\ \ B\ \ C\ \ D}{\begin{bmatrix} 0 & 1 & 4 & 7 \\ 0 & 4 & 5 & 0 \end{bmatrix}} + \begin{bmatrix} 3 & 3 & 3 & 3 \\ -2 & -2 & -2 & -2 \end{bmatrix} = \overset{A'\ \ B'\ \ C'\ \ D'}{\begin{bmatrix} 3 & 4 & 7 & 10 \\ -2 & 2 & 3 & -2 \end{bmatrix}}$$

The vertices of the image are $A'(3, -2)$, $B'(4, 2)$, $C'(7, 3)$, and $D'(10, -2)$.

**Use matrix addition to find the vertices of the image of the given figure under each translation.**

1. $\triangle TRI$ with vertices $T(-5, -5)$, $R(-3, -1)$, and $I(-1, -3)$
translation: $(x, y) \rightarrow (x + 6, y + 6)$
See margin.

2. square $SQRE$ with vertices $S(1, 2)$, $Q(4, 2)$, $R(4, 5)$, and $E(1, 5)$
translation: $(x, y) \rightarrow (x + 1, y - 3)$
See margin.

3. $\triangle NGL$ with vertices $N(4, 4)$, $G(7, 4)$, and $L(5, 0)$
translation matrix $\begin{bmatrix} -9 & -9 & -9 \\ -4 & -4 & -4 \end{bmatrix}$
See margin.

4. square $RECT$ with vertices $R(0, 0)$, $E(0, -4)$, $C(-4, -4)$, and $T(-4, 0)$
translation matrix $\begin{bmatrix} -1 & -1 & -1 & -1 \\ 2 & 2 & 2 & 2 \end{bmatrix}$
See margin.

5. a. What matrix would you use to translate a triangle 1 unit to the left and 4 units down? 5a. $\begin{bmatrix} -1 & -1 & -1 \\ -4 & -4 & -4 \end{bmatrix}$
b. Use your answer from part (a) to translate $\triangle ABC$ with vertices $A(2, 2)$, $B(3, 5)$, and $C(3, 0)$. See margin.



1. $\begin{bmatrix} -5 & -3 & -1 \\ -5 & -1 & -3 \end{bmatrix} + \begin{bmatrix} 6 & 6 & 6 \\ 6 & 6 & 6 \end{bmatrix} = \begin{bmatrix} 1 & 3 & 5 \\ 1 & 5 & 3 \end{bmatrix}$

The vertices of the image are $T'(1, 1)$, $R'(3, 5)$ and $I'(5, 3)$.

2. $\begin{bmatrix} 1 & 4 & 4 & 1 \\ 2 & 2 & 5 & 5 \end{bmatrix} + \begin{bmatrix} 1 & 1 & 1 & 1 \\ -3 & -3 & -3 & -3 \end{bmatrix} =$
$\begin{bmatrix} 2 & 5 & 5 & 2 \\ -1 & -1 & 2 & 2 \end{bmatrix}$

The vertices of the image are $S'(2, -1)$, $Q'(5, -1)$, $R'(5, 2)$ and $E'(2, 2)$.

### • Additional Example

Use a matrix to find the vertices of the image of rectangle *EFGH*, which has vertices $E(-2, 2)$, $F(2, 2)$, $G(2, -2)$, $H(-2, -2)$ using the rule $(x, y) \rightarrow (x - 1, y - 1)$. $E'(-3, 1)$, $F'(1, 1)$, $G'(1, -3)$, $H'(-3, -3)$

3. $\begin{bmatrix} 4 & 7 & 5 \\ 4 & 4 & 0 \end{bmatrix} + \begin{bmatrix} -9 & -9 & -9 \\ -4 & -4 & -4 \end{bmatrix} = \begin{bmatrix} -5 & -2 & -4 \\ 0 & 0 & -4 \end{bmatrix}$

The vertices of the image are $N'(-5, 0)$, $G'(-2, 0)$ and $L'(-4, -4)$.

4. $\begin{bmatrix} 0 & 0 & -4 & -4 \\ 0 & -4 & -4 & 0 \end{bmatrix} + \begin{bmatrix} -1 & -1 & -1 & -1 \\ 2 & 2 & 2 & 2 \end{bmatrix} =$
$\begin{bmatrix} -1 & -1 & -5 & -5 \\ 2 & -2 & -2 & 2 \end{bmatrix}$

The vertices of the image are $R'(-1, 2)$, $E'(-1, -2)$, $C'(-5, -2)$ and $T'(-5, 2)$.

5b. $\begin{bmatrix} 2 & 3 & 3 \\ 2 & 5 & 0 \end{bmatrix} + \begin{bmatrix} -1 & -1 & -1 \\ -4 & -4 & -4 \end{bmatrix} = \begin{bmatrix} 1 & 2 & 2 \\ -2 & 1 & -4 \end{bmatrix}$

The vertices of the image are $A'(1, -2)$, $B'(2, 1)$ and $C'(2, -4)$.

# Symmetry and Reflections

9-9

## Identifying Lines of Symmetry

A figure has **reflectional symmetry** when one half is a mirror image of the other half. A **line of symmetry** divides a figure with reflectional symmetry into two congruent halves.

A pattern for the back of a shirt is shown below. To make a shirt, you place the pattern on a folded piece of material, with the dashed lines of the pattern on the fold. After cutting the material, the back of the shirt will look like this.

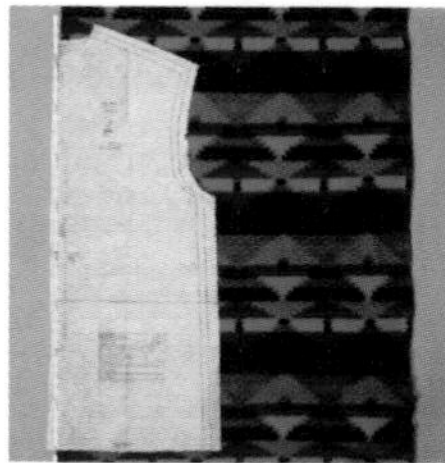

The fold is the line of symmetry.

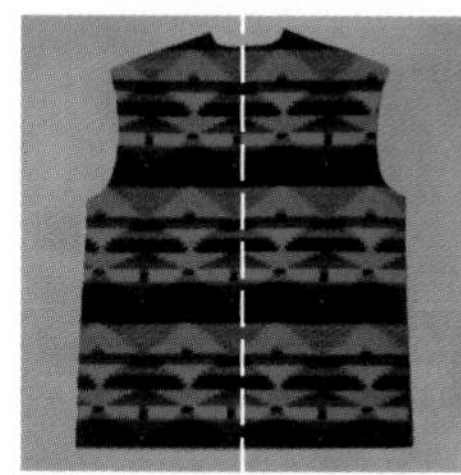

The shirt has one line of symmetry.

It is possible for a figure to have more than one line of symmetry.

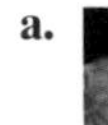

**EXAMPLE 1**

**Identify the lines of symmetry.**

**a.**

one line of symmetry

**b.**

six lines of symmetry

**TRY THIS** Copy each figure. Draw all lines of symmetry.

1. 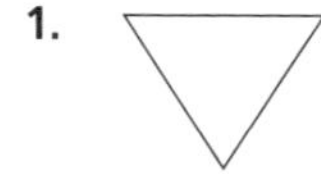 See back of book.

2. 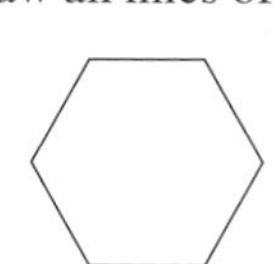 See back of book.

### What You'll Learn

1. To identify a line of symmetry
2. To graph a reflection of a geometric figure

### . . . And Why

To use symmetry and reflections in real-world situations, such as sewing



# Tools to Monitor Progress

**BEFORE THE LESSON**

**To check prerequisite skills:**

- Transforming figures

**Skills Intervention Kit,** Geometry

**DURING THE LESSON**

**To check understanding:**

**Try This** exercises on student page

- **Additional Example 1**

  Draw each item, and then identify the number of lines of symmetry.

  **a.** stop sign regular octagon; 8

  **b.** speed limit sign rectangle; 2

# 9-9

## Getting Ready

**Key Terms and Symbols** reflectional symmetry, line of symmetry, reflection, line of reflection

**Resources** A complete list of resources for this lesson is on p. 439H.

### Daily Skills Warm-Up

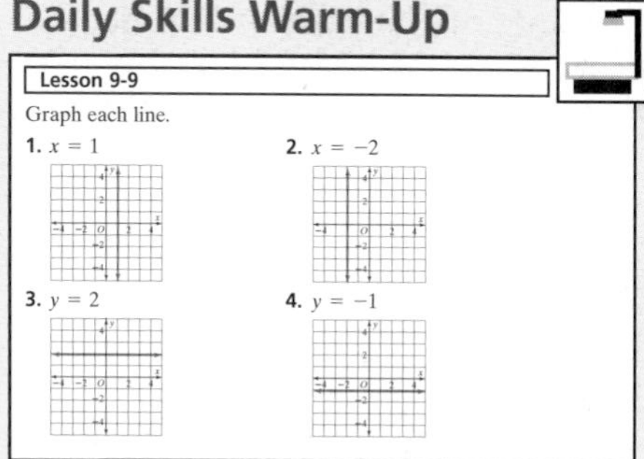

Lesson 9-9

Graph each line.

1. $x = 1$
2. $x = -2$
3. $y = 2$
4. $y = -1$

### Background for the Lesson

You can think of a line of symmetry as a line along which you could fold a figure so that both halves would match at every point. A line of reflection does not divide the figure in half. You could fold the plane along the line of reflection and the figures would then coincide. A reflection is a transformation that flips a figure over a line of reflection.

## 1 Focus

### Connecting to Students' Lives

Discuss a reflection of a figure in a mirror including how a reflection in a mirror is similar to the original object, and how it is different.

### Connecting to Prior Knowledge

In Lesson 9-8, students learned that a translation is a transformation in which all points on a figure move the same distance and direction. In this lesson, students learn about reflections, another type of transformation. In Lesson 9-10, students will learn about a third type of transformation, rotations.

# 2 Teach

## Part 1 Teaching Notes

Suggest that students visualize folding a figure along the line of symmetry.

### Example 1

**Build understanding.** Explain why a snowflake has six lines of symmetry. You could fold it along six different lines that produce two congruent images.

**Visual Learning** Have students search old newspapers, magazines, or the Internet for photos of objects with one or more lines of symmetry. Ask students to cut out the photos, draw the lines of symmetry (folding along them to check), and then display the pictures.

**Extension** How many lines of symmetry does a circle have? Explain. Infinitely many; each diameter is a line of symmetry.

## Part 2 Teaching Notes

Lead a discussion that compares and contrasts a line of reflection with a line of symmetry.

### Example 2

**Build understanding.** Ask: Describe the differences between $\Delta ABC$ and $\Delta A'B'C'$. The image is the same size and shape, but the left and right sides are reversed.

### Example 3

**Build understanding.** Ask: In which quadrant would the image lie if it were reflected over the line $x = -1$? It would lie in Quadrant II.

**Error Prevention** Remind students that lines where $y$ equals a constant are horizontal lines, and lines where $x$ equals a constant are vertical lines.

## Graphing Reflections

A **reflection** flips a figure over a **line of reflection.** The reflected figure, or image, is congruent to the original figure. Together, an image and its reflection have line symmetry, the line of reflection being the line of symmetry.

### Example 2

**Graph the image of $\triangle ABC$ after a reflection over the $y$-axis.**

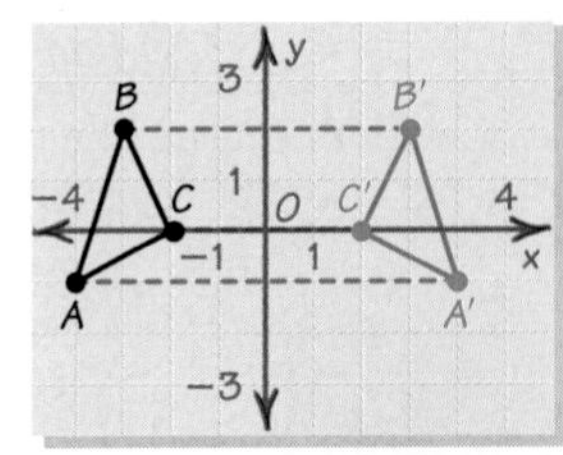


Since $A$ is 4 units to the left of the $y$-axis, $A'$ is 4 units to the right of the $y$-axis. Reflect the other vertices. Draw $\triangle A'B'C'$.

**Try This**

3. Graph the image of $\triangle ABC$ after a reflection over the $x$-axis. See back of book.

You can reflect images over lines other than the axes.

### Example 3

**Graph the image of $\triangle PQR$ after a reflection over $y = 2$.**

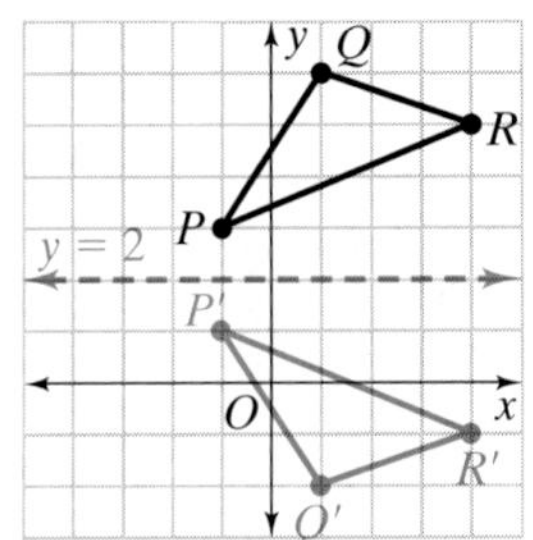


Graph $y = 2$. Since $P$ is 1 unit above the red line, $P'$ is 1 unit below the red line.

Reflect the other vertices. Draw $\triangle P'Q'R'$.

**Try This** Graph the image of $\triangle ABC$ with vertices $A(3, 0)$, $B(2, 3)$, and $C(5, -1)$ over each line.

4. $x = 2$ See back of book.
5. $y = -1$ See back of book.



- **Additional Examples 2–3**

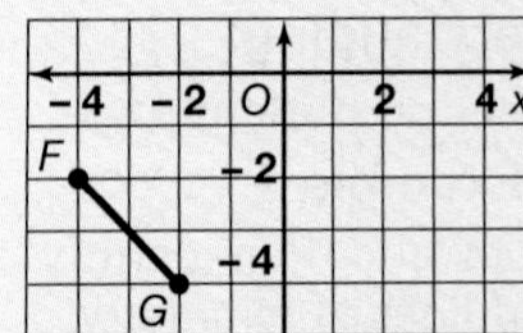


a. Graph the image of $\overline{FG}$ after a reflection over the $x$-axis. $F'(-4, 2)$, $G'(-2, 4)$

b. Graph the image of $\overline{FG}$ after a reflection over $y = -1$. $F'(-4, 0)$, $G'(-2, 2)$

### AFTER THE LESSON

**To assess knowledge: Lesson Quiz**

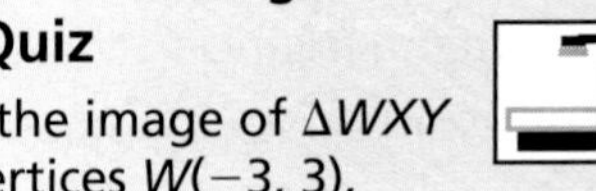

1. Graph the image of $\Delta WXY$ with vertices $W(-3, 3)$, $X(-2, 0)$, and $Y(0, 2)$ after a reflection over the $x$-axis. $W'(-3, -3)$, $X'(-2, 0)$, $Y'(0, -2)$
2. How many lines of symmetry does $\Delta WXY$ have? 1

- For enrichment and reteaching options see Resources on p. 439H.

# Exercises

## CHECK UNDERSTANDING

**Draw each figure. Draw all the lines of symmetry.** 1–3. See margin.

**1.** rhombus **2.** square **3.** isosceles triangle

**Graph each point and its image after a reflection over the given line.** 4–7. See back of book.

**4.** $R(7, 1)$; $x$-axis **5.** $S(5, -1)$; $y$-axis **6.** $F(-2, 9)$; $y = 1$ **7.** $N(-4, -6)$; $x = 4$

**The vertices of a triangle are listed. Reflect each triangle over the given line.** 8–9. See back of book.

**8.** $A(0, 0)$, $B(6, 0)$, $C(0, -6)$; $y = 1$ **9.** $K(-1, 4)$, $L(3, 3)$, $M(0, 2)$; $y = 0$

## PRACTICE AND PROBLEM SOLVING

**Copy each figure. Draw all the lines of symmetry. If a figure has no line of symmetry, explain why.** 10–13. See back of book for figures.

**10.** 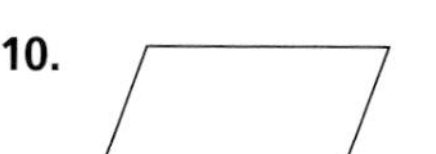  **11.** 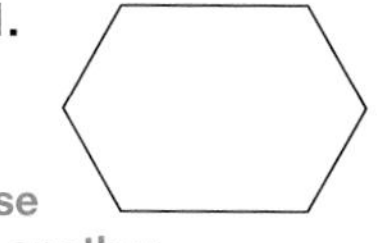 **12.** 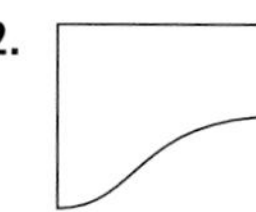 **13.** 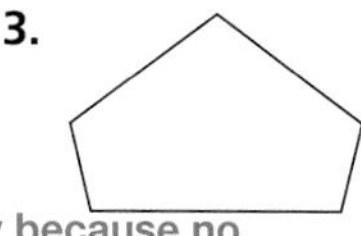

10. no line of symmetry because no part is a mirror reflection of another

12. no line of symmetry because no part is a mirror reflection of another

**Graph each point and its image after a reflection over the given line. Name the coordinates of the image.** 14–17. See back of book.

**14.** $H(-8, 3)$; $y = 4$ **15.** $J(-8, 3)$; $y = 2$ **16.** $V(5, 0)$; $x = -2$ **17.** $A(2, 5)$; $y = x$

**The vertices of a polygon are listed. Graph each polygon and its image after a reflection over the given line. Name the coordinates of the image.** 18–19. See back of book for graphs.

**18.** $F(0, 0)$, $G(6, 0)$, $H(8, 6)$, $I(2, 6)$; $x = 0$
$F'(0, 0)$, $G'(-6, 0)$, $H'(-8, 6)$, $I'(-2, 6)$

**19.** $W(-1, -1)$, $X(0, 0)$, $Y(-5, 0)$; $y = 2$
$W'(-1, 5)$, $X'(0, 4)$, $Y'(-5, 4)$

**20.** **TEST PREP** Which figure always has exactly two lines of symmetry? D
A. parallelogram
B. trapezoid
C. isosceles triangle
D. rhombus

**21.** *Writing* Will a reflection of an angle have a different measure than the original angle? Explain why or why not. No; a figure and its reflection are always congruent.



# 3 Practice/Assess

## Assignment Guide

To provide flexible scheduling, this lesson can be divided into parts.

**Part 1**
**Core** 1–3, 10–13, 20

**Part 2**
**Core** 4–9, 14–19, 21, 25–28
**Extension** 22–24, 29

Mixed Review can be assigned at any time for maintenance.

## Exercises

**Test Prep Exercise 20** Sketch the figures and draw the lines of symmetry to help you select an answer.

## Challenge

Describe a situation in which the image is exactly the same and in the same position as the original figure after a reflection. The image of a figure with reflectional symmetry that is reflected over one of its lines of symmetry will be exactly the same and in the same position as the original figure.

## Closure

A transformation is a change of position, shape, or size of a figure. The figure after the transformation is called the image. You can transform figures in a plane by reflection.

1. 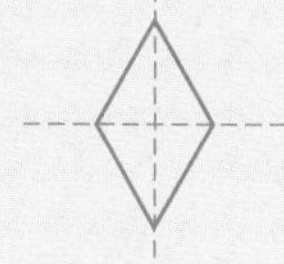

3. 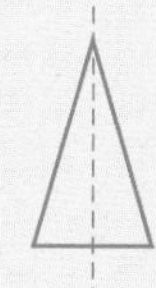

2. 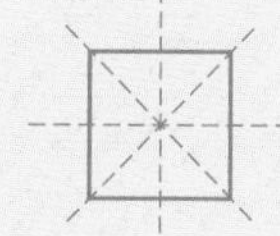

## Alternative Assessment

Give each student a clear plastic transparency. Have students write a set of instructions on the transparency to demonstrate how reflections work. Have students share their instructions with a partner or the class.

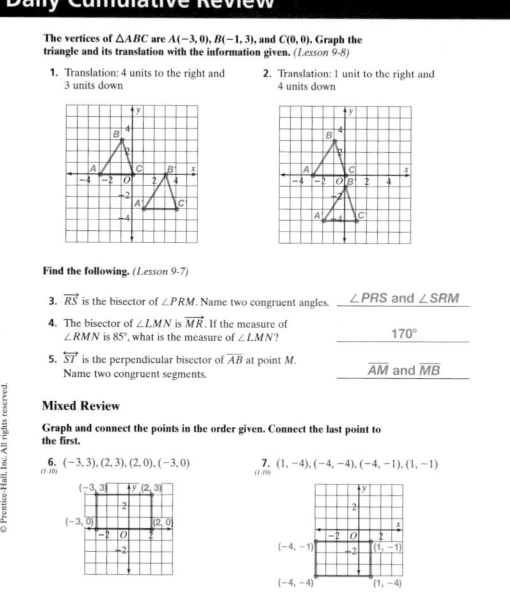

## Daily Cumulative Review

**The vertices of $\triangle ABC$ are $A(-3, 0)$, $B(-1, 3)$, and $C(0, 0)$. Graph the triangle and its translation with the information given.** *(Lesson 9-8)*

1. Translation: 4 units to the right and 3 units down
2. Translation: 1 unit to the right and 4 units down

**Find the following.** *(Lesson 9-7)*

3. $\overrightarrow{RS}$ is the bisector of $\angle PRM$. Name two congruent angles. $\angle PRS$ and $\angle SRM$
4. The bisector of $\angle LMN$ is $\overrightarrow{MR}$. If the measure of $\angle RMN$ is 85°, what is the measure of $\angle LMN$? 170°
5. $\overleftrightarrow{ST}$ is the perpendicular bisector of $\overline{AB}$ at point $M$. Name two congruent segments. $\overline{AM}$ and $\overline{MB}$

**Mixed Review**

**Graph and connect the points in the order given. Connect the last point to the first.**

6. (1-10) $(-3, 3), (2, 3), (2, 0), (-3, 0)$
7. (1-10) $(1, -4), (-4, -4), (-4, -1), (1, -1)$

## Practice

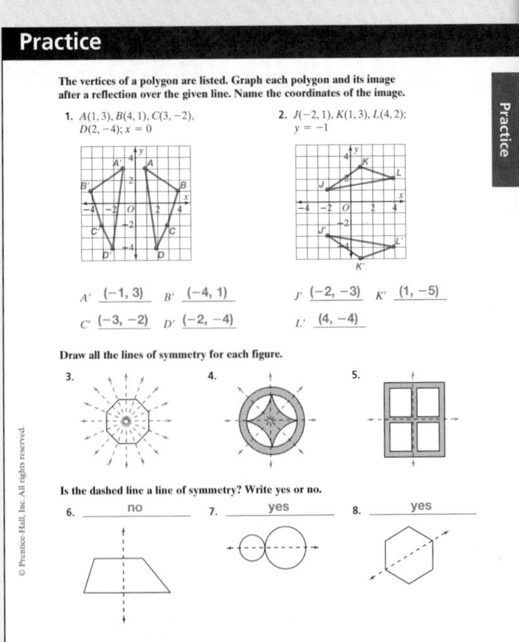
The vertices of a polygon are listed. Graph each polygon and its image after a reflection over the given line. Name the coordinates of the image.

1. $A(1, 3)$, $B(4, 1)$, $C(3, -2)$, $D(2, -4)$; $x = 0$
2. $J(-2, 1)$, $K(1, 3)$, $L(4, 2)$; $y = -1$

$A'$ (−1, 3) $B'$ (−4, 1) $C'$ (−3, −2) $D'$ (−2, −4)

$J'$ (−2, −3) $K'$ (1, −5) $L'$ (4, −4)

Draw all the lines of symmetry for each figure.

3. 4. 5.

Is the dashed line a line of symmetry? Write yes or no.

6. no 7. yes 8. yes



## Reteaching

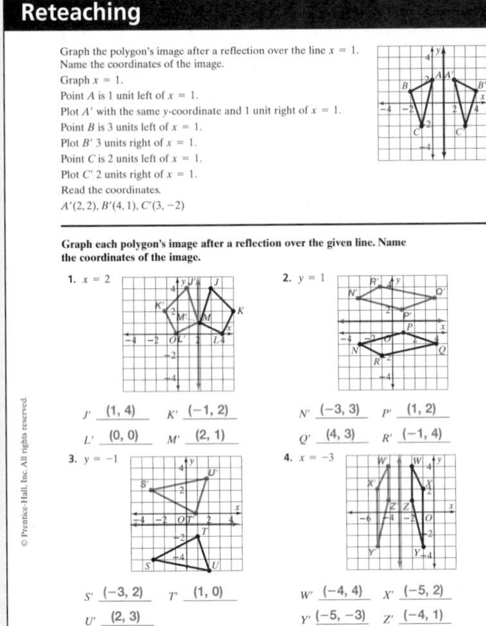
Graph the polygon's image after a reflection over the line $x = 1$. Name the coordinates of the image.

Graph $x = 1$.
Point $A$ is 1 unit left of $x = 1$.
Plot $A'$ with the same $y$-coordinate and 1 unit right of $x = 1$.
Point $B$ is 3 units left of $x = 1$.
Plot $B'$ 3 units right of $x = 1$.
Point $C$ is 2 units left of $x = 1$.
Plot $C'$ 2 units right of $x = 1$.
Read the coordinates.
$A'(2, 2)$, $B'(4, 1)$, $C'(3, -2)$

Graph each polygon's image after a reflection over the given line. Name the coordinates of the image.

1. $x = 2$
2. $y = 1$

$J'$ (1, 4) $K'$ (−1, 2) $L'$ (0, 0) $M'$ (2, 1)

$N'$ (−3, 3) $P'$ (1, 2) $Q'$ (4, 3) $R'$ (−1, 4)

3. $y = -1$
4. $x = -3$

$S'$ (−3, 2) $T'$ (1, 0) $U'$ (2, 3)

$W'$ (−4, 4) $X'$ (−5, 2) $Y'$ (−5, −3) $Z'$ (−4, 1)



## Enrichment

Herman Weyl, one of the twentieth century's greatest mathematicians, wrote that symmetry is an idea by which people through the ages have tried to comprehend and create three things. What are they?

To find the answer, solve the following puzzle.

Capital letters may have vertical symmetry or horizontal symmetry. Some letters have both vertical and horizontal symmetry, while others have neither.

| Vertical | Horizontal |
|---|---|
| M | D |
| Both | Neither |
| O | Z |

Varieties of symmetry: Vertical, Horizontal, Both, Neither

Choose the one letter beneath each letter space that is of a different symmetric variety than the other two. Write the letter in the space.

Example O is written in the first space because O is *both* vertically and horizontally symmetric, while S and F are *neither*.

O R D E R,

SOF RTV AMD EGP XRI

B E A U T Y, and

BUW JQE CAE NSU OTX YFZ

P E R F E C T I O N

EPB ETV ORH CBF WYE CGL NTS IDK AUO HNX



**The given point is reflected over line 1. Then the image is reflected over line 2. Name the coordinates of the second image.**

22. $A(3, -2)$
line 1: $y$-axis
line 2: $x$-axis
(−3, 2)

23. $B(-1, 5)$
line 1: $x$-axis
line 2: $y = 3$
(−1, 11)

24. $C(-5, -1)$
line 1: $x = 2$
line 2: $y$-axis
(−9, −1)

*Critical Thinking* **Decide whether each statement is *always* true, *sometimes* true, or *never* true.**

25. When a point is reflected over a horizontal line, the $x$–coordinate stays the same. always

26. When a point is reflected over a vertical line, the $y$–coordinate stays the same. always

27. The image of a polygon reflected over a line is congruent to the original polygon. always

28. When corresponding points of an original figure and its reflection are connected, the resulting segments are all perpendicular to the line of reflection. always

29. a. On a coordinate plane, graph the line $y = x$ and $\triangle ABC$ with vertices $A(5, 3)$, $B(6, -1)$, and $C(2, -1)$. See back of book.
 b. To graph the image of $\triangle ABC$ over the line $y = x$, trace the axes and $\triangle ABC$ on tracing paper. Fold the paper along $y = x$. Trace over the triangle so that it makes an impression on your original graph. Label $A'B'C'$ appropriately. See back of book.
 c. Connect $A$ to $A'$, $B$ to $B'$, and $C$ to $C'$. What do you notice about these segments and the line $y = x$? They are perpendicular.
 d. Complete the statement: The segment that connects a point to its image is _?_ to the line of reflection and forms a _?_ angle at the intersection. perpendicular, right
 e. Reflect $\triangle ABC$ over $y = x + 3$. See back of book.

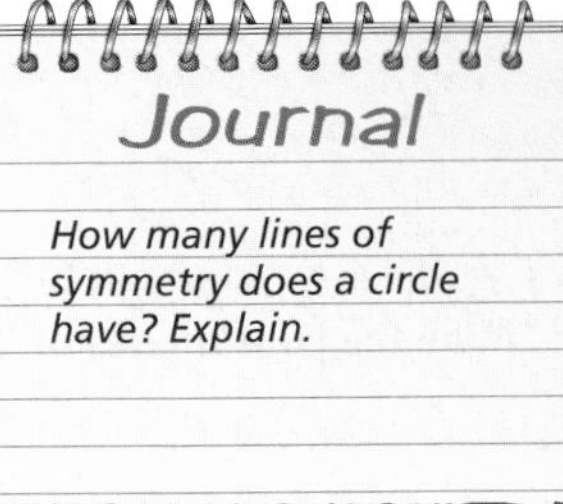

Journal
How many lines of symmetry does a circle have? Explain.


## Mixed Review

**The endpoints of a segment and a translation are given. Graph the segment and its image. Name the endpoints of the image.** *(Lesson 9-8)*

30. $A(4, 3)$, $B(5, 7)$; 3 units left, 2 units down
$A'(1, 1)$, $B'(2, 5)$; see margin for graph.

31. $X(0, -1)$, $Y(2, 7)$; 2 units right, 3 units up
$X'(2, 2)$, $Y'(4, 10)$; see margin for graph.

**Graph each equation.** *(Lesson 8-2)* 32–34. See back of book.

32. $x + 3 = y$
33. $y - 8 = x$
34. $2y = x + 10$

35. *Choose a Strategy* If six people meet, and each person shakes every other person's hand, how many handshakes are there in all? 15



See also Extra Practice section.

30.

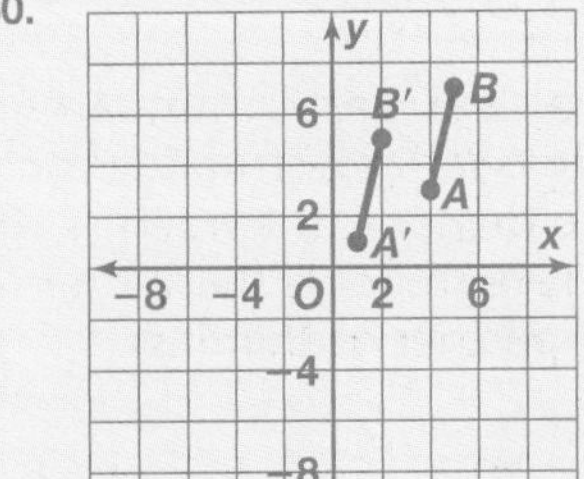


31.

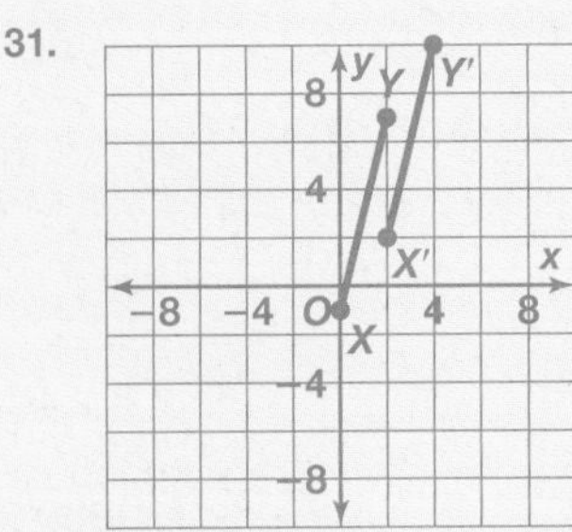

# Standardized Test Prep

## Multiple Choice

**Choose the best answer.**

1. Find the measure of the central angle that represents 46% in a circle graph. Round to the nearest degree. D
   A. 46° B. 83°
   C. 54° D. 166°

2. Identify the rule that describes the translation of $B(3, 5)$ to $B'(1, 1)$. G
   F. $(x + 2, y + 4)$ G. $(x - 2, y - 4)$
   H. $(x + 2, y - 4)$ J. $(x - 4, y - 2)$

3. Quadrilateral $JKLM \cong$ quadrilateral $PQRS$. Choose the correct congruence statement. C
   A. $\overline{JK} \cong \overline{RS}$ B. $\overline{LM} \cong \overline{QR}$
   C. $\angle K \cong \angle Q$ D. $\angle M \cong \angle P$

4. Choose the correct congruence statement. F

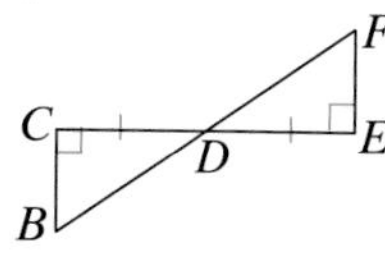


   F. $\triangle BCD \cong \triangle FED$ by **ASA**
   G. $\triangle BCD \cong \triangle FED$ by **SSS**
   H. $\triangle CDB \cong \triangle DEF$ by **ASA**
   J. $\triangle BDC \cong \triangle FED$ by **SAS**

5. A store receives a shipment of shirts. Each shirt costs the store \$18.00. The store sells each shirt for \$24.95. What is the percent of markup, to the nearest percent? C
   A. 139% B. 72% C. 39% D. 28%

6. Some taxicabs begin each trip by setting the meter to \$1.50. The meter then adds \$.40 for each $\frac{1}{4}$ mi traveled. If a trip costs \$7.90, how far did the cab travel? J
   F. 160 mi G. 16 mi
   H. 8 mi J. 4 mi

**Use the figure below for Exercises 7–9.**

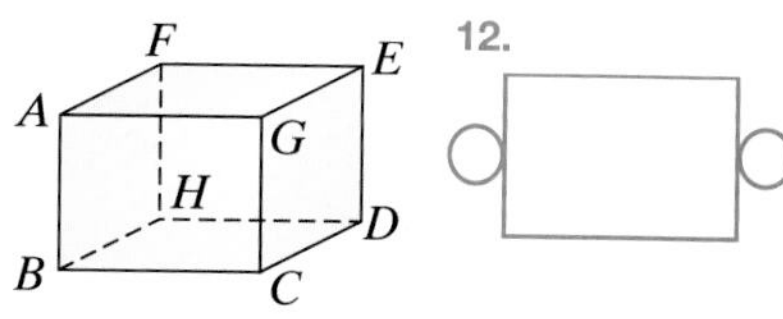


7. Name a segment skew to $\overline{AB}$. B
   A. $\overline{BC}$ B. $\overline{CD}$
   C. $\overline{DE}$ D. $\overline{GC}$

8. Name a segment parallel to $\overline{ED}$. H
   F. $\overline{BH}$ G. $\overline{AF}$
   H. $\overline{AB}$ J. $\overleftrightarrow{GE}$

9. Name a segment that does *not* intersect $\overline{AG}$. D
   A. $\overline{AB}$ B. $\overline{GC}$
   C. $\overline{AF}$ D. $\overline{BC}$

## Free Response

**For each exercise, show your work.**

10. Copy the segment below. Construct its perpendicular bisector. See margin.

11. Graph $\triangle XYZ$ with vertices $X(-2, 4)$, $Y(-3, 1)$ and $Z(-1, 5)$. Translate it 5 units to the right and 3 units down. Write the coordinates of the vertices of the translated image. $X'(3,1)$, $Y'(2,-2)$, $Z'(4, 2)$; see margin for graph.

12. *Open-ended* Draw a net for a cylinder. See above.

13. Company A charges \$29 per day to rent a car. For the same car, Company B charges \$19 per day and \$.15 per mile driven. Under what circumstances would you pay less at Company A? Explain your reasoning. See below.

14. How many diagonals does a hexagon have? 9

13. If I drive $66.\overline{6}$ miles, $19 + 66.\overline{6}(.15) = 29$, so for driving that distance the two companies charge the same. For a greater distance Company A charges less.



10.
C D

11.

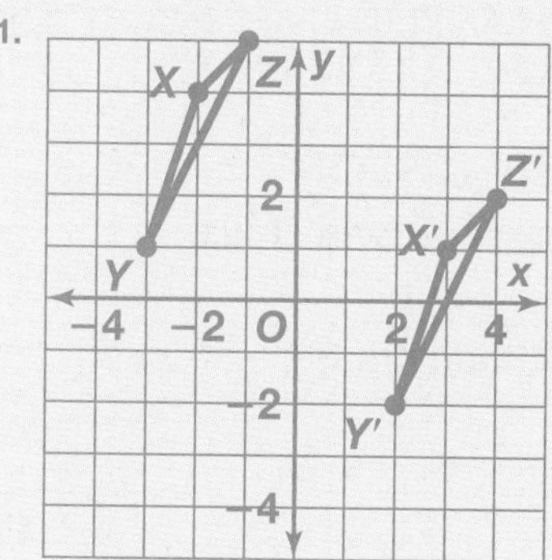


# Standardized Test Prep

Standardized tests, such as those administered for state assessment, SAT9, TerraNova™, ITBS, MAT7, or CAT5, may include multiple choice questions, free-response questions, and open-ended questions.

**Multiple Choice Questions** are followed usually by four choices, one of which is correct.

**Exercises 1–9** are multiple choice questions.

**Free-Response Questions** do not give answer choices. Student must provide the one correct answer on their own.

**Exercises 10–14** are free-response questions.

**Open-Ended Questions** allow for more than one solution. Students must construct their own responses instead of choosing from possible answers.

**Exercise 12** is an open-ended question.

## Resources

See p. 439G for a list of assessment options.

## Test-Taking Tip

For a question that involves geometry and geometric figures, you may find it helpful to draw and label a quick sketch of the figures described before you evaluate the answer choices.

### Test-Taking Tips on Transparency

1. Draw two rectangles of different lengths and widths, each with a perimeter of 20 units.

Scoring Guide

3 Draws 2 rectangles of different lengths and widths, with perimeter 20 units indicated by labels on sides.
2 Draws 2 identical rectangles, with perimeter 20 units, OR draws 2 rectangles of different widths and lengths, only 1 with perimeter 20 units.
1 Draws 1 or 2 rectangles, whose perimeters are not 20 units, OR draws 1 or 2 non-rectangles.
0 Answers inappropriately or not at all.

2. The Athletic Council is hosting a sports banquet. It costs \$300 to rent a hall, plus \$8 per person for food. Between 50 and 90 people will attend. What are the least and greatest amounts of money the banquet could cost? Explain.

Scoring Guide

3 Correctly computes least and greatest costs, AND explains adequately.
2 Computes least cost incorrectly, OR computes greatest cost incorrectly, OR explains inadequately.
1 Computes both costs incorrectly, OR computes one cost correctly, but explains inadequately.
0 Answers inappropriately or not at all.

# 9-10

## Getting Ready

**Key Terms and Symbols** rotation, center of rotation, angle of rotation, rotational symmetry

**Resources** A complete list of resources for this lesson is on p. 439H.

### Daily Skills Warm-Up

Lesson 9-10

Find the coordinates of each point.

1. $A$ (−3, 0)
2. $B$ (−2, 3)
3. $C$ (3, 2)
4. $D$ (0, −4)
5. $E$ (2, −1)

### Background for the Lesson

A rotation is a transformation in which a figure is rotated around a center of rotation. The amount a figure rotates is called the *angle of rotation*. For example, if a spot on a tire rotates halfway around the center of rotation, then the angle of rotation is 180°. Some figures rotate 180° or less than 180° around a center of rotation onto an image that matches the original figure. Such figures have *rotational symmetry*. For example, a five-pointed star rotated 72° appears the same as it did before you rotated it.

## 1 Focus

### Connecting to Students' Lives

Have students give examples of things that rotate and explain what that means.

### Connecting to Prior Knowledge

In Lesson 9-9, students learned that a reflection is a transformation in which a figure is reflected across a line. In this lesson, students learn about another type of transformation, the rotation. Students will learn more about circles in Lesson 10-3.

# 9-10 Rotations

**What You'll Learn**

1. To graph rotations
2. To identify rotational symmetry

**. . . And Why**

To use rotations in describing real objects

## Part 1 Graphing Rotations

A **rotation** is a transformation that turns a figure about a fixed point called the **center of rotation.** The angle measure of the rotation is the **angle of rotation.**

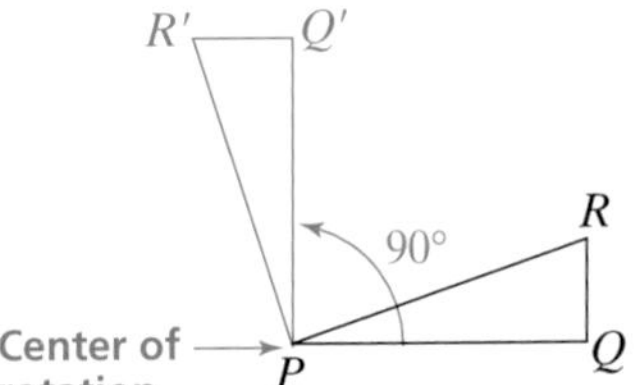


In the figure, $\triangle QPR$ is rotated 90° about the center of rotation, point $P$. Notice that $m\angle QPQ' = 90°$ and $m\angle RPR' = 90°$. A figure and its rotation image are congruent.

In the diagram, the direction of the rotation is *counterclockwise*. All rotations in this book will be counterclockwise.

You can graph rotations on a coordinate plane.

### Example 1

**Find the vertices of the image of $\triangle ABC$ after a rotation of 180° about the origin.**

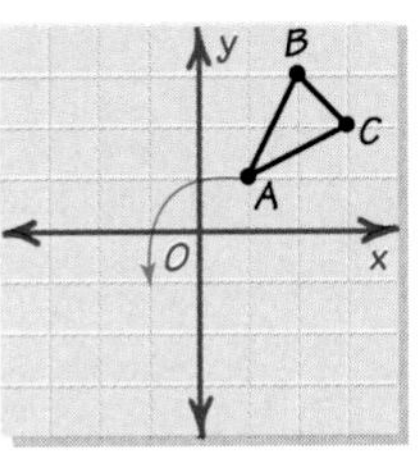


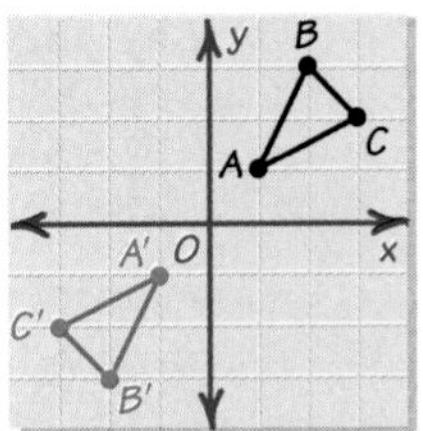


**Step 1** Draw $\triangle ABC$. Place a piece of tracing paper over the graph. Trace the vertices of the triangle, the $x$-axis, and the $y$-axis. Then place your pencil at the origin to rotate the paper.

**Step 2** Rotate the paper 180°. Make sure the axes line up. Mark the position of each vertex by pressing through the paper. Connect the vertices of the rotated triangle.

The vertices of the image are $A'(-1, -1)$, $B'(-2, -3)$, and $C'(-3, -2)$.



## Tools to Monitor Progress

**BEFORE THE LESSON**

**To check prerequisite skills:**

- Transforming a figure

**Skills Intervention Kit,** Geometry

**DURING THE LESSON**

**To check understanding:**

**Try This** exercises on student page

- **Additional Example 1**

  The figure $\Delta RST$ has vertices $R(1, -1)$, $S(1, -4)$, and $T(5, -4)$. Find the vertices of the image of $\Delta RST$ after a rotation of 90° about the origin.
  $R'(1, 1)$, $S'(4, 1)$, and $T'(4, 5)$

■ **TRY THIS**

1. Copy the graph of $\triangle ABC$. Draw its image after a rotation of 90° about the origin. Name the coordinates of the vertices of the image. See back of book.

## Identifying Rotational Symmetry

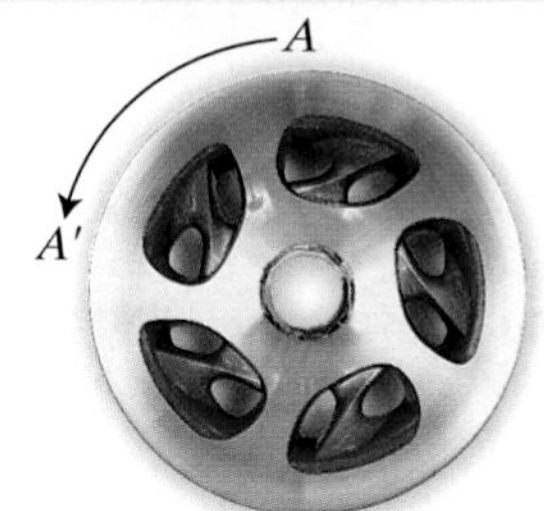


A figure has **rotational symmetry** if you can rotate it 180° or less so that its image matches the original figure. The angle that a figure rotates so that the image matches the original figure is the angle of rotation. When point $A$ moves to point $A'$ the wheel will look the same as it does now.

Since point $A$ can move to five different positions in which the wheel matches the original figure, the angle of rotation is 360° ÷ 5, or 72°. The figure has rotational symmetry.

REAL-WORLD CONNECTION

### ■ EXAMPLE 2

*Botany* **Judging from appearance, tell whether the flower has rotational symmetry. If so, what is the angle of rotation?**

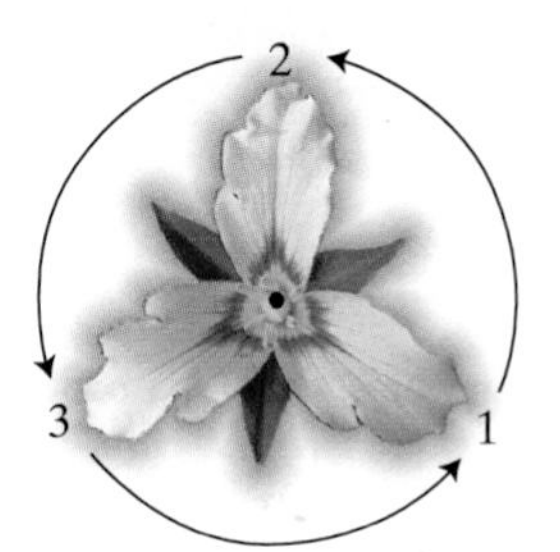


The flower can match itself in 3 positions.

The pattern repeats in 3 even intervals.
360° ÷ 3 = 120°

The figure has rotational symmetry. The angle of rotation is 120°.

■ **TRY THIS** Judging from appearance, tell whether each figure has rotational symmetry. If so, what is the angle of rotation?

2. 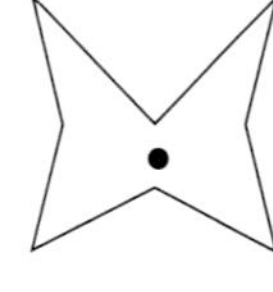
no

3. 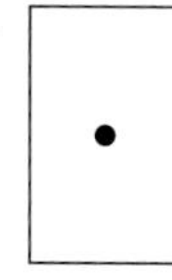
yes, 180°

4. 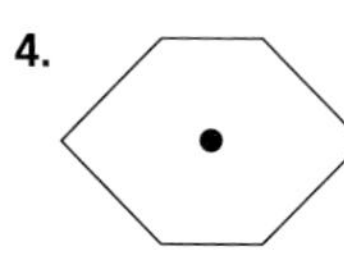
yes, 180°



• **Additional Example 2**
What is the angle of rotation of a 6-pointed star? 60°

### AFTER THE LESSON

**To assess knowledge:**
**Lesson Quiz**
The figure $\triangle DFG$ has vertices $D(-2, 4)$, $F(-3, 1)$, and $G(-1, 2)$. Find the vertices of the image of after a rotation of 180° about the origin. $D'(2, -4)$, $F'(3, -1)$, and $G'(1, -2)$

- For enrichment and reteaching options see Resources on p. 439H.

# 2 Teach

## PART 1 Part 1 Teaching Notes

Ask students to visualize the rotation of a figure by thinking of putting a pin through one vertex of a cut-out paper triangle and then rotating the triangle around the pin.

### ■ Example 1

**Build understanding.** Ask: How is the image that was produced in this rotation different from a reflection over the line $y = -x$? The point $A'$ is in the same place as it would be if the image is reflected. However, points $B'$ and $C'$ are reversed from their location in the reflection.

**ELL** Make sure students understand that *counterclockwise* describes a rotation that is the opposite of the direction in which the hands of a clock rotate.

**Error Prevention** While all the examples in this lesson are rotations about the origin, students may encounter problems that use a different center of rotation. Suggest that students make sure that they use whichever center of rotation is specified in a problem.

## PART 2 Part 2 Teaching Notes

Point out to students that the image of a figure with rotational symmetry will match the original only at certain angles of rotation. In between those angles, the image does not match the original.

### ■ Example 2

**Build understanding.** Ask: How far must you rotate the flower before the image matches the original? 120°

**Extension** Explain the relationship between the number of lines of symmetry that an object with rotational symmetry has and its angle of rotation. The angle, $A$, is equal to $\frac{360}{n}$, where $n$ equals the number of lines of symmetry the object has.

# 3 Practice/Assess

## Assignment Guide

To provide flexible scheduling, this lesson can be divided into parts.

▼ Part 1

**Core** 1–7, 12–16, 18

✪ **Extension** 17

▼ Part 2

**Core** 8–11, 19–28

✪ **Extension** 29

Mixed Review can be assigned at any time for maintenance.

### Exercises

**Tactile Learning** **Exercises 12–16** Draw the figures on a piece of tracing paper or on a transparency so you can rotate them and plot the new points.

### ✪ Challenge

Suppose you have a gear that has 50 teeth. What is its angle of rotation? 7.2°

### Closure

A transformation is a change of position, shape, or size of a figure. The figure after the transformation is called the image. You can transform figures in a plane by rotation.

# Exercises

## CHECK UNDERSTANDING

**Each figure below is an image formed by rotating the figure at the right. What is each angle of rotation?**

1.  90°
2. 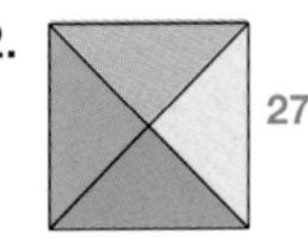 270°
3. 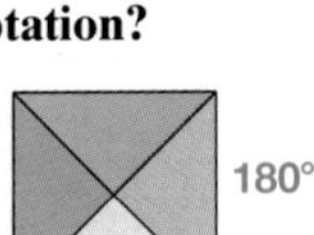 180°

**Graph each point. Then rotate it the given number of degrees about the origin. What are the coordinates of the image?** 4–7. See back of book.

4. $A(5, 5); 90°$
5. $B(0, -2); 180°$
6. $C(2, 4); 180°$
7. $D(-1, -3); 90°$

**Judging from appearance, tell whether each figure has rotational symmetry. If so, what is the angle of rotation?**

8. 
yes, 90°

9. 
yes, 60°

10. 
yes, 60°

11. 
no

## PRACTICE AND PROBLEM SOLVING

**The vertices of a triangle are given. On separate coordinate planes, graph each triangle and its image after a rotation of (a) 90° and (b) 180° about the origin.** 12. See margin. 13–16. See back of book.

12. $V(0, 0)$, $W(2, 5)$, $X(1, -5)$
13. $K(3, 0)$, $L(2, 2)$, $M(2, 4)$
14. $S(0, -4)$, $T(-4, -4)$, $U(-4, -3)$
15. $C(-2, 0)$, $D(-3, 5)$, $E(-1, 2)$
16. $G(-4, -1)$, $H(-2, -5)$, $I(-2, -1)$

✪ 17. $\triangle JKL$ has vertices $J(4, 4)$, $K(3, 2)$ and $L(5, 1)$.
   a. Graph its image after a rotation of 90° about the origin. Name the coordinates of the vertices of the image. See back of book for graph. $J'(-4, 4)$, $K'(-2, 3)$, $L'(-1, 5)$
   b. Graph the image of $\triangle J'K'L'$ after a reflection over the $y$-axis. See back of book for graph.

18. Explain how translations, reflections, and rotations affect the positions of figures. A translation slides a figure over the plane. A reflection flips a figure over a line. A rotation turns a figure around a point.



## Daily Cumulative Review

**Draw all the lines of symmetry.** *(Lesson 9-9)*

1. 2. 3. 4. 5. 6.

**Point B and its image after a translation are given. Write a rule to describe each translation.** *(Lesson 9-8)*

7. $B(8, -4), B'(-3, 2)$ $(x, y) \to (x - 11, y + 6)$
8. $B(-8, -4), B'(-3, 2)$ $(x, y) \to (x + 5, y + 6)$
9. $B(-8, 4), B'(3, -2)$ $(x, y) \to (x + 11, y - 6)$
10. $B(6, 8), B'(4, -5)$ $(x, y) \to (x - 2, y - 13)$
11. $B(-6, 8), B'(-4, -5)$ $(x, y) \to (x + 2, y - 13)$
12. $B(6, -8), B'(-4, 5)$ $(x, y) \to (x - 10, y + 13)$

**Mixed Review**

**Find the area of each rectangle.** *(From Last Year)*

13. 6 in., 3 in. — 18 in.$^2$
14. 8 cm, 2 cm — 16 cm$^2$
15. $l$ = 12 ft, $w$ = 8 ft — 96 ft$^2$

**Find the slope of the line through each pair of points.**

16. $B(3, 8), C(5, 6)$ slope = −1
17. $L(-9, 4), M(0, -5)$ slope = −1
18. $X(8, 8), Y(0, 3)$ slope = $\frac{5}{8}$



## Alternative Assessment

Have groups of students use a piece of poster board and transparencies, or other materials, to make a device on which they can draw figures on a coordinate plane and then rotate them.

12a.

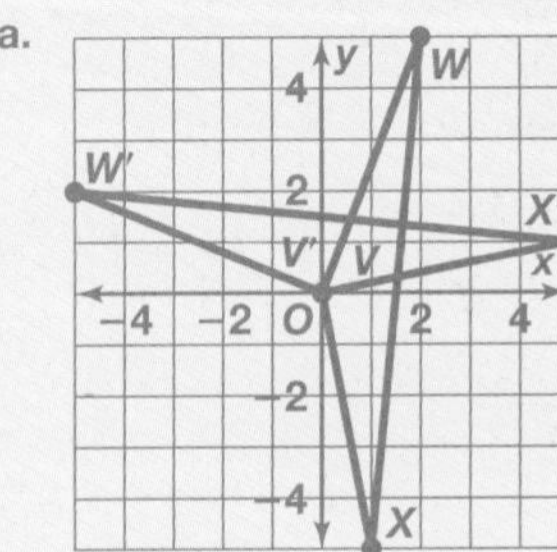

**Judging from appearance, tell whether each figure has rotational symmetry. If so, what is the angle of rotation?**

19. 
yes, 72°

20. 
yes, 180°

21. 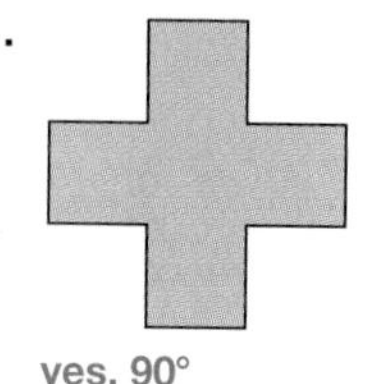
yes, 90°

22. 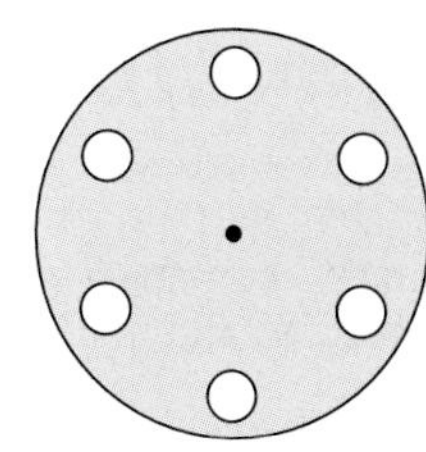
yes, 60°

**Does each figure have rotational symmetry? If so, what is the angle of rotation?**

23. equilateral triangle yes, 120°
24. rectangle yes, 180°
25. regular pentagon yes, 72°
26. trapezoid no
27. For Exercises 23–26, tell whether each figure has line symmetry. yes; yes; yes; yes if it is isosceles
28. *Writing* Describe something in your classroom that has rotational symmetry. What is the angle of rotation? Check students' work.
29. *Mathematical Reasoning* Is a rotation of 180° the same as a reflection across the $y$-axis? Justify your answer. No; the reflection of (2, 5) across the $y$-axis is (−2, 5). A 180° rotation image of (2, 5) is (−2, −5).

## Mixed Review

**The vertices of $\triangle ABC$ are $A(5, 6)$, $B(0, 3)$, and $C(3, 2)$. Reflect $\triangle ABC$ over the following lines.** *(Lesson 9-9)* 30–32. See back of book.

30. $x = -2$
31. $y = -2$
32. $x$-axis

**Find the slope of the line through each pair of points.** *(Lesson 8-3)*

33. $A(5, 9), B(5, 14)$ no slope or undefined
34. $C(-2, 4), D(-7, 14)$ −2
35. $E(2, 1), F(8, 4)$ $\frac{1}{2}$

36. *Choose a Strategy* How many three-digit numbers greater than 500 can you form using the digits 2, 6, and 8 exactly once each? four

Chapter Project 9

## Activity 3 Classifying

Here is the third clue: *An obtuse triangle connects Savannah, Everett, and the treasure island. The treasure is buried by the lighthouse on the island.* On which island is the treasure buried? Explain.
Sapelo Island; the line and circle intersect on Sapelo Island.

See also Extra Practice section.



## Project Activity 3

**Classifying** Remind students that an obtuse triangle has one obtuse angle. There are two islands that are 21 miles from Everett, but only one of them can be connected with Everett and Savannah with an obtuse triangle.

12b.

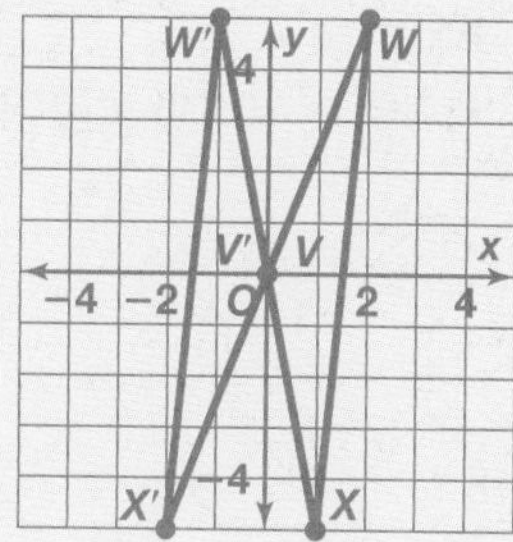


## Practice

**Judging from appearances, does each figure have rotational symmetry? If yes, what is the angle of rotation?**

1. no
2. yes; 180°
3. yes; 90°

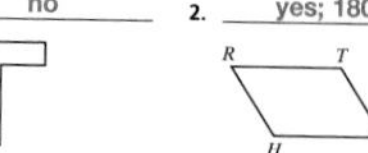


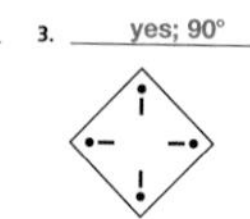

**The vertices of a triangle are given. Graph each triangle and its image after a rotation of (a) 90° and (b) 180° about the origin. Name the coordinates of the vertices of the images.**

4. $A(1, 4), B(1, 1), C(4, 2)$

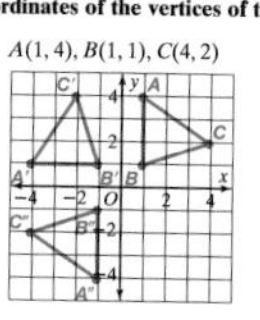


| 90° | | 180° | |
|---|---|---|---|
| $A'$ | (−4, 1) | $A''$ | (−1, −4) |
| $B'$ | (−1, 1) | $B''$ | (−1, −1) |
| $C'$ | (−2, 4) | $C''$ | (−4, −2) |

5. $S(2, 3), T(-2, 4), U(-4, 2)$

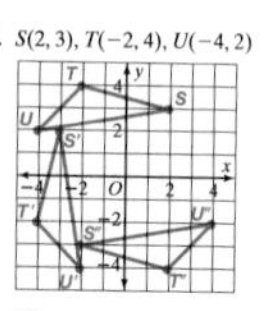


| 90° | | 180° | |
|---|---|---|---|
| $S'$ | (−3, 2) | $S''$ | (−2, −3) |
| $T'$ | (−4, −2) | $T''$ | (2, −4) |
| $U'$ | (−2, −4) | $U''$ | (4, −2) |

**Look for a pattern in Exercises 4 and 5 to complete the following.**

6. In a 90° rotation, $(x, y) \rightarrow$ (−y, x)
7. In a 180° rotation, $(x, y) \rightarrow$ (−x, −y)



## Reteaching

$\triangle PQR$ has vertices $P(1, 4)$, $Q(2, 1)$ and $R(4, 2)$. Graph the triangle and its image after a rotation of (a) 90° and (b) 180° about the origin.

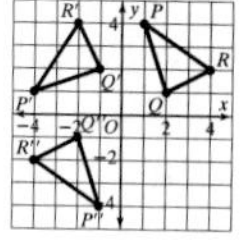


Graph $\triangle PQR$. Trace it onto tracing paper and label the vertices. Also trace the axes. Place your pencil at the origin. Turn the paper counterclockwise until the $y$-axis on the tracing paper is on top of the $x$-axis of the graph. Mark the position of each vertex by pressing through the paper. Connect the vertices of the rotated triangle and label them $P'$, $Q'$, and $R'$. The coordinates are $P'(-4, 1)$, $Q'(-1, 2)$, and $R'(-2, 4)$. Put your tracing paper back in its original position. Now turn it until +5 on the tracing paper $x$-axis is by −5 on the graph's $x$-axis. Mark the vertices, connect them, and label them $P''$, $Q''$, and $R''$. The coordinates are $P''(-1, -4)$, $Q''(-2, -1)$, and $R''(-4, -2)$.

1. The coordinates of $\triangle PQR$, its image after a 90° rotation $\triangle P'Q'R'$, and its image after a 180° rotation $\triangle P''Q''R''$ are listed in the table. Look for a pattern. What is the result on any point $(x, y)$ of (a) a 90° rotation, (b) an 180° rotation? Complete the table.

| Point | Image | |
|---|---|---|
| | 90° Rotation | 180° Rotation |
| $P(1, 4)$ | $P'(-4, 1)$ | $P''(-1, -4)$ |
| $Q(2, 1)$ | $Q'(-1, 2)$ | $Q''(-2, -1)$ |
| $R(4, 2)$ | $R'(-2, 4)$ | $R''(-4, -2)$ |
| $(x, y)$ | (−y, x) | (−x, −y) |

**The vertices of a triangle are given. Graph each triangle and its image after a rotation of (a) 90° and (b) 180° about the origin. Name the coordinates of the vertices of the images. Use tracing paper or the pattern you found.**

2. $J(1, 3), K(3, 3), L(1, 0)$

| 90° | | 180° | |
|---|---|---|---|
| $J'$ | (−3, 1) | $J''$ | (−1, −3) |
| $K'$ | (−3, 3) | $K''$ | (−3, −3) |
| $L'$ | (0, 1) | $L''$ | (−1, 0) |

3. $W(0, 4), Y(1, 2), Z(-1, 1)$

| 90° | | 180° | |
|---|---|---|---|
| $W'$ | (−4, 0) | $W''$ | (0, −4) |
| $Y'$ | (−2, 1) | $Y''$ | (−1, −2) |
| $Z'$ | (−1, −1) | $Z''$ | (1, −1) |



## Enrichment

The *gear ratio* of a 10-speed bicycle tells you how many times the wheels revolve each time the pedals revolve once. You can find the gear ratio by dividing the number of teeth engaged on the chain wheel by the number engaged on the flywheel.

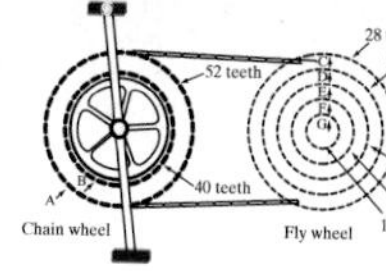


**Find the gear ratio when the given gears are engaged. Round to the nearest hundredth.**

1. $B$ and $E$ 2
2. $A$ and $C$ 1.86
3. $B$ and $F$ 2.35
4. What is the highest gear ratio? A to G = 3.71
5. What is the lowest gear ratio? B to C = 1.43

A rider's *cadence* is the number of pedal revolutions per minute.

6. A rider's cadence when the $B$ and $D$ gears are engaged is 32. Find the number of revolutions of the wheels in 5 min. Round to the nearest whole number. 267 revolutions
7. The diameter of a 10-speed bicycle wheel is 29 in., including tires. What is the circumference? Use 3.14 for $\pi$. Round to the nearest whole number. 91 in.

A rider's cadence is 25. The $A$ and $F$ gears are engaged.

8. How far does the bicycle travel in 1 min? Round to the nearest whole number. 6,959 in.
9. How far does the bicycle travel in 1 h? 417,540 in.
10. Find the rider's speed in mi/h (1 mi = 63,360 in.). Round to the nearest tenth. 6.6 mi/h
11. A rider's cadence is 80. The $B$ and $E$ gears are engaged. Find the rider's speed in mi/h. Round to the nearest tenth. 13.8 mi/h

## MATH TOOLBOX

### Tessellations

In Lesson 9-8, 9-9, and 9-10, students learned about three transformations: translations, rotations, and reflections. In this Math Toolbox, students use these transformations to create their own tessellation.

### Math Background

A tessellation is a mosaic pattern formed by fitting together (without overlapping or leaving spaces) a number of repeating polygons so that they could cover a plane. You can see tessellations in floor coverings, quilts, bathroom tiles, and in a honeycomb. The Greeks knew and proved that there are only three regular polygons that tile the plane using only one shape per tessellation. You can make these regular tessellations with equilateral triangles, squares, and regular hexagons. You may have seen tessellations in the designs of the famous artist M. C. Escher.

## Teaching Notes

**Error Prevention** To form a tessellation, the pattern must be capable of fitting together an infinite number of the repeating polygons. Verify that the design could continue in all directions in the same way to cover a plane.

**Monitoring Progress** Exercises 1–5
Success with tessellations depends on drawing the figures accurately and cutting out each one carefully.

**Block Scheduling** If you have block scheduling or extended periods, you may wish to insert this Math Toolbox lesson between Part 1 of Lesson 9-10 and Part 2 of Lesson 9-10.

1. 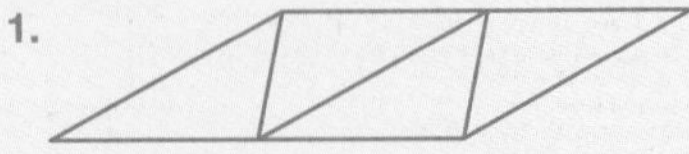

## MATH TOOLBOX

*Extension*
*After Lesson 9-10*

# *Tessellations*

A *tessellation* is a repeating pattern of figures that completely covers a plane without gaps or overlaps. You can see tessellations in art, architecture, and nature.

You can use translations, rotations, and reflections to create a tessellation.

### EXAMPLE

**Show how the figure at the right forms a tessellation.**

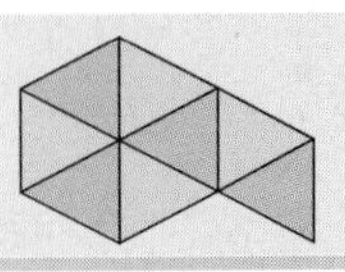

Rotate and translate the figure to cover the plane.

**Make multiple copies of each figure on graph paper. Determine whether each figure can form a tessellation. If it does, show the tessellation.**

1. 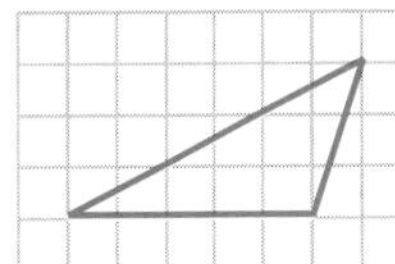
See margin.

2. 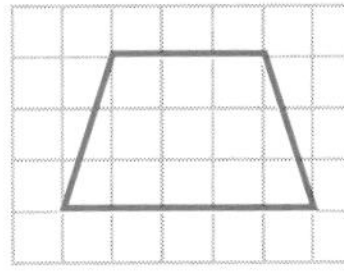
See margin.

3. 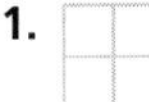
Will not tessellate.

4. 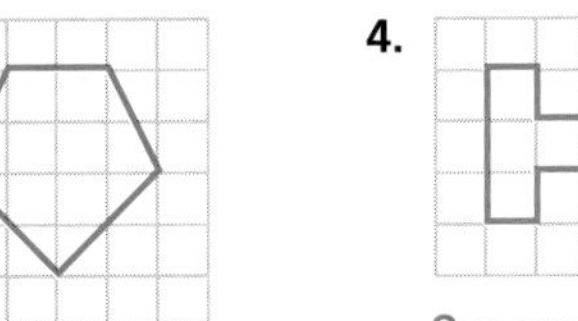
See margin.

5. *Open-ended* The diagram below shows how to create a shape to use as a repeating figure for a tessellation. Following the instructions shown, create your own tessellation. Check students' work.

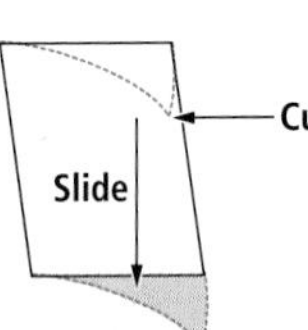

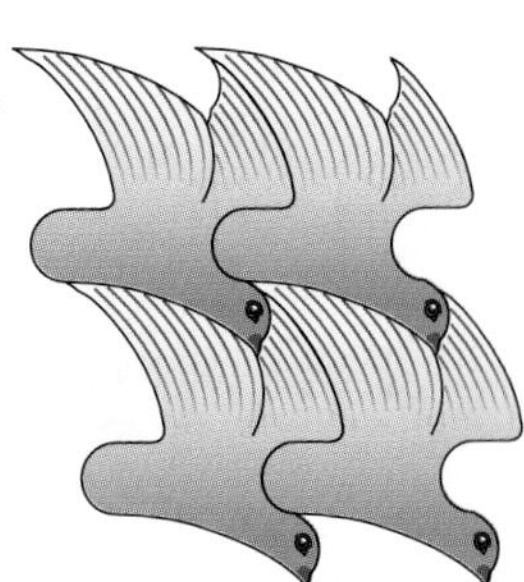

6. *Critical Thinking* Draw regular polygons with 3, 4, 5, 6, 7, and 8 sides. Which ones can you use to create a tessellation? 3, 4, and 6



• **Additional Example**
Show how this figure forms a tessellation.

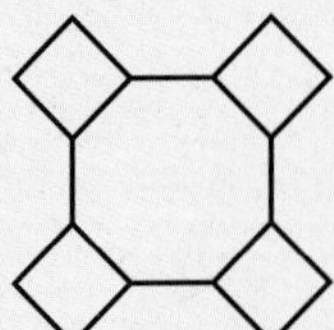

2. 

4. 

# FINISHING THE CHAPTER PROJECT

**Draw a Treasure Map** The Project Activities on pages 458, 478, and 493 will help you complete your project. Here is a checklist to help you gather the different parts.

- ✔ your drawing of the map, including the lines and figures defined in the activities
- ✔ your answers to the questions
- ✔ your explanations of your reasoning

Make a poster to display your map. Mark the location of the treasure. On the poster, include the clues you followed and an explanation of how your map relates to the clues.

*Reflect and Revise*

Ask a friend or someone at home to review your poster. Are your drawings neat and accurate? Are your explanations complete and clear? If necessary, make changes to improve your poster.

### *Web Extension*

**Visit Prentice Hall's Web site. You'll find some interesting links and ideas related to maps. You'll also be able to share information about your project.**

**www.phschool.com**

**Project Day** You may wish to plan a project day on which students share their completed projects. Encourage students to explain their processes as well as their products.

**Block Scheduling** If you have block scheduling or extended periods, you may wish to intersperse the sharing of projects over Days 3 and 4 between the completion of one lesson and the start of a new lesson.

### Project Notebook

Have students review their project work and bring their notebooks up to date. Call attention to the fact that they can share their projects with other students through the Web site **www.phschool.com**.

Be sure students include in their notebooks their completed Project Manager and Scoring Rubric forms.

**Portfolio** Students may wish to include their projects and/or their project notebooks in their portfolios.

### Web Extension

**Tell Us About Your Project**

Students may wish to share their projects with other students on the Web site: **www.phschool.com.**

### Scoring Rubric

**3** You draw all figures and find the treasure correctly. Your poster is complete, neat, well-organized, and easy to read. Your reasoning is appropriate and explained well.

**2** You make minor errors in your figures or your reasoning. Your poster is complete and descriptive, but it could be better organized or neater.

**1** You draw figures or reason incorrectly. Your poster is incomplete and lacks organization.

**0** Major elements of the project are incomplete or missing.

## Wrap Up

### Resources

Glossary, p. 748
Extra Practice, p. 718

For a complete list of resources for the chapter, see p. 439H.

### Quarterly Assessment Form A Page 1

1. Solve $3n - \frac{3}{4} = 5n$.
   (A.) $n = -\frac{3}{8}$  B. $n = -2\frac{1}{3}$
   C. $n = 6$  D. $n = -\frac{3}{32}$
2. Solve $-4 \leq 2x + 12$.
   F. $x \leq -8$  (G.) $x \geq -8$
   H. $x \leq -4$  J. $x \geq -4$
3. Solve $A = \frac{1}{2}bh$, for $h$.
   (A.) $h = \frac{2A}{b}$  B. $h = 2Ab$
   C. $h = \frac{2b}{A}$  D. $h = \frac{1}{2Ab}$
4. Find the simple interest on $860 deposited at an interest rate of 3.5% for 3 years.
   F. $30.10  G. $301
   (H.) $90.30  J. $77.40
5. Find the balance on $6,000 deposited at 4% compounded semi-annually for 2 years.
   A. $6,480.00  (B.) $6,494.59
   C. $6,489.60  D. $6,490.25
6. Which of the following relations is a function?
   F. $\{(4, 7), (-4, 7), (-4, -7)\}$
   G. $\{(-3, 5), (2, 4), (-3, 8)\}$
   (H.) $\{(2, 3), (3, 2), (-2, 3)\}$
   J. $\{(9, -1), (0, 5), (0, -6)\}$
7. The line with equation $2x - 3y = 5$ has slope
   (A.) $\frac{2}{3}$  B. $\frac{3}{2}$
   C. $-\frac{5}{3}$  D. $-\frac{2}{3}$
8. A board 36 in. long is cut in two pieces. Which equation describes the situation?
   F. $x + 2y = 36$  G. $x = y - 36$
   H. $x - y = 36$  (J.) $x = 36 - y$
9. A circle has diameter 70 ft. Find the circumference. Use 3.14 for $\pi$. Round to the nearest foot.
   A. 35 ft  B. 110 ft
   C. 440 ft  (D.) 220 ft
10. The length of a rectangle is 3 cm more than twice the width. The perimeter is 84 cm. Find the length.
    F. $40\frac{1}{2}$ cm  (G.) 29 cm
    H. 13 cm  J. 58 cm
11. Which of the following must be true if $\triangle BNR \cong \triangle QTA$?
    A. $\overline{NB} \cong \overline{AQ}$
    B. $\angle N \cong \angle A$
    C. $\overline{RB} \cong \overline{AT}$
    (D.) $\angle RBN \cong \angle AQT$
12. The lengths of the sides of a quadrilateral are 8 in., 4 in., 8 in., and 4 in. Which type of quadrilateral could it be?
    (F.) parallelogram  G. trapezoid
    H. square  J. rhombus
13. Which ordered pair is *not* a solution to $5x - 4y < 2$?
    A. (1, 2)  B. (2, 3)
    (C.) (−1, −2)  D. (0, 1)



### Quarterly Assessment Form A Page 2

14. Graph $y = -\frac{2}{3}x + 2$.

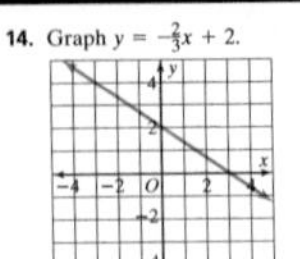

15. Graph $y > 2x - 3$.

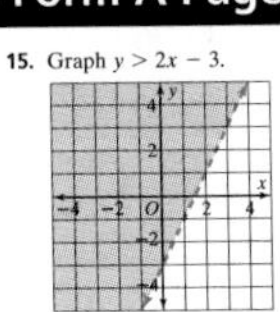

**Use the data in the table for 16–19.**

| Hours Spent Weekly | |
|---|---|
| Doing Homework | Watching TV |
| 2 | 10 |
| 5 | 6 |
| 8 | 3 |
| 4 | 6 |
| 6 | 4 |

16. Make a (homework, TV) scatter plot.
17. Is there a *positive correlation*, a *negative correlation*, or *no correlation* between the sets of data in your scatter plot?
    negative correlation
18. Draw a trend line and use it to predict how many hours a student who watches TV 8 hours a week would spend doing homework. Sample answer is shown.
    3 hours
19. Write an equation for your trend line. Sample answer is shown.
    $y = -x + 11$

**Find the coordinates of the image of a segment whose endpoints are $D(-1, -2)$ and $K(2, -3)$ after each transformation.**

20. a translation of left 3 and up 4 — $D'(-4, 2), K'(-1, 1)$
21. a reflection over the $x$-axis — $D'(-1, 2), K'(2, 3)$
22. a rotation of 90° about the origin — $D'(2, -1), K'(3, 2)$
23. Are the coordinates of the image of a point under a translation a function of the coordinates of the original point? Explain.
    Yes; for each point, there is only one image.





# 9 Wrap Up

## Key Terms

adjacent angles (p. 449)
alternate interior angles (p. 450)
angle bisector (p. 476)
angle of rotation (p. 490)
center of rotation (p. 490)
central angle (p. 470)
complementary angles (p. 449)
congruent angles (p. 449)
corresponding angles (p. 450)
image (p. 479)
line (p. 442)
line of reflection (p. 486)
line of symmetry (p. 485)
parallel (p. 443)
perpendicular bisector (p. 475)
perpendicular lines (p. 475)
plane (p. 442)
point (p. 442)
polygon (p. 454)
ray (p. 442)
reflection (p. 486)
reflectional symmetry (p. 485)
regular polygon (p. 456)
rotation (p. 490)
rotational symmetry (p. 491)
segment (p. 442)
segment bisector (p. 475)
skew (p. 443)
supplementary angles (p. 449)
transformation (p. 479)
translation (p. 479)
transversal (p. 450)
vertical angles (p. 449)

## Graphic Organizer

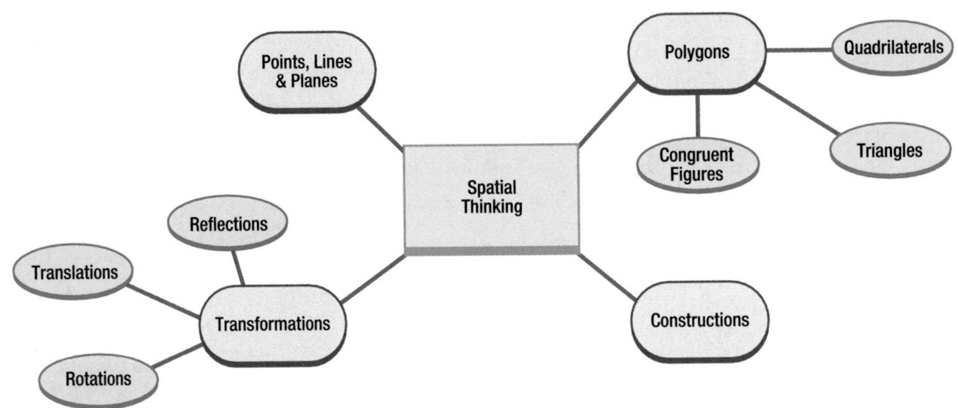


## Points, Lines, and Planes — 9-1

**Summary** A **point** is a position in space. All geometric figures are made up of points. A **line** is a series of points that extends in two directions without end. A **segment** is a part of a line and has two endpoints. A **ray** is a part of a line with exactly one endpoint. An angle is two rays that intersect at their endpoints.

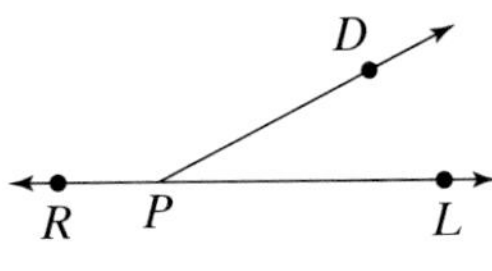


**Name the following in the figure above.**

1. three angles $\angle RPD, \angle DPL, \angle RPL$
2. three rays $\overrightarrow{PR}, \overrightarrow{PD}, \overrightarrow{PL}$
3. four segments $\overline{RP}, \overline{PD}, \overline{PL}, \overline{RL}$
4. four points $R, P, D, L$
5. a line $\overleftrightarrow{RL}$

## Angle Relationships and Parallel Lines — 9-2

*Summary* **Adjacent angles** share a vertex and a side but no points in their interiors. **Vertical angles** are formed by intersecting lines and are **congruent**. If parallel lines are crossed by a **transversal** their **corresponding angles** are congruent. **Alternate interior angles** of parallel lines are also congruent.

**Use the diagram at the right. $m \parallel n$**

6. Name all angles congruent to $\angle 1$. $\angle 3, \angle 5, \angle 7$
7. Name two pairs of supplementary angles. Answers may vary. Samples: $\angle 2$ and $\angle 3$, $\angle 5$ and $\angle 6$
8. Name all pairs of corresponding angles. $\angle 1$ and $\angle 5$, $\angle 2$ and $\angle 6$, $\angle 3$ and $\angle 7$, $\angle 4$ and $\angle 8$
9. Name all pairs of alternate interior angles. $\angle 4$ and $\angle 6$, $\angle 3$ and $\angle 5$
10. If $m\angle 2 = 75°$, find the measures of all the other angles. $m\angle 1 = 105°$, $m\angle 3 = 105°$, $m\angle 4 = 75°$, $m\angle 5 = 105°$, $m\angle 6 = 75°$, $m\angle 7 = 105°$, $m\angle 8 = 75°$

## Classifying Polygons and Congruent Polygons — 9-3 and 9-5

*Summary* A **polygon** is a closed figure with at least three sides. Polygons with the same size and shape are congruent. A triangle can be classified by its angles and its sides. You can show two triangles are congruent using **S**ide–**S**ide–**S**ide, **S**ide–**A**ngle–**S**ide, and **A**ngle–**S**ide–**A**ngle. You can classify some quadrilaterals as parallelograms, rectangles, squares, rhombuses, or trapezoids.

**Use the most precise name for each figure described.**

11. a triangle with all sides congruent equilateral triangle
12. a parallelogram with all sides congruent and four 90° angles square
13. a triangle with all acute angles and exactly two congruent sides isosceles acute triangle
14. a quadrilateral with exactly one pair of parallel sides trapezoid

**List the congruent corresponding parts of each of the triangles below. Write a congruence statement for the triangles.**

15. 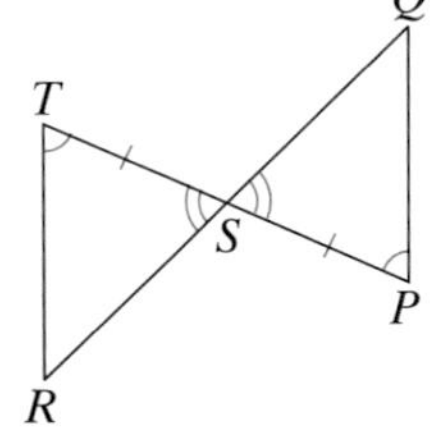


$\angle T \cong \angle P$, $\overline{ST} \cong \overline{SP}$, $\angle RST \cong \angle QSP$, $\triangle RST \cong \triangle QSP$ by ASA

16. 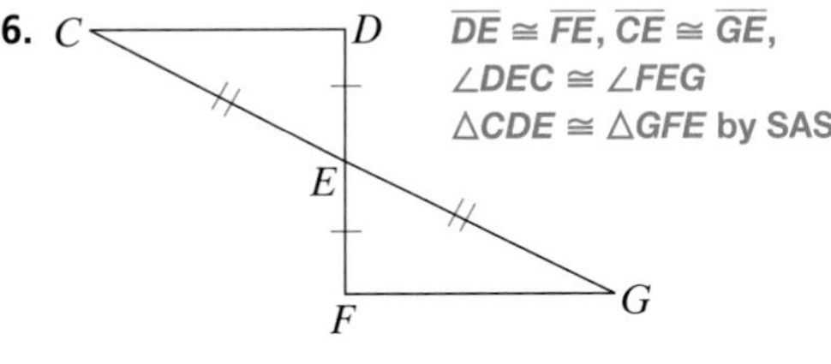


$\overline{DE} \cong \overline{FE}$, $\overline{CE} \cong \overline{GE}$, $\angle DEC \cong \angle FEG$, $\triangle CDE \cong \triangle GFE$ by SAS



**Portfolio** Students may wish to include their completed work for the Wrap Up in their portfolios.

**Web Site**

Students can find self-assessment materials on the Web site: **www.phschool.com.**

### Quarterly Assessment Form B Page 1

**Circle the letter of the best answer.**

1. Solve $\frac{2}{3}y + 4 = 12$.
   A. $y = 12$ B. $y = 5\frac{1}{3}$ C. $y = 14$ D. $y = 24$
2. Solve $3 - z < -1$.
   F. $z < 4$ G. $z \geq 3$ H. $z > 2$ J. $z > 4$
3. Solve $A = \pi r^2$, for $\pi$.
   A. $\pi = \frac{A}{r^2}$ B. $\pi = \frac{r^2}{A}$ C. $\pi = Ar^2$ D. $\pi = \frac{A}{r}$
4. Find the simple interest on $980 deposited at an interest rate of 2.5% for 4 years.
   F. $24.50 G. $98.00 H. $245.00 J. $101.74
5. Find the balance on $4,000 deposited at 6% compounded semi-annually for 2 years.
   A. $4,490.25 B. $4,480.00 C. $4,494.40 D. $4,502.04
6. Which of the following relations is a function?
   F. $\{(-8, 3), (3, 5), (-8, 5)\}$
   G. $\{(-7, 2), (-7, 5), (5, 2)\}$
   H. $\{(4, 9), (9, 4), (-4, 9)\}$
   J. $\{(1, 0), (-1, 6), (-1, 10)\}$
7. The line with equation $4x - 7y = 6$ has slope
   A. $-\frac{7}{4}$ B. $\frac{7}{4}$ C. $-\frac{4}{7}$ D. $\frac{4}{7}$
8. A number $x$ is three times a number $y$. Which equation describes the two numbers?
   F. $xy = 3$ G. $y = 3x$ H. $x = 3y$ J. $x = y + 3$
9. A circle has diameter 40 in. Find the circumference. Use 3.14 for $\pi$. Round to the nearest inch.
   A. 63 in. B. 126 in. C. 20 in. D. 1,256 in.
10. The length of a rectangle is 4 cm more than twice the width. The perimeter is 74 cm. Find the length.
    F. 26 cm G. 11 cm H. 52 cm J. 22 cm
11. Which of the following must be true if $\triangle PRK \cong \triangle CNJ$?
    A. $\angle RKP \cong \angle JNC$
    B. $\overline{RK} \cong \overline{CJ}$
    C. $\overline{KP} \cong \overline{JC}$
    D. $\angle K \cong \angle N$
12. The lengths of the sides of a quadrilateral are all 7 ft. The quadrilateral could *not* be which of the following?
    F. square G. trapezoid H. rectangle J. rhombus
13. Which ordered pair is *not* a solution to $3x - 5y < 4$?
    A. (2, 1) B. (2, 3) C. (−2, 1) D. (1, −2)



### Quarterly Assessment Form B Page 2

14. Graph $y = -\frac{3}{4}x + 1$.
15. Graph $y < 3x + 1$.

**Use the data in the table for 16–19.**

| Hours Spent Weekly | |
|---|---|
| Doing Homework | Playing Video games |
| 3 | 8 |
| 9 | 2 |
| 5 | 5 |
| 3 | 7 |
| 4 | 6 |

16. Make a (homework, video games) scatter plot.
17. Is there a *positive correlation*, a *negative correlation*, or *no correlation* between the sets of data in your scatter plot? negative correlation
18. Draw a trend line and use it to predict how many hours a student who plays video games 3 hours a week would spend doing homework. Sample answer is shown. 8 hours
19. Write an equation for your trend line. Sample answer is shown. $y = -\frac{9}{10}x + 10$

Hours Spent Weekly (Hours playing video games vs. Hours doing homework)

**Find the coordinates of the image of a segment whose endpoints are $D(2, -1)$ and $K(4, 2)$ after each transformation.**

20. a translation of left 5 and down 1 $D'(-3, -2)$, $K'(-1, 1)$
21. a reflection over the $y$-axis $D'(-2, -1)$, $K'(-4, 2)$
22. a rotation of 90° about the origin $D'(1, 2)$, $K'(-2, 4)$
23. Are the coordinates of the image of a point under a translation a function of the coordinates of the original point? Explain. Yes; for each point, there is only one image.

## Draw a Diagram 9-4

**Summary** Drawing a diagram helps you visualize a problem.

**17.** A house is to be built on a lot 70 ft wide by 100 ft deep. The shorter side of the lot faces the street. The house must be set back from the street at least 25 ft. It must be 20 ft from the back lot line and 10 ft from each side lot line. What are the maximum length and width of the house? 55 ft long, 50 ft wide

## Circles 9-6

**Summary** You can use these formulas to find the circumference of a circle: $C = \pi \cdot d$ and $C = 2\pi r$.
There are 360° in a circle. An angle whose vertex is the center of a circle is a **central angle.**

**18.** Find the circumference of a circle with a diameter of 14 cm. about 44 cm

**19.** *Television Programming* Suppose a survey indicates that at 8 P.M. 40% of viewers watched channel $X$, 25% watched channel $Y$, and 35% watched channel $Z$. Make a circle graph of the data. See margin.

## Constructions 9-7

**Summary** You can use a compass and straightedge to construct congruent segments, congruent angles, **segment bisectors,** and **angle bisectors**.

**Draw $\triangle CDE$ with an obtuse $\angle D$.**

**20.** Construct the bisector of $\angle D$. See margin.

**21.** Construct the perpendicular bisector of $\overline{DE}$. See margin.

## Translations, Reflections, and Rotations 9-8, 9-9 and 9-10

**Summary** A **transformation** is a change of position or size of a figure. The figure after the transformation is called the **image**. You can transform figures in a plane by a **translation**, a **reflection**, or a **rotation**.

**What is the image of point $A(7, -2)$ after each transformation?**

**22.** 4 units right, 3 units up $A'(11, 1)$

**23.** reflection over the $y$-axis $A'(-7, -2)$

**24.** rotation of 90° $A'(2, 7)$

**25.** reflection over the line $y = -1$ $A'(7, 0)$

**26.** *Writing* How do translations, reflections, and rotations affect the size and shape of an image? Explain. In each case the image is congruent to the original figure. None of these transformations affect size or shape.



19. Television Programming

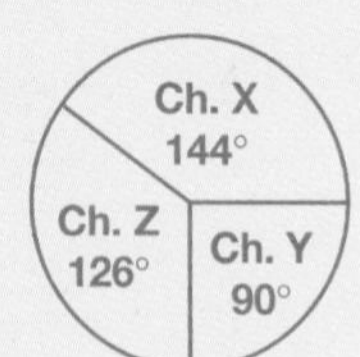


20.

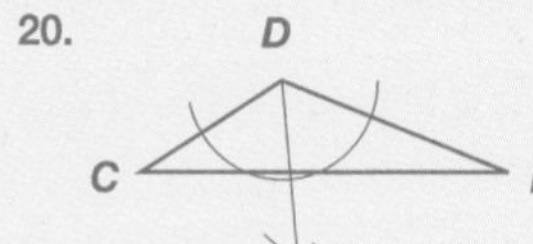


21.

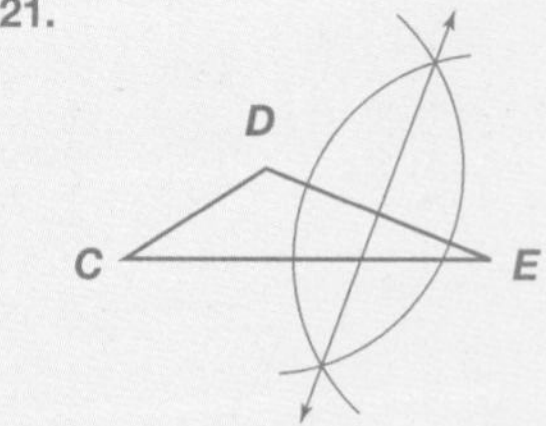


## Chapter Assessment Form A Page 1

**Circle the letter of the best answer.**

1. Find the perimeter of a square that has a side measure of 45 cm.
   A. 90 cm B. 135 cm (C.) 180 cm D. 225 cm
2. Find the perimeter of a rectangle that has length 15 in. and width 12 in.
   (F.) 54 in. G. 42 in. H. 39 in. J. 27 in.
3. A circle has a radius of 4.7 cm. Find the circumference to the nearest tenth. Use 3.14 for $\pi$.
   A. 14.8 cm B. 69.4 cm C. 19.5 cm (D.) 29.5 cm
4. The measures of two angles of a triangle are 28° and 58°. What is the measure of the third angle?
   F. 28° G. 16° (H.) 94° J. 58°
5. The measure of two angles of a triangle are 28° and 58°. Classify the triangle by its angles.
   (A.) obtuse B. acute C. right D. equilateral
6. Which of the following is a line perpendicular to $\overleftrightarrow{BE}$ in the diagram on the right?
   F. $\overleftrightarrow{CF}$ (G.) $\overleftrightarrow{GD}$
   H. $\overleftrightarrow{AE}$ J. $\overleftrightarrow{AF}$
7. Which of the following is an angle vertical to $\angle BAC$ in the diagram above?
   A. $\angle CAE$ B. $\angle CAD$ C. $\angle GAF$ (D.) $\angle FAE$
8. Which of the following is *not* a name for $\overleftrightarrow{CF}$ in the diagram above?
   F. $\overleftrightarrow{FC}$ (G.) $\overleftrightarrow{AE}$ H. $\overleftrightarrow{AC}$ J. $\overleftrightarrow{FA}$
9. Which of the following is *not* a ray on $\overleftrightarrow{GD}$ in the diagram above?
   A. $\overrightarrow{GD}$ B. $\overrightarrow{AD}$ (C.) $\overrightarrow{AC}$ D. $\overrightarrow{AG}$
10. Which of the following is *never* a quadrilateral with 4 right angles?
   F. parallelogram G. rectangle H. square (J.) trapezoid

**Find the coordinates of the image of a segment whose endpoints are $D(-2, 3)$ and $K(1, 2)$ after each transformation.**

11. a translation of right 4 and down 2 $D'(2, 1), K'(5, 0)$
12. a reflection over the $x$-axis $D'(-2, -3), K'(1, -2)$
13. a rotation of 90° about the origin $D'(-3, -2), K'(-2, 1)$



## Chapter Assessment Form A Page 2

14. Construct the bisector of $\angle A$.

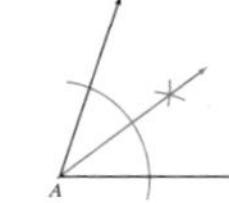


**Use the figure on the right for 15-17.**

15. Write an equation and use it to find the value of $x$.
    $9x - 32 = 7x + 4$; $x = 18$
16. Find $m\angle 1$ 130°
17. Find $m\angle 2$ 50°

**To make a circle graph of the following information, what should the measure of each central angle be?**

Fifty students were asked their favorite season. Thirty said summer, 15 said winter, and the rest said spring or fall.

18. Summer 216°
19. Winter 108°
20. Spring or Fall 36°

**Solve. A diagram may help.**

21. The perimeter of a triangle is 24 cm. One side is 2 centimeters longer than the shortest side. The longest side is 2 centimeters less than twice the length of the shortest side. Find the length of each side of the triangle.
    6 cm, 8 cm, and 10 cm
22. Draw two triangles that are congruent. Mark corresponding sides and angles congruent so that you could show the triangles are congruent by ASA. Sample answer is shown.

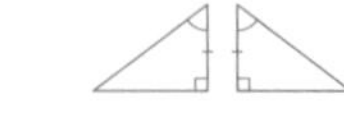



Assessment

# Assessment

**Use the diagram to name the following.**

1. all segments containing point $G$ $\overline{GQ}, \overline{GD}$
2. all vertical angles See below right.
3. all rays containing point $M$ $\overrightarrow{MQ}, \overrightarrow{QM}, \overrightarrow{TM}$
4. a line containing point $T$ $\overleftrightarrow{MT}$

2. $\angle GQT$ and $\angle MQD$, $\angle GQM$ and $\angle TQD$

**Use the diagram to name the following.**

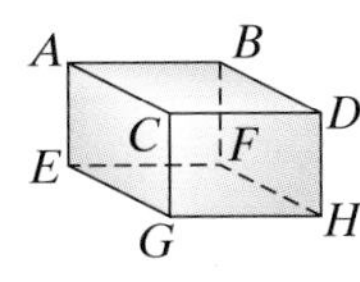


5. four segments that intersect $\overline{AB}$ $\overline{AC}, \overline{AE}, \overline{BD}, \overline{BF}$
6. three segments parallel to $\overline{AB}$ $\overline{CD}, \overline{EF}, \overline{GH}$

**For Exercises 7 and 8, name all possible polygons for each description.**

7. quadrilateral with at least one pair of parallel sides and at least two right angles trapezoid, rectangle, square
8. quadrilateral with one diagonal that divides it into two congruent equilateral triangles a rhombus that is not a square
9. Find the perimeter of an equilateral triangle that has a side measure of 60 cm. 180 cm
10. Find the perimeter of a square that has a side measure of 60 cm. 240 cm
11. The perimeter of a rectangle is 58 cm. One side is 18 cm. Find the lengths of the other three sides. 18 cm, 11 cm, 11 cm

**A segment has endpoints $A(-3, -6)$ and $M(-3, -4)$. Find the coordinates of the endpoints after each transformation.**

12. a translation of 4 units right and 3 units up $A'(1, -3), M'(1, -1)$
13. a reflection over the $y$-axis $A'(3, -6), M'(3, -4)$
14. a rotation of $90°$ $A'(6, -3), M'(4, -3)$
15. Draw a segment. Construct its perpendicular bisector. See margin.
16. *Open-ended* Draw an obtuse angle. Construct its angle bisector. See margin.

**Use the diagram for Exercises 17 and 18.**

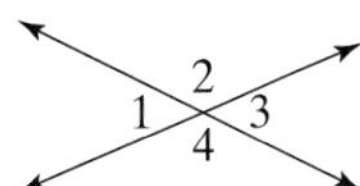


17. If $m\angle 2 = 130°$, find $m\angle 4$. 130°
18. *Writing* Describe how you can find $m\angle 1$ if you know $m\angle 2$. Subtract the measure of $\angle 2$ from 180°.
19. *Statistics* Forty two-year-old children were asked their favorite color. Five chose yellow, seven chose blue, and fourteen chose red. The rest chose other colors.
    a. To make a circle graph, what should be the measure of the central angle representing blue, red, and yellow? Round to the nearest degree. See below.
    b. Create a circle graph for the information. See margin.

19a. blue: 63°; red: 126°; yellow: 45°

20. If $\overline{AB} \cong \overline{CD}$, $\angle A \cong \angle D$, and $\angle B \cong \angle C$, what method can you use to show that $\triangle ABE \cong \triangle DCF$? ASA
21. *Open-ended* Draw and describe a figure that has rotational symmetry. Check students' work.
22. a. The measures of two angles of a triangle are 50° and 35°. What is the measure of the third angle? 95°
    b. Classify the triangle by its angles. obtuse
23. $\triangle CAB \cong \triangle DEB$. Find as many angle measures and side lengths as you can.

$DE = 3$, $BD = 5$, $m\angle C = 90°$, $m\angle D = 90°$, $m\angle ABC = 31°$, $m\angle EBD = 31°$, $m\angle A = 59°$

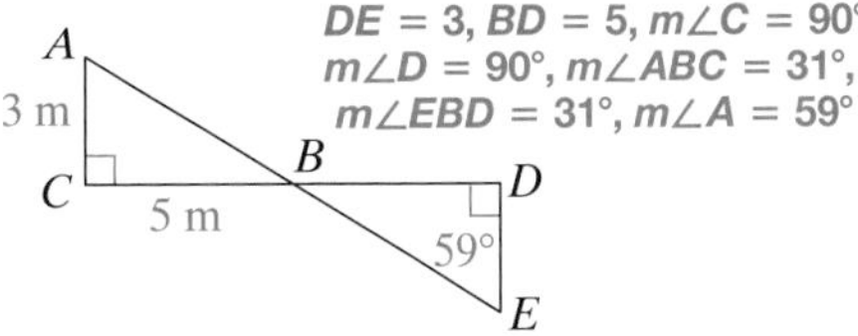

15.

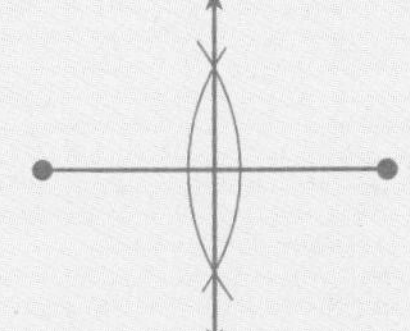

16.

19.b.

Favorite Colors

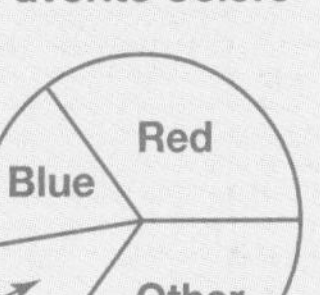


## Chapter Assessment

**Resources** For a complete list of resources for this chapter, see p. 439H.

### Chapter Assessment Form B Page 1

**Circle the letter of the best answer.**

1. Find the perimeter of an equilateral triangle that has a side measure of 45 cm.
   A. 90 cm  (B.) 135 cm  C. 180 cm  D. 225 cm
2. Find the perimeter of a rectangle that has length 19 in. and width 14 in.
   F. 33 in.  G. 47 in.  H. 52 in.  (J.) 66 in.
3. A circle has a radius of 6.2 cm. Find the circumference to the nearest tenth. Use 3.14 for $\pi$.
   (A.) 38.9 cm  B. 19.5 cm  C. 9.7 cm  D. 120.7 cm
4. The measure of two angles of a triangle are 36° and 54°. What is the measure of the third angle?
   F. 10°  (G.) 90°  H. 36°  J. 54°
5. The measure of two angles of a triangle are 36° and 54°. Classify the triangle by its angles.
   A. equilateral  B. obtuse  C. acute  (D.) right
6. Which of the following is a line parallel to $\overleftrightarrow{AB}$ in the diagram on the right?
   F. $\overleftrightarrow{BH}$  G. $\overleftrightarrow{BF}$
   (H.) $\overleftrightarrow{EG}$  J. $\overleftrightarrow{BA}$
7. Which of the following is an angle vertical to $\angle BFG$ in the diagram above?
   (A.) $\angle EFH$  B. $\angle EFB$  C. $\angle GFH$  D. $\angle ABD$
8. Which of the following is *not* a name for $\overleftrightarrow{BF}$ in the diagram above?
   F. $\overleftrightarrow{FB}$  G. $\overleftrightarrow{DB}$  (H.) $\overleftrightarrow{AB}$  J. $\overleftrightarrow{HD}$
9. Which of the following is *not* a ray on $\overleftrightarrow{FE}$ in the diagram above?
   A. $\overrightarrow{GE}$  (B.) $\overrightarrow{FB}$  C. $\overrightarrow{FG}$  D. $\overrightarrow{EF}$
10. Which of the following is *not* a quadrilateral with opposite sides parallel?
    F. parallelogram  G. rhombus  (H.) trapezoid  J. rectangle

**Find the coordinates of the image of a segment whose endpoints are $D(3, 2)$ and $K(1, -1)$ after each transformation.**

11. a translation of 4 units left and 2 units up $D'(-1, 4), K'(-3, 1)$
12. a reflection over the $y$-axis $D'(-3, 2), K'(-1, -1)$



### Chapter Assessment Form B Page 2

13. a rotation of 90° about the origin $D'(-2, 3), K'(1, 1)$
14. Construct an angle congruent to $\angle A$.

**Use the figure on the right for 15-17.**

15. Write an equation and use it to find the value of $x$.
    $9x - 24 = 5x + 40; x = 16$
16. Find $m\angle 1$. 120°
17. Find $m\angle 2$. 60°

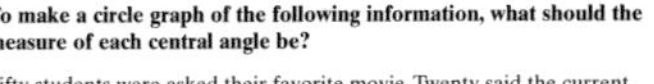

**To make a circle graph of the following information, what should the measure of each central angle be?**

Fifty students were asked their favorite movie. Twenty said the current number one movie, 25 said the current number two movie, and the rest said something else.

18. current number one movie 144°
19. current number two movie 180°
20. other 36°

**Solve. A diagram may help**

21. The perimeter of a triangle is 30 cm. One side is 7 centimeters longer than the shortest side. The longest side is 3 centimeters more than twice the length of the shortest side. Find the length of each side of the triangle.
    5 cm, 12 cm, 13 cm
22. Draw two triangles that are congruent. Mark corresponding sides and angles congruent so that you could show the triangles are congruent by SAS. Sample answer is shown.

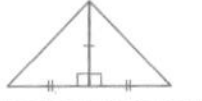



Assessment

# Cumulative Review

## Cumulative Review Page 1

**Circle the letter of the best answer.**

1. Which expression simplifies to $x + 2$?
   (A.) $\frac{1}{3}(3x + 6)$ B. $5 - x - 3$ C. $\frac{1}{3}(x + 12) - 2$ D. $7x - 5x + 2$
2. Find the mean of 12, 15, 18, and 23.
   F. 15 (G.) 17 H. 18 J. 16
3. Which expression is equivalent to $x \cdot x \cdot y \cdot 2 \cdot (-y) \cdot x \cdot 5$?
   A. $-10x^2y^3$ B. $10x^3y^2$ C. $10x^2y^3$ (D.) $-10x^3y^2$
4. Simplify $-5 + \frac{3}{5}$.
   F. $-5\frac{3}{5}$ G. $4\frac{2}{5}$ (H.) $-4\frac{2}{5}$ J. $5\frac{3}{5}$
5. Which measure is equivalent to $\frac{2}{3}$ yd?
   A. 1 ft (B.) 2 ft C. 12 in. D. 18 in.
6. 70% of $z$ is 140. Find $z$.
   F. 98 (G.) 200 H. 500 J. 0.005
7. Solve $5x - 3 = 7x + 11$.
   (A.) $x = -7$ B. $x = 4$ C. $x = \frac{3}{4}$ D. $x = 7$
8. Find the slope of the line through (4, 2) and (−2, 6).
   F. $-1\frac{1}{2}$ G. $1\frac{1}{2}$ (H.) $-\frac{2}{3}$ J. $\frac{2}{3}$
9. The measure of the complement of an angle with measure 18° is what?
   A. 81° (B.) 72° C. 162° D. 82°
10. Which number is less than 10?
    F. the LCM of 4 and 3 G. the GCF of 32 and 48
    H. the GCF of 24 and 36 (J.) the LCM of 3 and 9
11. In $\triangle PQR$, $m\angle P = 38°$ and $m\angle Q = 52°$. Classify $\triangle PQR$.
    A. acute (B.) right C. obtuse D. equilateral
12. Simplify $\frac{8 - 4(2 \cdot 4)}{4}$
    −6
13. Given: $\triangle JKL \cong \triangle PQR$. Complete the following:
    $\angle K \cong$ $\angle Q$  $\overline{LJ} \cong$ $\overline{RP}$
14. Name all the different rays shown in the figure.
    $\overrightarrow{DE}, \overrightarrow{ED}, \overrightarrow{EF}, \overrightarrow{FE}, \overrightarrow{DF}, \overrightarrow{FD}$



Assessment

## Cumulative Review Page 2

**For Exercises 15–17, use $\triangle STU$ with vertices $S(1, 4)$, $T(1, 1)$, and $U(3, 0)$.**

15. Graph $\triangle STU$ and then graph the image of its translation 4 units left and 3 units down.

16. Graph $\triangle STU$ and then graph its reflection over the $x$-axis.

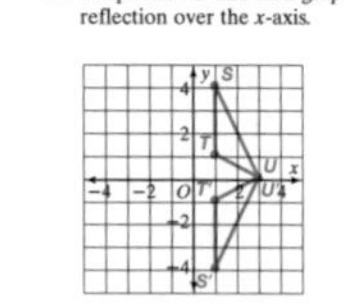

17. Graph $\triangle STU$ and then graph the image of its rotation 90°.

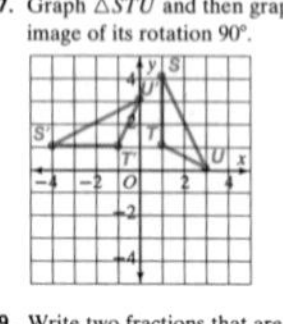

18. Construct the perpendicular bisector of $\overline{AB}$.

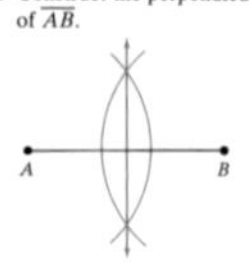

19. Write two fractions that are equivalent to $\frac{4a}{b}$.
    Sample answer is shown. $\frac{8a}{2b}, \frac{12a}{3b}$
20. Explain how you can show two triangles are congruent.
    Sample answer is shown. You can show SAS, that two sides and the angle between them in one triangle are congruent to corresponding parts of the other triangle.



# 9 Cumulative Review

**Preparing for Algebra**

**Choose the best answer.**

1. Simplify $\frac{10 - 5(5 \cdot 2)}{10}$. C
   A. 5 B. 4 C. −4 D. −1.5
2. Which expression simplifies to $x + 2$? F
   F. $\frac{1}{2}(2x + 4)$ G. $10 - x - 8$
   H. $\frac{1}{2}(x + 10) - 3$ J. $12x - 10x + 2$
3. Find the mean of the following prices: \$1.18, \$1.17, \$1.23, \$1.22, \$1.23, \$1.23. B
   A. \$1.20 B. \$1.21
   C. \$1.22 D. \$1.23
4. Which expression is equivalent to $-x \cdot x \cdot y \cdot y \cdot (-y) \cdot 2 \cdot 3$? J
   F. $-6x^2y^3$ G. $(6)(-x^2)(-y^2)$
   H. $-6x^3y^2$ J. $6x^2y^3$
5. Simplify $3\frac{1}{2} - 1\frac{5}{8}$. C
   A. $2\frac{2}{3}$ B. $2\frac{1}{8}$
   C. $1\frac{7}{8}$ D. $1\frac{2}{3}$
6. Which measure is equivalent to $\frac{1}{2}$ gal? J
   F. 4 qt G. 8 qt
   H. 8 pt J. 4 pt
7. 200 is 40% of what number? A
   A. 500 B. 80
   C. 5 D. 4,000
8. Solve $3(2x + 8) - 2x = 20$. H
   F. 3 G. 7
   H. −1 J. $-\frac{2}{3}$
9. Find the slope of the line through $A(1, -4)$ and $B(3, 2)$. C
   A. −3 B. $-\frac{1}{2}$
   C. 3 D. $\frac{1}{2}$
10. Two angles of a triangle have measures of 159° and 5°. What is the measure of the third angle? G
    F. 14° G. 16°
    H. 159° J. 164°
11. Angles 1 and 2 are supplementary. If $m\angle 1 = 40°$, what is $m\angle 2$? B
    A. 180° B. 140°
    C. 50° D. 40°
12. Which statement may be *false* if $\triangle ABC \cong \triangle DEF$? J
    F. $\angle A \cong \angle D$
    G. $\overline{BC} \cong \overline{EF}$
    H. $\overline{CA} \cong \overline{FD}$
    J. $\angle C \cong \angle E$
13. Name the figure. B

    A. $\overleftrightarrow{AB}$ B. $\overrightarrow{AB}$
    C. $\overrightarrow{BA}$ D. $\overline{AB}$
14. Classify the triangle. F
    4 m, 110°, 4 m, 35°, 35°, 6.6 m
    F. isosceles obtuse
    G. scalene right
    H. isosceles acute
    J. equilateral right

**For Exercises 15–17, use $\triangle STU$ with vertices $S(0, 0)$, $T(3, 4)$, and $U(3, -4)$.**

15. Graph $\triangle STU$ and then graph the image of its translation 2 units left and 3 units up. See back of book.
16. Graph the image of the reflection of $\triangle STU$ over the $y$-axis. List the vertices of the image. See back of book.
17. Graph $\triangle STU$ and an image of $\triangle STU$ rotated 90° about the origin. See back of book.

**For Exercises 18–20, show your work.**

18. Write two fractions that are equivalent to $\frac{5x}{z}$. Answers may vary. Samples: $\frac{10x}{2z}, \frac{25x}{5z}$
19. The GCF of 18 and $y$ is 1. Give two possible values of $y$. Answers may vary. Samples: 11, 17
20. Draw an acute angle. Construct its bisector. See back of book.



| Item | Chapter/ Lesson | Review Topic |
|---|---|---|
| 2 | 2-3 | Solving One-Step Equations and Inequalities |
| 3 | 3-3 | Decimals and Equations |
| 1, 4, 18, 19 | 4-3, 4-4, 4-7 | Factors, Fractions, and Exponents |
| 5, 6 | 5-3, 5-5 | Operations with Fractions |
| 7 | 6-7 | Ratios, Proportions, and Percents |
| 8 | 7-2 | Solving Equations and Inequalities |
| 9 | 8-3 | Linear Functions and Graphing |
| 10–17, 20 | 9-1, 9-2, 9-3, 9-5, 9-7, 9-8, 9-9, 9-10 | Spatial Thinking |

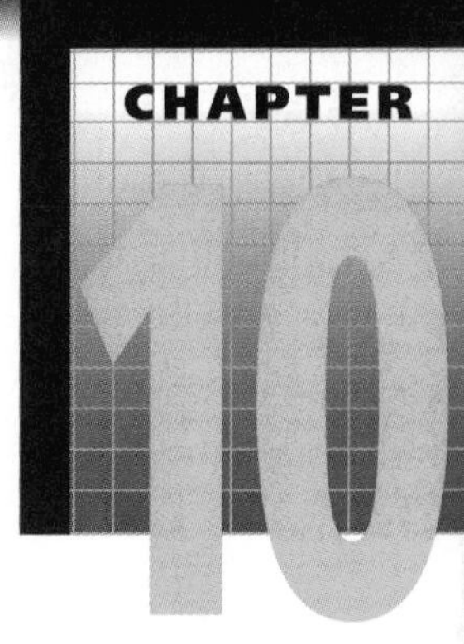


# Area and Volume

## Content Overview for Chapter 10

Chapter 10 shows how to find the area, surface area, and volume of some basic geometric forms. Area is the number of square units enclosed by a geometric figure. To find the area of a parallelogram, use the formula $A = bh$. To find the area of a triangle, use the formula $A = \frac{1}{2}bh$. To find the area of a trapezoid, use the formula $A = \frac{1}{2}h(b_1 + b_2)$. To find the area of a circle, use the formula $A = \pi r^2$. Use 3.14 for $\pi$.

Two-dimensional figures can be combined to create space figures. Pyramids and prisms are named by the shapes of their bases. A cylinder has two circular bases. A cone has one circular base and one vertex. Nets are flat patterns for space figures. You can find the surface area of prisms and cylinders by adding their lateral areas to the areas of their bases. The lateral area of a prism is the sum of the areas of the lateral faces. The lateral area of a cylinder is the area of the curved surface. For pyramids and cones, use the slant height, $\ell$, to find the lateral area. The lateral area of a pyramid is $n(\frac{1}{2}b\ell)$ and of a cone is $\pi r\ell$. The surface area of a sphere is $4\pi r^2$.

Volume is the measure of how much a space figure could hold if you could fill it. To find the volume of a prism or cylinder, use the formula $V = Bh$. To find the volume of pyramids and cones, use the formula $V = \frac{1}{3}Bh$. To find the volume of a sphere, use $V = \frac{4}{3}\pi r^3$.

**SCHOOL/HOME CONNECTION**
English and Spanish versions are available in the *Help at Home* book of copy masters.

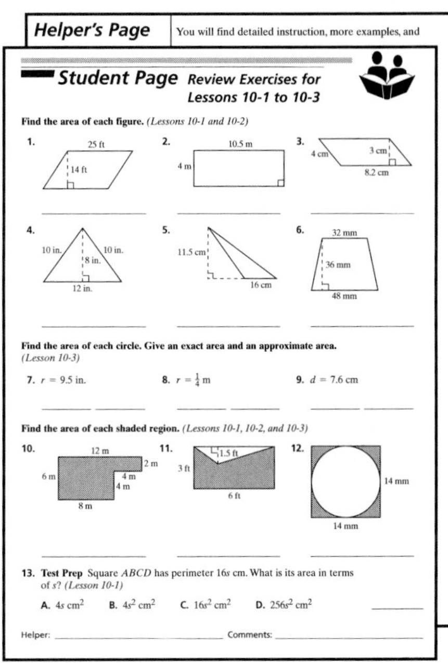
*Helper's Page* You will find detailed instruction, more examples, and

**Student Page** Review Exercises for Lessons 10-1 to 10-3

Find the area of each figure. *(Lessons 10-1 and 10-2)*

1. 2. 3. 4. 5. 6.

Find the area of each circle. Give an exact area and an approximate area. *(Lesson 10-3)*

7. $r = 9.5$ in. 8. $r = \frac{1}{2}$ m 9. $d = 7.6$ cm

Find the area of each shaded region. *(Lessons 10-1, 10-2, and 10-3)*

10. 11. 12.

13. **Test Prep** Square *ABCD* has perimeter $16s$ cm. What is its area in terms of $s$? *(Lesson 10-1)*

A. $4s$ cm² B. $4s^2$ cm² C. $16s^2$ cm² D. $256s^2$ cm²

Helper: ______ Comments: ______

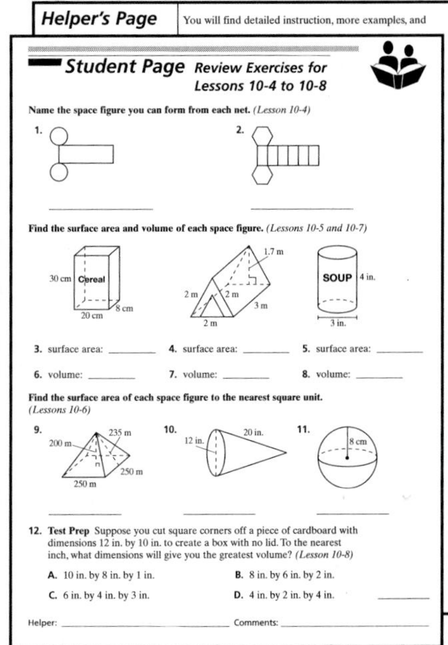
*Helper's Page* You will find detailed instruction, more examples, and

**Student Page** Review Exercises for Lessons 10-4 to 10-8

Name the space figure you can form from each net. *(Lesson 10-4)*

1. 2.

Find the surface area and volume of each space figure. *(Lessons 10-5 and 10-7)*

3. surface area: ______ 4. surface area: ______ 5. surface area: ______

6. volume: ______ 7. volume: ______ 8. volume: ______

Find the surface area of each space figure to the nearest square unit. *(Lessons 10-6)*

9. 10. 11.

12. **Test Prep** Suppose you cut square corners off a piece of cardboard with dimensions 12 in. by 10 in. to create a box with no lid. To the nearest inch, what dimensions will give you the greatest volume? *(Lesson 10-8)*

A. 10 in. by 8 in. by 1 in. B. 8 in. by 6 in. by 2 in.
C. 6 in. by 4 in. by 3 in. D. 4 in. by 2 in. by 4 in.

Helper: ______ Comments: ______

## Making Connections

| Lesson | Interdisciplinary and Real-World Connections | Math Integration |
|---|---|---|
| 10-1 | Landscaping | Coordinate Geometry |
| 10-2 | Geography | Algebra |
| 10-3 | Biology | Algebra |
| 10-4 | Art and Design | Geometry |
| 10-5 | Packaging | Geometry |
| 10-6 | Architecture | Algebra |
| 10-7 | Manufacturing | Algebra |
| 10-8 | Physics | Problem Solving |
| 10-9 | Physics | Geometry |

CHAPTER 10

# Chapter 10 at a Glance

To accommodate flexible scheduling, most lessons are divided into parts. Assignment Options are given in the Teacher's Edition for each lesson.

### Lesson 10-1
**Pages 504–508**
**Area: Parallelograms**

**NCTM 3, 4, 6, 7, 8, 9, 10**

Part 1 Finding Areas of Rectangles
Part 2 Finding Areas of Parallelograms
**Math at Work**

### Lesson 10-2
**Pages 509–513**
**Area: Triangles and Trapezoids**

**NCTM 3, 4, 7, 8, 9, 10**

Part 1 Finding Areas of Triangles
Part 2 Finding Areas of Trapezoids

### Lesson 10-3
**Pages 514–519**
**Area: Circles**

**NCTM 3, 4, 6, 8, 9, 10**

Part 1 Finding Areas of Circles
Part 2 Finding Areas of Irregular Figures
**Checkpoint 1**

### Lesson 10-7
**Pages 538–541**
**Volume: Prisms and Cylinders**

**NCTM 3, 4, 6, 8, 9, 10**

Part 1 Finding the Volumes of Prisms
Part 2 Finding the Volumes of Cylinders
▼ **Project Activity 2**

### Lesson 10-8
**Pages 542–545**
**Problem Solving Strategy**

**NCTM 3, 4, 6, 9, 10**

Make a Model
**Checkpoint 2**

### Lesson 10-9
**Pages 547–550**
**Volume: Pyramids, Cones, and Spheres**

**NCTM 3, 4, 6, 9, 10**

Part 1 Finding the Volumes of Cones and Pyramids
Part 2 Finding the Volumes of Spheres
▼ **Project Activity 3**

## Pacing Options

This chart suggests pacing for only the core lessons and their parts, and it is provided merely as a possible guide. It will help you determine how much time you have in your schedule to cover other features, such as the Chapter Project, Math Toolboxes, Standardized Test Prep, Wrap Up, and Assessment.

| | Day 1 | Day 2 | Day 3 | Day 4 | Day 5 | Day 6 | Day 7 | Day 8 | Day 9 | Day 10 | Day 11 |
|---|---|---|---|---|---|---|---|---|---|---|---|
| **Traditional** (40–45 min. class periods) | 10–1 ▼1, 10–1 ▼2 | 10–2 ▼1, 10–2 ▼2 | 10–3 ▼1 | 10–3 ▼2 | 10–4 ▼1, 10–4 ▼2 | 10–5 ▼1 | 10–5 ▼2 | 10–6 ▼1, 10–6 ▼2 | 10–7 ▼1, 10–7 ▼2 | 10–8 | 10–9 ▼1, 10–9 ▼2 |
| **Pre-Algebra Over 2 Years** (40–45 min. class periods) | 10–1 ▼1 | 10–1 ▼2 | 10–2 ▼1 | 10–2 ▼1 | 10–2 ▼2 | 10–3 ▼1 | 10–3 ▼1 | 10–3 ▼2 | 10–4 ▼1 | 10–4 ▼2 | 10–5 ▼1 |
| **Block Scheduling** (90 min. class periods) | 10–1 ▼1 ▼2, 10–2 ▼1 ▼2 | 10–3 ▼1 ▼2, 10–4 ▼1 | 10–4 ▼2, 10–5 ▼1 ▼2 | 10–6 ▼1 ▼2, 10–7 ▼1 | 10–7 ▼2, 10–8, 10–9 ▼1 ▼2 | | | | | | |

| Pages 521–525 | Lesson 10-4<br>Space Figures |
|---|---|
| NCTM<br>3, 8, 10 | Part 1 Naming Space Figures<br>Part 2 Identifying Space Figures from Nets |

| Pages 527–532 | Lesson 10-5<br>Surface Area: Prisms and Cylinders |
|---|---|
| NCTM<br>3, 4, 6, 7, 8, 9, 10 | Part 1 Finding Surface Areas of Prisms<br>Part 2 Finding Surface Areas of Cylinders<br>▼ **Project Activity 1** |

| Pages 533–537 | Lesson 10-6<br>Surface Area: Pyramids, Cones, and Spheres |
|---|---|
| NCTM<br>3, 4, 6, 7, 8, 9, 10 | Part 1 Finding Surface Areas of Pyramids<br>Part 2 Finding Surface Areas of Cones and Spheres |

**NCTM STANDARDS 2000**

1. Number and Operations
2. Algebra
3. Geometry
4. Measurement
5. Data Analysis and Probability
6. Problem Solving
7. Reasoning and Proof
8. Communication
9. Connections
10. Representation

| Day 12 | Day 13 | Day 14 | Day 15 | Day 16 | Day 17 | Day 18 | Day 19 | Day 20 | Day 21 | Day 22 | Day 23 | Day 24 |
|---|---|---|---|---|---|---|---|---|---|---|---|---|
| 10–5 ▼1 | 10–5 ▼2 | 10–6 ▼1 | 10–6 ▼2 | 10–6 ▼2 | 10–7 ▼1 | 10–7 ▼2 | 10–8 | 10–8 | 10–9 ▼1 | 10–9 ▼1 | 10–9 ▼2 | |

**Block Scheduling Notes**

Consider these suggestions:

- **Day 2** Before starting Lesson 10-4, teach Math Toolbox 1, p. 520.
- **Day 3** Before starting Lesson 10-5, teach Math Toolbox 2, p. 526.
- **Day 3** After completing Lesson 10-5, begin presentations for Finish the Project.
- **Day 5** Before starting Lesson 10-9, teach the Standardized Test Prep, p. 546.

# Math Background

## Lessons 10-1 and 10-2

### Area: Parallelograms, Triangles, and Trapezoids

The area of a plane figure is the number of square unit regions the figure contains. You calculate the area by counting or approximating the number of square unit regions covered by the surface. In many cases, you can use a formula to shortcut the counting process. With rectangular figures such as this one, you can easily divide the figure into square units.

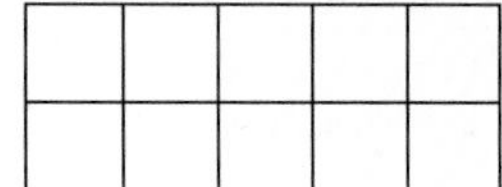

The area of this rectangle is 10 square units. The length, $\ell$, is 5; the width, $w$, is 2. The formula for the area of a rectangle is $A = \ell w$.

Notice in the following figures that the area of the rectangle does not change as it is skewed into a parallelogram.

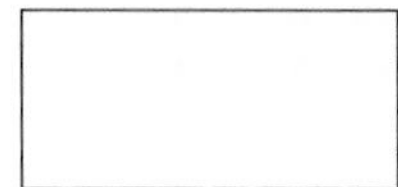

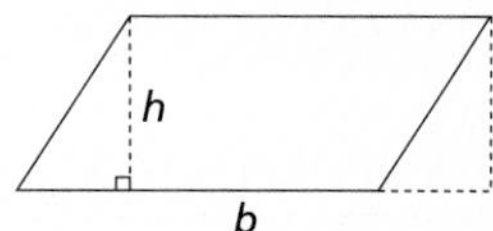


The formula for the area of a parallelogram is the same as that for a rectangle, but the length and width are usually called the *base* and the *height*. The formula for the area of a parallelogram is $A = bh$.

The following figure shows that the area of a triangle is one-half the area of the corresponding parallelogram.

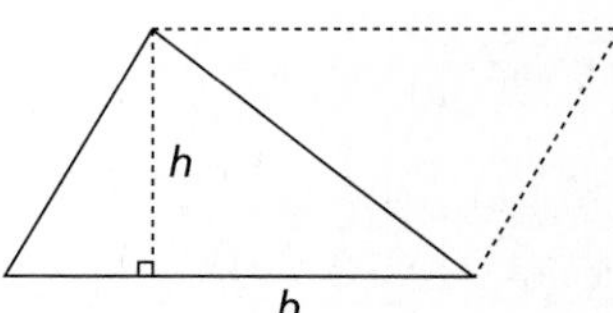


The formula for the area of a triangle is $A = \frac{1}{2}bh$. Notice that the height is a line from one vertex perpendicular to the opposite base. In the next figure, the height falls outside the triangle.

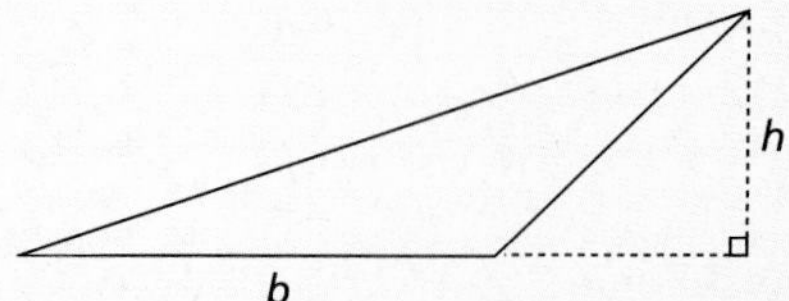


## Lesson 10-3

### Area: Circles

You can approximate the area of a circle by dividing it into polygons. One method, illustrated in the lesson, shows that a circle can be divided into wedges, or *sectors.* These sectors can be arranged to form a parallelogram with a height that is about the same as the radius of the circle and a base that is about the same as half the circumference of the circle. The following steps show how to substitute these measures of the circle to derive the formula for the area of a circle.

| | |
|---|---|
| $A = bh$ | area of a parallelogram |
| $A = \frac{1}{2}Cr$ | base is half the circumference and height is the radius |
| $A = \frac{1}{2}(2\pi r)r$ | substituting for $C = 2\pi r$ |
| $A = \pi r^2$ | simplify |

Notice that the formula for the area of a circle, $A = \pi r^2$, contains $r^2$. Since area is measured in square units, this will help students distinguish it from the formula for the circumference, $C = 2\pi r$.

## Lesson 10-4

### Space Figures

Solid geometry is the geometry that deals with figures in three-dimensional space. These figures are often called *space figures.* One space figure is the *prism.* A prism has two parallel bases that are congruent polygons and lateral faces that are parallelograms. Most boxes represent prisms of this kind. A *pyramid* has one base that is a polygon and lateral faces that are triangles, meeting at a vertex.

A *cylinder* has two congruent parallel circular bases and a curved lateral face. A *cone* has one base that is a circle and a curved lateral face that comes to a point called a *vertex.* A *sphere* is the space figure, modeled by a ball such as a basketball, that is made up of all the points in space that are a given distance, the radius, from a point that is the center of the sphere. There are illustrations of all these solids in the lesson.

A pattern that you can cut out and fold into a model for a space figure is called a *net.* If you take a shoe box with the top glued on, for example, and cut along the edges to flatten it out, the result is a net for a rectangular prism. You can draw several different nets for such a shoe box; this figure shows one of the possibilities.

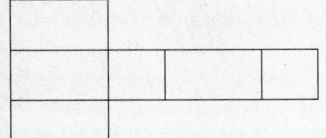

## LESSONS 10-5 AND 10-6

### Surface Area: Prisms, Cylinders, Pyramids, Cones, and Spheres

If the lateral face or faces of a cylinder or prism make right angles with the bases, then the figure is a *right* cylinder or prism; otherwise it is *oblique.* In this text, if it is not otherwise stated, figures are assumed to be right. The cones and pyramids are also right space figures because a line dropped from the vertex to the base is perpendicular to the base.

The surface area (S.A.) of a space figure is the sum of the area(s) of the base (or bases) and the area(s) of the lateral face (or faces) of the figure. The surface area is the same as the total area (in square units) of a net for the space figure.

In a prism, if the sides of the base are called $s_1$, $s_2$, $s_3$, and $s_4$, for example, then the lateral area (L.A.) of the faces is $hs_1 + hs_2 + hs_3 + hs_4$, where $h$ is the height of the prism. But this is $h(s_1 + s_2 + s_3 + s_4)$, which is the same as $h$(perimeter of the base, or $p$).

- For a prism, you can use these two formulas, L.A. $= ph$ and S.A. $=$ L.A. $+ 2B$, where $B$ is the area of one base.
- For a cylinder, since the perimeter, or circumference, of a circle is $2\pi r$, these two formulas become L.A. $= 2\pi rh$ and S.A. $=$ L.A. $+ 2B$.

All the pyramids in this text are *regular* pyramids with bases that are regular polygons and lateral faces that are congruent isosceles triangles. The height of one of the triangular faces is called the slant height ($\ell$) of the pyramid. For a pyramid, L.A. $= n(\frac{1}{2}b\ell)$, where $n$ is the number of lateral faces, and S.A. $=$ L.A. $+ B$.

- For a right circular cone with a slant height of $\ell$, L.A. $= \frac{1}{2}(2\pi r)\ell$ or L.A. $= \pi r\ell$ and S.A. $=$ L. A. $+ B$.
- For a sphere, S.A. $= 4\pi r^2$.

## LESSONS 10-7, 10-8, AND 10-9

### Volume: Prisms, Cylinders, Pyramids, Cones, and Spheres

The *volume* of a space figure is the number of cubic units needed to fill the figure. A *cubic unit* is the space occupied by a cube with edges of one unit. These are the formulas for the volumes of several space figures, where $B$ is the area of the base and $h$ is the height of the figure.

| | | | |
|---|---|---|---|
| prism | $V = Bh$ | cone | $V = \frac{1}{3}Bh$ |
| cylinder | $V = Bh$ | pyramid | $V = \frac{1}{3}Bh$ |
| sphere | $V = \frac{4}{3}\pi r^3$ | | |

An interesting experiment to convince students that the formula for the volume of a cone makes sense is to have them cut out of paper two figures: a cone and a cylinder that have exactly the same height and circumference. Then ask them to fill the cone with rice and pour the rice into the cylinder. Most students are surprised to discover that it takes three cones of rice to fill the cylinder.

For professional development tips visit our Web site **www.phschool.com.**

# Monitoring Progress

## Universal Access

### ▶ Preventing a Student from Falling Behind

These resources are particularly helpful in preventing a student from falling behind his or her appropriate math level. For a complete list of resources for this chapter, see page 501H.

#### Skills You Need for Chapter 10

Student Edition, p. 501
Teacher's Edition, p. 501

- Finding the areas of rectangles and squares
- Multiplying by a fraction
- Simplifying expressions with exponents
- Finding the circumferences of circles

#### Skills Handbook

Student Edition, pp. 723–741
Teacher's Edition, pp. 723–741

#### Reteaching Worksheets

There is a Reteaching worksheet for every lesson in this chapter.

- Chapter 10 Support File, Teaching Resources box
- See TE p. 501H for a complete list of resources

####  Skills Intervention Kit with CD-ROM

| For | Use |
|---|---|
| Lessons 10-1, 10-4 | Geometry |
| Lesson 10-6 | Operations with Fractions |
| Lessons 10-7–10-10 | Geometry |

#### Daily Cumulative Review Blackline Masters

There is a Daily Cumulative Review worksheet for every lesson in this chapter.

See TE p. 501H for a complete list of resources.

### ▶ Accommodating Diverse Learning Styles

#### Tactile Learning

Use floor tiles to find the area of a square. (Lesson 10-1)

Form space figures from nets. (Lesson 10-4)

Measure the slant heights of models of pyramids. (Lesson 10-6)

#### Advanced Learner

Every lesson has at least one challenge problem.

Fill cylindrical containers with water to create a conversion factor between cubic units and milliliters. (Lesson 10-7)

#### ELL (English Language Learner)

Picture a cross section of a carrot. (Lesson 10-2)

Examine that *lateral* comes from the Latin word that means *side*. (Lesson 10-5)

#### Auditory Learning

Say aloud the various formulas for circles. (Lesson 10-3)

Sketch and label solids named by a partner. (Lesson 10-4)

#### Visual Learning

Determine the volume of a box by filling it with small cubes. (Lesson 10-7)

Fill model boxes with popcorn to determine the one with the greatest volume. (Lesson 10-8)

# Aligning Assessment with Instruction

## Assessment Options

| | Chapter Opener | 10-1 | 10-2 | 10-3 | 10-4 | 10-5 | 10-6 | 10-7 | 10-8 | 10-9 | End |
|---|---|---|---|---|---|---|---|---|---|---|---|
| Chapter Project | ■ | | | ■ | | | ■ | | | | ■ |
| Try This Exercises | | ■ | ■ | ■ | ■ | ■ | ■ | ■ | ■ | ■ | |
| Mixed Reviews | | ■ | ■ | ■ | ■ | ■ | ■ | ■ | ■ | ■ | |
| Checkpoints | | | | ■ | | | | | ■ | | |
| Writing | | ■ | ■ | ■ | ■ | ■ | ■ | ■ | | | ■ |
| Chapter Assessment | | | | | | | | | | | ■ |
| Cumulative Review | | | | | | | | | | | ■ |
| Standardized Test Prep | | ■ | ■ | ■ | ■ | ■ | ■ | | ■ | ■ | |
| | Standardized Test Prep, p. 546 | | | | | | | | | | |
| Computer Item Generator | Can be used to create custom-made practice pages or assessment pages at any time. | | | | | | | | | | |

### Test-Taking Tips on Transparencies

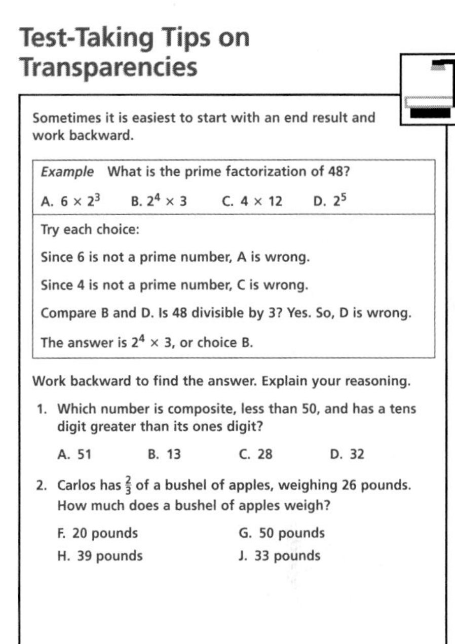

Sometimes it is easiest to start with an end result and work backward.

*Example* What is the prime factorization of 48?

A. $6 \times 2^3$ B. $2^4 \times 3$ C. $4 \times 12$ D. $2^5$

Try each choice:

Since 6 is not a prime number, A is wrong.

Since 4 is not a prime number, C is wrong.

Compare B and D. Is 48 divisible by 3? Yes. So, D is wrong.

The answer is $2^4 \times 3$, or choice B.

Work backward to find the answer. Explain your reasoning.

1. Which number is composite, less than 50, and has a tens digit greater than its ones digit?

   A. 51 B. 13 C. 28 D. 32

2. Carlos has $\frac{2}{3}$ of a bushel of apples, weighing 26 pounds. How much does a bushel of apples weigh?

   F. 20 pounds G. 50 pounds
   H. 39 pounds J. 33 pounds

*Use with Standardized Test Prep and Chapter Assessments.*

## Correlation to Standardized Tests

| Lesson | | CAT5 | CTBS/5 TerraNova™ | ITBS | MAT7 | SAT9 | LOCAL OBJECTIVES |
|---|---|---|---|---|---|---|---|
| 10-1 | Area: Parallelograms | ■ | | ■ | | ■ | |
| 10-2 | Area: Triangles and Trapezoids | ■ | | ■ | | ■ | |
| 10-3 | Area: Circles | | ■ | | ■ | ■ | |
| 10-4 | Space Figures | ■ | ■ | | | ■ | |
| 10-5 | Surface Area: Prisms and Cylinders | | | | | ■ | |
| 10-6 | Surface Area: Pyramids, Cones, and Spheres | | | | | ■ | |
| 10-7 | Volume: Prisms and Cylinders | | ■ | | ■ | ■ | |
| 10-8 | Problem Solving Strategy: Make a Model | | | | | ■ | |
| 10-9 | Volume: Pyramids, Cones, and Spheres | | | | | ■ | |

**CAT5** California Achievement Test, 5th edition
**CTBS TerraNova** Comprehensive Test of Basic Skills, 5th edition
**ITBS** Iowa Test of Basic Skills, Form M
**MAT7** Metropolitan Achievement Test, 7th edition
**SAT** Stanford Achievement Test, Advanced 1

For other standardized test correlations, follow the link to your state at **www.phschool.com**.

# Resources for Chapter 10

| | TEACHING RESOURCES BOX | | | | | | | | | | | | | | |
|---|---|---|---|---|---|---|---|---|---|---|---|---|---|---|---|
| | CHAPTER 10 SUPPORT FILE | | | | | | | | Cumulative Assessment | Lesson Planners Plus | Daily Cum Review | Teaching Transparencies | Warm-Up Transparencies | Help at Home | SE Answers Transparenci |
| | Practice | Reteach | Enrichment | Project Manager | Checkpoints | Cumulative Review | Chapter Assessment | Alternative Assessment | | | | | | | |
| Begin Chapter | | | | ■ | | | | | | ■ | | | | | |
| 10-1 | ■ | ■ | ■ | | | | | | | ■ | ■ | 12, 13 | ■ | | ■ |
| 10-2 | ■ | ■ | ■ | | | | | | | ■ | ■ | 74 | ■ | | ■ |
| 10-3 | ■ | ■ | ■ | | ■ | | | | | ■ | ■ | 14, 15 | ■ | ■ | ■ |
| 10-4 | ■ | ■ | ■ | | | | | | | ■ | ■ | | ■ | | ■ |
| 10-5 | ■ | ■ | ■ | | | | | | | ■ | ■ | 75 | ■ | | ■ |
| 10-6 | ■ | ■ | ■ | | | | | | | ■ | ■ | 76 | ■ | | ■ |
| 10-7 | ■ | ■ | ■ | | | | | | | ■ | ■ | 77 | ■ | | ■ |
| 10-8 | ■ | ■ | ■ | | ■ | | | | | ■ | ■ | | ■ | ■ | ■ |
| 10-9 | ■ | ■ | ■ | | | | | | | ■ | ■ | | ■ | | ■ |
| End Chapter | | | | | | ■ | ■ (2 forms) | ■ | After Ch. 3, 6, 9, 13 | | | | | | |

Also available for use with the chapter:

Solution Key
Computational Practice Skills Booklet
Mathematics Standardized Test Prep, Student Edition and Teacher's Edition
Overhead Manipulatives Kit
Practice Workbook
Algebra Readiness Kit
Student Manipulatives Kit
Test-Taking Tips on Transparencies
Assessment Success Kit
Teaching Aids and Letters
Graphing Calculator Handbook
Spanish Resources
Success-Building Puzzle and Problem Masters

## TECHNOLOGY

**Computer Item Generator with Standardized Test Prep**

CD-ROM with an unlimited supply of questions with varying degrees of difficulty for customized practice sheets, quizzes, and tests.

**Resource Pro® with Planning Express®**

CD-ROM with complete classroom planning tool and teaching resources for customizing and planning lessons.

**Interactive Math Lessons and Tools**

CD-ROM with lessons and tools to make abstract concepts visual and accessible.

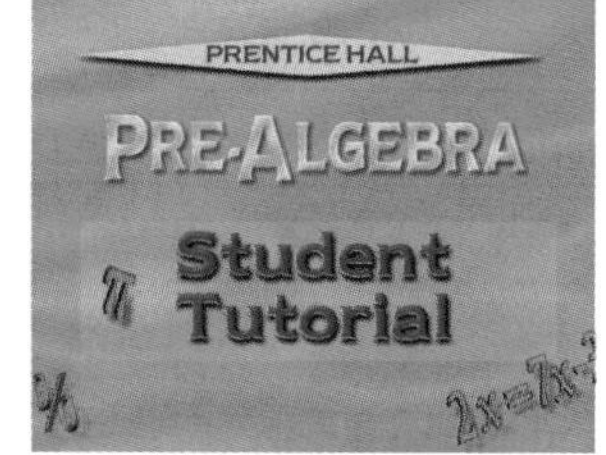


**Student Tutorial**

Test preparation software for students on CD-ROM with management system for teachers; includes Secondary Math Lab Toolkit™.

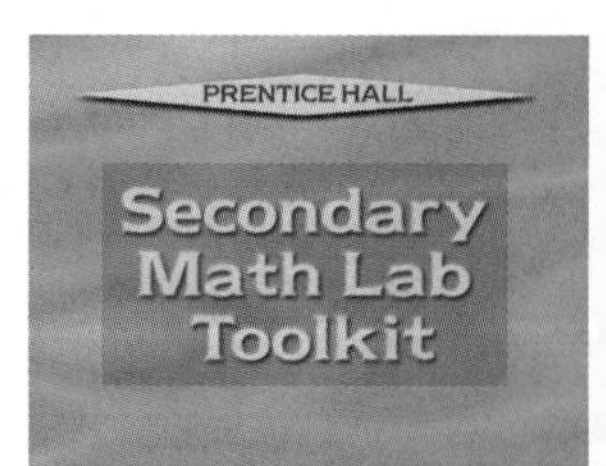


**Secondary Math Lab Toolkit™ with Integrated Math Labs**

Integrated software package with linkable math tools for exploring key concepts.

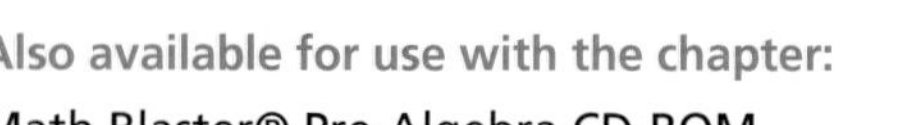

Also available for use with the chapter:

Math Blaster® Pre-Algebra CD-ROM
Video Fieldtrips, Vol. I: Algebra Applications
Video Fieldtrips, Vol. II: Geometry Applications
Wide World of Mathematics CD-ROM
Wide World of Mathematics Video

### *Web Extension*

**www.phschool.com**

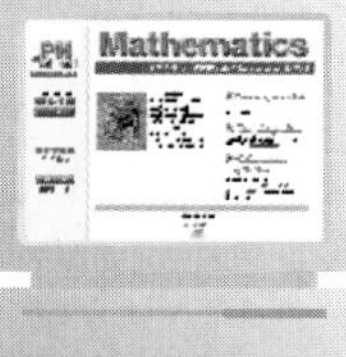


**For Students**
- Chapter Support with Internet Links
- Internet Activities

**For Teachers**
- Curriculum Support
- Professional Development
- Product Information
- Regional Support Information

# Skills You Need for Chapter 10

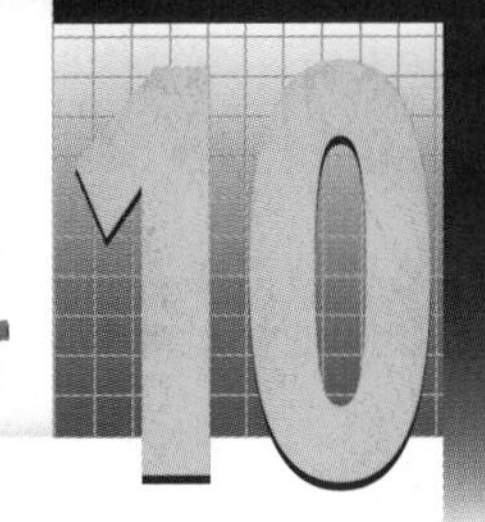

## ▶ *Finding the areas of rectangles and squares* — Use before Lesson 10-1.

**Find the area of each figure.**

1. 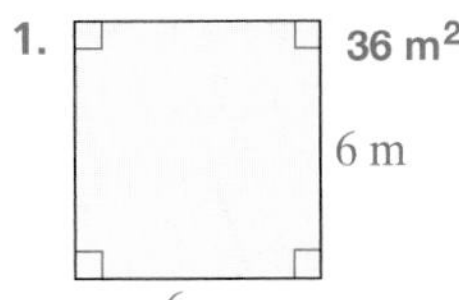

36 m²

2. 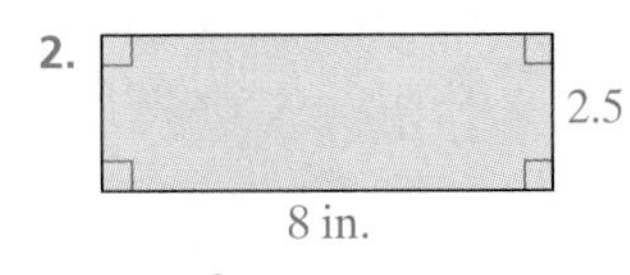

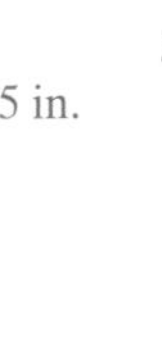

20 in.²

3. 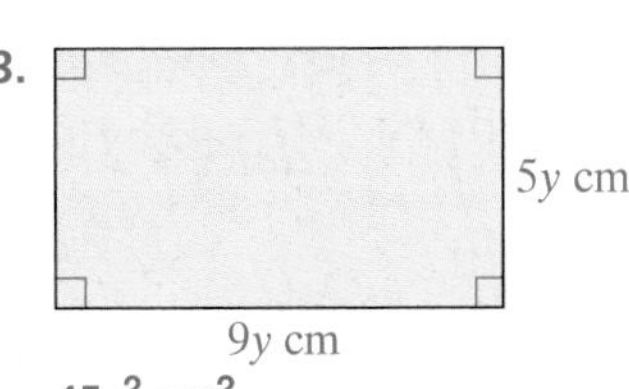

$45y^2$ cm²

## ▶ *Multiplying by a fraction* — Use before Lessons 10-2 and 10-6.

**Find each product.**

4. $\frac{1}{2} \cdot 12$ 6
5. $\frac{1}{2} \cdot 13 \cdot 3$ $\frac{39}{2}$
6. $\frac{1}{2}(10 + 8)$ 9
7. $\frac{1}{2} \cdot 20x$ $10x$
8. $\frac{1}{2} \cdot 5x \cdot 2x$ $5x^2$
9. $\frac{1}{2}(10)(6 + 5)$ 55
10. $\frac{1}{2}(62)(30 + 14)$ 1,364
11. $\frac{1}{3}(20)(35 + 40)$ 500
12. $\frac{1}{3}(3)(5 + 3)$ 8

## ▶ *Simplifying expressions with exponents* — Use before Lesson 10-3.

**Simplify each product.**

13. $5 \cdot 3^2$ 45
14. $3.14 \cdot 5^2$ 78.5
15. $6 \cdot 12^2$ 864
16. $4^2 \cdot 3$ 48
17. $10^2 \cdot 3$ 300
18. $3.14 \cdot 12^2$ 452.16

## ▶ *Finding the circumferences of circles* — Use before Lesson 10-5.

**Find the circumference of each circle. Use 3.14 for $\pi$.**

19. 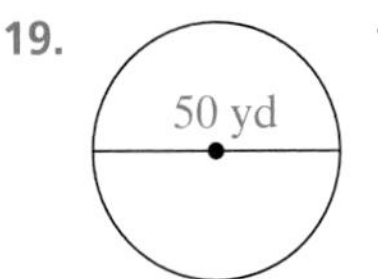

157 yd

20. 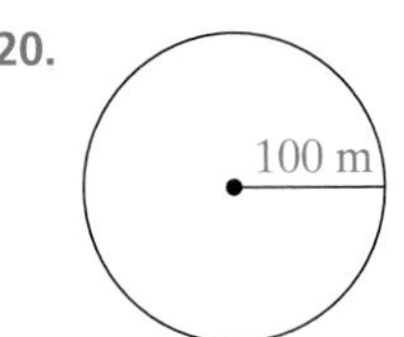

628 m

21. 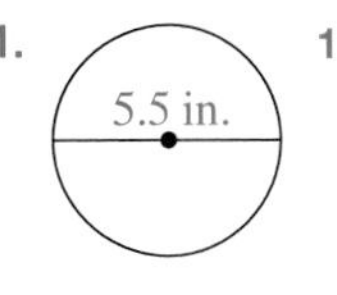

17.27 in.



# Skills You Need

### Finding the areas of rectangles and squares

**In Lesson 10-1** students will find the areas of rectangles and parallelograms.

### Multiplying by a fraction

**In Lesson 10-2** students will find the areas of triangles and trapezoids.

**In Lesson 10-6** students will find the surface areas of pyramids, cones, and spheres.

### Simplifying expressions with exponents

**In Lesson 10-3** students will find the areas of circles.

### Finding the circumference of circles

**In Lesson 10-5** students will find the surface areas of prisms and cylinders.

# Skills Trace

| SKILL | INTRODUCED | DEVELOPED IN LESSON(S) | REVIEWED/REINFORCED |
|---|---|---|---|
| Finding areas of polygons | 10-1 | 10-2 | pp. 513, 519, 617, 640, 688 |
| Finding areas of circles | 10-3 | 10-5 | pp. 525, 598, 649 |
| Identifying space figures and their nets | 10-4 | 10-5 | pp. 532, 576 |
| Finding surface areas of space figures | 10-5 | 10-6 | pp. 537, 541, 625 |
| Finding volumes of space figures | 10-7 | 10-8, 10-9 | pp. 545, 563, 645 |

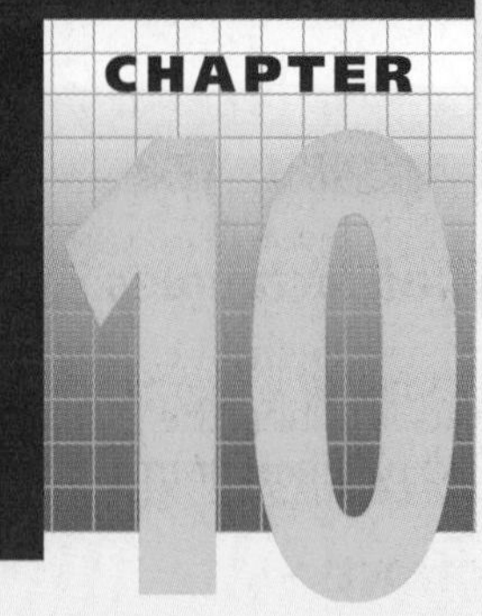


# Area and Volume

## Connecting to Students' Lives

Ask students to give examples of situations in which volume measurement might be important. Have them list common units that are used to measure volume.

## Interdisciplinary Connections

The Chapter Project connects math and science. You may want to contact your students' science teacher to find out how to instruct students on using a graduated cylinder to measure volume.

## About the Project

The Chapter Project directs students to apply their knowledge of finding the volume of solid objects to predict the volume of some actual objects. Then, students will use displacement to measure the actual volume of these objects, and compare the results with their predictions.

CHAPTER 10

## Area and Volume

**What you'll learn in this chapter:**

- How to find the areas of figures
- How to find the surface areas of space figures
- How to find the volumes of space figures

502 Chapter 10

*Web Extension*
**www.phschool.com**

For Students
Chapter Support with Internet links
Interactive Activities

For Teachers
Curriculum Support
Professional Development
Product Information
Regional Support Information

CHAPTER PROJECT 10

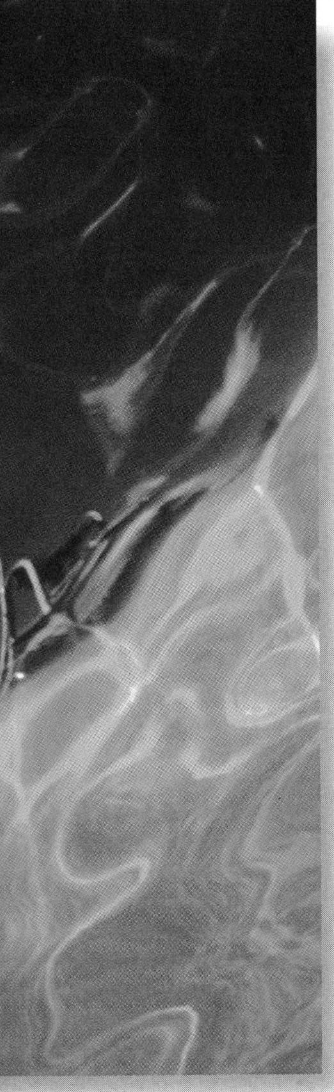

# MAKING A SPLASH

When you jump into a pool, or step into a bathtub, you cause the water level to rise. That's an example of water displacement. The volume of water displaced is equal to the volume of the object submerged—you.

***Use Water Displacement to Find Volume*** For your chapter project you will build a prism and a cylinder. You will calculate their volumes by using formulas. Then you will find their volumes by using water displacement.

***Steps to help you complete the project***


p. 532 Activity: Measuring
p. 541 Activity: Calculating
p. 550 Activity: Comparing
p. 551 Finishing the Chapter Project

***Web Extension***
**www.phschool.com**

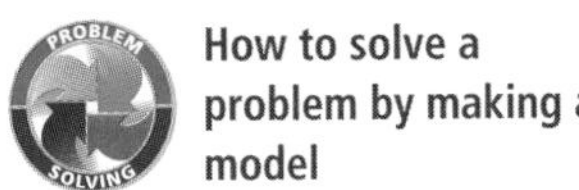

How to solve a problem by making a model

## LAUNCHING THE PROJECT

*The Chapter Project is optional and may be assigned at your discretion.*

Ask students:

- Where have you seen volume measurements before? Why are these measurements useful?
- How could you measure the volume of a solid object?
- If you place a full, one-gallon jug of water in a completely full bathtub, how much water will spill over the edge?

Distribute a copy of the Project Manager and Scoring Rubric to help students get an overview of the project.

Review the scoring rubric with students.

### Project Notebook

Encourage students to keep all project-related materials in a separate folder or notebook. Call attention to the fact that they will find much useful information on the Web site **www.phschool.com**.

**Tracking the Project** Set benchmark deadlines for students to show you their work in progress.

*Available in the Chapter 10 Support File in the Teaching Resources box.*

### Project Manager and Scoring Rubric

**Getting Started** You will be constructing a prism and a cylinder and then finding the volume of each with two methods. Read about the project in your textbook. As you work on the project, you will need centimeter cubes, pennies, tape, a metric ruler, a metric graduated cylinder, water, a calculator, materials to make your report, and materials to record your measurements.

**Checklist and Suggestions**

| | | |
|---|---|---|
| ❑ | Measure and calculate the base areas of your space figures. | Be sure to use the correct formula for each base. |
| ❑ | Calculate the volume of each space figure. | Remember the volume of a prism or cylinder is the area of its base times its height. |
| ❑ | Find the volume of each space figure with water displacement and compare. | Be careful not to measure the volume of your fingers. |
| ❑ | Make a table and write your report. | Be sure to compare and contrast the two procedures. |
| ❑ | Share your report with a friend. | Make any necessary changes. |

**Scoring Rubric**


3 You measure and calculate each volume accurately. You compare the values found with each method correctly, explain the differences appropriately, and describe advantages and disadvantages of each method clearly and thoroughly.

2 You make minor errors in your measurements, your calculations, or in your explanations. You describe advantages and disadvantages of each method, but your explanations could be clearer or more thorough.

1 You measure or calculate incorrectly. Your comparisons and explanations are incomplete or inappropriate.

0 Major elements of the project are incomplete or missing.


**Your Evaluation of the Project** Evaluate your work, based on the Scoring Rubric.

**Teacher's Evaluation of the Project**



## Scoring Rubric

**3** You measure and calculate each volume accurately. You compare the values found with each method correctly, explain the differences appropriately, and describe advantages and disadvantages of each method clearly and thoroughly.

**2** You make minor errors in your measurements, your calculations, or in your explanations. You describe advantages and disadvantages of each method, but your explanations could be clearer or more thorough.

**1** You measure or calculate incorrectly. Your comparisons and explanations are incomplete or inappropriate.

**0** Major elements of the project are incomplete or missing.

# 10-1

## Getting Ready

**Key Terms and Symbols** area, altitude, area of a parallelogram

**Materials** 3 in. by 5 in. index card, straightedge, scissors

**Resources** A complete list of resources for this lesson is on p. 501H.

### Daily Skills Warm-Up

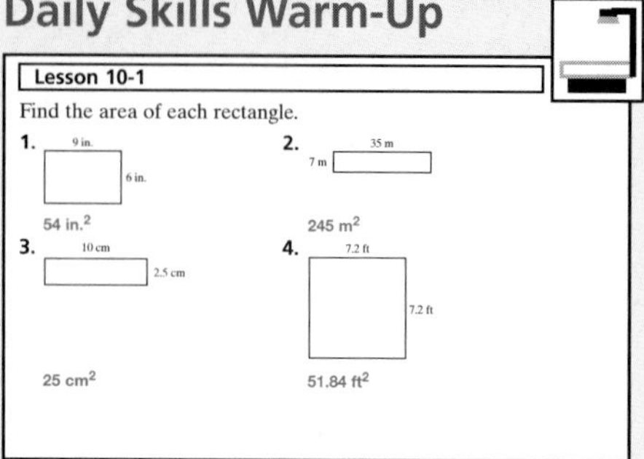
Lesson 10-1

Find the area of each rectangle.

1. 9 in. by 6 in. — 54 in.$^2$
2. 35 m by 7 m — 245 m$^2$
3. 10 cm by 2.5 cm — 25 cm$^2$
4. 7.2 ft by 7.2 ft — 51.84 ft$^2$

### Background for the Lesson

You calculate area by counting or approximating the number of square unit regions (one unit on a side) contained in a plane figure. For a rectangle, drawing a grid using units on the length and width shows clearly that the area is the product of the length and the width, measured in square units. You can cut a triangle off one end of a parallelogram and move it to the opposite end to form a rectangle of the same area. This leads to the formula for a parallelogram that $A = bh$ where $b$ is the base and $h$ is the perpendicular height drawn to that base.

## 1 Focus

### Investigate

To find the area of the index card, you can draw a 1-in. grid and count the square inches on the card.

### Connecting to Students' Lives

Discuss the various items that are sold by the square unit, such as carpeting, wallpaper, fabric, special papers, and various supplies for building models.

# 10-1 Area: Parallelograms

**What You'll Learn**

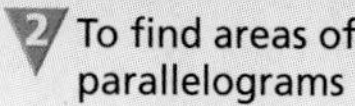

1. To find areas of rectangles
2. To find areas of parallelograms

**. . . And Why**

To use formulas in finding areas of objects, such as the area of a banner

*Investigate*

DISCOVERING AN AREA FORMULA

1. Use a 3-in. by 5-in. index card. Find the area of the card. 15 in.$^2$
2. Draw a line from one vertex to a point on another side to create a triangle. Cut along that line. Check students' work.
3. Use the pieces to form a parallelogram that is not a rectangle. Check students' work.
4. What is the area of your parallelogram? Explain. 15 in.$^2$; the shapes have the same amount of paper in them.

## PART 1 Finding Areas of Rectangles

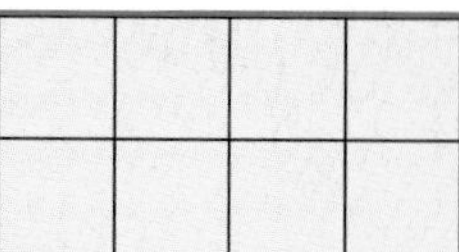

The **area** of a figure is the number of square units it encloses. The rectangle outlined in red encloses 8 square units, each with area 1 cm$^2$ (1 square centimeter). So, the area of the rectangle is 8 cm$^2$.

You can use the formula $A = bh$ to find the area of a rectangle, where $b$ is the length of one side and $h$ is the length of the other. For the rectangle above, $A = 2 \cdot 4 = 8$. So, the area is 8 cm$^2$.

Before you find the area of a figure, make sure the dimensions are in the same unit.

REAL-WORLD CONNECTION

**EXAMPLE 1**

**Find the area of the rectangular banner at the left.**

**Step 1** Change the units so that they are the same.

1 yd = 3 ft  Change 1 yard to feet.

**Step 2** Find the area.

$A = bh$  Use the formula for area of a rectangle.

$= (3)(7)$  Replace $b$ and $h$ with the dimensions 3 and 7.

$= 21$  Simplify.

The area of the banner is 21 ft$^2$.



## Tools to Monitor Progress

### BEFORE THE LESSON

**To check prerequisite skills:**

- Finding the area of rectangles and squares

**Skills You Need,** p. 501

**Skills Intervention Kit,** Geometry

### DURING THE LESSON

**To check understanding:**

**Try This** exercises on student page

- **Additional Example 1**

Find the area of the rectangle. 6 m$^2$

4 m by 150 cm

■ **TRY THIS** Find the area of each rectangle.

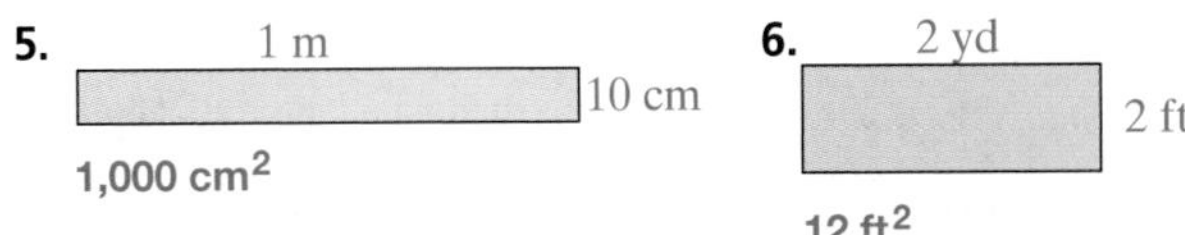


**1,000 cm²**

**12 ft²**

## Finding Areas of Parallelograms

A rectangle is a special kind of parallelogram. The formula for the area of a parallelogram follows from the formula for the area of a rectangle. The height $h$ of a parallelogram is the length of the *altitude*. The **altitude** is a line segment drawn from the side opposite the base and perpendicular to the base $b$ of the figure.

### Area of a Parallelogram

The area of a parallelogram is the product of any base length $b$ and the corresponding height $h$.

$A = bh$

b h | h b | h b

### EXAMPLE 2

**Find the area of each parallelogram.**

**a.**

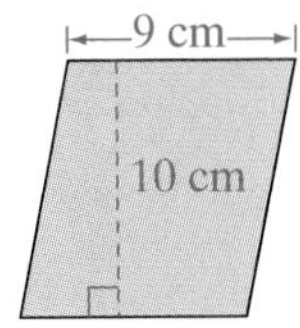


**b.**

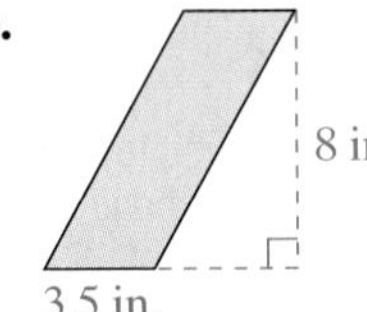


| a. | | b. |
|---|---|---|
| $A = bh$ | area formula | $A = bh$ |
| $= (9)(10)$ | Substitute. | $= (3.5)(8)$ |
| $= 90$ | Simplify. | $= 28$ |
| The area is 90 cm². | | The area is 28 in.². |

■ **TRY THIS** Find the area of each parallelogram.

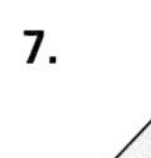

7.

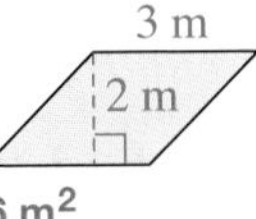


**6 m²**

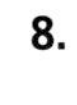

8.

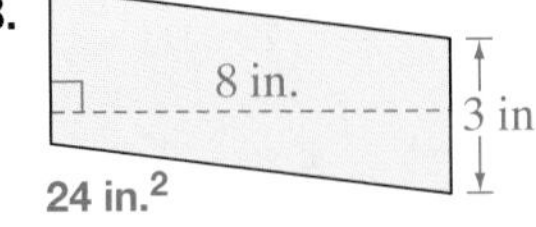


**24 in.²**



## 2 Teach

### Part 1 Teaching Notes

Some students may already know the formula for the area of a rectangle as $A = \ell w$, where $\ell$ is the length and $w$ is the width. Explain that *length* and *width* are just another way of saying *base* and *height*.

**Reading Math** If you find the area of a rectangle with sides measured in centimeters, the area will be in square centimeters. This is often abbreviated as cm², but it is still read as *square centimeters.*

#### ■ Example 1

**Build understanding.** Ask: If you changed the units to yards instead of feet, would the area be the same? Explain. **Yes, the area doesn't change, but the number would be $1(2\frac{1}{3})$ and the units would be in yd²; $2\frac{1}{3}$ yd² $= \frac{9 \text{ ft}^2}{1 \text{ yd}^2}\left(\frac{7}{3} \text{ yd}^2\right) = 21$ ft².**

**Tactile Learning** Many floor tiles are squares, 1 ft on a side. Give students a piece of cardboard that has exact side measurements such as 3 ft by 4 ft and have them find the area of the cardboard by counting the number of tiles it covers. Have them confirm their answers by measuring.

### Part 2 Teaching Notes

The parallelogram formed from a rectangle in the beginning of the lesson shows why the area formula is the same for rectangles and parallelograms.

#### ■ Example 2

**Build understanding.** Ask: If you rearranged the parallelogram in part b. into a rectangle, how many 1-in. squares would fit inside it? **28**

**Math Reasoning** Draw a parallelogram, and then draw a segment connecting two opposite corners. Then, use your figure and math reasoning to explain why the formula for the area of a triangle is $A = \frac{1}{2}bh$. **A triangle is half of a parallelogram, so the area equals half that of a parallelogram.**

### • Additional Example 2

Find the area of the parallelogram.
**16 m²**

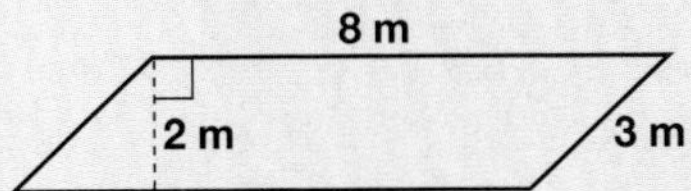


### AFTER THE LESSON

**To assess knowledge: Lesson Quiz**

Find each area.

1. Area of rectangle *ABFE*
**40 m²**

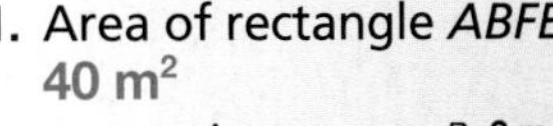

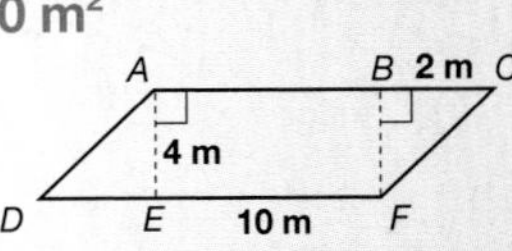


2. Area of parallelogram *ACFD* **48 m²**

• For enrichment and reteaching options see Resources on p. 501H.

# 3 Practice/Assess

## Assignment Guide

To provide flexible scheduling, this lesson can be divided into parts.

▼ Part 1

**Core** 1–2, 4, 10–13, 23, 25–27, 29

✪ **Extension** 20–22, 30

▼ Part 2

**Core** 3, 5–9, 14–19, 28

✪ **Extension** 24

Mixed Review can be assigned at any time for maintenance.

## Exercises

**Error Prevention Exercises 14–17** The side of a parallelogram is not usually equal to the height. Use the perpendicular height for the area calculations.

**Test Prep Exercise 25** Make a sketch. The *perimeter* is *x* units, which is four times the length of the side.

## ✪ Challenge

A parallelogram has an area of 180 in.$^2$ and a base of 1.5 ft. What is the height? 10 in.

## Closure

The area of a parallelogram is the number of square units enclosed by the parallelogram. To find the area of a parallelogram, use the formula $A = bh$.

# Exercises

## Check Understanding

**Find the area of each parallelogram.**

1. 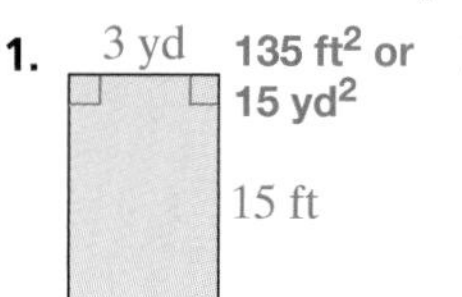

135 ft$^2$ or 15 yd$^2$

2. 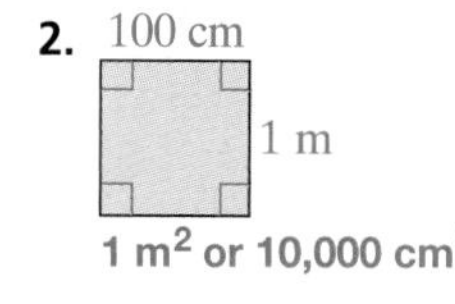

1 m$^2$ or 10,000 cm$^2$

3. 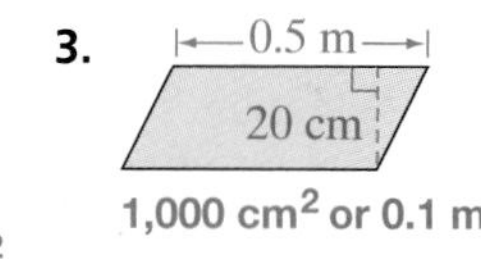

1,000 cm$^2$ or 0.1 m$^2$

4. 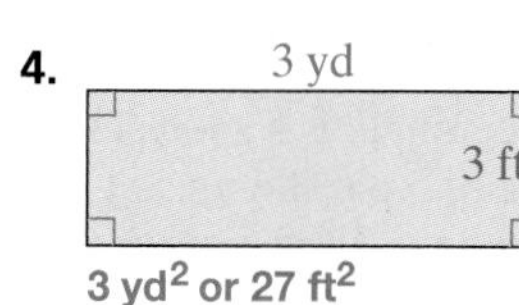

3 yd$^2$ or 27 ft$^2$

5. 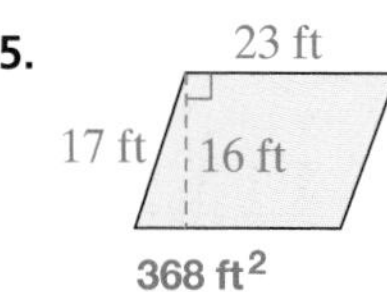

368 ft$^2$

6. 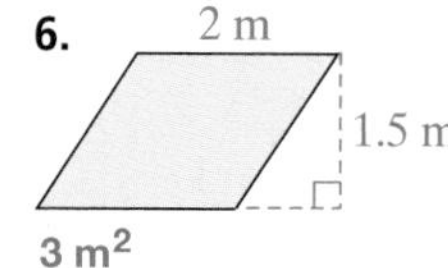

3 m$^2$

7. 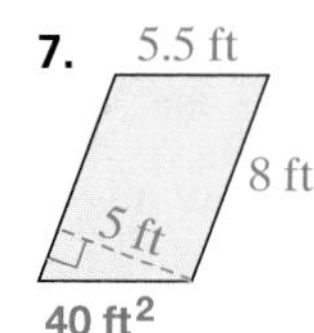

40 ft$^2$

8. 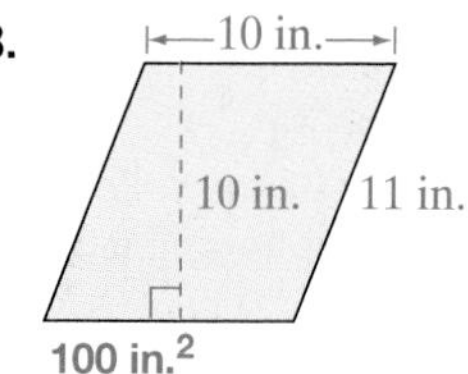

100 in.$^2$

9. Find the area of a parallelogram with base length 3 m and height 50 cm. 15,000 cm$^2$ or 1.5 m$^2$

## Practice and Problem Solving

**Find the area of each parallelogram.**

10. 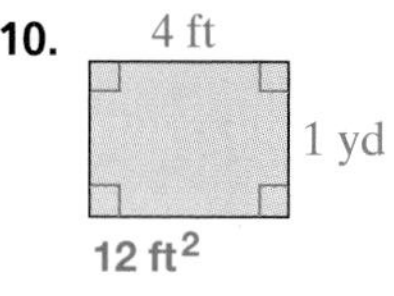

12 ft$^2$

11. 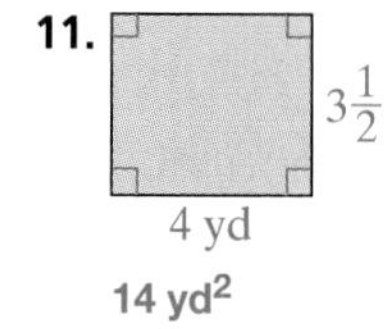

14 yd$^2$

12. 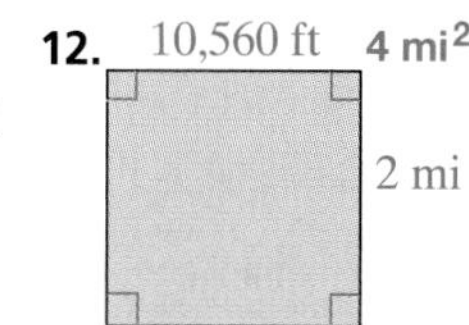

4 mi$^2$

13. 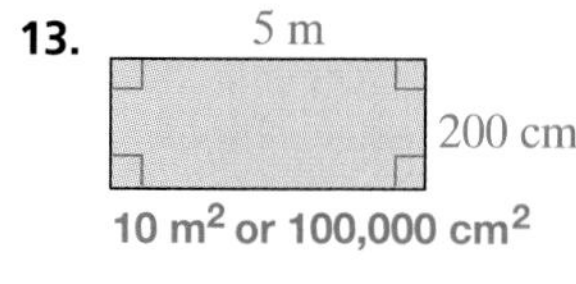

10 m$^2$ or 100,000 cm$^2$

14. 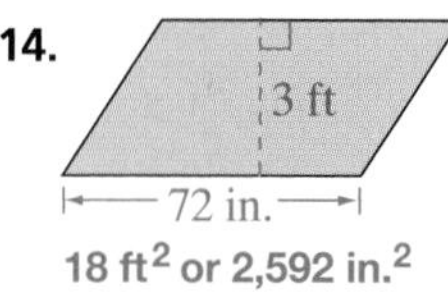

18 ft$^2$ or 2,592 in.$^2$

15. 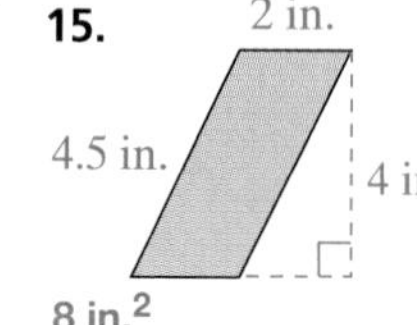

8 in.$^2$

16. 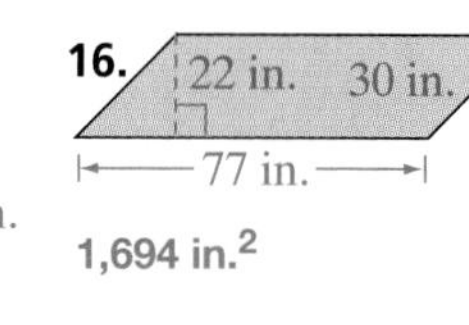

1,694 in.$^2$

17. 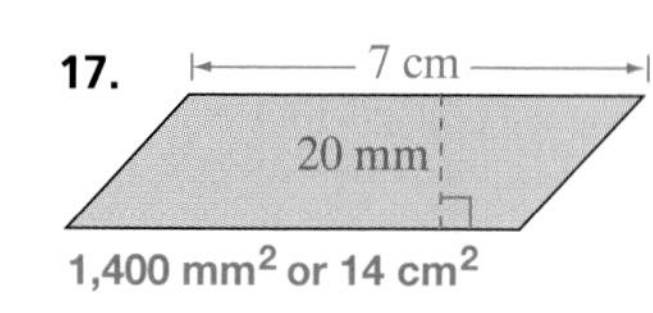

1,400 mm$^2$ or 14 cm$^2$

*Coordinate Geometry* **The vertices of a parallelogram are given. Draw each parallelogram. Find its area.**

18. $A(0, 0)$ $B(3, 0)$, $C(4, 3)$, $D(1, 3)$ 9 square units; see margin for graph.

19. $W(-2, 0)$, $X(-3, 3)$, $Y(2, 0)$, $Z(1, 3)$ 12 square units; see margin for graph.



## Alternative Assessment

Have students measure the length and width of the classroom (assuming it is rectangular) and calculate the area. Ask students to draw and label a parallelogram that is not a rectangle that has the same area.

18. 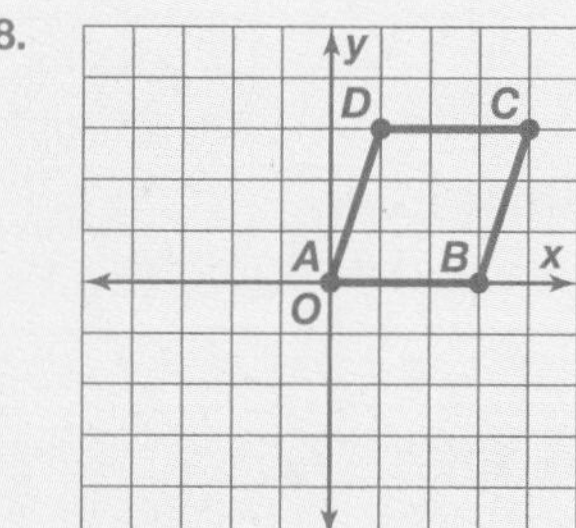


## Daily Cumulative Review

**The vertices of a rectangle are given. On the coordinate planes, graph each rectangle and its image after a rotation of 90° about the origin.** *(Lesson 9-10)*

1. $A(3, 4)$, $B(3, 1)$, $C(1, 1)$, $D(1, 4)$
2. $R(4, -3)$, $S(4, -4)$, $T(0, -4)$, $U(0, -3)$

**The vertices of a polygon are listed. Graph each polygon and its image after a reflection over the given line. Label the vertices of the image.** *(Lesson 9-9)*

3. $L(1, -4)$, $M(4, -2)$, $N(5, -4)$; $y = 1$
4. $W(1, -2)$, $X(2, 1)$, $Y(3, 1)$, $Z(2, -2)$; $x = -1$

**Mixed Review**

**Find each product.**

5. (5-4) $\frac{3}{4} \cdot \frac{8}{15}$ $\frac{2}{5}$
6. (5-4) $\frac{7}{8} \cdot \frac{4}{21}$ $\frac{1}{6}$
7. (5-4) $\frac{1}{3} \cdot \frac{6}{23}$ $\frac{2}{23}$

**Solve each equation.**

8. (3-6) $\frac{c}{4.5} = 6.4$ 28.8
9. (3-6) $32 = \frac{d}{4.3}$ 137.6
10. (3-6) $\frac{w}{0.7} = 7.4$ 5.18

**Find the area of each shaded region. Assume that all angles that appear to be right angles are right angles.**

**20.** 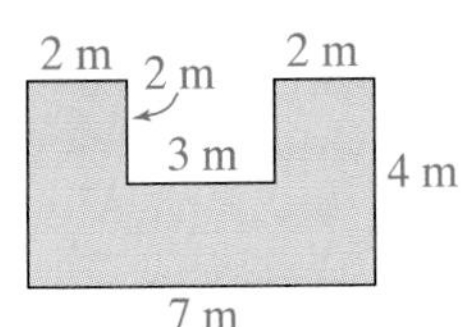

22 $m^2$

**21.** 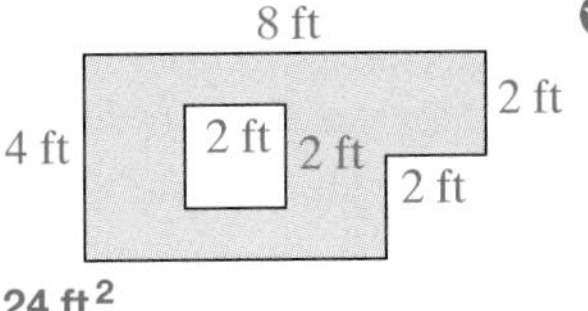

24 $ft^2$

**22.** 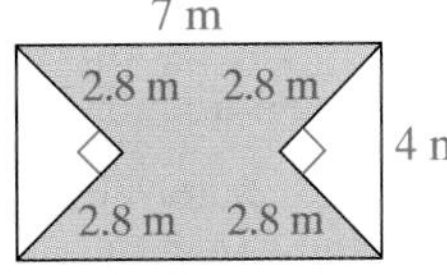

20.16 $m^2$

1 square = 1 square yard

**23.** *Estimation* Estimate the area of the small pond at the right. Each square represents 1 $yd^2$. 16 $yd^2$

**24. a.** *Mathematical Reasoning* The bases of two parallelograms are the same length. The height of the first parallelogram is half the height of the second. What is the ratio of the area of the first parallelogram to the area of the second? Justify your answer. See below right.

**b.** Suppose both the height and the length of the base of a parallelogram are twice those of another parallelogram. What is the ratio of the area of the smaller parallelogram to the larger parallelogram? Justify your answer. $\frac{1}{4}$; the area of a parallelogram is *bh*, so doubling both dimensions will quadruple the area.

**25.** **TEST PREP** Square *ABCD* has perimeter *x* units. What is its area in terms of *x*? A

**A.** $\frac{x^2}{16}$ square units **B.** $4x^2$ square units **C.** $\frac{x^2}{4}$ square units **D.** $\frac{x}{16}$ square units

*Math in the Media* Use the article below for exercises 26 and 27.

### Sign Regulations Set for Political Campaign

The City Council issued the following regulations for political signs in the upcoming election:

1. Only one sign may be posted on a single lot of land.
2. Sign areas may not exceed 32 $ft^2$.
3. Signs cannot be more than 6 ft in height.
4. All signs must be removed no later than 7 days after the election.

24a. $\frac{1}{2}$; the area of a parallelogram is *bh*, so doubling one dimension will double the area.

**26.** You wish to display a sign that is 6 ft high. What is the greatest width it can have? $5\frac{1}{3}$ ft

**27.** Draw rectangles to represent three different political signs that use the maximum possible area. Label the dimensions. Check students' work.

**28.** *Writing* At the right are two parallelograms with the same perimeter. Are the areas the same? Explain. No. The parallelogram on the left has an area of 6 $m^2$ while the one on the right has 4.5 $m^2$.

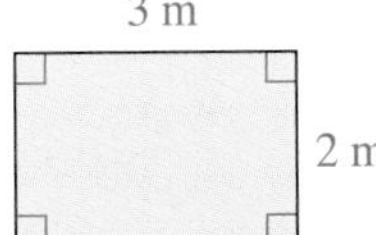


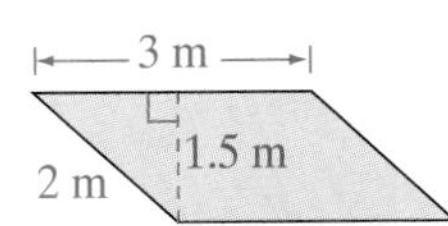




19.

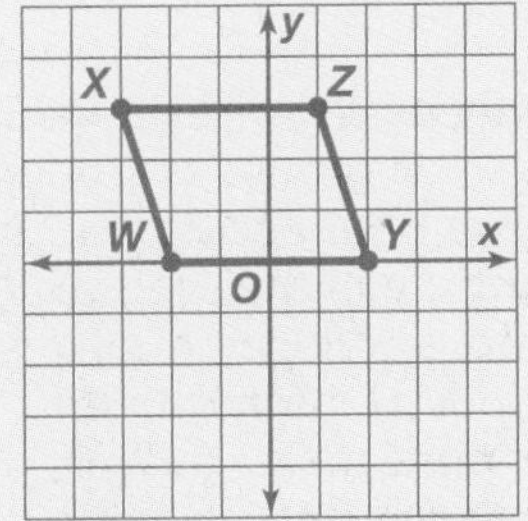

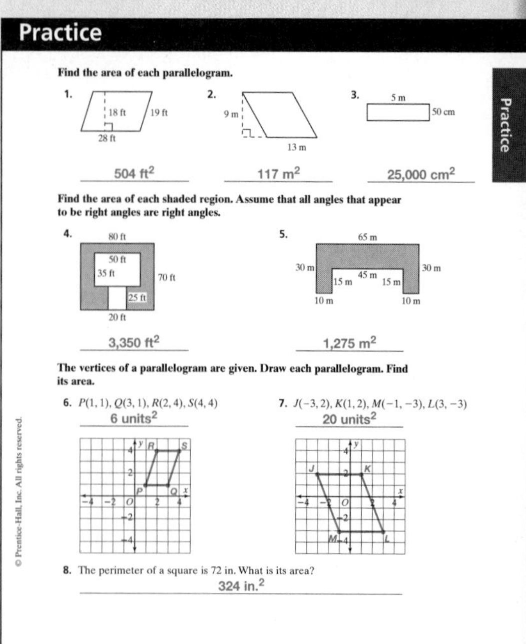

## Practice

Find the area of each parallelogram.

1. 504 ft²
2. 117 m²
3. 25,000 cm²

Find the area of each shaded region. Assume that all angles that appear to be right angles are right angles.

4. 3,350 ft²
5. 1,275 m²

The vertices of a parallelogram are given. Draw each parallelogram. Find its area.

6. $P(1, 1), Q(3, 1), R(2, 4), S(4, 4)$ 6 units²
7. $J(-3, 2), K(1, 2), M(-1, -3), L(3, -3)$ 20 units²
8. The perimeter of a square is 72 in. What is its area? 324 in.²



## Reteaching

Draw the parallelogram with vertices $A(-2, 4)$, $B(1, 4)$, $C(0, -2)$, and $D(-3, -2)$. Find its area.

Plot the four points and connect them to form the parallelogram. To find the area, find the length of a base and the height to that base. Any one of the four sides could be used as the base. The easiest side to use is $\overline{DC}$.

Count in the figure.
$DC = 3$ units, so $b = 3$.
Draw the height as a dashed line from $A$, perpendicular to $\overline{DC}$.
Count in the figure, $h = 6$.
So $A = bh = 3(6) = 18$ unit².

The vertices of a parallelogram are given. Draw each parallelogram. Find its area.

1. $E(-1, 2), F(3, 2), G(1, 1), H(-3, 1)$ 4 units²
2. $M(-2, 1), N(2, 1), Q(-3, -2), P(1, -2)$ 12 units²
3. $R(1, 3), S(3, 3), U(-1, -4), T(1, -4)$ 14 units²
4. $V(-3, -1), W(5, -1), Y(-4, -3), X(4, -3)$ 16 units²



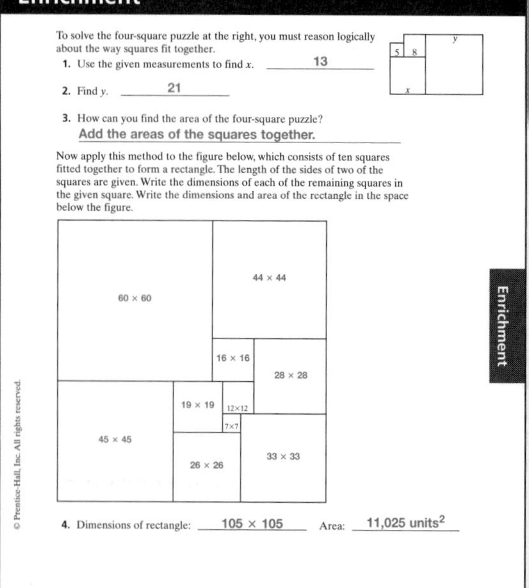

## Enrichment

To solve the four-square puzzle at the right, you must reason logically about the way squares fit together.

1. Use the given measurements to find $x$. 13
2. Find $y$. 21
3. How can you find the area of the four-square puzzle? Add the areas of the squares together.

Now apply this method to the figure below, which consists of ten squares fitted together to form a rectangle. The length of the sides of two of the squares are given. Write the dimensions of each of the remaining squares in the given square. Write the dimensions and area of the rectangle in the space below the figure.



4. Dimensions of rectangle: 105 × 105 Area: 11,025 units²



29. *Open-ended* You want to make a 400-ft² vegetable garden. You plan to build a fence to keep the rabbits out. To spend the least amount of money, you want to use as little fencing as possible.
    a. Draw and list three possible dimensions for your garden. Check students' work.
    b. Which of the three will need the least amount of fencing? Check students' work.

30. a. *Landscaping* Find the area of the yard at the right. Assume that all angles that appear to be right angles are right angles. 4,180 ft²
    b. How many square yards of sod would you need to cover the yard? 464.4 yd²
    c. One bag of fertilizer covers approximately 2,000 ft². How many bags should you buy to cover the yard? 3

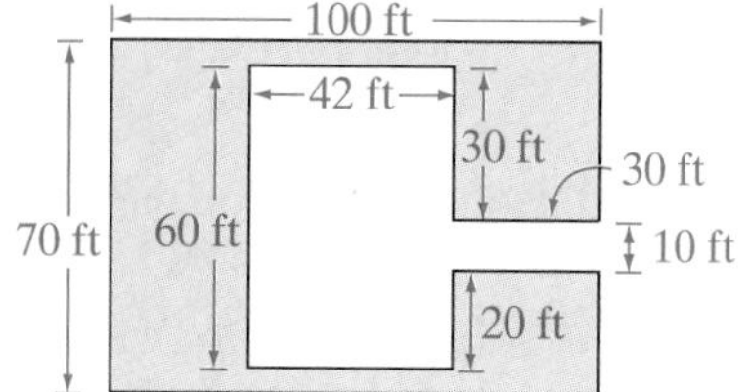


## Mixed Review

**The endpoints of a segment are given. Graph each segment and its image after a rotation of 90° about the origin.** *(Lesson 9-10)*

31. $A(5, 8), B(2, 4)$ See margin.
32. $C(0, 3), D(3, -5)$ See back of book.
33. $E(-2, -3), F(-2, 4)$ See back of book.

**Simplify each expression.** *(Lesson 5-4)*

34. $\frac{2}{5} \cdot 2\frac{1}{2}$ 1
35. $\frac{2}{5} \div 2\frac{1}{2}$ $\frac{4}{25}$
36. $3\frac{2}{3} \cdot \frac{3}{4}$ $\frac{11}{4}$
37. $3\frac{2}{3} \div \frac{3}{4}$ $\frac{44}{9}$

38. *Choose a Strategy* Find the measures of two supplementary angles if the difference of their measures is 56°. 118°, 62°

## Math at Work

### Pharmacist

Pharmacists dispense medications. They also talk to their customers about the possible side effects of medications. To do this, they must thoroughly understand how prescription drugs are made.

Sometimes a doctor prescribes a special medication that a pharmacist must mix. The pharmacist must measure the ingredients in the exact proportions that the patient needs. In a situation such as this, mathematics are essential.

For more information about pharmacists, visit the Prentice Hall Web site. www.phschool.com

See also Extra Practice section.

31.

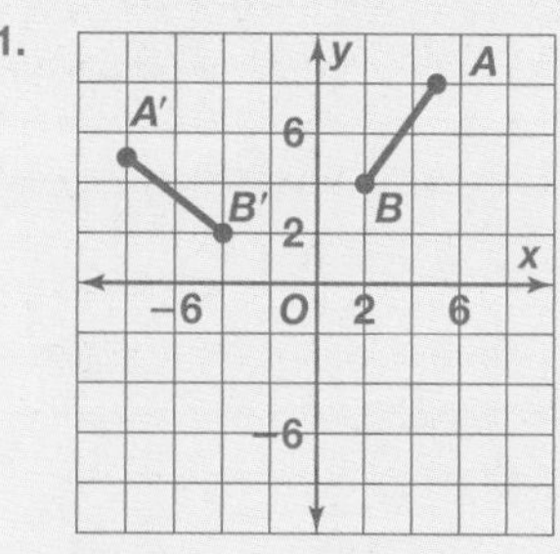


## Math at Work

If you have block scheduling or extended class periods, have small groups of students research the career of pharmacists and the math that they must use in their jobs. Suggest that students contact a college or university to find out what kinds of math courses pharmacy students must take. Students may also wish to interview pharmacists with questions about the math they use.

Students can find additional information on the Web site **www.phschool.com**.

# Area: Triangles and Trapezoids

10-2

## Part 1 Finding Areas of Triangles

### What You'll Learn

1. To find areas of triangles
2. To find areas of trapezoids

### . . . And Why

To find areas in real-world situations, such as construction

A diagonal divides a parallelogram into two congruent triangles.

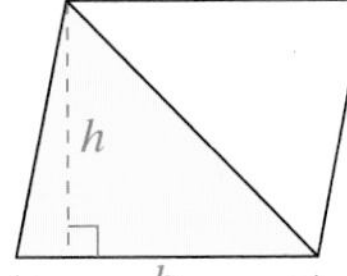


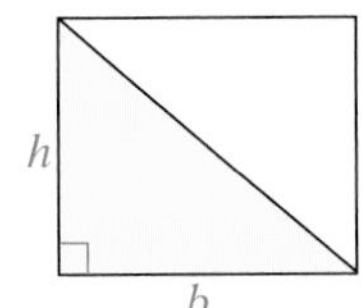


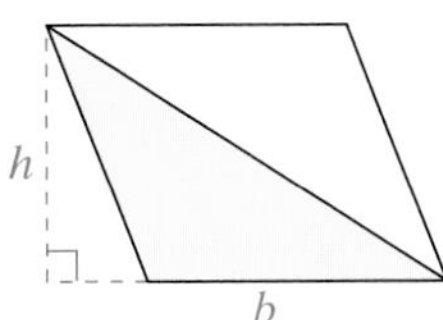


You can see that the area of a triangle is half the area of a parallelogram. An **altitude of a triangle** is the perpendicular segment from a vertex of a triangle to the line containing the opposite side. The height is the length of the altitude.

**Area of a Triangle**

The area of a triangle equals half the product of any base length $b$ and the corresponding height $h$.

$$A = \frac{1}{2}bh$$

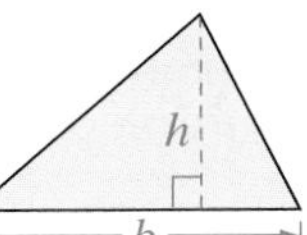


### Example 1

**Find the area of the triangle.**

$A = \frac{1}{2}bh$ Use the formula for area of a triangle.

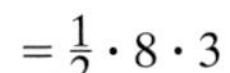
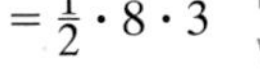

$= \frac{1}{2} \cdot 8 \cdot 3$ Replace $b$ with 8 and $h$ with 3.

$= 12$ Simplify.

The area is 12 $cm^2$.

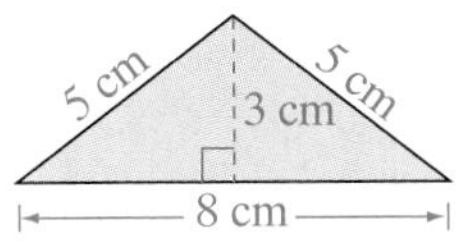


**Try This** Find the area of each triangle.

1. 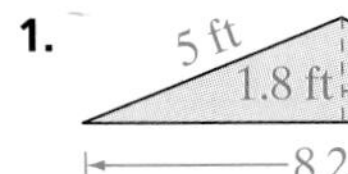
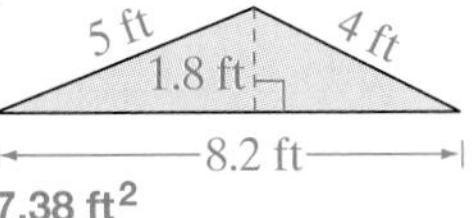

7.38 $ft^2$

2. 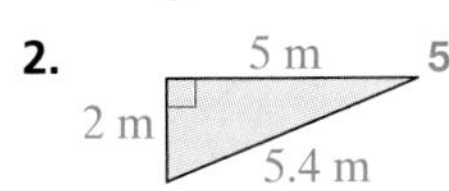

5 $m^2$



# Tools to Monitor Progress

## BEFORE THE LESSON

**To check prerequisite skills:**

- Multiplying by a fraction

**Skills You Need,** p. 501

## DURING THE LESSON

**To check understanding:**

**Try This** exercises on student page

- **Additional Example 1**

Find the area of the triangle.

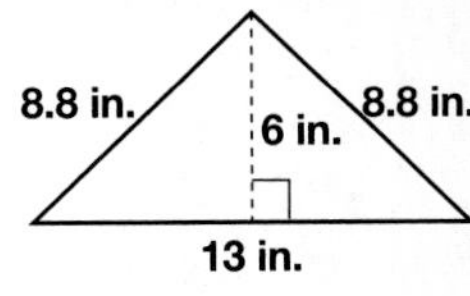


39 $in.^2$

# 10-2

## Getting Ready

**Key Terms and Symbols** altitude of a triangle, area of a triangle, area of a trapezoid.

**Resources** A complete list of resources for this lesson is on p. 501H.

### Daily Skills Warm-Up

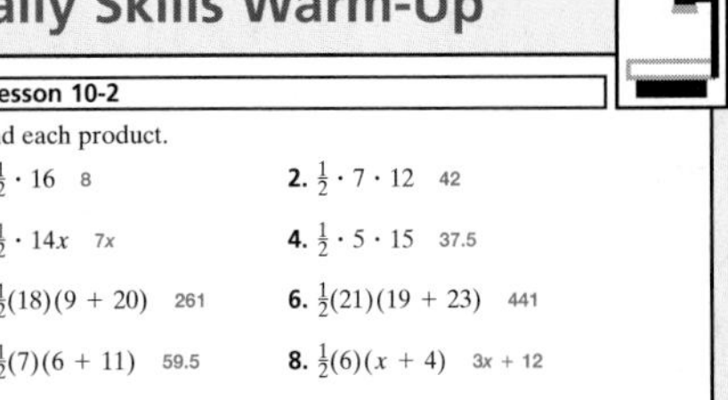

Lesson 10-2

Find each product.

1. $\frac{1}{2} \cdot 16$ 8
2. $\frac{1}{2} \cdot 7 \cdot 12$ 42
3. $\frac{1}{2} \cdot 14x$ 7x
4. $\frac{1}{2} \cdot 5 \cdot 15$ 37.5
5. $\frac{1}{2}(18)(9 + 20)$ 261
6. $\frac{1}{2}(21)(19 + 23)$ 441
7. $\frac{1}{2}(7)(6 + 11)$ 59.5
8. $\frac{1}{2}(6)(x + 4)$ $3x + 12$

### Background for the Lesson

Use the fact that a parallelogram can be divided in half by a diagonal to form two congruent triangles to find the area of a triangle. Since the area of a triangle is half that of the parallelogram, the area formula for a triangle is $A = \frac{1}{2}bh$. A trapezoid can be divided by a diagonal into two triangles with the same height as the trapezoid. One of the triangles has as its base the shorter base of the trapezoid, and the other triangle has as its base the longer base of the trapezoid. The area is the sum of the areas of these triangles.

## 1 Focus

### Connecting to Students' Lives

Ask students to find pictures or make sketches of trapezoids they see in buildings.

### Connecting to Prior Knowledge

In Lesson 10-1, students learned how to find the area of a parallelogram. In this lesson, students learn to adapt the formula for the area of a parallelogram to find the area of a triangle and a trapezoid. In Lesson 10-3, students will continue learning about area by finding the area of circles.

# 2 Teach

## Part 1 Teaching Notes

Point out to students that a *diagonal* connects two non-adjacent vertices of a parallelogram. The diagonal of a parallelogram forms two congruent triangles although this is not true for the diagonals of every quadrilateral.

### Example 1

**Build understanding.** Ask: What information in the diagram do you not need in order to find the area of this triangle? **the lengths of the 2 sides (other than the base)**

**Advanced Learners** Mark a point *A* on one side of a rectangle (such as an index card) and draw a triangle with sides from *A* to the two bottom corners. Imagine sliding *A* along the top of the rectangle to form various triangles. Which of these triangles will have the greatest area? **The areas will all be the same since the base and the height are the same for all of these triangles.**

**Visual Learning** Have students draw the parallelogram of which the triangle is one half to validate the formula for the area.

### Example 2

**Build understanding.** Ask: How do you know the length of the base of the triangle? **It is the same as the base of the rectangle.**

**Extension** The builder in Example 2 has to go to the lumber supply company to buy the siding. If the siding comes in 4-ft by 8-ft sheets, how many sheets does the builder have to buy? **8 sheets**

### EXAMPLE 2

*Construction* **How much siding does a builder need to cover the side of the house shown at the left?**

| Area of triangle | Area of rectangle |
|---|---|
| $A = \frac{1}{2}bh$ | $A = bh$ |
| $= \frac{1}{2} \cdot 16 \cdot 9$ | $= 16 \cdot 10$ |
| $= 72$ | $= 160$ |

Add to find the total: $72 + 160 = 232$.

The builder needs 232 ft$^2$ of siding.

**TRY THIS** Find the area of the shaded figure.

3\. 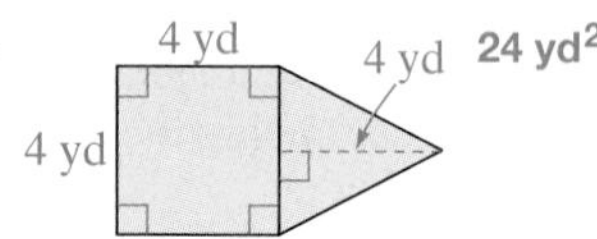

**24 yd$^2$**

## Part 2 Finding Areas of Trapezoids

A diagonal divides a trapezoid into two triangles. You can add the areas of the triangles to find the area of the trapezoid.

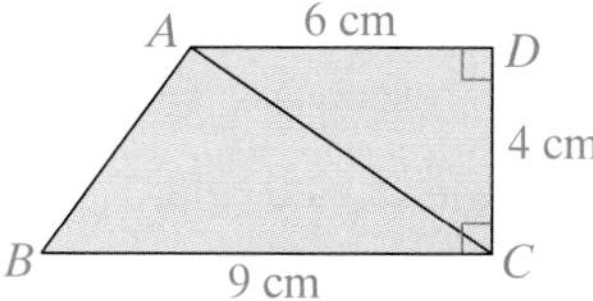


| Area of $\triangle ABC$ | Area of $\triangle ADC$ |
|---|---|
| $A = \frac{1}{2}bh$ | $A = \frac{1}{2}bh$ |
| $= \frac{1}{2} \cdot 9 \cdot 4$ | $= \frac{1}{2} \cdot 6 \cdot 4$ |
| $= 18$ | $= 12$ |

The areas of the two triangles are 18 cm$^2$ and 12 cm$^2$. The area of the trapezoid is the sum of the areas of the two triangles, 30 cm$^2$. Notice that the triangles have the same height but different bases. You can use this information to write a formula for the area of a trapezoid.



- **Additional Example 2**
  Find the area of the figure.

  20 cm
  45 cm
  30 cm

  **1,800 cm$^2$**

- **Additional Example 3**
  Suppose that, through the years, the Erie Canal filled up with silt and mud so that the depth is only 3 ft and the length of the bottom ($b_1$) increases to 31 ft. Find the area of the new trapezoidal cross section. **106.5 ft$^2$**

In a trapezoid, the parallel sides are its bases. For the figure at the right the bases are $b_1$ and $b_2$.

The area of the trapezoid is $\frac{1}{2}b_1h + \frac{1}{2}b_2h$.

By using the distributive property, you can see that $\frac{1}{2}b_1h + \frac{1}{2}b_2h$ is $\frac{1}{2}h(b_1 + b_2)$. So, the area of the trapezoid is $\frac{1}{2}h(b_1 + b_2)$.

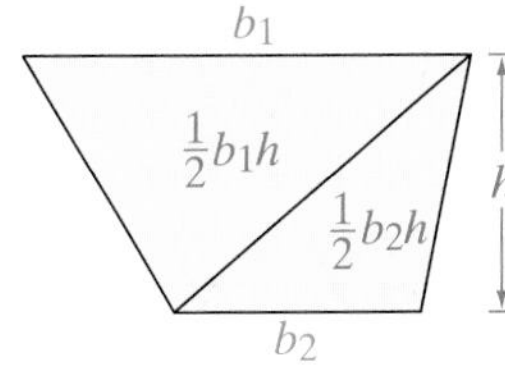


### Area of a Trapezoid

The area of a trapezoid is half the product of the height and the sum of the lengths of the bases.

$$A = \frac{1}{2}h(b_1 + b_2)$$

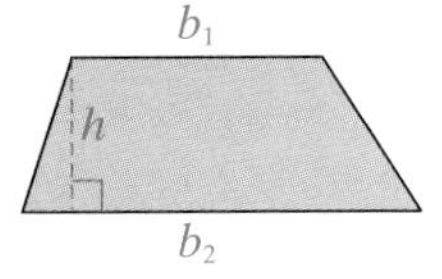


REAL-WORLD CONNECTION

## Example 3

*Erie Canal* **The Erie Canal opened in 1825 and was hailed as an engineering marvel. Below is a cross section of the Erie Canal. Find the area of the trapezoidal cross section.**

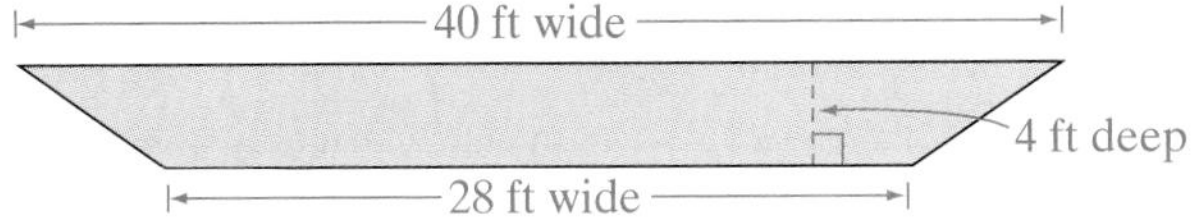


$A = \frac{1}{2}h(b_1 + b_2)$ Use the formula for the area of a trapezoid.

$A = \frac{1}{2} \cdot 4(28 + 40)$ Replace $h$ with 4, $b_1$ with 28, and $b_2$ with 40.

$= \frac{1}{2} \cdot 4(68)$ Simplify.

$= 2 \cdot 68$

$= 136$

The area of the cross section is 136 ft$^2$.

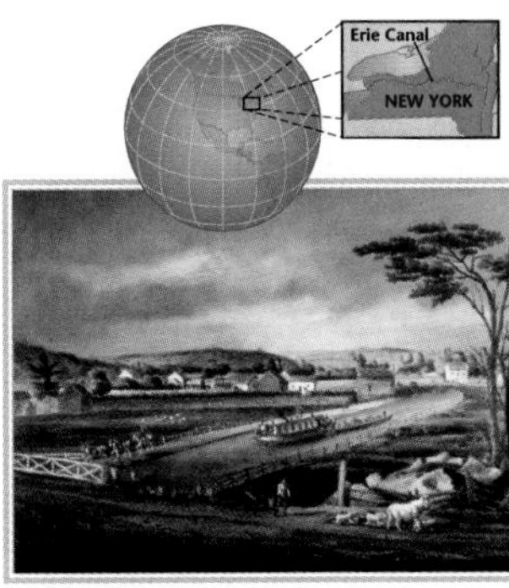


The Erie Canal is 363 miles in length.

**Try This** Find the area of each trapezoid.

**4.**

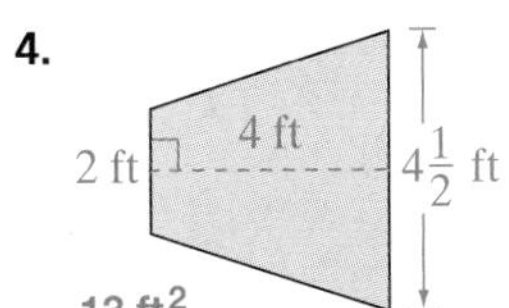


13 ft$^2$

**5.**

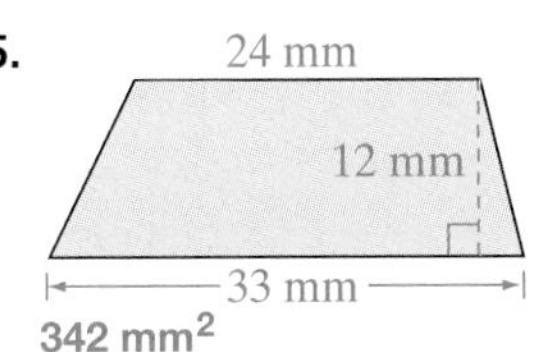


342 mm$^2$



## Part 2 Teaching Notes

Have a student compare a parallelogram and a trapezoid. Also ask a volunteer to review the distributive property with an example.

**Reading Math** Students may not understand that the subscript on $b_1$ and $b_2$ names the two bases and is not the same as a multiplier or exponent. Read this as "*b* sub one plus *b* sub two."

**Alternative Method** You can find the area of a trapezoid by dividing it into a rectangle with one or two triangles at the sides. Then find the area of the rectangle and the area of the triangle(s) and add them together to get the sum. This method only works if you have enough information to find the measure for the base of each triangle you create.

**ELL** Before Example 3, explain that a cross section is the geometric figure you get when you slice through a three-dimensional figure at right angles. Tell students to picture a carrot. The perpendicular cross section of a carrot is a circle.

### Example 3

**Build understanding.** Ask: Could two barges that are 10-ft wide pass each other in the canal? How do you know? Yes; The width of the canal at the top is 40 ft, which leaves more than enough room for the barges to pass each other.

**Error Prevention** Remind students that the bases of a trapezoid are the two sides that are parallel to each other, even if the figure is turned so that the bases are vertical. Use the lengths of these two sides when calculating the area of a trapezoid.

## AFTER THE LESSON

**To assess knowledge: Lesson Quiz**

Find each area.

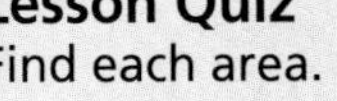

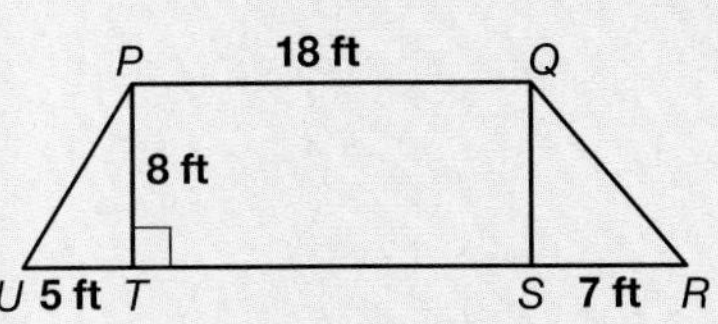


1. Area of trapezoid *PQRU* 192 ft$^2$
2. Area of triangle *PTU* 20 ft$^2$
3. Area of triangle *QRS* 28 ft$^2$

- For enrichment and reteaching options see Resources on p. 501H.

# 3 Practice/Assess

## Assignment Guide

To provide flexible scheduling, this lesson can be divided into parts.

**▼ Part 1**

**Core** 1–3, 7–10, 17–19, 21, 24–25

✪ **Extension** 22–23

**▼ Part 2**

**Core** 4–6, 11–16

✪ **Extension** 20

Mixed Review can be assigned at any time for maintenance.

## Exercises

**Test Prep Exercise 25** Find the value of $x$ first. Notice that the areas of the two triangles are equal.

## ✪ Challenge

What are the base lengths of a trapezoid that has an area of 240 m$^2$, and a height of 4 m, if one base is twice as long as the other base? 40 m and 80 m

## Closure

The area of a polygon is the number of square units enclosed by the polygon. To find the area of a triangle, use the formula $A = \frac{1}{2}bh$. To find the area of a trapezoid, use the formula $A = \frac{1}{2}h(b_1 + b_2)$.

# Exercises

## Check Understanding

**Find the area of each triangle.**

**1.**

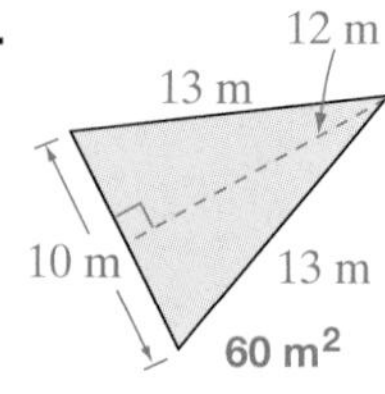


60 m$^2$

**2.**

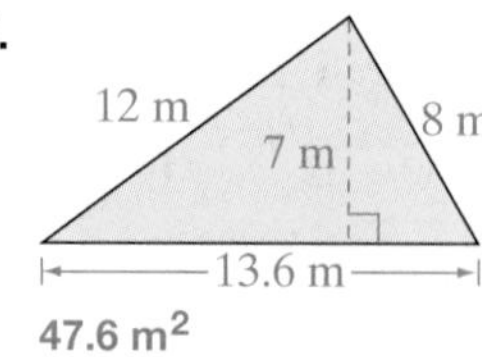


47.6 m$^2$

**3.**

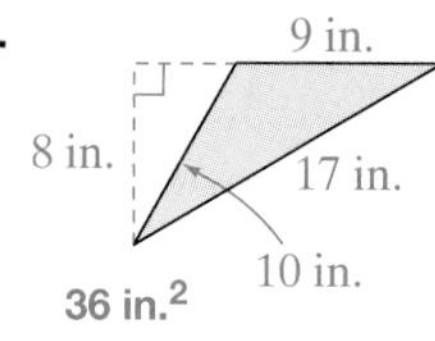


36 in.$^2$

**Find the area of each trapezoid.**

**4.**

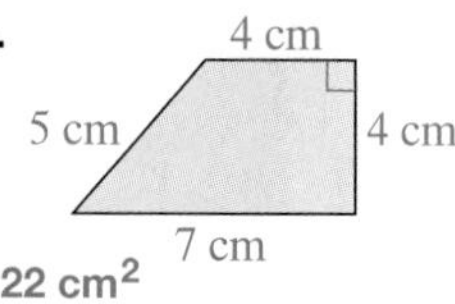


22 cm$^2$

**5.**

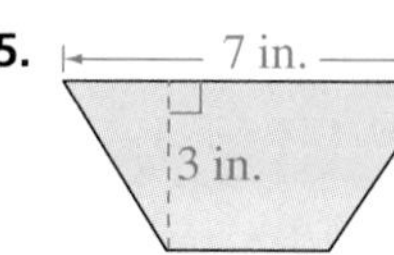


15 in.$^2$

**6.**

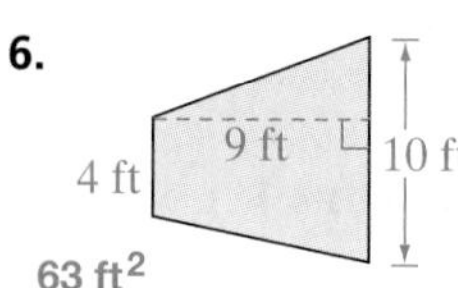


63 ft$^2$

**7.** *Critical Thinking* A triangle and a parallelogram both have areas of 20 cm$^2$ and bases of 5 cm. What do you know about the heights? The triangle is two times as high as the parallelogram.

## Practice and Problem Solving

**Find the area of each triangle.**

**8.**

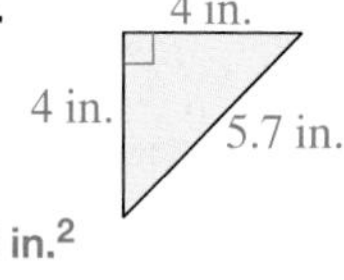


8 in.$^2$

**9.**

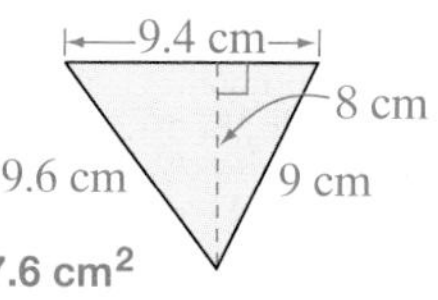


37.6 cm$^2$

**10.** 32 m, 80 m, 32 m

512 m$^2$

**Find the area of each trapezoid.**

**11.**

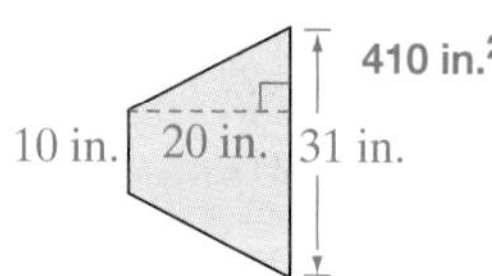


410 in.$^2$

**12.**

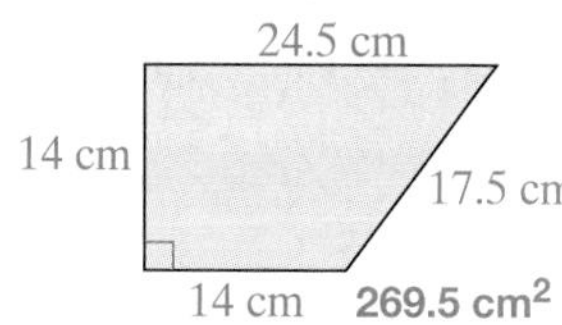


269.5 cm$^2$

**13.**

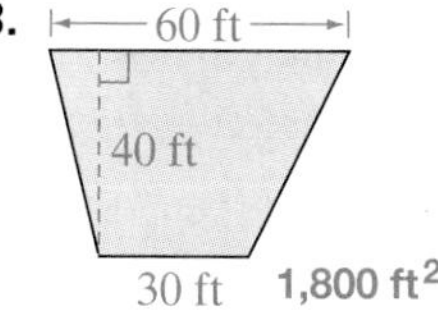


1,800 ft$^2$

**14.**

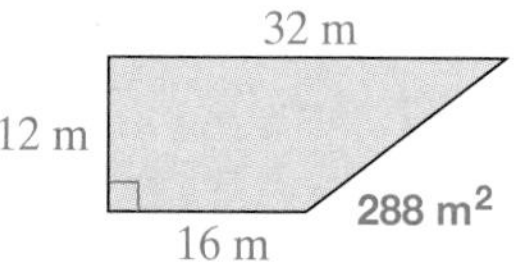


288 m$^2$

**15.**

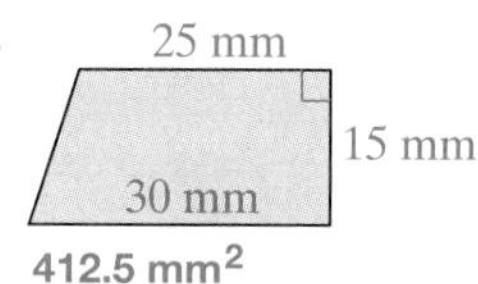


412.5 mm$^2$

**16.**

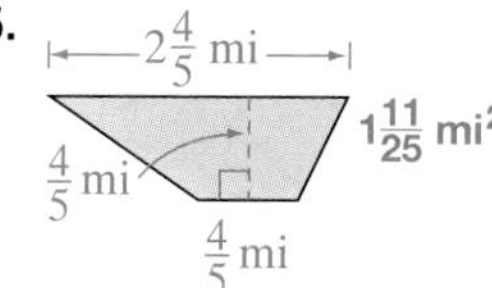


$1\frac{11}{25}$ mi$^2$



## Alternative Assessment

Have students verify the formula for the area of a parallelogram by first finding the area of a given parallelogram using the formula. Then have them find the area by adding the areas of the rectangle and the two triangles that make up the parallelogram.

## Daily Cumulative Review

**Find the area of each parallelogram.** *(Lesson 10-1)*

1. 3 yd, 2 yd — 6 yd$^2$
2. 4 ft, 6 ft, 16 ft — 64 ft$^2$
3. 24 in., 24 in. — 576 in.$^2$
4. 5 cm, 5 cm, 4 cm — 20 cm$^2$
5. 5 mi, 2 mi — 10 mi$^2$
6. 10 m, 5 m, 6 m — 50 m$^2$

**Judging from appearance, does each figure have a rotational symmetry? If yes, what is the angle of rotation?** *(Lesson 9-10)*

7. yes; 180°
8. no
9. yes; 90°

**Mixed Review**

**Evaluate each expression.**

10. $b^2$, for $b = 4$ (4-2) — 16
11. $c^3$, for $c = 6$ (4-2) — 216
12. $a^4$, for $a = 15$ (4-2) — 50,625

**Find the slope of the line through each pair of points.**

13. $A(4, 6), B(12, 1)$ (8-3) — slope $= -\frac{5}{8}$
14. $N(-5, 6), M(-1, 8)$ (8-3) — slope $= \frac{1}{2}$
15. $S(-3, -5), T(3, -3)$ (8-3) — slope $= \frac{1}{3}$

**Write each decimal as a fraction or mixed number in simplest form.**

16. 0.3 (5-2) — $\frac{3}{10}$
17. 6.75 (5-2) — $6\frac{3}{4}$
18. 3.21 (5-2) — $3\frac{21}{100}$

**Find the area of each shaded region.**

**17.** 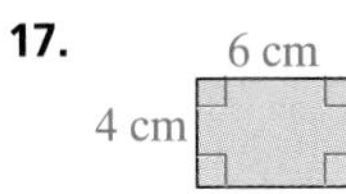


34 $cm^2$

**18.** 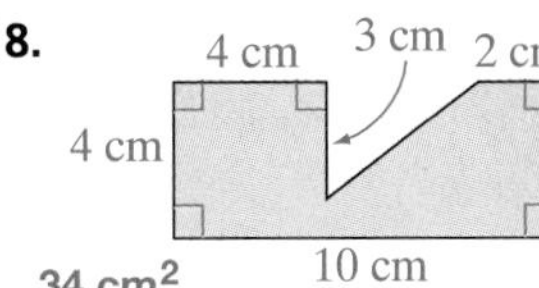


34 $cm^2$

**19.** 12 in. 4 in. 6 in. 10 in. 108 $in.^2$

✪ **20.** A trapezoid has area 50 $in.^2$. The two bases are 5 in. and 15 in. What is the height of the trapezoid? 5 in.

**21.** Find the area of the yellow region in the figure at the right. 50 $m^2$

10 m

✪ **22. a.** *Mathematical Reasoning* The bases of two triangles are the same length. The height of the first triangle is twice the height of the second. What is the ratio of the area of the second triangle to the area of the first? Justify your answer. See below.

**b.** Suppose the height and the base of a triangle are twice the length of the height and base of another triangle. What is the ratio of the area of the smaller triangle to the area of the larger triangle? Justify your answer. $\frac{1}{4}$; the area of a triangle is $\frac{1}{2}bh$, so doubling both dimensions will quadruple the area.

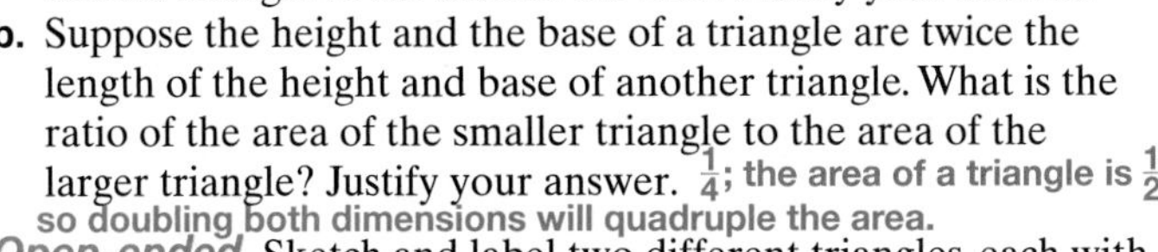

✪ **23.** *Open-ended* Sketch and label two different triangles, each with an area of 180 $in.^2$. Check students' work.

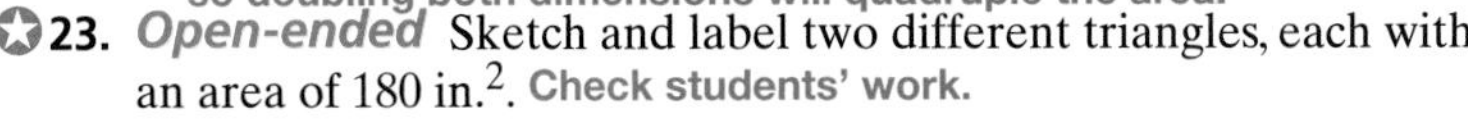

**24.** *Writing* Are $\left(\frac{1}{2} \cdot 3\right) \cdot 8$ and $3 \cdot \left(\frac{1}{2} \cdot 8\right)$ equal? Explain how this can help in finding the area of a triangle. Yes, you can multiply either the base or the height by $\frac{1}{2}$ to simplify the solution.

**25.** **TEST PREP** *ABCD* is a rectangle. What is the area of the shaded region? A

A. 15 $cm^2$ B. 20 $cm^2$ C. 35 $cm^2$ D. 50 $cm^2$

10 cm; A; B; 5 cm; D; C; x; 4 cm; x

22a. $\frac{1}{2}$; the area of a triangle is $\frac{1}{2}bh$, so doubling one dimension will double the area.

## MIXED REVIEW

**Find the area of each parallelogram.** *(Lesson 10-1)*

**26.** 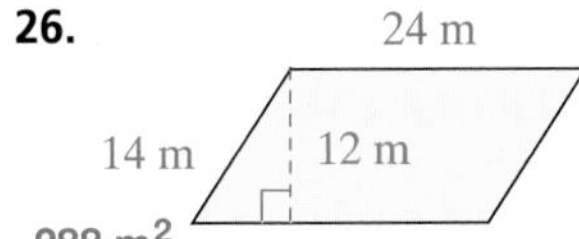


288 $m^2$

**27.** 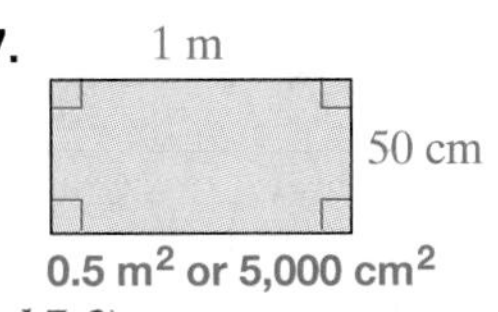


0.5 $m^2$ or 5,000 $cm^2$

**28.** 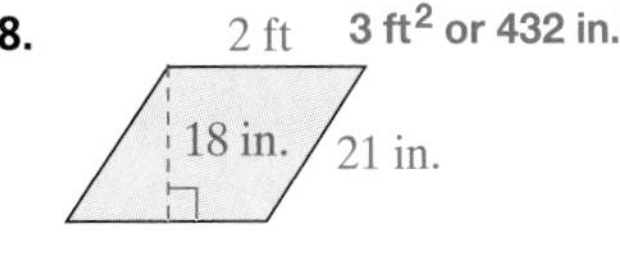


3 $ft^2$ or 432 $in.^2$

**Solve each equation.** *(Lessons 7-1 and 7-3)*

**29.** $13 + 3x = 7$ −2

**30.** $16 + 2y = 9$ −3.5

**31.** $5.5a + 2 = 10.5$ $1.\overline{54}$

**32.** $\frac{1}{2}b - 10 = 24$ 68

**33.** *Choose a Strategy* Suppose you bought two books for $15. The original price of the two books was the same, but you were able to buy one for full price and get the other for half price. What was the full price? $10

See also Extra Practice section.



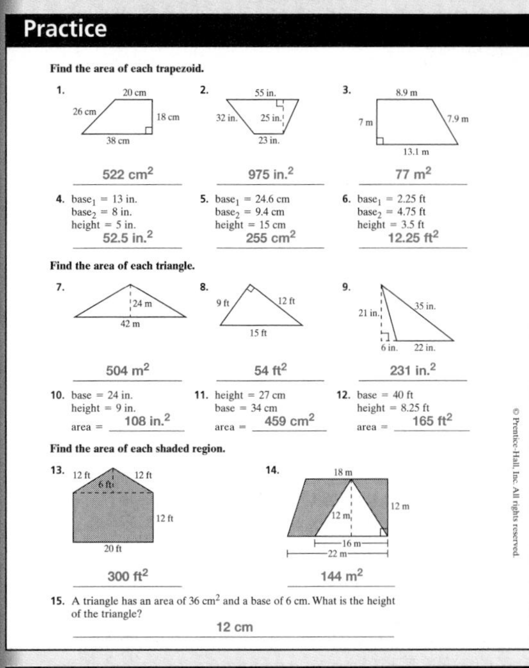

## Practice

**Find the area of each trapezoid.**

1. 20 cm, 26 cm, 18 cm, 38 cm — 522 $cm^2$
2. 55 in., 32 in., 25 in., 23 in. — 975 $in.^2$
3. 8.9 m, 7 m, 7.9 m, 13.1 m — 77 $m^2$
4. $base_1$ = 13 in., $base_2$ = 8 in., height = 5 in. — 52.5 $in.^2$
5. $base_1$ = 24.6 cm, $base_2$ = 9.4 cm, height = 15 cm — 255 $cm^2$
6. $base_1$ = 2.25 ft, $base_2$ = 4.75 ft, height = 3.5 ft — 12.25 $ft^2$

**Find the area of each triangle.**

7. 24 m, 42 m — 504 $m^2$
8. 9 ft, 12 ft, 15 ft — 54 $ft^2$
9. 21 in., 35 in., 6 in., 22 in. — 231 $in.^2$
10. base = 24 in., height = 9 in., area = 108 $in.^2$
11. height = 27 cm, base = 34 cm, area = 459 $cm^2$
12. base = 40 ft, height = 8.25 ft, area = 165 $ft^2$

**Find the area of each shaded region.**

13. 12 ft, 12 ft, 6 ft, 12 ft, 20 ft — 300 $ft^2$
14. 18 m, 12 m, 12 m, 16 m, 22 m — 144 $m^2$
15. A triangle has an area of 36 $cm^2$ and a base of 6 cm. What is the height of the triangle? 12 cm



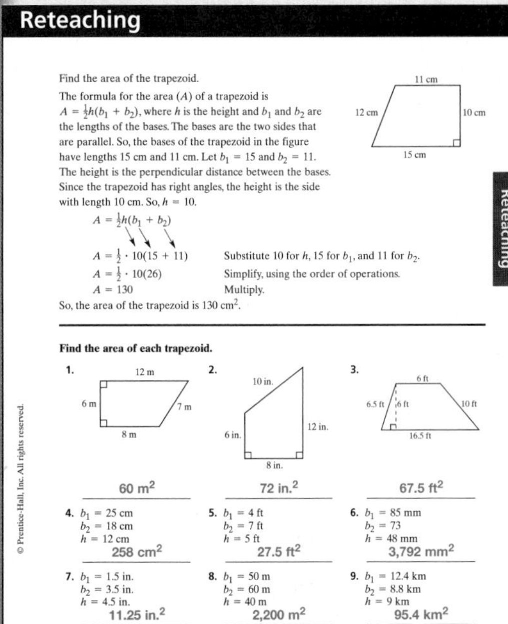

## Reteaching

Find the area of the trapezoid.

The formula for the area ($A$) of a trapezoid is $A = \frac{1}{2}h(b_1 + b_2)$, where $h$ is the height and $b_1$ and $b_2$ are the lengths of the bases. The bases are the two sides that are parallel. So, the bases of the trapezoid in the figure have lengths 15 cm and 11 cm. Let $b_1 = 15$ and $b_2 = 11$. The height is the perpendicular distance between the bases. Since the trapezoid has right angles, the height is the side with length 10 cm. So, $h = 10$.

11 cm, 12 cm, 10 cm, 15 cm

$A = \frac{1}{2}h(b_1 + b_2)$

$A = \frac{1}{2} \cdot 10(15 + 11)$ Substitute 10 for $h$, 15 for $b_1$, and 11 for $b_2$.

$A = \frac{1}{2} \cdot 10(26)$ Simplify, using the order of operations.

$A = 130$ Multiply.

So, the area of the trapezoid is 130 $cm^2$.

**Find the area of each trapezoid.**

1. 12 m, 6 m, 7 m, 8 m — 60 $m^2$
2. 10 in., 6 in., 12 in., 8 in. — 72 $in.^2$
3. 6 ft, 6.5 ft, 6 ft, 10 ft, 16.5 ft — 67.5 $ft^2$
4. $b_1$ = 25 cm, $b_2$ = 18 cm, $h$ = 12 cm — 258 $cm^2$
5. $b_1$ = 4 ft, $b_2$ = 7 ft, $h$ = 5 ft — 27.5 $ft^2$
6. $b_1$ = 85 mm, $b_2$ = 73, $h$ = 48 mm — 3,792 $mm^2$
7. $b_1$ = 1.5 in., $b_2$ = 3.5 in., $h$ = 4.5 in. — 11.25 $in.^2$
8. $b_1$ = 50 m, $b_2$ = 60 m, $h$ = 40 m — 2,200 $m^2$
9. $b_1$ = 12.4 km, $b_2$ = 8.8 km, $h$ = 9 km — 95.4 $km^2$



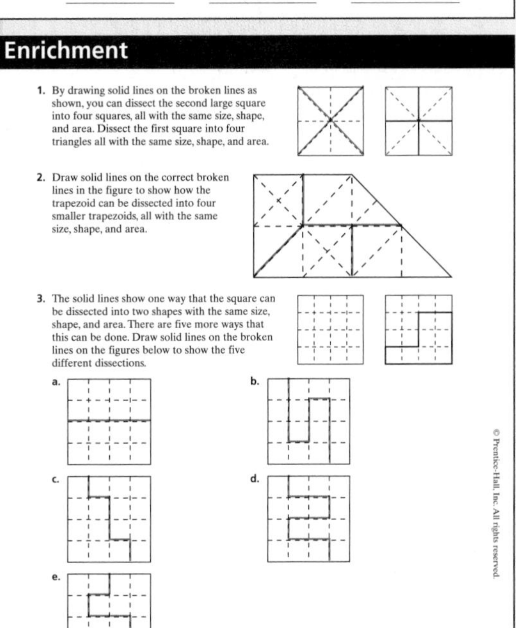

## Enrichment

1. By drawing solid lines on the broken lines as shown, you can dissect the second large square into four squares, all with the same size, shape, and area. Dissect the first square into four triangles all with the same size, shape, and area.

2. Draw solid lines on the correct broken lines in the figure to show how the trapezoid can be dissected into four smaller trapezoids, all with the same size, shape, and area.

3. The solid lines show one way that the square can be dissected into two shapes with the same size, shape, and area. There are five more ways that this can be done. Draw solid lines on the broken lines on the figures below to show the five different dissections.

a. b. c. d. e.

# 10-3

## Getting Ready

**Key Terms and Symbols** area of a circle

**Materials** protractor, scissors

**Resources** A complete list of resources for this lesson is on p. 501H.

### Daily Skills Warm-Up

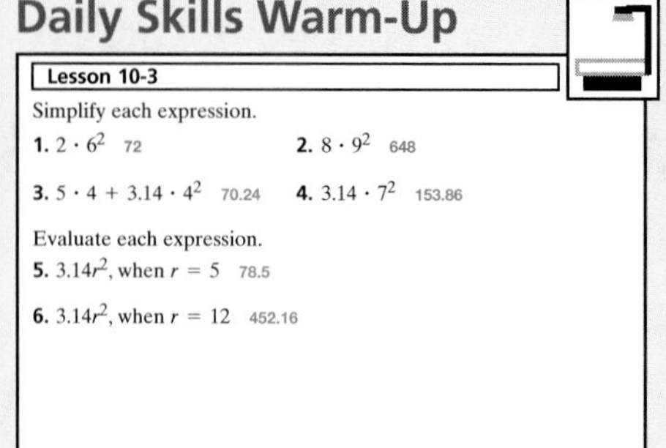
Lesson 10-3

Simplify each expression.

1. $2 \cdot 6^2$ 72
2. $8 \cdot 9^2$ 648
3. $5 \cdot 4 + 3.14 \cdot 4^2$ 70.24
4. $3.14 \cdot 7^2$ 153.86

Evaluate each expression.

5. $3.14r^2$, when $r = 5$ 78.5
6. $3.14r^2$, when $r = 12$ 452.16

### Background for the Lesson

The area of a circle is $A = \pi r^2$. Since $\pi$ is irrational and a decimal that never ends, you can only write the area of a circle exactly as the product of the radius squared and $\pi$. You can write the area of a circle as approximately equal to a decimal number.

## 1 Focus

### Investigate

Use round coffee filters as ready-made circles to demonstrate this activity. Explain that the resulting figure only *approximates* a parallelogram because the ends of each wedge are slightly curved. As the number of wedges increases, the area of the circle approaches that of a parallelogram. If you could use an infinite number of wedges, the two areas would be the same.

### Connecting to Prior Knowledge

In Lesson 10-1, students learned how to find the area of a parallelogram. In this lesson, students adapt that formula to find the area of a circle. In Lesson 10-5, students will find the surface area of space figures.

# 10-3 Area: Circles

### What You'll Learn

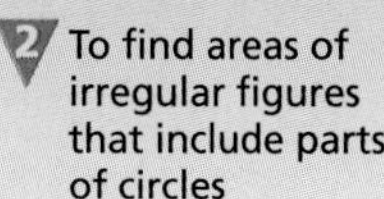

1. To find areas of circles
2. To find areas of irregular figures that include parts of circles

### . . . And Why

To use area formulas in real-world situations, such as finding the amount of grass seed needed to cover a circular region

## *Investigate*

**Finding the Formula for Area of a Circle**

1. Use your protractor to draw a circle. Cut out the circle. Check students' work.
2. Fold the circle in half, and then in half again. Fold it in half a third and fourth time. Check students' work.
3. Cut out the 16 wedges that you have formed with the folds. Check students' work.
4. Arrange the wedges in a row as shown below. Check students' work.

5. Notice that the new shape resembles a parallelogram. How does the base of the parallelogram (the side shown in red) relate to the circumference of the circle? How does the height of the parallelogram relate to the radius of the circle? The base is $\frac{1}{2}$ the circumference. The height is the radius of the circle.
6. Use the formula for the area of a parallelogram to estimate the area of your circle. Check students' work.

## Part 1 Finding Areas of Circles

The diagram above shows the relationship between the area of a circle and a figure that is like a parallelogram. The height $h$ of the parallelogram is about the same as the radius $r$ of the circle. The base $b$ is about half the circumference $C$ of the circle. You can use the formula for the area of a parallelogram to suggest the formula for the area of a circle.

| | |
|---|---|
| $A = bh$ | Use the formula for area of a parallelogram. |
| $A = (\frac{1}{2}C)(r)$ | Substitute $\frac{1}{2}C$ for $b$ and $r$ for $h$. |
| $A = \frac{1}{2}(2\pi r) \cdot r$ | Substitute $2\pi r$ for $C$. |
| $A = \pi r^2$ | Simplify. |



## Tools to Monitor Progress

### BEFORE THE LESSON

**To check prerequisite skills:**

- Simplifying expressions with exponents

**Skills You Need,** p. 501

### DURING THE LESSON

**To check understanding:**

**Try This** exercises on student page

- **Additional Example 1**
  Find the exact area of a circle with a diameter of 20 in. **$100\pi$ in.$^2$**
- **Additional Example 2**
  If a TV station's Doppler weather radar can detect precipitation up to 50 mi away, what is the area of the circular region covered by the radar? **about 7,850 mi$^2$**

### Area of a Circle

The area of a circle equals the product of $\pi$ and the square of the radius $r$.

$$A = \pi r^2$$

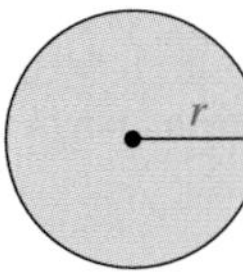


To find the *exact area* of a circle, you express the area using $\pi$.

### EXAMPLE 1

**Find the exact area of a circle with diameter 12 cm.**

$A = \pi r^2$

$= \pi(6)^2$    $r = \frac{1}{2}d$; $r = 6$

$= 36\pi$    Simplify.

The area is $36\pi$ cm$^2$.

**TRY THIS**

7. Find the exact area of a circle with diameter 100 in. $2{,}500\pi$ in.$^2$

For real-world situations, you usually want an approximate value for the area of a circle. If you are finding an approximate area, use 3.14 for $\pi$.

REAL-WORLD CONNECTION

### EXAMPLE 2

*Biology* **The size of a jaguar's territory depends on how much food is available. In a situation where there is plenty of food, such as in a forest, the circular territory of the jaguar may be as small as 3 mi in diameter. Find the area of the region.**

$A = \pi r^2$

$= \pi(1.5)^2$    $r = \frac{1}{2}d$; $r = 1.5$

$= 2.25\pi$    exact area

$\approx (2.25)(3.14)$    Use 3.14 for $\pi$.

$= 7.065$    approximate area

The area of the region is about 7 mi$^2$.

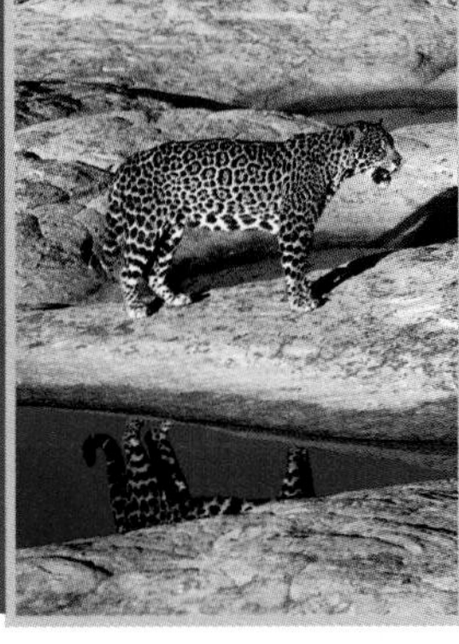

During a drought a jaguar may need to search for food in a territory as large as 6 mi in diameter.

**TRY THIS**

8. Find the approximate area of a circle with diameter 6 mi. 28.26 mi$^2$



## 2 Teach

### PART 1 Part 1 Teaching Notes

Remind students that $\pi$ is not a rational number, and it can only be approximated by a fraction or decimal. The most common approximation for $\pi$, used in this lesson, is 3.14.

#### Example 1

**Build understanding.** Ask: What is the radius of the circle? 6 cm

**Error Prevention** Students may multiply the radius by 2, rather than squaring it, when they find the area of a circle. A number squared is the number written 2 times as a factor, or the number multiplied by itself. Also remind students to read carefully to find whether the problem lists the *radius* or the *diameter.*

**Auditory Learning** Draw several circles on the board. Label the length of the radius in some of the circles, and the diameter in others. For each circle, have a volunteer say aloud the formula for the exact area of that circle.

#### Example 2

**Build understanding.** Ask: What is the farthest a jaguar would have to walk to cross its territory? Explain. 3 mi; Diameter is the greatest distance across a circle.

**Additional Example 3**

You decide to leave half of the curved area of the yard in Example 3 for a flower bed. What would be the approximate area of the yard covered by grass? about 1,302 ft$^2$

### AFTER THE LESSON

**To assess knowledge: Lesson Quiz**

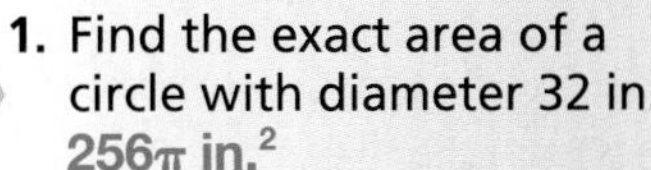

1. Find the exact area of a circle with diameter 32 in. $256\pi$ in.$^2$

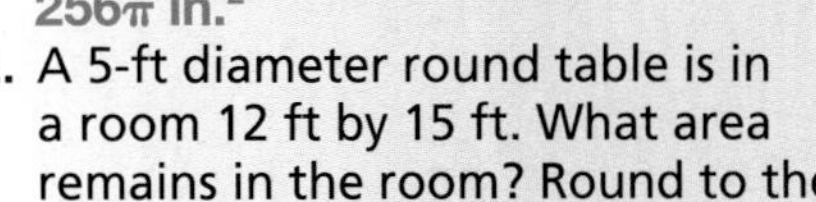

2. A 5-ft diameter round table is in a room 12 ft by 15 ft. What area remains in the room? Round to the nearest unit. 160 ft$^2$

- For enrichment and reteaching options see Resources on p. 501H.

## Part 2 Teaching Notes

In order to use this method of finding the area of irregular figures, the curved portions of the figures must be parts of a circle. Students can use a ruler to verify that the curved areas have a constant radius.

### Example 3

**Build understanding.** Ask: Why is the fraction $\frac{1}{2}$ used in the formula for the area of a circle in this problem? **because you are only looking for the area of a half-circle**

**Math Reasoning** Which has a larger area, a circle with radius 2 or a square with side 4? Explain. **The square has the larger area since the circle will fit inside the square.**

## Finding Areas of Irregular Figures

To find the area of an irregular figure, you can sometimes separate it into figures with areas you know how to find.

REAL-WORLD CONNECTION

### Example 3

*Landscaping* **A pound of grass seed covers approximately 675 ft$^2$. Find the area of the lawn below. Then find the amount of grass seed you need to buy to cover the lawn. Grass seed comes in 3-lb bags.**

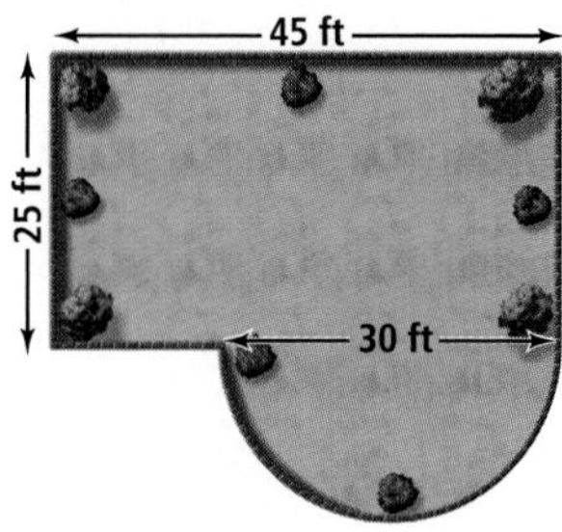


**Area of region that is one half of a circle**

area of circle $= \pi r^2$

area of half circle $= \frac{1}{2}\pi r^2$

$A \approx \frac{1}{2}(3.14)(15)^2$ — Replace $\pi$ with 3.14 and $r$ with 15.

$A = 353.25$

**Area of region that is a rectangle**

area of rectangle $= bh$

$A = 45 \cdot 25$ — Replace $b$ with 45 and $h$ with 25.

$A = 1{,}125$

The area of the lawn is about 353 ft$^2$ + 1,125 ft$^2$ = 1,478 ft$^2$.

$1{,}478 \div 675 \approx 2.19$ — Divide to find the amount of seed.

You will need to buy one 3-lb bag of grass seed.

### Try This

9. Find the area of the shaded region to the nearest tenth. **40.2 cm$^2$**

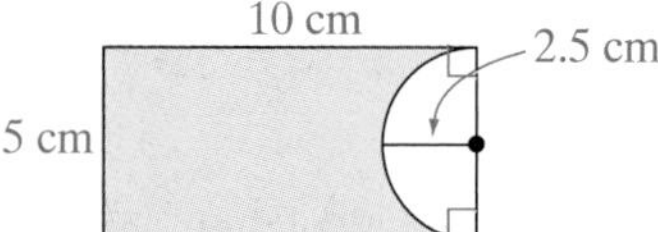

# Exercises

## Check Understanding

**Find the area of each circle. Give an exact area and an approximate area to the nearest square unit.**

1. $r = 3$ ft $9\pi$ ft$^2$; 28 ft$^2$
2. $d = 10$ m $25\pi$ m$^2$; 79 m$^2$
3. $r = 20$ cm $400\pi$ cm$^2$; 1,256 cm$^2$

4. 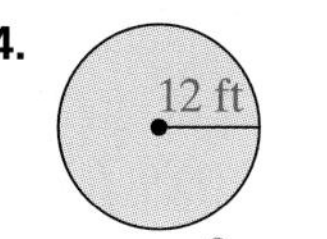

$144\pi$ ft$^2$; 452 ft$^2$

5. 16 m
$64\pi$ m$^2$; 201 m$^2$

6. 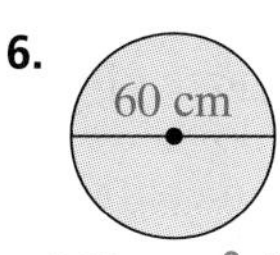

$900\pi$ cm$^2$; 2,826 cm$^2$

**Find the area of each figure to the nearest square unit.**

7. 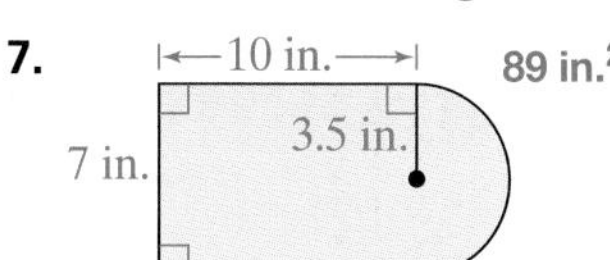

89 in.$^2$

8. 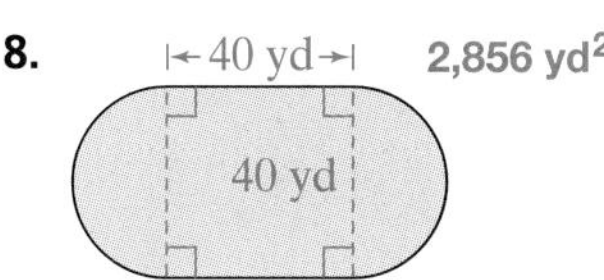

2,856 yd$^2$

9. Which has a greater area, a circle with radius 2 m or a square with side length 2 m? Explain. The circle has a greater area. A circle with radius 2 m has an area of $4\pi$ m$^2$, but a square of side length 2 m only has an area of 4 m$^2$.

## Practice and Problem Solving

**Find the area of each circle. Give an exact area and an approximate area to the nearest tenth.**

10. $r = 11$ mi $121\pi$ mi$^2$; 379.9 mi$^2$
11. $r = \frac{1}{2}$ m $\frac{1}{4}\pi$ m$^2$; 0.8 m$^2$
12. $d = 1.2$ in. $0.36\pi$ in.$^2$; 1.1 in.$^2$
13. $r = 5\frac{1}{2}$ mi $30.25\pi$ mi$^2$; 95 mi$^2$
14. $d = 3.2$ ft $2.56\pi$ ft$^2$; 8.0 ft$^2$
15. $d = 8.4$ mm $17.64\pi$ mm$^2$; 55.4 mm$^2$

**Find the area of each shaded region to the nearest square unit.**

16. 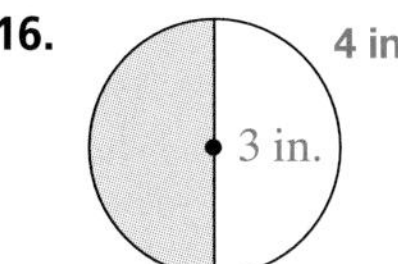

4 in.$^2$

17. 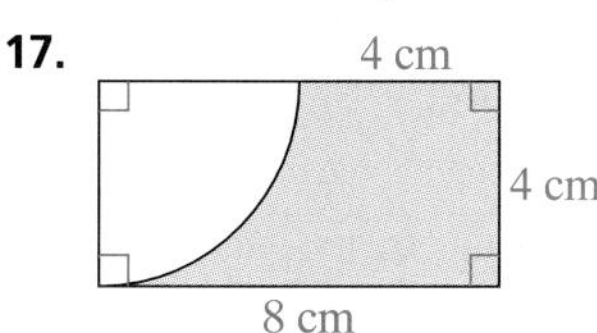

19 cm$^2$

18. 12 mm
6 mm
339 mm$^2$

19. 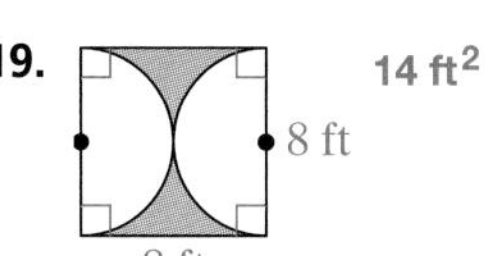

14 ft$^2$

20. 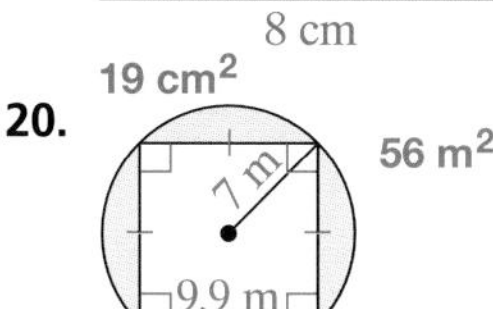

56 m$^2$

21. 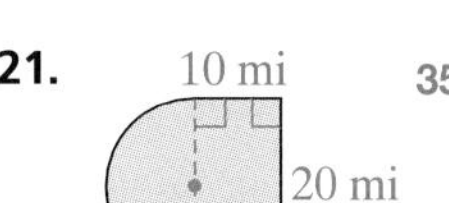

357 mi$^2$



# 3 Practice/Assess

## Assignment Guide

To provide flexible scheduling, this lesson can be divided into parts.

**Part 1**
**Core** 1–6, 9–18, 28, 31, 33
**Extension** 27, 30

**Part 2**
**Core** 7–8, 19–26
**Extension** 29, 32

Mixed Review can be assigned at any time for maintenance.

## Exercises

**Exercises 10–21** The area calculation requires the radius, which is $\frac{1}{2}$ the diameter. Use 3.14 to approximate $\pi$.

## Challenge

Find the area of this figure. Point $A$ is the center of the circle. $\angle BAD$ measures 110°. The radius of the part of the circle with center $A$ is 3 m.

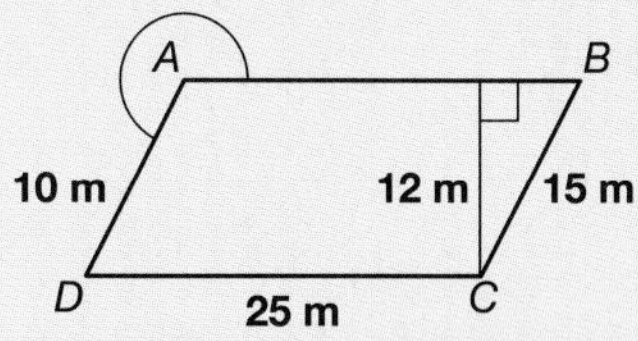


$25(12)$ m$^2$ $+ \frac{250}{360}(3^2\pi)$ m$^2$ $\approx 320$ m$^2$

## Closure

To find the area of a circle, use the formula $A = \pi r^2$. Use 3.14 for $\pi$.

## Alternative Assessment

Ask students to find irregularly shaped areas in the classroom and the school building and then to measure them to find their surface areas. Have students draw sketches of the figures to explain how they calculated the areas.

## Daily Cumulative Review

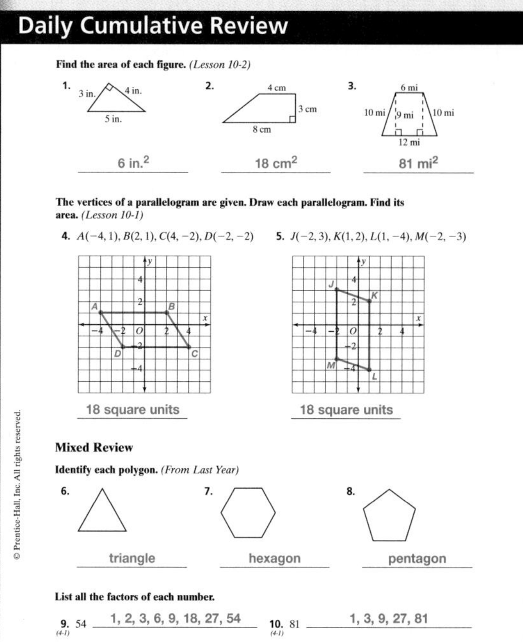

**Find the area of each figure.** *(Lesson 10-2)*

1. 3 in., 4 in., 5 in. — 6 in.$^2$
2. 4 cm, 3 cm, 8 cm — 18 cm$^2$
3. 6 mi, 10 mi, 9 mi, 10 mi, 12 mi — 81 mi$^2$

**The vertices of a parallelogram are given. Draw each parallelogram. Find its area.** *(Lesson 10-1)*

4. $A(-4, 1), B(2, 1), C(4, -2), D(-2, -2)$ — 18 square units
5. $J(-2, 3), K(1, 2), L(1, -4), M(-2, -3)$ — 18 square units

**Mixed Review**

**Identify each polygon.** *(From Last Year)*

6. triangle
7. hexagon
8. pentagon

**List all the factors of each number.**

9. 54 — 1, 2, 3, 6, 9, 18, 27, 54
10. 81 — 1, 3, 9, 27, 81

*Number Sense* **Match each object with the most reasonable area.**

| | |
|---|---|
| **22.** dinner plate E | **A.** 0.8 in.$^2$ |
| **23.** quarter A | **B.** 110 in.$^2$ |
| **24.** circle at the center of a basketball floor D | **C.** 7 in.$^2$ |
| **25.** jar lid C | **D.** 16,000 in.$^2$ |
| **26.** 12 in. pizza B | **E.** 80 in.$^2$ |

**27.** You need to carpet the border of the pool at the right.

**a.** What is the area of the border in square feet? 392.5 ft$^2$

**b.** Carpet is sold by the square yard. How many square feet does a square yard contain? 9 ft$^2$

**c.** How many square yards of carpet should you buy? 43.6 yd$^2$

**28.** *Open-ended* Describe a real-life situation, not used in this lesson, where you might use the formula for the area of a circle. Check students' work.

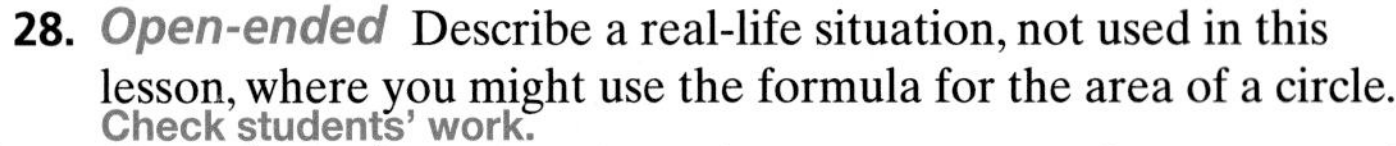

**29.** *Manufacturing* Lids of aluminum cans are cut from rectangular sheets of aluminum.

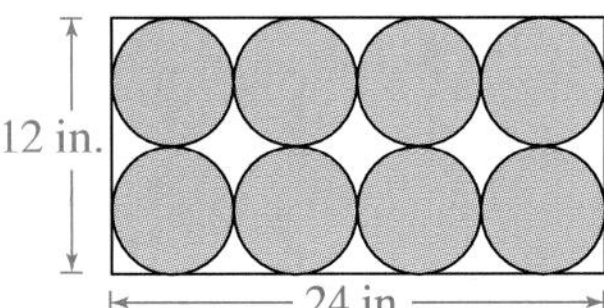


31. The circle with radius 4 m has greater area because the four circles will have a total area of $4\pi$ m$^2$, but the circle with radius 4 m will have an area of $16\pi$ m$^2$.

**a.** What is the radius of each lid? 3 in.

**b.** How many square inches of aluminum do the lids require? 226.08 in.$^2$

**c.** How many square inches of aluminum are wasted? 61.92 in.$^2$

**30. a.** *Consumer Issues* Each circle represents the area of a pizza. What is the area of each pizza? 79 in.$^2$, 113 in.$^2$, 154 in.$^2$

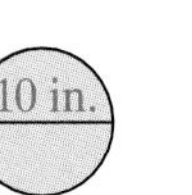


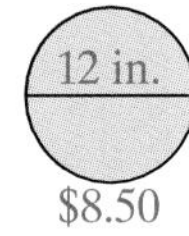


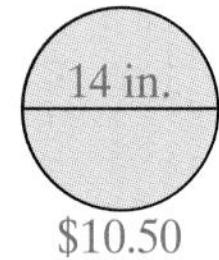


**b.** What is the price per square inch of each pizza? \$0.082/in.$^2$, \$0.075/in.$^2$, \$0.068/in.$^2$

**c.** *Critical Thinking* Is the largest pizza the best buy? Explain. Yes; it has the lowest cost per square inch of all the pizzas.

**31.** *Writing* Which has a greater area, four circles, each with the radius 1 m, or one circle with radius 4 m? Explain. See above right.

**32.** *Critical Thinking* What is the area of the largest circle that will fit in a square with area 64 cm$^2$? $16\pi$ cm$^2$

**33.** How many circles with radius 2 cm will have the same total area as a circle with radius 4 cm? 4

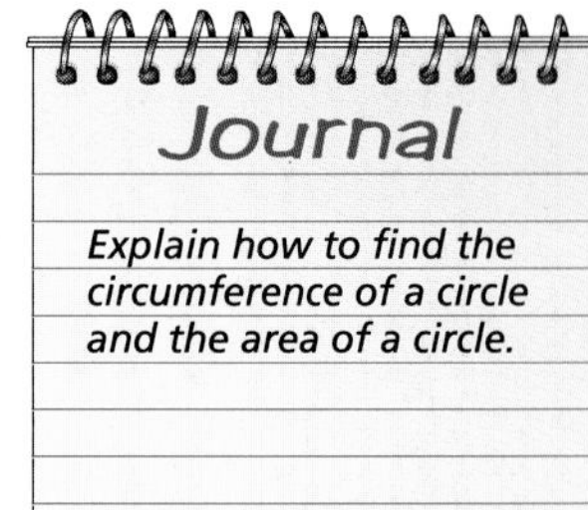

Journal
Explain how to find the circumference of a circle and the area of a circle.

## MIXED REVIEW

**Find the area of each triangle or trapezoid.** ***(Lesson 10-2)***

**34.**

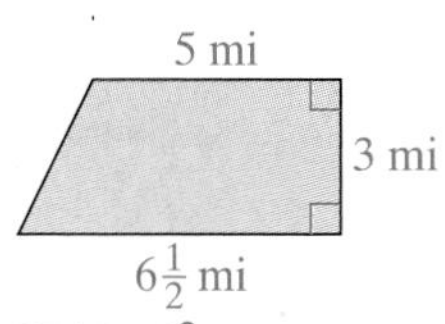


17.25 mi²

**35.** 1.5 yd, 7 yd

5.25 yd²

**36.**

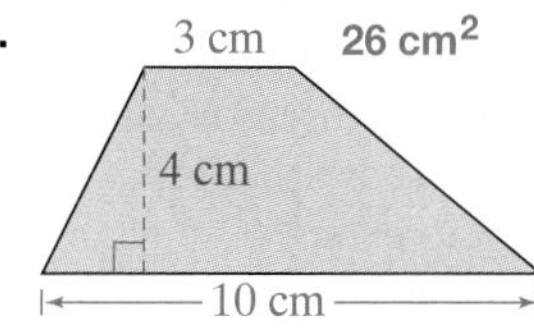


26 cm²

**Find each sum or difference.** ***(Lesson 5-3)***

**37.** $4\frac{3}{5} + 5\frac{2}{3}$ $10\frac{4}{15}$ **38.** $5\frac{2}{3} - 4\frac{3}{5}$ $1\frac{1}{15}$ **39.** $\frac{7}{8} + \frac{5}{6}$ $1\frac{17}{24}$ **40.** $\frac{7}{8} - \frac{5}{6}$ $\frac{1}{24}$

**41.** Square $ABCD$ has side length 8 in. $\triangle BXY$ is isosceles. The congruent sides have length 2 in. How many triangles congruent to $\triangle BXY$ can be cut from $ABCD$? ***(Lesson 9-4)*** 32

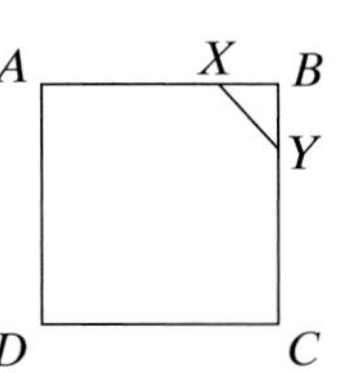


## CHECKPOINT 1 — Lessons 10-1 through 10-3

**Find the area of each figure.**

**1.**

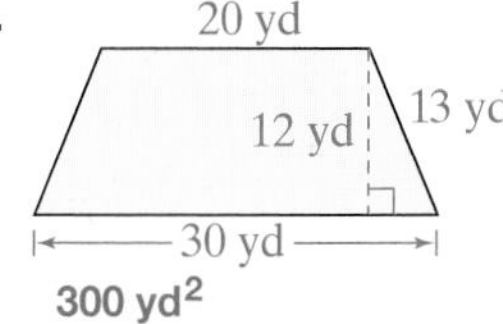


300 yd²

**2.**

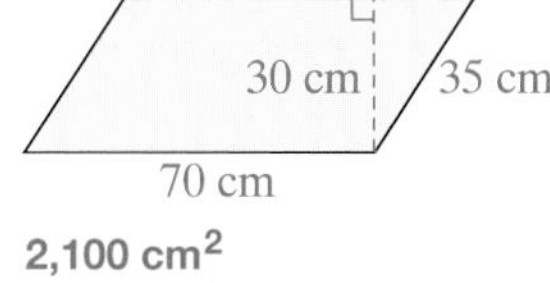


2,100 cm²

**3.**

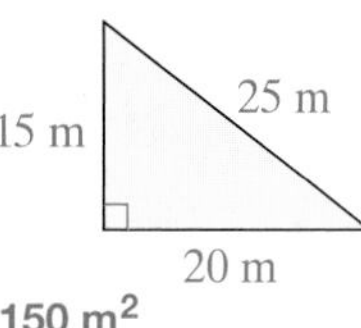


150 m²

**Find the area of each figure. Give an exact answer and an approximate answer to the nearest square unit.**

**4.**

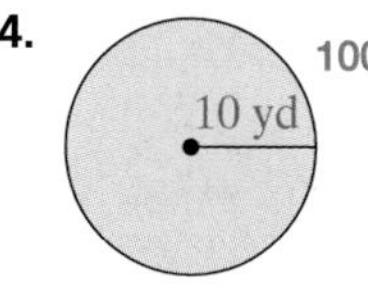


$100\pi$ yd²; 314 yd²

**5.**

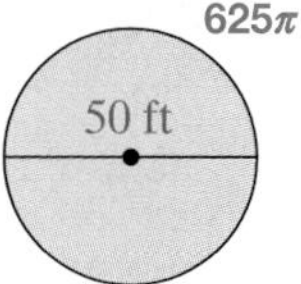


$625\pi$ ft²; 1,963 ft²

**6.**

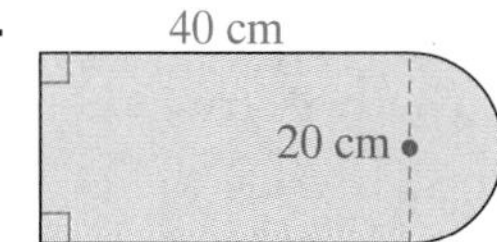


$(800 + 50\pi)$ cm²; 957 cm²

**7. TEST PREP** Which figure has an area that is about the same as the area of a circle with a radius of 10 in.? D

**A.**

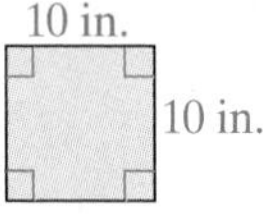


**B.**

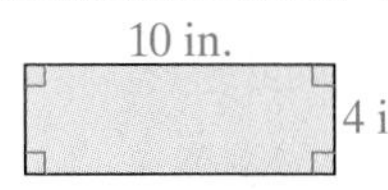


**C.**

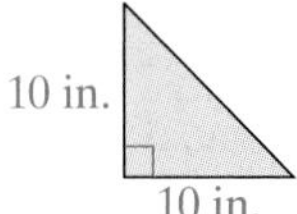


**D.**

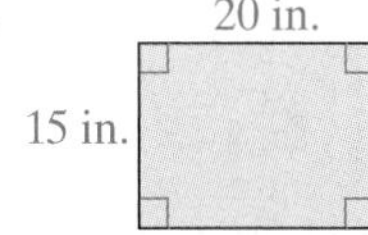


See also Extra Practice section.



## Checkpoint

**Find the area of each figure.**

**1.**

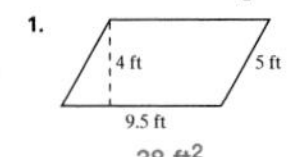


38 ft²

**2.** 8 m, 6 m, 4.5 m, 6 m

18 m²

**3.** 17 cm, 16 cm, 21 cm

304 cm²

**Find the area of each figure. Give an exact answer and an approximate answer to the nearest square unit.**

**4.** 17 in.

$A =$ $72.25\pi$ in.²

$A \approx$ 227 in.²

**5.** 24 mm, 16 mm

$A =$ $384 + 32\pi$ mm²

$A \approx$ 484 mm²

## Practice

**Find the area of each circle. Give an exact area and an approximate area to the nearest tenth.**

1. $r = 7$ m
   $A =$ $49\pi$ m²
   $A \approx$ 153.9 m²
2. $d = 18$ cm
   $A =$ $81\pi$ cm²
   $A \approx$ 254.3 cm²
3. $d = 42$ m
   $A =$ $441\pi$ m²
   $A \approx$ 1,384.7 m²
4. $r = 35$ km
   $A =$ $1{,}225\pi$ km²
   $A \approx$ 3,846.5 km²
5. $d = 22$ cm
   $A =$ $121\pi$ cm²
   $A \approx$ 379.9 cm²
6. $r = 25$ ft
   $A =$ $625\pi$ ft²
   $A \approx$ 1,962.5 ft²
7. $r = 3\frac{1}{2}$ mi
   $A =$ $12.25\pi$ mi²
   $A \approx$ 38.5 mi²
8. $d = 5$ in.
   $A =$ $6.25\pi$ in.²
   $A \approx$ 19.6 in.²
9. $d = 9.8$ mm
   $A =$ $24.01\pi$ mm²
   $A \approx$ 75.4 mm²

**Find the area of each shaded region to the nearest tenth.**

10. 8 m, 8 m, 12 m
    121.1 m²
11. 3 in., 4 in.
    22.0 in.²
12. 10 ft, 10 ft, 5 ft
    21.5 ft²
13. 7 cm, 9 cm, 12 cm
    99.9 cm²
14. A goat is tethered to a stake in the ground with a 5-m rope. The goat can graze to the full length of the rope a full 360° around the stake. How much area does the goat have in which to graze?
    78.5 m²



## Reteaching

Find the area of the circle. Give an exact area and an approximate area.

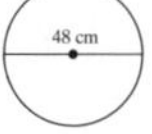


The formula for the area $A$ of a circle is $A = \pi r^2$, where $r$ is the radius of the circle and $\pi$ is a number that is close to 3.14, but not exactly 3.14.

In the circle shown, the diameter is 48 cm. The radius of any circle is half its diameter.

$\frac{1}{2} \cdot 48 = 24$

So, $r = 24$ cm.

$A = \pi r^2$

$A = \pi(24)^2$ Substitute 24 for $r$ in the formula.

$A = 576\pi$ Simplify.

The exact area of the circle is $576\pi$ cm².

To find the approximate area, substitute 3.14 for $\pi$.

$A = 576\pi \approx 576(3.14) = 1{,}808.64$

Note: The symbol ≈ is read "is approximately equal to."

The approximate area is 1,808.64 cm².

**Find the area of each circle. Give an exact area and an approximate area to the nearest tenth.**

1. 3 m
   $A =$ $9\pi$ m²
   $A \approx$ 28.3 m²
2. 140 in.
   $A =$ $4{,}900\pi$ in.²
   $A \approx$ 15,386 in.²
3. 4.5 ft
   $A =$ $20.25\pi$ ft²
   $A \approx$ 63.6 ft²
4. $r = 15$ cm
   $A =$ $225\pi$ cm²
   $A \approx$ 706.5 cm²
5. $d = 16$ in.
   $A =$ $64\pi$ in.²
   $A \approx$ 201.0 in.²
6. $d = 7$ m
   $A =$ $12.25\pi$ m²
   $A \approx$ 38.5 m²
7. $r = 3.4$ ft
   $A =$ $11.56\pi$ ft²
   $A \approx$ 36.3 ft²
8. $d = 29$ cm
   $A =$ $210.25\pi$ cm²
   $A \approx$ 660.2 cm²
9. $d = 284$ mi
   $A =$ $20{,}164\pi$ mi²
   $A \approx$ 63,315.0 mi²



## Enrichment

**Complete. Use 3.14 for $\pi$.**

| | Circle 1 | | | Circle 2 | | | Ratios | | |
|---|---|---|---|---|---|---|---|---|---|
| | radius ($r_1$) | circumference ($C_1$) | area ($A_1$) | radius ($r_2$) | circumference ($C_2$) | area ($A_2$) | $\frac{r_2}{r_1}$ | $\frac{C_2}{C_1}$ | $\frac{A_2}{A_1}$ |
| 1. | 2 | 12.56 | 12.56 | 4 | 25.12 | 50.24 | 2 | 2 | 4 |
| 2. | 3 | 18.84 | 28.26 | 6 | 37.68 | 113.04 | 2 | 2 | 4 |
| 3. | 4 | 25.12 | 50.24 | 8 | 50.24 | 200.96 | 2 | 2 | 4 |
| 4. | 2 | 12.56 | 12.56 | 6 | 37.68 | 113.04 | 3 | 3 | 9 |
| 5. | 3 | 18.84 | 28.26 | 9 | 56.52 | 254.34 | 3 | 3 | 9 |
| 6. | 4 | 25.12 | 50.24 | 12 | 75.36 | 452.16 | 3 | 3 | 9 |
| 7. | 2 | 12.56 | 12.56 | 10 | 62.8 | 314 | 5 | 5 | 25 |
| 8. | 3 | 18.84 | 28.26 | 15 | 94.2 | 706.5 | 5 | 5 | 25 |
| 9. | 4 | 25.12 | 50.24 | 20 | 125.6 | 1,256 | 5 | 5 | 25 |

**Study the patterns in the last three columns.**

10. Write a statement comparing the ratio of the radii of two circles to the ratio of their circumferences.
    The ratios will be the same.
11. Write a statement comparing the ratio of the radii of two circles to the ratio of their areas.
    The ratio of the areas of two circles equals the square of the ratio of their radii.
12. The radius of one circle is 12 times the radius of a smaller circle.
    a. Predict the ratio of the circumferences of the circles. 12:1
    b. Predict the ratio of the area of the circles. 144:1
13. The ratio of the areas of two circles is 49. How many times longer is the radius of the larger circle than the smaller circle?
    7

# MATH TOOLBOX

## Three Views of an Object

This Math Toolbox shows students how to draw views of three-dimensional figures.

## Math Background

A solid, or space figure, is a three-dimensional figure bounded by plane polygons. Another name for such a figure is a polyhedron. All the polyhedrons in this Toolbox have rectangular faces. You can build these solids by putting together one-inch cubes. Building a model helps you visualize the solid that the drawing represents. To draw a corner view, you can use isometric grid paper which uses three sets of parallel lines instead of the two sets of parallel lines used on rectangular grid paper.

## Teaching Notes

**Error Prevention** Encourage students to build models with cubes and then to look at them carefully from several sides. They can then use this experience to help them do the drawings.

**Monitoring Progress** **Exercises 1–5** The ability to visualize three-dimensional figures varies widely. Help students who are having difficulty by using models. It may take extra time for some students to "see" how the drawings relate to the solids.

**Block Scheduling** If you have block scheduling or extended periods, you may wish to insert this Math Toolbox lesson between the completion of Part 1 of Lesson 10-4 and the beginning of Part 2 of Lesson 10-4.

# MATH TOOLBOX

*Extension*
*Before Lesson 10-4*

## *Three Views of an Object*

A solid is a three-dimensional figure. Solids are often drawn in perspective to show that they are three-dimensional.

Isometric Dot

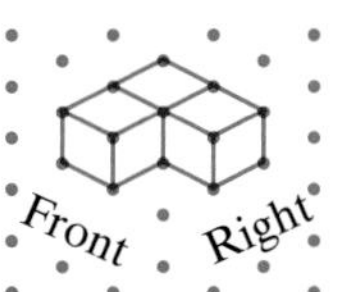


Solid lines are used for edges that show.

Isometric dot paper is helpful for drawing a corner view.

Rectangular Graph

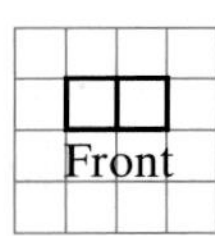


Rectangular graph paper is used for drawing the top, front, and side views.

### EXAMPLE

**Draw the top, front, and right-side views of the solid.**

Isometric

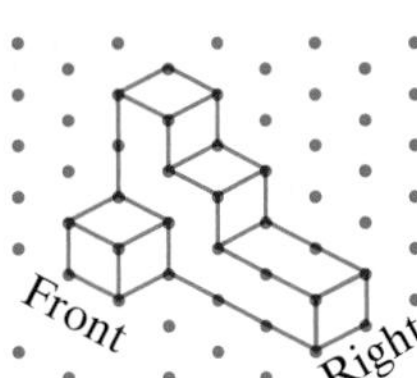


Top

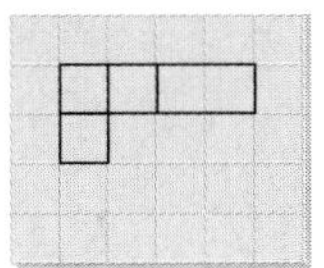

Front

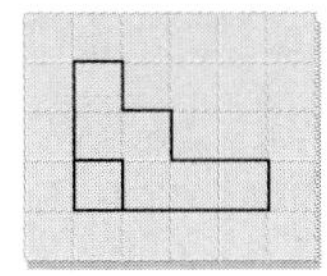

Right Side

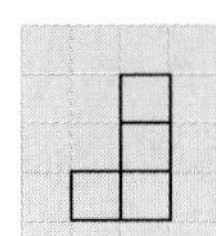

**Draw the top, front, and right-side views of each solid.** 1. See margin. 2–4. See back of book.

1. 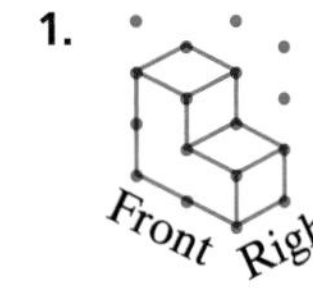


2. 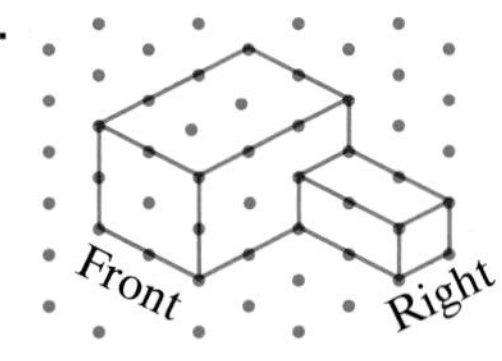


3. 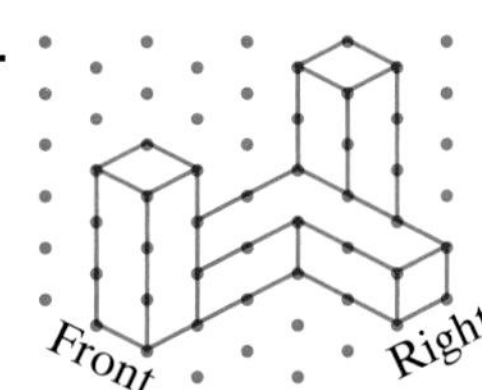


4. 

5. The top, front, and right-side views are given. Draw an isometric view on isometric dot paper.

Top

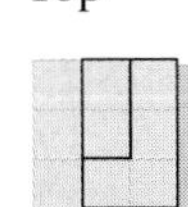

Front

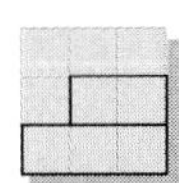

Right Side

5.



• **Additional Example**

Draw the top, front, and right-side views of this solid.

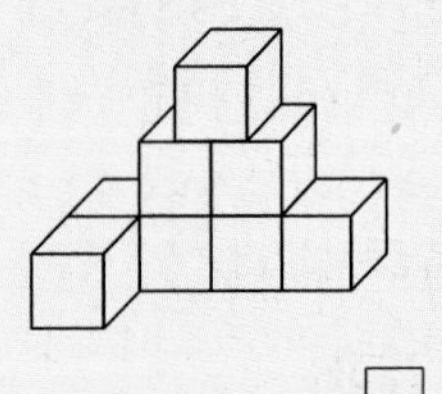

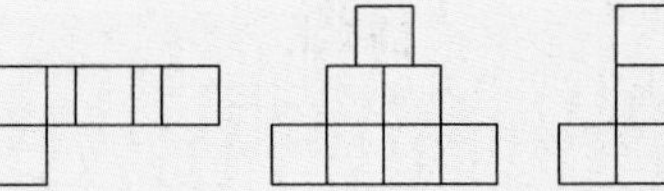

1.

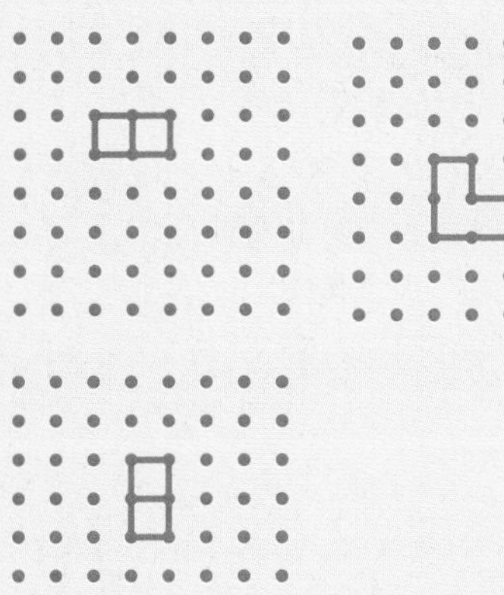

# Space Figures

## PART 1 Naming Space Figures

The figures below are common three-dimensional figures, also called **space figures** or solids. The space figures you will study in this book are prisms, pyramids, cylinders, cones, and spheres.

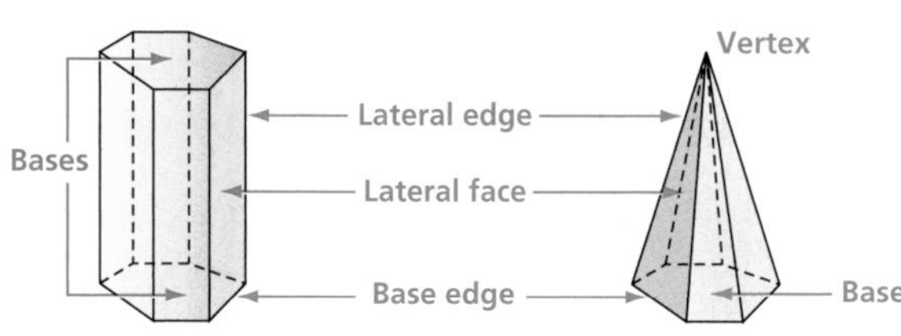


**Prism**

A **prism** has two parallel bases that are congruent polygons, and lateral faces that are parallelograms.

**Pyramid**

A **pyramid** has a base that is a polygon. The lateral faces are triangles.

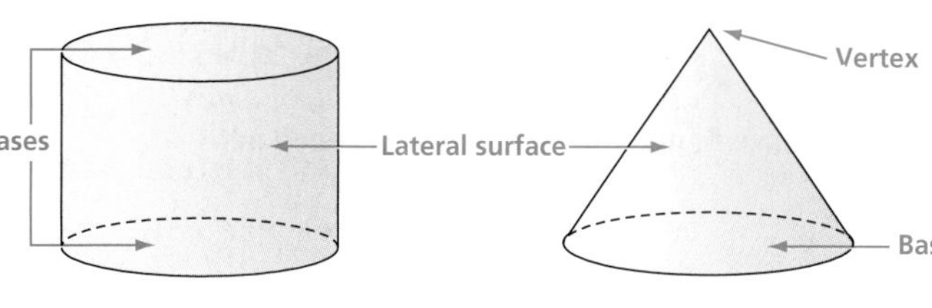


**Cylinder**

A **cylinder** has two parallel bases that are congruent circles.

**Cone**

A **cone** has one circular base and one vertex.

**Sphere**

A **sphere** is the set of all points in space that are a given distance from a given point called the center.

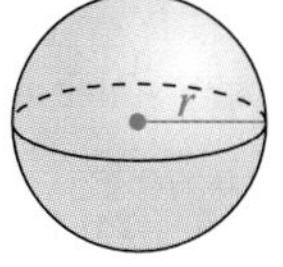


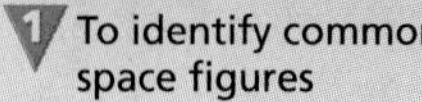

# 10-4

### What You'll Learn

1. To identify common space figures
2. To identify nets of space figures

### . . . And Why

To identify the space figures often used in constructing buildings

### Reading Math

*Lateral* means "on the side." The lateral faces of a figure are the surfaces that connect the bases.



# 10-4

## Getting Ready

**Key Terms and Symbols** space figures, prism, pyramid, cylinder, cone, sphere, net

**Resources** A complete list of resources for this lesson is on p. 501H.

### Daily Skills Warm-Up

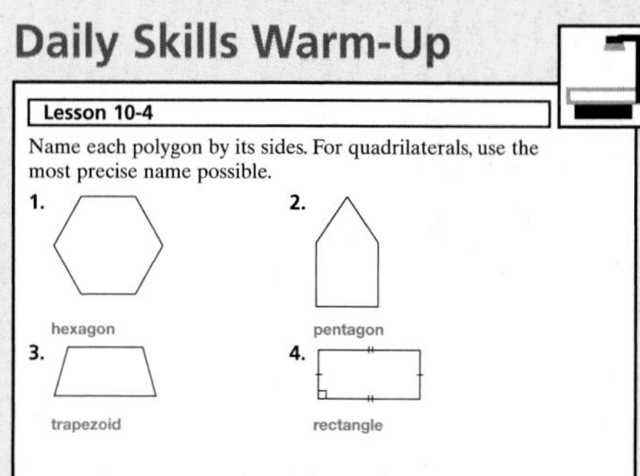
Lesson 10-4

Name each polygon by its sides. For quadrilaterals, use the most precise name possible.

1. hexagon
2. pentagon
3. trapezoid
4. rectangle

### Background for the Lesson

A *space figure* is a three-dimensional figure. A net is a two-dimensional pattern that you can fold to make a model of a space figure. To identify the kind of figure that is modeled by a net, look at the shape of the bases and faces.

## 1 Focus

### Connecting to Students' Lives

Discuss and name various space figures that you can see in the classroom. Ask students to name others outside the classroom.

### Connecting to Prior Knowledge

In Chapter 9, students learned about polygons and circles. In this lesson, students learn how these two-dimensional figures are combined to make space figures. In Lesson 10-5, students will use what they know about area to find the surface area of space figures.

## Tools to Monitor Progress

### BEFORE THE LESSON

**To check prerequisite skills:**

- Identifying polygons

**Skills Intervention Kit,** Geometry

a. two circular bases; cylinder

b. two rectangles; rectangular prism

### DURING THE LESSON

**To check understanding:**

**Try This** exercises on student page

- **Additional Example 1**

For each figure, describe the base and name the figure. See left.

a.

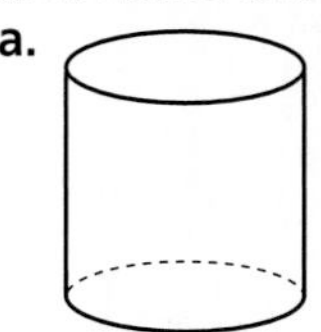

b.

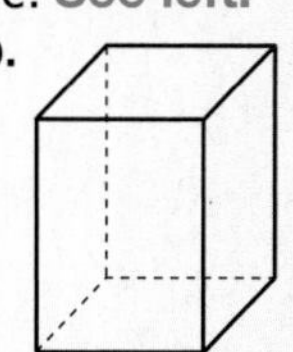

# 2 Teach

## Part 1 Teaching Notes

Explain that these solid figures occupy space in three dimensions: length, width, and depth. Contrast this to the two-dimensional geometric figures which lie in a plane and have length and width.

### Example 1

**Build understanding.** Ask: Which space figures have circular bases? How many bases do these figures have? Cones and cylinders have circular bases. A cone has only one base; a cylinder has two bases.

## Part 2 Teaching Notes

Students may have used nets to make models without knowing that they were called nets.

### Example 2

**Build understanding.** Ask: When you trace a net and use it to build a model, what do you have to add? tabs to glue or tape the edges together

**Tactile Learning** Have students trace one of the nets from the textbook then use scissors and tape to cut it out and form the space figure. If the nets in the text are too small, have a student enlarge the tracings on a photocopier until they are easier to cut out and fold.

**Math Reasoning** Use math reasoning to give an example of two different nets that form the same space figure.
sample answer:

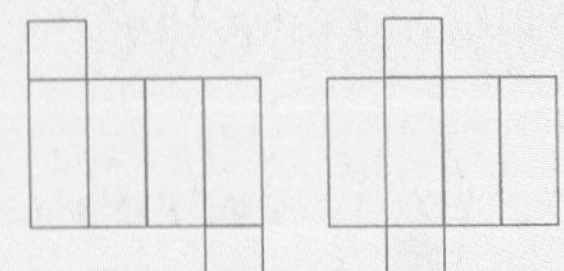

Describe the shapes that make up this tank.

You can use the shape of a base to help you name a space figure.

### Example 1

**For each figure, describe the base and name the figure.**

a.

The bases are triangles.
The figure is a triangular prism.

b.

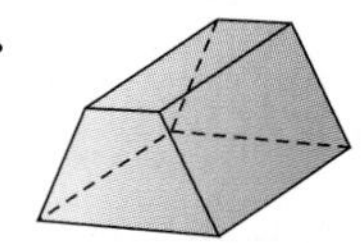

The bases of the prism are trapezoids. The figure is a trapezoidal prism.

**Try This** Name each figure.

1.

The figure is a cylinder.

2.

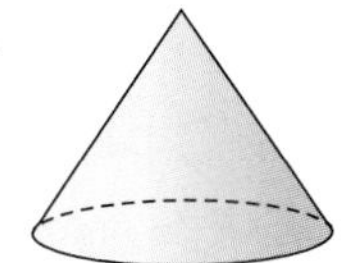

The figure is a cone.

## Part 2 Identifying Space Figures from Nets

A **net** is a pattern you can form into a space figure.

### Example 2

**Name the space figure you can form from each net.**

a.

With a hexagonal base and triangular sides, you can form a hexagonal pyramid.

b.

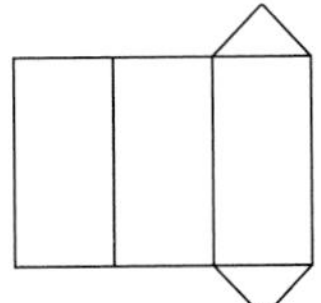

With two triangular bases and rectangular sides, you can form a triangular prism.

**Try This** Name the space figure you can form from each net.

3. With a triangular base and three faces that are triangles, you can form a triangular pyramid.

4. With two square bases and 4 faces that are squares, you can form a square prism.



• **Additional Example 2**
Name the space figure.

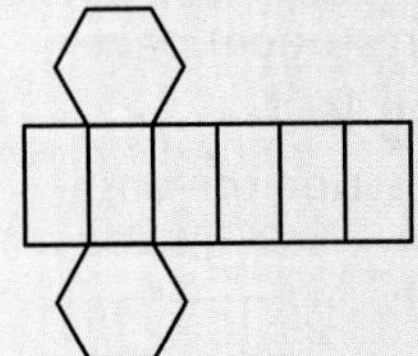

hexagonal prism

## AFTER THE LESSON

**To assess knowledge:**
**Lesson Quiz**

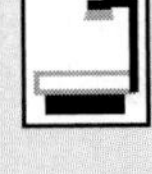

1. Identify the type of bases, number of bases, and the figure.

one octagonal base; octagonal pyramid

• For enrichment and reteaching options see Resources on p. 501H.

# Exercises

## Check Understanding

**For each figure, describe the base(s) and name the figure.**

1. 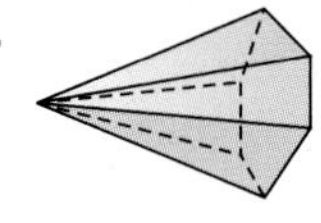 The base is a hexagon. The figure is a hexagonal pyramid.

2. 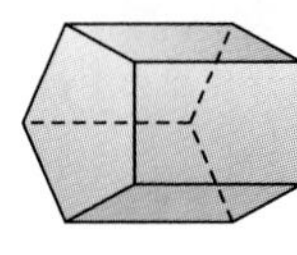 The bases are pentagons. The figure is a pentagonal prism.

3. 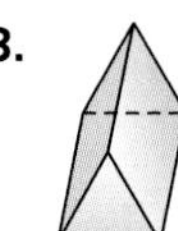 The bases are triangles. The figure is a triangular prism.

**Name the space figure you can form from each net.**

4. 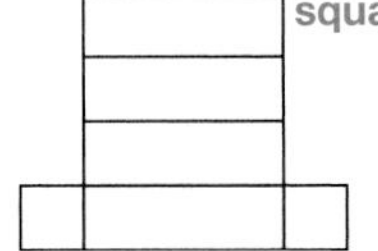 square prism

5.  triangular pyramid

6. 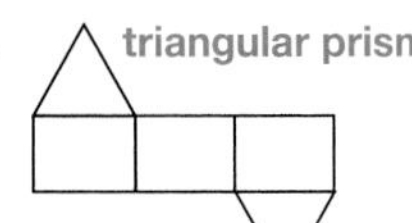 triangular prism

7. *Open-ended* Draw a net for a hexagonal prism. See margin.

## Practice and Problem Solving

**For each figure, describe the base(s) and name the figure.**

8. 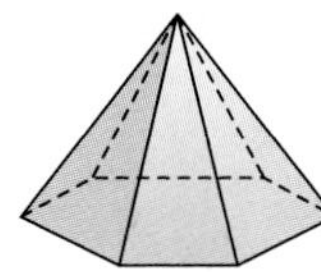 The base is a hexagon. The figure is a hexagonal pyramid.

9. 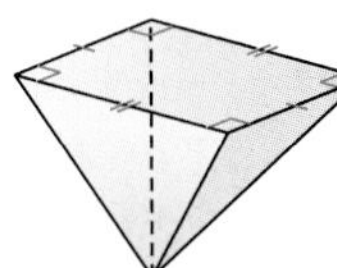 The base is a rectangle. The figure is a rectangular pyramid.

10. 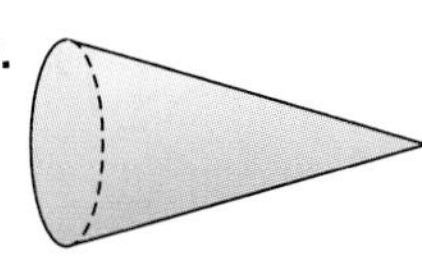 The base is a circle. The figure is a cone.

**Name the space figure you can form from each net.**

11. 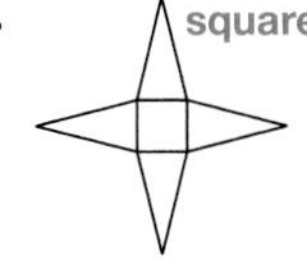 square pyramid

12. 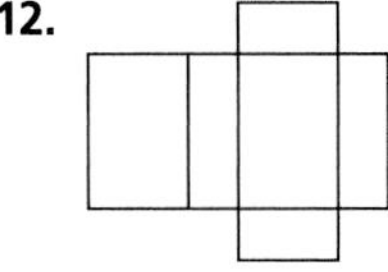 rectangular prism

13.  square prism 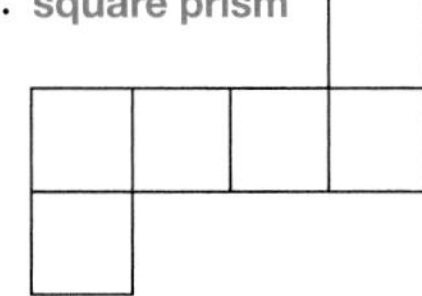

14. *Open-ended* Draw a net for a pentagonal pyramid. See margin.

15. **TEST PREP** Which of the following could be a net for a cylinder? B

A. 

B. 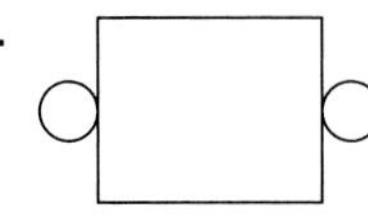

C. 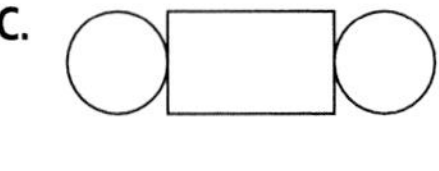

D. 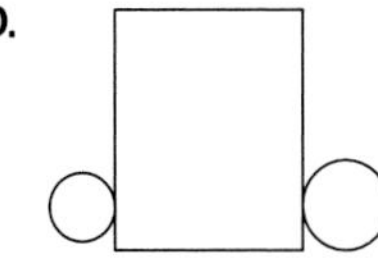



# 3 Practice/Assess

## Assignment Guide

To provide flexible scheduling, this lesson can be divided into parts.

**Part 1**

**Core** 1–3, 8–10, 20–22, 25

✪ **Extension** 27, 28

**Part 2**

**Core** 4–7, 11–18, 23, 26

✪ **Extension** 19, 24

Mixed Review can be assigned at any time for maintenance.

## Exercises

**Exercises 7, 14** Verify that your net forms the appropriate space figure.

**Test Prep Exercise 15** Consider that if the wall of a cylinder were split and laid flat, its width would have to be equal to the circumference of the circles at the bases.

## ✪ Challenge

There are many different nets for a cube. Draw as many as you can. Cut them out and fold them to check your work.

## Closure

Name pyramids and prisms by the shapes of their bases. A cylinder has two circular bases and a cone has one circular base and one vertex. Nets are flat patterns for space figures.

## Alternative Assessment

Give students space figures of paper or cardboard, such as paper cups and boxes. Have the students use the models to create nets of the figures. Have students demonstrate that their nets are accurate. Ask them to name the solids.

14. 

7. 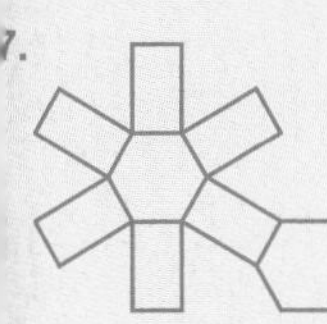

## Daily Cumulative Review

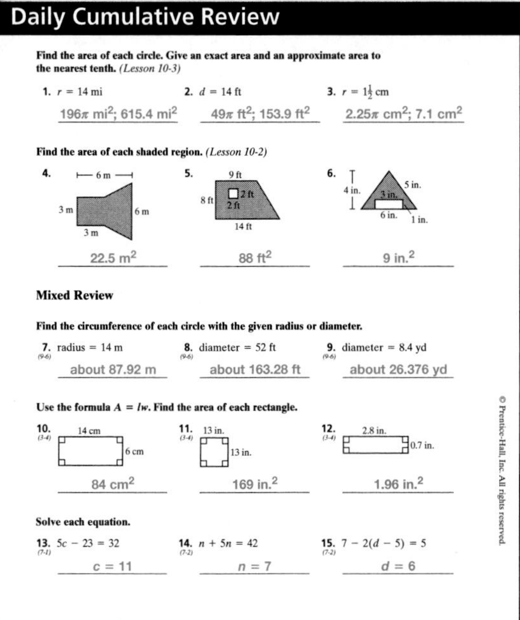

**Find the area of each circle. Give an exact area and an approximate area to the nearest tenth.** *(Lesson 10-3)*

1. $r = 14$ mi — $196\pi$ mi$^2$; 615.4 mi$^2$
2. $d = 14$ ft — $49\pi$ ft$^2$; 153.9 ft$^2$
3. $r = 1\frac{1}{2}$ cm — $2.25\pi$ cm$^2$; 7.1 cm$^2$

**Find the area of each shaded region.** *(Lesson 10-2)*

4. 22.5 m$^2$
5. 88 ft$^2$
6. 9 in.$^2$



**Mixed Review**

**Find the circumference of each circle with the given radius or diameter.**

7. (9-6) radius = 14 m — about 87.92 m
8. (9-6) diameter = 52 ft — about 163.28 ft
9. (9-6) diameter = 8.4 yd — about 26.376 yd

**Use the formula $A = lw$. Find the area of each rectangle.**

10. (3-4) 14 cm, 6 cm — 84 cm$^2$
11. (3-4) 13 in., 13 in. — 169 in.$^2$
12. (3-4) 2.8 in., 0.7 in. — 1.96 in.$^2$

**Solve each equation.**

13. (7-1) $5c - 23 = 32$ — $c = 11$
14. (7-2) $n + 5n = 42$ — $n = 7$
15. (7-2) $7 - 2(d - 5) = 5$ — $d = 6$

**Match each container with the correct net.**

**16.** C

**17.** A

**18.** B

**A.**

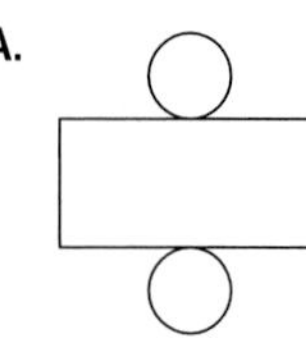

**B.**

**C.**

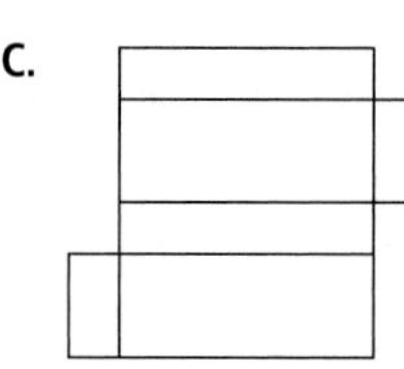

**19.** *Error Analysis* A student explains that since each figure below has six square faces, each can be folded to make a cube. Explain the error the student might have made.

Figure A

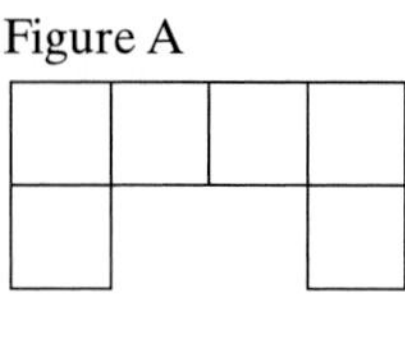

Figure B

Figure C

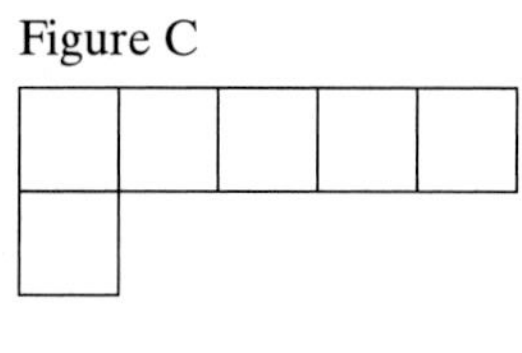

Figure D

The student forgot that there need to be bases on both sides of the vertical faces.

**For Exercises 20–22, write the most precise name for each figure.**

**20.** The figure has four lateral faces that are triangles. square pyramid

**21.** The figure has three lateral faces that are rectangles. triangular prism

**22.** The figure has one lateral face and one circular base. cone

**23.** *Writing* Suppose you see a net for a rectangular prism and a net for a rectangular pyramid. Explain how you can match each net with its name. The rectangular pyramid's net will have several triangles attached to a rectangular base. The rectangular prism's net will be made entirely of rectangles.

**24.** Draw a net to represent a rectangular box that is 10 cm long, 8 cm wide, and 4 cm high. Label dimensions on the net. See margin.

**25.** What mathematical name does each object suggest?

**a.** a shoe box rectangular prism

**b.** a teepee cone

**c.** a basketball sphere

**26.** *Open-ended* Draw a net for an object you find in your classroom. Check students' work.



24.

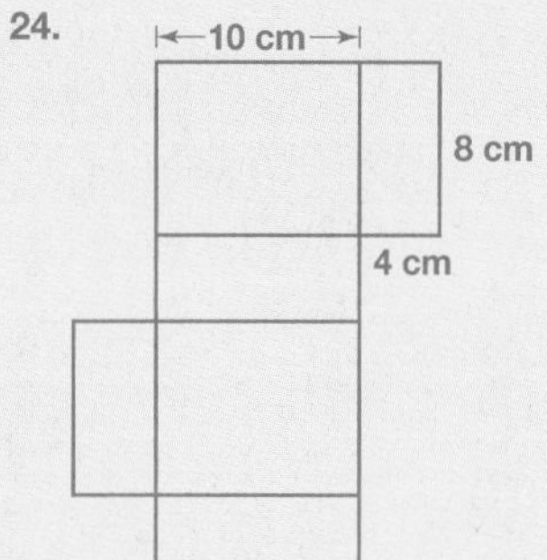

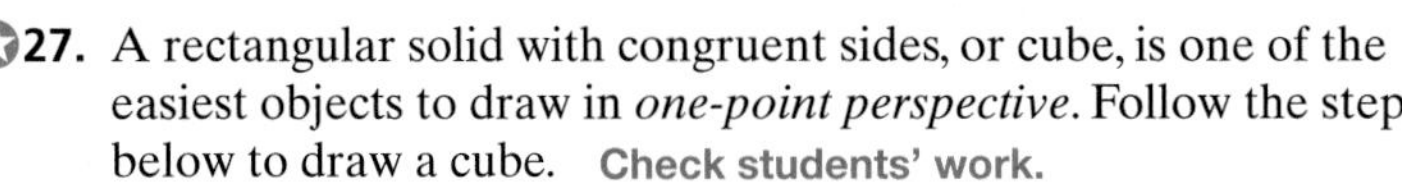

27. A rectangular solid with congruent sides, or cube, is one of the easiest objects to draw in *one-point perspective*. Follow the steps below to draw a cube. Check students' work.

Step 1

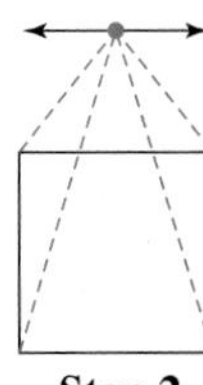
Step 2

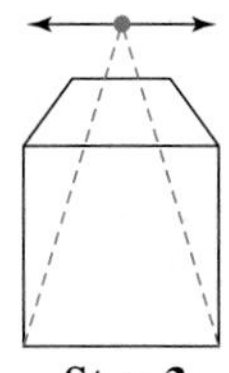
Step 3

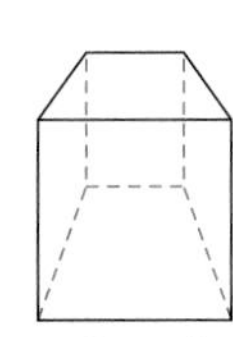
Step 4

**Step 1** Begin by drawing a square for the front. Draw a *horizon line* parallel to one horizontal edge of your square. Select a *vanishing point* on the horizon line.

**Step 2** Draw lines, called *vanishing lines*, from the vertices of the square to the vanishing point.

**Step 3** Draw a line segment parallel to the horizon line. Use this segment to determine the back edges.

**Step 4** Draw dashed lines for the hidden back vertical and horizontal edges. Erase the horizon line and unnecessary parts of the vanishing lines.

28. Using the steps from exercise 27, draw a rectangular solid in one-point perspective.

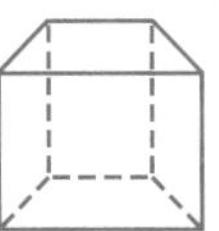

## Mixed Review

**Find the exact area and the approximate area of each circle.** *(Lesson 10-3)*

29.
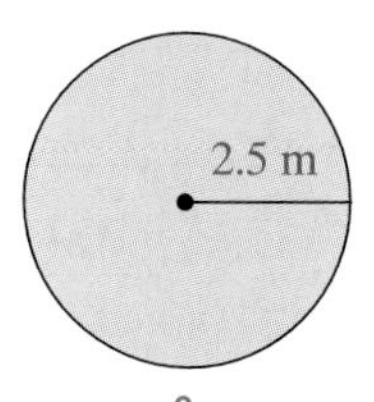

$6.25\pi$ m$^2$; 19.625 m$^2$

30.
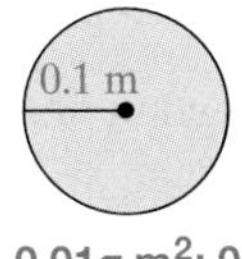

$0.01\pi$ m$^2$; 0.0314 m$^2$

31.
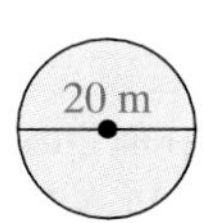

$100\pi$ m$^2$; 314 m$^2$

**Write each equation in slope-intercept form.** *(Lesson 8-3)*

32. $3x - y = 6$
$y = 3x - 6$

33. $2x - 2y = 10$
$y = x - 5$

34. $-8y - 16 = 24x$
$y = -3x - 2$

35. *Choose a Strategy* A rectangular yard is 20 ft by 40 ft. Your lawn mower will mow a 2-ft-wide path. What is the least number of turns you must make to mow the lawn? 9

See also Extra Practice section.



## Practice

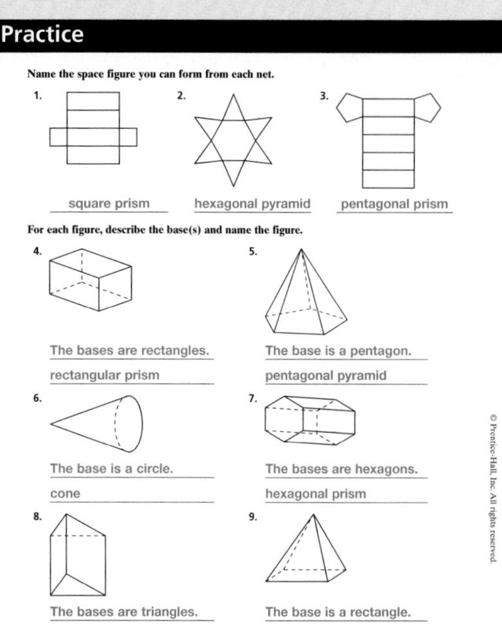

**Name the space figure you can form from each net.**

1. square prism
2. hexagonal pyramid
3. pentagonal prism

**For each figure, describe the base(s) and name the figure.**

4. The bases are rectangles. rectangular prism
5. The base is a pentagon. pentagonal pyramid
6. The base is a circle. cone
7. The bases are hexagons. hexagonal prism
8. The bases are triangles. triangular prism
9. The base is a rectangle. rectangular pyramid



## Reteaching

**Name the space figure you can form from the net.**

The net has a square and four triangles. So, the square must be the base. A pyramid has triangular sides and only one base. So, the net is for a triangular pyramid. You might try to picture what the figure looks like when it is cut out and folded. See the space figure at the right.

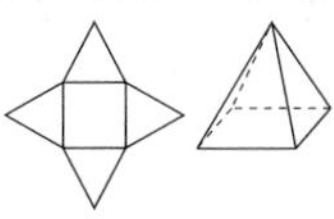

**Name the space figure you can form from each net. Start by naming the polygons in the net.**

1.

polygons: octagon, triangles
space figure: octagonal pyramid

2.
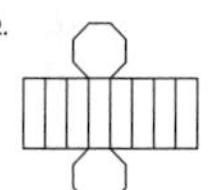
polygons: octagons, rectangles
space figure: octagonal prism

3.
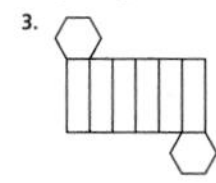
polygons: hexagons, rectangles
space figure: hexagonal prism

4.
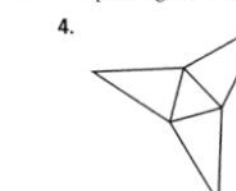
polygons: triangles
space figure: triangular pyramid



## Enrichment

Space figures made out of only polygons are called *polyhedra*. The sides of a polyhedron are called *faces*. A segment common to two faces is an *edge*. A point where edges intersect is a *vertex*. In the eighteenth century, Leonard Euler, a Swiss mathematician, discovered a remarkable relationship among the faces, edges, and vertices of any convex polyhedron. To discover the relationship, complete the chart for the given polyhedra.

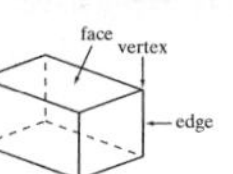


| | Figure | Number of faces ($F$) | Number of vertices ($V$) | Number of edges ($E$) | $F + V - E$ |
|---|---|---|---|---|---|
| 1. | | 5 | 5 | 8 | 2 |
| 2. | cube | 6 | 8 | 12 | 2 |
| 3. | | 7 | 10 | 15 | 2 |
| 4. | triangular pyramid | 4 | 4 | 6 | 2 |
| 5. | | 9 | 9 | 16 | 2 |

6. What do you find for $F + V - E$?
In each case, $F + V - E = 2$.

Euler proved that your result is true for any convex polyhedron.

7. A convex polyhedron has 18 edges and 12 vertices. How many faces does the polyhedron have?
8

8. A convex polyhedron has 10 faces and 16 vertices. How many edges does the polyhedron have?
24

# MATH TOOLBOX

### Cross Sections of Space Figures

In this Toolbox, students will consider various cross sections formed by the intersection of a plane and a solid.

### Math Background

When a plane intersects a space figure to form a cross section, the plane may slice the figure at right angles to the base, so the plane is perpendicular to the base of the figure. However, you can also form a cross section by cutting the figure with a plane that is parallel to the base of the figure. Many other cross sections are possible, depending on the angle of the plane to the base of the solid.

## Teaching Notes

**Error Prevention** Help students visualize these situations by using a model of a cube, perhaps built out of toothpicks held together at the corners with miniature marshmallows. A piece of paper or plastic can serve as the intersecting plane.

**Monitoring Progress** **Exercise 9** You may want to use an orange and a thin knife to model this situation.

**Block Scheduling** If you have block scheduling or extended periods, you may wish to insert this Math Toolbox between the completion of Part 1 of Lesson 10-5 and the beginning of Part 2 of Lesson 10-5.

# MATH TOOLBOX

*Extension*

*Before Lesson 10-5*

## *Cross Sections of Space Figures*

The intersection of a plane and a space figure is a *cross section* of the space figure. This cross section of a block of cheese is a rectangle.

### EXAMPLE

**Sketch a plane intersecting a cube in three different ways to show a rectangular cross section.**

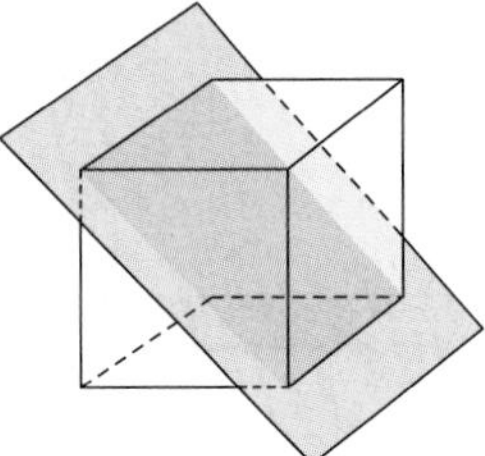

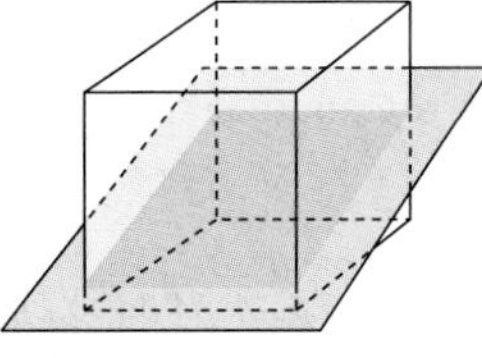

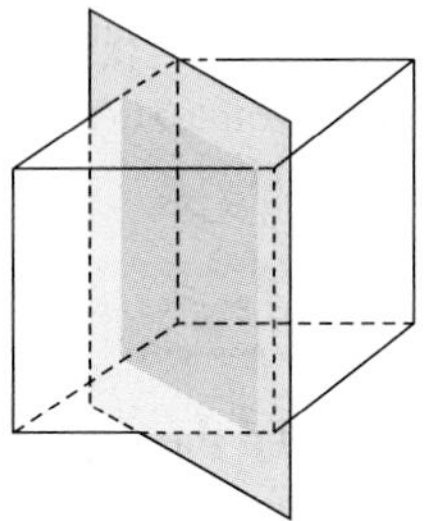

**Use the name of a polygon to describe each cross section of the cube. Points *M*, *N*, *P*, *Q*, and *R* are midpoints of edges.**

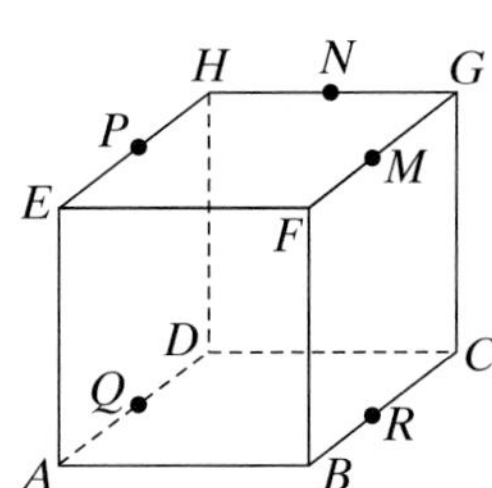


1. through $M, P, Q,$ and $R$ square
2. through $E, A, C,$ and $G$ rectangle
3. through $B, E,$ and $G$ equilateral triangle
4. through $M, N, D,$ and $B$ trapezoid

**Sketch a cube to show each cross section.** 5–8. Answers may vary. See margin for samples.

5. a scalene triangle
6. a rhombus
7. a square
8. an isosceles triangle
9. Describe the possible cross sections of a sphere. They are all circles.



- **Additional Example**

Sketch a cylinder to show two different cross sections: one that is a rectangle and one that is an ellipse (or oval).

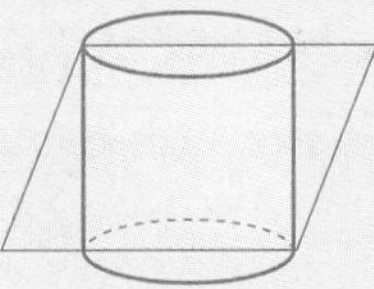

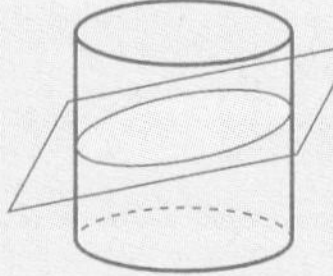

5.

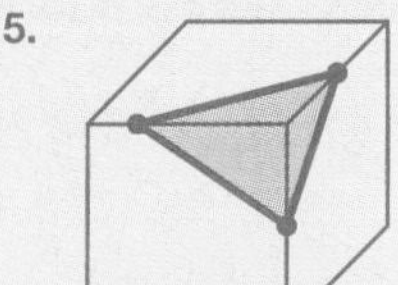

6.

7.

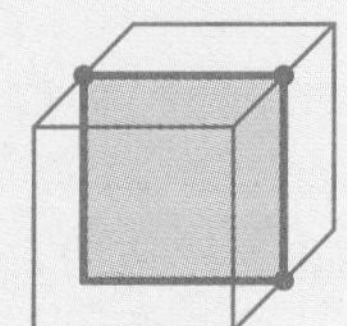

8.

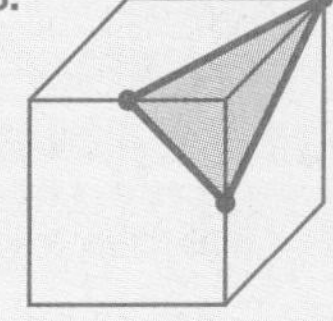

# Surface Area: Prisms and Cylinders

# 10-5

## Finding Surface Areas of Prisms

Prisms and cylinders can be *right* or *oblique*.

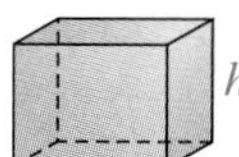


Right prism

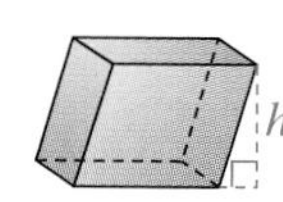


Oblique prism

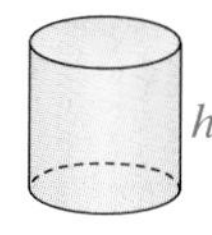


Right cylinder

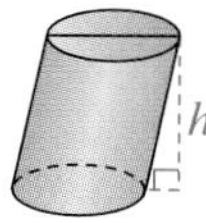


Oblique cylinder

In this text, you may assume that prisms and cylinders are right unless otherwise stated.

**Surface area (S.A.)** is the sum of the areas of the base(s) and the lateral faces of a space figure. One way to find the surface area of a space figure is to find the area of its net. You measure surface area in square units.

### What You'll Learn

1. To find surface areas of prisms
2. To find surface areas of cylinders

### . . . And Why

To find the amount of material needed in packaging

### Example 1

**Find the surface area of the rectangular prism using a net.**

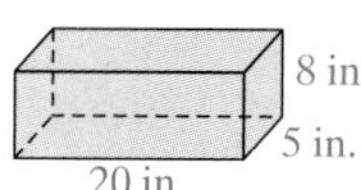


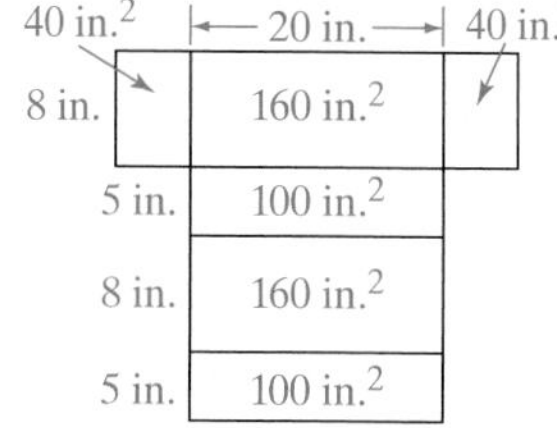


Draw and label a net.

Find the area of each rectangle in the net.

$40 + 40 + 160 + 100 + 160 + 100 = 600$ Add the areas.

The surface area is 600 in.$^2$.

### Try This

1. Find the surface area of the triangular prism at the right. **84 yd$^2$**

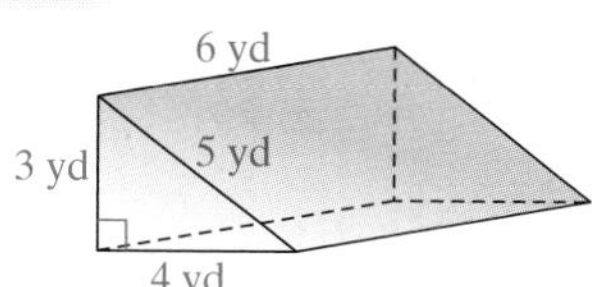




# 10-5

## Getting Ready

**Key Terms and Symbols** surface area, lateral area

**Resources** A complete list of resources for this lesson is on p. 501H.

### Daily Skills Warm-Up

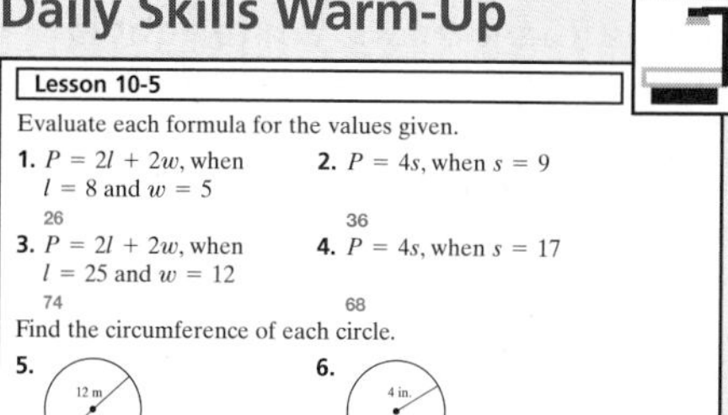
Lesson 10-5

Evaluate each formula for the values given.

1. $P = 2l + 2w$, when $l = 8$ and $w = 5$ 26
2. $P = 4s$, when $s = 9$ 36
3. $P = 2l + 2w$, when $l = 25$ and $w = 12$ 74
4. $P = 4s$, when $s = 17$ 68

Find the circumference of each circle.

5. (12 m) 37.68 m
6. (4 in.) 25.12 in.

Find the area of each figure.

### Background for the Lesson

The total surface area of a prism or cylinder is equal to the sum of the surface areas of all the sides and bases. One way to find the surface area is to add the area of the bases to the lateral area, which is the sum of the areas of the lateral faces. To find the lateral area of a prism, multiply the perimeter of the base by the height. The formula is the same for a cylinder, but the perimeter of the base is the circumference of a circle.

## 1 Focus

### Connecting to Students' Lives

Students who have wrapped a gift may know the problem of not having enough wrapping paper to cover the gift. Discuss how to estimate the amount of wrapping paper needed for a given solid.

### Connecting to Prior Knowledge

In Lesson 10-4, students learned about space figures, including prisms and cylinders. In this lesson, students learn how to find the surface area of prisms and cylinders. In Lesson 10-6, students will learn how to find the surface area of pyramids, cones, and spheres.

# Tools to Monitor Progress

### BEFORE THE LESSON

**To check prerequisite skills:**

- Finding the circumference of circles

**Skills You Need,** p. 501

### DURING THE LESSON

**To check understanding:**

**Try This** exercises on student page

- **Additional Example 1**

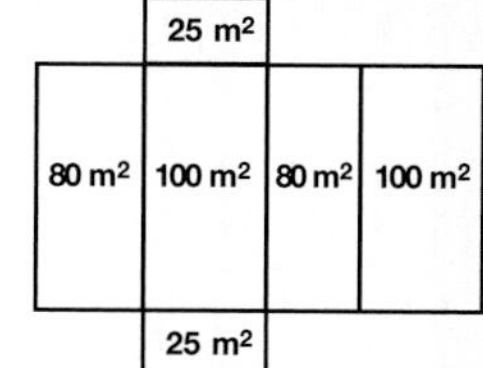


Find the surface area of the rectangular prism using the net. **410 m$^2$**

#  Teach

## Part 1 Teaching Notes

The formulas in this lesson for finding the surface area of prisms and cylinders apply only to right prisms and cylinders. The formulas *do not* apply to oblique cylinders and prisms. All cylinders and prisms in the text are right unless otherwise stated.

**Connecting to Science** The *prism* with which students may be most familiar is the glass triangular prism used by scientists to diffract white light into its seven constituent colors. White light is actually a combination of seven different visible wavelengths of light, each with its own color. When light rays enter a glass triangular prism, they are bent, or diffracted. Each of the seven different visible wavelengths of light is diffracted a slightly different amount. The result is that the seven colors of light are separated as they exit the prism, producing a rainbow-like pattern of colors.

### Example 1

**Build understanding.** Ask: Why isn't the area the same for all the sides of the prism? The sides have two different widths, corresponding to the length and width of the base rectangles.

**ELL** Explain that the word *lateral* comes from the Latin word that means *side,* so the lateral area is the area of the sides.

### Example 2

**Build understanding**. Ask: What is the perimeter of each base of the triangular prism? What is the lateral height of the prism? 16 cm; 12 cm

**Auditory Learning** Have students work in pairs on a drawing of two different prisms. The partners take turns shading the lateral area in a drawing and naming it aloud while writing a label for the shaded area. Then they do the same for the area of the bases and finally for the total surface area.

Another way to find the surface area of a prism is to use the *lateral area* and the base areas. **Lateral area (L.A.)** of a prism is the sum of the areas of the lateral faces.

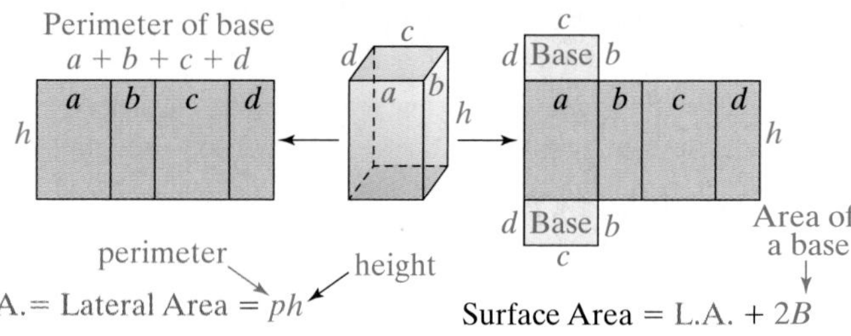


When you find the surface area of a prism, it is a good idea to find the lateral area first.

**Surface Area of a Prism**

The lateral area of a prism is the product of the perimeter of the base and the height.

$$\text{L.A.} = ph$$

The surface area of a prism is the sum of the lateral area and the areas of the two bases.

$$\text{S.A.} = \text{L.A.} + 2B$$

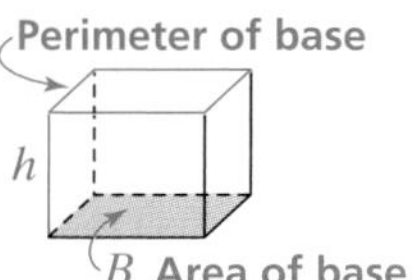


### Example 2

**Find the surface area of the triangular prism at the left.**

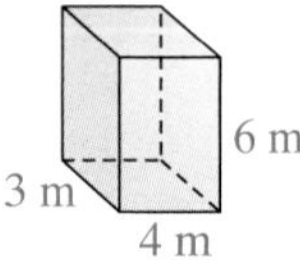


**Step 1** Find the lateral area.

$\text{L.A.} = ph$ — Use the formula for lateral area.

$= (5 + 5 + 6)12$ — $p = 5 + 5 + 6$ and $h = 12$

$= 192$

**Step 2** Find the surface area.

$\text{S.A.} = \text{L.A.} + 2B$

$= 192 + 2(\frac{1}{2} \cdot 6 \cdot 4)$ — L.A. = 192 and $B = \frac{1}{2} \cdot 6 \cdot 4$

$= 192 + 24$

$= 216$

The surface area of the triangular prism is 216 cm$^2$.

### Try This

2. Find the surface area of the figure at the left. 108 m$^2$



**• Additional Example 2**

Find the surface area of the rectangular prism. 500 in.$^2$

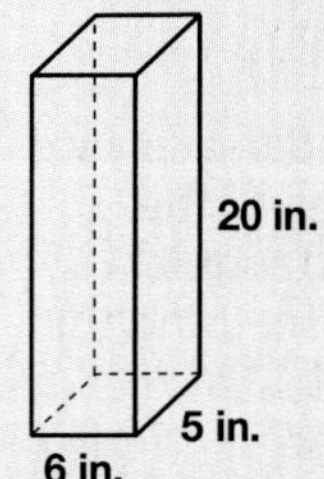


**• Additional Example 3**

Find the surface area of the cylindrical water tank below. about 1,156 ft$^2$

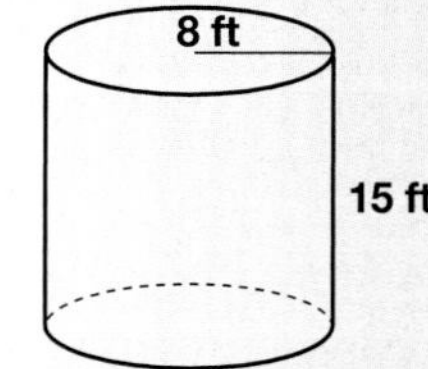

## Finding Surface Areas of Cylinders

If you cut a label from a soup can, you will see that the label is a rectangle. The height of the rectangle is the height of the can. The base length of the rectangle is the circumference of the can.

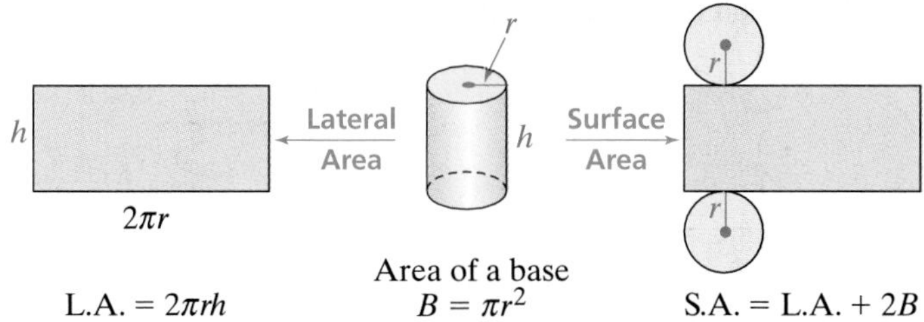


### Surface Area of a Cylinder

The lateral area of a cylinder is the product of the circumference of the base and the height of the cylinder.

$$\text{L.A.} = 2\pi rh$$

The surface area of a cylinder is the sum of the lateral area and the areas of the two bases.

$$\text{S.A.} = \text{L.A.} + 2B$$

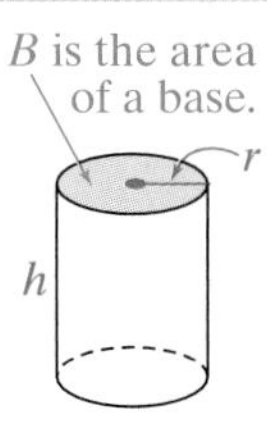


### Example 3

*Packaging* **Find the surface area of the can at the right.**

**Step 1** Find the lateral area.

$\text{L.A.} = 2\pi rh$ Use the formula for lateral area.

$\approx 2(3.14)(3.5)(11.5)$

$\approx 253$

**Step 2** Find the surface area.

$\text{S.A.} = \text{L.A.} + 2B$ Use the formulas for surface areas.

$= \text{L.A.} + 2(\pi r^2)$

$\approx 253 + 2(3.14)(3.5)^2 = 329.93$

The surface area of the can is about 330 $\text{cm}^2$.

### Try This

**3.** Find the surface area of a can with radius 5 cm and height 20 cm. $\approx 785\ \text{cm}^2$



## Part 2 Teaching Notes

Discuss the lateral area of a cylinder compared to the lateral area of a prism.

**Error Prevention** Make sure students understand that a cylinder has a lateral area, even though it has only one lateral surface, rather than faces like a prism.

### Example 3

**Build understanding.** Ask: Why is the area of the base ($\pi r^2$) multiplied by 2? **You are finding the area of both bases.**

**Extension** Write the formula for the surface area of a can that has had one end opened and removed. Explain how you came up with the formula.
**S.A. = L.A. + B; A can with one end removed is like a cylinder with only one base, so the formula is the same except the base, B, is not multiplied by 2.**

## After the Lesson

### To assess knowledge: Lesson Quiz

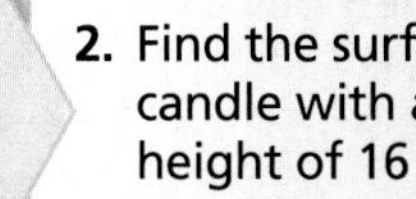

**1.** Find the surface area of a rectangular prism with a base perimeter of 30 cm, a base area of 50 $\text{cm}^2$ and a height of 150 cm. **4,600 $\text{cm}^2$**

**2.** Find the surface area of a cylindrical candle with a radius of 2 cm and a height of 16 cm. **about 226 $\text{cm}^2$**

- For enrichment and reteaching options see Resources on p. 501H.

# 3 Practice/Assess

## Assignment Guide

To provide flexible scheduling, this lesson can be divided into parts.

▼ **Part 1**

**Core** 1, 3, 5–8, 10–12, 15, 17, 25, 26
✪ **Extension** 19, 22

▼ **Part 2**

**Core** 2, 4, 9, 13–14, 16, 18, 20, 21, 24
✪ **Extension** 23, 27

Mixed Review can be assigned at any time for maintenance.

### Exercises

**Exercise 23** You can build models to compare these effects.

**Test Prep Exercise 24** Calculate the surface area of both figures before you select the correct response.

### ✪ Challenge

You want to paint all the surfaces of a cylindrical bucket. Write a formula to calculate the inside and outside surface area of the bucket. The bucket is open at one end. $S.A. = 2(L.A. + \pi r^2)$

### Closure

The lateral area of a prism is the sum of the areas of the lateral faces. The lateral area of a cylinder is the area of the curved surface. The surface area of prisms and cylinders is the sum of the lateral area and the area of the two bases.

### Daily Cumulative Review

**For each figure, describe the base(s) and name the figure.** *(Lesson 10-4)*

1. The bases are circles. The figure is a cylinder.
2. There is one base, a triangle. The figure is a triangular pyramid.
3. The bases of the prism are rectangles. The figure is a rectangular prism.

**Find the area of each shaded region.** *(Lesson 10-3)*

4. (20 ft, 20 ft) about 714 $ft^2$
5. (8 cm) about 50.24 $cm^2$
6. (6 yd, 3 yd) about 42.39 $yd^2$

**Mixed Review**

**Simplify each expression.**

7. *(1-2)* $13 + 4 \times 9$ 49
8. *(1-2)* $25 \div (19 - 14) + 7$ 12
9. *(1-2)* $(15 + 3) \div 3 \div 2$ 3

**Compare. Use <, >, or = to complete each statement.**

10. *(5-1)* $\frac{4}{15}$ [<] $\frac{5}{17}$
11. *(5-1)* $\frac{8}{43}$ [>] $\frac{3}{28}$
12. *(5-1)* $\frac{6}{8}$ [<] $\frac{13}{15}$



# Exercises

## Check Understanding

**For the space figure represented by each net, find the surface area to the nearest square unit.**

**1.**

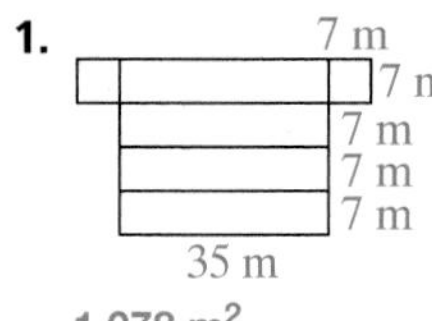


1,078 $m^2$

**2.**

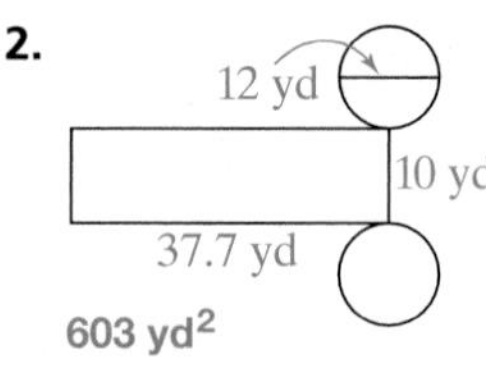


603 $yd^2$

**3.** 1,008 $m^2$

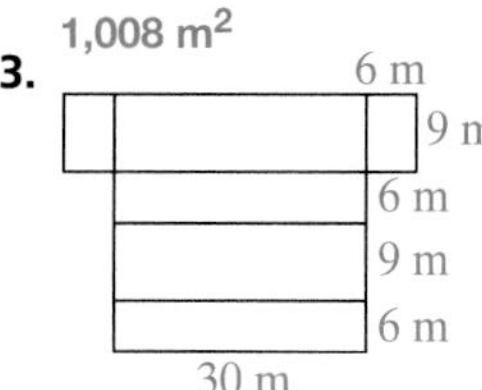


**Find the surface area of each space figure. If the answer is not a whole number, round to the nearest tenth.**

**4.**

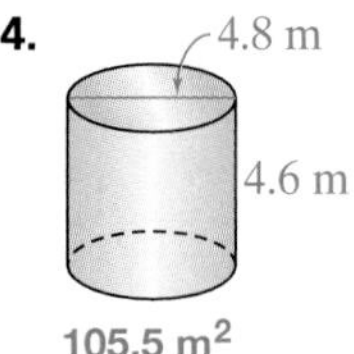


105.5 $m^2$

**5.**

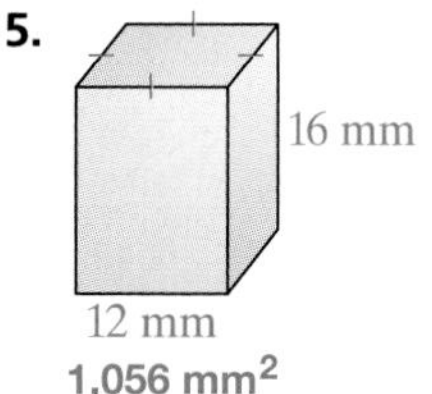


1,056 $mm^2$

**6.**

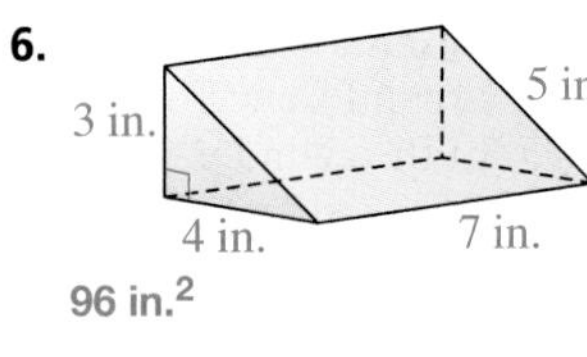


96 $in.^2$

**7.** The base of a rectangular prism is 3 in. by 5 in., and the height is 11 in. Draw and label a net for the prism. Find its surface area. 206 $in.^2$; see margin for net.

## Practice and Problem Solving

**For the space figure represented by each net, find the surface area to the nearest square unit.**

**8.** 16 $cm^2$

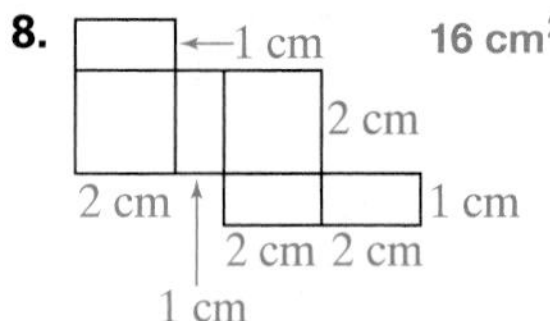


**9.**

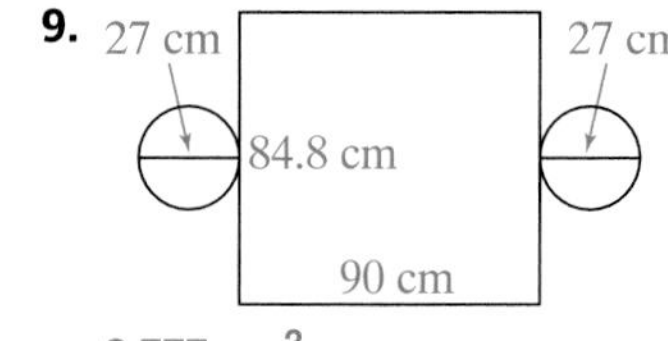


8,777 $cm^2$

**10.**

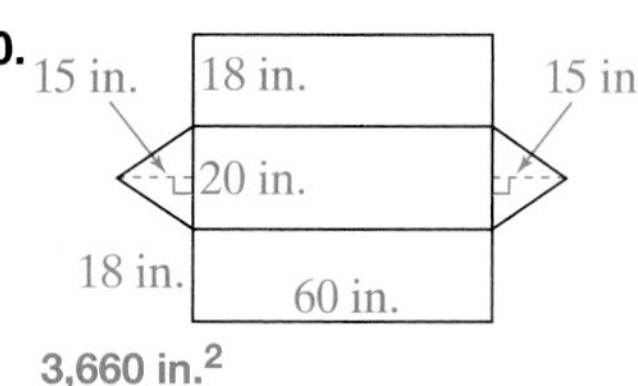


3,660 $in.^2$

**Find the surface area of each space figure. If the answer is not a whole number, round to the nearest tenth.**

**11.**

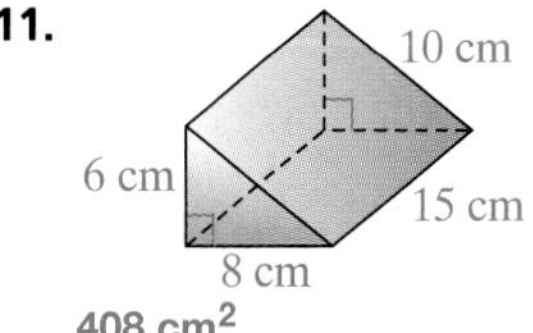


408 $cm^2$

**12.**

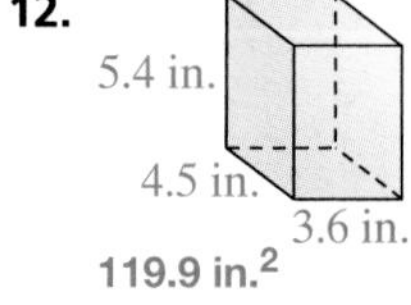


119.9 $in.^2$

**13.**

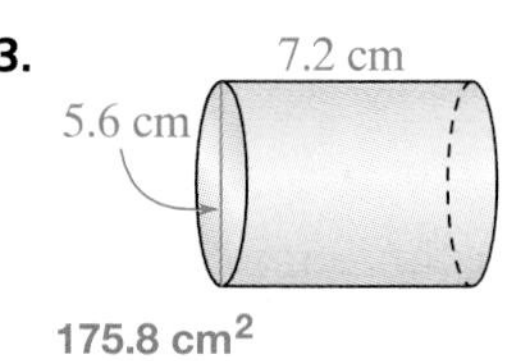


175.8 $cm^2$



## Alternative Assessment

With students in groups, give each group a model of a prism or cylinder and ask them to find a way, other than direct use of the formulas, to find the surface area of their solid. Have students check their methods by using the formulas from the lesson.

7.

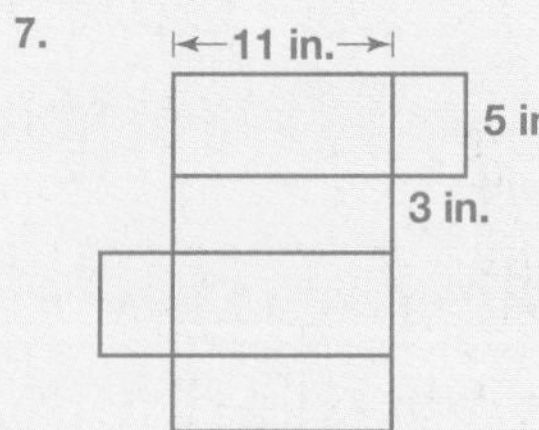

14. A cylinder has radius 8 ft and height 12 ft. Draw and label a net for the cylinder. Find its surface area. 1,004.8 ft$^2$; See below right for net.

15. Find the surface area of a square prism with base edge 7 m and height 15 m. 518 m$^2$

16. Find the area of the top and lateral surface of a cylindrical water tank with radius 20 ft and height 30 ft. 5,024 ft$^2$

17. The camping tent at the right is similar to a triangular prism. Find the surface area of the tent, including the bottom. 10,800 in.$^2$

42 in. 36 in. 42 in.
44 in. 72 in.

18. Find the surface area of a cylinder with radius 8 cm and height 10 cm. 904.32 cm$^2$

19. The neighborhood swimming pool needs to be painted. The pool is 40 ft by 60 ft. The depth of the pool is 6 ft throughout.
   a. How many sides need to be painted? 5
   b. What is the total number of square feet to be painted? 3,600 ft$^2$
   c. The materials for painting the pool cost $1.50 per square yard. What is the cost of the materials for painting the pool? $600

20. *Error Analysis* A student explains that the two cylinders below have the same surface area. Explain the student's error.
The student did not correctly apply the formula for surface area of a cylinder.

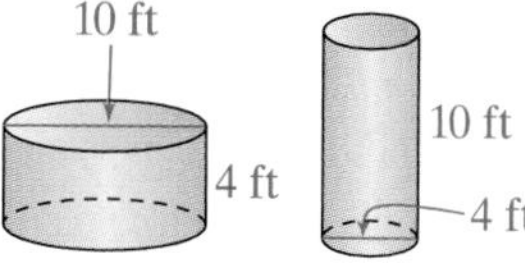


10 ft
4 ft

21. *Open-ended* Describe a real-world situation in which you need to know the surface area of a space figure. Check students' work.

22. *Critical Thinking* Use the cubes with side lengths of 1, 2, and 3 units to answer the following questions.

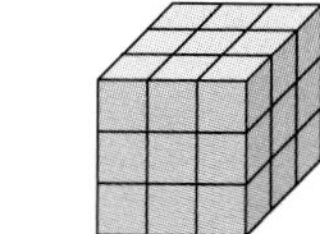

   a. Find the surface area of each cube. 6 square units; 24 square units; 54 square units
   b. If the length of each side of a cube is doubled, how does that affect the surface area? It is quadrupled.
   c. If the length of each side of a cube is tripled, how does that affect the surface area? It increases by a factor of nine.

23. *Mathematical Reasoning* Which has the greater effect on the surface area of a cylinder: doubling the base radius or doubling the height? Justify your answer. Doubling the radius has a greater effect on the surface area because the radius appears as a higher power than the height in determining surface area.

14.
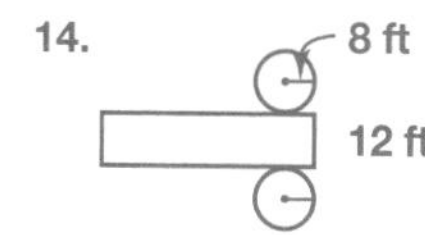

## Practice

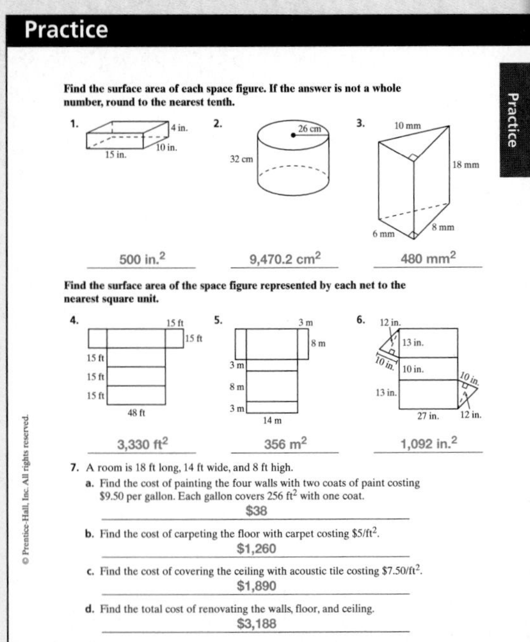

Find the surface area of each space figure. If the answer is not a whole number, round to the nearest tenth.

1. 4 in., 10 in., 15 in. — 500 in.$^2$
2. 26 cm, 32 cm — 9,470.2 cm$^2$
3. 10 mm, 18 mm, 6 mm, 8 mm — 480 mm$^2$

Find the surface area of the space figure represented by each net to the nearest square unit.

4. 15 ft, 15 ft, 15 ft, 15 ft, 15 ft, 48 ft — 3,330 ft$^2$
5. 3 m, 8 m, 3 m, 8 m, 3 m, 14 m — 356 m$^2$
6. 12 in., 13 in., 10 in., 10 in., 10 in., 13 in., 27 in., 12 in. — 1,092 in.$^2$

7. A room is 18 ft long, 14 ft wide, and 8 ft high.
   a. Find the cost of painting the four walls with two coats of paint costing \$9.50 per gallon. Each gallon covers 256 ft$^2$ with one coat. \$38
   b. Find the cost of carpeting the floor with carpet costing \$5/ft$^2$. \$1,260
   c. Find the cost of covering the ceiling with acoustic tile costing \$7.50/ft$^2$. \$1,890
   d. Find the total cost of renovating the walls, floor, and ceiling. \$3,188



## Reteaching

Find the surface area of the triangular prism.
Two methods can be used to find the surface area.

**Method 1**
Draw a net for the prism, find the area of each polygon in the net, and then add them together.

**Method 2**
Use the formula
S.A. = L.A. + 2*B*
L.A. = *ph*
$p = 3(8) = 24$
L.A. $= 24(12) = 288$ cm$^2$
$B = \frac{1}{2}bh = \frac{1}{2}(8)(7) = 28$ cm$^2$
S.A. = L.A. + 2*B*
$= 288 + 2(28)$
$= 344$ cm$^2$

The triangles have area:
$A = \frac{1}{2}bh = \frac{1}{2}(8)7 = 28$ cm$^2$
Each rectangle has area:
$A = bh = 8(12) = 96$ cm$^2$
The total area of the 2 triangles and 3 rectangles is:
$28 + 28 + 96 + 96 + 96 = 344$ cm$^2$

Find the surface area of each prism using the method you prefer.

1. 6 in., 6 in., 9 in., 5 in., 6 in. — 192 in.$^2$
2. 12 ft, 5 ft, 5 ft — 290 ft$^2$
3. 9 cm, 15 cm, 10 cm — 750 cm$^2$



## Enrichment

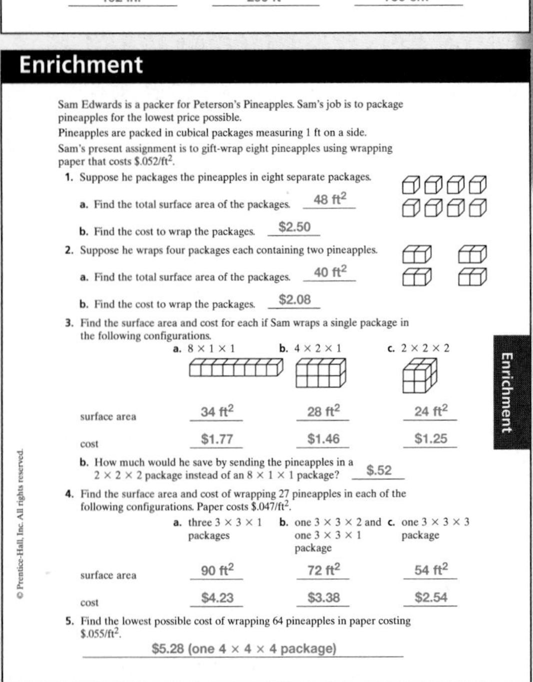

Sam Edwards is a packer for Peterson's Pineapples. Sam's job is to package pineapples for the lowest price possible.
Pineapples are packed in cubical packages measuring 1 ft on a side.
Sam's present assignment is to gift-wrap eight pineapples using wrapping paper that costs \$.052/ft$^2$.

1. Suppose he packages the pineapples in eight separate packages.
   a. Find the total surface area of the packages. 48 ft$^2$
   b. Find the cost to wrap the packages. \$2.50
2. Suppose he wraps four packages each containing two pineapples.
   a. Find the total surface area of the packages. 40 ft$^2$
   b. Find the cost to wrap the packages. \$2.08
3. Find the surface area and cost for each if Sam wraps a single package in the following configurations.

| | a. 8 × 1 × 1 | b. 4 × 2 × 1 | c. 2 × 2 × 2 |
|---|---|---|---|
| surface area | 34 ft$^2$ | 28 ft$^2$ | 24 ft$^2$ |
| cost | \$1.77 | \$1.46 | \$1.25 |

   b. How much would he save by sending the pineapples in a 2 × 2 × 2 package instead of an 8 × 1 × 1 package? \$.52
4. Find the surface area and cost of wrapping 27 pineapples in each of the following configurations. Paper costs \$.047/ft$^2$.

| | a. three 3 × 3 × 1 packages | b. one 3 × 3 × 2 and one 3 × 3 × 1 package | c. one 3 × 3 × 3 package |
|---|---|---|---|
| surface area | 90 ft$^2$ | 72 ft$^2$ | 54 ft$^2$ |
| cost | \$4.23 | \$3.38 | \$2.54 |

5. Find the lowest possible cost of wrapping 64 pineapples in paper costing \$.055/ft$^2$. \$5.28 (one 4 × 4 × 4 package)



24. **TEST PREP** Which figure would cost more to paint? A
    A. the square prism
    B. the cylinder
    C. They would cost the same.

8 cm, 5 cm, 5 cm; 10 cm, 5 cm

25. *Writing* In a triangular prism, what is the difference between the height of a base and the height of the prism? The height of the base is the height of the triangular base, but the height of the prism is the shortest distance between the two bases.

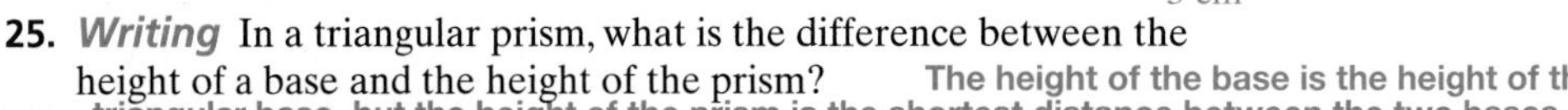

26. *Packaging* You have made two boxes with lids. Which box required more cardboard, a box 8 in. by 6.25 in. by 10.5 in., or a box 9 in. by 5.5 in. by 11.75 in.? Explain. See below right.

27. *Construction* The concrete figure at the right has a hole in it. The surface will be painted except for the inside of the hole. Find the total surface area to be painted to the nearest square foot. 658 ft$^2$

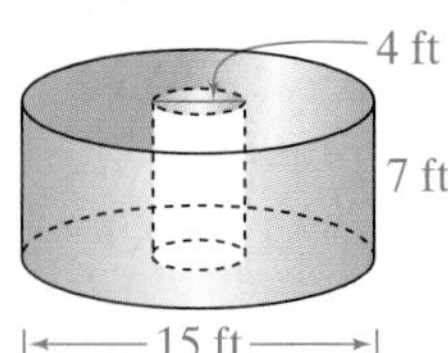


## Mixed Review

**Name each space figure.** ***(Lesson 10-4)***

28. hexagonal prism

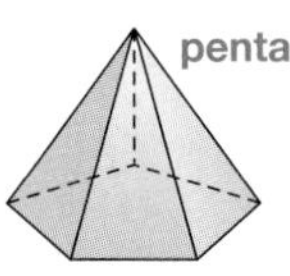

29. pentagonal pyramid

30. cone

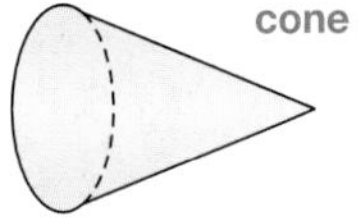

**Graph each point and its image after a reflection over the given line.** ***(Lesson 9-9)*** 31. See margin. 32–33. See back of book.

31. $A(0, 9)$; $x$-axis
32. $B(-3, 5)$; $y$-axis
33. $C(3, -1)$; $x = 2$

34. A recipe for 6 people calls for $\frac{1}{2}$ teaspoon of salt. In preparing this recipe for 25 people, how many teaspoons of salt should you use? ***(Lesson 6-2)*** about 2 teaspoons

26. The first box requires 399.25 in.$^2$ of cardboard, but the second requires 439.75 in.$^2$ of cardboard. So the second box requires more cardboard.

## Chapter Project 10 — Activity 1 Measuring

Use centimeter cubes to make a prism. Measure the dimensions of the prism's base. Calculate the area of the base.

Stack some pennies or nickels to make a cylinder. Measure the diameter of the cylinder's base. Calculate the area of the base.

Keep your space figures for use in Activities 2 and 3.



See also Extra Practice section.

31.

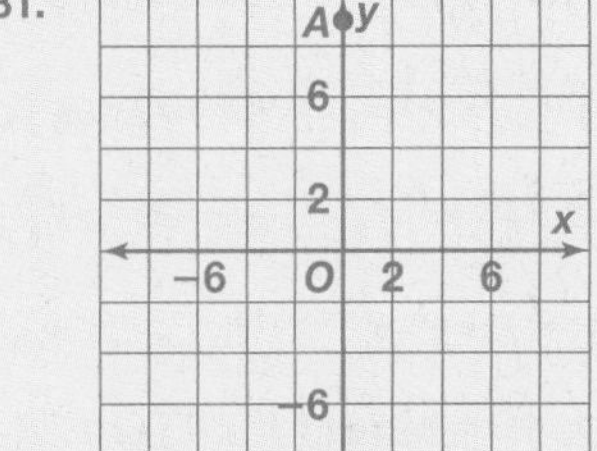


### Project Activity 1

**Measuring** Make sure students have rulers to measure the bases of their prisms and cylinders. Remind students that they need to find the radius of the base of the cylinder in order to find its area. Students should make their measurements in centimeters.

# Surface Area: Pyramids, Cones, and Spheres

# 10-6

## PART 1 Finding Surface Areas of Pyramids

In this text, all pyramids are *regular* pyramids. They have regular polygons for bases and congruent isosceles triangles for lateral faces.

You can use the **slant height** $\ell$, the height of a face, to find the area of the lateral faces.

If $n$ is the number of lateral triangular faces, L.A. is $n\left(\frac{1}{2}b\ell\right)$.

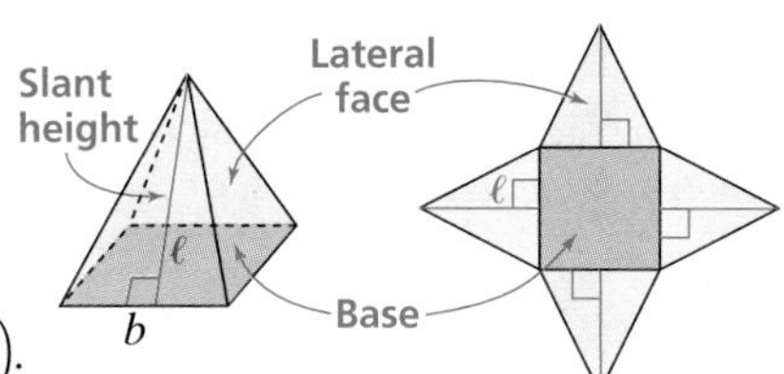


### What You'll Learn

1. To find surface areas of pyramids
2. To find surface areas of cones and spheres

### . . . And Why

To find surface areas of real-world objects, such as a basketball

### Surface Area of a Pyramid

The surface area of a pyramid is the sum of the lateral area and the area of the base.

$$\text{S.A.} = \text{L.A.} + B$$

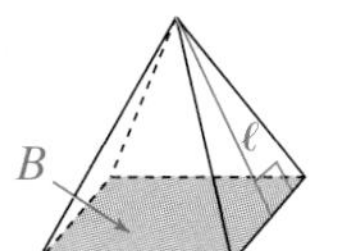


The entrance to the Louvre in Paris, France is a pyramid that is 66 ft tall.

### EXAMPLE 1

**Find the surface area of the square pyramid at the right.**

$\text{L.A.} = 4\left(\frac{1}{2}b\ell\right)$ There are 4 lateral faces.

$= 4\left(\frac{1}{2}\cdot 12\cdot 16\right) = 384$

$\text{S.A.} = \text{L.A.} + B$

$= 384 + 12^2$ The base is a square.

$= 384 + 144 = 528$

The surface area of the pyramid is 528 $\text{cm}^2$.

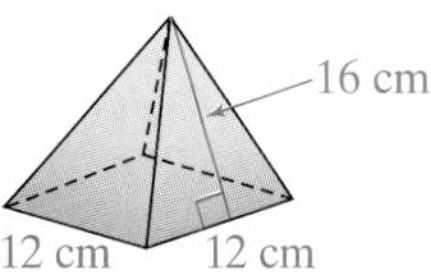


### TRY THIS

1. A pyramid has a square base with edge 20 ft. The slant height is 8 ft. Find the surface area. 720 $\text{ft}^2$



# 10-6

## Getting Ready

**Key Terms and Symbols** slant height, surface area of a pyramid, surface area of a cone, surface area of a sphere

**Resources** A complete list of resources for this lesson is on p. 501H.

### Daily Skills Warm-Up

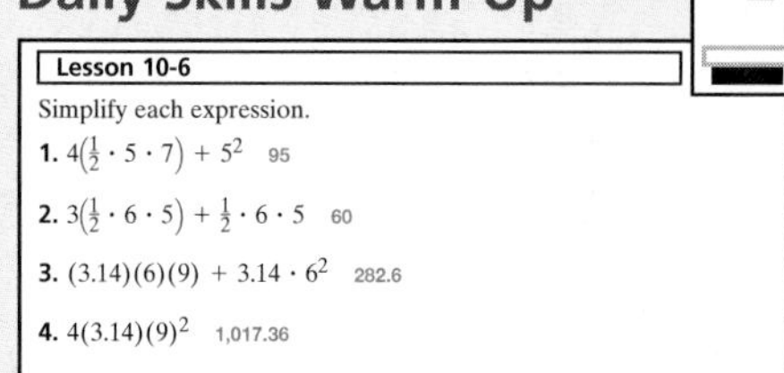
Lesson 10-6

Simplify each expression.

1. $4\left(\frac{1}{2}\cdot 5\cdot 7\right) + 5^2$ 95
2. $3\left(\frac{1}{2}\cdot 6\cdot 5\right) + \frac{1}{2}\cdot 6\cdot 5$ 60
3. $(3.14)(6)(9) + 3.14\cdot 6^2$ 282.6
4. $4(3.14)(9)^2$ 1,017.36

### Background for the Lesson

For a regular pyramid, the slant height, $\ell$, is the height of a triangle that is a side, or lateral face, of the pyramid. You find the lateral area of a pyramid by first finding the area of each lateral face $(\frac{1}{2}b\ell)$. For a right circular cone, the slant height is the shortest distance from the vertex to a point on the circle that forms the base. The lateral area of a cone is $\frac{1}{2}$ the product of the circumference of the base and the slant height. The surface area of a pyramid or a cone, like the surface area of a prism or a cylinder, is the sum of the lateral area and the area of the base.

## 1 Focus

### Connecting to Prior Knowledge

In Lesson 10-5, students learned how to find the surface areas of prisms and cylinders. In this lesson, students learn to find the surface areas of pyramids, cones, and spheres. In Lessons 10-7 and 10-9, students will learn how to find the volumes of prisms, cylinders, pyramids, cones, and spheres.

## Tools to Monitor Progress

### BEFORE THE LESSON

**To check prerequisite skills:**

- Multiplying by a fraction

**Skills You Need,** p. 501

**Skills Intervention Kit,** Operations with Fractions

### DURING THE LESSON

**To check understanding:**

**Try This** exercises on student page

- **Additional Example 1**

Find the surface area of the square pyramid. 105 $\text{m}^2$

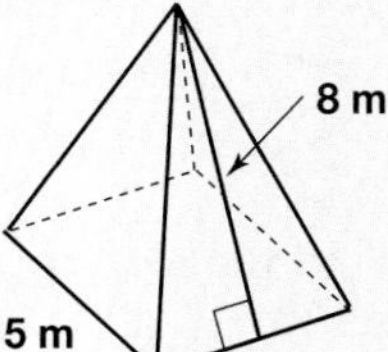

# 2 Teach

## Part 1 Teaching Notes

Discuss why this formula applies only to a regular pyramid with congruent isosceles triangles for lateral faces.

**ELL** The *slant height* is the altitude of the *slanted,* or tilted faces of the pyramid. It is different from the perpendicular distance from the vertex and the base (which is called the height of the pyramid). The slant height is not perpendicular to the base of the pyramid. It is perpendicular to the base of the triangle that is a lateral face.

**Tactile Learning** To clarify the difference between the slant height and height of a pyramid, give models of pyramids to groups of students. Have them measure the slant height and the height of the pyramid and compare the two measurements.

### Example 1

**Build understanding.** Ask: Can you use the formula L.A. $= 4(\frac{1}{2}b\ell)$ for all regular pyramids? Explain. **No, $n = 4$ in this case because the pyramid has 4 lateral faces.**

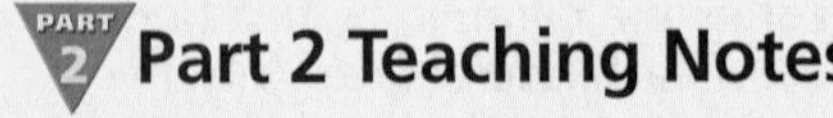

## Part 2 Teaching Notes

Making cones from paper circles, such as coffee filters, may help students understand these problems.

### Example 2

**Build understanding.** Ask: What would the formula for the lateral area be if you used the diameter of the base instead of the radius? **L.A. $= \frac{1}{2}\pi d\ell$**

### Example 3

**Build understanding.** Ask: Since the diameter of the basketball is 10 in., why is 5 used in the calculation? **The formula uses the radius, which is half of the diameter, or 5 in.**

## Finding Surface Areas of Cones and Spheres

In this text, every cone is a right circular cone with the vertex of the cone directly over the center of the circular base.

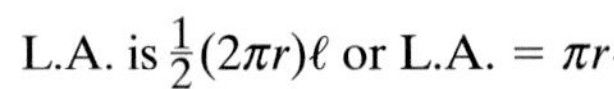

L.A. is $\frac{1}{2}(2\pi r)\ell$ or L.A. $= \pi r\ell$.

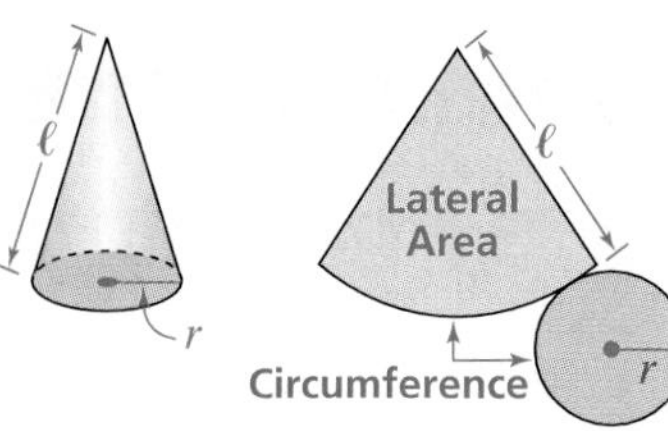


### Surface Area of a Cone

The surface area (S.A.) of a cone is the sum of the lateral area and base area, or S.A. = L.A. + $B$.

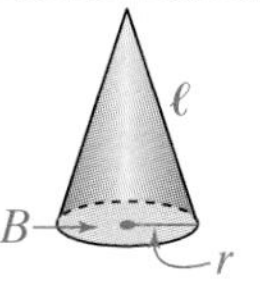


### EXAMPLE 2

**Find the surface area of the cone at the right.**

| | | |
|---|---|---|
| L.A. | $= \pi r\ell$ | |
| | $\approx 3.14(4)(10)$ | The radius is 4. |
| | $= 125.6$ | Simplify. |
| S.A. | $=$ L.A. $+ B$ | |
| | $\approx 125.6 + 3.14(4)^2$ | The radius is 4. |
| | $= 175.84$ | Simplify. |

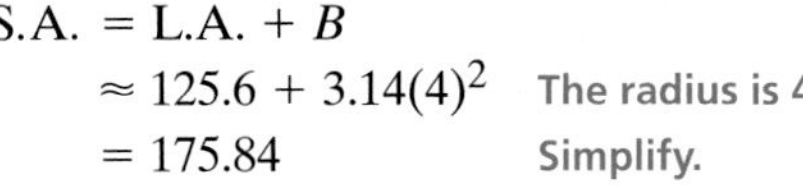

10 cm

4 cm

The total surface area of the cone is about 176 $cm^2$.

### TRY THIS

**2.** Find the surface area of a cone with lateral height 39 ft and diameter 14 ft. **1,011.08 $ft^2$**

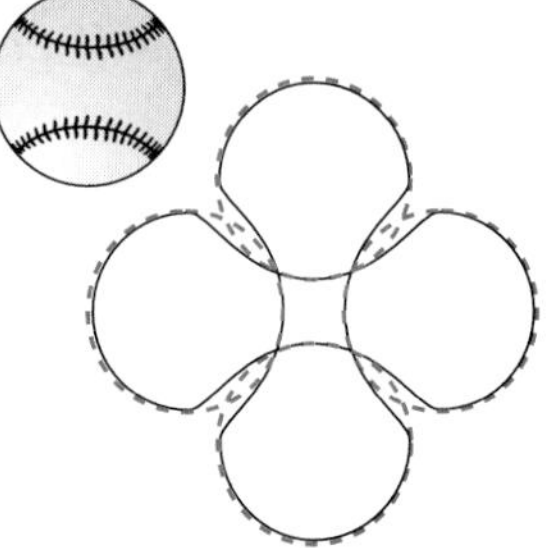

The figure at the left suggests how the cover of a baseball may help you remember the formula for surface area of a sphere.

### Surface Area of a Sphere

The surface area of a sphere of radius $r$ is S.A. $= 4\pi r^2$.

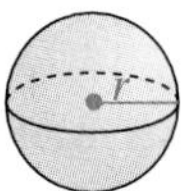




- **Additional Example 2**

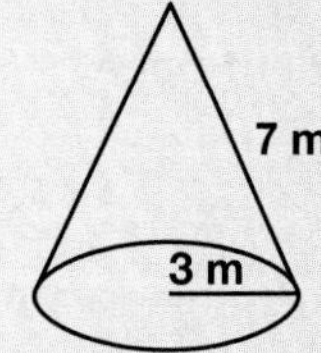


Find the surface area of the cone. **about 94 $m^2$**

- **Additional Example 3**

Earth has an average radius of 3,963 mi. Assume that Earth is a perfect sphere, without surface features, and calculate its surface area. **about 197,259,435 $mi^2$**

## EXAMPLE 3

REAL-WORLD CONNECTION

**Calculate the surface area of a basketball.**

$S.A. = 4\pi r^2$ surface area formula

$\approx 4(3.14)(5)^2$ Replace $\pi$ with 3.14 and $r$ with 5.

$= 314$ Simplify.

The surface area of the basketball is about 314 in.$^2$.

10 in.

You can find the surface area of a space figure that combines two or more of the figures you have studied.

## Different Ways to Solve a Problem

**Find the surface area of the silo formed by a half sphere and a cylinder. The diameter of the silo is 20 ft.**

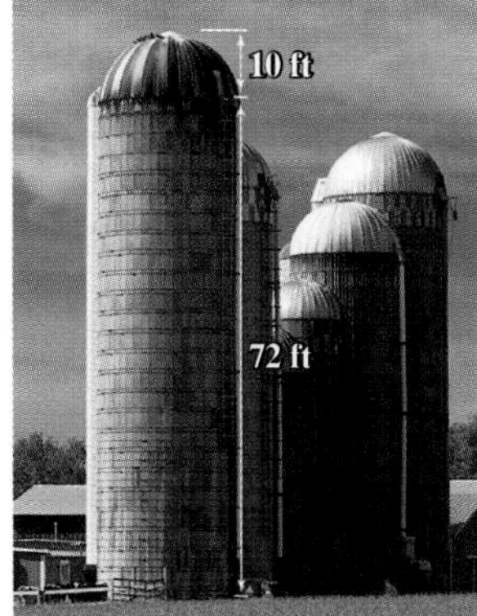


**Method 1**

Find the area of each space figure. Then find their sum.

One half sphere

$S.A. = \frac{1}{2}(4\pi r^2)$

$\approx \frac{1}{2}(4)(3.14)(10^2)$

$= 628$

Cylinder

$L.A. = 2\pi rh$

$\approx 2(3.14)(10)(72)$

$= 4{,}521.6$

Surface area of silo is 628 + 4,521.6, or 5,149.6 ft$^2$.

**Method 2**

Combine formulas before substituting values.

Surface area of silo $= \frac{1}{2}$ S.A. of sphere + L.A. of cylinder

$= \frac{1}{2}(4\pi r^2) + 2\pi rh$

$= 2\pi r^2 + 2\pi rh$

$\approx 2(3.14)(10^2) + 2(3.14)(10)(72)$

$= 5{,}149.6$

Surface area of silo is 5,149.6 ft$^2$.

**Choose a Method**

1. Which method do you prefer? Explain. Answers may vary. Sample: I prefer method 2 because it is easier to manipulate symbols than numbers.



**Connecting to Geology** Earth is not a perfect sphere, though a sphere is a good approximation for its shape. Earth is flattened a bit on the polar axis. Earth's diameter measured between the North and South Poles is 42 km less than the diameter measured at the equator. This difference is very slight considering that the average diameter is about 12,682 km.

### Different Ways to Solve a Problem

**Build understanding.** Ask: What mathematical property could you use to simplify the expression $2\pi r^2 + 2\pi rh$ in Method 2? What would be the resulting expression? You could use the distributive property to simplify the expression to $2\pi(r^2 + rh)$ or $2\pi r(r + h)$.

**Extension** Discuss the difference between the two methods described in the Different Ways to Solve a Problem. The methods are essentially the same but the combining is done at different times.

## AFTER THE LESSON

### To assess knowledge: Lesson Quiz

1. Find the surface area of a square pyramid with a base edge of 80 m and a lateral height of 100 m. 22,400 m$^2$

2. Find the surface area of a cone that has a lateral height of 22 cm and a radius of 7 cm. about 637 cm$^2$

- For enrichment and reteaching options see Resources on p. 501H.

# 3 Practice/Assess

## Assignment Guide

To provide flexible scheduling, this lesson can be divided into parts.

**Part 1**
**Core** 3, 5, 7, 9–10, 13
**Extension** 14

**Part 2**
**Core** 1–2, 4, 6, 8, 11–12, 18, 19–20
**Extension** 15–17

Mixed Review can be assigned at any time for maintenance.

### Exercises

**Test Prep Exercise 19** Set up the ratio with the radius of the smaller sphere in the numerator and the radius of the larger sphere in the denominator.

### Challenge

The sun has a diameter of approximately 864,000 mi. Assuming that the sun is a sphere, what is its approximate surface area? 2,343,997,440,000 mi$^2$

### Closure

For pyramids and cones, use the slant height, $\ell$, to find the lateral area. The lateral area of a pyramid is $n(\frac{1}{2}b\ell)$ and of a cone is $\pi r\ell$. The surface area of a pyramid or a cone is the sum of the lateral area and the base area. The surface area of a sphere is $4\pi r^2$.

### Daily Cumulative Review

**Find the surface area of the space figure represented by each net.** *(Lesson 10-5)*

1. 8 cm, 5 cm, 8 cm, 5 cm, 20 cm — 600 cm$^2$
2. 16 mm, 20 mm — about 1,406.72 mm$^2$
3. 10 m, 10 m, 6 m, 6 m, 8 m, 8 m, 30 m — 768 m$^2$

**Name the space figure you can form from each net.** *(Lesson 10-4)*

4. cylinder
5. pentagonal pyramid
6. hexagonal prism

**Mixed Review**

**Find the area of each figure.**

7. (10-1) 3 m, 17 m — 51 m$^2$
8. (10-2) 9 ft, 8 ft, 22 ft — 88 ft$^2$
9. (10-3) 24 mm — about 452.16 mm$^2$

**Find each discount.**

10. (6-9) regular price: \$15.99, percent of discount: 25% — \$4.00
11. (6-9) regular price: \$99.98, percent of discount: 30% — \$29.99
12. (6-9) regular price: \$12.55, percent of discount: 75% — \$9.41



# Exercises

## Check Understanding

**Find the surface area of each space figure, to the nearest square unit.**

1. 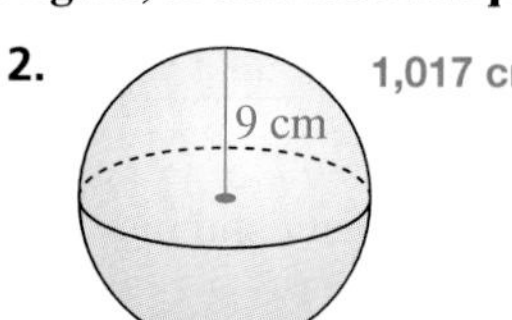

1,256 cm$^2$

2. 9 cm — 1,017 cm$^2$

3. 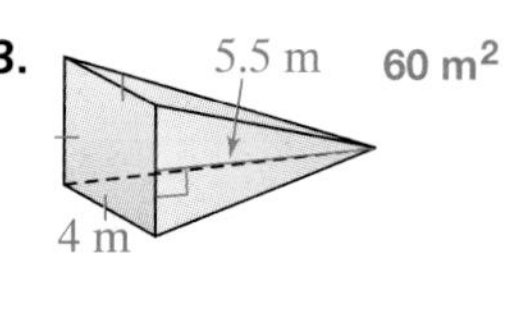

60 m$^2$

4. The base of a cone has radius 3 ft. Its slant height is 8 ft. Find the surface area of the cone. 104 ft$^2$

5. The length of the base of a square pyramid is 5 cm. Its slant height is 8 cm. Find the surface area of the square pyramid. 105 cm$^2$

6. *Mathematical Reasoning* Which has the greater surface area, a cylinder with height 2 in. and radius of base 2 in., or a sphere with radius 2 in.? Justify your answer. Both have the same surface area of $16\pi$ in.$^2$

## Practice and Problem Solving

**Find the surface area of each space figure, to the nearest square unit.**

7. 33 yd$^2$
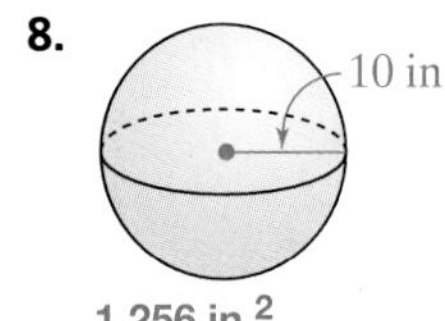


8. 10 in. — 1,256 in.$^2$

9. 540 cm$^2$
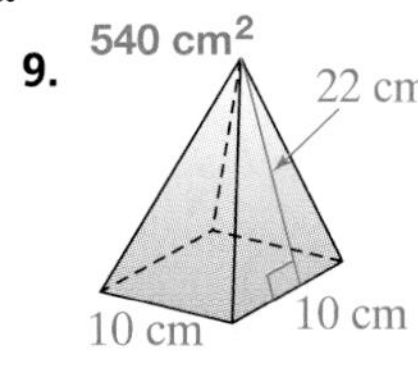


10. 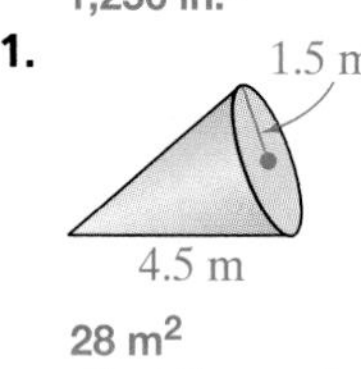

81 cm$^2$

11. 1.5 m, 4.5 m — 28 m$^2$

12. 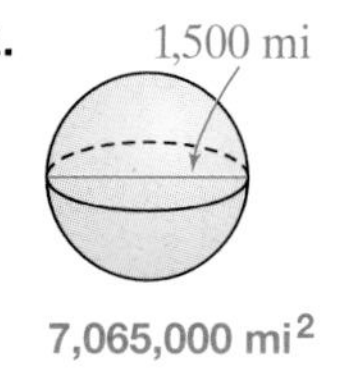

7,065,000 mi$^2$

13. *Error Analysis* A friend tells you that the surface area of a square prism with base length 4 m and height 5 m is the same as the area of a square pyramid with base length 4 m and height 5 m. Explain your friend's error. My friend forgot to add the area of the second base of the prism.



### Alternative Assessment

Give groups halves of oranges. Have them measure the diameter and calculate the surface area. Then, ask them to cut the peel of the orange into small squares and arrange them in a rectangle. Calculate the area and compare.

**Find the surface area of each figure. Give your answers to the nearest square unit.**

**14.** 216 m²

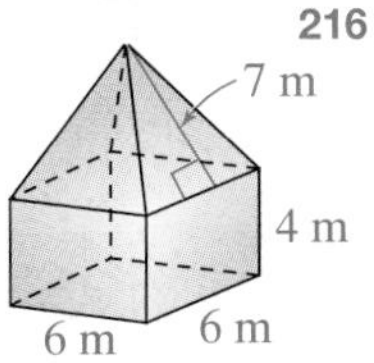


**15.** 122 m²

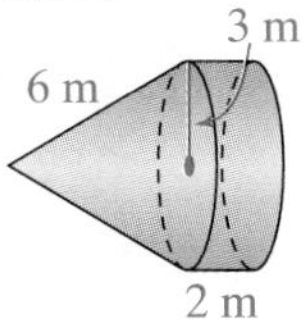


**16.** 2,185 ft²

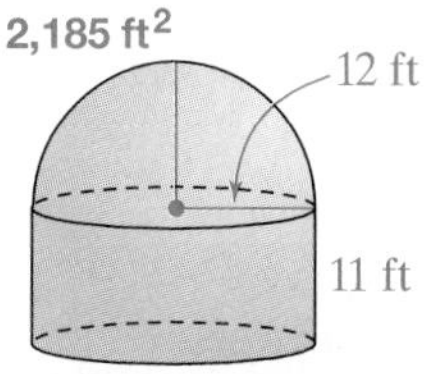


**17.** ***Architecture*** The American Museum of Natural History in New York City has built a spherical planetarium. The sphere measures 87 ft in diameter.

**a.** What is the surface area of the sphere? 23,766.66 ft²

**b.** The sphere is covered by 2,474 panels to absorb sound. What is the average area of each panel, to the nearest tenth of a square foot? 9.6 ft²

The American Museum of Natural History, New York City

**18.** ***Writing*** Write a paragraph explaining how to find the surface area of a cone with slant height 10 in. and base radius 8 in. See below right.

**19.** **TEST PREP** What is the ratio of the surface area of a sphere with radius 2 ft to the area of a sphere with radius 5 ft? B

**A.** 2 to 5 **B.** 4 to 25 **C.** 16 to 125 **D.** 18 to 20

**20.** ***Geography*** Approximately 70% of Earth's surface is covered by water. If the diameter of the earth is approximately 13,000 km, find the approximate area *not* covered by water. 159,198,000 km²

## Mixed Review

**Find the surface area, to the nearest square unit.** ***(Lesson 10-5)***

**21.**

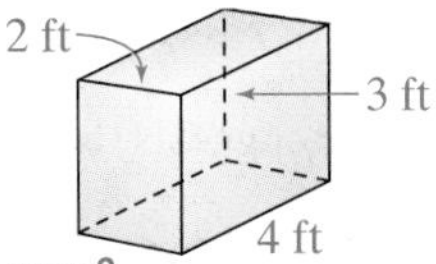


52 ft²

**22.**

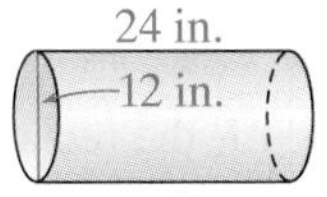


1,130 in.²

**23.**

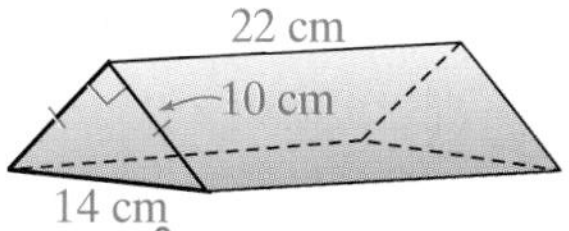


848 cm²

**List all the factors of each number.** ***(Lesson 4-1)***

**24.** 21 1, 3, 7, 21 **25.** 100 1, 2, 4, 5, 10, 20, 25, 50, 100 **26.** 25 1, 5, 25 **27.** 32 1, 2, 4, 8, 16, 32 **28.** 65 1, 5, 13, 65

**29.** Under rate plan A a new computer costs $200 down and $20 a month. Under rate plan B the computer costs $175 down and $25 a month. After how many months will the amount paid be the same for both plans? ***(Lesson 8-7)*** 5 months

18. Use the slant height to find the lateral area using the formula L.A. = $\pi r \ell$. Then, add the area of the base to the lateral area to find the total surface area.

See also Extra Practice section.



## Practice

**Find the surface area of each space figure to the nearest square unit.**

1. 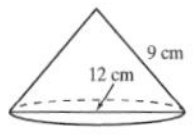

283 cm²

2. 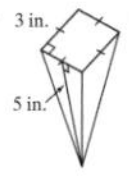

39 in.²

3. 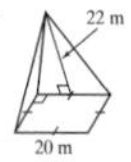

1,280 m²

4. 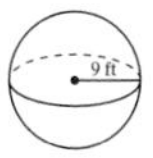

1,017 ft²

5. 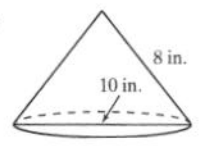

204 in.²

6. 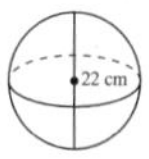

1,520 cm²

7. 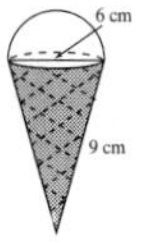

141 cm²

8. 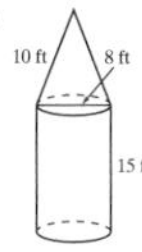

553 ft²

9. 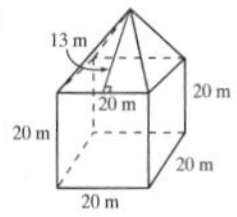

2,520 m²

10. A hemisphere with diameter 70 cm 11,540 cm²

11. A cone and a square-based pyramid have slant heights of 6 in. The diameter for the cone and the base edge of the pyramid are both 8 in.

a. Which space figure has the greater surface area? pyramid

b. By how much does the surface area of the greater space figure exceed that of the smaller? Use 3.14 for $\pi$. 34.4 in.²



## Reteaching

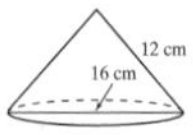


Find the surface area of the cone.

The formula for the surface area (S.A.) of a cone is S.A. = L.A. + $B$, where $B$ is the area of the base and L.A. is the lateral surface area.

L.A. = $\pi r l$, where $r$ is the radius of the cone and $l$ is the slant height.

In the cone, given $r = \frac{1}{2}(16) = 8$ and $l = 12$:

| | |
|---|---|
| L.A. = $\pi r l$ | |
| $= \pi(8)(12)$ | Substitute 8 for $r$ and 12 for $l$. |
| $\approx 301.44$ | Use 3.14 for $\pi$. |
| The base is a circle, so $B = \pi r^2$. | |
| $B = \pi r^2 = \pi(8)^2$ | Substitute 8 for $r$. |
| $\approx 200.96$ | Use 3.14 for $\pi$. |
| Thus, S.A. = L.A. + $B$ | |
| $\approx 301.44 + 200.96$ | Substitute 301.44 for L.A. and 200.96 for $B$. |
| $= 502.4$ | Add. |

The surface area is about 502 cm². Don't forget to use square units.

**Find the surface area of each space figure to the nearest square unit.**

1. 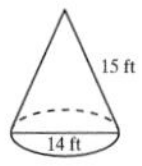

484 ft²

2. 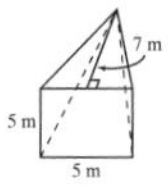

95 m²

3. 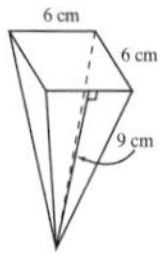

144 cm²

4. cone
$r = 10$ in.
$l = 14$ in.
754 in.²

5. square pyramid
$b = 11$ cm
$l = 8$ cm
297 cm²

6. cone
$d = 24$ m
$l = 25$ m
1,394 m²



## Enrichment

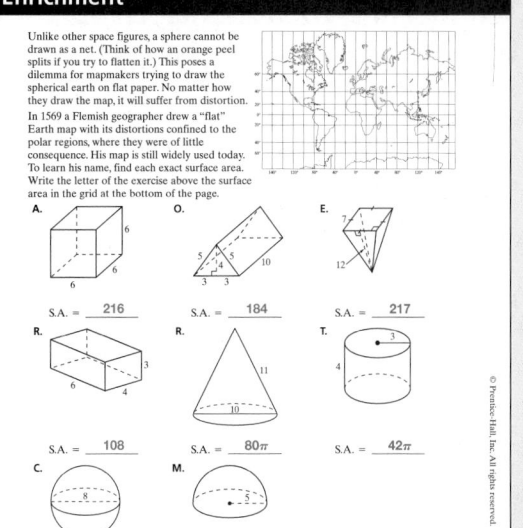

Unlike other space figures, a sphere cannot be drawn as a net. (Think of how an orange peel splits if you try to flatten it.) This poses a dilemma for mapmakers trying to draw the spherical earth on flat paper. No matter how they draw the map, it will suffer from distortion.

In 1569 a Flemish geographer drew a "flat" Earth map with its distortions confined to the polar regions, where they were of little consequence. His map is still widely used today. To learn his name, find each exact surface area. Write the letter of the exercise above the surface area in the grid at the bottom of the page.

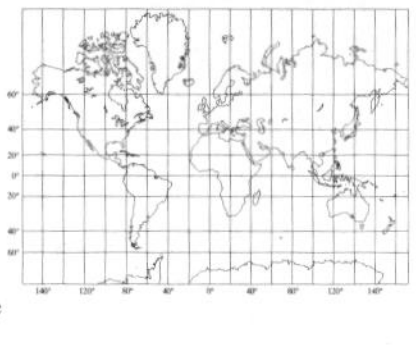

A. 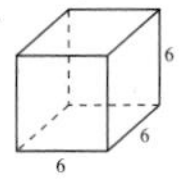

S.A. = 216

O. 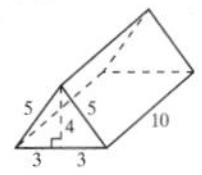

S.A. = 184

E. 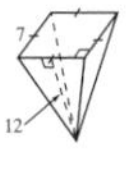

S.A. = 217

R. 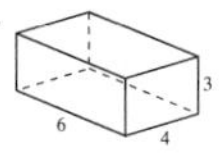

S.A. = 108

R. 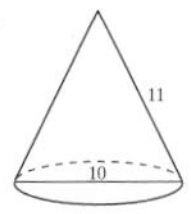

S.A. = 80$\pi$

T. 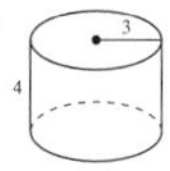

S.A. = 42$\pi$

C. 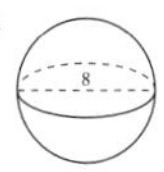

S.A. = 64$\pi$

M. 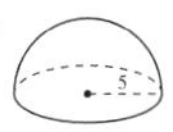

S.A. = 75$\pi$

Answer: Gerhardus

| M | E | R | C | A | T | O | R |
|---|---|---|---|---|---|---|---|
| 75$\pi$ | 217 | 80$\pi$ | 64$\pi$ | 216 | 42$\pi$ | 184 | 108 |

# 10-7

## Getting Ready

**Key Terms and Symbols** volume, cubic unit, volume of a prism, volume of a cylinder

**Resources** A complete list of resources for this lesson is on p. 501H.

### Daily Skills Warm-Up

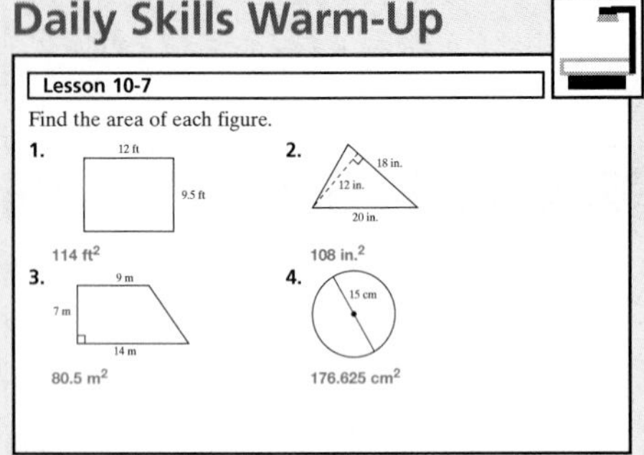


### Background for the Lesson

Volume is an amount of three-dimensional space, a measure of capacity. You calculate volume by counting or approximating the number of cubic units the object can contain. While cubic units are used for volumes in mathematics, you may be more familiar with other units of capacity such as gallons, quarts, or liters.

## 1 Focus

### Connecting to Students' Lives

Discuss using a measuring cup, graduated cylinder, or other container to measure a liquid or an amount of flour or cereal. Ask students to describe the markings on containers that measure volume.

### Connecting to Prior Knowledge

In Lesson 10-5, students learned how to calculate the surfaces area of prisms and cylinders. In this lesson, students learn to calculate the volumes of prisms and cylinders. In Lesson 10-9, students will learn how to calculate the volumes of pyramids, cones, and spheres.

# 10-7 Volume: Prisms and Cylinders

### What You'll Learn

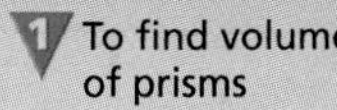
1 To find volumes of prisms

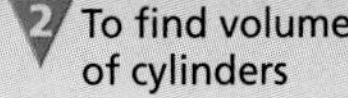
2 To find volumes of cylinders

### . . . And Why

To solve real-world problems, such as finding volumes of containers

## PART 1 Finding the Volumes of Prisms

The **volume** of a three-dimensional figure is the number of cubic units needed to fill it. A **cubic unit** is the space occupied by a cube with sides one unit long.

Consider filling the rectangular prism at the right with centimeter cubes.

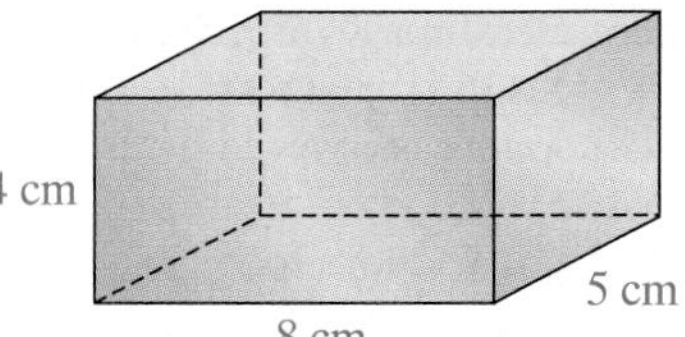


The bottom layer of the prism contains $8 \cdot 5 = 40$ centimeter cubes, or a volume of 40 $cm^3$.

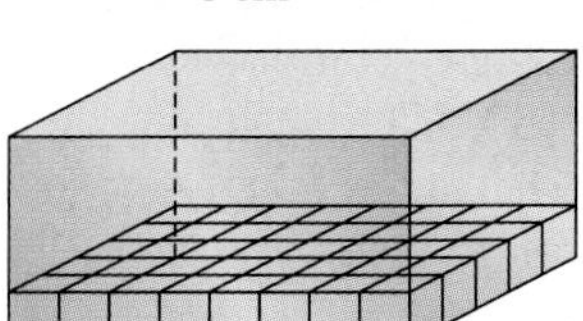

The prism has four layers of cubes, so it contains $4 \cdot 40$ or 160 centimeter cubes in all.

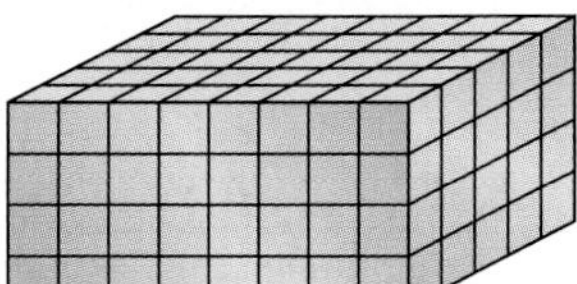

The volume of the prism is 160 $cm^3$.

The volume found for the rectangular prism above suggests the following formula.

### Volume of a Prism

The volume $V$ of a prism is the product of the base area $B$ and the height $h$.

$$V = Bh$$

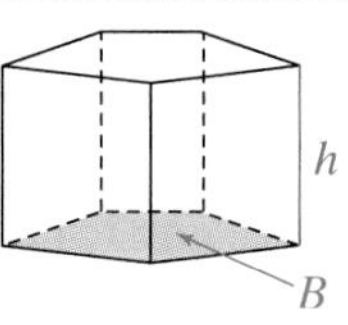




## Tools to Monitor Progress

### BEFORE THE LESSON

**To check prerequisite skills:**

- Finding areas

**Skills Intervention Kit,** Geometry

### DURING THE LESSON

**To check understanding:**

**Try This** exercises on student page

- **Additional Example 1**

Find the volume of the triangular prism. 1260 in.$^3$

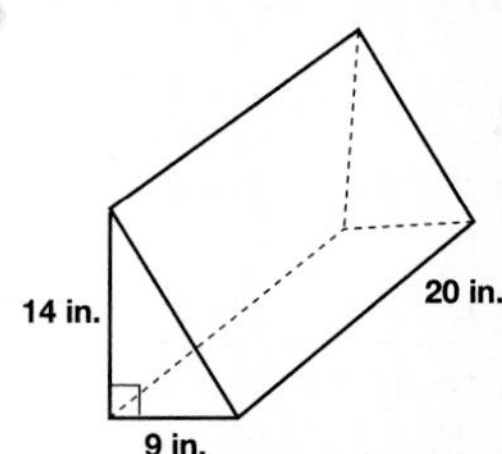

## EXAMPLE 1

**Find the volume of the triangular prism.**

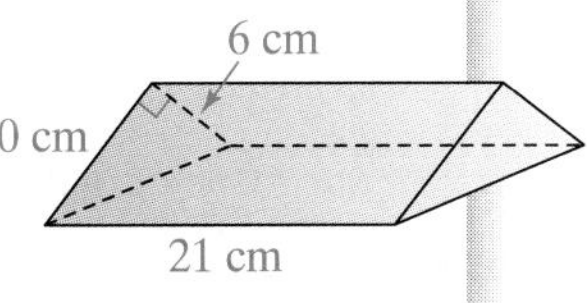


$V = Bh$ Use the formula for volume.

$= 30 \cdot 21$ $B = \frac{1}{2} \cdot 10 \cdot 6 = 30$ cm$^2$

$= 630$ Simplify.

The volume is 630 cm$^3$.

### TRY THIS

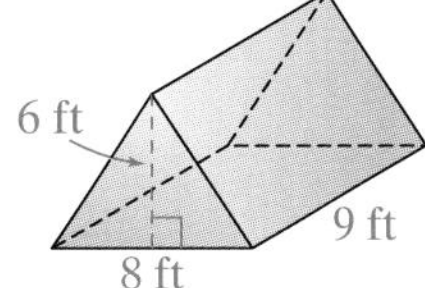


1. Find the volume of the triangular prism at the right. 216 ft$^3$

## Finding the Volumes of Cylinders

You can calculate the volume of a cylinder in much the same way that you calculate the volume of a prism.

### Volume of a Cylinder

The volume $V$ of a cylinder is the base area $B$ times the height $h$.

$$V = Bh$$

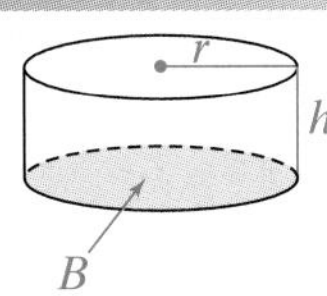

## EXAMPLE 2

*Packaging* **Find the volume of the juice can at the right to the nearest cubic centimeter.**

$V = Bh$ Use the formula for volume.

$V = \pi r^2 h$ $B = \pi r^2$.

$\approx 3.14 \cdot 3.4^2 \cdot 12$ Replace $\pi$ with 3.14, $r$ with 3.4, and $h$ with 12.

$= 435.5808$ Simplify.

The volume is about 436 cm$^3$.

### TRY THIS

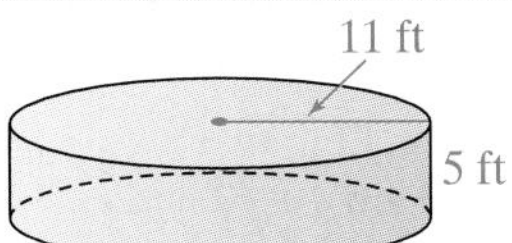


2. Find the volume of the cylinder to the nearest cubic foot. 1,900 ft$^3$



- **Additional Example 2**

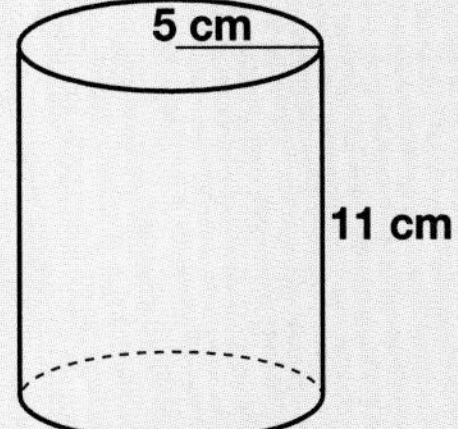


Find the volume of the cylinder.
about 864 cm$^3$

### AFTER THE LESSON

**To assess knowledge: Lesson Quiz**

Find the volume of each.

1. a rectangular prism with base of 12 m by 14 m and height of 50 m. 8,400 m$^3$
2. a cylindrical pool that has a diameter of 24 ft and a height of 4 ft. about 1,809 ft$^3$

- For enrichment and reteaching options see Resources on p. 501H.

# 2 Teach

## Part 1 Teaching Notes

Explain that the size of a cubic unit varies depending on the units you are using. For example, a cubic centimeter is a cube with a side of 1 cm. A cubic inch is a cube with a side of 1 in.

**Visual Learning** Give groups of students a small box and enough wooden, plastic, or sugar cubes to fill the box. Have students fill the box with cubes to determine the volume of the box in the cubic units they are using.

### Example 1

**Build understanding.** Ask: How does the measurement for the area of the base of the prism differ from the measurement of the volume of the prism? The area of the base is measured in square centimeters and the volume is measured in cubic centimeters.

**Error Prevention** When students find the area of the base of a triangular prism, they may forget to multiply the base and height by $\frac{1}{2}$. Remind them how this formula was derived by dividing a parallelogram in half with a diagonal.

## Part 2 Teaching Notes

Review finding the area of a circle before you discuss finding the volume of a cylinder.

### Example 2

**Build understanding.** Ask: Why do you use only the area of one base when you find the volume? You can think of the volume as moving one base along the height.

**Advanced Learners** Have students in groups measure and calculate the volume of a cylindrical container. Then have them fill the container with water and pour it into a graduated cylinder to find how many milliliters of water the container holds. Challenge students to use this information to create a conversion factor between cubic units and milliliters.

# 3 Practice/Assess

## Assignment Guide

To provide flexible scheduling, this lesson can be divided into parts.

▼ Part 1
**Core** 1–3, 7–10
✪ **Extension** 15

▼ Part 2
**Core** 4–6, 11–14, 16
✪ **Extension** 17–19

Mixed Review can be assigned at any time for maintenance.

## Exercises

**Error Prevention** **Exercises 4–6, 11–13** Pay careful attention to whether the given information is for the diameter or the radius when you calculate the volume of a cylinder.

**Math Reasoning** **Exercise 14** Be sure to explain also why you need to know the volume of the prism and the cylinder.

### ✪ Challenge

The size of a car's engine is measured by the volume of its cylinders, called displacement. What is the displacement of an 8-cylinder engine if each cylinder's diameter is 4 in. and its height is 3 in.? about 301 in.$^3$

## Closure

Volume is the measure of how much a space figure could hold if you could fill it. To find the volume of a prism or cylinder use the formula $V = Bh$.

# Exercises

## CHECK UNDERSTANDING

**Find the volume of each prism or cylinder to the nearest cubic unit.**

**1.** 24 cubic units

**2.** 54 cm$^3$

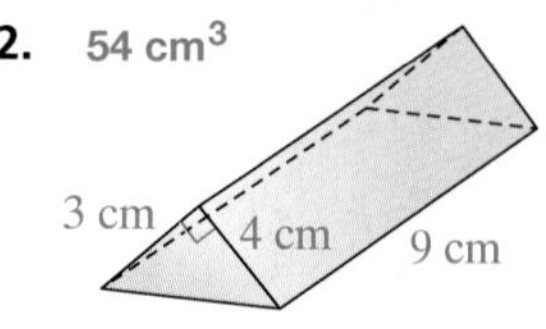


**3.** 480 cm$^3$

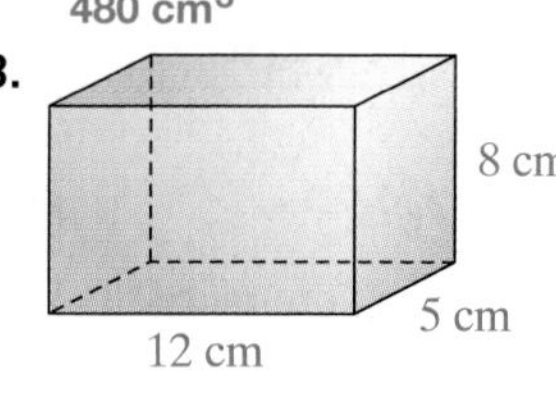


**4.**

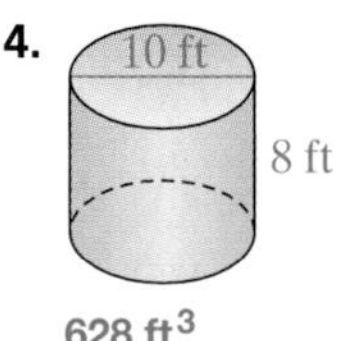


628 ft$^3$

**5.**

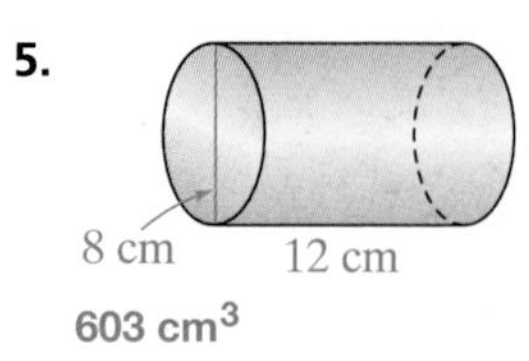


603 cm$^3$

**6.** 5,341 in.$^3$

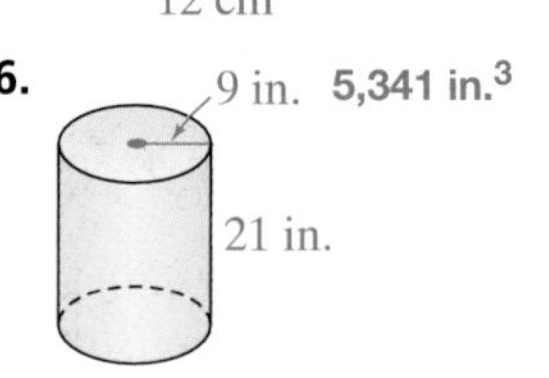


**7.** Wood for a fireplace is often sold by the cord. A cord is 8 ft by 4 ft by 4 ft. How many cubic feet are in a cord of wood? 128 ft$^3$

## PRACTICE AND PROBLEM SOLVING

**Find the volume of each prism or cylinder to the nearest tenth.**

**8.** 8 mm, 10 mm, 18 mm

720 mm$^3$

**9.** 166.4 in.$^3$

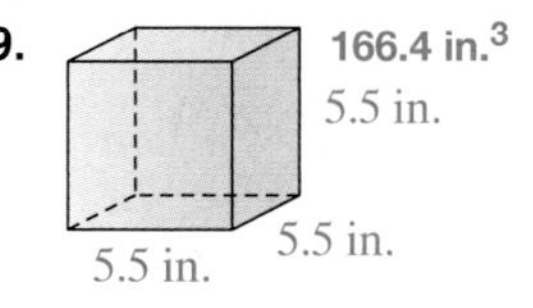


**10.** 34.4 ft$^3$

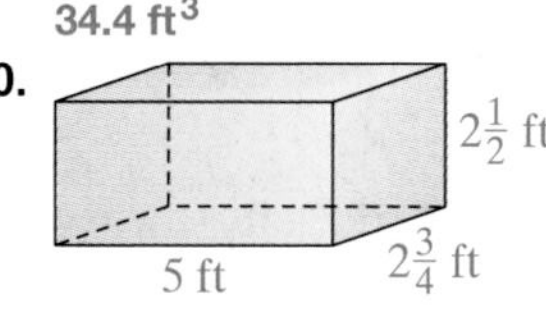


**11.**

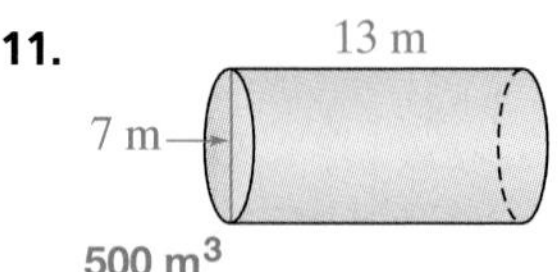


500 m$^3$

**12.**

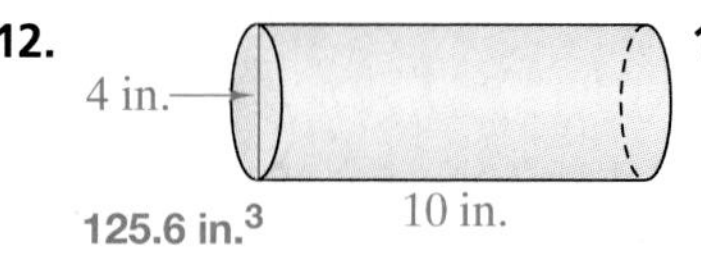


125.6 in.$^3$

**13.**

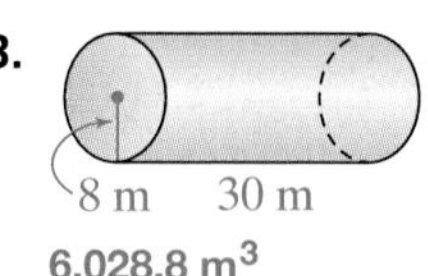


6,028.8 m$^3$

**14.** *Open-ended* Name at least one real prism and one real cylinder for which you may need to know the volumes. Check students' work.

✪ **15.** Concrete is sold by the yard, which means by the cubic yard. It costs \$70 per yard. How many cubic feet are in a cubic yard? How much would it cost to pour a slab 14 ft by 16 ft by 6 in. for a patio? 27; \$290.37

**16.** A box measures 24 in. by 12 in. by 3 in. Find its volume to the nearest cubic centimeter (1 in. = 2.54 cm). 14,158 cm$^3$



## Alternative Assessment

Have students write a lesson to teach the concept of volume to a class of younger students for the first time. Remind them not to use language or descriptions they think the younger students will not understand.

## Daily Cumulative Review

**Find the surface area of the space figure represented to the nearest square unit.** *(Lesson 10-6)*

1. 9 ft, 18 ft — 763 ft$^2$
2. 5 cm — 314 cm$^2$
3. 6 cm, 4 cm, 4 cm — 64 cm$^2$

**Find the surface area of each space figure.** *(Lesson 10-5)*

4. 16 in., 30 in. — about 4,622.08 in.$^2$
5. 2 yd, 2 yd, 6 yd — 56 yd$^2$
6. 18 in., 3 in., 6 in. — 360 in.$^2$

**Mixed Review**

**Solve using any strategy.**

7. *(9-4)* Ten basketball teams are to play each other two times in a season. How many games will be played? 90 games

**Write a function rule to describe the situation.**

8. *(8-4)* Express the number of ounces $n(d)$ as a function of the number of pounds $d$. $n(d) = 16d$

**Graph the solutions of each inequality on a number line.**

9. *(7-6)* $-6 + x \leq -3$

−5 −4 −3 −2 −1 0 1 2 3 4 5

10. *(7-6)* $-5x + 12 < -3$

−5 −4 −3 −2 −1 0 1 2 3 4 5

17. *Error Analysis* A student explains that a cylinder with radius 1 in. and height 3 in. has half the volume of one with radius 2 in. and height 3 in. Explain the student's error. **The student forgot to square the radius when calculating the area of the base.**

18. *Manufacturing* Table salt is usually packaged in cylinders.
   a. If a cylindrical box of salt has radius 4 cm and height 13.5 cm, what is its volume? What is its surface area? **678.24 cm³; 439.6 cm²**
   b. Would a rectangular prism 8 cm by 8 cm by 13.5 cm hold more or less salt than the cylindrical box? Explain. **More; such a box holds 864 cm³.**
   c. Would the rectangular prism need more or less cardboard to construct than the cylindrical box? Explain. **More; the box needs 560 cm² of cardboard.**
   d. Which type of box makes the more efficient use of cardboard? Explain. **Neither, since the ratio of the volume to the surface area is the same for both.**

19. *Critical Thinking* The two stacks of paper in the photo at the right contain the same number of sheets. The first stack forms an oblique prism; the second forms a right prism. The stacks have the same height, base, and volume. Use this information to find the volume of the oblique prism. **27 in.³**

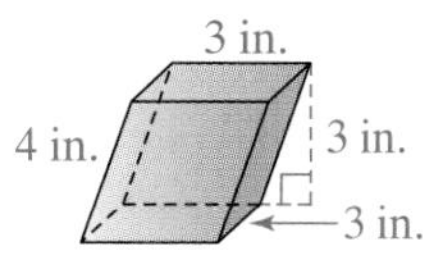


## Mixed Review

**Find the surface area of each figure, to the nearest square unit.** ***(Lesson 10-6)***

20. 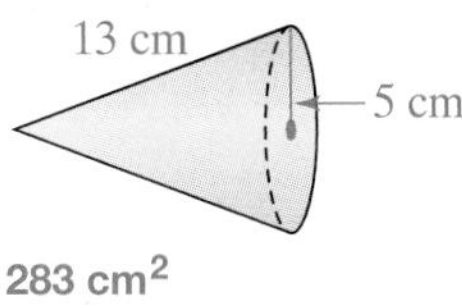

**283 cm²**

21. **120 cm²** 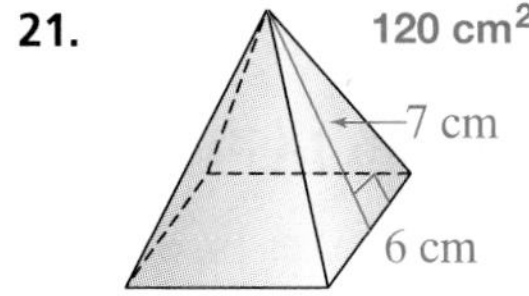


22. **61 in.²** 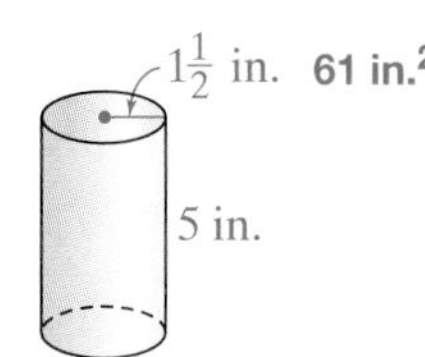


23. If $a \parallel b$, find the measures of the numbered angles in the figure at the right in terms of $x$. ***(Lesson 9-2)*** **$m\angle 4, m\angle 5, m\angle 8 = x°$; $m\angle 2, m\angle 3, m\angle 6, m\angle 7 = (180 - x)°$**

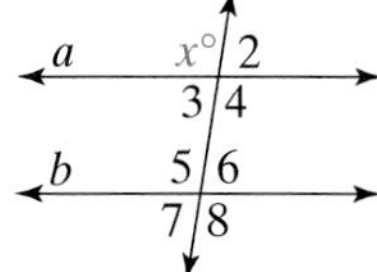


24. *Choose a Strategy* Juan has $3.80 in coins in his pocket. He has 6 quarters and 12 dimes. The rest are nickels. How many nickels does he have? **22**

CHAPTER PROJECT 10

## Activity 2 Calculating

Measure the heights of the prism and the cylinder you made for Activity 1. Use the heights and your results from Activity 1 to calculate the volume of each figure.

See also Extra Practice section.



## Project Activity 2

**Calculating** For both the rectangular prism and the cylinder, the volume is equal to the area of the base times the height. Make sure students record the volumes in cm³.

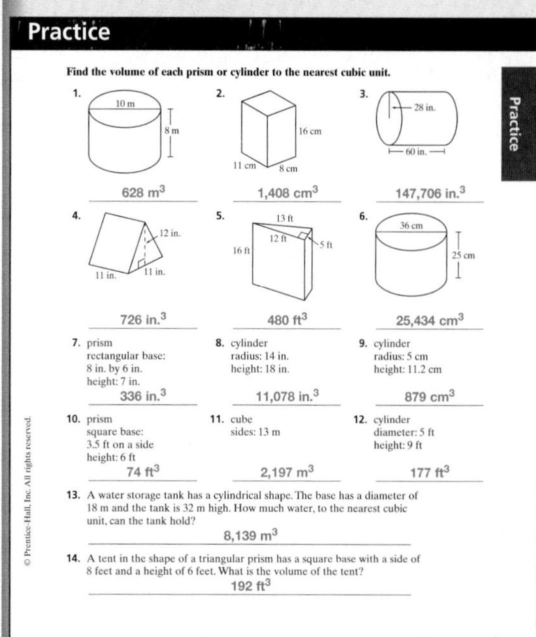

**Practice**

**Find the volume of each prism or cylinder to the nearest cubic unit.**

1. (10 m, 8 m) **628 m³**
2. (16 cm, 11 cm, 8 cm) **1,408 cm³**
3. (28 in., 60 in.) **147,706 in.³**
4. (12 in., 11 in., 11 in.) **726 in.³**
5. (13 ft, 12 ft, 5 ft, 16 ft) **480 ft³**
6. (36 cm, 25 cm) **25,434 cm³**
7. prism, rectangular base: 8 in. by 6 in., height: 7 in. **336 in.³**
8. cylinder, radius: 14 in., height: 18 in. **11,078 in.³**
9. cylinder, radius: 5 cm, height: 11.2 cm **879 cm³**
10. prism, square base: 3.5 ft on a side, height: 6 ft **74 ft³**
11. cube, sides: 13 m **2,197 m³**
12. cylinder, diameter: 5 ft, height: 9 ft **177 ft³**
13. A water storage tank has a cylindrical shape. The base has a diameter of 18 m and the tank is 32 m high. How much water, to the nearest cubic unit, can the tank hold? **8,139 m³**
14. A tent in the shape of a triangular prism has a square base with a side of 8 feet and a height of 6 feet. What is the volume of the tent? **192 ft³**



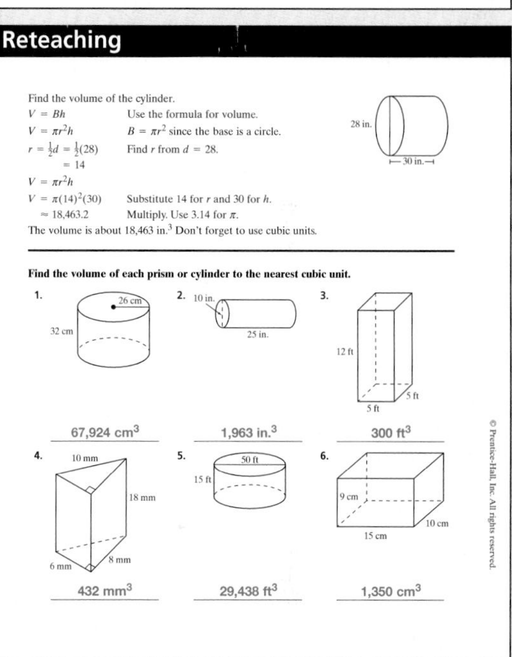

**Reteaching**

Find the volume of the cylinder.

$V = Bh$ — Use the formula for volume.
$V = \pi r^2 h$ — $B = \pi r^2$ since the base is a circle.
$r = \frac{1}{2}d = \frac{1}{2}(28) = 14$ — Find $r$ from $d = 28$.
$V = \pi r^2 h$
$V = \pi(14)^2(30)$ — Substitute 14 for $r$ and 30 for $h$.
$\approx 18{,}463.2$ — Multiply. Use 3.14 for $\pi$.

(28 in., 30 in.)

The volume is about 18,463 in.³ Don't forget to use cubic units.

**Find the volume of each prism or cylinder to the nearest cubic unit.**

1. (26 cm, 32 cm) **67,924 cm³**
2. (10 in., 25 in.) **1,963 in.³**
3. (12 ft, 5 ft, 5 ft) **300 ft³**
4. (10 mm, 18 mm, 8 mm, 6 mm) **432 mm³**
5. (50 ft, 15 ft) **29,438 ft³**
6. (9 cm, 15 cm, 10 cm) **1,350 cm³**



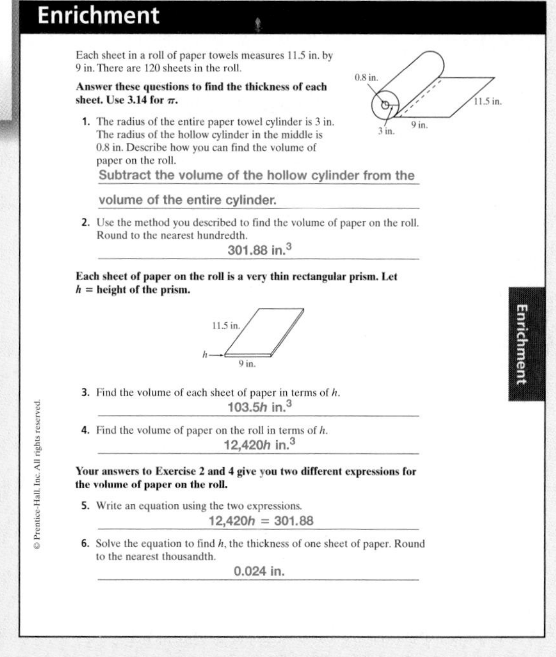

**Enrichment**

Each sheet in a roll of paper towels measures 11.5 in. by 9 in. There are 120 sheets in the roll.

**Answer these questions to find the thickness of each sheet. Use 3.14 for π.**

(0.8 in., 3 in., 9 in., 11.5 in.)

1. The radius of the entire paper towel cylinder is 3 in. The radius of the hollow cylinder in the middle is 0.8 in. Describe how you can find the volume of paper on the roll. **Subtract the volume of the hollow cylinder from the volume of the entire cylinder.**
2. Use the method you described to find the volume of paper on the roll. Round to the nearest hundredth. **301.88 in.³**

**Each sheet of paper on the roll is a very thin rectangular prism. Let $h$ = height of the prism.**

(11.5 in., 9 in., $h$)

3. Find the volume of each sheet of paper in terms of $h$. **103.5$h$ in.³**
4. Find the volume of paper on the roll in terms of $h$. **12,420$h$ in.³**

**Your answers to Exercise 2 and 4 give you two different expressions for the volume of paper on the roll.**

5. Write an equation using the two expressions. **12,420$h$ = 301.88**
6. Solve the equation to find $h$, the thickness of one sheet of paper. Round to the nearest thousandth. **0.024 in.**

# 10-8

## Getting Ready

**Materials** paper, ruler, scissors, tape

**Resources** A complete list of resources for this lesson is on p. 501H.

### Daily Skills Warm-Up

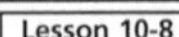

Lesson 10-8

Solve by drawing a diagram.

The 12 members of an Internet club decide to trade messages so each member has an exchange with each other member. One exchange involves one person sending a message to another and that person sending a "Reply to Author." How many exchanges will there be?

66 exchanges

### Background for the Lesson

Making a model to represent a problem is useful when you need to see, examine, or measure to solve a problem. Making a model can help you find the volume of a cardboard box by relating the three-dimensional object both to its volume and to the polygons that are its parts. A two-dimensional sketch, plan, or blueprint is still an abstract representation of a space figure. When you build a model, you create a concrete approximation of the actual object, although the size and exact materials may differ. If the model you build is a fairly accurate scale model, you can take measurements in order to answer questions.

## 1 Focus

### Connecting to Students' Lives

Discuss careers where making models is a common function of the job (building boats and planes, architecture, landscape design, sculpture, fashion design, safety engineering). Encourage students to think of computer models as well as physical models.



# 10-8

# Make a Model

**Problem Solving Strategies**

Account for All Possibilities
Draw a Diagram
Look for a Pattern
Make a Model
Make a Table
Simplify a Problem
Simulate a Problem
Solve by Graphing
Try, Test, Revise
Use Multiple Strategies
Work Backward
Write an Equation
Write a Proportion

***Math Strategies in Action*** Architects build and use models when they plan. When they design buildings, they experiment with models. When they design packaging, they first create prototype models.

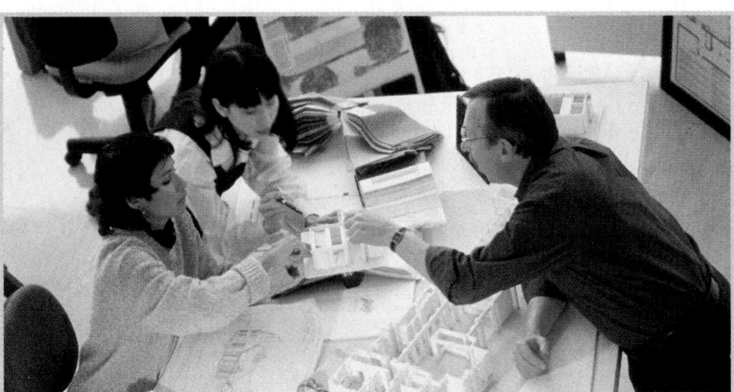

**SAMPLE PROBLEM**

A box company makes boxes to hold popcorn. Each box is made by cutting the square corners out of a rectangular sheet of cardboard. The rectangle is $8\frac{1}{2}$ in. by 11 in. What are the dimensions of the box that will hold the most popcorn if the square corners have side lengths 1 in., 2 in., 3 in., and 4 in.?

**Read**

1. What is the goal of the problem? The goal is to find the dimensions of the box that will hold the most popcorn.
2. What information do you have to help you build a model? The size of the piece of cardboard is known, as well as the size of the square corners.

**Plan**

To find the size that will hold the greatest amount of popcorn, you must find the dimensions that will give you the greatest volume.



## Tools to Monitor Progress

**BEFORE THE LESSON**

**To check prerequisite skills:**

- Finding areas

**Skills Intervention Kit,** Geometry

**DURING THE LESSON**

**To check understanding:**

- **Additional Sample Problem** A manufacturer makes cones by cutting a paper circle in half and bending it to make a cone with a circumference of 3 inches. To make a cone with a larger opening, the manufacturer begins with a paper circle congruent to the first paper circle and cuts out a pie-shaped piece, leaving $\frac{2}{3}$ of the original

Build four boxes using sheets of $8\frac{1}{2}$-in. by 11-in. paper. Test four whole-number lengths of cuts.

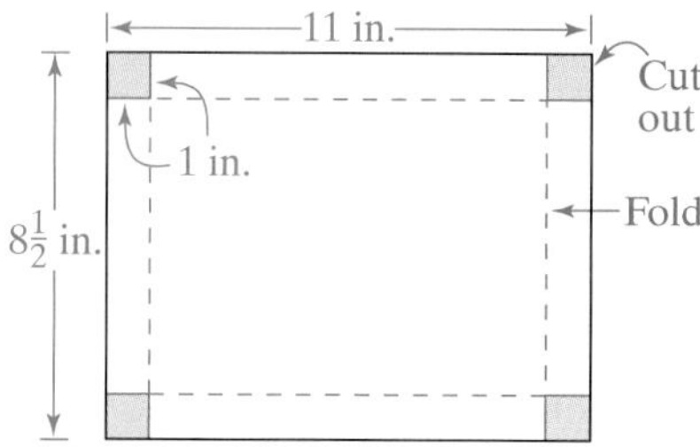


3a. $6\frac{1}{2}$ in. by 9 in. by 1 in.

3. **a.** What are the dimensions of the box with corners 1 in. by 1 in.?
   **b.** What is the volume of this box? 58.5 in.$^3$

4. When you cut a 2-in. by 2-in. square from each corner, what effect does that have on the length, width, and height of the box? The length and width are decreased by 4 in., and the height is increased by 2 in.

## Solve

Measure to find the dimensions of each of your boxes. Then find the volume of each box.

5. Which box has the greatest volume? The box with 2-in. by 2-in. corners.
6. Is it possible to create a box that has 5-in. by 5-in. corners? Explain. No, such a box would require more cardboard than is actually available in an $8\frac{1}{2}$-in. by 11-in. piece of cardboard.

## Look Back

A table is another way to organize your information and solve the problem. List the size of the cut, and then figure the length, width, and height of the box. Find each volume.

7.

| Size of Cut | Length | Width | Height | Volume |
|---|---|---|---|---|
| 1 in. | 9 in. | 6.5 in. | 1 in. | 58.5 in.$^3$ |
| 2 in. | 7 ■ | 4.5 ■ | 2 ■ | 63 ■ |
| 3 in. | 5 ■ | 2.5 ■ | 3 ■ | 37.5 ■ |
| 4 in. | 3 ■ | 0.5 ■ | 4 ■ | 6 ■ |

Use a table to find the volume of a box if the square corners are $1\frac{1}{2}$ in., $2\frac{1}{2}$ in., or $3\frac{1}{2}$ in.

8. Did you find dimensions of a box that holds a greater volume than you did in Question 5? Which dimensions are they? Yes, $5\frac{1}{2}$ in. by 8 in. by $1\frac{1}{2}$ in.



# 2 Teach

## Teaching Notes

As you discuss the Sample Problem, have students look at the diagram of the model to help them understand the situation. Give students time to make the model themselves and to try out the solutions so that they can develop the understanding of the connection between the 2-D abstract drawings and the concrete 3-D model.

### Sample Problem

**Build understanding.** Ask: As the area of the square corners increases, what happens to the areas of the base and sides? What happens to the volume? As the area of the square corners increases, the inside areas decrease, and the volume first increases, then decreases.

**Visual Learning** Bring popcorn to class and have students fill their model boxes to see which one holds the most, and thus has the greatest volume.

**Math Reasoning** Would the 2-in. cut result in the largest volume if your original piece of paper were 16 in. by 22 in. but the other conditions of the problem stayed the same? Explain. No, the largest volume for that piece of paper results from a corner cut of 3 in.

**Error Prevention** When you make models, measure and cut carefully so that your result is accurate.

circle to make the cone. What is the circumference of the opening of the new cone?
4 in.

How much greater is the area of the second cone than the first cone?
≈ 0.5 in.$^2$

## AFTER THE LESSON

**To assess knowledge:**

**Lesson Quiz**

You have 36 ft of fence to enclose a garden. What shape (rectangular or circular) and dimensions should you use in order to enclose the most area? a circle with a radius of about 5.7 ft

- For enrichment and reteaching options see Resources on p. 501H.

# 3 Practice/Assess

## Assignment Guide

Core 1–7
✪ Extension 8

Mixed Review can be assigned at any time for maintenance.

### Exercises

**Test Prep Exercise 5** Notice how the net must be folded. None of the circles will be next to the side of the triangle.

### ✪ Challenge

Suppose you had to guess how many dried beans it would take to fill a 55-gal barrel. How might you estimate the answer? **Sample answer: Build a model that is much smaller, but proportional, and fill it with beans. Then multiply the number of beans by the ratio of the model to the actual barrel.**

### Closure

You can solve some problems by making a model.

# Exercises

## Check Understanding

**Explain how to model each situation.**

1. You want to find how the length of a pendulum affects the time the pendulum takes to swing back and forth. Explain how you would model the situation. **1. Use several different lengths of string and a single weight. Record the time it takes the weight to swing back and forth when tied to each of the strings.**

2. Newspapers, books, and magazines often are printed in groups of 8, 16, or 32 pages, called signatures. The diagram at the right shows how pages should be positioned for an 8-page signature. The pages are positioned to print on both sides of the paper that is fed through the printing press. When the paper is folded, the pages are in order. Make a model to show one way to position the pages in a 16-page book. **Answers may vary. See margin for sample.**

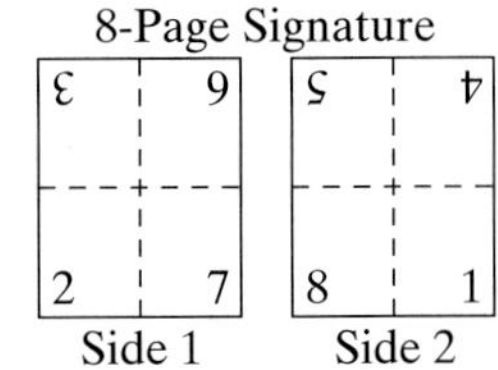


**Solve by making a model.**

3. *Packaging* A company packages snack mix in cylindrical tubes. Each tube will be made from a rectangle of cardboard. The bases of the cylinder will be plastic. The cardboard comes in $8\frac{1}{2}$-in. by 11-in. sheets. To hold the greatest amount of mix, should the longer side be the height, or should the shorter side? Justify your answer. **The shorter side should be the height because it will yield a volume of 81.8 in.$^3$, and using the longer side as the height yields a volume of only 63.3 in.$^3$.**

## Practice and Problem Solving

**Solve using any strategy.**

4. You cut square corners off a piece of cardboard with dimensions 16 in. by 20 in. You then fold the cardboard to create a box with no lid. To the nearest inch, what dimensions will give you the greatest volume? **10 in. by 14 in. by 3 in.**

5. **TEST PREP** The figure at the right represents the net of an unfolded box with designs on several panels. Below are three drawings of boxes with designs. Select the box that matches the net. **C**

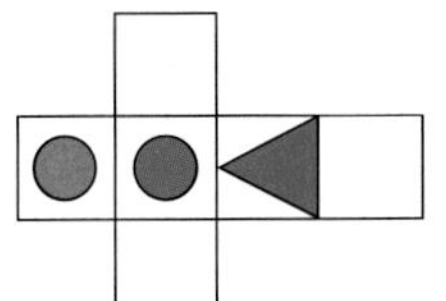

A. B. 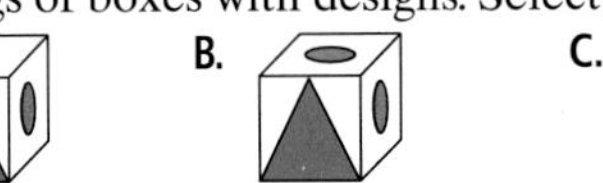

C. 

6. A dog owner wants to use 200 ft of fencing to enclose the greatest possible area for his dog. He wants the fenced area to be rectangular. What dimensions should he use? **50 ft by 50 ft**



## Daily Cumulative Review

**Find the volume of each prism or cylinder.** *(Lesson 10-7)*

1. about 1,004.8 cm$^3$
2. 67.575 yd$^3$
3. 576 ft$^3$

**Find the surface area of each space figure. Give your answers to the nearest square unit.** *(Lesson 10-6)*

4. 201 yd$^2$
5. 324 ft$^2$
6. 2,550 in.$^2$

**Mixed Review**

**Find the area of each figure.**

7. *(10-1)* 36 m$^2$
8. *(10-2)* 62.5 in.$^2$
9. *(10-3)* about 1,661.06 yd$^2$

**Given that $\triangle ABC \cong \triangle DEF$, complete the following.**

10. *(9-5)* $\angle B \cong$ $\angle E$
11. *(9-5)* $m\angle F =$ $m\angle C$
12. *(9-5)* $\angle C \cong$ $\angle F$
13. *(9-5)* $\overline{ED} \cong$ $\overline{BA}$
14. *(9-5)* $\angle D \cong$ $\angle A$
15. *(9-5)* $m\angle E =$ $m\angle B$
16. *(9-5)* $FE =$ 5
17. *(9-5)* $\triangle CBA \cong$ $\triangle FED$



## Alternative Assessment

Have students find a real-world problem that they can solve by building a model. Ask students to research the problem, build a model, then record their findings. Students can present their problems and models to the class.

**2. Answers may vary. Sample:**

| Sheet 1 front | Sheet 1 back | Sheet 2 front | Sheet 2 back |
|---|---|---|---|
| 6, 8 / 16, 1 | 7, 10 / 2, 15 | 11, 9 / 14, 3 | 5, 12 / 4, 13 |

7. The length of a rectangle is twice its width. The perimeter of the rectangle is 90 cm. What are the length and width? 30 cm, 15 cm

8. *Volume* The figure at the right shows a 3-by-3-by-3 cube.

a. How many 1-by-1-by-1 cubes are there? 27
b. How many 2-by-2-by-2-cubes are there? 8
c. How many 3-by-3-by-3 cubes are there? 1
d. How many 3-by-3-by-3 cubes would be in a 5-by-5-by-5 cube? 27

## Mixed Review

**Find the volume of each figure, to the nearest tenth.** ***(Lesson 10-7)***

9. 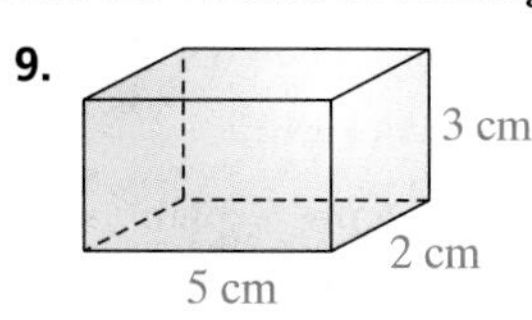

30 cm³

10. 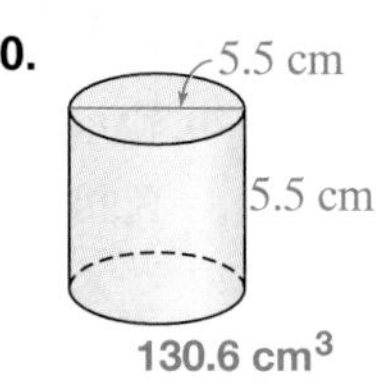

130.6 cm³

11. 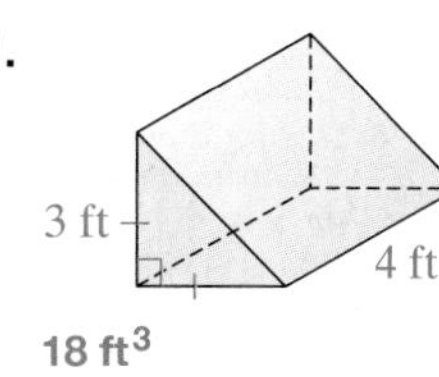

18 ft³

**Find the solutions of each equation when $x$ is 0, 1, and $-1$.** ***(Lesson 8-2)***

12. $2x - y = 10$ $-10, -8, -12$
13. $5x + y = 15$ 15, 10, 20
14. $2x + 3y = 6$ $2, 1\frac{1}{3}, 2\frac{2}{3}$

15. The wheels of a racing bike are about 70 cm in diameter. What is the circumference of the wheels? ***(Lesson 9-6)*** about 220 cm

## Checkpoint 2 — Lessons 10-4 through 10-8

**Name each space figure, and find its surface area, to the nearest square unit.**

1. 2 cm, 6 cm, 2 cm — square prism, 56 cm²

2. 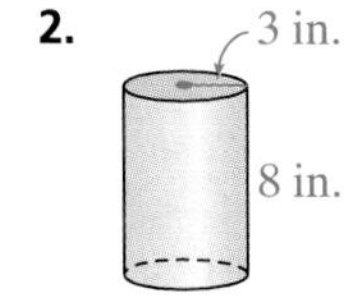

cylinder, 207 in.²

3. 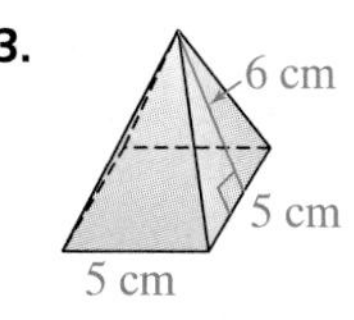

square pyramid, 85 cm²

4. 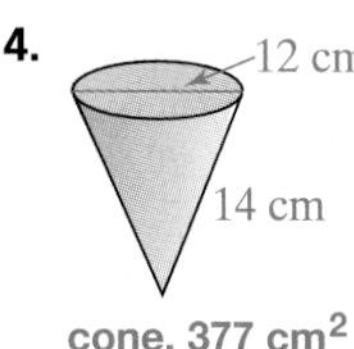

cone, 377 cm²

**Find the volume of each figure, to the nearest tenth.**

5. 3.1 cm, 3.6 cm, 7 cm — 78.1 cm³

6. 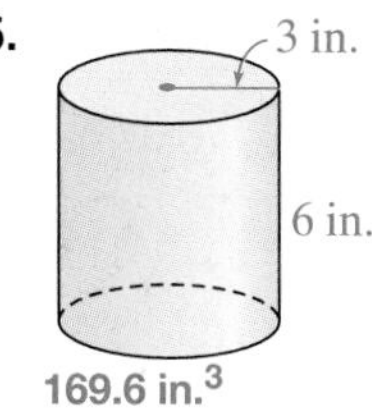

169.6 in.³

7. 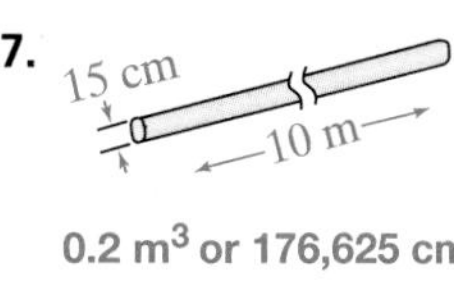

0.2 m³ or 176,625 cm³

8. *Open-ended* Choose a space figure. Draw its net. Check students' work.



## Checkpoint

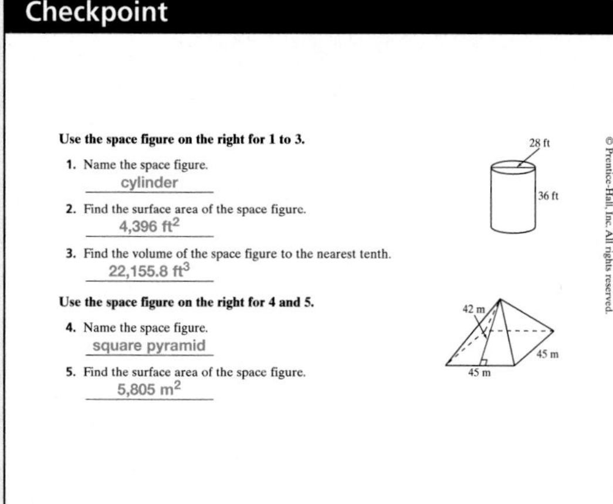

**Use the space figure on the right for 1 to 3.**

1. Name the space figure. cylinder
2. Find the surface area of the space figure. 4,396 ft²
3. Find the volume of the space figure to the nearest tenth. 22,155.8 ft³

**Use the space figure on the right for 4 and 5.**

4. Name the space figure. square pyramid
5. Find the surface area of the space figure. 5,805 m²





## Practice

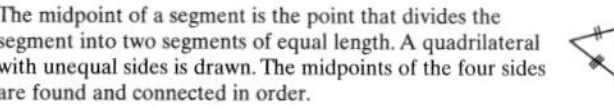

**Solve by making a model.**

1. A narrow strip of paper is twisted once, then joined at the ends with glue or tape. The strip is then cut lengthwise along the dotted line shown.

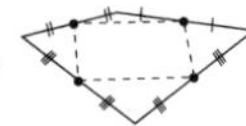

a. Guess the results. Answers may vary.
b. Make and cut a model as directed. What are the results? A single loop results.

2. The midpoint of a segment is the point that divides the segment into two segments of equal length. A quadrilateral with unequal sides is drawn. The midpoints of the four sides are found and connected in order.

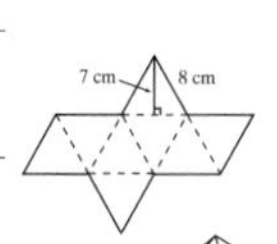

a. Guess what kind of quadrilateral is formed. Answers may vary.
b. Draw four quadrilaterals with unequal sides and connect the midpoints of adjacent sides. What kind of quadrilaterals appear to have been formed? parallelograms

3. A penny with Lincoln's head upright is rolled along the edge of another penny as shown in the figure.

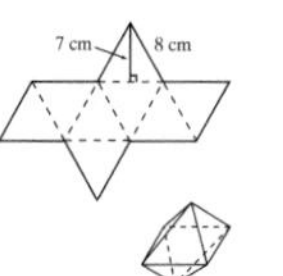

a. At the end, do you think Lincoln will be right-side-up or upside-down? Answers may vary.
b. Conduct an experiment to find out. What are your results? Lincoln is upright.

4. A net for an octahedron is shown. All the sides are congruent, equilateral triangles. Cut and fold on the dotted lines. Find the surface area of the octahedron. 224 cm²

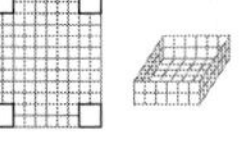




## Reteaching

Suppose you cut square corners off a piece of cardboard with dimensions 10 cm by 12 cm and fold up the sides to make an open box. To the nearest centimeter, what dimensions will give you the greatest volume?

Use a model to solve the problem. Cut out a 10 unit by 12 unit piece of grid paper. Cut a 1 by 1 square out of each corner. Fold to form a box.

The height of the box is the same as the height of the corner, 1 unit.

The length is 12 units minus the two corners or $12 - 2 = 10$ units. The width is 10 units minus the two corners or $10 - 2 = 8$.

$V = Bh = 10 \cdot 8 \cdot 1 = 80$ units³

Now cut 2 units by 2 unit squares out of the corners and fold the box.

$h = 2$

$l = 12 - 2(2) = 12 - 4 = 8$

$w = 10 - 2(2) = 10 - 4 = 6$

$V = Bh = 8 \cdot 6 \cdot 2 = 96$ units³

Now cut 3 unit by 3 unit squares out of the corners.

$V = (6 \cdot 4) \cdot 3 = 72$ units³

Then cut 4 unit by 4 unit squares out of the corners.

$V = (4 \cdot 2) \cdot 4 = 32$ units³

It is not possible to make a box by cutting 5 unit by 5 unit squares out of the corners. There would be no width.

So, to the nearest centimeter, a 2 cm by 6 cm by 8 cm box gives the greatest volume.

**Suppose you cut square corners off a piece of cardboard with dimensions 12 cm by 15 cm to make an open box. Use a model to find the dimensions, to the nearest centimeter of each box. Record your work in the table.**

| | Length of side of corner | Length | Width | Height | Volume |
|---|---|---|---|---|---|
| 1. | 1 cm | 13 cm | 10 cm | 1 cm | 130 cm³ |
| 2. | 2 cm | 11 cm | 8 cm | 2 cm | 176 cm³ |
| 3. | 3 cm | 9 cm | 6 cm | 3 cm | 162 cm³ |
| 4. | 4 cm | 7 cm | 4 cm | 4 cm | 112 cm³ |
| 5. | 5 cm | 5 cm | 2 cm | 5 cm | 50 cm³ |

6. Which dimensions give the greatest volume? 2 cm by 8 cm by 11 cm



## Enrichment

Polyhedra are space figures with polygons as sides. Regular polyhedra have regular polygons as sides and a special arrangement at each vertex. There are only five regular polyhedra.

You can use the patterns on this page to construct models of three of the five regular polyhedra.

Cut out the patterns. Fold on the dotted lines and fasten the edges with tape to construct the models.

Regular Tetrahedron

Regular Octahedron

Regular Dodecahedron

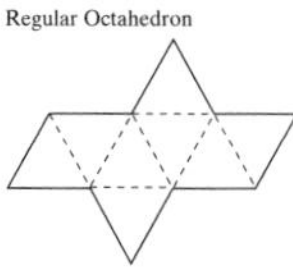

**Analyze Euler's Formula for these regular polyhedra.**

| | Regular Figure | Number of faces ($F$) | Number of vertices ($V$) | Number of edges ($E$) | $F + V - E$ |
|---|---|---|---|---|---|
| 1. | Tetrahedron | 4 | 4 | 6 | 2 |
| 2. | Octahedron | 8 | 6 | 12 | 2 |
| 3. | Dodecahedron | 12 | 15 | 25 | 2 |

4. Does $F + V - E = 2$ for each regular polyhedron? yes

# Standardized Test Prep

Standardized tests, such as those administered for state assessment, SAT9, TerraNova™, ITBS, MAT7, or CAT5, may include multiple choice questions, free-response questions, and open-ended questions.

**Multiple Choice Questions** are followed usually by four choices, one of which is correct.

**Exercises 1–7** are multiple choice questions.

**Free-Response Questions** do not give answer choices. Student must provide the one correct answer on their own.

**Exercises 8–11** are free-response questions.

## Resources

See p. 501G for a list of assessment options.

## Test-Taking Tip

A common question involves what happens to area when you multiply linear measures (Question 9, for example). If the side of a square is multiplied by 3, its new area is 9 times the old area.

### Test-Taking Tips on Transparency

Sometimes it is easiest to start with an end result and work backward.

*Example* What is the prime factorization of 48?

A. $6 \times 2^3$ B. $2^4 \times 3$ C. $4 \times 12$ D. $2^5$

Try each choice:

Since 6 is not a prime number, A is wrong.

Since 4 is not a prime number, C is wrong.

Compare B and D. Is 48 divisible by 3? Yes. So, D is wrong.

The answer is $2^4 \times 3$, or choice B.

Work backward to find the answer. Explain your reasoning.

1. Which number is composite, less than 50, and has a tens digit greater than its ones digit?
   A. 51 B. 13 C. 28 D. 32
2. Carlos has $\frac{2}{3}$ of a bushel of apples, weighing 26 pounds. How much does a bushel of apples weigh?
   F. 20 pounds G. 50 pounds
   H. 39 pounds J. 33 pounds



# Standardized Test Prep

## Multiple Choice

**Choose the best answer.**

1. Find the area of a circle that has a 7-ft diameter. Use 3.14 for $\pi$. A
   A. 38.465 ft$^2$ B. 153.86 ft$^2$
   C. 76.93 ft$^2$ D. 21.98 ft$^2$
2. What is the area of the trapezoid? H

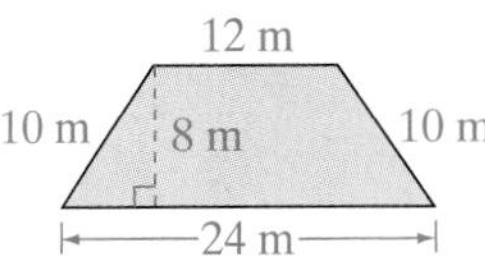


   F. 46 m$^2$ G. 120 m$^2$
   H. 144 m$^2$ J. 288 m$^2$
3. Each edge of a cube is 40 cm long. Find the surface area of the cube in square inches. Use 2.5 cm $\approx$ 1 in. D
   A. 3,840 in.$^2$ B. 9,600 in.$^2$
   C. 256 in.$^2$ D. 1,536 in.$^2$
4. A cylinder has a height of 10 in. Its base has a radius of 2.5 in. Find the cylinder's surface area. Use 3.14 for $\pi$. J
   F. 215.875 in.$^2$ G. 235.5 in.$^2$
   H. 188.4 in.$^2$ J. 196.25 in.$^2$
5. The volume of a rectangular box is 455 in.$^3$ The length of the box is 13 in. The width of the box is 7 in. How tall is the box? B
   A. 364 in.$^3$ B. 5 in.
   C. 6 in. D. 5 in.$^3$
6. Shari's recipe calls for 8 oz of dry milk powder. She recalls that 1 oz equals 28.4 g. How many ounces are in a 210-g can of milk powder? H
   F. between 5 and 6
   G. between 6 and 7
   H. between 7 and 8
   J. between 8 and 9
7. What is the surface area of the figure at the right? D

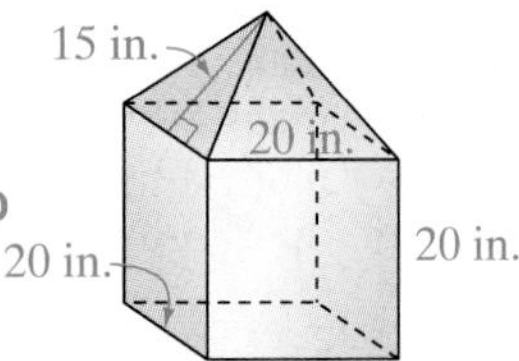


   A. 2,150 in.$^2$ B. 3,200 in.$^2$
   C. 3,000 in.$^2$ D. 2,600 in.$^2$

## Free Response

**For Exercises 8–11, show your work.**

8. Find the area of each figure. Explain two ways to find the area of the second figure.

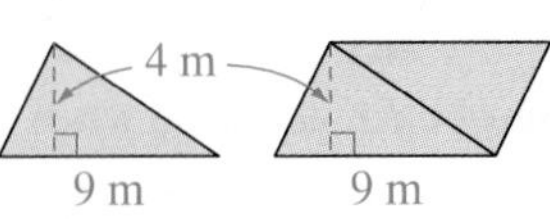


   18 m$^2$, 36 m$^2$; find the area of the triangle and multipl by 2 or find the area of the parallelogram
9. If the diameter of a circle is doubled, how are the area and the circumference of the circle affected? Use examples to explain.
   The area quadruples and the circumference doubles.
10. The cube below shows a rectangular cross section. Copy the cube and draw the following cross-sections.
    a. an equilateral triangle See margin.
    b. a square See margin.

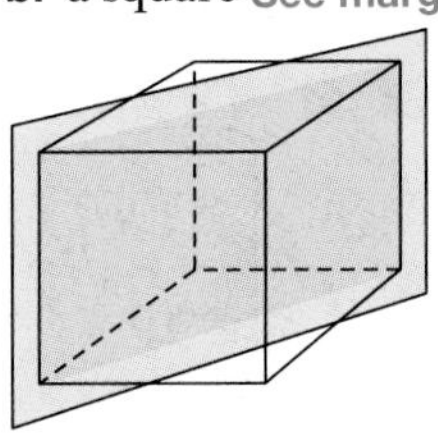

11. a. The circumference $C$ of a circle is expressed as a function of its diameter $d$ in the equation $C = \pi d$. Graph the equation. See margin.
    b. Find the slope of the line. $\pi$
    c. Explain the significance of the slope. The slope is the rate of change of $C$ per unit $d$.



10a.

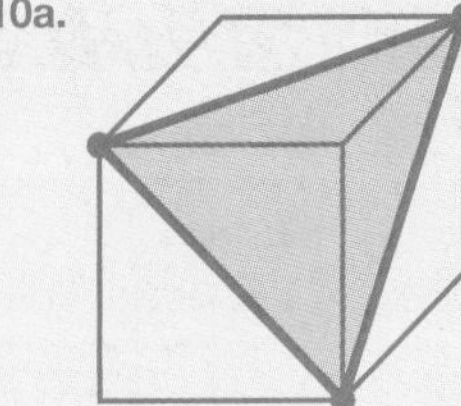

10b.

11.

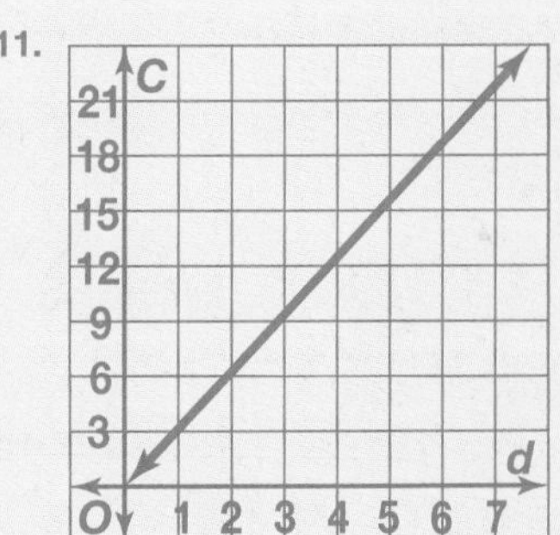

# Volume: Pyramids, Cones, and Spheres

## PART 1 Finding the Volumes of Cones and Pyramids

You can fill three cones with sand and pour the contents into a cylinder with the same height and radius. You will fill the cylinder evenly to the top.

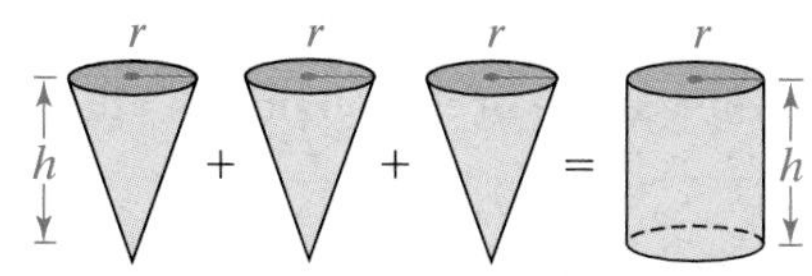


The volume of the cone is one third the volume of the cylinder. The same relationship is true of a pyramid and a prism with the same base and height.

### Volume of a Cone and of a Pyramid

The formula for volume of a cone or a pyramid is $\frac{1}{3}$ the base area $B$ times the height $h$.

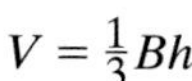

$V = \frac{1}{3}Bh$

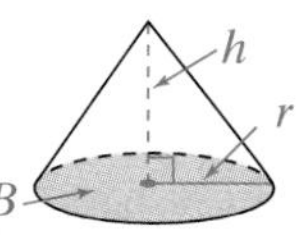


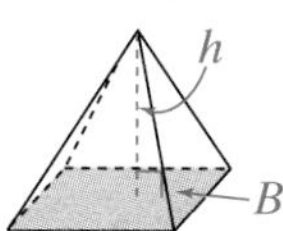


### EXAMPLE 1

**Find the volume of the cone at the right.**

$V = \frac{1}{3}Bh$ Use the formula for volume.

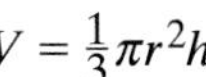

$V = \frac{1}{3}\pi r^2 h$ $B = \pi r^2$.

$\approx \frac{1}{3}(3.14)(3)^2(10)$ Replace $\pi$ with 3.14, $r$ with 3, and $h$ with 10.

$= 94.2$ Simplify.

10 ft

3 ft

The volume of the cone is about 94 ft$^3$.

### TRY THIS

1. Find the volume, to the nearest cubic unit, of a cone with height 5 cm and radius of base 2 cm. 21 cm$^3$

# 10-9

**What You'll Learn**

1 To find the volumes of pyramids and cones

2 To find the volumes of spheres

**. . . And Why**

To find out how much water is displaced by a space figure



# Tools to Monitor Progress

**BEFORE THE LESSON**

**To check prerequisite skills:**

- Finding volume

**Skills Intervention Kit**, Geometry

**DURING THE LESSON**

**To check understanding:**

**Try This** exercises on student page

- **Additional Examples 1–2**

Find the volume of the pyramid to the right with a height of 12 m. about 256 m$^3$

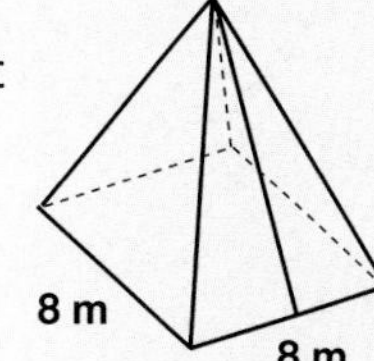


# 10-9

## Getting Ready

**Key Terms and Symbols** volume of a cone and pyramid, volume of a sphere

**Resources** A complete list of resources for this lesson is on p. 501H.

### Daily Skills Warm-Up

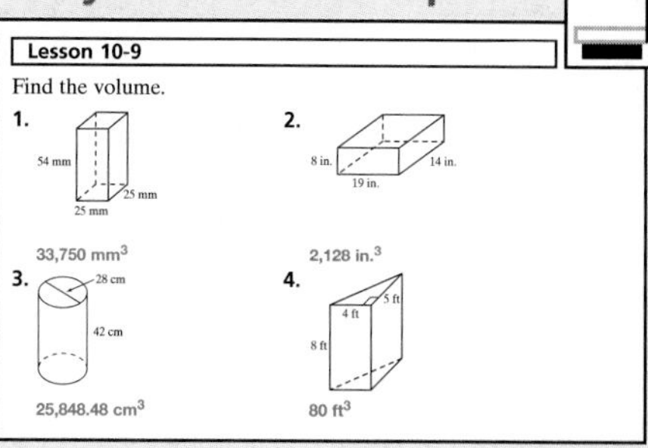

Lesson 10-9

Find the volume.

1. 54 mm, 25 mm, 25 mm — 33,750 mm$^3$
2. 8 in., 14 in., 19 in. — 2,128 in.$^3$
3. 28 cm, 42 cm — 25,848.48 cm$^3$
4. 4 ft, 5 ft, 8 ft — 80 ft$^3$

### Background for the Lesson

The formula for the volumes of a cone and pyramid is based on the fact that a cone has $\frac{1}{3}$ of the volume of a cylinder with the same base and height, and a pyramid has $\frac{1}{3}$ of the volume of a prism with the same base and height. It is important, however to notice that the formula, $V = \frac{1}{3}Bh$, contains the height of the cone (which is not the same as the slant height of the lateral surface). The height of a cone is the length of the segment from the vertex perpendicular to the base.

## 1 Focus

### Connecting to Students' Lives

Discuss whether any students have ever used a funnel to pour some substance from one container to another. Have them name the geometric shape that is closest to a funnel.

### Connecting to Prior Knowledge

In Lesson 10-7, students learned how to calculate the volumes of cylinders and prisms. In this lesson, students find the volumes of cones and pyramids. In Lesson 11-2, students continue learning about geometric figures by looking at special relationships in right triangles.

# 2 Teach

## Part 1 Teaching Notes

You may want to use a cone full of rice and a cylinder constructed of paper to demonstrate that three of the cones of rice will fill a cylinder of the same base and height.

**Error Prevention** The height used in the formula for the volume of a cone and pyramid is the height of the pyramid from the vertex to the base. Students may confuse this with the slant height, which they used in finding the surface area of pyramids and cones.

### Example 1

**Build understanding.** Ask: Since the radius of this cone is 3, and the whole expression must be multiplied by $\frac{1}{3}$, why can't the 3 and $\frac{1}{3}$ multiply to 1? You could simplify that way, but $3^2$ is $3 \bullet 3$ so you could only use one 3 to multiply by $\frac{1}{3}$.

### Example 2

**Build understanding.** Ask: Suppose the pyramid were rectangular instead of square. How would this affect the formula for the volume? The formula would stay the same, but you would have to multiply the base and height of the rectangle to get the area of the base before multiplying by the height.

## Part 2 Teaching Notes

Finding the volume of a sphere involves raising the radius to a power of 3. Have a student volunteer explain what this means.

### Example 3

**Build understanding.** Ask: Suppose the snowman is made of three spheres, each with a radius of 1.5 ft. How tall would it be? 9 ft

**Auditory Learning** Have students work with a partner who names a solid which the other person then sketches and labels to show which facts are needed to find the volume.

### EXAMPLE 2

**Find the volume of the square pyramid.**



| | |
|---|---|
| $V = \frac{1}{3}Bh$ | Use the volume formula. |
| $V = \frac{1}{3}s^2h$ | $B = s^2$. |
| $= \frac{1}{3}(6)^2(10)$ | Replace $s$ with 6 and $h$ with 10. |
| $= 120$ | Simplify. |

The volume of the pyramid is 120 ft$^3$.

**TRY THIS**

2. Find the volume of a square pyramid that has a side of 5 ft and a height of 20 ft. 167 ft$^3$

## PART 2 Finding the Volumes of Spheres

Below is the formula for the volume of a sphere.

**Volume of a Sphere**

The volume $V$ of a sphere with radius $r$ is $\frac{4}{3}\pi$ times the cube of the radius.

$$V = \frac{4}{3}\pi r^3$$

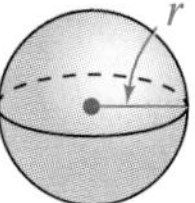


REAL-WORLD   CONNECTION

### EXAMPLE 3

**You build a snowman with spheres of snow. How much snow do you need to make the bottom sphere?**

| | |
|---|---|
| $V = \frac{4}{3}\pi r^3$ | Use the volume formula. |
| $\approx \frac{4}{3}(3.14)(1.5)^3$ | Replace $\pi$ with 3.14 and $r$ with 1.5. |
| $= 14.13$ | Simplify. |

The volume of the sphere of snow is about 14 ft$^3$.

**TRY THIS** Find the volume of each sphere.

3. radius = 15 m 14,130 m$^3$

4. diameter = 7,000 mi 179,503,333,333 mi$^3$



- **Additional Example 3**
  Earth has an average radius of 3,963 mi. Assume that Earth is a sphere and find its volume. about 260,579,713,159 mi$^3$

## AFTER THE LESSON

**To assess knowledge: Lesson Quiz**

1. Find the volume of a cone with a diameter of 9 cm and a height of 12 cm. about 254 cm$^3$
2. A basketball has a diameter of 10 in. Find its volume. about 523 in.$^3$

- For enrichment and reteaching options see Resources on p. 501H.

# Exercises

## Check Understanding

**Find the volume of each figure, to the nearest cubic unit.**

1. 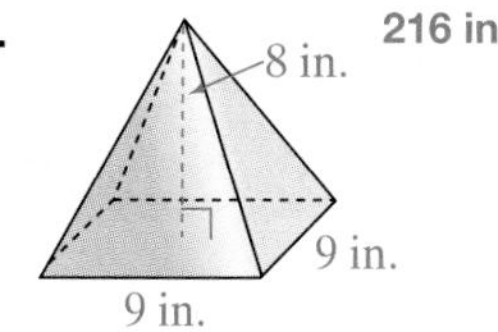

216 in.$^3$

2. 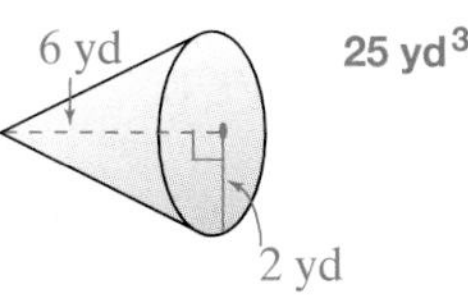

25 yd$^3$

3. 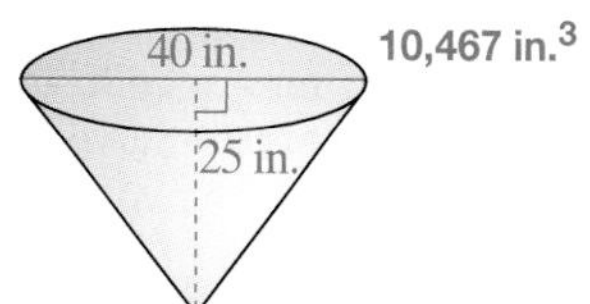

10,467 in.$^3$

4. 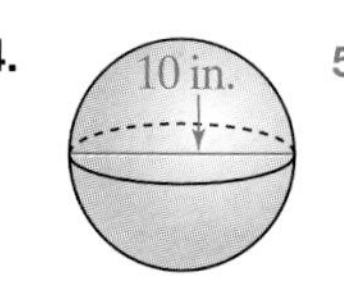

523 in.$^3$

5. 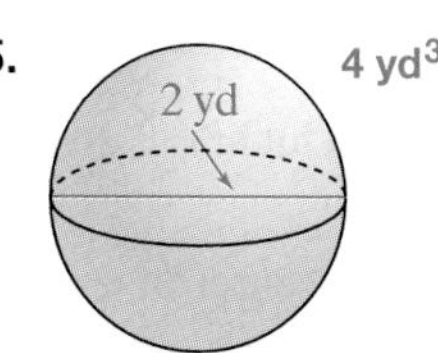

4 yd$^3$

6. 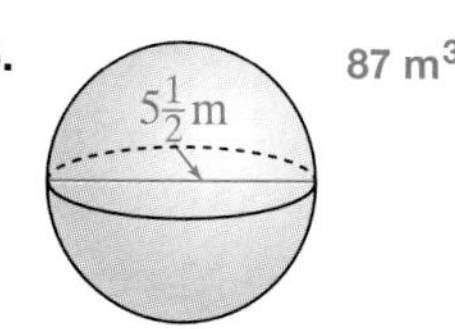

87 m$^3$

7. How many cones of radius 1 m and height 1 m have total volume equal to the volume of a sphere with radius 1 m? 4

## Practice and Problem Solving

**Find the volume of each figure, to the nearest cubic unit.**

8. 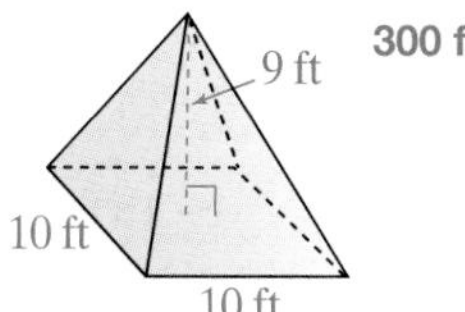

300 ft$^3$

9. 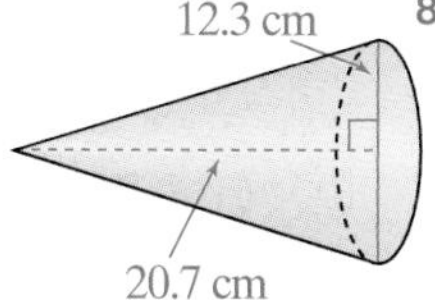

819 cm$^3$

10. 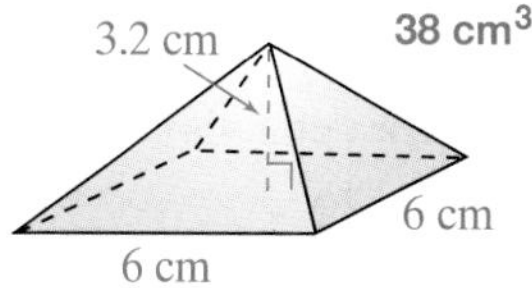

38 cm$^3$

11. 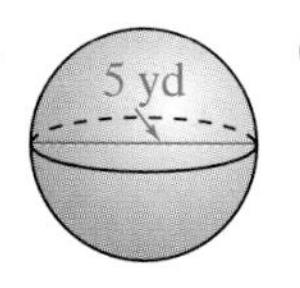

65 yd$^3$

12. 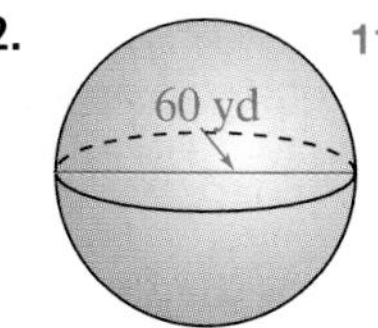

113,040 yd$^3$

13. 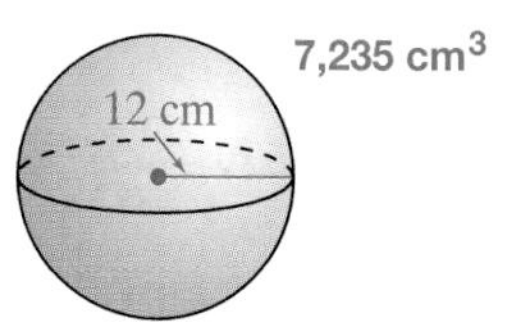

7,235 cm$^3$

14. Tennis balls with a diameter of 2.5 in. are sold in cans of three. The can is a cylinder. What is the volume of the space in the can not occupied by tennis balls? Assume the balls touch the can on the sides, top, and bottom. 12.3 in.$^3$

## Alternative Assessment

Have students create and solve a problem that involves either the relationship between the volumes of a cone and a cylinder with the same base, or the relationship between a pyramid and prism with the same base.

# 3 Practice/Assess

## Assignment Guide

To provide flexible scheduling, this lesson can be divided into parts.

**Part 1**

**Core** 1–3, 8–10, 20

**Extension** 15

**Part 2**

**Core** 4–7, 11–14, 17–19

**Extension** 16

Mixed Review can be assigned at any time for maintenance.

## Exercises

**Exercise 14** This exercise could be done in groups. A sketch may be helpful.

**Test Prep Exercise 20** Draw a sketch and label it before choosing.

## Challenge

How tall must a cone be if it is to hold the same amount of liquid as a sphere with a diameter of 8 in.? Assume that the base of the cone and the sphere have the same diameter. about 16 in.

## Closure

Volume is the measure of how much a space figure could hold if you could fill it. To find the volumes of pyramids and cones, use the formula $V = \frac{1}{3}Bh$. To find the volume of a sphere, use $V = \frac{4}{3}\pi r^3$.

## Daily Cumulative Review

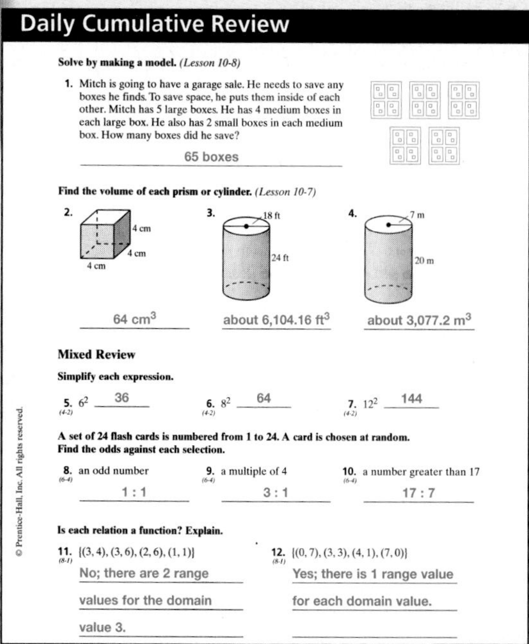

**Solve by making a model.** *(Lesson 10-8)*

1. Mitch is going to have a garage sale. He needs to save any boxes he finds. To save space, he puts them inside of each other. Mitch has 5 large boxes. He has 4 medium boxes in each large box. He also has 2 small boxes in each medium box. How many boxes did he save? 65 boxes

**Find the volume of each prism or cylinder.** *(Lesson 10-7)*

2. 4 cm, 4 cm, 4 cm — 64 cm$^3$

3. 18 ft, 24 ft — about 6,104.16 ft$^3$

4. 7 m, 20 m — about 3,077.2 m$^3$

**Mixed Review**

**Simplify each expression.**

5. $6^2$ (4-2) 36

6. $8^2$ (4-2) 64

7. $12^2$ (4-2) 144

**A set of 24 flash cards is numbered from 1 to 24. A card is chosen at random. Find the odds against each selection.**

8. an odd number (6-4) 1 : 1

9. a multiple of 4 (6-4) 3 : 1

10. a number greater than 17 (6-4) 17 : 7

**Is each relation a function? Explain.**

11. {(3, 4), (3, 6), (2, 6), (1, 1)} (8-1) No; there are 2 range values for the domain value 3.

12. {(0, 7), (3, 3), (4, 1), (7, 0)} (8-1) Yes; there is 1 range value for each domain value.

## Practice

**Find the volume of each figure to the nearest cubic unit.**

1. 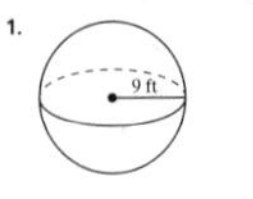

3,052 ft³

2. 16 in., 18 in., 18 in.
1,728 in.³

3. 15 in., 9 in.
1,272 in.³

4. 4 m, 5 m, 5 m
33 m³

5. 8 mm, 4 mm
33 mm³

6. 22 cm
5,572 cm³

7. square-based pyramid
$s = 9$ in.
$h = 12$ in.
324 in.³

8. cone
$r = 8$ cm
$h = 15$ cm
1,005 cm³

9. sphere
$r = 6$ in.
904 in.³

10. You make a snow figure using three spheres with radii of 12 in., 10 in., and 8 in., with the biggest on the bottom and the smallest for the head. You get snow from a rectangular area that is 6 ft by 7 ft.
   a. Find the volume of snow in your snow figure to the nearest hundredth of a cubic inch.
   bottom: 7,234.56 in.³ middle: 4,186.67 in.³
   head: 2,143.57 in.³ total: 13,564.8 in.³
   b. Find the area in square inches from which you get snow.
   6,048 in.²
   c. How deep does the snow need to be before you have enough snow to make a figure? State your answer to the nearest $\frac{1}{4}$ in.
   about $2\frac{1}{4}$ in.



## Reteaching

Find the volume of the cone.

Use the formula $V = \frac{1}{3}Bh$.

$r = \frac{1}{2}d = \frac{1}{2}(10) = 5$ The radius is half the diameter.

$B = \pi r^2$

$B = \pi(5)^2 \approx 78.5$ Substitute 5 for $r$ to find the area of the base and multiply.

$V = \frac{1}{3}Bh$

$V = \frac{1}{3}(78.5)(11)$ Substitute 78.5 for $B$ and 11 for $h$.

$= 287.83$ Multiply and round.

The volume is approximately 287.83 cm³.
Remember to use cubic units.

10 cm, 11 cm

**Find the volume of each figure to the nearest hundredth.**

1. 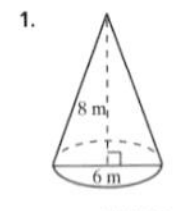

75.36 m³

2. 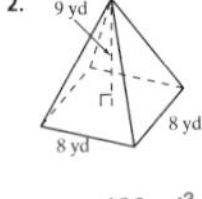

192 yd³

3. 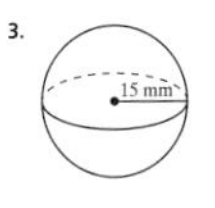

14,130 mm³

4. cone
$B = 93$ ft²
$h = 7$ ft
217 ft³

5. sphere
$r = \frac{3}{4}$ in.
1.77 in.³

6. pyramid
$B = 774$ cm²
$h = 42$ cm
10,836 cm³

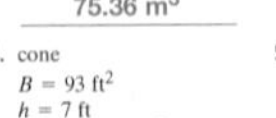

7. 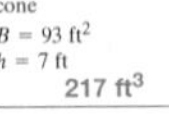

28,716.35 cm³

8. 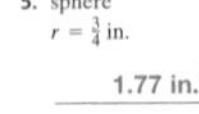
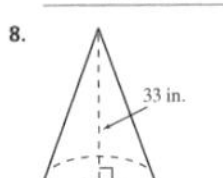

23,349.04 in.³

9. 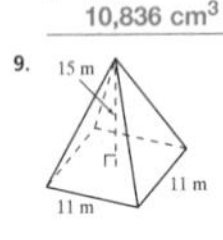

605 m³



## Enrichment

The *density* of an object is its mass per unit of volume:

density $= \frac{\text{mass}}{\text{volume}}$

**Example** A cube of zinc measuring 4 cm on a side has a mass of 454 g. Find the density.

**Solution** volume $= 4 \times 4 \times 4 = 64$ cm³

density $= \frac{454}{64} = 7.1$ g/cm³ (nearest tenth)

**Find the density. Round to the nearest tenth. Use 3.14 for $\pi$.**

| | Material | Shape | Dimensions (cm) | Mass (g) | Density |
|---|---|---|---|---|---|
| 1. | copper | rectangular prism | $7.1 \times 4 \times 2.9$ | 716 | 8.7 g/cm³ |
| 2. | tungsten | triangular prism | $B = 42$, $h = 24$ | 19,454 | 19.3 g/cm³ |
| 3. | iron | sphere | $r = 9$ | 24,111 | 7.9 g/cm³ |

**Find the mass. Round to the nearest tenth. Use 3.14 for $\pi$.**

4. a rectangular prism of silver measuring 4 cm × 2.5 cm × 1.8 cm
189 g

5. a lead cylinder with radius 6 cm and height 9.1 cm.
11,623.9 g

6. a chromium cone with radius 5 cm and height 8.1 cm
1,504.8 g

| Table of Densities | |
|---|---|
| **Material** | **Density (g/cm³)** |
| carbon | 2.3 |
| chromium | 7.1 |
| cobalt | 8.9 |
| gold | 19.3 |
| lead | 11.3 |
| magnesium | 1.7 |
| osmium | 22.4 |
| silver | 10.5 |
| titanium | 4.5 |

**Identify the material described.**

7. a rectangular prism measuring 6 cm × 5 cm × 3.7 cm, with a mass of 189 g
magnesium

8. a pyramid with a square base 2.5 cm on a side, height 4.2 cm, with a mass of 196 g
osmium

9. a cube measuring 1.2 cm on a side, with a mass of 33.4 g
gold





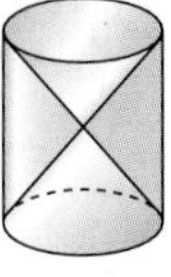

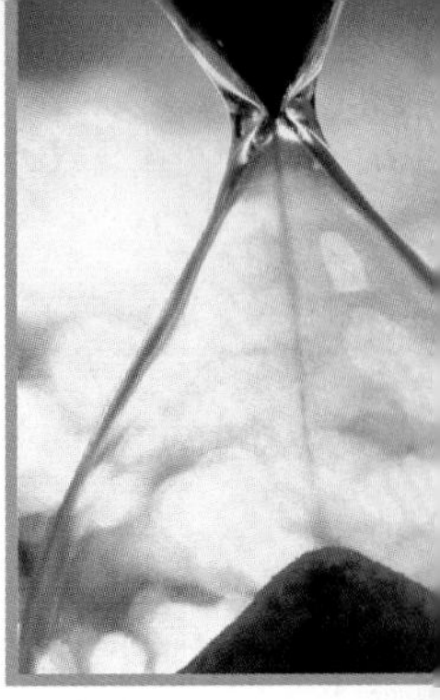

**15.** You want to fill the top part of an hourglass $\frac{2}{3}$ full of salt. The height of the hourglass is 20 cm and the radius of the base is 8 cm. Find the volume of salt needed. 447 cm³

**16.** *Error Analysis* A student tells a class that if you double the radius of a sphere, the volume will be multiplied by 6. Explain the student's error. The student multiplied 2 by three instead of taking $2^3$.

**17.** The diameter of the world's largest ball of string is 13 ft $2\frac{1}{2}$ in. The string was collected between 1989 and 1991.
   **a.** What is the surface area? 547.8 ft²
   **b.** What is the volume? 1,205.9 ft³

**18.** How much frozen yogurt can you pack inside a cone that is 5 in. high with a radius of 1.25 in.? 8.2 in.³

**19.** *Physics* You place a steel ball with diameter 4 cm in a water-filled cylinder that is 5 cm in diameter and 10 cm high. What volume of water will spill out of the cylinder? 33.5 cm³

**20.** **TEST PREP** The eight segments from the center of a cube to the four corners of the cube form the edges of six pyramids. If one edge of the cube is 4 in., what is the volume of each pyramid? B

**A.** 8 in.³ **B.** $\frac{32}{3}$ in.³ **C.** $\frac{64}{3}$ in.³ **D.** 64 in.³

### Journal

*Explain how you can remember the different formulas for finding volume.*

## Mixed Review

**Simplify each expression.** *(Lesson 5-9)*

**21.** $(3ab^2)^3$ $27a^3b^6$ **22.** $-(4x)^2$ $-16x^2$ **23.** $\left(-\frac{3}{8}\right)^2$ $\frac{9}{64}$ **24.** $\left(\frac{2x}{y^3}\right)^2$ $\frac{4x^2}{y^6}$

**Solve each equation.** *(Lesson 7-5)*

**25.** $\frac{5}{6}x = \frac{1}{6}x + 12$ 18 **26.** $3a + 10 = 12 - 2a$ $\frac{2}{5}$ **27.** $5y + 2 = 3y + 10$ 4

CHAPTER PROJECT 10

## Activity 3 Comparing

Pour 50 mL of water into a graduated cylinder. Add the cubes of your prism to the graduated cylinder. Measure the total volume. Find the volume of the prism by subtracting the water's volume from the total volume. Compare this volume to the value you found in Activity 2. (Recall that 1 mL equals 1 cm³.) Express the difference in volumes as a percent of change.

Repeat the steps above for your cylinder.

 See also Extra Practice section.

## Project Activity 3

**Comparing** Make sure students use graduated cylinders that measure volumes in milliliters. Each centimeter cube that students used to make up their prisms should displace 1 mL of water. When students find the volume of their cylinders, have them calculate the volume of an individual coin that makes up the cylinder.

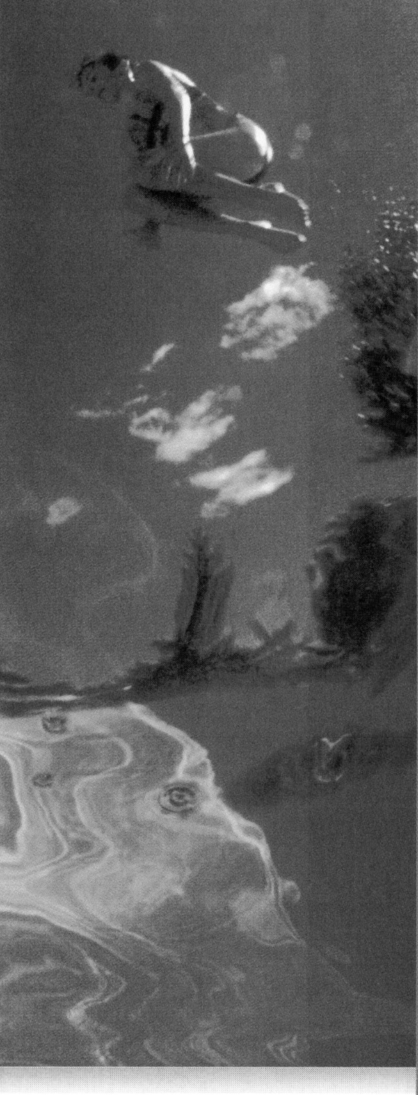

**Use Water Displacement to Find Volume** The Activities on pages 532, 541, and 550 will help you complete your project. Here is a checklist to help you gather the different parts.

- ✔ dimensions of your prism and cylinder
- ✔ volumes you found by using formulas
- ✔ volumes you found by using water displacement

Make a table to summarize your measurements and calculations. Write a paragraph in which you compare the values you found by different methods. Explain why the values are not exactly the same. Describe the advantages and disadvantages of each method.

***Reflect and Revise***

Ask a friend to review your table and your explanations. If necessary, make changes to improve your project.

### *Web Extension*

**Visit Prentice Hall's Web site. You'll find some interesting links and ideas related to volume. You'll also be able to share information about your project.**

**www.phschool.com**

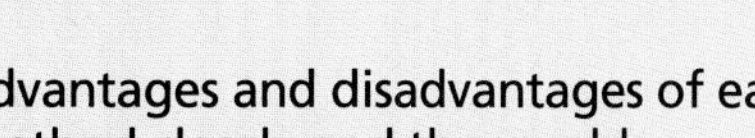

**Project Day** You may wish to plan a project day on which students share their completed projects. Encourage students to explain their process as well as their product.

**Block Scheduling** If you have block scheduling or extended periods, you may wish to intersperse the sharing of projects over Days 3, 4, and 5 between the completion of one lesson and the start of a new lesson.

### Project Notebook

Have students review their project work and bring their notebooks up to date. Call attention to the fact that they can share their projects with other students through the Web site **www.phschool.com.**

Be sure students include in their notebooks their completed Project Manager and Scoring Rubric forms.

**Portfolio** Students may wish to include their projects and/or their project notebooks in their portfolios.

### Web Extension

**Tell Us About Your Project**

Students may wish to share their projects with other students on the Web site: **www.phschool.com**.

### Scoring Rubric

**3** You measure and calculate each volume accurately. You compare the values found with each method correctly, explain the differences appropriately, and describe advantages and disadvantages of each method clearly and thoroughly.

**2** You make minor errors in your measurements, your calculations, or in your explanations. You describe advantages and disadvantages of each method, but your explanations could be clearer or more thorough.

**1** You measure or calculate incorrectly. Your comparisons and explanations are incomplete or inappropriate.

**0** Major elements of the project are incomplete or missing.

# Wrap Up

## Resources

Glossary, p. 748
Extra Practice, p. 719

For a complete list of resources for the chapter, see p. 501H.

# Wrap Up

## Key Terms



## Graphic Organizer

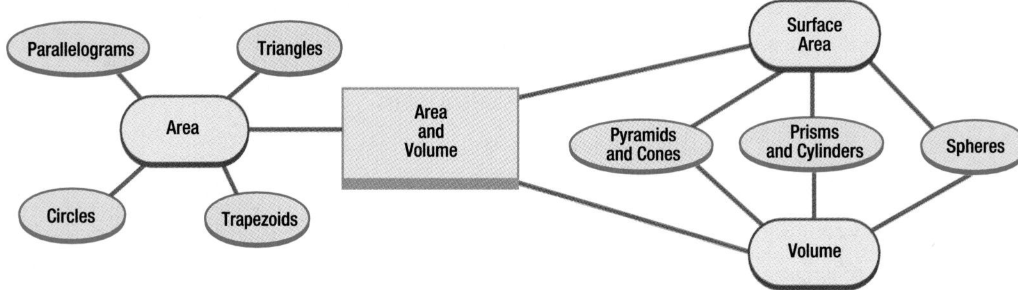


## Areas of Parallelograms, Triangles, and Trapezoids

10-1 and 10-2

*Summary* The **area** of a polygon is the number of square units enclosed by the polygon. To find the areas of parallelograms, triangles, or trapezoids, use the appropriate formulas.

| parallelogram | triangle | trapezoid |
|---|---|---|
| $A = bh$ | $A = \frac{1}{2}bh$ | $A = \frac{1}{2}h(b_1 + b_2)$ |

**Find the area of the shaded region in each figure.**

1. Parallelogram — 189 m$^2$

21 m
9 m

2. Trapezoid — 14 cm$^2$

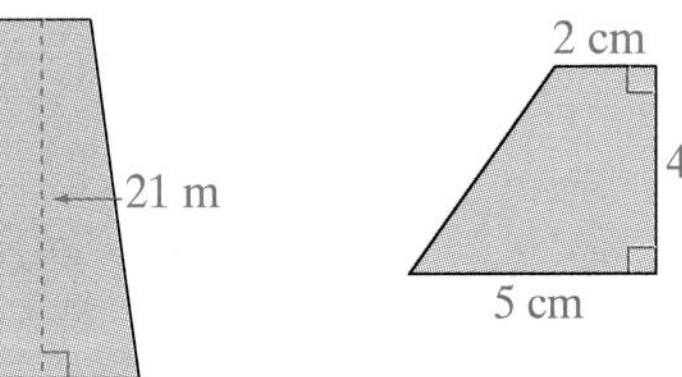


3. 6.25 yd$^2$

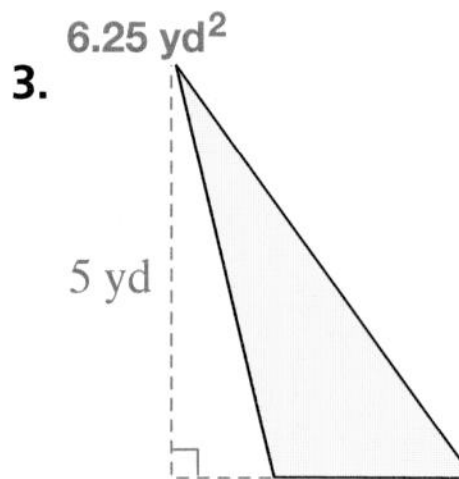


4. 17 in.$^2$

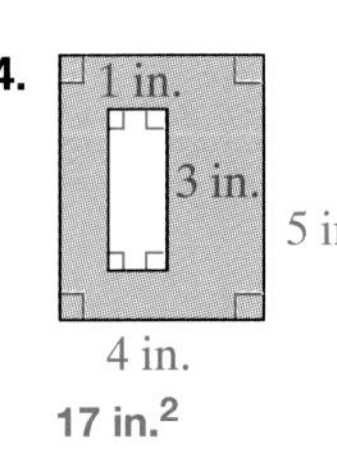

## Areas of Circles — 10-3

**Summary** To find the area of a circle, use the formula $A = \pi r^2$. Use 3.14 for $\pi$.

**Find the area of each figure to the nearest square unit.**

5. 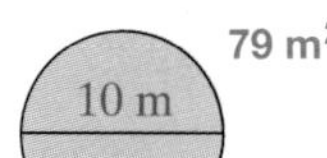

79 m²

6. 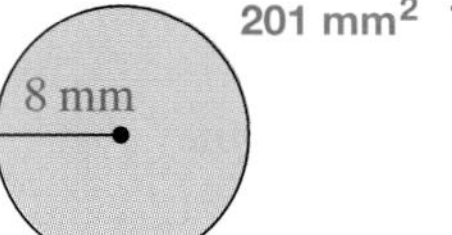

201 mm²

7. 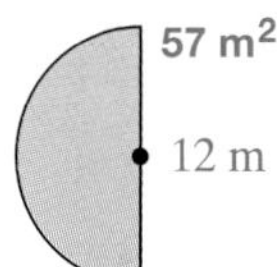

57 m²

8. 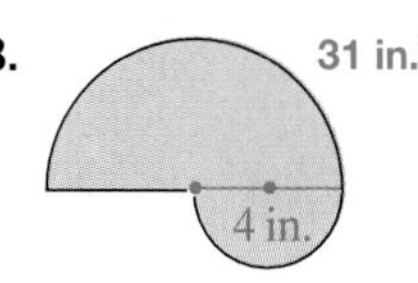

31 in.²

## Space Figures — 10-4

**Summary** Name **pyramids** and **prisms** by the shapes of their bases. A **cylinder** is a space figure with two circular bases. **Cones** have one circular base and one vertex. **Nets** are flat patterns for space figures.

**Name the space figure represented by each net.**

9. 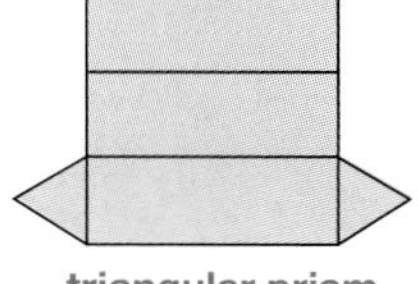
triangular prism

10. 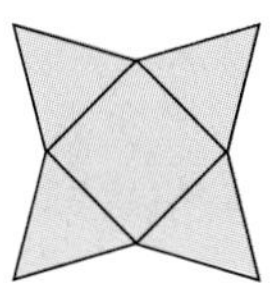
square pyramid

11. 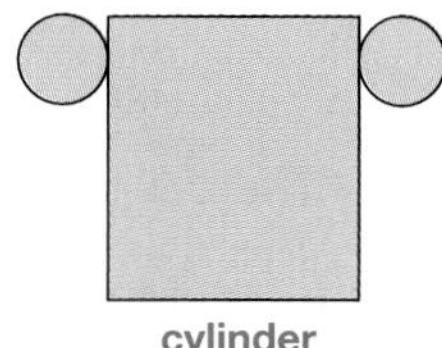
cylinder

## Surface Areas of Prisms and Cylinders — 10-5

**Summary** The **lateral area** of a prism is the sum of the areas of the lateral faces. The lateral area of a cylinder is the area of the curved surface. The **surface area** of a prism or a cylinder is the sum of the lateral area and the areas of the two bases.

To find surface area, use the appropriate formula.

| prism | cylinder |
|---|---|
| L.A. = $ph$ | L.A. = $2\pi rh$ |
| S.A. = L.A. + $2B$ | S.A. = L.A. + $2B$ |

**Find the surface area to the nearest square unit.**

12. 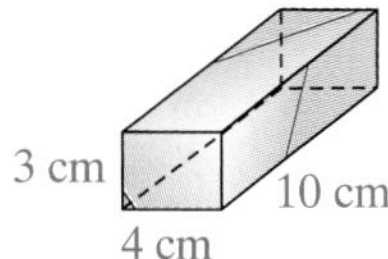

164 cm²

13. 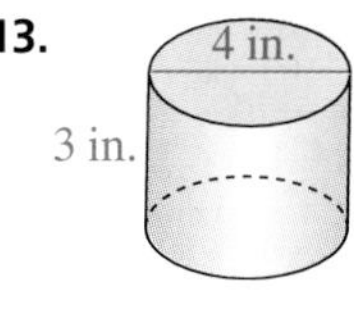

63 in.²

14. 84 cm² 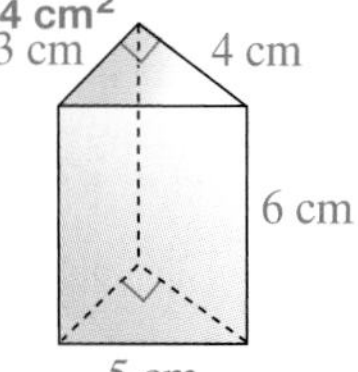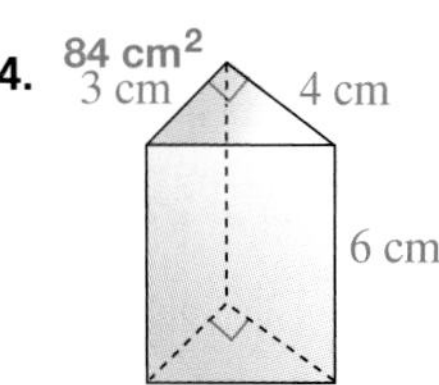


15. 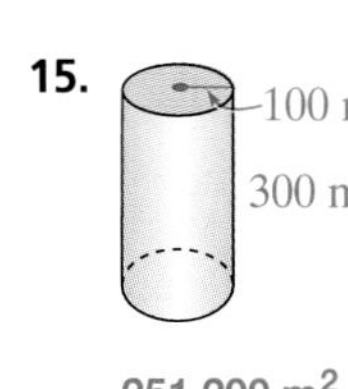

251,200 m²



**Portfolio** Students may wish to include their completed work for the Wrap Up in their portfolios.

### Web Site

Students can find self-assessment materials on the Web site: **www.phschool.com**.

## Surface Areas of Pyramids, Cones, and Spheres — 10-6

*Summary* For pyramids and cones, use **slant height** $\ell$ to find the lateral area. For a regular pyramid, if $n$ is the number of lateral faces, you can find the area of one face, and then multiply by $n$. The lateral area of a cone is the area of the curved surface. The surface area of a pyramid or a cone is the sum of the lateral area and the base area.

To find surface area, use the appropriate formula.

| pyramid | cone | sphere |
|---|---|---|
| L.A. $= n\left(\frac{1}{2}b\ell\right)$ | L.A. $= \pi r\ell$ | |
| S.A. $=$ L.A. $+ B$ | S.A. $=$ L.A. $+ B$ | S.A. $= 4\pi r^2$ |

**Find the surface area of each figure, to the nearest square unit.**

**16.** 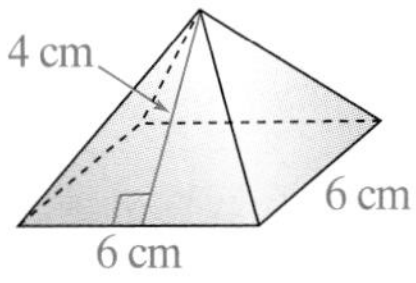

84 cm²

**17.** 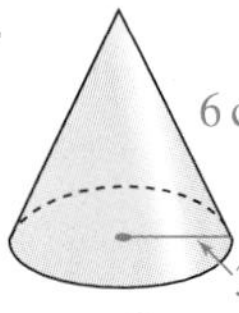

85 cm²

**18.** 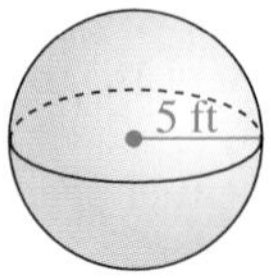

314 ft²

**19.** 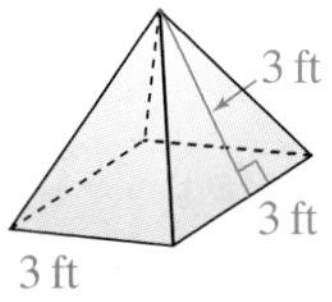

27 ft²

## Make a Model — 10-8

*Summary* To solve some problems, make a model.

**20.** A rectangular sheet of wrapping paper covers a gift box 6 in. by 6 in. by 6 in., without overlapping. What are the least possible dimensions of the sheet? 24 in. by 18 in.

**21.** *Writing* A 12-m by 15-m rectangular garden has a walk 1 m wide around it. Describe how you would find the area of the walk.
Find the area of the walk and garden, and then subtract the area of the garden.

## Volume — 10-7 and 10-9

*Summary* **Volume** is the measure of how much a space figure can hold.

To find volume, use the appropriate formula.

| prisms and cylinders | pyramids and cones | spheres |
|---|---|---|
| $V = Bh$ | $V = \frac{1}{3}Bh$ | $V = \frac{4}{3}\pi r^3$ |

**Find each volume to the nearest cubic unit.**

**22.** 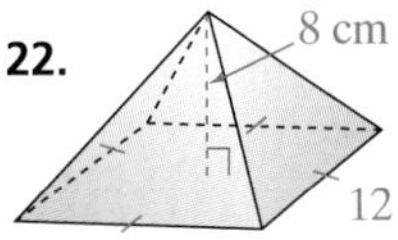

384 cm³

**23.** 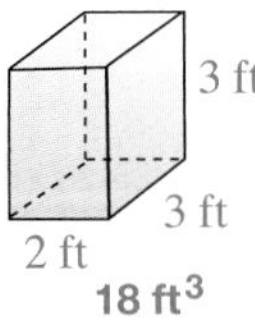

18 ft³

**24.** 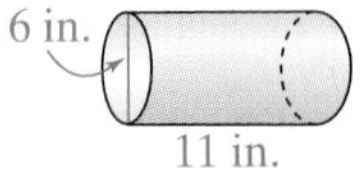

311 in.³

**25.** 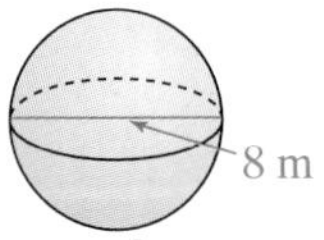

268 m³



## Chapter Assessment Form A Page 1

**Circle the letter of the best answer.**

1. Find the area.
   A. 24 in.² B. 18 in.² (C.) 16 in.² D. 32 in.²

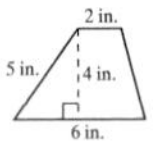


2. Find the approximate area.
   F. 69.08 cm² G. 1,519.76 cm² H. 138.16 cm² (J.) 379.94 cm²

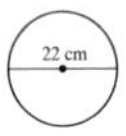


3. Find the approximate surface area.
   A. 191 ft² B. 64 ft² (C.) 205 ft² D. 572 ft²

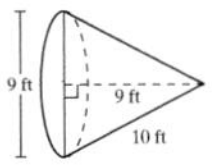


4. Find the approximate volume of the cone in number 3.
   (F.) 191 ft³ G. 64 ft³ H. 205 ft³ J. 572 ft³
5. In cubic meters, how much greater is the volume of a cylinder with height 21 m and a radius 12 m than the volume of a square prism with height 21 m and base 12 m on a side?
   A. 3,024 m³ (B.) 6,471 m³ C. 9,495 m³ D. 12,519 m³

**Find the area of each figure to the nearest square unit.**

6. 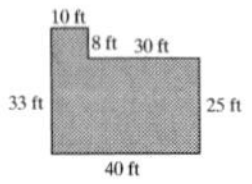

1,080 ft²

7. 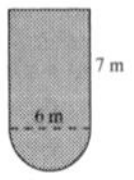

56 m²

8. Name the space figure that can be made out of the net.
   triangular prism

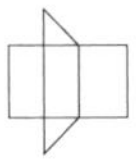



Assessment

## Chapter Assessment Form A Page 2

**For 9 to 12, use the space figure on the right.**

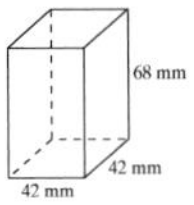


9. Name the space figure. square prism
10. Draw a net for the space figure.
    Sample answer is shown.

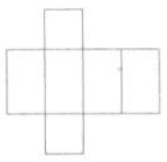

11. Find the surface area of the space figure.
    14,952 mm²
12. Find the volume of the space figure.
    119,952 mm³

**Find the volume and surface area of each space figure to the nearest tenth.**

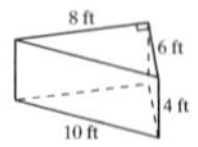


13. S.A. = 144 ft²
14. $V$ = 96 ft³

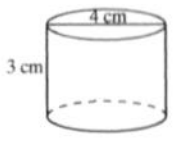


15. S.A. ≈ 62.8 cm²
16. $V$ ≈ 37.7 cm³

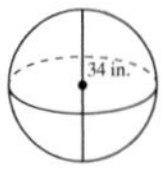


17. S.A. ≈ 3,629.8 in.²
18. $V$ ≈ 20,569.1 in.³

19. A rectangular piece of tin measures 36 in. by 25 in. A square measuring 4 in. by 4 in. is cut out of each corner and the sides are folded to form a box. What is the volume of the box?
    1,904 in.³
20. Describe the dimensions of a pyramid with a volume of 30 cm³.
    Sample answer: The pyramid has a square base that is 3 cm on a side and a height of 10 cm.

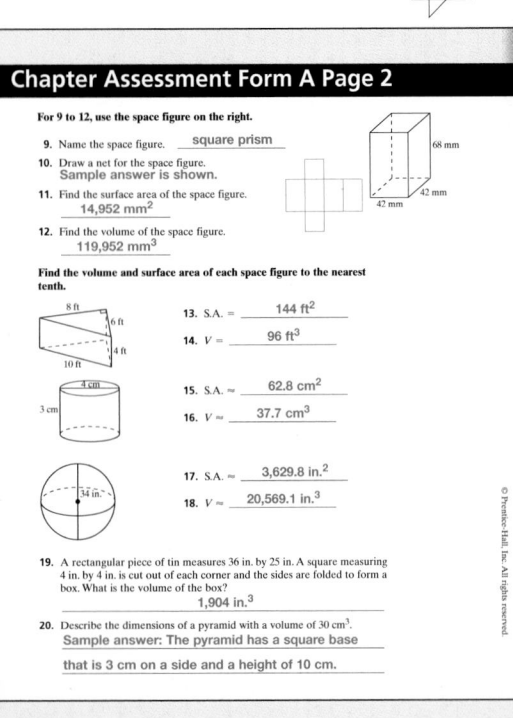

# Assessment

## Find the area of each figure.

1. 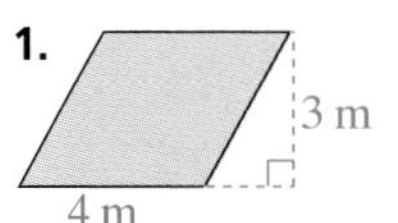

12 $m^2$

2. 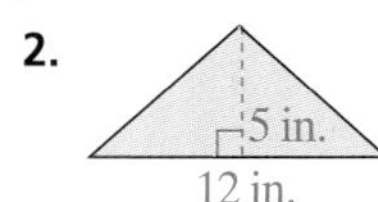

30 $in.^2$

3. 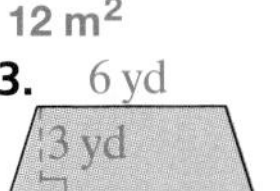

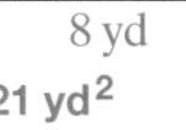
21 $yd^2$

4. 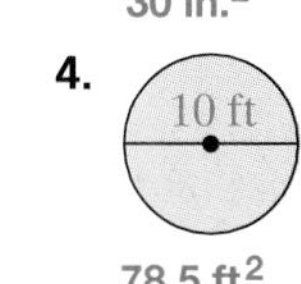

78.5 $ft^2$

5. 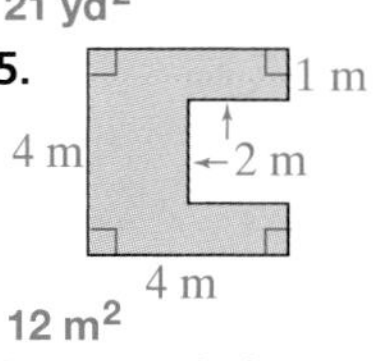

12 $m^2$

6. 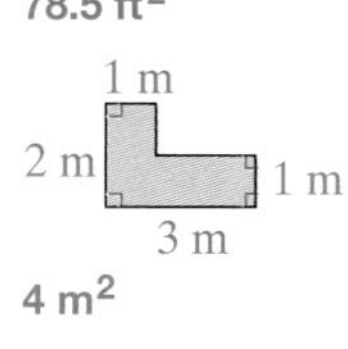

4 $m^2$

## Find the missing measures.

7. circle
$d = 4$ cm
$A = \blacksquare$ $cm^2$
12.56

8. triangle
$b = 7$ m
$h = 4$ m
$A = \blacksquare$ $m^2$
14

## Name the space figure for each net.

9. 
triangular pyramid

10. 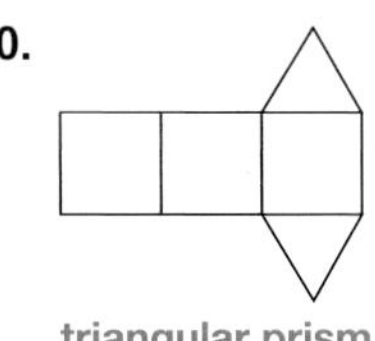
triangular prism

## Find the surface area of each figure.

11. 340 $m^2$
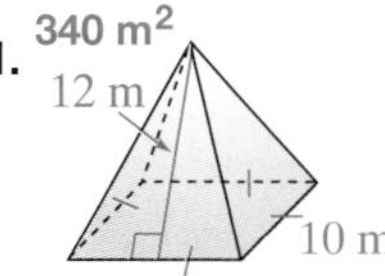


12. 31.4 $cm^2$
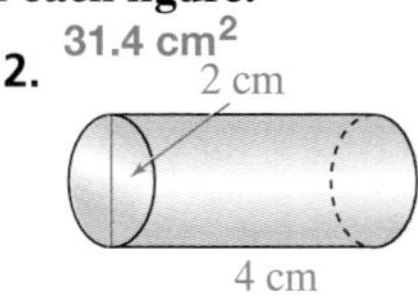


13. 
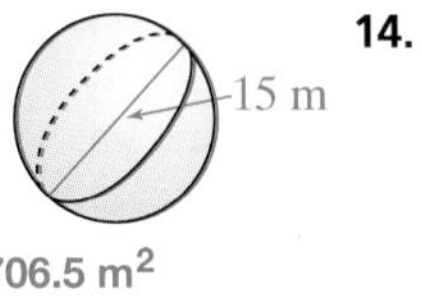

706.5 $m^2$

14. 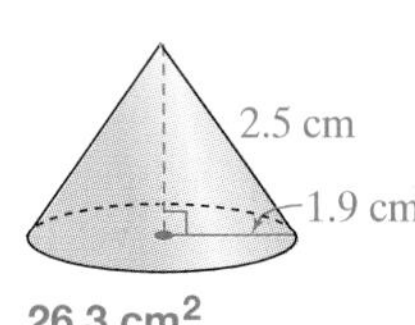

26.3 $cm^2$

## Find the volume of each figure.

15. 

65,416,666.7 $m^3$

16. 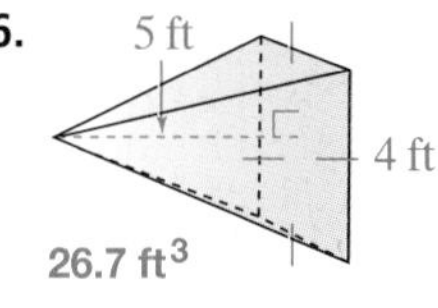

26.7 $ft^3$

17. 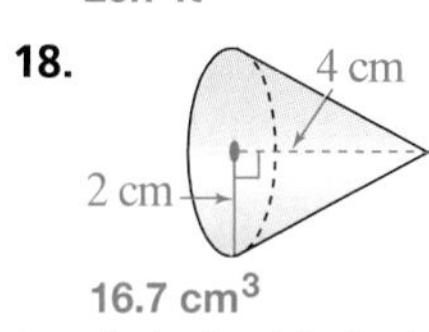

16 $in.^3$

18. 

16.7 $cm^3$

19. The height of a rectangle is doubled while the base is unchanged. How does this affect the area? Explain. See below.

20. In cubic feet, how much greater is the volume of a cone with height 10 ft and radius 6 ft than the volume of a square pyramid with height 10 ft and length of base 6 ft? 256.8 $ft^3$

21. The diameter of Mars is about 4,000 mi.
   a. Find the surface area. 50,240,000 $mi^2$
   b. Find the volume. 33,493,333,333 $mi^3$

22. A box is 25.5 cm by 17 cm by 5 cm.
   a. How much dry dishwashing detergent can it hold? 2,167.5 $cm^3$
   b. Without overlap, how much cardboard is needed to make the box ? 1,292 $cm^2$

23. *Writing* How is the formula for volume of a prism like the formula for volume of a pyramid? How are the formulas different? See margin.

24. A rectangular piece of sheet metal measures 26 in. by 20 in. A square measuring 2 in. by 2 in. is cut out of each corner, and the sides are folded to form a box. What is the volume of the box? 704 $in.^3$

25. *Open-ended* Draw a net for a rectangular prism. Check students' work.

19. Since the formula for the area of a rectangle is $A = bh$, doubling the height doubles the area.



23. Both formulas use the general form $V = Bh$ where $B$ is the area of the base, and $h$ the height. The formula for the volume of a pyramid has a factor of $\frac{1}{3}$.

# Chapter Assessment

**Resources** For a complete list of resources for this chapter, see p. 501H.

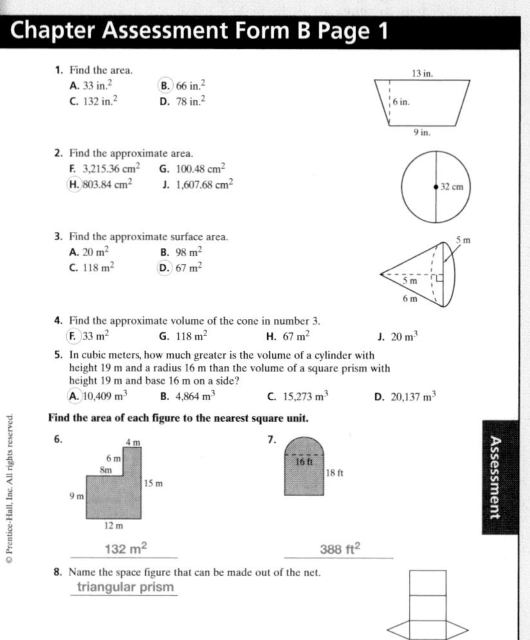

## Chapter Assessment Form B Page 1

1. Find the area.
   A. 33 $in.^2$ (B.) 66 $in.^2$ C. 132 $in.^2$ D. 78 $in.^2$



2. Find the approximate area.
   F. 3,215.36 $cm^2$ G. 100.48 $cm^2$ (H.) 803.84 $cm^2$ J. 1,607.68 $cm^2$



3. Find the approximate surface area.
   A. 20 $m^2$ B. 98 $m^2$ C. 118 $m^2$ (D.) 67 $m^2$



4. Find the approximate volume of the cone in number 3.
   (F.) 33 $m^2$ G. 118 $m^2$ H. 67 $m^2$ J. 20 $m^3$

5. In cubic meters, how much greater is the volume of a cylinder with height 19 m and a radius 16 m than the volume of a square prism with height 19 m and base 16 m on a side?
   (A.) 10,409 $m^3$ B. 4,864 $m^3$ C. 15,273 $m^3$ D. 20,137 $m^3$

**Find the area of each figure to the nearest square unit.**

6. 

132 $m^2$

7. 

388 $ft^2$

8. Name the space figure that can be made out of the net.
   triangular prism



Assessment

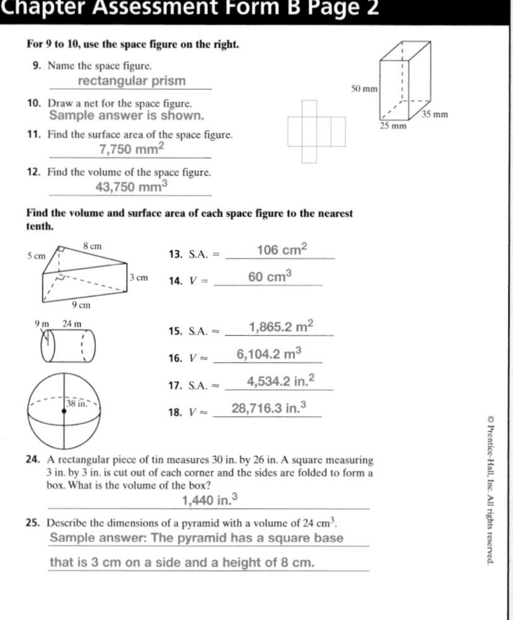

## Chapter Assessment Form B Page 2

**For 9 to 10, use the space figure on the right.**



9. Name the space figure.
   rectangular prism

10. Draw a net for the space figure.
   Sample answer is shown.

11. Find the surface area of the space figure.
   7,750 $mm^2$

12. Find the volume of the space figure.
   43,750 $mm^3$

**Find the volume and surface area of each space figure to the nearest tenth.**



13. S.A. = 106 $cm^2$

14. $V =$ 60 $cm^3$



15. S.A. ≈ 1,865.2 $m^2$

16. $V \approx$ 6,104.2 $m^3$



17. S.A. ≈ 4,534.2 $in.^2$

18. $V \approx$ 28,716.3 $in.^3$

24. A rectangular piece of tin measures 30 in. by 26 in. A square measuring 3 in. by 3 in. is cut out of each corner and the sides are folded to form a box. What is the volume of the box?
   1,440 $in.^3$

25. Describe the dimensions of a pyramid with a volume of 24 $cm^3$.
   Sample answer: The pyramid has a square base that is 3 cm on a side and a height of 8 cm.

# Cumulative Review

## Cumulative Review Page 1

**Circle the letter of the best answer.**

1. $3(x + y) - x + y =$
   A. $2x + 2y$ (B.) $2x + 4y$ C. $4x + 4y$ D. $4x + 2y$
2. Estimate $79.783 \times 31.6691$
   F. 240 (G.) 2,400 H. 24,000 J. 240,000
3. In standard notation, $9.03 \times 10^7$ is
   A. 9,030,000,000 B. 9,030,000 (C.) 90,300,000 D. 903,000,000
4. Which equation describes *four less than twice a number is negative eight?*
   (F.) $2x - 4 = -8$ G. $4 - 2x = -8$ H. $2(x - 4) = -8$ J. $4x - 2 = -8$
5. Which fraction is equal to 0.125?
   A. $\frac{1}{6}$ B. $\frac{1}{7}$ C. $\frac{1}{12}$ (D.) $\frac{1}{8}$
6. Which equation has $y$-intercept $-3$?
   (F.) $3x - y = 3$ G. $x - 3y = 3$ H. $x + 3y = 3$ J. $3x + 3 = y$
7. The measure of the supplement of a 71° angle is
   A. 19° B. 17° (C.) 109° D. 107°
8. Find the circumference of a circle with radius 18 cm.
   F. $18\pi$ cm G. $324\pi$ cm (H.) $36\pi$ cm J. $1{,}296\pi$ cm
9. What space figure can you form from the net at the right?
   (A.) square pyramid B. triangular prism
   C. triangular pyramid D. square prism
10. Figure $A$ is a rectangle 8 in. long and 6.5 in. high. Figure $B$ is a triangle 8 in. long and 6.5 in. high. Which statement is true about the areas of Figures $A$ and $B$?
    F. $A = B$ G. $A \propto B$ H. $A = \frac{1}{2}B$ (J.) $A = 2B$
11. A rectangle has a perimeter of 110 ft and a length of 23 ft. What is its area?
    A. 2,530 ft² B. 32 ft² C. 2,001 ft² (D.) 736 ft²

**Find the area of each figure to the nearest tenth.**

12. 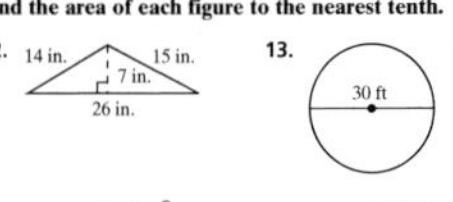

91 in.²

13. 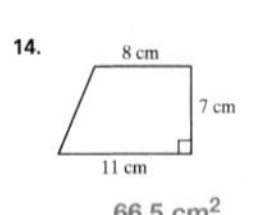

706.5 ft²

14. 8 cm, 7 cm, 11 cm
66.5 cm²



## Cumulative Review Page 2

**Find the surface area and volume of each figure to the nearest tenth.**

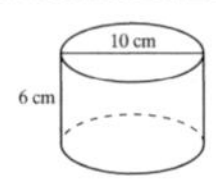


15. S.A. ≈ 345.4 cm²
16. $V \approx$ 471 cm³

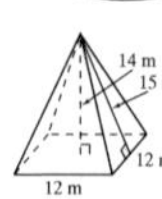


17. S.A. ≈ 504 m²
18. $V \approx$ 672 m³

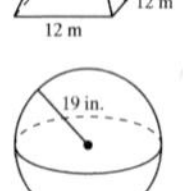


19. S.A. ≈ 4,534.2 in.²
20. $V \approx$ 28,716.3 in.³

21. Compare the volumes of the prism and pyramid shown.
    Since the prism and pyramid have congruent bases and the same heights, the volume of the pyramid is $\frac{1}{3}$ the volume of of the prism.

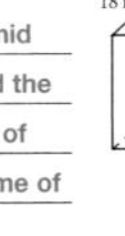


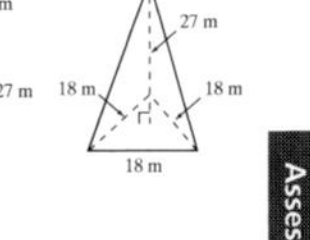




Assessment

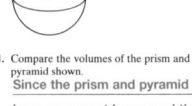

# Cumulative Review

**Preparing for Algebra**

**Choose the best answer.**

1. The average nose has about 6,000,000 cells that detect odors. Write this number in scientific notation. B
   A. $6 \cdot 10^5$ B. $6 \cdot 10^6$
   C. $6 \cdot 10^7$ D. $6 \cdot 10^8$
2. Which equation represents the statement *The sum of twice a number and five times another number is 40?* F
   F. $40 = 2x + 5y$ G. $5y = \frac{40}{2x}$
   H. $2x \cdot 5y = 40$ J. $5y = \frac{1}{2}x + 40$
3. Two angles are supplementary if A
   A. the sum of their measures is 180°.
   B. they share a vertex.
   C. the sum of their measures is 90°.
   D. they have the same measure.
4. What space figure can you form from the net below? H

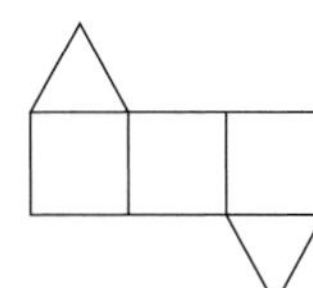

   F. square pyramid G. triangular pyramid
   H. triangular prism J. hexagonal prism
5. Figure $A$ is a rectangle 10 in. long and 7.5 in. wide. Figure $B$ is a parallelogram with height 12 in. and base length 7.5 in. Which statement is true? B
   A. area of $A >$ area of $B$
   B. area of $A <$ area of $B$
   C. area of $A =$ area of $B$
   D. Not here

**Find the area of each figure.**

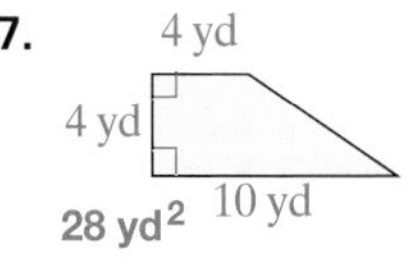


6. 30 m²
7. 28 yd²

**Find the approximate area of each circle to the nearest square unit.**

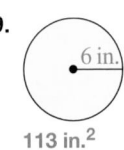

8. 24 ft — 452 ft²
9. 6 in. — 113 in.²

**Find the surface area of each figure to the nearest square unit.**

10. 6 m, 9 m, 6 m — 288 m²
11. 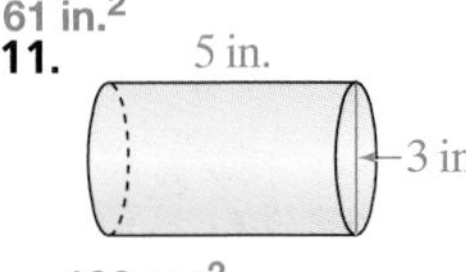

61 in.²
12. 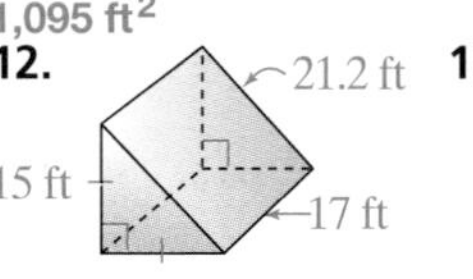

1,095 ft²
13. 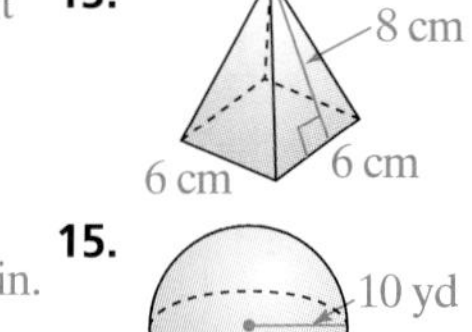

132 cm²
14. 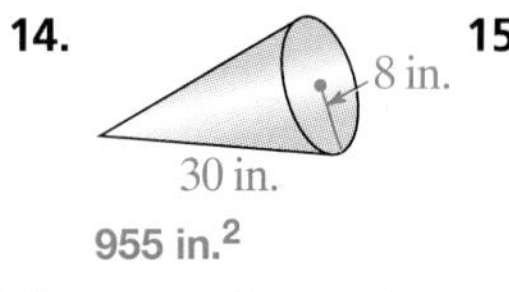

955 in.²
15. 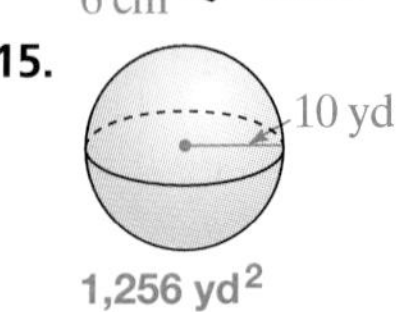

1,256 yd²

**Find the volume of each figure, to the nearest cubic unit.**

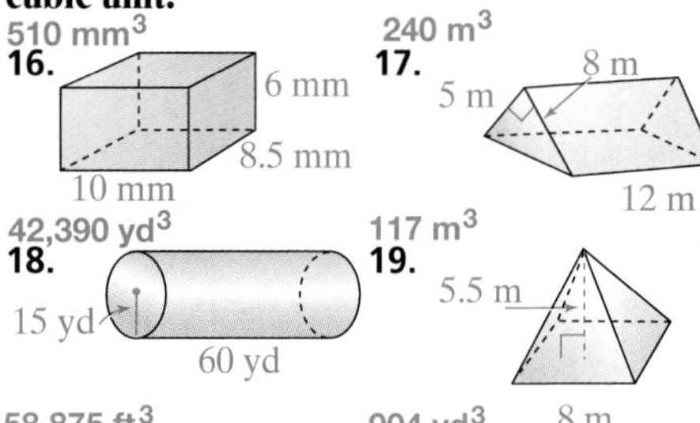


16. 510 mm³
17. 240 m³
18. 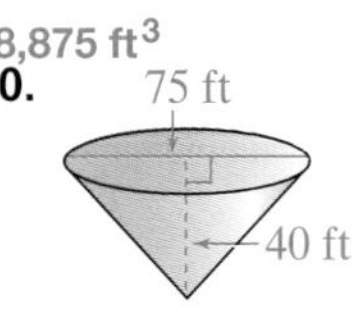

42,390 yd³
19. 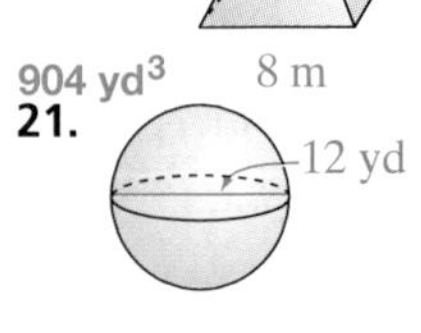

117 m³
20. 75 ft, 40 ft — 58,875 ft³
21. 12 yd — 904 yd³
22. Draw a net for a cylinder that has diameter 3 cm and height 6 cm. Label and find its surface area, to the nearest square centimeter. 71 cm²; see margin for net.



22. 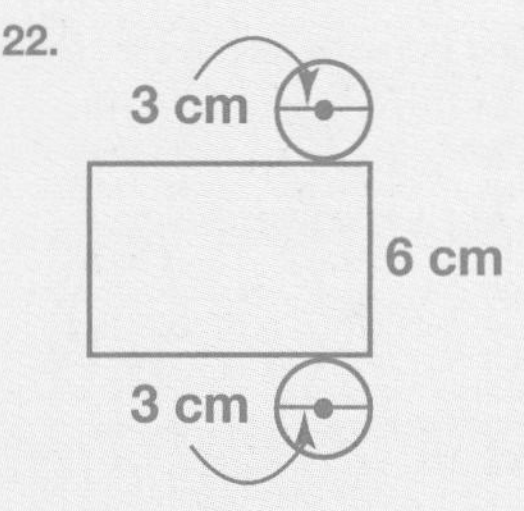


| Item | Chapter/ Lesson | Review Topic |
|---|---|---|
| 1 | 4-9 | Factors, Fractions, and Exponents |
| 2 | 8-2 | Linear Functions and Graphing |
| 3 | 9-2 | Spatial Thinking |
| 4–22 | 10-1, 10-2, 10-3, 10-4, 10-5, 10-6, 10-7, 10-9 | Area and Volume |

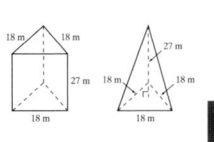

CHAPTER 11

# Right Triangles in Algebra

## Content Overview for Chapter 11

Chapter 11 begins with a lesson on square roots and irrational numbers. The square of an integer is a perfect square. The inverse of squaring is finding a square root. The symbol $\sqrt{\ }$ indicates the non-negative square root of a number. A number that cannot be expressed as the ratio of two integers, $\frac{a}{b}$, where $b$ is not zero, is irrational. If a positive integer is not a perfect square, then its square root is irrational.

The Pythagorean Theorem states that in any right triangle, the sum of the squares of the lengths of the legs is equal to the square of the length of the hypotenuse. You can derive the Distance Formula from the Pythagorean Theorem. The Distance Formula states that the distance $d$ between any two points $(x_1, y_1)$ and $(x_2, y_2)$ is $d = \sqrt{(x_2 - x_1)^2 + (y_2 - y_1)^2}$.

The Midpoint Formula states that the midpoint of a line segment with endpoints $A(x_1, y_1)$ and $B(x_2, y_2)$ is $\left(\frac{x_1 + x_2}{2}, \frac{y_1 + y_2}{2}\right)$.

You can use the Pythagorean Theorem to define relationships in special right triangles. In a 45°-45°-90° triangle, the length of the hypotenuse is the length of a leg times $\sqrt{2}$. In a 30°-60°-90° triangle, the length of the hypotenuse is 2 times the length of the shorter leg, and the length of the longer leg is $\sqrt{3}$ times the length of the shorter leg. The ratios of the lengths of two sides of a right triangle are trigonometric ratios. Three trigonometric ratios are sine, cosine, and tangent. For the angle $N$, $\sin N = \frac{\text{opposite}}{\text{hypotenuse}}$, $\cos N = \frac{\text{adjacent}}{\text{hypotenuse}}$, and $\tan N = \frac{\text{opposite}}{\text{adjacent}}$. You can use trigonometric ratios to find angles of elevation and depression.

## Making Connections

| Lesson | Interdisciplinary and Real-World Connections | Math Integration |
|---|---|---|
| 11-1 | Physics | Algebra, Geometry |
| 11-2 | Industrial Arts | Geometry, Algebra |
| 11-3 | | Geometry |
| 11-4 | Surveying | Problem Solving |
| 11-5 | Sports | Geometry |
| 11-6 | History | Measurement |
| 11-7 | Meteorology, Navigation | Measurement |

**SCHOOL/HOME CONNECTION**
English and Spanish versions are available in the *Help at Home* book of copy masters.

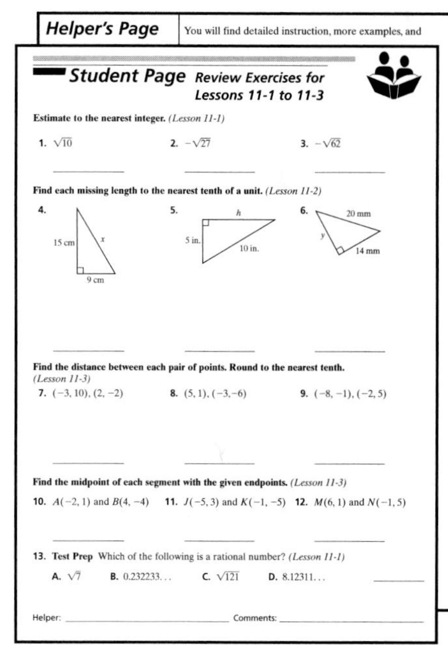

**Helper's Page** You will find detailed instruction, more examples, and

**Student Page** Review Exercises for Lessons 11-1 to 11-3

**Estimate to the nearest integer.** *(Lesson 11-1)*

1. $\sqrt{10}$ 2. $-\sqrt{27}$ 3. $-\sqrt{62}$

**Find each missing length to the nearest tenth of a unit.** *(Lesson 11-2)*

4. 5. 6.



**Find the distance between each pair of points. Round to the nearest tenth.** *(Lesson 11-3)*

7. (−3, 10), (2, −2) 8. (5, 1), (−3, −6) 9. (−8, −1), (−2, 5)

**Find the midpoint of each segment with the given endpoints.** *(Lesson 11-3)*

10. $A(-2, 1)$ and $B(4, -4)$ 11. $J(-5, 3)$ and $K(-1, -5)$ 12. $M(6, 1)$ and $N(-1, 5)$

13. **Test Prep** Which of the following is a rational number? *(Lesson 11-1)*

A. $\sqrt{7}$ B. 0.232233... C. $\sqrt{121}$ D. 8.12311...

Helper: ______ Comments: ______

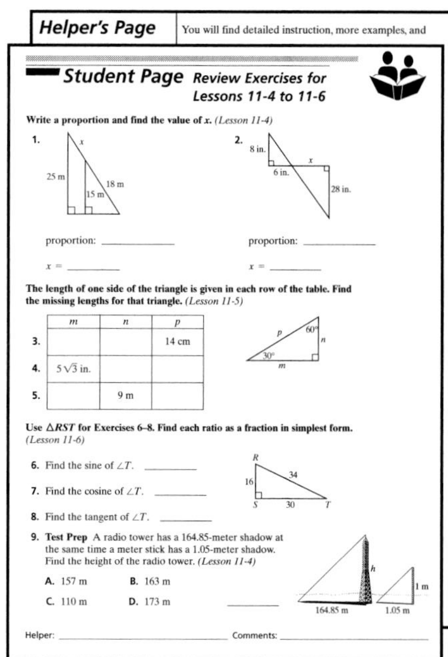

**Helper's Page** You will find detailed instruction, more examples, and

**Student Page** Review Exercises for Lessons 11-4 to 11-6

**Write a proportion and find the value of *x*.** *(Lesson 11-4)*

1. 2.



proportion: ______ proportion: ______

$x =$ ______ $x =$ ______

**The length of one side of the triangle is given in each row of the table. Find the missing lengths for that triangle.** *(Lesson 11-5)*

| | *m* | *n* | *p* |
|---|---|---|---|
| 3. | | | 14 cm |
| 4. | $5\sqrt{3}$ in. | | |
| 5. | | 9 m | |



**Use $\Delta RST$ for Exercises 6–8. Find each ratio as a fraction in simplest form.** *(Lesson 11-6)*

6. Find the sine of $\angle T$. ______
7. Find the cosine of $\angle T$. ______
8. Find the tangent of $\angle T$. ______



9. **Test Prep** A radio tower has a 164.85-meter shadow at the same time a meter stick has a 1.05-meter shadow. Find the height of the radio tower. *(Lesson 11-4)*

A. 157 m B. 163 m
C. 110 m D. 173 m



Helper: ______ Comments: ______

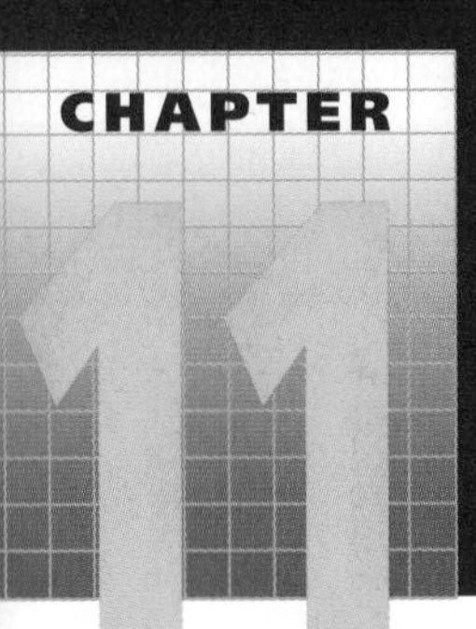


# Chapter 11 at a Glance

To accommodate flexible scheduling, most lessons are divided into parts. Assignment Options are given in the Teacher's Edition for each lesson.

| Pages 560–563 | **Lesson 11-1** **Square Roots and Irrational Numbers** |
|---|---|
| NCTM 1, 2, 3, 6, 8, 9 | Part 1 Finding Square Roots<br>Part 2 Classifying Real Numbers<br>▽ **Project Activity 1** |

| Pages 564–569 | **Lesson 11-2** **Geometry: The Pythagorean Theorem** |
|---|---|
| NCTM 1, 2, 3, 4, 6, 8, 9, 10 | Part 1 Using the Pythagorean Theorem<br>Part 2 Identifying Right Triangles<br>**Math at Work** |

| Pages 572–576 | **Lesson 11-3** **Distance and Midpoint Formulas** |
|---|---|
| NCTM 2, 3, 4, 10 | Part 1 Finding Distance<br>Part 2 Finding the Midpoint<br>**Checkpoint 1** |

| Pages 594–598 | **Lesson 11-7** **Measurement: Angles of Elevation and Depression** |
|---|---|
| NCTM 2, 3, 4, 6, 8, 9, 10 | Part 1 Angles of Elevation<br>Part 2 Angles of Depression<br>▽ **Project Activity 3** |

## Pacing Options

This chart suggests pacing for only the core lessons and their parts, and it is provided merely as a possible guide. It will help you determine how much time you have in your schedule to cover other features, such as the Chapter Project, Math Toolboxes, Standardized Test Prep, Wrap Up, and Assessment.

| | Day 1 | Day 2 | Day 3 | Day 4 | Day 5 | Day 6 | Day 7 | Day 8 | Day 9 | Day 10 | Day 11 |
|---|---|---|---|---|---|---|---|---|---|---|---|
| **Traditional** (40–45 min. class periods) | 11–1 ▽1, 11–1 ▽2 | 11–2 ▽1 | 11–2 ▽2 | 11–3 ▽1, 11–3 ▽2 | 11–4 | 11–5 ▽1, 11–5 ▽2 | 11–6 ▽1, 11–6 ▽2 | 11–7 ▽1, 11–7 ▽2 | | | |
| **Pre-Algebra Over 2 Years** (40–45 min. class periods) | 11–1 ▽1 | 11–1 ▽1 | 11–1 ▽2 | 11–2 ▽1 | 11–2 ▽1 | 11–2 ▽2 | 11–2 ▽2 | 11–3 ▽1 | 11–3 ▽1 | 11–3 ▽2 | 11–4 |
| **Block Scheduling** (90 min. class periods) | 11–1 ▽1 ▽2, 11–2 ▽1 | 11–2 ▽2, 11–3 ▽1 ▽2 | 11–4, 11–5 ▽1 ▽2 | 11–6 ▽1 ▽2, 11–7 ▽1 ▽2 | | | | | | | |

| Pages 578–581 | **Lesson 11-4** **Problem Solving Strategy** |
|---|---|
| **NCTM** 2, 3, 4, 6, 9, 10 | Write a Proportion |

| Pages 582–586 | **Lesson 11-5** **Special Right Triangles** |
|---|---|
| **NCTM** 1, 2, 3, 6, 8, 9, 10 | Part 1 Using 45°-45°-90° Triangles<br>Part 2 Using 30°-60°-90° Triangles<br>**Project Activity 2** |

| Pages 588–592 | **Lesson 11-6** **Measurement: Sine, Cosine, and Tangent Ratios** |
|---|---|
| **NCTM** 2, 3, 4, 6, 8, 9, 10 | Part 1 Finding Ratios in Right Triangles<br>Part 2 Using Ratios to Solve Problems<br>**Checkpoint 2** |

**NCTM STANDARDS 2000**

1 Number and Operations
2 Algebra
3 Geometry
4 Measurement
5 Data Analysis and Probability
6 Problem Solving
7 Reasoning and Proof
8 Communication
9 Connections
10 Representation

| Day 12 | Day 13 | Day 14 | Day 15 | Day 16 | Day 17 | Day 18 | Day 19 | Day 20 | Day 21 | Day 22 | Day 23 | Day 24 |
|---|---|---|---|---|---|---|---|---|---|---|---|---|
| 11–4 | 11–5 1 | 11–5 2 | 11–5 2 | 11–6 1 | 11–6 1 | 11–6 2 | 11–7 1 | 11–7 1 | 11–7 2 | | | |

**Block Scheduling Notes**

Consider these suggestions:

- **Day 2** Before starting Lesson 11-3, teach Math Toolbox 1, p. 570.
- **Day 3** Before starting Lesson 11-4, teach the Standardized Test Prep, p. 577.
- **Day 4** Before starting Lesson 11-6, teach Math Toolbox 2, p. 587.
- **Day 4** Before starting Lesson 11-7, teach Math Toolbox 3, p. 593.

# Math Background

## LESSON 11-1

### Square Roots and Irrational Numbers

The expression $3^2$ is read "three squared" because a number used twice as a factor gives the area of a square with sides that equal that number. $3 \bullet 3 = 3^2$

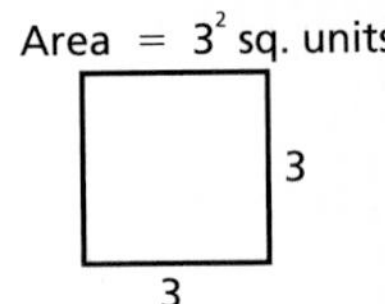


The inverse of squaring a number is finding the *square root.* If, for example, you know that the area of a square is 25 square units, to find the side of that square, you find the square root of 25 ($\sqrt{25}$).

The *radical sign* (from the Latin word *radix*, meaning "root") is used when you want the non-negative root. Since $(-5)(-5)$ also equals 25, $-5$ is a square root of 25, but $\sqrt{25} = 5$. The square of an integer (such as 3 or $-5$) is called a *perfect square.*

A rational number can be written as the ratio of two integers, $\frac{a}{b}$, where $b \neq 0$. A number that cannot be expressed as the ratio of integers, such as $\pi$ or $\sqrt{2}$, is irrational. The square root of an integer that is not a perfect square, such as $\sqrt{7}$, $\sqrt{101}$, or $\sqrt{33}$, is irrational. An irrational number can be expressed as a decimal that does not end or repeat a set of digits. Although 5.26226222622226 . . . shows a predictable pattern, it is an irrational number because it neither ends nor repeats.

## LESSON 11-2

### The Pythagorean Theorem

The longest side of a right triangle, which is always opposite the right angle, is called the *hypotenuse.* The other two sides, which form the sides of the right angle, are called the *legs.* If the hypotenuse of a right triangle is *c* and the legs are *a* and *b,* then $c^2 = a^2 + b^2$. This relationship is called the *Pythagorean Theorem,* and it is true for any right triangle. The *converse* of the Pythagorean Theorem is also true: if $c^2 = a^2 + b^2$ (where *c* is the longest side of the triangle) is true, then you can be sure that the triangle is a right triangle.

## LESSON 11-3

### Distance and Midpoint Formulas

One application of the Pythagorean Theorem is finding the distance between two points whose coordinates you know; for example, the points $(x_1, y_1)$ and $(x_2, y_2)$ are graphed here.

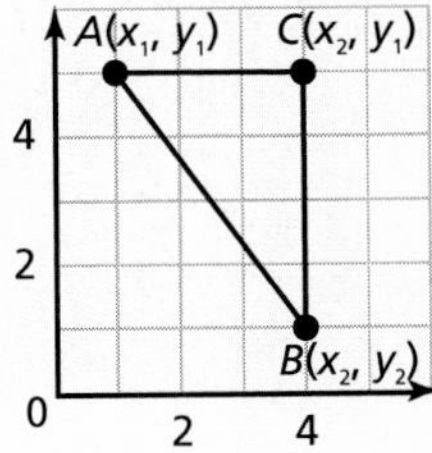


By drawing the right triangle shown, with point *C* at $(x_2, y_1)$, you can solve for *d,* the distance between points *A* and *B,* with the following steps.

$(AB)^2 = (AC)^2 + (CB)^2$

by the Pythagorean Theorem.

$(d)^2 = (x_2 - x_1)^2 + (y_2 - y_1)^2$

$d = \sqrt{(x_2 - x_1)^2 + (y_2 - y_1)^2}$

This is the *Distance Formula* for finding *d,* the distance between two points, $(x_1, y_1)$ and $(x_2, y_2)$.

You can use the *Midpoint Formula* to find the coordinates of a point that is halfway between points $A(x_1, y_1)$ and $B(x_2, y_2)$ on the segment $\overline{AB}$. The coordinates of *M*, the midpoint of $\overline{AB}$, are these: $\left(\frac{x_1 + x_2}{2}, \frac{y_1 + y_2}{2}\right)$.

## LESSON 11-5

### Special Right Triangles

You can use the Pythagorean Theorem with certain special right triangles. For example, in an isosceles right triangle (with equal legs), the two equal angles are each 45°. In any 45° right triangle, if each equal leg is $x$ units long, the following steps show why the length of the hypotenuse is always equal to $x\sqrt{2}$.

$h^2 = x^2 + x^2$ by the Pythagorean Theorem
$h^2 = 2x^2$ add
$h = \sqrt{2x^2}$ take the square root of both sides

To simplify $\sqrt{2x^2}$, use the Rule for Multiplying Square Roots, which says that if $a \geq 0$ and $b \geq 0$, then $\sqrt{ab} = \sqrt{a} \bullet \sqrt{b}$. So, $h = \sqrt{2x^2}$ simplifies to $\sqrt{2} \bullet \sqrt{x^2}$ and $h = x\sqrt{2}$ by the Commutative Property of Multiplication.

It is important to note that the Rule for Multiplying Square Roots does not apply if $a$ and $b$ are both negative; this means that $\sqrt{-4} \bullet \sqrt{-9}$ is *not* equal to $\sqrt{36}$. This is a key idea later on, when students study imaginary numbers.

In addition to a 45° right triangle, another special right triangle is the 30°-60°-90° triangle. In every 30°-60°-90° triangle, the side *opposite* the 30° angle is always one half the length of the hypotenuse.

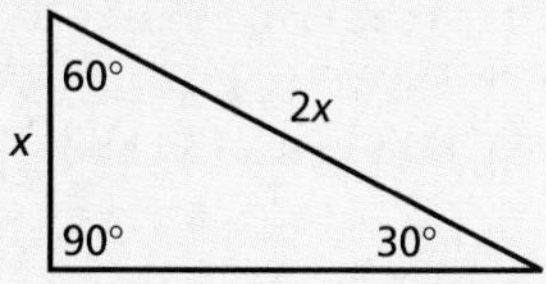


Solving for $b$, the third side, which is opposite the 60° angle, gives the result $b = x\sqrt{3}$. (The steps for solving are given in the text.)

In any 30°-60°-90° triangle, if the shorter leg opposite the 30° angle is $x$, then the hypotenuse is $2x$ and the longer leg is always equal to $x\sqrt{3}$.

## LESSONS 11-6 AND 11-7

### Sine, Cosine, and Tangent Ratios

There are other relationships that are always true in right triangles, and these are part of the branch of mathematics called *trigonometry*. Any two right triangles with a common acute angle are similar. This means that for all right triangles containing a given angle $A$, the ratio of side $a$ to side $c$ will be constant, as will other ratios of the sides.

There are six *trigonometric ratios* defined in terms of angle $A$: the hypotenuse ($c$), the side of the triangle that is opposite angle $A$ ($a$), and the side that is adjacent to angle $A$ ($b$). This text uses three of these six ratios.

$$\text{sine } \angle A = \frac{\text{side opposite}}{\text{hypotenuse}} = \frac{a}{c}$$

$$\text{cosine} \angle A = \frac{\text{side adjacent}}{\text{hypotenuse}} = \frac{b}{c}$$

$$\text{tangent } \angle A = \frac{\text{side opposite}}{\text{side adjacent}} = \frac{a}{b}$$

These ratios are usually abbreviated as sin $A$, cos $A$, and tan $A$.

You can use a scientific calculator or a table of trigonometric ratios to find the value of these ratios for any given angle. You can use these ratios to indirectly find the lengths of the measures of the angles in right triangles. You can use these trigonometric ratios to solve many real-world problems involving angle of elevation or angle of depression.

For professional development tips visit our Web site **www.phschool.com**.

# Monitoring Progress

## Universal Access

### ▶ Preventing a Student from Falling Behind

These resources are particularly helpful in preventing a student from falling behind his or her appropriate math level. For a complete list of resources for this chapter, see page 557H.

#### Skills You Need for Chapter 11

Student Edition, p. 557
Teacher's Edition, p. 557

- Simplifying numbers with exponents
- Understanding coordinates
- Solving proportions

#### Skills Handbook

Student Edition, pp. 723–741
Teacher's Edition, pp. 723–741

- Multiplying Whole Numbers, p. 725
- Multiplying and Dividing Fractions, p. 740

#### Reteaching Worksheets

There is a Reteaching worksheet for every lesson in this chapter.

- Chapter 11 Support File, Teaching Resources box
- See TE p. 557H for a complete list of resources

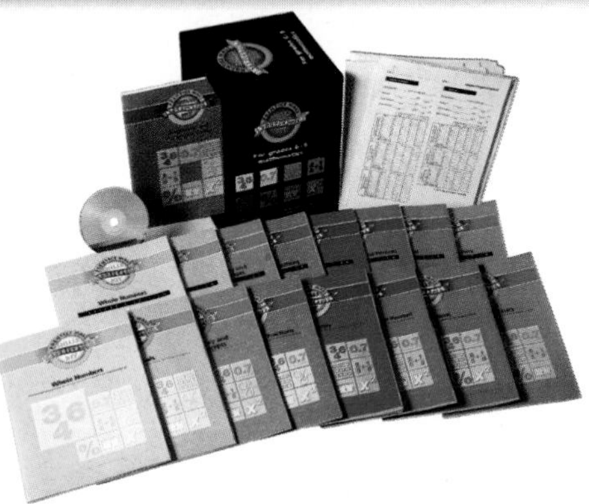

####  Skills Intervention Kit with CD-ROM

| For | Use |
|---|---|
| Lesson 11-2 | Whole Numbers |
| Lesson 11-3 | Geometry |
| Lesson 11-4 | Ratio, Proportion, and Percent |
| Lessons 11-6, 11-7 | Operations/Fractions |

#### Daily Cumulative Review Blackline Masters

There is a Daily Cumulative Review worksheet for every lesson in this chapter.

See TE p. 557H for a complete list of resources.

### ▶ Accommodating Diverse Learning Styles

#### Tactile Learning

Draw a diagram to help understand the situation. (Lesson 11-2)

Predict the length of the hypotenuse of a right triangle and then measure it to verify. (Lesson 11-5)

#### Advanced Learner

Every lesson has at least one challenge problem.

Find the length of the diagonal of the classroom by measuring the two sides and using the Distance Formula. (Lesson 11-3)

#### ELL (English Language Learner)

Pronounce the terms *sine, cosine,* and *tangent* correctly. (Lesson 11-6)

Understand the words *elevation* and *depression.* (Lesson 11-7)

#### Auditory Learning

Call out coordinates while a partner plots them on the coordinate plane. (Lesson 11-3)

Label one leg of an isosceles right triangle with a number or a variable while a partner says aloud the measurements of the other sides of the triangle. (Lesson 11-5)

#### Visual Learning

Devise a color code for writing trigonometric ratios. (Lesson 11-6)

Draw diagrams for problems involving angles of elevation and depression. (Lesson 11-7)

# Aligning Assessment with Instruction

## Assessment Options

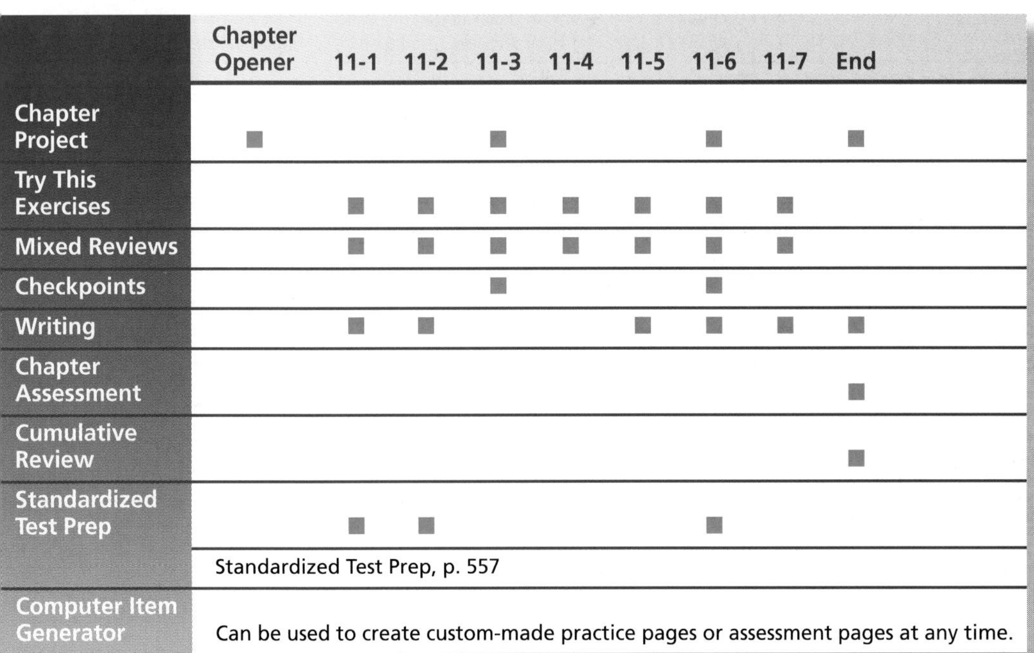

| | Chapter Opener | 11-1 | 11-2 | 11-3 | 11-4 | 11-5 | 11-6 | 11-7 | End |
|---|---|---|---|---|---|---|---|---|---|
| Chapter Project | ■ | | | ■ | | | ■ | | ■ |
| Try This Exercises | | ■ | ■ | ■ | ■ | ■ | ■ | ■ | |
| Mixed Reviews | | ■ | ■ | ■ | ■ | ■ | ■ | ■ | |
| Checkpoints | | | | ■ | | | ■ | | |
| Writing | | ■ | ■ | | | ■ | ■ | ■ | ■ |
| Chapter Assessment | | | | | | | | | ■ |
| Cumulative Review | | | | | | | | | ■ |
| Standardized Test Prep | | ■ | ■ | | | | ■ | | |
| | Standardized Test Prep, p. 557 | | | | | | | | |
| Computer Item Generator | Can be used to create custom-made practice pages or assessment pages at any time. | | | | | | | | |

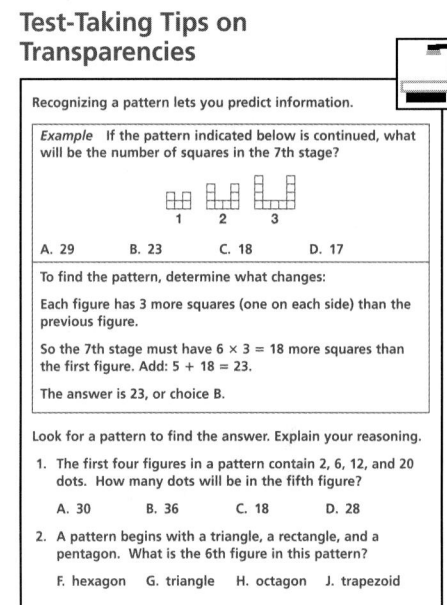

### Test-Taking Tips on Transparencies

Recognizing a pattern lets you predict information.

*Example* If the pattern indicated below is continued, what will be the number of squares in the 7th stage?

1 2 3

A. 29 B. 23 C. 18 D. 17

To find the pattern, determine what changes:

Each figure has 3 more squares (one on each side) than the previous figure.

So the 7th stage must have $6 \times 3 = 18$ more squares than the first figure. Add: $5 + 18 = 23$.

The answer is 23, or choice B.

Look for a pattern to find the answer. Explain your reasoning.

1. The first four figures in a pattern contain 2, 6, 12, and 20 dots. How many dots will be in the fifth figure?

   A. 30 B. 36 C. 18 D. 28

2. A pattern begins with a triangle, a rectangle, and a pentagon. What is the 6th figure in this pattern?

   F. hexagon G. triangle H. octagon J. trapezoid

*Use with Standardized Test Prep and Chapter Assessments.*

## Correlation to Standardized Tests

| Lesson | | CAT5 | CTBS/5 TerraNova™ | ITBS | MAT7 | SAT9 | LOCAL OBJECTIVES |
|---|---|---|---|---|---|---|---|
| 11-1 | Square Roots and Irrational Numbers | | | ■ | | ■ | |
| 11-2 | The Pythagorean Theorem | | ■ | | | ■ | |
| 11-3 | Distance and Midpoint Formulas | | | | | ■ | |
| 11-4 | Problem Solving Strategy: Write a Proportion | | | | | ■ | |
| 11-5 | Special Right Triangles | | | | | ■ | |
| 11-6 | Sine, Cosine, and Tangent Ratios | | | | | ■ | |
| 11-7 | Angles of Elevation and Depression | | | | | ■ | |

**CAT5** California Achievement Test, 5th edition
**CTBS TerraNova** Comprehensive Test of Basic Skills, 5th edition
**ITBS** Iowa Test of Basic Skills, Form M
**MAT7** Metropolitan Achievement Test, 7th edition
**SAT** Stanford Achievement Test, Advanced 1

For other standardized test correlations, follow the link to your state at **www.phschool.com**.

# Resources for Chapter 11

| | TEACHING RESOURCES BOX | | | | | | | | | | | | | | |
|---|---|---|---|---|---|---|---|---|---|---|---|---|---|---|---|
| | CHAPTER 11 SUPPORT FILE | | | | | | | | Cumulative Assessment | Lesson Planners Plus | Daily Cum Review | Teaching Transparencies | Warm-Up Transparencies | Help at Home | SE Answers c Transparenci |
| | Practice | Reteach | Enrichment | Project Manager | Checkpoints | Cumulative Review | Chapter Assessment | Alternative Assessment | | | | | | | |
| Begin Chapter | | | | ■ | | | | | | ■ | | | | | |
| 11-1 | ■ | ■ | ■ | | | | | | | ■ | ■ | 9 | ■ | | ■ |
| 11-2 | ■ | ■ | ■ | | | | | | | ■ | ■ | 78 | ■ | | ■ |
| 11-3 | ■ | ■ | ■ | | ■ | | | | | ■ | ■ | 79 | ■ | ■ | ■ |
| 11-4 | ■ | ■ | ■ | | | | | | | ■ | ■ | 80 | ■ | | ■ |
| 11-5 | ■ | ■ | ■ | | | | | | | ■ | ■ | | ■ | | ■ |
| 11-6 | ■ | ■ | ■ | | ■ | | | | | ■ | ■ | 81 | ■ | ■ | ■ |
| 11-7 | ■ | ■ | ■ | | | | | | | ■ | ■ | | ■ | | ■ |
| End Chapter | | | | | | ■ | ■ (2 forms) | ■ | After Ch. 3, 6, 9, 13 | | | | | | |

**Also available for use with the chapter:**

Solution Key
Computational Practice Skills Booklet
Mathematics Standardized Test Prep, Student Edition and Teacher's Edition
Overhead Manipulatives Kit
Practice Workbook
Algebra Readiness Kit
Student Manipulatives Kit
Test-Taking Tips on Transparencies
Assessment Success Kit
Teaching Aids and Letters
Graphing Calculator Handbook
Spanish Resources
Success-Building Puzzle and Problem Masters

## Technology

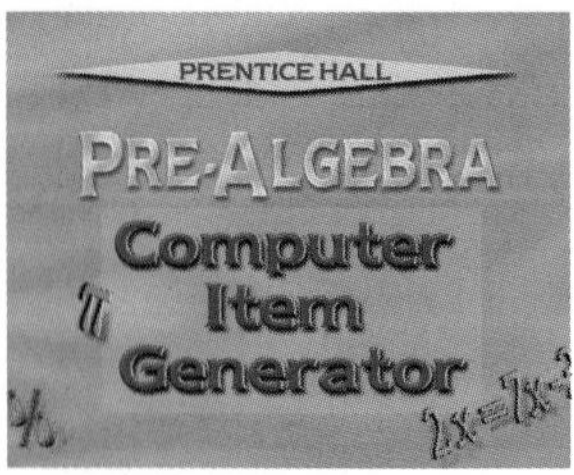


**Computer Item Generator with Standardized Test Prep**

CD-ROM with an unlimited supply of questions with varying degrees of difficulty for customized practice sheets, quizzes, and tests.

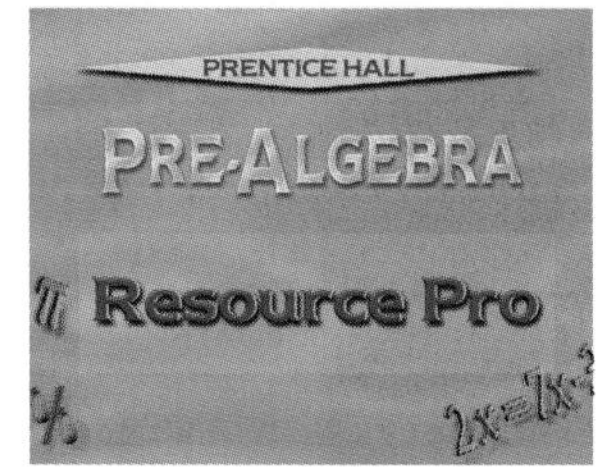


**Resource Pro® with Planning Express®**

CD-ROM with complete classroom planning tool and teaching resources for customizing and planning lessons.

**Interactive Math Lessons and Tools**

CD-ROM with lessons and tools to make abstract concepts visual and accessible.

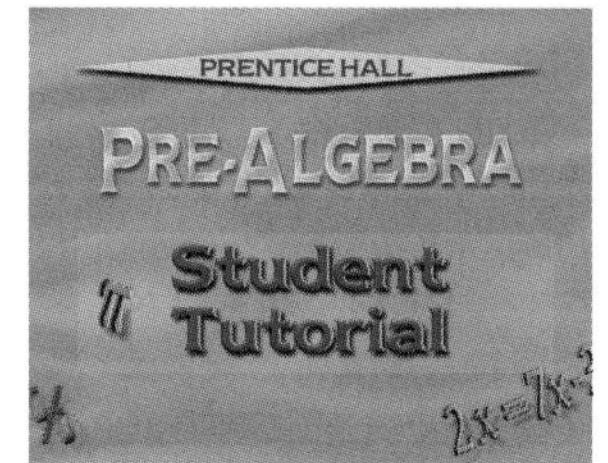


**Student Tutorial**

Test preparation software for students on CD-ROM with management system for teachers; includes Secondary Math Lab Toolkit™.

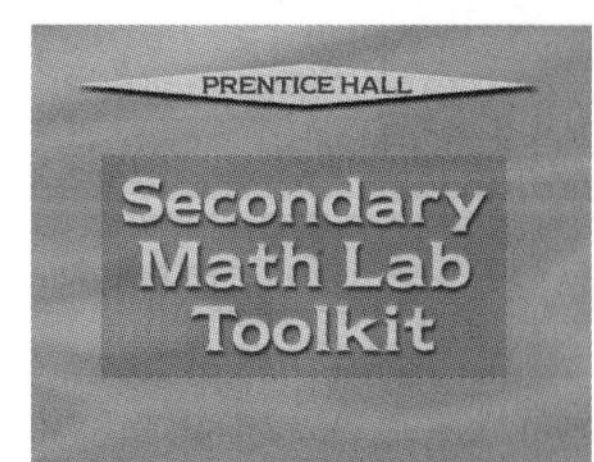


**Secondary Math Lab Toolkit™ with Integrated Math Labs**

Integrated software package with linkable math tools for exploring key concepts.

**Also available for use with the chapter:**

Math Blaster® Pre-Algebra CD-ROM
Video Fieldtrips, Vol. I: Algebra Applications
Video Fieldtrips, Vol. II: Geometry Applications
Wide World of Mathematics CD-ROM
Wide World of Mathematics Video

### *Web Extension*

**www.phschool.com**

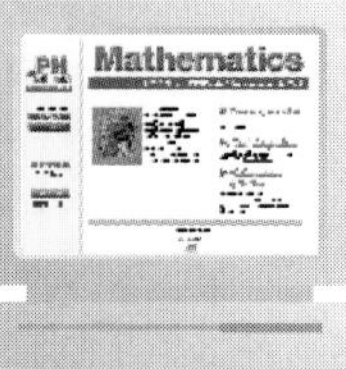


**For Students**
- Chapter Support with Internet Links
- Internet Activities

**For Teachers**
- Curriculum Support
- Professional Development
- Product Information
- Regional Support Information

# Skills You Need for Chapter 11

## Simplifying numbers with exponents
Use before Lesson 11-1.

**Simplify each expression.**

1. $10^2$ 100
2. $6^2$ 36
3. $2^2$ 4
4. $9^2$ 81
5. $11^2$ 121
6. $0.2^2$ 0.04
7. $7^2$ 49
8. $2.3^2$ 5.29
9. $4^2$ 16
10. $5^2$ 25

## Understanding coordinates
Use before Lesson 11-3.

**Name the point with the given coordinates.**

11. $(0, 3)$ G
12. $(1, -4)$ K
13. $(-2, 2)$ H
14. $(-5, -1)$ D
15. $(3, 5)$ B
16. $(6, -4)$ F
17. $(-3, 6)$ N
18. $(4, 2)$ Q

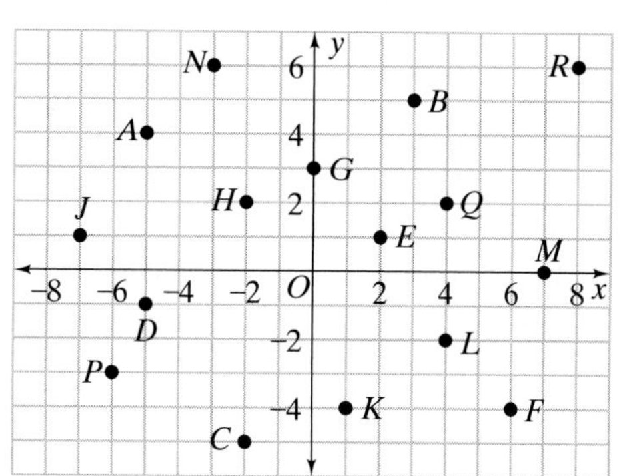


**Write the coordinates of each point.**

19. $A$ (−5, 4)
20. $C$ (−2, −5)
21. $E$ (2, 1)
22. $M$ (7, 0)
23. $J$ (−7, 1)
24. $L$ (4, −2)
25. $R$ (8, 6)
26. $P$ (−6, −3)

## Solving proportions
Use before Lesson 11-4.

**Solve each proportion.**

27. $\frac{1}{3} = \frac{a}{12}$ 4
28. $\frac{h}{5} = \frac{20}{25}$ 4
29. $\frac{24}{6} = \frac{4}{x}$ 1
30. $\frac{2}{7} = \frac{c}{35}$ 10
31. $\frac{e}{5} = \frac{32}{80}$ 2
32. $\frac{18}{g} = \frac{3}{10}$ 60
33. $\frac{4}{11} = \frac{28}{m}$ 77
34. $\frac{21}{13} = \frac{42}{a}$ 26
35. $\frac{2}{15} = \frac{c}{75}$ 10
36. $\frac{1}{4} = \frac{8}{x}$ 32
37. $\frac{13}{p} = \frac{39}{51}$ 17
38. $\frac{x}{20} = \frac{40}{100}$ 8
39. $\frac{1}{12} = \frac{5}{m}$ 60
40. $\frac{9}{a} = \frac{3}{21}$ 63
41. $\frac{h}{5} = \frac{12}{20}$ 3
42. $\frac{7}{17} = \frac{c}{51}$ 21



## Skills You Need

### Simplifying numbers with exponents
In **Lesson 11-1** students will simplify the square roots of perfect squares.

### Understanding coordinates
In **Lesson 11-3** students will find the distance between two coordinate points.

### Solving proportions
In **Lesson 11-4** students will find measurements indirectly by setting up proportions from similar right triangles.

# Skills Trace

| SKILL | INTRODUCED | DEVELOPED IN LESSON(S) | REVIEWED/REINFORCED |
|---|---|---|---|
| Finding square roots and identifying irrational numbers | 11-1 | 11-2 | pp. 569, 576 653 |
| Using the Pythagorean Theorem | 11-2 | 11-3 | pp. 576, 653 |
| Applying the Distance Formula and the Midpoint Formula | 11-3 | | pp. 581, 617, 631, 676 |
| Writing proportions to solve problems | 11-4 | 11-7 | p. 586 |
| Using relationships in 45°-45°-90° and 30°-60°-90° triangles | 11-5 | 11-6 | pp. 592, 598, 633, 679 |
| Finding and using trigonometric ratios | 11-6 | 11-7 | pp. 598, 611, 635, 681 |

# Right Triangles in Algebra

## Connecting to Students' Lives

Ask students to think of and describe some of the largest trees in your community. If any students have seen the giant sequoia trees in California, ask them to compare these trees with trees in your community. If you live in an area where there are no large trees, have students describe large trees that they have seen when traveling.

## Interdisciplinary Connections

The Chapter Project connects math and science. Consider contacting a local botanist or arborist about coming to your class to discuss how to measure trees according to the National Register of Big Trees formula.

## About the Project

The **Chapter Project** directs students to apply their knowledge of trigonometric ratios to measure the height of a large tree. Students will then apply a formula and several other measurements to calculate the Big Tree Points of the tree.

CHAPTER 11

## Right Triangles in Algebra

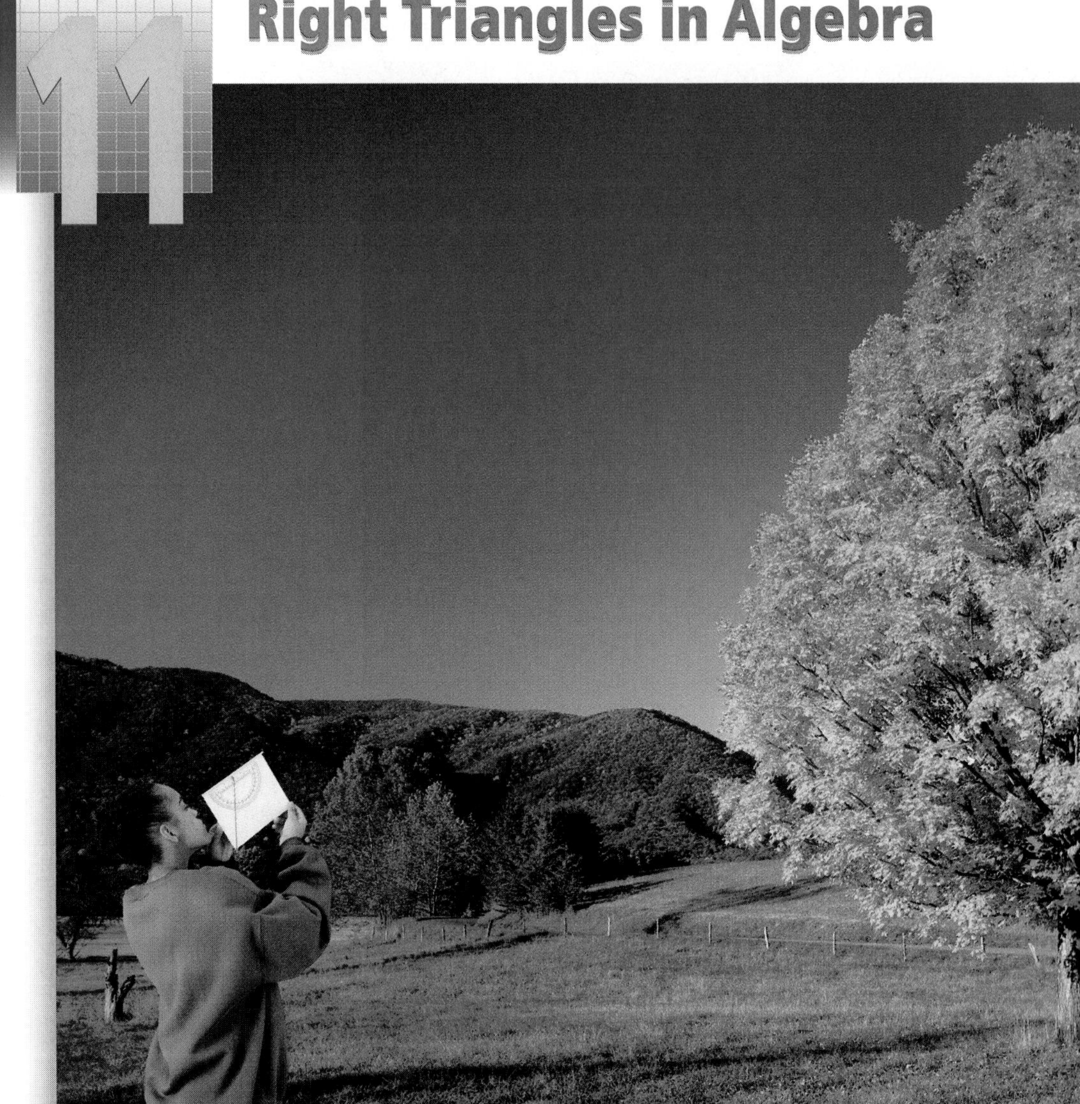

**What you'll learn in this chapter:**

- How to find the square roots of numbers
- How to find the missing measures of right triangles
- How to use the Distance and Midpoint Formulas

**558** Chapter 11

*Web Extension*
**www.phschool.com**

For Students
Chapter Support with Internet links
Interactive Activities

For Teachers
Curriculum Support
Professional Development
Product Information
Regional Support Information

CHAPTER PROJECT 11

# Tree Angles

A giant sequoia in California is the largest living thing on earth. It weighs about as much as 15 blue whales. What is the largest tree in your neighborhood? Maybe it is the largest of its species. You could nominate it to be in the National Register of Big Trees.

***Measure a Big Tree*** The National Register of Big Trees has a formula to compare the sizes of trees of the same species: Big Tree Points $= C + H + \frac{S}{4}$, where $C$ is the circumference in inches of the trunk at $4\frac{1}{2}$ feet above the ground, $H$ is the tree's height in feet, and $S$ is the average spread in feet of the tree's crown of branches.

For the chapter project, you will measure a tree and calculate its score in Big Tree Points.

### *Steps to help you complete the project*


p. 563 Activity: Creating

p. 586 Activity: Measuring

p. 598 Activity: Calculating

p. 599 Finishing the Chapter Project

***Web Extension***
**www.phschool.com**

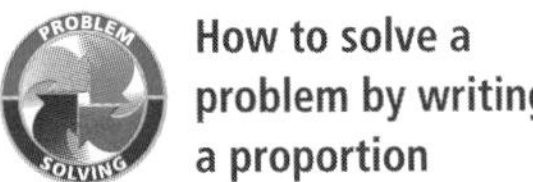

How to solve a problem by writing a proportion

## Scoring Rubric

3 You measure, calculate, and compare correctly. Your display is complete, well-organized, and informative. Your diagram is accurate and detailed, but easy to read.

2 You make minor errors in your measurements or calculations. Your display and diagram are complete, but could be better organized or more informative.

1 You measure or calculate incorrectly. Your display is incomplete or lacks organization.

0 Major elements of the project are incomplete or missing.

## LAUNCHING THE PROJECT

*The Chapter Project is optional and may be assigned at your discretion.*

Ask students:

- What kinds of trees are in your neighborhood?
- How can you measure the height of a tree?
- How would you describe a big tree?

Distribute a copy of the Project Manager and Scoring Rubric to help students get an overview of the project.

Review the scoring rubric with students.

### Project Notebook

Encourage students to keep all project-related materials in a separate folder or notebook. Call attention to the fact that they will find much useful information on the Web site **www.phschool.com**.

**Tracking the Project** Set benchmark deadlines for students to show you their work in progress.

*Available in the Chapter 11 Support File in the Teaching Resources box.*

### Project Manager and Scoring Rubric

**Getting Started** You will be creating a display showing how you compared the size of a tree in your neighborhood to similar trees in the National Registry of Big Trees. Read about the project in your textbook. As you work on the project, you will need a piece of cardboard, a drinking straw, a protractor, a piece of string, a washer, a tape measure, materials to record your measurements and calculations, and materials to create your display.

**Checklist and Suggestions**

| | | |
|---|---|---|
| ❑ | Make an inclinometer. | Attach the string to the protractor at the point where you put the vertex of an angle to measure it. |
| ❑ | Measure your tree. | Measure the circumference 4 feet above the ground. |
| ❑ | Calculate the height of your tree and your tree's Big Tree Points. | You will need to measure your horizontal distance from the highest point of the tree and the height of your eye above the ground. |
| ❑ | Create your display. | Include your inclinometer, calculations, diagrams, and comparison. |

**Scoring Rubric**

3 You measure, calculate, and compare correctly. Your display is complete, well-organized, and informative. Your diagram is accurate and detailed, but easy to read.

2 You make minor errors in your measurements or calculations. Your display and diagram are complete, but could be better organized or more informative.

1 You measure or calculate incorrectly. Your display is incomplete or lacks organization.

0 Major elements of the project are incomplete or missing.

**Your Evaluation of the Project** Evaluate your work, based on the Scoring Rubric.

**Teacher's Evaluation of the Project**

# 11-1

## Getting Ready

**Key Terms and Symbols** perfect square, square root, irrational

**Resources** A complete list of resources for this lesson is on p. 557H.

### Daily Skills Warm-Up

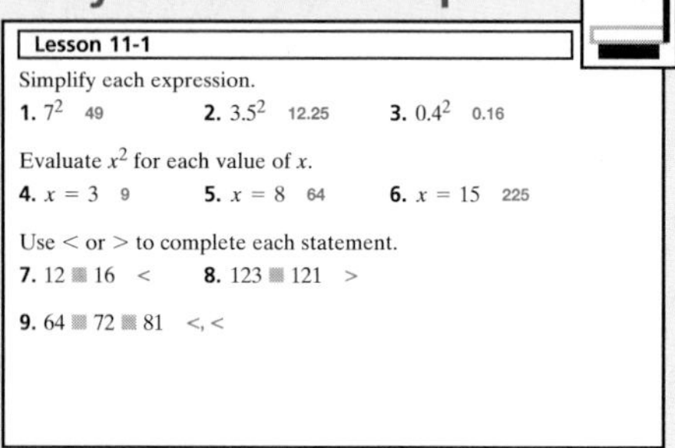

Lesson 11-1

Simplify each expression.

1. $7^2$ 49 2. $3.5^2$ 12.25 3. $0.4^2$ 0.16

Evaluate $x^2$ for each value of $x$.

4. $x = 3$ 9 5. $x = 8$ 64 6. $x = 15$ 225

Use < or > to complete each statement.

7. 12 ■ 16 < 8. 123 ■ 121 >

9. 64 ■ 72 ■ 81 <, <

### Background for the Lesson

The non-negative square root of a positive number $n$ (written $\sqrt{n}$) equals $r$ when $r \cdot r = n$ or $r^2 = n$. For example, since $(1.2)^2$ is 1.44, then $\sqrt{1.44}$ is 1.2. Square roots of positive integers other than perfect squares, such as $\sqrt{2}$, $\sqrt{5}$, and $\sqrt{24}$, are irrational numbers. Irrational numbers are decimals that neither terminate nor repeat. An irrational number may, however, have a pattern, such as 1.0110111011110 . . . The square root of a negative number is not a real number because the product of two nonzero numbers with the same sign is always positive. Later, students will learn that the square root of a negative number is defined in the complex number system.

## 1 Focus

### Connecting to Students' Lives

Remind students that if they know their multiplication tables, then they already know the first 10 to 12 perfect squares.

# 11-1 Square Roots and Irrational Numbers

**What You'll Learn**

1. To find square roots of numbers
2. To classify real numbers

**. . . And Why**

To use square roots in real-world situations, such as finding the distance to the horizon

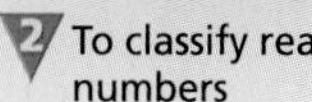

## Part 1 Finding Square Roots

Consider the three squares at the right.

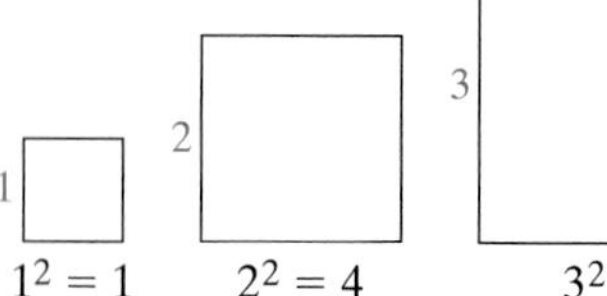


Each square has sides with integer length. The area of a square is the *square* of the length of a side. The square of an integer is a **perfect square.**

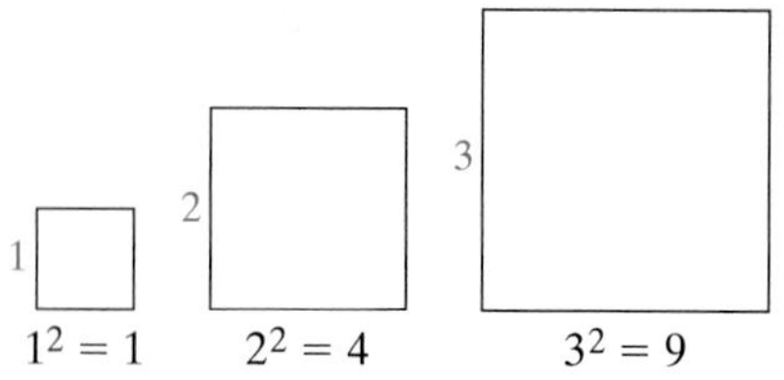

The inverse of squaring a number is finding a **square root.** The symbol $\sqrt{\phantom{x}}$ indicates the nonnegative square root of a number. Assume that an expression under a radical is greater than or equal to 0.

### Example 1

**Simplify each square root.**

**a.** $\sqrt{64}$

$\sqrt{64} = 8$

**b.** $-\sqrt{121}$

$-\sqrt{121} = -11$

**Try This** Simplify each square root.

1. $\sqrt{100}$ 10 2. $-\sqrt{100}$ −10 3. $\sqrt{16}$ 4 4. $-\sqrt{16}$ −4

The first thirteen perfect squares are 0, 1, 4, 9, 16, 25, 36, 49, 64, 81, 100, 121, and 144. Memorizing these will help you solve problems efficiently.

For an integer that is not a perfect square, you can estimate a square root. For example, 8 is between the perfect squares 4 and 9.

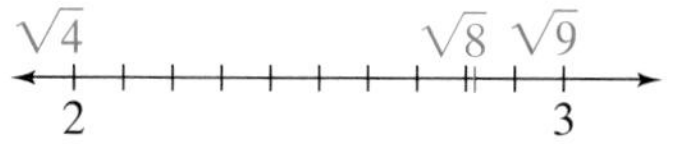

$\sqrt{4}$ ... $\sqrt{8}$ $\sqrt{9}$ (number line from 2 to 3) $\sqrt{8}$ is between $\sqrt{4}$ and $\sqrt{9}$.

Since 8 is closer to 9 than to 4, $\sqrt{8}$ is closer to 3 than to 2. So, $\sqrt{8} \approx 3$.



## Tools to Monitor Progress

**BEFORE THE LESSON**

**To check prerequisite skills:**

- Simplifying numbers with exponents

**Skills You Need,** p. 557

**Skills Handbook,** p. 725

**DURING THE LESSON**

**To check understanding:**

**Try This** exercises on student page

- **Additional Example 2**

If the eyes of the lifeguard in Example 2 are 20 ft above the ground, estimate the new distance to the horizon.
≈ 5 mi

## Example 2

**You can use the formula $d = \sqrt{1.5h}$ to estimate the distance $d$, in miles, to a horizon line. Here, $h$ is the height, in feet, of the viewer's eyes above the ground. Estimate the distance to the horizon seen by a lifeguard whose eyes are 10 feet above the ground.**

$d = \sqrt{1.5h}$ Use the formula.

$d = \sqrt{15}$ Replace $h$ with 10 and multiply.

$\sqrt{9} < \sqrt{15} < \sqrt{16}$ Find perfect squares close to 15.

$\sqrt{16} = 4$ Find the square root of the closest perfect square.

The lifeguard can see about 4 miles to the horizon.

**Try This** Estimate to the nearest integer.

**5.** $\sqrt{27}$ 5 **6.** $-\sqrt{72}$ −8 **7.** $\sqrt{50}$ 7 **8.** $-\sqrt{22}$ −5

## Part 2 Classifying Real Numbers

You can express a rational number as the ratio of two integers $\frac{a}{b}$, where $b$ is not zero. A number that *cannot* be expressed as such a ratio is **irrational.** In decimal form, rational numbers either terminate or repeat. Irrational numbers neither terminate nor repeat. If a positive integer is not a perfect square, its square root is irrational.

## Example 3

**Identify each number as rational or irrational.**

**a.** $\sqrt{18}$ irrational, because 18 is not a perfect square

**b.** $\sqrt{121}$ rational, because 121 is a perfect square

**c.** $-\sqrt{24}$ irrational, because 24 is not a perfect square

**d.** 432.8 rational, because it is a terminating decimal

**e.** 0.1212 . . . rational, because it is a repeating decimal

**f.** 0.120120012 . . . irrational, because it neither terminates nor repeats

**g.** $\pi$ irrational, because it cannot be represented as $\frac{a}{b}$, where $a$ and $b$ are integers

**Try This** Identify each number as rational or irrational.

**9.** $\sqrt{2}$ **10.** $-\sqrt{81}$ **11.** 0.53 **12.** $\sqrt{42}$

9–12. See right.

9. irrational
10. rational
11. rational
12. irrational



# 2 Teach

## Part 1 Teaching Notes

Discuss the fact that squaring and finding the square root are *inverse* operations that undo each other.

### Example 1

**Build understanding.** Ask: What difference does it make that the negative sign is outside the square root sign? A negative sign on the outside of the square root sign means to take the opposite of the square root. If the sign were inside, you couldn't find an integer that is the square root of −121.

**Reading Math** The expression $-\sqrt{121}$ is read, "the opposite of the square root of 121." When you simplify the expression, you find the square root of 121, 11, then express it as its opposite, −11.

**Error Prevention** Be sure students understand that the square root of a negative number is not a real number; no number on the real number line can be squared to give a negative result.

### Example 2

**Build understanding.** Ask: Would the lifeguard be able to see a little more than or a little less than 4 miles? Explain. a little less because $\sqrt{15} < \sqrt{16}$

## Part 2 Teaching Notes

Remind students that $\pi$ has been calculated with a computer to a great many places, and the decimal 3.1416 . . . does not end or repeat.

### Example 3

**Build understanding.** Ask: What is $11^2$? 121

**Extension** Is $\sqrt{18}$ close to 9? Estimate. No; It is between 4 ($\sqrt{16}$) and 5 ($\sqrt{25}$).

• **Additional Example 3**

Identify each as rational or irrational.

**a.** $\sqrt{49}$ **b.** 0.16 **c.** $\sqrt{3}$

rational; rational; irrational

## AFTER THE LESSON

**To assess knowledge: Lesson Quiz**

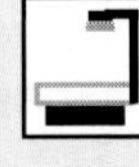

Simplify each square root. Estimate to the nearest integer if necessary.

**1.** $\sqrt{81}$ 9 **2.** $\sqrt{57}$ about 8

Identify each number as rational or irrational.

**3.** $\sqrt{48}$ irrational **4.** 0.0125 rational

• For enrichment and reteaching options see Resources on p. 557H.

# 3 Practice/Assess

## Assignment Guide

To provide flexible scheduling, this lesson can be divided into parts.

▼ Part 1
**Core** 1–10, 15–30, 36, 38, 46–48
✪ **Extension** 39–45

▼ Part 2
**Core** 11–14, 31–35
✪ **Extension** 37

Mixed Review can be assigned at any time for maintenance.

## Exercises

**Test Prep Exercise 38** Read this problem carefully; it asks for the *perimeter* of the square room, not the length of the side.

## ✪ Challenge

Does $\sqrt{36} = \sqrt{9} \cdot \sqrt{4}$? yes
Does $\sqrt{25} = \sqrt{9} + \sqrt{16}$? no

## Closure

The square of an integer is a perfect square. The inverse of squaring is finding a square root. The symbol $\sqrt{\ }$ indicates the non-negative square root of a number. A number that cannot be expressed as the ratio of two integers, $\frac{a}{b}$, where $b$ is not zero, is irrational. If a positive integer is not a perfect square, then its square root is irrational.

## Daily Cumulative Review

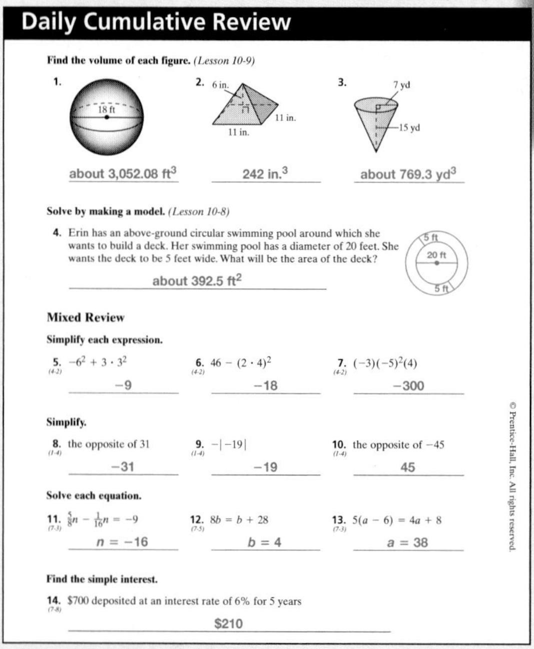

**Find the volume of each figure.** *(Lesson 10-9)*

1. about 3,052.08 $ft^3$
2. 242 $in.^3$
3. about 769.3 $yd^3$



**Solve by making a model.** *(Lesson 10-8)*

4. Erin has an above-ground circular swimming pool around which she wants to build a deck. Her swimming pool has a diameter of 20 feet. She wants the deck to be 5 feet wide. What will be the area of the deck?
about 392.5 $ft^2$



**Mixed Review**

**Simplify each expression.**

5. (4-2) $-6^2 + 3 \cdot 3^2$   −9
6. (4-2) $46 - (2 \cdot 4)^2$   −18
7. (4-2) $(-3)(-5)^2(4)$   −300

**Simplify.**

8. (1-4) the opposite of 31   −31
9. (1-4) $-|-19|$   −19
10. (1-4) the opposite of −45   45

**Solve each equation.**

11. (7-3) $\frac{5}{8}n - \frac{1}{16}n = -9$   $n = -16$
12. (7-5) $8b = b + 28$   $b = 4$
13. (7-3) $5(a - 6) = 4a + 8$   $a = 38$

**Find the simple interest.**

14. (7-8) $700 deposited at an interest rate of 6% for 5 years   $210



# Exercises

## Check Understanding

**Simplify each square root.**

1. $\sqrt{4}$ 2
2. $-\sqrt{36}$ −6
3. $\sqrt{64}$ 8
4. $\sqrt{25}$ 5
5. $-\sqrt{49}$ −7

**Estimate to the nearest integer.**

6. $\sqrt{10}$ 3
7. $-\sqrt{3}$ −2
8. $\sqrt{61}$ 8
9. $\sqrt{17}$ 4
10. $-\sqrt{39}$ −6

**Identify each number as rational or irrational.**

11. $\sqrt{0}$ rational
12. 4.1010010001 . . . irrational
13. $\sqrt{87}$ irrational
14. $-\sqrt{16}$ rational

15. *Critical Thinking* What number do you get when you square the square root of $x$? $x$

## Practice and Problem Solving

**Simplify each square root.**

16. $\sqrt{81}$ 9
17. $-\sqrt{9}$ −3
18. $-\sqrt{64}$ −8
19. $\sqrt{144}$ 12
20. $\sqrt{\frac{4}{9}}$ $\frac{2}{3}$

**Estimate to the nearest integer.**

21. $\sqrt{7}$ 3
22. $\sqrt{2}$ 1
23. $\sqrt{42}$ 6
24. $-\sqrt{80}$ −9
25. $\sqrt{58}$ 8
26. $\sqrt{43}$ 7
27. $-\sqrt{98}$ −10
28. $\sqrt{14}$ 4
29. $-\sqrt{55}$ −7
30. $\sqrt{105}$ 10

**Identify each number as rational or irrational.**

31. $-0.\overline{3}$ rational
32. $\sqrt{5}$ irrational
33. 2,222,222 rational
34. $\sqrt{144}$ rational
35. 0.31311 . . . irrational

36. *Writing* A classmate was absent for today's lesson. Explain to him or her how to estimate $\sqrt{30}$. Answers may vary. Sample: Think of the perfect squares closest to 30, one less than 30 and one greater than 30. Take the square root of the one closest to 30.

✪ 37. a. *Patterns* You can create irrational numbers. For example, the number 1.010010001 . . . shows a pattern, yet it is irrational. What pattern do you see? In each repetition of the pattern there is one more zero than in the previous one.
b. *Open-ended* Name three irrational numbers between 9 and 10. Answers may vary. Sample: 9.010010001 . . . , 9.121121112 . . . , 9.565665666 . . .

38. **TEST PREP** The floor of a square room has an area of 256 $ft^2$. What is the perimeter of the room? C
A. 16 ft B. 56 ft C. 64 ft D. 68 ft



## Alternative Assessment

With students in pairs, have one estimate the square root of a number that is not a perfect square (such as 11, 37, 84), while the other student finds the square root on a calculator. Ask the students to compare their findings, then exchange roles.

*Algebra* **Find two integers that make each equation true.**

39. $a^2 = 9$ 3, −3
40. $b^2 = 25$ 5, −5
41. $y^2 = 100$ 10, −10
42. $m^2 = \frac{100}{25}$ 2, −2

*Algebra* **Write a simplified expression for each product. Then simplify each expression.**

SAMPLE $\sqrt{8} \cdot \sqrt{2} = \sqrt{8 \cdot 2} = \sqrt{16} = 4$

43. $\sqrt{3} \cdot \sqrt{27}$ 9
44. $\sqrt{50} \cdot \sqrt{2}$ 10
45. $\sqrt{36} \cdot \sqrt{4}$ 12

46. *Geometry* Find the length of a side of a square with an area of 81 $cm^2$. 9 cm

47. *Geometry* The area of a circle is 12 $in.^2$. Estimate its radius to the nearest inch. 2 in.

48. The observation windows at the top of the Washington Monument in Washington, D.C. are 500 ft from the ground. Using the formula $d = \sqrt{1.5h}$, estimate the distance a visitor can see to the horizon from the observation windows. 27 mi

## MIXED REVIEW

**Find the volume of each figure.** ***(Lesson 10-9)***

49. sphere with $r = 0.03$ m 0.000113 $m^3$
50. cone with $r = 4$ cm and $h = 10$ cm 167.5 $cm^3$

**List all the factors of each number.** ***(Lesson 4-1)***

51. 18 1, 2, 3, 6, 9, 18
52. 22 1, 2, 11, 22
53. 33 1, 3, 11, 33
54. 45 1, 3, 5, 9, 15, 45
55. 50 1, 2, 5, 10, 25, 50
56. 90 1, 2, 3, 5, 6, 9, 10, 15, 18, 30, 45, 90

57. Shannon scored 17 correct on a 25-item test. The passing grade was 65%. Did Shannon pass? ***(Lesson 6-5)*** yes

## CHAPTER PROJECT 11 ACTIVITY 1 CREATING

An *inclinometer* is an instrument for measuring angles. You can build one from a piece of cardboard, a drinking straw, a protractor, a piece of string, and a washer. Practice using your inclinometer, reading it at the point where the string crosses the protractor. This reading measures $\angle XYZ$.

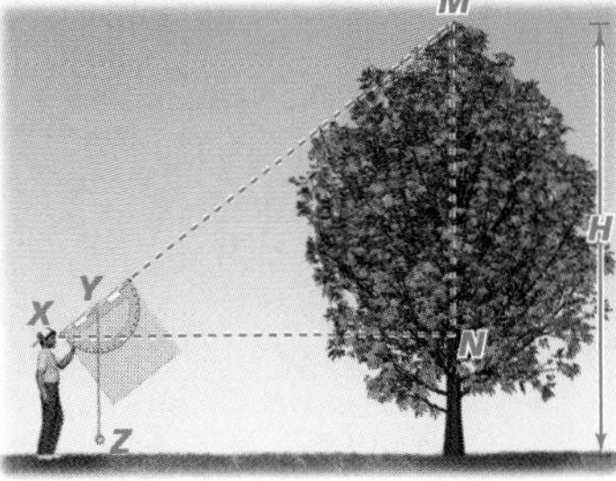


See also Extra Practice section.



## Project Activity 1

**Creating** To build the inclinometer, cut the drinking straw so that it is the same length as the base of the protractor. Then, tape the drinking straw to the edge of the base of the protractor. Tie the string through the hole that is closest to the base of the protractor. Tie the washer to the other end of the string. To use the inclinometer, sight through the straw to the top of the object you are measuring. Measure the acute angle where the string hits the protractor.

## Practice

**Estimate to the nearest integer.**

1. $\sqrt{18}$ 4
2. $\sqrt{24}$ 5
3. $\sqrt{50}$ 7
4. $\sqrt{8}$ 3
5. $\sqrt{62}$ 8
6. $\sqrt{78}$ 9
7. $\sqrt{98}$ 10
8. $\sqrt{46}$ 7
9. $\sqrt{38}$ 6

**Simplify each square root.**

10. $\sqrt{144}$ 12
11. $\sqrt{9 + 16}$ 5
12. $\sqrt{900}$ 30
13. $\sqrt{169}$ 13
14. $-\sqrt{100}$ −10
15. $\sqrt{0.16}$ 0.4
16. $\sqrt{\frac{16}{81}}$ $\frac{4}{9}$
17. $\sqrt{\frac{4}{25}}$ $\frac{2}{5}$
18. $\sqrt{\frac{121}{144}}$ $\frac{11}{12}$

**Identify each number as rational or irrational.**

19. $\sqrt{289}$ Rational
20. 5.7777... Rational
21. $\sqrt{41}$ Irrational
22. 0.62662... Irrational
23. $\sqrt{49}$ Rational
24. $\sqrt{52}$ Irrational

**Find two integers that make each equation true.**

25. $x^2 = 16$ 4, −4
26. $3m^2 = 147$ 7, −7

**Use the formula $d = \sqrt{1.5h}$ to estimate the distance to the horizon $d$ in miles for each viewer's eye height $h$, in feet.**

27. $h = 12$ ft about 4 mi
28. $h = 216$ ft 18 mi
29. $h = 412$ ft about 25 mi

30. The Moon has a surface area of approximately 14,650,000 $mi^2$. Estimate its radius to the nearest mile. 1,080 mi



## Reteaching

Estimate $\sqrt{27}$ to the nearest integer.
To estimate square roots, it is helpful to know the perfect squares in the following table.

| $n$ | 1 | 2 | 3 | 4 | 5 | 6 | 7 | 8 | 9 | 10 | 11 | 12 |
|---|---|---|---|---|---|---|---|---|---|---|---|---|
| $n^2$ | 1 | 4 | 9 | 16 | 25 | 36 | 49 | 64 | 81 | 100 | 121 | 144 |

Look at the $n^2$ row. These numbers are called perfect squares. Between which two perfect squares is 27?
$25 < 27 < 36$
so, $\sqrt{25} < \sqrt{27} < \sqrt{36}$
and $5 < \sqrt{27} < 6$
Since 27 is closer to 25 than to 36, $\sqrt{27}$ is closer to 5 than to 6.
Thus, $\sqrt{27}$ to the nearest integer is 5.

**Each square root is between what two integers? Circle the integer to which it is closer.**

1. $\sqrt{18}$ (4), 5
2. $\sqrt{60}$ 7, (8)
3. $-\sqrt{8}$ (−3), −2
4. $\sqrt{90}$ (9), 10
5. $\sqrt{29 + 8}$ (6), 7
6. $-\sqrt{21}$ (−5), −4
7. $\sqrt{133}$ 11, (12)
8. $-\sqrt{118}$ (−11), −10

**Estimate to the nearest integer.**

9. $\sqrt{48}$ 7
10. $\sqrt{80}$ 9
11. $\sqrt{119}$ 11
12. $\sqrt{141}$ 12
13. $\sqrt{67}$ 8
14. $\sqrt{95}$ 10
15. $\sqrt{6}$ 2
16. $\sqrt{20}$ 4
17. $\sqrt{12}$ 3
18. $-\sqrt{3}$ −2
19. $\sqrt{42}$ 6
20. $-\sqrt{22}$ −5
21. $-\sqrt{110}$ −10
22. $-\sqrt{31}$ −6
23. $\sqrt{45}$ 7



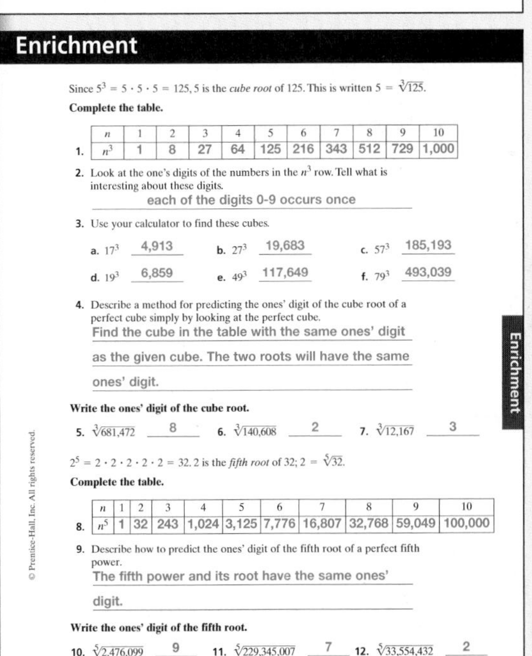

## Enrichment

Since $5^3 = 5 \cdot 5 \cdot 5 = 125$, 5 is the *cube root* of 125. This is written $5 = \sqrt[3]{125}$.

**Complete the table.**

1.

| $n$ | 1 | 2 | 3 | 4 | 5 | 6 | 7 | 8 | 9 | 10 |
|---|---|---|---|---|---|---|---|---|---|---|
| $n^3$ | 1 | 8 | 27 | 64 | 125 | 216 | 343 | 512 | 729 | 1,000 |

2. Look at the one's digits of the numbers in the $n^3$ row. Tell what is interesting about these digits.
each of the digits 0-9 occurs once

3. Use your calculator to find these cubes.
a. $17^3$ 4,913
b. $27^3$ 19,683
c. $57^3$ 185,193
d. $19^3$ 6,859
e. $49^3$ 117,649
f. $79^3$ 493,039

4. Describe a method for predicting the ones' digit of the cube root of a perfect cube simply by looking at the perfect cube.
Find the cube in the table with the same ones' digit as the given cube. The two roots will have the same ones' digit.

**Write the ones' digit of the cube root.**

5. $\sqrt[3]{681{,}472}$ 8
6. $\sqrt[3]{140{,}608}$ 2
7. $\sqrt[3]{12{,}167}$ 3

$2^5 = 2 \cdot 2 \cdot 2 \cdot 2 \cdot 2 = 32$. 2 is the *fifth root* of 32; $2 = \sqrt[5]{32}$.

**Complete the table.**

8.

| $n$ | 1 | 2 | 3 | 4 | 5 | 6 | 7 | 8 | 9 | 10 |
|---|---|---|---|---|---|---|---|---|---|---|
| $n^5$ | 1 | 32 | 243 | 1,024 | 3,125 | 7,776 | 16,807 | 32,768 | 59,049 | 100,000 |

9. Describe how to predict the ones' digit of the fifth root of a perfect fifth power.
The fifth power and its root have the same ones' digit.

**Write the ones' digit of the fifth root.**

10. $\sqrt[5]{2{,}476{,}099}$ 9
11. $\sqrt[5]{229{,}345{,}007}$ 7
12. $\sqrt[5]{33{,}554{,}432}$ 2

# 11-2

## Getting Ready

**Key Terms and Symbols** legs, hypotenuse, Pythagorean Theorem

**Materials** graph paper, straightedge

**Resources** A complete list of resources for this lesson is on p. 557H.

### Daily Skills Warm-Up

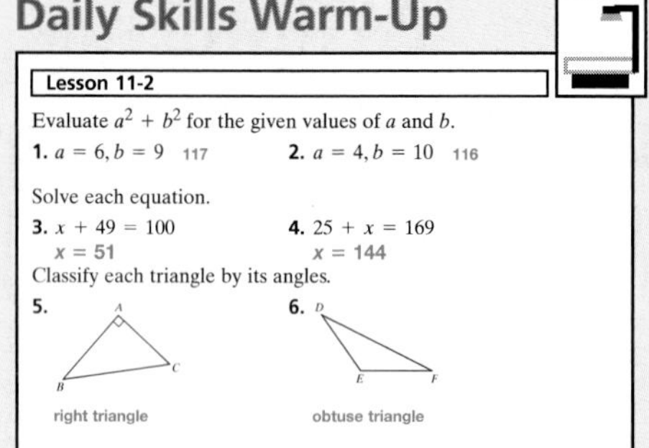
Lesson 11-2

Evaluate $a^2 + b^2$ for the given values of $a$ and $b$.

1. $a = 6, b = 9$ 117
2. $a = 4, b = 10$ 116

Solve each equation.

3. $x + 49 = 100$ $x = 51$
4. $25 + x = 169$ $x = 144$

Classify each triangle by its angles.

5. right triangle
6. obtuse triangle

### Background for the Lesson

The general theorem for any right triangle is named after the Greek mathematician Pythagoras, who lived about 580–500 B.C. Many examples of this theorem were known and used by the Babylonians as much as fifteen hundred years earlier. About 600 B.C. the theorem was stated in an ancient Hindu handbook for temple builders. Pythagoras is credited with first demonstrating the truth of this theorem. Since then, many people have written different proofs for the Pythagorean Theorem.

## 1 Focus

### Investigate

As students work through this exercise, make sure they square their measurements before comparing the sum of the legs squared to the hypotenuse squared.

### Connecting to Prior Knowledge

In Lesson 11-1, students learned about perfect squares and square roots. In this lesson, students learn to use the Pythagorean Theorem. In Lesson 11-3, students will use the Pythagorean Theorem to find the distance between two points on the coordinate plane.





# 11-2 The Pythagorean Theorem

### What You'll Learn

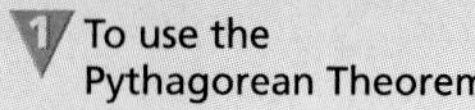
1 To use the Pythagorean Theorem

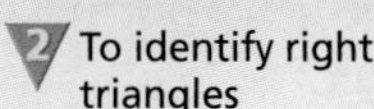
2 To identify right triangles

### . . . And Why

To use the Pythagorean Theorem in real-world situations, such as carpentry

## Investigate

EXPLORING RIGHT TRIANGLES

1. On graph paper, create right triangles with legs $a$ and $b$. Measure the length of the third side $c$ with another piece of graph paper. Copy and complete the table below.

| a | b | c | $a^2$ | $b^2$ | $c^2$ |
|---|---|---|---|---|---|
| 3 | 4 | ■ | 9 | 16 | ■ |
| 5 | 12 | ■ | 25 | 144 | ■ |
| 9 | 12 | ■ | 81 | 144 | ■ |

5, 25
13, 169
15, 225

2. Based on your table, use >, <, or = to complete the following statement.

$a^2 + b^2$ ■ $c^2$ =

## PART 1 Using the Pythagorean Theorem

**Quick Review**

A right triangle is a triangle with a 90° angle.

In a right triangle, the two shortest sides are **legs.** The longest side, which is opposite the right angle, is the **hypotenuse.** The Pythagorean Theorem shows how the legs and hypotenuse of a right triangle are related.

**Pythagorean Theorem**

In any right triangle, the sum of the squares of the lengths of the legs is equal to the square of the length of the hypotenuse.

$$a^2 + b^2 = c^2$$

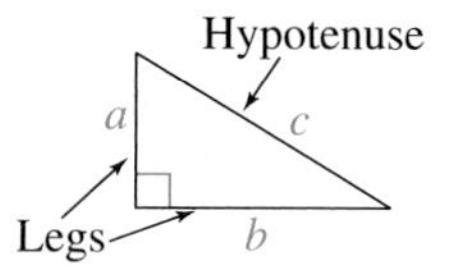


You will prove the Pythagorean Theorem in a future math class. For now, you will use the theorem to find the length of a leg or the length of a hypotenuse.



## Tools to Monitor Progress

**BEFORE THE LESSON**

**To check prerequisite skills:**

- Multiplying whole numbers

**Skills Handbook,** p. 725

**Skills Intervention Kit,** Whole Numbers

**DURING THE LESSON**

**To check understanding:**

**Try This** exercises on student page

- **Additional Examples 1–4**

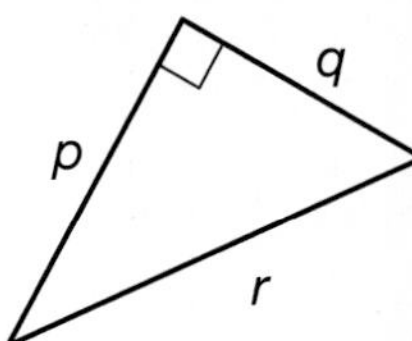

## EXAMPLE 1

**Find $c$, the length of the hypotenuse, in the triangle at the right.**

$c^2 = a^2 + b^2$ Use the Pythagorean Theorem.

$c^2 = 6^2 + 8^2$ Replace $a$ with 6 and $b$ with 8.

$c^2 = 100$ Simplify.

$c = \sqrt{100} = 10$ Find the positive square root of each side.

The length of the hypotenuse is 10 cm.

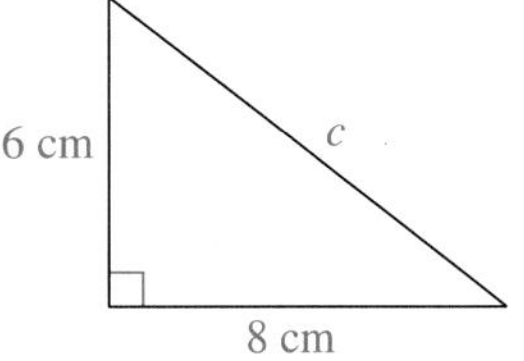


**TRY THIS** The lengths of two sides of a right triangle are given. Find the length of the third side.

**3.** legs: 3 ft and 4 ft 5 ft

**4.** leg: 12 m; hypotenuse: 15 m 9 m

You can use a calculator or a table of square roots to find approximate values for square roots.

## EXAMPLE 2

**Find the value of $x$ in the triangle at the right. Round to the nearest tenth.**

$a^2 + b^2 = c^2$ Use the Pythagorean Theorem.

$6^2 + x^2 = 9^2$ Replace $a$ with 6, $b$ with $x$, and $c$ with 9.

$36 + x^2 = 81$ Simplify.

$x^2 = 45$ Subtract 36 from each side.

$x = \sqrt{45}$ Find the positive square root.

Then, use one of the two methods below to approximate $\sqrt{45}$.

**Method 1** Use a calculator.

A calculator value for $\sqrt{45}$ is 6.708203932.

$x \approx 6.7$ Round to the nearest tenth.

**Method 2** Use a table of square roots.

Use the table on page 746. Find 45 in the $N$ column. Then find the corresponding value in the $\sqrt{N}$ column. It is 6.708.

$x \approx 6.7$ Round to the nearest tenth.

The value of $x$ is about 6.7 in.

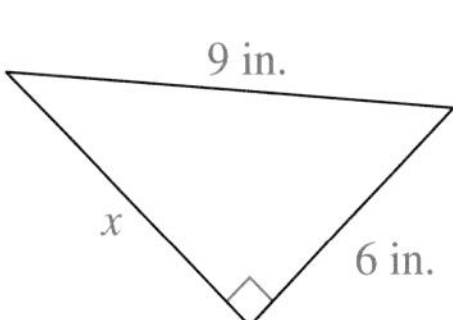


**TRY THIS**

**5.** In a right triangle the length of the hypotenuse is 15 m and the length of a leg is 8 m. What is the length of the other leg, to the nearest tenth of a meter? 12.7 m



# 2 Teach

## Part 1 Teaching Notes

Remind students that a right triangle has one right angle. To help students recognize right triangles, draw several on the board with the right angle in various positions and legs of different lengths. Have students label and name the right angle, the hypotenuse, and the legs.

### Example 1

**Build understanding.** Ask: What do you know about the length of $c$ as compared to $a$ and $b$? **$c$ is longer than $a$ or $b$.**

**Error Prevention** Students may assume that in order for the Pythagorean Theorem to work, $a^2 + b^2$ must sum to a perfect square so that $c$ can be an integer value. Explain that the relationship is true in every right triangle, even when the lengths of the sides are irrational numbers.

### Example 2

**Build understanding.** Ask: Why may finding $\sqrt{45}$ with a calculator or square root table sometimes be more useful than leaving the answer as the exact form $\sqrt{45}$? **sample answer: 6.7 is a measurement you can use to build something.**

**Connecting to History** The special relationship between the legs and hypotenuse of a right triangle, as described by the Pythagorean Theorem, has been known for thousands of years. Clay tablets from the Babylonian empire of ancient Mesopotamia have been found describing the relationship. These tablets were written in the second millennium B.C. (2000–1000 B.C.). Further evidence has been found that ancient Egyptians also knew about the relationship. It is also likely that ancient Asian cultures understood the relationship, though such artifacts do not exist.

**a.** Find the value of $r$, the hypotenuse, if $p = 28$ and $q = 21$. $r = 35$

**b.** Find the value of the leg $q$ if $r = 14$ and $p = 7$. Approximate the square root and round to the nearest tenth. $q \approx 12.1$

**c.** Is the triangle a right triangle if $p = 3.6$, $q = 2.7$, and $r = 4.5$? yes

## AFTER THE LESSON

**To assess knowledge: Lesson Quiz**

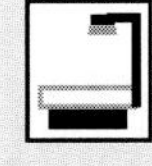

Find each missing length of the right triangle to the nearest tenth of a unit.

1. leg $a = 7$; leg $b = 8$ **hyp. $c$ 10.6**
2. hyp. $c = 17$, leg $a = 9$ **leg $b$ 14.4**
3. Is a triangle with sides 6.9 ft, 9.2 ft, and 11.5 ft a right triangle? **yes**

- For enrichment and reteaching options see Resources on p. 557H.

## Example 3

**Build understanding.** Ask: Which of these distances represent the legs of the triangle? Which represents the hypotenuse? The span and rise are the legs and the rafter length is the hypotenuse.

## Part 2 Teaching Notes

Before you introduce the topic of Part 2, ask students to describe ways to find out whether a triangle is a right triangle. Using a protractor to measure the largest angle might be one method. Then ask how they could do this without a protractor. Remind them of the Pythagorean Theorem.

**Visual Learning** Show students several examples of triangles that have one angle that is close to 90°. Ask them to explain whether they think the triangles are right triangles. Lead students to see that the only way to confirm whether they are right triangles, without measuring the angle, is to use the converse of the Pythagorean Theorem.

## Example 4

**Build understanding.** Ask: How do you know which sides are the legs and which is the hypotenuse? In a right triangle, the hypotenuse is always longer than either of the legs, so the side that is 20 m must be the hypotenuse.

**Math Reasoning** Use math reasoning to describe a way to draw a line that has a length of exactly $\sqrt{5}$. sample answer: Draw a right triangle with legs of 1 and 2. The hypotenuse has length $\sqrt{5}$.

### Example 3

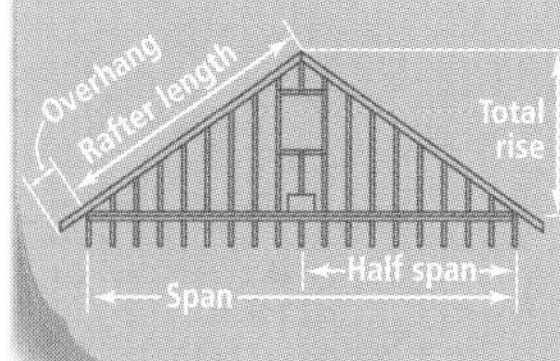


*Carpentry* **The carpentry terms *span*, *rise*, and *rafter length* are illustrated in the diagram at the left. A carpenter wants to make a roof that has a span of 24 ft and a rise of 8.5 ft. What should the rafter length be?**

| | |
|---|---|
| $c^2 = a^2 + b^2$ | Use the Pythagorean Theorem. |
| $c^2 = 12^2 + 8.5^2$ | Use half the span, 12 ft. Replace *a* with 12 and *b* with 8.5. |
| $c^2 = 144 + 72.25$ | Square 12 and 8.5. |
| $c^2 = 216.25$ | Add. |
| $c = \sqrt{216.25}$ | Find the positive square root. |
| $c \approx 14.70544117$ | Approximate the square root. |

The rafter length should be about 14.7 ft.

**Try This**

6. *Carpentry* What is the rise of a roof if the span is 22 feet and the rafter length is 14 feet? Round to the nearest tenth of a foot. 8.7 ft

## Part 2 Identifying Right Triangles

The *Converse of the Pythagorean Theorem* allows you to substitute the lengths of the sides of a triangle into the equation $a^2 + b^2 = c^2$ to check whether a triangle is a right triangle. It *is* a right triangle if the equation is true. It *is not* a right triangle if the equation is not true.

### Example 4

**Is a triangle with sides 12 m, 15 m, and 20 m a right triangle?**

| | |
|---|---|
| $a^2 + b^2 = c^2$ | Write the equation for the Pythagorean Theorem. |
| $12^2 + 15^2 \stackrel{?}{=} 20^2$ | Replace *a* and *b* with the shorter lengths and *c* with the longest length. |
| $144 + 225 \stackrel{?}{=} 400$ | Simplify. |
| $369 \neq 400$ | |

The triangle is not a right triangle.

**Try This** Can you form a right triangle with the three lengths given? Explain.

7. 7 in., 8 in., 9 in. No, $7^2 + 8^2 \neq 9^2$.
8. 5 mm, 6 mm, 10 mm No, $5^2 + 6^2 \neq 10^2$.

# Exercises

## CHECK UNDERSTANDING

**Find each square root. Use tables or a calculator. Round to the nearest tenth.**

1. $\sqrt{63}$ 7.9
2. $\sqrt{12}$ 3.5
3. $\sqrt{32}$ 5.7
4. $\sqrt{95}$ 9.7
5. $\sqrt{51}$ 7.1
6. $\sqrt{8}$ 2.8

**Name the legs and the hypotenuse.**

7. 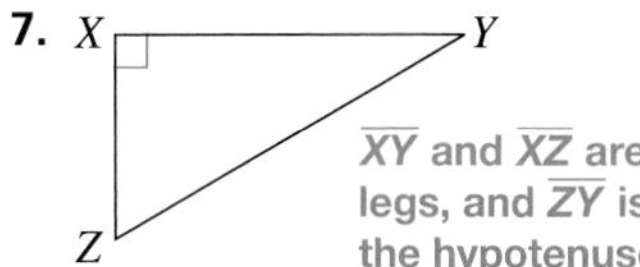

$\overline{XY}$ and $\overline{XZ}$ are legs, and $\overline{ZY}$ is the hypotenuse.

8. P Q R
$\overline{PR}$ and $\overline{QR}$ are legs, and $\overline{PQ}$ is the hypotenuse.

9. 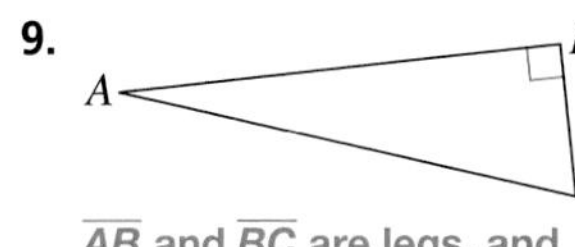

$\overline{AB}$ and $\overline{BC}$ are legs, and $\overline{AC}$ is the hypotenuse.

**Find each missing length to the nearest tenth of a unit.**

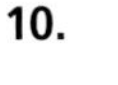

10. 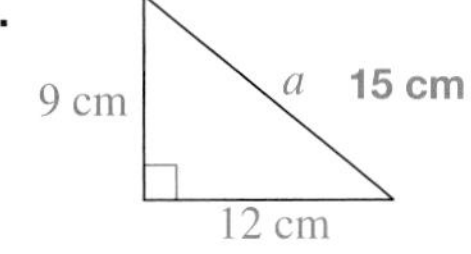

15 cm

11. 9.8 ft 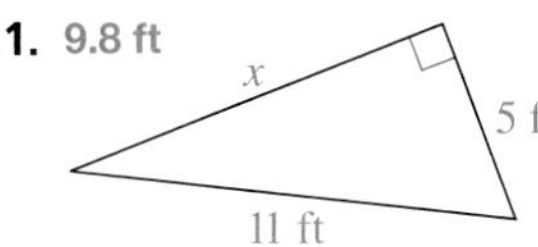


12. 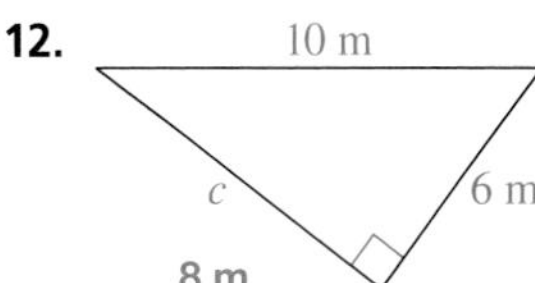

8 m

13. *Mental Math* Is a triangle with side lengths of $\sqrt{12}$ cm, $\sqrt{7}$ cm, and $\sqrt{5}$ cm a right triangle? yes

## PRACTICE AND PROBLEM SOLVING

**Find each missing length to the nearest tenth of a unit.**

14. 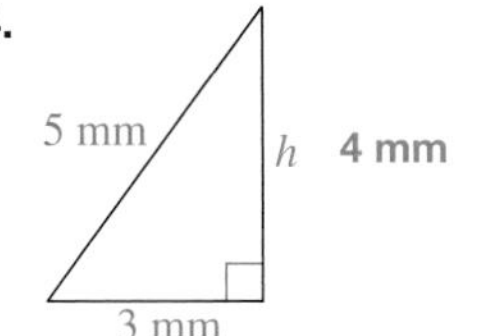

4 mm

15. 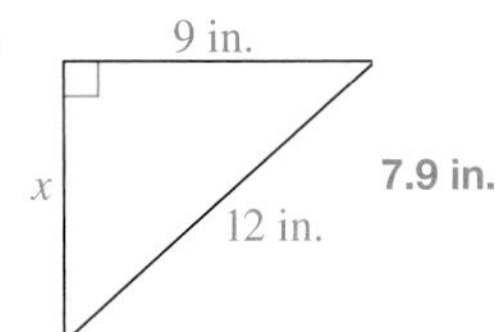

7.9 in.

16. 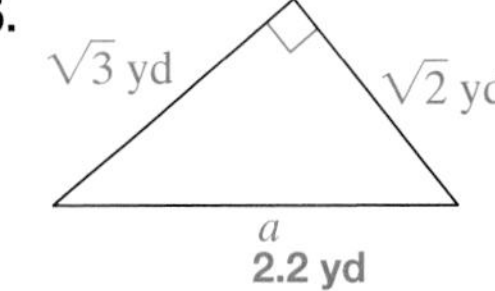

2.2 yd

17. 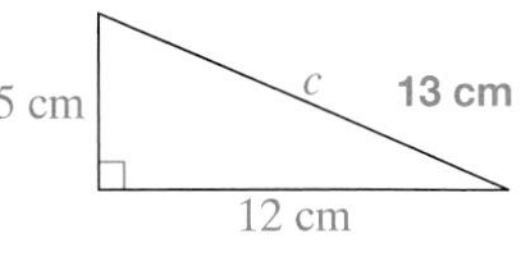

13 cm

18. 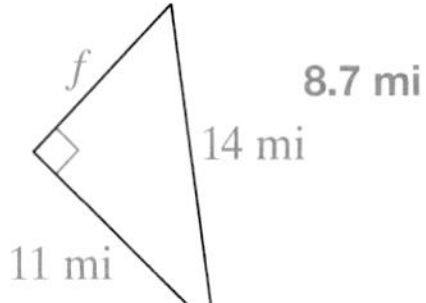

8.7 mi

19. 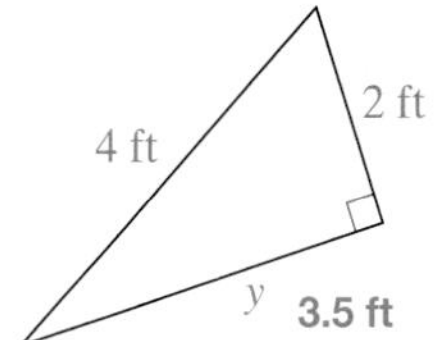

3.5 ft



# 3 Practice/Assess

## Assignment Guide

To provide flexible scheduling, this lesson can be divided into parts.

**Part 1**
**Core** 1–12, 14–19, 29–32, 40–42, 45
**Extension** 33–39, 43–44

**Part 2**
**Core** 13, 20–27
**Extension** 28

Mixed Review can be assigned at any time for maintenance.

## Exercises

**Tactile Learning Exercises 40–41** Drawing a diagram can help you understand the situation.

**Test Prep Exercise 45** Make a sketch and label the legs as $3x$ and $4x$.

## Challenge

Explain how you could use only a string and a pencil to draw a right triangle. Mark the string to indicate five equal segments. Mark one leg of the triangle using three units on the string, another using four. Then connect them with the hypotenuse of five segments.

## Closure

The Pythagorean Theorem states that in any right triangle, the sum of the squares of the lengths of the legs is equal to the square of the length of the hypotenuse.

## Alternative Assessment

Have students look for examples of right triangles either in their neighborhoods or in photos and illustrations in magazines and newspapers. Ask them to measure these right triangles to verify that the Pythagorean Theorem applies.

## Daily Cumulative Review

**Estimate to the nearest integer.** *(Lesson 11-1)*

1. $\sqrt{55}$ 7
2. $-\sqrt{90}$ −9
3. $\sqrt{47}$ 7
4. $-\sqrt{37}$ −6
5. $\sqrt{63}$ 8
6. $-\sqrt{29}$ −5

**Find the volume of each figure.** *(Lesson 10-9)*

7. 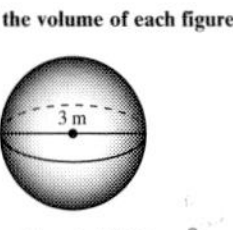

about 14.13 $m^3$

8. 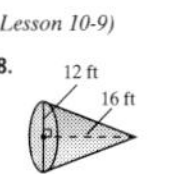

about 602.88 $ft^3$

9. 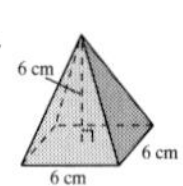

72 $cm^3$

**Mixed Review**

**Find the perimeter of each figure.**

10. (9-3) a square that has a side of 6.3 cm — 25.2 cm
11. (9-3) a regular hexagon that has a side of 4 yd — 24 yd
12. (9-3) an equilateral triangle that has a side of 5.3 ft — 15.9 ft

**Solve each equation.**

13. (2-5) $x - 3 = 9$ — $x = 12$
14. (2-5) $-36 = n - 12$ — $-24 = n$
15. (2-5) $r - 16 - 39 = 214$ — $r = 269$

**Simplify each expression.**

16. (4-2) $(5 - 2)^2 + (9 - 3)^2$ — 45
17. (4-2) $94 - (12 - 8)^2$ — 78
18. (4-2) $(16 - 14)^3 \div 2^2$ — 2
19. (2-3) $a + 3a + 16 - 2a$ — $2a + 16$
20. (2-3) $-5(b + 8) - b$ — $-6b - 40$
21. (2-3) $2(n + 3n) + 5(-7n)$ — $-27n$

**Can you form a right triangle with the three lengths given? Show your work.**

**20.** 4 m, 6 m, 7 m no
**21.** 5 cm, 12 cm, 13 cm yes
**22.** 7 in., 24 in., 25 in. yes
**23.** 1 ft, 3 ft, $\sqrt{12}$ ft no
**24.** 4 mi, 5 mi, 6 mi no
**25.** 1 m, 0.54 m, 0.56 m no
**26.** 8 in., 10 in., 12 in. no
**27.** $\sqrt{5}$ yd, $\sqrt{3}$ yd, $\sqrt{2}$ yd yes
**28.** $3p$ ft, $4p$ ft, $5p$ ft yes

**Use the triangle at the right. Find the missing length to the nearest tenth of a unit.**

**29.** $a = 2$ in., $b = 4$ in., $c = ■$ 4.5 in.
**30.** $a = 1.4$ m, $b = 2.8$ m, $c = ■$ 3.1 m
**31.** $a = 3$ ft, $c = 5$ ft, $b = ■$ 4 ft
**32.** $b = 2.7$ km, $c = 3.4$ km, $a = ■$ 2.1 km

*Algebra* **Find the value of $n$ in each diagram. Give your answer as a square root.**

**33.** 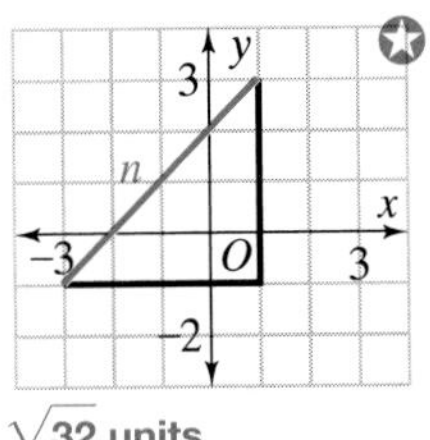
$\sqrt{32}$ units

**34.** 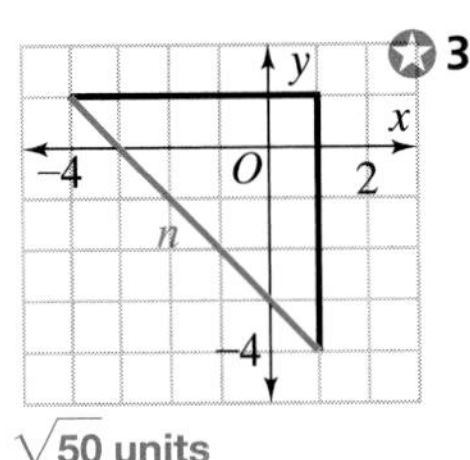
$\sqrt{50}$ units

**35.** 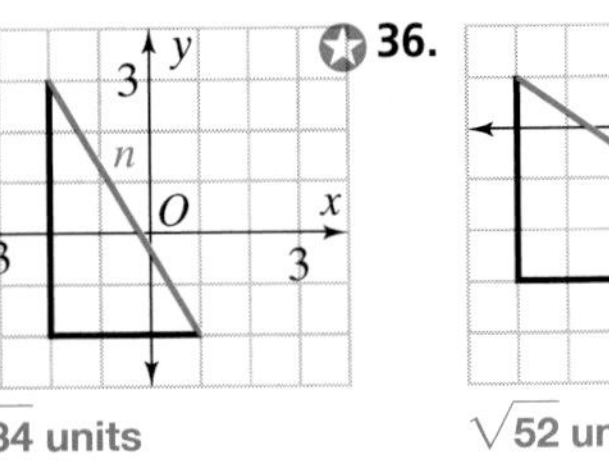
$\sqrt{34}$ units

**36.**
$\sqrt{52}$ units

**Any three positive integers that make $a^2 + b^2 = c^2$ true form a *Pythagorean triple*. Three sets of Pythagorean triples are given below. For each set, multiply each number by 2. Do the new numbers form a Pythagorean triple? Verify your answer.**

**37.** 3, 4, 5 6, 8, 10; yes 36 + 64 = 100
**38.** 7, 24, 25 14, 48, 50; yes, 196 + 2,304 = 2,500
**39.** 5, 12, 13 10, 24, 26; yes 100 + 576 = 676

**In Exercises 40–41, draw a sketch, and then solve.** 40–41. See margin.

**40.** The diagonals for a quilting frame must be the same length to ensure the frame is rectangular. What should the lengths of the diagonals be for a quilting frame 86 in. by 100 in.?

**41.** An 11-ft ladder is placed against a house by a painter. The base of the ladder is 3 ft from the house. How high on the house does the ladder reach?

**42.** Jim works for a landscaping company. He must plant and stake a tree. The stakes are 2 ft from the base of the tree and they are connected to wires that attach to the trunk at a height of 5 ft. If there is 6 in. of extra length at the ends of each wire, how long must each wire be, to the nearest tenth of a foot? 6.4 ft

40.
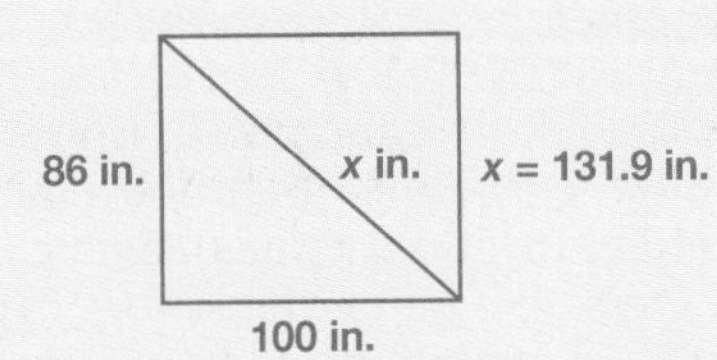


41.
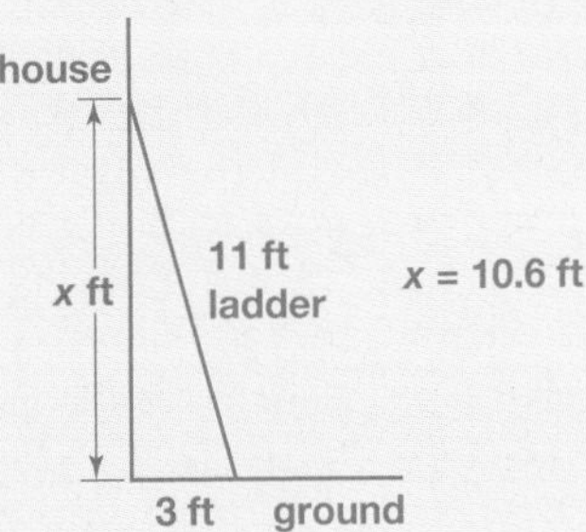

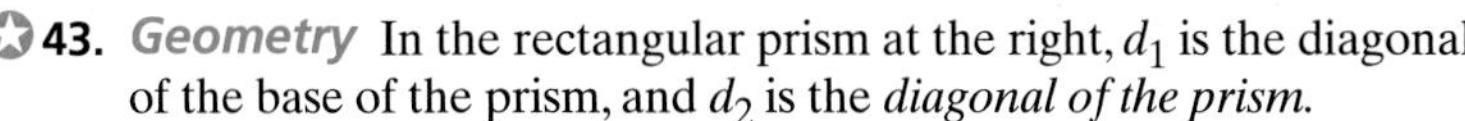

43. *Geometry* In the rectangular prism at the right, $d_1$ is the diagonal of the base of the prism, and $d_2$ is the *diagonal of the prism.*
   a. Find $d_1$. 10 in.
   b. The triangle formed by $d_1$, $d_2$, and the side that is 4 in. is a right triangle. Use your answer to part (a) to find $d_2$. 10.8 in.
   c. Find the diagonal of a rectangular prism with dimensions 9 in., 12 in., and 5 in. 15.8 in.

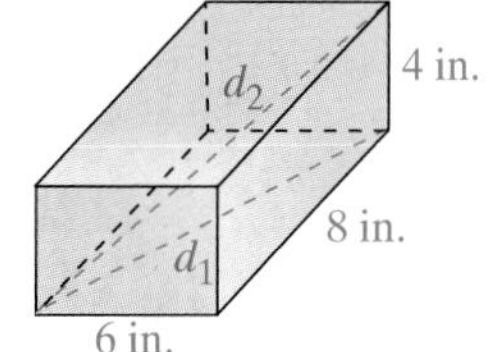


44. *Geometry* A circle has radius 6 in. What is the length of a diagonal of a square that has all four vertices on the circle? 12 in.

45. **TEST PREP** The lengths of the two legs of a right triangle are in the ratio 3 : 4. The perimeter of the triangle is 60 m. What is the length of the hypotenuse? C
   A. 15 m  B. 20 m  C. 25 m  D. 30 m

## Mixed Review

**Identify each number as rational or irrational.** *(Lesson 11-1)*

46. $\sqrt{36}$ rational
47. $0.\overline{6}$ rational
48. $-\sqrt{12}$ irrational
49. $-33.3$ rational
50. 0.654654 . . . rational

**Simplify each expression.** *(Lesson 5-9)*

51. $(bc)^5$ $b^5c^5$
52. $(2x^2)^4$ $16x^8$
53. $(-3b)^3$ $-27b^3$
54. $(a^5b^2)^4$ $a^{20}b^8$
55. $\left(\frac{3m}{5}\right)^2$ $\frac{9m^2}{25}$

56. Greenland is the world's largest island and has an area of 2,175,600 km$^2$. Express this area in scientific notation. *(Lesson 4-9)* $2.1756 \times 10^6$ km$^2$

## Math at Work

### Air Traffic Controller

When we think of airline safety, many of us think of pilots. But there is also a network of people, the air traffic controllers, who work hard to ensure the safe operation of aircraft. Using radar and visual observation, they closely monitor the location of each plane. They coordinate the movement of air traffic to make certain that aircraft stay a safe distance apart. They also coordinate landings and takeoffs to keep delays at a minimum.

In their jobs, air traffic controllers use angle measurements in some of the same ways you do when you solve problems in algebra and geometry.

For more information about air traffic controllers, visit the Prentice Hall Web site.
**www.phschool.com**

See also Extra Practice section.



## Math at Work

If you have block scheduling or extended class periods, have small groups of students research the career of air traffic controllers and the math that they must use in their jobs. Suggest that students conduct research using reference materials. They might contact the Federal Aviation Administration to find out more about the responsibilities of air traffic controllers and training requirements. Students can find additional information on the Web site **www.phschool.com**.

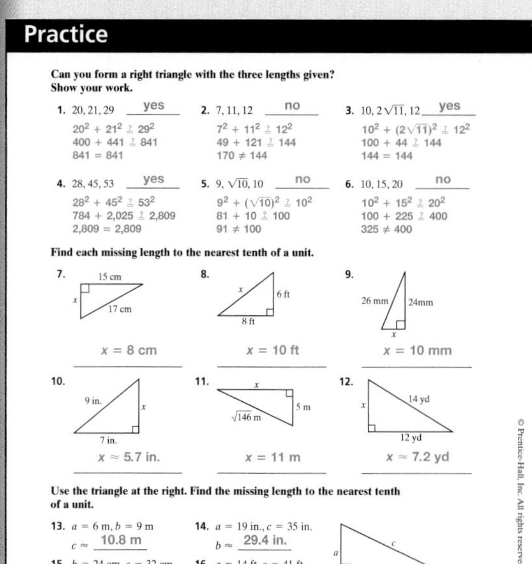

## Practice

**Can you form a right triangle with the three lengths given? Show your work.**

1. 20, 21, 29 yes
   $20^2 + 21^2 \stackrel{?}{=} 29^2$; $400 + 441 \stackrel{?}{=} 841$; $841 = 841$
2. 7, 11, 12 no
   $7^2 + 11^2 \stackrel{?}{=} 12^2$; $49 + 121 \stackrel{?}{=} 144$; $170 \neq 144$
3. $10, 2\sqrt{11}, 12$ yes
   $10^2 + (2\sqrt{11})^2 \stackrel{?}{=} 12^2$; $100 + 44 \stackrel{?}{=} 144$; $144 = 144$
4. 28, 45, 53 yes
   $28^2 + 45^2 \stackrel{?}{=} 53^2$; $784 + 2{,}025 \stackrel{?}{=} 2{,}809$; $2{,}809 = 2{,}809$
5. $9, \sqrt{10}, 10$ no
   $9^2 + (\sqrt{10})^2 \stackrel{?}{=} 10^2$; $81 + 10 \stackrel{?}{=} 100$; $91 \neq 100$
6. 10, 15, 20 no
   $10^2 + 15^2 \stackrel{?}{=} 20^2$; $100 + 225 \stackrel{?}{=} 400$; $325 \neq 400$

**Find each missing length to the nearest tenth of a unit.**

7. $x = 8$ cm
8. $x = 10$ ft
9. $x = 10$ mm
10. $x \approx 5.7$ in.
11. $x = 11$ m
12. $x \approx 7.2$ yd

**Use the triangle at the right. Find the missing length to the nearest tenth of a unit.**

13. $a = 6$ m, $b = 9$ m; $c \approx$ 10.8 m
14. $a = 19$ in., $c = 35$ in.; $b \approx$ 29.4 in.
15. $b = 24$ cm, $c = 32$ cm; $a \approx$ 21.2 cm
16. $a = 14$ ft, $c = 41$ ft; $b \approx$ 38.5 ft
17. A rectangular park measures 300 ft by 400 ft. A sidewalk runs diagonally from one corner to the opposite corner. Find the length of the sidewalk. 500 ft



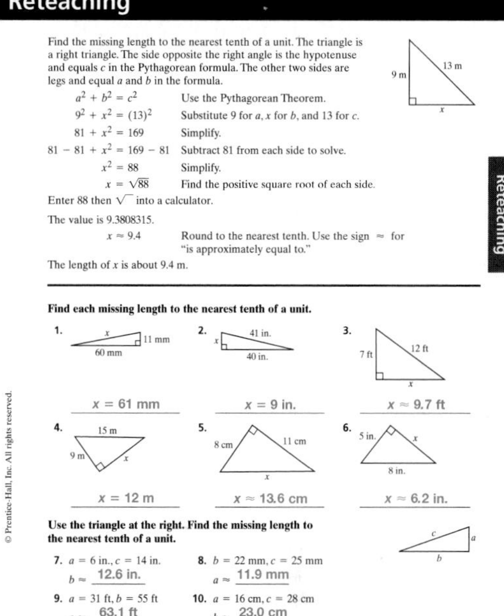

## Reteaching

Find the missing length to the nearest tenth of a unit. The triangle is a right triangle. The side opposite the right angle is the hypotenuse and equals $c$ in the Pythagorean formula. The other two sides are legs and equal $a$ and $b$ in the formula.

| | |
|---|---|
| $a^2 + b^2 = c^2$ | Use the Pythagorean Theorem. |
| $9^2 + x^2 = (13)^2$ | Substitute 9 for $a$, $x$ for $b$, and 13 for $c$. |
| $81 + x^2 = 169$ | Simplify. |
| $81 - 81 + x^2 = 169 - 81$ | Subtract 81 from each side to solve. |
| $x^2 = 88$ | Simplify. |
| $x = \sqrt{88}$ | Find the positive square root of each side. |

Enter 88 then $\sqrt{\ }$ into a calculator.
The value is 9.3808315.
$x \approx 9.4$ Round to the nearest tenth. Use the sign $\approx$ for "is approximately equal to."
The length of $x$ is about 9.4 m.

**Find each missing length to the nearest tenth of a unit.**

1. $x = 61$ mm
2. $x = 9$ in.
3. $x \approx 9.7$ ft
4. $x = 12$ m
5. $x \approx 13.6$ cm
6. $x \approx 6.2$ in.

**Use the triangle at the right. Find the missing length to the nearest tenth of a unit.**

7. $a = 6$ in., $c = 14$ in.; $b \approx$ 12.6 in.
8. $b = 22$ mm, $c = 25$ mm; $a \approx$ 11.9 mm
9. $a = 31$ ft, $b = 55$ ft; $c \approx$ 63.1 ft
10. $a = 16$ cm, $c = 28$ cm; $b \approx$ 23.0 cm



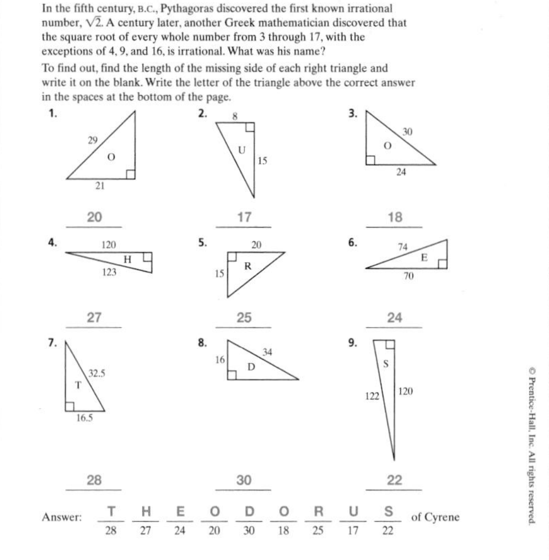

## Enrichment

In the fifth century, B.C., Pythagoras discovered the first known irrational number, $\sqrt{2}$. A century later, another Greek mathematician discovered that the square root of every whole number from 3 through 17, with the exceptions of 4, 9, and 16, is irrational. What was his name?

To find out, find the length of the missing side of each right triangle and write it on the blank. Write the letter of the triangle above the correct answer in the spaces at the bottom of the page.

1. 20
2. 17
3. 18
4. 27
5. 25
6. 24
7. 28
8. 30
9. 22

Answer: T H E O D O R U S of Cyrene

| T | H | E | O | D | O | R | U | S |
|---|---|---|---|---|---|---|---|---|
| 28 | 27 | 24 | 20 | 30 | 18 | 25 | 17 | 22 |

## MATH TOOLBOX

### The Pythagorean Theorem and Circles

This Math Toolbox leads students to discover that the perpendicular bisector of a chord passes through the center of the circle. Students also use the Pythagorean Theorem to find the distance from a chord to the center of the circle.

### Math Background

A *chord* of a circle is any line segment that connects two points on the circle. A *diameter* is a chord that passes through the center of the circle. The diameter is the longest chord in a circle.

The *distance* from a point to a line is defined to be the length of the line segment drawn from the point perpendicular to the line. This means that the distance of a chord from the center of the circle is the length of the line segment drawn from the center perpendicular to the chord.

### Teaching Notes

**Error Prevention** Emphasize that the radius of a circle is one half of the diameter and that the leg of the right triangle in the diagram is one half of the chord.

**Monitoring Progress** Exercises 6–11 Ask students, before they do the math, to name the segment labeled *x* in each diagram, for example, *chord, radius, distance from center to chord,* and so forth.

**Block Scheduling** If you have block scheduling or extended periods, you may wish to insert this Math Toolbox lesson between the completion of Part 1 of Lesson 11-3 and the beginning of Part 2 of Lesson 11-3.

## MATH TOOLBOX

Extension
After Lesson 11-2

# *The Pythagorean Theorem and Circles*

Follow the steps below to discover a characteristic of chords and their perpendicular bisectors.

**Step 1** With a compass, construct a large circle. Label the center $O$.

**Step 2** Draw a chord $\overline{AB}$ that is not a diameter.

**Step 3** Construct the perpendicular bisector of the chord with a compass and straightedge or by folding the circle so that $A$ lies on $B$.

**Step 4** Label the point where the perpendicular bisector intersects the chord $D$.

1. Write a conjecture about the perpendicular bisector of a chord and the center of the circle. The perpendicular bisector of a chord of a circle passes through the center of the circle.
2. Classify $\triangle AOD$ by its angles. right triangle

The distance from the center of a circle to a chord is the length of the perpendicular segment with endpoints at the center and on the chord. You can use the radius of a circle and the length of a chord to find the distance from the center of a circle to the chord.

### EXAMPLE 1

**Circle $O$ has a radius of 10 cm. Chord $FG$ is 12 cm long. How far is $\overline{FG}$ from $O$?**

$MG = 6$ cm. Use the Pythagorean Theorem to find the distance $x$ from the center to the chord.

$$\begin{aligned} 10^2 &= x^2 + 6^2 \\ 100 &= x^2 + 36 \\ 100 - 36 &= x^2 + 36 - 36 \\ 64 &= x^2 \\ 8 &= x \end{aligned}$$

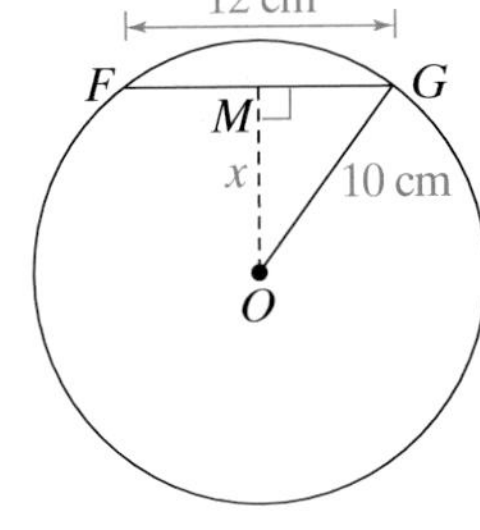


The distance from the center to the chord is 8 cm.



- **Additional Example 1**
  In the diagram for Example 1, if the circle has a diameter of 20 cm, and chord $\overline{FG}$ is 16 cm long, how far is chord $\overline{FG}$ from $O$? 6 cm
- **Additional Example 2**
  In the diagram for Example 2, if chord $\overline{PT}$ is 60 in. long and 16 in. from the center $O$ of the circle, what is the length of the radius? 34 in.

**Find $x$, the distance from the center $O$ of each circle to chord $\overline{JK}$. Round to the nearest tenth.**

**3.** 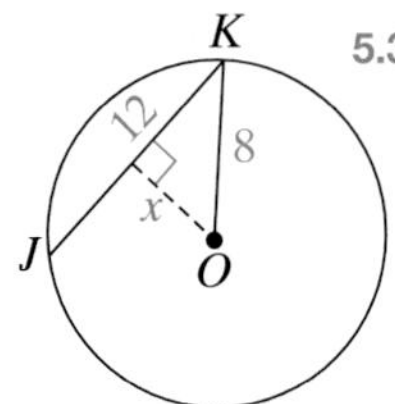

5.3

**4.** 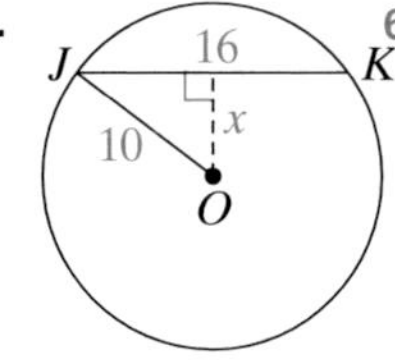

6

**5.** 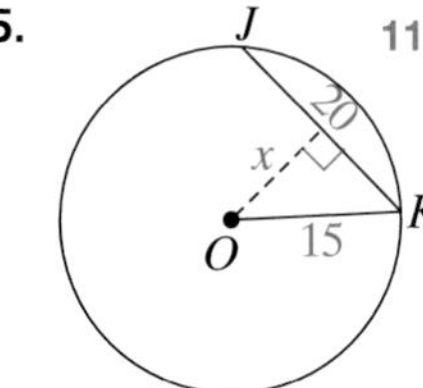

11.2

For a given circle, you can also find the length of a chord or the length of the radius if you know two other lengths.

## Example 2

**Chord $PT$ is 24 in. long and 5 in. from the center $O$ of the circle. Find the length of the radius.**

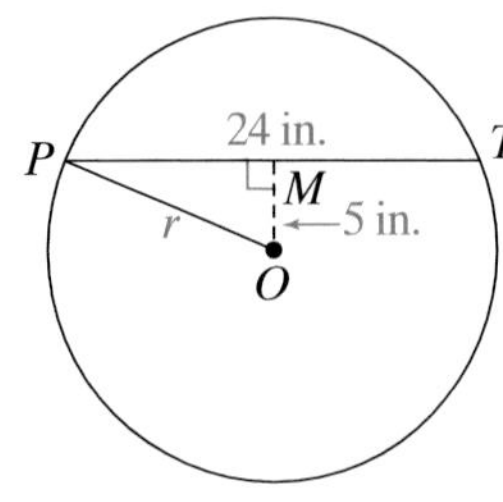


Use the Pythagorean Theorem to find the radius $r$.

$PM = \frac{1}{2}(PT) = 12$

$r^2 = 12^2 + 5^2$

$r^2 = 144 + 25$

$r^2 = 169$

$r = 13$

The radius is 13 in.

**Find the length of $x$ in each circle $O$. If your answer is not an integer, round to the nearest tenth.**

**6.** 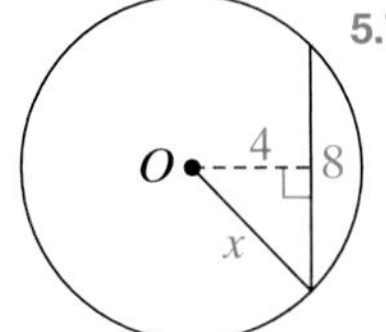

5.7

**7.** 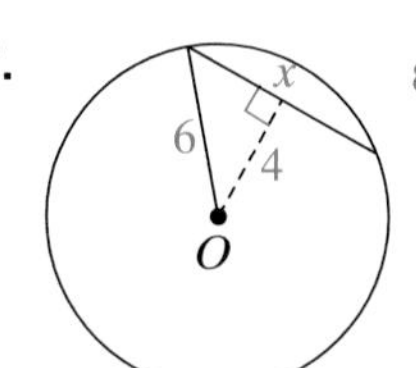

8.9

**8.** 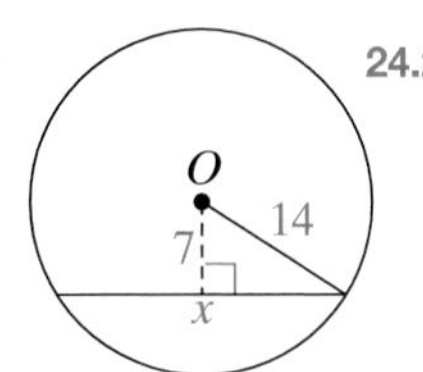

24.2

**9.** 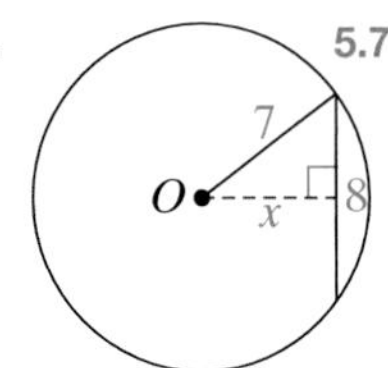

5.7

**10.** 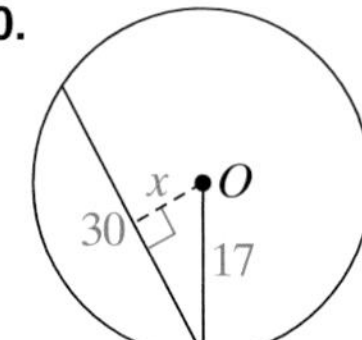

8

**11.** 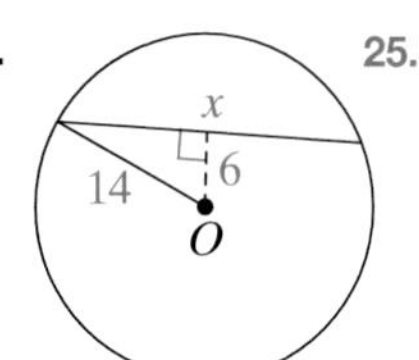

25.3

# 11-3

## Getting Ready

**Key Terms and Symbols** Distance Formula, distance, midpoint, Midpoint Formula

**Resources** A complete list of resources for this lesson is on p. 557H.

### Daily Skills Warm-Up

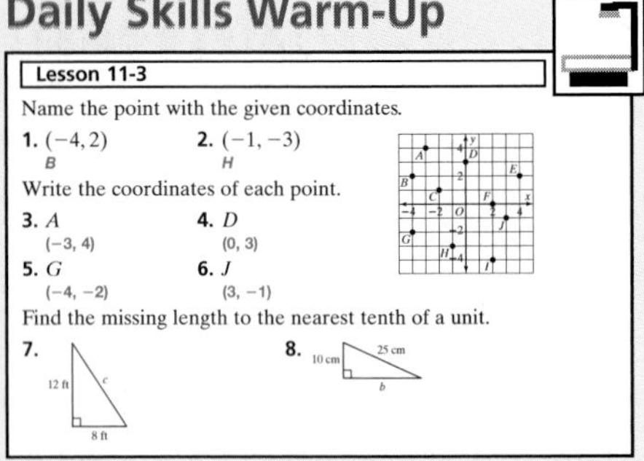
Lesson 11-3

Name the point with the given coordinates.

1. $(-4, 2)$ B
2. $(-1, -3)$ H

Write the coordinates of each point.

3. $A$ $(-3, 4)$
4. $D$ $(0, 3)$
5. $G$ $(-4, -2)$
6. $J$ $(3, -1)$

Find the missing length to the nearest tenth of a unit.

7. 
8. 

### Background for the Lesson

The Distance Formula uses the fact that any line segment between two points on the coordinate plane can form the hypotenuse of a right triangle. The difference in *x*-coordinates forms one leg of the right triangle, and the difference in *y*-coordinates forms the other leg. So, the length of the hypotenuse, or the distance between the two points, is the square root of the difference in *x*-coordinates squared, plus the difference in *y*-coordinates squared.

## 1 Focus

### Connecting to Students' Lives

Ask the class if anyone has seen surveyors working. Have a volunteer describe what surveyors do. Then, ask students to describe how the Pythagorean Theorem might be useful to surveyors.

### Connecting to Prior Knowledge

In Lesson 11-2, students used the Pythagorean Theorem to find the sides of a triangle. In this lesson students use the Pythagorean Theorem to find the distance between two points. In Lesson 11-5, students will use the Pythagorean Theorem to find relationships among the sides of special right triangles.

# 11-3 Distance and Midpoint Formulas

### What You'll Learn

1. To find the distance between two points using the Distance Formula
2. To find the midpoint of a segment using the Midpoint Formula

### . . . And Why

To find the perimeters of figures on the coordinate plane

## Part 1 Finding Distance

In the graph at the right, you can draw a point $C(7, 1)$ to form a right triangle with points $A(2, 1)$ and $B(7, 3)$. Using the Pythagorean Theorem, you can find $AB$.

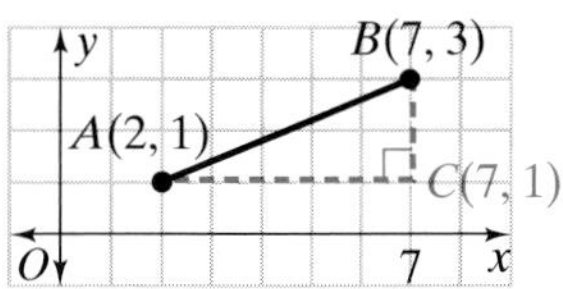


$(AB)^2 = (AC)^2 + (BC)^2$

$(AB)^2 = (7 - 2)^2 + (3 - 1)^2$ — *AC* equals the difference in *x*-values. *BC* equals the difference in *y*-values.

$(AB)^2 = 5^2 + 2^2$ — Subtract.

$AB = \sqrt{25 + 4} = \sqrt{29} \approx 5.4$ — Find the square root.

You can use the Pythagorean Theorem to find the length of a segment on a coordinate plane, or you can use the *Distance Formula*. The Distance Formula is based on the Pythagorean Theorem.

### Reading Math

Read the Distance Formula as "the distance between two points $(x_1, y_1)$ and $(x_2, y_2)$ equals the square root of the difference in *x* values squared plus the difference in *y* values squared."

### Distance Formula

You can find the **distance** $d$ between any two points $(x_1, y_1)$ and $(x_2, y_2)$:

$$d = \sqrt{(x_2 - x_1)^2 + (y_2 - y_1)^2}$$

### Example 1

**Find the distance between $A(6, 3)$ and $B(1, 9)$.**

$d = \sqrt{(x_2 - x_1)^2 + (y_2 - y_1)^2}$ — Use the Distance Formula.

$d = \sqrt{(1 - 6)^2 + (9 - 3)^2}$ — Replace $(x_2, y_2)$ with (1, 9) and $(x_1, y_1)$ with (6, 3).

$d = \sqrt{(-5)^2 + 6^2}$ — Simplify.

$d = \sqrt{61}$ — Find the exact distance.

$d \approx 7.8$ — Round to the nearest tenth.

The distance between $A$ and $B$ is about 7.8 units.



## Tools to Monitor Progress

### BEFORE THE LESSON

**To check prerequisite skills:**

- Understanding coordinates

**Skills You Need,** p. 557

**Skills Handbook,** p. 725

**Skills Intervention Kit,** Geometry

### DURING THE LESSON

**To check understanding:**

**Try This** exercises on student page

- **Additional Examples 1–3**

Use the following figure.

**a.** Find the distance between $T(4, -3)$ and $V(9, 2)$. Round the distance to the nearest tenth of a unit. **about 7.1 units**

**b.** Find the midpoint of $\overline{TV}$. **$(6\frac{1}{2}, -\frac{1}{2})$**

■ **Try This** Find the distance between each pair of points. Round to the nearest tenth.

**1.** $(3, 8), (2, 4)$ 4.1 **2.** $(10, -3), (1, 0)$ 9.5

You can also use the Distance Formula to solve geometry problems. Wait until the last step to round your answer.

**GEOMETRY** CONNECTION

## ■ Example 2

**Find the perimeter of *ABCD*.**

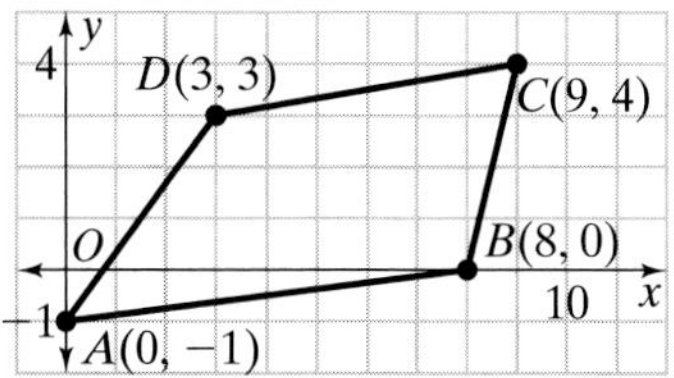


Use the Distance Formula to find the side lengths.

$AB = \sqrt{(8 - 0)^2 + (0 - (-1))^2}$ Replace $(x_2, y_2)$ with (8, 0) and $(x_1, y_1)$ with (0, −1).

$= \sqrt{64 + 1} = \sqrt{65}$ Simplify.

$BC = \sqrt{(9 - 8)^2 + (4 - 0)^2}$ Replace $(x_2, y_2)$ with (9, 4) and $(x_1, y_1)$ with (8, 0).

$= \sqrt{1 + 16} = \sqrt{17}$ Simplify.

$CD = \sqrt{(3 - 9)^2 + (3 - 4)^2}$ Replace $(x_2, y_2)$ with (3, 3) and $(x_1, y_1)$ with (9, 4).

$= \sqrt{36 + 1} = \sqrt{37}$ Simplify.

$DA = \sqrt{(0 - 3)^2 + ((-1) - 3)^2}$ Replace $(x_2, y_2)$ with (0, −1) and $(x_1, y_1)$ with (3, 3).

$= \sqrt{9 + 16} = \sqrt{25} = 5$ Simplify.

perimeter $= \sqrt{65} + \sqrt{17} + \sqrt{37} + 5 \approx 23.2681259$

The perimeter is about 23.3 units.

■ **Try This**

**3.** Find the perimeter of $\triangle DEF$ at the right. Round to the nearest tenth. 17.5

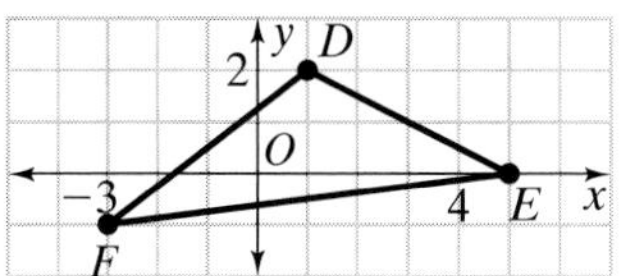




# 2 Teach

## Part 1 Teaching Notes

Help students understand that the distance between any two points on the coordinate plane forms the hypotenuse of a right triangle.

### ■ Example 1

**Build understanding.** Explain why it does not matter whether $x_2$ is subtracted from $x_1$ or vice versa to find the difference between *x*-coordinates. The difference is squared in the Distance Formula, so the result is the same whether the difference is positive or negative.

**Error Prevention** When you use the Distance Formula, carefully substitute the *x*- and *y*-coordinates.

**Reading Math** Remind students that the subscripts on the variables are not the same as exponents. Subscripts merely name the variables; they do not affect the value.

### ■ Example 2

**Advanced Learners** Have students find the length of a diagonal of the classroom by measuring the two sides of the classroom, then plotting the endpoints of the diagonal distance on a coordinate plane. Then, students can use the Distance Formula to find the diagonal distance. Have students check their work by measuring the actual diagonal distance.

## AFTER THE LESSON

**To assess knowledge:**

**Lesson Quiz**

Find the length of each segment to the nearest tenth of a unit. Then find the midpoint.

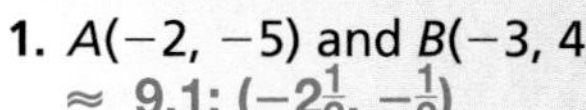

1. $A(-2, -5)$ and $B(-3, 4)$ $\approx 9.1; (-2\frac{1}{2}, -\frac{1}{2})$
2. $D(-4, 6)$ and $E(7, -2)$ $\approx 13.6; (1\frac{1}{2}, 2)$

- For enrichment and reteaching options see Resources on p. 557H.

## Part 2 Teaching Notes

Point out to students that the Midpoint Formula does not use the Pythagorean Theorem. It finds the averages of the *x*-coordinates and *y*-coordinates of the endpoints to find a coordinate pair halfway between two endpoints on a segment.

**ELL** Ask students to think of another way to express the term *midpoint*. Halfway point would be one example.

**Tactile Learning** Place students in pairs. Have one student find the midpoint of a segment on the coordinate plane using the Midpoint Formula. Have the other student find the midpoint of the segment by measuring and then halving the distance between the endpoints. Ask students to compare their findings.

### Example 3

**Build understanding.** Ask: What should be true about the distance between point *G* and the midpoint, and point *H* and the midpoint? **The distances between each endpoint and the midpoint should be the same.**

**Math Reasoning** Use math reasoning to explain how you could use the Distance Formula to verify that the Midpoint Formula works. **Use the Midpoint Formula to find the midpoint of a segment. Then use the Distance Formula to find the distance between the midpoint and one endpoint, and then the distance between the midpoint and the other endpoint. The distances should be the same.**

## Finding the Midpoint

The **midpoint** of a segment $\overline{AB}$ is the point $M$ on $\overline{AB}$ halfway between the endpoints $A$ and $B$ where $AM = MB$.

**Midpoint Formula**

You can find the midpoint of a line segment with endpoints $A(x_1, y_1)$ and $B(x_2, y_2)$:

$$M\left(\frac{x_1 + x_2}{2}, \frac{y_1 + y_2}{2}\right)$$

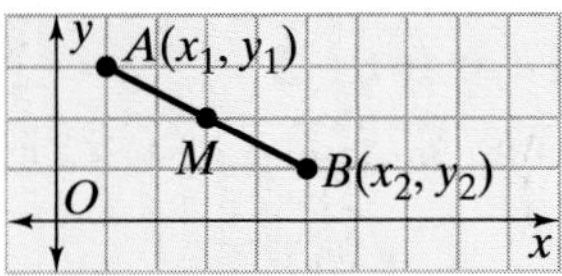


### Example 3

**Find the midpoint of $\overline{GH}$.**

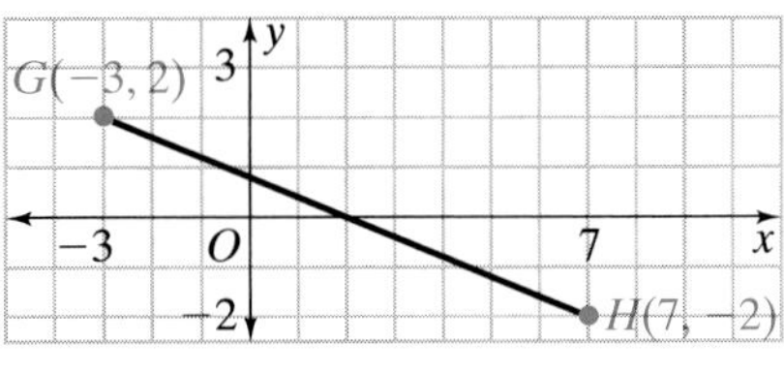


| | |
|---|---|
| $\left(\frac{x_1 + x_2}{2}, \frac{y_1 + y_2}{2}\right)$ | Use the Midpoint Formula. |
| $= \left(\frac{-3 + 7}{2}, \frac{2 + (-2)}{2}\right)$ | Replace $(x_1, y_1)$ with $(-3, 2)$ and $(x_2, y_2)$ with $(7, -2)$. |
| $= \left(\frac{4}{2}, \frac{0}{2}\right)$ | Simplify the numerators. |
| $= (2, 0)$ | Write the fractions in simplest form. |

The coordinates of the midpoint of $\overline{GH}$ are $(2, 0)$.

**Try This** Find the midpoint of each segment.

**4.**

(5, 3)

**5.**

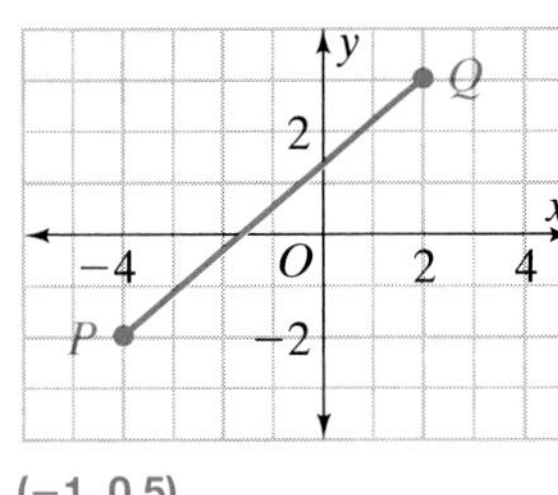


(−1, 0.5)

# Exercises

## CHECK UNDERSTANDING

**Find the distance between each pair of points.**

1. 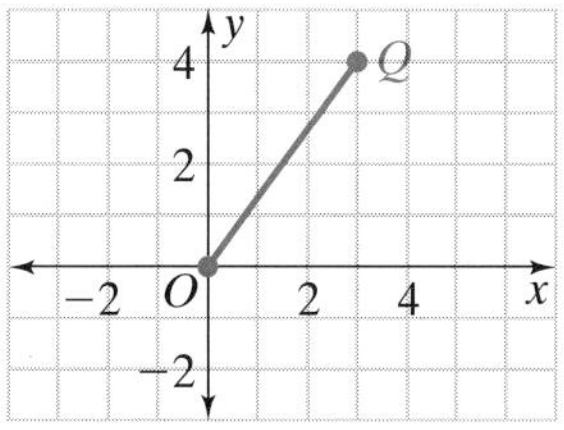

5 units

2. 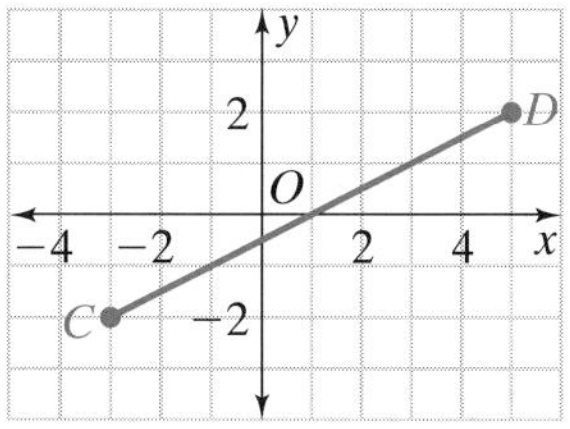

8.9 units

3. 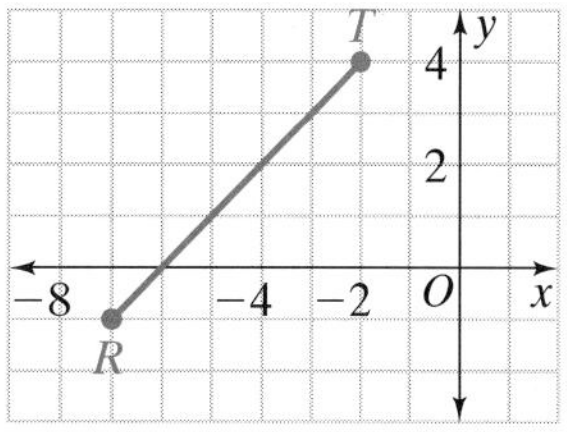

7.1 units

**Find the midpoint of each segment with the given endpoints.**

4. $P(4, 2)$ and $F(10, 0)$ (7, 1)
5. $L(6, -3)$ and $T(1, -7)$ (3.5, −5)
6. $G(-4, 9)$ and $K(-8, 10)$ (−6, 9.5)
7. *Critical Thinking* When you use the Distance Formula, does it matter which point you use as $(x_2, y_2)$? Explain. No, interchanging $x_1$ and $x_2$ will only affect the sign. Since you will square the difference, the sign is not important.

## PRACTICE AND PROBLEM SOLVING

**Find the distance between each pair of points. Round to the nearest tenth.**

8. (1, 5), (5, 2) 5
9. (6, 0), (−6, 5) 13
10. (−5, 10), (11, −7) 23.3
11. (−6, 12), (−3, −7) 19.2
12. (8, −1), (−5, 11) 17.7
13. (12, 3), (−12, 4) 24.0

**Find the midpoint of each segment with the given endpoints.**

14. $Z(3, 5)$ and $W(5, -3)$ (4, 1)
15. $G(-2, 0)$ and $J(7, -8)$ (2.5, −4)
16. $S(9, 12)$ and $U(-9, -12)$ (0, 0)
17. $B(10, -8)$ and $E(7, -7)$ (8.5, −7.5)
18. $K(23, 4)$ and $W(-2, 16)$ (10.5, 10)
19. $D(3.4, 6.5)$ and $P(-2.1, 3)$ (0.65, 4.75)

*Geometry* **Find the perimeter of each figure.**

✪ 20. 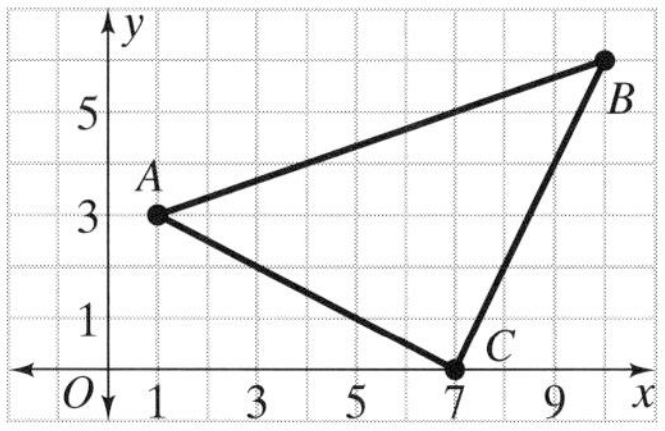

22.9 units

✪ 21. 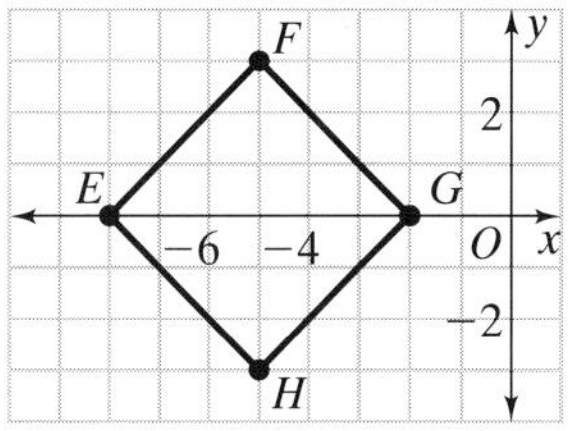

17 units



# 3 Practice/Assess

## Assignment Guide

To provide flexible scheduling, this lesson can be divided into parts.

▼ **Part 1**
**Core** 1–3, 7–13
✪ **Extension** 20–21, 24

▼ **Part 2**
**Core** 4–6, 14–19, 22, 25
✪ **Extension** 23

Mixed Review can be assigned at any time for maintenance.

## Exercises

**Auditory Learning Exercises 14–19**
Work with a partner. Have your partner say the coordinates while you plot them.

## ✪ Challenge

Explain how you could use a compass to check the Midpoint Formula. Find the midpoint of a segment with the formula. Then construct the perpendicular bisector. The midpoint should be the point where the bisector and the segment intersect.

## Closure

The Distance Formula states that the distance $d$ between any two points $(x_1, y_1)$ and $(x_2, y_2)$ is $d = \sqrt{(x_2 - x_1)^2 + (y_2 - y_1)^2}$. The Midpoint Formula states that the midpoint of a line segment with endpoints $A(x_1, y_1)$ and $B(x_2, y_2)$ is $\left(\frac{x_1 + x_2}{2}, \frac{y_1 + y_2}{2}\right)$.

## Daily Cumulative Review

**Find each missing length to the nearest tenth of a unit.** *(Lesson 11-2)*

1. 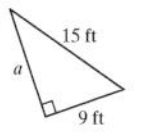

12 ft

2. 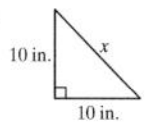

14.1 in.

3. 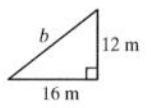

20 m

4. 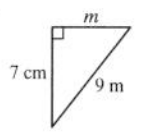

5.7 cm

5. 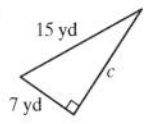

13.3 yd

6. 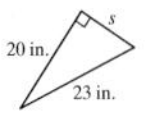

11.4 in.

**Identify each number as rational or irrational.** *(Lesson 11-1)*

7. $\sqrt{64}$ rational
8. 0.212112 . . . irrational
9. 6,329,521 rational
10. $-\sqrt{17}$ irrational
11. 0.6363 . . . rational
12. $\pi$ irrational

**Mixed Review**

**Evaluate. Write in simplest form.**

13. (4-6) $\frac{a}{b}$ for $a = -4, b = 6$ $-\frac{2}{3}$
14. (4-6) $\frac{s}{-r}$ for $r = 12, s = -10$ $\frac{5}{6}$
15. (4-6) $\frac{c - d}{-8}$ for $c = 16, d = 12$ $-\frac{1}{2}$

**Solve each proportion. Where necessary round to the nearest tenth.**

16. (6-2) $\frac{3}{8} = \frac{40}{a}$ $106.7 = a$
17. (6-2) $\frac{36}{17} = \frac{x}{81}$ $171.5 = x$
18. (6-2) $\frac{4}{9} = \frac{80}{b}$ $180 = b$



## Alternative Assessment

Give students an example of a real map or navigational chart. Have them use the Distance Formula to find the distance between two points on the map or chart.

## Practice

**The table has sets of endpoints of several segments. Find the distance between each pair of points and the midpoint of each segment. Round to the nearest tenth when necessary.**

| | Endpoints | Distance Between (Length of Segment) | Midpoint |
|---|---|---|---|
| 1. | $A(2, 6)$ and $B(4, 10)$ | 4.5 | (3, 8) |
| 2. | $C(5, -3)$ and $D(7, 2)$ | 5.4 | $\left(6, -\frac{1}{2}\right)$ |
| 3. | $E(0, 12)$ and $F(5, 0)$ | 13 | $\left(2\frac{1}{2}, 6\right)$ |
| 4. | $G(4, 7)$ and $H(-2, -3)$ | 11.7 | (1, 2) |
| 5. | $J(-1, 5)$ and $K(2, 1)$ | 5 | $\left(\frac{1}{2}, 3\right)$ |
| 6. | $L(-3, 8)$ and $M(-7, -1)$ | 9.8 | $\left(-5, 3\frac{1}{2}\right)$ |

**Find the perimeter of each figure. Round to the nearest tenth when necessary.**

7. 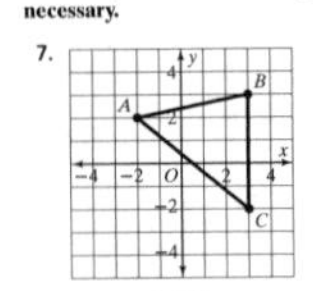
16.5

8. 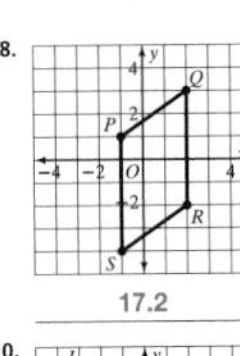
17.2

9. 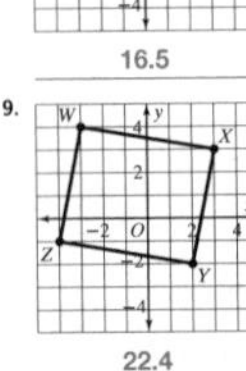
22.4

10. 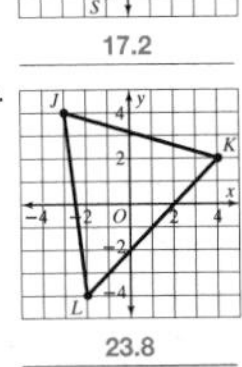
23.8



## Reteaching

Find the perimeter of the figure. Round to the nearest tenth where necessary.

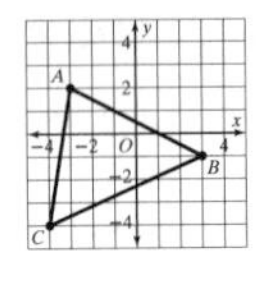

Use the distance formula to find the lengths of the sides.

$d = \sqrt{(x_2 - x_1)^2 + (y_2 - y_1)^2}$

First, find the coordinates of the vertices.

$A(-3, 2)$, $B(3, -1)$ and $C(-4, -4)$.

$AB = \sqrt{[3 - (-3)]^2 + [-1 - 2]^2}$ Replace $(x_2, y_2)$ with $(3, -1)$ and $(x_1, y_1)$ with $(-3, 2)$.

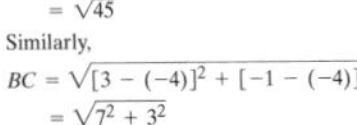

$= \sqrt{6^2 + (-3)^2}$ Simplify.

$= \sqrt{36 + 9}$ Find the squares.

$= \sqrt{45}$ Add.

Similarly,

$BC = \sqrt{[3 - (-4)]^2 + [-1 - (-4)]^2}$ $AC = \sqrt{[(-3) - (-4)]^2 + [2 - (-4)]^2}$

$= \sqrt{7^2 + 3^2}$ $= \sqrt{1^2 + 6^2}$

$= \sqrt{49 + 9}$ $= \sqrt{1 + 36}$

$= \sqrt{58}$ $= \sqrt{37}$

The perimeter is the sum of the lengths of the sides.

perimeter $= \sqrt{45} + \sqrt{58} + \sqrt{37} \approx 20.4$

The perimeter is about 20.4 units.

**Find the perimeter of each figure. Round to the nearest tenth when necessary.**

1. 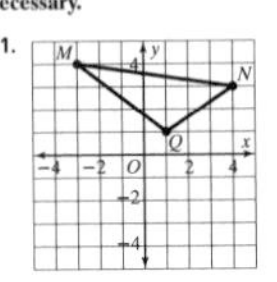

2. 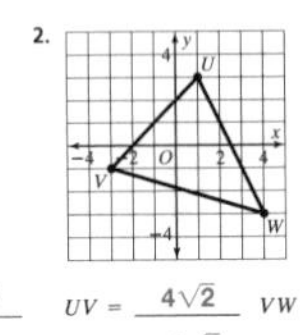

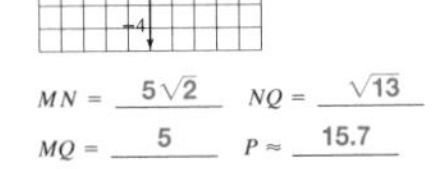

$MN =$ $5\sqrt{2}$ $NQ =$ $\sqrt{13}$ $UV =$ $4\sqrt{2}$ $VW =$ $\sqrt{53}$

$MQ =$ 5 $P \approx$ 15.7 $UW =$ $3\sqrt{5}$ $P \approx$ 19.6



## Enrichment

You can show that the triangle shown in the graph is isosceles by using the distance formula.

**Find the length of each side of the triangle. Leave your own answer as a square root.**

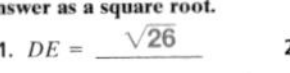
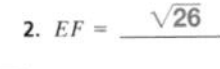

1. $DE =$ $\sqrt{26}$ 2. $EF =$ $\sqrt{26}$

Since $DE = EF$, $\overline{DE} \cong \overline{EF}$ and the triangle is isosceles.

**Show that the quadrilateral is a parallelogram by showing that opposite sides are congruent.**

3. $GH =$ $\sqrt{40}$ 4. $HJ =$ $\sqrt{17}$

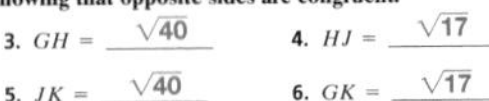

5. $JK =$ $\sqrt{40}$ 6. $GK =$ $\sqrt{17}$

7. Explain how you know $GHJK$ is a parallelogram.

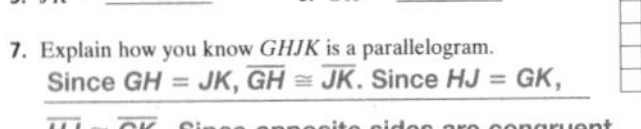

Since $GH = JK$, $\overline{GH} \cong \overline{JK}$. Since $HJ = GK$, $\overline{HJ} \cong \overline{GK}$. Since opposite sides are congruent, $GHJK$ is a parallelogram.

**Given that $\angle A$ and $\angle X$ are right angles and therefore congruent, show that $\triangle ABC \cong \triangle XYZ$. Find the side lengths indicated.**

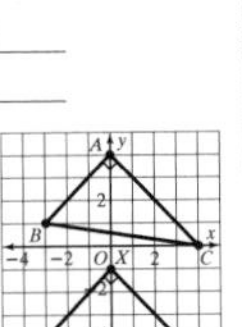

8. $AB =$ $\sqrt{18}$ 9. $AC =$ $\sqrt{32}$

10. $XY =$ $\sqrt{18}$ 11. $XZ =$ $\sqrt{32}$

12. Explain how you know $\triangle ABC \cong \triangle XYZ$.

Since $AB = XY$, $\overline{AB} \cong \overline{XY}$. Since $AC = XZ$, $\overline{AC} \cong \overline{XZ}$. $\angle A \cong \angle X$ is given. Therefore,

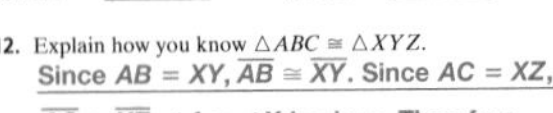

$\triangle ABC \cong \triangle XYZ$ by SAS.



22. *Error Analysis* A student's calculation of the midpoint of the segment with endpoints $A(-4, 2)$ and $B(6, 6)$ is shown at the right. What mistake did the student make? See margin.

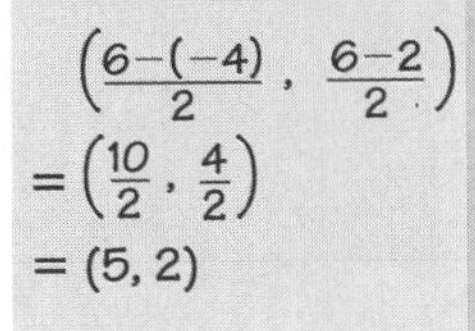

$\left(\frac{6-(-4)}{2}, \frac{6-2}{2}\right)$

$= \left(\frac{10}{2}, \frac{4}{2}\right)$

$= (5, 2)$

23. *Critical Thinking* The midpoint of $\overline{AB}$ is $(3, 5)$. The coordinates of $A$ are $(-6, 1)$. What are the coordinates of $B$? (12, 9)

24. *Geometry* The three vertices of a triangle have coordinates $P(-3, 1)$, $Q(2, -5)$, and $R(4, 6)$. Determine whether the triangle is scalene, isosceles, or equilateral. scalene

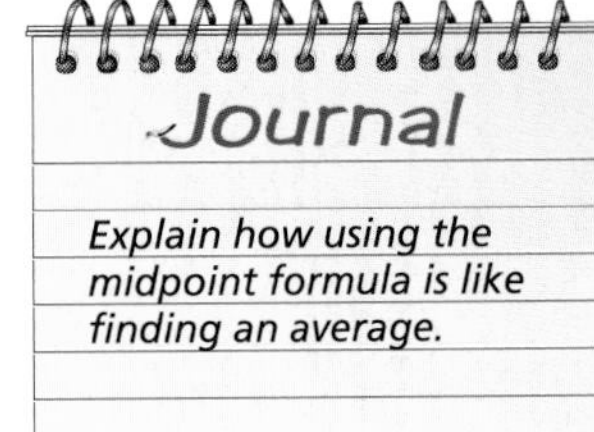

Journal
Explain how using the midpoint formula is like finding an average.



25. a. Find the midpoint $M$ of the line segment with endpoints $A(-3, 5)$ and $B(2, 1)$. (−0.5, 3)

b. Use the distance formula to verify that $AM = MB$.

$\sqrt{[-3 - (-0.5)]^2 + (5 - 3)^2} = \sqrt{(-0.5 - 2)^2 + (3 - 1)^2}$

$\sqrt{(-2.5)^2 + 2^2} = \sqrt{(-2.5)^2 + 2^2}$

## Mixed Review

**Can you form a right triangle with the three lengths given? *(Lesson 11-2)***

26. 8 cm, 15 cm, 17 cm yes
27. 5 in., 8 in., 5 in. no
28. 20 yd, 12 yd, 16 yd yes

**Solve each proportion. *(Lesson 6-2)***

29. $\frac{3}{8} = \frac{a}{24}$ 9
30. $\frac{11}{c} = \frac{66}{72}$ 12
31. $\frac{5}{6} = \frac{n}{15}$ 12.5
32. $\frac{b}{1.9} = \frac{7}{9.5}$ 1.4

33. *Geometry* Draw a net to represent a rectangular box that is 4 in. long, 3 in. wide, and 2 in. high. Label dimensions on the net. *(Lesson 10-4)* See margin.

## Checkpoint 1

Lessons 11-1 through 11-3

**Estimate to the nearest integer.**

1. $-\sqrt{3}$ −2
2. $\sqrt{14}$ 4
3. $\sqrt{27}$ 5
4. $\sqrt{90}$ 9
5. $-\sqrt{45}$ −7
6. $\sqrt{105}$ 10

**The lengths of two legs of a right triangle are given. Find the length of the hypotenuse. Round to the nearest tenth of a unit.**

7. 6 ft, 8 ft 10 ft
8. 8 m, 14 m 16.1 m
9. 7 yd, 24 yd 25 yd
10. 5 cm, 5 cm 7.1 cm

**Find the length of $\overline{AB}$ and the midpoint of $\overline{AB}$. Round the length of $\overline{AB}$ to the nearest tenth.**

11. $A(0, -2)$ and $B(-6, -9)$ 9.2; (−3, −5.5)
12. $A(8, 11)$ and $B(-5, 2)$ 15.8; (1.5, 6.5)
13. $A(-14, 12)$ and $B(-4, -7)$ 21.5; (−9, 2.5)

14. *Open-ended* Name three irrational numbers between 10 and 20. Answers may vary. Sample: $\sqrt{120}$, $\sqrt{299}$, 15.010010001 . . .



See also Extra Practice section.

## Checkpoint

**Estimate to the nearest integer.**

1. $\sqrt{40}$ 6
2. $\sqrt{85}$ 9
3. $-\sqrt{58}$ −8

**The lengths of two legs of a right triangle are given. Find the length of the hypotenuse. Round to the nearest tenth of a unit.**

4. 21 in., 28 in. 35 in.
5. 9 cm, 16 cm 18.4 cm
6. 12 m, 12 m 17.0 m

**Find the length of $\overline{AB}$ and the midpoint of $\overline{AB}$. Round the length of $\overline{AB}$ to the nearest tenth.**

$A(0, -3)$ and $B(6, 5)$ 7. length: 10 units 8. midpoint (3, 1)

$A(8, -4)$ and $B(-2, -1)$ 9. length: 10.4 units 10. midpoint $\left(3, -2\frac{1}{2}\right)$

22. When using the midpoint formula, the student subtracted in the numerators rather than adding.

33.

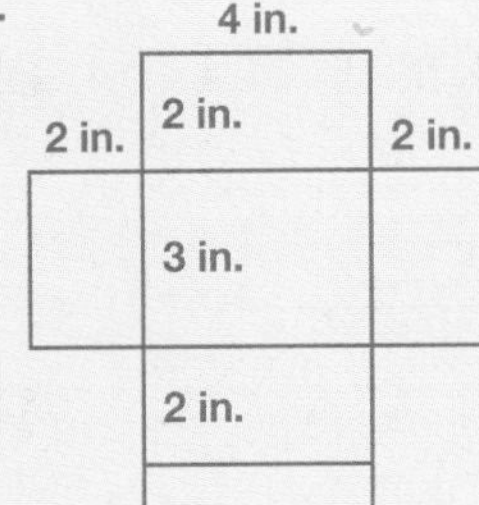

# Standardized Test Prep

## Multiple Choice

**Choose the best answer.**

1. Which statement is *false*? B

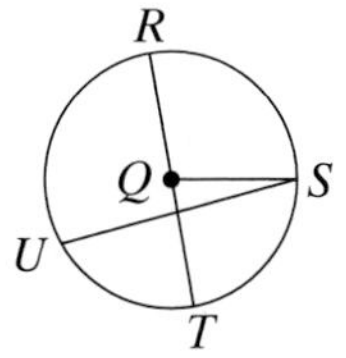


A. $\overline{QT}$ is a radius of circle $Q$.
B. $\overline{SU}$ is a radius of circle $Q$.
C. $\overline{SU}$ is a chord of circle $Q$.
D. $\overline{RT}$ is a diameter of circle $Q$.

2. The cost for a one-page advertisement at newspaper A is \$37 plus \$6.60 per week. newspaper B charges a single fee of \$14 per week. Which inequality can help you decide how many weeks an ad must run for newspaper A to be less expensive than newspaper B? J

F. $37 + 6.60x > 14x$
G. $37 + 6.60x \geq 14x$
H. $37 + 6.60x \leq 14x$
J. $37 + 6.60x < 14x$

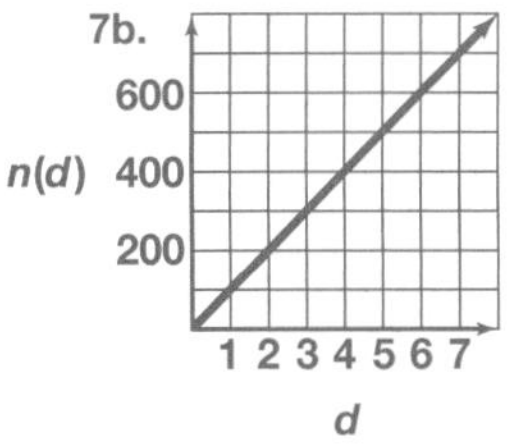


3. Find $x$. A

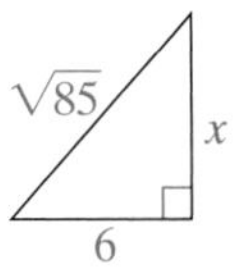


A. 7    B. 8    C. 9    D. 10

4. A rectangle's length is 60 mm, and its perimeter is 160 mm. What is the area of the rectangle in *square centimeters*? F

F. 12 $cm^2$    G. 30 $cm^2$
H. 1,200 $cm^2$    J. 3,000 $cm^2$

5. Name the coordinates of the image of polygon $ABCD$ reflected over the $y$-axis. B

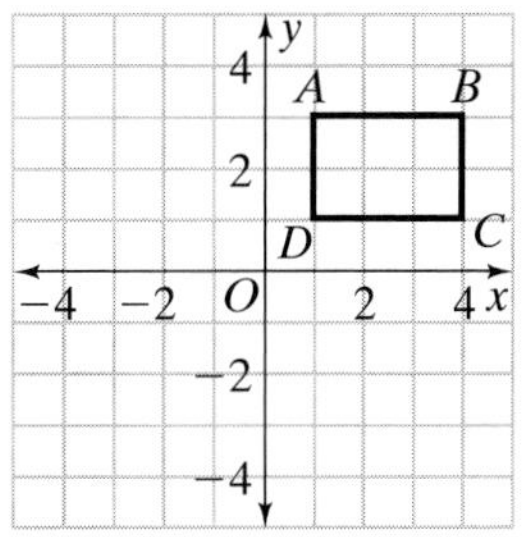


A. $A'(1, -1), B'(4, -1), C'(4, -3), D'(1, -3)$
B. $A'(-1, 3), B'(-4, 3), C'(-4, 1), D'(-1, 1)$
C. $A'(-4, 3), B'(-1, 3), C'(-1, 1), D'(-4, 1)$
D. $A'(1, -3), B'(4, -3), C'(4, -1), D'(1, -1)$

6. A scale model of a house has a flat rectangular roof 1 foot by 2 feet. Each inch on the model corresponds to 39 inches on the actual house. What is the area of the actual roof? H

F. 468 $in.^2$    G. 936 $in.^2$
H. 3,042 $ft^2$    J. 36,504 $ft^2$

## Free Response

**For Exercises 7 and 8, show your work.**

7. a. Express the number of centimeters as a function $n(d)$ of the number of meters $d$. $n(d) = 100d$
   b. Graph the function. See left.
   c. Find the slope of the line you graphed. 100
   d. Explain the significance of the slope. This is the number of centimeters per meter.

8. The area of Nevada is greater than the area of Utah by about what percent? Explain your reasoning.

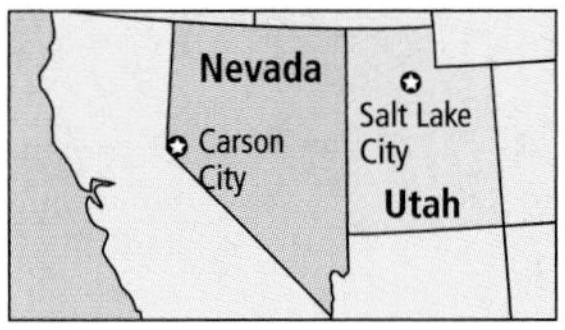


Accept answers between 20% and 35%.



## Standardized Test Prep

Standardized tests, such as those administered for state assessment, SAT9, TerraNova™, ITBS, MAT7, or CAT5, may include multiple choice questions, free-response questions, and open-ended questions.

**Multiple Choice Questions** are followed usually by four choices, one of which is correct.

**Exercises 1–6** are multiple choice questions.

**Free-Response Questions** do not give answer choices. Student must provide the one correct answer on their own.

**Exercises 7–8** are free-response questions.

### Resources

See p. 557G for a list of assessment options.

### Test-Taking Tip

When a question has a graph or diagram, read carefully all the labels and information in the graph. Make sure you understand what is pictured before you consider the answer choices.

### Test-Taking Tips on Transparency

Recognizing a pattern lets you predict information.

*Example* If the pattern indicated below is continued, what will be the number of squares in the 7th stage?

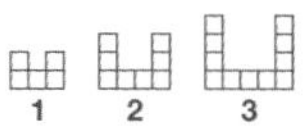


A. 29    B. 23    C. 18    D. 17

To find the pattern, determine what changes:

Each figure has 3 more squares (one on each side) than the previous figure.

So the 7th stage must have 6 × 3 = 18 more squares than the first figure. Add: 5 + 18 = 23.

The answer is 23, or choice B.

Look for a pattern to find the answer. Explain your reasoning.

1. The first four figures in a pattern contain 2, 6, 12, and 20 dots. How many dots will be in the fifth figure?
   A. 30    B. 36    C. 18    D. 28
2. A pattern begins with a triangle, a rectangle, and a pentagon. What is the 6th figure in this pattern?
   F. hexagon    G. triangle    H. octagon    J. trapezoid

# 11-4

## Getting Ready

**Resources** A complete list of resources for this lesson is on p. 557H.

### Daily Skills Warm-Up

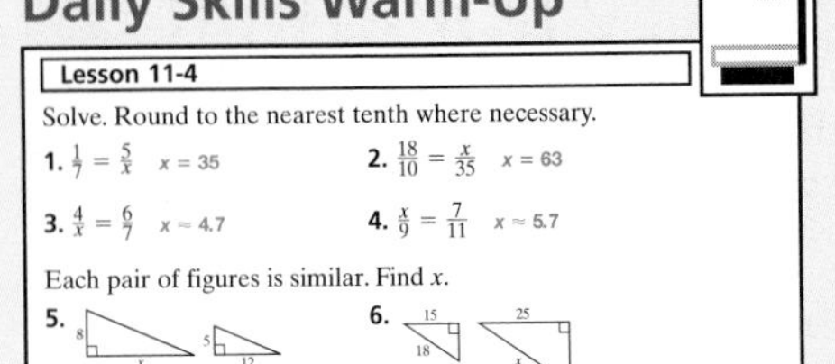

Lesson 11-4

Solve. Round to the nearest tenth where necessary.

1. $\frac{1}{7} = \frac{5}{x}$ $x = 35$
2. $\frac{18}{10} = \frac{x}{35}$ $x = 63$
3. $\frac{4}{x} = \frac{6}{7}$ $x \approx 4.7$
4. $\frac{x}{9} = \frac{7}{11}$ $x \approx 5.7$

Each pair of figures is similar. Find $x$.

5. $x = 19.2$
6. $x = 30$

### Background for the Lesson

You can write the sides of similar triangles as ratios in a proportion. So, if $\triangle ABC$ is similar to $\triangle DEF$, then $\frac{AB}{DE} = \frac{BC}{EF}$. You can use proportions such as this to find the lengths of the sides in similar triangles. Substitute three lengths you know or can measure in a proportion and solve for the length of the unknown side.

## 1 Focus

### Connecting to Students' Lives

Ask students if they have ever wondered how tall a building, tree, or a mountain is. Discuss possible ways to find such measurements without actually making them.

### Connecting to Prior Knowledge

In Lesson 11-2, students learned to use the Pythagorean Theorem to find sides of a right triangle. In this lesson, students use similar triangles and proportions to find an unknown side of a triangle. In Lesson 11-6, students will learn to use trigonometric ratios to find sides of triangles.

# 11-4 Write a Proportion

**Problem Solving Strategies**

- Account for All Possibilities
- Draw a Diagram
- Look for a Pattern
- Make a Model
- Make a Table
- Simplify a Problem
- Simulate a Problem
- Solve by Graphing
- Try, Test, Revise
- Use Multiple Strategies
- Work Backward
- Write an Equation
- **Write a Proportion**

***Math Strategies in Action*** You can't measure distance across the Grand Canyon with a tape measure. Yet, distances across it have been measured. How were they measured?

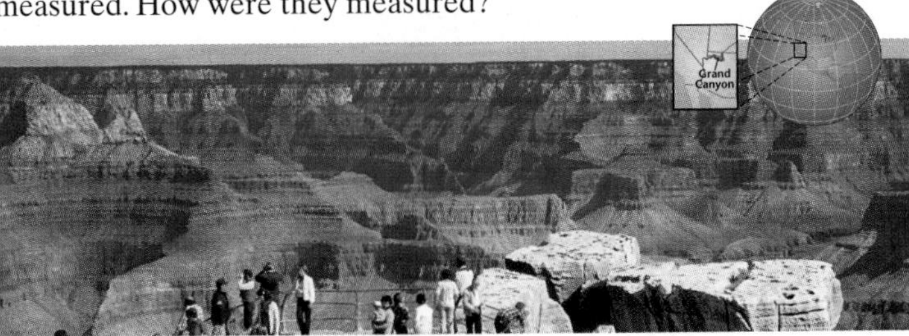


Surveyors sometimes find such distances indirectly using similar triangles. You learned about similar figures and proportions in Lesson 6-3. Now let's see how you can use similar right triangles to find measurements indirectly.

### Sample Problem

To find the distance from $Q$ to $P$ across a canyon, a surveyor picks points $R$ and $S$ such that $\overline{RS}$ is perpendicular to $\overline{RP}$. He locates point $T$ on $\overline{SP}$ such that $\overline{QT}$ is perpendicular to $\overline{RP}$. The two triangles, $\triangle PRS$ and $\triangle PQT$, are similar. He then measures $\overline{RS}$, $\overline{RQ}$, and $\overline{QT}$. What is the distance $QP$ across the canyon?

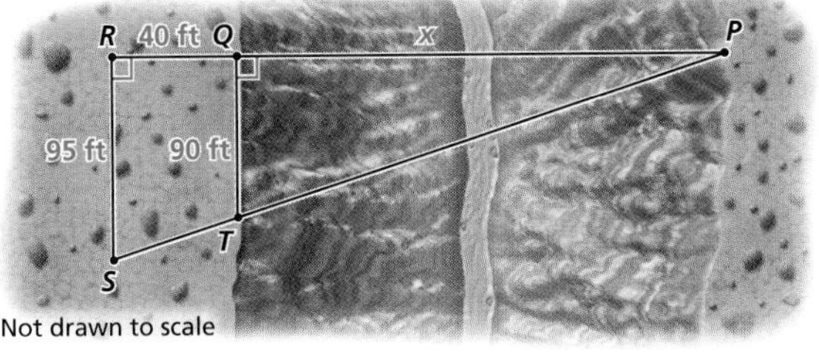


Not drawn to scale

### Read

1. What information is given? $\overline{RS} \perp \overline{RP}$, $\overline{QT} \perp \overline{RP}$, $\triangle PRS \sim \triangle PQT$, $RS$, $RQ$, and $QT$
2. What are you asked to find? $QP$



## Tools to Monitor Progress

### BEFORE THE LESSON

**To check prerequisite skills:**

- Solving proportions

**Skills You Need,** p. 557

**Skills Handbook,** p. 740

**Skills Intervention Kit,** Ratio, Proportion, and Percent

### DURING THE LESSON

**To check understanding:**

- **Additional Sample Problem**
  At a given time of day, a building of unknown height casts a shadow that is 24 feet long. At the same time of day, a lamppost that is 8 feet tall casts a shadow that is 4 feet long.

**Plan**

Since $\triangle PQT \sim \triangle PRS$, and you know three lengths, writing and solving a proportion is a good strategy to use. It is helpful to draw the triangles as separate figures.

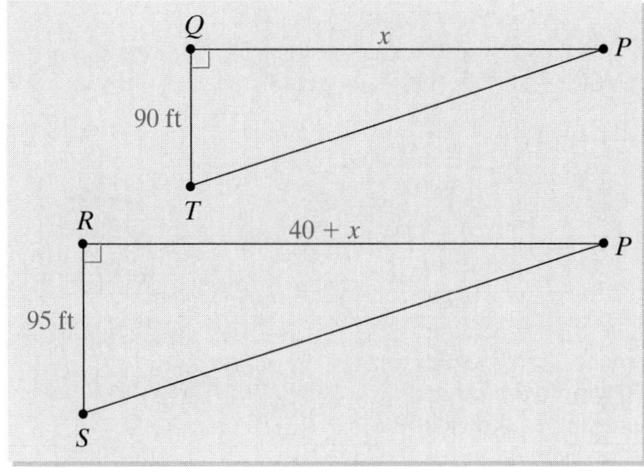

**Solve**

Write a proportion using the legs of the similar right triangles.

$\frac{x}{40 + x} = \frac{90}{95}$ Write a proportion.

$95x = 90(40 + x)$ Write cross products.

$95x = 3{,}600 + 90x$ Use the Distributive Property.

$5x = 3{,}600$ Subtract $90x$ from each side.

$x = 720$ Divide each side by 5.

The distance $QP$ across the canyon is 720 ft.

**Look Back**

Solving problems that involve indirect measurement often makes use of figures that *overlap*. Use the diagram on page 578 to answer the following questions.

**3.** Which segments overlap? **$\overline{RQ}$ and $\overline{RP}$, $\overline{ST}$ and $\overline{SP}$**

**4.** A common error students make is to use part of a side in a proportion. For example, some students might think $\frac{40}{95}$ is equal to $\frac{x}{90}$. How does drawing the triangles as separate figures help you avoid this error? **It forces you to draw the entire 40 + x side to complete the larger triangle.**



# 2 Teach

## Teaching Notes

Students may need a brief refresher on similar triangles. Remind students that similar triangles have corresponding congruent angles, and corresponding sides that are in proportion.

**Visual Learning** Some students may have difficulty envisioning the two similar triangles in the sample problem because the smaller triangle lies within the sides of the larger triangle. Suggest that students draw the triangles in two different colors to help them see the corresponding sides and angles.

**Reading Math** Remind students that the symbol ~ means "is similar to." So, you read the expression $\triangle PRS \sim \triangle PQT$ as "triangle *PRS* is similar to triangle *PQT*."

### Sample Problem

**Build understanding.** Explain why, once you have found the distance *QP* across the canyon, you still cannot find the distance *TP* using proportions. **You cannot find *TP* because you must know *ST* to be able to use proportions.**

**Math Reasoning** What is another method you could use to find *TP* once you know *QP* and *QT*? **You could use the Pythagorean Theorem to find *TP* because it is the hypotenuse of $\triangle PQT$.**

**Connecting to Geography** Scientists have tried, over many years, to use math to measure the height of Mt. Everest, the highest point above sea level on Earth. The methods tried include reflecting light from mirrors, using radar, and, most recently, bouncing signals off satellites to use the Global Positioning System. Actually all of the mountains in the Himalayas are increasing in height, but only a fraction of an inch per year.

What is the height *x* of the building? **48 ft**

## AFTER THE LESSON

**To assess knowledge:**

**Lesson Quiz**

Write a proportion and solve.

On the blueprints of a rectangular floor, the width of the floor is 6 in. The diagonal distance across the floor is 10 in. If the actual width of the building is 32 ft, what is the actual diagonal distance? **$53\frac{1}{3}$ ft**

- For enrichment and reteaching options see Resources on p. 557H.

# 3 Practice/Assess

## Assignment Guide

**Core** 1–12
✪ **Extension** 13, 14

Mixed Review can be assigned at any time for maintenance.

### Exercises

**Visual Learning** **Exercises 6–13** You may want to draw a sketch to help you solve some of these problems.

### ✪ Challenge

Explain how you could use proportions with similar polygons other than triangles to find unknown measurements. Similar polygons have sides that are in proportion.

### Closure

You can write a proportion to solve measurement problems using similar triangles.

# Exercises

## Check Understanding

**Write a proportion and find the value of each $x$.**

1. $\triangle PQT \sim \triangle PRS$

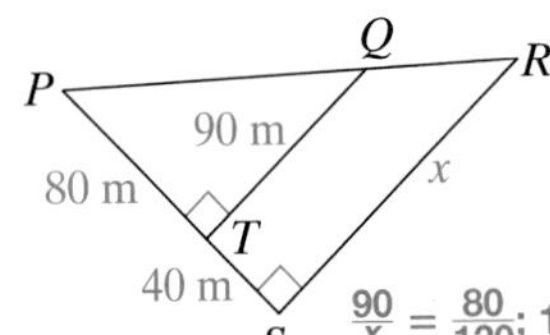


$\frac{90}{x} = \frac{80}{120}$; 135 m

2. $\triangle HGI \sim \triangle HFJ$ $\frac{x}{10 + x} = \frac{39}{48}$; $43\frac{1}{3}$ ft

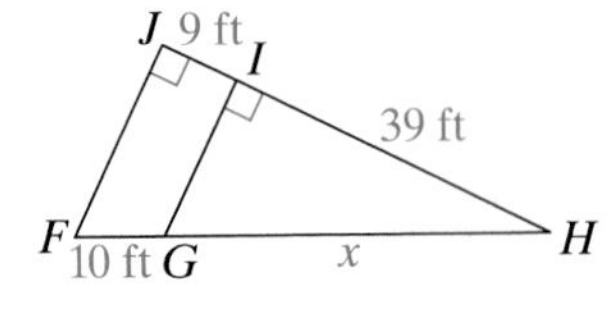


3. A swimmer needs to know the distance $x$ across a lake to help her decide whether it is safe to swim to the other side. She estimates the distance using the triangles shown at the right. $\triangle ABC \sim \triangle EDC$. How far is the distance across the lake? 1.2 mi

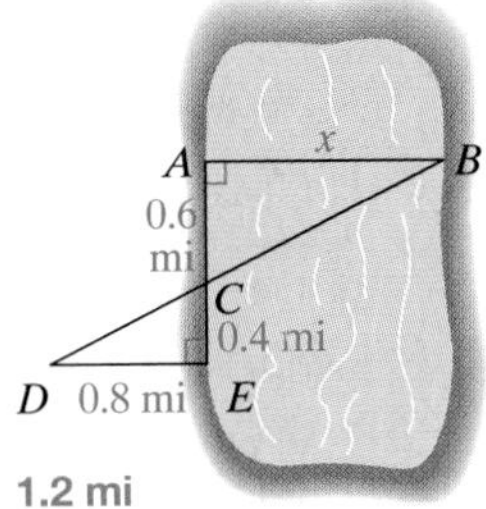


## Practice and Problem Solving

**Write a proportion, and find the value of each $x$.**

4. $\triangle ABE \sim \triangle ACD$

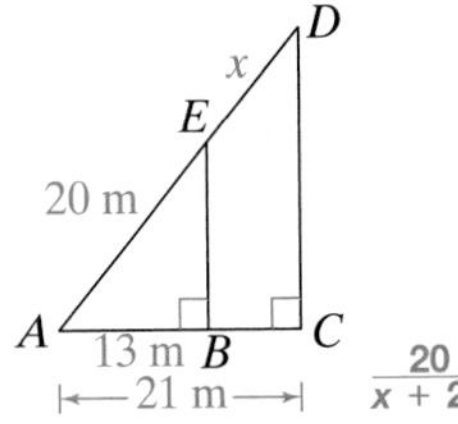


$\frac{20}{x + 20} = \frac{13}{21}$; 12.3 m

5. $\triangle GHI \sim \triangle KJI$ $\frac{x}{60} = \frac{15}{25}$; 36 yd

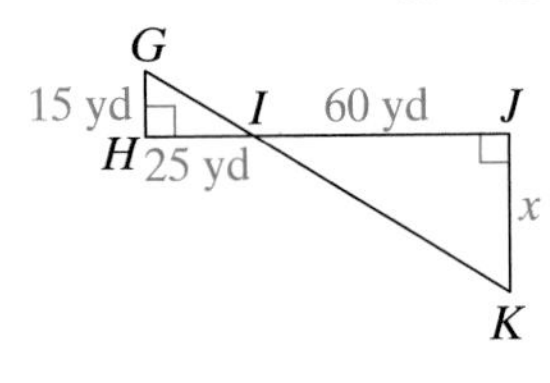


6. To estimate the height of a tree, Milton positions a mirror on the ground so he can see the top of the tree reflected in it. His height, his distance from the mirror, and his line of sight to the mirror determine a triangle. The tree's height, its distance from the mirror, and the distance from the top of the tree to the mirror form a similar triangle. Use the measurements at the right to determine the height of the tree. 28 ft

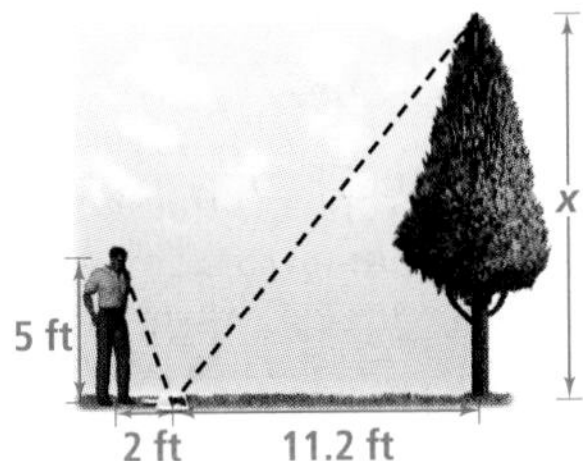


7. A landscaper needs to find the distance $x$ across a piece of land. He estimates the distance using the similar triangles at the right. What is the distance? 10.5 yd

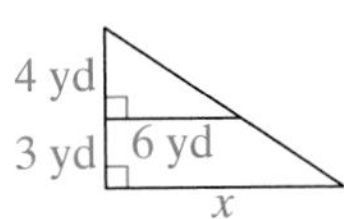




## Alternative Assessment

Place students in small groups. Ask each group to find a height around the school that they can measure by using similar triangles and proportions. Have students present their measurements and explain how they found them.

## Daily Cumulative Review

**Find the distance between each pair of points. Round to the nearest tenth.** *(Lesson 11-3)*

1. (2, 6), (6, 3) 5 units
2. (5, 0), (−5, 4) 10.8 units
3. (14, 5), (−10, 8) 24.2 units
4. (−5, 11), (−2, −6) 17.3 units
5. (9, −2), (−4, 12) 19.1 units
6. (−8, 6), (8, 5) 16.0 units

**Use the triangle at the right. Find the missing length to the nearest tenth of a unit.** *(Lesson 11-2)*

7. $a = 6$ in., $b = 3$ in., $c =$ 6.7 in.
8. $a = 12$ yd, $c = 20$ yd, $b =$ 16 yd
9. $b = 8$ ft, $c = 12$ ft, $a =$ 8.9 ft
10. $a = 14$ m, $c = 19$ m, $b =$ 12.8 m

**Mixed Review**

**Find the area of each figure.**

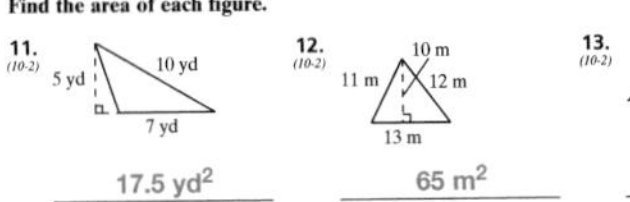


11. *(10-2)* 17.5 yd²
12. *(10-2)* 65 m²
13. *(10-2)* 105 mm²

**Find each sum or difference.**

14. *(5-3)* $\frac{3}{16} + \frac{4}{5}$ $\frac{79}{80}$
15. *(5-3)* $1\frac{6}{7} - \frac{3}{7}$ $1\frac{3}{7}$
16. *(5-3)* $2\frac{3}{5} + 3\frac{2}{5}$ 6

**Find each product or quotient.**

17. *(1-9)* $-8 \cdot 9$ −72
18. *(1-9)* $26 \div (-2)$ −13
19. *(1-9)* $-8 \cdot (-3)$ 24
20. *(5-4)* $\frac{5}{6} \div \frac{8}{9}$ $\frac{15}{16}$
21. *(5-4)* $\left(-\frac{3}{7}\right)\left(\frac{9}{15}\right)$ $-\frac{9}{35}$
22. *(5-4)* $6\frac{2}{3} \div 1\frac{5}{6}$ $3\frac{7}{11}$

**Solve using any strategy.**

8. The height of the Eiffel Tower is 984 ft. A souvenir model of the tower is 6 in. tall. At 5 P.M. in Paris, the shadow of the souvenir model is 8 in. long. The Eiffel Tower and its shadow determine two legs of a right triangle that are similar to the two legs of a right triangle determined by the souvenir model and its shadow. About how long is the shadow of the Eiffel Tower? 1,312 ft

9. There are 30 students in a math class. Twelve belong to the computer club, and eight belong to the photography club. Three belong to both clubs. How many belong to neither club? 13

10. Jake spent $\frac{3}{8}$ of his money on a videotape and $\frac{1}{2}$ of what was left on a cassette tape. He now has \$6.25. How much money did he start with? \$20

11. Hai takes 12 minutes to walk to school. He wants to get there 15 minutes early to meet with his lab partner. What time should he leave his house if school starts at 8:10 A.M.? 7:43 A.M.

12. *Number Sense* Christa thought of a number. She added 4, multiplied the sum by $-5$, and subtracted 12. She then doubled the result and got $-34$. What number did Christa start with? $-3$

13. Madison Square Garden in New York City is built in the shape of a circle. Its diameter is 404 ft and it accommodates 20,234 spectators. To the nearest tenth of a square foot, how much area is there for each spectator? 6.3 ft$^2$

14. A tennis ball is served from one end of a tennis court, 39 ft from the net. The ball is hit 9 ft above the ground, travels in a straight path down the middle of the court, and just clears the top of the 3-ft net. This is illustrated in the figure at the right. $\triangle PQR \sim \triangle MQS$. How far from the net does the ball land? 19.5 ft

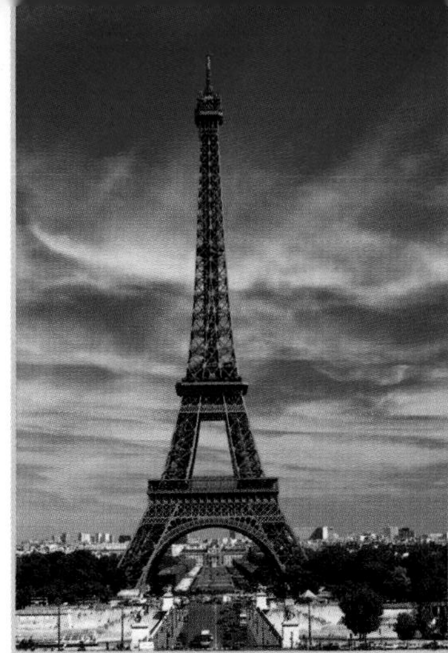

The Eiffel Tower was named for its designer, Gustave Eiffel. He was the same engineer who designed the framework of the Statue of Liberty.

## MIXED REVIEW

**Find the midpoint of each segment with the given endpoints.** ***(Lesson 11-3)***

15. $A(2, 3)$ and $B(4, 7)$ (3, 5)
16. $X(-1, 2)$ and $Y(2, 6)$ (0.5, 4)
17. $L(6, -5)$ and $M(-3, -8)$ (1.5, $-6.5$)

**Sketch each figure.** ***(Lesson 9-3)*** 18–20. See margin.

18. isosceles right triangle
19. equilateral triangle
20. scalene obtuse triangle

21. Keith collected twice as much money as Lucy for a walkathon. Together they collected \$120. How much money did each person collect? ***(Lesson 7-4)*** Keith \$80, Lucy \$40



18.

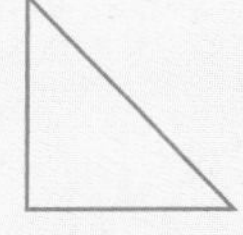

20.

19.

## Practice

**Write a proportion and find the value of each $x$.**
Sample proportions are shown.

1. $\triangle KLM \sim \triangle NPQ$
Proportion: $\frac{x}{17} = \frac{2}{8}$
$x =$ 4.25 m

2. $\triangle RST \sim \triangle RPQ$
Proportion: $\frac{x}{60} = \frac{32}{48}$
$x =$ 40 in.

3. $\triangle ABC \sim \triangle ADE$
Proportion: $\frac{x}{12} = \frac{49}{21}$
$x =$ 28 ft

4. $\triangle UVW \sim \triangle UYZ$
Proportion: $\frac{x + 9}{9} = \frac{20}{15}$
$x =$ 3 cm

**Solve. Show the proportion you use.**

5. A surveyor needs to find the distance across a canyon. She finds a tree on the edge of the canyon and a large rock on the other edge. The surveyor uses stakes to set up the similar right triangles shown. Find the distance across the canyon, $x$.
$\frac{15}{24} = \frac{x}{x + 12}$; 20 ft

6. Three cartons of juice cost \$4.77. Find the cost of 8 cartons.
$\frac{3}{4.77} = \frac{8}{x}$; \$12.72

7. If a pizza with a diameter of 12 inches costs \$10.99, based on area, how much should a 15-inch pizza cost?
$\frac{10.99}{113.04} = \frac{x}{176.625}$; about \$17.17



## Reteaching

Write a proportion, and find the value of $x$ given that $\triangle ABC \sim \triangle CBD$.

In similar triangles, corresponding sides are proportional. Thus, the first step is to decide which sides are proportional and can be used to find $x$. It is helpful to draw the triangles as separate figures.

Notice that the right angles are $\angle C$ and $\angle D$. So $C \leftrightarrow D$. The hypotenuses are $\overline{AB}$ and $\overline{CB}$. So $\overline{AB} \leftrightarrow \overline{CB}$. The longer legs are $\overline{BC}$ and $\overline{BD}$. So $\overline{BC} \leftrightarrow \overline{BD}$. You can also find these relationships in the similarity statement.

| | |
|---|---|
| So $\frac{AB}{CB} = \frac{BC}{BD}$ | Write corresponding sides in each ratio. Write sides in the same triangle in either the numerators or the denominators. |
| $\frac{x + 8}{10} = \frac{10}{8}$ | $AB = x + 8, CB = 10 = BC, BD = 8$ |
| $8(x + 8) = 10 \cdot 10$ | Write cross products. |
| $8x + 64 = 100$ | Use the Distributive Property. |
| $8x = 36$ | Subtract 64 from each side. |
| $x = 4.5$ | Divide each side by 8. |

The length of $x$ is 4.5 cm.

**Write a proportion to find the value of each $x$.**
Sample proportions are shown.

1. $\triangle EFG \sim \triangle HJG$
Proportion: $\frac{3}{5} = \frac{9}{x + 9}$
$x =$ 6 ft

2. $\triangle KLM \sim \triangle LNM$
Proportion: $\frac{6}{x + 5} = \frac{5}{6}$
$x =$ 2.2 m

Reteaching



## Enrichment

There are several methods for finding Pythagorean triples.

I. Calculate multiples of known Pythagorean triples.
7 ×③= 21  7 ×④= 28  7 ×⑤= 35
So, 21, 28, 35 is a Pythagorean triple: $21^2 + 28^2 = 35^2$.
You can show that two triangles are similar by showing that corresponding sides are proportional. In a triangle, if the sides are proportional, then the corresponding angles must be congruent.

1. Is the triangle with sides of length 3, 4, and 5 similar to the triangle of with sides of length 21, 28, and 35? Explain how you know.
Yes, the sides are proportional. $\frac{3}{21} = \frac{4}{28} = \frac{5}{35}$

2. The ratio of a side of a triangle to the corresponding side in a similar triangle is called the *scale factor*. What is the scale factor between the 3-4-5 right triangle and the 21-28-35 right triangle?
1:7

**Calculate multiples of the 3, 4, 5 triple that include the given numbers. The resulting triangle is similar to the 3-4-5 triangle. Give the scale factor.**

3. 18, 24, 30 scale factor: 1:6
4. 27, 36, 45 scale factor: 1:9
5. 150, 200, 250 scale factor: 1:50

II. Substitute whole number values of $n$ in the expressions $2n + 1$, $2n^2 + 2n$, and $2n^2 + 2n + 1$.
Using $n = 7$: $2n + 1 = 2(7) + 1 = 15$
$2n^2 + 2n = 2(7)^2 + 2(7) = 112$
$2n^2 + 2n + 1 = 2(7)^2 + 2(7) + 1 = 113$
So, 15, 112, 113 is a Pythagorean triple.

**Find a Pythagorean triple using the given value of $n$. If the resulting triangle is similar to the 15-112-113 triangle, give the scale factor. Otherwise, write "not similar."**

6. $n = 1$ 3, 4, 5 not similar
7. $n = 2$ 5, 12, 13 not similar
8. $n = 5$ 11, 60, 61 not similar
9. $n = 4$ 9, 40, 41 not similar

# 11-5

## Getting Ready

**Key Terms and Symbols** Rule for Multiplying Square Roots

**Resources** A complete list of resources for this lesson is on p. 557H.

### Daily Skills Warm-Up

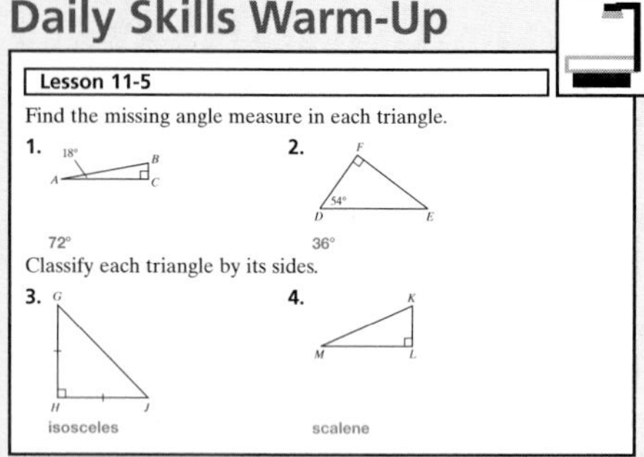

### Background for the Lesson

You can verify that the Rule for Multiplying Square Roots is true by finding $\sqrt{36}$ and comparing it to $\sqrt{9} \cdot \sqrt{4}$. As with a number of rules in mathematics, this one is true for multiplication, but it is not true for addition. To verify this, find $\sqrt{16} + \sqrt{9}$ and compare it to $\sqrt{25}$. You can use the Rule for Multiplying Square Roots to simplify many square roots by factoring perfect squares out of square roots. For example, you know that $\sqrt{27} = \sqrt{9} \cdot \sqrt{3}$. Since 9 is a perfect square, this expression simplifies to $3\sqrt{3}$.

## 1 Focus

### Connecting to Students' Lives

When you fold paper to create origami figures, you are using the relationships in certain special right triangles.

### Connecting to Prior Knowledge

In Lesson 11-2, students learned how to use the Pythagorean Theorem to find the sides of a triangle. In this lesson, students use the Pythagorean Theorem to define relationships in special right triangles. In Lesson 11-6, students will use trigonometric ratios to find the sides of triangles.

# 11-5 Special Right Triangles

**What You'll Learn**

1. To use the relationships in 45°-45°-90° triangles
2. To use the relationships in 30°-60°-90° triangles

**. . . And Why**

To find distances in real-world situations, such as in sports

## PART 1 Using 45°-45°-90° Triangles

The Pythagorean Theorem requires that you understand square roots. The rule for Multiplying Square Roots will help you work with square roots more efficiently.

**Multiplying Square Roots**

For nonnegative numbers, the square root of a product equals the product of the square roots.

| Arithmetic | Algebra |
|---|---|
| | If $a \geq 0$ and $b \geq 0$, |
| $\sqrt{9 \cdot 2} = \sqrt{9} \cdot \sqrt{2}$ | then $\sqrt{ab} = \sqrt{a} \cdot \sqrt{b}$. |

The rule for Multiplying Square Roots is especially useful with an isosceles right triangle, which is also known by its angle measures as a 45°-45°-90° triangle.

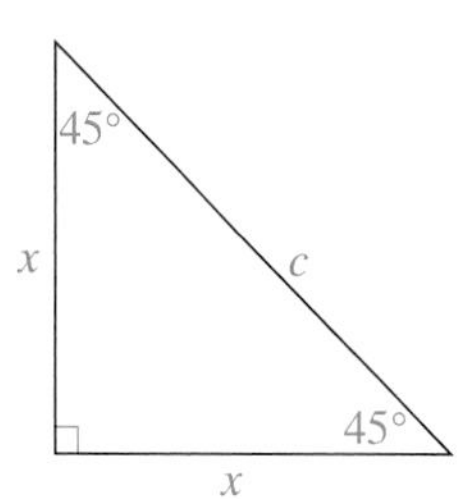


For the figure at the left, you can use the Pythagorean Theorem to find the length of the hypotenuse.

| | |
|---|---|
| $c^2 = a^2 + b^2$ | Use the Pythagorean Theorem. |
| $c^2 = x^2 + x^2$ | Replace *a* and *b* with *x*. |
| $c^2 = 2x^2$ | Simplify. |
| $c = \sqrt{2x^2}$ | Find the square root. |
| $c = \sqrt{2} \cdot \sqrt{x^2}$ | Use the rule for Multiplying Square Roots. |
| $c = \sqrt{2} \cdot x$, or $x\sqrt{2}$ | Simplify. |

This shows the special relationship of the hypotenuse and the legs of a 45°-45°-90° triangle.

**45°-45°-90° Triangles**

In a 45°-45°-90° triangle, the legs are congruent and the length of the hypotenuse is the length of a leg times $\sqrt{2}$.

$$\text{hypotenuse} = \text{leg} \cdot \sqrt{2}$$

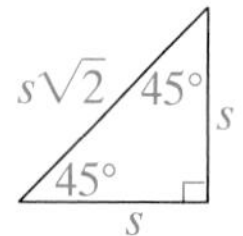




# Tools to Monitor Progress

**BEFORE THE LESSON**

**To check prerequisite skills:**

- Multiplying whole numbers

**Skills Handbook,** p. 725

**DURING THE LESSON**

**To check understanding:**

**Try This** exercises on student page

- **Additional Examples 1–2**

  Patrice folds the square napkins diagonally to put on the table. What is the length of the diagonal if the side length is 20 in.? Round your answer to the nearest tenth. 28.3 in.

## Example 1

**Find the length of the hypotenuse in the figure at the right.**

$\text{hypotenuse} = \text{leg} \cdot \sqrt{2}$

$x = 6 \cdot \sqrt{2}$ The length of the leg is 6.

$\approx 8.5$ Use a calculator.

The length of the hypotenuse is about 8.5 in.

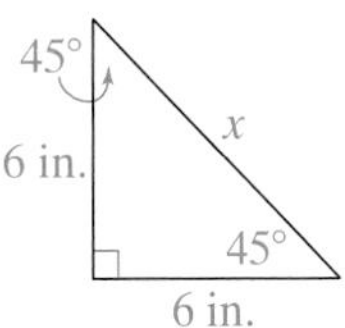


### Try This

1. The length of the legs of an isosceles right triangle is 4.2 cm. Find the length of the hypotenuse. Round to the nearest tenth. 5.9 cm

You can use 45°-45°-90° triangles in real-world situations.

REAL-WORLD CONNECTION

## Example 2

**A baseball diamond is a square. The distance from any base to the next is 90 ft. How far is it from home plate to second base?**

$\text{hypotenuse} = \text{leg} \cdot \sqrt{2}$ Use the 45°-45°-90° relationship.

$= 90 \cdot \sqrt{2}$ The length of the leg is 90.

$\approx 127.28$ Use a calculator.

The distance from home plate to second base is about 127 ft.

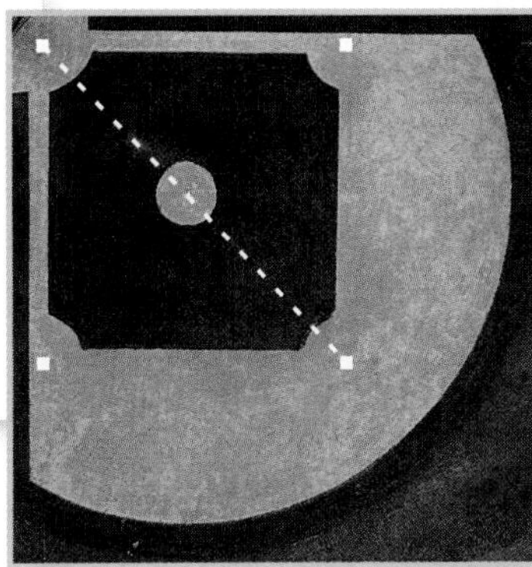

### Try This

2. Gymnasts use mats that are 12 m by 12 m for floor exercises. A gymnast does cartwheels across the diagonal of a mat. What is the length of the diagonal to the nearest meter? 17 m

## PART 2 Using 30°-60°-90° Triangles

Another special right triangle is the 30°-60°-90° triangle. You can form two congruent 30°-60°-90° triangles by bisecting an angle of an equilateral triangle. This is shown in the diagram at the right.

In the diagram, the length of the hypotenuse of each 30°-60°-90° triangle is twice the length of the shorter leg. You can use the Pythagorean Theorem to find the length of the longer leg.

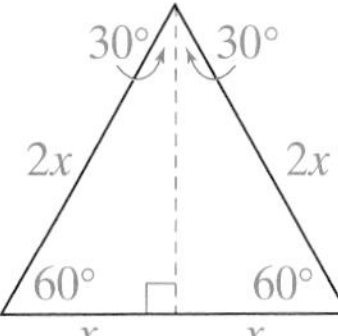

# 2 Teach

## PART 1 Part 1 Teaching Notes

Discuss the meaning of *isosceles right triangle.*

**Reading Math** The expression $x\sqrt{2}$ is read "*x* times the square root of 2."

### Example 1

**Build understanding.** Ask: How do you express the exact length of the hypotenuse? 8.5 or $6\sqrt{2}$? $6\sqrt{2}$

**Error Prevention** To find $6 \cdot \sqrt{2}$ on most non-graphing calculators, you press [6], then [×], then [2], then [√ ], then [=]. You enter [2] before you press the square root key even though when you read the problem, you say "square root" before you say "two." This difference may lead some students to reverse these steps in the procedure.

### Example 2

**Build understanding.** Explain why it might be safer for a gymnast to do cartwheels across the diagonal of the mat, rather than straight across. The length of the diagonal is greater than the length of the sides, giving her more room.

**Extension** Based on Example 2, what would be the formula for the diagonal of a square of side length *s*? diagonal $= s\sqrt{2}$

**Auditory Learning** Have one partner draw an isosceles right triangle, label one leg with a number or a variable (such as *x*), and hand it to the other. The second partner labels the other leg and the hypotenuse, while saying the measurements aloud (such as $x$ and $x\sqrt{2}$). Then exchange roles.

- **Additional Example 3**

Find the length of the longer leg of a 30°-60°-90° triangle with a hypotenuse of 14 ft. Round your answer to the nearest tenth. 12.1 ft

## AFTER THE LESSON

### To assess knowledge: Lesson Quiz

Find each missing length.

1. Find the hypotenuse of a 45°-45°-90° triangle with legs of 4*y* cm. $4y\sqrt{2}$ cm
2. Find the longer leg of a 30°-60°-90° triangle with a hypotenuse of *b* ft. $\frac{b\sqrt{3}}{2}$

- For enrichment and reteaching options see Resources on p. 557H.

## Part 2 Teaching Notes

When you know the relationships among the sides of a 30°-60°-90° triangle, with just one side length you can find the other two side lengths.

### Example 3

**Build understanding.** Ask: How would you find the missing lengths if the length of the hypotenuse were given? The short leg equals half the hypotenuse. The long leg equals the short leg times $\sqrt{3}$.

**Advanced Learners** What are the missing lengths of a 30°-60°-90° triangle that has a longer leg length of 2? shorter leg $= \frac{2}{\sqrt{3}}$; hypotenuse $= \frac{4}{\sqrt{3}}$

**Math Reasoning** Use math reasoning to explain why you might choose not to use the Pythagorean Theorem to find the hypotenuse of a 30°-60°-90° triangle, if you know the length of both legs. Doubling the shorter leg to find the hypotenuse might be much easier than using the Pythagorean Theorem.

**Tactile Learning** Have students draw right triangles with one leg that is 4 cm long and the other leg 6.9 cm (which $\approx 4\sqrt{3}$ long.) Have them predict the length of the hypotenuse and the size of the angles, and then have them measure to verify.

**Error Prevention** Students sometimes confuse which square root to use with which special right triangle. To help them, remind them that there are two congruent angles in the 45°–45°–90° triangles. So the two congruent triangles can remind them of the 2 in the $\sqrt{2}$. There are three different angles in 30°–60°–90° triangles, and all angles are divisible by 3. So the number 3 can remind them of the 3 in $\sqrt{3}$.

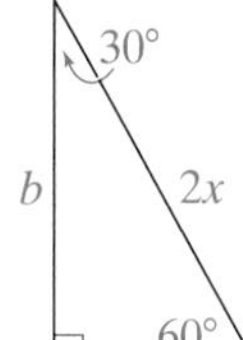


For the figure at the left, find the length of the longer leg.

| | |
|---|---|
| $(2x)^2 = x^2 + b^2$ | Use the Pythagorean Theorem. |
| $4x^2 = x^2 + b^2$ | Simplify. |
| $3x^2 = b^2$ | Subtract $x^2$ from each side. |
| $\sqrt{3x^2} = b$ | Find the square root. |
| $\sqrt{3} \cdot \sqrt{x^2} = b$ | Use the rule for Multiplying Square Roots. |
| $b = \sqrt{3} \cdot x$, or $x\sqrt{3}$ | Simplify. |

This shows the special relationship of the hypotenuse and the legs in a 30°-60°-90° triangle.

**30°-60°-90° Triangle**

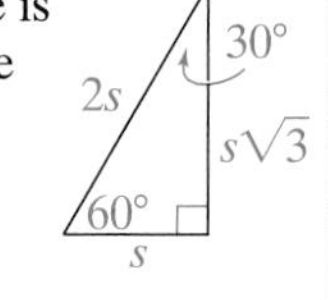


In a 30°-60°-90° triangle, the length of the hypotenuse is 2 times the length of the shorter leg. The length of the longer leg is $\sqrt{3}$ times the length of the shorter leg.

hypotenuse = 2 · shorter leg

longer leg = shorter leg · $\sqrt{3}$

### Example 3

30°, y, x, 60°, 5 ft

**Find the missing lengths in the triangle at the left.**

hypotenuse = 2 · shorter leg

| | |
|---|---|
| $x = 2 \cdot 5$ | The length of the shorter leg is 5. |
| $x = 10$ | Simplify. |

longer leg = shorter leg · $\sqrt{3}$

| | |
|---|---|
| $y = 5 \cdot \sqrt{3}$ | The length of the shorter leg is 5. |
| $y \approx 8.7$ | Use a calculator. |

The length of the hypotenuse is 10 ft, and the length of the longer leg is about 8.7 ft.

**Try This** Find the missing lengths in each 30°-60°-90° triangle.

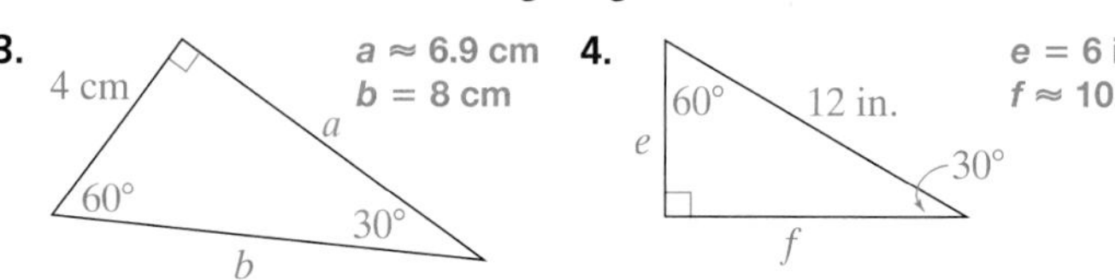

# Exercises

## Check Understanding

**Tell whether a triangle with sides of the given lengths could be 45°-45°-90° or 30°-60°-90°. Explain.** 1–3. See margin.

1. 6, 8, 10
2. $5, 5, 5\sqrt{2}$
3. $15, 7.5\sqrt{3}, 7.5$

**Find the missing lengths.**

4. 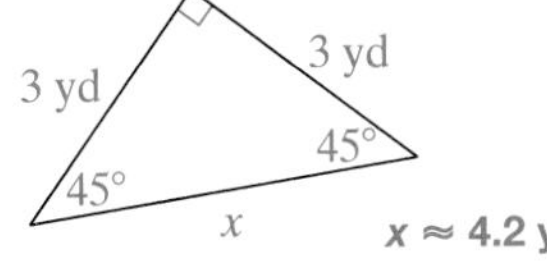

$x \approx 4.2$ yd

5. 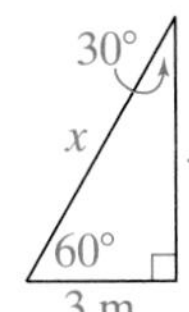

$x = 6$ m, $y \approx 5.2$ m

6. 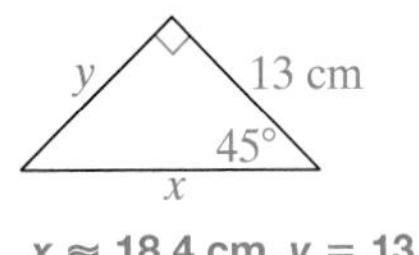

$x \approx 18.4$ cm, $y = 13$ cm

7. *Mathematical Reasoning* The smaller angles of a 30°-60°-90° triangle are in the ratio 1 : 2. Are the shorter sides also in the ratio 1 : 2? Explain. No, because the hypotenuse is twice the shorter leg.

## Practice and Problem Solving

**The length of one side of the triangle is given in each row of the table. Find the missing lengths for that triangle.**

| | a | b | c |
|---|---|---|---|
| 8. | 3 m | 3 m | 4.2 m |
| 9. | 9 cm | 9 cm | 12.7 cm |
| 10. | 5.4 in. | 5.4 in. | 7.6 in. |

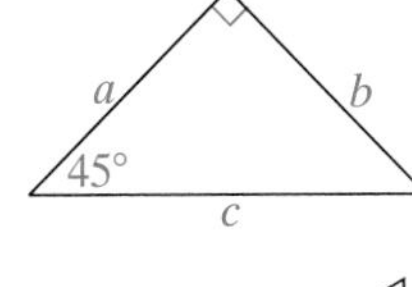


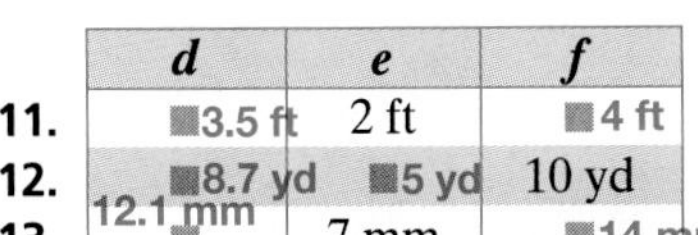
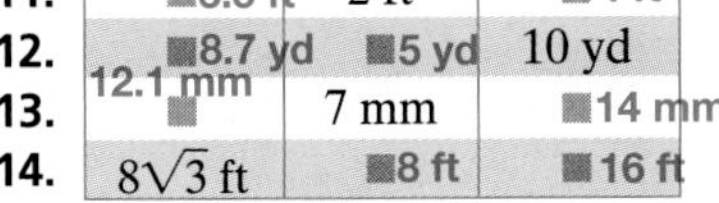

| | d | e | f |
|---|---|---|---|
| 11. | 3.5 ft | 2 ft | 4 ft |
| 12. | 8.7 yd | 5 yd | 10 yd |
| 13. | 12.1 mm | 7 mm | 14 mm |
| 14. | $8\sqrt{3}$ ft | 8 ft | 16 ft |

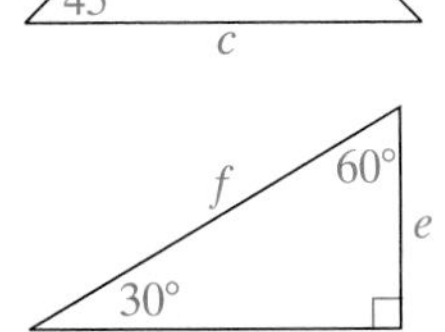


15. Answers may vary. Sample: The hypotenuse is twice the shorter leg. Since the shorter leg is 10 ft, the hypotenuse is 20 ft. The longer leg is $\sqrt{3}$ times the shorter leg, which is $10\sqrt{3}$.

16. Answers may vary. Sample: Perhaps the student is assuming that if $\sqrt{2}$ is a factor of the hypotenuse, the triangle must be a 45°-45°-90° triangle.

15. *Writing* Explain how to find the lengths of the longer leg and hypotenuse of a 30°-60°-90° triangle if the shorter leg is 10 ft. See above right.

16. *Error Analysis* A student says that a right triangle with a hypotenuse of length $2\sqrt{2}$ in. has to be an isosceles right triangle. What mistake might the student have made? See above right.



1. Neither. In a 45°-45°-90° triangle two sides are congruent. In a 30°-60°-90° triangle the hypotenuse is twice the shorter leg.

2. This is a 45°-45°-90° triangle because two sides are congruent and the hypotenuse is $\sqrt{2}$ times a leg.

3. This is a 30°-60°-90° triangle because the hypotenuse is twice the shorter leg and the longer leg is $\sqrt{3}$ times the shorter leg.

## Alternative Assessment

Have students use a protractor, ruler, and graph paper to draw a 45°-45°-90° triangle and a 30°-60°-90° triangle. Then have students measure the sides and calculate to confirm that the relationships they learned in this lesson are true.

# 3 Practice/Assess

## Assignment Guide

To provide flexible scheduling, this lesson can be divided into parts.

**Part 1**
Core 1–2, 4, 6, 8–10
Extension 16

**Part 2**
Core 3, 5, 7, 11–15
Extension 17–18

Mixed Review can be assigned at any time for maintenance.

## Exercises

**Exercise 18** Recall that a regular hexagon has 6 equal sides.

## Challenge

Find the length of the hypotenuse of a 45°-45°-90° triangle with legs that measure $\sqrt{2}$ m. 2 m

## Closure

In a 45°-45°-90° triangle, the length of the hypotenuse is the length of a leg times $\sqrt{2}$. In a 30°-60°-90° triangle, the length of the hypotenuse is 2 times the length of the shorter leg, and the length of the longer leg is $\sqrt{3}$ times the length of the shorter leg.

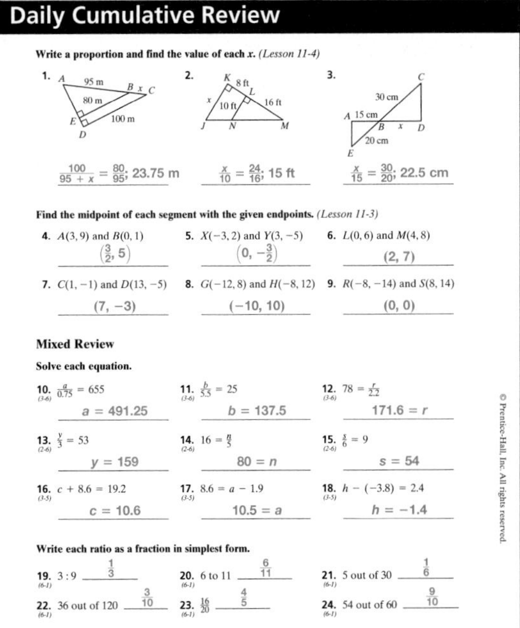

## Daily Cumulative Review

**Write a proportion and find the value of each x.** *(Lesson 11-4)*

1. $\frac{100}{95 + x} = \frac{80}{95}$; 23.75 m
2. $\frac{x}{10} = \frac{24}{16}$; 15 ft
3. $\frac{x}{15} = \frac{30}{20}$; 22.5 cm

**Find the midpoint of each segment with the given endpoints.** *(Lesson 11-3)*

4. $A(3, 9)$ and $B(0, 1)$ $\left(\frac{3}{2}, 5\right)$
5. $X(-3, 2)$ and $Y(3, -5)$ $\left(0, -\frac{3}{2}\right)$
6. $L(0, 6)$ and $M(4, 8)$ (2, 7)
7. $C(1, -1)$ and $D(13, -5)$ (7, −3)
8. $G(-12, 8)$ and $H(-8, 12)$ (−10, 10)
9. $R(-8, -14)$ and $S(8, 14)$ (0, 0)

**Mixed Review**

**Solve each equation.**

10. (3-6) $\frac{a}{0.75} = 655$ $a = 491.25$
11. (3-6) $\frac{b}{5.5} = 25$ $b = 137.5$
12. (3-6) $78 = \frac{r}{2.2}$ $171.6 = r$
13. (2-6) $\frac{y}{3} = 53$ $y = 159$
14. (2-6) $16 = \frac{n}{5}$ $80 = n$
15. (2-6) $\frac{s}{6} = 9$ $s = 54$
16. (3-5) $c + 8.6 = 19.2$ $c = 10.6$
17. (3-5) $8.6 = a - 1.9$ $10.5 = a$
18. (3-5) $h - (-3.8) = 2.4$ $h = -1.4$

**Write each ratio as a fraction in simplest form.**

19. (6-1) 3 : 9 $\frac{1}{3}$
20. (6-1) 6 to 11 $\frac{6}{11}$
21. (6-1) 5 out of 30 $\frac{1}{6}$
22. (6-1) 36 out of 120 $\frac{3}{10}$
23. (6-1) $\frac{16}{20}$ $\frac{4}{5}$
24. (6-1) 54 out of 60 $\frac{9}{10}$

## Practice

**The length of one side of the triangle is given in each row of the table. Find the missing lengths for that triangle.**

| | *m* | *n* | *p* |
|---|---|---|---|
| 1. | 14 | $14\sqrt{3}$ | 28 |
| 2. | 18 | $18\sqrt{3}$ | 36 |
| 3. | 9 | $9\sqrt{3}$ | 18 |
| 4. | 5 | $5\sqrt{3}$ | 10 |

| | *x* | *y* | *z* |
|---|---|---|---|
| 5. | 11 | 11 | $11\sqrt{2}$ |
| 6. | 8.7 | 8.7 | $8.7\sqrt{2}$ |
| 7. | 7 | 7 | $7\sqrt{2}$ |
| 8. | 17 | 17 | $17\sqrt{2}$ |

**Tell whether a triangle with sides of the given lengths could be 45°-45°-90° or 30°-60°-90°. Explain.**

9. $3\sqrt{2}, 3\sqrt{2}, 6$
   45°-45°-90°; Two sides are equal, and $(3\sqrt{2})\sqrt{2} = 6$, so the hypotenuse = leg · $\sqrt{2}$.
10. 10, 24, 26
    Neither; This triangle is similar to the 3-4-5 triangle.

**In the figure, $BD = 6\sqrt{2}$. Find each value.**

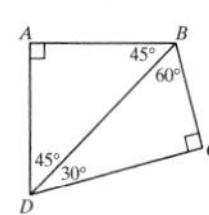

11. $AB$ 6
12. $AD$ 6
13. $BC$ $3\sqrt{2}$
14. $CD$ $3\sqrt{6}$
15. One leg of a 45°-45°-90° right triangle measures 14 cm. Find the exact perimeter.
    $28 + 14\sqrt{2}$ cm



## Reteaching

Find the length of each missing side in the figure.
$\triangle ABC$ is a 45°-45°-90° triangle.
$BC = AC = 8$ in.
$AB = AC \cdot \sqrt{2} = 8\sqrt{2}$ in. $\approx 11.3$ in.
$\triangle ACD$ is a 30°-60°-90° triangle and $\overline{AC}$ is the shorter leg.
$AD = 2 \cdot AC = 2 \cdot 8 = 16$ in.
$DC = \sqrt{3} \cdot AC = 8\sqrt{3}$ in. $\approx 13.9$ in.

Remember:

In a 45°-45°-90° triangle:
leg = leg
hypotenuse = leg$\sqrt{2}$.

In a 30°-60°-90° triangle:
hypotenuse = 2 · shorter leg
longer leg = $\sqrt{3}$ · shorter leg.

**Find the length of each missing side in each figure to the nearest tenth of a unit.**

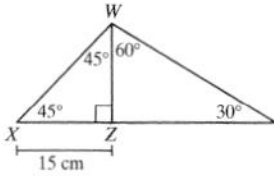

1. $WZ =$ 15 cm
2. $WX \approx$ 21.2 cm
3. $WY =$ 30 cm
4. $ZY \approx$ 26.0 cm

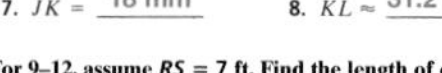

5. $LM =$ 36 mm
6. $JM \approx$ 50.9 mm

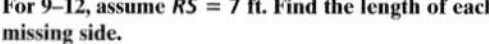

7. $JK =$ 18 mm
8. $KL \approx$ 31.2 mm

**For 9–12, assume $RS = 7$ ft. Find the length of each missing side.**

9. $RU =$ 14 ft
10. $SU \approx$ 12.1 ft
11. $ST =$ 7 ft
12. $RT \approx$ 9.9 ft

**For 13–16, assume $SU = 11\sqrt{3}$ ft. Find the length of each missing side.**

13. $RS =$ 11 ft
14. $RU =$ 22 ft
15. $ST =$ 11 ft
16. $RT \approx$ 15.6 ft



## Enrichment

You can use your knowledge of special right triangles to find information about space figures.

**The base of the pyramid is a square with sides 10 units long. The slant height is $EF$ and the height of the pyramid is $EG$. $m\angle BEF = m\angle CEF = 30°$.**

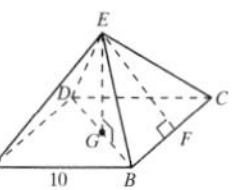

**Find the following information about the pyramid. Give exact answers.**

1. $m\angle EBF$ 60°
2. $m\angle ECF$ 60°
3. $BF$ 5 units
4. $FC$ 5 units
5. $EB$ 10 units
6. $EF$ $5\sqrt{3}$ units
7. $DB$ $10\sqrt{2}$ units
8. $GB \left(GB = \frac{1}{2} \cdot DB\right)$ $5\sqrt{2}$ units
9. $EG$ (Use the Pythagorean Theorem in $\triangle EGB$.) $\sqrt{50}$ or $5\sqrt{2}$ units
10. What type of special right triangle is $\triangle EGB$? 45°-45°-90°
11. $m\angle GEB$ 45°
12. $m\angle GBE$ 45°
13. area of $\square ABCD$ 100 units$^2$
14. area of $\triangle EBC$ $25\sqrt{3}$ units$^2$
15. surface area of pyramid $100 + 100\sqrt{3}$ units$^2$
16. volume of pyramid $\frac{500\sqrt{2}}{3}$ units$^3$

**The radius of the cone's base is 12. $m\angle OPQ = 30°$. Find the following information about the cone. Give exact answers.**

17. height $OP$ $12\sqrt{3}$ units
18. slant height $PQ$ 24 units
19. area of base $144\pi$ units$^2$
20. lateral area $288\pi$ units$^2$
21. surface area $432\pi$ units$^2$
22. volume $576\pi\sqrt{3}$ units$^3$





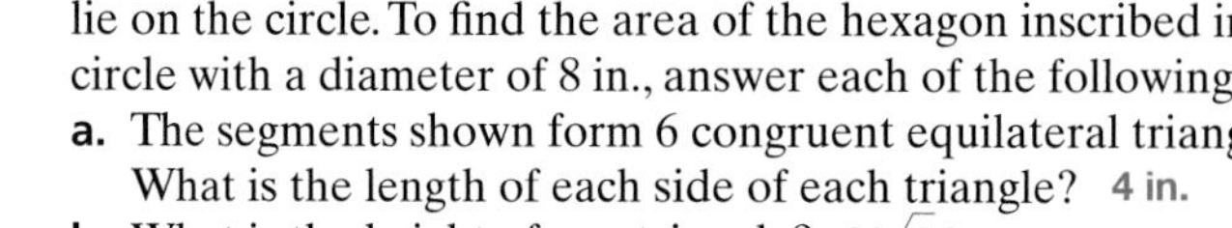

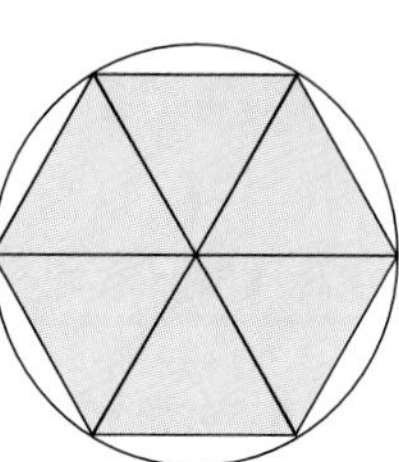

17. *Geometry* A polygon is inscribed in a circle if all of its vertices lie on the circle. To find the area of the hexagon inscribed in a circle with a diameter of 8 in., answer each of the following.
    a. The segments shown form 6 congruent equilateral triangles. What is the length of each side of each triangle? 4 in.
    b. What is the height of one triangle? $2\sqrt{3}$ in.
    c. What is the area of one triangle? $4\sqrt{3}$ in.$^2$
    d. What is the area of the hexagon? $24\sqrt{3}$ in.$^2$

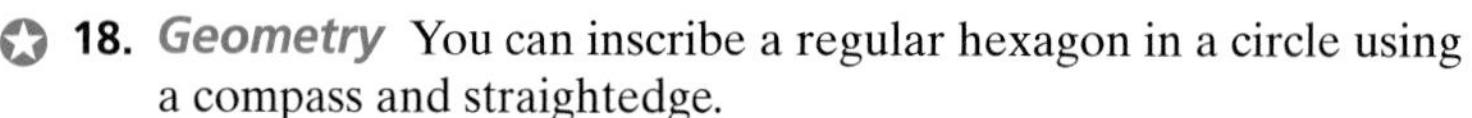

18. *Geometry* You can inscribe a regular hexagon in a circle using a compass and straightedge.
    a. Use your compass to construct a circle. Keep the compass at the same setting. Place the tip of the compass on the circle. Mark an arc on the circle. Place the tip of the compass where the arc intersects the circle and mark another arc. Continue around the circle until you have six arcs on the circle. Join consecutive arcs with segments. Check students' work.
    b. Measure the diameter of the circle. Use this measure and Exercise 17 to find the area of your hexagon. Check students' work.

**Journal**
*Sketch a 45°-45°-90° triangle and a 30°-60°-90° triangle. Use x for the length of the shorter side in each triangle. Explain how to find the lengths of the other sides of each triangle.*

## Mixed Review

**Is each relation a function? Explain.** *(Lesson 8-1)*

19. $\{(-1,3), (0,4), (1,5)\}$ Yes, for each domain value there is only one range value.
20. $\{(2,3), (3,4), (4,5), (5,6)\}$ Yes, for each domain value there is only one range value.

**Find the circumference of each circle with the given radius or diameter.** *(Lesson 9-6)*

21. radius = 4 in. 25.1 in.
22. diameter = 6 m 18.8 m
23. radius = 2.5 ft 15.7 ft
24. *Surveying* A surveyor needs to find the distance across a lake. He estimates the distance using the similar triangles at the right. What is the distance? *(Lesson 11-4)* 33 m

## Chapter Project 11 — Activity 2 Measuring

Choose a big tree in your neighborhood. Find the following:
- the measure of $\angle XYZ$ as explained in Activity 1 on page 563
- the distance you are from the tree when you measure $\angle XYZ$
- the circumference $C$, as explained on page 559
- $s_1$ and $s_2$, the maximum and minimum spread of the tree (See the diagram at the right.)
- $S$, the average of $s_1$ and $s_2$

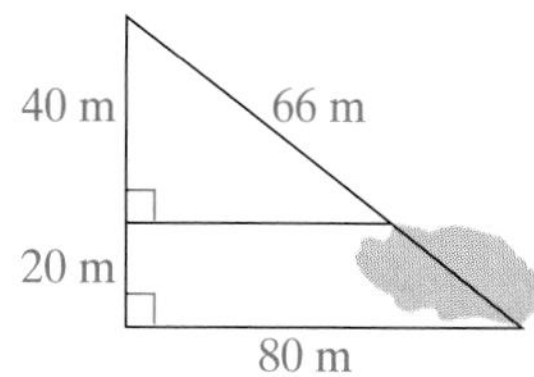



See also Extra Practice section.

### Project Activity 2

**Measuring** You may want to have students work in groups to measure big trees near the school or in a nearby park. If students work in pairs to measure the same tree, they can check each other's work.

# MATH TOOLBOX

Extension

After Lesson 11-5

## Square Roots of Expressions with Variables

You can simplify square roots of expressions that contain variables. Assume that the value of each variable is not negative.

### EXAMPLE 1

**a. Simplify $\sqrt{25x^2}$.**

$\sqrt{25x^2} = \sqrt{(5x)^2}$ Write $25x^2$ as the square of $5x$.

$= 5x$ Simplify.

**b. Simplify $\sqrt{p^6}$.**

$\sqrt{p^6} = \sqrt{(p^3)^2}$ Use the rule for the Power of a Power.

$= p^3$ Simplify.

**Simplify each square root.**

1. $\sqrt{49y^2}$ $7y$
2. $\sqrt{100m^{12}}$ $10m^6$
3. $-\sqrt{25x^6}$ $-5x^3$
4. $\sqrt{a^2b^{10}}$ $ab^5$

You can also simplify expressions that have nonsquare factors by using the rule for Multiplying Square Roots.

### EXAMPLE 2

**a. Simplify $\sqrt{x^9}$.**

$\sqrt{x^9} = \sqrt{x^8 \cdot x}$ Use the rule for Multiplying Powers with the Same Base.

$= \sqrt{x^8} \cdot \sqrt{x}$ Use the rule for Multiplying Square Roots.

$= x^4\sqrt{x}$ Simplify.

**b. Simplify $\sqrt{48x}$.**

$\sqrt{48x} = \sqrt{16 \cdot 3x}$ Find a perfect square factor.

$= \sqrt{16} \cdot \sqrt{3x}$ Use the rule for Multiplying Square Roots.

$= 4\sqrt{3x}$ Simplify.

**Simplify each square root.**

5. $\sqrt{a^{12}}$ $a^6$
6. $\sqrt{36x^4}$ $6x^2$
7. $\sqrt{81b^8}$ $9b^4$
8. $-\sqrt{64a^{16}}$ $-8a^8$
9. $-\sqrt{x^4y^{12}}$ $-x^2y^6$
10. $\sqrt{c^7}$ $c^3\sqrt{c}$
11. $\sqrt{x^{23}}$ $x^{11}\sqrt{x}$
12. $-\sqrt{20m}$ $-2\sqrt{5m}$
13. $\sqrt{27b^{11}}$ $3b^5\sqrt{3b}$
14. $-\sqrt{72a^{19}}$ $-6a^9\sqrt{2a}$



- **Additional Example 1**

  Simplify each square root.

  a. $\sqrt{81r^4}$ $9r^2$

  b. $\sqrt{s^{14}}$ $s^7$

- **Additional Example 2**

  Simplify each square root.

  a. $\sqrt{q^7}$ $q^3\sqrt{q}$

  b. $\sqrt{50n}$ $5\sqrt{2n}$

## MATH TOOLBOX

### Square Roots of Expressions with Variables

This Math Toolbox shows students how to find square roots of expressions with variables.

### Math Background

Finding the square root of a variable expression is very similar to finding the square root of a constant. You can simplify variables that are perfect squares so $\sqrt{x^2} = x$, or $\sqrt{x^4} = x^2$. If a variable expression also contains constants, you simplify both the constants and the variables. So, $\sqrt{36p^2} = 6p$. You can use the Rule for Multiplying Square Roots to factor perfect squares from variable expressions in order to simplify them. For example, $\sqrt{32v^3} = \sqrt{16v^2 \cdot 2v} = 4v\sqrt{2v}$.

### Teaching Notes

**Error Prevention** Students may want to write $\sqrt{x^{10}}$ as a power of a power to make simplification easier. To do so, they can rewrite $x^{10}$ as $(x^5)^2$, [and *not* $(x^8)^2$] because exponents are *multiplied*, not *added*, when you are finding the power of a power.

**Monitoring Progress** Exercises 5–14 Pay careful attention to the negative sign when simplifying expressions that involve the opposite of a square root.

**Block Scheduling** If you have block scheduling or extended periods, you may wish to insert this Math Toolbox lesson between the completion of Part 1 of Lesson 11-5 and the beginning of Part 2 of Lesson 11-5.

# 11-6

## Getting Ready

### Key Terms and Symbols

trigonometry, trigonometric ratio, sine, cosine, tangent

**Resources** A complete list of resources for this lesson is on p. 557H.

### Daily Skills Warm-Up

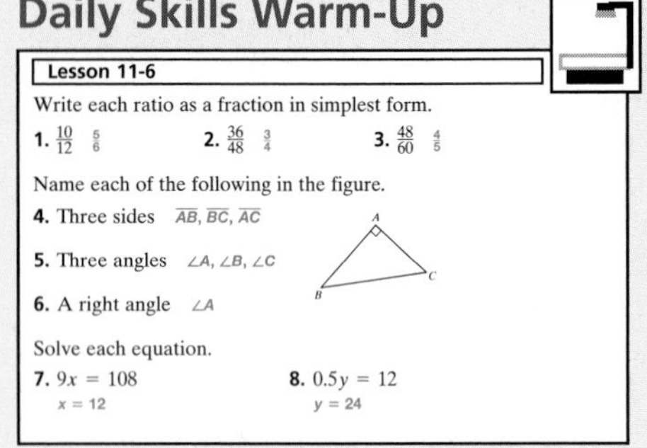
Lesson 11-6

Write each ratio as a fraction in simplest form.

1. $\frac{10}{12}$ $\frac{5}{6}$ 2. $\frac{36}{48}$ $\frac{3}{4}$ 3. $\frac{48}{60}$ $\frac{4}{5}$

Name each of the following in the figure.

4. Three sides $\overline{AB}, \overline{BC}, \overline{AC}$
5. Three angles $\angle A, \angle B, \angle C$
6. A right angle $\angle A$

Solve each equation.

7. $9x = 108$ $x = 12$ 8. $0.5y = 12$ $y = 24$

### Background for the Lesson

For similar right triangles the ratios of two corresponding sides are the same. The size of the triangle makes no difference. These ratios for a given angle are called the trigonometric ratios for that angle. The ratio of the side opposite the angle to the hypotenuse is called the *sine* of the angle. For example the sine of 50° ≈ 0.7660. You can find these values with a calculator, a table, or by measuring.

## 1 Focus

### Investigate

Help students recognize that the pairs of ratios they wrote are equivalent.

### Connecting to Prior Knowledge

In Lesson 11-4, students learned how to write ratios for right triangles. In this lesson, students learn about trigonometric ratios. In Lesson 11-7, students will use their knowledge of trigonometric ratios to find angles of elevation and depression.





# 11-6 Sine, Cosine, and Tangent Ratios

**What You'll Learn**

1. To find trigonometric ratios in right triangles
2. To use trigonometric ratios to solve problems

**. . . And Why**

To find lengths that cannot be measured directly

## Investigate

EXPLORING RATIOS IN SIMILAR RIGHT TRIANGLES

1. In the diagram at the right, $\triangle PQR \sim \triangle XYZ$. Find the length of the hypotenuse of each triangle. 16 m, 8 m

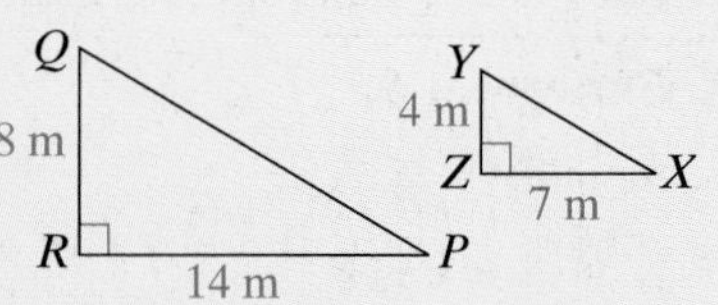


2. In the triangles above, $\angle P$ is the smallest angle of $\triangle PQR$ and $\angle X$ is the smallest angle of $\triangle XYZ$. For each figure, write the following ratios in simplest form.
   a. $\frac{\text{length of leg opposite smallest angle}}{\text{length of hypotenuse}}$ $\frac{8}{16} = \frac{1}{2}, \frac{4}{8} = \frac{1}{2}$
   b. $\frac{\text{length of leg adjacent to smallest angle}}{\text{length of hypotenuse}}$ $\frac{14}{16} = \frac{7}{8}, \frac{7}{8}$
   c. $\frac{\text{length of leg opposite smallest angle}}{\text{length of leg adjacent to smallest angle}}$ $\frac{8}{14} = \frac{4}{7}, \frac{4}{7}$
3. What do you notice about each pair of ratios you wrote for Question 2? Each pair of ratios are identical.

## PART 1 Finding Ratios in Right Triangles

The word **trigonometry** means triangle measure. The ratio of two sides of a right triangle is a **trigonometric ratio.** To write trigonometric ratios, you must identify sides that are opposite and adjacent to the acute angles of a triangle.

**Trigonometric Ratios**

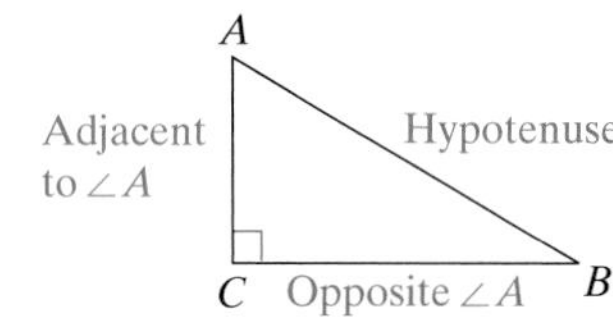


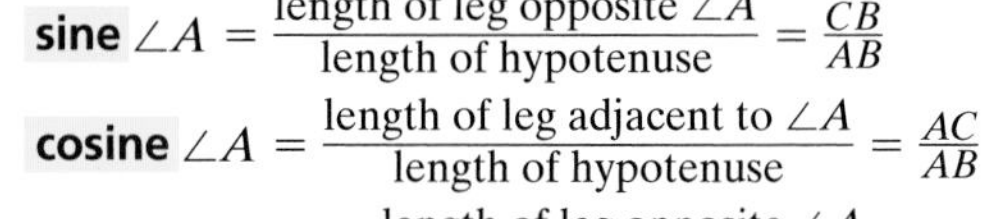

**sine** $\angle A = \frac{\text{length of leg opposite } \angle A}{\text{length of hypotenuse}} = \frac{CB}{AB}$

**cosine** $\angle A = \frac{\text{length of leg adjacent to } \angle A}{\text{length of hypotenuse}} = \frac{AC}{AB}$

**tangent** $\angle A = \frac{\text{length of leg opposite } \angle A}{\text{length of leg adjacent to } \angle A} = \frac{CB}{AC}$



## Tools to Monitor Progress

### BEFORE THE LESSON

**To check prerequisite skills:**

- Multiplying and dividing fractions

**Skills Handbook,** p. 740

**Skills Intervention Kit,** Operations with Fractions

### DURING THE LESSON

**To check understanding:**

**Try This** exercises on student page

- **Additional Example 1**

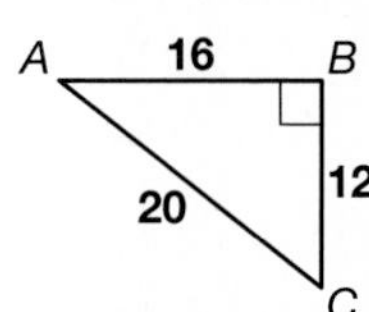

You can use these abbreviations when you find trigonometric ratios for a given acute $\angle N$.

$\sin N = \frac{\text{opposite}}{\text{hypotenuse}}$ $\cos N = \frac{\text{adjacent}}{\text{hypotenuse}}$ $\tan N = \frac{\text{opposite}}{\text{adjacent}}$

**EXAMPLE 1**

**For $\triangle XYZ$, find the sine, cosine, and tangent of $\angle X$.**

$\sin X = \frac{\text{opposite}}{\text{hypotenuse}} = \frac{5}{13}$

$\cos X = \frac{\text{adjacent}}{\text{hypotenuse}} = \frac{12}{13}$

$\tan X = \frac{\text{opposite}}{\text{adjacent}} = \frac{5}{12}$

Y, 13, 5, Z, 12, X

**TRY THIS** 4. $\sin Y = \frac{12}{13}$, $\cos Y = \frac{5}{13}$, $\tan Y = \frac{12}{5}$

**4.** For $\triangle XYZ$ in Example 1, find the sine, cosine, and tangent of $\angle Y$.

Trigonometric ratios are usually expressed in decimal form as approximations. If you know the measure of an acute angle of a right triangle, you can use a calculator or a table of trigonometric ratios to find approximate values for the sine, cosine, and tangent of the angle.

**EXAMPLE 2**

**Find the trigonometric ratios of 42° using a scientific calculator or the table on page 747. Round to four decimal places.**

$\sin 42° \approx 0.6691$
$\cos 42° \approx 0.7431$
$\tan 42° \approx 0.9004$

Scientific calculator: Enter 42 and press the key labeled SIN, COS, or TAN.
Table: Find 42° in the first column. Look across to find the appropriate ratio.

*Graphing Calculator HINT*

If you are using a graphing calculator, the trigonometric ratio name is entered before the angle measure. Be sure the calculator is in degree mode.

**TRY THIS** Find each value. Round to four decimal places.

**5.** sin 10° 0.1736 **6.** cos 75° 0.2588 **7.** tan 53° 1.3270 **8.** cos 22° 0.9272

## PART 2 Using Ratios to Solve Problems

You can use trigonometric ratios to find measures in right triangles indirectly. The advantage to using trigonometric ratios is that you need only an acute angle measure and the length of one side to find the lengths of the other two sides.



# 2 Teach

## PART 1 Part 1 Teaching Notes

Suggest that students think of mnemonic devices to help them remember the three trigonometric ratios in this lesson. Mention that they will later learn three more trigonometric ratios that are the reciprocals of these three.

**ELL** *Sine*, *cosine*, and *tangent* are likely to be terms that students have never seen before. Make sure students know how to pronounce the terms (sign, co´-sign, tan´-jent). Have students record the definitions of each ratio in their Math Journals or on index cards for easy reference.

### Example 1

**Build understanding.** Ask: Is this the only triangle with these particular trigonometric ratios? Explain. **No; Any triangle similar to $\triangle XYZ$ will have the same trigonometric ratios.**

**Error Prevention** Students may be confused about which leg is adjacent to an angle. A leg adjacent to an angle in a triangle forms one side of the angle. A side opposite an angle in a triangle is not one of the sides of the angle.

**Visual Learning** Suggest that students devise a color code for writing trigonometric ratios. For example, they may want to always write the hypotenuse in green, the opposite side in blue, and the adjacent side in red in their ratios to make sure they are writing the correct values.

### Example 2

**Build understanding.** Explain what $\sin 42° \approx 0.6691$ means. **In a right triangle, the ratio of the side opposite the 42° angle to the hypotenuse is equal to approximately 0.6691, or approximately $\frac{6691}{10{,}000}$.**

Find the sine, cosine, and tangent of $\angle A$. $\frac{12}{20}, \frac{16}{20}, \frac{12}{16}$

- **Additional Example 2**

Find the trigonometric ratios of 18°. Round to four decimal places.
**$\sin 18° \approx 0.3090$; $\cos 18° \approx 0.9511$; $\tan 18° \approx 0.3249$**

- **Additional Example 3**

Find the length of the hypotenuse of a triangle with one acute angle of 40° and the side opposite that angle measuring 10 feet. **about 15.6 ft**

## AFTER THE LESSON

### To assess knowledge: Lesson Quiz

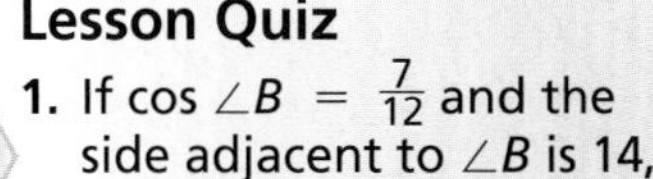

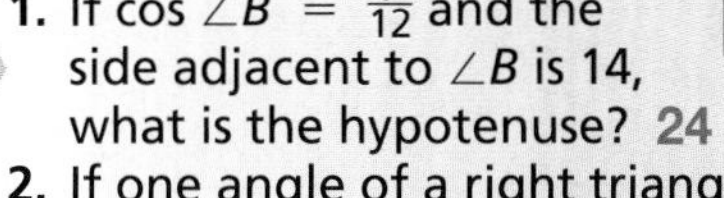

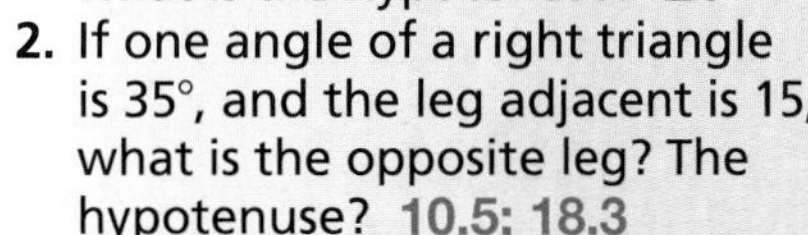

1. If $\cos \angle B = \frac{7}{12}$ and the side adjacent to $\angle B$ is 14, what is the hypotenuse? **24**
2. If one angle of a right triangle is 35°, and the leg adjacent is 15, what is the opposite leg? The hypotenuse? **10.5; 18.3**

- For enrichment and reteaching options see Resources on p. 557H.

## Part 2 Teaching Notes

You can use any of the trigonometric ratios to find measures in right triangles. The ratio you use depends on which side and angle measure you know, and on which side you are trying to find.

### Example 3

**Build understanding.** Ask: Suppose you were given the measure of the other acute angle, 86°. What trigonometric ratio would you have used to find the hypotenuse? What would be the result? **Since you know the angle and the side adjacent to it, you would use the cosine ratio. The result would be the same, about 14.34 ft.**

**Math Reasoning** Use math reasoning to explain the relationship between the sine of an angle $A$, and the cosine of angle $(90° - m\angle A)$. **These ratios are the same. $A$ and $(90° - m\angle A)$ are the two angles in the same right triangle. Therefore, the sine of $A$ and the cosine of $(90° - m\angle A)$ both describe the ratio of the same side length over the hypotenuse.**

### Different Ways to Solve a Problem

**Build understanding.** Ask: What is the measurement of the other angles in the triangle? **90° and 22°**

### Example 3

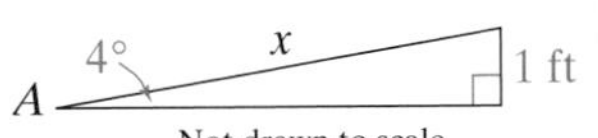

Not drawn to scale

*Ramps* **The diagram at the left shows a wheelchair ramp for a school. What is the length of the ramp?**

You know the angle and the side opposite the angle. You want to find $x$, the length of the hypotenuse.

| | |
|---|---|
| $\sin A = \frac{\text{opposite}}{\text{hypotenuse}}$ | Use the sine ratio. |
| $\sin 4° = \frac{1}{x}$ | Substitute 4° for the angle and 1 for the height. |
| $x(\sin 4°) = 1$ | Multiply each side by $x$. |
| $x = \frac{1}{\sin 4°}$ | Divide each side by sin 4°. |
| $x \approx 14.34$ | Use a calculator. Round to the nearest hundredth. |

The ramp is about 14.34 ft long.

### Try This

9. What is the length of the longer leg of the ramp in Example 3? **14.3 ft**

### Different Ways to Solve a Problem

*Ladders* **Find $x$, the height the ladder reaches up the building.**

**Method 1**

Use the Pythagorean theorem.

$3^2 + x^2 = 8^2$

$9 + x^2 = 64$

$x^2 = 55$

$x = \sqrt{55} \approx 7.4$

The ladder reaches about 7.4 ft.

**Method 2**

Use a trigonometric ratio.

$\sin 68° = \frac{x}{8}$

$8(\sin 68°) = x$

$7.4 \approx x$

The ladder reaches about 7.4 ft.

1. **Answers may vary. Sample: Method 2; it usually requires fewer steps.**

2. **the acute angle measure; the distance between the foot of the ladder and the building**

### Choose a Method

1. Which method do you prefer to use? Explain. **See above.**
2. What information is not needed for Method 1? For Method 2? **See left.**

# Exercises

## Check Understanding

**Use $\triangle ABC$ for Exercises 1 and 2.**

2. $\sin A = \frac{4}{5}$, $\cos A = \frac{3}{5}$, $\tan A = \frac{4}{3}$

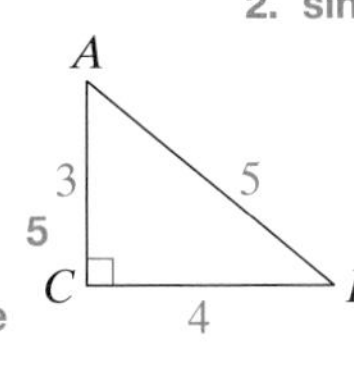


1. a. What is the length of the leg opposite $\angle A$? 4
   b. What is the length of the leg adjacent to $\angle A$? 3
   c. What is the length of the hypotenuse of $\triangle ABC$? 5
2. Find the sine, cosine, and tangent of $\angle A$. See above right.

**Find each value. Round to four decimal places.**

3. tan 89° 57.2900
4. sin 30° 0.5
5. cos 14° 0.9703
6. sin 67° 0.9205
7. tan 28° 0.5317

*Mental Math* **Use right triangles to find the ratios. Show your diagrams.**

8. tan 45° 1

9. cos 60° $\frac{1}{2}$

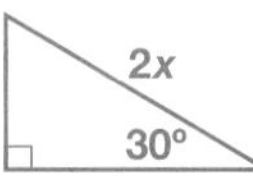


10. sin 30° $\frac{1}{2}$ x 2x 30°

## Practice and Problem Solving

**Use $\triangle QRS$ for Exercises 11 and 12.** 11–12. See right.

11. Find the sine, cosine, and tangent of $\angle R$.
12. Find the sine, cosine, and tangent of $\angle S$.

S 15 9 R Q 12

11. $\frac{9}{15}, \frac{12}{15}, \frac{9}{12}$ 12. $\frac{12}{15}, \frac{9}{15}, \frac{12}{9}$
13. 0 14. 0.1944
15. 0.8290 16. 0.9657
17. 0.3746 18. 0.9455

**Find each value. Round to four decimal places.** 13–18. See above right.

13. cos 90°
14. tan 11°
15. sin 56°
16. tan 44°
17. sin 22°
18. cos 19°
19. sin 83° 0.9925
20. cos 39° 0.7771
21. tan 60° 1.7321
22. tan 84° 9.5144
23. cos 77° 0.2250
24. sin 2° 0.0349
25. A hot air balloon climbs continuously along a 30° angle to a height of 5,000 feet. To the nearest tenth of a foot, how far has the balloon traveled to reach 5,000 feet? Draw a sketch, and then solve. See margin.
26. *Writing* Tom says the missing length in the triangle at the right can be found using the tangent ratio. Jed says it can be found using the sine ratio. Who is correct? Explain.

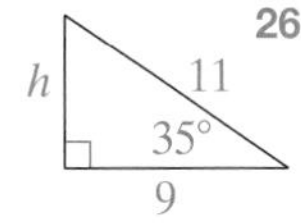


26. Both are correct. Both ratios include *h* and a known number.

27. *Mathematical Reasoning* Find the sine of an acute angle and the cosine of its complement. Do this for several angles. Make a conjecture based on your results. The two ratios are equal.



# 3 Practice/Assess

## Assignment Guide

To provide flexible scheduling, this lesson can be divided into parts.

**Part 1**
**Core** 1–24, 26
**Extension** 27

**Part 2**
**Core** 25, 28
**Extension** 29

Mixed Review can be assigned at any time for maintenance.

## Exercises

**Tactile Learning** **Exercises 28–29** You may want to draw diagrams to help you solve these problems.

## Challenge

Use what you know about a 30°-60°-90° triangle to explain why the cosine of a 60° angle is 0.5. **The shorter leg of a 30°-60°-90° triangle is adjacent to the 60° angle. Also, the hypotenuse is two times the length of the shorter leg. If the shorter leg is x, then cos 60° $= \frac{x}{2x}$ or $\frac{1}{2}$.**

## Closure

The ratios of the lengths of two sides of a right triangle are trigonometric ratios. Three trigonometric ratios are sine, cosine, and tangent. For the angle *N*, $\sin N = \frac{\text{opposite}}{\text{hypotenuse}}$, $\cos N = \frac{\text{adjacent}}{\text{hypotenuse}}$, and $\tan N = \frac{\text{opposite}}{\text{adjacent}}$.

25.

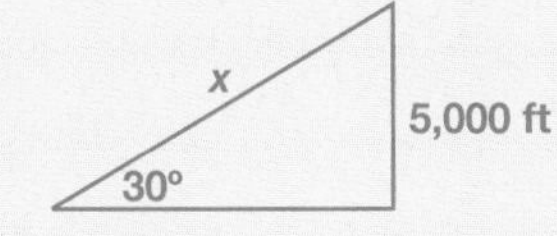


10,000 ft

## Alternative Assessment

Give students one angle measurement of a right triangle and have them use a calculator to find the trigonometric ratios. From the ratios, have students figure out possible side lengths for the triangle.

## Daily Cumulative Review

**Tell whether a triangle with sides of the given lengths could be a 45°-45°-90° or 30°-60°-90°. Explain.** *(Lesson 11-5)*

1. $6\sqrt{3}$, 12, 6 — 30°-60°-90°; the length of the hypotenuse is 2 times the shorter leg and the longer leg is $\sqrt{3}$ times the shorter leg.
2. 9.5, 19, $9.5\sqrt{3}$ — 30°-60°-90°; the length of the hypotenuse is 2 times the shorter leg and the longer leg is $\sqrt{3}$ times the shorter leg.
3. 12, 12, $12\sqrt{2}$ — 45°-45°-90°; the legs are congruent (12) and the hypotenuse is the length of a leg times $\sqrt{2}$.

**Solve using a proportion.** *(Lesson 11-4)*

4. An interior designer needs to find the distance from the floor to the top of the widow in the cathedral. She uses the similar triangles at the right to estimate the distance. What is the distance? 18.75 ft

**Mixed Review**

**Judging by appearances, classify each triangle by its angles.**

5. (9-3) obtuse triangle
6. (9-3) right triangle
7. (9-3) acute triangle

## Practice

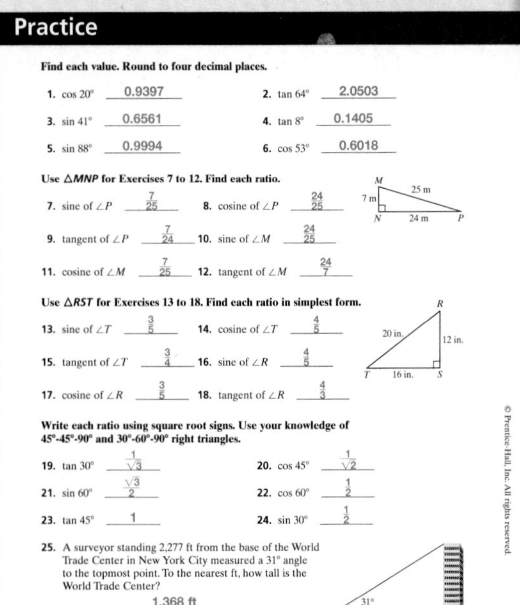

**Find each value. Round to four decimal places.**

1. cos 20° 0.9397
2. tan 64° 2.0503
3. sin 41° 0.6561
4. tan 8° 0.1405
5. sin 88° 0.9994
6. cos 53° 0.6018

**Use $\triangle MNP$ for Exercises 7 to 12. Find each ratio.**

7. sine of $\angle P$ $\frac{7}{25}$
8. cosine of $\angle P$ $\frac{24}{25}$
9. tangent of $\angle P$ $\frac{7}{24}$
10. sine of $\angle M$ $\frac{24}{25}$
11. cosine of $\angle M$ $\frac{7}{25}$
12. tangent of $\angle M$ $\frac{24}{7}$

**Use $\triangle RST$ for Exercises 13 to 18. Find each ratio in simplest form.**

13. sine of $\angle T$ $\frac{3}{5}$
14. cosine of $\angle T$ $\frac{4}{5}$
15. tangent of $\angle T$ $\frac{3}{4}$
16. sine of $\angle R$ $\frac{4}{5}$
17. cosine of $\angle R$ $\frac{3}{5}$
18. tangent of $\angle R$ $\frac{4}{3}$

**Write each ratio using square root signs. Use your knowledge of 45°-45°-90° and 30°-60°-90° right triangles.**

19. tan 30° $\frac{1}{\sqrt{3}}$
20. cos 45° $\frac{1}{\sqrt{2}}$
21. sin 60° $\frac{\sqrt{3}}{2}$
22. cos 60° $\frac{1}{2}$
23. tan 45° 1
24. sin 30° $\frac{1}{2}$
25. A surveyor standing 2,277 ft from the base of the World Trade Center in New York City measured a 31° angle to the topmost point. To the nearest ft, how tall is the World Trade Center? 1,368 ft





## Reteaching

Find the sine, cosine, and tangent of $\angle K$.

The side opposite $\angle K$ is $\overline{JL}$.

The side adjacent to $\angle K$ is $\overline{KL}$.

The hypotenuse is $\overline{JK}$.

$\sin K = \frac{\text{opposite}}{\text{hypotenuse}} = \frac{9}{15} = \frac{3}{5}$

$\cos K = \frac{\text{adjacent}}{\text{hypotenuse}} = \frac{12}{15} = \frac{4}{5}$

$\tan K = \frac{\text{opposite}}{\text{adjacent}} = \frac{9}{12} = \frac{3}{4}$

J, 15 in., 9 in., K, 12 in., L

**Use $\triangle ABC$ for Exercises 1–6. Find each ratio.**

1. sine of $\angle A$ $\frac{40}{41}$
2. cosine of $\angle A$ $\frac{9}{41}$
3. tangent of $\angle A$ $\frac{40}{9}$
4. sine of $\angle C$ $\frac{9}{41}$
5. cosine of $\angle C$ $\frac{40}{41}$
6. tangent of $\angle C$ $\frac{9}{40}$

C, 41 m, 40 m, A, B, 9 m

**Use $\triangle PQR$ for Exercises 7–12. Find each ratio in simplest form.**

7. sine of $\angle R$ $\frac{5}{13}$
8. cosine of $\angle R$ $\frac{12}{13}$
9. tangent of $\angle R$ $\frac{5}{12}$
10. sine of $\angle P$ $\frac{12}{13}$
11. cosine of $\angle P$ $\frac{5}{13}$
12. tangent of $\angle P$ $\frac{12}{5}$

R, 24 cm, 26 cm, Q, 10 cm, P

**Use $\triangle UVW$ for Exercises 13–18. Find each ratio.**

13. sine of $\angle U$ $\frac{24}{25}$
14. cosine of $\angle U$ $\frac{7}{25}$
15. tangent of $\angle U$ $\frac{24}{7}$
16. sine of $\angle V$ $\frac{7}{25}$
17. cosine of $\angle V$ $\frac{24}{25}$
18. tangent of $\angle V$ $\frac{7}{24}$

W, 7 cm, 24 cm, U, 25 cm, V

Reteaching



## Enrichment

1. Find each value.

| sin 20° 0.3420 | sin 32° 0.5299 | sin 71° 0.9455 | sin 83° 0.9925 |
|---|---|---|---|
| cos 70° 0.3420 | cos 58° 0.5299 | cos 19° 0.9455 | cos 7° 0.9925 |

2. How are the two angles in each of the above boxes related? They are complementary angles. The sum of their measures is 90°.
3. Predict the answers without using the trigonometric table or a calculator.
   sin 50° = cos 40° cos 75° = sin 15° cos 27° = sin 63°

**Complete. Use the table of trigonometric values or a calculator. Round answers to 4 decimal places.**

| | $\angle A$ | sin $A$ | cos $A$ | $(\sin A)^2$ | $(\cos A)^2$ | $(\sin A)^2 + (\cos A)^2$ |
|---|---|---|---|---|---|---|
| 4. | 5° | 0.0872 | 0.9962 | 0.0076 | 0.9924 | 1 |
| 5. | 27° | 0.4540 | 0.8910 | 0.2061 | 0.7939 | 1 |
| 6. | 41° | 0.6561 | 0.7547 | 0.4304 | 0.5696 | 1 |

7. What do you notice about the results in the last column? They all equal one.
8. Predict the answers without using the trigonometric table.
   $(\sin 16°)^2 + (\cos 16°)^2$ 1 $(\sin 57°)^2 + (\cos 57°)^2$ 1

**Complete. Use the table of trigonometric values or a calculator. Round answers to 4 decimal places.**

| | $\angle A$ | sin $A$ | cos $A$ | $\frac{\sin A}{\cos A}$ | tan $A$ |
|---|---|---|---|---|---|
| 9. | 13° | 0.2250 | 0.9744 | 0.2309 | 0.2309 |
| 10. | 34° | 0.5592 | 0.8290 | 0.6745 | 0.6745 |
| 11. | 51° | 0.7771 | 0.6293 | 1.2349 | 1.2349 |

12. Describe the results in the last two columns. They are equal.
13. Write a statement relating the tangent of an angle $A$ to its sine and cosine. $\tan A = \frac{\sin A}{\cos A}$



*Math in the Media* **Use the article below for Exercises 28 and 29.**

### The Tilting Tower

Building began on the bell tower at Pisa, Italy, in 1173. Shortly after that, the tower began to lean and has continued to lean even more over the centuries. In 1993, the tower had a tilt that was 5.5° from the vertical.

In the spring of 1999, engineering experts began to remove soil at the base to correct some of the lean. The team hopes to reduce the lean by about a tenth, which would stabilize the tower for the next 300 years.

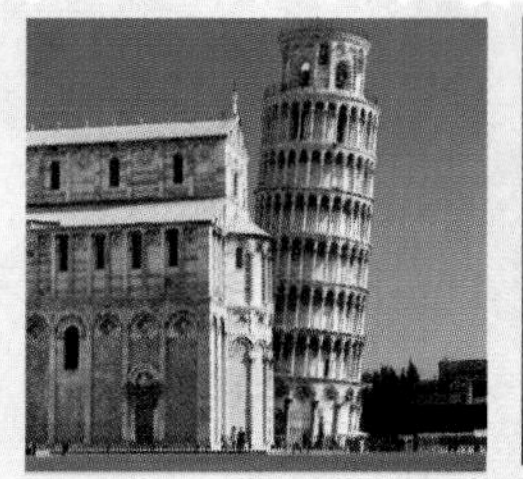

28. From base to top, the height of the tower is about 55.9 m. About how many meters from the vertical was the top in 1993? 5.4 m
29. Determine how many meters the top will be from the vertical when the tilt is reduced by a tenth. 4.8 m

## Mixed Review

**Find the missing lengths.** ***(Lesson 11-5)***

30. $4\sqrt{2}$ m

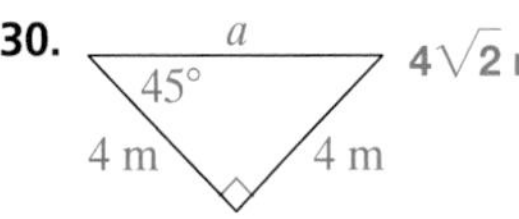



31. 14 ft

y, 7 ft, 30°

32.

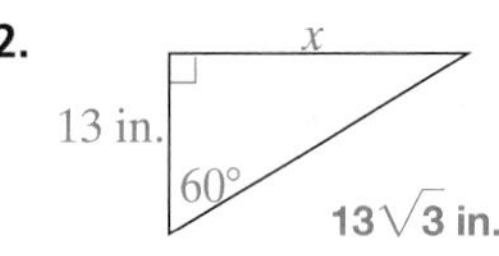



**Find the solutions of each equation for $x = -1, 0,$ and $3$.** ***(Lesson 8-2)***

33. $y = 2x - 4$ −6, −4, 2
34. $y = -3x + 2$ 5, 2, −7
35. $x + y = 20$ 21, 20, 17
36. $6x - 2y = 12$ −9, −6, 3
37. *Geometry* $\overleftrightarrow{GT}$ is the perpendicular bisector of $\overline{RA}$ at point $E$. Name two congruent segments. ***(Lesson 9-7)*** $\overline{RE} \cong \overline{EA}$

## Checkpoint 2

**Lessons 11-4 through 11-6**

**Tell whether a triangle with sides of the given lengths is 45°-45°-90°, 30°-60°-90°, or neither.**

1. $8, 8, 8\sqrt{2}$ 45°-45°-90°
2. $1, 2, \sqrt{3}$ 30°-60°-90°
3. $12\sqrt{3}, 12, 24$ 30°-60°-90°

**Find each value. Round to four decimal places.**

4. cos 61° 0.4848
5. tan 30° 0.5774
6. sin 32° 0.5299
7. sin 87° 0.9986
8. **TEST PREP** A wire from a radio tower is supported by a 23-ft brace. How high is the radio tower? B
   A. 46 ft B. 69 ft C. 83 ft D. 176 ft

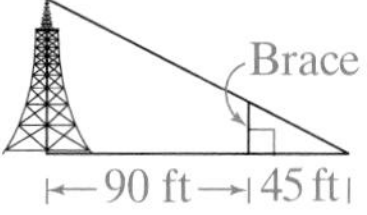





See also Extra Practice section.

## Checkpoint

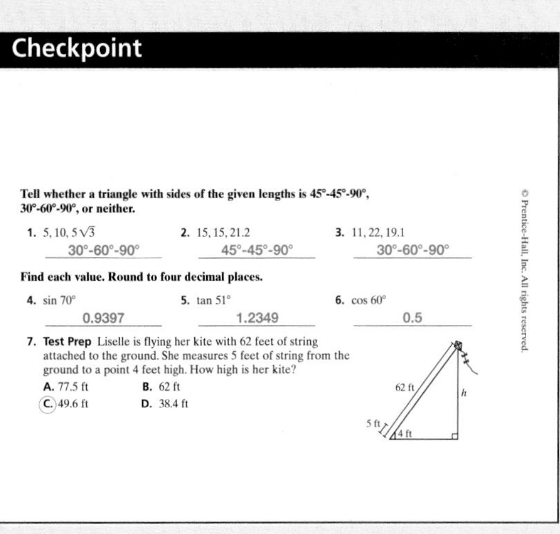

**Tell whether a triangle with sides of the given lengths is 45°-45°-90°, 30°-60°-90°, or neither.**

1. $5, 10, 5\sqrt{3}$ 30°-60°-90°
2. 15, 15, 21.2 45°-45°-90°
3. 11, 22, 19.1 30°-60°-90°

**Find each value. Round to four decimal places.**

4. sin 70° 0.9397
5. tan 51° 1.2349
6. cos 60° 0.5
7. **Test Prep** Liselle is flying her kite with 62 feet of string attached to the ground. She measures 5 feet of string from the ground to a point 4 feet high. How high is her kite?
   A. 77.5 ft B. 62 ft (C.) 49.6 ft D. 38.4 ft

# MATH TOOLBOX

*Technology*
*After Lesson 11-6*

# *Finding the Angles of a Right Triangle*

You can use a calculator or a trigonometric ratio table to find the degree measure of an acute angle of a right triangle if two sides of the triangle are known. If you are using a graphing calculator, be sure you are in degree mode.

## EXAMPLE

**You have a map charting a ship's course. The ship is traveling from the port along the course shown. What is the angle from due north of the ship's course?**

The angle formed by due north, the port, and the ship is the angle at which the ship is traveling. This is angle $X$.

$\cos X = \frac{191}{325}$

To find $m\angle X$ with a calculator:

Press 191 ÷ 325 = 2nd COS.

$m\angle X \approx 54°$

To find $m\angle X$ using the table of trigonometric ratios on p. 747:

$\cos X = \frac{191}{325} \approx 0.587692308$ Divide.

$m\angle X \approx 54°$ In the cosine column, find the decimal closest to 0.5877, which is 0.5878. Read the angle measure across from 0.5878.

The ship is traveling at a 54° angle from due north.

**Find the measure of each acute angle. Round to the nearest degree.**

1. $m\angle X \approx 44°, m\angle Y \approx 46°$

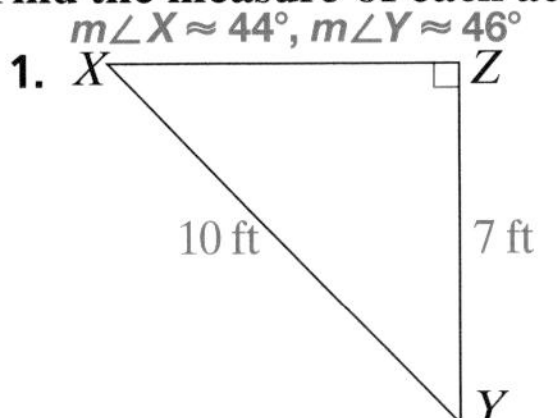


2. $m\angle H \approx 28°, m\angle K \approx 62°$

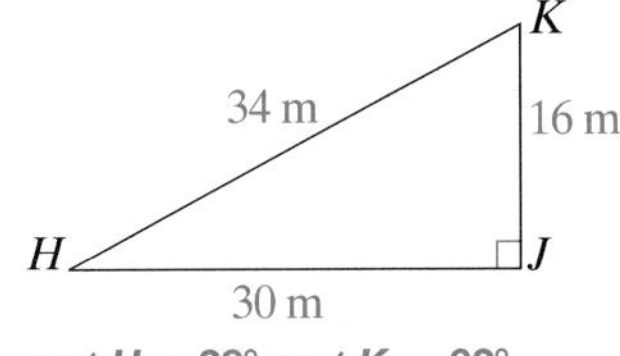


3. $m\angle C \approx 36°, m\angle D \approx 54°$

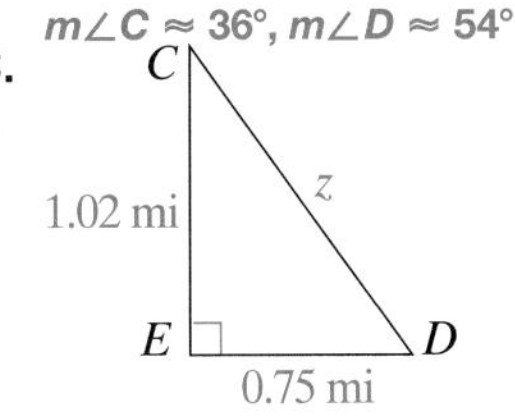




- **Additional Example**
  A pilot points a helicopter due north, facing a mountain. The airport where the helicopter lifted off is 10 miles from the mountain. The pilot's destination is 76 miles due east of the mountain. What angle should the compass read for the pilot to head directly toward the destination? Assume a 0° reading on the compass is north. Round your answer to the nearest degree. 82°

## MATH TOOLBOX

### Finding the Angles of a Right Triangle

This Math Toolbox shows students how to find the degree measure of an angle using trigonometric ratios.

### Math Background

Inverse operations are operations that undo each other. Subtraction is the inverse operation for addition, and division is the inverse operation for multiplication. Similarly, the trigonometric functions sine, cosine, and tangent have inverse operations. They are called *arcsine*, *arccosine*, and *arctangent*. So, the function $y = \sin x$ is equivalent to $x = \arcsin y$. Read this as "$x$ is the angle whose sin is $y$." If you know the length of the side opposite $\angle A$ is 3, and the length of the hypotenuse is 5, you can say $\sin A = \frac{3}{5}$, or $\arcsin \frac{3}{5} = m\angle A$. To find the value of $m\angle A$, you first find the decimal equivalent of $\frac{3}{5}$, or 0.6. Then find the angle (in the table) whose sine equals 0.6. You can also use a graphing calculator to find the inverses of trigonometric functions.

### Teaching Notes

**Error Prevention** Have your students check the sequence of key strokes for finding sine, cosine, and tangent on their calculators. Different calculators may require a different sequence of steps.

**Monitoring Progress Exercises 1–3** To check the answer, add the two angle measures. The sum should be 90.

**Block Scheduling** If you have block scheduling or extended periods, you may wish to insert this Math Toolbox lesson between the completion of Part 1 of Lesson 11-6 and the beginning of Part 2 of Lesson 11-6.

# 11-7

## Getting Ready

**Key Terms and Symbols** angle of elevation, angle of depression

**Resources** A complete list of resources for this lesson is on p. 557H.

### Daily Skills Warm-Up

Lesson 11-7

Find each value. Round to four decimal places.

1. sin 40° 0.6428
2. cos 25° 0.9063
3. tan 68° 2.4751

Solve each equation. Round to the nearest tenth.

4. $0.2354 = \frac{x}{18}$ $x \approx 4.2$
5. $\frac{b}{35} = 0.6894$ $b \approx 24.1$
6. $0.4812x = 40$ $x \approx 83.1$
7. $1.3579a = 58$ $a \approx 42.7$

### Background for the Lesson

You can use trigonometric ratios to solve many real-world measurement problems. If you are looking for an unknown distance, you can find that distance by forming a right triangle that contains it. You can then use the measure of an angle of the triangle, plus a known side, to find the unknown distance. The angles formed in these problems are either angles of elevation or angles of depression. An angle of elevation is formed by a horizontal line at eye level and a line of sight from the eye to an object above the observer. An angle of depression is formed by a horizontal line and a line of sight to an object below the observer.

## 1 Focus

### Connecting to Students' Lives

Ask students what they think of when they hear the terms *elevation* and *depression*. How are these two terms related? What do they describe?

### Connecting to Prior Knowledge

In Lesson 11-6, students learned about trigonometric ratios. In this lesson, students use trigonometric ratios to find angles of elevation and depression.



# 11-7 Angles of Elevation and Depression

**What You'll Learn**

1. To use trigonometry for finding angles of elevation
2. To use trigonometry for finding angles of depression

**. . . And Why**

To solve real-world problems in subjects such as surveying and navigation

## Part 1 Angles of Elevation

Civil engineers and navigators use the terms *angle of elevation* and *angle of depression* to describe the angles at which they observe things. An **angle of elevation** is formed by a horizontal line and a line of sight above it. It is used when you must look up at an object.

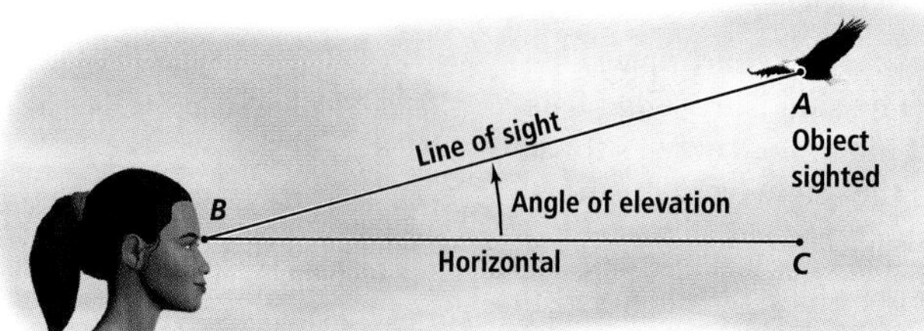


$\angle ABC$ is an angle of elevation.

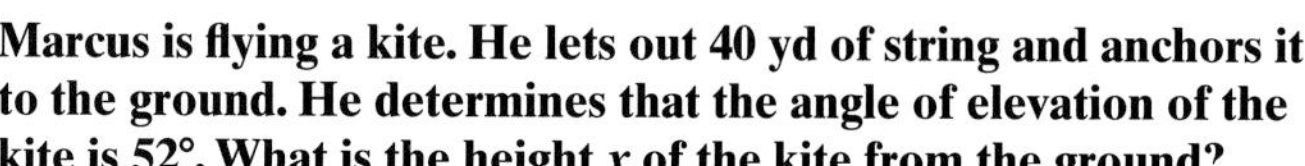


### Example 1

**Marcus is flying a kite. He lets out 40 yd of string and anchors it to the ground. He determines that the angle of elevation of the kite is 52°. What is the height $x$ of the kite from the ground?**

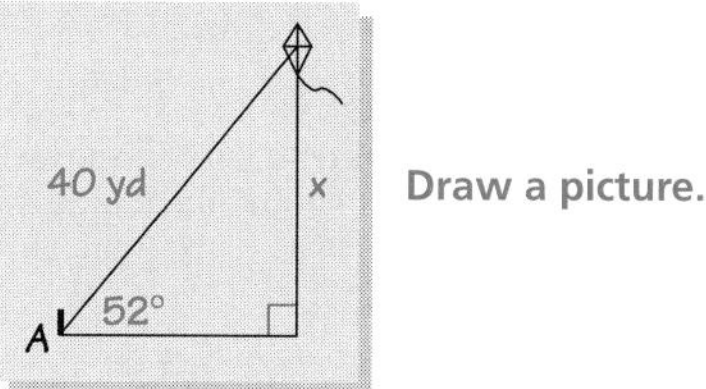


Draw a picture.

$\sin A = \frac{\text{opposite}}{\text{hypotenuse}}$ Choose an appropriate trigonometric ratio.

$\sin 52° = \frac{x}{40}$ Substitute.

$40(\sin 52°) = x$ Multiply each side by 40.

$32 \approx x$ Simplify.

The kite is about 32 yd from the ground.



## Tools to Monitor Progress

### BEFORE THE LESSON

**To check prerequisite skills:**

- Multiplying and dividing fractions

**Skills Handbook,** p. 740

**Skills Intervention Kit,** Operations with Fractions

### DURING THE LESSON

**To check understanding:**

**Try This** exercises on student page

- **Additional Example 1**
  Suppose Marcus reels the kite in 10 yards, but the angle of elevation stays the same. What is the height $x$ above the ground? Round to the nearest yard. about 24 yd

■ **TRY THIS**

1. The angle of elevation from a ship to the top of a lighthouse is 12°. The lighthouse is known to be 30 m tall. How far is the ship from the base of the lighthouse? **141 m**

In real life, a person's line of sight is parallel to the ground at eye height. In some problems you must account for this.

■ **EXAMPLE 2**

**Felicia wants to determine the height of a tree. From her position 20 ft from the base of the tree, she sees the top of the tree at an angle of elevation of 73°. Felicia's eyes are 5 ft from the ground. How tall is the tree, to the nearest foot?**

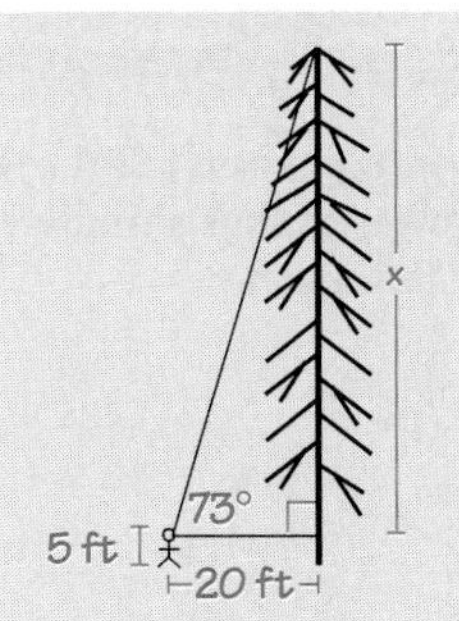


Draw a picture.

| | |
|---|---|
| $\tan = \frac{\text{opposite}}{\text{adjacent}}$ | Choose an appropriate trigonometric ratio. |
| $\tan 73° = \frac{x}{20}$ | Substitute 73 for the angle measure and 20 for the adjacent side. |
| $20(\tan 73°) = x$ | Multiply each side by 20. |
| $65 \approx x$ | Use a calculator or a table. |
| $65 + 5 = 70$ | Add 5 to account for the height of Felicia's eyes from the ground. |

The tree is about 70 ft tall.

■ **TRY THIS**

2. A rock climber looks at the top of a vertical rock wall at an angle of elevation of 74°. He is standing 4.2 m from the base of the wall and his eyes are 1.5 m from the ground. How high is the wall, to the nearest tenth of a meter? **16.1 m**



# 2 Teach

## PART 1 Part 1 Teaching Notes

Students should be aware that horizontal lines are parallel to the horizon. Have a student distinguish between a horizontal and vertical line.

**ELL** Explain to students that the term *elevation* is usually associated with height (as in the path of an elevator). Depression is usually associated with something that is lower or below.

**Tactile Learning** To demonstrate the idea of an angle of elevation, have students hold their outstretched left arm parallel to the floor to form a horizontal line. Then, ask students to locate an object in the room that is higher than the imaginary horizontal line (a corner or a clock, for example) that they formed with their left arm. Then have students point their outstretched right arm at the object. An angle of elevation describes the angle formed by a student's arms.

### ■ Example 1

**Build understanding.** Ask: In order for this problem to work, what do you have to assume about the kite string? **The kite string must form a straight line and can't be sagging.**

### ■ Example 2

**Build understanding.** Ask: Why is the tangent ratio better than the sine ratio for working this problem? **The length of the hypotenuse is not given.**

- **Additional Example 3**

Suppose the plane in Example 3 began its 3° descent from an altitude of 1.5 miles. How far is the plane from the runway (in ground distance) rounded to the nearest tenth of a mile? **about 28.6 mi**

## AFTER THE LESSON

### To assess knowledge: Lesson Quiz

Round to the nearest unit.

When Ming launched a model rocket she was standing 20 m away. The rocket traveled straight up until it was at an angle of 70° from Ming. How high did the rocket fly? **about 55 m**

- For enrichment and reteaching options see Resources on p. 557H.

# Part 2 Teaching Notes

Explain that an angle of depression is the opposite of an angle of elevation. It is the angle formed when you must look down to see an object.

**Error Prevention** A common error when solving problems with angle of elevation or angle of depression is not using the correct trigonometric ratio. Tell students to label the opposite side, adjacent side, and hypotenuse on the diagram of the problem.

## Example 3

**Build understanding.** Ask: If the pilot were closer to the runway, would the angle of descent (angle of depression) have to be greater than or less than 3°? Explain. **Greater than 3°; The plane still must travel 0.5 mi down to the ground, but it would have a shorter distance to do it.**

**Math Reasoning** Using Example 3, find the distance the airplane must fly through the air from its current position to the runway (the hypotenuse). Then, compare your results to the ground distance from the runway, using math reasoning to explain your findings. **The distances are almost the same because the angle of depression is so small.**

**Advanced Learners** Suggest that students conduct research to find out how airplane pilots use angle and distance calculations when they fly. Students should be able to find information about flight planning and procedures through reference materials or on the internet. Have students report their findings to the class.

## Part 2 Angles of Depression

An **angle of depression** is formed by a horizontal line and a line of sight below it. It is used when you must look down at an object.

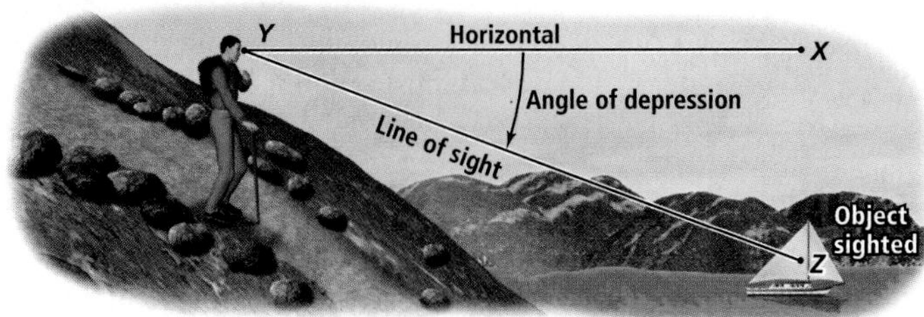


$\angle XYZ$ is an angle of depression.

### Example 3

*Navigation* **An airplane is flying 0.5 mi above the ground. If the pilot must begin a 3° descent to an airport runway at that altitude, how far is the airplane from the beginning of the runway (in ground distance)?**

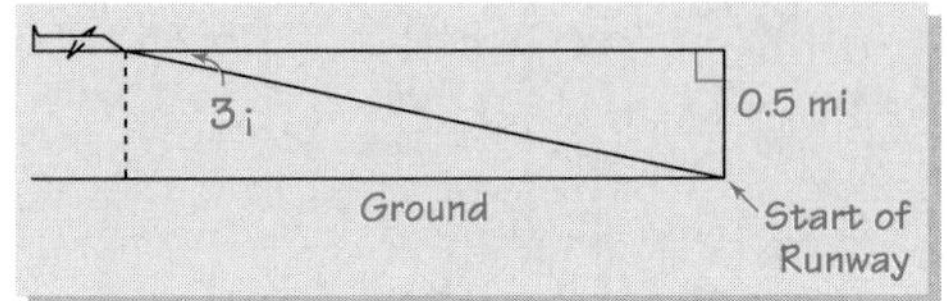


Not drawn to scale

Draw a picture.

$\tan 3° = \frac{0.5}{d}$ Choose an appropriate trigonometric ratio.

$d \tan 3° = 0.5$ Multiply each side by $d$.

$\frac{d \tan 3°}{\tan 3°} = \frac{0.5}{\tan 3°}$ Divide each side by tan 3°.

$d = \frac{0.5}{\tan 3°}$ Simplify.

$d \approx 9.5$ Use a calculator.

The airplane is about 9.5 mi from the airport.

### Try This

3. A group of people in a hang-gliding class are standing on top of a cliff 70 m high. They spot a hang glider landing on the beach below them. The angle of depression from the top of the cliff to the hang glider is 72°. How far is the hang glider from the base of the cliff? 22.7 m

# Exercises

## Check Understanding

**Name the acute angles of elevation and depression in each figure.**

**1.**

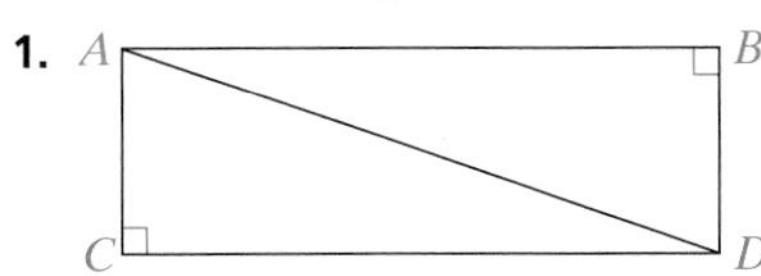


angle of elevation = ∠ADC, angle of depression = ∠BAD

**2.**

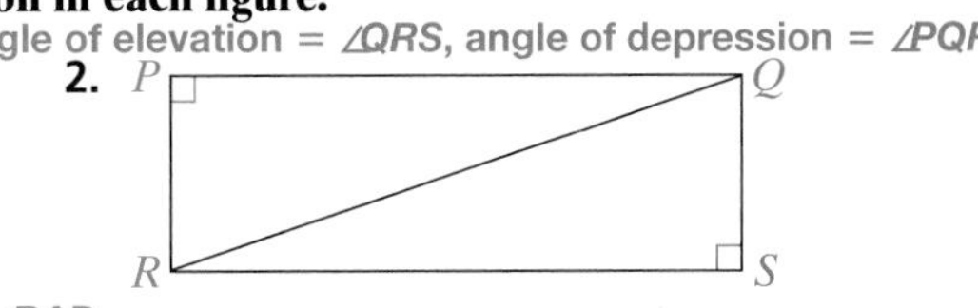


angle of elevation = ∠QRS, angle of depression = ∠PQR

**Find $x$ to the nearest tenth.**

**3.**

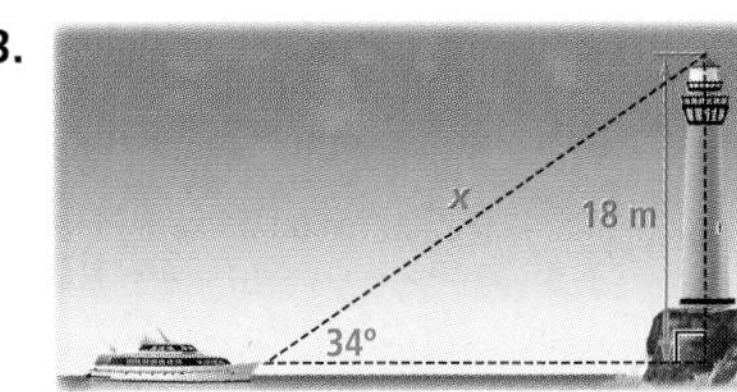


32.2 m

**4.**

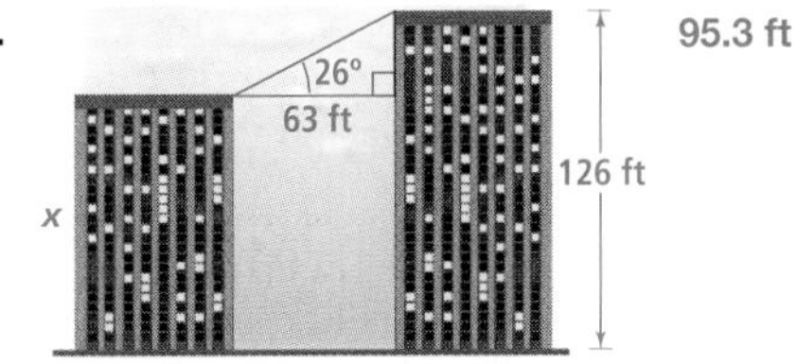


95.3 ft

**5.** *Error Analysis* The drawing at the right was drawn by a student to solve an angle of depression problem. What mistake has the student made? The angle of depression is between the line of sight and the horizontal.

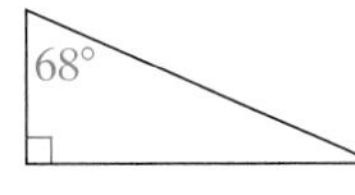


## Practice and Problem Solving

**Find $x$ to the nearest tenth.**

**6.**

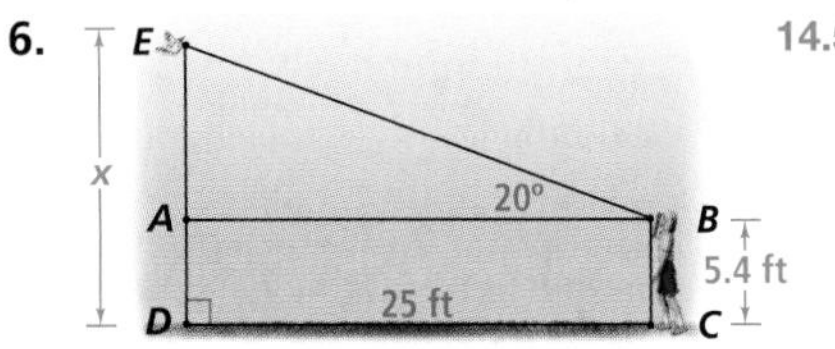


14.5 ft

**7.**

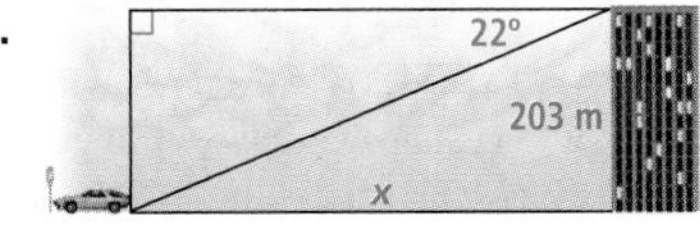


502.4 m

**Solve. If the answer is not a whole number, round to the nearest tenth.**

**8.** *Navigation* The angle of elevation from a ship to the top of a lighthouse is 4°. If the top of the lighthouse is known to be 50 m above sea level, how far is the ship from the lighthouse? 715 m

**9.** *Meteorology* A meteorologist measures the angle of elevation of a weather balloon as 53°. A radio signal from the balloon indicates that it is 1,620 m from the meteorologist's location. How high above ground is the weather balloon? 1,293.8 m



# 3 Practice/Assess

## Assignment Guide

To provide flexible scheduling, this lesson can be divided into parts.

**Part 1**

**Core** 3–4, 6, 8–9, 13

**Part 2**

**Core** 1–2, 5, 7, 12

✪ **Extension** 10–11, 14

Mixed Review can be assigned at any time for maintenance.

## Exercises

**Visual Learning Exercises 3–14** Use the diagrams to help you solve each problem. If no diagram is given, draw one.

## ✪ Challenge

Suppose you are standing 15 meters from a 15-meter high building. If your head were at ground level, at what angle would you need to look up to see the top of the building? How do you know? The height of the building and your distance from it are the same, so these two distances are legs of a 45°-45°-90° triangle, which means the angle is 45°.

## Closure

A horizontal line and a line of sight above it form an angle of elevation. A horizontal line and a line of sight below it form an angle of depression.

## Alternative Assessment

Have students estimate the height of the school's flagpole using the methods in this lesson. They will need to find a way to measure the angle of elevation. Suggest that they use a meter stick, string, and protractor. After students make their estimates, suggest that they see if anyone knows the actual height.

## Daily Cumulative Review

**Find each value. Round to four decimal places.** *(Lesson 11-6)*

1. sin 60° 0.8660  2. tan 58° 1.6003  3. cos 19° 0.9455
4. tan 85° 11.4301  5. cos 6° 0.9945  6. sin 40° 0.6428
7. cos 50° 0.6428  8. sin 27° 0.4540  9. tan 36° 0.7265

**Find the missing lengths. Round to the nearest tenth.** *(Lesson 11-5)*

10. (8 cm, 45°, $x$, 45°, 8 cm) $x \approx 11.3$ cm
11. ($y$, 4 in., 45°, 45°, $x$) $x \approx 5.7$ in.; $y = 4$ in.
12. (8 ft, 60°, $b$, 30°, $a$) $b = 4$ ft; $a \approx 6.9$ ft

**Mixed Review**

**Find the mean, median, and mode. Round to the nearest tenth where necessary. Identify any outliers.**

13. *(3-3)* \$2,698 \$3,598 \$260 \$3,010
Mean \$2,391.50 Median \$2,854
Mode None Outlier \$260

14. *(3-3)* 4 6 8 5 7 19 5
Mean 7.7 Median 6
Mode 5 Outlier 19

**Write each number in scientific notation.**

15. *(4-9)* 0.00000008 $8 \times 10^{-8}$
16. *(4-9)* 3,902,000 $3.902 \times 10^{6}$
17. *(4-9)* $0.008 \times 10^{13}$ $8 \times 10^{10}$

**Write and solve an equation.**

18. *(6-7)* 180 is 20% of what number? $180 = 0.20n$; 900
19. *(6-7)* 75% of $x$ is 203,655. What is $x$? $0.75x = 203,655$; 271,540

## Practice

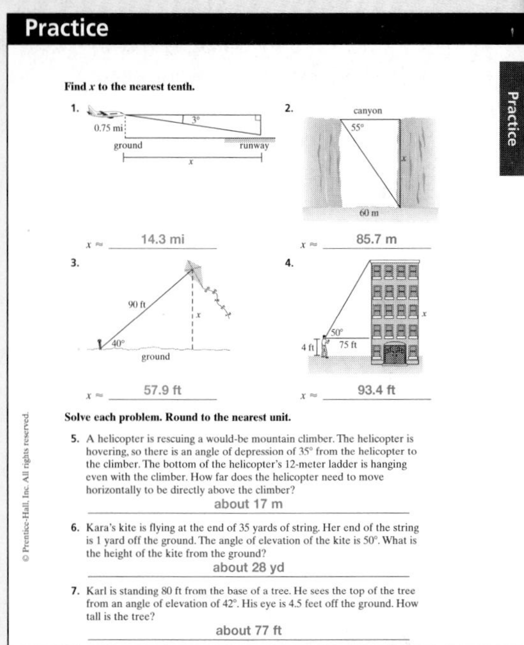
Find $x$ to the nearest tenth.

1. (figure: 0.75 mi, 3°, ground, runway, $x$) $x \approx$ 14.3 mi
2. (figure: canyon, 55°, 60 m, $x$) $x \approx$ 85.7 m
3. (figure: 90 ft, 40°, ground, $x$) $x \approx$ 57.9 ft
4. (figure: 50°, 75 ft, 4 ft, $x$) $x \approx$ 93.4 ft

Solve each problem. Round to the nearest unit.

5. A helicopter is rescuing a would-be mountain climber. The helicopter is hovering, so there is an angle of depression of 35° from the helicopter to the climber. The bottom of the helicopter's 12-meter ladder is hanging even with the climber. How far does the helicopter need to move horizontally to be directly above the climber? about 17 m
6. Kara's kite is flying at the end of 35 yards of string. Her end of the string is 1 yard off the ground. The angle of elevation of the kite is 50°. What is the height of the kite from the ground? about 28 yd
7. Karl is standing 80 ft from the base of a tree. He sees the top of the tree from an angle of elevation of 42°. His eye is 4.5 feet off the ground. How tall is the tree? about 77 ft



## Reteaching

A surveyor stands 38 meters from the base of a sheer cliff. Using equipment that sites from 1 meter off the ground, the surveyor measures the angle of elevation from her position to the top of the cliff as 58°. What is the height of the cliff?

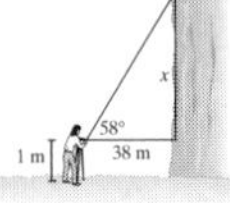


Start by drawing a diagram and labeling it with the information given. Label $x$ in the right triangle. Remember the height $h$ of the cliff is actually $x + 1$, since the surveyor is siting from one meter off the ground.

Determine what information is given. The angle of elevation is 58°. The side adjacent to the 58° angle is 38 meters.

The surveyor needs to determine $x$, the side opposite the 58° angle.

The tangent ratio uses the opposite side and the adjacent side, so use that.

$\tan = \frac{\text{opposite}}{\text{adjacent}}$

$\tan 58° = \frac{x}{38}$ Substitute 58° for the angle measure, 38 for the adjacent side, and $x$ for the opposite side.

$38(\tan 58°) = x$ Multiply each side by 38.

$61 \approx x$ Use a calculator or a table.

$h = x + 1 = 61 + 1 = 62$ Add one meter for the tripod's height.

The cliff is about 62 meters high.

Find $x$ to the nearest whole unit.

1. 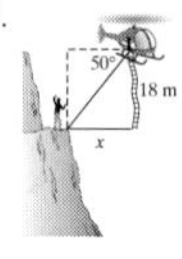

$x \approx$ 15 m

2. 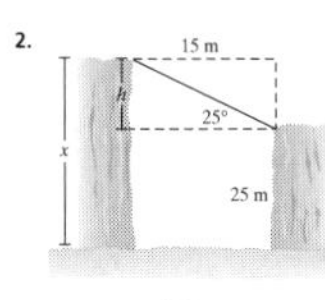

$x \approx$ 32 m

3. Thomas' kite is flying at the end of 82 feet of string. His end of the string is 3 feet off the ground. The angle of elevation of the kite is 55°. What is the height of the kite from the ground? about 70 ft



## Enrichment

In Chapter 8, you graphed points using rectangular coordinates. You can also graph points using *polar coordinates*. Point $G$ has polar coordinates (3, 60°). The first number is the point's *distance* from the origin. The second number is the *angle* formed by a line segment drawn to the point and the positive horizontal axis.

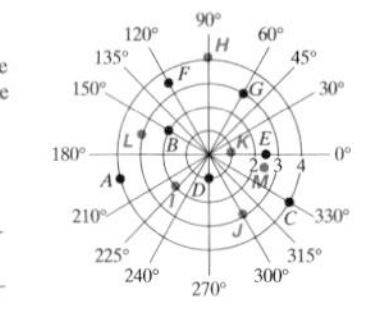


Write the polar coordinates of the point.

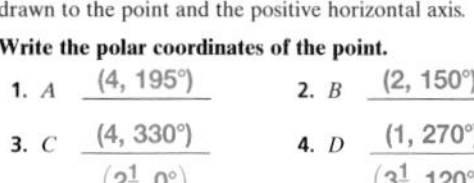

1. $A$ (4, 195°)
2. $B$ (2, 150°)
3. $C$ (4, 330°)
4. $D$ (1, 270°)
5. $E$ $(2\frac{1}{2}, 0°)$
6. $F$ $(3\frac{1}{2}, 120°)$

Graph these points. Write the letter beside the point.

7. $H(4, 90°)$
8. $I(2, 225°)$
9. $J(3, 300°)$
10. $K(1, 0°)$
11. $L(3, 165°)$
12. $M(2\frac{1}{2}, 345°)$

Point $P$ has polar coordinates $(r, x°)$ and rectangular coordinates $(a, b)$.

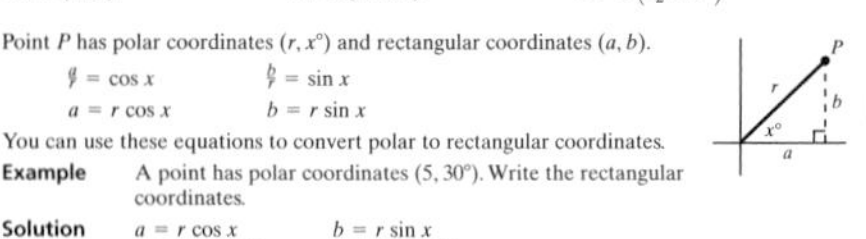

$\frac{a}{r} = \cos x$ $\quad \frac{b}{r} = \sin x$

$a = r \cos x$ $\quad b = r \sin x$

You can use these equations to convert polar to rectangular coordinates.

**Example** A point has polar coordinates (5, 30°). Write the rectangular coordinates.

**Solution** $a = r \cos x = 5 \cos 30° = 5(0.8660)$, $a = 4.33$ $\quad b = r \sin x = 5 \sin 30° = 5(0.5)$, $b = 2.5$

The rectangular coordinates are (4.33, 2.5).

Write the rectangular coordinates of the point with these polar coordinates. Round to the nearest hundredth.

13. (6, 45°) (4.24, 4.24)
14. (10, 62°) (4.69, 8.83)
15. (2, 73°) (0.58, 1.91)
16. (8.1, 24°) (7.40, 3.29)
17. (4.2, 81°) (0.66, 4.15)
18. (16, 8°) (15.84, 2.23)





10. *Astronomy* The figure at the right illustrates a method for determining depths of moon craters from observations on Earth. Astronomers calculate that the distance from $R$ to $H$ is 3 km when the angle of depression of the sun's rays is 12°. How high is the rim of the moon crater from the floor of the crater? 0.6 km

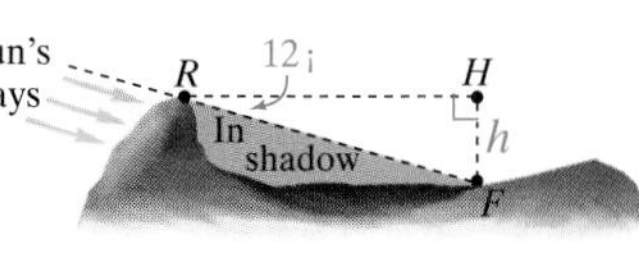


11. From an aerial photograph, rangers determine that a canyon is 9 km wide. From one rim of the canyon, the angle of depression to the floor of the canyon at the other rim is 20°. How deep is the canyon? Draw a sketch, and then solve. 3.3 km

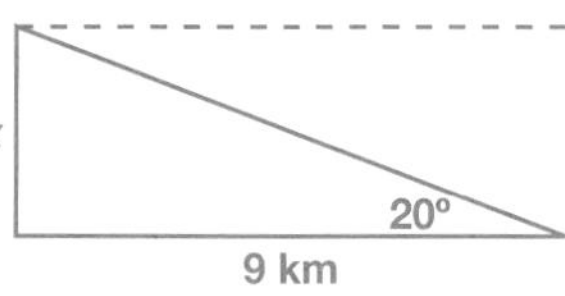


12. *Writing* How do you decide which trigonometric ratio to use to solve a problem? Answers may vary. Sample: You need to use a ratio that involves the number you are looking for and a known number.
13. A rare bird is spotted in a tree by a bird watching group. The group is 9.5 yd from the base of the tree. The angle of elevation to the bird is 57°. How far is the bird from the group along the line of sight? Draw a sketch, and then solve. 17.4 yd

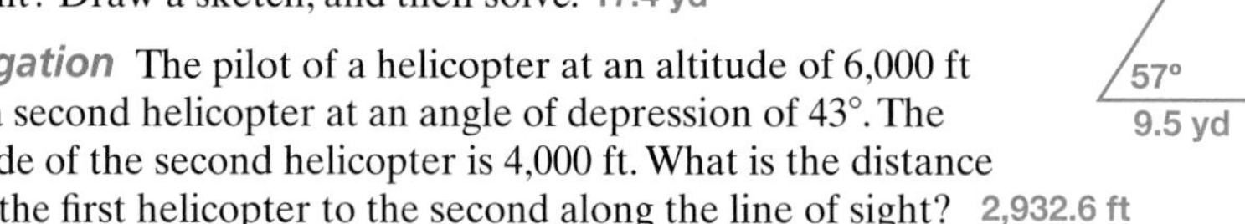

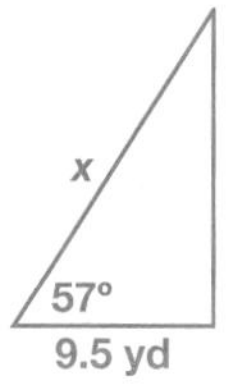

14. *Navigation* The pilot of a helicopter at an altitude of 6,000 ft sees a second helicopter at an angle of depression of 43°. The altitude of the second helicopter is 4,000 ft. What is the distance from the first helicopter to the second along the line of sight? 2,932.6 ft

## Mixed Review

**Find each value. Round to four decimal places.** *(Lesson 11-6)*

15. tan 29° 0.5543
16. sin 80° 0.9848
17. cos 34° 0.8290
18. sin 76° 0.9703
19. tan 68° 2.4751

**Find the area of each circle. Give an exact area and an approximate area to the nearest tenth.** *(Lesson 10-3)*

20. $r = 8$ in. $64\pi$ in.$^2 \approx 201$ in.$^2$
21. $r = 1.9$ cm $3.61\pi$ cm$^2 \approx 11.3$ cm$^2$
22. $r = 10$ mm $100\pi$ mm$^2 \approx 314$ mm$^2$
23. $r = 4.5$ in. $20.25\pi$ in.$^2 \approx 63.6$ in.$^2$
24. A recipe that serves four people calls for $1\frac{1}{2}$ c of flour. How many cups of flour are needed to make enough to serve ten people? *(Lesson 6-2)* $3\frac{3}{4}$ c

## Chapter Project 11 — Activity 3 Calculating

Refer to the diagram for Activity 1 on page 563. Use your measurement of $\angle XYZ$ from Activity 2 to find the angle of elevation. Then calculate $H$. Use your values for $C$, $H$, and $S$ to find your tree's score in Big Tree Points using the formula on page 559.

 See also Extra Practice section.

### Project Activity 3

**Calculating** As an interim check on student work, ask students to compare with each other (before they finish calculating). For example, before students calculate $H$, compare the size of their angles of elevation to make sure all are reasonable. Discuss what values for $C$, $H$, and $S$ are reasonable.

# FINISHING THE CHAPTER PROJECT

CHAPTER PROJECT 11

# Tree Angles

**Measure a Big Tree** The Project Activities on pages 563, 586, and 598 will help you complete your project. Here is a checklist to help you gather the different parts.

- ✔ your inclinometer
- ✔ your measurements for $\angle XYZ$, $C$, and $S$
- ✔ your calculation of $H$ and of your tree's score in Big Tree Points

Create a display. Include your inclinometer, your calculations, and a diagram of your tree with its measurements. If possible, find out the species of your tree. Compare your tree's score to the scores of other trees of the same species, which are available at the Web address given below.

***Reflect and Revise***

Ask a friend or someone at home to review your display. Are your diagrams and calculations accurate and clear? If necessary, make changes to improve them.

***Web Extension***

**Visit Prentice Hall's Web site. You'll find some interesting links and ideas related to angles and Big Trees. You'll also be able to share information about your project.**
**www.phschool.com**



## FINISHING THE PROJECT

CHAPTER PROJECT 11

**Project Day** You may wish to plan a project day on which students share their completed projects. Encourage students to explain their process as well as their product.

**Block Scheduling** If you have block scheduling or extended periods, you may wish to intersperse the sharing of projects over Days 3 and 4 between the completion of one lesson and the start of a new lesson.

###  Project Notebook

Have students review their project work and bring their notebooks up to date. Call attention to the fact that they can share their projects with other students through the Web site **www.phschool.com**.

Be sure students include in their notebooks their completed Project Manager and Scoring Rubric forms.

**Portfolio** Students may wish to include their projects and/or their project notebooks in their portfolios.

###  Web Extension

**Tell Us About Your Project**

Students may wish to share their projects with other students on the Web site: **www.phschool.com**.

### Scoring Rubric

3 You measure, calculate, and compare correctly. Your display is complete, well-organized, and informative. Your diagram is accurate and detailed, but easy to read.

2 You make minor errors in your measurements or calculations. Your display and diagram are complete, but could be better organized or more informative.

1 You measure or calculate incorrectly. Your display is incomplete or lacks organization.

0 Major elements of the project are incomplete or missing.

# Wrap Up

## Resources

Glossary, p. 748
Extra Practice, p. 720

For a complete list of resources for the chapter, see p. 557H.

# Wrap Up

## Key Terms

angle of elevation (p. 594)
angle of depression (p. 596)
cosine (p. 588)
distance (p. 572)
hypotenuse (p. 564)
irrational number (p. 561)
legs (p. 564)
midpoint (p. 574)
perfect square (p. 560)
sine (p. 588)
square root (p. 560)
tangent (p. 588)
trigonometry (p. 588)
trigonometric ratio (p. 588)

## Graphic Organizer

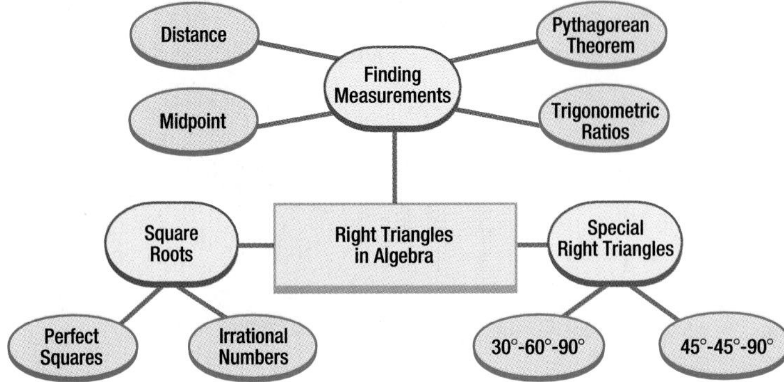


## Square Roots and Irrational Numbers 11-1

*Summary* The square of an integer is a **perfect square.** The inverse of squaring a number is finding a **square root.** The symbol $\sqrt{\ }$ indicates the positive square root of a number. A number that cannot be expressed as the ratio of two integers $\frac{a}{b}$, where $b$ is not zero, is **irrational.** If a positive integer is not a perfect square, its square root is irrational.

**Simplify each square root.**

**1.** $\sqrt{1}$ 1 **2.** $-\sqrt{16}$ −4 **3.** $\sqrt{49}$ 7 **4.** $\sqrt{64}$ 8 **5.** $-\sqrt{36}$ −6

**Estimate to the nearest integer.**

**6.** $\sqrt{5}$ 2 **7.** $\sqrt{11}$ 3 **8.** $\sqrt{33}$ 6 **9.** $\sqrt{62}$ 8 **10.** $\sqrt{91}$ 10

**Identify each number as rational or irrational.**

**11.** 0.55 rational **12.** $\sqrt{64}$ rational **13.** $0.\overline{45}$ rational **14.** $\sqrt{15}$ irrational **15.** 0.123123 . . . rational

16. *Writing* Explain why 0.12122122212222 . . . is an irrational number. It is irrational because there is not a block of identical repeating digits.

## The Pythagorean Theorem 11-2

*Summary* In a right triangle, the two shortest sides are the **legs.** The longest side, which is opposite the right angle, is the **hypotenuse.** The Pythagorean Theorem states that in any right triangle the sum of the squares of the lengths of the legs is equal to the square of the length of the hypotenuse ($a^2 + b^2 = c^2$).

**Can you form a right triangle with the three lengths given? Show your work.**

17. 1 mi, 3 mi, 3 mi No, $1 + 9 \neq 9$.
18. 9 yd, 12 yd, 15 yd Yes, 81 + 144 = 225.
19. $\sqrt{6}$ ft, $\sqrt{10}$ ft, 4 ft Yes, 6 + 10 = 16.
20. 30 m, 40 m, 50 m Yes, 900 + 1,600 = 2,500.

## Distance and Midpoint Formulas 11-3

*Summary* The Distance Formula states that the **distance** $d$ between any two points $(x_1, y_1)$ and $(x_2, y_2)$ is $d = \sqrt{(x_2 - x_1)^2 + (y_2 - y_1)^2}$. The Midpoint Formula states that the **midpoint** of a line segment with endpoints $A(x_1, y_1)$ and $B(x_2, y_2)$ is $\left(\frac{x_1 + x_2}{2}, \frac{y_1 + y_2}{2}\right)$.

**Find the distance between each pair of points. Round to the nearest tenth.**

21. (3, 0), (0, 2) 3.6
22. (−1, 7), (3, 10) 5
23. (4, −5), (−8, −1) 12.6
24. (−10, −12), (−8, −11) 2.2
25. (2, −14), (9, −20) 9.2
26. (10, 4), (−2, −2) 13.4

**Find the midpoint of each segment with the given endpoints.**

27. $H(0, 1)$ and $J(4, 7)$ (2, 4)
28. $K(2, 6)$ and $L(4, 2)$ (3, 4)
29. $M(-7, 8)$ and $P(3, -4)$ (−2, 2)
30. $A(4, 9)$ and $B(5, 11)$ (4.5, 10)
31. $X(-15, -12)$ and $Y(-9, -4)$ (−12, −8)
32. $D(20, 18)$ and $E(-15, -19)$ (2.5, −0.5)

## Write a Proportion 11-4

*Summary* You can write a proportion to solve indirect measurement problems using similar triangles.

33. *Engineering* An engineer needs to know what length to plan for a bridge across a river. She estimates the distance using the similar triangles $\triangle ABC$ and $\triangle DEC$ in the figure at the right. What is the distance across the river? 337.5 ft

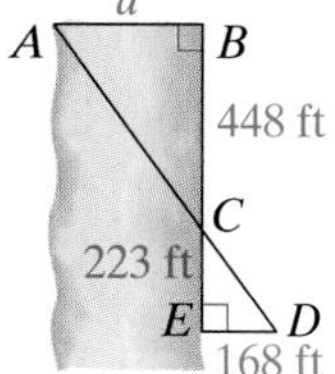




**Portfolio** Students may wish to include their completed work for the Wrap Up in their portfolios.

**Web Site**

Students can find self-assessment materials on the Web site: **www.phschool.com.**

## ■ Special Right Triangles 11-5

*Summary* In a 45°-45°-90° triangle, the length of the hypotenuse is the length of a leg times $\sqrt{2}$.

In a 30°-60°-90° triangle, the length of the hypotenuse is 2 times the length of the shorter leg and the length of the longer leg is $\sqrt{3}$ times the length of the shorter leg.

**Find the values of the variables.**

**34.**

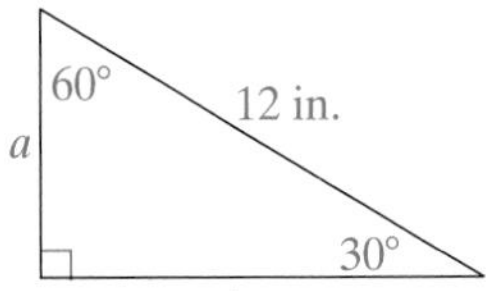


$a = 6$ in., $b \approx 10.4$ in.

**35.**

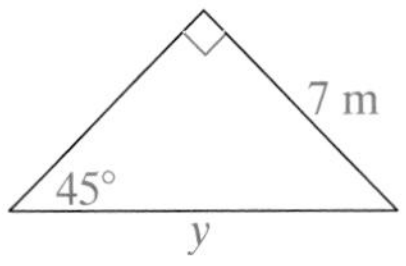


$y \approx 9.9$ m

**36.**

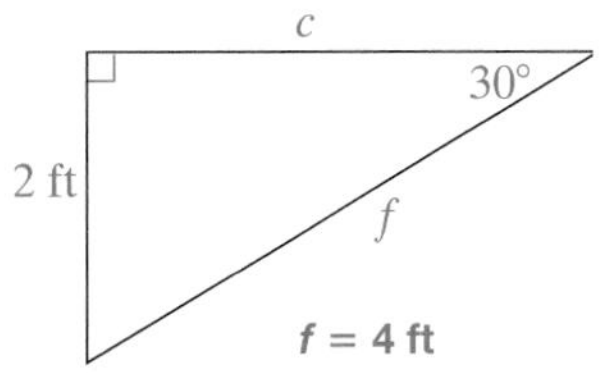


$f = 4$ ft

$c \approx 3.5$ ft

## ■ Using Trigonometric Ratios 11-6 and 11-7

*Summary* The ratios of the lengths of two sides of a right triangle are **trigonometric ratios.** Three trigonometric ratios are **sine, cosine,** and **tangent.** You can use these abbreviations when you find trigonometric ratios for a given acute $\angle N$.

$$\sin N = \frac{\text{opposite}}{\text{hypotenuse}} \qquad \cos N = \frac{\text{adjacent}}{\text{hypotenuse}} \qquad \tan N = \frac{\text{opposite}}{\text{adjacent}}$$

An **angle of elevation** is formed by a horizontal line and a line of sight above it. An **angle of depression** is formed by a horizontal line and a line of sight below it.

**Find each value. Round to four decimal places.**

**37.** sin 16° 0.2756 **38.** tan 82° 7.1154 **39.** cos 25° 0.9063 **40.** tan 3° 0.0524 **41.** sin 87° 0.9986

**42.** cos 73° 0.2924 **43.** cos 46° 0.6947 **44.** tan 45° 1 **45.** sin 79° 0.9816 **46.** tan 13° 0.2309

**Solve each problem. Round to the nearest unit.**

**47.** A loading ramp forms a 28° angle with the ground. If the base of the ramp is 15 ft long, how high does the ramp reach? 8 ft

**48.** Melanie is flying a kite and lets out 100 ft of string. Rosa determines that from Melanie's hands the angle of elevation of the kite is 71°. Melanie's hands are 4.3 ft from the ground. What is the height of the kite? about 99 ft



## Chapter Assessment Form A Page 1

**Circle the letter of the best answer.**

1. Which of the following is the best estimate of $\sqrt{76}$?
A. 6 B. 7 C. 8 (D.) 9

2. Which of the following is the best estimate of $\sqrt{119}$?
F. 9 G. 10 (H.) 11 J. 12

3. Which of the following is a rational number?
(A.) $\sqrt{36}$ B. 0.93993 . . . C. $\sqrt{85}$ D. 3.474477 . . .

4. Which of the following is an irrational number?
F. 743,743 G. $\sqrt{169}$ H. 0.2323 . . . (J.) 0.151155 . . .

5. Which of the following could be the lengths of the sides of a right triangle?
A. 2, 6, $\sqrt{38}$ (B.) 5, 12, 13 C. 36, 64, 100 D. 7, 8, 11

6. Which of the following could be the lengths of the sides of a 30°-60°-90° right triangle?
F. 3, 3, $3\sqrt{2}$ G. 9, $18\sqrt{3}$, 18 (H.) 6, $6\sqrt{3}$, 12 J. 5, $5\sqrt{2}$, $5\sqrt{3}$

7. Find sin 28° to four decimal places.
(A.) 0.4695 B. 0.8829 C. 0.5317 D. 0.6157

8. A right triangle has legs of lengths 7 m and 9 m. Which of the following is the best estimate of the length of the hypotenuse?
F. 10 m (G.) 11 m H. 12 m J. 13 m

**Simplify each square root.**

9. $\sqrt{144}$ 12 10. $-\sqrt{49}$ −7

**Find each missing length to the nearest tenth of a unit.**

11.

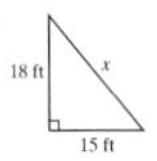


23.4 ft

12.

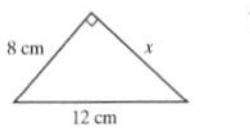


8.9 cm

13.

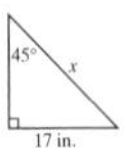


24.0 in.

Assessment



## Chapter Assessment Form A Page 2

14.

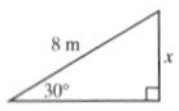


4 m

15.

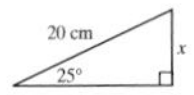


8.5 cm

16. Find the distance between the points $A(-7, 6)$ and $B(-1, 1)$ to the nearest tenth of a unit.
7.8 units

17. Find the midpoint of the segment with endpoints $A(-7, 6)$ and $B(-1, 1)$.
$\left(-4, 3\frac{1}{2}\right)$

18. A building casts a 52-foot shadow at the same time Tonya casts a 4-foot shadow. Tonya and her shadow form a triangle that is similar to the triangle formed by the building and its shadow. If Tonya is 5 feet tall, what is the height $h$ of the building?
65 ft

19. An airplane is flying 0.75 miles above the ground. If the pilot must begin a 4° descent to an airport runway, how far is the airplane from the beginning of the runway (in ground distance) to the nearest tenth of a mile?
10.7 mi

20. Explain why the tangent of 45° = 1. Sample answer is shown.
A right triangle with a 45° angle is isosceles, so the legs have the same measure. Therefore $\frac{\text{opposite}}{\text{adjacent}} = 1$.

# Assessment

**Simplify each square root.**

1. $\sqrt{25}$ 5
2. $-\sqrt{81}$ −9
3. $\sqrt{100}$ 10
4. $-\sqrt{4}$ −2
5. $\sqrt{16}$ 4
6. $\sqrt{49}$ 7

**Estimate to the nearest integer.**

7. $\sqrt{6}$ 2
8. $\sqrt{12}$ 3
9. $\sqrt{45}$ 7
10. $\sqrt{78}$ 9
11. $\sqrt{85}$ 9
12. $\sqrt{118}$ 11

**Identify each number as rational or irrational.**

13. 0.999 . . . rational
14. $\sqrt{24}$ irrational
15. $\sqrt{100}$ rational
16. 420,420 rational

**Find each missing length to the nearest tenth of a unit.**

17. 5.3 mm

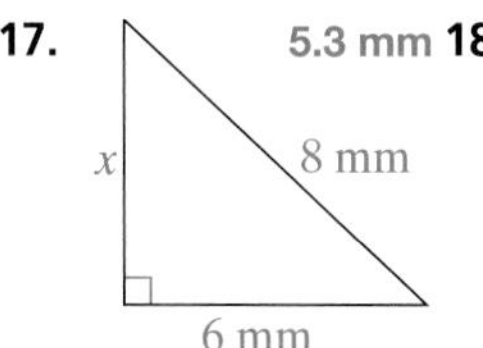


18. 

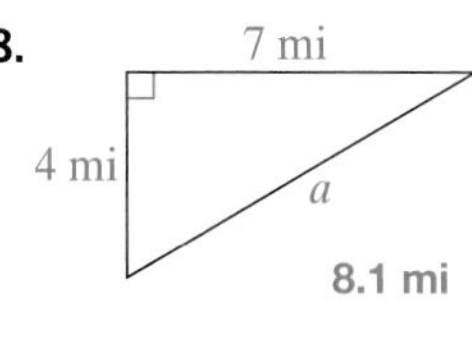


8.1 mi

19. 

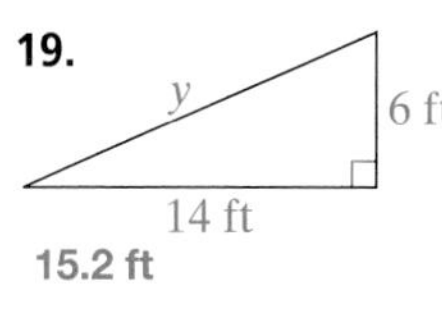


15.2 ft

20. 

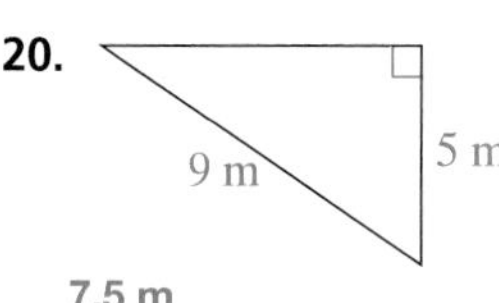


7.5 m

**Find the distance between each pair of points. Round to the nearest tenth.**

21. $(0, 0), (4, 6)$ 7.2
22. $(5, -3), (-6, 2)$ 12.1
23. $(-8, -9), (1, 2)$ 14.2
24. $(-1, -3), (-4, -7)$ 5

**Find the midpoint of each segment with the given endpoints.**

25. $C(5, 0)$ and $D(3, 6)$ (4, 3)
26. $M(9, -4)$ and $P(2, 8)$ (5.5, 2)

27. To estimate the height of a tree, Joan positions a mirror on the ground so she can see the top of the tree reflected in it. Joan's height, her distance from the mirror, and her line of sight to the mirror determine a triangle. The tree's height, its distance from the mirror, and the distance from the top of the tree to the mirror determine a similar triangle. Use the measurements below to find the height of the tree.
16 ft

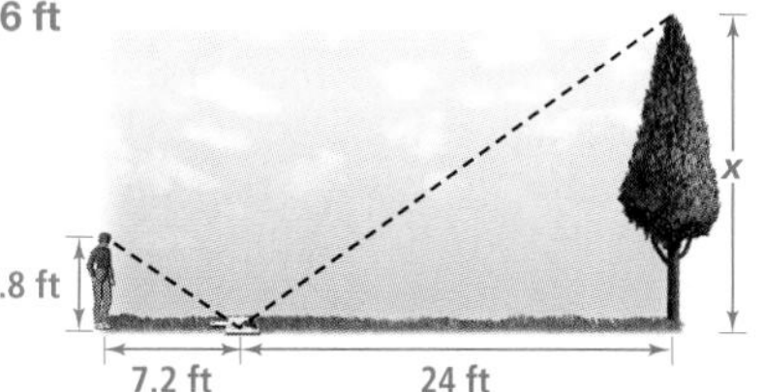


**Find the missing lengths.**

28. 

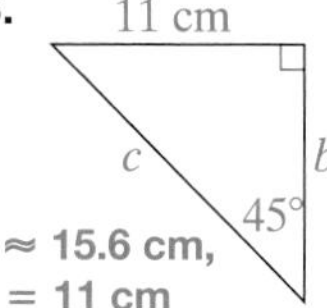


$c \approx 15.6$ cm, $b = 11$ cm

29. 

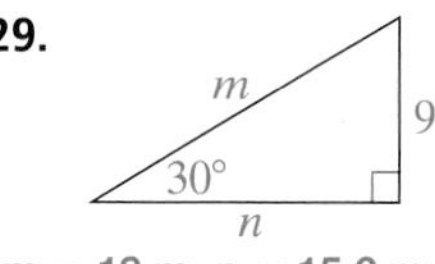


$m = 18$ m, $n \approx 15.6$ m

**Find each value. Round to four decimal places.**

30. sin 47°
31. tan 75°
32. cos 86°
33. tan 29°
34. cos 60°
35. sin 67°

30–35. See margin.

36. ***Writing*** Explain how a trigonometric ratio can be used to find a measurement indirectly. See margin.

37. ***Navigation*** The captain of a ship sights the top of a lighthouse at an angle of elevation of 12°. The captain knows that the top of the lighthouse is 24 m above sea level. What is the distance from the ship to the lighthouse? 112.9 m



30. 0.7314

31. 3.7321

32. 0.0698

33. 0.5543

34. 0.5

35. 0.9205

36. Answers may vary. Sample: If an unknown measurement can be placed into a trigonometric ratio with two known measurements, you can solve for the unknown measurement.

## Chapter Assessment

**Resources** For a complete list of resources for this chapter, see p. 557H.

### Chapter Assessment Form B Page 1

**Circle the letter of the best answer.**

1. Which of the following is the best estimate of $\sqrt{52}$?
   A. 6 (B.) 7 C. 8 D. 9
2. Which of the following is the best estimate of $\sqrt{138}$?
   F. 9 G. 10 H. 11 (J.) 12
3. Which of the following is a rational number?
   A. 0.58558 . . . B. $\sqrt{10}$ (C.) $\sqrt{64}$ D. 7.91911 . . .
4. Which of the following is an irrational number?
   F. $\sqrt{121}$ (G.) 0.343344 . . . H. 540,540 J. 0.2323 . . .
5. Which of the following could be the lengths of the sides of a right triangle?
   (A.) $3, 7, \sqrt{58}$ B. 6, 7, 9 C. $5, 8, \sqrt{90}$ D. 9, 16, 25
6. Which of the following could be the lengths of the sides of a 30°-60°-90° right triangle?
   F. $4, 4\sqrt{2}, 4\sqrt{3}$ G. $7, 7, 7\sqrt{2}$ H. $5, 10\sqrt{3}, 10$ (J.) $8, 8\sqrt{3}, 16$
7. Find cos 34° to four decimal places.
   (A.) 0.8290 B. 0.5592 C. 0.6745 D. 0.7193
8. A right triangle has legs of lengths 4 m and 6 m. Which of the following is the best estimate of the length of the hypotenuse?
   F. 5 m G. 6 m (H.) 7 m J. 8 m

**Simplify each square root.**

9. $\sqrt{625}$ 25
10. $-\sqrt{64}$ −8

**Find each missing length to the nearest tenth of a unit.**

11. 22 ft, x, 10 ft — 24.2 ft
12. 10 cm, x, 15 cm — 11.2 cm
13. 45°, 19 in., x — 26.9 in.



Assessment

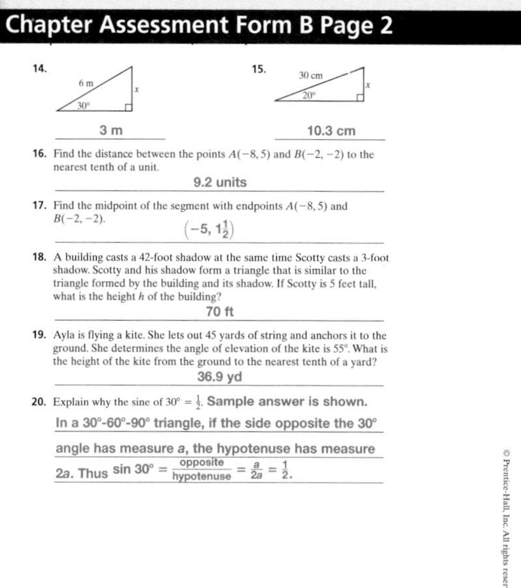
### Chapter Assessment Form B Page 2

14. 6 m, 30°, x — 3 m
15. 30 cm, 20°, x — 10.3 cm
16. Find the distance between the points $A(-8, 5)$ and $B(-2, -2)$ to the nearest tenth of a unit.
    9.2 units
17. Find the midpoint of the segment with endpoints $A(-8, 5)$ and $B(-2, -2)$.
    $\left(-5, 1\frac{1}{2}\right)$
18. A building casts a 42-foot shadow at the same time Scotty casts a 3-foot shadow. Scotty and his shadow form a triangle that is similar to the triangle formed by the building and its shadow. If Scotty is 5 feet tall, what is the height $h$ of the building?
    70 ft
19. Ayla is flying a kite. She lets out 45 yards of string and anchors it to the ground. She determines the angle of elevation of the kite is 55°. What is the height of the kite from the ground to the nearest tenth of a yard?
    36.9 yd
20. Explain why the sine of $30° = \frac{1}{2}$. Sample answer is shown.
    In a 30°-60°-90° triangle, if the side opposite the 30° angle has measure $a$, the hypotenuse has measure $2a$. Thus $\sin 30° = \frac{\text{opposite}}{\text{hypotenuse}} = \frac{a}{2a} = \frac{1}{2}$.

# Cumulative Review

## Cumulative Review Page 1

**Circle the letter of the best answer.**

1. Which integer is less than −63?
   A. 0 B. −81 C. −53 D. 29
2. Which property is used?
   $5(3 + 8) = 5(8 + 3)$
   F. commutative property of addition G. distributive property
   H. associative property of addition J. commutative property of multiplication
3. Find the mean of the following numbers.
   15 8 −14 −6 22
   A. 65 B. 5 C. 25 D. 125
4. Which number has 3 as a factor?
   F. 311 G. 419 H. 223 J. 528
5. Solve $-3.5 - x = 7.2$.
   A. $x = -10.7$ B. $x = 10.7$ C. $x = 3.7$ D. $x = -3.7$
6. In $\triangle PQR$, $m\angle P = 21°$ and $m\angle Q = 17°$. Find $m\angle R$.
   F. 142° G. 52° H. 322° J. 232
7. If $\triangle ABC \sim \triangle XYZ$, which statement is necessarily true?
   A. $\frac{AB}{XY} = \frac{BC}{XZ}$ B. $\angle B \cong \angle X$ C. $\angle C \cong \angle Z$ D. $\frac{AC}{XZ} = \frac{BA}{YZ}$
8. Find the area of a trapezoid with bases 8 in. and 2 in. and height 4 in.
   F. 20 in.$^2$ G. 40 in.$^2$ H. 25 in.$^2$ J. 34 in.$^2$
9. Find the volume of a cone with diameter 9 cm and height 6 cm.
   A. 508.68 cm$^3$ B. 127.17 cm$^3$ C. 381.51 cm$^3$ D. 254.34 cm$^3$
10. Which numbers could be the lengths of the sides of a right triangle?
    F. 16, 30, 35 G. 5, 12, 14 H. 9, 12, 15 J. 6, 8, 9
11. Find cos 43°.
    A. 0.6820 B. 0.9325 C. 0.7314 D. 1.0724
12. Which expression represents the area of the figure?
    F. $(5 + 4)^2$ G. $9 \cdot 5 + \frac{1}{2}(5 \cdot 4)$
    H. $5^2 + 4 \cdot 5$ J. $5^2 + \frac{1}{2}(4 \cdot 5)$

5 m
5 m
4 m



## Cumulative Review Page 2

13. Which estimate is closest to the distance between $A$ and $B$?
    A. 4 units B. 5 units
    C. 6 units D. 7 units
14. Find the midpoint of $\overline{AB}$. $\left(-1, \frac{1}{2}\right)$
15. Find the slope of the line containing points $A$ and $B$. $\frac{5}{4}$
16. Find $x$. 82 mm

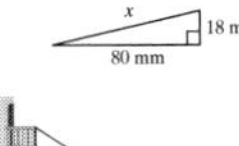


17. In the diagram, the angle of elevation from the ground to the balcony is 32°. Find the height $h$ of the balcony. about 5 m

h
32°
ground
8 m

18. Give an example of an irrational number and explain why it is irrational.
    Sample answer is shown. $\sqrt{2}$; It cannot be written as the ratio of two integers.

Assessment



# 11 Cumulative Review

Preparing for Algebra

**Choose the best answer.**

1. What is the best description of the figure? C

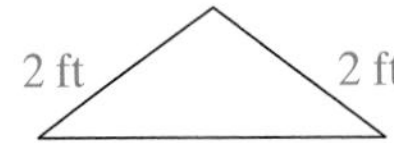


   A. obtuse equilateral triangle
   B. acute equilateral triangle
   C. obtuse isosceles triangle
   D. acute isosceles triangle

2. Which formula is correct for finding the area of a half circle? G
   F. $A = \frac{\pi d}{2}$ G. $A = \frac{\pi d^2}{8}$
   H. $A = \pi r$ J. $A = \pi r^2$

3. Which expression represents the area of the figure below? B

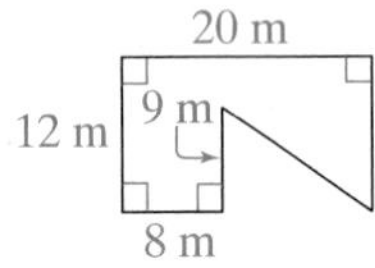


   A. $(20 \cdot 12) + \frac{1}{2}(12 \cdot 9)$
   B. $(20 \cdot 12) - \frac{1}{2}(12 \cdot 9)$
   C. $(12 \cdot 8) + \frac{1}{2}(12 \cdot 12)$
   D. $(12 \cdot 8) - \frac{1}{2}(12 \cdot 12)$

4. What is the surface area of a rectangular prism that is 8 in. long, $5\frac{1}{2}$ in. wide, and 3 in. tall? H
   F. 132 in.$^2$ G. 99 in.$^2$
   H. 169 in.$^2$ J. $84\frac{1}{2}$ in.$^2$

5. Simplify $\sqrt{36x^6}$. A
   A. $6x^3$ B. $\sqrt{6x^3}$
   C. $\sqrt{6x}$ D. $6x^6$

6. Find $x$. H

10 in.
x
24 in.

   F. 17 in. G. 28 in.
   H. 26 in. J. 338 in.

7. Which could be the side lengths of a right triangle? D
   A. 4 m, 4 m, 4 m B. 8 m, 11 m, 14 m
   C. 3 m, 4 m, 6 m D. 9 m, 12 m, 15 m

8. Which estimate is closest to the distance between $A$ and $B$? G

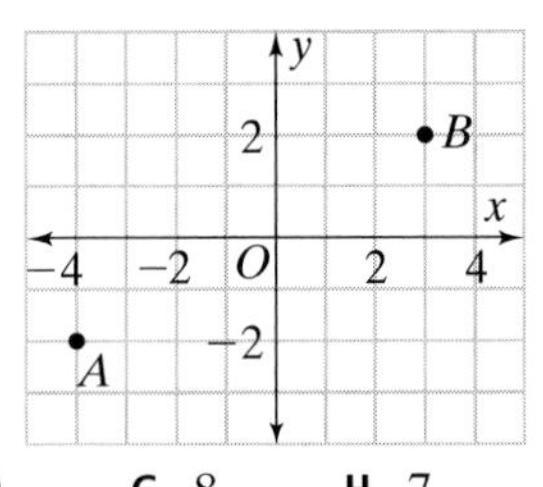


   F. 9 G. 8 H. 7 J. 6

**For Exercises 9–15, use a calculator or the Trigonometric Ratios Table on page 747. Find each value. Round to the nearest ten thousandth.**

9. sin 34° 0.5592
10. tan 79° 5.1446
11. cos 79° 0.1908
12. tan 22° 0.4040
13. cos 9° 0.9877
14. sin 75° 0.9659

15. In the diagram, the angle of depression between the parking lot and the ramp is 10°. Find the height $h$ of the loading dock. 2.1 ft

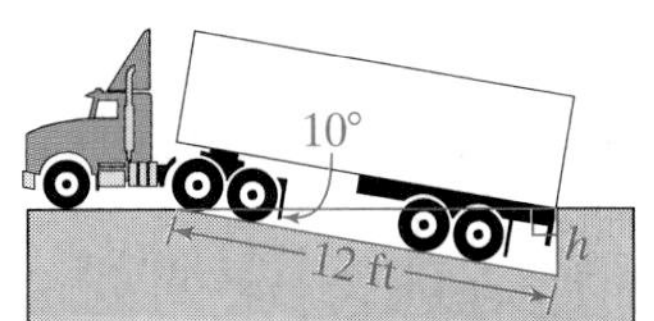




| Item | Chapter/ Lesson | Review Topic |
|---|---|---|
| 1 | 9-3 | Spatial Thinking |
| 2, 3, 4 | 10-2, 10-3, 10-5 | Area and Volume |
| 5–15 | 11-2, 11-3, 11-5, 11-6, 11-7 | Right Triangles in Algebra |

CHAPTER 12

# Data Analysis and Probability

## Content Overview for Chapter 12

Chapter 12 covers various techniques of analyzing data and probability. You can show data in a frequency table or in a line plot. The range is the difference between the greatest and least values in a set of data. A box-and-whisker plot displays data items below a number line. Quartiles divide the data into four parts. The median is the middle quartile. Graphs can be misleading when they include a break in the scale or when the scale is otherwise distorted.

A sample space is all the possible outcomes of an event. You can use a tree diagram or the Counting Principle to count the number of outcomes to find theoretical probability. Independent events are events in which one event does not affect the other event. If *A* and *B* are independent events, the probability of both *A* and *B* happening is $P(A \text{ and } B) = P(A) \bullet P(B)$. Dependent events are events in which one event does affect the other event. If *A* and *B* are dependent events, the probability of both *A* and *B* happening is $P(A \text{ and } B) = P(A) \bullet P(B \text{ after } A)$.

You can extend the Counting Principle to finding permutations and combinations. An arrangement in which order is important is a permutation. An arrangement in which order does not matter is a combination.

Theoretical probability is the ratio of favorable outcomes to the total number of possible outcomes; experimental probability is based on experimental data. A population is a group about which you want information. A sample is a part of the population you use to make predictions about the population. In a random sample, each member of the population has an equal chance to be selected.

**SCHOOL/HOME CONNECTION**

English and Spanish versions are available in the *Help at Home* book of copy masters.

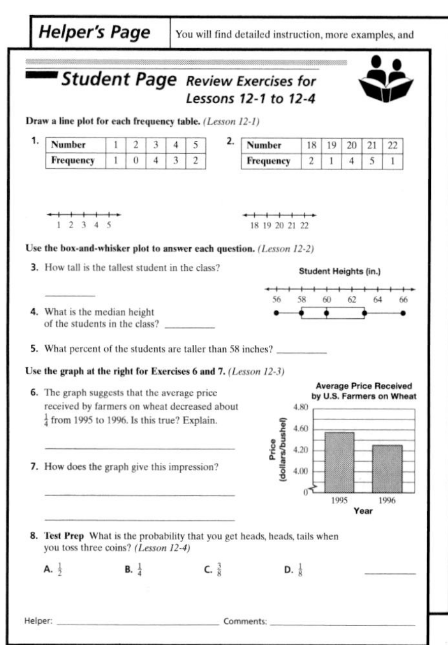

**Helper's Page** You will find detailed instruction, more examples, and

**Student Page** Review Exercises for Lessons 12-1 to 12-4

**Draw a line plot for each frequency table.** *(Lesson 12-1)*

1.

| Number | 1 | 2 | 3 | 4 | 5 |
|---|---|---|---|---|---|
| Frequency | 1 | 0 | 4 | 3 | 2 |

2.

| Number | 18 | 19 | 20 | 21 | 22 |
|---|---|---|---|---|---|
| Frequency | 2 | 1 | 4 | 5 | 1 |



**Use the box-and-whisker plot to answer each question.** *(Lesson 12-2)*

3. How tall is the tallest student in the class? ______

4. What is the median height of the students in the class? ______

5. What percent of the students are taller than 58 inches? ______



**Use the graph at the right for Exercises 6 and 7.** *(Lesson 12-3)*

6. The graph suggests that the average price received by farmers on wheat decreased about $\frac{1}{4}$ from 1995 to 1996. Is this true? Explain. ______

7. How does the graph give this impression? ______



8. **Test Prep** What is the probability that you get heads, heads, tails when you toss three coins? *(Lesson 12-4)*

A. $\frac{1}{2}$ B. $\frac{1}{4}$ C. $\frac{3}{8}$ D. $\frac{1}{8}$ ______

Helper: ______ Comments: ______

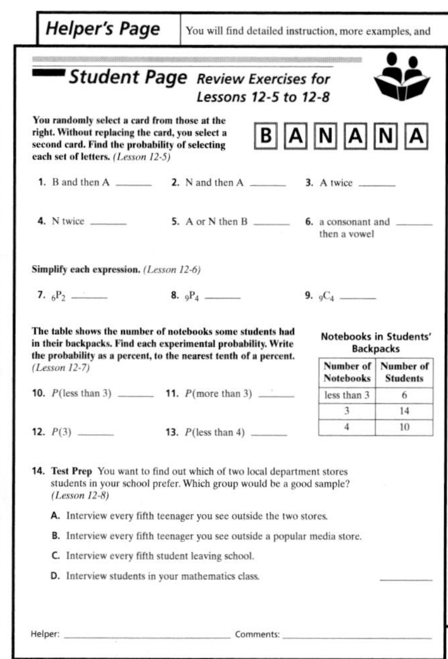

**Helper's Page** You will find detailed instruction, more examples, and

**Student Page** Review Exercises for Lessons 12-5 to 12-8

**You randomly select a card from those at the right. Without replacing the card, you select a second card. Find the probability of selecting each set of letters.** *(Lesson 12-5)*



1. B and then A ______
2. N and then A ______
3. A twice ______
4. N twice ______
5. A or N then B ______
6. a consonant and then a vowel ______

**Simplify each expression.** *(Lesson 12-6)*

7. ${}_6P_2$ ______
8. ${}_9P_4$ ______
9. ${}_9C_4$ ______

**The table shows the number of notebooks some students had in their backpacks. Find each experimental probability. Write the probability as a percent, to the nearest tenth of a percent.** *(Lesson 12-7)*

Notebooks in Students' Backpacks

| Number of Notebooks | Number of Students |
|---|---|
| less than 3 | 6 |
| 3 | 14 |
| 4 | 10 |

10. *P*(less than 3) ______
11. *P*(more than 3) ______
12. *P*(3) ______
13. *P*(less than 4) ______

14. **Test Prep** You want to find out which of two local department stores students in your school prefer. Which group would be a good sample? *(Lesson 12-8)*

A. Interview every fifth teenager you see outside the two stores.
B. Interview every fifth teenager you see outside a popular media store.
C. Interview every fifth student leaving school.
D. Interview students in your mathematics class. ______

Helper: ______ Comments: ______

## Making Connections

| Lesson | Interdisciplinary and Real-World Connections | Math Integration |
|---|---|---|
| 12-1 | Literature | Statistics |
| 12-2 | Biology, Social Studies | Statistics |
| 12-3 | Economics | Statistics |
| 12-4 | Clothing | Probability |
| 12-5 | Botany, Meteorology | Probability |
| 12-6 | Geography | Probability |
| 12-7 | Medical Science | Statistics, Probability |
| 12-8 | Recycling | Statistics |
| 12-9 | Sports | Problem Solving |

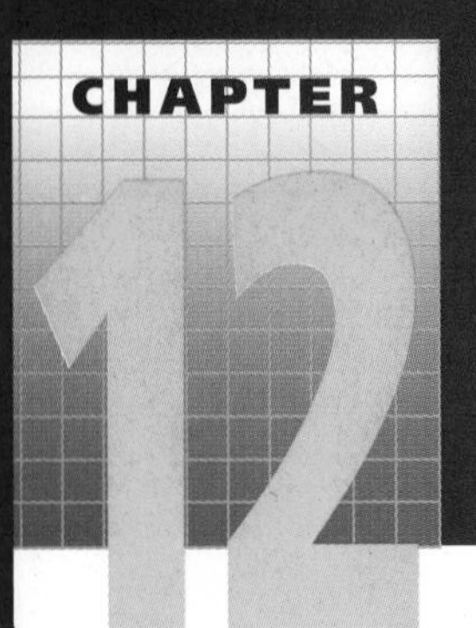

# Chapter 12 at a Glance

To accommodate flexible scheduling, most lessons are divided into parts. Assignment Options are given in the Teacher's Edition for each lesson.

| Pages | Lesson | NCTM | Parts |
|---|---|---|---|
| 608–611 | **Lesson 12-1** Frequency Tables and Line Plots | 1, 5, 6, 7, 9, 10 | Part 1 Using Frequency Tables to Display Data<br>Part 2 Using Line Plots to Display Data |
| 613–617 | **Lesson 12-2** Box-and-Whisker Plots | 5, 6, 7, 8, 9, 10 | Part 1 Making Box-and-Whisker Plots<br>Part 2 Analyzing Box-and-Whisker Plots |
| 620–625 | **Lesson 12-3** Using Graphs to Persuade | 5, 6, 8, 9, 10 | Part 1 Using Breaks in Scales<br>Part 2 Using Different Scales |
| 642–645 | **Lesson 12-7** Experimental Probability | 5, 6, 7, 8, 9 | Part 1 Finding Experimental Probability<br>Part 2 Simulating Events<br>**Project Activity 2** |
| 646–649 | **Lesson 12-8** Random Samples and Surveys | 5, 6, 8, 9 | Part 1 Choosing Samples for Surveys<br>Part 2 Making Estimates about Populations<br>**Checkpoint 2** |
| 650–653 | **Lesson 12-9** Problem Solving Strategy | 5, 6, 9 | Simulate a Problem<br>**Project Activity 3** |

## Pacing Options

This chart suggests pacing for only the core lessons and their parts, and it is provided merely as a possible guide. It will help you determine how much time you have in your schedule to cover other features, such as the Chapter Project, Math Toolboxes, Standardized Test Prep, Wrap Up, and Assessment.

| | Day 1 | Day 2 | Day 3 | Day 4 | Day 5 | Day 6 | Day 7 | Day 8 | Day 9 | Day 10 | Day 11 |
|---|---|---|---|---|---|---|---|---|---|---|---|
| **Traditional** (40–45 min. class periods) | 12–1 (1), 12–1 (2) | 12–2 (1) | 12–2 (2) | 12–3 (1), 12–3 (2) | 12–4 (1) | 12–4 (2) | 12–5 (1), 12–5 (2) | 12–6 (1) | 12–6 (2) | 12–7 (1), 12–7 (2) | 12–8 (1), 12–8 (2) |
| **Pre-Algebra Over 2 Years** (40–45 min. class periods) | 12–1 (1) | 12–1 (2) | 12–2 (1) | 12–2 (1) | 12–2 (2) | 12–3 (1) | 12–3 (2) | 12–3 (2) | 12–4 (1) | 12–4 (1) | 12–4 (2) |
| **Block Scheduling** (90 min. class periods) | 12–1 (1, 2), 12–2 (1) | 12–2 (2), 12–3 (1, 2) | 12–4 (1, 2), 12–5 (1, 2) | 12–6 (1, 2), 12–7 (1, 2) | 12–8 (1, 2), 12–9 | | | | | | |

| Pages 626–630 | Lesson 12-4 Counting Outcomes and Theoretical Probability |
|---|---|
| NCTM 5, 6, 7, 8, 9, 10 | Part 1 Counting Possible Choices<br>Part 2 Counting Outcomes to Find Probability<br>**Checkpoint 1** |

| Pages 631–635 | Lesson 12-5 Independent and Dependent Events |
|---|---|
| NCTM 5, 6, 8, 9 | Part 1 Independent Events<br>Part 2 Dependent Events<br>**Project Activity 1** |

| Pages 636–640 | Lesson 12-6 Permutations and Combinations |
|---|---|
| NCTM 5, 6, 8, 9 | Part 1 Permutations<br>Part 2 Combinations<br>**Math at Work** |

**NCTM STANDARDS 2000**

1. Number and Operations
2. Algebra
3. Geometry
4. Measurement
5. Data Analysis and Probability
6. Problem Solving
7. Reasoning and Proof
8. Communication
9. Connections
10. Representation

| Day 12 | Day 13 | Day 14 | Day 15 | Day 16 | Day 17 | Day 18 | Day 19 | Day 20 | Day 21 | Day 22 | Day 23 | Day 24 |
|---|---|---|---|---|---|---|---|---|---|---|---|---|
| 12–9 | | | | | | | | | | | | |
| 12–5 ▽1 | 12–5 ▽1 | 12–5 ▽2 | 12–6 ▽1 | 12–6 ▽2 | 12–6 ▽2 | 12–7 ▽1 | 12–7 ▽2 | 12–8 ▽1 | 12–8 ▽2 | 12–9 | 12–9 | |

**Block Scheduling Notes**

Consider these suggestions:
- **Day 1** Before starting Lesson 12-2, teach Math Toolbox 1, p. 612.
- **Day 2** Before starting Lesson 12-3, teach Math Toolbox 2, p. 618.
- **Day 4** Before starting Lesson 12-7, teach the Standardized Test Prep, p. 641.
- **Day 5** After completing Lesson 12-9, teach Math Toolbox 3, p. 654.

# Math Background

## Lesson 12-1

### Frequency Tables and Line Plots

One method of organizing data is to show the number of items in each category. This is called a *frequency table.* The table lists each data item with a tally or number that shows how many times (or how frequently) that value occurs.

A frequency table orders the data. Other ways to order the data include tally marks, a bar graph, or a line plot. A *line plot* uses a number line. Above each value, make an x-mark for each time that value occurs in a set of data. The following line plot shows how many times each digit appears in the counting numbers from 5 to 15, inclusive.

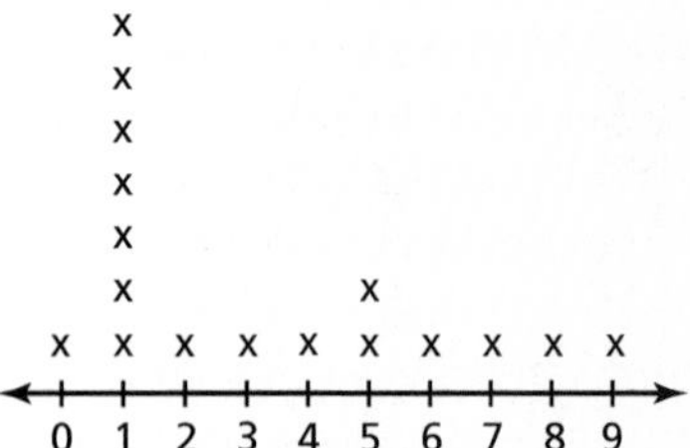

## Lessons 12-2 and 12-3

### Box-and-Whisker Plots; Using Graphs to Persuade

In addition to organizing and displaying data, you may want to summarize the data. One way to do this along a number line is to use a *box-and-whisker plot.* A box-and-whisker plot groups the data into four equal parts, or *quartiles.* To make such a plot, you first arrange the data in order from least to greatest. The median of all the scores is the point called the *middle quartile.* The point that is the median of the lower half is the *lower quartile.* The median of the upper half is the *upper quartile*. The *least value* is the first point of the plot and the *greatest value* is the last point of the plot. The box includes the values from the lower quartile to the upper quartile (the middle half of the values). The whiskers are the lines from the box to the least value and the greatest value. The text shows several plots of this type.

You can use a box-and-whisker plot to show where the data are concentrated and how they are spread out. You can organize and summarize collected facts and display them in ways that communicate clearly or in ways that may distort the data or mislead the reader.

Some ways of picturing data that may distort the data include using different units on the *x*-axis and *y*-axis, using a break in the scale on either axis, and using different widths for the bars on a bar graph.

## Lessons 12-4 and 12-5

### Counting Outcomes and Theoretical Probability; Independent and Dependent Events

The Counting Principle states that if *m* choices can be made for the first place and *n* choices can be made for the second place, then the total number of choices for both places is the product $m \times n$.

For example, if you toss two number cubes (marked with 1 to 6 dots), you can make a list of all possible outcomes. This list of all possible outcomes for an event is called a *sample space.* The sample space for tossing two cubes has 6 choices for the first cube and 6 choices for the second, so there are $6 \times 6$, or 36, possible results, or outcomes.

The *theoretical probability* of an event in which all outcomes are equally likely is this:
$P(\text{event}) = \frac{\text{favorable outcomes}}{\text{possible outcomes}}$

If you want to find the theoretical probability of tossing two cubes and getting a 2 and a 6 in either order, use the sample space of 36 possible outcomes. The favorable outcomes would be either (2 and 6) or (6 and 2). The theoretical probability is this:
$P(\text{2 and 6 in either order}) = \frac{2}{36}$ or $\frac{1}{18}$.

Does this mean that if you toss two cubes 18 times you are sure to get one toss of 2 and 6? No, the theoretical probability of $\frac{1}{18}$ is the number that the results will approach if the cubes are tossed a great many times. If you toss two cubes and record the results, you are finding the *experimental probability* for a given outcome (as described in Lesson 12-7).

When you toss one number cube and then toss a second, the result you get on the first toss has no influence on the second toss. Two events such that the outcome of one does not affect the outcome of the other are called *independent events.*

For two independent events, *A* and *B*, the probability of both events occurring is the product of the probabilities of each event occurring. For independent events, $P(A \text{ and } B) = P(A) \bullet P(B)$.

What happens when the outcome of one event does affect the outcome of the other? Suppose you want to select two *different* numbers from cards numbered 1 to 9. On your first choice, you have 9 possible outcomes. You choose and do not replace that card. For the second choice, you now have only 8 possible outcomes. This means that the outcome of the first event affects the outcome of the second; if you choose a 7 at first, then 7 is no longer a possibility for the second choice. Events in which the first event does affect the second are called *dependent events.*

For two dependent events *A* and *B*, the probability of both events occurring is the product of the probability of the first event and the probability that, after the first event, the second event occurs. For dependent events, $P(A \text{ and } B) = P(A) \bullet P(B \text{ after } A)$.

You can write probabilities as fractions, decimals, or percents.

## Lesson 12-6
### Permutations and Combinations

When the *order* of an arrangement matters, then the arrangement is a *permutation.* When the order of an arrangement is not important, then the arrangement is a *combination.*

For example, if you choose 3 people from a club of 10 members to represent the club at a meeting, then the order does not matter. The choice of (Bill, Irene, and Lynn) is the same as the choice of (Lynn, Bill, and Irene). You can write this as ${}_{10}C_3$, where ${}_nC_r$ represents the number of combinations of *n* objects chosen *r* at a time.

However, if you choose 3 people from the 10-member club to be the president, vice-president, and secretary of the club, the order does matter. The choice of (Bill as secretary, Irene as vice-president, and Lynn as president) is not the same as the choice of (Lynn as secretary, Bill as vice-president, and Irene as president). You can write this as ${}_{10}P_3$, where ${}_nP_r$ represents the number of permutations of *n* objects chosen *r* at a time.

You can find ${}_{10}P_3$ by using the Counting Principle.
${}_{10}P_3 = 10 \bullet 9 \bullet 8$

The number of ${}_nP_n$, or permutations of *n* things taken *n* at a time, is given by
${}_nP_n = n(n - 1)(n - 2)\ldots(1)$ so
${}_{10}P_{10} = 10 \bullet 9 \bullet 8 \bullet 7 \bullet 6 \bullet 5 \bullet 4 \bullet 3 \bullet 2 \bullet 1$

In later courses, students will learn that this product of all the integers from 10 to 1 is called 10 *factorial* (symbolized as 10!), or, in general, ${}_nP_n = n!$

To find the number of combinations, use the following formula. ${}_nC_r = \frac{{}_nP_r}{{}_rP_r}$

## Lesson 12-7
### Experimental Probability

When you find the probability of an event based on performing an actual experiment, you find *experimental probability.* One way to find experimental probability is with a model or *simulation.*

For professional development tips visit our Web site **www.phschool.com.**

# Monitoring Progress

## Universal Access

### ▶ Preventing a Student from Falling Behind

These resources are particularly helpful in preventing a student from falling behind his or her appropriate math level. For a complete list of resources for this chapter, see page 605H.

#### Skills You Need for Chapter 12

Student Edition, p. 605
Teacher's Edition, p. 605

- Finding the median
- Finding probability
- Multiplying fractions
- Fractions, decimals, and percents

#### Skills Handbook

Student Edition, pp. 723–741
Teacher's Edition, pp. 723–741

- Comparing and Ordering Whole Numbers, p. 723
- Multiplying Whole Numbers, p. 725
- Dividing Whole Numbers, p. 726
- Comparing and Ordering Decimals, p. 728

#### Reteaching Worksheets

There is a Reteaching worksheet for every lesson in this chapter.

- Chapter 12 Support File, Teaching Resources box
- See TE p. 605H for a complete list of resources

####  Skills Intervention Kit with CD-ROM

| For | Use |
| --- | --- |
| Lessons 12-1, 12-2, 12-4, 12-6, 12-8, 12-9 | Whole Numbers |
| Lesson 12-3 | Decimals |
| Lesson 12-7 | Operations/Fractions |

#### Daily Cumulative Review Blackline Masters

There is a Daily Cumulative Review worksheet for every lesson in this chapter.

See TE p. 605H for a complete list of resources.

### ▶ Accommodating Diverse Learning Styles

#### Tactile Learning

Write data values on cards and place them on a masking tape number line. (Lesson 12-2)

Use real coins and number cubes to find sample spaces. (Lesson 12-4)

#### Advanced Learner

Every lesson has at least one challenge problem.

Describe why a person might want to make a graph and suggest different ideas by drawing it in different ways. (Lesson 12-3)

Research factorial notation. (Lesson 12-6)

#### ELL (English Language Learner)

Relate the term *quartile* to quarter. (Lesson 12-2)

Use the words *odds* and *chances* to help understand the term *probability*. (Lesson 12-5)

#### Auditory Learning

Mark data points on a line plot as a partner calls them out. (Lesson 12-1)

Take turns explaining all the parts of the plots in the examples to a partner. (Lesson 12-2)

#### Visual Learning

Use visual cues on graphs that show a break in the scale. (Lesson 12-3)

Use index cards labeled blue and black to represent the blue and black socks in the exercises. (Lesson 12-5)

# Aligning Assessment with Instruction

## Assessment Options

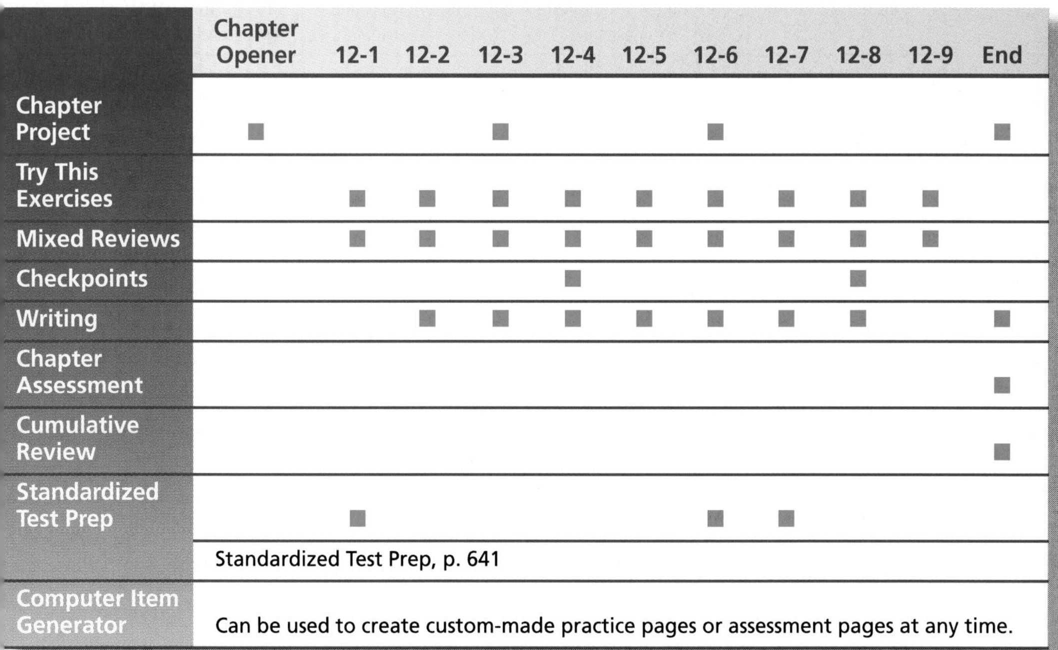

| | Chapter Opener | 12-1 | 12-2 | 12-3 | 12-4 | 12-5 | 12-6 | 12-7 | 12-8 | 12-9 | End |
|---|---|---|---|---|---|---|---|---|---|---|---|
| Chapter Project | ■ | | | ■ | | | ■ | | | | ■ |
| Try This Exercises | | ■ | ■ | ■ | ■ | ■ | ■ | ■ | ■ | ■ | |
| Mixed Reviews | | ■ | ■ | ■ | ■ | ■ | ■ | ■ | ■ | ■ | |
| Checkpoints | | | | | ■ | | | | ■ | | |
| Writing | | | ■ | ■ | ■ | ■ | ■ | ■ | ■ | | ■ |
| Chapter Assessment | | | | | | | | | | | ■ |
| Cumulative Review | | | | | | | | | | | ■ |
| Standardized Test Prep | | ■ | | | | | ■ | ■ | | | |
| | Standardized Test Prep, p. 641 | | | | | | | | | | |
| Computer Item Generator | Can be used to create custom-made practice pages or assessment pages at any time. | | | | | | | | | | |

### Test-Taking Tips on Transparencies

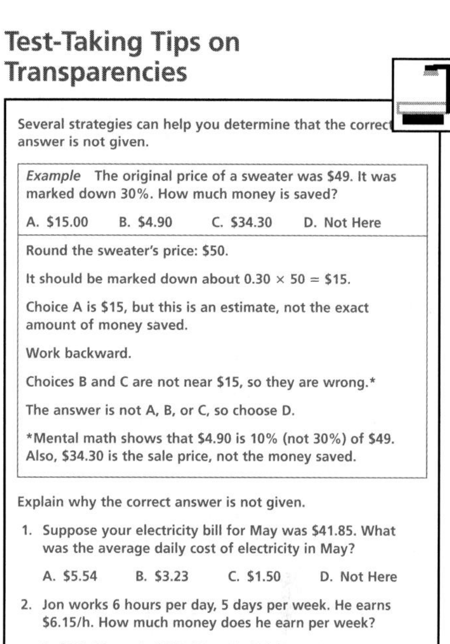

Several strategies can help you determine that the correct answer is not given.

*Example* The original price of a sweater was $49. It was marked down 30%. How much money is saved?

A. $15.00 B. $4.90 C. $34.30 D. Not Here

Round the sweater's price: $50.

It should be marked down about 0.30 × 50 = $15.

Choice A is $15, but this is an estimate, not the exact amount of money saved.

Work backward.

Choices B and C are not near $15, so they are wrong.*

The answer is not A, B, or C, so choose D.

*Mental math shows that $4.90 is 10% (not 30%) of $49. Also, $34.30 is the sale price, not the money saved.

Explain why the correct answer is not given.

1. Suppose your electricity bill for May was $41.85. What was the average daily cost of electricity in May?

   A. $5.54 B. $3.23 C. $1.50 D. Not Here

2. Jon works 6 hours per day, 5 days per week. He earns $6.15/h. How much money does he earn per week?

   F. $180.00 G. $738.00 H. $36.90 J. Not Here

*Use with Standardized Test Prep and Chapter Assessments.*

## Correlation to Standardized Tests

| Lesson | | CAT5 | CTBS/5 TerraNova™ | ITBS | MAT7 | SAT9 | LOCAL OBJECTIVES |
|---|---|---|---|---|---|---|---|
| 12-1 | Frequency Tables and Line Plots | | | | | ■ | |
| 12-2 | Box-and-Whisker Plots | | | | | ■ | |
| 12-3 | Using Graphs to Persuade | | ■ | ■ | ■ | ■ | |
| 12-4 | Counting Outcomes and Theoretical Probability | | | ■ | | ■ | |
| 12-5 | Independent and Dependent Events | | ■ | | | ■ | |
| 12-6 | Permutations and Combinations | ■ | | ■ | | ■ | |
| 12-7 | Experimental Probability | | | | ■ | ■ | |
| 12-8 | Random Samples and Surveys | | ■ | | | ■ | |
| 12-9 | Problem Solving Strategy: Simulate a Problem | | | | | ■ | |

**CAT5** California Achievement Test, 5th edition
**CTBS** TerraNova Comprehensive Test of Basic Skills, 5th edition
**ITBS** Iowa Test of Basic Skills, Form M
**MAT7** Metropolitan Achievement Test, 7th edition
**SAT** Stanford Achievement Test, Advanced 1

For other standardized test correlations, follow the link to your state at **www.phschool.com**.

# Resources for Chapter 12

| | TEACHING RESOURCES BOX | | | | | | | | | | | | | | |
|---|---|---|---|---|---|---|---|---|---|---|---|---|---|---|---|
| | CHAPTER 12 SUPPORT FILE | | | | | | | | Cumulative Assessment | Lesson Planners Plus | Daily Cum Review | Teaching Transparencies | Warm-Up Transparencies | Help at Home | SE Answers Transparenc |
| | Practice | Reteach | Enrichment | Project Manager | Checkpoints | Cumulative Review | Chapter Assessment | Alternative Assessment | | | | | | | |
| Begin Chapter | | | | ■ | | | | | | ■ | | | | | |
| 12-1 | ■ | ■ | ■ | | | | | | | ■ | ■ | 82 | ■ | | ■ |
| 12-2 | ■ | ■ | ■ | | | | | | | ■ | ■ | 83, 84, 85 | ■ | | ■ |
| 12-3 | ■ | ■ | ■ | | | | | | | ■ | ■ | | ■ | | ■ |
| 12-4 | ■ | ■ | ■ | | ■ | | | | | ■ | ■ | | ■ | ■ | ■ |
| 12-5 | ■ | ■ | ■ | | | | | | | ■ | ■ | | ■ | | ■ |
| 12-6 | ■ | ■ | ■ | | | | | | | ■ | ■ | | ■ | | ■ |
| 12-7 | ■ | ■ | ■ | | | | | | | ■ | ■ | | ■ | | ■ |
| 12-8 | ■ | ■ | ■ | | ■ | | | | | ■ | ■ | | ■ | ■ | ■ |
| 12-9 | ■ | ■ | ■ | | | | | | | ■ | ■ | | ■ | | ■ |
| End Chapter | | | | | | ■ | ■ (2 forms) | ■ | After Ch. 3, 6, 9, 13 | | | | | | |

**Also available for use with the chapter:**

Solution Key
Computational Practice Skills Booklet
Mathematics Standardized Test Prep, Student Edition and Teacher's Edition
Overhead Manipulatives Kit
Practice Workbook
Algebra Readiness Kit
Student Manipulatives Kit
Test-Taking Tips on Transparencies
Assessment Success Kit
Teaching Aids and Letters
Graphing Calculator Handbook
Spanish Resources
Success-Building Puzzle and Problem Masters

## TECHNOLOGY

**Computer Item Generator with Standardized Test Prep**

CD-ROM with an unlimited supply of questions with varying degrees of difficulty for customized practice sheets, quizzes, and tests.

**Resource Pro® with Planning Express®**

CD-ROM with complete classroom planning tool and teaching resources for customizing and planning lessons.

**Interactive Math Lessons and Tools**

CD-ROM with lessons and tools to make abstract concepts visual and accessible.

**Student Tutorial**

Test preparation software for students on CD-ROM with management system for teachers; includes Secondary Math Lab Toolkit™.

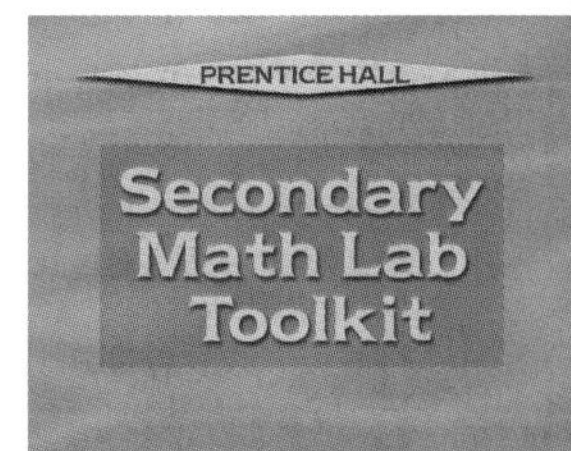


**Secondary Math Lab Toolkit™ with Integrated Math Labs**

Integrated software package with linkable math tools for exploring key concepts.

**Also available for use with the chapter:**

Math Blaster® Pre-Algebra CD-ROM
Video Fieldtrips, Vol. I: Algebra Applications
Video Fieldtrips, Vol. II: Geometry Applications
Wide World of Mathematics CD-ROM
Wide World of Mathematics Video

### *Web Extension*

**www.phschool.com**

**For Students**
- Chapter Support with Internet Links
- Internet Activities

**For Teachers**
- Curriculum Support
- Professional Development
- Product Information
- Regional Support Information

# Skills You Need for Chapter 12

## Finding the median — Use before Lesson 12-2.

**Find the median.**

1. 12, 14, 10, 9, 13, 12, 15, 12, 11 12
2. 55, 53, 67, 52, 50, 49, 51, 52, 52 52
3. 101, 100, 100, 105, 102, 101 101
4. 0.2, 0.5, 0.11, 0.25, 0.34, 0.19 0.225

## Finding probability — Use before Lessons 12-4, 12-5, and 12-7.

**Find the probability for one roll of a number cube.**

5. $P(2)$ $\frac{1}{6}$
6. $P(5)$ $\frac{1}{6}$
7. $P(2 \text{ or } 5)$ $\frac{1}{3}$
8. $P(8)$ 0
9. $P(1, 2, \text{or } 3)$ $\frac{1}{2}$
10. $P(\text{greater than } 4)$ $\frac{1}{3}$
11. $P(\text{not } 3)$ $\frac{5}{6}$
12. $P(\text{less than } 1)$ 0

**A student is chosen at random from a class of 15 boys and 18 girls. Find each probability.**

13. $P(\text{girl})$ $\frac{6}{11}$
14. $P(\text{boy})$ $\frac{5}{11}$
15. $P(\text{not a girl})$ $\frac{5}{11}$

## Multiplying fractions — Use before Lesson 12-5.

**Find each product.**

16. $\frac{2}{3} \cdot \frac{1}{2}$ $\frac{1}{3}$
17. $\frac{7}{8} \cdot \frac{6}{7}$ $\frac{3}{4}$
18. $\frac{9}{10} \cdot \frac{8}{9}$ $\frac{4}{5}$
19. $\frac{5}{6} \cdot \frac{4}{5}$ $\frac{2}{3}$
20. $\frac{3}{4} \cdot \frac{2}{3}$ $\frac{1}{2}$
21. $\frac{1}{2} \cdot \frac{1}{2} \cdot \frac{1}{2}$ $\frac{1}{8}$
22. $\frac{7}{8} \cdot \frac{6}{7} \cdot \frac{5}{6}$ $\frac{5}{8}$
23. $\frac{2}{5} \cdot \frac{1}{4}$ $\frac{1}{10}$

## Fractions, decimals, and percents — Use before Lessons 12-5 and 12-7.

**Write each percent as a decimal.**

24. 50% 0.5
25. 36% 0.36
26. 20% 0.2
27. 5% 0.05

**Write each decimal or fraction as a percent.**

28. $\frac{1}{5}$ 20%
29. $\frac{7}{8}$ 87.5%
30. 0.28 28%
31. 0.3 30%



# Skills You Need

### Finding the median

**In Lesson 12-2** students will find the median to create box-and-whisker plots.

### Finding probability

**In Lessons 12-4, 12-5, and 12-7** students will find theoretical and experimental probabilities and calculate probabilities of independent and dependent events.

### Multiplying fractions

**In Lesson 12-5** students will multiply fractions to calculate probabilities of independent and dependent events.

### Fractions, decimals, and percents

**In Lessons 12-5 and 12-7** students will use fractions, decimals, and percents in problems involving independent and dependent events and experimental probability.

# Skills Trace

| SKILL | INTRODUCED | DEVELOPED IN LESSON(S) | REVIEWED/REINFORCED |
|---|---|---|---|
| Displaying data | 12-1 | 12-2 | Math Toolbox p. 618; pp. 617, 625, 630, 672, 692, 697 |
| Finding theoretical probability | 12-4 | 12-5 | p. 640 |
| Using permutations and combinations | 12-6 | 12-6 | pp. 676, 697 |
| Finding experimental probability | 12-7 | 12-8 | p. 649 |
| Making estimates and predictions | 12-8 | Math Toolbox p. 654 | pp. 653, 668 |

# Data Analysis and Probability

## Connecting to Students' Lives

Ask students to describe any survey results they have heard or read—perhaps a Top Ten music poll or a news story about the average amount of money that teenagers spend per month.

## Interdisciplinary Connections

The Chapter Project connects math and social studies. You may want to display news stories and graphs that show the results of various surveys and polls.

## About the Project

The Chapter Project directs students to apply their knowledge of statistics, samples, graphing, and surveys to conduct a survey to determine the amount of time students spent per week at the school on organized extracurricular activities.

**What you'll learn in this chapter:**

- How to use graphs to represent data
- How to find theoretical probability and experimental probability
- How to find permutations and combinations

606 Chapter 12

*Web Extension*
**www.phschool.com**

For Students
Chapter Support with Internet links
Interactive Activities

For Teachers
Curriculum Support
Professional Development
Product Information
Regional Support Information

CHAPTER PROJECT 12

# The Good Times Poll

**D**o you participate in an organized extracurricular activity, such as a sport or a club? How much time do you devote to such activities each week? How does the amount of time you spend compare to the averages for students in your class and your school?

***Conduct a Survey*** For the chapter project, you will do a survey of your class and a survey of your school. You will use graphs and statistical measures to display and analyze the results.

### *Steps to help you complete the project*


**p. 635** ACTIVITY: INTERVIEWING
**p. 645** ACTIVITY: GRAPHING
**p. 653** ACTIVITY: COMPARING
**p. 655** FINISHING THE CHAPTER PROJECT

*Web Extension*
**www.phschool.com**

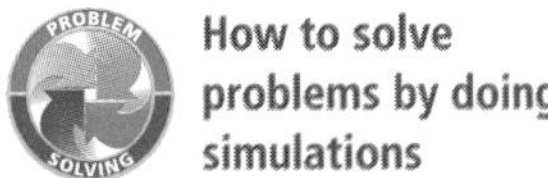

How to solve problems by doing simulations

## Scoring Rubric

**3** You conduct your surveys accurately and draw your graphs correctly. Your analysis and conclusions are insightful and justified by the data. Your report is complete and well written.
**2** You make minor errors in your survey, graphs, or analysis. Your report is complete, but it could be written better or could be more insightful.
**1** Your survey methods, graphs, or analysis are incorrect. Your report is incomplete.
**0** Major elements of the project are incomplete or missing.

## CHAPTER PROJECT 12 LAUNCHING THE PROJECT

*The Chapter Project is optional and may be assigned at your discretion.*

Ask students:
- Does it make a difference whether you ask the question exactly the same way every time?
- Will the data from your class be representative of the entire school?
- What are different ways to communicate your results to others?

Distribute a copy of the Project Manager and Scoring Rubric to help students get an overview of the project.

Review the scoring rubric with students.

###  Project Notebook

Encourage students to keep all project-related materials in a separate folder or notebook. Call attention to the fact that they will find much useful information on the Web site **www.phschool.com**.

**Tracking the Project** Set benchmark deadlines for students to show you their work in progress.

*Available in the Chapter 12 Support File in the Teaching Resources box.*

### Project Manager and Scoring Rubric

**Getting Started** You will be writing a report analyzing and comparing two surveys on students' extracurricular activities. Read about the project in your textbook. As you work on the project, you will need materials to record your survey results, to do your calculations, to make your graphs, and to write your report.

**Checklist and Suggestions**

| | | |
|---|---|---|
| ❑ | Survey members of your class. | Decide how to record the results before you start surveying your classmates. |
| ❑ | Draw graphs of your data. | Decide what is average for the class. |
| ❑ | Survey the school. | Choose a sample that represents the whole school. |
| ❑ | Compare your surveys. | Choose the scale for your box-and whisker plot to fit the results of both surveys. |
| ❑ | Write your report. | Describe your survey plan and your conclusions. |
| ❑ | Share your report with a friend. | Make any necessary changes. |

**Scoring Rubric**

**3** You conduct your surveys accurately and draw your graphs correctly. Your analysis and conclusions are insightful and justified by the data. Your report is complete and well written.
**2** You make minor errors in your survey, graphs, or analysis. Your report is complete, but it could be written better or could be more insightful.
**1** Your survey methods, graphs, or analysis are incorrect. Your report is incomplete.
**0** Major elements of the project are incomplete or missing.

**Your Evaluation of the Project** Evaluate your work, based on the Scoring Rubric.

**Teacher's Evaluation of the Project**

# 12-1

## Getting Ready

**Key Terms and Symbols** frequency table, line plot, range

**Resources** A complete list of resources for this lesson is on p. 605H.

### Daily Skills Warm-Up

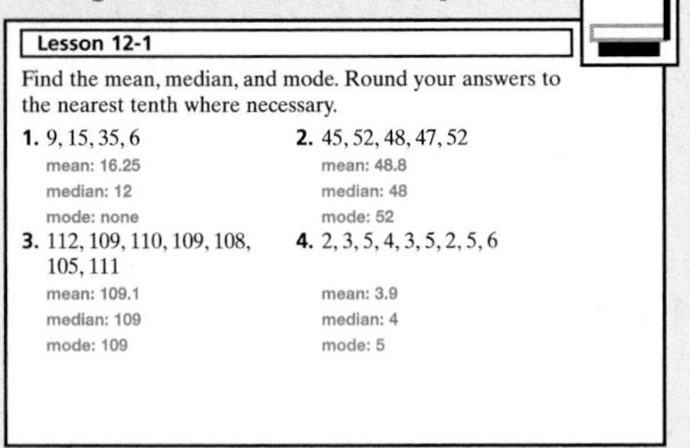
Lesson 12-1

Find the mean, median, and mode. Round your answers to the nearest tenth where necessary.

1. 9, 15, 35, 6
   mean: 16.25
   median: 12
   mode: none
2. 45, 52, 48, 47, 52
   mean: 48.8
   median: 48
   mode: 52
3. 112, 109, 110, 109, 108, 105, 111
   mean: 109.1
   median: 109
   mode: 109
4. 2, 3, 5, 4, 3, 5, 2, 5, 6
   mean: 3.9
   median: 4
   mode: 5

### Background for the Lesson

You can change data into information that people can quickly understand by organizing the numbers into frequency tables and line plots. A frequency table shows each data item and a count of how many times that item occurs. A line plot pictures the data from a frequency table in the form of marks above a number line. Label a point for each possible data item along a number line. Plot the count for each item by making marks above the number to show the count. For example, if the count for an item, such as carrying 20 books, is 4, you make 4 marks above 20 on the line plot.

## 1 Focus

### Investigate

Help students see how much more quickly they can get information (such as which result is most common) from the data when it is organized into the frequency table.

### Connecting to Students' Lives

Ask students if they have ever been involved in a survey, either asking or answering questions. Discuss why people take surveys and the information people look for when they take surveys.

# 12-1 Frequency Tables and Line Plots

**What You'll Learn**

1. To display data in frequency tables
2. To display data in line plots

**. . . And Why**

To analyze data collected in surveys

## Investigate

EXPLORING FREQUENCY TABLES

*Surveys* Many people have favorite colors. Do people also have favorite numbers? Take a survey of your classmates.

1. Ask each person to choose an integer from 0 to 9. Use a table to record the responses. 1–3. Check students' work.
2. Which number was chosen most frequently? How many times was each of the other numbers chosen?
3. Suppose you want to continue your survey by asking more people. Looking back, would you use the same type of table you used for Question 1? Can you make improvements? Explain.

### PART 1 Using Frequency Tables to Display Data

You can display data in a **frequency table,** which lists each data item with the number of times it occurs.

#### EXAMPLE 1

**A number cube was rolled 20 times. The results are shown at the right. Display the data in a frequency table.**

5 2 5 4 1 6 5 2 5 1
3 6 1 3 4 5 3 5 3 4

List the numbers on the cube in order. Use a tally mark for each result. Count the tally marks and record the frequency.

| Number | Tally | Frequency |
|---|---|---|
| 1 | III | 3 |
| 2 | II | 2 |
| 3 | IIII | 4 |
| 4 | III | 3 |
| 5 | ~~IIII~~ I | 6 |
| 6 | II | 2 |



## Tools to Monitor Progress

### BEFORE THE LESSON

**To check prerequisite skills:**

- Comparing and ordering whole numbers

**Skills Handbook,** p. 723

**Skills Intervention Kit,** Whole Numbers

### DURING THE LESSON

**To check understanding:**

**Try This** exercises on student page

- **Additional Examples 1–2**

  Here are results of a survey of 24 students on the hours of TV they watch daily. Display the data in a line plot. Then find the range.

  1 3 4 3 1 1 2 3 4 1 3
  2 2 1 3 2 1 2 3 2 4 3

■ **Try This**

4. Display the data below in a frequency table.
10 12 13 15 10 11 14 13 10 11 11 12 10 10 15

4.

| Number | Frequency |
|---|---|
| 10 | 5 |
| 11 | 3 |
| 12 | 2 |
| 13 | 2 |
| 14 | 1 |
| 15 | 2 |

## PART 2 Using Line Plots to Display Data

A **line plot** displays data with X marks above a number line.

The **range** of the data is the difference between the greatest and the least values in the data set.

### Example 2

*Surveys* **Twenty-five students in a school hallway were asked how many books they were carrying. The frequency table at the right shows their responses. Display the data in a line plot. Then find the range.**

**"How many books are you carrying?"**

| Number | Frequency |
|---|---|
| 0 | 3 |
| 1 | 7 |
| 2 | 6 |
| 3 | 2 |
| 4 | 4 |
| 5 | 3 |

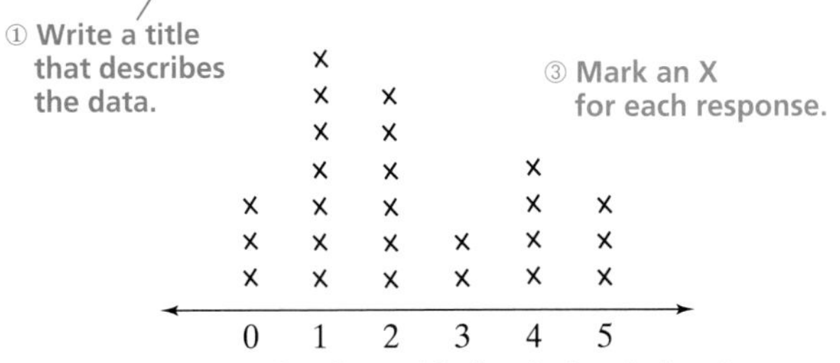


The greatest value in the data set is 5 and the least value is 0. So the range is 5 − 0, or 5.

■ **Try This**

5. Display the data below in a line plot. Then find the range.
miles from home to the mall: 2, 4, 3, 7, 3, 1, 4, 2, 2, 6, 3, 5, 1, 8, 3
See above right; 7.

6. What is the range of the data below? $0.19
prices of a gallon of regular gas at different gas stations:
$1.48, $1.32, $1.30, $1.35, $1.41, $1.29, $1.32, $1.43, $1.36

5.

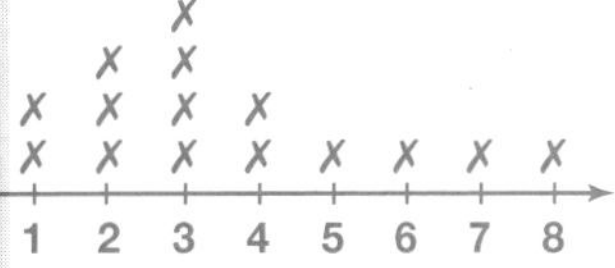


**Reading Math**

The word *range* is used in different ways in mathematics. The range of a data set is the difference between the greatest and the least values. The range of a function is its set of functional values.



range: 3

Hours of TV

| X | X | X | |
|---|---|---|---|

1 2 3 4

# 2 Teach

## Part 1 Teaching Notes

Explain that data items can be such things as colors or makes of cars as well as numbers. If you survey people to see the number of each coin they have, the data items would be penny, nickel, dime, quarter, half-dollar and dollar.

### ■ Example 1

**Build understanding.** Ask: Were there any results that were rolled the same number of times? How can you tell? Two and six (each 2 times) and one and four (each 3 times); You can tell by the count shown in the frequency column.

**Error Prevention** Clear and accurate labels on frequency tables, especially those where the data items are numbers, help the reader to tell the difference between the data items and the count.

## Part 2 Teaching Notes

Ask students to compare line plots with frequency tables. How are the two similar? How are they different?

**Reading Math** Help students distinguish between a line *plot* (marks above a number line) and a line *graph* they may have drawn on the coordinate plane.

### ■ Example 2

**Build understanding.** Ask: Suppose 25 more students were asked how many books they were carrying, but none had more than five. Would the range change? Explain. No; The greatest value would still be 5 and the least would still be 0.

**Extension** Suggest that students conduct a survey, similar to the one in Example 2, in their school. Ask students to report on how the number of students they survey affects their data.

## AFTER THE LESSON

### To assess knowledge:

**Lesson Quiz**

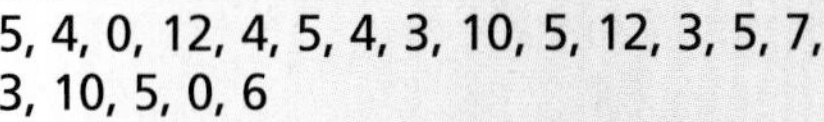

Display the data in a line plot. Find the range. Books read in the last month:
5, 4, 0, 12, 4, 5, 4, 3, 10, 5, 12, 3, 5, 7, 3, 10, 5, 0, 6
range: 12 See right for plot.

- For enrichment and reteaching options see Resources on p. 605H.

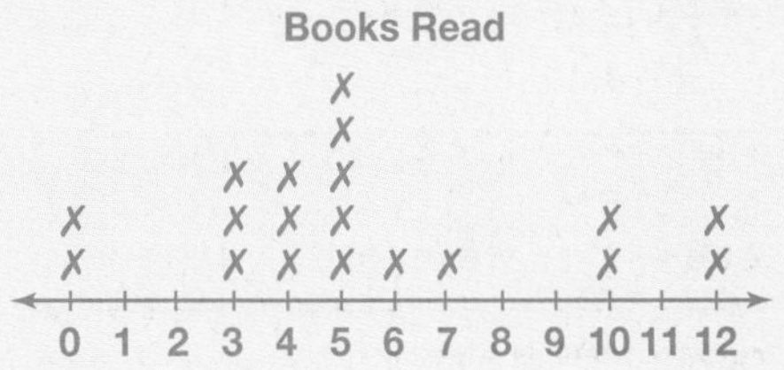

# 3 Practice/Assess

## Assignment Guide

To provide flexible scheduling, this lesson can be divided into parts.

**Part 1**
**Core** 1–2, 6–11, 24
✪ **Extension** 21–23

**Part 2**
**Core** 3–5, 12–20, 25–27
✪ **Extension** 28

Mixed Review can be assigned at any time for maintenance.

## Exercises

**Auditory Learning** **Exercises 12–15, 17–20** Work with a partner to draw and label the line and the data points. Then, as your partner calls out each data point, mark it on the line plot.

## ✪ Challenge

What is the range of the data in a line plot that shows the results of a survey of eye colors? Explain your answer. There is no range because the data have no numerical values.

## Closure

You can show data in a frequency table, which lists each data item with the number of times it occurs, or in a line plot, which displays data with X marks on a number line. The range is the difference between the greatest and least values in a set of data.

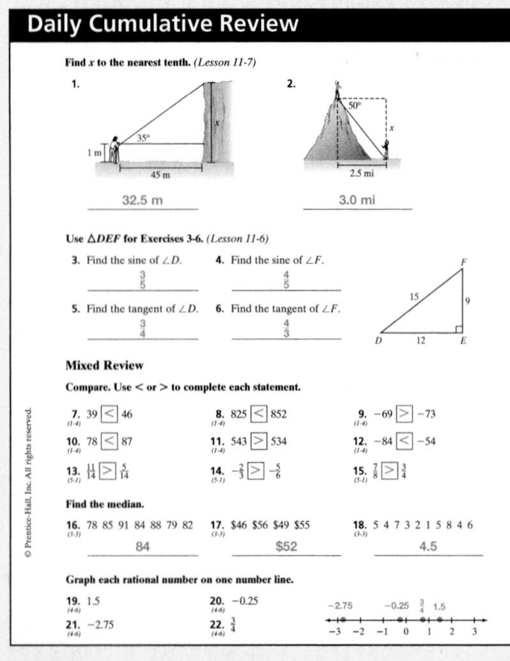

**Daily Cumulative Review**

**Find $x$ to the nearest tenth.** *(Lesson 11-7)*



1. 32.5 m
2. 3.0 mi

**Use $\triangle DEF$ for Exercises 3-6.** *(Lesson 11-6)*



3. Find the sine of $\angle D$. $\frac{3}{5}$
4. Find the sine of $\angle F$. $\frac{4}{5}$
5. Find the tangent of $\angle D$. $\frac{3}{4}$
6. Find the tangent of $\angle F$. $\frac{4}{3}$

**Mixed Review**

**Compare. Use $<$ or $>$ to complete each statement.**

7. (1-4) $39 \; \boxed{<} \; 46$
8. (1-4) $825 \; \boxed{<} \; 852$
9. (1-4) $-69 \; \boxed{>} \; -73$
10. (1-4) $78 \; \boxed{<} \; 87$
11. (1-4) $543 \; \boxed{>} \; 534$
12. (1-4) $-84 \; \boxed{<} \; -54$
13. (5-1) $\frac{11}{14} \; \boxed{>} \; \frac{5}{14}$
14. (5-1) $-\frac{2}{3} \; \boxed{>} \; -\frac{5}{6}$
15. (5-1) $\frac{7}{8} \; \boxed{>} \; \frac{3}{4}$

**Find the median.**

16. (3-3) 78 85 91 84 88 79 82 — 84
17. (3-3) \$46 \$56 \$49 \$55 — \$52
18. (3-3) 5 4 7 3 2 1 5 8 4 6 — 4.5

**Graph each rational number on one number line.**

19. (4-6) 1.5
20. (4-6) −0.25
21. (4-6) −2.75
22. (4-6) $\frac{3}{4}$





# Exercises

## Check Understanding

**Display each set of data in a frequency table.** 1–2. See margin.

1. 1 4 0 3 0 1 3 2 2 4
2. 6 2 8 7 9 3 5 4 8 2 4 6 4 1

**Display each set of data in a line plot. Find the range.**

3. 0 2 1 1 4 0 4 3 2

X X X X
X X X X X
0 1 2 3 4 ;4

4. 5 0 2 1 4 3 4 0 2 5 4 3 2 0 4

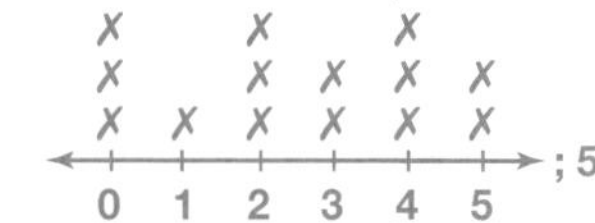


5. *Critical Thinking* Describe a set of data that would be easier to display with a frequency table than with a line plot. Answers may vary. Sample: Data in which one number occurs with a high frequency.

## Practice and Problem Solving

**Display each set of data in a frequency table.** 6–7. See margin. 8–11. See back of book.

6. 10 30 20 30 50 10 40 30 50 40 30 50
7. 25 29 28 28 30 25 26 28 27 29 26 30
8. rolls of a number cube: 4 1 3 4 2 1 2 5 2 3 5 1 6 1 3 5 6
9. test scores: 100 90 70 60 95 65 85 70 70 75 80 85 75 70 100 90
10. ages of club members: 14 16 14 16 14 13 12 15 16 12 12 15 14 15 15
11. heights of plants (inches): 25 25 20 25 16 20 25 30 25 31 26 28 30

**Display each set of data in a line plot.** 12–15. See back of book.

12. 5 2 1 3 3 6 4 5 4 2
13. 4 2 4 12 8 12 10 6 4 8 6 8 12
14. 7 11 10 10 8 11 9 7 9 8 11 11
15. 17 20 16 17 19 18 17 20 17 18 18 19 18 17

16. **TEST PREP** What is the range of the data below? E
99.2 101.5 97.9 102.1 98.6 100.4 102.2 99.9
**A.** 3.7 **B.** 3.9 **C.** 4.0 **D.** 4.2 **E.** Not here

**Draw a line plot for each frequency table.** 17–20. See back of book.

17.

| Number | 1 | 2 | 3 | 4 | 5 | 6 |
|---|---|---|---|---|---|---|
| Frequency | 2 | 5 | 7 | 8 | 4 | 3 |

18.

| Number | 1 | 2 | 3 | 4 | 5 | 6 |
|---|---|---|---|---|---|---|
| Frequency | 1 | 3 | 5 | 8 | 8 | 5 |

19.

| Number | 1 | 2 | 3 | 4 | 5 | 6 |
|---|---|---|---|---|---|---|
| Frequency | 7 | 5 | 3 | 2 | 6 | 7 |

20.

| Number | 1 | 2 | 3 | 4 | 5 | 6 |
|---|---|---|---|---|---|---|
| Frequency | 5 | 5 | 5 | 5 | 5 | 5 |



## Alternative Assessment

Have groups of students use number cubes or spinners from various board games. Have them record their results and their frequency count resulting from rolling the number cubes and spinning the spinner. Students record their data in a frequency table and as a line plot, and find the range for their data.

1.

| Number | Frequency |
|---|---|
| 0 | 2 |
| 1 | 2 |
| 2 | 2 |
| 3 | 2 |
| 4 | 2 |

**Construct a frequency table from each line plot.** 21–23. See back of book.

21.
```
            X
        X   X       X
X       X   X   X   X
<-+---+---+---+---+---+->
  1   2   3   4   5   6
```

22.
```
X                       X
X         X         X   X
X    X    X    X    X   X
X    X    X    X    X   X
<-+----+----+----+----+----+->
 15   16   17   18   19   20
```

23.
```
X         X              X
X    X    X    X    X    X
X    X    X    X    X    X
X    X    X    X    X    X
<-+----+----+----+----+----+->
 70   75   80   85   90   95
```

24. In the World Series, the first team to win four games is the champion. Sometimes the series lasts for seven games, but sometimes a team is able to win in fewer games. Below are data for 1970–1999. Make a frequency table and use it to find the mode.

Numbers of World Series Games, 1970–1999: 5, 7, 7, 7, 5, 7, 4, 6, 6, 7, 6, 6, 7, 5, 5, 7, 7, 7, 5, 4, 4, 7, 6, 6, 0, 6, 6, 7, 4, 4 See back of book.

25. Use a line plot to display the data at the right. See back of book.

26. Below are the numbers of letters in each of the first twenty-five words of *Alice's Adventures in Wonderland* by Lewis Carroll.
4 3 10 5 3 9 2 3 4 5 2 7 2 3 6 2 3 4 3 2 6 7 2 2 4
 a. Draw a line plot for the data. 26a–b. See back of book.
 b. Make a frequency table.
 c. Find the range. 8

27. Here are the weekly earnings in dollars of the employees at Industrial Enterprises: 320, 320, 320, 400, 400, 400, 400, 400, 400, 480, 480, 480, 720, 720, 720, 1000.
 a. Draw a line plot for the data. 27a–b. See back of book.
 b. Make a frequency table.
 c. Find the range. $680

28. *Mathematical Reasoning* You are given a line plot of the results of a survey. Explain how you could use the line plot to find the number of people who answered the survey. Count the x's.

**Distribution of Gold Medals 1998 Winter Olympics**

| Country | Medals |
|---|---|
| Germany | 12 |
| Norway | 10 |
| Russia | 9 |
| Canada | 6 |
| United States | 6 |
| Netherlands | 5 |
| Japan | 5 |
| Austria | 3 |
| Korea | 3 |
| Italy | 2 |
| Finland | 2 |
| Switzerland | 2 |
| France | 2 |
| Czech Republic | 1 |
| Bulgaria | 1 |

SOURCE: *The World Almanac*

## MIXED REVIEW

**Find the mean, the median, and the mode of each data set.** *(Lesson 3-2)*

29. 12 13 14 16 16 17 18 18 15.5, 16, 16 and 18 30. 8 15 22 9 11 16 20 10 13.875, 13, no mode

**Given that $\triangle LMN \cong \triangle PQR$, complete each statement.** *(Lesson 9-5)*

31. $\angle N \cong$ ■ $\angle R$ 32. $\overline{MN} \cong$ ■ $\overline{QR}$ 33. $PQ =$ ■ $LM$

34. *Measurement* The angle of elevation to the top of a tree from a point 10 ft from the tree's base is 70°. Find the height of the tree. *(Lesson 11-8)* about 27.5 ft

See also Extra Practice section.



2.

| Number | Frequency |
|---|---|
| 1 | 1 |
| 2 | 2 |
| 3 | 1 |
| 4 | 3 |
| 5 | 1 |
| 6 | 2 |
| 7 | 1 |
| 8 | 2 |
| 9 | 1 |

6.

| Number | Frequency |
|---|---|
| 10 | 2 |
| 20 | 1 |
| 30 | 4 |
| 40 | 2 |
| 50 | 3 |

7.

| Number | Frequency |
|---|---|
| 25 | 2 |
| 26 | 2 |
| 27 | 1 |
| 28 | 3 |
| 29 | 2 |
| 30 | 2 |

## Practice

**Draw a line plot for each frequency table. Find the range.**

1.

| Number | 1 | 2 | 3 | 4 | 5 | 6 |
|---|---|---|---|---|---|---|
| Frequency | 2 | 0 | 4 | 1 | 2 | 4 |

range: 5

2.

| Number | 1 | 2 | 3 | 4 | 5 | 6 |
|---|---|---|---|---|---|---|
| Frequency | 4 | 4 | 0 | 0 | 3 | 2 |

range: 5

**Display each set of data in a frequency table.**

3. 5 1 4 6 2 6 4 5 1 3 2 6 4 5 4 6

| Number | 1 | 2 | 3 | 4 | 5 | 6 |
|---|---|---|---|---|---|---|
| Frequency | 2 | 2 | 1 | 4 | 3 | 4 |

4. 4 3 1 2 1 3 3 1 3 2 1

| Number | 1 | 2 | 3 | 4 |
|---|---|---|---|---|
| Frequency | 4 | 2 | 4 | 1 |

**Construct a frequency table from the line plot.**

5. State Average Pupils per Teacher

| Pupils per Teacher | 14 | 15 | 16 | 17 | 18 | 19 | 20 | 21 | 22 | 23 | 24 |
|---|---|---|---|---|---|---|---|---|---|---|---|
| Frequency | 6 | 7 | 10 | 13 | 4 | 4 | 4 | 0 | 0 | 0 | 2 |

6. What is the range in pupil-teacher ratios? 10 pupils per teacher



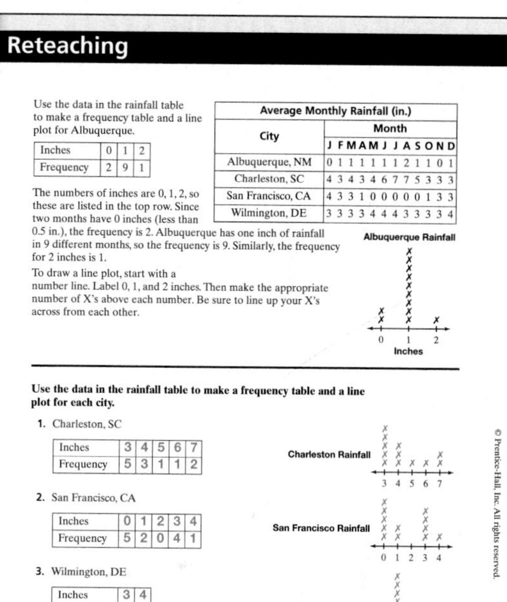

## Reteaching

Use the data in the rainfall table to make a frequency table and a line plot for Albuquerque.

| Inches | 0 | 1 | 2 |
|---|---|---|---|
| Frequency | 2 | 9 | 1 |

**Average Monthly Rainfall (in.)**

| City | J | F | M | A | M | J | J | A | S | O | N | D |
|---|---|---|---|---|---|---|---|---|---|---|---|---|
| Albuquerque, NM | 0 | 1 | 1 | 1 | 1 | 1 | 1 | 2 | 1 | 1 | 0 | 1 |
| Charleston, SC | 4 | 3 | 4 | 3 | 4 | 6 | 7 | 7 | 5 | 3 | 3 | 3 |
| San Francisco, CA | 4 | 3 | 3 | 1 | 0 | 0 | 0 | 0 | 0 | 1 | 3 | 3 |
| Wilmington, DE | 3 | 3 | 3 | 3 | 4 | 4 | 4 | 3 | 3 | 3 | 3 | 4 |

The numbers of inches are 0, 1, 2, so these are listed in the top row. Since two months have 0 inches (less than 0.5 in.), the frequency is 2. Albuquerque has one inch of rainfall in 9 different months, so the frequency is 9. Similarly, the frequency for 2 inches is 1.

To draw a line plot, start with a number line. Label 0, 1, and 2 inches. Then make the appropriate number of X's above each number. Be sure to line up your X's across from each other.

Albuquerque Rainfall (Inches: 0, 1, 2)

**Use the data in the rainfall table to make a frequency table and a line plot for each city.**

1. Charleston, SC

| Inches | 3 | 4 | 5 | 6 | 7 |
|---|---|---|---|---|---|
| Frequency | 5 | 3 | 1 | 1 | 2 |

Charleston Rainfall

2. San Francisco, CA

| Inches | 0 | 1 | 2 | 3 | 4 |
|---|---|---|---|---|---|
| Frequency | 5 | 2 | 0 | 4 | 1 |

San Francisco Rainfall

3. Wilmington, DE

| Inches | 3 | 4 |
|---|---|---|
| Frequency | 8 | 4 |

Wilmington Rainfall



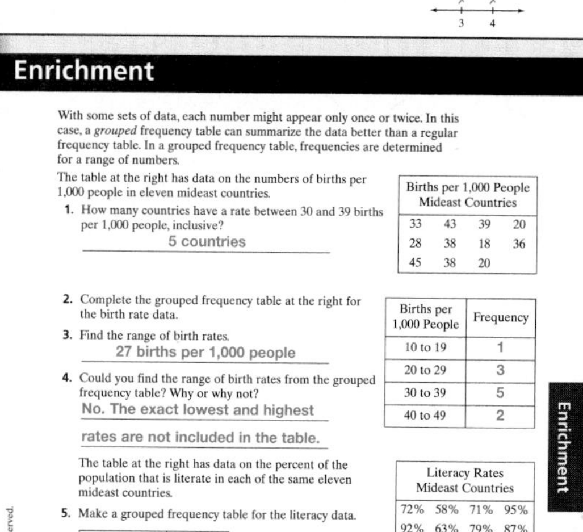

## Enrichment

With some sets of data, each number might appear only once or twice. In this case, a *grouped* frequency table can summarize the data better than a regular frequency table. In a grouped frequency table, frequencies are determined for a range of numbers.

The table at the right has data on the numbers of births per 1,000 people in eleven mideast countries.

**Births per 1,000 People Mideast Countries**

| | | | |
|---|---|---|---|
| 33 | 43 | 39 | 20 |
| 28 | 38 | 18 | 36 |
| 45 | 38 | 20 | |

1. How many countries have a rate between 30 and 39 births per 1,000 people, inclusive? 5 countries
2. Complete the grouped frequency table at the right for the birth rate data.
3. Find the range of birth rates. 27 births per 1,000 people
4. Could you find the range of birth rates from the grouped frequency table? Why or why not? No. The exact lowest and highest rates are not included in the table.

| Births per 1,000 People | Frequency |
|---|---|
| 10 to 19 | 1 |
| 20 to 29 | 3 |
| 30 to 39 | 5 |
| 40 to 49 | 2 |

The table at the right has data on the percent of the population that is literate in each of the same eleven mideast countries.

**Literacy Rates Mideast Countries**

| | | | |
|---|---|---|---|
| 72% | 58% | 71% | 95% |
| 92% | 63% | 79% | 87% |
| 43% | 59% | 79% | |

5. Make a grouped frequency table for the literacy data.

| Literacy Rate | Frequency |
|---|---|
| 40–49% | 1 |
| 50–59% | 2 |
| 60–69% | 1 |
| 70–79% | 4 |
| 80–89% | 1 |
| 90–99% | 2 |

# MATH TOOLBOX

## Making Histograms

This Math Toolbox shows students how to use a graphing calculator to make a histogram.

## Math Background

A histogram is a bar graph (or column graph) that has no spaces between the bars. Before you begin to do any problem with a graphing calculator, first clear all old numbers and data so that the memory is empty. When you use a calculator to do statistics, you first put it into statistics mode so that all the numbers that follow will be interpreted as data points rather than simply as numbers for calculations.

Since the designs of graphing calculators differ, discuss with your students the keystrokes on their calculators.

## Teaching Notes

**Error Prevention** With students in pairs, ask one to be the *coach* and the other to be the *athlete.* The coach carefully watches the athlete press the sequence of keys on the calculator, pointing out any errors for correction. They then exchange roles.

**Monitoring Progress** Exercises 1–4 After each exercise, have students compare results and correct their work to make sure they are on track.

**Block Scheduling** If you have block scheduling or extended periods, you may wish to insert this Math Toolbox lesson between the completion of Part 1 of Lesson 12-1 and the beginning of Part 2 of Lesson 12-1.

# MATH TOOLBOX

Technology
After Lesson 12-1

## Making Histograms

A histogram shows the frequencies of data items as a graph. You can use a graphing calculator to make a histogram.

### EXAMPLE

**Make a histogram of the data below.**
**21, 23, 20, 22, 23, 21, 24, 26, 23, 21, 20, 23, 21, 23, 20, 24**

**Step 1** Press STAT ENTER to set up lists for the data. If necessary, press ▲ CLEAR ENTER to clear an old list. Enter the data under L1, pressing ENTER after each item.

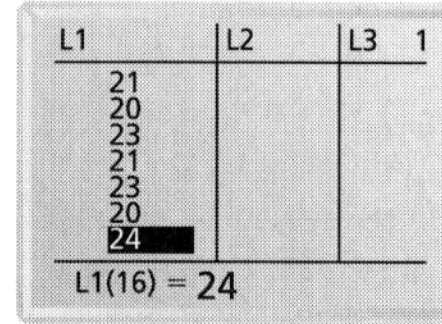


**Step 2** Press 2nd Y= to use the StatPlot feature. Press ENTER. Use the arrow keys and ENTER to select **On** and to select a histogram in the **Type:** row.

**Step 3** Press ZOOM 9 to graph the histogram.

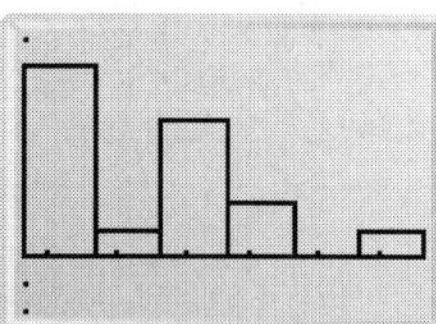

**Step 4** To see the frequency of each number, press WINDOW and set Xscl = 1. Then press GRAPH. Sketch the histogram.

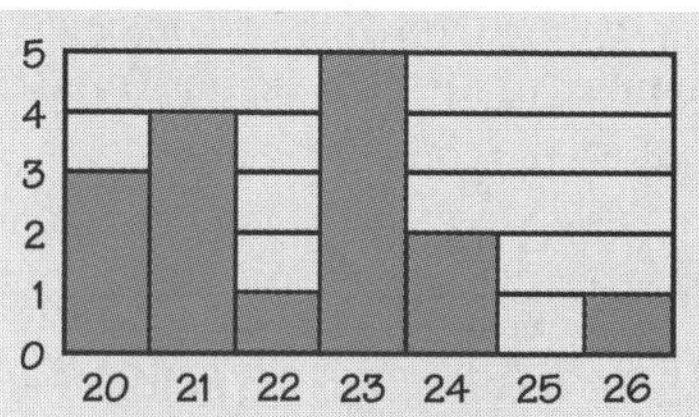


**Use a graphing calculator to make a histogram of each set of data. Then sketch the histogram.** 1–4. See margin.

1. 11, 12, 12, 11, 10, 12, 13, 15, 9, 10, 12, 13
2. 9, 7, 6, 9, 8, 5, 9, 2, 2, 5, 8, 4, 6, 3, 8, 7, 8, 5
3. 23, 26, 25, 26, 23, 25, 25, 24, 21, 21, 22, 23
4. 95, 90, 92, 91, 95, 94, 93, 92, 94, 93, 95, 91

612 Math Toolbox

• **Additional Example**

Make a histogram of the number of pets that each person in your class has. **Have students compare their work to check for reasonableness.**

1.

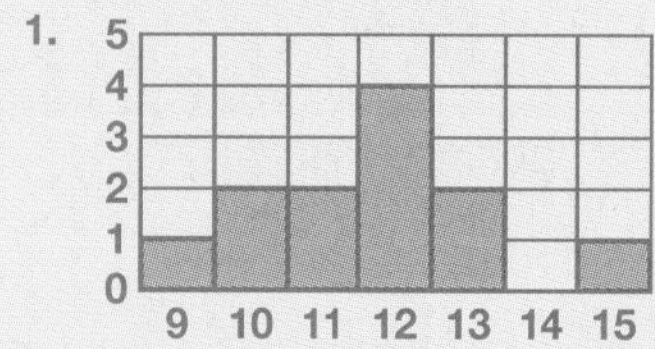


2.

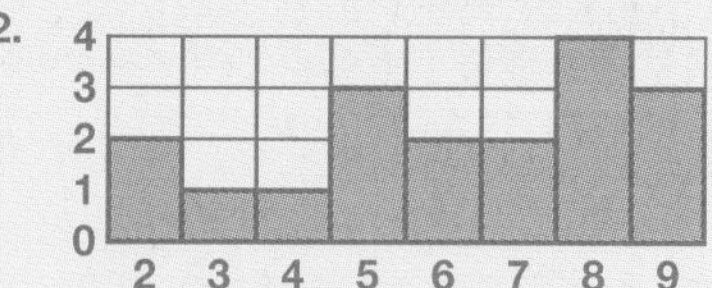


3.

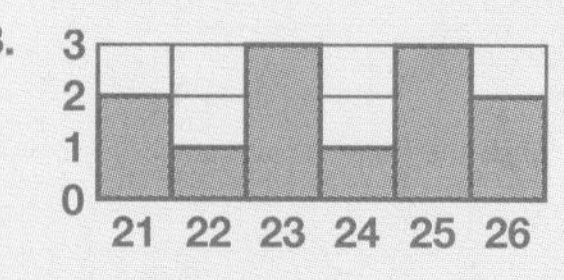


4.

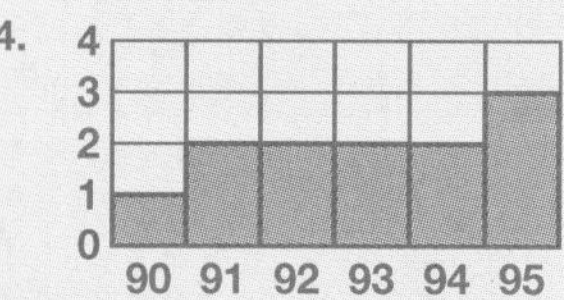

# Box-and-Whisker Plots

12-2

## Part 1 Making Box-and-Whisker Plots

A **box-and-whisker plot** displays the distribution of data items along a number line. **Quartiles** divide the data into four equal parts. The median is the middle quartile.

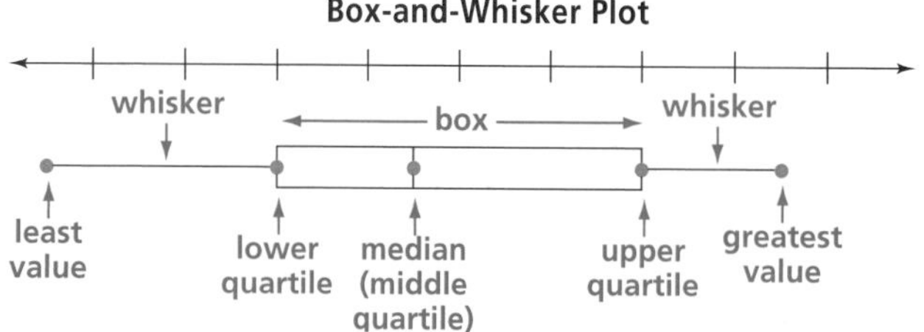


### What You'll Learn

1. To make box-and-whisker plots
2. To analyze data in box-and-whisker plots

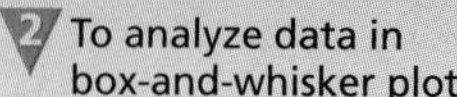

### . . . And Why

To analyze large data sets, such as crop acreages and animal weights

REAL-WORLD  CONNECTION

### Example 1

*Statistics* **Use the data at the right to make a box-and-whisker plot for crops harvested in the years 1985–1997.**

**Step 1** Arrange the data in order from least to greatest. Find the median.

293 298 308 314 316 317 318 318 321 322 326 333 342

**Step 2** Find the lower quartile and upper quartile, which are the medians of the lower and upper halves.

293 298 308 314 316 317 318 318 321 322 326 333 342

lower quartile $= \frac{308 + 314}{2} = \frac{622}{2} = 311$

upper quartile $= \frac{322 + 326}{2} = \frac{648}{2} = 324$

**Step 3** Draw a number line. Mark the least and greatest values, the median, and the quartiles. Draw a box from the first to the third quartiles. Mark the median with a vertical segment. Draw whiskers from the box to the least and greatest values.

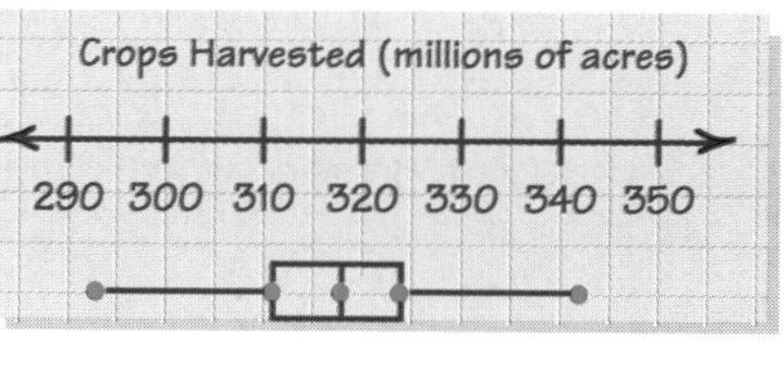


**Crops Harvested in the United States**

| Year | Acres (millions) |
|---|---|
| 1985 | 342 |
| 1986 | 316 |
| 1987 | 293 |
| 1988 | 298 |
| 1989 | 318 |
| 1990 | 322 |
| 1991 | 318 |
| 1992 | 317 |
| 1993 | 308 |
| 1994 | 321 |
| 1995 | 314 |
| 1996 | 326 |
| 1997 | 333 |

SOURCE: *Statistical Abstract of the United States*



# 12-2

## Getting Ready

**Key Terms and Symbols** box-and-whisker plot, quartiles

**Resources** A complete list of resources for this lesson is on p. 605H.

### Daily Skills Warm-Up

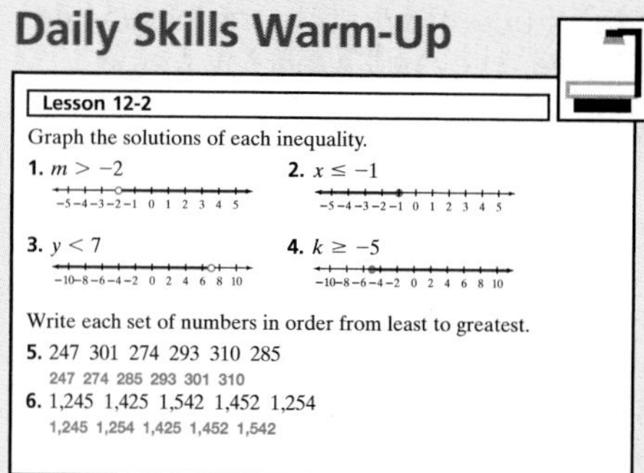

Lesson 12-2

Graph the solutions of each inequality.

1. $m > -2$
2. $x \leq -1$
3. $y < 7$
4. $k \geq -5$

Write each set of numbers in order from least to greatest.

5. 247 301 274 293 310 285
   247 274 285 293 301 310
6. 1,245 1,425 1,542 1,452 1,254
   1,245 1,254 1,425 1,452 1,542

### Background for the Lesson

You can summarize data in a picture by grouping the data in fourths with a *box-and-whisker plot.* The middle two fourths of the data are grouped inside a *box.* You show the first fourth and the last fourth as lines (*whiskers*) extending from the central box. Five points (least value at the left end, first fourth of the data, median of the data, third fourth, and greatest value at the right end) divide the whole line into fourths. The middle point, or *quartile,* is the median of the data. The lower quartile is the median of the lower half of the data and the upper quartile is the median of the upper half of the data.

## 1 Focus

### Connecting to Students' Lives

After a test, students often want to know how many people made A's, B's, and C's. This lesson shows a way to show such comparisons.

### Connecting to Prior Knowledge

In Lesson 12-1, students organized data into line plots. In this lesson, students organize data into box-and-whisker plots. In Lesson 12-3, students will use plots and graphs as tools to persuade.

## Tools to Monitor Progress

### BEFORE THE LESSON

**To check prerequisite skills:**

- Finding the median

**Skills You Need,** p. 605

**Skills Handbook,** p. 723

**Skills Intervention Kit,** Whole Numbers

### DURING THE LESSON

**To check understanding:**

**Try This** exercises on student page

- **Additional Example 1**

Make a box-and-whisker plot for this set of data: 61, 35, 61, 40, 22, 33, 29, 40, 62, 21, 49, 72, 75, 28, 21, 54.

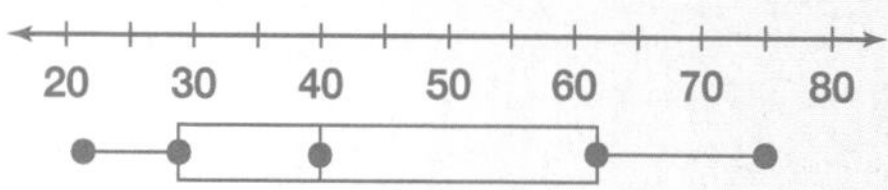

# 2 Teach

## PART 1 Part 1 Teaching Notes

The median of a set of data is the middle value when the data is arranged in order. If there is an even number of data items, add the two middle values and divide by two to find the median. Then include a middle value in the lower quartile when finding a median of the lower quartile. Include a middle value in the upper quartile when finding the median of that quartile.

**ELL** Ask students what the term *quartile* sounds like. They will likely say that it sounds like *quarter.* Tell students that just like quarters are fourths of a dollar, quartiles divide a set of data into fourths.

**Visual Learning** To help students remember the name and form of a box-and-whisker plot, draw a box-and-whisker plot on the board without a number line. Make the box short and the whiskers long so that the box looks like a cat's nose and the lines form whiskers.

### Example 1

**Build understanding.** Ask: Is 318 the median because there were two years where 318 crops were harvested? Explain. **No, 318 is the median because it is the middle value; it also happens to be the mode.**

### Example 2

**Build understanding.** Ask: Does the heaviest orca weigh as much as the lightest hippopotamus? How can you tell? **No; The whiskers on the two plots do not overlap.**

**Math Reasoning** If quartiles divide the data into four equal parts, then why are parts of a box-and-whisker plot usually different sizes? **Quartiles divide the *number* of data items into four equal parts. However, the range of the *values* of the data points in each quarter may be different, which leads to the different sizes.**

**Tactile Learning** Students can use masking tape to make a number line with labels. Then they write each data value on a small card and place the cards where they belong on the line. Use this model to help draw the plot.

### Try This

1. Draw a box-and-whisker plot for the distances of migration of birds (thousands of miles): 5, 2.5, 6, 8, 9, 2, 1, 4, 6.2, 18, 7. **See margin.**

You can compare two sets of data by making two box-and-whisker plots on one number line.

### Example 2

*Biology* **Use box-and-whisker plots to compare orca whale masses and hippopotamus masses.**

**Orca whale masses (kg)**

3,900 2,750 2,600 3,100 4,200 2,600 3,700 3,000 2,200

**Hippopotamus masses (kg)**

1,800 2,000 3,000 2,500 3,600 2,700 1,900 3,100 2,300

Draw a number line for both sets of data. Use the range of data points to choose a scale.

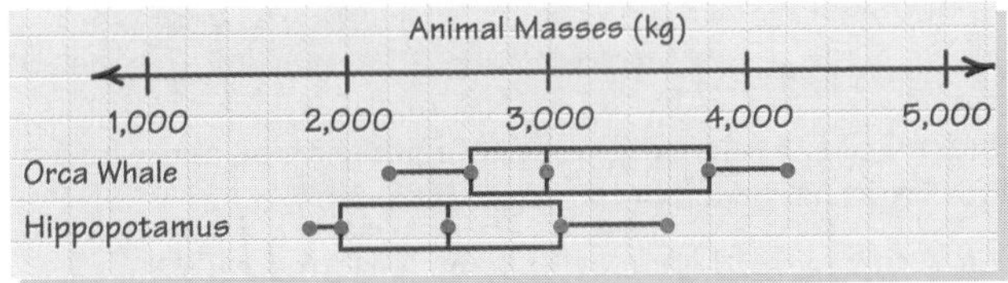


Draw the second box-and-whisker plot below the first one.

DNA evidence suggests that whales and hippopotamuses are closely related genetically.

### Try This

2. Compare annual video sales and album sales by making two box-and-whisker plots on one number line. **See margin.**

   videos (millions of units): 28, 24, 15, 21, 22, 16, 22, 30, 24, 17

   albums (millions of units): 16, 17, 22, 16, 18, 24, 15, 16, 25, 18

## PART 2 Analyzing Box-and-Whisker Plots

Although you cannot see every data point in a box-and-whisker plot, you can use the quartiles and the greatest and least values to analyze a data set.



### • Additional Example 2

Use box-and-whisker plots to compare test scores from two math classes.

**Class A**: 92, 84, 76, 68, 90, 67, 82, 71, 79, 85, 79

**Class B**: 78, 93, 81, 98, 69, 95, 74, 87, 81, 75, 83

60 70 80 90 100

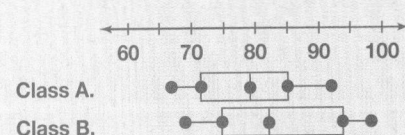

Class A.

Class B.

### • Additional Examples 3–4

**Percentage of students who were eligible and participated in extracurricular activities from 1995 to 2000**

40 50 60 70 80 90 100

eligible

participated

a. Describe the data for the percentage of students who were

## Example 3

**Describe the data in the box-and-whisker plot at the right.**

The highest score is 90 and the lowest is 50. At least half of the scores are within 10 points of the median, 75. Since the median is not in the center of the box, the scores are not evenly distributed.

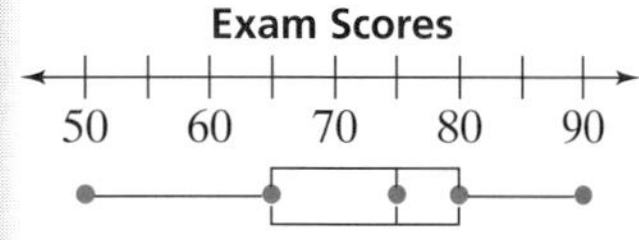


**Try This** Describe the data in each box-and-whisker plot.

3. 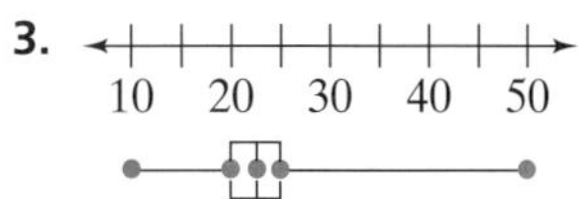


4. 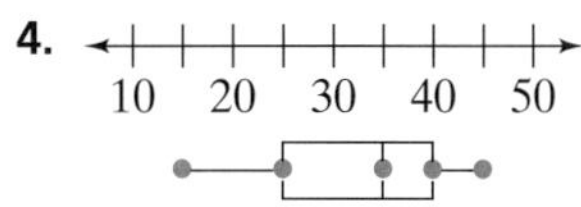


3. The values range from 10 to 50. The median is 22.5. At least half of the values are within 2.5 units of the median.
4. The values range from 15 to 45. The median is 35. At least half of the values are within 10 units of the median.

You can compare box-and-whisker plots to analyze two sets of data.

**DATA ANALYSIS** CONNECTION

## Example 4

*Social Studies* **The plots below compare the percents of the voting-age population who said they registered to vote in U.S. elections to the percents who said they voted. What conclusions can you draw?**

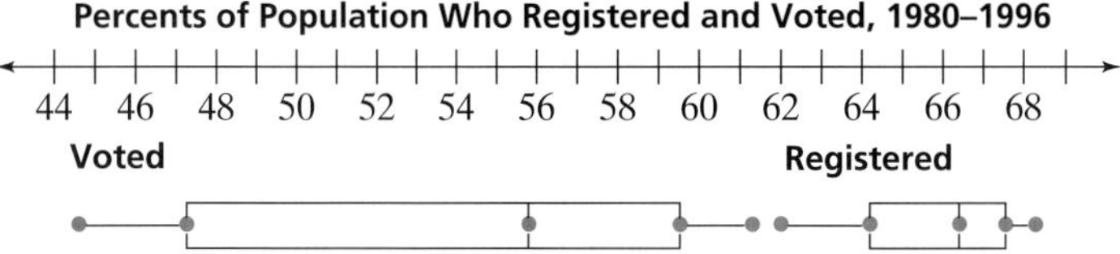


The percent registered was fairly constant, since the box-and-whisker plot is narrow. The percent who voted varied more, but it was always less than the percent who registered. Therefore, you can conclude that many who were registered did not vote.

5. The women's heights have a median of 71 in. and a range of only 10 in. The men's heights have a median of 79 in. and a range of 12 in. Most of the men are taller than the tallest woman.

**Try This**

5. Use the box-and-whisker plots below. What conclusions can you draw about heights of Olympic basketball players?

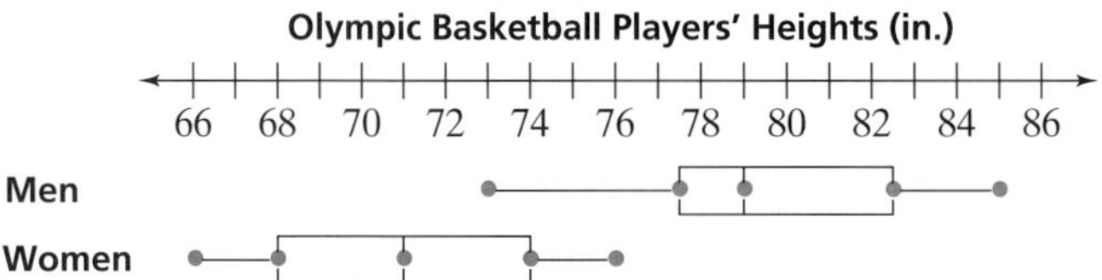




## Part 2 Teaching Notes

Have students list the things that they know about a set of data just from looking at a box-and-whisker plot. Discuss how these things could help make a comparison between two sets of data.

### Example 3

**Build understanding.** Ask: What are the only two exam scores that you can be certain are part of the data set? **50 and 90, the lowest and highest scores indicated by the ends of the whiskers**

**Extension** Explain why you can't be sure from looking at a box-and-whisker plot that the median and quartiles are actual data values from the data set. **If the number of data values in the set is even, then the median is the average of the two middle data points, which may not be an actual data point.**

**Error Prevention** Suggest that students copy the plots onto their paper, and then label the points. Finally, label the percentages represented by the box and whiskers.

### Example 4

**Build understanding.** Ask: What is the median percentage of people registered to vote? What is the median percentage of people who actually voted? **about 66%; about 56%**

**Auditory Learning** Have partners take turns explaining to each other all the parts of the plots in the examples.

1. 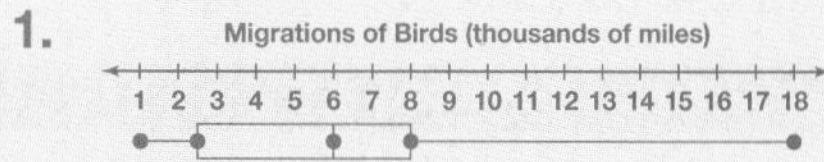


2. 

eligible for extra-curricular activities. **highest and lowest percentages: 100 and 85; 25% above about 97; 25% below about 89; half between about 89 and 97 and within 6 percentage points of the median, 95**
**b.** Draw conclusions by comparing the percentages of students who were eligible and who participated. **The percentages of students who participated were always less than the number who were eligible, and they varied more.**

### AFTER THE LESSON

**To assess knowledge:**

**Lesson Quiz**

Make a box-and-whisker plot for the data.

1. student heights (in.): 60, 66, 59, 67, 68, 63, 62, 61, 69, 64, 61 **See right.**
2. What is the median height? **63 in.**
3. Between what heights do 50% of the students fall? **between 61 and 67 in.**

- For enrichment and reteaching options see Resources on p. 605H.

1. 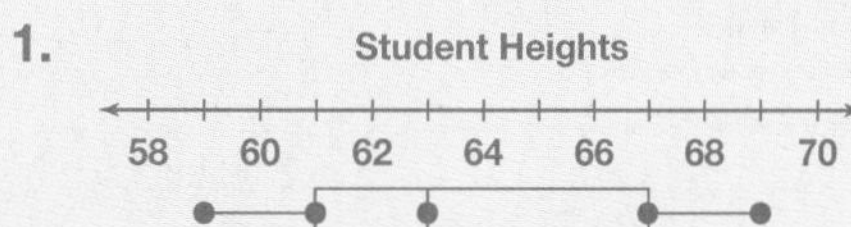

# 3 Practice/Assess

## Assignment Guide

To provide flexible scheduling, this lesson can be divided into parts.

**▼ Part 1**
Core 1–2, 8–14, 17
✪ Extension 16

**▼ Part 2**
Core 3–7, 15, 18, 20
✪ Extension 21

Mixed Review can be assigned at any time for maintenance.

### Exercises

**Exercise 15** Recall that quartiles are points on the line.

**Exercise 20** Note that for the ages of the men players the median of the data is 22 and the median of the upper quartile is also 22.

### ✪ Challenge

Suppose you want to create box-and-whisker plots to compare two sets of data. However, the data points all fall between two whole numbers on the number line. How can you make the plots meaningful? Change the scale on the number line so that you can plot fractions of a whole number.

### Closure

A box-and-whisker plot displays data items below a number line. Quartiles divide the data into four parts. The median is the middle quartile. You can compare two sets of related data by making two box-and-whisker plots.

### Daily Cumulative Review

**Display each set of data in a frequency table.** *(Lesson 12-1)*

1. 77 79 78 77 80 75 76 79 77 75 78 77
2. 13 14 14 14 15 13 14 12 13 13 15 16 15 14 12

| Number | Frequency |
|---|---|
| 75 | 2 |
| 76 | 1 |
| 77 | 4 |
| 78 | 2 |
| 79 | 2 |
| 80 | 1 |

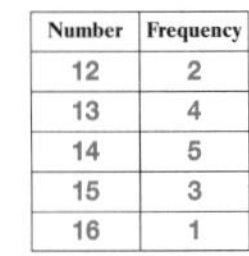

| Number | Frequency |
|---|---|
| 12 | 2 |
| 13 | 4 |
| 14 | 5 |
| 15 | 3 |
| 16 | 1 |

**Solve. Round to the nearest unit.** *(Lesson 11-7)*

3. Scientists determine that a canyon is 4 miles wide. From one rim of the canyon, the angle of depression to the floor of the canyon at the other rim is 37°. How deep is the canyon?

about 3 mi

**Mixed Review**

**Write a rule for each function.**

4. $y = 3x - 2$

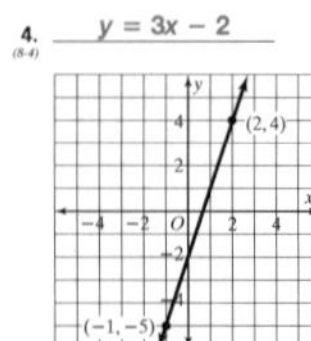


5. $y = -\frac{2}{3}x + 1$

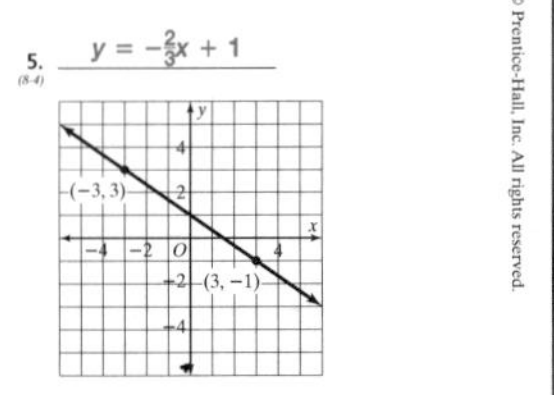






# Exercises

## Check Understanding

**Make a box-and-whisker plot for each set of data.**

1. 16, 18, 59, 75, 30, 34, 25, 49, 27, 16, 21, 58, 71, 19, 50
2. 138, 149, 200, 101, 128, 196, 186, 150, 129, 176, 192, 190
See below right.

1.
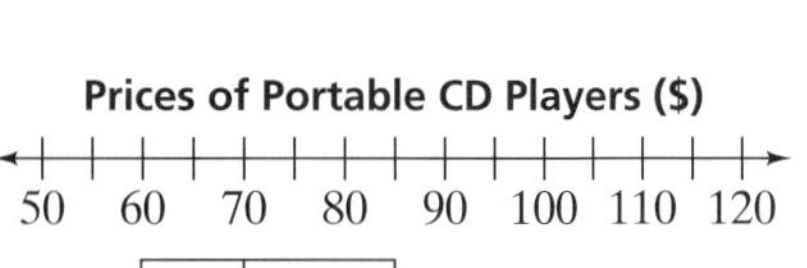


**Use the box-and-whisker plot to answer each question.**

Prices of Portable CD Players ($)

50 60 70 80 90 100 110 120

3. What are the highest and lowest prices for the CD players? $115, $50
4. What is the median price? $70
5. What is the lower quartile price? $60
6. What is the upper quartile price? $85
7. Are the prices evenly distributed? Explain.
No; the median is not in the middle of the box.

2.
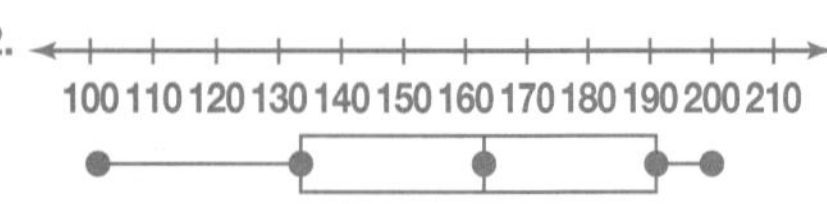


## Practice and Problem Solving

**Make a box-and-whisker plot for each set of data.** 8–11. See margin.

8. flamingo heights (cm):
92, 101, 96, 85, 126, 124, 116, 97, 109
9. wingspans of eagles (m):
2.3, 2, 2.5, 2.1, 1.9, 1.7, 2.2, 2.3, 2, 2.4
10. wingspans of butterflies (mm):
90, 100, 35, 90, 10, 30, 35, 60, 37, 63, 18, 38
11. numbers of pages in books:
205, 198, 312, 258, 185, 268, 279, 242, 356

**Use box-and-whisker plots to compare data sets. Use a single number line for each comparison.**

12. first set: 12, 16, 62, 48, 16, 59, 43
second set: 34, 92, 73, 71, 59, 68, 49
13. first set: 36, 9, 4, 3, 12, 29, 50, 16, 25, 21
second set: 18, 22, 7, 4, 11, 16, 40, 18, 33, 9
14. first set: 3, 7, 9, 12, 2, 1, 6, 5, 4, 3, 7, 10, 13, 8, 1, 9
second set: 9, 8, 1, 7, 6, 3, 7, 9, 8, 6, 4, 7, 8, 9, 10, 10
See below right.
15. *Writing* Explain how you can find the quartiles of a set of data.
✪16. *Open-ended* Write a set of data that has a wide box and narrow whiskers. Check students' work.

12. 5 10 15 20 25 30 35 40 45 50 55 60 65 70 75 80 85 90 95
1st set
2nd set

13. 0 5 10 15 20 25 30 35 40 45 50 55 60
1st set
2nd set

15. The lower quartile is the median of the lower half of the data; the upper quartile is the median of the upper half of the data. The middle quartile is the median of the data.

14. 0 1 2 3 4 5 6 7 8 9 10 11 12 13 14 15 16
1st set
2nd set



## Alternative Assessment

Have students find data from newspapers or magazines that they can represent with a box-and-whisker plot. Have students cut or photocopy the article from which they got their data, create the plot, and then share the article and plot with the class.

8.
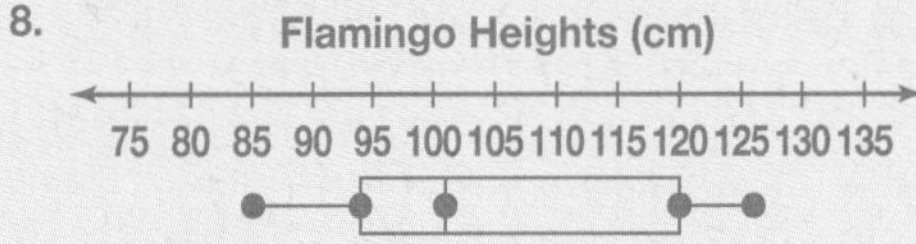


9.
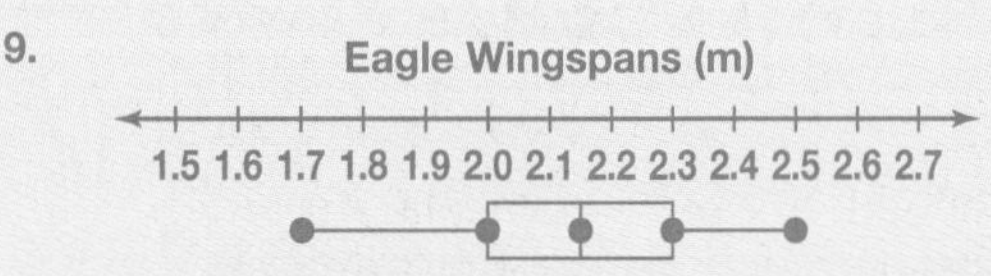


10.
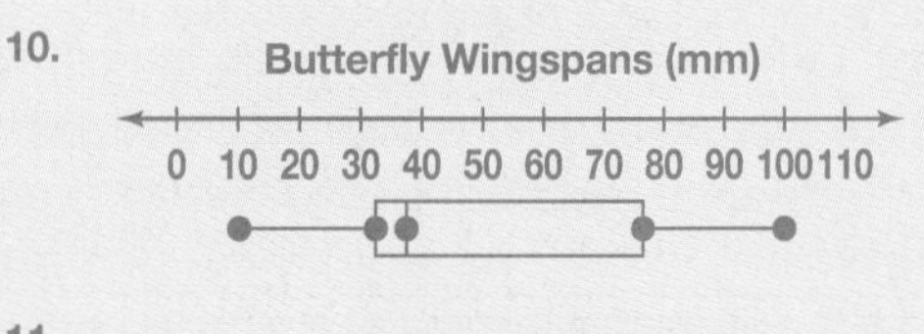


11.
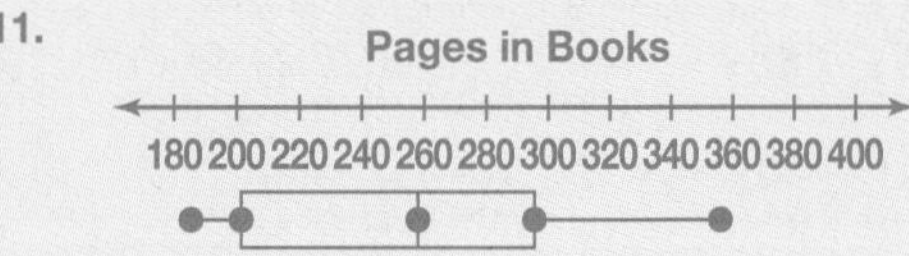

17. *Biology* Use the data at the right to make a box-and-whisker plot for the maximum speeds of animals. See margin.

18. *Error Analysis* A student made a box-and-whisker plot. The student marked the greatest and least data values and then divided the distance between those points into four equal parts. What error did the student make? See below.

19. Use the box-and-whisker plot below. What can you conclude about acreages of state parks? See below.

**Areas of State Parks (acres)**

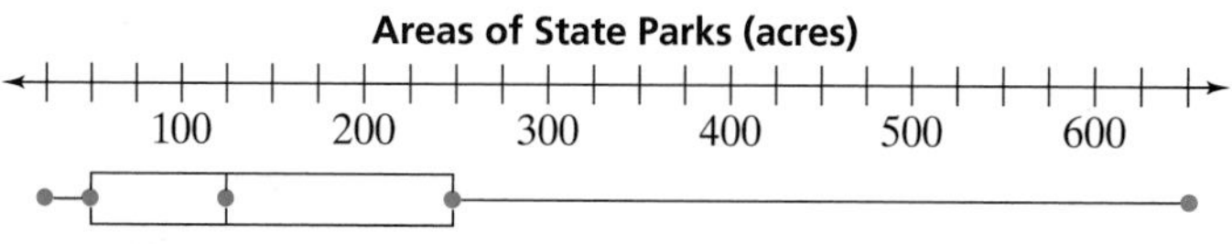


**Maximum Speeds of Animals for a Quarter Mile**

| Animal | Maximum Speed (mi/h) |
|---|---|
| Cheetah | 70 |
| Lion | 50 |
| Quarter horse | 47.5 |
| Coyote | 43 |
| Hyena | 40 |
| Rabbit | 35 |
| Giraffe | 32 |
| Grizzly bear | 30 |
| Cat (domestic) | 30 |
| Elephant | 25 |
| Squirrel | 12 |

SOURCE: *The World Almanac*

20. a. Use the data below to make two box-and-whisker plots on one number line. See margin.

**Ages of U.S. Olympic Soccer Team Players**

**men:** 22, 21, 22, 26, 20, 26, 23, 21, 22, 22, 22, 22, 21, 22, 23, 21, 20, 22

**women:** 30, 27, 28, 25, 31, 24, 31, 24, 21, 23, 27, 18, 19, 24, 23, 20

b. Compare the two box-and-whisker plots. What can you conclude?

21. *Mathematical Reasoning* Can you find the mean, median, and mode of a set of data by looking at a box-and-whisker plot? Explain. The median can be determined from the line across the box. The mean and mode are not indicated, and the detailed data to calculate them is not shown in the plot.

18. The student divided the total range into four equal parts. It is the number of data points that should be divided into four equal parts.

19. The acreages vary considerably, from about 25 acres to about 650 acres. However, most of the parks are between 50 and 250 acres, with a median of 125 acres.

## MIXED REVIEW

**Display each set of data in a frequency table.** ***(Lesson 12-1)***

22. 6 8 7 6 5 8 5 6 4 8 7 5 4 7 6 8 6 7
See below.

23. 32 31 29 33 31 32 35 33 32 31 32 30
See margin.

**Find the distance between each pair of points.** ***(Lesson 11-3)***

24. $D(3, -2), S(-3, 2)$ 7.2

25. $A(0, 4), W(-7, -5)$ 11.4

26. $Y(6, 4), K(-1, 3)$ 7.1

27. $Z(9, 0), M(-8, 11)$ 20.2

28. Lawns can have 850 blades of grass per square foot.

a. A grass lawn is 3 yd by 6 yd. About how many blades of grass are in the yard? ***(Lesson 10-1)*** 137,700 blades of grass

b. The area of all the lawns in the United States equals an area twice as large as that of Pennsylvania. Pennsylvania's area is 46,058 mi$^2$. Estimate the number of blades of grass in lawns in the United States. Write your answer in scientific notation. (*Hint*: A mile equals 5,280 feet.) ***(Lesson 4-9)*** $2.18 \times 10^{15}$ blades of grass

22.

| Number | Frequency |
|---|---|
| 4 | 2 |
| 5 | 3 |
| 6 | 5 |
| 7 | 4 |
| 8 | 4 |

See also Extra Practice section.



17. **Maximum Speeds of Animals (mi/h)**

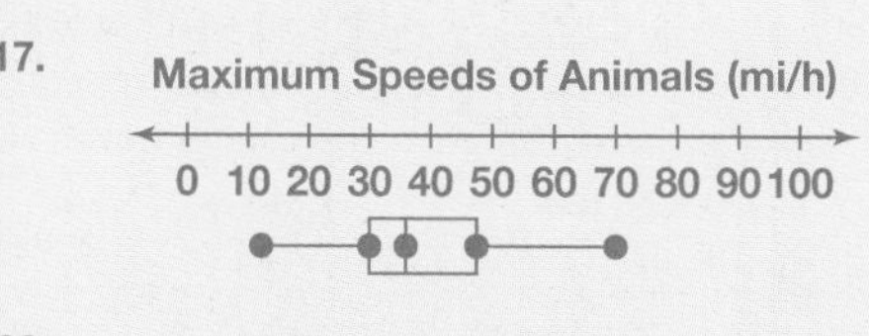


20a. Ages of U.S. Olympic Soccer Team Players

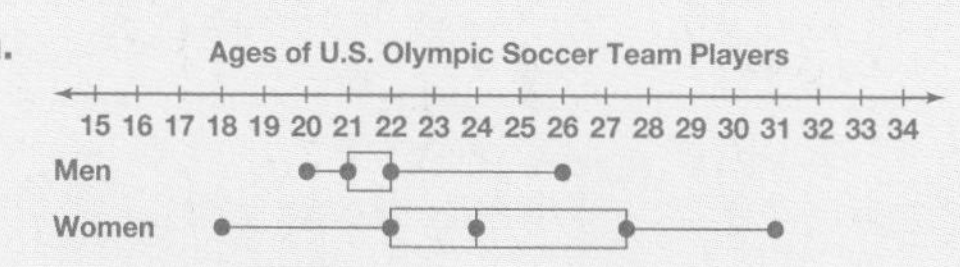


b. The men are all from 20 to 26 years old, and 50% are aged 21 to 22. The upper quartile also is 22. The women's ages are much more spread out, ranging from 18 to 31. The median age for women is two years greater than the median age for men.

23.

| Number | Frequency |
|---|---|
| 29 | 1 |
| 30 | 1 |
| 31 | 3 |
| 32 | 4 |
| 33 | 2 |
| 34 | 0 |
| 35 | 1 |

## Practice

**Use the box-and-whisker plot to answer each question.**

**Weekly Mileage Totals, 24 Runners**

10 15 20 25 30 35 40 45 50 55 60

1. What is the highest weekly total? 55 miles the lowest? 15 miles
2. What is the median weekly total? 35 miles
3. What percent of runners run less than 40 miles a week? 75%
4. How many runners run less than 20 miles a week? 6 runners

**Make a box-and-whisker plot for each set of data.**

5. 16 20 30 15 23 11 15 21 30 29 13 16 (10 15 20 25 30)
6. 9 12 10 3 2 3 9 11 5 1 10 4 7 12 3 10 (0 5 10 15)
7. 70 77 67 65 79 82 70 68 75 73 69 66 70 73 89 72 (60 65 70 75 80 85 90)

**Use box-and-whisker plots to compare data sets. Use a single number line for each comparison.**

8. 1st set: 7 12 25 3 1 29 30 7 15 2 5 10 29 1 10 30 18 8 7 29
2nd set: 37 17 14 43 27 19 32 1 8 48 26 16 28 6 25 18
(0 5 10 15 20 25 30 35 40 45 50; 1st Set; 2nd Set)

9. Area in 1,000 mi$^2$
midwestern states:
45 36 58 97 56 65 87 82 77
southern states:
52 59 48 52 42 32 54 43 70 53 66
(30 40 50 60 70 80 90 100; Midwestern States; Southern States)



## Reteaching

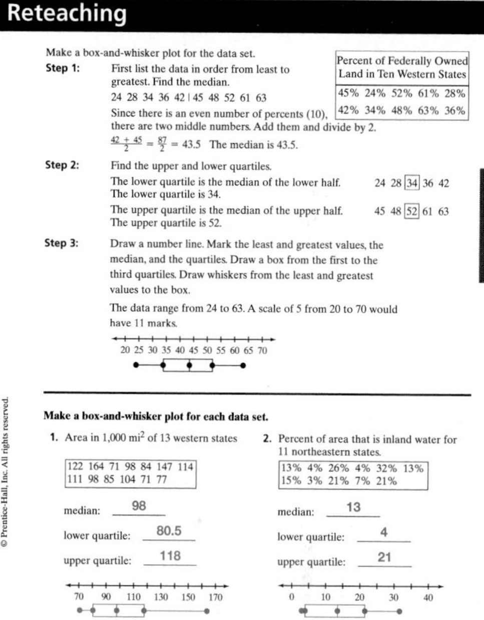

Make a box-and-whisker plot for the data set.

| Percent of Federally Owned Land in Ten Western States | | | | |
|---|---|---|---|---|
| 45% | 24% | 52% | 61% | 28% |
| 42% | 34% | 48% | 63% | 36% |

**Step 1:** First list the data in order from least to greatest. Find the median.
24 28 34 36 42 | 45 48 52 61 63
Since there is an even number of percents (10), there are two middle numbers. Add them and divide by 2.
$\frac{42 + 45}{2} = \frac{87}{2} = 43.5$ The median is 43.5.

**Step 2:** Find the upper and lower quartiles.
The lower quartile is the median of the lower half. 24 28 [34] 36 42
The lower quartile is 34.
The upper quartile is the median of the upper half. 45 48 [52] 61 63
The upper quartile is 52.

**Step 3:** Draw a number line. Mark the least and greatest values, the median, and the quartiles. Draw a box from the first to the third quartiles. Draw whiskers from the least and greatest values to the box.

The data range from 24 to 63. A scale of 5 from 20 to 70 would have 11 marks.

20 25 30 35 40 45 50 55 60 65 70

**Make a box-and-whisker plot for each data set.**

1. Area in 1,000 mi$^2$ of 13 western states

122 164 71 98 84 147 114
111 98 85 104 71 77

median: 98
lower quartile: 80.5
upper quartile: 118

70 90 110 130 150 170

2. Percent of area that is inland water for 11 northeastern states.

13% 4% 26% 4% 32% 13%
15% 3% 21% 7% 21%

median: 13
lower quartile: 4
upper quartile: 21

0 10 20 30 40

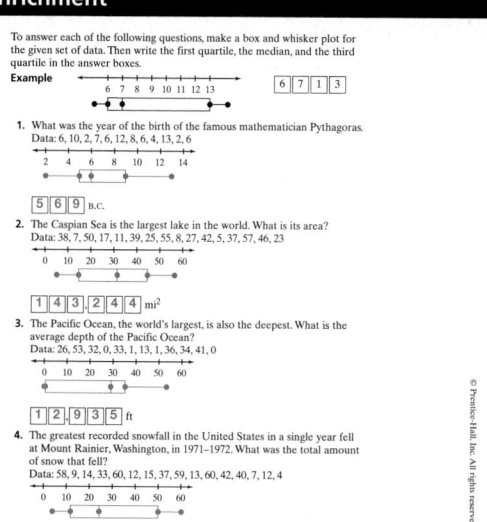

## Enrichment

To answer each of the following questions, make a box and whisker plot for the given set of data. Then write the first quartile, the median, and the third quartile in the answer boxes.

**Example** (6 7 8 9 10 11 12 13) [6][7][1][3]

1. What was the year of the birth of the famous mathematician Pythagoras.
Data: 6, 10, 2, 7, 6, 12, 8, 6, 4, 13, 2, 6
(2 4 6 8 10 12 14)
[5][6][9] B.C.

2. The Caspian Sea is the largest lake in the world. What is its area?
Data: 38, 7, 50, 17, 11, 39, 25, 55, 8, 27, 42, 5, 37, 57, 46, 23
(0 10 20 30 40 50 60)
[1][4][3],[2][4][4] mi$^2$

3. The Pacific Ocean, the world's largest, is also the deepest. What is the average depth of the Pacific Ocean?
Data: 26, 53, 32, 0, 33, 1, 13, 1, 36, 34, 41, 0
(0 10 20 30 40 50 60)
[1][2],[9][3][5] ft

4. The greatest recorded snowfall in the United States in a single year fell at Mount Rainier, Washington, in 1971–1972. What was the total amount of snow that fell?
Data: 58, 9, 14, 33, 60, 12, 15, 37, 59, 13, 60, 42, 40, 7, 12, 4
(0 10 20 30 40 50 60)
[1],[2][2][4].[5][0] in.

## MATH TOOLBOX

### Stem-and-Leaf Plots

In this Math Toolbox, students learn to make and interpret stem-and-leaf plots.

### Math Background

Stem-and-leaf plots are similar to the box-and-whisper plots that are the subject of Lesson 12-2. You begin plotting both of these with a frequency distribution that arranges the data in order from least to greatest. A stem-and-leaf plot differs from the box-and-whisper plot in that a stem-and-leaf plot is a special kind of table. You arrange the data by separating the last digit (leaves) of each data value from the previous digits (stems) of each value to make two separate lists of the data in order. A back-to-back stem-and-leaf plot uses the same stems but two columns of leaves, one to the left and one to the right of the column that shows the common stems.

## Teaching Notes

**Error Prevention** Copy the data, arrange in order, and circle the last digit, or leaves. Underline the other digits, or stems.

**Monitoring Progress** **Exercise 1** To check understanding, ask which animal has the life span shown by the entry 4|1? hippopotamus

**Block Scheduling** If you have block scheduling or extended periods, you may wish to insert this Math Toolbox lesson between the completion of Part 1 of Lesson 12-3 and the beginning of Part 2 of Lesson 12-3.

## MATH TOOLBOX

Extension
*After Lesson 12-2*

# *Stem-and-Leaf Plots*

A *stem-and-leaf plot* organizes data by showing each item in order. The leaf is the last digit to the right. The stem is the remaining digit or digits.

stem→ 15.7 ←leaf    stem→ 32 ←leaf

### EXAMPLE 1

**Use the table at the right to construct a stem-and-leaf plot. Then find the median, mode, and range.**

**Broadway Productions**

| Season | New Shows |
|---|---|
| 1990–1991 | 28 |
| 1991–1992 | 37 |
| 1992–1993 | 33 |
| 1993–1994 | 37 |
| 1994–1995 | 29 |
| 1995–1996 | 38 |
| 1996–1997 | 37 |
| 1997–1998 | 33 |

SOURCE: *The World Almanac*

Choose the stems. For this data set, use the values in the tens place. Draw a line to the right of the stems.

stems →
2 |
3 |

Leaves are single digits, so for this data set the leaves will be the values in the ones place.

2 | 8 9
3 | 7 3 7 8 7 3
← leaves

Arrange the leaves on each stem from least to greatest. Include a key that shows how to read your stem-and-leaf plot.

**Broadway Productions**

2 | 8 9
3 | 3 3 7 7 7 8

2 | 3 means 23 ← key

Since the data items are in order, the median is the midpoint. The median is the mean of the fourth and fifth items, or 35.

The mode corresponds to the most repeated leaf. The mode is 37.

The range is the difference of the greatest and least values, or 10.

1. *Biology* Use the table at the right.
   a. *Critical Thinking* What number should you use as the stem for the kangaroo and the opossum? 0
   b. Construct a stem-and-leaf plot. See margin.
   c. Find the median. 13.5
   d. Find the mode. 15
   e. Find the range. 40

**Average Longevity**

| Animal | Years | Animal | Years |
|---|---|---|---|
| Grizzly bear | 25 | Hippopotamus | 41 |
| Kangaroo | 7 | Pig | 10 |
| Cow | 15 | Lion | 15 |
| Dog | 12 | Opossum | 1 |
| Giraffe | 10 | Cat | 12 |
| Gorilla | 20 | Zebra | 15 |

SOURCE: *The World Almanac*



- **Additional Example 1**
  Make a stem-and-leaf plot to show the ages of the people in your class.
  Check students' plots.
- **Additional Example 2**
  Make a back-to-back stem-and-leaf plot for the last page number in the hardback books and the paperback books in one shelf of a bookcase in your school or home. Check students' plots.

1b. Animal Life Spans

0 | 1 7
1 | 0 0 2 2 3 5 5
2 | 0 5
3 | 2
4 | 1

1 | 6 means 16

2.

1 | 0 5 5 8
2 | 2 5 8
3 | 5 6

2 | 4 means 24

22, 15, 26

**Make a stem-and-leaf plot for each set of data. Then find the median, the mode, and the range.** 2–5. See margin.

**2.** 15, 22, 25, 10, 36, 15, 28, 35, 18

**3.** 47, 41, 60, 75, 85, 53, 57, 76, 79, 81, 84, 86

**4.** 785, 785, 776, 772, 792, 788, 761, 768, 768

**5.** 4.5, 4.3, 0.8, 3.5, 2.6, 1.4, 0.2, 0.8, 4.3, 6.0

A back-to-back stem-and-leaf plot uses two sets of data. The side-by-side display makes the data easier to compare.

### Example 2

**Draw a back-to-back stem-and-leaf plot for the winning times in the Olympic 100-m dash. Find each median and mode.**

Use seconds for the stem and tenths of seconds for the leaves. Put the leaves in ascending order starting at the stem.

**Winning Times, 100-m Dash**

| Men's Times (tenths of second) | Stem (seconds) | Women's Times (tenths of second) |
|---|---|---|
| 9 9 8 | 9 | |
| 3 2 1 1 0 0 0 | 10 | 5 8 9 |
| | 11 | 0 0 0 1 1 1 4 |

means 10.1 ⟵ 1 | 10 | 5 ⟶ means 10.5

**Winning Times, 100-m Dash (seconds)**

| Year | Men | Women |
|---|---|---|
| 1960 | 10.2 | 11.0 |
| 1964 | 10.0 | 11.4 |
| 1968 | 9.9 | 11.0 |
| 1972 | 10.1 | 11.1 |
| 1976 | 10.1 | 11.1 |
| 1980 | 10.3 | 11.1 |
| 1984 | 10.0 | 11.0 |
| 1988 | 9.9 | 10.5 |
| 1992 | 10.0 | 10.8 |
| 1996 | 9.8 | 10.9 |

SOURCE: *Sports Illustrated Sports Almanac*

The median of the times for men is 10.0 s. The median of the times for women is 11.0 s. The mode of the times for men is 10.0 s. The modes of the times for women are 11.0 s and 11.1 s.

**Make a back-to-back stem-and-leaf plot for each pair of data sets. Then find each median and mode.** 6–7. See margin.

**6.** Set A: 9.1, 8.2, 7.3, 6.4, 7.3, 8.5 Set B: 7.6, 9.2, 8.2, 8.3, 9.7, 7.6

**7.** Set C: 236, 237, 241, 250, 242 Set D: 262, 251, 248, 243, 257

**Use the stem-and-leaf plot at the right. The plot shows the time two classes spent on homework.**

**Time Spent on Homework (min)**

| Class A | | Class B |
|---|---|---|
| 7 4 3 | 6 | 1 1 3 5 5 |
| 9 9 8 5 4 4 | 7 | 0 2 2 4 |
| 5 2 1 0 | 8 | 4 5 8 9 |
| 7 6 6 4 2 | 9 | 3 6 7 9 9 9 |

means 63 ⟵ 3 | 6 | 1 ⟶ means 61

**8.** Which numbers are the stems? 6, 7, 8, and 9

**9.** What is the least time spent for each set of data? See below.

**10.** What is the median for each set of data? See below.

**11.** What is the mode for each set of data? See below.

**12.** What is the range for each set of data? See below.

9. Class A: 63 min; Class B: 61 min 10. Class A: 79.5 min; Class B: 84 min 11. Class A: 74, 79, and 96 min; Class B: 99 min 12. Class A: 34 min; Class B: 38 min



3.

| | |
|---|---|
| 4 | 1 7 |
| 5 | 3 7 |
| 6 | 0 |
| 7 | 5 6 9 |
| 8 | 1 4 5 6 |

7 | 5 means 75

75.5; no mode; 45

4.

| | |
|---|---|
| 76 | 1 8 8 |
| 77 | 2 6 |
| 78 | 5 5 8 |
| 79 | 2 |

76 | 1 means 761

776; 768 and 785; 31

5.

| | |
|---|---|
| 0 | 2 8 8 |
| 1 | 4 |
| 2 | 6 |
| 3 | 5 |
| 4 | 3 3 5 |
| 5 | |
| 6 | 0 |

4 | 3 means 4.3

3.05; 0.8 and 4.3; 5.8

6.

| Set B | | Set A |
|---|---|---|
| | 6 | 4 |
| 6 6 | 7 | 3 3 |
| 3 2 | 8 | 2 5 |
| 7 2 | 9 | 1 |

means 8.3 ⟵ 3 | 8 | 2 ⟶ means 8.2

Set A: 7.75; 7.3
Set B: 8.25; 7.6

7.

| Set D | | Set C |
|---|---|---|
| | 23 | 6 7 |
| 8 3 | 24 | 1 2 |
| 7 1 | 25 | 0 |
| 2 | 26 | |

means 251 ⟵ 1 | 25 | 0 ⟶ means 250

Set C: 241, no mode
Set D: 251, no mode

# 12-3

## Getting Ready

**Resources** A complete list of resources for this lesson is on p. 605H.

### Daily Skills Warm-Up

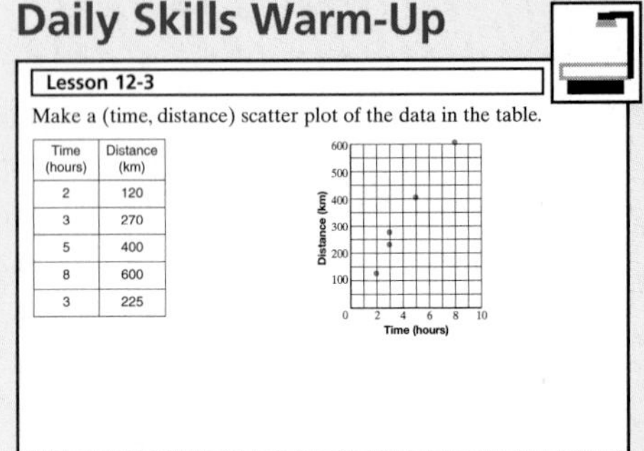

Lesson 12-3

Make a (time, distance) scatter plot of the data in the table.

| Time (hours) | Distance (km) |
|---|---|
| 2 | 120 |
| 3 | 270 |
| 5 | 400 |
| 8 | 600 |
| 3 | 225 |

### Background for the Lesson

Graphs help you compare data because they provide visual representations of the relative sizes. On a bar graph, for example, you can immediately see which bars are longer or shorter than the others. However, to interpret the graph accurately, pay attention to all the labels of the graph: the title, the labels on the axes, and the scales on both axes. Using different scales on the horizontal and vertical axes or a break in the scale can cause the graph to be misleading.

## 1 Focus

### Connecting to Students' Lives

Ask students to describe a graph they have seen. Where was the graph? What kinds of data did it compare?

### Connecting to Prior Knowledge

In Lesson 12-2, students learned how to organize data into box-and-whisker plots. In this lesson, students learn how the scales of graphs can be manipulated to suggest different ideas. In Lesson 12-4, students will learn about another kind of graph—a tree diagram.

# 12-3 Using Graphs to Persuade

**What You'll Learn**

1. To recognize the use of breaks in the scales of graphs
2. To recognize the use of different scales

**. . . And Why**

To interpret graphical data correctly

## PART 1 Using Breaks in Scales

You can use a graph to give different impressions by drawing it in different ways.

When you make a line or bar graph, you can use a break in the scale on one or both axes. Using a break lets you show more detail, but it can also give a distorted picture of the data.

### EXAMPLE 1

*Population* **Which title would be more appropriate for the graph below: "Los Angeles Overwhelms Chicago" or "Populations of Chicago and Los Angeles"? Explain.**

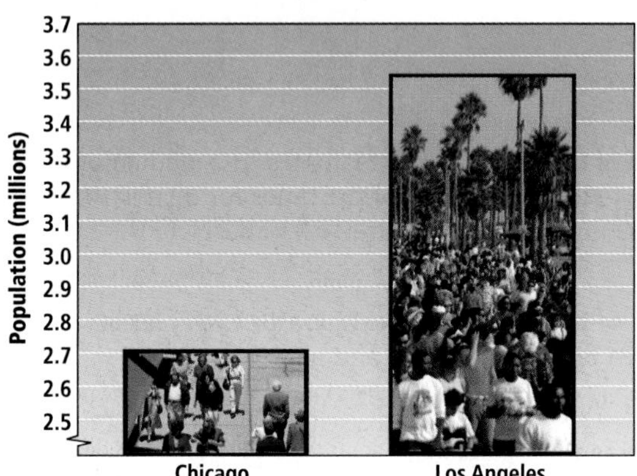


Because of the break in the vertical axis, the bar for Los Angeles appears to be about three times as tall as the bar for Chicago. Actually, the population of Los Angeles is a little less than 3.6 million, and the population of Chicago is about 2.7 million. So the population of Los Angeles is about 1.3 times that of Chicago.

The title "Los Angeles Overwhelms Chicago" could be misleading. "Populations of Chicago and Los Angeles" better describes the information in the graph.



## Tools to Monitor Progress

### BEFORE THE LESSON

**To check prerequisite skills:**

- Comparing and ordering decimals

**Skills Handbook,** p. 728

**Skills Intervention Kit,** Decimals

### DURING THE LESSON

**To check understanding:**

**Try This** exercises on student page

- **Additional Example 3**

  Use the graph on the next page to answer the following question. What are two things that were done to this graph to make the decrease in students who buy lunch look greater?

■ **TRY THIS**

1. Use the data in the graph in Example 1. Redraw the graph without a break.

1. Populations of Chicago and Los Angeles

Population (millions): 0, 1, 2, 3, 4

Chicago L.A.

## Using Different Scales

You can use a graph to give different impressions by choosing longer or shorter spaces between units on the graph's axes.

REAL-WORLD CONNECTION

### ■ EXAMPLE 2

*Cost of Living* **Study the graphs below. Which graph gives the impression of a sharper increase in price? Explain.**

**Average Gasoline Prices**

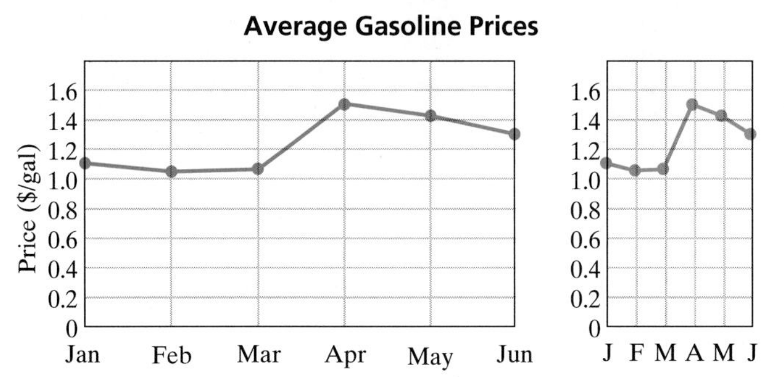


In the graph at the right, the months are much closer together, so the line appears to climb more rapidly. This graph suggests that prices are going up faster than the graph at the left suggests.

■ **TRY THIS** Use the data in the table at the right.

2. Make a graph that suggests a rapid decrease in the total weight of fish caught. See margin p. 622.
3. Make a graph that suggests a slow decrease in the total weight of fish caught. See margin p. 622.
4. *Critical Thinking* A group is planning a campaign to protect the supply of fish. They are proposing a regulation that would limit the number of pounds of fish caught annually. Would they more likely use the graph from Question 2 or Question 3 in their proposal? Explain. Answers may vary. Sample: They would use the graph from Question 2 to show that the supply of fish is decreasing rapidly. Using this graph emphasizes the need for the limit.

**Fish Caught for Food in the U.S.**

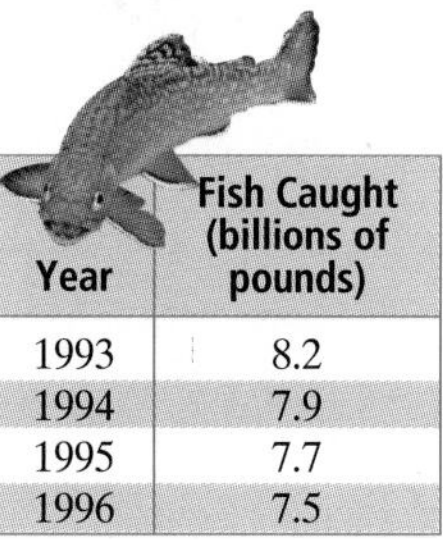

| Year | Fish Caught (billions of pounds) |
|---|---|
| 1993 | 8.2 |
| 1994 | 7.9 |
| 1995 | 7.7 |
| 1996 | 7.5 |

SOURCE: *Statistical Abstract of the United States*



# 2 Teach

## Part 1 Teaching Notes

A break in scale means that the numbers on one or both of the axes is not continuous. When there is a break, the length of the bar or line does not accurately represent the size of the data.

**Visual Learning** Help students use the visual cues on the graph that show a break in the scale, such as a crooked line and a gap.

### ■ Example 1

**Build understanding.** Ask: According to the graph, about how many more people live in Los Angeles than Chicago? about 0.9 million, or 900,000

## Part 2 Teaching Notes

The scale you choose to represent the data can make the *y*-value seem greater or lesser relative to the *x*-value. Choosing a small unit makes the bar longer and the data seem greater than if you choose a large unit.

### ■ Example 2

**Build understanding.** Ask: How can you confirm that the two graphs represent the same data? For each month, the price is the same on both graphs.

**Advanced Learners** Ask students to describe some reasons why a person or group might want to make a graph. Have students share and discuss their ideas with the class.

**Students Who Buy Cafeteria Lunches**

370, 360, 350, 340, 330, 320, 310, 300, 0

1998–1999 1999–2000

It has a break in scale, and the second bar was made narrower than the first bar.

## AFTER THE LESSON

**To assess knowledge: Lesson Quiz**

Name three different techniques you can use to give different impressions when presenting data in a graph.

You can use breaks in scales, longer or shorter spaces between units on the axis, or different-sized bars.

- For enrichment and reteaching options see Resources on p. 605H.

**Error Prevention** Checking to make sure that the data is accurate is especially important when you choose to use different scales because you may accidentally use the wrong scale to draw a point.

**Connecting to Statistics** Newspapers, magazines, and television use graphs to report the results of public opinion polls. Nationwide public opinion polls got their start in the United States in 1935 when George Gallup began asking questions about social issues. Gallup formed the American Institute of Public Opinion, also known as the Gallup Poll, to conduct nationwide public opinion surveys. Since the 1930s, the use of public opinion polls has grown in the United States. News organizations, government agencies, opinion research centers, and universities often sponsor public opinion polls.

## Example 3

**Build understanding.** Ask: Read the scales on the axes of this graph. Can you see any reason why the second bar is wider than the first bar? Explain. The only quantitative difference is on the vertical axis, so there is no reason why the second bar should be wider than the first.

**Extension** Now that students know some of the ways that graphs can be manipulated to suggest different ideas, have students write a set of rules or procedures to follow before drawing conclusions about the information in a graph. Ask students to share their procedures with the class.

Bar graphs can be misleading if their bars change in more than one dimension.

REAL-WORLD CONNECTION

### EXAMPLE 3

*Critical Thinking* **What makes the graph misleading? Explain.**

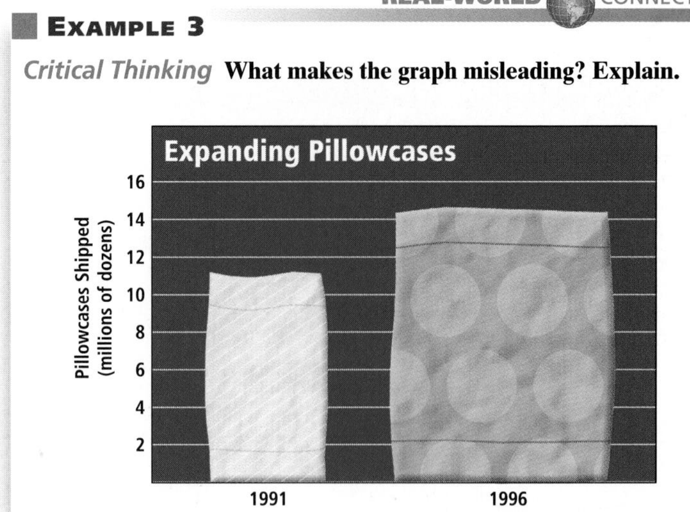


By reading the vertical axis, you can see that the number of pillowcases shipped increased by about one fourth. However, the bar on the right has not only increased in height, but has also nearly doubled in width. Since the area of the second bar is more than two times the area of the first bar, you might get the impression that the increase was much greater than it really was.

6.

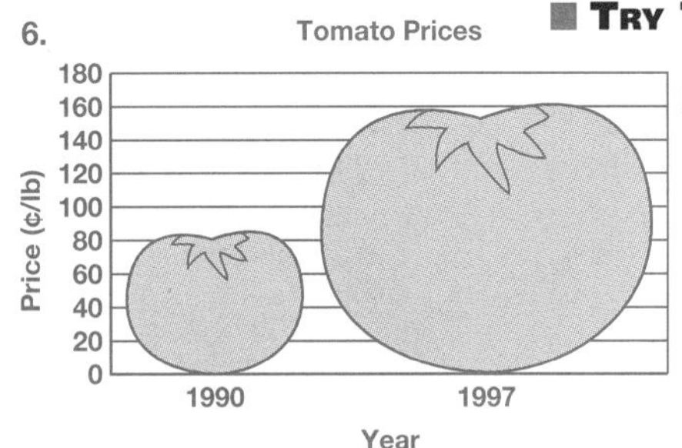


**TRY THIS** Use the data in the table below.

**Prices of Field-Grown Tomatoes in the United States**

| Year | Price of Tomatoes (cents per pound) |
|---|---|
| 1990 | 86 |
| 1997 | 162 |

SOURCE: *Statistical Abstract of the United States*

5.

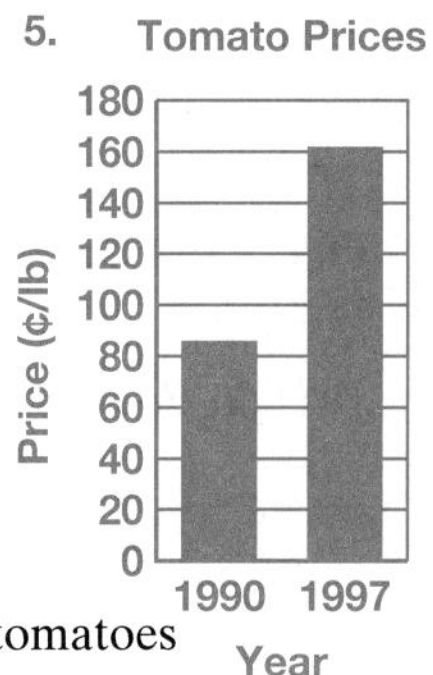


5. Draw a graph that suggests that the price of tomatoes nearly doubled. Answers may vary. See sample at right.
6. Draw a graph that suggests that the price of tomatoes more than doubled. Answers may vary. See sample above left.



2. Answers may vary. Sample:

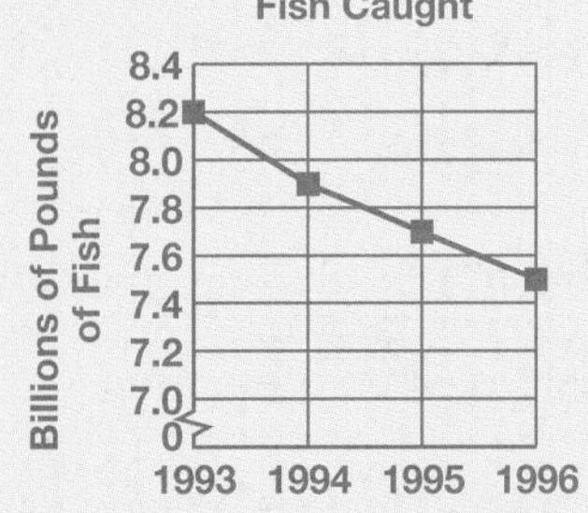


3. Answers may vary. Sample:

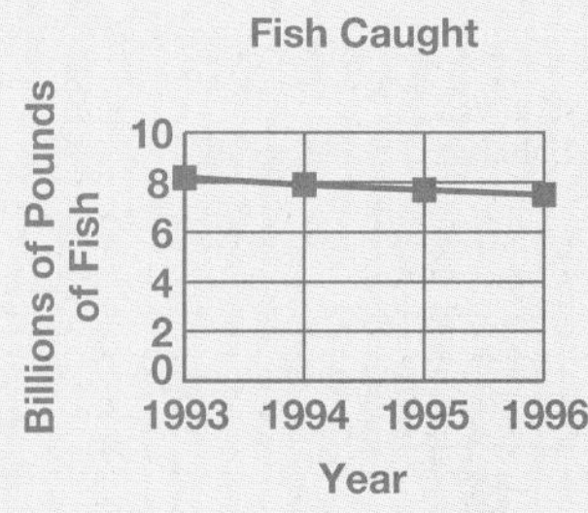

# Exercises

## CHECK UNDERSTANDING

**Use the graph at the right for Exercises 1–4.**

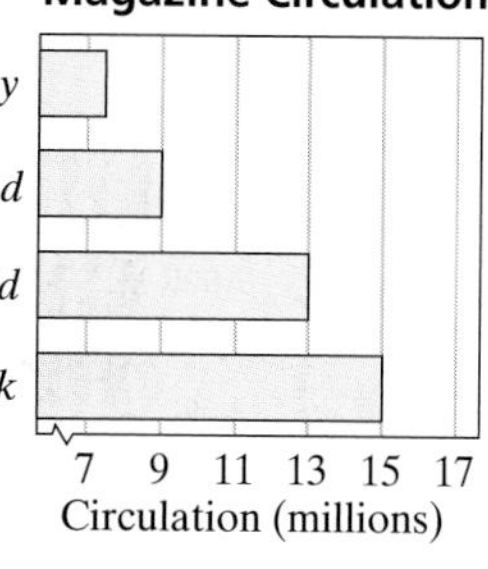


1. Which magazine *appears* to have about twice the circulation of *Circuitry Today?* American Ampersand
2. Which magazine *actually* has twice the circulation of *Circuitry Today?* Fossil Week
3. *Writing* Explain why the graph is misleading. One tends to compare the lengths of the bars without noticing the break in the scale.
4. Improve the graph by redrawing it without a break. See right.
5. a. *Statistics* Use the data below. Draw a graph with a break that suggests that the enrollment in 2000 was many times the enrollment in 1990. See margin p. 624.

4.

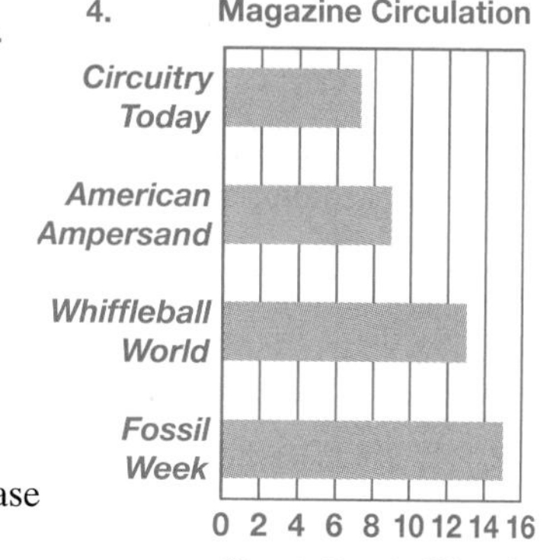


**U.S. College Enrollment**

| Year | Enrollment |
|---|---|
| 1990 | 13.8 million |
| 1995 | 14.2 million |
| 2000 | 14.9 million |

SOURCE: U.S. Education Department

   b. Draw a second graph of the data, without using a break. Choose a scale that suggests that enrollment did not increase much from 1990 to 2000. See margin p. 624.

## PRACTICE AND PROBLEM SOLVING

**Use the graph at the right for Exercises 6–8.**

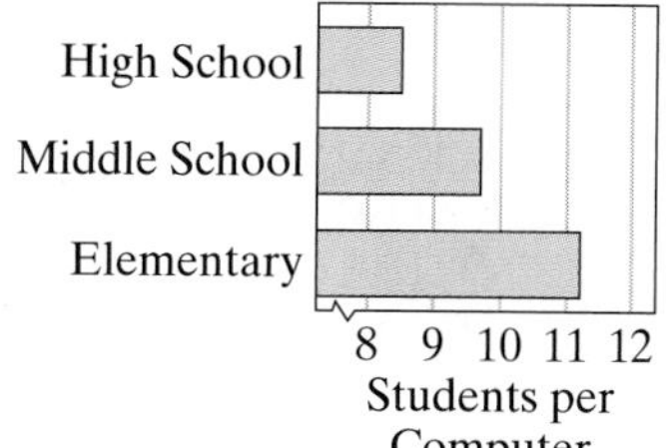


6. The graph suggests that the number of students per computer in elementary schools is three times the number of students per computer in high schools. Is this true? Explain. No; 11.2 is only about 1.3 times 8.5. The break in the axis causes the misinterpretation.
7. What does the graph suggest is the ratio of middle school students per computer to high school students per computer? What is the actual ratio? nearly 2 to 1; about 1.14 to 1
8. Redraw the graph without a break. Describe the effect this has on what the graph suggests. See margin p. 624.



## Alternative Assessment

Have students create an advertisement for a product that includes graphs comparing the product to competitive products. Ask them to manipulate the graphs so that the advertised product looks much better than the products with which it is compared. Have the class analyze these advertisements to point out how the graphs may be misleading.

# 3 Practice/Assess

## Assignment Guide

To provide flexible scheduling, this lesson can be divided into parts.

**Part 1**
**Core** 1–4, 6–8, 13–14

**Part 2**
**Core** 5, 9–12, 16
**Extension** 17–18

Mixed Review can be assigned at any time for maintenance.

## Exercises

**Auditory Learning** Exercises 6–10
Work with a partner. Have your partner read the information from the graphs while you record it in a data table. Then to answer the questions, compare the data in the table rather than by looking at the graphs.

## Challenge

How could you make a graph show what appears to be a significant difference between two sets of data that are only a few tenths of a percent different from each other? Make the scale increase by only tenths of a percentage point.

## Closure

Graphs can be misleading when they include a break in the scale or when the scale is otherwise distorted.

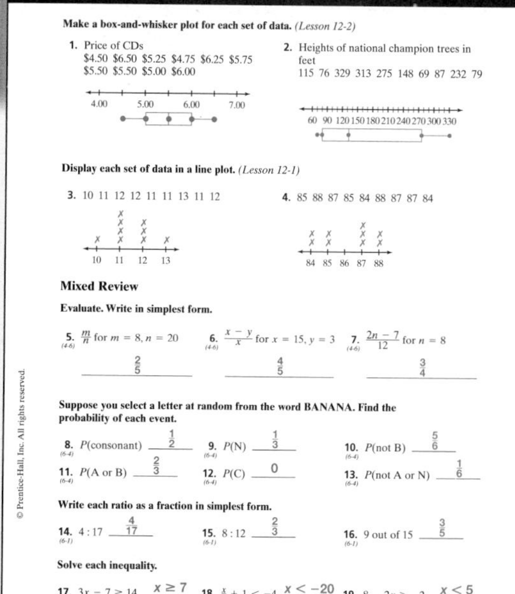

## Daily Cumulative Review

**Make a box-and-whisker plot for each set of data.** *(Lesson 12-2)*

1. Price of CDs
$4.50 $6.50 $5.25 $4.75 $6.25 $5.75 $5.50 $5.50 $5.00 $6.00
2. Heights of national champion trees in feet
115 76 329 313 275 148 69 87 232 79

**Display each set of data in a line plot.** *(Lesson 12-1)*

3. 10 11 12 12 11 11 13 11 12
4. 85 88 87 85 84 88 87 87 84

**Mixed Review**

**Evaluate. Write in simplest form.**

5. (4-6) $\frac{m}{n}$ for $m = 8, n = 20$ $\frac{2}{5}$
6. (4-6) $\frac{x-y}{x}$ for $x = 15, y = 3$ $\frac{4}{5}$
7. (4-6) $\frac{2n-7}{12}$ for $n = 8$ $\frac{3}{4}$

**Suppose you select a letter at random from the word BANANA. Find the probability of each event.**

8. (6-4) P(consonant) $\frac{1}{2}$
9. (6-4) P(N) $\frac{1}{3}$
10. (6-4) P(not B) $\frac{5}{6}$
11. (6-4) P(A or B) $\frac{2}{3}$
12. (6-4) P(C) 0
13. (6-4) P(not A or N) $\frac{1}{6}$

**Write each ratio as a fraction in simplest form.**

14. (6-1) 4 : 17 $\frac{4}{17}$
15. (6-1) 8 : 12 $\frac{2}{3}$
16. (6-1) 9 out of 15 $\frac{3}{5}$

**Solve each inequality.**

17. (7-6) $3x - 7 \geq 14$ $x \geq 7$
18. (7-6) $\frac{x}{4} + 1 < -4$ $x < -20$
19. (7-6) $8 - 2x > -2$ $x < 5$

5. Answers may vary. Samples:

a.

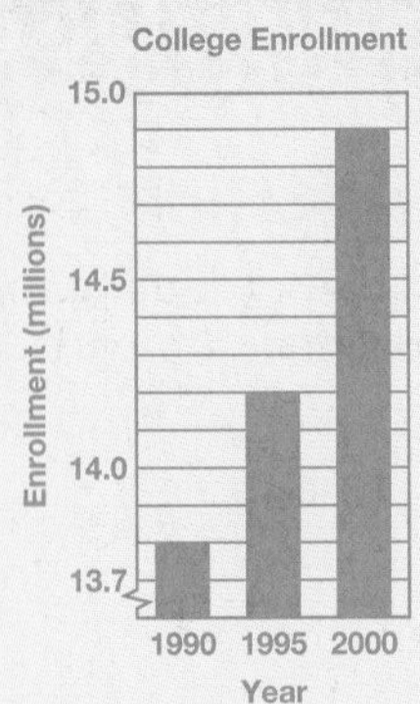


b.

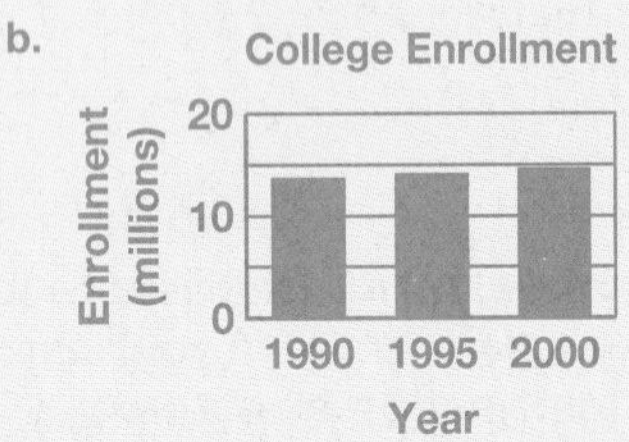


8. Answers may vary. Sample:

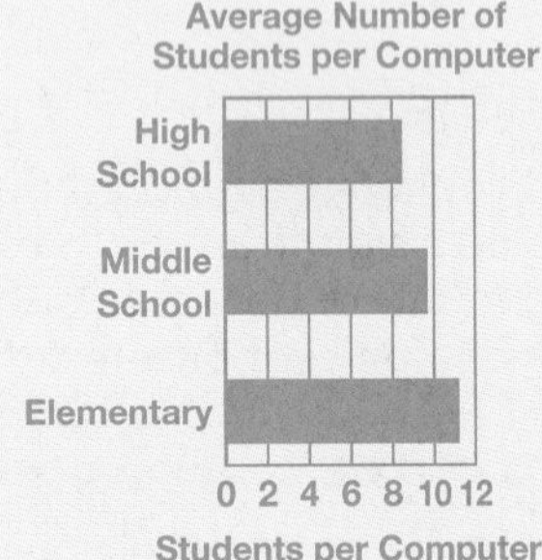


There is only a small decrease in the number of students per computer between elementary and middle school and between middle school and high school.

10. Answers may vary. Sample:

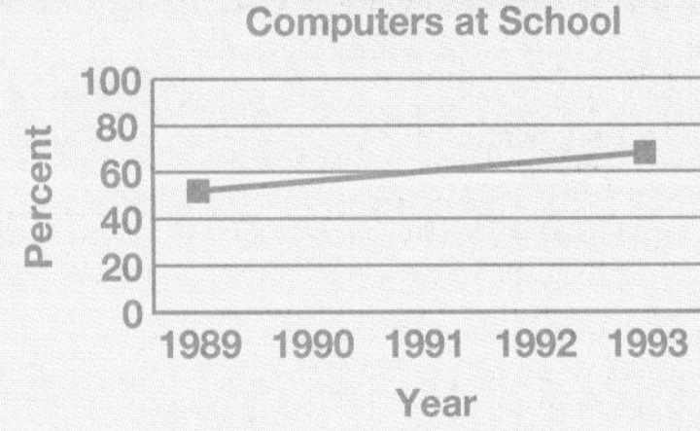


*Statistics* **Use the graph at the right for Exercises 9 and 10.**

**Percent of Students Using Computers at School**

Percent: 0, 10, 20, 30, 40, 50, 60, 70, 80

Year: 1989, 1993

9. Does the graph suggest that the percent of students using a computer at school is rising rapidly or rising slowly? How does it make that suggestion? It suggests that the percent is rising rapidly, by putting 1989 and 1993 very close together.

10. Redraw the graph to suggest less of an increase from 1989 to 1993. See margin.

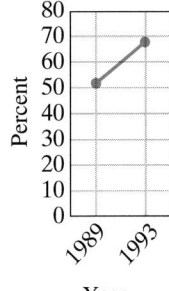

**Use the graph below for Exercises 11 and 12.**

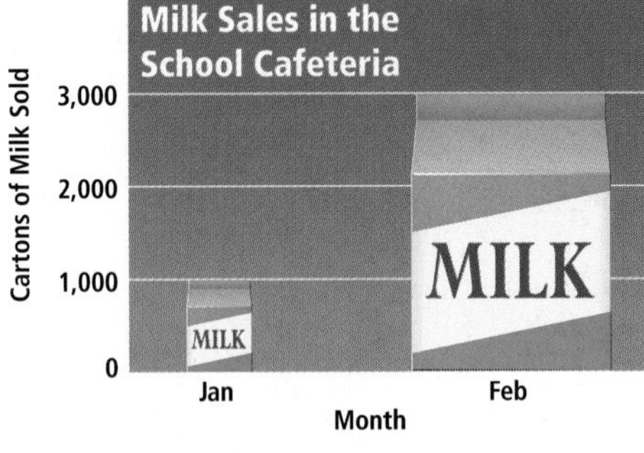


12. Yes. Rather than looking at just the heights of the boxes, one tends to compare areas. The big box looks like it could contain perhaps five times as much milk.

11. What impression does the graph give you about milk sales in the school cafeteria? that sales more than quadrupled

12. *Critical Thinking* Is the graph misleading? Explain. See above.

*Math in the Media* **Use the cartoon at the right for Exercises 13 and 14.**

13. *Writing* Based on this sales presentation, would you buy stock in this company? Explain. See below.

14. a. Explain how you could redraw the graph so it gives a better picture of the company's sales. See below.
 b. Redraw the graph. See margin.

15. Use the data below to make two different graphs. Draw one of the graphs to suggest that the percent of low-fat milk sold in 1990 was double the percent in 1980. See margin.

**Percent of Milk Sold That Was Low-Fat**

| Year | Percent |
|---|---|
| 1980 | 38% |
| 1990 | 59% |

13. No. The break in the vertical axis shows that the presenter is intending to be deceptive.

14a. Avoid using the break, and use appropriate times on the horizontal axis.



14b. Answers may vary. Sample:

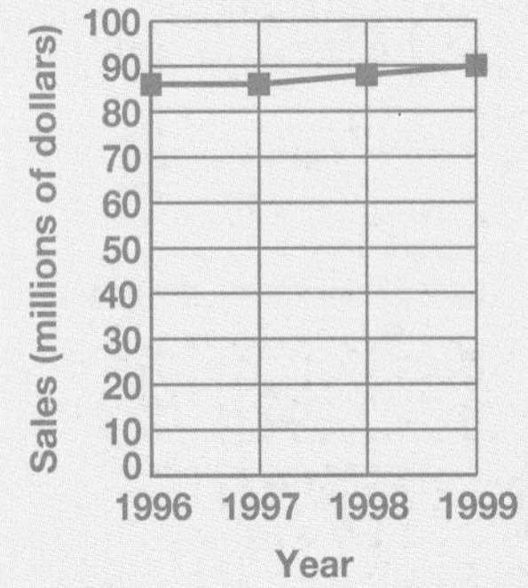

16. Use the data at the right. Draw a line graph that gives the impression that college costs increased sharply from 1984 to 1995. See below right.

**Average Annual Costs of College**

| Year | Cost |
|---|---|
| 1984–1985 | $4,563 |
| 1989–1990 | $6,207 |
| 1994–1995 | $8,306 |

SOURCE: *Wall Street Journal Almanac*

17. *Open-ended* Find a graph in a newspaper or magazine that could be misleading. Explain why and how it could be misleading. Check students' work.

18. *Statistics* Use the graph below. Explain why the intervals on the horizontal axis could make the graph misleading.

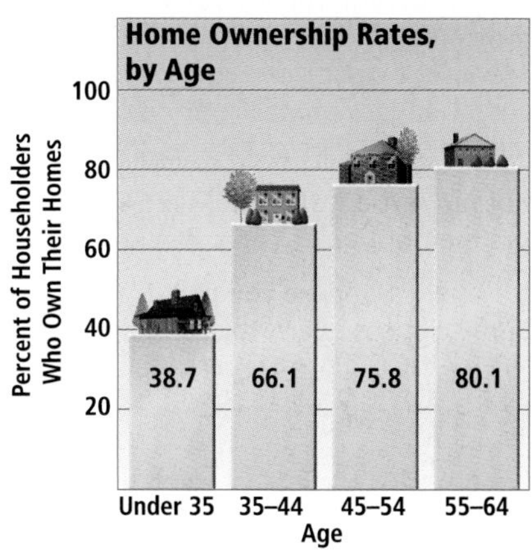


16.

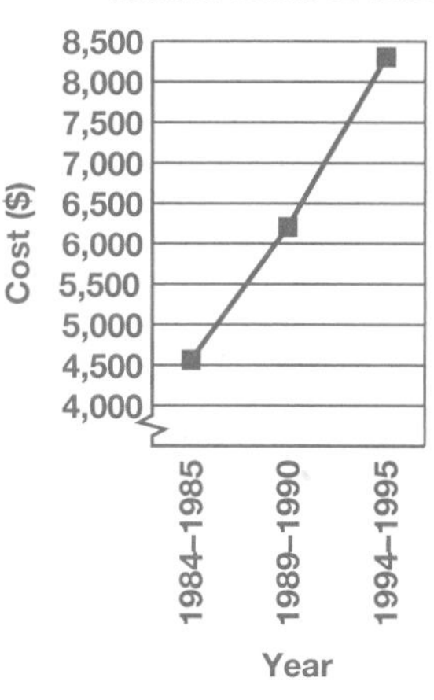


18. The intervals are not comparable. Each of the three tallest bars includes a span of 10 years, while the shorter one contains many more.

## MIXED REVIEW

**Make a box-and-whisker plot for each set of data.** ***(Lesson 12-2)***

19. 27, 25, 23, 29, 25, 28, 26, 27, 23, 21, 20, 24, 25, 28, 30, 19, 25

20. 2, 6, 3, 9, 15, 4, 9, 20, 6, 7, 2, 3, 8, 4, 1, 5, 6, 8, 5, 4, 9, 3, 2, 8, 7

21. 100, 95, 102, 101, 96, 100, 104, 115, 102, 108, 92, 97, 103, 106 See below.

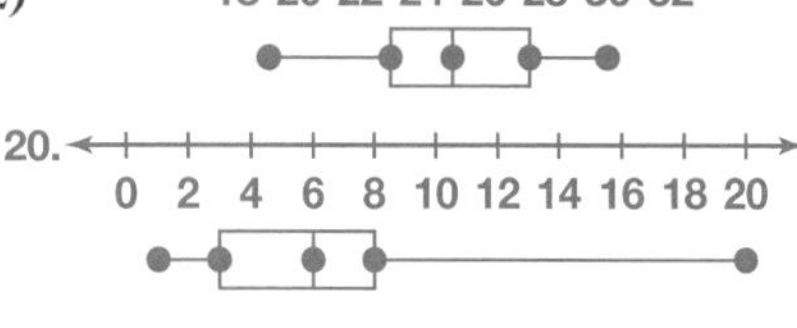


**Find each probability for choosing a letter at random from the word STATISTICS.** ***(Lesson 6-4)***

22. $P$(vowel) $\frac{3}{10}$ 23. $P$(S) $\frac{3}{10}$ 24. $P$(not T) $\frac{7}{10}$ 25. $P$(A or C) $\frac{1}{5}$

26. *Geometry* The Museum of Health and Medical Science in Houston, Texas, has one of the largest kaleidoscopes in the world. It is a cylinder 10 feet long and 22 inches in diameter. What is the surface area of the kaleidoscope? ***(Lesson 10-6)*** 9,049.5 in.$^2$ or 62.9 ft$^2$

21.

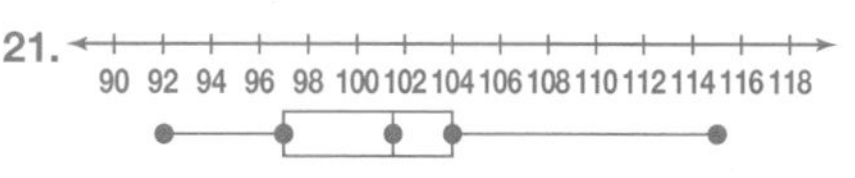

See also Extra Practice section.



15. Answers may vary. Sample:

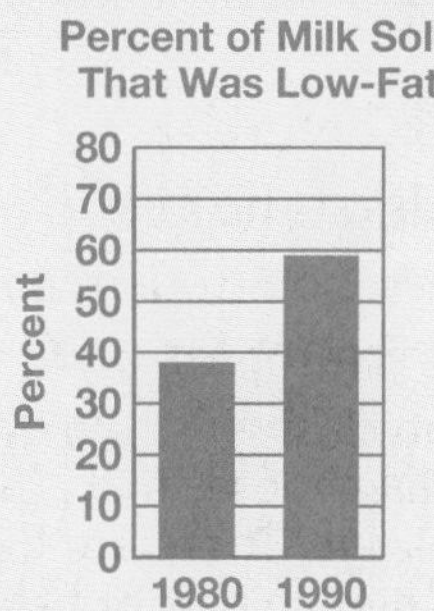


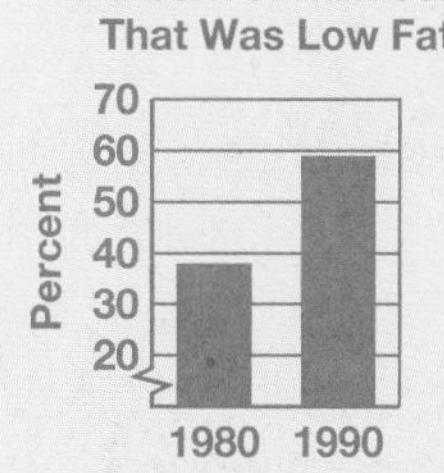


## Practice

**Use the graph at the right for Exercises 1–5.**

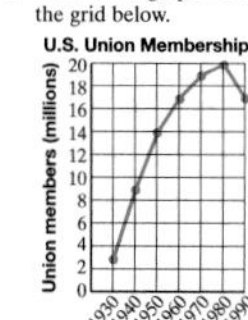


1. Which group of animals appears to have more than twice as many endangered species as mammals? birds
2. Does one group actually have twice as many endangered species as mammals? no
3. What gives the impression that one group has twice as many endangered species as mammals? The break in the vertical axis.
4. Redraw the graph without a break.
5. Describe the effect the change in scale has on what the graph suggests. The differences seem much less.

**Use the data in the table for Exercises 6–10.**

| U.S. Union Membership | | | | | | | |
|---|---|---|---|---|---|---|---|
| Year | 1930 | 1940 | 1950 | 1960 | 1970 | 1980 | 1990 |
| Union members (millions) | 3 | 9 | 14 | 17 | 19 | 20 | 17 |

6. Draw a line graph of the data using the grid below.

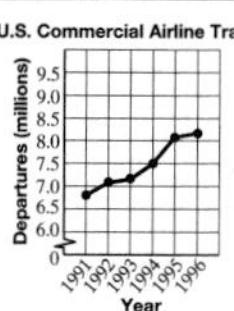


7. Draw a line graph of the data using the grid below.

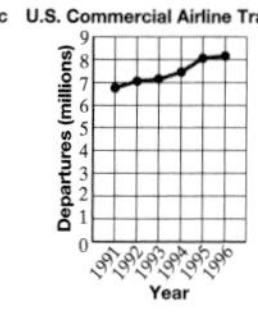


8. What gives the different impressions in the two graphs? The horizontal scales are different.



## Reteaching

Use the data in the table. Draw a line graph on each grid at the right. Discuss the impressions given by the graphs.

| U.S. Commercial Airline Traffic | | | | | | |
|---|---|---|---|---|---|---|
| Year | 1991 | 1992 | 1993 | 1994 | 1995 | 1996 |
| Departures (millions) | 6.8 | 7.1 | 7.2 | 7.5 | 8.1 | 8.2 |

The first graph gives the impression that airline traffic increased rapidly from 1991 to 1996. The second graph implies a much more gradual increase. The different impressions are given by the vertical scales. The vertical scale in the first graph is broken and increases by half millions. The vertical scale in the second graph is unbroken and increases by millions.

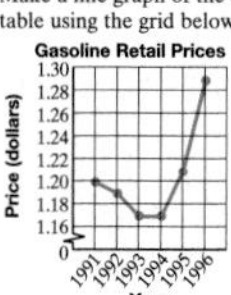


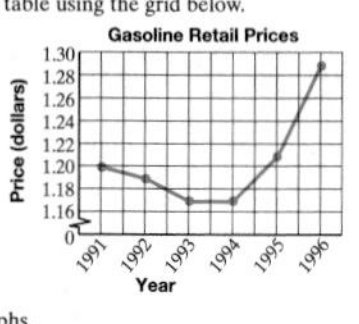


| U.S. City Average Gasoline Retail Prices | | | | | | |
|---|---|---|---|---|---|---|
| Year | 1991 | 1992 | 1993 | 1994 | 1995 | 1996 |
| Price | $1.20 | $1.19 | $1.17 | $1.17 | $1.21 | $1.29 |

1. Make a line graph of the data in the table using the grid below.
2. Make a line graph of the data in the table using the grid below.
3. Compare the impressions given in the two graphs. The first graph implies that prices decreased rapidly from 1991 to 1993 and increased rapidly from 1994 to 1996. The second graph implies slower changes.



## Enrichment

The 20 members of the Student Council sold T-shirts as a school fund raiser. Four teams of 5 students sold 1,000 T-shirts at $6.50 each.

Use a computer to graph and analyze the data.

| Teams | Number Sold |
|---|---|
| blue | 250 |
| red | 375 |
| gold | 125 |
| white | 250 |

**Construct a bar graph that shows the number of shirts sold by each team. Use unbroken axes.**

1. Which team sold the greatest number of shirts? red
2. About how many times as great as the gold team was the number of shirts sold by the white team? two times
3. Change the graph so there is a break in one axis. Also change the scale. Make your new graph give the impression that the white team sold about three times as many shirts as the gold team. What scale did you use for the number sold? Sample answer is shown. 62.5 to 412.5 by 50
4. About how many times as great as the gold team was the number of shirts sold by the red team? 3 times
5. About how many times as great as the gold team does the number of shirts sold by the red team seem based on your second graph? Sample answer is shown: 5 times
6. Which bar graph would members of the red team prefer? the second graph

**Construct a line graph that compares the number of shirts sold and the amount of money raised. Show data for 100, 200, 300, . . . 1,000 shirts sold.**

7. What scale did you use for "Money Raised"? Sample answer is shown. 0 to 6,500 by 500's
8. What unbroken scale could you use for "shirts sold" to give the impression that the money raised increases more rapidly with each shirt sold than your first graph implies? Sample answer is shown. 0 to 1,000 by 200's
9. Which line graph would members of the gold team prefer? the first graph

# 12-4

## Getting Ready

**Key Terms and Symbols** Counting Principle, theoretical probability, sample space

**Resources** A complete list of resources for this lesson is on p. 605H.

### Daily Skills Warm-Up

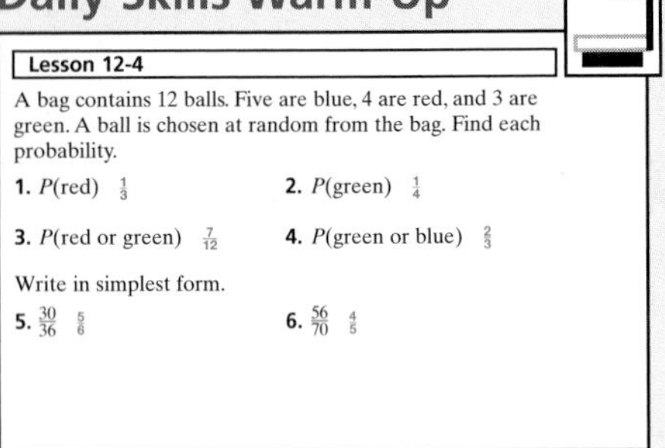
Lesson 12-4

A bag contains 12 balls. Five are blue, 4 are red, and 3 are green. A ball is chosen at random from the bag. Find each probability.

1. $P(\text{red})$ $\frac{1}{3}$
2. $P(\text{green})$ $\frac{1}{4}$
3. $P(\text{red or green})$ $\frac{7}{12}$
4. $P(\text{green or blue})$ $\frac{2}{3}$

Write in simplest form.

5. $\frac{30}{36}$ $\frac{5}{6}$
6. $\frac{56}{70}$ $\frac{4}{5}$

### Background for the Lesson

When you use the *Counting Principle,* you *multiply* to find the number of possible outcomes. For example, for a four-digit combination lock there are 10 possible choices (0–9) for each digit. To find the total number of possible choices, you multiply the choices for the first digit by those for the second, third, and fourth digits, or $10 \times 10 \times 10 \times 10$.

The *theoretical probability* of an event is the ratio of favorable outcomes to the total number of possible outcomes. For the four-digit combination lock, the theoretical probability of guessing the right combination is $\frac{1}{10{,}000}$.

## 1 Focus

### Investigate

Help students realize that each different choice (size, crust, and topping) makes a different type of pizza.

### Connecting to Students' Lives

Ask students if they have ever forgotten the combination to the lock on their school locker. In this lesson, they learn how likely it is that they might guess the correct combination.

# 12-4 Counting Outcomes and Theoretical Probability

### What You'll Learn

1. To use a tree diagram and the Counting Principle to find the number of possible outcomes
2. To find theoretical probability by counting outcomes

### . . . And Why

To find outcomes and probabilities in real-world problems

## *Investigate*

**EXPLORING POSSIBLE OUTCOMES**

Congratulations! Your application to run the pizza stand at school home games has been accepted. Now you have to decide which pizzas to sell. You plan to offer two or three choices in each of three categories—size, crust, and topping. The more types of pizza the better, but you're limited by kitchen space to a total of 18 types.

1. Decide which types of pizza you will offer. Make a menu that shows your customers their options. Check students' work.
2. *Mathematical Reasoning* Suppose you decide to offer three choices of size and three choices of crust. How many toppings can you offer? 2 toppings

## PART 1 Counting Possible Choices

You can use a tree diagram to display and count possible choices.

### EXAMPLE 1

**A school team sells caps in two colors (blue or white), two sizes (child or adult), and two fabrics (cotton or polyester). Draw a tree diagram to find the number of cap choices.**

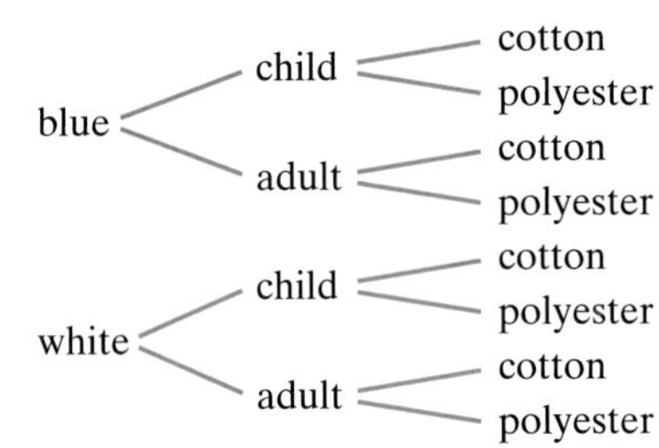


Each branch of the "tree" represents one choice—for example, blue-child-cotton.

There are 8 possible cap choices.



# Tools to Monitor Progress

### BEFORE THE LESSON

**To check prerequisite skills:**

- Finding probability

**Skills You Need,** p. 605

**Skills Handbook,** p. 725

**Skills Intervention Kit,** Whole Numbers

### DURING THE LESSON

**To check understanding:**

**Try This** exercises on student page

- **Additional Examples 1–4**

The freshman class sells cold drinks. Customers can choose small, medium, or large. There are five drinks: cola, diet cola, root beer, lemonade, and water. Customers may choose ice or no ice.

**■ TRY THIS**

3. Suppose the caps in Example 1 also come in black. Draw a tree diagram. How many cap choices are there? 12 choices; see margin for diagram.

Another way to count choices is to use the Counting Principle.

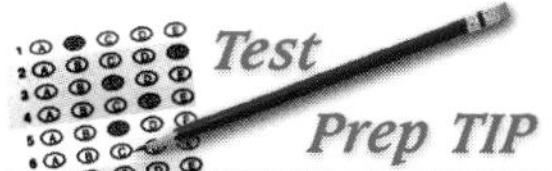


The Counting Principle is sometimes called the Multiplication Counting Principle.

**Counting Principle**

If there are $m$ ways of making one choice, and $n$ ways of making a second choice, then there are $m \cdot n$ ways of making the first choice followed by the second.

The Counting Principle is particularly useful when a tree diagram would be too large to draw.

REAL-WORLD CONNECTION

**■ EXAMPLE 2**

**How many two-letter monograms are possible?**

| first letter possible choices | | second letter possible choices | | monograms possible choices |
|---|---|---|---|---|
| 26 | · | 26 | = | 676 |

There are 676 possible two-letter monograms.

A monogram is a figure made up of two or more letters, such as the initials of your name.

**■ TRY THIS**

4. How many three-letter monograms are possible? 17,576 three-letter monograms

## PART 2 Counting Outcomes to Find Probability

You can count outcomes to help you find the **theoretical probability** of an event in which outcomes are equally likely.

**Theoretical Probability**

$$P(\text{event}) = \frac{\text{number of favorable outcomes}}{\text{number of possible outcomes}}$$

A **sample space** is a list of all possible outcomes. You can use a tree diagram to find a sample space. Then you can calculate probability.



# 2 Teach

## PART 1 Part 1 Teaching Notes

Tree diagrams are useful for counting possible choices when the number of choices is small. However, when the number of choices is very large the Counting Principle is much easier to use.

### ■ Example 1

**Build understanding.** Ask: How many different white cap choices are there? How many blue cap choices are there? 4; 4

### ■ Example 2

**Math Reasoning** In Example 2, the answer is the same as $26^2$. This result makes sense because there are two letters in the monogram, each with 26 choices, or $26 \times 26$. Use math reasoning to describe some situations in which you could use powers to find the total number of possible choices. sample answer: when there are multiple letters or digits in a combination

## Part 2 Teaching Notes

*Theoretical probability* is the mathematical prediction of the frequency of an event over a large number of trials. A number cube, for example, has six sides. Only one side is marked with a 1. If you toss a number cube, there are six possible sides that could come up. The theoretical probability of tossing a 1, which will be true in a very large number of trials, is one out of six, or $\frac{1}{6}$. However, if you actually toss a number cube just a few times, a 1 may or may not come up one sixth of the time.

**a.** Find the total number of possible choices. 30
**b.** What is the theoretical probability that a customer will order a medium diet cola with no ice? $\frac{1}{30}$

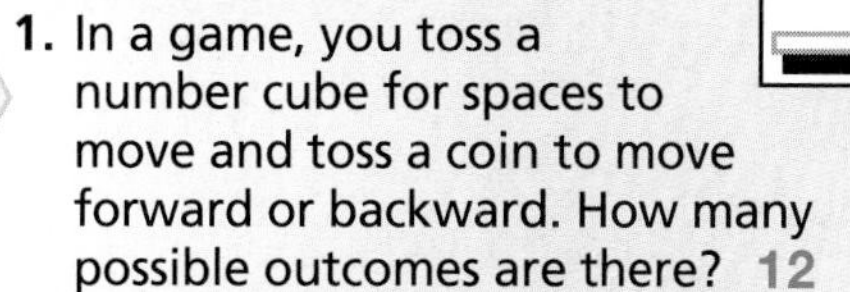

**AFTER THE LESSON**

**To assess knowledge: Lesson Quiz**

1. In a game, you toss a number cube for spaces to move and toss a coin to move forward or backward. How many possible outcomes are there? 12
2. What is the theoretical probability you will move four spaces? $\frac{2}{12}$; or $\frac{1}{6}$

- For enrichment and reteaching options see Resources on p. 605H.

3.

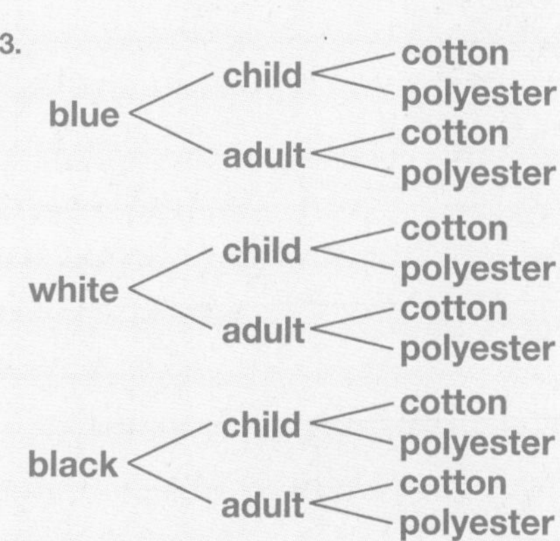

## ■ Example 3

**Build understanding.** Ask: How is the probability of tossing two heads related to the probability of tossing two tails? **With two heads, like two tails, there is only one favorable outcome out of four possible outcomes, so the probability is the same.**

**Extension** In Example 3, you used a tree diagram to find that there are four possible outcomes when you toss two coins. How could you use the counting principle to find the number of possible outcomes? **The first coin has two outcomes, and the second has two. You multiply 2 times 2 to get 4 possible outcomes.**

**Error Prevention** In Example 3, help students understand that the combinations of heads-tails and tails-heads are two *separate* possible outcomes in the sample space.

**Connecting to Science** Heredity is the study of the biological processes by which traits are passed from parents to their offspring. In the mid 1800s, the Austrian monk Gregor Mendel discovered that the probability of whether certain traits would be passed from parents to offspring could be predicted. Mendel conducted experiments with pea plants. Through his experiments, Mendel identified seven traits in pea plants and their seeds that he could predict with mathematical probability principles.

## ■ Example 4

**Build understanding.** Which type of number, one with random digits like 8376, or one with "special digits," like 1111, is more likely to be a winning number? **They are equally likely.**

### EXAMPLE 3

**Use a tree diagram to find the sample space for tossing two coins. Then find the probability of tossing two tails.**

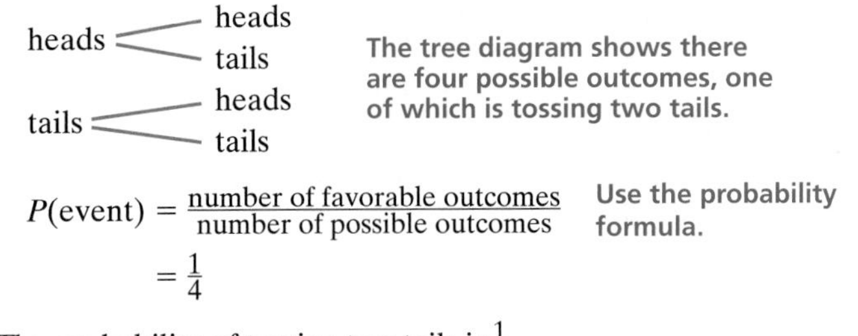
heads
heads
tails
tails
heads
tails
The tree diagram shows there are four possible outcomes, one of which is tossing two tails.

$P(\text{event}) = \dfrac{\text{number of favorable outcomes}}{\text{number of possible outcomes}}$ Use the probability formula.

$= \dfrac{1}{4}$

The probability of tossing two tails is $\frac{1}{4}$.

### ■ TRY THIS

**5.** You toss two coins. Find $P$(one head and one tail). $\frac{1}{2}$

You can also use the Counting Principle to find probability.

REAL-WORLD CONNECTION

### EXAMPLE 4

**Many people play lottery games without knowing the probability of winning. In some state lotteries, the winning number is made up of four digits chosen at random. Suppose a player buys two tickets with different numbers. What is the probability that the player has a winning ticket?**

First find the number of possible outcomes. For each digit, there are 10 possible outcomes, 0 through 9.

| $1^{st}$ digit | | $2^{nd}$ digit | | $3^{rd}$ digit | | $4^{th}$ digit | | total |
|---|---|---|---|---|---|---|---|---|
| outcomes | | outcomes | | outcomes | | outcomes | | outcomes |
| 10 | · | 10 | · | 10 | · | 10 | = | 10,000 |

Then find the probability when there are two favorable outcomes.

$P(\text{event}) = \dfrac{\text{number of favorable outcomes}}{\text{number of possible outcomes}} = \dfrac{2}{10{,}000}$

The probability is $\frac{2}{10{,}000}$, or $\frac{1}{5{,}000}$.

### ■ TRY THIS

**6.** A lottery uses five digits chosen at random. Find the probability of buying a winning ticket. $\frac{1}{100{,}000}$

# Exercises

## Check Understanding

1. There are 3 ways of performing Task A. There are 4 ways of performing Task B. Use a tree diagram to find the number of ways there are to perform Task A and then Task B. 12 ways; see diagram below.
2. There are 8 roads leading from Marsh to Taft and 7 roads leading from Taft to Polk. How many possible routes are there for driving from Marsh to Polk through Taft? 56
3. Find the probability of rolling a 3 on each of two number cubes. $\frac{1}{36}$

## Practice and Problem Solving

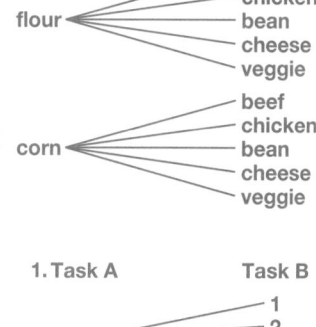

4. You can buy a burrito made from a flour tortilla or a corn tortilla. You have a choice of five fillings: beef, chicken, bean, triple-cheese, or grilled vegetables. Draw a tree diagram. How many burrito choices do you have? 10 choices
5. There are 6 roads leading from Seymour to Clarksville and 3 roads leading from Clarksville to Belleview. Use a tree diagram to find the number of possible routes from Seymour to Belleview through Clarksville. 18 routes; see margin.
6. a. A student has eight shirts and six pairs of pants. How many different shirt-pants outfits can he choose? 48 outfits
   b. The student also has three neckties. How many shirt-pants-tie outfits can he choose? 144 outfits
7. An automobile manufacturer makes four different car styles. Each style comes in 11 colors. Each car comes in one of five different interior styles and with an automatic or a manual transmission. A car dealer wants to order one of each kind of car. How many cars will the dealer order? 440 cars
8. *Open-ended* Write a problem that you can solve by using the Counting Principle. Then solve the problem. Check students' work.

4. flour — beef, chicken, bean, cheese, veggie; corn — beef, chicken, bean, cheese, veggie

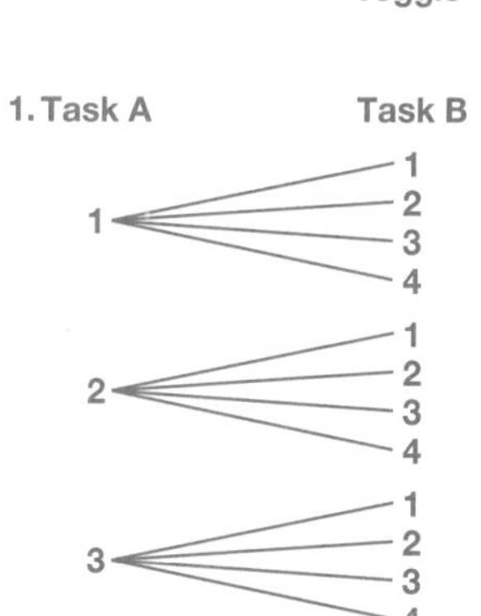


**Find each sample space.**

9. tossing 3 coins HHH, HHT, HTH, THH, HTT, THT, TTH, TTT
10. tossing one coin and rolling one number cube H1, H2, H3, H4, H5, H6, T1, T2, T3, T4, T5, T6
11. scheduling an appointment for a weekday during the morning or the afternoon Mon. A.M., Mon. P.M., Tue. A.M., Tue. P.M., Wed. A.M., Wed. P.M., Thur. A.M., Thur. P.M., Fri. A.M., Fri. P.M.



# 3 Practice/Assess

## Assignment Guide

To provide flexible scheduling, this lesson can be divided into parts.

**Part 1**
Core 1–2, 4–7
Extension 8

**Part 2**
Core 3, 9–17
Extension 18

Mixed Review can be assigned at any time for maintenance.

## Exercises

**Tactile Learning Exercises 9–10, 12–14** You may want to use real coins and number cubes to help you find each sample space.

## Challenge

Use two number cubes and theoretical probability to explain why the number seven is considered by many to be a lucky number. The theoretical probability for a sum of seven is $\frac{1}{6}$, greater than that of any other sum.

## Closure

A sample space is all the possible outcomes of an event. Use a tree diagram or the Counting Principle to count the number of outcomes. You can count outcomes to help find theoretical probability.

## Alternative Assessment

Place students in groups. Have groups create a simple board game based on probability. Ask students to write instructions on how to play their games. Then have the groups rotate to play each other's games.

5.

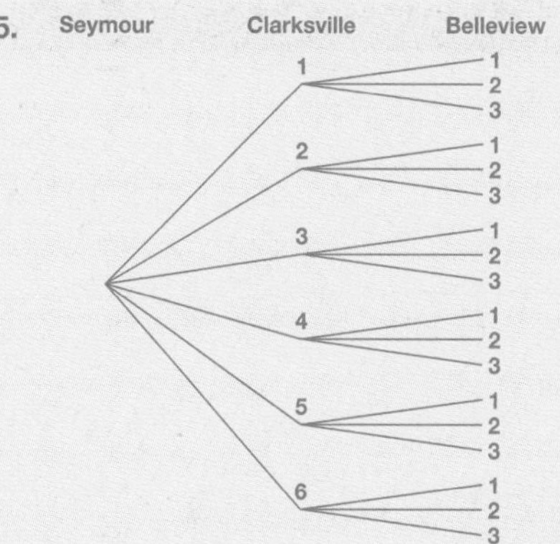


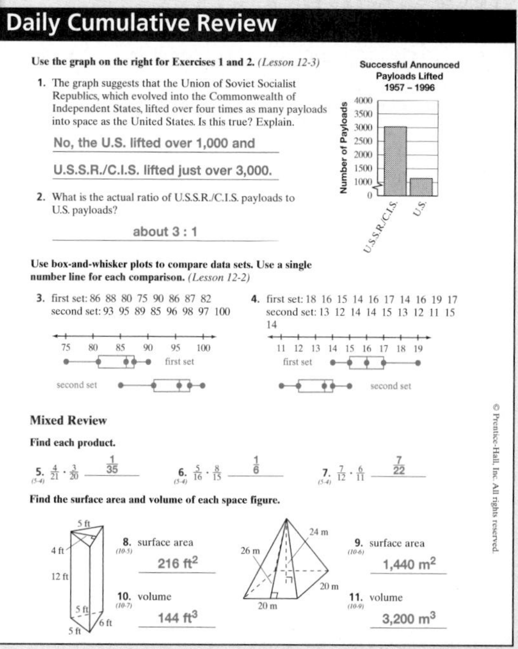

## Daily Cumulative Review

**Use the graph on the right for Exercises 1 and 2.** *(Lesson 12-3)*

1. The graph suggests that the Union of Soviet Socialist Republics, which evolved into the Commonwealth of Independent States, lifted over four times as many payloads into space as the United States. Is this true? Explain.
   No, the U.S. lifted over 1,000 and U.S.S.R./C.I.S. lifted just over 3,000.
2. What is the actual ratio of U.S.S.R./C.I.S. payloads to U.S. payloads?
   about 3 : 1



**Use box-and-whisker plots to compare data sets. Use a single number line for each comparison.** *(Lesson 12-2)*

3. first set: 86 88 80 75 90 86 87 82
   second set: 93 95 89 85 96 98 97 100
4. first set: 18 16 15 14 16 17 14 16 19 17
   second set: 13 12 14 14 15 13 12 11 15 14



**Mixed Review**

**Find each product.**

5. (5-4) $\frac{4}{21} \cdot \frac{3}{20}$ $\frac{1}{35}$
6. (5-4) $\frac{5}{16} \cdot \frac{8}{15}$ $\frac{1}{6}$
7. (5-4) $\frac{7}{12} \cdot \frac{6}{11}$ $\frac{7}{22}$

**Find the surface area and volume of each space figure.**



8. (10-5) surface area 216 $ft^2$
9. (10-6) surface area 1,440 $m^2$
10. (10-7) volume 144 $ft^3$
11. (10-9) volume 3,200 $m^3$

## Practice

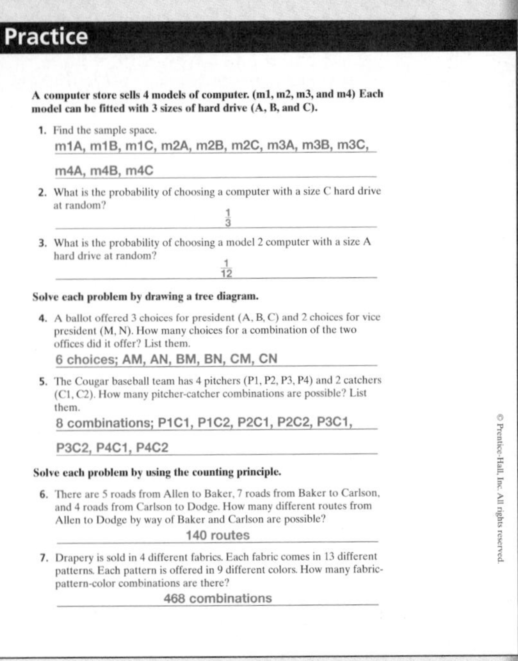

A computer store sells 4 models of computer. (m1, m2, m3, and m4) Each model can be fitted with 3 sizes of hard drive (A, B, and C).

1. Find the sample space.
   m1A, m1B, m1C, m2A, m2B, m2C, m3A, m3B, m3C, m4A, m4B, m4C
2. What is the probability of choosing a computer with a size C hard drive at random?
   $\frac{1}{3}$
3. What is the probability of choosing a model 2 computer with a size A hard drive at random?
   $\frac{1}{12}$

**Solve each problem by drawing a tree diagram.**

4. A ballot offered 3 choices for president (A, B, C) and 2 choices for vice president (M, N). How many choices for a combination of the two offices did it offer? List them.
   6 choices; AM, AN, BM, BN, CM, CN
5. The Cougar baseball team has 4 pitchers (P1, P2, P3, P4) and 2 catchers (C1, C2). How many pitcher-catcher combinations are possible? List them.
   8 combinations; P1C1, P1C2, P2C1, P2C2, P3C1, P3C2, P4C1, P4C2

**Solve each problem by using the counting principle.**

6. There are 5 roads from Allen to Baker, 7 roads from Baker to Carlson, and 4 roads from Carlson to Dodge. How many different routes from Allen to Dodge by way of Baker and Carlson are possible?
   140 routes
7. Drapery is sold in 4 different fabrics. Each fabric comes in 13 different patterns. Each pattern is offered in 9 different colors. How many fabric-pattern-color combinations are there?
   468 combinations



## Reteaching

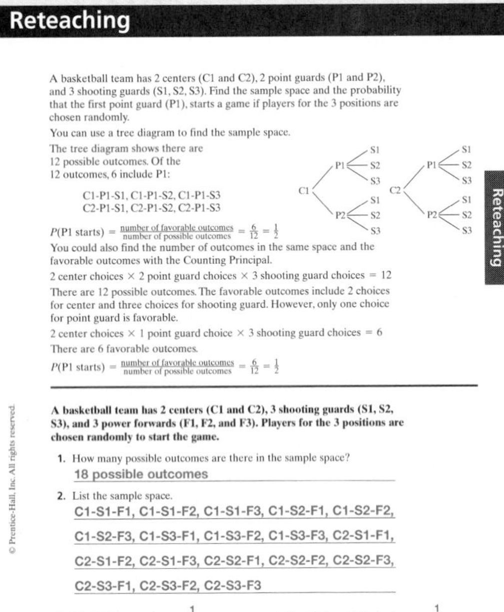

A basketball team has 2 centers (C1 and C2), 2 point guards (P1 and P2), and 3 shooting guards (S1, S2, S3). Find the sample space and the probability that the first point guard (P1), starts a game if players for the 3 positions are chosen randomly.

You can use a tree diagram to find the sample space.

The tree diagram shows there are 12 possible outcomes. Of the 12 outcomes, 6 include P1:

C1-P1-S1, C1-P1-S2, C1-P1-S3
C2-P1-S1, C2-P1-S2, C2-P1-S3



$P(\text{P1 starts}) = \frac{\text{number of favorable outcomes}}{\text{number of possible outcomes}} = \frac{6}{12} = \frac{1}{2}$

You could also find the number of outcomes in the same space and the favorable outcomes with the Counting Principle.

2 center choices × 2 point guard choices × 3 shooting guard choices = 12

There are 12 possible outcomes. The favorable outcomes include 2 choices for center and three choices for shooting guard. However, only one choice for point guard is favorable.

2 center choices × 1 point guard choice × 3 shooting guard choices = 6

There are 6 favorable outcomes.

$P(\text{P1 starts}) = \frac{\text{number of favorable outcomes}}{\text{number of possible outcomes}} = \frac{6}{12} = \frac{1}{2}$

**A basketball team has 2 centers (C1 and C2), 3 shooting guards (S1, S2, S3), and 3 power forwards (F1, F2, and F3). Players for the 3 positions are chosen randomly to start the game.**

1. How many possible outcomes are there in the sample space?
   18 possible outcomes
2. List the sample space.
   C1-S1-F1, C1-S1-F2, C1-S1-F3, C1-S2-F1, C1-S2-F2, C1-S2-F3, C1-S3-F1, C1-S3-F2, C1-S3-F3, C2-S1-F1, C2-S1-F2, C2-S1-F3, C2-S2-F1, C2-S2-F2, C2-S2-F3, C2-S3-F1, C2-S3-F2, C2-S3-F3
3. Find $P$(F2 starts). $\frac{1}{3}$
4. Find $P$(S1 and F1) start. $\frac{1}{9}$

Reteaching



## Enrichment

The diagram shows trails leading from Camp Alpha (A), where you are camped, to the river. You may walk only in a southerly direction.

**How many routes can you choose to get from A to:**

1. B? 1 2. C? 1
3. D? 1 4. F? 1
5. G? 1 6. J? 1
7. Find the number of routes you can choose to get from A to E. 2
8. Find the number of choices you have for walking from A to H and from A to I.
   A to H 3 A to I 3
9. Use the above method to find the number of trails from Camp Alpha to the Rainbow Desert. Write the number of choices to each point in the open circles.

Camp Alpha

1
1 1
1 2 1
1 3 3 1
1 4 6 4 1
1 5 10 10 5 1
1 6 15 20 15 6 1

Rainbow Desert

You may recognize the triangle of numbers you have written as Pascal's triangle, an array with wide applications in mathematics.



**Find each event's probability.**

12. You toss three coins and get three heads. $\frac{1}{8}$
13. You toss three coins. You get one head and two tails. $\frac{3}{8}$
14. You toss a coin and roll a number cube. You toss tails and roll an even number. $\frac{1}{4}$

**Use the table. You have one sweater for each possible color and style.**

15. Find the sample space. How many sweaters do you have? See above.
16. What is the probability of choosing a brown sweater at random? $\frac{1}{5}$
17. What is the probability of choosing a cardigan at random? $\frac{1}{3}$
18. *Mathematical Reasoning* You have a bag containing an equal number of nickels, dimes, and quarters. You reach into the bag and choose a coin. Are all outcomes equally likely? Explain. No. You might tend to pick up a larger coin. Also, larger coins might tend to go to the bottom, so you might be more likely to pick a lighter coin.

15. blue cardigan, blue crewneck, blue V-neck, pink cardigan, pink crewneck, pink V-neck, red cardigan, red crewneck, red V-neck, brown cardigan, brown crewneck, brown V-neck, black cardigan, black crewneck, black V-neck; 15 sweaters.

**Sweaters**

| Colors | Styles |
|---|---|
| Blue | Cardigan |
| Pink | Crewneck |
| Red | V-neck |
| Brown | |
| Black | |

## Mixed Review

**Display each data set in a line plot. Find the range.** *(Lesson 12-1)*

19. 3 4 5 4 7 7 3 6 5 range = 4
20. 19 18 19 17 17 16 19 18 17 19 range = 3

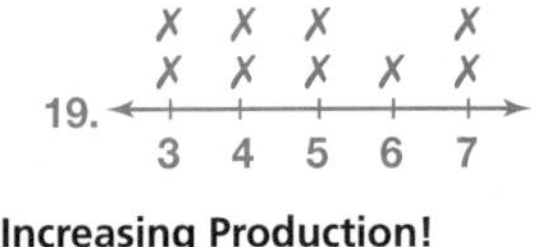


20. line plot: 16 17 18 19

**Find the midpoint of a segment with the given endpoints.** *(Lesson 11-3)*

21. $X(3, -2)$ and $Y(-3, 6)$ (0, 2)
22. $A(-1, 0)$ and $B(2, 1)$ (0.5, 0.5)
23. *Writing* Explain why the graph at the right could be misleading. *(Lesson 12-3)* While the height of the 1990 bar is $1\frac{2}{3}$ times the height of the 1980 bar, the area is 5 times as great.

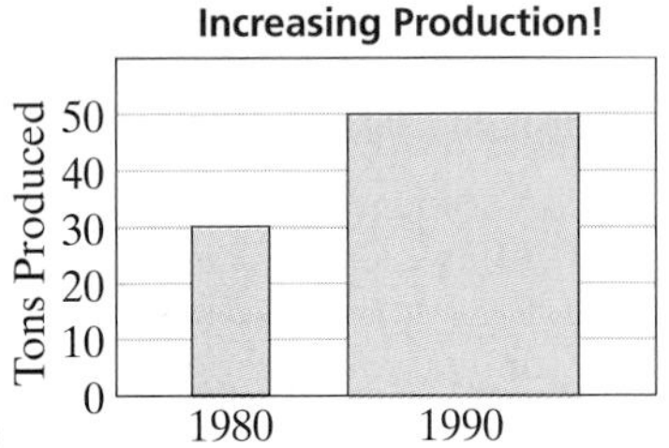


## Checkpoint 1

Lessons 12-1 through 12-4

1. Display the data below in a frequency table.
   47 51 50 52 50 47 48 50 49 51 48 52
   See margin.
2. Make a box-and-whisker plot for the data below.
   31, 33, 74, 90, 44, 49, 40, 64, 42, 31, 36, 73, 86, 34, 46, 65
   See right.
3. *Open-ended* Use the data in the table. Check students' work.
   a. Draw a graph that could be misleading. Explain.
   b. Redraw the graph so it is not misleading.
4. Two numbers from 1 to 10 are chosen at random. Find the probability that both numbers are odd numbers. $\frac{1}{4}$

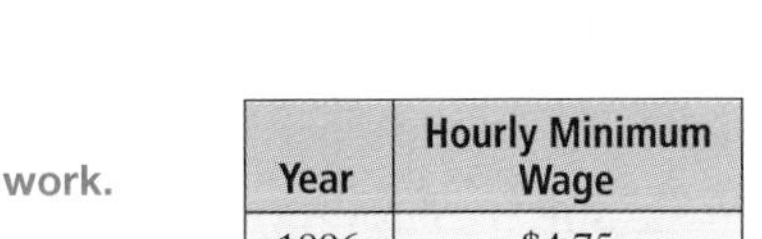


| Year | Hourly Minimum Wage |
|---|---|
| 1996 | $4.75 |
| 1997 | $5.15 |

SOURCE: *Wall Street Journal Almanac*



See also Extra Practice section.

## Checkpoint

1. Display the data below in a frequency table.
   95 94 91 94 93 93 91 95 94 93 94 92

| Number | Frequency |
|---|---|
| 91 | 2 |
| 92 | 1 |
| 93 | 3 |
| 94 | 4 |
| 95 | 2 |

2. Make a box-and-whisker plot for the data below.
   81 97 85 86 75 95 82 87 92 90
   70 75 80 85 90 95 100
   median: 86.5
   lower quartile: 82
   upper quartile: 92
   range: 75 to 97
3. Two numbers from 1 to 12 are chosen at random. Find the probability that both are greater than 8. $\frac{1}{9}$

1.

| Number | Frequency |
|---|---|
| 47 | 2 |
| 48 | 2 |
| 49 | 1 |
| 50 | 3 |
| 51 | 2 |
| 52 | 2 |

# Independent and Dependent Events

# 12-5

## *Investigate*

EXPLORING PROBABILITY IN GAMES

You have four cards with an M written on them, two with an A, six with a T, and eight with an H.

1. You draw an M card at random and replace it. What is the probability that the next card you draw at random will also be an M card? $\frac{1}{5}$
2. You draw an M card at random and do not replace the card. What is the probability that the next card you draw at random will also be an M card? $\frac{3}{19}$
3. Make a table to find the probability of matching cards.

**Probability *With* Replacement**

| First Card | Second Card Matches |
|---|---|
| $P(M) = ■$ | $P(M) = ■$ |
| $P(A) = ■$ | $P(A) = ■$ |
| $P(T) = ■$ | $P(T) = ■$ |
| $P(H) = ■$ | $P(H) = ■$ |

**Probability *Without* Replacement**

| First Card | Second Card Matches |
|---|---|
| $P(M) = ■$ | $P(M) = ■$ |
| $P(A) = ■$ | $P(A) = ■$ |
| $P(T) = ■$ | $P(T) = ■$ |
| $P(H) = ■$ | $P(H) = ■$ |

4. *Critical Thinking* For any letter, why is the probability for selecting the second card with replacement of the first card different from the probability of selecting the second card without replacement of the first card? Without replacement, both the number of matching cards and the total number of cards have been reduced by one.

## PART 1 Independent Events

Suppose you select a card from a stack of cards. You then select a second card *after replacing* the first card. Your first selection does not affect your second selection. The cards available for the second selection are the same as those for the first.

**Independent events** are events in which the first event *does not* affect the second event.

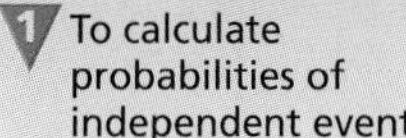

### What You'll Learn

1. To calculate probabilities of independent events
2. To calculate probabilities of dependent events

### . . . And Why

To find probabilities in games and science

3.

| | | | |
|---|---|---|---|
| $\frac{1}{5}$ | $\frac{1}{5}$ | $\frac{1}{5}$ | $\frac{3}{19}$ |
| $\frac{1}{10}$ | $\frac{1}{10}$ | $\frac{1}{10}$ | $\frac{1}{19}$ |
| $\frac{3}{10}$ | $\frac{3}{10}$ | $\frac{3}{10}$ | $\frac{5}{19}$ |
| $\frac{2}{5}$ | $\frac{2}{5}$ | $\frac{2}{5}$ | $\frac{7}{19}$ |



# Tools to Monitor Progress

## BEFORE THE LESSON

**To check prerequisite skills:**

- Finding probability
- Multiplying fractions
- Fractions, decimals, and percents

**Skills You Need,** p. 605

## DURING THE LESSON

**To check understanding:**

**Try This** exercises on student page

- **Additional Example 1**

  You roll a number cube once, then again. What is the probability that you get 5 on the first roll and a number less than 4 on the second roll? $\frac{1}{12}$

# 12-5

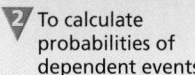

## Getting Ready

**Key Terms and Symbols** independent events, probability of independent events, dependent events, probability of dependent events

**Resources** A complete list of resources for this lesson is on p. 605H.

### Daily Skills Warm-Up

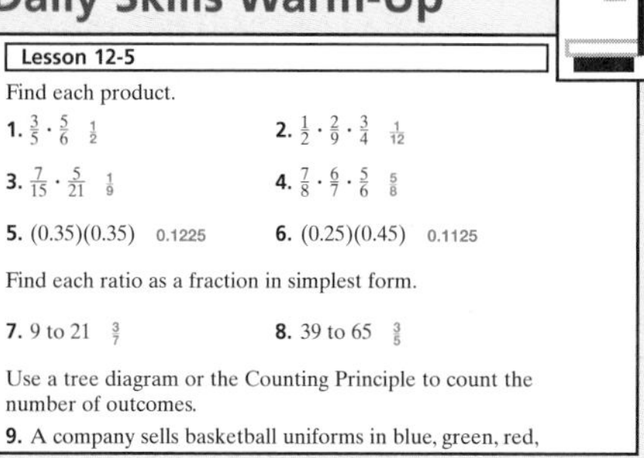

Lesson 12-5

Find each product.

1. $\frac{3}{5} \cdot \frac{5}{6}$ $\frac{1}{2}$
2. $\frac{1}{2} \cdot \frac{2}{9} \cdot \frac{3}{4}$ $\frac{1}{12}$
3. $\frac{7}{15} \cdot \frac{5}{21}$ $\frac{1}{9}$
4. $\frac{7}{8} \cdot \frac{6}{7} \cdot \frac{5}{6}$ $\frac{5}{8}$
5. $(0.35)(0.35)$ 0.1225
6. $(0.25)(0.45)$ 0.1125

Find each ratio as a fraction in simplest form.

7. 9 to 21 $\frac{3}{7}$
8. 39 to 65 $\frac{3}{5}$

Use a tree diagram or the Counting Principle to count the number of outcomes.

9. A company sells basketball uniforms in blue, green, red,

### Background for the Lesson

Suppose you put five white marbles and one red marble in a bag. You reach in without looking to draw a marble, look at it, and put it back in the bag. A second person draws a marble. The probability that the second person will draw the red marble is the same because the bag contains the same five white marbles and one red marble. These are *independent* events. However, if you keep your marble when you draw it, the probability that the second person will draw a red marble is different because there is one less marble in the bag. These are *dependent* events.

## 1 Focus

### Investigate

Help students understand that when the cards are not replaced there are fewer possible outcomes.

### Connecting to Prior Knowledge

In Lesson 12-4, students learned to find theoretical probability. In this lesson, they learn the difference in the probability of independent and dependent events. In Lesson 12-7, students will learn about experimental probability.

# 2 Teach

## Part 1 Teaching Notes

To start the discussion about finding the probability of independent events, ask students to think back to an example problem from Lesson 12-4. In this problem, students used a tree diagram to find the probability of tossing two tails when tossing two coins. The probability was $\frac{1}{4}$. Help students see that this is the same as multiplying the probability of tossing tails on one coin $\left(\frac{1}{2}\right)$ by the probability of tossing tails on the second coin $\left(\frac{1}{2}\right)$.

### Example 1

**Build understanding.** Ask: What is the probability that you get a 3 on the first roll and a number greater than 4 on the second roll? What is the probability that you get a 4 on the first roll and a number less than 3 on the second roll? $\frac{1}{18}$, $\frac{1}{18}$

### Example 2

**Build understanding.** Ask: If you plant 10 bluebonnet seeds, how many would you expect to grow? Explain. 2; because 20% of 10 is 2

**Math Reasoning** Use math reasoning to explain why the probability that two seeds will grow as in Example 2 is less than the probability that one seed will grow. Only 2 out of every 10 seeds will grow, so the likelihood that you will pick the two that will grow is very small.

**Connecting to Science** Bluebonnet seeds have a very tough outer covering, and it may take several years for them to germinate. With this delayed germination, only about 20% of bluebonnet seeds will germinate in any year. Delayed germination assures that the plant species will survive periods of drought or other adverse growing conditions.

**Probability of Independent Events**

For two independent events $A$ and $B$, the probability of both events occurring is the product of the probabilities of each event occurring.

$$P(A \text{ and } B) = P(A) \cdot P(B)$$

### Example 1

**You roll a number cube once. Then you roll it again. What is the probability that you get 2 on the first roll and a number greater than 4 on the second roll?**

$P(2) = \frac{1}{6}$ There is one 2 among 6 numbers on a cube.

$P(\text{greater than } 4) = \frac{2}{6}$ There are two numbers greater than 4 on a cube.

$$P(2 \text{ and greater than } 4) = P(2) \cdot P(\text{greater than } 4) = \frac{1}{6} \cdot \frac{2}{6} = \frac{2}{36}, \text{ or } \frac{1}{18}$$

The probability of rolling 2 and then a number greater than 4 is $\frac{1}{18}$.

### Try This

5. You toss a coin twice. Find the probability of getting two heads. $\frac{1}{4}$

You can use fractions, decimals, or percents to represent probabilities and to find the probability of two events occurring.

If you randomly select *three* bluebonnet seeds like those in Example 2, what is the probability that all three will grow?

REAL-WORLD CONNECTION

### Example 2

***Botany*** **Bluebonnets grow wild in the southwest United States. Under the best conditions, each bluebonnet seed has a 20% probability of growing. If you select two seeds at random, what is the probability that both will grow, under the best conditions?**

$P(\text{a seed grows}) = 20\%, \text{ or } 0.20$ Write the percent as a decimal.

$P(\text{two seeds grow}) = P(\text{a seed grows}) \cdot P(\text{a seed grows})$

$= 0.20 \cdot 0.20$ Substitute.

$= 0.04 = 4\%$ Multiply. Write 0.04 as a percent.

The probability that two seeds grow is 4%.



- **Additional Example 2**
  Suppose you use a fertilizer that increases the probability to 50% that a bluebonnet seed will grow. What is the probability that two seeds grow? 25%
- **Additional Example 3**
  Suppose in Example 3 that the group consisted of three boys and two girls. Then what is the probability that the teacher will select two girls? $\frac{1}{10}$

## AFTER THE LESSON

### To assess knowledge: Lesson Quiz

Suppose you spin a spinner that is numbered 1–10, then toss a number cube. What is the probability that you will spin and toss an even number? Are these independent or dependent events? $\frac{1}{4}$; independent

- For enrichment and reteaching options see Resources on p. 605H.

■ **TRY THIS**

6. *Botany* Chemically treated bluebonnet seeds have a 30% probability of growing. You select two such seeds at random. What is the probability that both will grow? 9%

## PART 2 Dependent Events

Suppose you select a card from a stack of cards. You then select a second card *without replacing* the first card. Your first selection affects your second selection because there is one card fewer in the stack when you select the second card.

**Dependent events** are events in which the first event *does* affect the second event.

**Probability of Dependent Events**

For two dependent events $A$ and $B$, the probability of both events occurring is the product of the probability of the first event and the probability that, after the first event, the second event occurs.

$$P(A \text{ and } B) = P(A) \cdot P(B \text{ after } A)$$

### EXAMPLE 3

**Three girls and two boys volunteer to represent their class at a school assembly. The teacher selects one name and then another from a bag containing the five students' names. What is the probability that both representatives will be girls?**

$P(\text{girl}) = \frac{3}{5}$ Three of five students are girls.

$P(\text{girl after girl}) = \frac{2}{4}$ If a girl's name is drawn, two of the four remaining students are girls.

$P(\text{girl and girl}) = P(\text{girl}) \cdot P(\text{girl after girl})$

$= \frac{3}{5} \cdot \frac{2}{4}$ Substitute.

$= \frac{6}{20}$, or $\frac{3}{10}$ Simplify.

The probability that both representatives will be girls is $\frac{3}{10}$.

■ **TRY THIS**

7. For Example 3, find $P(\text{boy and girl})$. $\frac{3}{10}$

## Part 2 Teaching Notes

Help students understand that dependent events are so named because the probability of the second event *depends* on the first event taking place.

**Tactile Learning** To demonstrate the concept of dependent events, place one white marble and one black marble in a paper sack. Get students to agree that the probability of drawing either a white or black marble from the bag is $\frac{1}{2}$. Have a student draw a marble.

Then, ask students what the probability of drawing the other marble (depending on which one the first student drew) is. Students should see that drawing the first marble affected the probability of drawing the second marble.

### ■ Example 3

**Build understanding.** Ask: Is the teacher more likely to select a boy with the first selection or with the second selection, if the first is a girl? if the first is a boy? Explain. boy first selection: 2:5; boy second (after girl) 2:4; boy second (after boy) 1:4; since 2:4 > 2:5 > 1:4, boy more likely on second than first only if first was girl

**ELL** Explain that the probability that an event will occur is the same as the *chances* that it will occur. *Chances* is a term that may be more familiar to students than probability.

**Error Prevention** Remind students that when finding the probability of dependent events, the probability of the second event *should* be *different* from the probability of the first event.

# 3 Practice/Assess

## Assignment Guide

To provide flexible scheduling, this lesson can be divided into parts.

**Part 1**

**Core** 1–4, 12–17

**Extension** 27–28

**Part 2**

**Core** 5–11, 18–25, 29

**Extension** 26

Mixed Review can be assigned at any time for maintenance.

## Exercises

**Visual Learning** **Exercises 5–8** Use index cards labeled blue and black to represent the blue and black socks in these exercises.

## Challenge

A bag contains red and white buttons. Suppose you choose two buttons without replacement. The probability of choosing two red buttons is $\frac{3}{10}$. If the probability of choosing a red button first is $\frac{3}{5}$, what is the probability of choosing a second red button? $\frac{1}{2}$

## Closure

Independent events are events in which one event does not affect the other event. If *A* and *B* are independent events, the probability of both *A* and *B* happening is $P(A \text{ and } B) = P(A) \bullet P(B)$. Dependent events are events in which one event does affect the other event. If *A* and *B* are dependent events, the probability of both *A* and *B* happening is $P(A \text{ and } B) = P(A) \bullet P(B \text{ after } A)$.

## Daily Cumulative Review

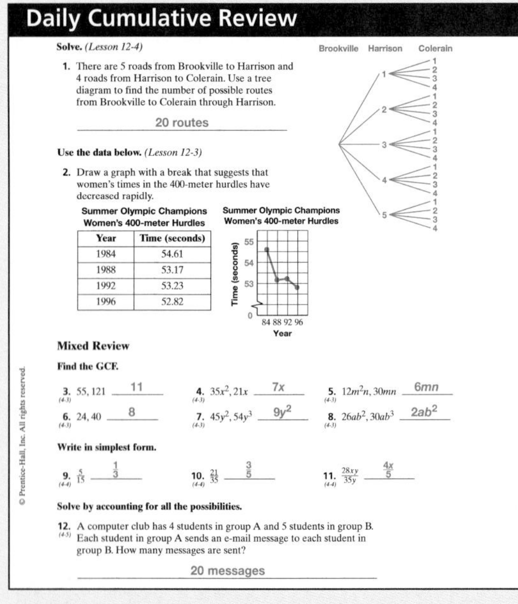

**Solve.** *(Lesson 12-4)*

1. There are 5 roads from Brookville to Harrison and 4 roads from Harrison to Colerain. Use a tree diagram to find the number of possible routes from Brookville to Colerain through Harrison. 20 routes



**Use the data below.** *(Lesson 12-3)*

2. Draw a graph with a break that suggests that women's times in the 400-meter hurdles have decreased rapidly.

**Summer Olympic Champions Women's 400-meter Hurdles**

| Year | Time (seconds) |
|---|---|
| 1984 | 54.61 |
| 1988 | 53.17 |
| 1992 | 53.23 |
| 1996 | 52.82 |



**Mixed Review**

**Find the GCF.**

3. (4-3) 55, 121 11
4. (4-3) $35x^2, 21x$ $7x$
5. (4-3) $12m^2n, 30mn$ $6mn$
6. (4-3) 24, 40 8
7. (4-3) $45y^2, 54y^3$ $9y^2$
8. (4-3) $26ab^2, 30ab^3$ $2ab^2$

**Write in simplest form.**

9. (4-4) $\frac{5}{15}$ $\frac{1}{3}$
10. (4-4) $\frac{21}{35}$ $\frac{3}{5}$
11. (4-4) $\frac{28xy}{35y}$ $\frac{4x}{5}$

**Solve by accounting for all the possibilities.**

12. (4-5) A computer club has 4 students in group A and 5 students in group B. Each student in group A sends an e-mail message to each student in group B. How many messages are sent? 20 messages



# Exercises

## Check Understanding

**You pick a marble from a bag containing 1 green marble, 4 red marbles, 2 yellow marbles, and 3 black marbles. You replace the first marble and select a second one. Find each probability.**

1. *P*(red and yellow) $\frac{2}{25}$ or 8%
2. *P*(black and black) $\frac{9}{100}$ or 9%
3. *P*(red and black) $\frac{3}{25}$ or 12%
4. *P*(yellow and black) $\frac{3}{50}$ or 6%

**A student has 5 blue socks and 4 black socks. He selects one sock at random. Without replacing the sock, he selects a second sock at random. Find each probability.**

5. *P*(blue and black) $\frac{5}{18}$
6. *P*(black and blue) $\frac{5}{18}$
7. *P*(black and black) $\frac{1}{6}$
8. *P*(blue and blue) $\frac{5}{18}$

**Are the events independent or dependent? Explain.**

9. You select a card. Without putting the card back, you select a second card. Dependent. The total number of cards has been reduced by 1.
10. You select a card. After putting it back, you select a second card. Independent. The total number of cards is unchanged.
11. You roll a number cube. You roll it again. Independent. The possibilities on the second roll are the same as on the first.

## Practice and Problem Solving

**You roll a number cube twice. What is the probability that you roll each of the following pairs of numbers?**

12. 6 and then 5 $\frac{1}{36}$
13. 6 and then 2 or 5 $\frac{1}{18}$
14. 6 and then a number less than 4 $\frac{1}{12}$
15. 1 and then 1 $\frac{1}{36}$
16. an even number and then 2 or 5 $\frac{1}{6}$
17. an even number and then an odd number $\frac{1}{4}$

**You select a card at random from those at the right. Without replacing the card, you select a second card. Find the probability of selecting each set of letters.**

P R E A L G E B R A

18. P and then G $\frac{1}{90}$
19. E and then A $\frac{2}{45}$
20. E and then a second vowel $\frac{1}{15}$
21. G and then R or A $\frac{2}{45}$
22. P or E and then A $\frac{1}{15}$
23. a consonant and then a vowel $\frac{4}{15}$
24. *Writing* Explain the difference between independent and dependent events. In independent events the occurrence of the first does not affect the probability of the occurrence of the second. In dependent events it does.



## Alternative Assessment

Have students create a poster or other visual aid that explains the difference between independent and dependent events, and also explains how to find the probability of each type of event.

25. *Open-ended* Give an example of dependent events different from the ones used in this lesson. Check students' work.

26. A refrigerator contains 12 orange drinks, 4 grape drinks, and 25 apple drinks. Ann is first in the line for drinks. Mark is second. What is the probability that Ann gets an apple drink and Mark gets a grape drink, if they are given drinks at random? $\frac{5}{82}$

27. Mrs. Kendall's wallet contains 3 one-dollar bills, 2 five-dollar bills, and 3 ten-dollar bills. She randomly selects one bill and then another from the wallet. Find the probability that she selects the given bills.

a. a one-dollar bill and then a ten-dollar bill $\frac{9}{56}$

b. a ten-dollar bill and then a five-dollar bill $\frac{3}{28}$

28. On a multiple-choice test you randomly guess the answers to two questions. Each question has five choices.

a. What is the probability that you get both answers correct? $\frac{1}{25}$

b. What is the probability that you get both answers incorrect? $\frac{16}{25}$

29. *Weather Forecasting* Weather forecasters are accurate 91% of the time when predicting precipitation for the following day. What is the probability that a forecaster will make a correct precipitation prediction on Friday for the following Saturday, two weeks in a row? 83%

## MIXED REVIEW

**Find the sine, cosine, and tangent of angle *A* for each triangle.** ***(Lesson 11-6)***

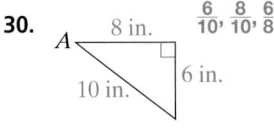

30. $\frac{6}{10}, \frac{8}{10}, \frac{6}{8}$

A
8 in.
6 in.
10 in.

31. $\frac{7}{25}, \frac{24}{25}, \frac{7}{24}$

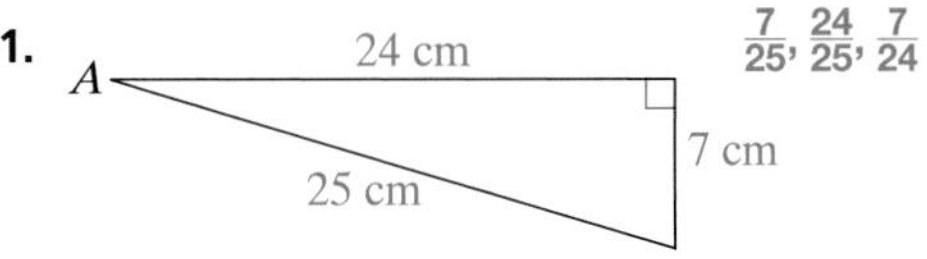


32. From Compt there are four ways to get to Murch. From Murch there are five ways to get to Toll. How many ways are there from Compt to Toll through Murch? ***(Lesson 12-4)*** 20 ways

CHAPTER PROJECT 12

## ACTIVITY 1 INTERVIEWING

Survey the members of your class. Ask each person how much time per week he or she spends on organized extracurricular activities. Record the results.

See also Extra Practice section.



## Project Activity 1

**Interviewing** Have students write the question they want to ask so they can be sure to say it exactly the same way every time. Before they begin the interviews, have them design the form they will use to record and tabulate the answers.

## Practice

**A shelf holds 3 novels, 2 biographies and 1 history book. Two students in turn choose a book at random. What is the probability that the students choose each of the following?**

1. both novels $\frac{1}{5}$
2. both biographies $\frac{1}{15}$
3. a history, then a novel $\frac{1}{10}$
4. both history books 0

**Meg flipped a penny the given number of times. What is the probability the results were as follows?**

5. 2; two heads $\frac{1}{4}$
6. 3; three tails $\frac{1}{8}$
7. 2; a tail, then a head $\frac{1}{4}$
8. 5; five tails $\frac{1}{32}$

**Two puppies are chosen at random from a box at the mall. What is the probability of these outcomes?**

Free Puppies for Adoption!
5 black retrievers
3 brown hounds
4 black setters

9. both black $\frac{6}{11}$
10. both brown $\frac{1}{22}$
11. a setter, then a hound $\frac{1}{11}$
12. a retriever, then a setter $\frac{5}{33}$
13. both setters $\frac{1}{11}$

**Are the events independent or dependent? Explain.**

14. A guest at a party takes a sandwich from a tray. A second guest then takes a sandwich. Dependent; the second guest's choice is limited by the first guest's choice.
15. Sam flips a coin and gets heads. He flips again and gets tails. Independent; the second flip is not affected by the first.

**You can select only two cards from the right. Find the probability of selecting a T and an N for each condition.**

M A T H
I S
F U N

16. You replace the first card before drawing the second. $\frac{1}{81}$
17. You do not replace the first card before drawing the second. $\frac{1}{72}$



## Reteaching

You can select only two cards from the right. Find the probability both are T if you replace the first card before drawing the second and if you do not.

S T A T I S T I C S

If you replace the first card before drawing the second, then the two events of drawing a card are independent. The first draw *does not* affect the second draw.

Use $P(A \text{ and } B) = P(A) \cdot P(B)$.

$P(\text{T}) = \frac{\text{number of favorable outcomes}}{\text{number of possible outcomes}} = \frac{3}{10}$

$P(2\text{T}) = P(\text{T and T}) = P(\text{T}) \cdot P(\text{T}) = \frac{3}{10} \cdot \frac{3}{10} = \frac{9}{100}$

If you do not replace the first card before drawing the second, the two events of drawing a card are dependent. The first draw *does* affect the second draw.

Use $P(A \text{ and } B) = P(A) \cdot P(B \text{ after } A)$.

For the first draw, $P(\text{T}) = \frac{3}{10}$.

If the card is not replaced, there are only 9 cards left on the second draw.

If a T is drawn the first time and not replaced, there are only 2 T's left on the second draw.

$P(\text{T after T}) = \frac{\text{number of favorable outcomes}}{\text{number of possible outcomes}} = \frac{2}{9}$

$P(2\text{T}) = P(\text{T}) \cdot P(\text{T after T}) = \frac{3}{10} \cdot \frac{2}{9} = \frac{1}{15}$

So, with replacement, $P(2\text{T}) = \frac{9}{100}$ and, without replacement, $P(2\text{T}) = \frac{1}{15}$.

**You randomly select a card from those above. You replace the card and select a second card. Find the probability of selecting each set of letters.**

1. two I's $\frac{1}{25}$
2. S and then I $\frac{3}{50}$
3. C and then T $\frac{3}{100}$
4. T and then S $\frac{9}{100}$

**You randomly select a card from those above and, without replacing the card, you select a second card. Find the probability of selecting each set of letters.**

5. two I's $\frac{1}{45}$
6. S and then I $\frac{1}{15}$
7. C and then T $\frac{1}{30}$
8. T and then S $\frac{1}{10}$



## Enrichment

Odds are a way of comparing favorable and unfavorable outcomes.

odds in favor $= \frac{\text{number of favorable outcomes}}{\text{number of unfavorable outcomes}}$

odds against $= \frac{\text{number of unfavorable outcomes}}{\text{number of favorable outcomes}}$

**A record is chosen at random from a sale bin. Find the odds.**

Record Sale!
8 jazz
6 classical
2 rock

1. in favor of classical $\frac{3}{5}$
2. in favor of rock $\frac{1}{7}$
3. against jazz $\frac{1}{1}$

**Example:** Two records are chosen at random from the sale bin. Find the odds in favor of both being jazz.

**Solution:** You can use probability to find odds.

$P(\text{both jazz}) = \frac{8}{16} \cdot \frac{7}{15} = \frac{7}{30}$

There are $30 - 7 = 23$ unfavorable outcomes out of 30.

Odds in favor of both being jazz $= \frac{7}{23}$

**Two records are chosen at random from the sale bin described above. Find the odds in favor of each.**

4. both are rock $\frac{1}{119}$
5. the first is jazz and the second is rock $\frac{1}{14}$
6. the first is classical and the second is jazz $\frac{1}{4}$
7. both are classical $\frac{1}{7}$

**Two records are chosen at random from the sale bin described above. Find the odds against each.**

8. both are rock $\frac{119}{1}$
9. the first is jazz and the second is rock $\frac{14}{1}$
10. the first is classical and the second is jazz $\frac{4}{1}$
11. both are classical $\frac{7}{1}$

# 12-6

## Getting Ready

**Key Terms and Symbols** permutation, permutation notation, combination, combination notation

**Resources** A complete list of resources for this lesson is on p. 605H.

### Daily Skills Warm-Up

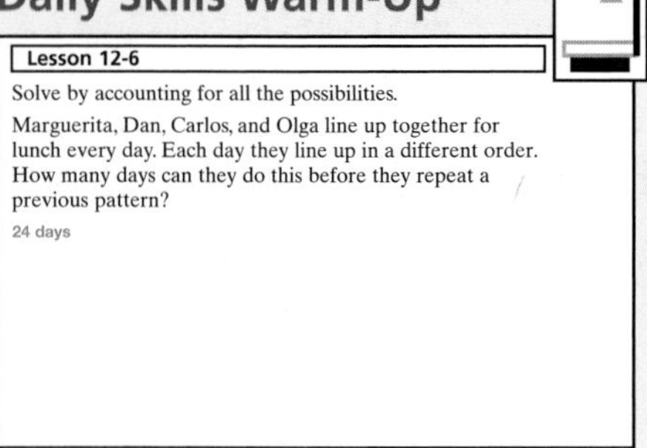

Lesson 12-6
Solve by accounting for all the possibilities.
Marguerita, Dan, Carlos, and Olga line up together for lunch every day. Each day they line up in a different order. How many days can they do this before they repeat a previous pattern?
24 days


### Background for the Lesson

In a group photograph, there are many ways the group can be arranged. Suppose the group has four members and you photograph them in a row. Each way to arrange the four is a *permutation.* Now, suppose you want to take photographs of only two members at a time but you don't care who is on the left or right. You would need to take six photographs to get each possible pair. An arrangement when the order of the group does not matter is a *combination.*

## 1 Focus

### Connecting to Students' Lives

Discuss solving word puzzles with scrambled letters. This lesson shows how to calculate the number of ways the letters of a word can be scrambled.

### Connecting to Prior Knowledge

In Lesson 12-4, students used the counting principle to find outcomes. In this lesson, students extend that to permutations and combinations. In Lesson 12-7, students will learn another method, using experimental probability.



12-6

# Permutations and Combinations

**What You'll Learn**

1. To use permutations
2. To use combinations

**. . . And Why**

To make choices in real-world problems involving sports and earth science

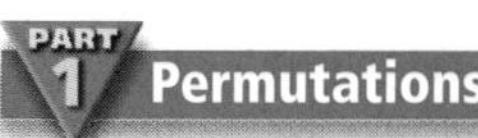

## Part 1 Permutations

An arrangement in which order is important is a **permutation.** For the letters O, P, S, and T, the permutations *STOP* and *POTS* are different because the order of the letters is different. You can use the Counting Principle to find the number of possible permutations.

### Example 1

**Find the number of permutations of the letters O, P, S, and T.**

| 1st letter | | 2nd letter | | 3rd letter | | 4th letter | | |
|---|---|---|---|---|---|---|---|---|
| 4 choices | | 3 choices | | 2 choices | | 1 choice | | |
| 4 | · | 3 | · | 2 | · | 1 | = | 24 |

There are 24 permutations of the letters O, P, S, and T.

### Try This

1. Use the Counting Principle to find the number of permutations possible for the letters W, A, T, E, and R. 120

A track team has seven members. In how many ways can four members line up for a relay race?

You can use *permutation notation* to represent this problem.

7 members → Choose 4.

$$_7P_4 = 7 \cdot 6 \cdot 5 \cdot 4 = 840$$

(7: 1st member; 6: 2nd member; 5: 3rd member; 4: 4th member)

Four of seven team members can line up in 840 ways.

**Permutation Notation**

The expression $_nP_r$ stands for the number of permutations of $n$ objects chosen $r$ at a time.



# Tools to Monitor Progress

### BEFORE THE LESSON

**To check prerequisite skills:**

- Multiplying whole numbers

**Skills Handbook,** p. 725

**Skills Intervention Kit,** Whole Numbers

### DURING THE LESSON

**To check understanding:**

**Try This** exercises on student page

- **Additional Example 1**
  Find the number of permutations of the letters H, O, M, E, and S. 120
- **Additional Example 2**
  In how many ways can you arrange 3 out of 7 students in a line for a group photograph? 210

## EXAMPLE 2

**In how many ways can you arrange five books out of nine books on a shelf?**

9 books — Choose 5.

$_9P_5 = 9 \cdot 8 \cdot 7 \cdot 6 \cdot 5 = 15{,}120$ Simplify.

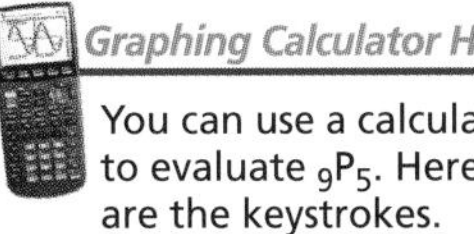

*Graphing Calculator HINT*

You can use a calculator to evaluate $_9P_5$. Here are the keystrokes.

9 MATH < 2 5 ENTER

The result is 15,120.

**TRY THIS** Simplify each expression.

**2.** $_5P_2$ 20 **3.** $_5P_3$ 60 **4.** $_5P_4$ 120 **5.** $_5P_5$ 120

## PART 2 Combinations

Sometimes the order of a group of items is not important. For instance, a ham and cheese sandwich is the same as a cheese and ham sandwich. An arrangement in which order does not matter is a **combination.**

REAL-WORLD CONNECTION

## EXAMPLE 3

*Geography* **In how many ways can you choose two countries from the table when you write reports about inland water?**

Make an organized list of all the combinations.

| | | | | |
|---|---|---|---|---|
| AC | AE | AI | AT | AU |
| | CE | CI | CT | CU |
| | | EI | ET | EU |
| | | | IT | IU |
| | | | | TU |

Abbreviate by using the first letter of each country's name. First list all pairs containing Australia. Continue until every pair of countries is listed.

There are fifteen ways to choose two countries from a list of six.

**Inland Water**

| Country | Water Area (mi²) |
|---|---|
| Australia | 26,610 |
| Canada | 291,573 |
| Ethiopia | 46,680 |
| India | 121,391 |
| Tanzania | 22,799 |
| United States | 79,541 |

SOURCE: *The Top 10 of Everything*

**TRY THIS**

**6.** In how many ways can you choose three different items from a menu containing six items? 20 ways

**Combination Notation**

The expression $_nC_r$ stands for the number of combinations of $n$ objects chosen $r$ at a time.



# 2 Teach

## PART 1 Part 1 Teaching Notes

Explain that a permutation is each unique arrangement of the letters. For example, there are 24 unique ways in which the letters S, T, O, and P can be arranged.

**Error Prevention** Students may think that the only permutations of the letters S, T, O, and P are the ones that spell a word. Explain that each unique way that the letters can be arranged, regardless of whether it spells a word, is a permutation of those letters.

### Example 1

**Build understanding.** Explain why there are fewer choices for the second, third, and fourth letters. Once the first letter is chosen, there are only three letters from which to choose the second letter and two from which to choose the third letter, and so forth.

**Tactile Learning** Have students in groups write the letters S, T, O, and P on four pieces of paper. Ask them to arrange and record their 24 permutations.

**Reading Math** Read the expression $_6P_2$ as, "The number of permutations of six objects chosen two at a time."

**Advanced Learners** Have students research factorial notation ($n$!) and compare this operation to the counting principle. Then ask them to explain factorial notation to the class.

### Example 2

**Build understanding.** Ask: Suppose you wanted to include 7 out of the 9 books in your arrangement. How would you express this in permutation notation? What is the answer? $_9P_7$; 181,440

**Technology Option** On some scientific calculators, the keystrokes may be 9 <shift> <$_nP_r$> 5.

- **Additional Examples 3–4**
  How many different pizzas can you make if you can choose exactly 5 out of 9 toppings? 126
- **Additional Example 5**
  Does the following question involve a permutation or a combination? How many different outfits of a shirt and a sweater can you make from those hanging in a closet? combination

## AFTER THE LESSON

**To assess knowledge:**

**Lesson Quiz**

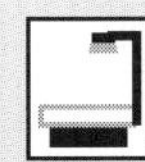

Find the given permutations or combinations.

1. Find the number of permutations in the phone number 390-5847. 5,040
2. $_8P_6$ 20,160
3. $_{12}P_3$ 1,320
4. $_7C_3$ 35

- For enrichment and reteaching options see Resources on p. 605H.

## Part 2 Teaching Notes

Help students understand that ${}_rP_r$ describes the number of duplicate groups because, according to the definition of a combination, each of these permutations is the same combination.

### Example 3

**Build understanding.** Ask: Why was the combination CA left out of the list? **CA is the same combination as AC, which was already included.**

**ELL** Emphasize that *order* is the distinguishing factor between permutations and combinations. If you arrange the letters *T, H,* and *E* as *THE* and *HTE,* their order is different, so they are different permutations. If order is not a factor, the three letters arranged as *THE* and *HTE* are the same combination.

### Example 4

**Build understanding.** Ask: Why are there fewer combinations than permutations? **Some of the permutations are duplicate combinations.**

**Extension** Use math reasoning to explain why ${}_nC_n = 1$. **Since order is not important in combinations, then there is only one combination for all of the items in a group taken as a whole.**

### Example 5

**Build understanding.** Ask: What are key words in these questions that help you identify the problems as combinations or permutations? Explain. **The word *group* does not specify an order, so you are looking for combinations. The second question specifies order, so you are looking for permutations.**

For combinations, a group with the same items as another is a *duplicate group*. For *r* items, the number of duplicate groups is ${}_rP_r$. The number of combinations equals the number of permutations divided by the number of duplicates of each group. So,

$${}_nC_r = \frac{{}_nP_r}{{}_rP_r}.$$

*Graphing Calculator HINT*

You can use a calculator to evaluate ${}_5C_3$. Here are the keystrokes.

5 MATH < 3 3 ENTER

The result is 10.

### EXAMPLE 4

**How many different sandwiches can you make if you can choose exactly three items out of five?**

5 food items — Choose 3.

$${}_5C_3 = \frac{{}_5P_3}{{}_3P_3}$$

$$= \frac{5 \cdot 4 \cdot 3}{3 \cdot 2 \cdot 1} = 10 \quad \text{Simplify.}$$

You can make 10 different sandwiches.

**TRY THIS** Simplify each expression.

**7.** ${}_8C_2$ 28 **8.** ${}_8C_3$ 56 **9.** ${}_8C_4$ 70 **10.** ${}_8C_5$ 56

You can tell whether a problem requires permutations or combinations by asking yourself *Does order matter?* If the answer is *yes*, use permutations. If it is *no*, use combinations.

### EXAMPLE 5

**Tell which type of arrangement each problem involves.**

**a. How many different groups of three books can you choose from five books?**
Combinations: the order of the books selected does not matter.

**b. In how many different orders can you play three CDs?**
Permutations: the order in which you play the CDs matters.

**TRY THIS** Tell which type of arrangement is involved.

**11.** A teacher selects a committee of 4 students from 25 students. How many different committees can the teacher select? combinations

**12.** Class officers are president, vice-president, secretary, and treasurer. From a class of 25 students, how many different groups of officers can be chosen? permutations

# Exercises

## Check Understanding

**Use the Counting Principle to find the number of permutations possible for each group of letters. Use all the letters.**

1. S, I, T 6
2. W, O, R, L, D 120
3. D, E, C, I, M, A, L 5,040

**Make a list to find the number of combinations using two different letters you can form from each group of letters.**

4. C, A, T CA, CT, AT; 3
5. M, A, T, H MA, MT, MH, AT, AH, TH; 6
6. V, A, L, U, E VA, VL, VU, VE, AL, AU, AE, LU, LE, UE; 10

**Simplify each expression.**

7. ${}_4P_2$ 12
8. ${}_6P_4$ 360
9. ${}_9P_4$ 3,024
10. ${}_{10}P_8$ 1,814,400
11. ${}_3P_2$ 6
12. ${}_4C_2$ 6
13. ${}_6C_4$ 15
14. ${}_9C_4$ 126
15. ${}_{10}C_8$ 45
16. ${}_3C_2$ 3

## Practice and Problem Solving

**Use the Counting Principle to find the number of three-letter permutations possible for each group of letters.**

17. P, L, U, S 24
18. F, A, C, T, O, R 120
19. T, R, I, A, N, G, L, E 336

**Make a list to find the number of three-letter combinations you can form from each group of letters.**

20. F, O, R, T, Y FOR, FOT, FOY, FRT, FRY, FTY, ORT, ORY, OTY, RTY; 10 combinations
21. S, I, X SIX; 1 combination
22. E, I, G, H, T, Y EIG, EIH, EIT, EIY, EGH, EGT, EGY, EHT, EHY, ETY, IGH, IGT, IGY, IHT, IHY, ITY, GHT, GHY, GTY, HTY; 20 combinations

**Simplify each expression.**

23. ${}_6P_3$ 120
24. ${}_2P_1$ 2
25. ${}_{10}P_5$ 30,240
26. ${}_7P_4$ 840
27. ${}_{12}P_9$ 79,833,600
28. ${}_6C_3$ 20
29. ${}_2C_1$ 2
30. ${}_{10}C_5$ 252
31. ${}_7C_4$ 35
32. ${}_{12}C_9$ 220

33. Use the letters E, P, S, and T.
   a. How many possible arrangements of the letters are there? 24
   b. How many arrangements form real English words? See below.
   c. *Probability* What is the probability that an arrangement of these letters chosen at random will form an English word? $\frac{1}{8}$

34. *Writing* The lock at the right has a combination consisting of three whole numbers. Explain why it is not likely to be opened by someone who does not know the correct numbers. because there are 64,000 possible combinations

33b. three: pest, pets, and step



# 3 Practice/Assess

## Assignment Guide

To provide flexible scheduling, this lesson can be divided into parts.

**Part 1**
**Core** 1–3, 7–11, 17–19, 23–27
**Extension** 34

**Part 2**
**Core** 4–6, 12–16, 20–22, 28–32, 35–39
**Extension** 33

Mixed Review can be assigned at any time for maintenance.

## Exercises

**Test Prep Exercise 39** Think back to how you read ${}_{10}C_2$ and write down the phrase before you select your answer.

## Challenge

Find the number of permutations of the letters in your first and last names. Answers will vary.

## Closure

An arrangement in which order is important is a permutation. An arrangement in which order does not matter is a combination.

## Alternative Assessment

Ask students to write a paragraph or two comparing and contrasting permutations and combinations. In their paragraphs, students should use examples to help convey their point.

## Daily Cumulative Review

**You randomly select a card from those at the right. Without replacing the card, you select a second card. Find the probability of selecting each set of letters.** *(Lesson 12-5)*

B A L L O O N

1. L and then O $\frac{2}{21}$
2. L twice $\frac{1}{21}$
3. N and then A $\frac{1}{42}$

**Find each sample space. Then find the event's probability.** *(Lesson 12-4)*

4. A bag has one red, one green, one yellow, and one blue marble. You draw a marble from the bag and toss a coin. You get yellow and heads. RH, GH, YH, BH, RT, GT, YT, BT; $\frac{1}{8}$
5. A spinner has 5 equal sections numbered 1 to 5. You spin the spinner and toss a coin. You get an even number and tails. 1H, 2H, 3H, 4H, 5H, 1T, 2T, 3T, 4T, 5T; $\frac{1}{5}$

**Mixed Review**

**Write each fraction as a decimal.**

6. $\frac{8}{25}$ 0.32
7. $\frac{5}{6}$ $0.8\overline{3}$
8. $3\frac{7}{8}$ 3.875

**Write each number as a percent. Round to the nearest tenth of a percent.**

9. 0.79 79%
10. 0.0421 4.2%
11. 1.09 109%
12. $\frac{11}{20}$ 55%
13. $\frac{5}{48}$ 10.4%
14. 0.0083 0.8%

**To make a circle graph of the following information, what should the measure of each central angle be? Round to the nearest degree.**

Fifty students were asked their favorite weekend entertainment. Eighteen said going to a movie, 12 said going to a video arcade, 16 said going to a school dance, and 4 said going bowling.

15. movie 130°
16. video arcade 86°

## Practice

**Simplify each expression.**

1. ${}_7P_2$ 42
2. ${}_7C_2$ 21
3. ${}_8P_3$ 336
4. ${}_9P_4$ 3,024
5. ${}_3C_2$ 3
6. ${}_{10}C_4$ 210

7. Art, Becky, Carl, and Denise are lined up to buy tickets.
   a. How many different permutations of the four are possible? 24
   b. Suppose Ed was also in line. How many permutations would there be? 120
   c. In how many of the permutations of the five is Becky first? 24
   d. What is the probability that a permutation of this five chosen at random will have Becky first? $\frac{1}{5}$
8. Art, Becky, Carl, Denise, and Ed all want to go to the concert. However, there are only 3 tickets. How many ways can they choose the 3 who get to go to the concert? 10
9. A combination lock has 36 numbers on it. How many different 3-number combinations are possible if no number may be repeated? 42,840

**Numbers are to be formed using the digits 1, 2, 3, 4, 5, and 6. No digit may be repeated.**

10. How many two-digit numbers can be formed? 30
11. How many three-digit numbers can be formed? 120
12. How many four-digit numbers can be formed? 360
13. How many five-digit numbers can be formed? 720
14. How many six-digit numbers can be formed? 720



## Reteaching

Ayla, Brandon, Juan, Li, and Marguerita want to go to see a ballet. They only have 3 tickets. How many ways can they choose the 3 that go? One way to solve the problem is to use the first letter of each student's name and list the combinations.

ABJ BJL JLM
ABL BJM
ABM BLM
AJL
AJM
ALM

There are 10 choices. You can also compute the number. There are 3 tickets. Five students want the first ticket. After one is chosen for the first ticket, only 4 want the second ticket. Then, only 3 want the third ticket. So, there are $5 \cdot 4 \cdot 3 = 60$ permutations. The 60 includes different orders, like ABJ, BAJ, and JBA. However, in all cases, the same 3 students would be going to the ballet. Therefore, the *order doesn't matter*.

How many times are Ayla, Brandon, and Juan counted in the 60 permutations found?

ABJ BAJ JAB
AJB BJA JBA

Notice, each of the 3 is listed first. After one is chosen first, 2 can be listed second. After the first two are determined, only one is left for last. So, there are $3 \cdot 2 \cdot 1 = 6$ arrangements for each group of 3.

So, the five students have the following number of choices of 3 to go to the ballet.

$\frac{5 \cdot 4 \cdot 3}{3 \cdot 2 \cdot 1} = \frac{60}{6} = 10$ choices

1. How many choices would Ayla, Brandon, Juan, Li, and Marguerita have if they only had 2 tickets? 10 choices
2. How many choices would the 5 students have if they had 4 tickets? 5 choices
3. Three-digit numbers are to be formed using only the digits 1, 2, 4, 7, and 9. No digit may be repeated. How many different numbers can be formed? 60 numbers
4. An ice cream shop has 21 flavors. How many different two-dip cones can you have if the dips are not the same flavor? 210 cones

Reteaching



## Enrichment

**Find each.**

1. ${}_5P_3$ 60
2. $6 \cdot ({}_5P_3)$ 360
3. ${}_6P_4$ 360
4. ${}_7P_4$ 840
5. $8({}_7P_4)$ 6,720
6. ${}_8P_5$ 6,720
7. Look for a pattern. Explain how you could find ${}_{10}P_3$ using ${}_9P_2 = 72$
   ${}_{10}P_3 = 10 \cdot {}_9P_2 = 10 \cdot 72 = 720$

**Find each. Look for a pattern.**

8. ${}_8C_5$ 56
9. ${}_8C_3$ 56
10. ${}_{12}C_4$ 495
11. ${}_{12}C_8$ 495

**What combination should be equal to each of the following?**

12. ${}_9C_3$ ${}_9C_6$
13. ${}_{15}C_4$ ${}_{15}C_{11}$
14. Find each combination in the triangle on the left. Write the amount in the corresponding circle in the triangle on the right.
    ${}_nC_0 = 1$ for any $n$ since the only combination is to choose nothing.

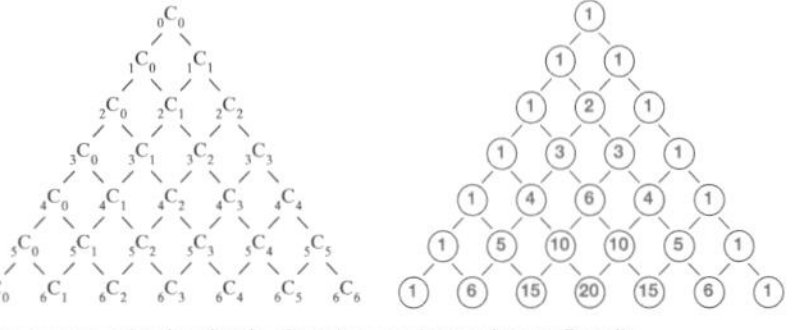

You may recognize the triangle of numbers you have written as Pascal's triangle.





35. *Open-ended* Use the different letters from your last name. Check students' work.
    a. Find the number of two-letter permutations.
    b. Find the number of two-letter combinations.
36. Louisa May Alcott published 13 novels during her lifetime. In how many ways could you select and read three of these books? 286 ways

**Does each problem involve *permutations* or *combinations*? Explain.**

37. In how many different ways can three students form a line? Permutations; order is important in a line.
38. In how many orders can you play three different games? Permutations; order is important in games.
39. **TEST PREP** Which question can you answer by evaluating ${}_{10}C_2$? C
    A. In how many ways can you arrange 10 books on 2 shelves?
    B. In how many ways can 10 people line up 2 at a time?
    C. In how many ways can you choose 2 people from 10 for tennis?
    D. In how many ways can you choose first-place and second-place winners from 10 finalists?

**Journal**

*Explain the difference between a permutation and a combination.*

## Mixed Review

**On each of five cards there is one of the letters A, B, C, D, and E. You select two cards. Find each probability.** ***(Lesson 12-5)***

40. $P(A, \text{then } B \text{ with } A \text{ replaced})$ $\frac{1}{25}$
41. $P(A, \text{then } B \text{ without } A \text{ replaced})$ $\frac{1}{20}$
42. Find the area of the triangle at the right. ***(Lessons 10-2 and 11-2)*** 120 in.$^2$

43. *Consumer Issues* A coat is on sale for \$80. Its original price was \$120. What is the percent of discount? ***(Lesson 6-9)*** $33.\overline{3}\%$

## Math at Work

### Wildlife Statistician

Wildlife statisticians study the growth or decline of plant and animal life in a geographical region. They make observations and collect data for a small portion, or sample, of an animal or plant population. Then they draw conclusions about the entire population. If you enjoy studying wildlife, this may be the job for you.

For more information about careers in wildlife statistics, visit the Prentice Hall Web site. **www.phschool.com**

See also Extra Practice section.

## Math at Work

If you have block scheduling or extended class periods, have small groups of students research the career of a wildlife statistician, or any other statistician, to discover the ways in which statisticians use math. Ask the groups to prepare a report of their findings to share with the class.

Students can find additional information on the Web site **www.phschool.com**.

# Standardized Test Prep

## Multiple Choice

**Choose the best answer.**

1. You are writing a three-digit number. The first digit must be 2 or 8. The second digit must be 1, 3, or 9. The third digit must be 4, 5, 6, 7, or 8. Which expression can you use to determine how many different numbers you can write? A
   A. $2 \cdot 3 \cdot 5$
   B. $5 \cdot 4 \cdot 3 \cdot 2 \cdot 1$
   C. $(1 \cdot 2) + (2 \cdot 3) + (3 \cdot 5)$
   D. $2 + 3 + 5$

2. Which expression shows the prime factorization of the numerator and denominator of $\left(\frac{42}{22}\right)\left(\frac{75}{63}\right)$? G
   F. $\frac{42 \cdot 75}{22 \cdot 63}$
   G. $\frac{2 \cdot 3^2 \cdot 5^2 \cdot 7}{2 \cdot 3^2 \cdot 7 \cdot 11}$
   H. $2\frac{27}{100}$
   J. $\frac{6 \cdot 7 \cdot 5 \cdot 25}{2 \cdot 11 \cdot 7 \cdot 9}$

3. Name the figure. C

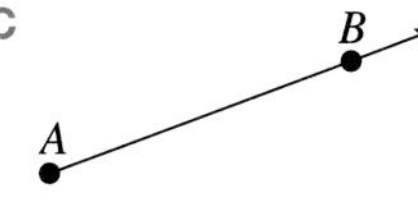


   A. $\overleftrightarrow{AB}$
   B. $\overline{AB}$
   C. $\overrightarrow{AB}$
   D. $\angle AB$

4. Each solid has a height of 5 in. Which has the greatest volume? H

F. 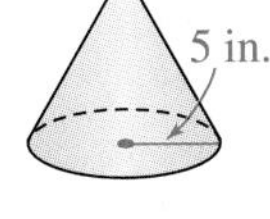


G. 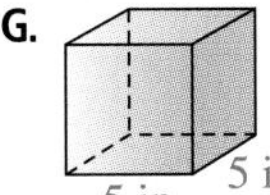


H. 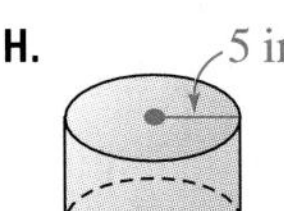


J. 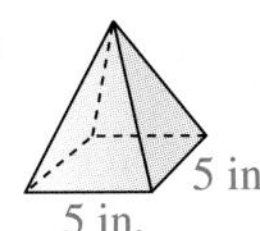


5. Which figure *cannot* be a net for the prism shown? D

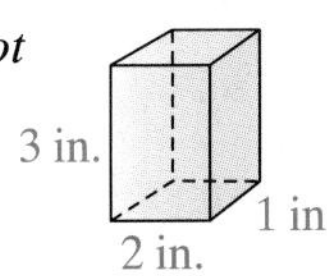


A. 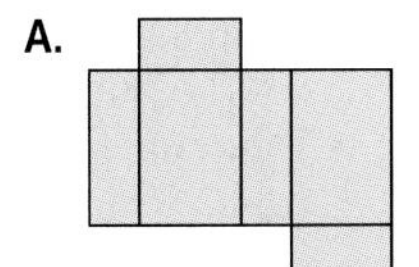

B. 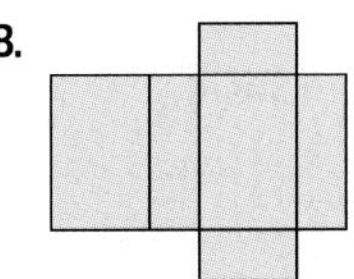

C. 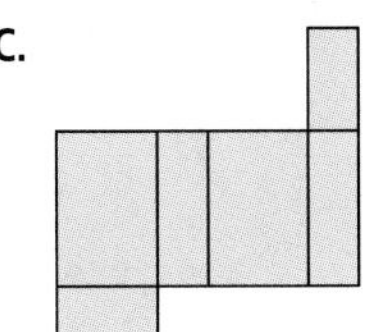

D. 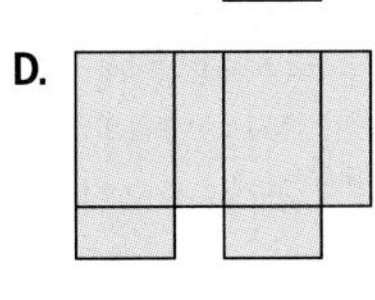

## Free Response

**For Exercises 6–8, show your work.**

6. $\angle ABC$ is an acute angle. Write an inequality for $x$. $x < 60$

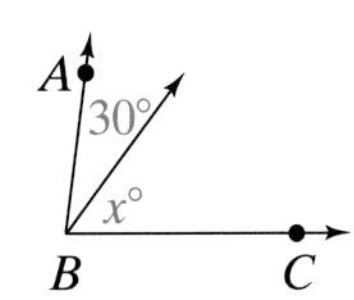


7. Explain how you can use the Pythagorean Theorem to find the height of an equilateral triangle with side length 12. See margin.

8. a. The table below shows the maximum life span of some mammals. Create a box-and-whisker plot for the data. See margin.
   b. Write the values of the lower quartile, the median, and the upper quartile. 18, 31, 50

| | | | |
|---|---|---|---|
| **Beaver** | 50 yr | **Goat** | 18 yr |
| **Black bear** | 36 yr | **Horse** | 50 yr |
| **Chimpanzee** | 53 yr | **Mouse** | 6 yr |
| **Chipmunk** | 8 yr | **Squirrel** | 23 yr |
| **Elephant** | 77 yr | **Tiger** | 26 yr |



## Standardized Test Prep

Standardized tests, such as those administered for state assessment, SAT9, TerraNova™, ITBS, MAT7, or CAT5, may include multiple choice questions, free-response questions, and open-ended questions.

**Multiple Choice Questions** are followed usually by four choices, one of which is correct.

Exercises 1–5 are multiple choice questions.

**Free-Response Questions** do not give answer choices. Student must provide the one correct answer on their own.

Exercises 6–8 are free-response questions.

### Resources

See p. 605G for a list of assessment options.

### Test-Taking Tip

Before you calculate an answer, try to eliminate one or two of the answer choices that you recognize as clearly incorrect.

7. The height is the length of an altitude. The altitude divides the triangle into two right triangles, both with leg 6 and hypotenuse 12. The altitude is the other leg. $h^2 + 6^2 = 12^2$ and $h = 10.4$.

8a. Life Spans of Mammals

0 10 20 30 40 50 60 70 80

### Test-Taking Tips on Transparency

Several strategies can help you determine that the correct answer is not given.

*Example* The original price of a sweater was $49. It was marked down 30%. How much money is saved?

A. $15.00 B. $4.90 C. $34.30 D. Not Here

Round the sweater's price: $50.

It should be marked down about 0.30 × 50 = $15.

Choice A is $15, but this is an estimate, not the exact amount of money saved.

Work backward.

Choices B and C are not near $15, so they are wrong.*

The answer is not A, B, or C, so choose D.

*Mental math shows that $4.90 is 10% (not 30%) of $49. Also, $34.30 is the sale price, not the money saved.

Explain why the correct answer is not given.

1. Suppose your electricity bill for May was $41.85. What was the average daily cost of electricity in May?
   A. $5.54 B. $3.23 C. $1.50 D. Not Here
2. Jon works 6 hours per day, 5 days per week. He earns $6.15/h. How much money does he earn per week?
   F. $180.00 G. $738.00 H. $36.90 J. Not Here

# 12-7

## Getting Ready

**Key Terms and Symbols** experimental probability, simulation

**Resources** A complete list of resources for this lesson is on p. 605H.

### Daily Skills Warm-Up

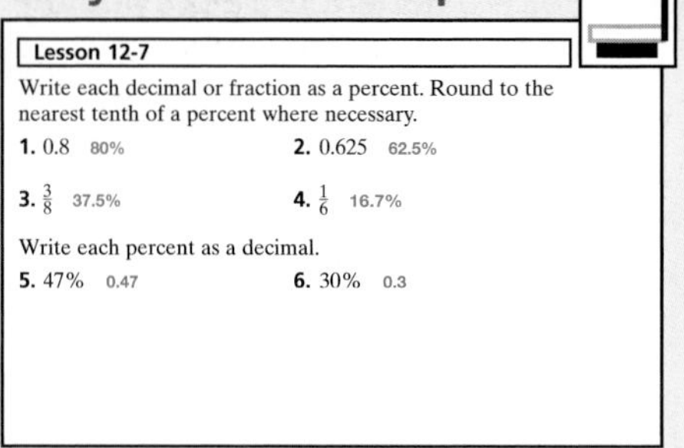
Lesson 12-7

Write each decimal or fraction as a percent. Round to the nearest tenth of a percent where necessary.

**1.** 0.8 80% **2.** 0.625 62.5%

**3.** $\frac{3}{8}$ 37.5% **4.** $\frac{1}{6}$ 16.7%

Write each percent as a decimal.

**5.** 47% 0.47 **6.** 30% 0.3

### Background for the Lesson

Remember that theoretical probability is the ratio of the number of times an event occurs to the number of possible outcomes. The theoretical probability of tossing a 1 on a number cube is $\frac{1}{6}$. In contrast, *experimental probability* is based on data you gather in actual trials. For example, you could toss a number cube several times to see how often the number 1 comes up. There are often differences between the theoretical and experimental probability of an event. As you increase the number of trials, the experimental probability gets closer to the theoretical probability.

## 1 Focus

### Connecting to Students' Lives

Discuss students' experiences when flipping coins. Why might someone want to decide by using two out of three flips?

### Connecting to Prior Knowledge

In Lesson 12-4, students learned how to calculate theoretical probability. In this lesson, students learn the difference between theoretical and experimental probability. In Lesson 12-9, students will simulate problems to determine experimental probability.



# 12-7 Experimental Probability

**What You'll Learn**

1. To find experimental probability
2. To use simulations

**. . . And Why**

To solve problems in medical science and test-taking

## Part 1 Finding Experimental Probability

You have learned to find theoretical probability, which is the ratio of the number of favorable outcomes to the number of possible outcomes. You can also find probability based on experimental data, which is known as **experimental probability.**

**Experimental Probability**

$$P(\text{event}) = \frac{\text{number of times an event occurs}}{\text{number of times experiment is done}}$$

### Example 1

*Medical Science* **A medical study tests a new medicine on 3,500 participants. It is effective for 3,010 participants. Find the experimental probability that the medicine is effective.**

$$P(\text{event}) = \frac{\text{number of times an event occurs}}{\text{number of times experiment is done}}$$

$$= \frac{3{,}010}{3{,}500} = 0.86$$

The experimental probability that the medicine is effective is 0.86, or 86%.

**Try This**

1. Another medicine is effective for 1,183 of 2,275 participants. Find the experimental probability that the medicine is effective. 52%

## Part 2 Simulating Events

A **simulation** is a model used to find experimental probability. Experimental probability found by simulation can differ from theoretical probability. The more trials you do in a simulation, the closer the two types of probability values are likely to be.



# Tools to Monitor Progress

### BEFORE THE LESSON

**To check prerequisite skills:**

- Finding probability
- Fractions, decimals, and percents

**Skills You Need,** p. 605

**Skills Intervention Kit,** Operations with Fractions

### DURING THE LESSON

**To check understanding:**

**Try This** exercises on student page

- **Additional Example 1**

  **a.** Suppose 1,715 of the 3,500 participants developed side effects. Find the experimental probability that the medicine will cause side effects. 49%

## Different Ways to Solve a Problem

**Use theoretical and experimental probabilities to find the probability of correctly guessing all 4 answers on a 4-question true-false quiz.**

**Method 1: Theoretical Probability**

Each guess is an independent event. Find the probability of one correct guess. Then find the probability of four independent correct guesses.

$P(\text{1 correct guess}) = \frac{1}{2}$

$P(\text{4 correct guesses}) = \frac{1}{2} \cdot \frac{1}{2} \cdot \frac{1}{2} \cdot \frac{1}{2} = \frac{1}{16}$

The theoretical probability is $\frac{1}{16}$.

**Method 2: Experimental Probability**

Simulate the problem by tossing a coin. Let heads stand for a correct guess and tails for an incorrect guess. Use the results of 120 tosses given at the right.

Separate the results into 30 groups of 4. Count the groups with 4 heads. There are two.

| | | | | | |
|---|---|---|---|---|---|
| HTTT | HTTT | HHHT | TTTT | TTHT | THTT |
| THHH | THHH | HTTT | TTHH | HTTT | HTHH |
| HTHH | THTT | TTHT | THTH | HHTT | THTH |
| HHHH | TTHT | HHHH | THTT | TTTH | HHHT |
| HHTT | HTTT | THTT | HHTT | HHTH | HTHH |

Find the experimental probability.

$P(\text{event}) = \frac{\text{number of times an event occurs}}{\text{number of times experiment is done}}$

$= \frac{2}{30} = \frac{1}{15}$

The experimental probability is $\frac{1}{15}$.

**120 Coin Tosses**

H T T T H T T T H H H T
T T T T T T H T T H T T
T H H H T H H H H T T T
T T H H H T T T H T H H
H T H H T H T T T T H T
T H T H H H T T T H T H
H H H H T T H T H H H H
T H T T T T T H H H H T
H H T T H T T T T H T T
H H T T H H T H H T H H

For this simulation, the experimental probability is a little greater than the theoretical probability. Another simulation might give different results. As you do more trials, the experimental probability is likely to approach the theoretical probability.

**Choose a Method**

1. Which method would you use to solve the problem? Explain. Check students' work.



# 2 Teach

### Part 1 Teaching Notes

Explain that to find experimental probability, you actually have to create the event or a simulation of the event. This means that if you want to know the experimental probability of rolling a 6 on a number cube, you must roll the number cube repeatedly.

**Connecting to Medicine** Drug testing is regulated by the United States Food and Drug Administration (FDA). Before a new drug can be tested on humans, it must undergo hundreds or thousands of lab and animal tests. Then, the drug must undergo many human tests before it can be approved for general use.

#### Example 1

**Build understanding.** Ask: Does the experimental probability of this medicine mean that if you gave it to 10 people, it would be effective for 8? not necessarily with such a small sample

**Error Prevention** The denominator in an experimental probability ratio is the number of trials that were undertaken, not the number of possible outcomes. If you toss a coin 100 times, the denominator of the ratio will be 100, not 2 as in theoretical probability.

### Part 2 Teaching Notes

Explain that a simulation is a mathematical way to model chance occurrences in an experiment that is difficult to actually carry out.

#### Different Ways to Solve a Problem

**Build understanding.** The theoretical probability and experimental probability of an event are likely to be different. Explain how you can make their values approach each other. The more trials you do, the closer the experimental probability will be to the theoretical probability.

**b.** What if 4,500 people had participated in the trials with 1,715 participants developing side effects? Would there be an increase or a decrease in the experimental probability that the medicine will cause side effects? Explain. decrease; a lesser percentage (38%) would have side effects

### AFTER THE LESSON

**To assess knowledge: Lesson Quiz**

1. Jenny made 42 out of 70 free throws. What is the experimental probability that she will make her next free throw? 60%
2. If 152 of 722 students chose fish, what is the experimental probability that the next student will choose fish? about 21%

- For enrichment and reteaching options see Resources on p. 605H.

# 3 Practice/Assess

## Assignment Guide

To provide flexible scheduling, this lesson can be divided into parts.

**Part 1**
**Core** 1–4, 6–12
**Extension** 16

**Part 2**
**Core** 5, 13–15, 18
**Extension** 17

Mixed Review can be assigned at any time for maintenance.

## Exercises

**Auditory Learning Exercise 5** Work with a partner to discuss ways you could simulate this problem. After you and your partner agree on a simulation, record your ideas.

**Test Prep Exercise 12** If you read this problem carefully, you will realize that it is actually asking for the number of baseballs that are OK.

## Challenge

If you toss a coin only one time and get heads, what experimental probability have you found for tossing heads? 100%

## Closure

Experimental probability is based on experimental data. You can use a simulation to model real-world problems.

# Exercises

## CHECK UNDERSTANDING

**Students were surveyed about the number of pencils in their bookbags. The table shows the results. Write each experimental probability as a fraction in simplest form.**

**Pencils in Students' Bookbags**

| Number of pencils | Number of students |
|---|---|
| 0 | 4 |
| 1 | 16 |
| 2 or more | 12 |

1. $P$(one pencil) $\frac{1}{2}$
2. $P$(no pencils) $\frac{1}{8}$
3. $P$(two or more pencils) $\frac{3}{8}$
4. $P$(at least one pencil) $\frac{7}{8}$
5. *Calendar* Design a simulation you could use to find the experimental probability of your birthday falling on a Saturday in a year chosen at random. Check students' work.

## PRACTICE AND PROBLEM SOLVING

**A student took a survey of some of the vehicles in a parking lot. Use the results in the table to find the experimental probability that a random vehicle in the lot is the given color. Write the probability as a percent, to the nearest tenth of a percent.**

| Color | Number of Vehicles |
|---|---|
| Black | 9 |
| Blue | 10 |
| Brown | 13 |
| Green | 7 |
| Red | 12 |
| White | 11 |
| Gray | 6 |

6. red 17.6%
7. white 16.2%
8. black 13.2%
9. blue or green 25%
10. not black or gray 77.9%
11. purple 0%
12. **TEST PREP** A baseball manufacturer checked 250 of its baseballs and found that 8 were defective. Find the experimental probability that a baseball was *not* defective. D
    A. 9.68% B. 32% C. 3.2% D. 96.8%
13. a. How would you find the experimental probability of tossing three coins and getting three heads? See below right.
    b. *Mathematical Reasoning* How would you compare the experimental probability of getting three heads to the theoretical probability? Would you expect the probabilities to be equal? Explain. See below right.
14. You take a 5-question multiple-choice test. Each question has 4 choices. Use a simulation to find the experimental probability of guessing the correct answers to exactly 4 questions. Check students' work.
15. *Data Analysis* Roll a number cube 100 times. Record the results.
    a. Find the experimental probability of rolling an even number.
    b. Compare the experimental probability to the theoretical probability. Check students' work.

13a. Toss 3 coins repeatedly, perhaps 100 times, and record the results. The percent of the time that you get 3 heads is the experimental probability.

13.b. Find the experimental probability as in part (a). Calculate the theoretical probability $\left(\frac{1}{2} \cdot \frac{1}{2} \cdot \frac{1}{2} = \frac{1}{8}\right)$. Compare the probabilities. They will not necessarily be the same. As one performs many experiments, experimental probability will approach theoretical.



## Daily Cumulative Review

**Use the Counting Principle to find the number of three-letter permutations possible for each group of letters.** *(Lesson 12-6)*

1. E I G H T Y 120
2. H E X A G O N 210
3. T R I A N G L E S 504

**Solve.** *(Lesson 12-5)*

4. Parents of one of the players brought 9 apples, 8 oranges, and 4 peaches for the players after the game. Michelle is first in line and Juanita is second. What is the probability that Michelle gets an orange and Juanita gets an apple if they are given fruit at random? $\frac{6}{35}$

**Mixed Review**

**Solve each proportion. Round to the nearest tenth where necessary.**

5. (6-2) $\frac{5}{16} = \frac{x}{30}$ 9.4
6. (6-2) $\frac{a}{6} = \frac{9}{20}$ 2.7
7. (6-2) $\frac{4}{b} = \frac{6}{17}$ 11.3

**Write a proportion, and find the value of each $x$.**

8. (11-4) $\triangle JKL \sim \triangle JMN$

   $\frac{12}{18} = \frac{15}{x + 15}$; 7.5 ft

9. (11-4) $\triangle PQR \sim \triangle TSR$

   $\frac{0.25}{0.4} = \frac{0.3}{x}$; 0.48 mi

**Use the triangle at the right. Find the missing length to the nearest tenth of a unit.**

10. (11-2) $a = 7$ in., $b = 9$ in., $c \approx$ 11.4 in.
11. (11-2) $a = 4$ m, $c = 10$ m, $b \approx$ 9.2 m



## Alternative Assessment

Have students use computer spreadsheet software to simulate tossing a coin so they can find the experimental probability. Students should simulate as many trials as possible. Ask them to share their findings with the class.

**16.** Two players played a game with a number cube. The table shows the results.

**Game Results**

| A Wins | B Wins |
|---|---|
| 卌卌卌卌 卌 IIII | 卌卌卌卌 卌卌卌卌 卌卌 II |

**a.** Find Probability(A wins) and Probability(B wins). $\frac{29}{81}$, $\frac{52}{81}$

**b.** *Writing* A *fair game* is one in which each player has the same chance of winning. Do you think the game that A and B played is fair? Explain. Probably not a fair game, because B is winning far more often than A.

**17. a.** *Open-ended* Write a problem you can solve with a simulation. Check students' work.

**b.** Solve the problem.

**18.** *Error Analysis* A student wants to do a simulation to find the probability of correctly guessing a number from 1 to 5 two times in a row. He decides to roll a number cube 100 times, separating the results into 50 groups of two and letting a roll of 1 stand for a correct guess. Explain why the student's simulation will not give good results.

18. In the actual situation, the students' probability of making a correct guess is $\frac{1}{5}$. In the simulation, using a six-sided number cube, the probability of rolling a 1 is $\frac{1}{6}$.

## MIXED REVIEW

**Evaluate each expression.** ***(Lesson 12-6)***

**19.** ${}_4P_2$ 12 **20.** ${}_{10}P_3$ 720 **21.** ${}_4C_3$ 4 **22.** ${}_6C_3$ 20

*Spatial Thinking* **Write a rule to describe each translation.** ***(Lesson 9-8)***

**23.**

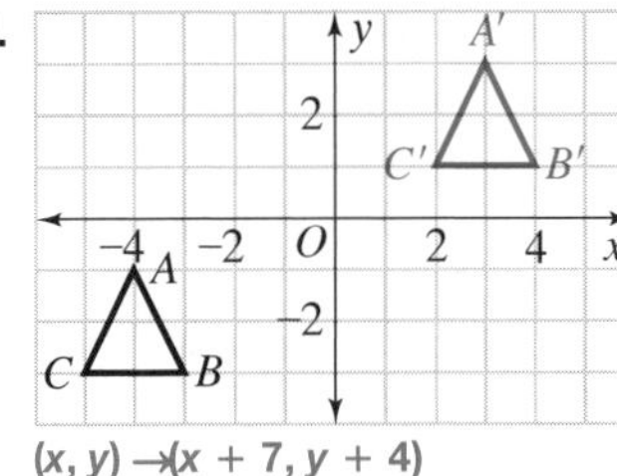


$(x, y) \rightarrow (x + 7, y + 4)$

**24.**

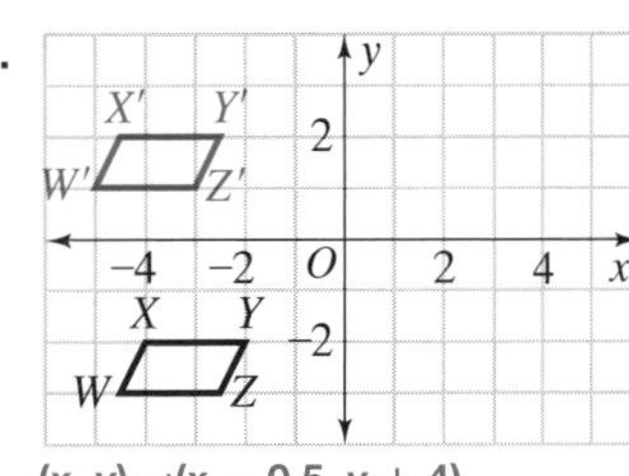


$(x, y) \rightarrow (x - 0.5, y + 4)$

**25.** *Geometry* Find the volume of a spherical globe with a diameter of 0.9 m. Use 3.14 for $\pi$. Round to the nearest tenth. ***(Lesson 10-9)*** 0.4 $m^3$

CHAPTER PROJECT 12

## ACTIVITY 2 GRAPHING

Display your data from Activity 1 in a line plot and a box-and-whisker plot. Which type of graph is better for comparing the amount of time you spend on extracurricular activities to the class average? Explain.

See also Extra Practice section.



## Project Activity 2

**Graphing** Ask students to consider these questions: Which graph represents the data most accurately? Which graph communicates the results most clearly to someone else?

## Practice

**The table shows the colors of Rahmi's soccer shirts. For each color, find the experimental probability that a random shirt from Rahmi's collection is that color. Write the probability as a percent, to the nearest tenth of a percent.**

| Color | Number of shirts |
|---|---|
| red | 6 |
| white | 4 |
| orange | 3 |
| blue | 2 |

1. red 40%
2. white 26.7%
3. orange 20%
4. blue 13.3%
5. red or blue 53.3%
6. not white 73.3%
7. not orange or red 40%
8. green 0%

**Your school's basketball team has an equal chance of winning or losing the first three games of the season. You simulate the probability by tossing a coin 60 times, letting heads stand for a win and tails stand for a loss. Use the data below. Find each experimental probability as a percent.**

HHH THH THT TTH THH
HTH THH THH HTH HHH
THH TTH THH HTT TTT
HTT HHT TTH HTH THH

9. $P$(win all 3) 10%
10. $P$(win exactly 2) 55%
11. $P$(win exactly 1) 30%
12. $P$(win none) 5%
13. $P$(win at least 2) 65%
14. $P$(win at least 1) 95%
15. $P$(win less than 2) 35%

**Students were surveyed about the number of children living in their household. The table shows the results. Write each experimental probability as a fraction in simplest form.**

| Number of children | Number of students |
|---|---|
| 0 | 0 |
| 1 | 11 |
| 2 | 15 |
| 3 | 3 |
| 4 or more | 4 |

16. $P$(one child) $\frac{1}{3}$
17. $P$(2 or more children) $\frac{2}{3}$
18. $P$(at least 3 children) $\frac{7}{33}$



Practice

## Reteaching

The table shows the colors of Lisa's baseball caps. Find the probability that a random cap from Lisa's collection is green or orange. Round to the nearest tenth of a percent.

$P(\text{event}) = \frac{\text{number of times the event occurs}}{\text{number of trials}}$

Since there are 30 caps in Lisa's collection, the number of trials is 30. Five caps are green and 3 are orange, so $5 + 3 = 8$ are either green or orange.

$P(\text{green or orange}) = \frac{8}{30} \approx 26.7\%$

| Color | Number of Caps |
|---|---|
| blue | 7 |
| green | 5 |
| orange | 3 |
| white | 9 |
| red | 6 |

**Use the data in the table above. For each color, find the experimental probability that a random cap from Lisa's collection is that color. Write the probability as a percent, to the nearest tenth of a percent.**

1. blue 23.3%
2. green 16.7%
3. red 20%
4. red or white 50%
5. blue or orange 33.3%
6. not white 70%
7. not green or red 63.3%
8. pink 0%
9. not pink 100%
10. red, white, or blue 73.3%
11. green, orange, or white 56.7%
12. not green, orange, or white 43.3%



## Enrichment

You and a partner can conduct a probability experiment to approximate the value of $\pi$. First, recall this definition: Two numbers are *relatively prime* if their only common factor is 1.

Each partner should choose a 2-digit number at random from a phone book or the page numbers of a book. Record the numbers as Trial 1. Conduct as many trials as possible. The more pairs you choose, the closer will be your approximation to $\pi$. Check student's tables.

| Trial | First number | Second number |
|---|---|---|
| 1 | | |
| 2 | | |
| 3 | | |
| 4 | | |
| 5 | | |
| 6 | | |
| 7 | | |
| 8 | | |
| 9 | | |
| 10 | | |
| 11 | | |
| 12 | | |
| 13 | | |
| 14 | | |
| 15 | | |
| 16 | | |
| 17 | | |
| 18 | | |
| 19 | | |
| 20 | | |

| Trial | First number | Second number |
|---|---|---|
| 21 | | |
| 22 | | |
| 23 | | |
| 24 | | |
| 25 | | |
| 26 | | |
| 27 | | |
| 28 | | |
| 29 | | |
| 30 | | |
| 31 | | |
| 32 | | |
| 33 | | |
| 34 | | |
| 35 | | |
| 36 | | |
| 37 | | |
| 38 | | |
| 39 | | |
| 40 | | |

**Now find the following.**

1. number of trials ($N$) 40
2. number of relatively prime pairs ($R$) Answer should be close to 24.
3. To approximate $\pi$, find $\sqrt{\frac{6N}{R}}$ using your calculator. Answer should be about 3.16.
4. To the nearest thousandth, how far off is your approximation? Use $\pi \approx 3.142$. Check students' calculations.



Enrichment

# 12-8

## Getting Ready

**Key Terms and Symbols** population, sample, random sample

**Resources** A complete list of resources for this lesson is on p. 605H.

### Daily Skills Warm-Up

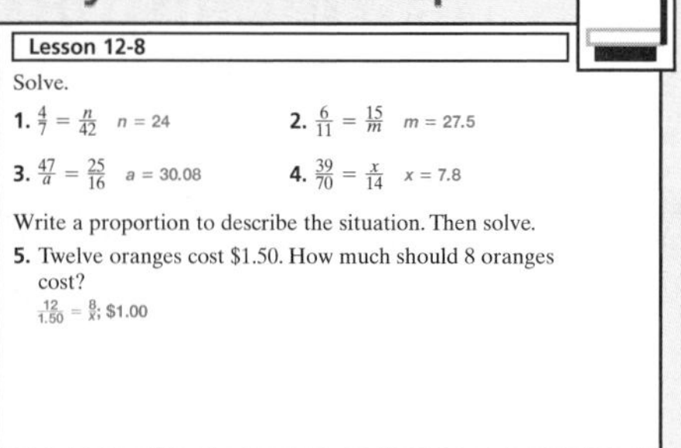

Lesson 12-8

Solve.

1. $\frac{4}{7} = \frac{n}{42}$ $n = 24$
2. $\frac{6}{11} = \frac{15}{m}$ $m = 27.5$
3. $\frac{47}{a} = \frac{25}{16}$ $a = 30.08$
4. $\frac{39}{70} = \frac{x}{14}$ $x = 7.8$

Write a proportion to describe the situation. Then solve.

5. Twelve oranges cost $1.50. How much should 8 oranges cost?
$\frac{12}{1.50} = \frac{8}{x}$; $1.00

### Background for the Lesson

A *sample* is a small part of a *population* you choose to represent the entire population that you are studying. You use the sample to make predictions about the population as a whole. The results from the sample are supposed to reflect the results you would get if you had surveyed the population as a whole. The larger the sample, the more reliable the results will be. A choice is *random* if each member of the sample had the same chance to be selected.

## 1 Focus

### Connecting to Students' Lives

Find out if any students have been part of a survey. Discuss what kinds of questions the survey asked.

### Connecting to Prior Knowledge

In Lesson 12-1, students learned to organize the data from a survey into frequency tables and line plots. In this lesson, students learn how to choose samples for a survey and how to use a sample to make an estimate about a population. In Lesson 12-9, students will learn to make predictions by simulating a problem.



# 12-8 Random Samples and Surveys

**What You'll Learn**

1. To choose a sample for a survey of a population
2. To make estimates about populations

**. . . And Why**

To solve problems involving recycling and quality control

## PART 1 Choosing Samples for Surveys

How many books do you read each week? What are your hobbies? Statisticians use questions like these in surveys to get information about specific groups. A **population** is a group about which you want information. A **sample** is a part of the population you use to make estimates about the population. The larger your sample, the more reliable your estimates will be.

For a **random sample** each member of the population has an equal chance to be selected. A random sample is likely to be representative of the whole population.

### EXAMPLE 1

**You want to find out whether students will participate if you start a recycling program at your school. Tell whether each survey plan describes a good sample.**

**a. Interview every tenth teenager you see at a mall.**
This sample will probably include students who do not go to your school. It is not a good sample because it is not taken from the population you want to study.

**b. Interview the students in your ecology class.**
The views of students in an ecology class may not represent the views about recycling of students in other classes. This is not a good sample because it is not random.

**c. Interview every tenth student leaving a school assembly.**
This is a good sample. It is selected at random from the population you want to study.

**TRY THIS** Explain whether each plan describes a good sample.

1. You want to know which bicycle is most popular. You plan to survey entrants in a bicycle race. **Not a good sample, because these students would be most interested in racing bikes.**
2. You want to know how often teens rent videos. You plan to survey teens going into the local video rental store. **Not a good sample, because this sample would not include teens who do not rent videos.**



## Tools to Monitor Progress

### BEFORE THE LESSON

**To check prerequisite skills:**

- Dividing whole numbers

**Skills Intervention Kit,** Whole Numbers

### DURING THE LESSON

**To check understanding:**

**Try This** exercises on student page

- **Additional Example 1**
To find out how many people in the community use computers on a daily basis, Sergio surveyed every tenth student who arrived to school on a school bus. Explain why this is or is not a good survey plan. **sample answer: The sample is composed**

3. You want to know the most popular breakfast cereal. You plan to survey people entering a grocery store. This is a good sample, because there is no built-in bias for or against any cereal.

## Part 2 Making Estimates about Populations

You can use a sample to make an estimate about a population by writing and solving a proportion.

REAL-WORLD CONNECTION

### Example 2

*Quality Control* **From 20,000 calculators produced, a manufacturer takes a random sample of 500 calculators. The sample has 3 defective calculators. Estimate the total number of defective calculators.**

$$\frac{\text{defective sample calculators}}{\text{sample calculators}} = \frac{\text{defective calculators}}{\text{calculators}}$$ Write a proportion.

$$\frac{3}{500} = \frac{n}{20{,}000}$$ Substitute.

$$3(20{,}000) = 500n$$ Write cross products.

$$\frac{3(20{,}000)}{500} = \frac{500n}{500}$$ Divide each side by 500.

$$120 = n$$ Simplify.

Estimate: About 120 calculators are defective.

**Try This** Use the data in the table below.

**Calculator Samples**

| Sample | Number Sampled | Number Defective |
|---|---|---|
| A | 500 | 3 |
| B | 200 | 2 |
| C | 50 | 0 |

4. Using Sample B, how many of 20,000 calculators would you estimate to be defective? 200 calculators
5. *Mathematical Reasoning* Would you expect an estimate based on Sample C to be more accurate or less accurate than one based on Sample B? Explain. Less accurate. A larger sample is likely to be more representative of the population.
6. Explain why you would take a sample rather than counting or surveying an entire population. The entire population might be too large to be surveyed. Also, the testing might be destructive, as in testing flash bulbs.

# 2 Teach

## Part 1 Teaching Notes

Discuss the fact that random samples produce a more reliable survey result because there are no intentional or unintentional biases in selecting the sample.

### Example 1

**Build understanding.** Ask: What is the population you want to study with this survey? Why must your sample be taken from that population? students at your school; to help you answer the question accurately

**Math Reasoning** Use math reasoning to explain why the views about recycling among students in an ecology class might be different from the views of students in other classes. They might be more aware of the benefits and more likely to be in favor of recycling.

## Part 2 Teaching Notes

Have a student volunteer review how to set up and solve a proportion.

### Example 2

**Build understanding.** Ask: If the manufacturer tested 2,000 calculators, would the prediction about the total number of defective calculators be more or less likely to be accurate? Explain. more likely; the larger the sample, the more reliable the results

**Error Prevention** Remind students that a sample can be used only to make an *estimate* about a population. Whether the estimate is true depends on many factors. In Example 2, there *may* be 120 defective calculators in the group of 20,000, based on the number of defective calculators in the sample group.

entirely of students, but the population is the whole community.

- **Additional Example 2**
After correcting some faults in the manufacturing process, a second random sample of 300 from 20,000 calculators shows 2 with defects. Did the corrections lower the number of defects? no; About 133 are now defective.

## AFTER THE LESSON

### To assess knowledge:

### Lesson Quiz

To select the school colors for a new school, you decide to survey one out of five students who will attend a new school for their favorite colors. Explain why this is or is not a good survey plan. good; sample selected at random from the population

- For enrichment and reteaching options see Resources on p. 605H.

# 3 Practice/Assess

## Assignment Guide

To provide flexible scheduling, this lesson can be divided into parts.

**▼ Part 1**
**Core** 1–3, 5–8
✪ **Extension** 9

**▼ Part 2**
**Core** 4, 10–11
✪ **Extension** 12

Mixed Review can be assigned at any time for maintenance.

## Exercises

**Test Prep Exercise 8** Think about which of the choices represents a random sample of the *whole* population.

## ✪ Challenge

You use a survey to buy drinks for field day. However, you run out of a brand of soda that your survey predicted was the least popular. If your sample was good, large, and selected at random from the population, why might the prediction have been wrong? Sample answer: Perhaps the students surveyed did not answer truthfully or changed their mind.

## Closure

A population is a group about which you want information. A sample is a part of the population you use to make predictions about the population. In a random sample, each member of the population has an equal chance to be selected.

## Daily Cumulative Review

**The table shows the colors of shirts in Olga's closet. For each color, find the experimental probability that a random shirt in the closet is that color. Write the probability as a percent, to the nearest tenth of a percent.** *(Lesson 12-7)*

| Color | Number of shirts |
|---|---|
| Blue | 8 |
| Red | 4 |
| Green | 2 |
| Gray | 3 |
| Black | 1 |

1. blue 44.4%
2. green 11.1%
3. not gray 83.3%
4. red or blue 66.7%
5. gray or black 22.2%
6. pink 0%

**Simplify each expression.** *(Lesson 12-6)*

7. ${}_{10}P_3$ 720
8. ${}_{11}C_4$ 330
9. ${}_{15}C_5$ 3,003

**Mixed Review**

**Display each set of data in a frequency table.**

10. (12-1) 8 9 6 5 7 6 8 7 6 8 4 5 7 7 8

| Number | Frequency |
|---|---|
| 4 | 1 |
| 5 | 2 |
| 6 | 3 |
| 7 | 4 |
| 8 | 4 |
| 9 | 1 |

11. (12-1) 48 51 50 49 49 50 47 52 50 49 49 48

| Number | Frequency |
|---|---|
| 47 | 1 |
| 48 | 2 |
| 49 | 4 |
| 50 | 3 |
| 51 | 1 |
| 52 | 1 |

**Find the sample space. Then find the event's probability.**

12. (12-4) A spinner has 6 equal sections, numbered 1 to 6. You toss a coin and spin the spinner. You get heads and an odd number.
H1, H2, H3, H4, H5, H6, T1, T2, T3, T4, T5, T6; $\frac{1}{4}$

13. (12-4) You toss 3 coins. You get 3 tails.
HHH, HHT, HTH, THH, HTT, THT, TTH, TTT; $\frac{1}{8}$



# Exercises

## Check Understanding

**You want to find out how popular basketball is at your school. State whether each survey plan describes a good sample. Explain your reasoning.** 1–3. See right.

1. You interview the 10 tallest students in the school.
2. You choose 20 student identification numbers at random to find students to interview.
3. You interview 30 students watching a basketball game.
4. *Quality Control* A worker takes 100 eggs at random from a shipment of 144,000 eggs. The worker finds that four eggs are bad. Estimate the total number of bad eggs. 5,760 eggs

1. Not a good sample, since tall students are more likely to be basketball players than other students.
2. This is a good sample, since there is no bias built into the sample.
3. Not a good sample, since it excludes students not interested in basketball.

## Practice and Problem Solving

**You want to find out which restaurants in your city are most popular. State whether each survey plan describes a good sample. Explain your reasoning.**

5. You choose people to interview at random from the city telephone book. A good sample, since there is no bias built into it.
6. You interview every fifth person leaving a restaurant in the city. See right.
7. You interview all the restaurant critics in the state. See right.
8. **TEST PREP** You want to find how many students in the local elementary school bring their lunches. Which group would be a good sample? D
   A. the entire student population
   B. one first-grade homeroom
   C. the cafeteria workers
   D. students on one school bus
9. ✪ *Open-ended* Describe a survey question, a population, and a sample you could use to make an estimate. Check students' work.
10. *Estimation* Of 75 pairs of jeans, 7 have flaws. Estimate how many of 24,000 pairs of jeans are flawed. 2,240
11. *Writing* From 50,000 computer chips produced, the manufacturer samples 250 chips and finds 2 that are defective. Explain how you could estimate the total number of defective chips. See right.

6. Not a good sample, since it excludes people who dislike that particular restaurant.
7. Not a good sample, because restaurant critics may be looking for things the general public pays little attention to.
11. Write and solve the equation that states that the ratio of defective chips to the 250 chips in the sample is equal to the ratio of defective chips to the 50,000 chips produced.



## Alternative Assessment

Ask students to find the results of surveys in newspapers or magazines. Have students identify the sample size and the population that is represented by the sample. Ask students to share their findings with the class.

12. *Error Analysis* Eight of the 32 students in your math class have a cold. The school population is 450. A student estimates that 112 students in the school have a cold.

a. Why is your math class not representative of the population?

b. Describe a survey plan you could use to better estimate the number of students who have a cold. Check students' work.

12a. The cold virus may be passed from student to student in that class so that more of them have colds than in the total school population.

## Mixed Review

**Use the survey data at the right. Write each experimental probability as a fraction in simplest form.** *(Lesson 12-7)*

13. $P$(no pets) $\frac{9}{26}$

14. $P$(one pet) $\frac{6}{13}$

15. $P$(two or more pets) $\frac{5}{26}$

16. $P$(at least one pet) $\frac{17}{26}$

**Students' Pets**

| Number of Pets | Number of Students |
|---|---|
| 0 | 9 |
| 1 | 12 |
| 2 or more | 5 |

*Geometry* **Find the area of each circle. Give the exact area and an approximate area.** *(Lesson 10-3)*

17. $r = 24$ cm
$576\pi$ cm$^2$; 1,809 cm$^2$

18. $d = 45$ in.
$506.25\pi$ in.$^2$; 1,590 in.$^2$

19. $r = 50$ mi
$2{,}500\pi$ mi$^2$; 7,850 mi$^2$

20. How many combinations of four flowers can you choose from a bouquet of one dozen different flowers? *(Lesson 12-6)* 495

## Checkpoint 2

**Lessons 12-5 through 12-8**

1. A bag contains 10 cards labeled 1–10. You draw one card and then another, without replacing the first card before drawing the second. Find the probability of drawing two even numbers. D

A. $\frac{1}{5}$  B. $\frac{5}{10}$  C. $\frac{9}{10}$  D. $\frac{2}{9}$

2. a. A club of 20 students chooses a president and a vice-president. How many different outcomes are possible? 380 outcomes

b. A club of 20 students chooses two committee members. How many different committees may be chosen? 190 committees

3. A hockey player attempts 15 goals and makes 2.

a. Find the experimental probability of the player's making a goal. $\frac{2}{15}$

b. Predict the number of goals the player will make in the next game if the player attempts 23 goals. 3

c. Can the player expect to make the same percent of goals in each game? Explain. No. The player will have off days, and lucky days, and may improve with experience.

4. An orange farmer picks 450 oranges. Of these, 85 are "premium." Estimate the number of premium oranges the farmer will pick from a crop of 50,000 oranges. 9,444 oranges

See also Extra Practice section.



## Practice

**A school has 800 students. Two random surveys are conducted to determine students' favorite sport. Use the data in the table to estimate the total number of students who prefer each sport.**

| Sport Samples | | | | |
|---|---|---|---|---|
| Sample | Number Sampled | Favorite sport | | |
| | | Basketball | Football | Baseball |
| A | 40 | 16 | 14 | 10 |
| B | 50 | 22 | 16 | 12 |

1. basketball based on Sample A 320 students
2. basketball based on Sample B 352 students
3. baseball based on Sample A 200 students
4. baseball based on Sample B 192 students

**You want to find out if a school bond issue for a new computer center is likely to pass in the next election. State whether each survey plan describes a good sample. Explain your reasoning.**

5. You interview people coming out of a computer store in your town.
The views of people coming out of a computer store may not represent the views of other voters. This is not a good sample because it is not random.

6. You choose people to interview at random from the city telephone book.
The city telephone book may cover more than one school district. It would also include people who do not vote. This is not a good sample because it does not represent the population.

7. You interview every tenth person leaving each voting place in your school district.
This is a good sample. It is selected at random from the population you want to study.



## Reteaching

From 8,000 sports shirts produced, a manufacturer takes several random samples. Use the data in the table to estimate the total number of defective shirts based on Sample A.

| Sample | Number Sampled | Number Defective |
|---|---|---|
| A | 250 | 6 |
| B | 400 | 8 |
| C | 500 | 9 |

Set up a proportion.

$\frac{\text{defective sample shirts}}{\text{sample shirts}} = \frac{\text{defective shirts}}{\text{shirts produced}}$

$\frac{6}{250} = \frac{x}{8{,}000}$ Substitute.

$250x = 6(8{,}000)$ Find cross products.

$250x = 48{,}000$ Simplify.

$\frac{250x}{250} = \frac{48{,}000}{250}$ Divide each side by 250.

$x = 192$ Simplify.

The total number of defective shirts based on Sample A is about 192.

**Use the data in the table above to estimate the number of defective shirts out of 8,000 based on each sample.**

1. Sample B 160 shirts proportion used: $\frac{8}{400} = \frac{x}{8{,}000}$
2. Sample C 144 shirts proportion used: $\frac{9}{500} = \frac{x}{8{,}000}$

**From 12,000 computer games produced, a manufacturer takes several random samples. Use the data in the table to estimate the total number of defective games based on each sample.**

| Sample | Number Sampled | Number Defective |
|---|---|---|
| A | 400 | 16 |
| B | 800 | 30 |
| C | 500 | 19 |

3. Sample A 480 games
proportion: $\frac{16}{400} = \frac{x}{12{,}000}$
4. Sample B 450 games
proportion: $\frac{30}{800} = \frac{x}{12{,}000}$
5. Sample C 456 games
proportion: $\frac{19}{500} = \frac{x}{12{,}000}$
6. All 3 samples combined: 459 games
proportion: $\frac{65}{1{,}700} = \frac{x}{12{,}000}$

Reteaching



## Enrichment

The following computer program simulates the toss of a coin. The program instructs the computer to pick random numbers between 0 and 0.999999999. It assigns "heads" to those random numbers with values less than 0.5 and "tails" to those greater than or equal to 0.5. You can control the number of tosses by inputting the number when you are prompted by the computer.

**Enter the program carefully into the computer.**

```
10   PRINT "THIS PROGRAM SIMULATES A COIN TOSS"
20   INPUT "HOW MANY TIMES DO YOU WANT THE COIN
     TOSSED"; N
30   A=0:B=0
40   FOR C=1 TO N
50   T=RND(1)
60   IF T<.5 THEN PRINT "HEADS":A=A+1
70   IF T>=.5 THEN PRINT "TAILS":B=B+1
80   NEXT C
90   PRINT "THE TOTAL NUMBER OF HEADS IS "; A
100  PRINT "THE TOTAL NUMBER OF TAILS IS "; B
110  END
```

1. The probability of getting heads when tossing a coin is $\frac{1}{2}$. If a coin is tossed 10 times, how many times can you expect heads to result?
5 times

Answers may vary for exercises 2-4 and 6.

2. Toss a coin 10 times by hand. What results did you get.
heads ________ tails ________
3. Instruct the computer to toss the coin 10 times. Write the results.
heads ________ tails ________
4. How do the results compare to what you expected?
________
5. Do you think the results of the tosses will be closer to the expected probability if the number of tosses is increased?
yes
6. Test your answer. Run the program for 1,000 tosses. Write the results.
heads ________ tails ________
7. Do you think tossing one coin 1,000 times is the same as tossing 1,000 coins once?
yes



## Checkpoint

**Aysha has 8 pictures to hang over her couch. She wants to hang only 3 of them.**

1. Find how many ways she can choose the 3 pictures from the 8. 56 ways
2. Find how many ways she can choose the 3 pictures from the 8 and arrange them in a row on the wall. 336 ways

**A baseball player gets 2 hits in 9 times at bat.**

3. Find the probability that the player gets a hit as a percent to the nearest percent. 22%
4. Estimate how many hits the player will get in the next 12 times at bat. 3 hits
5. A bag contains 8 marbles. Four are blue, three are green, and one is orange. You draw out one marble and then another, without replacing the first marble. Find the probability of drawing two blue marbles.
A. $\frac{1}{2}$  B. $\frac{1}{4}$  (C.) $\frac{3}{14}$  D. $\frac{3}{28}$

# 12-9

## Getting Ready

**Resources** A complete list of resources for this lesson is on p. 605H.

### Daily Skills Warm-Up

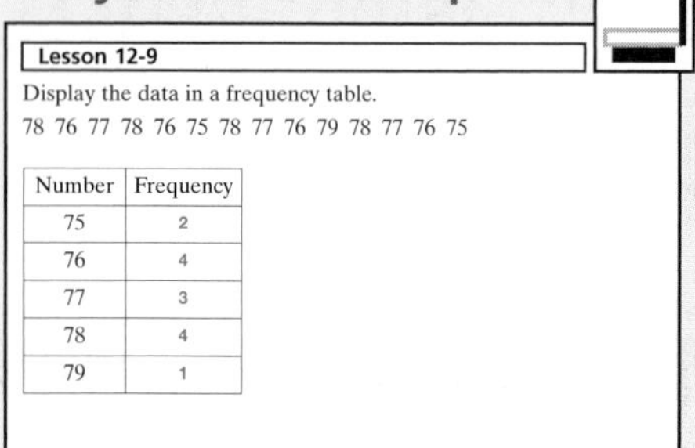
Lesson 12-9

Display the data in a frequency table.

78 76 77 78 76 75 78 77 76 79 78 77 76 75

| Number | Frequency |
|---|---|
| 75 | 2 |
| 76 | 4 |
| 77 | 3 |
| 78 | 4 |
| 79 | 1 |

### Background for the Lesson

When you use a simulation to find the experimental probability of the event, your simulation must have the same theoretical probability as the event. For example, suppose you want to design a simulation to find the experimental probability of a batter making a base hit. If the batter's batting average is 0.300, then he hits 30% of the time, or 3 out of every 10 at bats. The theoretical probability of your simulation must also be 30%, so you might use a spinner where 3 of the 10 sections represent hits. You then conduct trials with the spinner to get an experimental probability, which may or may not be 30%.

## 1 Focus

### Connecting to Students' Lives

Ask students who play team sports if they have ever participated in a scrimmage or practice game. Have volunteers explain the purpose of practice games.

### Connecting to Prior Knowledge

In Lesson 12-7, students learned that experimental probability is often determined through simulations. In this lesson, students learn how to design simulations to find experimental probability. In the Math Toolbox that follows this lesson, students will learn how to use random numbers for simulations.



12-9

# Simulate a Problem

**Problem Solving Strategies**

Account for All Possibilities
Draw a Diagram
Look for a Pattern
Make a Model
Make a Table
Simplify the Problem
Simulate a Problem
Solve by Graphing
Try, Test, Revise
Use Multiple Strategies
Work Backward
Write an Equation
Write a Proportion

*Math Strategies in Action*

Do you dream of flying your own airplane? Can you picture yourself in a space shuttle? Flight simulators help pilots train for real flying. Simulators are models of the real experience.

You can use simulations to investigate real-world problems. First develop a model, and then conduct an experiment.

### SAMPLE PROBLEM

As time is running out in the basketball game, your team is behind by one point. You are fouled and go to the free-throw line. If you miss the shot, your team loses. If you make it, the score is tied and you get another shot. If you miss the second shot, the game ends in a tie. If you make both shots, your team wins. Your average at free throws is four out of five. What is the experimental probability that you tie or win the game?

### Read

Think about the problem.

1. Based on your average, what is the probability of making one free throw? $\frac{4}{5}$
2. What methods could you use to simulate the problem? Answers may vary. Sample: toss coins.

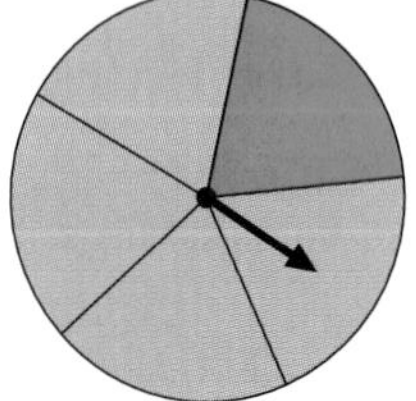

### Plan

You can use a spinner to simulate the problem. Construct a spinner with five congruent sections. Make four of the sections blue and one of them red. The blue section represents *makes the shot* and the red section represents *misses the shot.* Each spin represents one shot.



## Tools to Monitor Progress

### BEFORE THE LESSON

**To check prerequisite skills:**

**Skills Handbook,** p. 726

**Skills Intervention Kit,** Whole Numbers

### DURING THE LESSON

**To check understanding:**

- **Additional Sample Problem**
  A softball player has a batting average of 0.300, which means she gets a base hit 3 times out of every 10 at bats. What is the experimental probability that she will get a base

3. How many spins will you make for each experiment? one or two spins
4. How many experiments will you do? many—perhaps 100

## Solve

Use the results given in the table below. "B" stands for blue and "R" stands for red. Note that there is no second shot when the first shot is a miss (R).

**Results of 100 Experiments**

| | | | | | | | | | |
|---|---|---|---|---|---|---|---|---|---|
| BR | BB | BB | BB | BB | BR | BB | BB | BB | BB |
| BR | BB | BR | BB | R | BB | R | BB | BR | BB |
| BB | BB | BB | R | BB | BB | BB | BB | BB | BB |
| BB | R | BB | BB | BB | BB | BB | BB | BB | BB |
| BB | R | BR | BR | BB | BB | BB | R | BB | BR |
| BB | BR | BB | BB | BB | R | BB | R | BB | BB |
| BB | R | BR | BB | BB | R | BB | BR | BB | R |
| BB | BB | BB | BB | BB | BB | BB | BR | BB | BB |
| BB | R | BR | BB | R | BB | BB | BB | R | BB |
| BR | BR | BB | R | BB | R | BB | BB | BB | BB |

Make a frequency table.

| Misses the first shot (R) | Makes the first shot and misses the second shot (BR) | Makes the first shot and makes the second shot (BB) |
|---|---|---|
| 𝍸 𝍸 𝍸 \| | 𝍸 𝍸 𝍸 | 𝍸 𝍸 𝍸 𝍸 𝍸 𝍸 𝍸 𝍸 𝍸 𝍸 𝍸 𝍸 𝍸 \|\|\|\| |

5. Find each experimental probability.
   a. Your team wins the game. 69%
   b. Your team ties the game. 15%
   c. Your team wins or ties the game. 84%

## Look Back

Simulations can give different results. You may find a different probability if you do another simulation. The more experiments you do, the closer the results of different simulations are likely to be.

6. Continue the simulation with another 100 experiments. Combine the results with the results of the first 100 experiments. Check students' work.
7. Based on the second simulation, what is the probability that your team wins? Check students' work.

# 2 Teach

## Part 1 Teaching Notes

The most important part of setting up a simulation is to make sure that the simulation accurately reproduces the probability of the actual event. In the sample problem, the player makes four out of five free throws. So, the spinner that is used to simulate making free throws must have a theoretical probability of $\frac{4}{5}$.

**Visual Learning** Suggest that students organize the information in this problem into a table with two columns. In the first column, the students can record information they know. In the second column, students can record what they need to find.

### Example 1

**Build understanding.** Ask: What might be another way that this situation could be simulated? **Sample answer: Use five index cards. Mark four of them with an H for *hit the shot* and one of them with an M for *miss the shot.* Then pick a card at random, replacing it and shuffling after each pick.**

**Extension** Suppose the theoretical probability of you making a shot is $\frac{4}{5}$. What would be the probability of you making two shots? How does this probability compare with the experimental probability shown in the table? **The theoretical probability of making two shots would be $\frac{4}{5} \cdot \frac{4}{5} = \frac{16}{25}$, which is 64%. The experimental probability was 69%, very close to what could be expected.**

**Error Prevention** Make sure students differentiate between the number of trials and the number of shots in this simulation. While there were 100 trials, many of the trials involved more than one shot, so the total number of shots is greater than 100.

hit for each of the next two times she will be at bat? **Answers will vary but should be near the theoretical probability, which is 0.09, or 9%.**

## AFTER THE LESSON

**To assess knowledge: Lesson Quiz**

Solve by simulation.

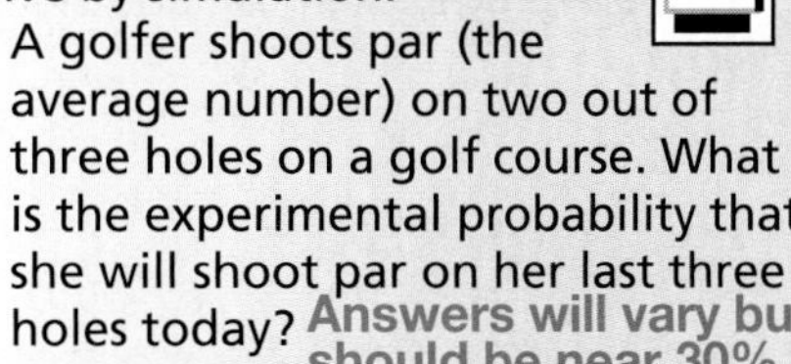

A golfer shoots par (the average number) on two out of three holes on a golf course. What is the experimental probability that she will shoot par on her last three holes today? **Answers will vary but should be near 30%.**

- For enrichment and reteaching options see Resources on p. 605H.

# 3 Practice/Assess

## Assignment Guide

**Core** 1–5, 7–11
✪ **Extension** 6

Mixed Review can be assigned at any time for maintenance.

## Exercises

**Exercise 3** Think about the implications of this problem. How does guessing on multiple questions on a test change your probability of getting the questions right?

## ✪ Challenge

What are some aspects of making a free throw that a simulation cannot re-create, even if it has the same theoretical probability as a player making the shot? sample answer: crowd noise, stress, fatigue

## Closure

Experimental probability is based on experimental data. You can use a simulation to model real-world problems.

# Exercises

## Check Understanding

**Solve by simulating the problem.**

1. What is the probability that exactly three children in a family of five children will be boys? Assume that $P(\text{boy}) = P(\text{girl})$. Check students' work. (Theoretical probability is 31.25%.)
2. On a TV game show, you try to win a prize that is hidden behind one of three doors. After you choose a door, but before it is opened, the host opens one of the other doors, behind which there is no prize. You can then switch to the remaining closed door or stay with your original choice.
   a. Find the experimental probability of winning if your strategy is to stay with your original choice. (*Hint:* Simulate by using one marked index card and two unmarked index cards.) Check students' work. (Theoretical probability is $\frac{1}{3}$.)
   b. Find the experimental probability of winning if your strategy is to switch to the other door. Check students' work. (Theoretical probability is $\frac{2}{3}$.)
   c. *Writing* Should you stay or switch in this game? Explain. Check students' work.

## Practice and Problem Solving

**Solve using any strategy.**

3. You take a three-question multiple-choice test. Each question has four choices. You don't know any of the answers. What is the probability that you will guess exactly two out of three correctly? Check students' work. (Theoretical probability is $\frac{9}{64}$.)
4. Thirteen of 25 students are going on a field trip. Six students are traveling in a van. What is the theoretical probability that a student chosen at random from those going on the trip is *not* traveling in the van? $\frac{7}{13}$
5. *Prices* The original cost of a jacket is \$72. During a sale, the store reduces the jacket price by 25%. After the sale, the store raises the reduced jacket price by 25%. What is the price of the jacket after it is increased? \$67.50
6. ✪ Each box of Tastycrunch cereal contains a prize. There are four possible prizes. The prizes are equally likely. You purchase 10 boxes of Tastycrunch. Find the probability that you will get all four prizes. Check students' work. (Theoretical probability is about 78%.)
7. *Geometry* A farmer uses 24 yd of fencing to make a rectangular pen. The pen is 6 yd longer than it is wide. What are the dimensions of the pen? 3 yd × 9 yd



## Daily Cumulative Review

**Solve.** *(Lesson 12-8)*

1. Of 125 t-shirts, 6 have flaws. Estimate how many of 8,000 t-shirts are flawed.
   384 t-shirts

**The table shows the number of consonants in several puzzles from a game show. For each letter, find the experimental probability that a random consonant appears in a puzzle. Write the probability as a percent, to the nearest tenth of a percent.** *(Lesson 12-7)*

| Letter | Frequency |
|---|---|
| R | 8 |
| S | 7 |
| T | 9 |
| L | 3 |
| N | 5 |
| others | 10 |

2. R 19.0%
3. T 21.4%
4. not S 83.3%
5. L or S 23.8%
6. N or T 33.3%
7. S or N 28.6%

**Mixed Review**

**Write a rule for continuing each pattern. Find the next three numbers in the pattern.**

8. (1-7) 6, 11, 16, 21, 26, 31, 36
   Rule: Start with 6 and add 5 repeatedly.
9. (1-7) 2, 4, 8, 16, 32, 64, 128, 256
   Rule: Start with 2 and multiply by 2 repeatedly.

**Use a pattern to solve.**

10. (1-8) Forty-nine students are needed for the middle school pagent. The faculty advisor wants twice as many 8th grade students as 7th grade students and twice as many 7th grade students as 6th grade students. How many students from each grade should be in the pagent?
    28 8th grade, 14 7th grade, and 7 6th grade



## Alternative Assessment

Suggest that groups of students go to a basketball court to gather data on actual free throws. If there is someone in the group who consistently makes four out of five shots, then have this person make the shots. If no one in the group has this average, then use another average.

8. A student draws a card at random from the cards below. What is the probability that the student will draw a card showing A or B? Check students' work. (Theoretical probability is $\frac{3}{11}$.)

9. You toss five coins. What is the probability that you will get five heads? Check students' work. (Theoretical probability is $\frac{1}{32}$.)

10. Many sweepstakes contests have an elimination round. In the elimination round, half of the entrants are chosen at random to go on to the final round. Then one person is chosen as the winner. What is the theoretical probability that a person who enters a contest with 10,000 entrants will be the winner? $\frac{1}{10{,}000}$

11. The circumference of the peg is 3 in. Will the peg go through the hole? Explain. Yes. Since circumference equals $\pi d$, $d = \frac{3 \text{ in.}}{\pi} \approx \frac{3 \text{ in.}}{3.14}$, which is less than 1 in.

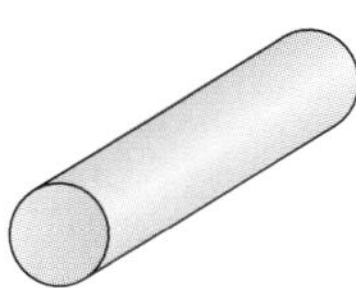

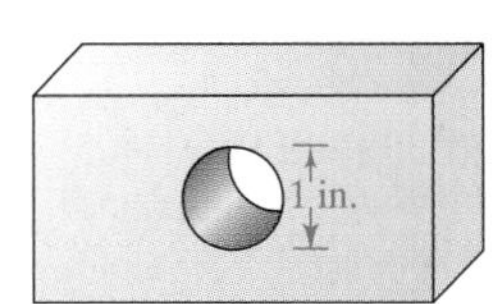


**Journal**

*Explain the difference between experimental probability and theoretical probability.*

## Mixed Review

**Estimate to the nearest integer.** ***(Lesson 11-1)***

12. $\sqrt{15}$ 4

13. $\sqrt{10}$ 3

14. $\sqrt{50}$ 7

15. $-\sqrt{82}$ −9

16. *Quality Control* Six out of every 80 wrenches are found to be defective. For a batch of 3,200 wrenches, estimate the number of wrenches that will *not* have any flaw. ***(Lesson 12-8)*** 2,960 wrenches

17. *Geometry* You are building a kite in the shape of a square. Each side is 20 in. long. To the nearest inch, what length of wood do you need to make the diagonals? ***(Lesson 11-2)*** 57 in.

## Chapter Project 12 — Activity 3 Comparing

Design a survey plan for your entire school. The survey question will be the same as in Activity 1. Choose a sample and conduct the survey. Compare the results of your school survey to the results of your class survey by graphing them in a double box-and-whisker plot.



### Project Activity 3

**Comparing** Students will need to find out the total number of students in the entire school and how the students are distributed across the grades. Have students plan how they will choose their sample and how large it will be.

## Practice

**Solve by simulating the problem.**

1. Twenty people seated in a circle counted to seven, beginning with the number one. The seventh person dropped out and those remaining counted to seven again. If every seventh person dropped out, what was the number of the last person remaining in the circle? Use the number circle to simulate the problem.
3

2. The Rockets played their first volleyball game on Friday, October 18, and played a game every Friday thereafter.
   a. What was the date of their ninth game?
   December 13
   b. What was the number of the game they played on February 7?
   17

3. Five coins are placed side by side as shown. A move consists of sliding two adjacent coins to an open spot without changing the order of the two coins. (The move "2-3 right" is illustrated.) Find three successive moves that will leave the coins in this order: 3-1-5-2-4
Sample answer is shown. 1-2 right, 4-5 right, 2-4 right

4. An irresponsible TV weatherperson forecasts the weather by throwing a number cube and consulting the weather key shown here. The weather during one 5-day stretch is given in the table. What is the probability that the forecaster was right at least 3 days out of 5? Use a number cube to simulate the forecaster's predictions. A successful trial occurs when you roll the correct weather three or more times out of five.

| Weather Key |
|---|
| 1–clear and warm |
| 2–clear and cool |
| 3–cloudy and cool |
| 4–intermittent showers |
| 5–continual rain |
| 6–snow |

| Mon | Tue | Wed | Thu | Fri |
|---|---|---|---|---|
| continual rain | continual rain | clear and cool | cloudy and cool | snow |

Work with a partner. Carry out 50 trials. Write the probability after the given number of trials. Sample answers are shown.

a. 10 $\frac{1}{10}$  b. 30 $\frac{1}{15}$  c. 50 $\frac{1}{25}$



## Reteaching

Each carton of monster yogurt contains a card with a monster cartoon character on it. Each of the 6 characters is equally likely. You purchase 8 cartons of yogurt. Find the probability that you get at least 5 different cards. Simulate the problem.

Since there are 6 characters, you can use a number cube to simulate the problem. A trial consists of rolling the cube 8 times. The results of 5 trials are shown in the table.

In trials 1, 4, and 5, four different numbers were rolled, representing 4 different cards. In trials 2 and 3, five different numbers were rolled, representing 5 different cards.

| Trial 1 | 6 6 1 5 1 6 6 4 |
|---|---|
| Trial 2 | 1 6 2 4 4 2 6 5 |
| Trial 3 | 5 6 3 1 1 6 2 1 |
| Trial 4 | 6 2 1 2 3 3 2 6 |
| Trial 5 | 3 5 4 4 3 4 2 4 |

So, at least 5 different cards were found in 2 of the 5 trials and the probability is $\frac{2}{5}$ or 40%. Note that "at least 5" means 5 or 6.

**Use the table above combined with the one on the right to find each probability based on 10 trials. Write each probability as a percent.**

| Trial 6 | 5 6 1 1 5 1 1 3 |
|---|---|
| Trial 7 | 2 4 4 6 5 6 2 6 |
| Trial 8 | 2 4 4 2 2 6 6 4 |
| Trial 9 | 1 4 6 4 4 2 3 4 |
| Trial 10 | 4 4 4 2 4 5 3 6 |

1. Complete the frequency table for the ten trials.

| Number of Different Cards | Tally | Frequency (number of trials) |
|---|---|---|
| 3 | \| | 1 |
| 4 | ~~\|\|\|\|~~ | 5 |
| 5 | \|\|\|\| | 4 |
| 6 | | 0 |

2. Find the probability that you get exactly 4 different cards.
50%

3. Find the probability that you get exactly 5 different cards.
40%

4. Find the probability that you get at least 4 different cards.
90%

5. Find the probability that you get at least 5 different cards.
40%

6. Find the probability that you get no more than 4 different cards.
60%



## Enrichment

Photos of the ten starters in the NBA All-star game are given out at random to ticket buyers, one photo per ticket. How many tickets would you have to buy to obtain all ten photos?

You can simulate the purchase of tickets using random numbers generated by computer. Let each of the digits 0 through 9 represent a different photo. A trial occurs when you scan the digits left to right, counting digits until one of each has appeared.

| | | | |
|---|---|---|---|
| 76245 | 40901 | 97017 | 70762 |
| 88449 | 01912 | 07436 | 50813 |
| 36607 | 11458 | 30440 | 52639 |
| 32378 | 68038 | 89351 | 37005 |
| 59960 | 70408 | 29812 | 83126 |
| 78071 | 17456 | 96104 | 18327 |
| 70009 | 23233 | 65438 | 59685 |
| 88598 | 47821 | 00265 | 82525 |
| 43989 | 90770 | 22965 | 44247 |
| 76210 | 22467 | 83275 | 32286 |
| 36782 | 00268 | 97121 | 57676 |
| 36270 | 77786 | 89578 | 21059 |
| 58581 | 95331 | 78629 | 73344 |
| 07648 | 70164 | 34994 | 67662 |
| 49475 | 50558 | 34698 | 71800 |
| 54728 | 81972 | 58975 | 30761 |
| 79178 | 33692 | 57352 | 72862 |
| 21252 | 12746 | 37554 | 97775 |
| 45557 | 96345 | 33271 | 53464 |
| 46717 | 72364 | 86954 | 55580 |
| 05822 | 46760 | 44294 | 07672 |
| 01055 | 79044 | 19308 | 83623 |
| 49044 | 95495 | 81256 | 53214 |
| 30883 | 89660 | 96142 | 18354 |
| 24290 | 01551 | 80092 | 82118 |

1. Begin the first trial at the upper left of the table. According to the first trial, how many tickets must you buy in order to obtain all ten photos?
34 tickets

2. Conduct as many trials as possible. Begin each trial where the last one left off. Record the results in the table.

| Trial number | Number of Tickets Purchased | Trial number | Number of Tickets Purchased |
|---|---|---|---|
| 1 | 34 | 8 | 29 |
| 2 | 26 | 9 | 46 |
| 3 | 28 | 10 | 26 |
| 4 | 21 | 11 | 19 |
| 5 | 23 | 12 | 45 |
| 6 | 19 | 13 | 51 |
| 7 | 33 | 14 | 33 |

3. Find the mean number of ticket purchases you must make in order to obtain all ten photos. Round to the nearest whole number.
31 (in 14 trials)

4. If you used a different table of random digits, would you get the same answer?
The average of many trials using different tables would result in approximately the same answer.

5. How can you get a more accurate answer?
by conducting more trials

## MATH TOOLBOX

### Using Random Numbers

This Math Toolbox shows students how to use random numbers generated by a calculator for simulations of experimental probability.

### Math Background

*Experimental probability* is the result of conducting an actual experiment and tabulating the results you get. In this case, random numbers are used, instead of actual cars and stop lights, to represent the experimental results. Experimental probability is very different from *theoretical probability.* For example, the theoretical probability of tossing a coin and getting heads is exactly 50%, but you would have to toss a very large number of times to get that result reliably with an experiment. Tossing a coin ten times, for instance, could give you almost any experimental probability and probably would *not* give you 50%.

Since the designs of graphing calculators differ, discuss with your students the keystrokes on their calculators.

## Teaching Notes

**Error Prevention** Help students understand that this simulation of an experiment involves too little data to predict accurately what might actually happen with real cars and lights.

**Monitoring Progress** Exercises 2–4 Explain that to get a *random number* of 4 digits means that every four-digit number has an *equal chance* of showing up on the calculator. Have students compare the random numbers generated by their calculators.

**Block Scheduling** If you have block scheduling or extended periods, you may wish to teach this Math Toolbox lesson together with Lesson 12-9.

## MATH TOOLBOX

Technology
*After Lesson 12-9*

# *Using Random Numbers*

Some calculators and computer programs can generate *random numbers*. You can use random numbers for simulations.

On a graphing calculator, the command *randInt* generates random integers. To create a list of random integers, press MATH ◄ 5. You will see **randInt(**. After the parenthesis, type "0,9999" and press ENTER to create a 4-digit random number. Each time you press ENTER you will get a different number. The calculator suppresses any zeros at the front of a number, so write 456, for example, as 0456.

### EXAMPLE

**There is a 30% probability of being stopped by a red light at each of four stoplights. Use a simulation to find the experimental probability of being stopped by at least two red lights.**

Use your calculator to generate 20 random 4-digit numbers.

There is a 30% chance of a red light, so let three of the ten digits represent a red light. For this simulation let 1, 2, and 3 represent a red light. Let 4, 5, 6, 7, 8, 9, and 0 represent a yellow or green light.

| | | | |
|---|---|---|---|
| 5186 | 8918 | 4275 | 4285 |
| 8124 | 9619 | 2517 | 9964 |
| 0912 | 2759 | 2329 | 1666 |
| 8938 | 0357 | 6755 | 2227 |
| 0201 | 6325 | 1905 | 6885 |

Any group with two or more of the digits 1, 2, or 3 represents being stopped by at least two red lights. There are seven such groups in this list.

$P(\text{at least two red lights}) = \frac{7}{20}$, or 35%

1. Use the information in the Example. What is the probability of being stopped by exactly three red lights? By four red lights? 10%; 0
2. a. Create a new random number list by using randInt(0,999) in place of randInt(0,9999). How many digits are in each random number? 3
   b. How can you make a 6-digit random number? randInt (0, 999999) enter
3. *Writing* Suppose the probability of being stopped by a red light at each of four lights is 50%. Describe how you would use random numbers to find the probability of getting a red light at two or more lights. Let an even digit represent being stopped by a red light. Look for groups with 2 or more even digits.
4. About 20% of high school students in the United States say they would like to be President. Use random numbers to find the probability that at least three of the next five high school students you see would like to be President. Check students' work. (Theoretical probability is about 5.8%.)

654 Math Toolbox

- **Additional Example**

Describe what you would do differently in the Example if 30% were replaced by 40%. Select any 4 digits to represent a red light.

# FINISHING THE CHAPTER PROJECT

**Conduct a survey** The Project Activities on pages 635, 645, and 653 will help you complete your project. Here is a checklist to help you gather the different parts.

- ✔ the results of your class survey
- ✔ your graphs of the data from your class survey
- ✔ your double box-and-whisker plot comparing the results of your two surveys

Write a report that summarizes the results of your surveys. Include a description of your school survey plan and how you chose a sample. Also include your double box-and-whisker plot. Analyze the plot and write a paragraph that explains the conclusions you draw from your analysis.

***Reflect and Revise***

Ask a friend or someone at home to review your report. Are your graphs and explanations accurate and clear? If necessary, make changes to improve your report.

### *Web Extension*

**Visit Prentice Hall's Web site. You'll find some interesting links and ideas related to surveys. You'll also be able to share information about your project.**

**www.phschool.com**

**Project Day** You may wish to plan a project day on which students share their completed projects. Encourage students to explain their process as well as their product.

**Block Scheduling** If you have block scheduling or extended periods, you may wish to intersperse the sharing of projects over Days 3, 4, 5 between the completion of one lesson and the start of a new lesson.

Have students review their project work and bring their notebooks up to date. Call attention to the fact that they can share their projects with other students through the Web site **www.phschool.com**.

Be sure students include in their notebooks their completed Project Manager and Scoring Rubric forms.

**Portfolio** Students may wish to include their projects and/or their project notebooks in their portfolios.

## Web Extension

### Tell Us About Your Project

Students may wish to share their projects with other students on the Web site: **www.phschool.com**.

## Scoring Rubric

3 You conduct your surveys accurately and draw your graphs correctly. Your analysis and conclusions are insightful and justified by the data. Your report is complete and well written.

2 You make minor errors in your survey, graphs, or analysis. Your report is complete, but it could be written better or could be more insightful.

1 Your survey methods, graphs, or analysis are incorrect. Your report is incomplete.

0 Major elements of the project are incomplete or missing.

# Wrap Up

## Resources

Glossary, p. 748
Extra Practice, p. 721

For a complete list of resources for the chapter, see p. 605H.

1.

| Number | Frequency |
|---|---|
| 9 | 1 |
| 10 | 3 |
| 11 | 3 |
| 12 | 4 |
| 13 | 1 |

2.

| Number | Frequency |
|---|---|
| 45 | 1 |
| 46 | 3 |
| 47 | 2 |
| 48 | 3 |
| 49 | 2 |
| 50 | 1 |

3. ; 5

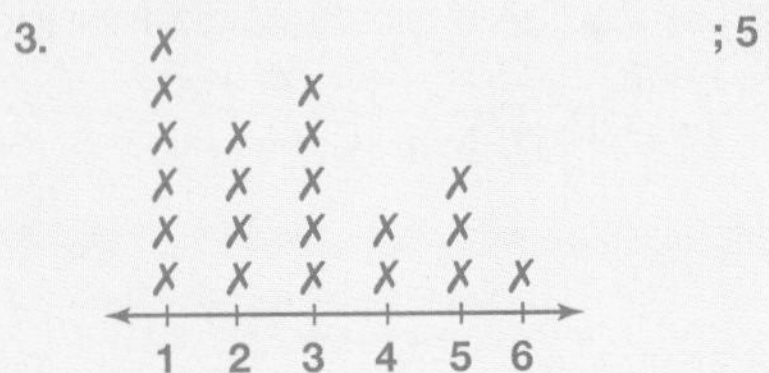


4. ; 5

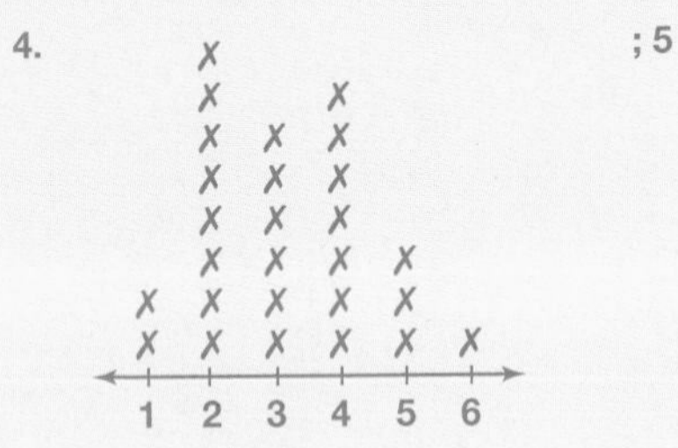


5.

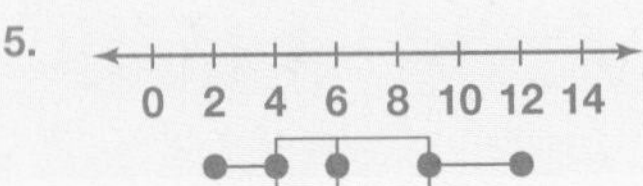


6.

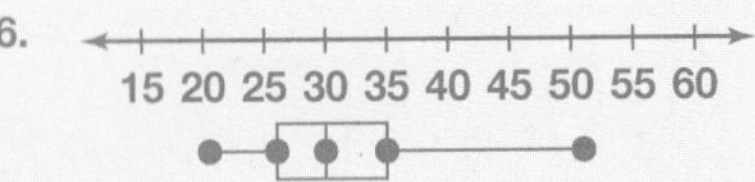

# Wrap Up

## Key Terms

box-and-whisker plot (p. 613)
combination (p. 637)
counting principle (p. 627)
dependent events (p. 633)
experimental probability (p. 642)
frequency table (p. 608)
independent events (p. 631)
line plot (p. 609)
permutation (p. 636)
population (p. 646)
quartile (p. 613)
random sample (p. 646)
range (p. 609)
sample (p. 646)
sample space (p. 627)
simulation (p. 642)
theoretical probability (p. 627)

## Graphic Organizer

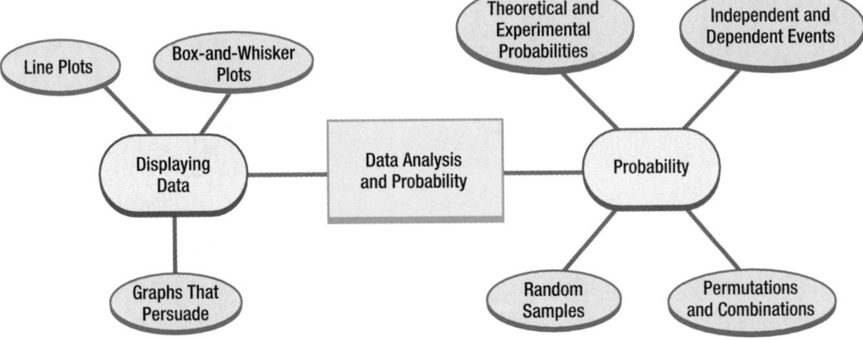


## Frequency Tables and Line Plots 12-1

*Summary* You can show data in a **frequency table**, which lists each data item with the number of times it occurs, or a **line plot**, which displays data with **X** marks on a number line. The **range** is the difference between the greatest and the least values in a set of data.

**Display each set of data in a frequency table.**

**1.** 11 10 12 10 12 11 13 12 11 9 12 10
See margin.

**2.** 47 48 46 47 45 49 46 48 50 48 46 49
See margin.

**Draw a line plot for each frequency table. Find the range.**

**3.**

| Number | 1 | 2 | 3 | 4 | 5 | 6 |
|---|---|---|---|---|---|---|
| Frequency | 6 | 4 | 5 | 2 | 3 | 1 |

See margin.

**4.**

| Number | 1 | 2 | 3 | 4 | 5 | 6 |
|---|---|---|---|---|---|---|
| Frequency | 2 | 8 | 6 | 7 | 3 | 1 |

See margin.

## Box-and-Whisker Plots 12-2

*Summary* A **box-and-whisker plot** displays data items below a number line. **Quartiles** divide the data into four parts. The median is the middle quartile. You can compare two sets of related data by making two box-and-whisker plots on one number line.

**Make a box-and-whisker plot for each set of data.**

5. 6 9 6 5 8 2 3 9 4 8 5 7 12 9 4
   See margin.
6. 21 35 26 32 24 30 29 38 27 32 51
   See margin.

## Using Graphs to Persuade 12-3

*Summary* Graphs can be misleading when a break is used in the scale or when the scale is distorted.

**Use the graph at the right for Exercises 7 and 8.**

7. *Writing* Explain why the graph could be misleading.
   See below right.
8. Explain how you could redraw the graph so that production seems to be increasing dramatically.
   Answers may vary. Sample: Use a vertical scale that goes from 50 to 60.

**Wheat Production in the United States**

Wheat Produced (millions of metric toms)

200
100
0
1995 1996 1997

## Counting Outcomes and Theoretical Probability 12-4

*Summary* A **sample space** is all the possible outcomes of an event. Use a tree diagram or the **Counting Principle** to count the number of outcomes. You can count outcomes to help find **theoretical probability**.

9. Volunteers have made a large number of sandwiches for a school party. The sandwiches come on white bread, whole wheat bread, or a roll. Each contains one of five fillings: turkey, chicken, egg salad, cheese, or peanut butter.
   a. How many different types of sandwich are possible? 15
   b. There are 20 of each type of sandwich. You receive one sandwich at random. Find the theoretical probability of getting a sandwich on bread with a meat filling. $\frac{4}{15}$

7. Because the vertical axis is short, the bars appear to be nearly the same height.

## Independent and Dependent Events 12-5

*Summary* **Independent events** are events in which one event *does not* affect the other event. If $A$ and $B$ are independent events, the probability of both $A$ and $B$ happening is $P(A \text{ and } B) = P(A) \cdot P(B)$.

**Dependent events** are events in which one event *does* affect the other event. If $A$ and $B$ are dependent events, the probability of both $A$ and $B$ happening is $P(A \text{ and } B) = P(A) \cdot P(B \text{ after } A)$.



**Portfolio** Students may wish to include their completed work for the Wrap Up in their portfolios.

**Web Site**

Students can find self-assessment materials on the Web site: **www.phschool.com**.

**You select a card at random from those at the right. Find the probability of each event.**

10. You select E, replace the card, and then select V. $\frac{2}{25}$

11. You select T, do not replace the card, and then select N. $\frac{1}{20}$

## Permutations and Combinations — 12-6

*Summary* An arrangement in which order is important is a **permutation**. An arrangement in which order does not matter is a **combination**.

**Tell whether each question is a *permutation* or a *combination* problem. Explain. Then find each answer.**

12. In how many different ways can five people line up for a photo? Permutation, since order is important; 120 ways.

13. How many groups of three pens can you select from a box of twelve pens? Combination, since order does not matter; 220 groups.

## Experimental Probability and Simulations — 12-7 and 12-9

*Summary* **Experimental probability** is based on experimental data. You can use a simulation to model real-world problems.

**Use the survey data at the right. Write each experimental probability as a fraction in simplest form.**

**Notebooks in Students' Lockers**

| Number of Notebooks | Frequency |
|---|---|
| 0 | 1 |
| 1 | 9 |
| 2 | 6 |
| 3 or more | 4 |

14. *P*(one notebook) $\frac{9}{20}$

15. *P*(at least two notebooks) $\frac{1}{2}$

16. You take a 3-question multiple-choice quiz. Each question has 3 choices. You don't know any of the answers. Use a simulation to find the probability that you will guess 2 out of 3 correctly. Check student's work. (Theoretical probability is $\frac{2}{9}$.)

## Random Samples and Surveys — 12-8

*Summary* A **population** is a group about which you want information. A **sample** is a part of the population you use to make estimates for the population. In a **random sample** each member of the population has an equal chance to be selected.

**You want to find the favorite brand of in-line skates in your town. Does each survey plan describe a good sample? Explain.**

17. You interview students in your homeroom. Not a good sample, because it includes students not in the skating population.

18. You interview every tenth student entering the building. Not a good sample, because it includes students not in the skating population.

19. You interview people skating at the local park. A good sample. These students are all in the skating population, and there is no built-in bias.



## Chapter Assessment Form A Page 1

**Circle the letter of the best answer.**

G E O M E T R Y

1. You randomly select two cards from those at the right, replacing the first before you select the second. Find the probability you select two E's.
   A. $\frac{1}{64}$ B. $\frac{1}{28}$ (C.) $\frac{1}{16}$ D. $\frac{1}{56}$
2. You randomly select two cards from those at the right, not replacing the first before you select the second. Find the probability you select two E's
   F. $\frac{1}{64}$ (G.) $\frac{1}{28}$ H. $\frac{1}{16}$ J. $\frac{1}{56}$
3. How many ways can Leonardo select 3 movies to rent from the top 10 rentals?
   A. 720 ways B. 240 ways C. 90 ways (D.) 120 ways
4. How many ways can Leonardo select 3 movies to rent from the top 10 rentals and arrange them into a triple feature?
   (F.) 720 ways G. 240 ways H. 90 ways J. 120 ways
5. The table shows the shirt colors of a random sample of students in your school. Find the experimental probability a student chosen at random is wearing a white shirt.
   A. $\frac{4}{15}$ (B.) $\frac{2}{5}$
   C. $\frac{1}{10}$ D. $\frac{7}{30}$

| Color | Number of shirts |
|---|---|
| Blue | 8 |
| Red | 7 |
| White | 12 |
| Other | 3 |

6. You want to find out who is likely to win the election for student council president in your school. Which survey plan describes the best sample?
   F. You survey students in your social studies class.
   G. You survey students in Drama Club.
   (H.) You survey students outside the cafeteria during lunch hour.
   J. You survey basketball players.
7. What is the median of the data shown in the box-and-whisker plot?
   (A.) 44 B. 46
   C. 48 D. 38
8. In the box-and-whisker plot, what percent of the scores are greater than 46?
   F. 100% G. 75% H. 50% (J.) 25%
9. From 80,000 jars produced, a manufacturer samples 1,200 and finds 7 of those defective. Estimate the total number of defective jars.
   about 467 jars



Assessment

## Chapter Assessment Form A Page 2

**Use the data below for 10 to 12.**
12 15 17 14 15 16 12 16 15 14 15 12 14 16 15

10. Display the data in a frequency table.

| Number | Frequency |
|---|---|
| 12 | 3 |
| 13 | 0 |
| 14 | 3 |
| 15 | 5 |
| 16 | 3 |
| 17 | 1 |

11. Display the data in a line plot.

12. Find the range of the data. 5

13. Make a box-and-whisker plot for the data.
42 48 43 65 58 47 60 56 52 64 51 66 56 62

14. Find the sample space for spinning the two spinners shown.
GB, GY, GR, GW, YB, YY,
YR, YW, BB, BY, BR, BW

Green (G) Yellow (Y) Blue (B)
Blue (B) Yellow (Y) Red (R) White (W)

15. Find the theoretical probability of spinning blue on both. $\frac{1}{12}$

**The table shows the money spent on non-durable toys and sports supplies. Use the table for 16 and 17.**
Sample answers are shown.

| Year | 1993 | 1994 | 1995 | 1996 |
|---|---|---|---|---|
| Dollars (billions) | 37 | 40 | 42 | 45 |

16. Draw a graph that emphasizes the increase in money spent over time.

17. Draw a graph that shows the money spent has not changed much over time.

Money Spent on Toys

# Assessment

**Use the box-and-whisker plot for Exercises 1 and 2.**

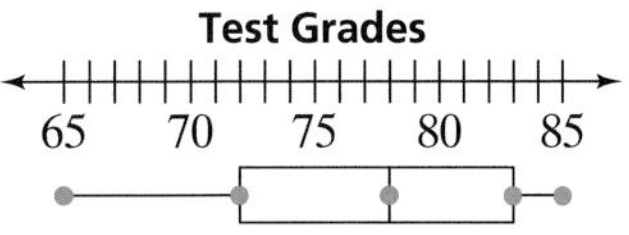


1. What is the median grade on the test? 78
2. What is the range in grades? 20
3. Make a box-and-whisker plot for the data. 75, 70, 80, 85, 85, 55, 60, 60, 65, 85, 75, 95, 50 See margin.
4. Use the data below. See margin.
   8, 4, 5, 1, 8, 4, 7, 9, 10, 5, 0, 5, 3, 4, 2
   a. Display the data in a frequency table.
   b. Display the data in a line plot.
   c. Find the range of the data. 10

**The table shows the money spent on movie tickets. Use the table for Exercises 5 and 6.**

| Year | Dollars (billions) |
|---|---|
| 1994 | 5.6 |
| 1995 | 6.0 |
| 1996 | 6.3 |

5. Draw a graph that emphasizes the increase in money spent over time. See margin.
6. Draw a graph to show that the money spent has not changed much over time. See back of book.

**Use the word TRAIN. Find the probability of each event when a letter is drawn at random.**

7. selecting an R, replacing it, and then selecting an N $\frac{1}{25}$
8. selecting an R, not replacing it, and then selecting an N $\frac{1}{20}$
9. a. Find the sample space for tossing 3 coins. See back of book.
   b. Find the theoretical probability of tossing 2 heads and 1 tail. $\frac{3}{8}$

**Simplify each expression.**

10. ${}_3P_2$ 6
11. ${}_5C_2$ 10

**Find the number of three-letter permutations you can make using each group of letters.**

12. F, O, U, R 24
13. L, U, N, C, H 60

**A student has 4 blue shirts and 2 white shirts. He selects one shirt at random. Without replacing the shirt, he selects a second shirt at random. Find each probability.**

14. $P$(blue and white)
15. $P$(white and blue)
16. $P$(blue and blue)
17. $P$(white and white)

14. $\frac{4}{15}$ 15. $\frac{4}{15}$ 16. $\frac{2}{5}$ 17. $\frac{1}{15}$

**The table below shows the colors of a random sample of the bicycles in a rack at school. Use the table for Exercises 18–21.**

| Color | Number of Bicycles |
|---|---|
| Black | 9 |
| Blue | 10 |
| Red | 14 |

**Find each experimental probability for a bicycle chosen at random from the rack. Write each probability as a percent, to the nearest tenth of a percent.**

18. $P$(red) 42.4%
19. $P$(blue) 30.3%
20. $P$(black) 27.3%
21. How many bicycles would you expect to be black if there are 50 bicycles in the rack? 14 bicycles
22. You roll a pair of number cubes once. What is the probability of rolling doubles?
    a. Find the sample space. Then find the theoretical probability. See back of book.
    b. Use a simulation to find the experimental probability. Check students' work.
    c. *Writing* Should you expect your answers to (a) and (b) to be the same? Explain. The answers should be close. The more trials there are in the simulation, the closer they will be.



# Chapter Assessment

**Resources** For a complete list of resources for this chapter, see p. 605H.

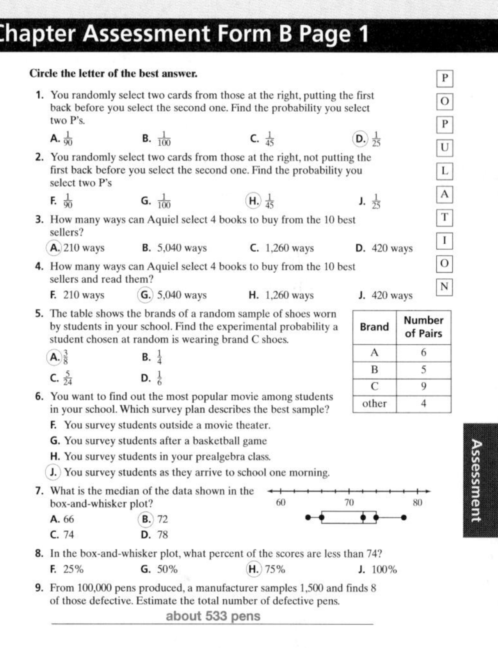

## Chapter Assessment Form B Page 1

**Circle the letter of the best answer.**

1. You randomly select two cards from those at the right, putting the first back before you select the second one. Find the probability you select two P's.
   A. $\frac{1}{90}$ B. $\frac{1}{100}$ C. $\frac{1}{45}$ (D.) $\frac{1}{25}$
2. You randomly select two cards from those at the right, not putting the first back before you select the second one. Find the probability you select two P's
   F. $\frac{1}{90}$ G. $\frac{1}{100}$ (H.) $\frac{1}{45}$ J. $\frac{1}{25}$
3. How many ways can Aquiel select 4 books to buy from the 10 best sellers?
   (A.) 210 ways B. 5,040 ways C. 1,260 ways D. 420 ways
4. How many ways can Aquiel select 4 books to buy from the 10 best sellers and read them?
   F. 210 ways (G.) 5,040 ways H. 1,260 ways J. 420 ways

P O P U L A T I O N

5. The table shows the brands of a random sample of shoes worn by students in your school. Find the experimental probability a student chosen at random is wearing brand C shoes.
   (A.) $\frac{3}{8}$ B. $\frac{1}{4}$ C. $\frac{5}{24}$ D. $\frac{1}{6}$

| Brand | Number of Pairs |
|---|---|
| A | 6 |
| B | 5 |
| C | 9 |
| other | 4 |

6. You want to find out the most popular movie among students in your school. Which survey plan describes the best sample?
   F. You survey students outside a movie theater.
   G. You survey students after a basketball game
   H. You survey students in your prealgebra class.
   (J.) You survey students as they arrive to school one morning.
7. What is the median of the data shown in the box-and-whisker plot? (60 70 80)
   A. 66 (B.) 72 C. 74 D. 78
8. In the box-and-whisker plot, what percent of the scores are less than 74?
   F. 25% G. 50% (H.) 75% J. 100%
9. From 100,000 pens produced, a manufacturer samples 1,500 and finds 8 of those defective. Estimate the total number of defective pens.
   about 533 pens



Assessment

3.



4. a.

| Number | Frequency |
|---|---|
| 0 | 1 |
| 1 | 1 |
| 2 | 1 |
| 3 | 1 |
| 4 | 3 |
| 5 | 3 |
| 6 | 0 |
| 7 | 1 |
| 8 | 2 |
| 9 | 1 |
| 10 | 1 |

b.

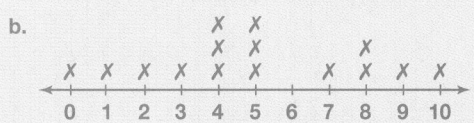

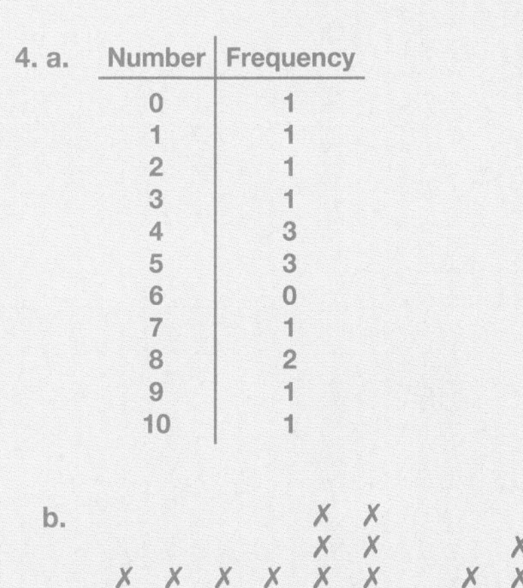


5. Answers may vary. Sample:

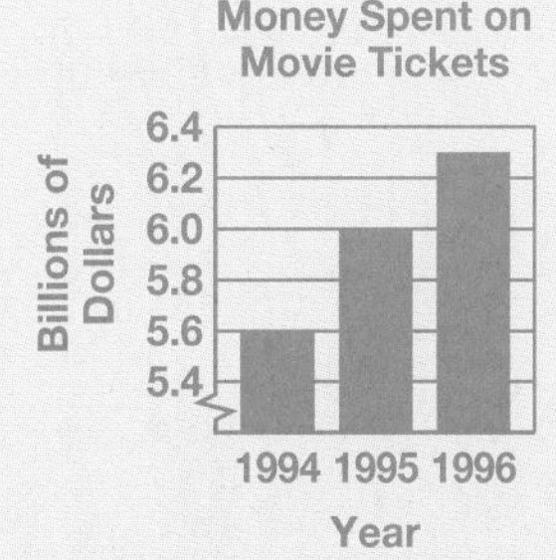


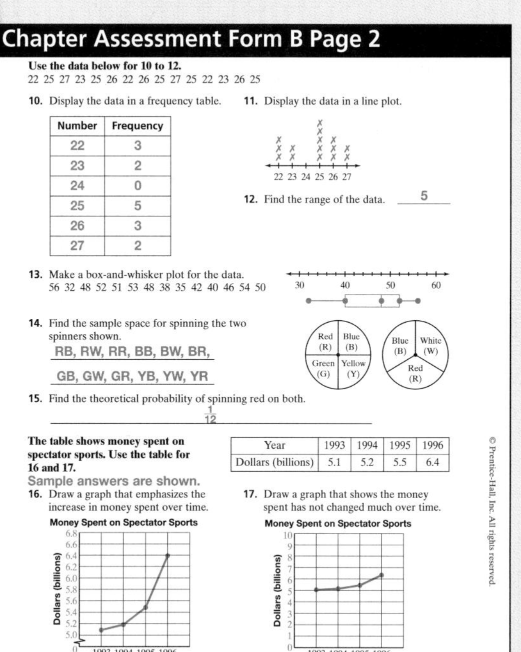

## Chapter Assessment Form B Page 2

**Use the data below for 10 to 12.**
22 25 27 23 25 26 22 26 25 27 25 22 23 26 25

10. Display the data in a frequency table.

| Number | Frequency |
|---|---|
| 22 | 3 |
| 23 | 2 |
| 24 | 0 |
| 25 | 5 |
| 26 | 3 |
| 27 | 2 |

11. Display the data in a line plot. (22 23 24 25 26 27)
12. Find the range of the data. 5
13. Make a box-and-whisker plot for the data.
    56 32 48 52 51 53 48 38 35 42 40 46 54 50 (30 40 50 60)
14. Find the sample space for spinning the two spinners shown.
    RB, RW, RR, BB, BW, BR,
    GB, GW, GR, YB, YW, YR
    (Red (R), Blue (B), Green (G), Yellow (Y); Blue (B), White (W), Red (R))
15. Find the theoretical probability of spinning red on both. $\frac{1}{12}$

**The table shows money spent on spectator sports. Use the table for 16 and 17.**

| Year | 1993 | 1994 | 1995 | 1996 |
|---|---|---|---|---|
| Dollars (billions) | 5.1 | 5.2 | 5.5 | 6.4 |

Sample answers are shown.

16. Draw a graph that emphasizes the increase in money spent over time.
    Money Spent on Spectator Sports (Dollars (billions) 0, 5.0–6.8; 1993 1994 1995 1996)
17. Draw a graph that shows the money spent has not changed much over time.
    Money Spent on Spectator Sports (Dollars (billions) 0–10; 1993 1994 1995 1996)

# Cumulative Review

## Cumulative Review Page 1

**Circle the letter of the best answer.**

1. Simplify $24 - 12 \div 2 + 2$.
   (A.) 20  B. 21  C. 8  D. 16
2. Find the GCF: 30, 52.
   F. 16  G. 4  H. 6  (J.) 2
3. Solve $\frac{2}{3}x - 4 = \frac{1}{2}$.
   A. $x = -5\frac{1}{4}$  (B.) $x = 6\frac{3}{4}$  C. $x = 3$  D. $x = 6$
4. Find the slope of the line that contains the points $(-3, 5)$ and $(7, 10)$.
   F. $-\frac{1}{2}$  G. 2  H. $-2$  (J.) $\frac{1}{2}$
5. $\frac{5}{6} =$
   (A.) $83\frac{1}{3}\%$  B. 120%  C. $62\frac{1}{2}\%$  D. 71.4%
6. Find the supplementary angles.
   F. 35° and 155°  G. 61° and 19°  (H.) 84° and 96°  J. 72° and 18°
7. Find the surface area of the rectangular prism.
   A. 192 $ft^2$  (B.) 208 $ft^2$  C. 176 $ft^2$  D. 188 $ft^2$
8. Find the volume of the rectangular prism.
   F. 176 $ft^3$  G. 188 $ft^3$  (H.) 192 $ft^3$  J. 208 $ft^3$

4 ft
6 ft
8 ft

9. The hypotenuse of a 30°-60°-90° triangle is 8 cm. What is the length of the shorter side?
   (A.) 4 cm  B. $4\sqrt{3}$ cm  C. $4\sqrt{2}$ cm  D. $8\sqrt{3}$ cm
10. Use the data in the table to find the experimental probability of getting tails.

20 coin tosses

| T | T | H | T | H | H | H | T | H | T |
|---|---|---|---|---|---|---|---|---|---|
| H | T | T | H | H | T | H | T | T | T |

   F. 50%  (G.) 55%  H. 45%  J. 20%
11. Use the data in the table to predict the number of tails you would get in 75 coin tosses.
   A. 35 tails  B. 40 tails  (C.) 41 tails  D. 45 tails



## Cumulative Review Page 2

**Simplify each expression.**

12. $(x^3)^5$ $x^{15}$
13. $8a^7 \cdot 9a^3$ $72a^{10}$
14. $\left(\frac{5k}{m^2}\right)^3$ $\frac{125k^3}{m^6}$
15. $\frac{9y^8}{15xy^3}$ $\frac{3y^5}{5x}$
16. Graph $y = 4x - 3$.

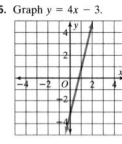

**Marisa has seven pairs of shoes. Three are white and four are black. She randomly chooses a pair to wear each day. Find the probability that Marisa chooses a white pair two days in a row under each condition.**

17. Marisa will wear the same pair two days in a row. $\frac{9}{49}$
18. Marisa will not wear the same pair two days in a row. $\frac{1}{7}$
19. Make a box-and-whisker plot for the set of data.
   6 7 9 5 7 4 2 10 8 7 5
20. Explain the difference between a population and a sample.
   Sample answer is shown. A population is a group about which you want information. A sample is just part of the population you use to make predictions about the whole population.

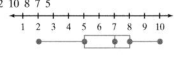

Assessment

# 12 Cumulative Review

**Preparing for Algebra**

**Choose the best answer.**

1. $\overleftrightarrow{MN} \parallel \overleftrightarrow{OP}$. Which angles are supplementary? B

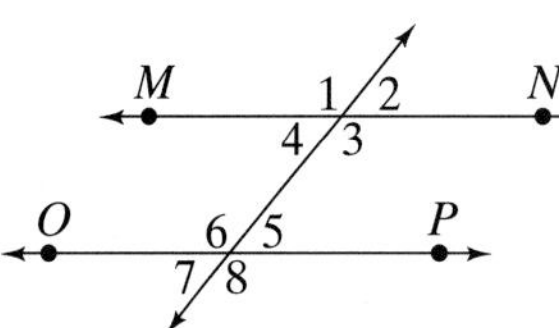


   A. $\angle 1$ and $\angle 3$  B. $\angle 4$ and $\angle 6$
   C. $\angle 2$ and $\angle 5$  D. $\angle 7$ and $\angle 5$

2. How many shaded triangles can fit inside the trapezoid? J

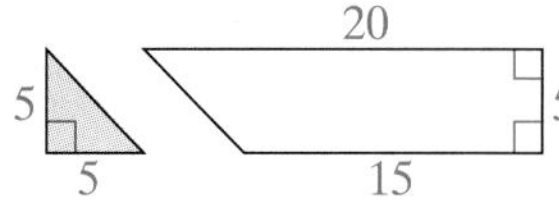


   F. four  G. five
   H. six  J. seven

3. Each of the six faces of a cube is painted either yellow or green. When the cube is tossed, the probability is $\frac{2}{3}$ that the cube will land with a green face up. How many faces are yellow? B
   A. one  B. two
   C. three  D. four

4. Simplify ${}_6P_3$. H
   F. 20  G. 2  H. 120  J. 18

5. A student has 3 blue T-shirts and 2 white T-shirts. He selects one T-shirt at random. Without replacing the T-shirt, he selects another T-shirt at random. Find the probability that the student will pick a white T-shirt and then a blue T-shirt. A
   A. $\frac{3}{10}$  B. $\frac{1}{6}$  C. $\frac{1}{6}$  D. $\frac{5}{6}$

6. A shoe manufacturer checks 150 pairs of walking shoes and finds three pairs to be defective. Find the probability that a pair of walking shoes is defective. F
   F. 2%  G. 98%  H. 148%  J. 50%

**For Exercises 7–11, show your work.**

7. Make a box-and-whisker plot for the data.
   55, 50, 60, 65, 65, 35, 40, 40, 45, 65, 55, 75, 30, 35, 55, 60, 45, 55 See margin.

8. Use the data in the table. Make a graph that shows each situation. See margin.
   a. sales decreasing sharply
   b. sales staying about the same

| Year | Sales (dollars) |
|---|---|
| 1997 | 18.2 million |
| 1998 | 17.9 million |
| 1999 | 17.7 million |
| 2000 | 17.5 million |

9. You toss two coins.
   a. Find the theoretical probability of tossing two tails. $\frac{1}{4}$
   b. Find the experimental probability of tossing two tails. Check students' work.
   c. Summarize your results. Compare the two probabilities. Check students' work.

**State whether each survey plan describes a good sample. Explain your reasoning.**

10. You want to find out how many people who buy stamps are buying them for a stamp collection. You plan to survey people going into the post office. This is a good sample, with no built-in bias.

11. You want to find out how popular the national women's soccer team is in your school. You survey all the young women in your school. This is not a good sample, since it excludes men, who are part of the total population.



| Item | Chapter/ Lesson | Review Topic |
|---|---|---|
| 1 | 9-2 | Spatial Thinking |
| 2 | 10-2 | Area and Volume |
| 3–11 | 12-2, 12-3, 12-4, 12-6, 12-7, 12-8 | Data Analysis and Probability |

7.

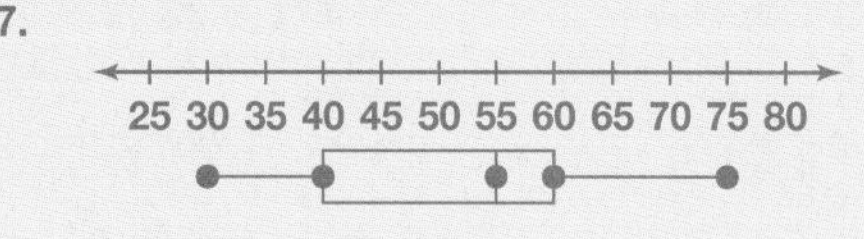


8. a

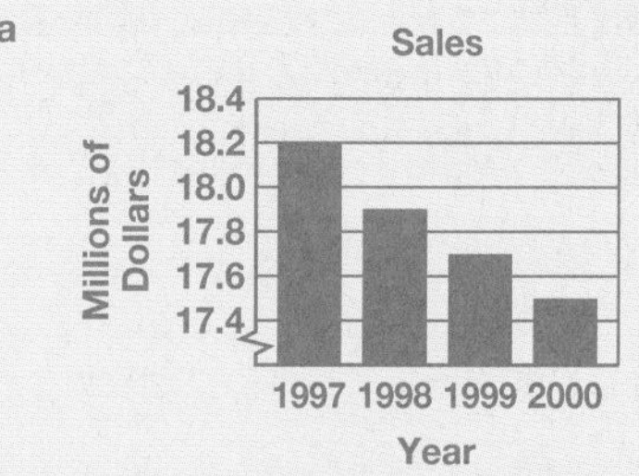


8. b

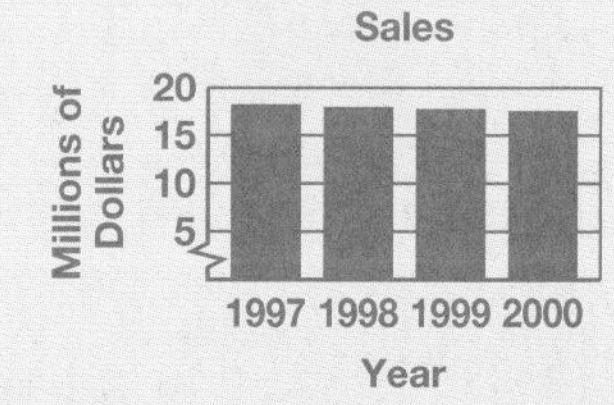

CHAPTER 13

# Nonlinear Functions and Polynomials

## Content Overview for Chapter 13

Chapter 13 begins by exploring patterns and sequences. A sequence is a set of numbers that follow a pattern. Each number in the sequence is a term of the sequence. You can find a term of an arithmetic sequence by adding a fixed number, the common difference, to the previous term. You can find a term of a geometric sequence by multiplying the previous term by a fixed number, a common ratio.

The graph of a quadratic function is a U-shaped curve called a *parabola* that opens upward or downward. The graph of an absolute value function is V-shaped. A function like $y = 2^x$ models exponential growth. Its graph curves upward as input values increase. A function like $y = (\frac{1}{2})^x$ models exponential decay. Its graph curves downward as input values increase.

A monomial is a real number, a variable, or a product of a real number and variables with whole number exponents. A polynomial is a monomial or a sum or difference of monomials. You name a polynomial by the number of its terms. A binomial has two terms and a trinomial has three terms. You add or subtract polynomials by using models, combining like terms, or aligning like terms vertically.

You use the Distributive Property to simplify the product of a monomial and a polynomial and to write some polynomials as the product of two factors. You can use tiles to model the product of two binomials.

**SCHOOL/HOME CONNECTION**
English and Spanish versions are available in the *Help at Home* book of copy masters.

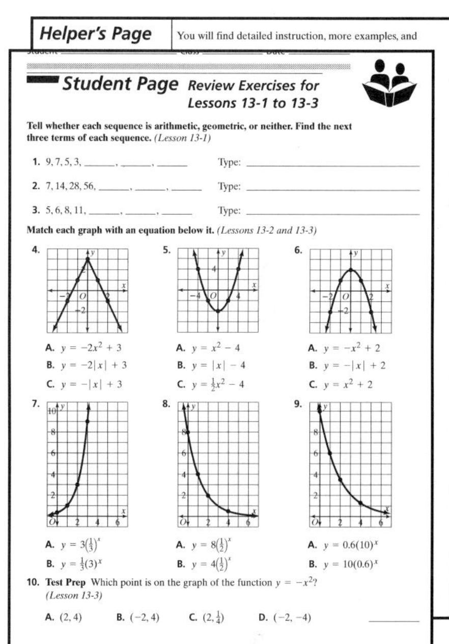

**Helper's Page** You will find detailed instruction, more examples, and

**Student Page** Review Exercises for Lessons 13-1 to 13-3

**Tell whether each sequence is arithmetic, geometric, or neither. Find the next three terms of each sequence.** *(Lesson 13-1)*

1. 9, 7, 5, 3, ____, ____, ____ Type: ____
2. 7, 14, 28, 56, ____, ____, ____ Type: ____
3. 5, 6, 8, 11, ____, ____, ____ Type: ____

**Match each graph with an equation below it.** *(Lessons 13-2 and 13-3)*

4. A. $y = -2x^2 + 3$ B. $y = -2|x| + 3$ C. $y = -|x| + 3$
5. A. $y = x^2 - 4$ B. $y = |x| - 4$ C. $y = \frac{1}{2}x^2 - 4$
6. A. $y = -x^2 + 2$ B. $y = -|x| + 2$ C. $y = x^2 + 2$
7. A. $y = 3(\frac{1}{3})^x$ B. $y = \frac{1}{3}(3)^x$
8. A. $y = 8(\frac{1}{2})^x$ B. $y = 4(\frac{1}{2})^x$
9. A. $y = 0.6(10)^x$ B. $y = 10(0.6)^x$

10. **Test Prep** Which point is on the graph of the function $y = -x^2$? *(Lesson 13-3)*
A. (2, 4) B. (−2, 4) C. $(2, \frac{1}{4})$ D. (−2, −4) ____

## Making Connections

| Lesson | Interdisciplinary and Real-World Connections | Math Integration |
|---|---|---|
| 13-1 | Accounting | Algebra |
| 13-2 | | Algebra, Geometry |
| 13-3 | Biology | Algebra |
| 13-4 | Science | Algebra, Geometry |
| 13-5 | | Algebra, Geometry |
| 13-6 | Botany | Algebra, Geometry |
| 13-7 | | Algebra, Measurement, Geometry |
| 13-8 | Construction | Problem Solving, Geometry |

**Helper's Page** You will find detailed instruction, more examples, and

**Student Page** Review Exercises for Lessons 13-4 to 13-7

**Evaluate each polynomial for $x = -4$ and $y = 5$.** *(Lesson 13-4)*

1. $x^2 - y$ ____ 2. $3 + xy$ ____ 3. $3x + y$ ____
4. $xy - x$ ____ 5. $x^2 - 2y - 1$ ____ 6. $\frac{x^2}{8} - y$ ____

**Simplify each sum or difference.** *(Lesson 13-5)*

7. $(2x + 3y) + (4x - 7y)$ 8. $(x^2 - 9) + (x^2 - 2x)$
9. $(x^2 - 5x + 3) + (-x^2 + 2x - 10)$ 10. $(4y - 9x) - (3y - 5x)$
11. $(x^2 - 5x + 3) - (2x^2 - x)$ 12. $(x^2 - 6x) - (5x - 7)$

**Simplify each product.** *(Lessons 13-6 and 13-7)*

13. $5x(x - 6)$ 14. $-3b(b - 7)$ 15. $2x^2(x^2 - 5x + 3)$
16. $(x + 10)(x + 4)$ 17. $(y + 5)(y - 9)$ 18. $(2a - b)(a + 3b)$

19. **Test Prep** Which of the following is a binomial? *(Lesson 13-4)*
A. $\frac{1}{x} - 5$ B. $x^2 + 3x - 9$
C. $6x^2$ D. $x^2 - 5$ ____

Helper: ____ Comments: ____

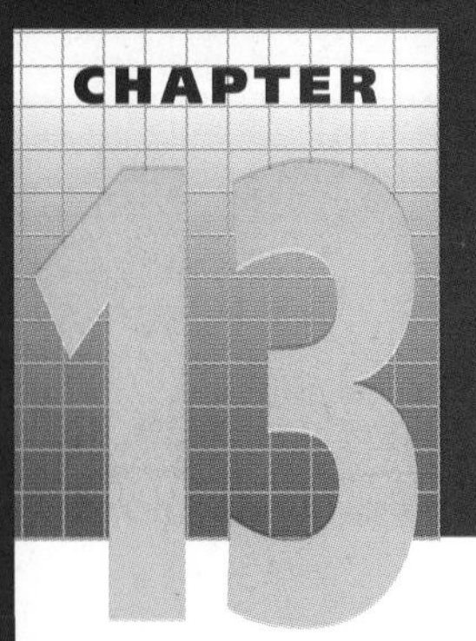

# Chapter 13 at a Glance

To accommodate flexible scheduling, most lessons are divided into parts. Assignment Options are given in the Teacher's Edition for each lesson.

### Lesson 13-1 Patterns and Sequences
**Pages 664–668**

**NCTM 1, 2, 6, 7, 8, 9, 10**

- Part 1 Arithmetic Sequences
- Part 2 Geometric and Other Sequences

### Lesson 13-2 Graphing Nonlinear Functions
**Pages 669–672**

**NCTM 2, 3, 4, 6, 8, 9, 10**

- Part 1 Graphing Quadratic Functions
- Part 2 Graphing Absolute Value Functions

**Math at Work**

### Lesson 13-3 Exponential Growth and Decay
**Pages 673–676**

**NCTM 2, 6, 8, 9, 10**

- Part 1 Exponential Growth
- Part 2 Exponential Decay

**Checkpoint 1**

### Lesson 13-7 Measurement: Multiplying Binomials
**Pages 694–697**

**NCTM 2, 3, 4, 7, 8, 10**

- Part 1 Using Models
- Part 2 Using the Distributive Property

**Checkpoint 2**

### Lesson 13-8 Problem Solving Strategy
**Pages 699–702**

**NCTM 2, 3, 4, 6, 7, 9, 10**

Use Multiple Strategies

## Pacing Options

This chart suggests pacing for only the core lessons and their parts, and it is provided merely as a possible guide. It will help you determine how much time you have in your schedule to cover other features, such as the Chapter Project, Math Toolboxes, Standardized Test Prep, Wrap Up, and Assessment.

| | Day 1 | Day 2 | Day 3 | Day 4 | Day 5 | Day 6 | Day 7 | Day 8 | Day 9 | Day 10 | Day 11 |
|---|---|---|---|---|---|---|---|---|---|---|---|
| **Traditional** (40–45 min. class periods) | 13–1 (1) | 13–1 (2) | 13–2 (1) 13–2 (2) | 13–3 (1) 13–3 (2) | 13–4 (1) 13–4 (2) | 13–5 (1) 13–5 (2) | 13–6 (1) 13–6 (2) | 13–7 (1) 13–7 (2) | 13–8 | | |
| **Pre-Algebra Over 2 Years** (40–45 min. class periods) | 13–1 (1) | 13–1 (2) | 13–1 (2) | 13–2 (1) | 13–2 (2) | 13–2 (2) | 13–3 (1) | 13–3 (2) | 13–4 (1) | 13–4 (1) | 13–4 (2) |
| **Block Scheduling** (90 min. class periods) | 13–1 (1) (2) 13–2 (1) (2) | 13–3 (1) (2) 13–4 (1) (2) | 13–5 (1) (2) 13–6 (1) (2) | 13–7 (1) (2) 13–8 | | | | | | | |

| Pages 678–681 | Lesson 13-4 Polynomials |
|---|---|
| NCTM 2, 6, 8, 9, 10 | Part 1 Identifying Polynomials<br>Part 2 Evaluating Polynomials<br>▼ **Project Activity 1** |

| Pages 684–688 | Lesson 13-5 Adding and Subtracting Polynomials |
|---|---|
| NCTM 2, 3, 7, 9, 10 | Part 1 Adding Polynomials<br>Part 2 Subtracting Polynomials<br>▼ **Project Activity 2** |

| Pages 689–692 | Lesson 13-6 Multiplying a Polynomial by a Monomial |
|---|---|
| NCTM 2, 3, 4, 7, 8, 10 | Part 1 Using the Area Model<br>Part 2 Writing a Polynomial as a Product<br>▼ **Project Activity 3** |

**NCTM STANDARDS 2000**

1 Number and Operations
2 Algebra
3 Geometry
4 Measurement
5 Data Analysis and Probability
6 Problem Solving
7 Reasoning and Proof
8 Communication
9 Connections
10 Representation

| Day 12 | Day 13 | Day 14 | Day 15 | Day 16 | Day 17 | Day 18 | Day 19 | Day 20 | Day 21 | Day 22 | Day 23 | Day 24 |
|---|---|---|---|---|---|---|---|---|---|---|---|---|
| 13–5 ▼1 | 13–5 ▼1 | 13–5 ▼2 | 13–6 ▼1 | 13–6 ▼1 | 13–6 ▼2 | 13–7 ▼1 | 13–7 ▼1 | 13–7 ▼2 | 13–8 | 13–8 | | |

**Block Scheduling Notes**

Consider these suggestions:

- **Day 2** Before starting Lesson 13-4, teach Math Toolbox 1, p. 677.
- **Day 3** Before starting Lesson 13-5, teach Math Toolbox 2, p. 682.
- **Day 4** Before starting Lesson 13-7, teach the Standardized Test Prep, p. 693.
- **Day 4** Before starting Lesson 13-8, teach Math Toolbox 3, p. 698.

# Math Background

## Lesson 13-1

### Patterns and Sequences

A set of numbers ordered in some specified way is called a *sequence.* One famous sequence was discovered by Fibonacci, an Italian mathematician in the thirteenth century who also popularized the use of Arabic numerals in Europe. The Fibonacci sequence begins like this. 1, 1, 2, 3, 5, 8, 13, 21, 34, 55, 89, . . . The pattern for this sequence is that, after the first two terms, each number is the sum of the two terms that go before. This sequence of numbers describes many natural phenomena, such as the arrangement of the spirals in a sunflower, pineapple, or pine cone.

Each number in a sequence is called a *term.* Consider these two sequences.
6, 9, 12, 15, 18, . . .
6, 18, 54, 162, 486, . . .

In the sequence 6, 9, 12, 15, 18 . . ., there is a *common difference* between successive terms. You can find the next term by adding this common difference to the preceding term. In this case, you add 3 each time to the term before. A sequence that has a common difference between the terms is called an *arithmetic sequence* (pronounced a-rith-mé-tic, with the accent on the third syllable).

In the sequence 6, 18, 54, 162, 486, . . . , there is a *common ratio* between successive terms. You can find the next term by multiplying this common ratio by the preceding term. In this case, you multiply by 3 each time. A sequence that has a common ratio between the terms is called a *geometric sequence.*

The Fibonacci sequence is neither arithmetic nor geometric; there is no common difference or ratio between the terms.

## Lessons 13-2 and 13-3

### Graphing Nonlinear Functions and Exponential Growth and Decay

In a quadratic function, the $x$, or input variable, is squared. The graph of a quadratic function is always a parabola. A parabola is a specific U-shaped curve defined by having an equation of the form $y = ax^2 + bx + c$. In this lesson, most of the quadratic functions have $b = 0$, so they are of the general form $y = ax^2 + c$.

When a quadratic function is in this form, the sign of $a$, the coefficient of the $x$ term, tells you whether the curve opens upward or downward. The graph of $y = ax^2 + c$ opens upward ("holds water") when $a > 0$. When $a > 0$, the parabola has a *least* value for $y$, which is the lowest point on the graph and the vertex of the parabola. The graph opens *downward* ("spills water") when $a < 0$. When $a < 0$, the parabola has a *greatest* value for $y$, which is the highest point on the graph and the vertex of the parabola.

The graph of $y = a|x| + c$ is similar to that of $y = ax^2 + c$ except that the graph of this absolute value function is V-shaped instead of being a parabola.

A function of the form $y = a^x$, where $a > 1$, models *exponential growth.* The graph of such an equation, for example, $y = 2^x$, is shown below on the left. A function of the form $y = a^x$, where $0 < a < 1$, models *exponential decay*. The graph of such an equation, for example, $y = (\frac{1}{2})^x$, is shown below on the right.

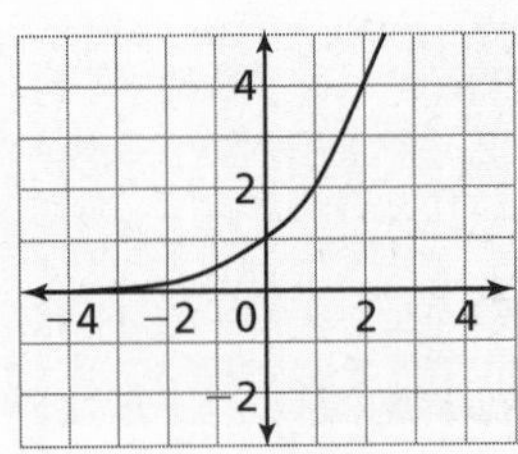


$y = 2^x$

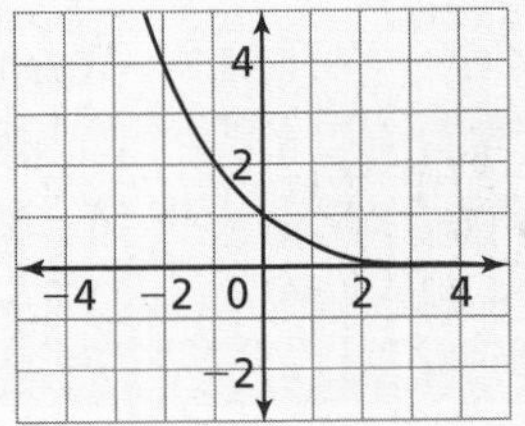


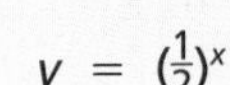

$y = (\frac{1}{2})^x$

## ▶ Lesson 13-4

### Polynomials

A *monomial* is an algebraic expression that has exactly one term and contains neither a variable in the denominator nor a root of a variable. Here are some examples of monomials: 4, $4x$, $4x^2$, $-3xy^2$, and $\frac{2}{5}abc$. The following are not monomials: $4 + 4x$, $\frac{3}{y}$ or $3y^{-1}$, $\sqrt{4x}$, and $\frac{2a}{5bc}$

A *polynomial* is a monomial or the sum or difference of monomials. You name a polynomial by how many terms it has. A polynomial is in *standard form* when the terms are simplified and combined and when the polynomial is written in order of the descending degree of the exponents on the variable.

## ▶ Lessons 13-5 and 13-6

### Adding and Subtracting Polynomials and Multiplying a Polynomial by a Monomial

You can use algebra tiles to model the addition and subtraction of polynomials. Here are the models for adding $2x^2 + 3x - 4$ and $x^2 + 2x + 5$.

Adding the tiles together gives a model for the sum of $3x^2 + 5x + 1$.

When you add polynomials, you combine like terms (terms that have exactly the same variable with the same exponent). You subtract polynomials by adding the opposite of each term in the second polynomial.
$x^2 + 2x + 5 - (2x^2 + 3x - 4)$ is
$x^2 + 2x + 5 - 2x^2 - 3x + 4$,
which is $-x^2 - x + 9$.

You can use the Distributive Property to simplify the product of a monomial and a polyomial.
$-2x(x^3 - 4x^2 + 3x - 5)$ is
$(-2x)(x^3) + (-2x)(-4x^2) + (-2x)(3x) + (-2x)(-5)$,
or $-2x^4 + 8x^3 - 6x^2 + 10x$.

## ▶ Lessons 13-7 and 13-8

### Multiplying Binomials and Using Multiple Strategies

To model the multiplication of binomials with algebra tiles, you can use a frame to set a length equal to one binomial and a width equal to the other binomial. Then within the frame, use tiles to build a rectangle with those dimensions. For example, a model of $(x + 1)(x + 3)$ might look like this

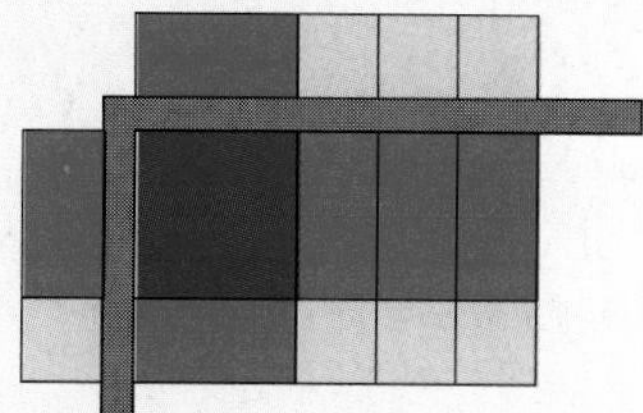

The rectangle within the frame has an area of $(x + 1)(x + 3)$, which is equal to $x^2 + 4x + 3$.

You can also multiply binomials by distributing each term in the first binomial to each term in the second.
$(x + 1)(x + 3)$ distribute the first binomial
$(x + 1)(x) + (x + 1)(3)$ distributing again
$x^2 + x + 3x + 3$ collecting terms
$x^2 + 4x + 3$

There are many strategies for problem solving. Sometimes, you may want to combine two or more strategies to help you solve one problem. For example, it may be helpful to make a table or draw a diagram before you write an equation.

For professional development tips visit our Web site **www.phschool.com**.

# Monitoring Progress

## Universal Access

### ▶ Preventing a Student from Falling Behind

These resources are particularly helpful in preventing a student from falling behind his or her appropriate math level. For a complete list of resources for this chapter, see page 661H.

#### Skills You Need for Chapter 13

Student Edition, p. 661
Teacher's Edition, p. 661

- Equations with two variables
- Evaluating expressions
- Simplifying variable expressions
- Using the Distributive Property

#### Skills Handbook

Student Edition, pp. 723–741
Teacher's Edition, pp. 723–741

- Multiplying Whole Numbers, p. 725
- Dividing Whole Numbers, p. 726
- Multiplying and Dividing Fractions, p. 740
- Working with Integers, p. 741

#### Reteaching Worksheets

There is a Reteaching worksheet for every lesson in this chapter.

- Chapter 13 Support File, Teaching Resources box
- See TE p. 661H for a complete list of resources

#### Skills Intervention Kit with CD-ROM

| For | Use |
|---|---|
| Lesson 13-1 | Operations with Fractions |
| Lessons 13-2, 13-3, 13-4 | Pre-Algebra Basics |
| Lessons 13-5, 13-6, 13-7,13-8 | Whole Numbers |

#### Daily Cumulative Review Blackline Masters

There is a Daily Cumulative Review worksheet for every lesson in this chapter.

See TE p. 661H for a complete list of resources.

### ▶ Accommodating Diverse Learning Styles

#### Tactile Learning

Write separate terms of each polynomial on a note card, then arrange the like terms in columns. (Lesson 13-5)

Use algebra tiles to model multiplying binomials with the factors exchanged. (Lesson 13-7)

#### Advanced Learner

Every lesson has at least one challenge problem.

Write a rule for finding the *n*th term of an arithmetic sequence. (Lesson 13-1)

#### ELL (English Language Learner)

Pronounce *arithmetic* with the accent correctly placed on the word as a noun and a modifier. (Lesson 13-1)

Understand the word *warren.* (Lesson 13-3)

#### Auditory Learning

Name like terms to a partner before combining those terms. (Lesson 13-5)

Discuss problem solving strategies with a partner before attempting to solve them. (Lesson 13-8)

#### Visual Learning

Use number lines to help find the common difference and additional terms in arithmetic sequences. (Lesson 13-1)

Cross out each term in a polynomial as they multiply it. (Lesson 13-6)

# Aligning Assessment with Instruction

## Assessment Options

| | Chapter Opener | 13-1 | 13-2 | 13-3 | 13-4 | 13-5 | 13-6 | 13-7 | 13-8 | End |
|---|---|---|---|---|---|---|---|---|---|---|
| Chapter Project | ■ | | | ■ | | | ■ | | | ■ |
| Try This Exercises | | ■ | ■ | ■ | ■ | ■ | ■ | ■ | ■ | |
| Mixed Reviews | | ■ | ■ | ■ | ■ | ■ | ■ | ■ | ■ | |
| Checkpoints | | | | ■ | | | | ■ | | |
| Writing | | ■ | ■ | ■ | ■ | | | ■ | | ■ |
| Chapter Assessment | | | | | | | | | | ■ |
| Cumulative Review | | | | | | | | | | ■ |
| Standardized Test Prep | | ■ | | ■ | ■ | | | ■ | | |
| | Standardized Test Prep, p. 693 | | | | | | | | | |
| Computer Item Generator | Can be used to create custom-made practice pages or assessment pages at any time. | | | | | | | | | |

### Test-Taking Tips on Transparencies

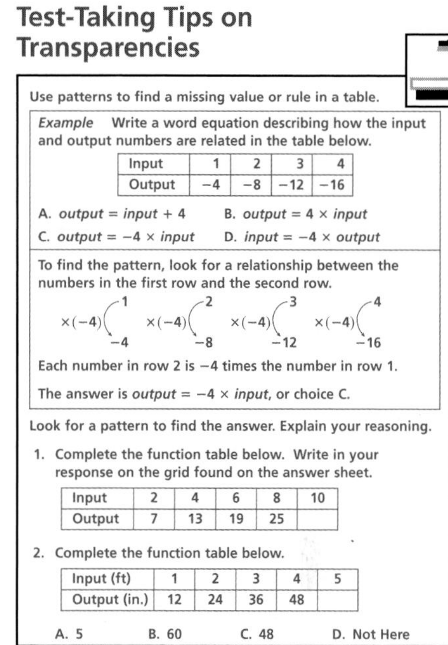

Use patterns to find a missing value or rule in a table.

*Example* Write a word equation describing how the input and output numbers are related in the table below.

| Input | 1 | 2 | 3 | 4 |
|---|---|---|---|---|
| Output | −4 | −8 | −12 | −16 |

A. *output* = *input* + 4 B. *output* = 4 × *input*
C. *output* = −4 × *input* D. *input* = −4 × *output*

To find the pattern, look for a relationship between the numbers in the first row and the second row.

$\times(-4)$: 1 → −4, 2 → −8, 3 → −12, 4 → −16

Each number in row 2 is −4 times the number in row 1.

The answer is *output* = −4 × *input*, or choice C.

Look for a pattern to find the answer. Explain your reasoning.

1. Complete the function table below. Write in your response on the grid found on the answer sheet.

| Input | 2 | 4 | 6 | 8 | 10 |
|---|---|---|---|---|---|
| Output | 7 | 13 | 19 | 25 | |

2. Complete the function table below.

| Input (ft) | 1 | 2 | 3 | 4 | 5 |
|---|---|---|---|---|---|
| Output (in.) | 12 | 24 | 36 | 48 | |

A. 5 B. 60 C. 48 D. Not Here

*Use with Standardized Test Prep and Chapter Assessments.*

## Correlation to Standardized Tests

| Lesson | | CAT5 | CTBS/5 TerraNova™ | ITBS | MAT7 | SAT9 | LOCAL OBJECTIVES |
|---|---|---|---|---|---|---|---|
| 13-1 | Patterns and Sequences | ■ | ■ | ■ | | ■ | |
| 13-2 | Graphing Nonlinear Functions | | | | | ■ | |
| 13-3 | Growth and Decay | | | | | ■ | |
| 13-4 | Polynomials | | | | | ■ | |
| 13-5 | Adding and Subtracting Polynomials | | | | | ■ | |
| 13-6 | Multiplying a Polynomial by a Monomial | | | | | ■ | |
| 13-7 | Multiplying Binomials | ■ | ■ | ■ | ■ | ■ | |
| 13-8 | Problem Solving Strategy: Use Multiple Strategies | | ■ | ■ | | ■ | |

**CAT5** California Achievement Test, 5th edition
**CTBS** TerraNova Comprehensive Test of Basic Skills, 5th edition
**ITBS** Iowa Test of Basic Skills, Form M
**MAT7** Metropolitan Achievement Test, 7th edition
**SAT** Stanford Achievement Test, Advanced 1

For other standardized test correlations, follow the link to your state at **www.phschool.com**.

# Resources for Chapter 13

| | TEACHING RESOURCES BOX | | | | | | | | | | | | | | |
|---|---|---|---|---|---|---|---|---|---|---|---|---|---|---|---|
| | CHAPTER 13 SUPPORT FILE | | | | | | | | | | | | | | |
| | Practice | Reteach | Enrichment | Project Manager | Checkpoints | Cumulative Review | Chapter Assessment | Alternative Assessment | Cumulative Assessment | Lesson Planners Plus | Daily Cum Review | Teaching Transparencies | Warm-Up Transparencies | Help at Home | SE Answers Transparenc |
| Begin Chapter | | | | ■ | | | | | | ■ | | | | | |
| 13-1 | ■ | ■ | ■ | | | | | | | ■ | ■ | | ■ | | ■ |
| 13-2 | ■ | ■ | ■ | | | | | | | ■ | ■ | 88 | ■ | | ■ |
| 13-3 | ■ | ■ | ■ | | ■ | | | | | ■ | ■ | | ■ | ■ | ■ |
| 13-4 | ■ | ■ | ■ | | | | | | | ■ | ■ | 89 | ■ | | ■ |
| 13-5 | ■ | ■ | ■ | | | | | | | ■ | ■ | | ■ | | ■ |
| 13-6 | ■ | ■ | ■ | | | | | | | ■ | ■ | | ■ | | ■ |
| 13-7 | ■ | ■ | ■ | | ■ | | | | | ■ | ■ | 90 | ■ | ■ | ■ |
| 13-8 | ■ | ■ | ■ | | | | | | | ■ | ■ | | ■ | | ■ |
| End Chapter | | | | | | ■ | ■ (2 forms) | ■ | After Ch. 3, 6, 9, 13 | | | | | | |

Also available for use with the chapter:

Solution Key
Computational Practice Skills Booklet
Mathematics Standardized Test Prep, Student Edition and Teacher's Edition
Overhead Manipulatives Kit
Practice Workbook
Algebra Readiness Kit
Student Manipulatives Kit
Test-Taking Tips on Transparencies
Assessment Success Kit
Teaching Aids and Letters
Graphing Calculator Handbook
Spanish Resources
Success-Building Puzzle and Problem Master

## TECHNOLOGY

**Computer Item Generator with Standardized Test Prep**
CD-ROM with an unlimited supply of questions with varying degrees of difficulty for customized practice sheets, quizzes, and tests.

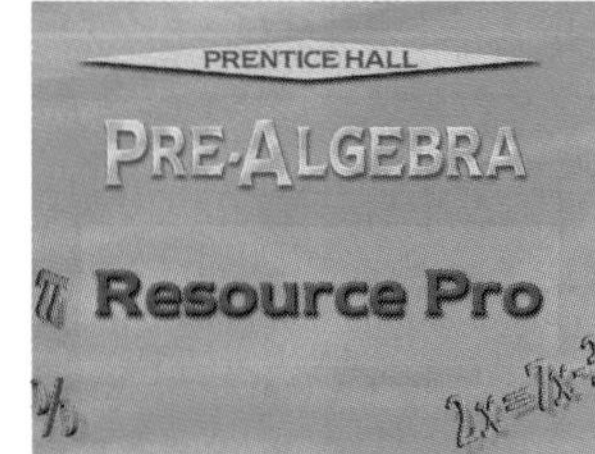


**Resource Pro® with Planning Express®**
CD-ROM with complete classroom planning tool and teaching resources for customizing and planning lessons.

**Interactive Math Lessons and Tools**
CD-ROM with lessons and tools to make abstract concepts visual and accessible.

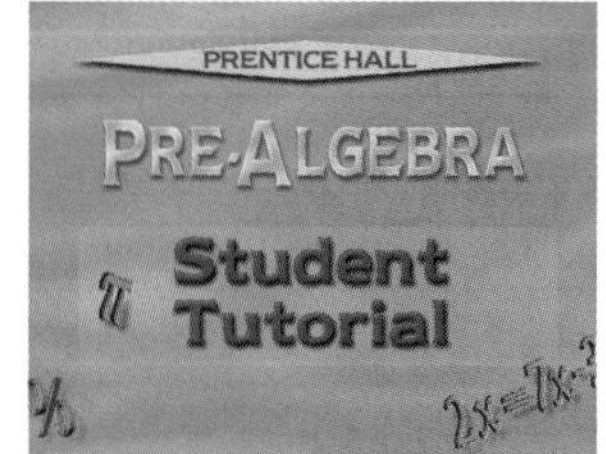


**Student Tutorial**
Test preparation software for students on CD-ROM with management system for teachers; includes Secondary Math Lab Toolkit™.

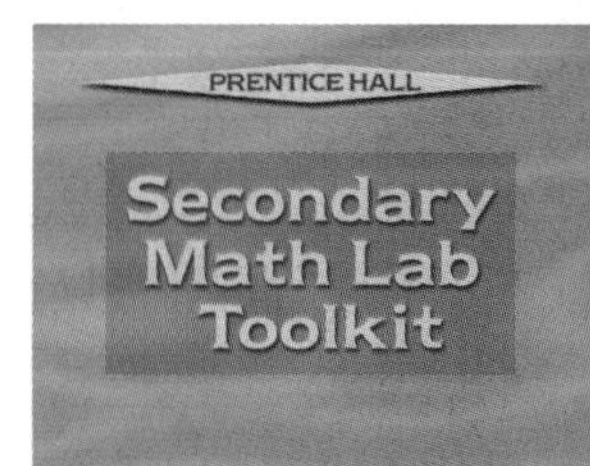


**Secondary Math Lab Toolkit™ with Integrated Math Labs**
Integrated software package with linkable math tools for exploring key concepts.

Also available for use with the chapter:

Math Blaster® Pre-Algebra CD-ROM
Video Fieldtrips, Vol. I: Algebra Applications
Video Fieldtrips, Vol. II: Geometry Applications
Wide World of Mathematics CD-ROM
Wide World of Mathematics Video

***Web Extension***
**www.phschool.com**

**For Students**
- Chapter Support with Internet Links
- Internet Activities

**For Teachers**
- Curriculum Support
- Professional Development
- Product Information
- Regional Support Information

# Skills You Need for Chapter 13

### ▶ *Equations with two variables*

Use before Lessons 13-2 and 13-3.

**Find the $y$ values of each equation for $x = -2, 0$, and 2.**

1. $y = 3x - 4$ −10, −4, 2
2. $y = -3x$ 6, 0, −6
3. $y = 4x - 2$ −10, −2, 6
4. $y = \frac{1}{2}x$ −1, 0, 1
5. $y = \frac{3}{5}x - 5$ $-6\frac{1}{5}, -5, -3\frac{4}{5}$
6. $y = 6 - 2x$ 10, 6, 2
7. $y = -\frac{1}{4}x - 8$ $-7\frac{1}{2}, -8, -8\frac{1}{2}$
8. $y = \frac{1}{4}x + 6$ $5\frac{1}{2}, 6, 6\frac{1}{2}$
9. $y = -3x - 1$ 5, −1, −7

### ▶ *Evaluating expressions*

Use before Lesson 13-4.

**Evaluate each expression.**

10. $8b$, for $b = 5$ 40
11. $x - 5$, for $x = 16$ 11
12. $104z$, for $z = 2$ 208
13. $4a + 4$, for $a = 6$ 28
14. $19 - (n - 6)$, for $n = 8$ 17
15. $55 - 3mn$, for $m = 2, n = 5$ 25
16. $c^2 + 5$, for $c = -4$ 21
17. $n^2$, for $n = 0.8$ 0.64
18. $(-h)^5$, for $h = 2$ −32
19. $\frac{120}{s + r}$, for $s = 25$ and $r = 35$ 2
20. $\frac{j - k}{9}$, for $j = 75$ and $k = 12$ 7

### ▶ *Simplifying variable expressions*

Use before Lesson 13-5.

**Simplify each expression.**

21. $5a - 4 + 6a$ $11a - 4$
22. $x - 4x + 3x + 5$ 5
23. $g + 4 - 3g + g$ $4 - g$
24. $5t + 5s + 5t$ $10t + 5s$
25. $9b - 3d + 7d - 2b$ $7b + 4d$
26. $-4(9c) + 2(-4c) - c$ $-45c$

### ▶ *Using the Distributive Property*

Use before Lessons 13-6 and 13-7.

**Simplify each expression.**

27. $7(v + 3)$ $7v + 21$
28. $(d - 4)3$ $3d - 12$
29. $5(3x + 1)$ $15x + 5$
30. $-5(6 - 3t)$ $15t - 30$
31. $3(u - 8)$ $3u - 24$
32. $(p + 8)9$ $9p + 72$
33. $-4(-2y - 7)$ $8y + 28$
34. $4(-3d + 1)$ $-12d + 4$
35. $10(5 - 3s)$ $50 - 30s$
36. $-3(7 - 2w)$ $-21 + 6w$
37. $6(h + 9)$ $6h + 54$
38. $(9 - 2b)3$ $27 - 6b$



## Skills You Need

### Equations with two variables

In Lessons 13-2 and 13-3 students will use equations with two variables when graphing quadratic and absolute value functions and functions that model growth and decay.

### Evaluating expressions

In Lesson 13-4 students will evaluate polynomial expressions.

### Simplifying variable expressions

In Lesson 13-5 students will simplify variable expressions when adding and subtracting polynomials.

### Using the Distributive Property

In Lessons 13-6 and 13-7 students will use the Distributive Property when multiplying polynomials by monomials and when multiplying binomials.

## Skills Trace

| SKILL | INTRODUCED | DEVELOPED IN LESSON(S) | REVIEWED/REINFORCED |
|---|---|---|---|
| Finding arithmetic and geometric sequences | 13-1 | 13–1 | p. 672 |
| Graphing non linear functions | 13-2 | 13-3 | Math Toolbox p. 677; pp. 676, 681 |
| Operations with polynomials | 13-4 | 13-5, 13-6, 13-7 | Math Toolboxes pp. 682, 698; pp. 688, 692, 697, 702 |

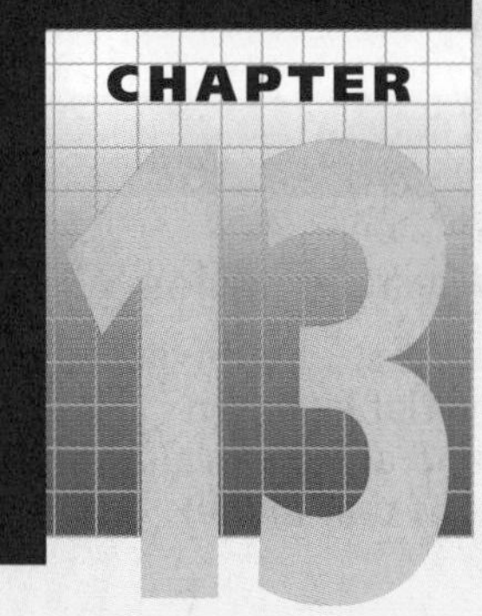

# Nonlinear Functions and Polynomials

## Connecting to Students' Lives

Discuss with students how plans or blueprints for boxes, buildings, and other 3-D objects are made. Ask students if they have seen computer graphics of 3-D models.

## Interdisciplinary Connections

The Chapter Project connects math, architecture, and art. You may want to display model buildings, airplanes, and other 3-D models.

## About the Project

The Chapter Project directs students to apply their knowledge of algebra and geometric solids to create a 3-D model that represents the algebraic expression $(a + b)^3$.

CHAPTER 13

# Nonlinear Functions and Polynomials

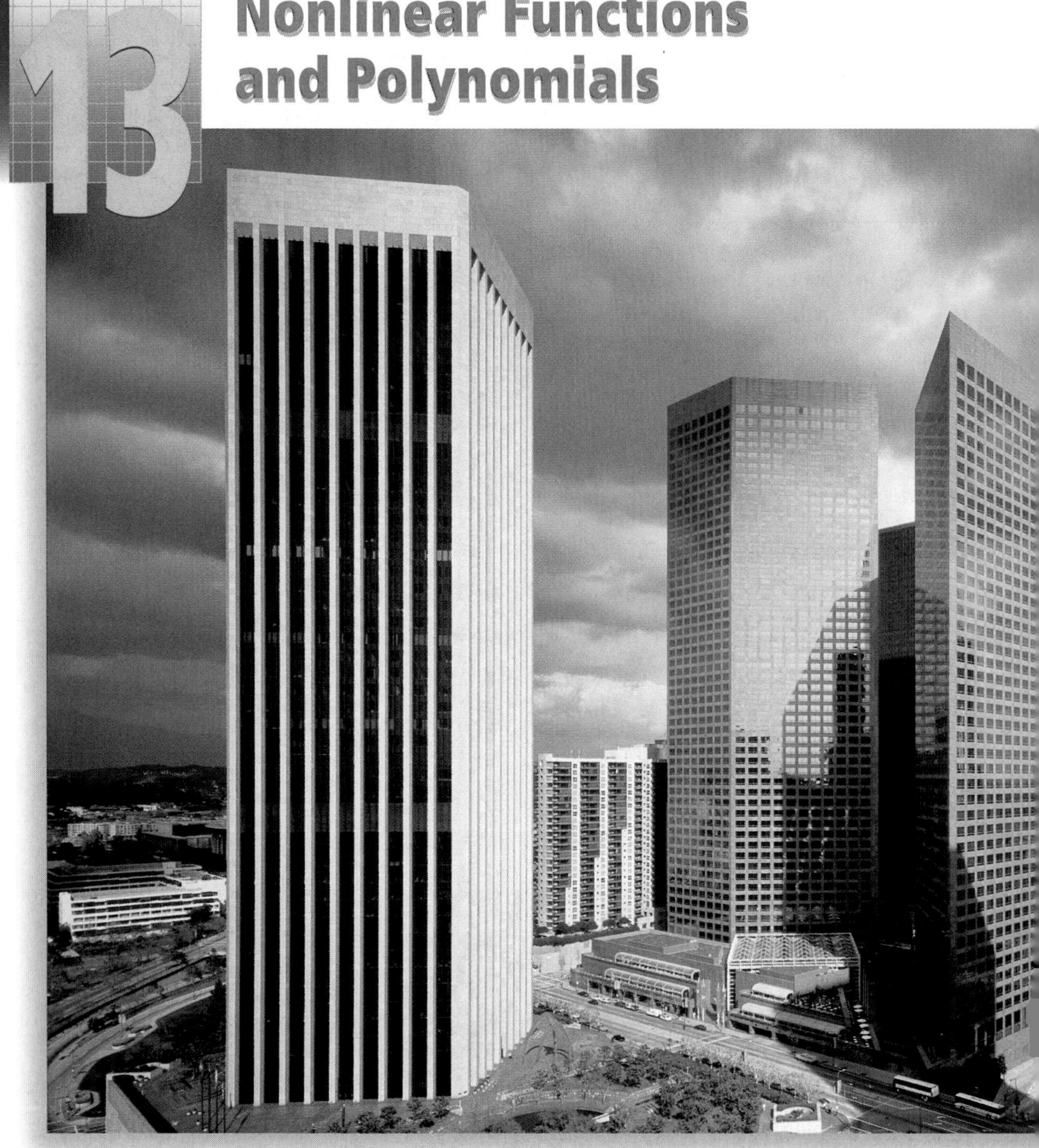

**What you'll learn in this chapter:**

- How to use arithmetic and geometric sequences
- How to graph nonlinear functions
- How to perform operations with polynomials

*Web Extension*
**www.phschool.com**

For Students
Chapter Support with Internet links
Interactive Activities

For Teachers
Curriculum Support
Professional Development
Product Information
Regional Support Information

The prismatic shapes of the buildings at the left can be described using mathematical expressions such as $(a + b)^3$. Is $(a + b)^3$ equal to $a^3 + b^3$? No, but many students make that mistake. Sometimes it helps to have a concrete representation of a mathematical expression.

***Make a 3-D Polynomial Model*** For the chapter project, you will make a three-dimensional model of a polynomial. You will analyze the model and its parts. You will use the model to see how polynomials can represent real-world objects.

### *Steps to help you complete the project*

**p. 681** Activity: Creating
**p. 688** Activity: Writing
**p. 692** Activity: Writing
**p. 703** Finishing the Chapter Project

*Web Extension*
**www.phschool.com**

How to solve a problem by using multiple strategies

*The Chapter Project is optional and may be assigned at your discretion.*

Ask students:

- What is the product of $(a + b)$ times $(a + b)$?
- What is the area of a square that is $(a + b)$ units in length and $(a + b)$ units in width?
- What is the volume of a cube that is $(a + b)$ units in length and $(a + b)$ units in width and $(a + b)$ units deep?

Distribute a copy of the Project Manager and Scoring Rubric to help students get an overview of the project.

Review the scoring rubric with students.

###  Project Notebook

Encourage students to keep all project-related materials in a separate folder or notebook. Call attention to the fact that they will find much useful information on the Web site **www.phschool.com**.

**Tracking the Project** Set benchmark deadlines for students to show you their work in progress.

## Scoring Rubric

**3** You write your equations correctly. Your polynomial model is neat, accurate, and well-labeled. Your display is complete, well-organized, and easy to read.

**2** You make minor errors in your equations. Your polynomial model is accurate, but could be constructed better. Your display is complete, but could be organized better.

**1** You write your equations or construct your polynomial model incorrectly. Your display is incomplete and lacks organization.

**0** Major elements of the project are incomplete or missing.

*Available in the Chapter 13 Support File in the Teaching Resources box.*

### Project Manager and Scoring Rubric

**Getting Started** You will be creating a display of a three-dimensional polynomial model. Read about the project in your textbook. As you work on the project, you will need cardboard, scissors, tape, a ruler, materials to record your calculations, and materials to create your display.

**Checklist and Suggestions**

| | | |
|---|---|---|
| ❑ | Create the polynomial model. | Make $a$ and $b$ different lengths. |
| ❑ | Write polynomials for the area of a face. Write an equation. | Remember the face of a cube is a square with area $s^2$. |
| ❑ | Write polynomials for the volume of the cube. Write an equation. | Add the volumes of each of the eight prisms you originally constructed. |
| ❑ | Create your display. | Label your models and explain their connections to the equations clearly. |
| ❑ | Share your display with a friend. | Make any necessary changes. |

**Scoring Rubric**

**3** You write your equations correctly. Your polynomial model is neat, accurate, and well-labeled. Your display is complete, well-organized, and easy to read.

**2** You make minor errors in your equations. Your polynomial model is accurate, but could be constructed better. Your display is complete, but could be organized better.

**1** You write your equations or construct your polynomial model incorrectly. Your display is incomplete and lacks organization.

**0** Major elements of the project are incomplete or missing.

**Your Evaluation of the Project** Evaluate your work, based on the Scoring Rubric.

**Teacher's Evaluation of the Project**

# 13-1

## Getting Ready

**Key Terms and Symbols** sequence, term, arithmetic sequence, common difference, geometric sequence, common ratio

**Resources** A complete list of resources for this lesson is on p. 661H.

### Daily Skills Warm-Up

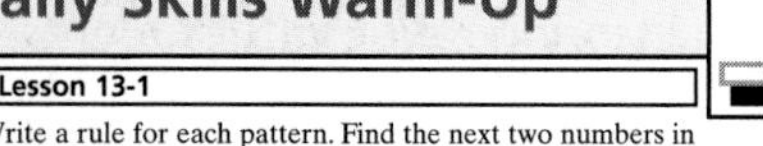

Lesson 13-1

Write a rule for each pattern. Find the next two numbers in the pattern.

1. 8, 14, 20, 26, 32
   Start with 8 and add 6 repeatedly.
2. 4, 20, 100, 500, 2,500
   Start with 4 and multiply by 5 repeatedly.
3. 7, 19, 31, 43, 55, 67
   Start with 7 and add 12 repeatedly.
4. 6, 5, 10, 9, 18, 17, 34
   Start with 6 and alternate subtracting 1 and multiplying by 2.

### Background for the Lesson

A *sequence* is a set of elements ordered in some specific way. The elements in a sequence are called *terms*. In an arithmetic sequence, there is a common difference between the terms. For example, in the sequence 3, 6, 9, 12, . . . , the *common difference*, added to each term, is 3. In a *geometric sequence*, there is a *common ratio* between the terms. For example, in the sequence 3, 9, 27, 81, . . . , the common ratio that multiplies each successive term is 3.

## 1 Focus

### Investigate

Many students will instinctively choose \$500 over \$1 for the first day. Point out to them that using mathematics can change their first reaction.

### Connecting to Students' Lives

Discuss with students any patterns or sequences that they know in their daily lives.

# 13-1 Patterns and Sequences

### What You'll Learn

1. To describe number patterns with arithmetic sequences
2. To describe number patterns with geometric sequences

### . . . And Why

To use sequences in making predictions

### Investigate

**Discovering a Pattern**

You win a contest and can choose one of two options for 30 days.

| Option A | Option B |
|---|---|
| You receive \$500 the first day, \$550 the second, \$600 the third, \$650 the fourth, and so on. | You receive \$1 the first day, \$2 the second, \$4 the third, \$8 the fourth, and so on. |

1. Make a table of values for both options for the first 10 days. See margin.
   a. Which option gives you more money in 10 days? Option A
   b. Which option would you choose for 30 days? Explain.
   Option B. Option A increases at a steady \$50 a day. From day 7 on, Option B is increasing faster, and will soon pass Option A.

### Reading Math

In the phrase *arithmetic sequence*, the word *arithmetic* is pronounced "a rith MET ik." The third syllable, *met*, is emphasized.

## Part 1 Arithmetic Sequences

A **sequence** is a set of numbers that follow a pattern. Each number in the sequence is a **term** of the sequence. You find a term of an **arithmetic sequence** by adding a fixed number to the previous term. This fixed number is called the **common difference.**

| Term Number | 1st | 2nd | 3rd | 4th |
|---|---|---|---|---|
| Arithmetic Sequence | 2 | 6 | 10 | 14 |

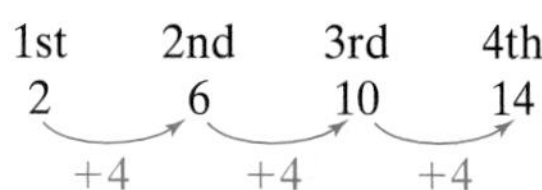

Common Difference +4 +4 +4

### Example 1

**What is the common difference in the sequence 4, 2, 0, −2, . . .?**

4 2 0 −2

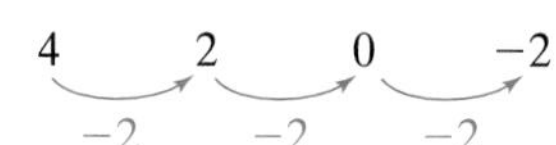

−2 −2 −2 Find the common difference.

The common difference is −2.

**Try This** What is the common difference in each sequence?

2. 8, 13, 18, 23, . . . 5
3. 12, 9, 6, 3, . . . −3



## Tools to Monitor Progress

### BEFORE THE LESSON

**To check prerequisite skills:**

- Multiplying and dividing fractions

**Skills Handbook,** p. 740

**Skills Intervention Kit,** Operations with Fractions

### DURING THE LESSON

**To check understanding:**

**Try This** exercises on student page

- **Additional Examples 1–4**
  One of the following sequences is arithmetic, one is geometric, and the other is neither. Identify the type of sequence. For the arithmetic and geometric sequences, give the common difference or ratio, and find the next three terms. For the other sequence, find the next three terms.

You can continue a sequence and write a rule to describe it.

REAL-WORLD  CONNECTION

### Example 2

**A runner training for a race runs 2 mi the first day, $2\frac{1}{4}$ mi the second day, $2\frac{1}{2}$ mi the third day, and so on. Find the next three terms of the sequence. Then write a rule to describe the sequence.**

$2 \quad 2\frac{1}{4} \quad 2\frac{1}{2} \quad 2\frac{3}{4} \quad 3 \quad 3\frac{1}{4}$

$+\frac{1}{4} \quad +\frac{1}{4} \quad +\frac{1}{4} \quad +\frac{1}{4} \quad +\frac{1}{4}$

Find the common difference. Use it to find the next three terms.

The next three terms are $2\frac{3}{4}$, 3, and $3\frac{1}{4}$. The rule for the sequence is *Start with 2 and add $\frac{1}{4}$ repeatedly.*

**Try This** Find the next three terms of each sequence. Then write a rule to describe each sequence.

4. 23, 19, 15, 11, . . . 7, 3, −1; start with 23 and add −4 repeatedly.

5. $-6, -4\frac{2}{3}, -3\frac{1}{3}, -2, \ldots$ $-\frac{2}{3}, \frac{2}{3}, 2$; start with −6 and add $1\frac{1}{3}$ repeatedly.

## Geometric and Other Sequences

You find a term of a **geometric sequence** by *multiplying* the previous term by a fixed number called the **common ratio.**

| Term Number | 1st | 2nd | 3rd | 4th |
|---|---|---|---|---|
| Geometric Sequence | 2 | 6 | 18 | 54 |
| Common Ratio | ×3 | ×3 | ×3 | |

You can find the common ratio for a geometric sequence by dividing a term by the previous term in the sequence.

### Example 3

**Find the common ratio in the sequence 4, 8, 16, 32, . . . Find the next three terms of the sequence. Then write a rule to describe the sequence.**

4 8 16 32 64 128 256

×2 ×2 ×2 ×2 ×2 ×2

Find the common ratio. Use it to find the next three terms.

The next three terms are 64, 128, and 256. The rule for the sequence is *Start with 4 and multiply by 2 repeatedly*.

During a two-mile run, a runner's feet strike the ground about 3,000 times. About how many times will the feet of the runner in Example 2 strike the ground on the fifth day? 4,500

### Reading Math

The word *common* means "shared by all." The common ratio is called that because you get the same value when you divide each term in a geometric sequence by the previous term. The ratio is shared by every pair of consecutive terms.



# 2 Teach

## Part 1 Teaching Notes

Explain that students can find the next term of an arithmetic sequence by adding the same number (positive or negative) each time. Point out that the sequences in this lesson are infinite and have no last term.

**ELL** Help students pronounce math words correctly by telling them that arithmetic (as a noun) has the accent on the second syllable (*-rith*) but in arithmetic sequence (where arithmetic is a modifier), the accent is on the third syllable (*-met*).

### Example 1

**Build understanding.** Ask: What will be the next three terms in this sequence? −4, −6, −8

**Error Prevention** The common difference is always added to the previous term, so the common difference is negative when a sequence is decreasing.

### Example 2

**Build understanding.** Ask: On which day will the runner run 4 miles? How do you know? 8th day; answers may vary.

**Advanced Learners** Write a rule for finding the *n*th term of an arithmetic sequence. $a + (n - 1)d$; $a$ is the first term; $d$ is the common difference.

**Visual Learning** Suggest that students use number lines to help find the common difference and additional terms in arithmetic sequences.

1a.

| Day | Option A | Option B |
|---|---|---|
| 1 | $500 | $1 |
| 2 | $550 | $2 |
| 3 | $600 | $4 |
| 4 | $650 | $8 |
| 5 | $700 | $16 |
| 6 | $750 | $32 |
| 7 | $800 | $64 |
| 8 | $850 | $128 |
| 9 | $900 | $256 |
| 10 | $950 | $512 |

a. 3, 5, 9, 15, . . . neither; 23, 33, 45

b. 12, 10.5, 9, 7.5, . . . arithmetic; −1.5; 6, 4.5, 3

c. 2, −4, 8, −16, . . . geometric; −2; 32, −64, 128

## After the Lesson

### To assess knowledge: Lesson Quiz

Tell whether the sequence is arithmetic, geometric, or neither. Find the next three terms of each sequence.

1. $9, 3, 1, \frac{1}{3}, \ldots$ G; $\frac{1}{9}, \frac{1}{27}, \frac{1}{81}$
2. 1, 4, 9, 16, . . . N; 25, 36, 49
3. 66, 77, 88, 99, . . . A; 110, 121, 132

- For enrichment and reteaching options see Resources on p. 661H.

## Part 2 Teaching Notes

A geometric sequence replaces the common difference of an arithmetic sequence by a common ratio to find the next term from the previous one.

### Example 3

**Build understanding.** Ask: Because the common ratio is 2, what is the relationship between a given term and the previous term? Any given term in the sequence is double the previous term.

**Error Prevention** Students may assume that a common ratio must be a fraction. When the first term is half the second, then the common ratio (or multiplier) is 2, an integer.

### Example 4

**Build understanding.** Ask: How can you tell that a sequence is neither arithmetic nor geometric? The terms do not increase by a single number that is the common difference or ratio.

**Math Reasoning** Use math reasoning to explain the relationship between the terms in the sequence in part c of Example 4. The number added to each term increases by one each time, starting with 2.

6. The common ratio is 3. 162, 486, 1,458; start with 2 and multiply by 3 repeatedly.
7. The common ratio is $\frac{1}{2}$. 0.25, 0.125, 0.0625; start with 4 and multiply by $\frac{1}{2}$ repeatedly.

**TRY THIS** Find the common ratio and the next three terms of each sequence. Then write a rule to describe each sequence.

**6.** 2, 6, 18, 54, . . . **7.** 4, 2, 1, 0.5, . . .

6–7. See left.

Not every sequence is arithmetic or geometric. You can determine whether any sequence of numbers *is* arithmetic or geometric by looking for a common difference or a common ratio. You can look for patterns to continue any sequence.

### EXAMPLE 4

**Tell whether each sequence is *arithmetic, geometric,* or *neither.* Find the next three terms of each sequence.**

**a. 4, 6, 8, 10, . . .**

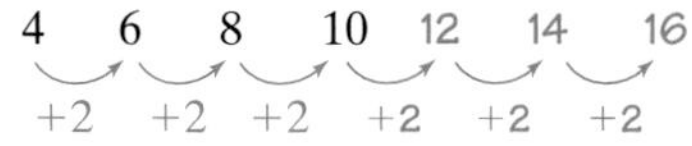


There is a common difference of 2. The sequence is arithmetic. The next three terms are 12, 14, and 16.

**b. 4, 6, 9, $13\frac{1}{2}$, . . .**

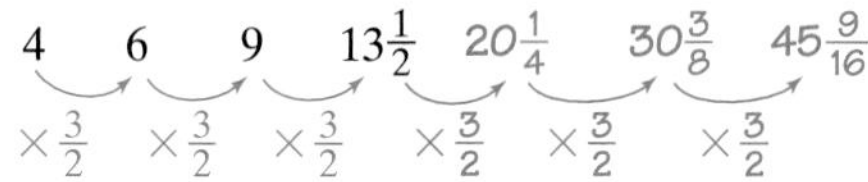


The ratio determined by the first three terms is $\frac{6}{4}$ or $\frac{9}{6}$. These equal $\frac{3}{2}$, which is the common ratio. The sequence is geometric. The next three terms are $20\frac{1}{4}$, $30\frac{3}{8}$, and $45\frac{9}{16}$.

**c. 4, 6, 9, 13, . . .**

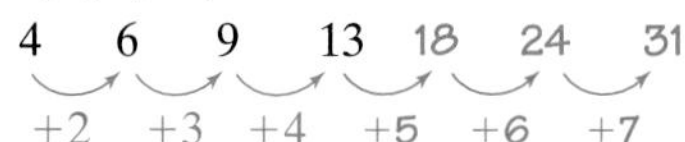


The sequence is neither arithmetic nor geometric. Following the pattern above, the next three terms are 18, 24, and 31.

8. geometric; 243, 729, 2,187
9. neither; 34, 45, 58
10. geometric; −12, 12, −12
11. arithmetic; 650, 800, 950

**TRY THIS** Tell whether each sequence is *arithmetic, geometric,* or *neither.* Find the next three terms of each sequence. 8–11. See left.

**8.** 3, 9, 27, 81, . . . **9.** 10, 13, 18, 25, . . .

**10.** −12, 12, −12, 12, . . . **11.** 50, 200, 350, 500, . . .

# Exercises

## Check Understanding

**What is the common difference of each arithmetic sequence?**

**1.** $5, 4, 3, 2, \ldots$ −1　**2.** $4, 11, 18, 25, \ldots$ 7　**3.** $1, 1\frac{1}{2}, 2, 2\frac{1}{2}, \ldots$ $\frac{1}{2}$　**4.** $7, 1, -5, -11, \ldots$ −6

**What is the common ratio of each geometric sequence?**

**5.** $45, 90, 180, 360, \ldots$ 2　**6.** $3, 6, 12, 24, \ldots$ 2　**7.** $5, 1, \frac{1}{5}, \frac{1}{25}, \ldots$ $\frac{1}{5}$　**8.** $-3, -15, -75, \ldots$ 5

**Find the next three terms of each sequence. Then write a rule to describe each sequence.**

**9.** $1, 4, 16, 64, \ldots$ 256, 1,024, 4,096; start with 1 and multiply by 4 repeatedly.

**10.** $-21, -18, -15, -12, \ldots$ −9, −6, −3; start with −21 and add 3 repeatedly.

**11.** $6.5, 6.7, 6.9, 7.1, \ldots$ 7.3, 7.5, 7.7; start with 6.5 and add 0.2 repeatedly.

## Practice and Problem Solving

**What is the common difference of each arithmetic sequence?**

**12.** $-6, -5, -4, -3, \ldots$ 1　**13.** $3, 9, 15, 21, \ldots$ 6　**14.** $80, 60, 40, 20, \ldots$ −20　**15.** $5, 6.4, 7.8, 9.2, \ldots$ 1.4

**What is the common ratio of each geometric sequence?**

**16.** $5, 10, 20, 40, \ldots$ 2　**17.** $-4, 12, -36, 108, \ldots$ −3　**18.** $8, 40, 200, 1{,}000, \ldots$ 5　**19.** $12, 4, 1\frac{1}{3}, \frac{4}{9}, \ldots$ $\frac{1}{3}$

**Find the next three terms of each sequence. Then write a rule to describe each sequence.** 20–27. See margin.

**20.** $0, 5, 10, 15, \ldots$　**21.** $9, 18, 36, 72, \ldots$　**22.** $2, 20, 200, 2{,}000, \ldots$　**23.** $21, 15, 9, 3, \ldots$

**24.** $25, 50, 75, 100, \ldots$　**25.** $80, 50, 20, -10, \ldots$　**26.** $3, 1, -1, -3, \ldots$　**27.** $2, 8, 32, 128, \ldots$

**Tell whether each sequence is *arithmetic, geometric,* or *neither.* Find the next three terms of each sequence.** 28–39. See margin p. 668.

**28.** $1, 3, 9, 27, \ldots$　**29.** $10, 5, 0, -5, \ldots$　**30.** $4.5, 4, 3.5, 3, \ldots$

**31.** $2, 2, 4, 6, \ldots$　**32.** $-1, 3, -9, 27, \ldots$　**33.** $\frac{1}{2}, \frac{5}{6}, 1\frac{1}{6}, 1\frac{1}{2}, \ldots$

**34.** $7, 7.03, 7.06, 7.09, \ldots$　**35.** $0, 5, 12, 21, \ldots$　**36.** $1, 10, 2, 20, \ldots$

**37.** $13, 12, 10, 7, \ldots$　**38.** $50, 150, 450, 950, \ldots$　**39.** $-\frac{1}{5}, -\frac{1}{10}, -\frac{1}{20}, -\frac{1}{40}, \ldots$

**40.** *Writing* The first two numbers of a sequence are 4 and 8. Can you tell what kind of sequence this is? Explain. No. It could be arithmetic, such as 4, 8, 12, 16, . . . , or it could be geometric, such as 4, 8, 16, 32, . . . , or it could be neither, such as 4, 8, 13, 19, 26, . . .



20. 20, 25, 30; Start with 0 and add 5 repeatedly.

21. 144, 288, 576; Start with 9 and multiply by 2 repeatedly.

22. 20,000, 200,000, 2,000,000; Start with 2 and multiply by 10 repeatedly.

23. −3, −9, −15; Start with 21 and add −6 repeatedly.

24. 125, 150, 175; Start with 25 and add 25 repeatedly.

25. −40, −70, −100; Start with 80 and add −30 repeatedly.

## Alternative Assessment

Have students write two word problems with each kind of sequence. Have them exchange with a partner to solve each other's problems.

26. −5, −7, −9; Start with 3 and add −2 repeatedly.

27. 512, 2,048, 8,192; Start with 2 and multiply by 4 repeatedly.

# 3 Practice/Assess

## Assignment Guide

To provide flexible scheduling, this lesson can be divided into parts.

**Part 1**
**Core** 1–4, 10–15, 20, 23–26, 49

**Part 2**
**Core** 5–9, 16–19, 21–22, 27–40, 42–46
**Extension** 41, 47–48

Mixed Review can be assigned at any time for maintenance.

## Exercises

**Test Prep Exercise 49** Find the difference between the terms and how many terms there are between the two terms given. Then divide.

## Challenge

Write a geometric series where all of the terms are the same, except the first term. What is the common ratio? sample answer: 5, 0, 0, 0, . . .; 0

## Closure

A sequence is a set of numbers that follows a pattern. Each number in the sequence is a term of the sequence. You can find a term of an arithmetic sequence by adding a fixed number, the common difference, to the previous term. You can find a term of a geometric sequence by multiplying the previous term by a fixed number, called a common ratio.

## Daily Cumulative Review

**Solve.** *(Lesson 12-9)*

1. You take a four-question multiple choice test. Each question has four choices. You don't know any of the answers. What is the probability that you guess exactly 3 out of 4 correctly?
Answers may vary but should be about 6%

**Solve.** *(Lesson 12-8)*

2. A chicken farmer collects 200 eggs. Of these, 30 are grade AA large. Estimate the number of grade AA large eggs the farmer will collect out of 850 eggs.
about 128 eggs

**Mixed Review**

**Evaluate each expression.**

3. $a^2$, for $a = -7$ (4-2) 49
4. $2x^2$, for $x = 5$ (4-2) 50
5. $y^2 - 3y + 4$, for $y = -2$ (4-2) 14
6. $h^3$, for $h = -10$ (4-2) −1,000
7. $3y^2$, for $y = 0.4$ (4-2) 0.48
8. $x^2 + 2x + 7$, for $x = -3$ (4-2) 10

**Simplify.**

9. $|-36|$ (1-4) 36
10. $-|-47|$ (1-4) −47
11. $-|-18|$ (1-4) −18

**Complete the table of ordered pairs and graph the equation.**

12. $y = -\frac{2}{3}x + 1$ (8-2)

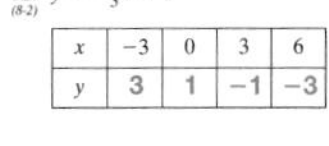

| $x$ | −3 | 0 | 3 | 6 |
|---|---|---|---|---|
| $y$ | 3 | 1 | −1 | −3 |

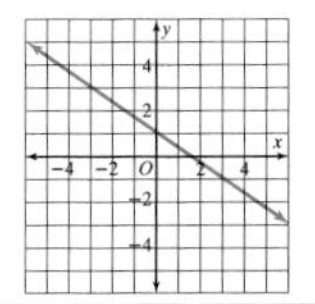

*Math in the Media* **Use the article at the right for Exercise 41.**

**41.** Write the data as a sequence. Then answer the questions below. 12, 11, and 14 million

**a.** Find the difference between each pair of consecutive terms of the sequence.

**b.** Find the ratio between each pair of consecutive terms of the sequence. 1.053, 1.046, 1.056

**c.** Does an arithmetic or a geometric sequence best model the data? geometric

**d.** Use your choice in part (c) to predict what the population will be in the year 2005. 290 million

> **Population Watch**
>
> The population of the United States in 1980 was about 226 million, in 1985 it was about 238 million, in 1990 it was about 249 million, and in 1995 it was about 263 million.

**Evaluate each expression for $n = -2, -1, 0$, and 1. Is the sequence formed *arithmetic, geometric,* or *neither*?** 42–46. See right.

**42.** $3n$ **43.** $n(n + 1)$ **44.** $2^n$ **45.** $2n$ **46.** $n^2$

42. −6, −3, 0, 3; arithmetic
43. 2, 0, 0, 2; neither
44. $\frac{1}{4}, \frac{1}{2}$, 1, 2; geometric
45. −4, −2, 0, 2; arithmetic
46. 4, 1, 0, 1; neither

**47.** You open a savings account with $2,000. The account earns 4% interest compounded semiannually.

**a.** Write the balance in the savings account after each interest payment for two years. $2,040, $2,080.80, $2,122.42, $2,164.86

**b.** Does the pattern of balances form an arithmetic or geometric sequence? Explain. Geometric; each balance is 1.02 times the previous balance.

**48.** *Patterns* In the Fibonacci sequence 1, 1, 2, 3, 5, 8, . . . , you find each term (after the first two terms) by adding the two previous terms together. Write the next three terms of the sequence. 13, 21, 34

**49.** **TEST PREP** If the first term of an arithmetic sequence is 35 and the tenth term is 107, what is the third term? B

A. 50 B. 51 C. 52 D. 53

**Quick Review**

The formula for compound interest is $B = p(1 + r)^n$, where $B$ is the balance, $p$ is the principal, $r$ is the interest rate for each interest period, and $n$ is the number of interest periods. For interest that is compounded semiannually, the interest rate is $\frac{1}{2}$ the yearly rate.

## Mixed Review

**Find the circumference of each circle.** ***(Lesson 9-6)***

**50.** diameter = 14 cm 44 cm **51.** radius = 5 in. 31.4 in. **52.** radius = 8.5 m 53.4 m

**53.** List the congruent corresponding parts of the triangles at the right. Write a congruence statement for the triangles. ***(Lesson 9-5)*** $\overline{GH} \cong \overline{RP}$, $\overline{IG} \cong \overline{QR}$, $\angle G \cong \angle R$, $\triangle GHI \cong \triangle RPQ$ by SAS

G H Q I P R

**54.** *Surveys* You want to find out which presidential candidate is most popular in your city. You plan to interview people who visit the city's art museum. State whether the survey plan describes a good sample. Explain your reasoning. ***(Lesson 12-8)*** It is not a good sample, because it excludes many groups, such as people with no interest in art.



See also Extra Practice section.

28. geometric; 81, 243, 729
29. arithmetic; –10, –15, –20
30. arithmetic; 2.5, 2, 1.5
31. neither; 10, 16, 26
32. geometric; –81, 243, –729
33. arithmetic; $1\frac{5}{6}, 2\frac{1}{6}, 2\frac{1}{2}$
34. arithmetic; 7.12, 7.15, 7.18
35. neither; 32, 45, 60
36. neither; 3, 30, 4
37. neither; 3, −2, −8
38. neither; 1,650, 2,550, 3,650
39. geometric; $-\frac{1}{80}, -\frac{1}{160}, -\frac{1}{320}$

## Practice

**Tell whether each sequence is *arithmetic, geometric,* or *neither*. Find the next three terms of each sequence. If the sequence is arithmetic or geometric, write a rule to describe the sequence.**

1. 7, 14, 28, 56, 112, 224, 448 type: geometric
   rule: Start with 7 and multiply by 2 repeatedly.
2. 5, 11, 17, 23, 29, 35, 41 type: arithmetic
   rule: Start with 5 and add 6 repeatedly.
3. 32, 16, 8, 4, 2, 1, $\frac{1}{2}$ type: geometric
   rule: Start with 32 and multiply by $\frac{1}{2}$ repeatedly.
4. 25, 21, 17, 13, 9, 5, 1 type: arithmetic
   rule: Start with 25 and add −4 repeatedly.
5. 9, 3, −3, −9, −15, −21, −27 type: arithmetic
   rule: Start with 9 and add −6 repeatedly.
6. 8, 3, −3, −10, −18, −27, −37 type: neither
   rule:
7. 2, −6, 18, −54, 162, −486, 1,458 type: geometric
   rule: Start with 2 and multiply by −3 repeatedly.
8. 1, 4, 9, 16, 25, 36, 49 type: neither
   rule:

**What is the common difference of each arithmetic sequence?**

9. 16, 19, 22, 25, . . . 3
10. 3, 5.8, 8.6, 11.4, . . . 2.8

**What is the common ratio of each geometric sequence?**

11. 6, 24, 96, 384, . . . 4
12. 12, 3, $\frac{3}{4}$, $\frac{3}{16}$, . . . $\frac{1}{4}$



## Reteaching

Tell whether the sequence is *arithmetic, geometric,* or *neither*. Find the next three terms and write a rule to describe the sequence.

9, 18, 36, 72, . . .

Find the difference between each term and the one before it to see if the sequence is arithmetic.

9, 18, 36, 72, . . .
18 − 9 = 9 36 − 18 = 18 72 − 36 = 36

There is no common difference, so the sequence is not arithmetic. Find the ratio between each term and the one before it to see if the sequence is geometric.

9, 18, 36, 72, . . .
$\frac{18}{9} = 2$ $\frac{36}{18} = 2$ $\frac{72}{36} = 2$

There is a common ratio of 2. The sequence is geometric. The rule is: *Start with 9 and multiply by 2 repeatedly.*

The next three terms are:

$72 \cdot 2 = 144$
$144 \cdot 2 = 288$
$288 \cdot 2 = 576$

9, 18, 36, 72, 144, 288, 576

**Tell whether each sequence is *arithmetic, geometric,* or *neither*. Find the next three terms of each sequence. If the sequence is arithmetic or geometric, write a rule to describe the sequence.**

1. 8, 11, 14, 17, 20, 23, 26 type: arithmetic
   rule: Start with 8 and add 3 repeatedly.
2. 4, 2, 0, −2, −4, −6, −8 type: arithmetic
   rule: Start with 4 and add −2 repeatedly.
3. 2, 10, 50, 250, 1,250, 6,250, 31,250 type: geometric
   rule: Start with 2 and multiply by 5 repeatedly.



## Enrichment

All arithmetic sequences have the same general form, so you can find a general expression for any arithmetic sequence. The same is true for geometric sequences.

**Find an expression for the $n^{th}$ term of the arithmetic sequence 3, 7, 11, 15, . . . by completing the table.**

| | Term Number | Term | Expression |
|---|---|---|---|
| | 1 | 3 | $3 + 0 = 3 + 4(0)$ |
| | 2 | 7 | $3 + 4 = 3 + 4(1)$ |
| | 3 | 11 | $(3 + 4) + 4 = 3 + 4(2)$ |
| 1. | 4 | 15 | $3 + 4(2) + 4 = 3 + 4(3)$ |
| 2. | 5 | 19 | $3 + 4(3) + 4 = 3 + 4(4)$ |
| 3. | 6 | 23 | $3 + 4(4) + 4 = 3 + 4(5)$ |
| 4. | $n$ | — | $3 + 4(n - 1)$ |

5. Let $a$ be the first term of any arithmetic sequence and $d$ be the common difference. Write an expression for the $n^{th}$ term in terms of $a$, $d$, and $n$. $a + d(n - 1)$

**Find an expression for the $n^{th}$ term of the geometric sequence 8, 16, 32, 64, . . . by completing the table.**

| | Term Number | Term | Expression |
|---|---|---|---|
| | 1 | 8 | $8 = 8 \cdot 2^0$ |
| | 2 | 16 | $8 \cdot 2 = 8 \cdot 2^1$ |
| | 3 | 32 | $(8 \cdot 2) \cdot 2 = 8 \cdot 2^2$ |
| 6. | 4 | 64 | $8 \cdot 2^2 \cdot 2 = 8 \cdot 2^3$ |
| 7. | 5 | 128 | $8 \cdot 2^3 \cdot 2 = 8 \cdot 2^4$ |
| 8. | 6 | 256 | $8 \cdot 2^4 \cdot 2 = 8 \cdot 2^5$ |
| 9. | $n$ | — | $8 \cdot 2^{n-1}$ |

10. Let $a$ be the first term of any geometric sequence and $r$ be the common ratio. Write an expression for the $n^{th}$ term in terms of $a$, $r$, and $n$. $a \cdot r^{n-1}$

# Graphing Nonlinear Functions

13-2

## Investigate

GRAPHING DATA

You can graph the area of a square as a function of the length of a side of the square.

1. Complete the table at the right.
2. Draw a graph of the data. Does your graph appear to be a linear function? Explain. See below right.

| Side $x$ | Area $f(x)$ |
|---|---|
| 1 | 1 |
| 2 | ■ 4 |
| 3 | ■ 9 |
| 4 | ■ 16 |
| 5 | ■ 25 |
| 6 | 36 |

### What You'll Learn

1. To graph quadratic functions
2. To graph absolute value functions

### ... And Why

To use nonlinear functions in modeling real-world situations, such as finding the area of an enclosed space

## PART 1 Graphing Quadratic Functions

In a **quadratic function,** the input variable is squared. The graph of a quadratic function is a U-shaped curve, called a *parabola*. The curve may open upward or downward.

### Reading Math

A *nonlinear function* is a function that cannot be graphed as a line.

### EXAMPLE 1

**For the function $y = 2x^2$, make a table with integer values of $x$ from −2 to 2. Then graph the function.**

Make a table.

| $x$ | $2x^2 = y$ | $(x, y)$ |
|---|---|---|
| −2 | $2(-2)^2 = 8$ | $(-2, 8)$ |
| −1 | $2(-1)^2 = 2$ | $(-1, 2)$ |
| 0 | $2(0)^2 = 0$ | $(0, 0)$ |
| 1 | $2(1)^2 = 2$ | $(1, 2)$ |
| 2 | $2(2)^2 = 8$ | $(2, 8)$ |

Make a graph.

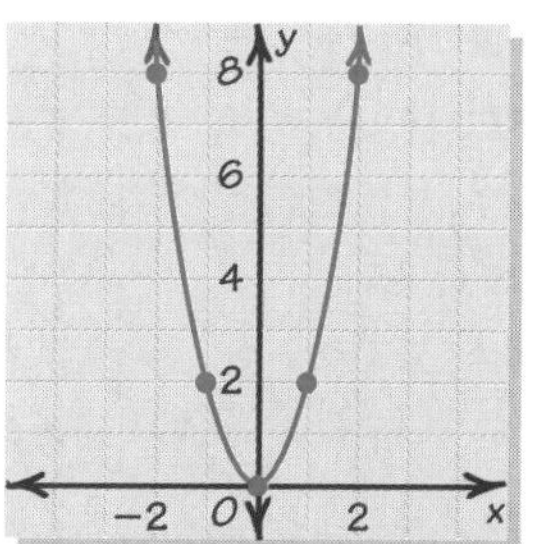


2.

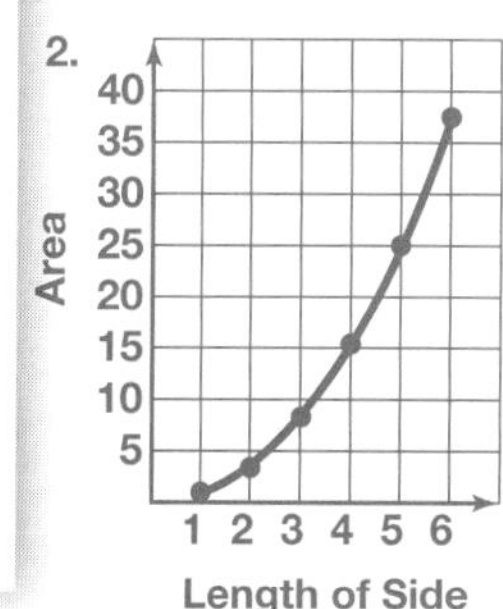


This is not a linear function because its graph is a curve.

■ **TRY THIS** For each function, make a table with integer values of $x$ from –2 to 2. Then graph each function. 3. See margin p. 670. 4. See back of book.

3. $y = \frac{1}{2}x^2 + 3$
4. $y = -x^2 + 3$



# Tools to Monitor Progress

## BEFORE THE LESSON

**To check prerequisite skills:**

- Equations with two variables

**Skills You Need,** p. 659

**Skills Handbook,** p. 725

**Skills Intervention Kit,** Pre-Algebra Basics

## DURING THE LESSON

**To check understanding:**

**Try This** exercises on student page

- **Additional Examples 1–3**

Graph the functions
$y = \frac{3}{4}|x| - 1$,
and
$y = -x^2 + x$
for $x$-values from −2 to 2.

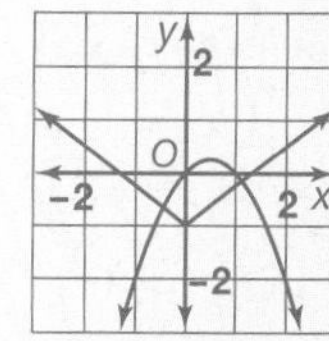



13-2


## Getting Ready

**Key Terms and Symbols** quadratic function, absolute value function

**Resources** A complete list of resources for this lesson is on p. 661H.

## Daily Skills Warm-Up

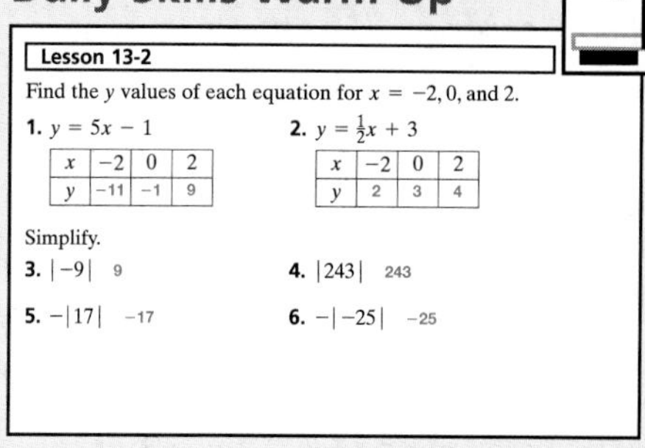

Lesson 13-2

Find the $y$ values of each equation for $x = -2, 0,$ and 2.

1. $y = 5x - 1$

| $x$ | −2 | 0 | 2 |
|---|---|---|---|
| $y$ | −11 | −1 | 9 |

2. $y = \frac{1}{2}x + 3$

| $x$ | −2 | 0 | 2 |
|---|---|---|---|
| $y$ | 2 | 3 | 4 |

Simplify.

3. $|-9|$ 9
4. $|243|$ 243
5. $-|17|$ −17
6. $-|-25|$ −25

## Background for the Lesson

The graph of a quadratic function of the standard form $y = ax^2 + bx + c$ is a U-shaped curve, called a *parabola*, that opens either upward ($a > 0$) or downward ($a < 0$). In the equation $y = x^2$, for $x = 2$ and $-2$, $y = 4$; for $x = 3$ and $-3$, $y = 9$; and so on. Notice that $y$ is increasing much faster than $x$, so the graph forms a curve instead of a straight line.

# 1 Focus

## Investigate

Students may try to connect the points on this graph with individual straight lines. Help them understand that the graph of this function is actually a curved line.

## Connecting to Students' Lives

Discuss the fact that connect-the-dots pictures often have jagged edges as a result of connecting the dots with straight lines instead of with curved lines.

# 2 Teach

## Part 1 Teaching Notes

Help students identify whether the graph of a parabola opens upward or downward by looking at the coefficient of the $x^2$-term.

### Example 1

**Build understanding.** Ask: Explain why the $y$-values of this function increase more rapidly than the $x$-values. **Each $y$-value equals twice the square of the $x$-value.**

**Tactile Learning** Some students may need practice graphing curved lines. Give them a table of $x$- and $y$-values from a quadratic function such as the one in Example 1. Have them practice plotting the points and drawing the curves of a parabola.

### Example 2

**Build understanding.** Ask: Why is the value of $y$ greatest at $x = 5$? **The difference between $x^2$ and $10x$ (which equals the value of $y$) is greatest when $x = 5$.**

## Part 2 Teaching Notes

Suggest that students picture the graph of an absolute value function as a straight beam of light reflecting off a mirror.

### Example 3

**Build understanding.** Ask: How is this function similar to $y = x^2$? **They both produce only nonnegative values for $y$.**

**Math Reasoning** Use math reasoning to explain what would change the width of a V-shaped graph of an absolute value function. **the coefficient of $x$; the greater the coefficient, the narrower the graph**

**Technology Option** The Graphing Calculator feature on a computer, or a graphing calculator, can show quickly how changing the numbers affects the graph.

Suppose the area of this kid's pen is 24 $yd^2$. What are the pen's width and length?
**width = 4 yd**
**length = 6 yd**

GEOMETRY CONNECTION

### Example 2

**The function $A = 10x - x^2$, where $x$ is the width in yards, gives the area $A$ of a goat pen in square yards. Graph the function. Use the graph to find the width that gives the greatest area.**

| x | $10x - x^2 = y$ | (x, y) |
|---|---|---|
| 0 | $10(0) - 0^2 = 0$ | (0, 0) |
| 1 | $10(1) - 1^2 = 9$ | (1, 9) |
| 2 | $10(2) - 2^2 = 16$ | (2, 16) |
| 3 | $10(3) - 3^2 = 21$ | (3, 21) |
| 4 | $10(4) - 4^2 = 24$ | (4, 24) |
| 5 | $10(5) - 5^2 = 25$ | (5, 25) |
| 6 | $10(6) - 6^2 = 24$ | (6, 24) |

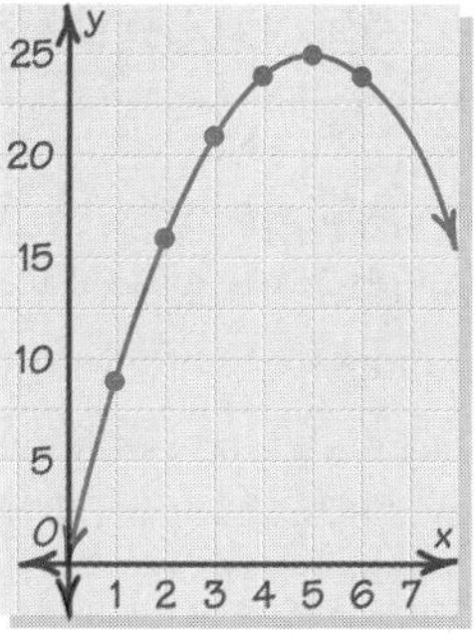

The ordered pair (5, 25) shows what appears to be the highest point. So the width 5 yards gives the greatest area.

**Try This** Graph each function. **5–6. See left.**

5. $y = -2x^2$

6. $y = 6x - x^2$

5. 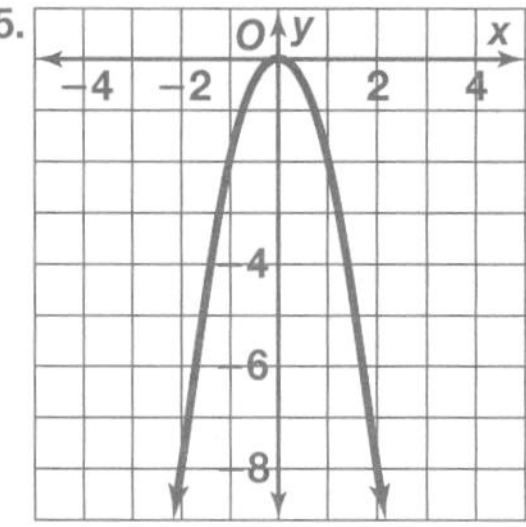

6.

## Part 2 Graphing Absolute Value Functions

The equation $y = |x|$ is an **absolute value function.** The graph of $y = |x|$ is V-shaped.

### Example 3

**Graph the function $y = |x|$.**

| x | $\|x\| = y$ | (x, y) |
|---|---|---|
| −2 | $\|-2\| = 2$ | (−2, 2) |
| −1 | $\|-1\| = 1$ | (−1, 1) |
| 0 | $\|0\| = 0$ | (0, 0) |
| 1 | $\|1\| = 1$ | (1, 1) |
| 2 | $\|2\| = 2$ | (2, 2) |

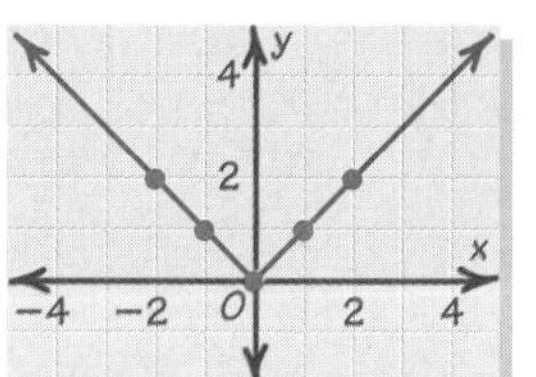

**Try This** Graph each function. **7–8. See back of book.**

7. $y = -|x| + 1$

8. $y = 2|x|$



3.

| x | $\frac{1}{2}x^2 + 3 = y$ | (x, y) |
|---|---|---|
| −2 | $\frac{1}{2}(-2)^2 + 3 = 5$ | (−2, 5) |
| −1 | $\frac{1}{2}(-1)^2 + 3 = 3\frac{1}{2}$ | $(-1, 3\frac{1}{2})$ |
| 0 | $\frac{1}{2}(0)^2 + 3 = 3$ | (0, 3) |
| 1 | $\frac{1}{2}(1)^2 + 3 = 3\frac{1}{2}$ | $(1, 3\frac{1}{2})$ |
| 2 | $\frac{1}{2}(2)^2 + 3 = 5$ | (2, 5) |

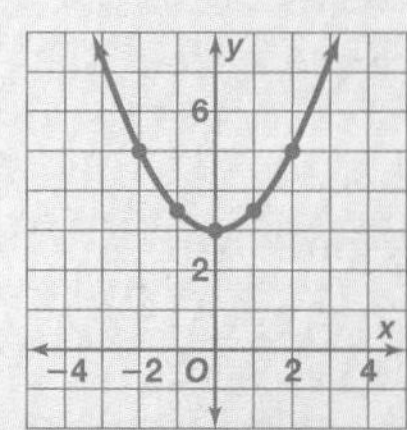

## AFTER THE LESSON

### To assess knowledge:

**Lesson Quiz**

What is the shape of the graph of each function? Does the graph open upward or downward?

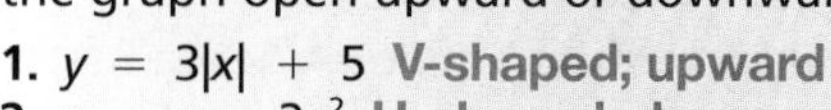

1. $y = 3|x| + 5$ **V-shaped; upward**
2. $y = x - 2x^2$ **U-shaped; downward**
3. $y = 14 + x^2$ **U-shaped; upward**
4. $y = 25 - \frac{1}{3}|x|$ **V-shaped; downward**

- For enrichment and reteaching options see Resources on p. 659H.

# Exercises

## Check Understanding

**What is the shape of the graph of each function?**

1. $y = |x| + 1$ V-shape
2. $y = x^2 - 8$ U-shape
3. $y = -4x^2$ U-shape
4. $y = -|x| - 3$ V-shape

**For each function, make a table with integer values of $x$ from $-2$ to 2. Then graph each function.** 5. See margin. 6–8. See back of book.

5. $y = x^2 + 1$
6. $y = |x| - 2$
7. $y = -x^2 + 2$
8. $y = -3|x|$

## Practice and Problem Solving

**TEST PREP** **Match each graph with an equation.**

9. 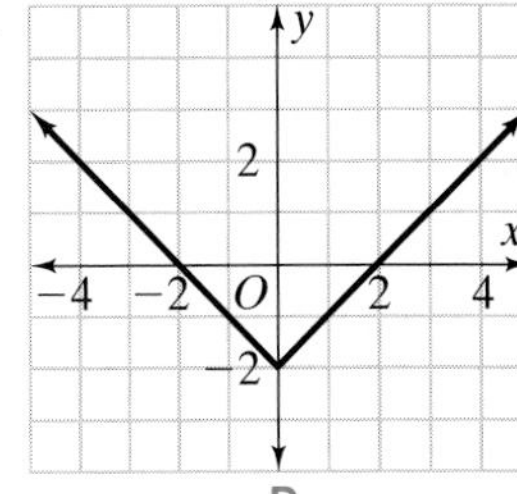

D

A. $y = -2|x|$
B. $y = x^2 - 2$
C. $y = |x - 2|$
D. $y = |x| - 2$

10. 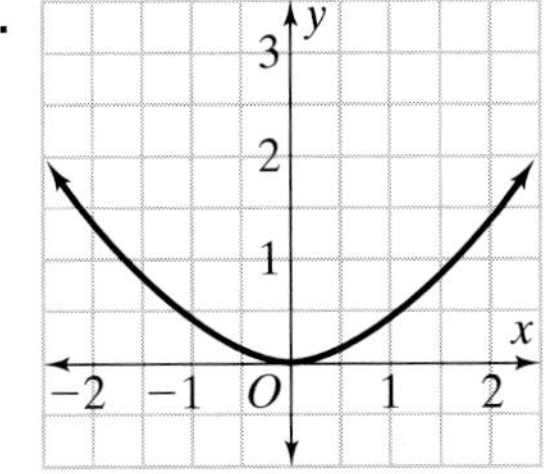

D

A. $y = 3x^2$
B. $y = |x| - \frac{1}{3}$
C. $y = x^2 - \frac{1}{2}$
D. $y = \frac{1}{3}x^2$

11. 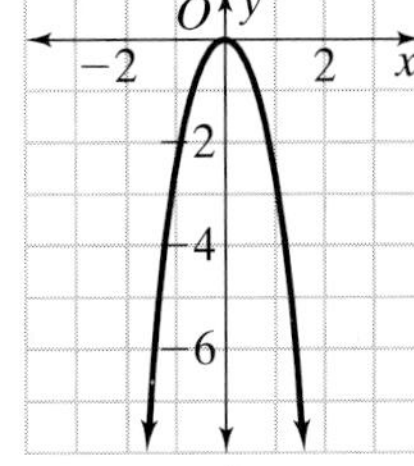

A

A. $y = -3x^2$
B. $y = x^2 - 3$
C. $y = -x^2 - 2$
D. $y = |x| - 3$

**For each function, make a table with integer values of $x$ from $-2$ to 2. Then graph each function.** 12–19. See back of book.

12. $y = x^2 - 2$
13. $y = x^2 + 4$
14. $y = 2x^2 - 2$
15. $y = -x^2 + 5$
16. $y = |x| + 3$
17. $y = |x| - 4$
18. $y = -|x| - 1$
19. $y = -2|x|$

20. *Open-ended* Write an absolute value function of your own. Graph the function. Check students' work.

21. *Mathematical Reasoning* For the function $y = x^3$, make a table with integer values of $x$ from $-2$ to 2. Then graph the function. Is the function quadratic? Explain. See back of book.



5.

| $x$ | $x^2 + 1$ | $y$ | $(x, y)$ |
|---|---|---|---|
| −2 | $(-2)^2 + 1$ | 5 | (−2, 5) |
| −1 | $(-1)^2 + 1$ | 2 | (−1, 2) |
| 0 | $0^2 + 1$ | 1 | (0, 1) |
| 1 | $1^2 + 1$ | 2 | (1, 2) |
| 2 | $2^2 + 1$ | 5 | (2, 5) |

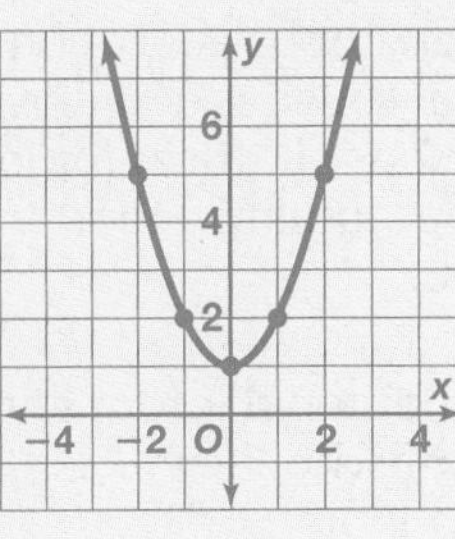

# 3 Practice/Assess

## Assignment Guide

To provide flexible scheduling, this lesson can be divided into parts.

**Part 1**
Core 2–3, 5, 10–15
Extension 21, 23

**Part 2**
Core 1, 4, 6–9, 16–20
Extension 22

Mixed Review can be assigned at any time for maintenance.

## Exercises

**Test Prep Exercises 9–11** Look at each graph to determine whether it is a quadratic or absolute value function to eliminate some answer choices. Substitute 0 for $x$ to find the $y$-value. Check to see if $(0, y)$ is on the given graph.

## Challenge

What kind of quadratic equation has a graph that opens to the right or left of the origin? What kind of absolute value equation has a graph that opens to the right or left of the origin? sample answer: $x = y^2$; $x = |y|$

## Closure

The graph of a quadratic function is a U-shaped curve, called a *parabola*, that opens upward or downward. The graph of an absolute value function is V-shaped.

## Alternative Assessment

Have students use the graph of the function $A = s^2$ to predict how the area of a square increases as the length of a side increases.

## Daily Cumulative Review

**Tell whether each sequence is *arithmetic*, *geometric*, or *neither*. Find the next three terms of each sequence.** *(Lesson 13-1)*

1. −2, 12, −72, 432, −2,592, 15,552, −93,312 Type: geometric
2. 3, 12, 27, 48, 75, 108, 147 Type: neither
3. 8.04, 8.08, 8.12, 8.16, 8.20, 8.24, 8.28 Type: arithmetic

**Solve.** *(Lesson 12-9)*

4. There is a 50% chance of rain each day for three days in a row. What is the probability that it rains all 3 days?
Anwers may vary but should be about 12.5%.

**Mixed Review**

**Simplify each expression.**

5. (5-9) $(2a^3)^4$ $16a^{12}$
6. (5-9) $(m^3 \cdot n^2)^5$ $m^{15}n^{10}$
7. (5-9) $(4x^2y^3)^2$ $16x^4y^6$
8. (5-9) $\left(\frac{b^4}{3}\right)^2$ $\frac{b^8}{9}$
9. (5-9) $\left(\frac{c^3}{d}\right)^4$ $\frac{c^{12}}{d^4}$
10. (5-9) $\left(\frac{9a^4}{b}\right)^2$ $\frac{81a^8}{b^2}$

**Find the balance. Use the formula $B = p(1 + r)^n$.**

11. (7-8) \$2,500 at 7% compounded annually for 4 years \$3,276.99
12. (7-8) \$6,700 at 4% compounded semi-annually for 3 years \$7,545.29
13. (7-8) \$850 at 6% compounded semi-annually for 5 years \$1,142.33
14. (7-8) \$500 at 8% compounded semi-annually for 2 years \$584.93

**Write and solve an equation.**

15. (6-7) What percent of 85 is 51?
$85x = 51$; 60%

16. (6-7) 7.5% of $n$ is 4.5. What is $n$?
$0.075n = 4.5$; $n = 60$

## Practice

**For each function, complete the table for integer values of $x$ from $-2$ to 2. Then graph each function.**

1. $y = |x| - 2$

| $x$ | $y = \|x\| - 2$ | $(x, y)$ |
|---|---|---|
| −2 | $y = \|-2\| - 2 = 0$ | $(-2, 0)$ |
| −1 | $y = \|-1\| - 2 = -1$ | $(-1, -1)$ |
| 0 | $y = \|0\| - 2 = -2$ | $(0, -2)$ |
| 1 | $y = \|1\| - 2 = -1$ | $(1, -1)$ |
| 2 | $y = \|2\| - 2 = 0$ | $(2, 0)$ |

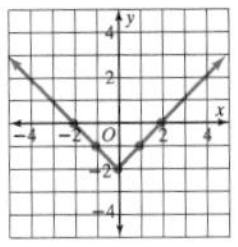

2. $y = -x^2 + 3$

| $x$ | $y = -x^2 + 3$ | $(x, y)$ |
|---|---|---|
| −2 | $y = -(-2)^2 + 3 = -1$ | $(-2, -1)$ |
| −1 | $y = -(-1)^2 + 3 = 2$ | $(-1, 2)$ |
| 0 | $y = -(0)^2 + 3 = 3$ | $(0, 3)$ |
| 1 | $y = -(1)^2 + 3 = 2$ | $(1, 2)$ |
| 2 | $y = -(2)^2 + 3 = -1$ | $(2, -1)$ |

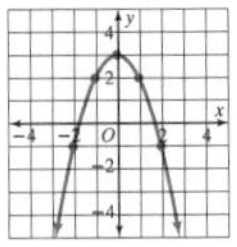

3. $y = 2x^2 - 4$

| $x$ | $y = 2x^2 - 4$ | $(x, y)$ |
|---|---|---|
| −2 | $y = 2(-2)^2 - 4 = 4$ | $(-2, 4)$ |
| −1 | $y = 2(-1)^2 - 4 = -2$ | $(-1, -2)$ |
| 0 | $y = 2(0)^2 - 4 = -4$ | $(0, -4)$ |
| 1 | $y = 2(1)^2 - 4 = -2$ | $(1, -2)$ |
| 2 | $y = 2(2)^2 - 4 = 4$ | $(2, 4)$ |

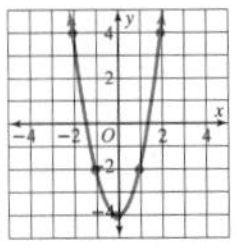

4. $y = 2|x| + 3$

| $x$ | $y = -2\|x\| + 3$ | $(x, y)$ |
|---|---|---|
| −2 | $y = -2\|-2\| + 3 = -1$ | $(-2, -1)$ |
| −1 | $y = -2\|-1\| + 3 = 1$ | $(-1, 1)$ |
| 0 | $y = -2\|0\| + 3 = 3$ | $(0, 3)$ |
| 1 | $y = -2\|1\| + 3 = 1$ | $(1, 1)$ |
| 2 | $y = -2\|2\| + 3 = -1$ | $(2, -1)$ |

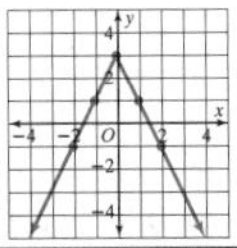



## Reteaching

Complete the table and graph $y = -2x^2 + 4$.
Substitute each value for $x$ in $y = -2x^2 + 4$ to find the corresponding value of $y$.

| $x$ | $y = -2x^2 + 4$ | $(x, y)$ |
|---|---|---|
| −2 | $y = -2(-2)^2 + 4 = -2(4) + 4 = -8 + 4 = -4$ | $(-2, -4)$ |
| −1 | $y = -2(-1)^2 + 4 = -2(1) + 4 = -2 + 4 = 2$ | $(-1, 2)$ |
| 0 | $y = -2(0)^2 + 4 = -2(0) + 4 = 0 + 4 = 4$ | $(0, 4)$ |
| 1 | $y = -2(1)^2 + 4 = -2(1) + 4 = -2 + 4 = 2$ | $(1, 2)$ |
| 2 | $y = -2(2)^2 + 4 = -2(4) + 4 = -8 + 4 = -4$ | $(2, -4)$ |

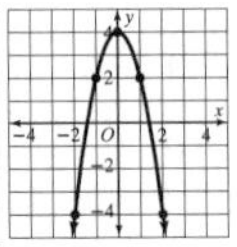

Plot the ordered pairs in the graph. The function is of the form $y = ax^2 + b$ so it is a quadratic function. The graph of a quadratic function is a U-shaped curve called a *parabola*. Connect the plotted points with a parabola.
A function of the form $y = a|x| + b$ is an absolute value function. The graph is V-shaped.

**Complete the table and graph the function for the values in the table.**

$y = 2|x| - 2$

| $x$ | $y = 2\|x\| - 2$ | $(x, y)$ |
|---|---|---|
| −2 | $y = 2\|-2\| - 2 = 4 - 2 = 2$ | $(-2, 2)$ |
| −1 | $y = 2\|-1\| - 2 = 2 - 2 = 0$ | $(-1, 0)$ |
| 0 | $y = 2\|0\| - 2 = 0 - 2 = -2$ | $(0, -2)$ |
| 1 | $y = 2\|1\| - 2 = 2 - 2 = 0$ | $(1, 0)$ |
| 2 | $y = 2\|2\| - 2 = 4 - 2 = 2$ | $(2, 2)$ |

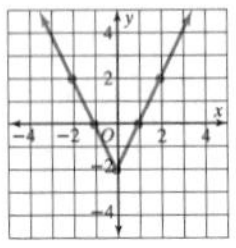



## Enrichment

Marnie has 16 m of fencing with which to enclose three sides of a rectangular garden adjacent to a wall. The wall will form the fourth side of the garden. Marnie wants the garden to have the greatest possible area. Answer these questions to find a graphical solution of the problem.

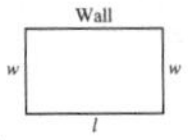


1. Complete the table. Remember that 16 m of fencing will be used to enclose two widths and one length of the garden. (That is, $2w + l = 16$.)

| width | $\frac{1}{2}$ | 1 | 2 | 3 | 4 | 5 | 6 | 7 | $7\frac{1}{2}$ |
|---|---|---|---|---|---|---|---|---|---|
| length (m) | 15 | 14 | 12 | 10 | 8 | 6 | 4 | 2 | 1 |
| $2w + l$ | 16 | 16 | 16 | 16 | 16 | 16 | 16 | 16 | 16 |
| area ($m^2$) | $7\frac{1}{2}$ | 14 | 24 | 30 | 32 | 30 | 24 | 14 | $7\frac{1}{2}$ |

2. Use values of width and area from the table as ordered pairs to draw a graph. Connect the points in the way that seems most reasonable to you.

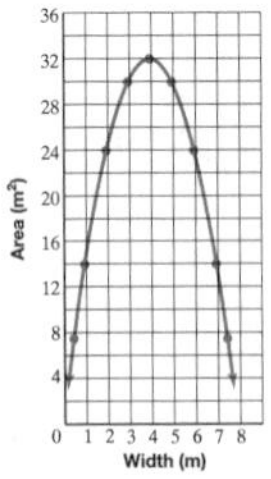


The graph you have drawn is called a *parabola*. It clearly illustrates that as the width increases, the area increases too, but only to a certain point. After that the area begins to decrease.

3. What value of the width gives the greatest possible area?
   4



**22. a.** *Geometry* Make a table to show side lengths and volumes of four cubes. The four cubes have integer side lengths from 1 m to 4 m. See back of book.
**b.** Graph the ordered pairs from your table. See back of book.
**c.** Using your graph from part (b), estimate the volume of a cube with side length 3.5 m. Answers may vary. Sample: 43 $m^3$

**23. a.** Graph $y = x^2$, $y = 2x^2$, and $y = \frac{1}{2}x^2$ on a coordinate plane. See margin.
**b.** *Writing* Describe how the coefficient of $x^2$ affects the width of the graph of the functions. The greater the coefficient of $x^2$, the narrower the graph.

### Journal

*How are quadratic and absolute value functions alike? How are they different?*

## Mixed Review

**Find the next three terms of each sequence. Then write a rule to describe each sequence.** *(Lesson 13-1)*

**24.** 4, 11, 18, 25, . . . 32, 39, 46; start with 4 and add 7 repeatedly.
**25.** 12, 27, 42, 57, . . . 72, 87, 102; start with 12 and add 15 repeatedly.
**26.** 3, 6, 9, 12, . . . 15, 18, 21; start with 3 and add 3 repeatedly.

**Name all points, segments, lines, and rays shown.** *(Lesson 9-1)*

**27.**
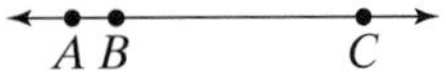


A, B, C, $\overline{AB}$, $\overline{BC}$, $\overline{AC}$, $\overleftrightarrow{AC}$ (or $\overleftrightarrow{AB}$), $\overrightarrow{AC}$, $\overrightarrow{BC}$, $\overrightarrow{BA}$, $\overrightarrow{CA}$, $\overrightarrow{CB}$, $\overrightarrow{AB}$

**28.**
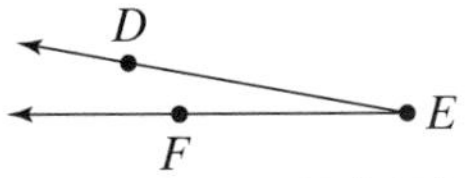


D, E, F, $\overline{DE}$, $\overrightarrow{EF}$, $\overrightarrow{ED}$, $\overrightarrow{EF}$

**29.** *Statistics* The data at the right show the prices of an evening movie at eighteen different movie theaters. Use the data to draw a frequency table. *(Lesson 12-1)* See margin.

**Cost of a Movie**

$7.00, $6.50, $7.50, $7.00, $7.50, $8.00, $7.00, $8.50, $8.00, $6.00, $7.00, $7.50, $8.00, $7.00, $7.50, $8.50, $7.50, $6.50

## Math at Work

### Computer Systems Analyst

Systems analysts are responsible for upgrading hardware and designing and installing new software. They also respond to problems users have with hardware or software. Logic skills are necessary for writing programs, isolating problems, and solving problems.

Systems analysts have backgrounds in computer programming. Since computer technology is constantly changing, they must continue their education throughout their careers.

Internet Connection

For more information about systems analysts, visit the Prentice Hall Web site. www.phschool.com



See also Extra Practice section.

23. a.

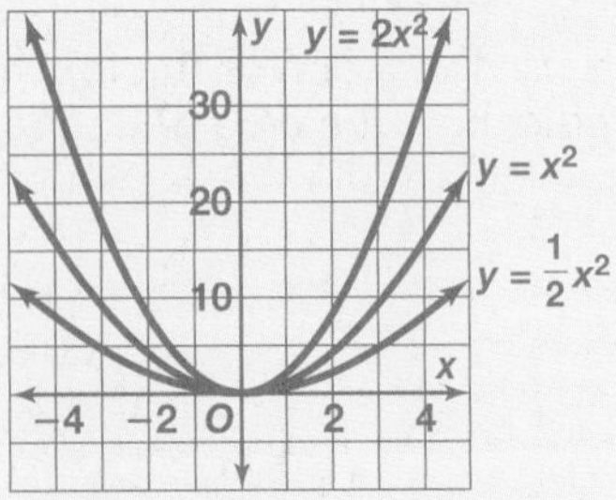


29.

| Price | Frequency |
|---|---|
| $6.00 | 1 |
| $6.50 | 2 |
| $7.00 | 5 |
| $7.50 | 5 |
| $8.00 | 3 |
| $8.50 | 2 |

### Math at Work

If you have block scheduling or extended class periods, have small groups of students research what math is involved in the career of a computer systems analyst. Perhaps students can interview an analyst. Students may find information about education for these careers at local colleges and universities or by talking to personnel offices for local technical firms. Have students report their findings to the class.

Students can find additional information on the Web site **www.phschool.com**.

# Exponential Growth and Decay

## Exponential Growth

A function like $y = 2^x$ has input, or domain, values that are exponents. It models *exponential growth*. Its graph curves upward as input values increase.

### EXAMPLE 1

*Biology* **A warren of rabbits starts with one male and one female. The number of rabbits then doubles each month. The function $y = 2^x$ models the number of rabbits in the warren. For the function $y = 2^x$, make a table with integer values of $x$ from 2 to 5. Then graph the function.**

| $x$ | $2^x$ | $y$ | $(x, y)$ |
|---|---|---|---|
| 2 | $2^2$ | 4 | (2, 4) |
| 3 | $2^3$ | 8 | (3, 8) |
| 4 | $2^4$ | 16 | (4, 16) |
| 5 | $2^5$ | 32 | (5, 32) |

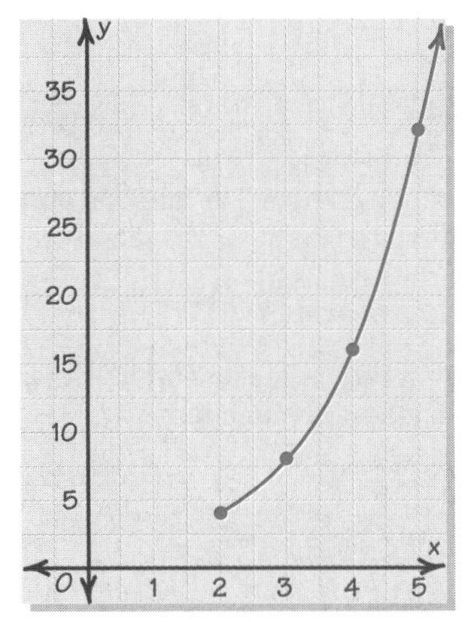


### TRY THIS

1. For the function $y = 3^x$, make a table with integer values of $x$ from 1 to 4. Then graph the function. See right.

You can multiply the power in a function by a number. For example, in $y = 0.25(4^x)$, the power $4^x$ is multiplied by 0.25.

# 13-3

### What You'll Learn

1. To use tables, rules, and graphs with functions modeling growth
2. To use tables, rules, and graphs with functions modeling decay

### . . . And Why

To model real-world situations involving population growth

1.

| $x$ | $3^x$ | $y$ | $(x, y)$ |
|---|---|---|---|
| 1 | $3^1$ | 3 | (1, 3) |
| 2 | $3^2$ | 9 | (2, 9) |
| 3 | $3^3$ | 27 | (3, 27) |
| 4 | $3^4$ | 81 | (4, 81) |

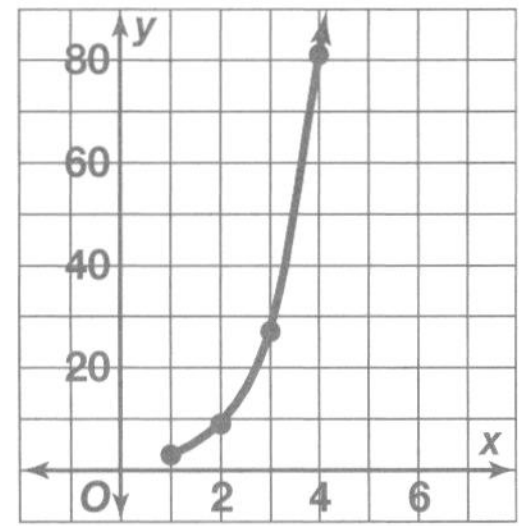




# Tools to Monitor Progress

### BEFORE THE LESSON

**To check prerequisite skills:**

- Equations with two variables

**Skills You Need,** p. 659

**Skills Handbook,** p. 725

**Skills Intervention Kit,** Pre-Algebra Basics

### DURING THE LESSON

**To check understanding:**

**Try This** exercises on student page

- **Additional Examples 1–2**

  Which function models exponential growth?
  Which models exponential decay?
  **a.** $y = 0.6(3)^x$ growth
  **b.** $y = 2(0.5)^x$ decay

# 13-3

## Getting Ready

**Resources** A complete list of resources for this lesson is on p. 661H.

### Daily Skills Warm-Up

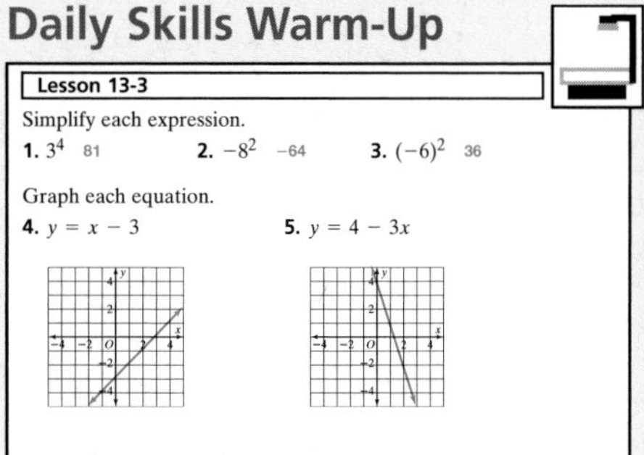

Lesson 13-3

Simplify each expression.

**1.** $3^4$ 81 **2.** $-8^2$ −64 **3.** $(-6)^2$ 36

Graph each equation.

**4.** $y = x - 3$ **5.** $y = 4 - 3x$

### Background for the Lesson

Growth and decay can often be shown by functions of the form $y = a^x$, where $x$ is a nonnegative number representing a period of time. Their graphs form a curve, but the shape is different from that of a parabola. If $a > 1$, the curve slopes upward, getting steeper as $x$-values increase to model exponential growth, such as the way populations of bacteria grow. If $a$ is between 0 and 1, the curve slopes downward, getting less steep as $x$-values increase to model exponential decay, such as the half-life of a radioactive element.

## 1 Focus

### Connecting to Students' Lives

Discuss possible ways to model the change in population in your town and whether a straight line would be an accurate model for such change.

### Connecting to Prior Knowledge

In Lesson 13-2, students were introduced to the nonlinear graphs of quadratic and absolute value functions. In this lesson, students learn how to graph exponential functions that model real-world situations. In Lesson 13-4, students will use polynomials to model situations.

# 2 Teach

## Part 1 Teaching Notes

You may wish to review powers with students before discussing exponential growth and decay.

### Example 1

**Build understanding.** Ask: What is represented by the *x*- and *y*-values in this function? *x*-values: number of months; *y*-values: number of rabbits in the warren

**ELL** A *warren* is a hole or tunnel in the ground where a family or group of rabbits lives.

### Example 2

**Build understanding.** Ask: What effect does multiplying the power by 0.25 have on the curve of this function? It causes the curve to increase in steepness a bit more gradually.

## Part 2 Teaching Notes

Remind students that raising a fraction to a power decreases the value. An example is $\left(\frac{1}{3}\right)^2$ or $\frac{1}{3} \bullet \frac{1}{3}$, which equals $\frac{1}{9}$.

### Example 3

**Build understanding.** Ask: As *x* increases from 0 to 5, what happens to the value of *y*? It decreases.

**Math Reasoning** Use math reasoning to explain why the graphs of $y = 2^x$ and $y = \left(\frac{1}{2}\right)^x$ will never touch the *x*-axis. There is no value of *x* that will make $2^x$ or $\left(\frac{1}{2}\right)^x$ equal to zero.

**Auditory Learning** Have students work in pairs to complete the Try This exercises in this lesson. As one student substitutes *x*-values into the equation, have the other record the *y*-values in the table.

2.

| $x$ | $0.5(2)^x$ | $y$ | $(x, y)$ |
|---|---|---|---|
| 0 | $0.5(2)^0$ | 0.5 | (0, 0.5) |
| 1 | $0.5(2)^1$ | 1 | (1, 1) |
| 2 | $0.5(2)^2$ | 2 | (2, 2) |
| 3 | $0.5(2)^3$ | 4 | (3, 4) |
| 4 | $0.5(2)^4$ | 8 | (4, 8) |
| 5 | $0.5(2)^5$ | 16 | (5, 16) |

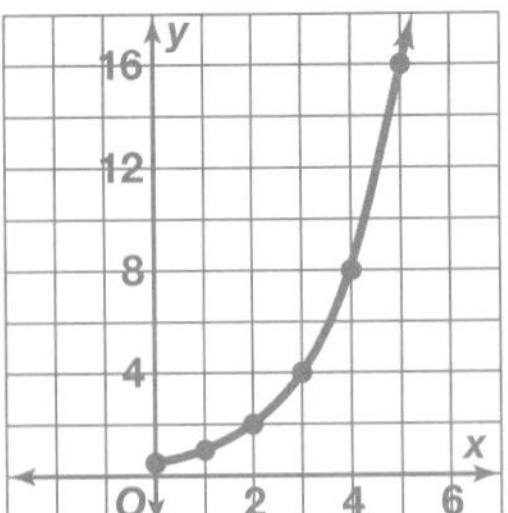


Doctors use the element technetium to make bone scans. Technetium decays exponentially. After 6 hours, only 15 mg of a 30-mg dose remains. After 12 hours, only 7.5 mg remains. How much remains after 18 h? 3.75 mg

### EXAMPLE 2

**For the function $y = 0.25(4)^x$, make a table with integer values of $x$ from 0 to 4. Then graph the function.**

| $x$ | $0.25(4)^x$ | $y$ | $(x, y)$ |
|---|---|---|---|
| 0 | $0.25(4)^0$ | 0.25 | (0, 0.25) |
| 1 | $0.25(4)^1$ | 1 | (1, 1) |
| 2 | $0.25(4)^2$ | 4 | (2, 4) |
| 3 | $0.25(4)^3$ | 16 | (3, 16) |
| 4 | $0.25(4)^4$ | 64 | (4, 64) |

### TRY THIS

2. For $y = 0.5(2)^x$, make a table with integer values of $x$ from 0 to 5. Then graph the function. See left.

## PART 2 Exponential Decay

A function like $y = \left(\frac{1}{2}\right)^x$ models *exponential decay*. Its graph slopes downward as input values increase.

### EXAMPLE 3

**For $y = 60\left(\frac{1}{2}\right)^x$, make a table with integer values of $x$ from 0 to 5. Then graph the function.**

| $x$ | $60\left(\frac{1}{2}\right)^x$ | $y$ | $(x, y)$ |
|---|---|---|---|
| 0 | $60\left(\frac{1}{2}\right)^0$ | 60 | (0, 60) |
| 1 | $60\left(\frac{1}{2}\right)^1$ | 30 | (1, 30) |
| 2 | $60\left(\frac{1}{2}\right)^2$ | 15 | (2, 15) |
| 3 | $60\left(\frac{1}{2}\right)^3$ | 7.5 | (3, 7.5) |
| 4 | $60\left(\frac{1}{2}\right)^4$ | 3.75 | (4, 3.75) |
| 5 | $60\left(\frac{1}{2}\right)^5$ | 1.875 | (5, 1.875) |

### TRY THIS

3. For the function $y = 90\left(\frac{1}{3}\right)^x$, make a table with integer values of $x$ from 0 to 5. Then graph the function. See back of book.



- **Additional Examples 3–4**
  The functions below could possibly describe which of the graphs?
  a. $y = x^2$ neither
  b. $y = 0.4(3)^x$ B
  c. $y = \left(\frac{3}{4}\right)^x$ A

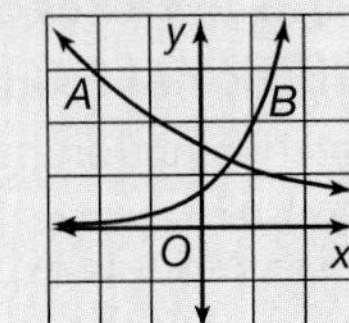


## AFTER THE LESSON

**To assess knowledge:**

**Lesson Quiz**

Does the given function model exponential growth, exponential decay, or neither?

1. $y = \left(\frac{7}{8}\right)^x$ decay
2. $y = \frac{1}{6}(8)^x$ growth
3. $y = 0.875(10)^x$ growth
4. $y = 11 + 3|x|$ neither

- For enrichment and reteaching options see Resources on p. 661H.

# Exercises

## Check Understanding

**Complete the table for each function.**

**1.** $f(x) = 0.5(2)^x$

| x | 0 | 1 | 2 | 3 | 4 | 5 |
|---|---|---|---|---|---|---|
| f(x) | 0.5 | ■ | ■ | 4 | ■ | 16 |
| | | 1 | 2 | | 8 | |

**2.** $y = 30\left(\frac{1}{3}\right)^x$

| x | 0 | 1 | 2 | 3 | 4 | 5 |
|---|---|---|---|---|---|---|
| y | ■ | 10 | ■ | ■ | ■ | ■ |
| | 30 | | $3\frac{1}{3}$ | $1\frac{1}{9}$ | $\frac{10}{27}$ | $\frac{10}{81}$ |

**3.** $y = 4(0.5)^x$

| x | 0 | 1 | 2 | 3 | 4 | 5 |
|---|---|---|---|---|---|---|
| y | 4 | ■ | 1 | ■ | ■ | ■ |
| | | 2 | | $\frac{1}{2}$ | $\frac{1}{4}$ | $\frac{1}{8}$ |

**For each function, make a table with integer values of $x$ from 0 to 5. Then graph each function.** 4. See margin. 5–6. See back of book.

**4.** $y = 3^x$ **5.** $g(x) = 3 \cdot 2^x$ **6.** $y = 100(0.6)^x$

## Practice and Problem Solving

**Match each graph with an equation.**

**7.** 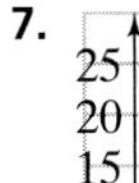
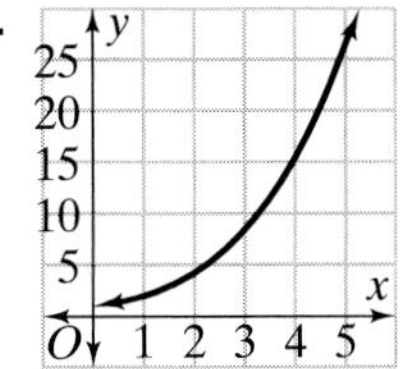
B

A. $y = 3^x$
B. $y = 2^x$

**8.** 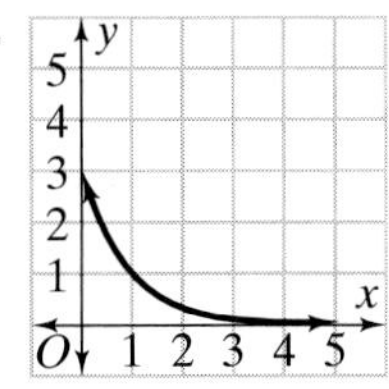
A

A. $y = 3\left(\frac{1}{3}\right)^x$
B. $y = 2\left(\frac{1}{2}\right)^x$

**9.** 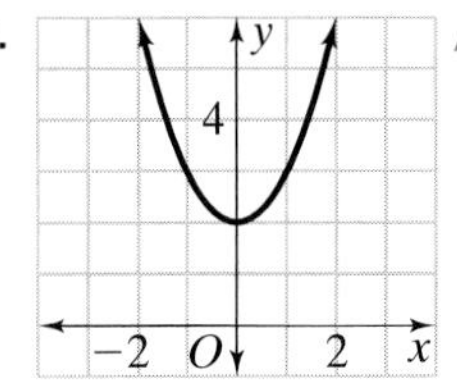
A

A. $y = x^2 + 2$
B. $y = x^2$

**Is the point (2, 8) on the graph of each function?**

**10.** $y = 4x$ yes **11.** $y = 2^x$ no **12.** $y = x^2$ no **13.** $y = \left(\frac{1}{2}\right)^x$ no

**For each function, make a table with integer values of $x$ from 0 to 4. Then graph each function.** 14–19. See back of book.

**14.** $y = 2 \cdot 3^x$ **15.** $f(x) = \frac{1}{2} \cdot 2^x$ **16.** $y = \frac{1}{5} \cdot 5^x$

**17.** $g(x) = 20\left(\frac{1}{2}\right)^x$ **18.** $y = 6(0.5)^x$ **19.** $y = 200(0.4)^x$

**20. a.** For the functions $y = 2x$, $y = x^2$, and $y = 2^x$, make tables with integer values of $x$ from 0 to 5. Then graph the functions. See back of book.

**b.** *Writing* Describe how the graphs are similar. Describe how they are different.



4.

| x | $3^x$ | y | (x, y) |
|---|---|---|---|
| 0 | $3^0$ | 1 | (0, 1) |
| 1 | $3^1$ | 3 | (1, 3) |
| 2 | $3^2$ | 9 | (2, 9) |
| 3 | $3^3$ | 27 | (3, 27) |
| 4 | $3^4$ | 81 | (4, 81) |
| 5 | $3^5$ | 243 | (5, 243) |

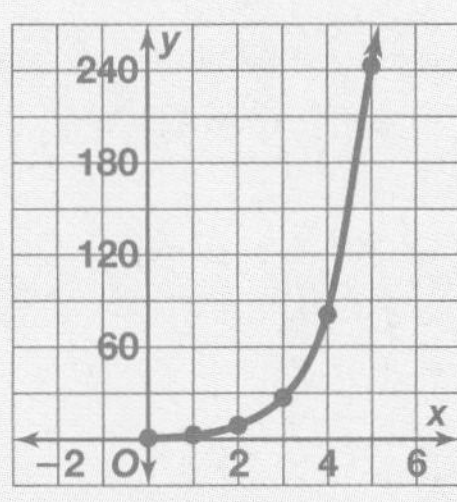

## Alternative Assessment

Have students make a poster showing the differences in the graphs of $y = 1^x$, $y = 2^x$, and $y = 3^x$.

# 3 Practice/Assess

## Assignment Guide

To provide flexible scheduling, this lesson can be divided into parts.

**Part 1**
**Core** 1, 4–5, 7, 9–12, 14–16, 22
**Extension** 20, 23

**Part 2**
**Core** 2–3, 6, 8, 13, 17–19
**Extension** 21

Mixed Review can be assigned at any time for maintenance.

## Exercises

**Connecting to Biology** Exercise 22
Many cells, including bacteria, reproduce by a process called binary fission. The cell's DNA produces a copy of itself, then the rest of the cell simply divides. The number of cells in a culture can double each time they all divide.

## Challenge

What happens to the $y$-values of the equation $y = 2^x$ when the $x$-values are negative? $2^{-1}$ is the same as $\frac{1}{2^1}$, so as the $x$-values decrease, the $y$-values get smaller and smaller, approaching but never equaling zero.

## Closure

A function like $y = 2^x$ models exponential growth. Its graph curves upward as input values increase. A function like $y = \left(\frac{1}{2}\right)^x$ models exponential decay. Its graph curves downward as input values increase.

## Daily Cumulative Review

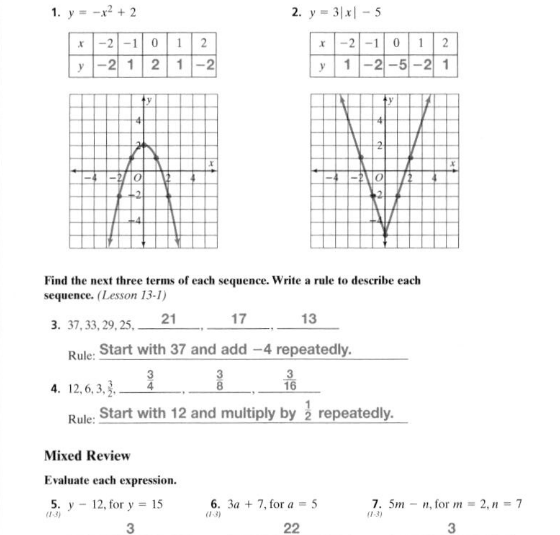

**Graph each function for $x$ values from −2 to 2.** *(Lesson 13-2)*

1. $y = -x^2 + 2$

| x | −2 | −1 | 0 | 1 | 2 |
|---|---|---|---|---|---|
| y | −2 | 1 | 2 | 1 | −2 |

2. $y = 3|x| - 5$

| x | −2 | −1 | 0 | 1 | 2 |
|---|---|---|---|---|---|
| y | 1 | −2 | −5 | −2 | 1 |

**Find the next three terms of each sequence. Write a rule to describe each sequence.** *(Lesson 13-1)*

3. 37, 33, 29, 25, 21, 17, 13
Rule: Start with 37 and add −4 repeatedly.

4. 12, 6, 3, $\frac{3}{2}$, $\frac{3}{4}$, $\frac{3}{8}$, $\frac{3}{16}$
Rule: Start with 12 and multiply by $\frac{1}{2}$ repeatedly.

**Mixed Review**

**Evaluate each expression.**

5. $y - 12$, for $y = 15$ — 3
6. $3a + 7$, for $a = 5$ — 22
7. $5m - n$, for $m = 2, n = 7$ — 3
8. $\frac{3x}{x^2}$, for $x = 9$ — $\frac{1}{3}$
9. $\frac{2x - y}{5}$, for $x = 6, y = 2$ — 2
10. $\frac{m - n}{3}$, for $m = -5, n = 10$ — −5

## Practice

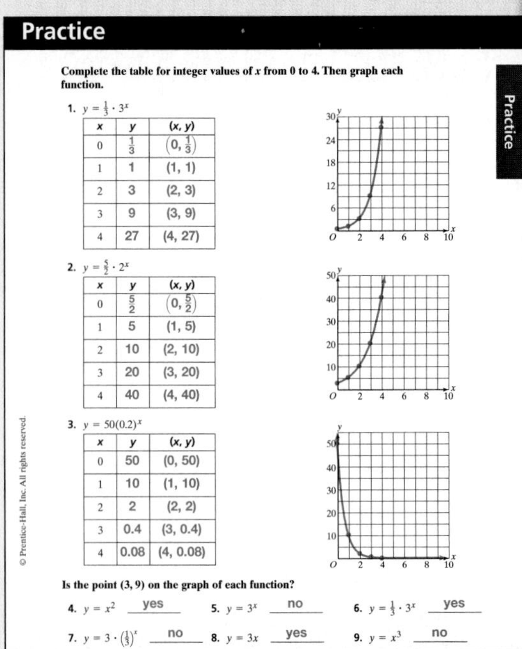

Complete the table for integer values of $x$ from 0 to 4. Then graph each function.

1. $y = \frac{1}{3} \cdot 3^x$

| $x$ | $y$ | $(x, y)$ |
|---|---|---|
| 0 | $\frac{1}{3}$ | $(0, \frac{1}{3})$ |
| 1 | 1 | (1, 1) |
| 2 | 3 | (2, 3) |
| 3 | 9 | (3, 9) |
| 4 | 27 | (4, 27) |

2. $y = \frac{5}{2} \cdot 2^x$

| $x$ | $y$ | $(x, y)$ |
|---|---|---|
| 0 | $\frac{5}{2}$ | $(0, \frac{5}{2})$ |
| 1 | 5 | (1, 5) |
| 2 | 10 | (2, 10) |
| 3 | 20 | (3, 20) |
| 4 | 40 | (4, 40) |

3. $y = 50(0.2)^x$

| $x$ | $y$ | $(x, y)$ |
|---|---|---|
| 0 | 50 | (0, 50) |
| 1 | 10 | (1, 10) |
| 2 | 2 | (2, 2) |
| 3 | 0.4 | (3, 0.4) |
| 4 | 0.08 | (4, 0.08) |

Is the point (3, 9) on the graph of each function?

4. $y = x^2$ yes 5. $y = 3^x$ no 6. $y = \frac{1}{3} \cdot 3^x$ yes

7. $y = 3 \cdot (\frac{1}{3})^x$ no 8. $y = 3x$ yes 9. $y = x^3$ no



## Reteaching

Complete the table and graph the function $y = 8(\frac{1}{2})^x$. Substitute each value of $x$ into the equation and find the corresponding value of $y$.

| $x$ | $y = 8(\frac{1}{2})^x$ | $(x, y)$ |
|---|---|---|
| 0 | $y = 8(\frac{1}{2})^0 = 8 \cdot 1 = 8$ | (0, 8) |
| 1 | $y = 8(\frac{1}{2})^1 = 8 \cdot \frac{1}{2} = 4$ | (1, 4) |
| 2 | $y = 8(\frac{1}{2})^2 = 8 \cdot \frac{1}{4} = 2$ | (2, 2) |
| 3 | $y = 8(\frac{1}{2})^3 = 8 \cdot \frac{1}{8} = 1$ | (3, 1) |
| 4 | $y = 8(\frac{1}{2})^4 = 8 \cdot \frac{1}{16} = \frac{1}{2}$ | $(4, \frac{1}{2})$ |

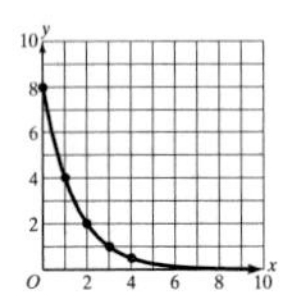

Plot the ordered pairs in the graph and connect them with a smooth curve. Put arrows at the end of the curve to show it continues.

Complete the table and graph the function.

$y = \frac{5}{8} \cdot 2^x$

| $x$ | $y = \frac{5}{8} \cdot 2^x$ | $(x, y)$ |
|---|---|---|
| 0 | $y = \frac{5}{8} \cdot 2^0 = \frac{5}{8} \cdot 1 = \frac{5}{8}$ | $(0, \frac{5}{8})$ |
| 1 | $y = \frac{5}{8} \cdot 2^1 = \frac{5}{8} \cdot 2 = \frac{5}{4}$ | $(1, \frac{5}{4})$ |
| 2 | $y = \frac{5}{8} \cdot 2^2 = \frac{5}{8} \cdot 4 = \frac{5}{2}$ | $(2, \frac{5}{2})$ |
| 3 | $y = \frac{5}{8} \cdot 2^3 = \frac{5}{8} \cdot 8 = 5$ | (3, 5) |
| 4 | $y = \frac{5}{8} \cdot 2^4 = \frac{5}{8} \cdot 16 = 10$ | (4, 10) |

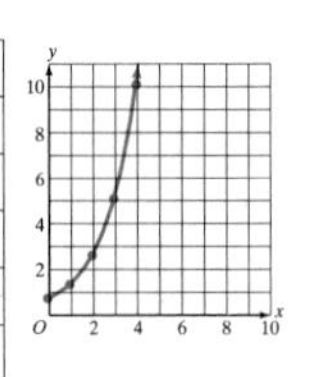



## Enrichment

Remember $x^{-3} = \frac{1}{x^3}$. So $2^{-3} = \frac{1}{2^3} = \frac{1}{8}$.

1. Graph $y = 2^x$ and $y = (\frac{1}{2})^x$ on the same coordinate plane.

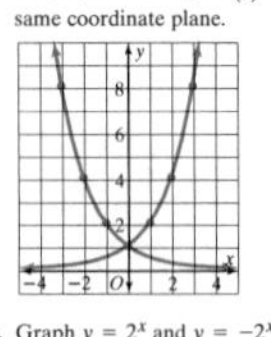

2. Describe the relationship between the graphs of $y = 2^x$ and $y = (\frac{1}{2})^x$.

The graph of $y = (\frac{1}{2})^x$ is the reflection of the graph of $y = 2^x$ in the $y$-axis.

3. Graph $y = 2^x$ and $y = -2^x$ on the same coordinate plane.

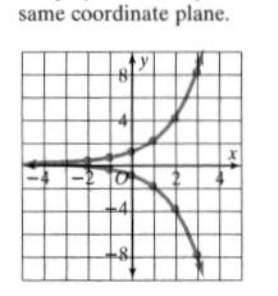

4. Describe the relationship between the graphs of $y = 2^x$ and $y = -2^x$.

The graph of $y = -2^x$ is the reflection of the graph of $y = 2^x$ in the $x$-axis.

The equation is given for one graph on each coordinate plane. Use the equation and patterns you found to find the equation of the other graph. Plot points to check.

5. $y = -(\frac{1}{2})^x$

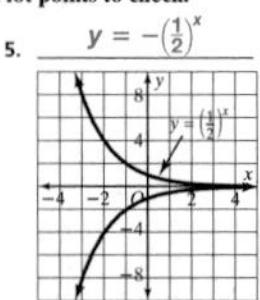

6. $y = (\frac{1}{3})^x$

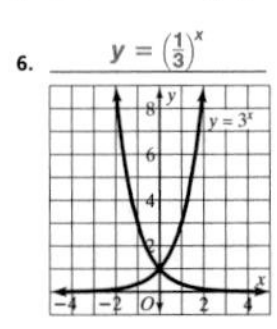

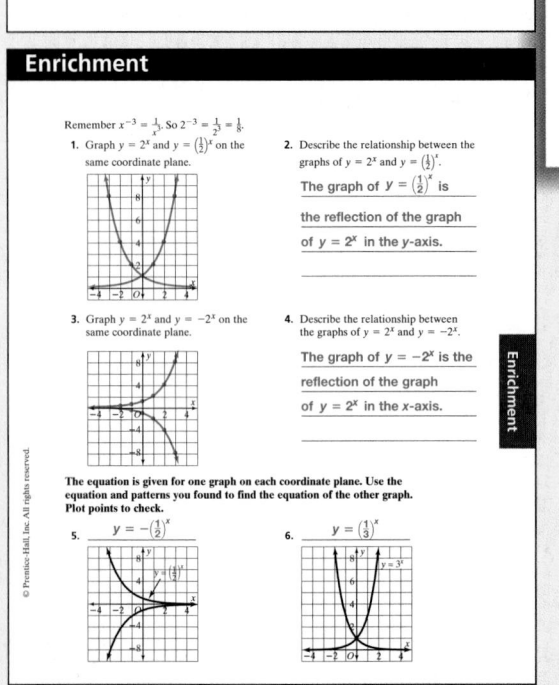

21. **Critical Thinking** Without graphing, predict whether each function shows exponential growth or exponential decay. Explain how you came to your conclusion.

a. $y = 5^x$ b. $y = (\frac{1}{2})^x$ c. $y = 3(0.2)^x$ d. $y = 3(2)^x$

21. a. growth, because $5 > 1$
b. decay, because $\frac{1}{2} < 1$
c. decay, because $0.2 < 1$
d. growth, because $2 > 1$

22. **Biology** A bacteria culture starts with 10 cells and doubles every hour. The function $y = 10(2)^x$ models the number of cells $y$ in the culture after $x$ hours. How many bacteria are in the culture after 3 hours? 80 cells

23. **Finance** You put $100 in a stock that has an annual return of 20% of its value. This is the same as 20% interest compounded annually. The function $b = 100(1.2)^x$ describes the balance $b$ in the account after $x$ years. 144; this is the value of the stock after 2 years.

a. Evaluate the function for $x = 2$. What does the value represent?

b. For the function, make a table with integer values of $x$ from 1 to 6. Graph the function. See margin.

c. **Critical Thinking** Estimate how long it will take for the balance to be twice the initial investment. Answers may vary. Sample: 3 years 9 months

## Mixed Review

**Graph each function. (Lesson 13-2)** 24–27. See back of book.

24. $y = |x| + 2$ 25. $f(x) = 3|x|$ 26. $y = x^2 - 5$ 27. $g(x) = -x^2 + 1$

**Find the midpoint of each segment with the given endpoints. (Lesson 11-3)**

28. $A(4, -6)$ and $B(-2, 5)$ (1, −0.5)

29. $X(-3, -8)$ and $Y(1, 6)$ (−1, −1)

30. $Q(7, 9)$ and $R(-7, -9)$ (0, 0)

31. Janelle is buying a sweatshirt. She has a choice of red, purple, or green; zipper or no zipper; and hooded or not hooded. How many different sweatshirt choices does she have? *(Lesson 12-4)* 12

## Checkpoint 1 — Lessons 13-1 through 13-3

**Find the next three terms of each sequence. Then write a rule to describe the sequence.**

1. 100, 85, 70, 55, . . . 40, 25, 10; start with 100 and add −15 repeatedly.

2. 17, 24, 31, 38, . . . 45, 52, 59; start with 17 and add 7 repeatedly.

3. 13, 26, 52, 104, . . . 208, 416, 832; start with 13 and multiply by 2 repeatedly.

**For each function, make a table with integer values of $x$ from 0 to 4. Then graph each function.** 4–7. See back of book.

4. $y = \frac{1}{4}x^2$ 5. $f(x) = \frac{1}{4}|x|$ 6. $y = 0.25(2)^x$ 7. $f(x) = 0.5(3)^x$

8. **TEST PREP** The graph of which function has points in Quadrant IV? C

A. $y = x^2 + 2$ B. $y = 0.2(2)^x$ C. $y = |x| - 2$ D. $y = 2(\frac{1}{2})^x$



See also Extra Practice section.

## Checkpoint

**Find the next three terms of the sequence. Then write a rule to describe the sequence.**

1. 56, 28, 14, 7, $\frac{7}{2}$, $\frac{7}{4}$, $\frac{7}{8}$

rule: Start with 56 and multiply by $\frac{1}{2}$ repeatedly.

**Make a table for integer values of $x$ from 0 to 4. Then graph the function.**

2. $y = 4(0.5)^x$

| $x$ | $y = 4(0.5)^x$ | $(x, y)$ |
|---|---|---|
| 0 | $y = 4(0.5)^0 = 4(1) = 4$ | (0, 4) |
| 1 | $y = 4(0.5)^1 = 4(0.5) = 2$ | (1, 2) |
| 2 | $y = 4(0.5)^2 = 4(0.25) = 1$ | (2, 1) |
| 3 | $y = 4(0.5)^3 = 4(0.125) = 0.5$ | (3, 0.5) |
| 4 | $y = 4(0.5)^4 = 4(0.0625) = 0.25$ | (4, 0.25) |

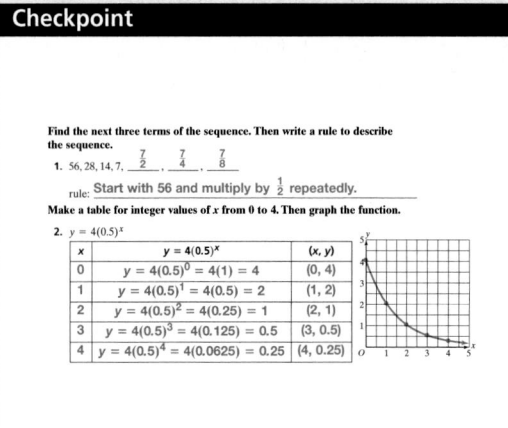

23. b.

| $x$ | $100(1.2)^x$ | $y$ | $(x, y)$ |
|---|---|---|---|
| 1 | $100(1.2)^1$ | 120 | (1, 120) |
| 2 | $100(1.2)^2$ | 144 | (2, 144) |
| 3 | $100(1.2)^3$ | 172.80 | (3, 172.80) |
| 4 | $100(1.2)^4$ | 207.36 | (4, 207.36) |
| 5 | $100(1.2)^5$ | 248.83 | (5, 248.83) |
| 6 | $100(1.2)^6$ | 298.60 | (6, 298.60) |

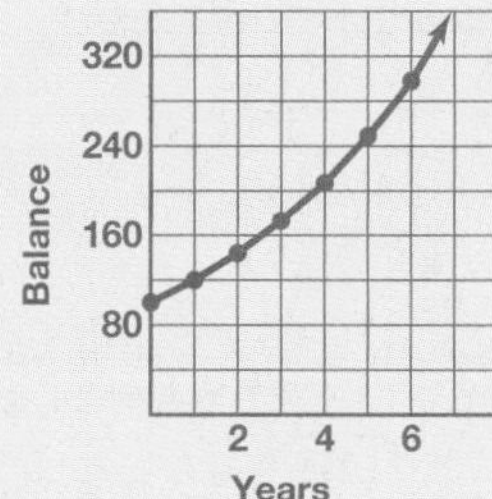

# MATH TOOLBOX

Technology
*After Lesson 13-3*

# *Nonlinear Functions and Graphing Calculators*

You can use a graphing calculator to graph nonlinear functions. For the exponent 2, you can use the $x^2$ key or press ^ 2.

## EXAMPLE

**Graph $y = |3x|$.**

**Step 1** Press Y= MATH ▶ ▶ 5. Then press 3 X,T,θ,n ) .

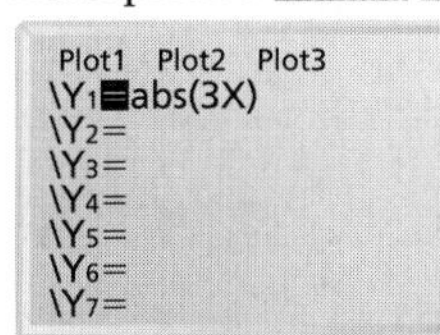


**Step 2** Set your viewing window.

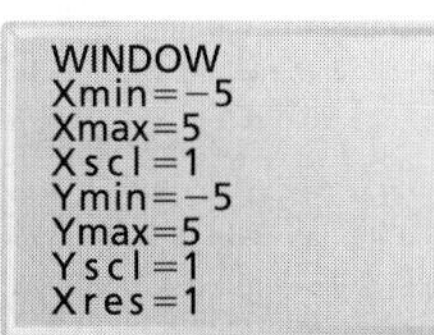


**Step 3** Use GRAPH to see your graph.

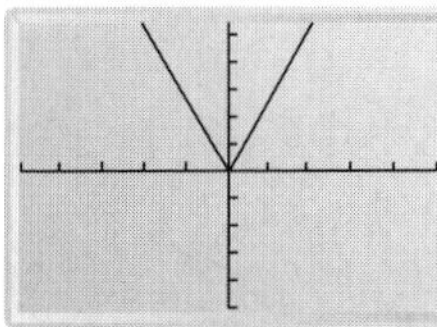

**Step 4** Use the TABLE feature to see solutions.

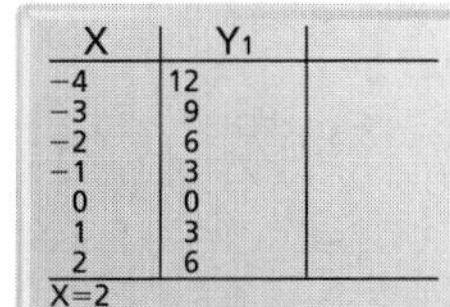

| X | Y1 |
|---|---|
| −4 | 12 |
| −3 | 9 |
| −2 | 6 |
| −1 | 3 |
| 0 | 0 |
| 1 | 3 |
| 2 | 6 |

X=2

**Graph each equation using a graphing calculator. For each function, use the solutions you see in the TABLE feature to create a table with integer values of $x$ from −5 to 5. Then sketch the graph.** 1. See margin. 2–9. See back of book.

**1.** $y = |2x|$

**2.** $y = -|2x|$

**3.** $y = |2x| + 1$

**4.** $y = x^2 - 1$

**5.** $y = -x^2 - 1$

**6.** $y = 3(2)^x$

**7.** $y = -3(2)^x$

**8.** $y = 3\left(\frac{1}{2}\right)^x$

**9.** $y = -3\left(\frac{1}{2}\right)^x$

**10.** *Open-ended* Write a nonlinear function that you can graph using a graphing calculator. Graph your function. Make a table of values and sketch your graph. Check students' work.



MATH TOOLBOX

## Nonlinear Functions and Graphing Calculators

This Math Toolbox shows students how to use a graphing calculator to graph absolute value functions and other nonlinear functions.

## Math Background

The graph of an absolute value function is V-shaped. The graph of a quadratic function is U-shaped, a parabola. The graph of an exponential function like $y = 2^x$ curves upward, and the graph of an exponential function like $y = \left(\frac{1}{2}\right)^x$ curves downward.

Since the designs of graphing calculators differ, discuss with your students the keystrokes on their calculators.

## Teaching Notes

**Error Prevention** Have students in pairs monitor each other's keystrokes. Remind students that the key to enter a negative number may be different from the key for subtracting.

**Monitoring Progress Exercises 1–9** Have students predict the shape of the graph before they enter the equation.

**Block Scheduling** If you have block scheduling or extended periods, you may wish to insert this Math Toolbox lesson between the completion of Part 1 of Lesson 13-4 and the beginning of Part 2 of Lesson 13-4.

1.

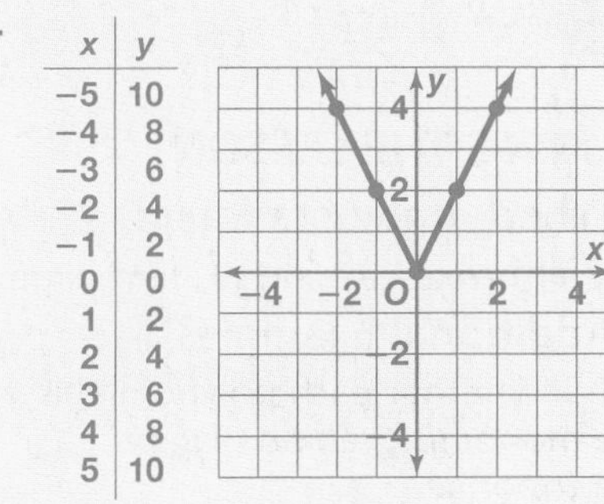

| x | y |
|---|---|
| −5 | 10 |
| −4 | 8 |
| −3 | 6 |
| −2 | 4 |
| −1 | 2 |
| 0 | 0 |
| 1 | 2 |
| 2 | 4 |
| 3 | 6 |
| 4 | 8 |
| 5 | 10 |



• **Additional Example**

Graph $y = |-3x|$ for $x$-values from −5 to 5 using a graphing calculator. Compare to the graph in the Example. The graphs are the same.

# 13-4

## Getting Ready

**Key Terms and Symbols** monomial, polynomial, binomial, trinomial

**Resources** A complete list of resources for this lesson is on p. 661H.

### Daily Skills Warm-Up

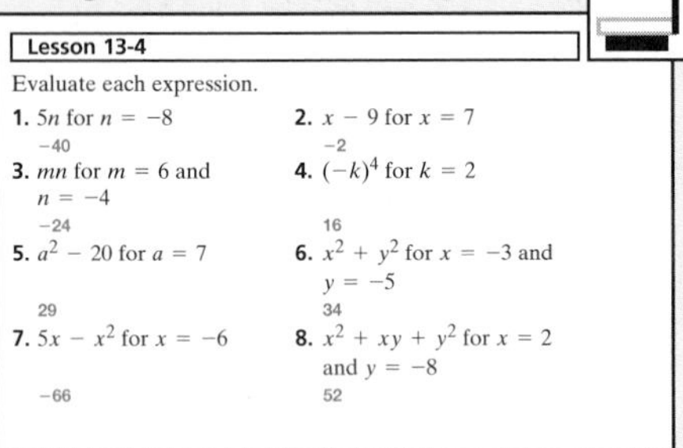

Lesson 13-4

Evaluate each expression.

1. $5n$ for $n = -8$ $-40$
2. $x - 9$ for $x = 7$ $-2$
3. $mn$ for $m = 6$ and $n = -4$ $-24$
4. $(-k)^4$ for $k = 2$ $16$
5. $a^2 - 20$ for $a = 7$ $29$
6. $x^2 + y^2$ for $x = -3$ and $y = -5$ $34$
7. $5x - x^2$ for $x = -6$ $-66$
8. $x^2 + xy + y^2$ for $x = 2$ and $y = -8$ $52$

### Background for the Lesson

When plus or minus signs separate an algebraic expression into parts, each part is a *term*. You can name algebraic expressions by the number of terms: $-3x^2$ is a *mono*mial (one term); $-3x^2 + 5x$ is a *bi*nomial (two terms); $-3x^2 + 5x - 15y$ is a *tri*nomial (three terms). A *polynomial* is an algebraic expression of one or more terms in which there are no variables in a denominator, no variables under a radical ($\sqrt{\ }$) sign, and any exponents on the variables are positive integers.

## 1 Focus

### Connecting to Students' Lives

Ask students the difference between a *bi*cycle and a *tri*cycle. Discuss the meaning of the prefixes in these names.

### Connecting to Prior Knowledge

In Lesson 13-3, students learned how to graph exponential functions. In this lesson, students learn the language of polynomials. In Lesson 13-5, students will learn how to add and subtract polynomials.

# 13-4 Polynomials

### What You'll Learn

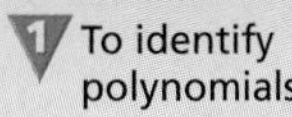
To identify polynomials

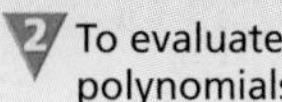
To evaluate polynomials

### . . . And Why

To model real-world applications in science

## PART 1 Identifying Polynomials

You have seen how mathematics uses algebraic expressions to represent real-world situations. Some of these expressions are monomials. A **monomial** is a real number, a variable, or a product of a real number and variables with whole-number exponents.

Monomials: $3$ $\quad m$ $\quad 5xy$ $\quad 0.35bc^3$ $\quad \frac{w}{9}$ $\quad \frac{1}{4}p^2q$

*Not* monomials: $a - 8$ $\quad \sqrt{m}$ $\quad y^{-1}$ (or $\frac{1}{y}$) $\quad \frac{ab}{c}$

### Example 1

**Is each expression a monomial? Explain.**

**a.** $7x^2y$ Yes, the expression is the product of the real number 7 and the variables $x$ and $y$.

**b.** $8 + a$ No, the expression is a sum.

**c.** $\frac{a}{7y}$ No, the denominator contains a variable.

**d.** $\frac{5x}{4}$ Yes, the expression is the product of the real number $\frac{5}{4}$ and the variable $x$.

**Try This** Is each expression a monomial? Explain.

**1.** $\frac{6}{m}$ **2.** $\frac{m}{6}$ **3.** 45 **4.** $mx + b$

1–4. See left.

1. No, the denominator contains a variable.
2. Yes, it is the product of the variable $m$ and the real number $\frac{1}{6}$.
3. Yes, it is a real number.
4. No, it is a sum.

A **polynomial** is a monomial or a sum or difference of monomials. We call the monomials that make up a polynomial its *terms*. You can name a polynomial by the number of its terms.

| Polynomial | Number of terms | Examples |
|---|---|---|
| Monomial | 1 | $4, 32, x, 2x^2$ |
| **Binomial** | 2 | $x - 3, 5x + 1, x^3 - x$ |
| **Trinomial** | 3 | $x^2 + x + 1, x^4 - 2x - 5$ |



## Tools to Monitor Progress

### BEFORE THE LESSON

**To check prerequisite skills:**

- Evaluating expressions

**Skills You Need,** p. 661

**Skills Handbook,** p. 726

**Skills Intervention Kit,** Pre-Algebra Basics

### DURING THE LESSON

**To check understanding:**

**Try This** exercises on student page

- **Additional Examples 1–2**

Tell whether each polynomial is a *monomial*, a *binomial*, or a *trinomial*.

a. $14x^2 + 2xy - 7y^2$ trinomial

b. $\frac{11a^2bc}{3}$ monomial

c. $z + 10$ binomial

## EXAMPLE 2

**Tell whether each polynomial is a *monomial,* a *binomial,* or a *trinomial.***

**a.** $x - y$ binomial **b.** $8xyz$ monomial **c.** $y^2 + 8y + 18$ trinomial

**TRY THIS** Tell whether each polynomial is a monomial, a binomial, or a trinomial.

**5.** 10 monomial **6.** $9x^2 + xy$ binomial **7.** $8 - y$ binomial **8.** $5 + x - 3y$ trinomial

## PART 2 Evaluating Polynomials

You evaluate polynomials by substituting values for the variables.

## EXAMPLE 3

**Evaluate each polynomial for $m = 8$ and $p = -3$.**

**a.** $2mp$

$2mp = 2(8)(-3)$ Replace $m$ with 8 and $p$ with −3.

$= -48$ Simplify.

**b.** $3m - 2p$

$3m - 2p = 3(8) - 2(-3)$
$= 24 + 6$
$= 30$

**TRY THIS** Evaluate each polynomial for $x = -2$ and $y = 5$.

**9.** $5xy$ −50 **10.** $x + 3y$ 13 **11.** $y^2 - 2y + x$ 13

REAL-WORLD CONNECTION

## EXAMPLE 4

*Science* **The polynomial $-16t^2 + 140t$ gives the height, in feet, reached by fireworks in $t$ seconds. If the fireworks explode 4 seconds after launch, at what height do they explode?**

$-16t^2 + 140t$
$-16(4)^2 + 140(4)$ Replace $t$ with 4.
304 Simplify.

The fireworks explode at 304 feet.

**TRY THIS**

**12.** Fireworks are set to explode 6 seconds after launch. At what height will they explode? 264 ft

During a twenty-minute show, fireworks technicians can set off as many as 6,000 different fireworks. How many fireworks is that per minute? 300



# 2 Teach

## PART 1 Part 1 Teaching Notes

Point out to students that addition and subtraction signs are the key to identifying types of polynomials.

### Example 1

**Build understanding.** Ask: How can you rewrite $(4z - 2) + (3z + 2)$ as a monomial? $7z$

**Error Prevention** Help students understand why $\frac{a}{3}$ is a monomial when $\frac{3}{a}$ is not. You can rewrite $\frac{a}{3}$ as the product $\frac{1}{3} \bullet a$ but $\frac{3}{a}$ rewritten as $3 \bullet \frac{1}{a}$ still does not fit the definition of a polynomial.

### Example 2

**Build understanding.** Part b contains three variables. Explain why it is not a trinomial. **A trinomial has three *terms*, not three variables.**

**Extension** Is part b in Example 2 a polynomial? Explain. **Yes; A monomial is one kind of polynomial.**

## PART 2 Part 2 Teaching Notes

Remind students that they evaluate expressions by substituting values for variables.

### Example 3

**Build understanding.** Ask: Why do you rewrite the operation in part b as addition? **Subtracting a number is the same as adding its opposite; the product of two negative numbers is positive.**

### Example 4

**Build understanding.** Ask: What value will you substitute for $t$? 4

- **Additional Examples 3–4**

Evaluate each polynomial for $r = 2$ and $s = 7$.

**a.** $5r^2 - s$ 13
**b.** $\frac{6rs}{3}$ 28

## AFTER THE LESSON

### To assess knowledge:

**Lesson Quiz**

Tell whether the expression is a polynomial. If it is, is it a *monomial*, *binomial*, or *trinomial*?

1. $\frac{14c^2}{b}$ **not a polynomial**
2. $s + 14 - t$ **yes; trinomial**
3. 8 **yes; monomial**
4. $6x + 2y$ **yes; binomial**

- For enrichment and reteaching options see Resources on p. 661H.

# 3 Practice/Assess

## Assignment Guide

To provide flexible scheduling, this lesson can be divided into parts.

▼ Part 1
**Core** 1–10, 15–29, 42–43
✪ **Extension** 38–41

▼ Part 2
**Core** 11–14, 30–37
✪ **Extension** 44, 45

Mixed Review can be assigned at any time for maintenance.

## Exercises

**Visual Learning Exercises 22–29** Copy each expression and then circle each term to identify the type of polynomial.

**Test Prep Exercise 42** To help you choose, try to write an example that fits each answer choice.

## ✪ Challenge

Explain why $\frac{15x^2y}{2x}$ is or is not a polynomial. It is a polynomial because it simplifies to $\frac{15xy}{2}$ $(x \neq 0)$.

## Closure

A monomial is a real number, a variable, or a product of a real number and variables with whole number exponents. A polynomial is a monomial or a sum or difference of monomials. You can name a polynomial by the number of its terms. A binomial has two terms and a trinomial has three terms.

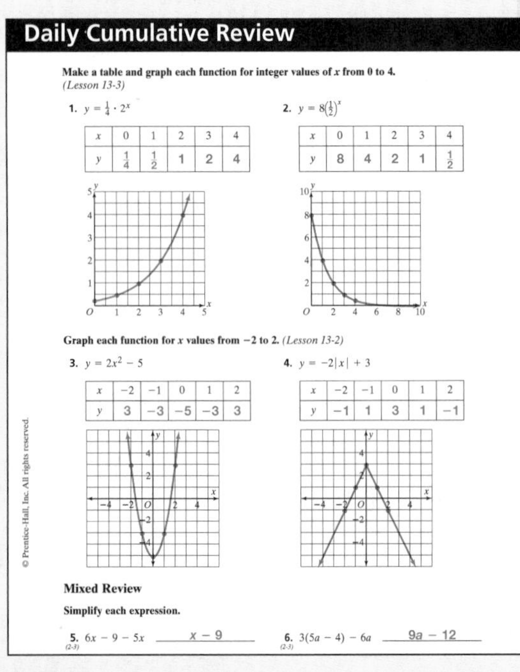

### Daily Cumulative Review

**Make a table and graph each function for integer values of $x$ from 0 to 4.** *(Lesson 13-3)*

1. $y = \frac{1}{4} \cdot 2^x$

| $x$ | 0 | 1 | 2 | 3 | 4 |
|---|---|---|---|---|---|
| $y$ | $\frac{1}{4}$ | $\frac{1}{2}$ | 1 | 2 | 4 |

2. $y = 8\left(\frac{1}{2}\right)^x$

| $x$ | 0 | 1 | 2 | 3 | 4 |
|---|---|---|---|---|---|
| $y$ | 8 | 4 | 2 | 1 | $\frac{1}{2}$ |

**Graph each function for $x$ values from −2 to 2.** *(Lesson 13-2)*

3. $y = 2x^2 - 5$

| $x$ | −2 | −1 | 0 | 1 | 2 |
|---|---|---|---|---|---|
| $y$ | 3 | −3 | −5 | −3 | 3 |

4. $y = -2|x| + 3$

| $x$ | −2 | −1 | 0 | 1 | 2 |
|---|---|---|---|---|---|
| $y$ | −1 | 1 | 3 | 1 | −1 |

**Mixed Review**

**Simplify each expression.**

5. $6x - 9 - 5x$ (2-3) ______ $x - 9$

6. $3(5a - 4) - 6a$ (2-3) ______ $9a - 12$



# Exercises

1. No, it is a sum.
2. Yes, it is a product of the real number 18 and the variables $a$ and $b$.
3. No, the denominator contains a variable.
4. Yes, it is a real number.
5. No, a variable has an exponent that is not a whole number.
6. Yes, it is a product of the real number 0.82 and the variable $k$.

## CHECK UNDERSTANDING

**Is each expression a monomial? Explain.**

**1.** $2 + x$ **2.** $18ab^2$ **3.** $\frac{4}{b}$ **4.** $1$ **5.** $pq^{-3}$ **6.** $0.82k$

1–6. See above right.

**Tell whether each polynomial is a *monomial,* a *binomial,* or a *trinomial.***

**7.** $3xy + 4y^2$ binomial **8.** $5c - 2 + a$ trinomial **9.** $7y^2 + 2y - 9$ trinomial **10.** $658$ monomial

**Evaluate each polynomial for $a = 2$ and $b = -4$.**

**11.** $a - 3b$ 14 **12.** $5a + 7b$ −18 **13.** $ab^2 + 5$ 37 **14.** $2a^2 - b + 4$ 16

**15.** *Open-ended* Write a trinomial. Answers may vary. Sample: $x + 2 + y$

## PRACTICE AND PROBLEM SOLVING

**Is each expression a monomial? Explain.** 16–21. See margin.

**16.** $2x$ **17.** $-0.3y$ **18.** $\frac{a}{3}$ **19.** $82$ **20.** $\frac{3}{p}$ **21.** $10bc + b$

**Tell whether each polynomial is a *monomial,* a *binomial,* or a *trinomial.***

**22.** $3x^2 + 2x$ binomial **23.** $21$ monomial **24.** $7p^2$ monomial **25.** $56 - x$ binomial

**26.** $x^2 + 7x + 4$ trinomial **27.** $15 + w$ binomial **28.** $abc$ monomial **29.** $4.5 + 3.7m$ binomial

**Evaluate each polynomial for $x = -5$ and $y = 3$.**

**30.** $y - x$ 8 **31.** $2x + 2y$ −4 **32.** $7 + x^2y$ 82 **33.** $7y^2 + 6x - 20$ 13

**34.** $xy - y$ −18 **35.** $3y + x$ 4 **36.** $x^2 + 2x - 3$ 12 **37.** $\frac{x^2}{5} + x$ 0

✪**38. a.** *Writing* Name other words with the prefixes *mono, bi, tri,* and *poly.* How do the prefixes help you understand the meanings of the words? Answers may vary. Sample: Monotone, bicycle, trilogy, polygon; the prefixes tell you the number of things involved.

**b.** What would you call a polynomial with four terms? Answers may vary. Sample: quadrinomial

*Critical Thinking* **Tell why each expression is not a polynomial.**

✪**39.** $x^2 + 2x + \frac{1}{x}$ The term $\frac{1}{x}$ contains a variable in the denominator.

✪**40.** $2ab + b^2 + \sqrt{a}$ $\sqrt{a}$ is not always a real number.

✪**41.** $(y^2 + 4) \div y$ The expression is a quotient with a variable in the denominator.



## Alternative Assessment

Say the words *monomial, binomial,* and *trinomial* and have students write examples of each.

16. Yes, it is a product of the real number 2 and the variable $x$.
17. Yes, it is a product of the real number − 0.3 and the variable $y$.
18. Yes, it is a product of the real number $\frac{1}{3}$ and the variable $a$.
19. Yes, it is real number.
20. No, the denominator contains a variable.
21. No, it is a sum.

42. **TEST PREP** Which of the following statements is *not* true? C
A. A monomial is a polynomial.
B. A binomial consists of two monomials.
C. A polynomial must have more than one term.
D. An integer is a monomial.

43. *Geometry* You can write the formula for the area of a trapezoid as $\frac{1}{2}b_1h + \frac{1}{2}b_2h$. What kind of polynomial is this? binomial

44. a. The polynomial $34x^2 - 945x + 46{,}971$ models U.S. public school enrollment, in thousands, from 1970 to 1998. The value of $x$ for 1970 is 1 and the value of $x$ for 1998 is 29. How many students were enrolled in public schools in 1970? In 1998? See below.
b. Use the polynomial to predict enrollment in 2010. 65,380,000 students

45. *Geometry* A polygon is convex if no diagonal has points outside the polygon. The polynomial $\frac{n^2}{2} - \frac{3n}{2}$ gives the number of diagonals that you can draw in a convex polygon with $n$ sides. How many diagonals does a 20-sided convex polygon have? 170

46.

| $x$ | $2 \cdot 2^x$ | $y$ | $(x, y)$ |
|---|---|---|---|
| 1 | $2 \cdot 2^1$ | 4 | (1, 4) |
| 2 | $2 \cdot 2^2$ | 8 | (2, 8) |
| 3 | $2 \cdot 2^3$ | 16 | (3, 16) |
| 4 | $2 \cdot 2^4$ | 32 | (4, 32) |

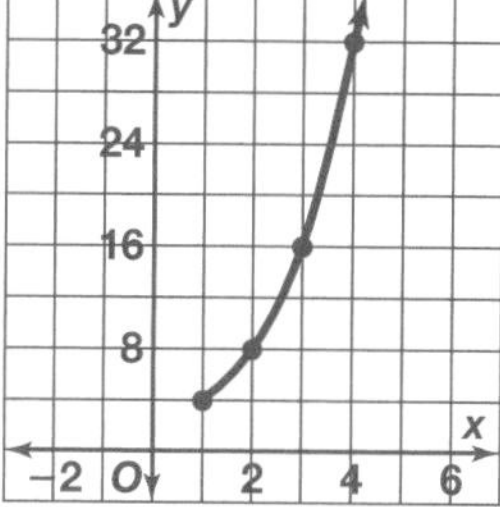

44a. 46,060,000; 48,160,000

## Mixed Review

**For each function, make a table with integer values of $x$ from 1 to 4. Then graph each function.** ***(Lesson 13-3)***

46. $y = 2 \cdot 2^x$ See above right.
47. $f(x) = \frac{1}{3} \cdot 3^x$ See margin.
48. $y = 18(0.2)^x$ See back of book.

**Simplify each expression.** ***(Lesson 2-3)***

49. $m + 5 + 3m$ $4m + 5$
50. $2y - 12 + 6x + 5$ $6x + 2y - 7$
51. $-4a + 10b + 7a - 2$ $3a + 10b - 2$

52. *Navigation* A plane is flying 6.3 mi above the ground. The angle of depression to an airport is 14°. How far is the plane from the airport (in ground distance)? ***(Lesson 11-7)*** 25.3 mi

## Chapter Project 13 — Activity 1 Creating

Use poster board to make two cubes, one with edge length $a$, and one with edge length $b$. You can use any values you choose for $a$ and $b$. Next make six rectangular prisms, three with dimensions $a \times a \times b$, and three with dimensions $a \times b \times b$. Assemble the eight prisms into one large cube. Use tape to hold the prisms together. What is the edge length of the large cube, in terms of $a$ and $b$?

See also Extra Practice section.



## Project Activity 1

**Creating** In order to help students connect the abstract algebraic representation $(a + b)$ with the real models, you may want to make or draw cubes with edges of 2 inches and 3 inches and use these models to demonstrate this activity.

47.

| $x$ | $\frac{1}{3} \cdot 3^x$ | $y$ | $(x, y)$ |
|---|---|---|---|
| 1 | $\frac{1}{3} \cdot 3^1$ | 1 | (1, 1) |
| 2 | $\frac{1}{3} \cdot 3^2$ | 3 | (2, 3) |
| 3 | $\frac{1}{3} \cdot 3^3$ | 9 | (3, 9) |
| 4 | $\frac{1}{3} \cdot 3^4$ | 27 | (4, 27) |

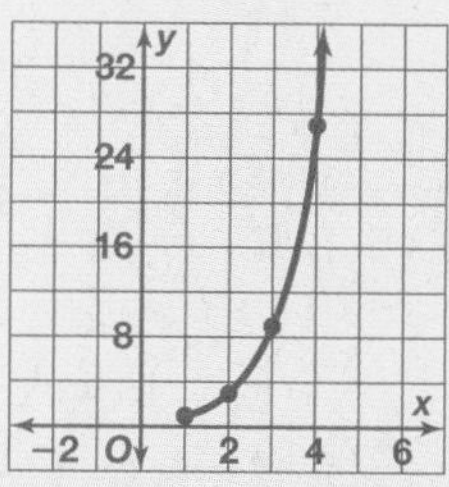

## Practice

**Evaluate each polynomial for $x = -1$, $y = 3$, and $z = 2$.**

1. $x^2 + z$ 3
2. $3y + x$ 8
3. $2z + y$ 7
4. $x + y + z$ 4
5. $x^2 + y^2$ 10
6. $z - x - y$ 0

**Evaluate each polynomial for $m = 21$, $n = -9$, and $p = 28$.**

7. $3m - 2p$ 7
8. $2n^2 - 5m$ 57
9. $m^2 - n^2$ 360
10. $n^2 + 5n - 6$ 30
11. $5p^2 - 5p$ 3,780
12. $7m + 6p$ 315

**Solve using the given polynomials.**

13. Find the number of diagonals that can be drawn in a polygon with 24 sides.
$N = \frac{1}{2}n^2 - \frac{3}{2}n$
$N$ = number of diagonals
$n$ = number of sides
252 diagonals

14. A rock thrown from the top of a cliff at an initial velocity of 3 m/s takes 6.2 s to reach the bottom. To the nearest meter, how tall is the cliff?
$d = 4.9t^2 - vt$
$d$ = distance fallen
$t$ = time falling
$v$ = initial velocity
170 m

**Tell whether each polynomial is a *monomial*, a *binomial*, or a *trinomial*.**

15. $36abc$ monomial
16. $10 - h^3$ binomial
17. $95xy + y$ binomial
18. $a^2 + b^2 + cd$ trinomial
19. $3k$ monomial
20. $-12e + 12f^2$ binomial



## Reteaching

The polynomial $d = 4.9t^2 - vt$ gives the distance $d$ in meters an object has fallen after $t$ seconds if it is thrown down with an initial velocity $v$. A rock is thrown from the top of a cliff with an initial velocity of 2 m/s. The rock takes 7.3 s to reach the bottom. To the nearest meter, how tall is the cliff?

$d = 4.9t^2 - vt$ Substitute 7.3 for $t$ and 2 for $v$.
$d = 4.9(7.3)^2 - 2(7.3)$
$d = 4.9(53.29) - 2(7.3)$ Evaluate using the order of operations. Evaluate the exponent first.
$d = 261.121 - 14.6$ Multiply.
$d = 246.521$ Subtract.
$d \approx 247$ meters Round.

**Use the polynomial $d = 4.9t^2 - vt$ to find the distance each object falls for the given time and initial velocity. Round to the nearest meter.**

1. $t = 7$ s, $v = 3$ m/s 219 m
2. $t = 6$ s, $v = 3.5$ m/s 155 m
3. $t = 5.7$ s, $v = 2$ m/s 148 m
4. $t = 6.4$ s, $v = 2.8$ m/s 183 m

**Evaluate each polynomial for $x = -2$ and $y = 3$.**

5. $x^2 - 2x - 5$ 3
6. $xy + y^2 + 2x$ −1
7. $9 - 3x^2$ −3
8. $x^2 - 2xy - y^2$ 7
9. The polynomial $S = 2\pi r^2 + 2\pi rh$ gives the surface area of a cylinder with radius $r$ and height $h$. Find the surface area of a cylinder with radius 8 cm and height 14 cm, to the nearest cm$^2$.
1,105 cm$^2$



## Enrichment

The following problem uses polynomials.
Jason is 16 years old. Each year, beginning with his 13th birthday, his mother has given him $100. He invests the money at an annual yield of 6%.

1. How much money did Jason get on his 13th birthday? $100

If 6% is the interest rate, we can express the interest as 100(0.06). We can express the total amount in the account at the end of the first year as 100 + 100(0.06). Another way is 106% of $100 or 100(1.06).

2. Money in the account after Jason's 14th birthday: 100(1.06) + $100
3. During the year the amount in the account earns 6% interest. Use the distributive property to write the addition expression another way so that it represents the total amount in the account.
Money in the account after earning 6% interest: 1.06[100(1.06) + 100] =
$100(1.06)^2 + 100(1.06)$
4. Money in the account after Jason's 15th birthday:
$100(1.06)^2 + 100(1.06) +$ $100
5. Money in the account after earning 6% interest:
$1.06[100(1.06)^2 + 100(1.06) + 100] =$
$100(1.06)^3 + 100(1.06)^2 + 100(1.06)$

A spreadsheet can be used to organize and evaluate the data.

| | A | B | C | D |
|---|---|---|---|---|
| 1 | amount before birthday | birthday year | amount added | total |
| 2 | 0 | 13 | 100 | 100 |
| 3 | 106 | 14 | 100 | 206 |

6. Write a formula for each of the following cells.
A4 = D3 * 1.06 D4 = A4 + C4 A5 = D4 * 1.06
D5 = A5 + C5 A6 = D5 * 1.06 D6 = A6 + C6
7. How much money is in his account after his 16th birthday? $437.46
8. Explain how the polynomial, $100y^3 + 100y^2 + 100y + 100$ represents the amount of money in Jason's account just after his 16th birthday.
y represents 1.06 in the expression $100(1.06)^3 + 100(1.06)^2 + 100(1.06) + 100$

## MATH TOOLBOX

### Degree of a Polynomial

This Math Toolbox shows students how to identify the degree of a polynomial.

### Math Background

The degree of a polynomial is the highest sum of the exponents of the variables that appear in one term. For example, the degree of $6a^2b^3$ is 5; the degree of $6a^2b + ab^2$ is 3. A polynomial is in *standard form* when the terms are arranged in descending powers of one variable, with the constant term at the end.

## Teaching Notes

**Error Prevention** Point out that you need to look at only one term to find the degree of a polynomial—the term that has the highest sum of the exponents on the variables. Exponents on numbers, rather than on variables, do not influence the degree of the polynomial.

**Monitoring Progress Exercises 18–29** Suggest that, after students copy the problem, they use circles, underlines, or boxes to indicate the like terms they will combine.

**Block Scheduling** If you have block scheduling or extended periods, you may wish to insert this Math Toolbox between the completion of Part 1 of Lesson 13-5 and the beginning of Part 2 of Lesson 13-5.

## MATH TOOLBOX

Extension
After Lesson 13-4

# Degree of a Polynomial

Just as you can get information about a polynomial by counting the number of terms, you can get other information by looking at the exponents. The *degree of a term* is the sum of the exponents of the variables in the term. The *degree of a polynomial* is the greatest degree of its terms.

polynomial → $x^3 + 4x^2 + xy - 5x + 9$ ← The degree of a nonzero constant is zero.

degree of each term → 3  2  2  1  0

Degree of the polynomial is 3.

### EXAMPLE 1

**Identify each polynomial by name and by degree.**

**a.** $2 - a$

0  1 ← degree of each term

Greatest degree of the terms is 1.

The polynomial is a binomial of degree 1.

**b.** $3y^3x$

4 ← Add the exponents: 3 + 1 = 4.

Degree of the term is 4.

The polynomial is a monomial of degree 4.

**c.** $5x^2 + x + 4$

2  1  0 ← degree of each term

Greatest degree of the terms is 2.

The polynomial is a trinomial of degree 2.

**Identify each polynomial by name and by degree.** 1–8. See above right.

1. $9c + 5$
2. $12a^2b$
3. $6x^2 - 3x + 2$
4. $p^2q^3$
5. $d^4 + 6d$
6. $4a^3 + 8a^2 - 11$
7. $24x^3yz$
8. $15x - 2x^2$

1. binomial of degree 1
2. monomial of degree 3
3. trinomial of degree 2
4. monomial of degree 5
5. binomial of degree 4
6. trinomial of degree 3
7. monomial of degree 5
8. binomial of degree 2



- **Additional Example**

Simplify the polynomial and write the result in standard form. Then identify the result by name and by degree.

$8 + 7d - 2d^2 - 5 - 3d + d^2$

$-d^2 + 4d + 3$; trinomial of degree 2

When you write a polynomial with the terms in order of decreasing degree, the polynomial is in *standard form.* When terms need to be moved, first use the Commutative Property of Addition to reorganize terms that are subtracted. For example, you can write $4 - x^2$ as $4 + (-x^2)$. Then you can rewrite the polynomial as $-x^2 + 4$.

13. $b^3 + 2b^2 - b - 2$
14. $6y^2 - y + 11$
15. $4x^5 + 4x^4 + 2x^3 + x^2$
16. $p^6 - 7p^3 + p^2 + p - 4$
17. $6a^3 - 5a^2 + 9a - 5$

## EXAMPLE 2

**Write each polynomial in standard form.**

**a.** $x^4 + 2 - x^2$

4 0 2 ← degree of each term

standard form: $x^4 - x^2 + 2$

**b.** $-2y + y^3 + y^2 - 3$

1 3 2 0 ← degree of each term

standard form: $y^3 + y^2 - 2y - 3$

21. $-2p^2 + 10p$
22. $9c^2 - 6c - 8$
23. $x^2 + 2x + 8$
24. $5b^2 + 1$
25. $5m^3 + 8m^2 + 11m + 14$
26. $-5a^6 + 3a^4 - 9a + 6$
27. $-y^2 - 6y - 11$
28. $15p^2 + 11p$
29. $18x^2 + 26x + 6$

**Write each polynomial in standard form.** 13–17. See top right.

**9.** $8 + 5a$ $5a + 8$ **10.** $3y^2 + 16 + y$ $3y^2 + y + 16$ **11.** $2c + 4c^2 - 7$ $4c^2 + 2c - 7$

**12.** $5x - 4x^2 + 3$ $-4x^2 + 5x + 3$ **13.** $2b^2 - 2 + b^3 - b$ **14.** $11 + 6y^2 - y$

**15.** $4x^4 + 4x^5 + x^2 + 2x^3$ **16.** $p^6 - 4 + p + p^2 - 7p^3$ **17.** $9a - 5 + 6a^3 - 5a^2$

When you simplify a polynomial, you should write your answer in standard form.

## EXAMPLE 3

**Simplify each polynomial.**

**a.** $5a + a^2 + 3a^2 + 2$

$5a + (1 + 3)a^2 + 2$ Combine like terms.

$5a + 4a^2 + 2$ Simplify.

$4a^2 + 5a + 2$ Write in standard form.

**b.** $3x - 8x + 2x^2 + 4x^2$

$(3 - 8)x + (2 + 4)x^2$

$-5x + 6x^2$

$6x^2 - 5x$

21–29. See above right.

**Simplify each polynomial.**

**18.** $x + 3x^2 + x^2$ $4x^2 + x$ **19.** $3a + 5a^2 + 2a + 6$ $5a^2 + 5a + 6$ **20.** $4m^2 + m^2 + 10 + 4m$ $5m^2 + 4m + 10$

**21.** $6p - 5p^2 + 4p + 3p^2$ **22.** $c + 9c^2 - 7c - 8$ **23.** $-2x^2 + 5 + 3x^2 + 2x + 3$

**24.** $3b + 1 + 7b^2 - 3b - 2b^2$ **25.** $5m^3 + 8m^2 + 11m + 14$ **26.** $3a^4 - 5a^6 - 9a + 6$

**27.** $-11 - y^2 - 8y + 2y$ **28.** $6p + 8p^2 + 5p + 7p^2$ **29.** $22x + 18x^2 + 6 + 4x$

# 13-5

## Getting Ready

**Materials** algebra tiles

**Resources** A complete list of resources for this lesson is on p. 661H.

### Daily Skills Warm-Up

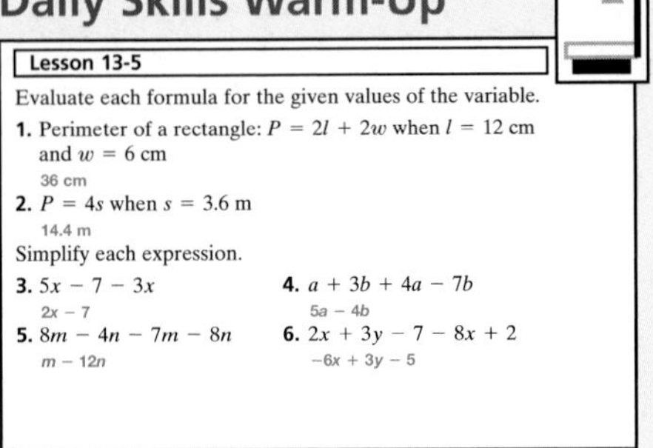
Lesson 13-5

Evaluate each formula for the given values of the variable.

1. Perimeter of a rectangle: $P = 2l + 2w$ when $l = 12$ cm and $w = 6$ cm
   36 cm
2. $P = 4s$ when $s = 3.6$ m
   14.4 m

Simplify each expression.

3. $5x - 7 - 3x$
   $2x - 7$
4. $a + 3b + 4a - 7b$
   $5a - 4b$
5. $8m - 4n - 7m - 8n$
   $m - 12n$
6. $2x + 3y - 7 - 8x + 2$
   $-6x + 3y - 5$

### Background for the Lesson

When you add or subtract polynomials, you combine like terms. Like terms have the same variables to the same degree. For example, $-3xy^2$ and $5xy^2$ are like terms; $xy$ and $xy^2$ are not like terms. To add or subtract like terms, you add or subtract their coefficients and use the sum or difference as the coefficient of the result.

## 1 Focus

### Connecting to Students' Lives

Discuss whether it would be easier to count the coins in a cash register or savings bank by combining all of the coins of the same denomination or by counting the coins individually as they occur.

### Connecting to Prior Knowledge

In Lesson 13-4, students were introduced to polynomials. In this lesson, students add and subtract polynomials. In Lesson 13-6, students will multiply a polynomial by a monomial.

# 13-5 Adding and Subtracting Polynomials

**What You'll Learn**

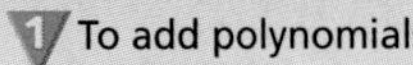
1 To add polynomials

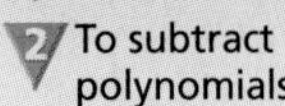
2 To subtract polynomials

**. . . And Why**

To solve problems involving area and volume

## PART 1 Adding Polynomials

In Chapter 2 you saw models for variables and numbers. You can also model the square of a variable.

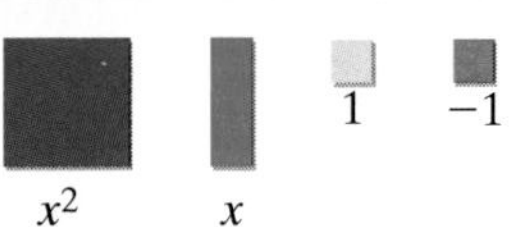


You can use models or properties to add polynomials.

### EXAMPLE 1

**Simplify $(2x^2 + 3x + 1) + (x^2 + x + 3)$.**

**Method 1** Add using tiles.

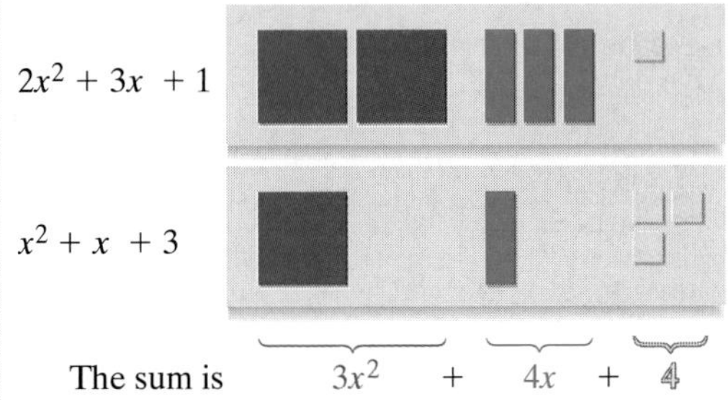


**Method 2** Add by combining like terms.

$(2x^2 + 3x + 1) + (x^2 + x + 3)$

$= (2x^2 + x^2) + (3x + x) + (1 + 3)$ — Use the Commutative and Associative Properties of Addition to group like terms.

$= (2 + 1)x^2 + (3 + 1)x + (1 + 3)$ — Use the Distributive Property to combine like terms.

$= 3x^2 + 4x + 4$ — Simplify.

**Quick Review**

*Like terms* are terms with the same variable(s), raised to the same power(s). Like terms are combined by adding their coefficients.

$3b + 12b = (3 + 12)b$
$= 15b$

**TRY THIS** Simplify.

1. $(7d^2 + 7d) + (2d^2 + 3d)$ $9d^2 + 10d$
2. $(x^2 + 2x + 5) + (3x^2 + x + 12)$ $4x^2 + 3x + 17$



## Tools to Monitor Progress

**BEFORE THE LESSON**

**To check prerequisite skills:**

- Simplifying variable expressions

**Skills You Need,** p. 661

**Skills Handbook,** p. 741

**Skills Intervention Kit,** Whole Numbers

**DURING THE LESSON**

**To check understanding:**

**Try This** exercises on student page

- **Additional Examples 1–3**

Simplify each sum or difference.

a. $(4b^2 + 2b + 1) + (7b^2 + b - 3)$ $11b^2 + 3b - 2$

b. $(2z^2 - 9z - 15) + (8z + 11)$ $2z^2 - z - 4$

You can also add polynomials in a column by aligning like terms and then adding their coefficients.

**EXAMPLE 2**

**Find the sum of $z^2 + 5z + 4$ and $2z^2 - 5$.**

Align like terms.

$$\begin{array}{r} z^2 + 5z + 4 \\ +\ \ 2z^2 \phantom{+ 5z} - 5 \\ \hline 3z^2 + 5z - 1 \end{array}$$

Add the terms in each column.

**TRY THIS** Simplify.

**3.** $\begin{array}{r} 4x + 9y \\ +\ 3x - 5y \\ \hline \end{array}$ $7x + 4y$

**4.** $\begin{array}{r} a^2 + 6a - 4 \\ +\ 8a^2 - 8a \phantom{- 4} \\ \hline \end{array}$ $9a^2 - 2a - 4$

**5.** $(4g^2 - 2g + 2) + (2g^2 - 3)$ $6g^2 - 2g - 1$

**6.** $(-2t^2 + t + 5) + (2t + 4)$ $-2t^2 + 3t + 9$

## PART 2 Subtracting Polynomials

You subtract polynomials by adding the opposite of each term in the second polynomial.

**EXAMPLE 3**

**Simplify $(5x^2 + 10x) - (3x - 12)$.**

$(5x^2 + 10x) - (3x - 12)$

$= 5x^2 + 10x - 3x + 12$ Write the opposite of each term in the second polynomial.

$= 5x^2 + (10x - 3x) + 12$ Group like terms.

$= 5x^2 + (10 - 3)x + 12$ Use the Distributive Property.

$= 5x^2 + 7x + 12$ Simplify.

**TRY THIS** Simplify.

**7.** $(7a^2 - 2a) - (5a^2 + 3a)$ $2a^2 - 5a$

**8.** $(10z^2 + 6z + 5) - (z^2 - 8z + 7)$ $9z^2 + 14z - 2$

**9.** $(3w^2 + 8 + v) - (5w^2 - 3 - 7v)$ $-2w^2 + 8v + 11$



**c.** $(12y^2 + 10y - 5) - (6y^2 + 8y - 11)$ $6y^2 + 2y + 6$

### AFTER THE LESSON

**To assess knowledge:**

**Lesson Quiz**

Simplify each sum or difference.

**1.** $(5c^2 + 4c + 2) + (3c^2 - 5c - 7)$ $8c^2 - c - 5$

**2.** $(4a^2 - a + 3) - (9a^2 - 6a + 2)$ $-5a^2 + 5a + 1$

- For enrichment and reteaching options see Resources on p. 661H.

# 2 Teach

## PART 1 Part 1 Teaching Notes

Using algebra tiles to model the addition of polynomials as you introduce these procedures gives students a concrete representation to help them understand the abstract mathematics. Help students connect what they do with the concrete models to the written abstract symbols.

### Example 1

**Build understanding.** Ask: What are the coefficients of the $x^2$- and $x$-terms in the second polynomial? How do you know? The coefficients are 1 because any variable by itself has an understood coefficient of 1.

### Example 2

**Build understanding.** Ask: The second polynomial has no $z$-term. How does this affect the sum? Think of adding 0 to $5z$.

**Auditory Learning** Have pairs of students name the like terms to each other before they combine those terms.

**Extension** If you add two polynomials, one with two terms and another with three terms, how many terms will the sum have? Explain your answer. The answer depends on whether the terms are like terms and can be combined.

## PART 2 Part 2 Teaching Notes

Remind students that subtracting a quantity is the same as adding its opposite.

### Example 3

**Build understanding.** Ask: Why is 12 added instead of subtracted? You are subtracting −12, which is the same as adding 12.

**Error Prevention** Make sure students add the opposite of *each* term in the second polynomial when they subtract polynomials.

# 3 Practice/Assess

## Assignment Guide

To provide flexible scheduling, this lesson can be divided into parts.

▼ **Part 1**
**Core** 1–6, 9–20, 29–34, 36
✪ **Extension** 27, 38

▼ **Part 2**
**Core** 7–8, 21–26, 35, 39–44
✪ **Extension** 28, 37

Mixed Review can be assigned at any time for maintenance.

## Exercises

**Tactile Learning Exercises 15–26** Write the separate terms of each polynomial (with the sign) on a note card or small piece of paper. Arrange like terms in columns.

## ✪ Challenge

Simplify $(\frac{1}{3}x^2 + \frac{5}{7}x - \frac{3}{4}) - (\frac{1}{2}x^2 - \frac{2}{7}x + 2)$. $(-\frac{1}{6}x^2 + x - 2\frac{3}{4})$

## Closure

You can add polynomials by using models, combining like terms, or aligning like terms vertically and then adding their coefficients. You subtract polynomials by adding the opposite of each term in the second polynomial.

### Daily Cumulative Review

**Evaluate each polynomial for $x = -3$ and $y = 2$.** *(Lesson 13-4)*

1. $y - x$ 5
2. $2y + 5x$ −11
3. $8 + xy^2$ −4
4. $x^2 - y - 4$ 3
5. $\frac{x^2}{3} + y$ 5
6. $xy - 2y$ −10

**Make a table and graph each function for integer values of $x$ from 0 to 4.** *(Lesson 13-3)*

7. $y = \frac{1}{9} \cdot 3^x$

| $x$ | 0 | 1 | 2 | 3 | 4 |
|---|---|---|---|---|---|
| $y$ | $\frac{1}{9}$ | $\frac{1}{3}$ | 1 | 3 | 9 |

8. $y = 9(\frac{1}{3})^x$

| $x$ | 0 | 1 | 2 | 3 | 4 |
|---|---|---|---|---|---|
| $y$ | 9 | 3 | 1 | $\frac{1}{3}$ | $\frac{1}{9}$ |

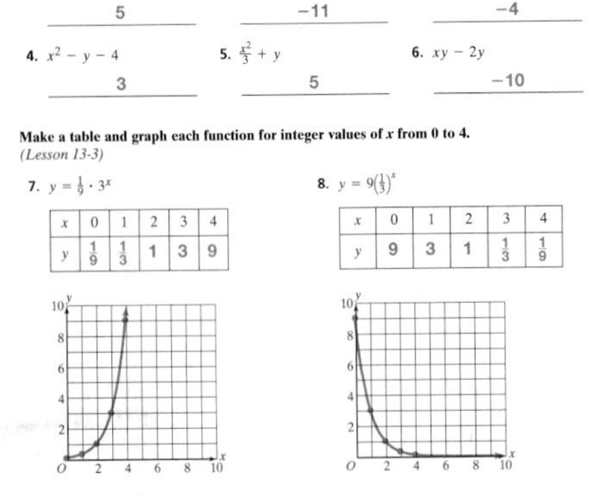


**Mixed Review**

**Use the Distributive Property to multiply.**

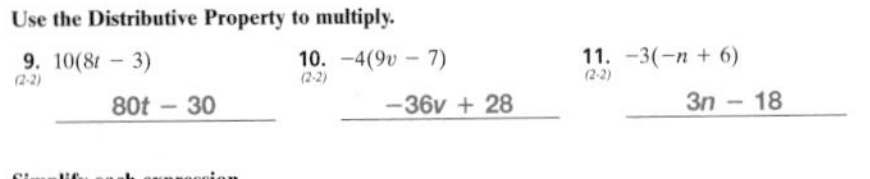

9. $10(8t - 3)$ (2-2) $80t - 30$
10. $-4(9v - 7)$ (2-2) $-36v + 28$
11. $-3(-n + 6)$ (2-2) $3n - 18$

**Simplify each expression.**

12. $5^4 \cdot 5^{12}$ (4-7) $5^{16}$
13. $n^6 \cdot n^9$ (4-7) $n^{15}$
14. $6x^2 \cdot (-8x^3)$ (4-7) $-48x^5$



# Exercises

## Check Understanding

**Write the sum modeled in each exercise. Then simplify the sum.**

1. 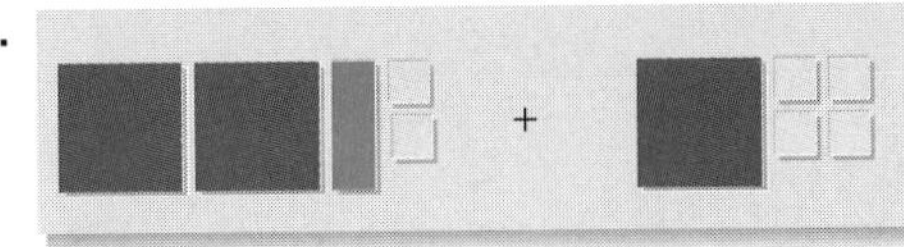

$(2x^2 + x + 2) + (x^2 + 4) = 3x^2 + x + 6$

2. $(x^2 + 2x - 4) + (x^2 + 2x + 2) = 2x^2 + 4x - 2$

**Use a model to simplify each sum.**

3. $(x^2 + 3x + 1) + (x^2 + x + 6)$ $2x^2 + 4x + 7$
4. $(x^2 + 5x + 2) + (3x^2 + x + 1)$ $4x^2 + 6x + 3$

**Simplify each sum or difference.**

5. $\begin{array}{r} 5a + 7b \\ + \quad -3a + 2b \\ \hline \end{array}$ $2a + 9b$
6. $\begin{array}{r} x^2 + 4x - 2 \\ + \quad 8x^2 - 3x + 7 \\ \hline \end{array}$ $9x^2 + x + 5$
7. $(5x + 9) - (2x + 1)$ $3x + 8$
8. $(-11a^2 + 2a - 1) - (7a^2 + 4a - 1)$ $-18a^2 - 2a$

## Practice and Problem Solving

**Use a model to simplify each sum.**

9. $(3x + 2) + (-4x + 3)$ $-x + 5$
10. $(5x^2 + 3x + 7) + (7x - 2)$ $5x^2 + 10x + 5$

**Simplify each sum or difference.**

11. $\begin{array}{r} x^4 + 3x^3 - x^2 + x - 2 \\ + \quad 7x^3 + x^2 - 5x - 9 \\ \hline \end{array}$ $x^4 + 10x^3 - 4x - 11$
12. $\begin{array}{r} xy + 5x - 2y + 4 \\ + \quad 2xy - 3x - 3y - 8 \\ \hline \end{array}$ $3xy + 2x - 5y - 4$
13. $\begin{array}{r} x^3 + 5x^2 + 3x - 2 \\ + \quad x^3 \qquad - 2x + 6 \\ \hline \end{array}$ $2x^3 + 5x^2 + x + 4$
14. $\begin{array}{r} 4x^2 - 5xy \qquad + 7 \\ + \quad 8x^2 + 3xy - 3y - 4 \\ \hline \end{array}$ $12x^2 - 2xy - 3y + 3$
15. $(3x - 2y) + (5x + 4y)$ $8x + 2y$
16. $(x^2 + 3x - 7) + (x^2 - 6x - 9)$ $2x^2 - 3x - 16$
17. $(-4x^2 + 2x - 1) + (x^2 - x + 8)$ $-3x^2 + x + 7$
18. $(ab - 4) + (3ab - 6)$ $4ab - 10$
19. $(13a^2b - 3ab^2) + (2a^2b + 5ab^2)$ $15a^2b + 2ab^2$
20. $(w^2 + 5w) + (2w - 6)$ $w^2 + 7w - 6$
21. $(2x^2 + 3x) - (x^2 + 2x)$ $x^2 + x$
22. $(x^2 + 3x + 5) - (x^2 + x + 2)$ $2x + 3$
23. $(8j - 3k + 6m) - (-2j + 3m)$ $10j - 3k + 3m$
24. $(3x^2 + x + 7) - (2x^2 + x + 2)$ $x^2 + 5$
25. $(6y - 8) - (2y + 7)$ $4y - 15$
26. $(x^2 - 3x - 9) - (5x - 4)$ $x^2 - 8x - 5$



## Alternative Assessment

Have students create a poster that explains how to add and subtract polynomials. Include examples of polynomials that have the same number of terms and different numbers of terms.

*Mathematical Reasoning* **Justify each step.**

27. $(x^2 + 3x - 2) + (3x^2 + 2x + 4)$
$(x^2 + 3x^2) + (3x + 2x) + (-2 + 4)$
$(1 + 3)x^2 + (3 + 2)x + (-2 + 4)$
$4x^2 + 5x + 2$
commutative and associative properties; distributive property; simplify

28. $(x^2 + 2x + 1) - (2x^2 - 3x - 4)$
$(x^2 + 2x + 1) + -(2x^2 - 3x - 4)$
$(x^2 + 2x + 1) + (-2x^2) + 3x + 4$
$(x^2 + -2x^2) + (2x + 3x) + (1 + 4)$
$(1 + -2)x^2 + (2 + 3)x + (1 + 4)$
$-x^2 + 5x + 5$ definition of subtraction; distributive property; commutative and associative properties; distributive property; simplify

**Write the perimeter of each figure as a polynomial. Simplify.**

29. 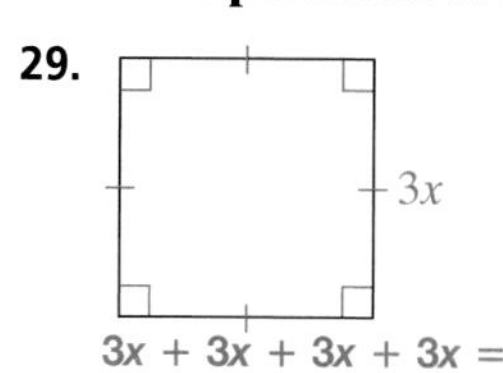


$3x + 3x + 3x + 3x = 12x$

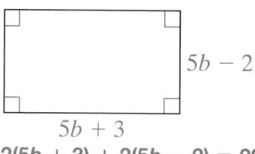

30. $5b - 2$, $5b + 3$
$2(5b + 3) + 2(5b - 2) = 20b + 2$

31. $2m$, $m^2 + 1$, $3m - 1$
$(m^2 + 1) + (3m - 1) + 2m = m^2 + 5m$

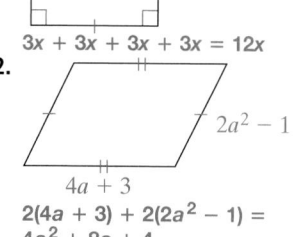

32. $2a^2 - 1$, $4a + 3$
$2(4a + 3) + 2(2a^2 - 1) = 4a^2 + 8a + 4$

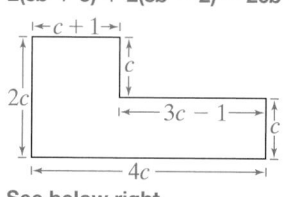

33. $c + 1$, $c$, $2c$, $3c - 1$, $c$, $4c$
See below right.

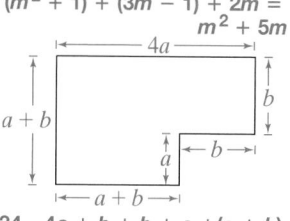

34. $4a$, $b$, $a + b$, $b$, $a$, $a + b$

34. $4a + b + b + a + (a + b) + (a + b) = 7a + 4b$

35. *Error Analysis* Tian simplified $(5x^2 + 4x - 3) - (2x^2 - x)$ as shown below. What is his error?

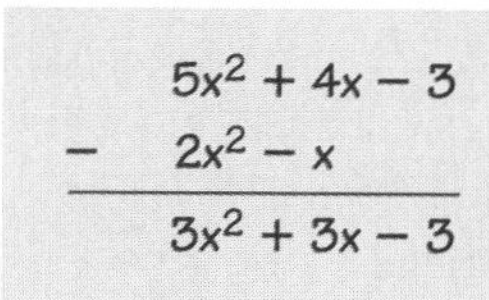


35. Answers may vary. Sample: Tian added $4x$ and $-x$. He should have added $4x$ and the opposite of $-x$, since this is a subtraction problem.

33. $(c + 1) + c + (3c - 1) + c + 4c + 2c = 12c$

36. a. Write an expression for the sum of three consecutive numbers. Let $x$ be the first number. Then simplify the expression. $x + (x + 1) + (x + 2) = 3x + 3$
b. What three consecutive numbers have the sum 108? 35, 36, 37

37. a. *Geometry* The volume of a cube is $(3x^3 + 9)$ in.$^3$. A smaller cube with volume $(x^3 - 3)$ in.$^3$ is cut out of the cube. Write a polynomial for the remaining volume. $(3x^3 + 9) - (x^3 - 3) = 2x^3 + 12$
b. Evaluate your polynomial for $x = 2$. 28 in.$^3$
c. *Reasoning* Will the original cube fit into a box with dimensions 10 in. × 9 in. × 15 in.? Explain. With $x = 2$, the original volume is 33 in.$^3$, so its side is less than 4 in. It will fit into the box.

38. a. *Critical Thinking* What polynomial is the opposite of $2x^2 + 3x - 5$? $-2x^2 - 3x + 5$
b. What is the sum of $2x^2 + 3x - 5$ and its opposite? 0

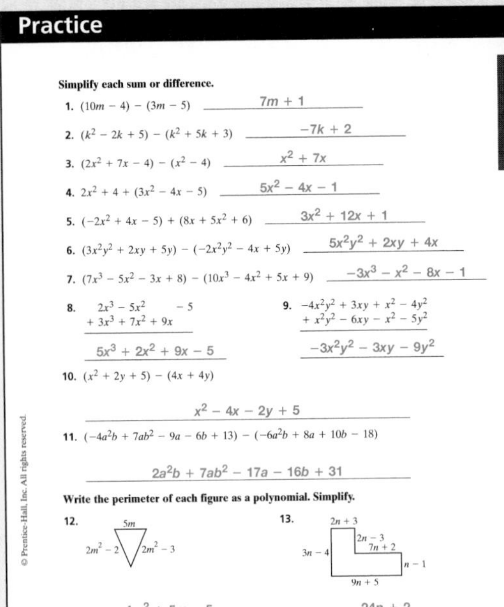

## Practice

**Simplify each sum or difference.**

1. $(10m - 4) - (3m - 5)$ $7m + 1$
2. $(k^2 - 2k + 5) - (k^2 + 5k + 3)$ $-7k + 2$
3. $(2x^2 + 7x - 4) - (x^2 - 4)$ $x^2 + 7x$
4. $2x^2 + 4 + (3x^2 - 4x - 5)$ $5x^2 - 4x - 1$
5. $(-2x^2 + 4x - 5) + (8x + 5x^2 + 6)$ $3x^2 + 12x + 1$
6. $(3x^2y^2 + 2xy + 5y) - (-2x^2y^2 - 4x + 5y)$ $5x^2y^2 + 2xy + 4x$
7. $(7x^3 - 5x^2 - 3x + 8) - (10x^3 - 4x^2 + 5x + 9)$ $-3x^3 - x^2 - 8x - 1$
8. $2x^3 - 5x^2 \quad - 5$ / $+ 3x^3 + 7x^2 + 9x$ $5x^3 + 2x^2 + 9x - 5$
9. $-4x^2y^2 + 3xy + x^2 - 4y^2$ / $+ x^2y^2 - 6xy - x^2 - 5y^2$ $-3x^2y^2 - 3xy - 9y^2$
10. $(x^2 + 2y + 5) - (4x + 4y)$ $x^2 - 4x - 2y + 5$
11. $(-4a^2b + 7ab^2 - 9a - 6b + 13) - (-6a^2b + 8a + 10b - 18)$ $2a^2b + 7ab^2 - 17a - 16b + 31$

**Write the perimeter of each figure as a polynomial. Simplify.**

12. $5m$, $2m^2 - 2$, $2m^2 - 3$ $4m^2 + 5m - 5$
13. $2n + 3$, $2n - 3$, $7n + 2$, $3n - 4$, $n - 1$, $9n + 5$ $24n + 2$



## Reteaching

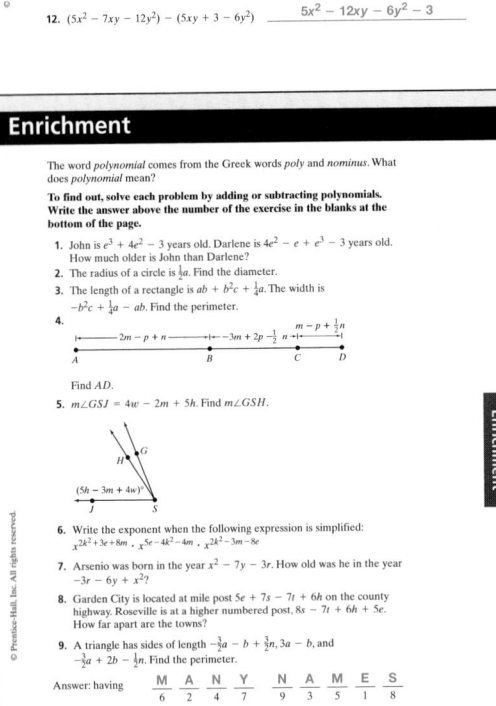

Simplify $(5x^2 - 4x + 7) - (2x^2 - 3x + 12)$.
Add the opposite of each term in the second polynomial.

| | |
|---|---|
| $(5x^2 - 4x + 7) - (2x^2 - 3x + 12)$ | |
| $= 5x^2 - 4x + 7 - 2x^2 + 3x - 12$ | Write the opposite of each term in the second polynomial. |
| $= (5x^2 - 2x^2) + (-4x + 3x) + (7 - 12)$ | Group like terms. |
| $= 3x^2 - x - 5$ | Simplify. Notice $-4x + 3x = -x$. Write $-x$ as subtraction. |

**Simplify each sum or difference.**

1. $(3x - 2) - (4x + 3)$ $-x - 5$
2. $(2x^2 - 4x + 1) - (x^2 - 2x + 1)$ $x^2 - 2x$
3. $(2x^2 + 5x + 4) + (x^2 - 3x - 3)$ $3x^2 + 2x + 1$
4. $(-x^2 + 3x - 1) + (3x^2 - x + 2)$ $2x^2 + 2x + 1$
5. $(4x^2 - 3x + 8) - (3x^2 - 2x + 10)$ $x^2 - x - 2$
6. $(2x^2 - 7x - 9) + (x^2 - 3x + 2)$ $3x^2 - 10x - 7$
7. $(y^2 - 8y - 6) - (y^2 - 10y + 3)$ $2y - 9$
8. $(4xy - 2x^2 + 3y^2) + (x^2 - 5xy - 7y^2)$ $-x^2 - xy - 4y^2$
9. $(7x^2 - 5xy - 6y) - (3xy + 5x^2 - 11y)$ $2x^2 - 8xy + 5y$
10. $(6k^2 - 9) - (4k + 3)$ $6k^2 - 4k - 12$
11. $(8ab - 7b) + (6b - 9ab)$ $-ab - b$
12. $(5x^2 - 7xy - 12y^2) - (5xy + 3 - 6y^2)$ $5x^2 - 12xy - 6y^2 - 3$



## Enrichment

The word *polynomial* comes from the Greek words *poly* and *nominus*. What does *polynomial* mean?

**To find out, solve each problem by adding or subtracting polynomials. Write the answer above the number of the exercise in the blanks at the bottom of the page.**

1. John is $e^3 + 4e^2 - 3$ years old. Darlene is $4e^2 - e + e^3 - 3$ years old. How much older is John than Darlene?
2. The radius of a circle is $\frac{1}{2}a$. Find the diameter.
3. The length of a rectangle is $ab + b^2c + \frac{1}{4}a$. The width is $-b^2c + \frac{1}{4}a - ab$. Find the perimeter.
4. $AB = 2m - p + n$, $BC = -3m + 2p - \frac{1}{2}n$, $CD = m - p + \frac{1}{2}n$

   Find $AD$.
5. $m\angle GSJ = 4w - 2m + 5h$. Find $m\angle GSH$.

   $(5h - 3m + 4w)^\circ$ (angle $HSJ$)
6. Write the exponent when the following expression is simplified: $x^{2k^2 + 3e + 8m} \cdot x^{5e - 4k^2 - 4m} \cdot x^{2k^2 - 3m - 8e}$
7. Arsenio was born in the year $x^2 - 7y - 3r$. How old was he in the year $-3r - 6y + x^2$?
8. Garden City is located at mile post $5e + 7s - 7t + 6h$ on the county highway. Roseville is at a higher numbered post, $8s - 7t + 6h + 5e$. How far apart are the towns?
9. A triangle has sides of length $-\frac{3}{2}a - b + \frac{3}{2}n$, $3a - b$, and $-\frac{3}{2}a + 2b - \frac{1}{2}n$. Find the perimeter.

Answer: having

| M | A | N | Y | | N | A | M | E | S |
|---|---|---|---|---|---|---|---|---|---|
| 6 | 2 | 4 | 7 | | 9 | 3 | 5 | 1 | 8 |



*Geometry* **Find each missing length.**

39. perimeter $= 11x + 6$

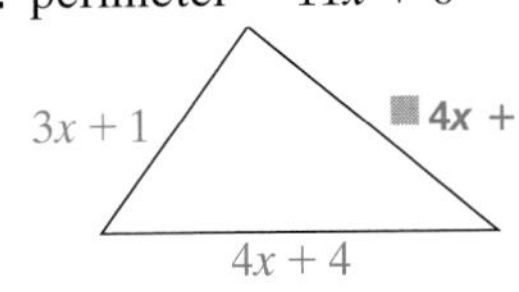


40. perimeter $= 12b - 2$

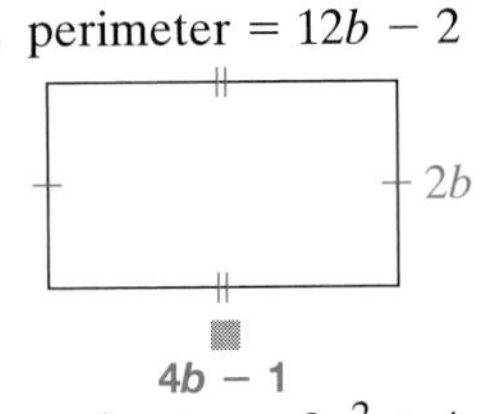


41. perimeter $= 5m^2 + 3m$

$m^2$, $2m^2 + m$, $2m^2 + 2m$

42. perimeter $= 6a + 3$

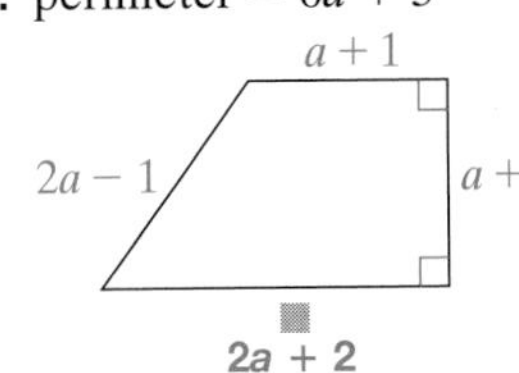


43. perimeter $= 8x^2 + 4$

$2x^2$, $2x^2 + 2$

44. perimeter $= 11y - 2$

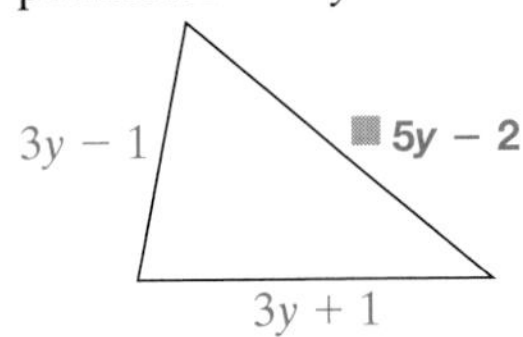


## Mixed Review

**Evaluate each polynomial for $a = 2$, $b = -1$, and $c = \frac{1}{2}$.** ***(Lesson 13-4)***

45. $8ab + 1$ $-15$
46. $5 + 4ab - c$ $-3\frac{1}{2}$
47. $a^2 + ab + b^2$ $3$
48. $5c - b - 1$ $2\frac{1}{2}$

**Find the area of each figure.** ***(Lesson 10-2)***

49. 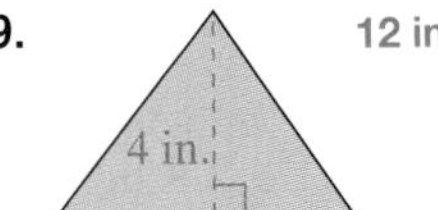

12 in.²

50. 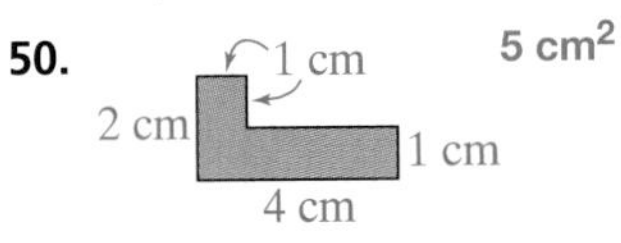

5 cm²

51. 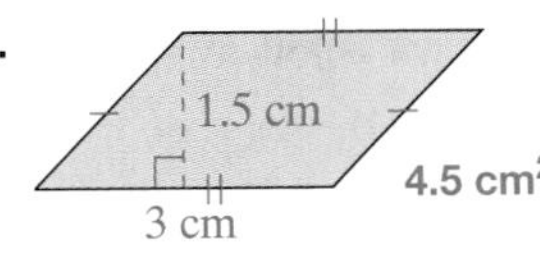

4.5 cm²

52. A student participated in a walk for charity. His friends pledged a total of \$3.20 for each mile he walked. The student earned \$22.40 for the charity. How many miles did he walk? ***(Lesson 3-6)*** 7 mi

CHAPTER PROJECT 13

## ACTIVITY 2 WRITING

For the area of one face of the large cube that you created in Activity 1, write a polynomial in terms of the cube's edge length. Then write a polynomial for the area of the face as the sum of the areas of the parts of the face. Write an equation that compares the two polynomials.



See also Extra Practice section.

## Project Activity 2

**Writing** The large cube has an edge length of $(a + b)$, so the area of one face is $(a + b)^2$ or $(a^2 + 2ab + b^2)$. The sum of the areas of the rectangles that are the parts of this face is equal to the total area of the face, or $(a + b)^2$. Suggest that students first write the two expressions for the area using the numbers for their model (such as 2 in. and 3 in.) and then write the same polynomials using variables.

# Multiplying a Polynomial by a Monomial

# 13-6

## Part 1 Using an Area Model

You can model the product of a monomial and a polynomial using algebra tiles. You can find the area of a rectangle that is $2x$ units long and $(x + 4)$ units wide by counting the tiles.

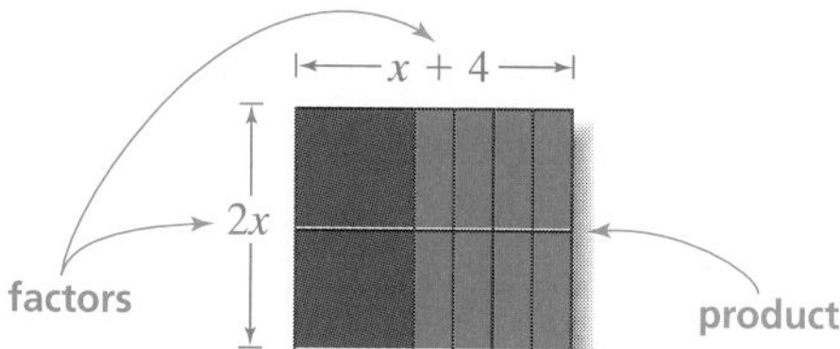


The area is $2x^2 + 8x$. So $2x(x + 4) = 2x^2 + 8x$.

You can also use the Distributive Property to simplify a product of a monomial and a polynomial. Multiply each term of the polynomial by the monomial.

REAL-WORLD CONNECTION

**EXAMPLE 1**

**Find the area of the garden. All measurements are in feet.**

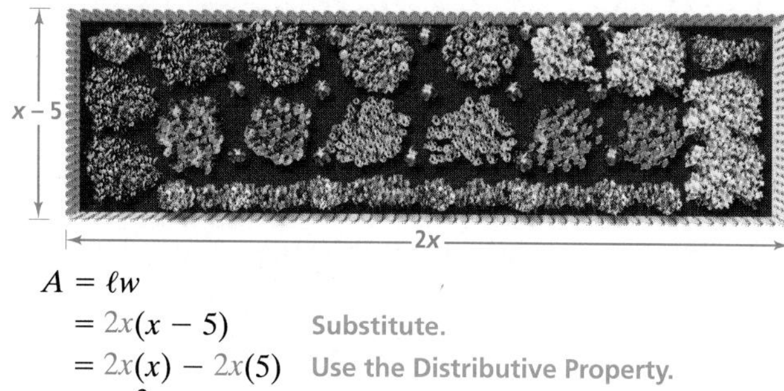


$A = \ell w$

$= 2x(x - 5)$ Substitute.

$= 2x(x) - 2x(5)$ Use the Distributive Property.

$= 2x^2 - 10x$ Simplify.

The area of the garden is $(2x^2 - 10x)$ ft$^2$.

**TRY THIS** Simplify each product.

1. $3x(x + 4)$ $3x^2 + 12x$
2. $x(2x - 3)$ $2x^2 - 3x$

### What You'll Learn

1. To use an area model for multiplication
2. To write a polynomial as the product of a monomial and a polynomial

### . . . And Why

To use area formulas with polynomials



# 13-6

## Getting Ready

**Materials** algebra tiles

**Resources** A complete list of resources for this lesson is on p. 661H.

### Daily Skills Warm-Up

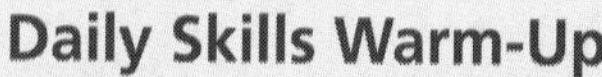

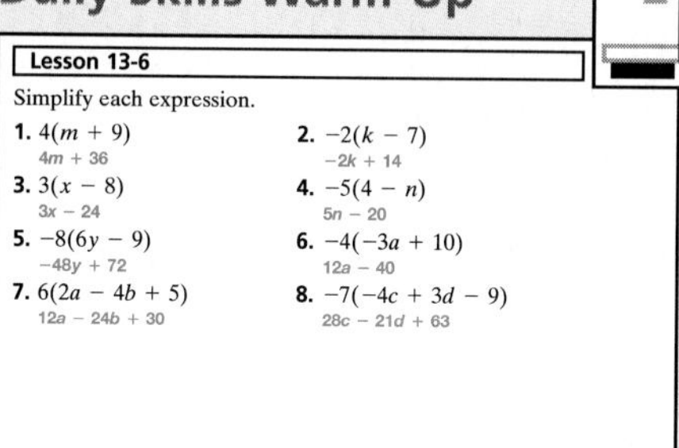

Lesson 13-6

Simplify each expression.

1. $4(m + 9)$ $4m + 36$
2. $-2(k - 7)$ $-2k + 14$
3. $3(x - 8)$ $3x - 24$
4. $-5(4 - n)$ $5n - 20$
5. $-8(6y - 9)$ $-48y + 72$
6. $-4(-3a + 10)$ $12a - 40$
7. $6(2a - 4b + 5)$ $12a - 24b + 30$
8. $-7(-4c + 3d - 9)$ $28c - 21d + 63$

### Background for the Lesson

As is usually true in mathematics, the process for multiplication and division of polynomials is different from, and somewhat easier than, the process for addition and subtraction. You can only add like terms; you can multiply any terms. To multiply a polynomial by a monomial, use the distributive property to multiply each term of the polynomial by the monomial. To do this, you find the product of the constants and the product of the variables. For example, $2x(3xy) = 6x^2y$.

## 1 Focus

### Connecting to Prior Knowledge

In Lesson 13-5, students added and subtracted polynomials. In this lesson, students multiply a polynomial by a monomial. In Lesson 13-7, students will multiply binomials.

# Tools to Monitor Progress

## BEFORE THE LESSON

**To check prerequisite skills:**

- Using the Distributive Property

**Skills You Need,** p. 661

**Skills Handbook,** p. 725

**Skills Intervention Kit,** Whole Numbers

## DURING THE LESSON

**To check understanding:**

**Try This** exercises on student page

- **Additional Example 1**
  Find the area of a rectangle that has a length of $4v$ and a width of $7 + v$.
  $28v + 4v^2$
- **Additional Example 2**
  Simplify $5n^2(2n^3 - 4n^2 + n)$.
  $10n^5 - 20n^4 + 5n^3$

# 2 Teach

## Part 1 Teaching Notes

Encourage students to look carefully at a problem before they begin to calculate in order to decide whether they will be adding or multiplying.

### Example 1

**Build understanding.** Ask: Which expression represents the length of the garden? Which represents the width? $2x$; $(x - 5)$

### Example 2

**Build understanding.** Ask: What is the rule for multiplying powers with the same base? To multiply two powers with the same base, add the exponents.

**Error Prevention** Caution students to double-check the signs in the product, especially if the multiplying monomial is negative.

**Visual Learning** On their paper, have students cross out each term in the polynomial as they multiply it.

## Part 2 Teaching Notes

Factoring a common monomial out of a polynomial is the inverse, or opposite, of multiplying a polynomial by a monomial. You may want to review finding the Greatest Common Factor (GCF) with students.

### Example 3

**Build understanding.** Ask: What does it mean to say that $3x$ is the GCF of $6x^3 + 3x^2 + 9x$? $3x$ is the greatest term that can be factored from all three of the terms.

**Extension** If you multiply a monomial by a polynomial, what is the relationship between the original monomial and the product of the multiplication? The original monomial is a factor of the product.

You can often use other properties to simplify the product of a monomial and a polynomial.

**Quick Review**

When multiplying powers with the same base, add exponents.

### EXAMPLE 2

**Simplify $3x^2(8x^2 - 5x + 2)$.**

| | |
|---|---|
| $3x^2(8x^2 - 5x + 2)$ | |
| $= 3x^2(8x^2) + 3x^2(-5x) + 3x^2(2)$ | Use the Distributive Property. |
| $= (3)(8)x^{2+2} + (3)(-5)x^{2+1} + (3)(2)x^2$ | Use the Commutative Property of Multiplication. |
| $= (3)(8)x^4 + (3)(-5)x^3 + (3)(2)x^2$ | Add exponents. |
| $= 24x^4 - 15x^3 + 6x^2$ | Simplify. |

**TRY THIS** Simplify each product.

3. $x(x^2 + 2x + 4)$ $x^3 + 2x^2 + 4x$
4. $2a^2(2a^3 - 3a^2 + 3)$ $4a^5 - 6a^4 + 6a^2$

## PART 2 Writing a Polynomial as a Product

**Quick Review**

The Distributive Property
$10a + 20 = 10(a + 2)$
$5y - y = (5 - 1)y$

You can sometimes use the Distributive Property to write a polynomial as the product of two factors. You will usually want to find the GCF of all the terms of a polynomial and use that as one of the factors.

### EXAMPLE 3

**Write $6x^3 + 3x^2 + 9x$ as a product of two factors.**

$6x^3 = 2 \cdot 3 \cdot x \cdot x \cdot x$
$3x^2 = 3 \cdot x \cdot x$
$9x = 3 \cdot 3 \cdot x$
Write the prime factorization of each term.

GCF $= 3x$ — Find the GCF.

Write each term as the product of $3x$ and another factor.

$6x^3 = 3x \cdot 2x^2$ $\quad 3x^2 = 3x \cdot x$ $\quad 9x = 3x \cdot 3$

$6x^3 + 3x^2 + 9x = 3x(2x^2 + x + 3)$ — Use the Distributive Property.

**TRY THIS** Use the GCF of the terms to write each expression as the product of two factors.

5. $2x^2 + x$ $x(2x + 1)$
6. $2b^3 + 6b^2 - 12b$ $2b(b^2 + 3b - 6)$



- **Additional Example 3**
  Write $6r^4 + 10r^3 - 14r^2$ as a product of two factors. $2r^2(3r^2 + 5r - 7)$

## AFTER THE LESSON

**To assess knowledge:**

**Lesson Quiz**

Simplify each product.

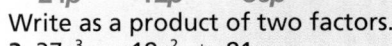

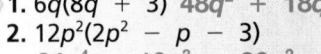

1. $6q(8q + 3)$ $48q^2 + 18q$
2. $12p^2(2p^2 - p - 3)$ $24p^4 - 12p^3 - 36p^2$

Write as a product of two factors.

3. $27y^3 - 18y^2 + 81y$ $9y(3y^2 - 2y + 9)$

- For enrichment and reteaching options see Resources on p. 661H.

# Exercises

## Check Understanding

**Use an area model to simplify each product.**

**1.** $3x(x + 1)$ $3x^2 + 3x$ **2.** $x(x + 5)$ $x^2 + 5x$ **3.** $2x(x + 3)$ $2x^2 + 6x$ **4.** $2x(3x + 1)$ $6x^2 + 2x$

**Use the Distributive Property to simplify each product.**

**5.** $3x(x + 5)$ $3x^2 + 15x$ **6.** $-4x(2x - 3)$ $-8x^2 + 12x$ **7.** $5x(-3x^2 + 2x)$ $-15x^3 + 10x^2$

**8.** $x(5x^2 + x - 4)$ $5x^3 + x^2 - 4x$ **9.** $3a(a^2 + 2a + 1)$ $3a^3 + 6a^2 + 3a$ **10.** $3b(2b^2 - b + 4)$ $6b^3 - 3b^2 + 12b$

**Use the GCF of the terms to write each expression as the product of two factors.**

**11.** $3d^4 + d^2$ $d^2(3d^2 + 1)$ **12.** $10x^5 - 5x^3 + 10x$ $5x(2x^4 - x^2 + 2)$ **13.** $4y^3 - 8y^2 - 12y$ $4y(y^2 - 2y - 3)$ **14.** $-9b^2 - 3b$ $3b(-3b - 1)$

## Practice and Problem Solving

**Use an area model to simplify each product.**

**15.** $2x(x + 6)$ $2x^2 + 12x$ **16.** $x(2x + 6)$ $2x^2 + 6x$ **17.** $2x(3x - 1)$ $6x^2 - 2x$ **18.** $3x(2x + 4)$ $6x^2 + 12x$

**Simplify each product.**

**19.** $2x(x + 4)$ $2x^2 + 8x$ **20.** $-4a(a - 9)$ $-4a^2 + 36a$ **21.** $3y(y + 7)$ $3y^2 + 21y$

**22.** $-2b(3b - 1)$ $-6b^2 + 2b$ **23.** $5x(x + 3)$ $5x^2 + 15x$ **24.** $7c(4 + c)$ $28c + 7c^2$

**25.** $3y(4y - 1)$ $12y^2 - 3y$ **26.** $a(a^2 + 3)$ $a^3 + 3a$ **27.** $x(2x - 5)$ $2x^2 - 5x$

**28.** $\frac{1}{2}b(b - 8)$ $\frac{1}{2}b^2 - 4b$ **29.** $-8y(2y + 3)$ $-16y^2 - 24y$ **30.** $-3(2c^2 - 3c - 1)$ See below.

**31.** $12x^2(5x + 2)$ $60x^3 + 24x^2$ **32.** $a^3(a + a^2 + 5)$ $a^4 + a^5 + 5a^3$ **33.** $6y^2\left(y^2 - 2y - \frac{1}{3}\right)$ See below.

**34.** $7b^2(2b^2 + b - 3)$ See below. **35.** $4x^2(x^3 + x^2 - x)$ See below. **36.** $5c(c + 5 - c^2)$ See below.

**37.** $-14a(a^2 + 3a - 4)$ $-14a^3 - 42a^2 + 56a$ **38.** $17y(2y^2 - 8y + 9)$ $34y^3 - 136y^2 + 153y$

✪ **39.** $-3xy(2x^2y + xy + y^2 - 3)$ $-6x^3y^2 - 3x^2y^2 - 3xy^3 + 9xy$ ✪ **40.** $4z(2z^6 - 3z^5 - 12z^2 + 8)$ $8z^7 - 12z^6 - 48z^3 + 32z$

**Write an expression for the area of each shaded region.**

✪ **41.**

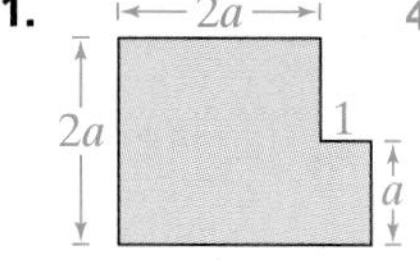

$4a^2 + a$

✪ **42.**

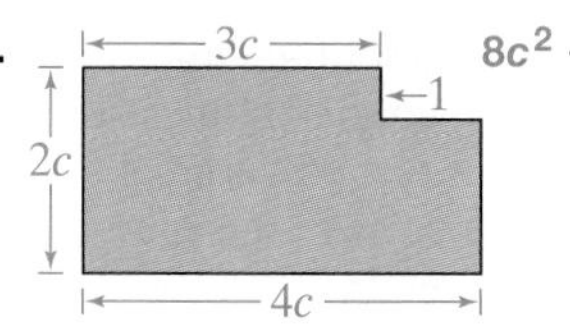


$8c^2 - c$

30. $-6c^2 + 9c + 3$
33. $6y^4 - 12y^3 - 2y^2$
34. $14b^4 + 7b^3 - 21b^2$
35. $4x^5 + 4x^4 - 4x^3$
36. $5c^2 + 25c - 5c^3$



# 3 Practice/Assess

## Assignment Guide

To provide flexible scheduling, this lesson can be divided into parts.

**Part 1**
**Core** 1–10, 15–38, 55
✪ **Extension** 39–42, 56–59

**Part 2**
**Core** 11–14, 43–52
✪ **Extension** 53–54

Mixed Review can be assigned at any time for maintenance.

## Exercises

**Auditory Learning** Exercises 43–54
Working with a partner, name the Greatest Common Factor before you write the expression as a product.

## ✪ Challenge

Simplify $9c^5(7c^2 + 4cd + 11d^2)$.
$63c^7 + 36c^6d + 99c^5d^2$

## Closure

You can use properties to simplify the product of a monomial and a polynomial. You can also use the Distributive Property to write some polynomials as the product of two factors.

## Alternative Assessment

Have students draw a rectangle with dimensions given as a monomial and a polynomial. Then have them find the area as the product of the two. Then exchange the areas, and have a partner find the two dimensions.

### Daily Cumulative Review

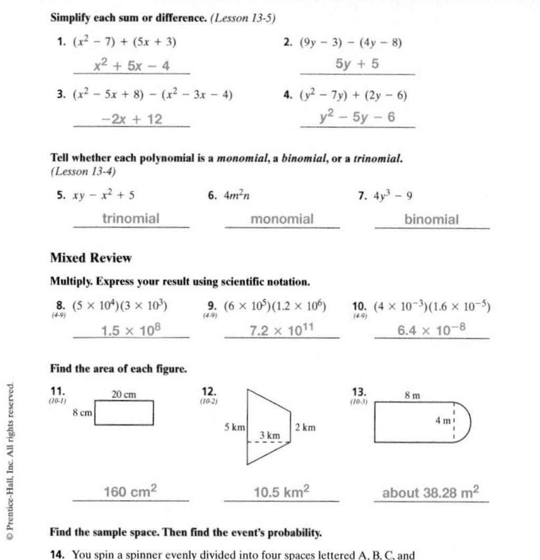

**Simplify each sum or difference.** *(Lesson 13-5)*

1. $(x^2 - 7) + (5x + 3)$ $x^2 + 5x - 4$
2. $(9y - 3) - (4y - 8)$ $5y + 5$
3. $(x^2 - 5x + 8) - (x^2 - 3x - 4)$ $-2x + 12$
4. $(y^2 - 7y) + (2y - 6)$ $y^2 - 5y - 6$

**Tell whether each polynomial is a *monomial*, a *binomial*, or a *trinomial*.** *(Lesson 13-4)*

5. $xy - x^2 + 5$ trinomial
6. $4m^2n$ monomial
7. $4y^3 - 9$ binomial

**Mixed Review**

**Multiply. Express your result using scientific notation.**

8. (4-9) $(5 \times 10^4)(3 \times 10^3)$ $1.5 \times 10^8$
9. (4-9) $(6 \times 10^5)(1.2 \times 10^6)$ $7.2 \times 10^{11}$
10. (4-9) $(4 \times 10^{-3})(1.6 \times 10^{-5})$ $6.4 \times 10^{-8}$

**Find the area of each figure.**

11. (10-1) 20 cm, 8 cm — 160 cm²
12. (10-2) 5 km, 3 km, 2 km — 10.5 km²
13. (10-3) 8 m, 4 m — about 38.28 m²

**Find the sample space. Then find the event's probability.**

14. (12-4) You spin a spinner evenly divided into four spaces lettered A, B, C, and D twice. You get A exactly once.
AA, AB, AC, AD, BA, BB, BC, BD, CA, CB, CC, CD, DA, DB, DC, DD; $\frac{3}{8}$

## Practice

**Simplify each product.**

1. $4x(3x - 5)$ $12x^2 - 20x$
2. $-8x(x - 7)$ $-8x^2 + 56x$
3. $7xy^2(y - 2x + x^2)$ $7xy^3 - 14x^2y^2 + 7x^3y^2$
4. $3xy(2xy + 5)$ $6x^2y^2 + 15xy$
5. $-9xyz(-2xy + 3yz - 4xz)$ $18x^2y^2z - 27xy^2z^2 + 36x^2yz^2$
6. $12ab\left(-\frac{1}{2}b + \frac{1}{4}a^3\right)$ $-6ab^2 + 3a^4b$
7. $-15a^2(a - b + 3c)$ $-15a^3 + 15a^2b - 45a^2c$
8. $-3x^2a^2(2a^3 + ab - x)$ $-6x^2a^5 - 3x^2a^3b + 3x^3a^2$

**Write an expression for the area of each shaded region. Simplify.**

9. 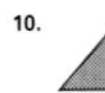


10. 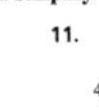


11. 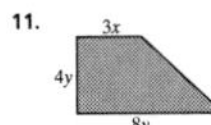


9. $x(12x - 6y)$; $12x^2 - 6xy$
10. $\frac{1}{2}(2ab)(a + b)$; $a^2b + ab^2$
11. $\frac{1}{2}(4y)(3x + 8y)$; $6xy + 16y^2$

**Use the GCF of the terms to write each expression as the product of two factors.**

12. $8x + 8y$ $8(x + y)$
13. $13a - 13b$ $13(a - b)$
14. $2x^3 + 2x^2$ $2x^2(x + 1)$
15. $11a + 11b + 11c$ $11(a + b + c)$
16. $x^3y^2 + x^2y^3 + x^4y$ $x^2y(xy + y^2 + x^2)$
17. $-12ab^2c + 18a^2bc^2 - 30ab^3c^3$ $-6abc(2b - 3ac + 5b^2c^2)$
18. $90w^3x + 144w^2$ $18w^2(5wx + 8)$



## Reteaching

**Use the GCF to write $36x^2y - 90x^2y^2$ as the product of two factors. Multiply to check.**

Write the prime factorization of each term to find the GCF.

$36x^2y = 2 \cdot 2 \cdot 3 \cdot 3 \cdot x \cdot x \cdot y$

$90x^2y^2 = 2 \cdot 3 \cdot 3 \cdot 5 \cdot x \cdot x \cdot y \cdot y$

$\text{GCF} = 2 \cdot 3 \cdot 3 \cdot x \cdot x \cdot y = 18x^2y$

Write each term as the product of $18x^2y$ and another factor.

$36x^2y - 90x^2y^2 = 18x^2y(2) - 18x^2y(5y)$

$= 18x^2y(2 - 5y)$ Use the Distributive Property.

Thus $36x^2y - 90x^2y^2 = 18x^2y(2 - 5y)$.

Check by multiplying $18x^2y(2 - 5y)$.

$18x^2y(2 - 5y) = (18x^2y)(2) - (18x^2y)5y$ Use the Distributive Property.

$= (2 \cdot 18x^2y) - 5(18)x^2y \cdot y$ Use the Commutative and Associative Properties to rearrange terms.

$= 36x^2y - 90x^2y^2$ Simplify.

The solution checks.

**Complete to show how the given expression can be written as the product of two factors.**

1. $5x + 5y = 5(\underline{x} + \underline{y})$
2. $-3m - 3n = -3(\underline{m} + \underline{n})$
3. $4x^3 + 4x^2y = \underline{4x^2}(x + y)$
4. $6ab + 12b = \underline{6b}(a + 2)$

**Use the GCF of the terms to write each expression as the product of two factors.**

5. $12x - 16y$ $4(3x - 4y)$
6. $6a + 9b$ $3(2a + 3b)$
7. $-9x^2 - 9y^2$ $-9(x^2 + y^2)$
8. $20m + 25n - 35k$ $5(4m + 5n - 7k)$

**Simplify each product.**

9. $y(4x + y - 2x^2)$ $4xy + y^2 - 2x^2y$
10. $3y(5y - 2x + 4xy)$ $15y^2 - 6xy + 12xy^2$



## Enrichment

You can use what you have learned about polynomials when working with formulas.

rectangle

w

l

perimeter

$p = 2l + 2w$

1. Complete to show how the polynomial $2l + 2w$ can be written as a product:
$p = 2l + 2w = 2(\underline{l} + \underline{w})$
2. A rectangle has length 13.7 cm and width 6.3 cm.
   a. Find the perimeter using the formula $p = 2l + 2w$.
   40 cm
   b. Find the perimeter using the new formula you wrote in Exercise 1.
   40 cm
3. Which formula is easier to use? Explain your answer.

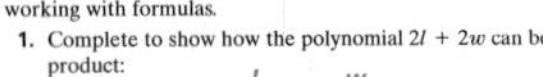
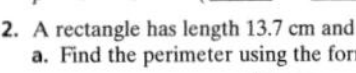
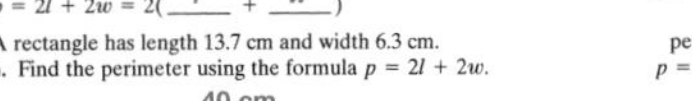
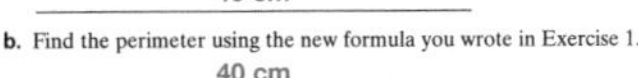

Sample answer is shown. The formula $p = 2(l + w)$ is easier to use because you only have to multiply by 2 once.

4. Complete to show how the polynomial $2\pi r^2 + 2\pi rh$ can be written as a product:
$S = 2\pi r^2 + 2\pi rh = 2\pi r(\underline{r} + \underline{h})$
5. A cylinder has radius 3 ft and height 5 ft.
   a. Find the surface area using the formula $S = 2\pi r^2 + 2\pi rh$. Use $\pi = 3.14$.
   150.72 $ft^2$
   b. Find the surface area using the new formula you wrote in Exercise 4.
   150.72 $ft^2$

cylinder

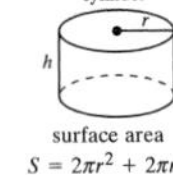


surface area

$S = 2\pi r^2 + 2\pi rh$

6. Which formula is easier to use? Explain your answer.
Sample answer is shown. The formula $S = 2\pi r(r + h)$ is easier to use because it involves fewer operations.
7. The formula for the amount ($A$) of money after a principle ($p$) is invested for $t$ years at an interest rate of $r$ is $A = p + prt$. Give another way to write the formula:
$A = p + prt = \underline{p}(\underline{1} + \underline{rt})$



**Use the GCF of the terms to write each expression as the product of two factors.** 50. $3g^2(6g^5 - 2g^2 + 1)$

43. $7x^2 - 14x$ $7x(x - 2)$
44. $24y^3 + 6y^2 - 20y$ $2y(12y^2 + 3y - 10)$
45. $14a^2 + 7a - 7$ $7(2a^2 + a - 1)$
46. $7p^2 + p$ $p(7p + 1)$
47. $5z^2 - 20z$ $5z(z - 4)$
48. $15x^3 + 4x^2 - 7x$ $x(15x^2 + 4x - 7)$
49. $-4x^5 - 4x^4 + 8x^2$ $4x^2(-x^3 - x^2 + 2)$
50. $18g^7 - 6g^4 + 3g^2$ See above.
51. $12a^3 - 16a^2 - 4a$ $4a(3a^2 - 4a - 1)$
52. $4m^9 + 6m^5 - 2m^2$ $2m^2(2m^7 + 3m^3 - 1)$
53. $2a^2 + ab$ $a(2a + b)$
54. $2m^3n - 6m^2n^2 + 8mn$ $2mn(m^2 - 3mn + 4)$
55. *Open-ended* Write a monomial and a polynomial with 4 terms. Multiply them and then simplify the product. Check students' work.

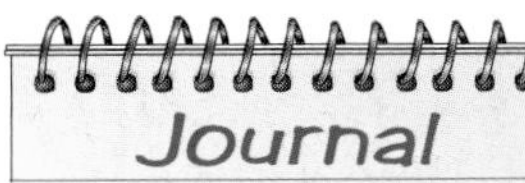

**Journal**

*Explain how to use the GCF to write the polynomial $15a^3 + 20a^2 + 45a$ as the product of two factors.*

*Geometry* **Write an expression to represent the area of each figure. Then simplify the expression.** 56. $\ell\left(\frac{1}{2}\ell + 7\right) = \frac{1}{2}\ell^2 + 7\ell$

56. The width of a rectangle is 7 more than $\frac{1}{2}$ its length. See above.
57. The length of a rectangle is 5 less than 4 times its width. $w(4w - 5) = 4w^2 - 5w$
58. The base length of a triangle is $8x$. The triangle's height is twice the base length plus 5. $\frac{1}{2} \cdot 8x(2 \cdot 8x + 5) = 64x^2 + 20x$
59. The height of an isosceles triangle is 3 less than $\frac{1}{3}$ its base. $\frac{1}{2}b\left(\frac{1}{3}b - 3\right) = \frac{1}{6}b^2 - \frac{3}{2}b$

## Mixed Review

**Find each sum or difference.** *(Lesson 13-5)*

60. $(2x + 8) + (3x^2 + 5x - 2)$ $3x^2 + 7x + 6$
61. $(-7x^2 - 8x + 4) - (2x^2 - 3x - 9)$ $-9x^2 - 5x + 13$

**Display each set of data in a line plot.** *(Lesson 12-1)*

62. 1.7, 2.1, 1.9, 2.1, 2.2, 2.4, 2.3, 2.1, 1.9 See margin.
63. 13, 17, 15, 14, 12, 14, 11, 13, 15

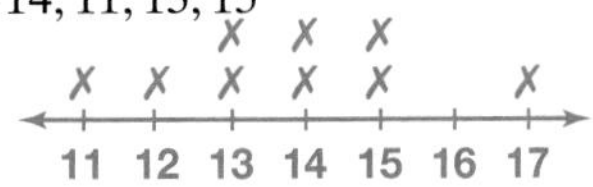


64. *Choose a Strategy* A college student received a bank statement. The new balance was $200. It showed deposits of $400, interest of $1, and checks totaling $650. What was the beginning balance? $449

## Chapter Project 13

## Activity 3 Writing

For the volume of the large cube that you created in Activity 1, write a polynomial in terms of the cube's edge length. Then write and simplify a polynomial for the volume as the sum of the volumes of the parts of the cube. Write an equation that compares the two polynomials.



See also Extra Practice section.

62.

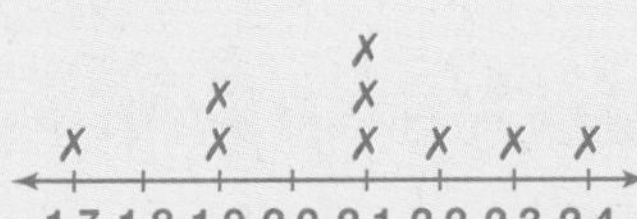


### Project Activity 3

**Writing** Again, you may wish to have students write these polynomials using the numbers they chose originally as values for $a$ and $b$. The volume of the large cube is $(a + b)^3$, which is equal to $(a^3 + 3a^2b + 3ab^2 + b^3)$.

# Standardized Test Prep

## Multiple Choice

**Choose the best answer.**

1. In the figure, $m\angle LPN = 70°$, $m\angle MPO = 60°$, and $m\angle LPO = 100°$. Find $m\angle MPN$. C

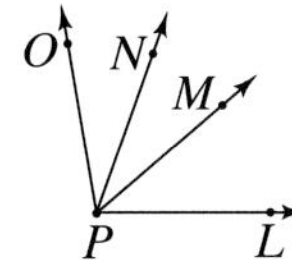


A. 40° B. 20° C. 30° D. 10°

2. U.S. car sales are shown in the graph below. Suppose the total number of cars sold was 8 million. How many luxury cars were sold? F

**U.S. Car Sales**

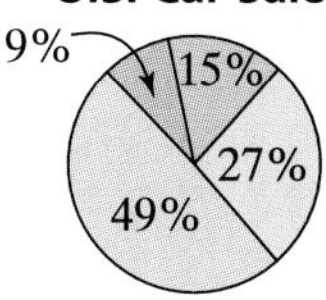


Luxury
Small
Midsize
Large

F. 1,200,000 G. 21,600,000
H. 2,160,000 J. 120,000,000

3. The box-and-whisker plot represents the scores on a 100-point test. What is the difference between the upper quartile and lower quartile scores? D

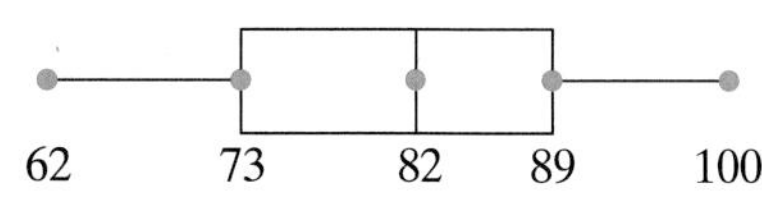


A. 27 B. 20 C. 38 D. 16

4. How many *C* boxes are needed to balance one *A* box? J

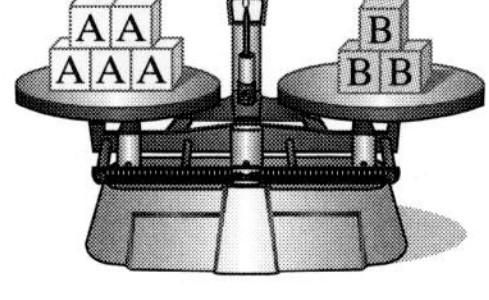


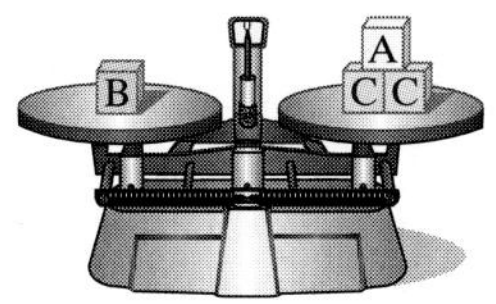


F. 2 G. 6 H. 4.5 J. 3

## Free Response

**For Exercises 5–13, show your work.**

5. A bird flying 200 ft above the ground drops a stick from its beak. The equation $d = 200 - 16t^2$ gives the vertical distance $d$, in feet, that the stick drops in $t$ seconds.
   a. Make a table with integer values of $t$ from 0 to 4. Then graph the function. See back of book
   b. Use your graph to estimate the vertical distance the stick falls in $1\frac{1}{2}$ s. about 160 ft
   c. Estimate the time until the stick hits the ground. 3.5 sec

**Graph each linear equation or inequality.** 6–9. See back of book.

6. $y = -2x$
7. $y = 2x$
8. $y = 2x - 1$
9. $y \leq 2x - 2$

**The table lists the grams of fat and the number of calories in 1-oz servings of cheese.**

| Type of Cheese | Fat (g) | Calories |
|---|---|---|
| American | 8.9 | 106 |
| Blue | 8.2 | 100 |
| Cheddar | 9.4 | 114 |
| Colby | 9.1 | 112 |
| Limburger | 7.7 | 93 |
| Mozzarella | 6.1 | 80 |
| Provolone | 7.6 | 100 |
| Swiss | 7.8 | 107 |

SOURCE: *The T-Factor Fat Gram Counter*

10. Make a (fat, calories) scatter plot. See back of book.
11. Use the scatter plot to describe the correlation between the number of grams of fat and the number of calories. It is a positive correlation.

**For each function, make a table with integer values of *x* from 0 to 3. Then graph each function.** 12–13. See margin.

12. $y = -3(2)^x$
13. $y = 2x^3$



12.

| $x$ | $-3(2)^x$ | $y$ | $(x, y)$ |
|---|---|---|---|
| 0 | $-3(2)^0$ | −3 | (0, −3) |
| 1 | $-3(2)^1$ | −6 | (1, −6) |
| 2 | $-3(2)^2$ | −12 | (2, −12) |
| 3 | $-3(2)^3$ | −24 | (3, −24) |

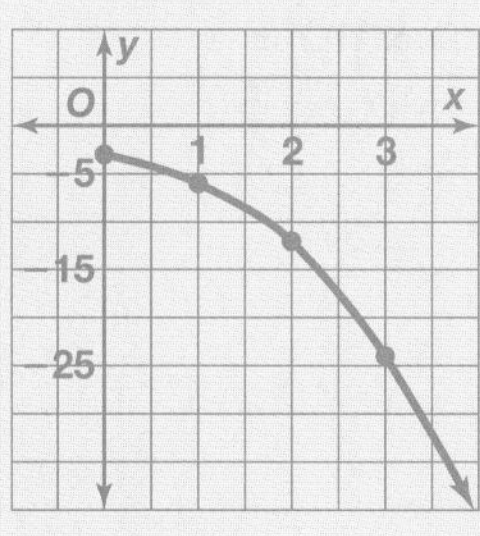


13.

| $x$ | $2x^3$ | $y$ | $(x, y)$ |
|---|---|---|---|
| 0 | $2 \cdot 0^3$ | 2 | (0, 2) |
| 1 | $2 \cdot 1^3$ | 2 | (1, 2) |
| 2 | $2 \cdot 2^3$ | 16 | (2, 16) |
| 3 | $2 \cdot 3^3$ | 54 | (3, 54) |

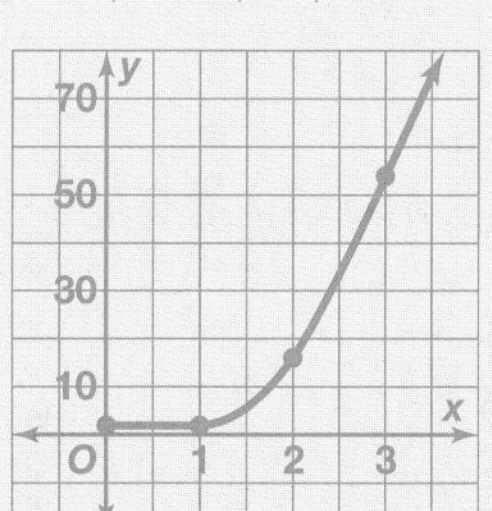


## Standardized Test Prep

Standardized tests, such as those administered for state assessment, SAT9, TerraNova™, ITBS, MAT7, or CAT5, may include multiple choice questions, free-response questions, and open-ended questions.

**Multiple Choice Questions** are followed usually by four choices, one of which is correct.

**Exercises 1–4** are multiple choice questions.

**Free-Response Questions** do not give answer choices. Student must provide the one correct answer on their own.

**Exercises 5–13** are free-response questions.

### Resources

See p. 661G for a list of assessment options.

### Test-Taking Tip

Be sure to label completely and clearly the graphs to answer free-response questions.

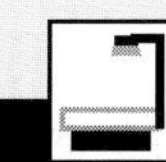

**Test-Taking Tips on Transparency**

Use patterns to find a missing value or rule in a table.

*Example* Write a word equation describing how the input and output numbers are related in the table below.

| Input | 1 | 2 | 3 | 4 |
|---|---|---|---|---|
| Output | −4 | −8 | −12 | −16 |

A. *output* = *input* + 4 B. *output* = 4 × *input*
C. *output* = −4 × *input* D. *input* = −4 × *output*

To find the pattern, look for a relationship between the numbers in the first row and the second row.

×(−4) 1 → −4 ×(−4) 2 → −8 ×(−4) 3 → −12 ×(−4) 4 → −16

Each number in row 2 is −4 times the number in row 1.

The answer is *output* = −4 × *input*, or choice C.

Look for a pattern to find the answer. Explain your reasoning.

1. Complete the function table below. Write in your response on the grid found on the answer sheet.

| Input | 2 | 4 | 6 | 8 | 10 |
|---|---|---|---|---|---|
| Output | 7 | 13 | 19 | 25 | |

2. Complete the function table below.

| Input (ft) | 1 | 2 | 3 | 4 | 5 |
|---|---|---|---|---|---|
| Output (in.) | 12 | 24 | 36 | 48 | |

A. 5 B. 60 C. 48 D. Not Here

# 13-7

## Getting Ready

**Materials** algebra tiles

**Resources** A complete list of resources for this lesson is on p. 661H.

### Daily Skills Warm-Up

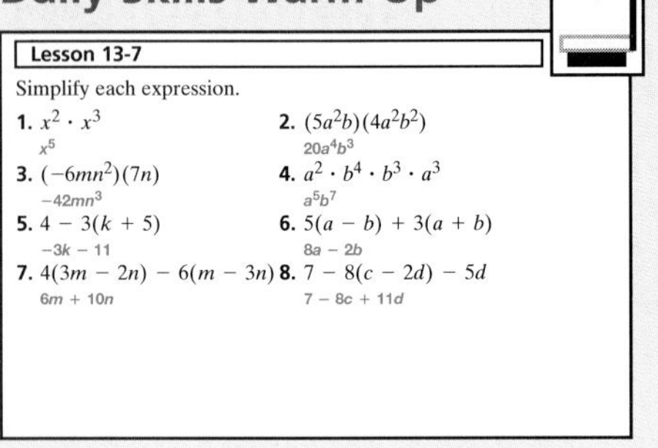
Lesson 13-7

Simplify each expression.

1. $x^2 \cdot x^3$ — $x^5$
2. $(5a^2b)(4a^2b^2)$ — $20a^4b^3$
3. $(-6mn^2)(7n)$ — $-42mn^3$
4. $a^2 \cdot b^4 \cdot b^3 \cdot a^3$ — $a^5b^7$
5. $4 - 3(k + 5)$ — $-3k - 11$
6. $5(a - b) + 3(a + b)$ — $8a - 2b$
7. $4(3m - 2n) - 6(m - 3n)$ — $6m + 10n$
8. $7 - 8(c - 2d) - 5d$ — $7 - 8c + 11d$

### Background for the Lesson

To multiply a binomial by another binomial, you can use the Distributive Property. After students have practiced using the Distributive Property, they may want to use a shorter method called the FOIL method. FOIL stands for First, Outer, Inner, Last. This mnemonic reminds you that the first step is to multiply the First terms in each binomial. Then, multiply the Inner terms and add their product to the product of the Outer terms. Finally, multiply the Last terms.

### Connecting to Prior Knowledge

In Lesson 13-6, students multiplied a polynomial by a monomial. In this lesson, students learn how to multiply binomials. In the Math Toolbox, students will use the inverse of this process.



# 13-7 Multiplying Binomials

**What You'll Learn**

1. To use models in multiplying binomials
2. To multiply two binomials

**. . . And Why**

To find the areas of geometric figures

## Part 1 Using Models

You can use tiles to find the product of two binomials.

### Example 1

**Simplify $(x + 2)(x + 4)$.**

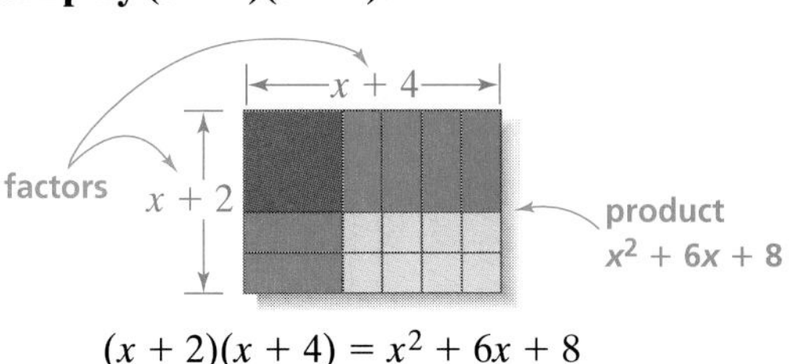


$$(x + 2)(x + 4) = x^2 + 6x + 8$$

The area is $x^2 + 6x + 8$.

**Try This** Simplify each product using models.

1. $(x + 2)(x + 3)$ $x^2 + 5x + 6$
2. $(y + 1)(y + 4)$ $y^2 + 5y + 4$

## Part 2 Using the Distributive Property

You can use the Distributive Property to simplify the product of two binomials. If you think of one binomial as a single expression, you can use the distributive property twice to simplify the product.

### Example 2

**Simplify $(x + 4)(x - 3)$.**

$(x + 4)(x - 3)$

$= x(x - 3) + 4(x - 3)$ Use the Distributive Property.

$= x^2 - 3x + 4x - 12$ Use the Distributive Property again!

$= x^2 + x - 12$ Simplify.



# Tools to Monitor Progress

**BEFORE THE LESSON**

**To check prerequisite skills:**

- Using the Distributive Property

**Skills You Need,** p. 661

**Skills Handbook,** p. 725

**Skills Intervention Kit,** Whole Numbers

**DURING THE LESSON**

**To check understanding:**

**Try This** exercises on student page

- **Additional Example 1**

  Simplify $(x + 3)(x + 5)$.
  $x^2 + 8x + 15$

■ **TRY THIS** Simplify each product.

**3.** $(x + 2)(x - 5)$ $x^2 - 3x - 10$ **4.** $(m + 2)(2m + 3)$ $2m^2 + 7m + 6$

## ■ Different Ways to Solve a Problem

**Write a polynomial to express the area of the square at the right.**

$(2x + 1)$ in.

**Method 1**

Use a model.

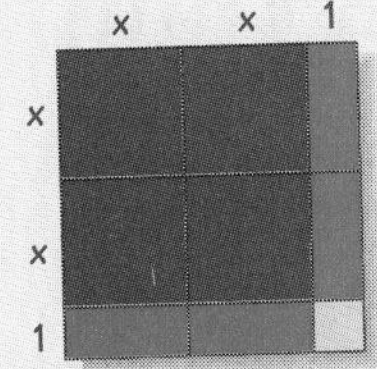


The area of the square is $(4x^2 + 4x + 1)$ in.$^2$.

**Method 2**

Use the formula for the area of a square and the Distributive Property.

$$\begin{aligned} \text{Area} &= \text{side}^2 \\ A &= (2x + 1)^2 \\ &= (2x + 1)(2x + 1) \\ &= 2x(2x + 1) + 1(2x + 1) \\ &= 2x(2x) + 2x(1) + 1(2x) + 1(1) \\ &= 4x^2 + 2x + 2x + 1 \\ &= 4x^2 + 4x + 1 \end{aligned}$$

The area of the square is $(4x^2 + 4x + 1)$ in.$^2$.

**Choose a Method**

1. Which method do you prefer to use? Explain.
2. Which method would you use to simplify $(3x + 4)(3x + 4)$?

1. Answers may vary. Sample: Method 1; it helps me see the relationship between the polynomial and the area.

2. Answers may vary. Sample: Method 2; method 1 requires too many pieces.



# 2 Teach

## Part 1 Teaching Notes

You may wish to have students work in small groups for the examples with tiles.

### ■ Example 1

**Build understanding.** Ask: Why does the product of the two binomials have an $x^2$-term when the binomials do not? The $x$-term in one of the binomials is multiplied by the $x$-term in the other binomial, resulting in an $x^2$-term.

## Part 2 Teaching Notes

Write two binomials on the board and ask students to suggest ways to multiply them. One way is to use long multiplication to multiply each term of one by each term of the other.

### ■ Example 2

**Build understanding.** Describe how the Distributive Property is used in the first step of the simplification. One binomial is multiplied by each of the terms of the other binomial.

**Error Prevention** When using the Distributive Property to multiply binomials, multiply *both* terms in the first binomial by *both* terms in the second binomial.

**Extension** Suggest that students research the FOIL method of multiplying binomials and then share their results to the class.

### ■ Different Ways to Solve a Problem

**Build understanding.** Ask: Why might knowing how to multiply binomials without tiles be useful? sample answer: in case you need to solve a problem and you do not have tiles

- **Additional Example 2**

Simplify $(b + 2)(3b - 1)$. $3b^2 + 5b - 2$

**AFTER THE LESSON**

**To assess knowledge:**

**Lesson Quiz**

Simplify each product.

1. $(r + 7)(r - 8)$

$r^2 - r - 56$
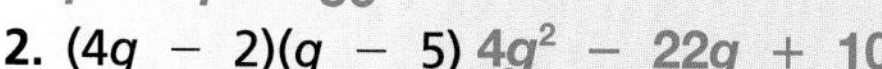
2. $(4g - 2)(g - 5)$ $4g^2 - 22g + 10$
3. $(9 + z)(1 + 2z)$ $9 + 19z + 2z^2$
4. $(n - 15)(n + 16)$ $n^2 + n - 240$

- For enrichment and reteaching options see Resources on p. 661H.

# 3 Practice/Assess

## Assignment Guide

To provide flexible scheduling, this lesson can be divided into parts.

▼ Part 1

**Core** 1–6, 14–16

▼ Part 2

**Core** 7–13, 17–31, 34–36

✪ **Extension** 32–33

Mixed Review can be assigned at any time for maintenance.

## Exercises

**Tactile Learning** **Exercises 1–6** Use your tiles to model the same problem with the factors exchanged.

## ✪ Challenge

Simplify $(w + x)(y + z)$.

$wy + xy + wz + xz$

## Closure

You can use tiles to model the product of two binomials. When you use the Distributive Property to find the product of two binomials, you use the Distributive Property twice.

# Exercises

## CHECK UNDERSTANDING

**Simplify each product using a model.**

**1.** $(x + 2)(x + 1)$ $x^2 + 3x + 2$
**2.** $(x + 2)(x + 2)$ $x^2 + 4x + 4$
**3.** $(x + 3)(x + 1)$ $x^2 + 4x + 3$

**4.** $(x + 3)(x + 4)$ $x^2 + 7x + 12$
**5.** $(x + 4)(x + 5)$ $x^2 + 9x + 20$
**6.** $(x + 9)(x + 3)$ $x^2 + 12x + 27$

**Simplify each product.**

**7.** $(x + 2)(x - 1)$ $x^2 + x - 2$
**8.** $(c + 7)(c + 9)$ $c^2 + 16c + 63$
**9.** $(x - 5)(x + 3)$ $x^2 - 2x - 15$

**10.** $(a - 4)(a - 2)$ $a^2 - 6a + 8$
**11.** $(x + 5)(x + 5)$ $x^2 + 10x + 25$
**12.** $(b + 6)(b - 6)$ $b^2 - 36$

**13.** *Error Analysis* A student simplifies $(x + 5)(x - 3)$. Find the error in the work at the right.
The student neglected to distribute the 5 to the −3. The third line should read $x^2 - 3x + 5x - 15$.

$(x + 5)(x - 3)$
$x(x - 3) + 5(x - 3)$
$x^2 - 3x + 5x - 3$
$x^2 - 2x - 3$

24. $n^2 + 4n - 320$
26. $b^2 + 13b + 12$
27. $m^2 - 11m + 24$

## PRACTICE AND PROBLEM SOLVING

**Find the area of each rectangle.**

**14.**

$x + 3$

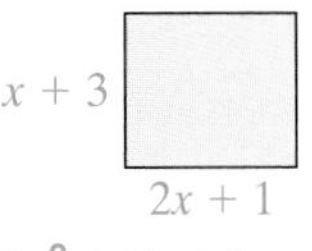

$2x + 1$

$2x^2 + 7x + 3$

**15.**

$2c + 4$

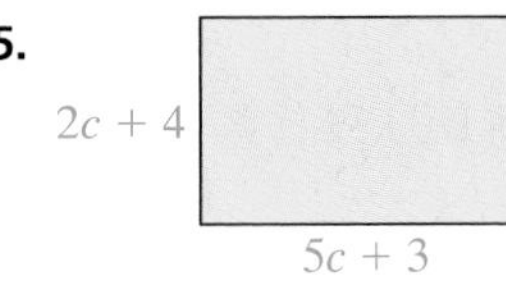

$5c + 3$

$10c^2 + 26c + 12$

**16.**

$4n - 5$

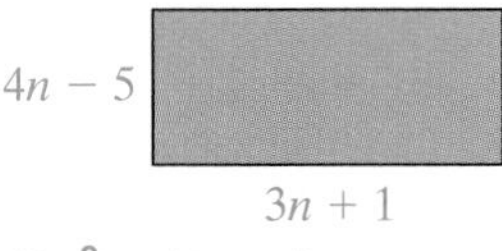

$3n + 1$

$12n^2 - 11n - 5$

**Simplify each product.**

**17.** $(x + 3)(x + 6)$ $x^2 + 9x + 18$
**18.** $(a - 7)(a + 5)$ $a^2 - 2a - 35$
**19.** $(m + 1)(m + 6)$ $m^2 + 7m + 6$

**20.** $(c + 3)(c - 4)$ $c^2 - c - 12$
**21.** $(x + 3)(x - 2)$ $x^2 + x - 6$
**22.** $(y + 3)(y + 8)$ $y^2 + 11y + 24$

**23.** $(x + 4)(2x + 1)$ $2x^2 + 9x + 4$
**24.** $(n - 16)(n + 20)$ See above right.
**25.** $(x + 2)(x + 8)$ $x^2 + 10x + 16$

**26.** $(b + 1)(b + 12)$ See above right.
**27.** $(m - 8)(m - 3)$ See above right.
**28.** $(3 + x)(5 - x)$ $15 + 2x - x^2$

**29.** $(3c + 1)(2c - 4)$ $6c^2 - 10c - 4$
**30.** $(2a + b)(4c - 2d)$ $8ac - 4ad + 4bc - 2bd$
**31.** $\left(\frac{1}{2}x + 9\right)(4x + 8)$ $2x^2 + 40x + 72$

✪**32.** *Patterns* Simplify $(y + 2)^2$, $(y + 3)^2$, and $(y + 4)^2$. What pattern do you see? $y^2 + 4y + 4$; $y^2 + 6y + 9$; $y^2 + 8y + 16$. The product is the sum of the square of the first term, twice the product of the two terms, and the square of the second term.

✪**33.** *Patterns* Simplify $(y + 1)(y - 1)$, $(y + 2)(y - 2)$, and $(y + 5)(y - 5)$. What pattern do you see? $y^2 - 1$; $y^2 - 4$; $y^2 - 25$. The product is a binomial consisting of the square of the first term minus the square of the second term.



## Daily Cumulative Review

**Simplify each product.** *(Lesson 13-6)*

1. $b(b^2 - 12)$ $b^3 - 12b$
2. $2n(5n - 3)$ $10n^2 - 6n$
3. $4x^2\left(x^2 - 6x + \frac{1}{2}\right)$ $4x^4 - 24x^3 + 2x^2$
4. $-5y(9y - 8)$ $-45y^2 + 40y$
5. $\frac{1}{2}a(6a - 10)$ $3a^2 - 5a$
6. $7y^2(y^2 - 5y - 4)$ $7y^4 - 35y^3 - 28y^2$

**Simplify each sum or difference.** *(Lesson 13-5)*

7. $(y^2 - 7y) + (2y - 5)$ $y^2 - 5y - 5$
8. $(3y^2 - 4y - 6) - (2y^2 + 10y - 5)$ $y^2 - 14y - 1$

**Mixed Review**

**Solve by drawing a diagram.**

9. *(9-4)* A class of 24 students voted on two choices of field trips. Fourteen students wanted to go to the art museum, 15 wanted to go to the science museum, and 8 wanted to go to both. How many didn't want to go to either? 3 students

**Write an equation. Solve.**

10. *(7-4)* Nathan is working in a fast food restaurant for $7.25 per hour. As an incentive to sell more hamburgers, the manager offers him $.02 bonus for each hamburger he rings up on the cash register. Last week Nathan worked 20 hours and earned $153.60 gross. How many hamburgers did he sell?
$145 + 0.02h = 153.60$; 430 hamburgers

**Find the distance between each pair of points. Round to the nearest tenth.**

11. *(11-3)* $(2, -3), (-4, 5)$ 10
12. *(11-3)* $(12, 7), (9, -1)$ 8.5

**Solve each equation.**

13. *(3-5)* $k + 7 = 2.8$ $k = -4.2$
14. *(3-5)* $y - (-2.1) = -5.63$ $y = -7.73$



## Alternative Assessment

Ask students to describe and explain the patterns and shortcuts they might use to multiply two binomials.

34. *Writing* Explain the similarities between multiplying two binomials and multiplying a polynomial by a monomial.

34. Answers may vary. Sample: Both can be done using the distributive property; one term is distributed when multiplying by a monomial, and two terms are distributed when multiplying two binomials.

35. *Geometry* The base of a parallelogram is $(w + 5)$ cm. The height is 2 cm less than the base. Find the area of the parallelogram. $(w^2 + 8w + 15)$ cm$^2$

36. **TEST PREP** Assume $m$ is an even integer. What is the product of the next two consecutive even integers? B

A. $m^2 + 3m + 2$ B. $m^2 + 6m + 8$
C. $m^2 + 2m$ D. $2m + 6$

## MIXED REVIEW

**Find each product.** *(Lesson 13-6)*

37. $7a(a + 5b + 2c)$ $7a^2 + 35ab + 14ac$

38. $-3xy(2x + 9y - 6)$ $-6x^2y - 27xy^2 + 18xy$

39. $8m^2(-4m^3 + mp + 2p^4)$ $-32m^5 + 8m^3p + 16m^2p^4$

**Make a box-and-whisker plot for the data.** *(Lesson 12-2)*

40. 8, 9, 27, 39, 14, 17, 13, 25, 15, 8, 11, 29, 36, 10, 15, 25

40. 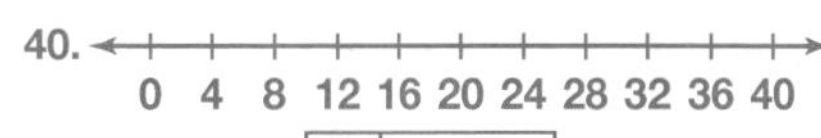


41. Does the problem below require *permutations* or *combinations?* Explain. *(Lesson 12-6)* Combinations, since the order of the colors is not important. There are 56 possible choices.

You select three colors from a choice of eight colors to paint a picture. How many 3-color choices are possible?

## CHECKPOINT 2 — Lessons 13-4 through 13-7

**Tell whether each polynomial is a *monomial,* a *binomial,* or a *trinomial.***

1. 178 monomial
2. $x + 15y$ binomial
3. $7pq$ monomial
4. $m^2 + 4m - 12$ trinomial

**Evaluate each polynomial for $x = -1$ and $y = 3$.**

5. $5x - y$ $-8$
6. $x + 3y$ 8
7. $-7x + x^2y$ 10
8. $4y^2 + 11x - 16$ 9

**Simplify each expression.** 11. $10p^2q + 16p^2q^2 + 4pq$

9. $(4a - b) + (3a + 5b)$ $7a + 4b$
10. $(x^2 + 7x - 4) + (x^2 + 9)$ $2x^2 + 7x + 5$
11. $2pq(5p + 8pq + 2)$ See above.
12. $(g + 6)(g + 4)$ $g^2 + 10g + 24$
13. $3m(-6m - 2m^2p - 10p)$ $-18m^2 - 6m^3p - 30mp$

14. *Open-ended* Write a binomial expression for the length of the side of a square. Write a polynomial to express the area of the square. Check students' work.

See also Extra Practice section.



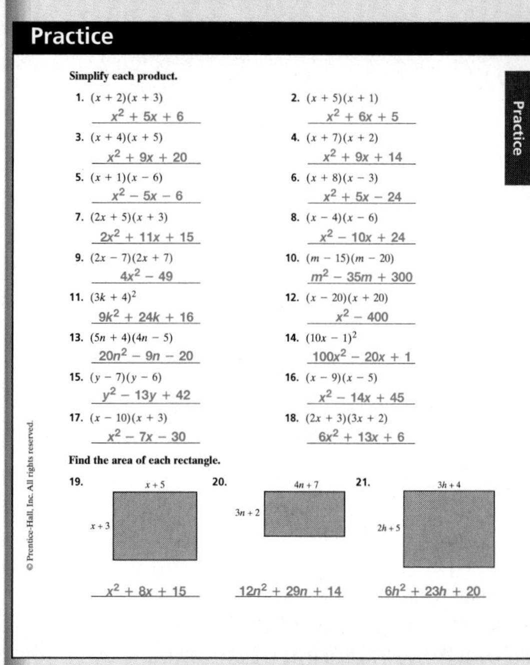

**Practice**

Simplify each product.

1. $(x + 2)(x + 3)$ $x^2 + 5x + 6$
2. $(x + 5)(x + 1)$ $x^2 + 6x + 5$
3. $(x + 4)(x + 5)$ $x^2 + 9x + 20$
4. $(x + 7)(x + 2)$ $x^2 + 9x + 14$
5. $(x + 1)(x - 6)$ $x^2 - 5x - 6$
6. $(x + 8)(x - 3)$ $x^2 + 5x - 24$
7. $(2x + 5)(x + 3)$ $2x^2 + 11x + 15$
8. $(x - 4)(x - 6)$ $x^2 - 10x + 24$
9. $(2x - 7)(2x + 7)$ $4x^2 - 49$
10. $(m - 15)(m - 20)$ $m^2 - 35m + 300$
11. $(3k + 4)^2$ $9k^2 + 24k + 16$
12. $(x - 20)(x + 20)$ $x^2 - 400$
13. $(5n + 4)(4n - 5)$ $20n^2 - 9n - 20$
14. $(10x - 1)^2$ $100x^2 - 20x + 1$
15. $(y - 7)(y - 6)$ $y^2 - 13y + 42$
16. $(x - 9)(x - 5)$ $x^2 - 14x + 45$
17. $(x - 10)(x + 3)$ $x^2 - 7x - 30$
18. $(2x + 3)(3x + 2)$ $6x^2 + 13x + 6$

Find the area of each rectangle.

19. $x + 5$ by $x + 3$: $x^2 + 8x + 15$
20. $4n + 7$ by $3n + 2$: $12n^2 + 29n + 14$
21. $3h + 4$ by $2h + 5$: $6h^2 + 23h + 20$



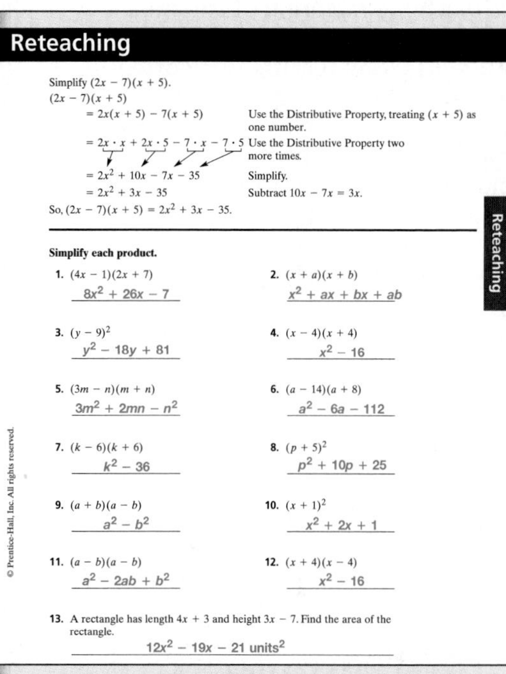

**Reteaching**

Simplify $(2x - 7)(x + 5)$.

$(2x - 7)(x + 5)$
$= 2x(x + 5) - 7(x + 5)$ Use the Distributive Property, treating $(x + 5)$ as one number.
$= 2x \cdot x + 2x \cdot 5 - 7 \cdot x - 7 \cdot 5$ Use the Distributive Property two more times.
$= 2x^2 + 10x - 7x - 35$ Simplify.
$= 2x^2 + 3x - 35$ Subtract $10x - 7x = 3x$.

So, $(2x - 7)(x + 5) = 2x^2 + 3x - 35$.

Simplify each product.

1. $(4x - 1)(2x + 7)$ $8x^2 + 26x - 7$
2. $(x + a)(x + b)$ $x^2 + ax + bx + ab$
3. $(y - 9)^2$ $y^2 - 18y + 81$
4. $(x - 4)(x + 4)$ $x^2 - 16$
5. $(3m - n)(m + n)$ $3m^2 + 2mn - n^2$
6. $(a - 14)(a + 8)$ $a^2 - 6a - 112$
7. $(k - 6)(k + 6)$ $k^2 - 36$
8. $(p + 5)^2$ $p^2 + 10p + 25$
9. $(a + b)(a - b)$ $a^2 - b^2$
10. $(x + 1)^2$ $x^2 + 2x + 1$
11. $(a - b)(a - b)$ $a^2 - 2ab + b^2$
12. $(x + 4)(x - 4)$ $x^2 - 16$

13. A rectangle has length $4x + 3$ and height $3x - 7$. Find the area of the rectangle. $12x^2 - 19x - 21$ units$^2$



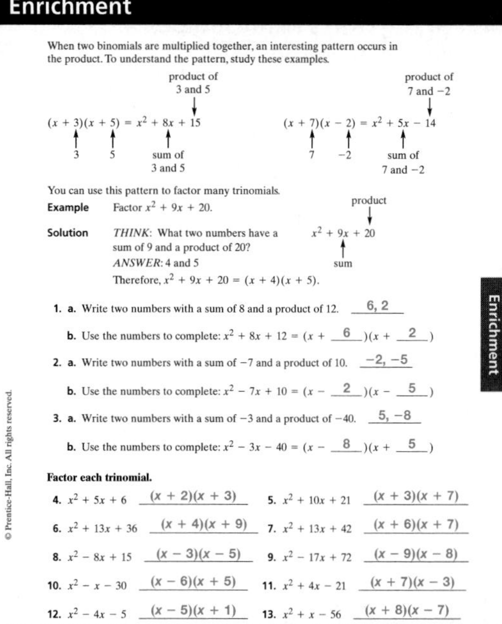

**Enrichment**

When two binomials are multiplied together, an interesting pattern occurs in the product. To understand the pattern, study these examples.

$(x + 3)(x + 5) = x^2 + 8x + 15$ (product of 3 and 5; sum of 3 and 5)

$(x + 7)(x - 2) = x^2 + 5x - 14$ (product of 7 and −2; sum of 7 and −2)

You can use this pattern to factor many trinomials.

Example Factor $x^2 + 9x + 20$.

Solution *THINK:* What two numbers have a sum of 9 and a product of 20? *ANSWER:* 4 and 5. Therefore, $x^2 + 9x + 20 = (x + 4)(x + 5)$.

1. a. Write two numbers with a sum of 8 and a product of 12. 6, 2
b. Use the numbers to complete: $x^2 + 8x + 12 = (x + 6)(x + 2)$
2. a. Write two numbers with a sum of −7 and a product of 10. −2, −5
b. Use the numbers to complete: $x^2 - 7x + 10 = (x - 2)(x - 5)$
3. a. Write two numbers with a sum of −3 and a product of −40. 5, −8
b. Use the numbers to complete: $x^2 - 3x - 40 = (x - 8)(x + 5)$

Factor each trinomial.

4. $x^2 + 5x + 6$ $(x + 2)(x + 3)$
5. $x^2 + 10x + 21$ $(x + 3)(x + 7)$
6. $x^2 + 13x + 36$ $(x + 4)(x + 9)$
7. $x^2 + 13x + 42$ $(x + 6)(x + 7)$
8. $x^2 - 8x + 15$ $(x - 3)(x - 5)$
9. $x^2 - 17x + 72$ $(x - 9)(x - 8)$
10. $x^2 - x - 30$ $(x - 6)(x + 5)$
11. $x^2 + 4x - 21$ $(x + 7)(x - 3)$
12. $x^2 - 4x - 5$ $(x - 5)(x + 1)$
13. $x^2 + x - 56$ $(x + 8)(x - 7)$



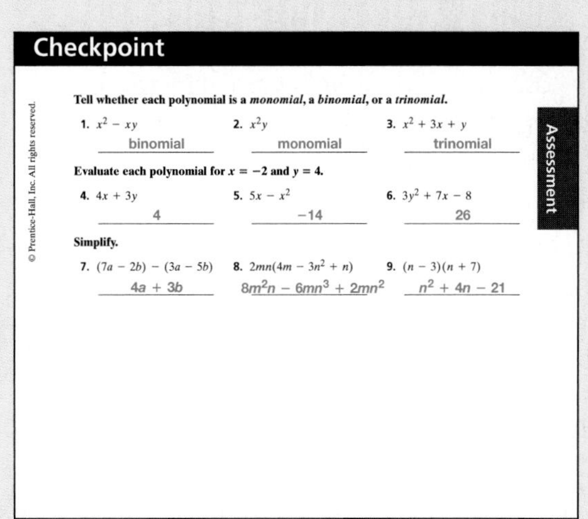

**Checkpoint**

Tell whether each polynomial is a *monomial,* a *binomial,* or a *trinomial.*

1. $x^2 - xy$ binomial
2. $x^2y$ monomial
3. $x^2 + 3x + y$ trinomial

Evaluate each polynomial for $x = -2$ and $y = 4$.

4. $4x + 3y$ 4
5. $5x - x^2$ −14
6. $3y^2 + 7x - 8$ 26

Simplify.

7. $(7a - 2b) - (3a - 5b)$ $4a + 3b$
8. $2mn(4m - 3n^2 + n)$ $8m^2n - 6mn^3 + 2mn^2$
9. $(n - 3)(n + 7)$ $n^2 + 4n - 21$

## MATH TOOLBOX

### Binomial Factors of a Trinomial

This Math Toolbox introduces students to factoring trinomials by modeling with algebra tiles.

### Math Background

Factoring a trinomial reverses the process of multiplying two binomial factors. There are a number of different ways to teach the factoring of trinomials. No matter which algebraic techniques students ultimately use, they often develop a better understanding of why those techniques work if you introduce the idea with the concrete models of algebra tiles so they can discover the principles involved.

## Teaching Notes

**Error Prevention** Give students plenty of time to explore and discover for themselves. Remind them that the width of the $x$-tile is 1 but the length of the $x$-tile is unknown and not a multiple of the unit tiles.

**Monitoring Progress** Exercises 1–9 At least two arrangements of the tiles (depending on which factor is first) are correct.

**Block Scheduling** If you have block scheduling or extended periods, you may wish to insert this Math Toolbox after the completion of Lesson 13-7.

MATH TOOLBOX

Extension

After Lesson 13-7

# *Binomial Factors of a Trinomial*

You can sometimes write a trinomial as the product of two binomial factors. You can use algebra tiles to find the factors. Use tiles to form a rectangle. The lengths of the sides of the rectangle are the factors of the trinomial.

**EXAMPLE**

**Write $x^2 + 4x + 3$ as the product of two binomial factors.**

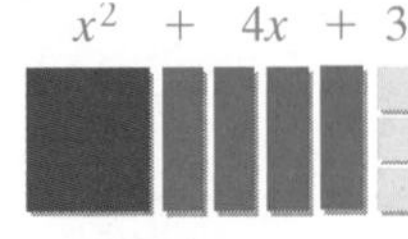


Model the trinomial.

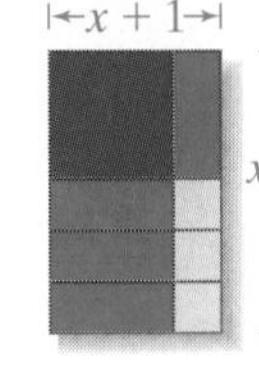


Use the tiles to form a rectangle. The length is $(x + 3)$ and the width is $(x + 1)$.

$x^2 + 4x + 3 = (x + 3)(x + 1)$

**Use tiles to find binomial factors of each trinomial.**

1. $x^2 + 2x + 1$ $(x + 1)^2$
2. $x^2 + 5x + 6$ $(x + 2)(x + 3)$
3. $x^2 + 7x + 10$ $(x + 2)(x + 5)$
4. $x^2 + 6x + 5$ $(x + 5)(x + 1)$
5. $x^2 + 4x + 4$ $(x + 2)^2$
6. $x^2 + 5x + 4$ $(x + 4)(x + 1)$
7. $x^2 + 9x + 8$ $(x + 8)(x + 1)$
8. $2x^2 + 5x + 3$ $(2x + 3)(x + 1)$
9. $2x^2 + 9x + 10$ $(2x + 5)(x + 2)$
10. *Critical Thinking* Complete $x^2 + \blacksquare x + 12$ with three different integers so that each trinomial has two binomial factors. For each trinomial, write the binomial factors. $x^2 + 13x + 12 = (x + 12)(x + 1)$; $x^2 + 8x + 12 = (x + 6)(x + 2)$; $x^2 + 7x + 12 = (x + 3)(x + 4)$
11. **a.** What two numbers have a sum of 11 and a product of 30? 5 and 6
    **b.** *Mathematical Reasoning* Use your answer to part (a) to find the binomial factors of $x^2 + 11x + 30$. $(x + 5)(x + 6)$



**• Additional Example**

Use tiles to find the binomial factors of $3x^2 + 4x + 1$. $(3x + 1)(x + 1)$

# Use Multiple Strategies

13-8

*Math Strategies in Action*

After a natural disaster such as an earthquake, a tornado, or a flood, relief workers help rescue survivors. They also bring food, clothing, and blankets to people who need them. Relief organizers use multiple strategies as they plan and coordinate their efforts.

In simple and complex situations in your own life, you already use multiple strategies. Remember when you learned how to ride a bike or fly a kite. The more you practiced, the less you had to think about the steps required to be successful.

In mathematics, you can use multiple strategies to solve problems. The more strategies you learn and the more you use them, the better problem solver you will be. Solving problems can become as easy as riding a bike or flying a kite!

**Problem Solving Strategies**

- Account for All Possibilities
- Draw a Diagram
- Look for a Pattern
- Make a Model
- Make a Table
- Simplify a Problem
- Simulate a Problem
- Solve by Graphing
- Try, Test, Revise
- Use Multiple Strategies
- Work Backward
- Write an Equation
- Write a Proportion

## SAMPLE PROBLEM

Suppose you receive instructions for building a kite. The writer of the instructions presents them as a puzzle:

> I fly above the clouds with my tail flowing behind me. My tail is 12 ft plus twice my length. Together, our length is 21 ft. How long am I? How long is my tail?

### Read

Read the problem carefully.

1. What do you want to find? the length of the kite and the length of the tail
2. What is the relationship between the length of the kite's tail and the length of the kite's body? The tail is 12 ft plus twice the length of the kite. Together, the two lengths total 21 ft.



# 13-8

## Getting Ready

**Resources** A complete list of resources for this lesson is on p. 661H.

### Daily Skills Warm-Up

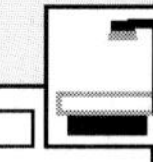

Lesson 13-8

Solve. What strategy did you use?

Leonardo invested some money and made a 6% profit. The current value of his investment is \$593.60. How much did he invest initially?

\$560 Sample answer: Write an equation.

### Background for the Lesson

The first task in solving a problem is to understand the situation that is described in the problem. Often it is helpful to use more than one problem solving strategy to solve a problem. You may want to Draw a Diagram, Make a Model, or Make a Table to grasp what is happening and what you need to find. You might then Work Backward, Simplify a Problem, or Look for a Pattern. If you can represent the situation mathematically, you might Write an Equation, Write a Proportion, or Solve by Graphing.

## 1 Focus

### Connecting to Students' Lives

Ask if any students fly kites regularly. Have these students explain the purpose of a kite's tail.

### Connecting to Prior Knowledge

In this textbook, students learned many problem solving strategies. In this lesson, students apply these strategies along with algebraic skills they have learned.

# Tools to Monitor Progress

## BEFORE THE LESSON

**To check prerequisite skills:**

- Dividing whole numbers

**Skills You Need,** p. 661

**Skills Handbook,** p. 726

**Skills Intervention Kit,** Whole Numbers

## DURING THE LESSON

**To check understanding:**

- **Additional Sample Problem**

For a given rectangle, the length is four ft more than three times the width. The perimeter of the same rectangle is 72 ft. Find the length and width. length = 28 ft, width = 8 ft

# 2 Teach

## Teaching Notes

You may want to have students work in groups to solve the sample problem. After students solve the problem by following the methods outlined in the text, have each group come up with one or two alternative methods for solving the problem. Ask the groups to share their alternative methods with the class.

### ■ Sample Problem

**Build understanding.** Ask: Why does finding the length of the kite's body allow you to find the length of the tail? You know the relationship between the length of the kite's body and the length of its tail.

**Extension** Using the same proportions, how long would the tail of the kite be if the body were 5 ft long? 32 ft

**Visual Learning** Challenge students to explain why drawing a diagram can help solve this problem. Could the problem be solved without the diagram?

**Error Prevention** Suggest that when students use multiple strategies to solve problems, they use strategies they are most familiar with to solve the problem. Explain that any strategies are valid as long as they work and can be understood by others.

**Connecting to History** There is no written record of when the first kite was invented. People in Asia have been flying kites for countless centuries. In the United States, the most famous kite in history has to be the one that Benjamin Franklin flew in a thunderstorm to test his hypothesis that lightning was a form of electricity. By the beginning of the 20th century, militaries were experimenting with large kites for aerial observations. However, this use was never fully developed because of the invention of the airplane.

### Plan

To get a visual picture of the problem, draw a diagram. Then write an equation to solve the problem.

### Solve

Draw a diagram.

Let $b$ = length of the body of the kite.

Write an equation.

| | |
|---|---|
| $3b + 12 = 21$ | Use the diagram to write an equation. |
| $3b + 12 - 12 = 21 - 12$ | Subtract 12 from each side. |
| $3b = 9$ | Simplify. |
| $\frac{3b}{3} = \frac{9}{3}$ | Divide each side by 3. |
| $b = 3$ | |

The kite is 3 ft long. Now find the length of the tail.

| | |
|---|---|
| length of tail $= 2b + 12$ | Use the diagram to write an expression for the length of the tail. |
| $= 2(3) + 12$ | Replace $b$ with the length of the kite's body. |
| $= 18$ | Simplify. |

The tail is 18 ft long.

### Look Back

Check the answer using the original problem.

**3. a.** The original problem says that the tail must be 12 ft plus twice the length of the kite's body. Show that the lengths found meet this condition. $18 = 12 + 2 \cdot 3$

**b.** The length of the kite's body plus the length of its tail must be 21 ft. Show that the lengths found meet this condition. $18 + 3 = 21$



- **Additional Sample Problem**
  A grocer stacks apples in the shape of a square pyramid. How many apples will he use if the bottom edge of the pyramid has 6 apples? 91 apples

## AFTER THE LESSON

**To assess knowledge:**
**Lesson Quiz**

Solve using multiple strategies.

Emilio is four years more than half his sister Rosa's age. The sum of their ages is 28. How old are they? Emilio is 12 and Rosa is 16.

- For enrichment and reteaching options see Resources on p. 661H.

# Exercises

## CHECK UNDERSTANDING

**Use multiple strategies to solve each problem.**

1. A bus traveling 40 mi/h left Freetown at noon. A car following the bus at 60 mi/h left Freetown at 1:30 P.M.
   a. At what time did the car catch up with the bus? 4:30 P.M.
   b. How many miles were the car and the bus from Freetown when the car caught up with the bus? 180 mi
2. A student playing a computer chess game gets 5 points every time he wins a round. The computer gets 3 points every time it wins a round. They play 64 rounds and end with a tie score. How many rounds did the computer win? 40 rounds
3. A kite and its tail total 36 ft in length. The tail is five times the length of the body. How long is the kite's tail? 30 ft

## PRACTICE AND PROBLEM SOLVING

**Solve using any strategy.**

4. A student has \$8 to spend on a phone call to a friend. The cost of a call is \$.34 for the first minute and \$.24 for each additional minute. How long can the student talk to his friend? 32 min
5. *Construction* A painter places an 8.5-ft-long ladder against a wall. The bottom of the ladder is 4 ft from the base of the wall. How high up the wall does the ladder reach? 7.5 ft
6. *Geometry* There are 27 white cubes assembled to form a large cube. The outside surface of the large cube is painted red. The large cube is then separated into the 27 smaller cubes. How many of the small cubes will have red paint on exactly the following number of faces?
   a. three faces 8 b. two faces 12 c. one face 6 d. no face 1
7. A room has a floor area of 1,025 $ft^2$ and a 10-ft-high ceiling. Occupancy guidelines recommend at least 200 $ft^3$ per person. What is the maximum number of people allowed in the room? 51 people
8. A student weighs her hamsters two at a time. Sandy and White Ears weigh 209 g together. White Ears and Sport weigh 223 g together. Sandy and Sport weigh 216 g together. How much does each hamster weigh? Sandy 101 g, White Ears 108 g, Sport 115 g



# 3 Practice/Assess

## Assignment Guide

**Core** 1–8, 10–12, 14, 15
**Extension** 9, 13

Mixed Review can be assigned at any time for maintenance.

## Exercises

### Auditory Learning Exercises 1–3

Discuss these problems with a partner to decide on your problem solving strategies before you attempt to solve them.

### Challenge

Carlo has an equation for the height of a model rocket *s* seconds after takeoff. As he increases the number of seconds, he notices that the height first goes up, then goes down. Use multiple strategies to explain why. The rocket eventually runs out of fuel and begins falling back to Earth.

## Closure

You can use multiple strategies to solve problems.

## Alternative Assessment

Have students write a problem that may be solved by using multiple problem solving strategies. Have students test their problems with a partner, and then share them with the class.

## Daily Cumulative Review

**Simplify each product.** *(Lesson 13-7)*

1. $(x + 7)(x + 8)$ $x^2 + 15x + 56$
2. $(x + 6)(x - 5)$ $x^2 + x - 30$
3. $(2x - 1)(x - 9)$ $2x^2 - 19x + 9$
4. $(y - 4)(y - 10)$ $y^2 - 14y + 40$
5. $(y + 3)(y + 11)$ $y^2 + 14y + 33$
6. $(3x - 2)(x + 5)$ $3x^2 + 13x - 10$

**Use the GCF of the terms to write each expression as the product of two factors.** *(Lesson 13-6)*

7. $9x^2 - 18x$ $9x(x - 2)$
8. $7a^2 + 3ab$ $a(7a + 3b)$
9. $5m^6 - 15m^4 + 30m^2$ $5m^2(m^4 - 3m^2 + 6)$

**Mixed Review**

**Display each set of data in a line plot.**

10. (12-1) 5 4 3 5 3 5 8 6 5 5 3 6 4 6

3 4 5 6 7 8

11. (12-1) 29 30 27 28 25 30 27 27 26 30 25 26 28 29 28 26

25 26 27 28 29 30

**You randomly select a card from those at the right. Without replacing the card, you select a second card. Find the probability of selecting each set of letters.**

S P R I N G
T I M E S

12. (12-5) N and then I $\frac{1}{55}$
13. (12-5) two vowels $\frac{3}{55}$
14. (12-5) two consonants $\frac{28}{55}$

**Solve each equation.**

15. (7-1) $4x - 7 = 13$ 5
16. (7-1) $\frac{b}{3} + 8 = 4$ −12
17. (7-2) $7x - 5x = 24$ 12
18. (7-2) $y - 8y = -42$ 6
19. (7-5) $8n - 7 = 9n$ −7
20. (7-5) $3x + \frac{1}{3}(15x - 18) = -22$ −2

## Practice

**Use multiple strategies to solve each problem.**

1. A rectangle has length $(x - 3)^2$ and width 4. The perimeter of the rectangle is 40. Find the length.
   16
2. A rectangular prism has length $x + 2$, width $x + 1$, height 4, and volume 24. Find the length and the width.
   3 and 2
3. A piece of cardboard measures 12 ft by 12 ft. Corners are to be cut from it as shown by the broken lines, and the sides folded up to make a box with an open top. What size corners should be cut from the cardboard to make a box with the greatest possible volume?
   2 ft by 2 ft
4. What size corners should be cut from a piece of cardboard that measures 30 in. by 30 in. to make an open-top box with the greatest possible volume?
   5 in. by 5 in.
5. What is the maximum number of small boxes that can fit inside the large box?
   64 boxes
   
6. The perimeter of a right triangle is 24 in. Find the dimensions of the triangle if the sides are all whole-number lengths.
   6 in., 8 in., 10 in.



## Reteaching

A rectangular prism has length 5 cm, width $(x + 1)$ cm, height $(x + 3)$ cm, and volume 120 $cm^3$. Find the width and the height.



To get a visual picture of the problem, draw a diagram. Label the dimensions. Next, write an equation.

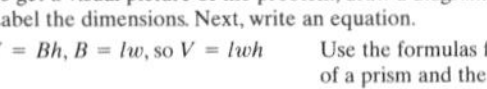

$V = Bh, B = lw$, so $V = lwh$ — Use the formulas for the volume of a prism and the area of a rectangle.

$V = lwh$

$120 = 5(x + 1)(x + 3)$ — Substitute 120 for $V$, 5 for $l$, $x + 1$ for $w$ and $x + 3$ for $h$.

$\frac{120}{5} = \frac{5(x + 1)(x + 3)}{5}$ — Divide each side by 5.

$24 = (x + 1)(x + 3)$ — Simplify.

**Use Try, Test, Revise to find $x$. Organize tests in a table.**

| $x$ | $x + 1$ | $x + 3$ | $(x + 1)(x + 3)$ | Comment |
|---|---|---|---|---|
| 2 | 3 | 5 | 15 | Too low |
| 4 | 5 | 7 | 35 | Too high |
| 3 | 4 | 6 | 24 | $x = 3$ |

If $x = 3, x + 1 = 3 + 1 = 4$
$x + 3 = 3 + 3 = 6$

The width of the prism is 4 cm and the height is 6 cm.
Check: $V = 5 \cdot 4 \cdot 6 = 120\ cm^3$ ✓

**Use multiple strategies to solve each problem.**

1. The product of two whole numbers is 36. What is the greatest possible sum that the numbers can have?
   37 (1 and 36)
2. The sum of two numbers is 14. What is the greatest possible product that the numbers can have?
   49 (7 and 7)
3. A rectangle has length $k + 6$ and width $k - 6$. The area of the rectangle is 64. Find the length and the width.
   16 and 4



## Enrichment

Because of gravity, a free falling object falls faster and faster, or *accelerates*, as it descends. The distance ($d$) in feet that an object falls in $t$ seconds is given by the equation $d = 16t^2$.

1. A penny thrown into a wishing well takes 3 s to reach the bottom. How deep is the well?
   144 ft
2. Complete the table showing how far an object falls each of the first 8 s.

| $t$ (s) | 1 | 2 | 3 | 4 | 5 | 6 | 7 | 8 |
|---|---|---|---|---|---|---|---|---|
| $d$ (ft) | 16 | 64 | 144 | 256 | 400 | 576 | 784 | 1,024 |

3. How far does an object fall during the fifth second (from $t = 4$ to $t = 5$)?
   144 ft
   during the sixth second? 176 ft
   during the seventh second? 208 ft
4. How much farther does an object fall during the eighth second than it falls during the seventh second?
   32 ft
   during the fifth second than during the fourth second? 32 ft
   during the third second than during the second second? 32 ft

You can use the division property to write a new free-fall equation.

5. Complete: If $d = 16t^2$, then $t^2 = \frac{d}{16}$

**Use your new equation to solve. You may wish to use a calculator.**

6. A rock fell from the top of a 2,304-ft cliff to the base of the cliff. For how long did the rock fall?
   12 s
7. A rivet falls off an airplane from 28,224 ft. How long does is take the rivet to hit the ground?
   42 s





9. *Geometry* A circle has a circumference of 20 cm and a square has a perimeter of 20 cm.
   a. What is the area of the circle? 31.8 $cm^2$
   b. What is the area of the square? 25 $cm^2$
   c. Which figure has the greater area? the circle
10. A student decided to purchase a new telephone. He could choose from 8 different models, 2 different cord lengths, and 4 different colors. How many possible choices did he have? 64 choices
11. A clerk starts working at a beginning salary of $10,400 with an annual increase of $400. An assistant clerk who starts at the same time has a starting salary of $9,600 per year with an annual increase of $600.
    a. Who earns more after 3 years? the clerk
    b. After how many years will the assistant be earning more money than the clerk? after 5 years
12. *Geometry* A lot measures 50 ft by 100 ft. The house on the lot measures 25 ft by 50 ft. What is the area of the lawn? 3,750 $ft^2$
13. A student spends $\frac{1}{3}$ of her money on a movie and $\frac{1}{4}$ of the remaining amount on a snack after the movie. She now has $12 left. How much money did she originally have? $24
14. List the different ways you can give change from a $100 bill for a $78 purchase without using coins and without giving a customer more than seven singles.
15. Each face of a cube can be painted either red or yellow. How many different ways can you paint the cube? 7

14. 1 ten, 1 five, 7 ones; 3 fives, 7 ones; 2 tens, 2 ones; 4 fives, 2 ones; 1 ten, 2 fives, 2 ones; 1 twenty, 2 ones

## Mixed Review

**Simplify.** ***(Lesson 13-7)***

16. $(x + 1)(x - 3)$ $x^2 - 2x - 3$
17. $(d + 2)(2d + 5)$ $2d^2 + 9d + 10$
18. $(x + 3)^2$ $x^2 + 6x + 9$

**Make a list to find the number of two-letter combinations you can form from each group of letters.** ***(Lesson 12-6)***

19. G, O, A, T GO, GA, GT, OA, OT, AT; 6
20. A, P, E AP, AE, PE; 3
21. H, Y, E, N, A HY, HE, HN, HA, YE, YN, YA, EN, EA, NA; 10
22. *Choose a Strategy* A boy jogs in the park every other day. His sister jogs every third day. They both jogged together on April 2. On how many more of the 30 days in April will they jog together if they maintain this schedule? four more days

# FINISHING THE CHAPTER PROJECT

**Make a 3-D Polynomial Model** The Project Activities on pages 681, 688, and 692 will help you complete your project. Here is a checklist to help you gather the different parts.

- ✔ your prisms, assembled into a cube
- ✔ your equation of two polynomials for the area of a cube face
- ✔ your equation of two polynomials for the volume of the cube

Make a display for your polynomial model. Label the parts of the cube with their dimensions. Include an explanation of the connection between the cube's dimensions and your polynomial expressions.

***Reflect and Revise***

Ask a friend or someone at home to review your display. Are your polynomials correct? Are your explanations clear? If necessary, make changes to improve your display.

## *Web Extension*

**Visit Prentice Hall's Web site. You'll find some interesting links and ideas related to models. You'll also be able to share information about your project.**

**www.phschool.com**

## FINISHING THE PROJECT

**Project Day** You may wish to plan a project day on which students share their completed projects. Encourage students to explain their process as well as their product.

**Block Scheduling** If you have block scheduling or extended periods, you may wish to intersperse the sharing of projects over Days 3 and 4 between the completion of one lesson and the start of a new lesson.

### Project Notebook

Have students review their project work and bring their notebooks up to date. Call attention to the fact that they can share their projects with other students through the Web site **www.phschool.com**.

Be sure students include in their notebooks their completed Project Manager and Scoring Rubric forms.

**Portfolio** Students may wish to include their projects and/or their project notebooks in their portfolios.

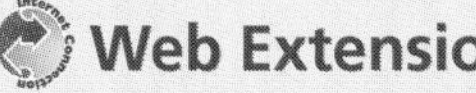

### Web Extension

**Tell Us About Your Project**

Students may wish to share their projects with other students on the Web site: **www.phschool.com**.

### Scoring Rubric

**3** You write your equations correctly. Your polynomial model is neat, accurate, and well-labeled. Your display is complete, well-organized, and easy to read.

**2** You make minor errors in your equations. Your polynomial model is accurate, but could be constructed better. Your display is complete, but could be organized better.

**1** You write your equations or construct your polynomial model incorrectly. Your display is incomplete and lacks organization.

**0** Major elements of the project are incomplete or missing.

# Wrap Up

## Resources

Glossary, p. 748
Extra Practice, p. 722

For a complete list of resources for the chapter, see p. 661H.

### Quarterly Assessment Form A Page 1

**Circle the letter of the best answer.**

1. Find the area of a circle with diameter 8 cm.
   (A.) $50.24 \text{ cm}^2$ B. $12.56 \text{ cm}^2$
   C. $25.12 \text{ cm}^2$ D. $200.96 \text{ cm}^2$

2. Find the surface area of a sphere with radius 7 m.
   F. $1{,}436.03 \text{ m}^2$ (G.) $615.44 \text{ m}^2$
   H. $43.96 \text{ m}^2$ J. $2{,}461.76 \text{ m}^2$

3. Which of the following is the best estimate of $\sqrt{99}$?
   A. 7 B. 8
   C. 9 (D.) 10

4. Which of the following could be the lengths of the sides of a 30°-60°-90° right triangle?
   F. 9 cm, 9 cm, $9\sqrt{2}$ cm
   G. 10 cm, $20\sqrt{3}$ cm, 20 cm
   (H.) 11 cm, $11\sqrt{3}$ cm, 22 cm
   J. 7 cm, $7\sqrt{2}$ cm, $7\sqrt{3}$ cm

5. A bag has 8 marbles. Three are green, three are blue, and two are yellow. You randomly select two marbles from the bag, putting the first back before you select the second one. Find the probability you select two yellow.
   A. $\frac{1}{4}$ B. $\frac{1}{6}$
   C. $\frac{1}{12}$ (D.) $\frac{1}{16}$

6. A bag has 8 marbles. Three are green, three are blue, and two are yellow. You randomly select two marbles from the bag, without putting the first back before you select the second one. Find the probability you select two yellow.
   F. $\frac{1}{6}$ G. $\frac{1}{12}$
   (H.) $\frac{1}{28}$ J. $\frac{1}{16}$

7. Six pennants are to be hung from a flagpole. In how many different orders can they be hung?
   A. 6 orders (B.) 720 orders
   C. 20 orders D. 360 orders

**Use the line plot for 8 and 9.**

35 36 37 38 39 40

8. What is the mode of the data in the line plot?
   (F.) 36 G. 38
   H. 39 J. 37

9. What is the range of the data in the line plot?
   A. 3 B. 4
   (C.) 5 D. 6

10. Evaluate $x^2 - 4x - 9$ for $x = -1$.
    F. −5 G. 5
    (H.) −4 J. 4

11. Find the volume of a rectangular prism with height 7 in., width $3x$ in., and length $(x + 4)$ in.
    A. $(21x + 4) \text{ in.}^3$
    B. $(21x + 28) \text{ in.}^3$
    C. $(21x^2 + 84) \text{ in.}^3$
    (D.) $(21x^2 + 84x) \text{ in.}^3$



### Quarterly Assessment Form A Page 2

**For 12 to 14, use the space figure at the right.**

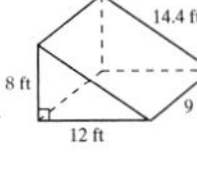


12. Name the space figure. triangular prism

13. Find the surface area of the space figure. $405.6 \text{ ft}^2$

14. Find the volume of the space figure. $432 \text{ ft}^3$

15. Find the missing length $x$ to the nearest tenth of a unit. Use $\sin 47° \approx 0.7314$, $\cos 47° \approx 0.6820$, or $\tan 47° \approx 1.0724$.

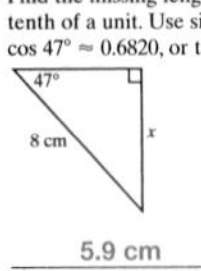


5.9 cm

16. Graph $y = -3|x| + 5$

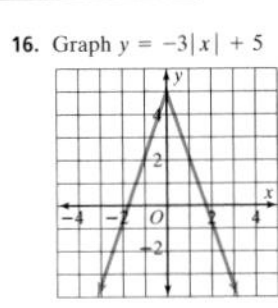


**Simplify.**

17. $(3x^2 - 5xy + y^2) - (x^2 - 8xy - y^2)$ $2x^2 + 3xy + 2y^2$

18. $(x - 7)(x - 4)$ $x^2 - 11x + 28$

19. Tell whether the sequence is *arithmetic*, *geometric*, or *neither*. Find the next three terms. Write a rule to describe the sequence.
    5, 2, −1, −4, −7, −10 type: arithmetic
    rule: Start with 5 and add −3 repeatedly.

20. Explain what impression the graph gives and how it gives that impression. Sample answer is shown.
    The graph gives the impression that sales increased rapidly in 2001 by using a broken vertical scale of 0.1 million.

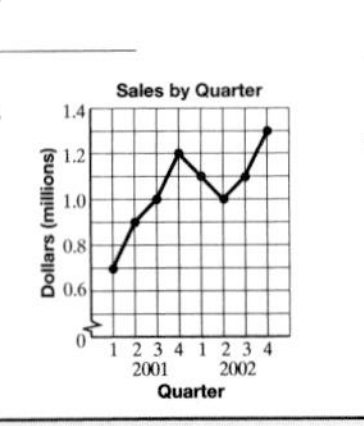




# 13 Wrap Up

## Key Terms

absolute value function (p. 670)
arithmetic sequence (p. 664)
binomial (p. 678)
common difference (p. 664)
common ratio (p. 665)
geometric sequence (p. 665)
monomial (p. 678)
polynomial (p. 678)
quadratic function (p. 669)
sequence (p. 664)
term (p. 664)
trinomial (p. 678)

## Graphic Organizer

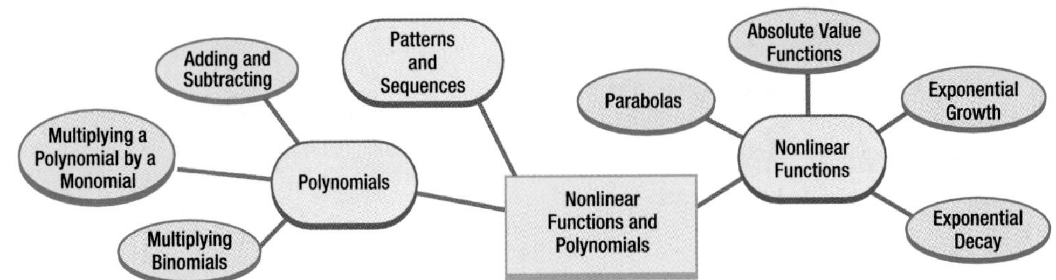


## Patterns and Sequences 13-1

*Summary* A **sequence** is a set of numbers that follow a pattern. Each number in the sequence is a **term** of the sequence. You find a term of an **arithmetic sequence** by adding a fixed number, called the **common difference,** to the previous term.

You find a term of a **geometric sequence** by multiplying the previous term by a fixed number. This fixed number is called a **common ratio.**

**Find the next three terms of each sequence. Then write a rule to describe each sequence.** 1–6. See margin.

1. 1, 5, 9, 13, . . .
2. −60, −30, −15, −7.5, . . .
3. 100, 107, 114, 121, . . .
4. 0, −5, −10, −15, . . .
5. 26, 15, 4, −7, . . .
6. $\frac{1}{10}, \frac{1}{2}, 2.5, 12.5, \ldots$

**Tell whether each sequence is *arithmetic, geometric,* or *neither.* Find the next three terms of each sequence.**

7. 9, 13, 17, 21, . . . arithmetic; 25, 29, 33
8. −8, −4, −2, −1, . . . geometric; $-\frac{1}{2}, -\frac{1}{4}, -\frac{1}{8}$
9. 3, 4, 5, 6, . . . arithmetic; 7, 8, 9
10. −22, −11, 0, 11, . . . arithmetic; 22, 33, 44
11. 10, 1, 20, 2, . . . neither; 30, 3, 40
12. $\frac{1}{200}, \frac{1}{100}, \frac{1}{50}, \frac{1}{25}, \ldots$ geometric; $\frac{2}{25}, \frac{4}{25}, \frac{8}{25}$



1. 17, 21, 25; Start with 1 and add 4 repeatedly.
2. −3.75, −1.875, −0.9375; Start with −60 and multiply by $\frac{1}{2}$ repeatedly.
3. 128, 135, 142; Start with 100 and add 7 repeatedly.
4. −20, −25, −30; Start with 0 and add −5 repeatedly.
5. −18, −29, −40; Start with 26 and add −11 repeatedly.
6. 62.5, 312.5, 1,562.5; Start with $\frac{1}{10}$ and multiply by 5 repeatedly.

14.

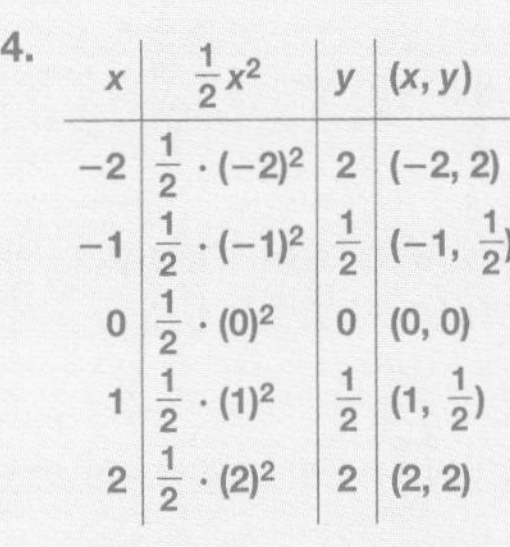

| $x$ | $\frac{1}{2}x^2$ | $y$ | $(x, y)$ |
|---|---|---|---|
| −2 | $\frac{1}{2} \cdot (-2)^2$ | 2 | (−2, 2) |
| −1 | $\frac{1}{2} \cdot (-1)^2$ | $\frac{1}{2}$ | $(-1, \frac{1}{2})$ |
| 0 | $\frac{1}{2} \cdot (0)^2$ | 0 | (0, 0) |
| 1 | $\frac{1}{2} \cdot (1)^2$ | $\frac{1}{2}$ | $(1, \frac{1}{2})$ |
| 2 | $\frac{1}{2} \cdot (2)^2$ | 2 | (2, 2) |

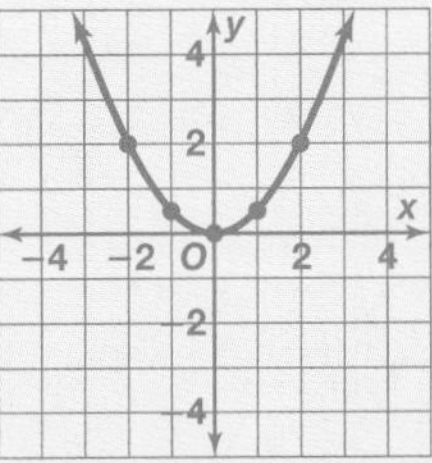

**13.** *Open-ended* Describe a situation that you can represent with an arithmetic sequence. Write a sequence of numbers for that situation and identify the common difference. Check students' work.

## Graphing Nonlinear Functions — 13-2 and 13-3

*Summary* Two types of nonlinear functions are **quadratic functions** and **absolute value functions.** The graph of a quadratic function is a U-shaped curve called a *parabola* that opens upward or downward. The graph of an absolute value function is V-shaped.

A function like $y = 2^x$ models *exponential growth*. Its graph curves upward as input values increase. A function like $y = \left(\frac{1}{2}\right)^x$ models *exponential decay*. Its graph slopes downward as input values increase.

**For each function, make a table with integer values of $x$ from −2 to 2. Then graph each function.** 14–19. See margin pp. 704–706. 20–25. See back of book.

**14.** $y = \frac{1}{2}x^2$ **15.** $y = 2|x|$ **16.** $y = |x| + 1$ **17.** $y = x^2 + 5$

**18.** $y = -|x|$ **19.** $y = \frac{1}{2}|x|$ **20.** $y = -x^2 - 3$ **21.** $y = -x^2 + 4$

**For each function, make a table with integer values of $x$ from 0 to 4. Then graph each function.**

**22.** $y = \left(\frac{1}{4}\right)^x$ **23.** $y = \frac{1}{2} \cdot 2^x$ **24.** $y = 3^x$ **25.** $y = \left(\frac{1}{2}\right)^x$

## Polynomials — 13-4

*Summary* A **monomial** is a real number, a variable, or a product of a real number and variables with whole-number exponents. A **polynomial** is a monomial or a sum or difference of monomials. You can name a polynomial by the number of its terms. A **binomial** has two terms and a **trinomial** has three terms.

**Tell whether each polynomial is a *monomial*, a *binomial*, or a *trinomial*.**

**26.** $3x$ monomial **27.** $2x^2 - 1$ binomial **28.** $\frac{2}{3}x$ monomial **29.** $x^4 - x^3 + 2$ trinomial **30.** $15$ monomial

**31.** $mn$ monomial **32.** $z^2 + z$ binomial **33.** $7d + f$ binomial **34.** $-2x^2 - 12$ binomial **35.** $3 + 2x - x^2$ trinomial

**Evaluate each polynomial for $x = -3$ and $y = 2$.**

**36.** $y^5$ 32 **37.** $x^2 - y$ 7 **38.** $y^2 - x - 1$ 6 **39.** $2xy$ −12 **40.** $3 - xy$ 9



15.

| $x$ | $2\|x\|$ | $y$ | $(x, y)$ |
|---|---|---|---|
| −2 | $2\|-2\|$ | 4 | (−2, 4) |
| −1 | $2\|-1\|$ | 2 | (−1, 2) |
| 0 | $2\|0\|$ | 0 | (0, 0) |
| 1 | $2\|1\|$ | 2 | (1, 2) |
| 2 | $2\|2\|$ | 4 | (2, 4) |

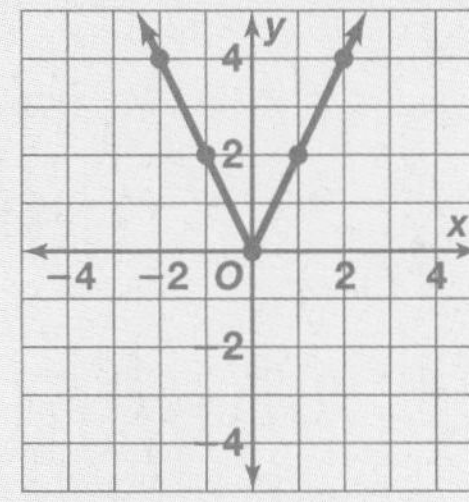

16.

| $x$ | $\|x\| + 1$ | $y$ | $(x, y)$ |
|---|---|---|---|
| −2 | $\|-2\| + 1$ | 3 | (−2, 3) |
| −1 | $\|-1\| + 1$ | 2 | (−1, 2) |
| 0 | $\|0\| + 1$ | 1 | (0, 1) |
| 1 | $\|1\| + 1$ | 2 | (1, 2) |
| 2 | $\|2\| + 1$ | 3 | (2, 3) |

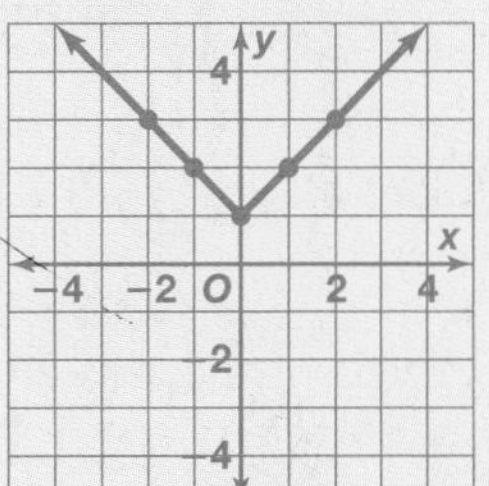

**Portfolio** Students may wish to include their completed work for the Wrap Up in their portfolios.

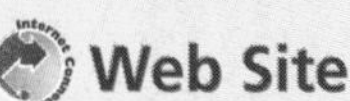

### Web Site

Students can find self-assessment materials on the Web site: www.phschool.com.

### Quarterly Assessment Form B Page 1

**Circle the letter of the best answer.**

1. Find the area of a circle with diameter 12 cm.
   A. 37.68 $cm^2$  B. 452.16 $cm^2$
   C. 18.84 $cm^2$  (D.) 113.04 $cm^2$
2. Find the surface area of a cone with radius 5 m and slant height 13 m.
   F. 204.1 $m^2$  (G.) 282.6 $m^2$
   H. 314 $m^2$  J. 78.5 $m^2$
3. Which of the following is the best estimate of $\sqrt{79}$?
   A. 10  (B.) 9
   C. 8  D. 7
4. Which of the following could be the length of the sides of a 30°-60°-90° right triangle?
   (F.) 7 in, $7\sqrt{3}$ in., 14 in.
   G. 8 in., 16 in., $16\sqrt{3}$ in.
   H. 10 in., 10 in., $10\sqrt{2}$ in.
   J. 15 in., $15\sqrt{2}$ in., $15\sqrt{3}$ in.
5. A bag has 9 marbles. Four are yellow, three are blue, and two are green. You randomly select two marbles from the bag, putting the first back before you select the second one. Find the probability you select two blue.
   A. $\frac{1}{6}$  B. $\frac{1}{8}$
   (C.) $\frac{1}{9}$  D. $\frac{1}{12}$
6. A bag has 9 marbles. Four are yellow, three are blue, and two are green. You randomly select two marbles from the bag, without putting the first back before you select the second one. Find the probability you select two blue.
   F. $\frac{1}{6}$  G. $\frac{1}{8}$
   H. $\frac{1}{9}$  (J.) $\frac{1}{12}$
7. A club with 30 members is electing 4 officers. How many different sets of officers are possible?
   A. 24  B. 120
   C. 657,720  (D.) 27,405

**Use the line plot for 8 and 9.**

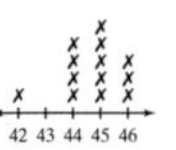


8. What is the mode of the data in the line plot?
   F. 43  G. 44
   (H.) 45  J. 46
9. What is the range of the data in the line plot?
   A. 3  (B.) 4
   C. 5  D. 6
10. Evaluate $x^2 - 5x - 10$ for $x = -1$.
   (F.) −4  G. 4
   H. −5  J. 5
11. Find the volume of a rectangular prism with height 6 cm, width $4x$ cm, and length $(x + 5)$ cm.
   A. $(24x + 30)$ $cm^3$
   B. $(24x + 5)$ $cm^3$
   C. $(24x^2 + 120)$ $cm^3$
   (D.) $(24x^2 + 120x)$ $cm^3$



### Quarterly Assessment Form B Page 2

**For 12 to 14, use the space figure at the right.**

12. Name the space figure. square pyramid
13. Find the surface area of the space figure. 800 in.$^2$
14. Find the volume of the space figure. 1,280 in.$^2$

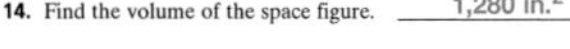

15. Find the missing length $y$ to the nearest tenth of a unit. Use $\sin 25° \approx 0.4226$, $\cos 25° \approx 0.9063$, or $\tan 25° \approx 0.4663$.
   11.8 m
16. Graph $y = 2x^2 - 5$

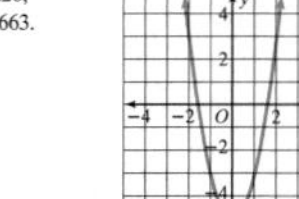

**Simplify.**

17. $(x^2 - 2xy + y^2) - (x^2 - 5xy)$ $3xy + y^2$
18. $(x - 10)(x + 3)$ $x^2 - 7x - 30$
19. Tell whether the sequence is *arithmetic*, *geometric*, or *neither*. Find the next three terms. Write a rule to describe the sequence.
   54, 18, 6, 2, $\frac{2}{3}$, $\frac{2}{9}$  type: geometric
   rule: Start with 54 and multiply by $\frac{1}{3}$ repeatedly.
20. Explain what impression the graph gives and how it gives that impression. Sample answer is shown. The graph gives the impression sales have been decreasing less rapidly than they actually have been by using a vertical range of 2 million.

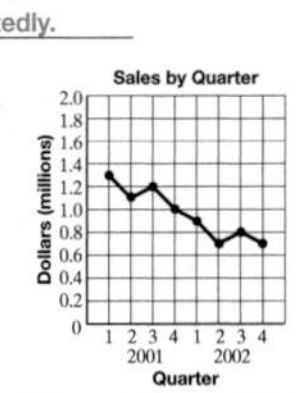

17.

| $x$ | $x^2 + 5$ | $y$ | $(x, y)$ |
|---|---|---|---|
| $-2$ | $(-2)^2 + 5$ | 9 | $(-2, 9)$ |
| $-1$ | $(-1)^2 + 5$ | 6 | $(-1, 6)$ |
| 0 | $0^2 + 5$ | 5 | $(0, 5)$ |
| 1 | $1^2 + 5$ | 6 | $(1, 6)$ |
| 2 | $2^2 + 5$ | 9 | $(2, 9)$ |

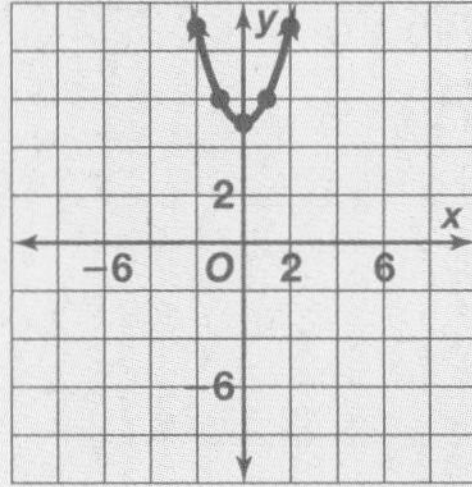


## Adding and Subtracting Polynomials 13-5


**Summary** You can add polynomials by using models, combining like terms, or aligning like terms vertically and then adding their coefficients. You can subtract polynomials by adding the opposite of each term in the second polynomial.


**Simplify each sum or difference.**

**41.** $(a^2 + a + 1) + (2a^2 + a + 7)$ $3a^2 + 2a + 8$

**42.** $(m^2 - 5m - 2) + (3m^2 + 3m - 10)$ $4m^2 - 2m -$

**43.** $(3x^2 - 4) + (x^2 - 2x + 6)$ $4x^2 - 2x + 2$

**44.** $(7p - 5q + 2) - (3p + 2q + 4)$ $4p - 7q - 2$

**45.** $(10w^2 + 6w) - (7w^2 - 3w + 5)$ $3w^2 + 9w - 5$

**46.** $(9x - 3y) - (3x - 9y)$ $6x + 6y$

## Multiplying Polynomials 13-6 and 13-7


**Summary** You can use properties to simplify the product of a monomial and a polynomial. You can sometimes use the Distributive Property to write a polynomial as the product of two factors.

You can use tiles to model the product of two binomials. When you use the Distributive Property to find the product of two binomials, you use the Distributive Property twice.


**Simplify each product.** 50. $3x^3 - 3x^2 - 15x$

**47.** $a(2a + 5)$ $2a^2 + 5a$

**48.** $4c(3c - 7)$ $12c^2 - 28c$

**49.** $-6y(5y + 3)$ $-30y^2 - 18y$

**50.** $3x(x^2 - x - 5)$ See above.

**51.** $x^2(x + 7)$ $x^3 + 7x^2$

**52.** $2x^2(x^2 - 3x - 6)$ $2x^4 - 6x^3 - 1$

**53.** $(x + 3)(x + 4)$ $x^2 + 7x + 12$

**54.** $(x + 1)(x - 5)$ $x^2 - 4x - 5$

**55.** $(x - 2)(x - 4)$ $x^2 - 6x + 8$

**Use the GCF of the terms to write each expression as the product of two factors.**

**56.** $x^2 - x$ $x(x - 1)$

**57.** $9p^2 + 27$ $9(p^2 + 3)$

**58.** $3x^3 - 9x^2 + 6x$ $3x(x^2 - 3x + 2)$

**59.** $5b^5 + 20b^3 - 30$ $5(b^5 + 4b^3 - 6)$

**60.** $8x^3 + 2x^2 + 4x$ $2x(4x^2 + x + 2)$

**61.** $28a^2 - 4ab$ $4a(7a - b)$

## Use Multiple Strategies 13-8


**Summary** You can use multiple strategies to solve problems.


**62.** A gardener plans to use 196 feet of fencing to enclose a garden. What is the largest possible area of the garden? 2,401 ft²

**63.** *Writing* Explain your choice of strategies for Exercise 62. See right.

63. Answers may vary. Sample: A diagram gives a visual picture of the problem. A table organizes possible dimensions and their related areas. Looking for a pattern leads to the answer.

706 Chapter 13 Wrap Up

## Chapter Assessment Form A Page 1

**Circle the letter of the best answer.**

1. The expression $5y^2 + 3y + x$ is which of the following?
   A. a monomial B. a binomial C. not a polynomial (D.) a trinomial
2. Evaluate $5m - 2n$ for $m = -3$ and $n = -2$.
   F. $-19$ (G.) $-11$ H. 19 J. 11
3. Simplify $(4x + 1) + (-3x + 9)$.
   (A.) $x + 10$ B. $7x - 8$ C. $7x + 10$ D. $x - 8$
4. Simplify $(b^2c + 7bc - 3) - (12b^2c - 2bc + 5)$.
   F. $-11bc^2 + 9bc - 8$ (G.) $-11b^2c + 9bc - 8$
   H. $13b^2c + 5bc + 2$ J. $-11b^2c + 5bc + 2$
5. Simplify $3fg(f^2g + 5f - 4)$.
   A. $3f^2g^2 + 15fg - 12$ B. $3f^3g^3 + 15f^2g - 12$
   C. $3f^3g^2 + 15f^2g - 12$ (D.) $3f^3g^2 + 15f^2g - 12fg$

**Tell whether each sequence is *arithmetic*, *geometric*, or *neither*. Find the next three terms of each sequence. Write a rule to describe the sequence.**

6. $-3, -12, -48,$ $-192$, $-768$, $-3{,}072$ type: geometric
   rule: Start with −3 and multiply by 4 repeatedly.
7. 6, 11, 16, 21, 26, 31, 36 type: arithmetic
   rule: Start with 6 and add 5 repeatedly.

**Complete the table and graph each function.**

8. $y = -x^2 + 2$

| $x$ | $y = -x^2 + 2$ | $(x, y)$ |
|---|---|---|
| $-2$ | $y = -(-2)^2 + 2 = -2$ | $(-2, -2)$ |
| $-1$ | $y = -(-1)^2 + 2 = 1$ | $(-1, 1)$ |
| 0 | $y = -(0)^2 + 2 = 2$ | $(0, 2)$ |
| 1 | $y = -(1)^2 + 2 = 1$ | $(1, 1)$ |
| 2 | $y = -(2)^2 + 2 = -2$ | $(2, -2)$ |

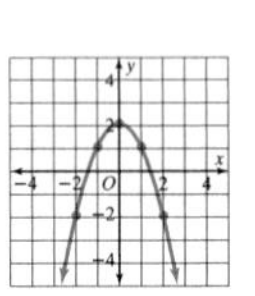




## Chapter Assessment Form A Page 2

9. $y = \frac{1}{2}|x| - 4$

| $x$ | $y = \frac{1}{2}\|x\| - 4$ | $(x, y)$ |
|---|---|---|
| $-4$ | $y = \frac{1}{2}\|-4\| - 4 = -2$ | $(-4, -2)$ |
| $-2$ | $y = \frac{1}{2}\|-2\| - 4 = -3$ | $(-2, -3)$ |
| 0 | $y = \frac{1}{2}\|0\| - 4 = -4$ | $(0, -4)$ |
| 2 | $y = \frac{1}{2}\|2\| - 4 = -3$ | $(2, -3)$ |
| 4 | $y = \frac{1}{2}\|4\| - 4 = -2$ | $(4, -2)$ |

**Simplify.**

10. $(n^2 - 3n + 1) - (4n^2 + n - 5)$ $-3n^2 - 4n + 6$
11. $4y^2z(2y + 3z - 5)$ $8y^3z + 12y^2z^2 - 20y^2z$
12. $(x - 8)(x + 5)$ $x^2 - 3x - 40$
13. $(d - 2b)(d + 4b)$ $d^2 + 2bd - 8b^2$

**Write each expression as the product of a monomial and a polynomial.**

14. $10x^2 - 15x + 25$ $5(2x^2 - 3x + 5)$
15. $9x^3 - 6x^2 - 15x$ $3x(x^2 - 2x - 5)$
16. Joe remembered that the three digits in his locker combination were 3, 5, and 7, but he forgot the order of the numbers. What is the maximum number of combinations he must check in order to open his lock? What are they?
    6 combinations; 357, 375, 537; 573; 735; 753
17. Describe the relationship between a binomial and a polynomial.
    Sample answer is shown. A binomial is a polynomial with two terms.



Assessment

18.

| $x$ | $-\|x\|$ | $y$ | $(x, y)$ |
|---|---|---|---|
| $-2$ | $-\|-2\|$ | $-2$ | $(-2, -2)$ |
| $-1$ | $-\|-1\|$ | $-1$ | $(-1, -1)$ |
| 0 | $-\|0\|$ | 0 | $(0, 0)$ |
| 1 | $-\|1\|$ | $-1$ | $(1, -1)$ |
| 2 | $-\|2\|$ | $-2$ | $(2, -2)$ |

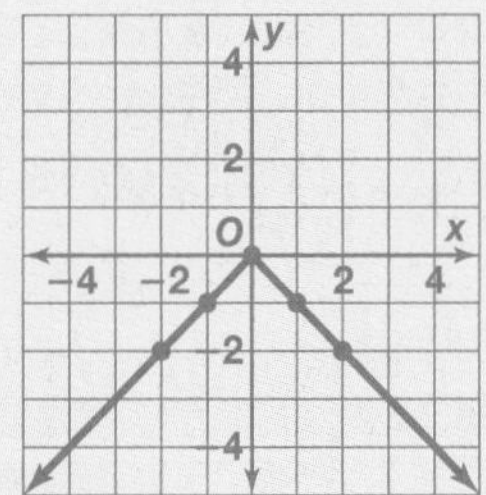


19.

| $x$ | $\frac{1}{2}\|x\|$ | $y$ | $(x, y)$ |
|---|---|---|---|
| $-2$ | $\frac{1}{2}\|-2\|$ | 1 | $(-2, 1)$ |
| $-1$ | $\frac{1}{2}\|-1\|$ | $\frac{1}{2}$ | $(-1, \frac{1}{2})$ |
| 0 | $\frac{1}{2}\|0\|$ | 0 | $(0, 0)$ |
| 1 | $\frac{1}{2}\|1\|$ | $\frac{1}{2}$ | $(1, \frac{1}{2})$ |
| 2 | $\frac{1}{2}\|2\|$ | 1 | $(2, 1)$ |

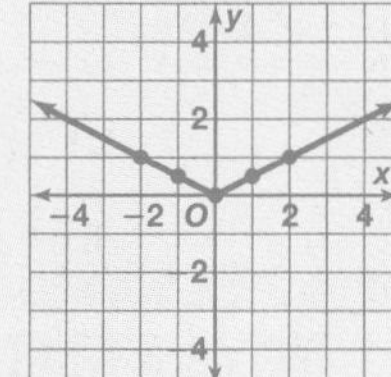

# 13 Assessment

**Find the next three terms of each sequence. Then write a rule to describe each sequence.**

1. $5, 8, 11, 14, \ldots$
2. $-1.5, -3, -6, -12, \ldots$
3. $50, 10, 2, 0.4, \ldots$
4. $100, 93, 86, 79, \ldots$

1–10. See margin.

**Tell whether each sequence is *arithmetic*, *geometric*, or *neither*. Find the next three terms of the sequence.**

5. $5, 2, -1, -4, \ldots$
6. $1, 1, 2, 3, 5, \ldots$
7. $15, 13, 11, 9, \ldots$
8. $-48, -12, -3, -\frac{3}{4}, \ldots$
9. $2, 4, 8, 16, \ldots$
10. $0, 7, 14, 21, \ldots$

**For each function, make a table with integer values of $x$ from $-2$ to 2. Then graph each function.** 11–20. See back of book.

11. $y = x^2$
12. $y = x^2 - 1$
13. $y = -x^2 + 1$
14. $y = -x^2 - 2$
15. $y = |x| - 1$
16. $y = \frac{1}{2}|x|$

**For each function, make a table with integer values of $x$ from 0 to 4. Then graph each function.**

17. $y = 2^x$
18. $y = 3^x$
19. $y = 2\left(\frac{1}{2}\right)^x$
20. $y = \left(\frac{1}{3}\right)^x$

**Tell whether each polynomial is a *monomial*, a *binomial*, or a *trinomial*.**

21. $4x - 1$ binomial
22. $c^2 + c + 1$ trinomial
23. $xyz$ monomial
24. $a^5 - 7$ binomial
25. $h^4 - h^3 - h$ trinomial
26. $ab$ monomial

**Evaluate each polynomial for $x = 4$ and $y = 10$.**

27. $x + y$ 14
28. $y - x^2$ −6
29. $xy - 15$ 25
30. $x^2 + xy - y^2$ −44

31. *Open-ended* Write a polynomial with two different variables. Assign a value to each variable. Evaluate your polynomial for those values. Check students' work.

**Simplify each sum or difference.**

32. $(x^2 + 4x + 3) + (x^2 - 3x + 7)$ $2x^2 + x + 10$
33. $(2x^2 - 3) + (x + 4)$ $2x^2 + x + 1$
34. $(3x^2 + 2x + 4) + (x^2 + 3)$ $4x^2 + 2x + 7$
35. $(x^2 + 10x + 9) - (x^2 + x + 1)$ $9x + 8$
36. $(3x^2 - x + 3) - (2x^2 - 2x - 4)$ $x^2 + x + 7$
37. $(2x^2 - 4x) - (x^2 - 3x - 5)$ $x^2 - x + 5$

**Simplify each product.**

38. $x(x - 4)$ $x^2 - 4x$
39. $2x(x^2 - x + 2)$ $2x^3 - 2x^2 + 4x$
40. $x^2(3x^2 + 2x - 5)$ $3x^4 + 2x^3 - 5x^2$
41. $(x + 2)(x + 4)$ $x^2 + 6x + 8$
42. $(x + 1)(x + 5)$ $x^2 + 6x + 5$
43. $(x + 3)(x - 1)$ $x^2 + 2x - 3$
44. $(x + 2)(x - 4)$ $x^2 - 2x - 8$
45. $(x - 1)(x - 6)$ $x^2 - 7x + 6$
46. $(x - 2)(x - 3)$ $x^2 - 5x + 6$

**Write each expression as the product of a monomial and a polynomial.**

47. $2x^3 + 4x^2 + 12x$ $2x(x^2 + 2x + 6)$
48. $x^2 - x$ $x(x - 1)$
49. $9x^3 - 18x^2 - 3x$ $3x(3x^2 - 6x - 1)$

50. *Writing* Explain how you can use the Distributive Property to write the expression $3x^2 + 6x$ as the product of a monomial and a polynomial. See margin.

51. A customer gives a clerk a \$100 bill for a \$76 purchase. In how many ways can the clerk give change without using coins? in ten ways



1. 17, 20, 23; Start with 5 and add 3 repeatedly.
2. −24, −48, −96; Start with −1.5 and multiply by 2 repeatedly.
3. 0.08, 0.016, 0.0032; Start with 50 and divide by 5 repeatedly.
4. 72, 65, 58; Start with 100 and add −7 repeatedly.
5. arithmetic; −7, −10, −13
6. neither; 8, 13, 21
7. arithmetic; 7, 5, 3
8. geometric; $-\frac{3}{16}, -\frac{3}{64}, -\frac{3}{256}$
9. geometric; 32, 64, 128
10. arithmetic; 28, 35, 42

50. Answers may vary. Sample: After finding the GCF of $3x$, use the Distributive Property to bring $3x$ to the front as a factor. This gives you $3x(x + 2)$, which is the product of a monomial and a binomial.

## Chapter Assessment

**Resources** For a complete list of resources for this chapter, see p. 661H.

### Chapter Assessment Form B Page 1

**Circle the letter of the best answer.**

1. Which expression is a trinomial?
   A. $3x^2y^2z^2$ (B.) $x^2 + y^2 + z^2$ C. $x^2 + y + \frac{1}{z}$ D. $x + z^2$
2. Evaluate $a(2a + b)$ for $a = -5$ and $b = 4$.
   (F.) 30 G. −30 H. 70 J. −70
3. Simplify $(3z^2 + 5z - 3) + (2z + 4)$.
   A. $5z^2 + 5z + 1$ B. $3z^2 + 7z - 7$ (C.) $3z^2 + 7z + 1$ D. $5z^2 + 7z + 1$
4. Simplify $(2n^2 + 3n - 5) - (7n^2 - n + 4)$.
   F. $9n^2 - 1$ (G.) $-5n^2 + 4n - 9$ H. $9n^2 - 9$ J. $-5n^2 + 2n - 1$
5. Simplify $4vw(v^2w - 8v - 5)$.
   (A.) $4v^3w^2 - 32v^2w - 20vw$ B. $4v^3w^2 - 32v^2w - 20$
   C. $4v^2w^2 - 32v^2w - 20$ D. $4v^2w^2 - 32v^2w - 20vw$

**Tell whether each sequence is arithmetic, geometric, or neither. Find the next three terms of each sequence. Write a rule to describe the sequence.**

6. 8, 8.5, 9, 9.5, 10, 10.5, 11 type: arithmetic
   rule: Start with 8 and add 0.5 repeatedly.
7. 5, −10, 20, −40, 80, −160, 320 type: geometric
   rule: Start with 5 and multiply by −2 repeatedly.

**Complete the table and graph each function.**

8. $y = -\frac{1}{2}x^2 - 4$

| $x$ | $y = -\frac{1}{2}x^2 - 4$ | $(x, y)$ |
|---|---|---|
| −4 | $y = \frac{1}{2}(-4)^2 - 4 = 4$ | (−4, 4) |
| −2 | $y = \frac{1}{2}(-2)^2 - 4 = -2$ | (−2, −2) |
| 0 | $y = \frac{1}{2}(0)^2 - 4 = -4$ | (0, −4) |
| 2 | $y = \frac{1}{2}(2)^2 - 4 = -2$ | (2, −2) |
| 4 | $y = \frac{1}{2}(4)^2 - 4 = 4$ | (4, 4) |

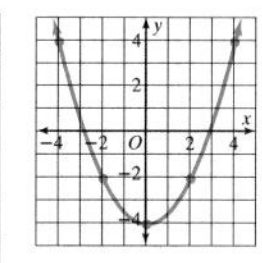



### Chapter Assessment Form B Page 2

9. $y = -|x| + 3$

| $x$ | $y = -\|x\| + 3$ | $(x, y)$ |
|---|---|---|
| −2 | $y = -\|-2\| + 3 = 1$ | (−2, 1) |
| −1 | $y = -\|-1\| + 3 = 2$ | (−1, 2) |
| 0 | $y = -\|0\| + 3 = 3$ | (0, 3) |
| 1 | $y = -\|1\| + 3 = 2$ | (1, 2) |
| 2 | $y = -\|2\| + 3 = 1$ | (2, 1) |

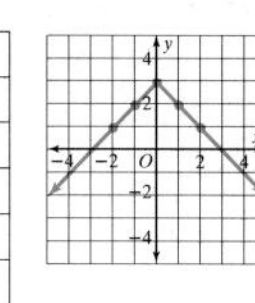

**Simplify.**

10. $(p^2 + 3p - 6) - (5p - 1)$ $p^2 - 2p - 5$
11. $mn^2(m + 4n)$ $m^2n^2 + 4mn^3$
12. $(x + 7)(x - 10)$ $x^2 - 3x - 70$
13. $(7a + 2)(3a - 4)$ $21a^2 - 22a - 8$

**Write each expression as the product of a monomial and a polynomial.**

14. $12x^2 - 16x - 24$ $4(3x^2 - 4x - 6)$
15. $20x^3 + 30x^2 - 50x$ $10x(2x^2 + 3x - 5)$
16. The first digit of a 3-digit telephone area code is 6 or 7. The second digit is 9. How many codes are possible?
    20 codes
17. Describe the relationship between a monomial and a trinomial.
    Sample answer is shown. A trinomial is actually three monomials added together.



Assessment

## Cumulative Review Page 1

**Circle the letter of the best answer.**

1. Write an inequality for the *total, t, is not more than eighteen.*
   A. $t \geq 18$ (B.) $t \leq 18$ C. $t > 18$ D. $t < 18$
2. Solve $k + 3 < -2$.
   F. $k < 5$ G. $k > -5$ (H.) $k < -5$ J. $k > 5$
3. Evaluate $3x^2(2x + 1)$ for $x = -3$.
   A. 189 B. −189 (C.) −135 D. 135
4. 85% of $z$ is 170. Find $z$.
   F. 144.5 G. 1,445 (H.) 200 J. 50
5. In the figure at the right, $\triangle JKL \sim \triangle PQR$. Find $KL$.
   A. 42 cm (B.) 77 cm C. 39.3 cm D. 40.7 cm
   P 40 cm Q; 30 cm; 55 cm; R; J 56 cm K; L
6. On a scale drawing of a house, the kitchen is $4\frac{1}{2}$ in. long. The actual room is 18 ft long. Find the scale.
   (F.) 1 in. : 4 ft G. 1 in. : 2 ft H. 1 in. : 8 ft J. 1 in. : 4.5 ft
7. Approximate the volume of a sphere with diameter 6 in. Use 3.14 for $\pi$.
   A. 904.32 in.$^3$ B. 452.16 in.$^3$ C. 37.68 in.$^3$ (D.) 113.04 in.$^3$
8. $(2z - 3)^2 =$
   (F.) $4z^2 - 12z + 9$ G. $2z^2 - 6z + 9$ H. $4z^2 + 12z + 9$ J. $2z^2 - 12z + 9$
9. A rectangle 15 cm wide has perimeter 80 cm. Find the length of the rectangle.
   (A.) 25 cm B. 50 cm C. 12.5 cm D. 65 cm
10. Match the graph with an equation below.
    F. $y = -4|x| + 4$ G. $4|x| - 4$
    H. $y = 4x^2 - 4$ (J.) $y = -4x^2 + 4$
11. Which figure has a volume greater than 400 cm$^3$?
    (A.) a cylinder with radius 6 cm and height 4 cm
    B. a cylinder with radius 4 cm and height 6 cm
    C. a cone with radius 6 cm and height 6 cm
    D. a cone with radius 4 cm and height 4 cm
12. An item on sale for \$8.75 is 70% of the original price. What was the original price?
    (F.) \$12.50 G. \$9.75 H. \$14.25 J. \$6.13



Assessment

## Cumulative Review Page 2

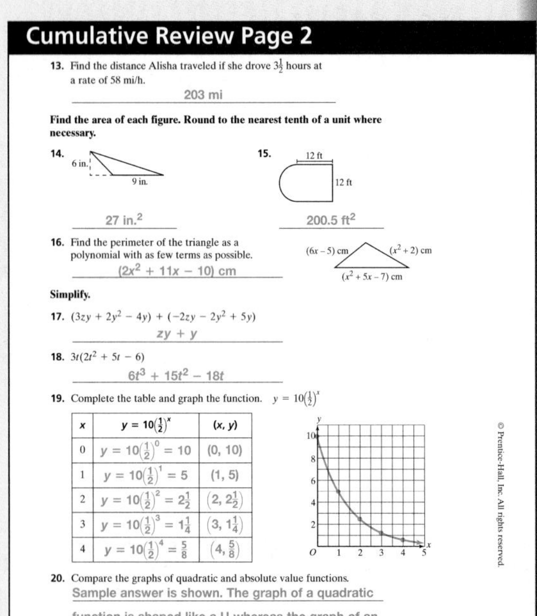

13. Find the distance Alisha traveled if she drove $3\frac{1}{2}$ hours at a rate of 58 mi/h.
    203 mi

**Find the area of each figure. Round to the nearest tenth of a unit where necessary.**

14. 6 in.; 9 in.
    27 in.$^2$
15. 12 ft; 12 ft
    200.5 ft$^2$
16. Find the perimeter of the triangle as a polynomial with as few terms as possible.
    $(6x - 5)$ cm; $(x^2 + 2)$ cm; $(x^2 + 5x - 7)$ cm
    $(2x^2 + 11x - 10)$ cm

**Simplify.**

17. $(3zy + 2y^2 - 4y) + (-2zy - 2y^2 + 5y)$
    $zy + y$
18. $3t(2t^2 + 5t - 6)$
    $6t^3 + 15t^2 - 18t$
19. Complete the table and graph the function. $y = 10\left(\frac{1}{2}\right)^x$

| $x$ | $y = 10\left(\frac{1}{2}\right)^x$ | $(x, y)$ |
|---|---|---|
| 0 | $y = 10\left(\frac{1}{2}\right)^0 = 10$ | (0, 10) |
| 1 | $y = 10\left(\frac{1}{2}\right)^1 = 5$ | (1, 5) |
| 2 | $y = 10\left(\frac{1}{2}\right)^2 = 2\frac{1}{2}$ | $\left(2, 2\frac{1}{2}\right)$ |
| 3 | $y = 10\left(\frac{1}{2}\right)^3 = 1\frac{1}{4}$ | $\left(3, 1\frac{1}{4}\right)$ |
| 4 | $y = 10\left(\frac{1}{2}\right)^4 = \frac{5}{8}$ | $\left(4, \frac{5}{8}\right)$ |

20. Compare the graphs of quadratic and absolute value functions.
    Sample answer is shown. The graph of a quadratic function is shaped like a U whereas the graph of an absolute value function is shaped like a V.



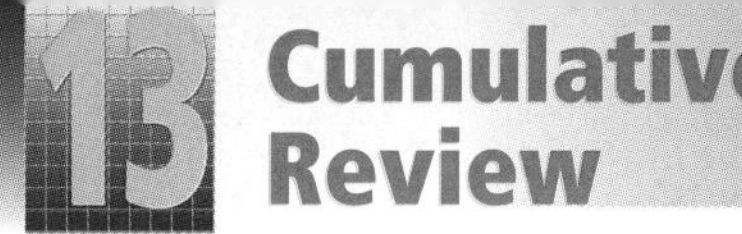

# Cumulative Review

Preparing for Algebra

**Choose the best answer.**

1. Solve $-3x + 1 < 25$. C
   A. $x > 8$ B. $x < -8$
   C. $x > -8$ D. Not here
2. 32% of $b$ is 8,000. Find $b$. G
   F. 2,560 G. 25,000
   H. 250 J. 25,600
3. Find the distance Joe traveled if he drove for $2\frac{1}{2}$ h at a rate of 62 mi/h. D
   A. 24.8 mi B. 124 mi
   C. 154 mi D. 155 mi
4. Which decimal is between $(-0.1)^2$ and 0.05? F
   F. 0.03 G. 0.2
   H. 0.3 J. −0.02
5. Evaluate $\frac{a^5b^3c}{a^6b^2}$ for $a = 2, b = -3$, and $c = -4$. C
   A. 12 B. −6 C. 6 D. −2
6. An artist created this scale drawing of a lighthouse. What is the height of the actual lighthouse? Use your centimeter ruler. G
   Scale: 1 cm = 12 m
   F. 36 m G. 48 m
   H. 72 m J. 120 m
7. Which ordered pair is a solution of $x - 2y = 3$ and $3x + y = 2$? A
   A. $(1, -1)$ B. $(-1, 1)$
   C. $(3, 2)$ D. $\left(2, -\frac{1}{2}\right)$
8. What number is next in the pattern $-1, \sqrt{1}, -2, \sqrt{4}, -3, \ldots$? J
   F. $\sqrt{3}$ G. $\sqrt{5}$
   H. $\sqrt{7}$ J. $\sqrt{9}$
9. In $\triangle ABC$, $m\angle A = 55°$, and $m\angle C = 15°$. Name the triangle. D
   A. acute B. equiangular
   C. right D. obtuse
10. $\triangle ABC \sim \triangle DEF$. Find $AC$. F

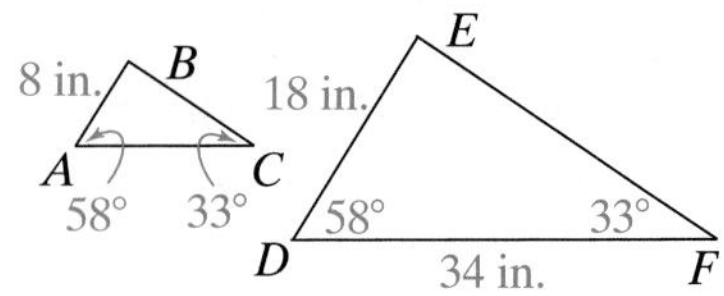


    F. 15.11 in. G. 76.5 in.
    H. 24 in. J. 17.25 in.
11. $ABCD$ is a rectangle. Which of the following is *not* true? D

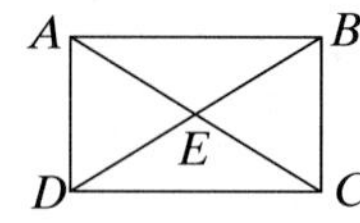


    A. $\overline{AC} \cong \overline{DB}$
    B. $\angle ADC \cong \angle CBA$
    C. $\triangle DAE \cong \triangle BCE$
    D. $\angle CBD \cong \angle DAB$
12. Find the volume of a cone in which $r = 4$ and $h = 12$. G
    F. $16\pi$ G. $64\pi$
    H. $192\pi$ J. $96\pi$
13. Write an inequality for *The number t is at least 35.* C
    A. $t > 35$ B. $t < 35$
    C. $t \geq 35$ D. $t \leq 35$
14. Find the area of the shaded region. G

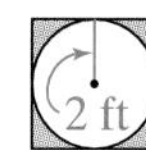


    F. 4.2 ft$^2$ G. 3.4 ft$^2$
    H. 2.4 ft$^2$ J. 4.3 ft$^2$



| Item | Chapter/ Lesson | Review Topic |
|---|---|---|
| 3 | 3-4 | Decimals and Equations |
| 4, 5 | 4-2, 4-4 | Fractions and Exponents |
| 2, 6, 10, 17 | 6-3, 6-4, 6-7 | Ratios, Proportions, and Percents |
| 1, 7, 13 | 2-8, 7-1, 8-7 | Solving Equations and Inequalities |
| 9, 11–12, 14–15 | 9-3, 9-5, 10-2, 10-3, 10-9 | Spatial Thinking; Area and Volume |
| 16 | 12-4 | Data Analysis and Probability |
| 8, 18–28 | 13-1, 13-2, 13-3, 13-4, 13-5, 13-6 | Nonlinear Functions and Polynomials |

15. Find the area of $\triangle CDE$. A

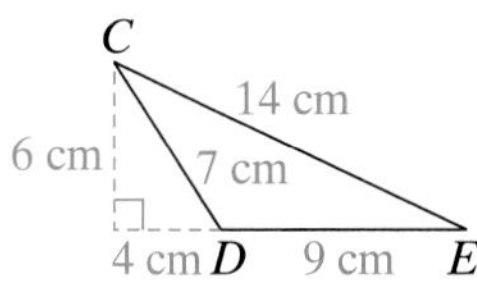


A. 27 $cm^2$  B. 36 $cm^2$
C. 12 $cm^2$  D. 39 $cm^2$

16. A bicycle company makes 3 different bicycle styles. Each style comes in 4 colors. Each style is made in 6 frame sizes with a choice of 2 types of seat. The bicycle shop would like to order one of each type of bicycle. How many bicycles is that? H
F. 60 bicycles  G. 120 bicycles
H. 144 bicycles  J. 240 bicycles

17. In a box filled with 60 colored chips, $\frac{1}{6}$ are blue, $\frac{1}{12}$ are white, $\frac{1}{4}$ are yellow, and $\frac{1}{2}$ are purple. Find the probability of picking at random a purple chip or a white chip. D
A. $\frac{2}{3}$  B. $\frac{1}{24}$  C. 35  D. $\frac{7}{12}$

18. If the first term in an arithmetic sequence is 15 and the tenth term is 69, what is the fourth term in the sequence? G
F. 32  G. 33  H. 34  J. 35

19. Simplify $6z(4 - 2z^2)$. A
A. $24z - 12z^3$  B. $24z - 12z^2$
C. $24z - 2z^2$  D. $24z + 12z^3$

20. Which expression is represented by the model shown below? J

F. $2(x^2 + 2x) + 3$  G. $2x^2 + 2 + 3^2$
H. $x^2 + 2x + 3$  J. $2x^2 + 2x + 3$

21. Which phrase best describes the expression $9xyz$? A
A. monomial  B. binomial
C. trinomial  D. Not here

22. Match the graph with an equation below. F

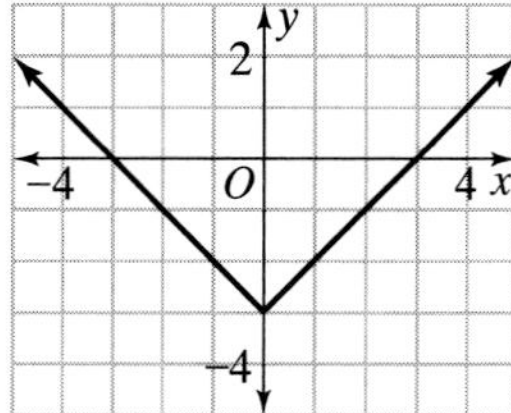


F. $y = |x| - 3$
G. $y = x^2 - 3$
H. $y = -3|x|$
J. $y = |x - 3|$

23. Find the sum. D

$$\begin{array}{r} x^4 + 2x^3 - x^2 + x - 3 \\ +\quad 6x^3 + x^2 - 4x - 8 \\ \hline \end{array}$$

A. $x^4 + 4x^3 - 2x^2 - 5x - 5$
B. $x^4 + 8x^3 - 4x - 5$
C. $x^4 + 8x^3 + 2x^2 - 3x - 11$
D. $x^4 + 8x^3 - 3x - 11$

24. Find the difference.
$(5r - 4s) - (2r - s)$ G
F. $10r - 4s$  G. $3r - 3s$
H. $10r^2 - 4s^2$  J. $3r - 5s$

**Write the perimeter of each figure as a polynomial. Simplify.**

25. 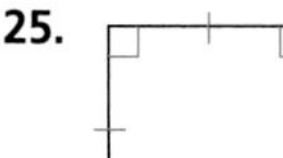


$5b + 5b + 5b + 5b = 20b$

26. 

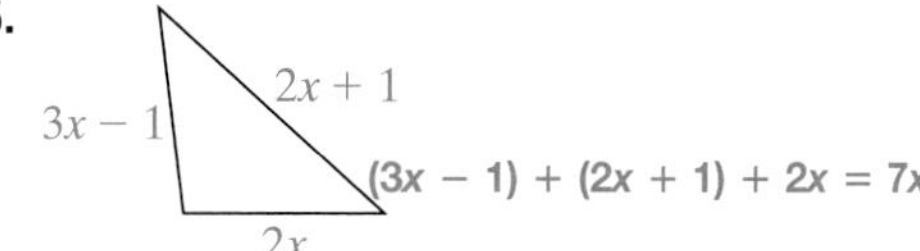


$(3x - 1) + (2x + 1) + 2x = 7x$

**For each function, make a table with integer values of *x* from 0 to 4. Then graph each function.** 27–28. See margin.

27. $y = 3^x$  28. $y = 20\left(\frac{1}{2}\right)^x$



27.

| $x$ | $3^x$ | $y$ | $(x, y)$ |
|---|---|---|---|
| 0 | $3^0$ | 1 | (0, 1) |
| 1 | $3^1$ | 3 | (1, 3) |
| 2 | $3^2$ | 9 | (2, 9) |
| 3 | $3^3$ | 27 | (3, 27) |
| 4 | $3^4$ | 81 | (4, 81) |

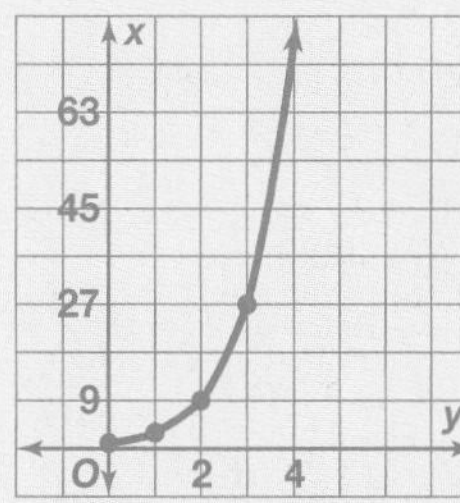


28.

| $x$ | $20(\frac{1}{2})^x$ | $y$ | $(x, y)$ |
|---|---|---|---|
| 0 | $20(\frac{1}{2})^0$ | 20 | (0, 20) |
| 1 | $20(\frac{1}{2})^1$ | 10 | (1, 10) |
| 2 | $20(\frac{1}{2})^2$ | 5 | (2, 5) |
| 3 | $20(\frac{1}{2})^3$ | 2.5 | (3, 2.5) |
| 4 | $20(\frac{1}{2})^4$ | 1.25 | (4, 1.25) |

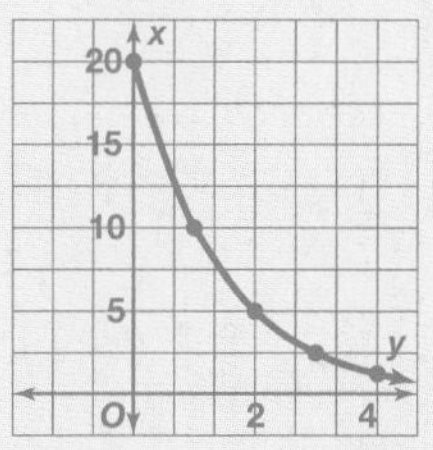

page 710 Extra Practice

42–50.

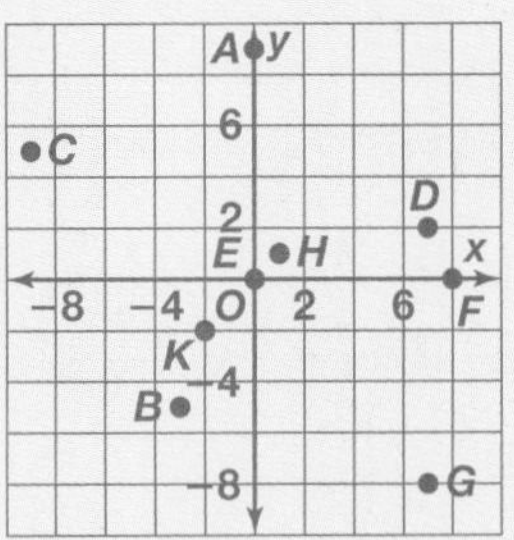


CHAPTER 1

# Extra Practice

**Write a variable expression for each word phrase.** Lesson 1-1

1. 6 less than $x$ $x - 6$
2. $y$ less than 12 $12 - y$
3. the sum of $z$ and 2 $z + 2$
4. a number $m$ increased by 34 $m + 34$
5. the product of 8 and $p$ $8p$
6. $t$ divided by 5 $\frac{t}{5}$

**Simplify each expression.** Lesson 1-2

7. $15 + 20 \cdot 3$ 75
8. $46 - 4(2 + 8)$ 6
9. $16 \div 4 + 10 \div 2$ 9
10. $100 \div (30 + 20)$ 2
11. $5(8 + 4) \div 6 \div 2$ 5
12. $9 \cdot 6 - 12 \div 2$ 48

**Evaluate each expression.** Lesson 1-3

13. $3x + 6$, for $x = 12$ 42
14. $15a - 2a$, for $a = 20$ 260
15. $38 - 3y$, for $y = 9$ 11
16. $25 - (t + 18)$, for $t = 7$ 0
17. $\frac{x + y}{10}$, for $x = 35$ and $y = 65$ 10

**Compare. Use >, <, or = to complete each statement.** Lesson 1-4

18. $-12 \blacksquare -9$ <
19. $|-4| \blacksquare |4|$ =
20. $-|-7| \blacksquare |-7|$ <
21. $0 \blacksquare -100$ >

**Simplify each expression.** Lessons 1-5 and 1-6

22. $-56 + 60$ 4
23. $18 + -25$ −7
24. $-34 + -36$ −70
25. $19 - (-5)$ 24
26. $80 - (-125)$ 205
27. $-82 - (-50)$ −32
28. $-7 + 35 + -22$ 6
29. $-44 - 20 - 80$ −144
30. $-8 + (-13) - (24)$ −45

**Write a rule for continuing each pattern. Find the next three numbers in the pattern.** Lesson 1-7

31. $-12, -3, 6, 15, 24, \ldots$ Start with −12, and add 9 to the previous term. 33, 42, 51 . . .
32. $0.15, 0.3, 0.45, 0.6, \ldots$ Start with 0.15, and add 0.15 to the previous term. 0.75, 0.90, 1.05, . . .
33. $1, 1, 2, 3, 5, 8, 13, \ldots$ Add the two previous terms. 21, 34, 55, . . .

**Simplify each expression.** Lesson 1-9

34. $-4 \cdot 12$ −48
35. $-15(-8)$ 120
36. $30 \cdot (-5)$ −150
37. $-1(-2)(-3)(-4)$ 24
38. $-78 \div (-3)$ 26
39. $-150 \div 25$ −6
40. $\frac{120}{-15}$ −8
41. $-1{,}125 \div (-125)$ 9

**Draw a coordinate plane. Graph each point.** 42–50. See margin. Lesson 1-10

42. $A(0, 9)$
43. $B(-3, -5)$
44. $C(-9, 5)$
45. $D(7, 2)$
46. $E(0, 0)$
47. $F(8, 0)$
48. $G(7, -8)$
49. $H(1, 1)$
50. $K(-2, -2)$

CHAPTER

# 2 Extra Practice

**Simplify each expression. Justify each step.** 1–6. See margin. Lesson 2-1

1. $99 + (-46) + (-99) + 45$
2. $225 + 320 + 75$
3. $18 + 12 + (-25) + 13$
4. $5 \cdot 678 \cdot 2$
5. $58 \cdot 2 \cdot 50$
6. $20 \cdot 4 \cdot 5 \cdot 25$

**Use the Distributive Property to simplify.** Lessons 2-2 and 2-3

7. $7(5) - 3(5)$ 20
8. $3 \cdot 6 + 7 \cdot 6$ 60
9. $15 \cdot 32 - 12 \cdot 32$ 96
10. $7b + 25 - 4b$ $3b + 25$
11. $3(a - 2c)$ $3a - 6c$
12. $3q + 2(q + 1)$ $5q + 2$
13. $-3(4y - 1) + 5(7 - y)$ $-17y + 38$
14. $41 - 2(m + 1) - m$ $-3m + 39$
15. $12 + 5x - 2(3x + 5)$ $-x + 2$

**Write an equation for each sentence. Is each equation *true*, *false*, or an *open sentence*?** Lesson 2-4

16. Twice the sum of a number and one is twenty-two. $2(x + 1) = 22$; open sentence
17. Negative three divided by negative one is three. $\frac{-3}{-1} = 3$; true
18. Forty-five plus five equals negative fifty. $45 + 5 = -50$; false

**Solve each equation.** Lessons 2-5 and 2-6

19. $40 + x = 25$ $-15$
20. $-5 = y - 12$ 7
21. $z + (-23) = -47$ $-24$
22. $14 = a - 9$ 23
23. $t - 453 = -520$ $-67$
24. $78 = b + 100$ $-22$
25. $4k = 96$ 24
26. $300 = -15j$ $-20$
27. $-12c = 180$ $-15$
28. $\frac{d}{7} = -14$ $-98$
29. $-4 = \frac{w}{16}$ $-64$
30. $\frac{k}{-9} = -20$ 180

**Graph the solutions of each inequality.** Lesson 2-8

31. $x > -12$
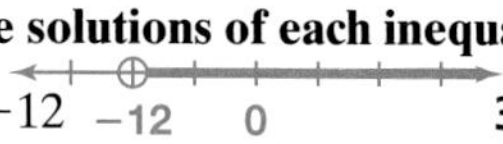
$-12$ 0

32. $y \leq 3$

0 3

33. $0 \geq z$

0

34. $p < -9$

$-9$ 0

35. $7 < n$

0 7

36. $f \leq -3$

$-3$ 0

**Solve each inequality.** Lessons 2-9 and 2-10

37. $a + 3 < -1$ $a < -4$
38. $-2 > b - 4$ $2 > b$
39. $5 + x > -8$ $x > -13$
40. $-12 < -2 + y$ $-10 < y$
41. $w - 32 \leq 15$ $w \leq 47$
42. $-20 \geq z - 13$ $-7 \geq z$
43. $\frac{c}{5} \leq -3$ $c \leq -15$
44. $8p \geq -96$ $p \geq -12$
45. $0 < 8r$ $0 < r$
46. $\frac{t}{-6} < -3$ $t > 18$
47. $\frac{a}{11} > -22$ $a > -242$
48. $-12k \geq -144$ $k \leq 12$



Extra Practice

## CHAPTER 2

### page 711 Extra Practice

1. 99 + (−99) + 45 + (−46)
   Commutative Property of Addition
   0 + 45 + (−46)
   additive inverse
   −1
2. 225 + 75 + 320
   Commutative Property of Addition
   300 + 320
   Add from left to right.
   620
3. 18 + 12 + 13 + (−25)
   Commutative Property of Addition
   18 + −25 + (12 + 13)
   Associative Property of Addition
   18 + −25 + 25
   Commutative Property of Addition
   18
4. 5 • 2 • 678
   Commutative Property of Multiplication
   10 • 678
   Multiply from left to right.
   6,780
5. 2 • 50 • 58
   Commutative Property of Multiplication
   100 • 58
   Multiply from left to right.
   5,800
6. 20 • 5 • 4 • 25
   Commutative Property of Multiplication
   100 • 4 • 25
   100 • 100
   Associative Property of Multiplication
   10,000

Extra Practice

CHAPTER 3

page 712 Extra Practice

13. mean: 12.9
median: 12
modes: 10 and 12
outlier: 19

14. mean: 81.8
median: 85.5
modes: 85 and 90
outlier: 50

CHAPTER 3

# Extra Practice

**Estimate. State the method you used.** 1–6. Answers may vary. Samples are given. Lesson 3-1

1. 5.35 + 7.953 about 13; rounding
2. 25.68 − 3.7 about 22; rounding
3. 6.877 + 3.521 + 8.5 about 19; front-end
4. 103.890 − 25.6 about 70; rounding
5. 42.875 + 36.982 + 45.7 about 120; clustering
6. 42.651 − 12.8 about 30; rounding

**Estimate each product or quotient.** Lesson 3-2

7. 9.5(12.31) about 120
8. 24.8 ÷ 5.03 about 5
9. 2.8 · 6.11 about 18
10. −5.78 ÷ 1.95 about −3
11. (−2.468)(−9.031) about 18
12. −19.32 ÷ 4.025 about −5

**Find the mean, median, and mode. When the answer is not an integer, round to the nearest tenth. Identify any outliers.** Lesson 3-3

13. 10 13 10 15 12 11 12 19 14 See margin.
14. 85 86 80 85 90 90 50 88 See margin.
15. \$25 \$30 \$32 \$28 \$30 \$15 \$28 \$30 mean: \$27.30; median: \$29; mode: \$30; outlier: \$15
16. 6.2 4.5 4.8 12.3 5.7 4.8 6.0 mean: 6.3; median: 5.7; mode: 4.8; outlier: 12.3

**Evaluate each formula for the values given.** Lesson 3-4

17. perimeter of a rectangle: $P = 2\ell + 2w$ when $\ell = 45$ yd and $w = 20$ yd 130 yd
18. circumference of a circle: $C = 2\pi r$ when $r = 6.8$ in.; use 3.14 for $\pi$ 42.704 in.
19. distance traveled: $d = rt$ when $r = 50$ mi/h and $t = 3.5$ h 175 mi
20. perimeter of a square: $P = 4s$ when $s = 12$ cm 48 cm

**Solve each equation.** Lessons 3-5 and 3-6

21. $t + 4.5 = 17.2$ 12.7
22. $15.5 + y = 10.5$ −5
23. $x - 70.2 = 23.6$ 93.8
24. $1.2b = 6$ 5
25. $c \div 5.3 = 12$ 63.6
26. $-21.2 = p - 12.7$ −8.5
27. $f \div 5.25 = 7.8$ 40.95
28. $6.4m = 38.4$ 6
29. $-3.1 = -31a$ 0.1
30. $h + 25.8 = 76$ 50.2
31. $101.5 = j - 82.8$ 184.3
32. $-50.8 = d + 36.2$ −87
33. $4.5v = 13.5$ 3
34. $s \div 10.5 = 42$ 441
35. $26.2 = z - 6.55$ 32.75

**Complete each statement.** Lesson 3-7

36. 0.95 m = ■ cm 95
37. 250 mL = ■ L 0.25
38. 2.5 kg = ■ g 2,500
39. 60 g = ■ kg 0.060
40. 0.54 L = ■ mL 540
41. 5.62 m = ■ cm 562
42. 58 cm = ■ m 0.58
43. 564 mm = ■ m 0.564
44. 345 g = ■ mg 345,000
45. 36 mg = ■ g 0.036
46. 234 cm = ■ m 2.34
47. 567 mg = ■ g 0.567

CHAPTER 4 Extra Practice

1. 1, 2, 3, 4, 5, 6, 10, 12, 15, 20, 30, 60

6. 1, 2, 4, 5, 10, 20, 25, 50, 100

**List all the factors of each number.** Lesson 4-1

1. 60 See above right.
2. 45 1, 3, 5, 9, 15, 45
3. 64 1, 2, 4, 8, 16, 32, 64
4. 46 1, 2, 23, 46
5. 36 1, 2, 3, 4, 6, 9, 12, 18, 36
6. 100 See above.

**Evaluate each expression.** Lesson 4-2

7. $x^2$, for $x = 8$ 64
8. $-2v^3$, for $v = 2$ −16
9. $5t^2 - 4$, for $t = 4$ 76
10. $a^3 + 10$, for $a = -5$ −115
11. $mn^2$, for $m = 3$ and $n = 4$ 48
12. $6(2r - 4)^2$, for $r = 7$ 600

**Is each number *prime*, *composite*, or *neither*? For each composite number, write the prime factorization. Use exponents where possible.** Lesson 4-3

13. 25 composite; $5^2$
14. 36 composite; $2^2 \cdot 3^2$
15. 47 prime
16. 38 composite; $2 \cdot 19$
17. 1 neither
18. 117 composite; $3^2 \cdot 13$

**Find the GCF.** Lesson 4-3

19. 20, 30 10
20. 8, 12, 18 2
21. $5x, 40x$ $5x$
22. $6y, 108$ 6

**Write in simplest form.** Lesson 4-4

23. $\frac{12}{20}$ $\frac{3}{5}$
24. $\frac{4}{20}$ $\frac{1}{5}$
25. $\frac{35}{80}$ $\frac{7}{16}$
26. $\frac{18}{36}$ $\frac{1}{2}$
27. $\frac{13}{52}$ $\frac{1}{4}$
28. $\frac{75}{100}$ $\frac{3}{4}$
29. $\frac{16}{50}$ $\frac{8}{25}$
30. $\frac{5x}{65x^2}$ $\frac{1}{13x}$
31. $\frac{3x^2}{45x}$ $\frac{x}{15}$
32. $\frac{50a^2}{5a}$ $10a$
33. $\frac{36x}{16}$ $\frac{9x}{4}$
34. $\frac{100pq}{625q}$ $\frac{4p}{25}$

**Graph each rational number on one number line.** 35–39. See below. Lesson 4-6

35. 0.2
36. $\frac{3}{10}$
37. −2
38. −1
39. $-\frac{1}{2}$

**Evaluate each expression for $a = 10$ and $b = -4$. Write in simplest form.** Lesson 4-6

40. $\frac{a+b}{a}$ $\frac{3}{5}$
41. $\frac{b}{a}$ $-\frac{2}{5}$
42. $\frac{a-b}{3a}$ $\frac{7}{15}$
43. $\frac{b^2}{a^2}$ $\frac{4}{25}$

**Simplify each expression.** Lessons 4-7 and 4-8

44. $8a^2 \cdot 3a^4$ $24a^6$
45. $3y^2 \cdot 2y^3$ $6y^5$
46. $(p^5)^6$ $p^{30}$
47. $(x^3)(y)(x^5)$ $x^8y$
48. $\frac{6x^2}{2x^5}$ $\frac{3}{x^3}$
49. $\frac{18t^{20}}{6t^5}$ $3t^{15}$
50. $\frac{b^2}{b^3}$ $\frac{1}{b}$
51. $12^0$ 1

**Multiply. Express each result in scientific notation.** Lesson 4-9

52. $(5 \times 10^4)(8 \times 10^9)$ $4 \times 10^{14}$
53. $(1.1 \times 10^6)(6 \times 10^{10})$ $6.6 \times 10^{16}$
54. $(3 \times 10^{12})(4 \times 10^8)$ $1.2 \times 10^{21}$



35–39.

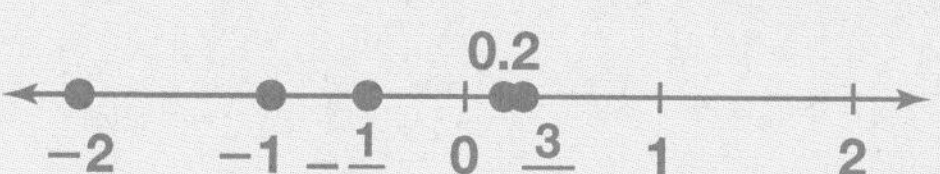

CHAPTER 5

# Extra Practice

**Find the LCM of each group of numbers or expressions.** Lesson 5-1

**1.** 15, 30 30 **2.** 4, 8, 10 40 **3.** $8x, 12y$ $24xy$ **4.** $3t^2, 5t$ $15t^2$

**Compare. Use >, <, or = to complete each statement.** Lesson 5-1

**5.** $\frac{5}{8}$ ■ $\frac{3}{5}$ > **6.** $\frac{3}{10}$ ■ $\frac{1}{3}$ < **7.** $\frac{3}{4}$ ■ $\frac{6}{8}$ = **8.** $-\frac{1}{5}$ ■ $-\frac{1}{4}$ >

**Write each fraction or mixed number as a decimal.** Lesson 5-2

**9.** $\frac{7}{8}$ 0.875 **10.** $2\frac{3}{5}$ 2.6 **11.** $\frac{3}{11}$ $0.\overline{27}$ **12.** $\frac{16}{5}$ 3.2 **13.** $-\frac{7}{10}$ −0.7 **14.** $-2\frac{1}{9}$ $-2.\overline{1}$

**Write each decimal as a fraction or mixed number in simplest form.** Lesson 5-2

**15.** 1.3 $1\frac{3}{10}$ **16.** 0.605 $\frac{121}{200}$ **17.** $0.\overline{6}$ $\frac{2}{3}$ **18.** $-0.\overline{15}$ $-\frac{5}{33}$ **19.** 0.35 $\frac{7}{20}$ **20.** 5.4 $5\frac{2}{5}$

**Add or subtract.** Lesson 5-3

**21.** $\frac{2}{5} + \frac{3}{5}$ 1 **22.** $3\frac{3}{4} - 1\frac{5}{6}$ $\frac{23}{12} = 1\frac{11}{12}$ **23.** $-\frac{5}{8} + \frac{1}{4}$ $-\frac{3}{8}$ **24.** $\frac{10}{x} - \frac{12}{x}$ $-\frac{2}{x}$

**25.** $\frac{1}{2} - \frac{3}{4}$ $-\frac{1}{4}$ **26.** $4\frac{5}{6} + 5\frac{2}{9}$ $10\frac{1}{18}$ **27.** $\frac{5}{t} + \frac{3}{4}$ $\frac{20 + 3t}{4t}$ **28.** $5\frac{1}{3} - \frac{7}{8}$ $4\frac{11}{24}$

**Find each product or quotient.** Lesson 5-4

**29.** $\frac{3}{5} \cdot \frac{2}{3}$ $\frac{2}{5}$ **30.** $\frac{5}{6} \div 1\frac{2}{3}$ $\frac{1}{2}$ **31.** $-\frac{7}{10} \cdot 1\frac{3}{7}$ −1 **32.** $\frac{5y}{6} \div \frac{2y}{3}$ $\frac{5}{4}$ **33.** $-\frac{2}{3} \cdot \left(-\frac{9}{22}\right)$ $\frac{3}{11}$

**34.** $10\frac{5}{8} \div \frac{5}{8}$ 17 **35.** $\frac{5x}{7} \cdot \frac{1}{5}$ $\frac{x}{7}$ **36.** $\left(-\frac{1}{2}\right)\left(-\frac{3}{4}\right)$ $\frac{3}{8}$ **37.** $\frac{2}{5} \div \left(-\frac{1}{5}\right)$ −2 **38.** $\frac{6}{7} \cdot \frac{3}{7}$ $\frac{18}{49}$

**Complete each statement.** Lesson 5-5

**39.** 60 in. = ■ ft 5 ft **40.** 15 qt = ■ pt 30 pt **41.** 4 lb = ■ oz 64 oz

**Solve each equation.** Lessons 5-7 and 5-8

**42.** $\frac{3}{5} + a = 1\frac{2}{3}$ $1\frac{1}{15}$ **43.** $b - 3\frac{1}{2} = 5$ $8\frac{1}{2}$ **44.** $-\frac{4}{5}c = \frac{7}{10}$ $-\frac{7}{8}$

**45.** $5d = \frac{3}{4}$ $\frac{3}{20}$ **46.** $1\frac{4}{7} = f + \frac{3}{14}$ $1\frac{5}{14}$ **47.** $\frac{7}{8} = g - \frac{2}{3}$ $1\frac{13}{24}$

**Simplify each expression.** Lesson 5-9

**48.** $(8a^3)^2$ $64a^6$ **49.** $(x^2y^3)^4$ $x^8y^{12}$ **50.** $(-2v)^3$ $-8v^3$ **51.** $(abc^3)^5$ $a^5b^5c^{15}$ **52.** $(f^2g^3)^6$ $f^{12}g^{18}$

**53.** $(2xy)^3$ $8x^3y^3$ **54.** $\left(\frac{2}{5}\right)^3$ $\frac{8}{125}$ **55.** $\left(\frac{2c}{d^3}\right)^2$ $\frac{4c^2}{d^6}$ **56.** $\left(\frac{3t}{4v}\right)^2$ $\frac{9t^2}{16v^2}$ **57.** $\left(\frac{1}{4}\right)^3$ $\frac{1}{64}$

# CHAPTER 6 Extra Practice

**Write each ratio as a fraction in simplest form.** Lesson 6-1

**1.** 15 : 30 $\frac{1}{2}$ **2.** 25 to 10 $\frac{5}{2}$ **3.** 4 out of 16 $\frac{1}{4}$ **4.** $\frac{15}{35}$ $\frac{3}{7}$

**Find each unit rate.** Lesson 6-1

**5.** 40 mi/h = ■ ft/s $58.\overline{6}$ ft/s **6.** 8 cm/s = ■ m/h 288 m/h **7.** 5.5 qt/min = ■ gal/h 82.5 gal/h

**Solve each proportion. Round to the nearest tenth where necessary.** Lesson 6-2

**8.** $\frac{3}{5} = \frac{a}{60}$ 36 **9.** $\frac{8}{7} = \frac{96}{b}$ 84 **10.** $\frac{8}{c} = \frac{40}{85}$ 17 **11.** $\frac{d}{36} = \frac{2}{3}$ 24

**12.** $\frac{105}{200} = \frac{x}{40}$ 21 **13.** $\frac{8}{15} = \frac{y}{50}$ 26.7 **14.** $\frac{z}{40} = \frac{11}{15}$ 29.3 **15.** $\frac{t}{2} = \frac{1.5}{8}$ 0.4

**The scale of a map is 4 in. : 25 mi. Find the actual distance for each map distance. Round to the nearest tenth where necessary.** Lesson 6-3

**16.** 10 in. 62.5 mi **17.** 5.5 in. 34.4 mi **18.** $\frac{1}{2}$ in. 3.1 mi **19.** 3 in. 18.8 mi

**Find each probability for one roll of a number cube. Then find the odds in favor of the event.** Lesson 6-4

**20.** $P(4)$ $\frac{1}{6}$; 1 to 5 **21.** $P(8)$ 0; 0 to 6 **22.** $P$(even number) $\frac{1}{2}$; 1 to 1 **23.** $P$(1 or 2) $\frac{1}{3}$; 1 to 2

**Write each percent as a fraction in simplest form and as a decimal.** Lesson 6-5

**24.** 10% $\frac{1}{10}$; 0.1 **25.** 200% $\frac{2}{1}$; 2 **26.** 6% $\frac{3}{50}$; 0.06 **27.** 1.75% $\frac{7}{400}$; 0.0175 **28.** 8.5% $\frac{17}{200}$; 0.085

**Write each number as a percent. Where necessary, round to the nearest tenth of a percent.** Lesson 6-5

**29.** 0.15 15% **30.** 1.2 120% **31.** $\frac{5}{12}$ 41.7% **32.** $\frac{1}{8}$ 12.5% **33.** 0.345 34.5%

**Solve each percent problem by using a proportion or an equation.** Lessons 6-6 and 6-7

**34.** Find 12% of 80. 9.6 **35.** 30% of $x$ is 12. What is $x$? 40

**36.** What percent of 50 is 2.5? 5% **37.** Find 30% of 121. 36.3

**Find each percent of change. Tell whether the change is an increase or a decrease.** Lesson 6-8

**38.** 120 to 80 33.3% decrease **39.** 40 to 100 150% increase **40.** 175 to 231 32% increase **41.** \$4 to \$3.50 12.5% decrease

**Find each sale price.** Lesson 6-9

**42.** regular price, \$100; discount, 20% \$80 **43.** regular price, \$60; discount, 25% \$45

Extra Practice



Extra Practice

## CHAPTER 7

**page 716 Extra Practice**

22.
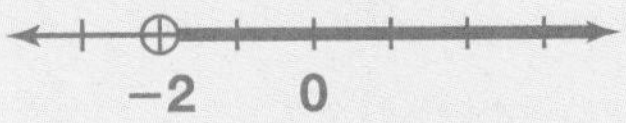


23.

24.
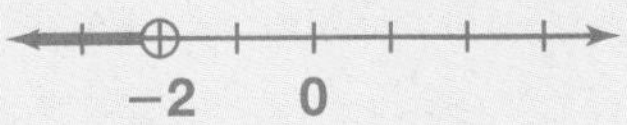


25.

26.
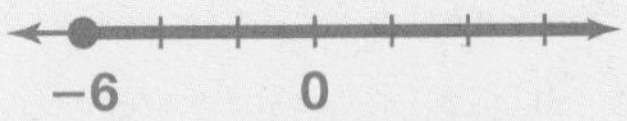


27.
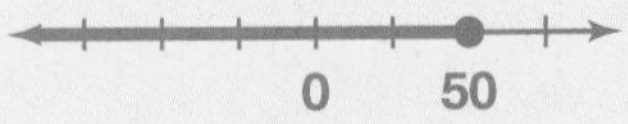


28.
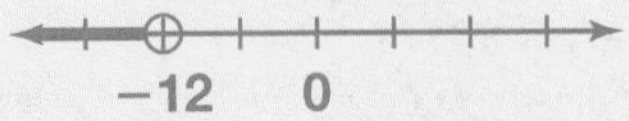


29.
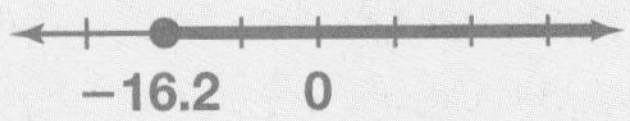


30.
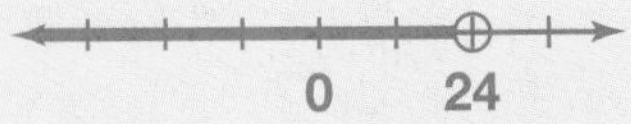


## CHAPTER 7 Extra Practice

**Solve and check each equation.** Lessons 7-1, 7-2, 7-3, and 7-5

1. $10 - 5x = 15$ −1
2. $3y + 17 = -13$ −10
3. $62 = -12z + 14$ −4
4. $6x - 2x = 12$ 3
5. $t + 5 - 2t = -10$ 15
6. $24 = 2(b - 2) - 4b$ −14
7. $5 - 2(y - 5) = 27$ −6
8. $-56a + 90 + 58a = 92$ 1
9. $8 = 3(c + 8)$ $-\frac{16}{3}$
10. $8 - \frac{t}{2} = 53$ −90
11. $75 = \frac{m}{3} + 10$ 195
12. $\frac{3}{5}p + 18 = 24$ 10
13. $0.05x - 0.08 + x = 0.97$ 1
14. $2.5y + 3.5 = -1.5$ −2
15. $6.3p + 1.2p = 22.5$ 3
16. $2x + 6 = 5x$ 2
17. $3a + 2 = a - 8$ −5
18. $3(b - 2) = 9b$ −1
19. $8(f + 3) = 10f - 32$ 28
20. $\frac{1}{4}(x - 8) = \frac{3}{4}x$ −4
21. $4(w - 2.1) = w + 0.6$ 3

**Solve and graph each inequality.** See margin for graphs. Lesson 7-6

22. $3x + 18 > 12$ $x > -2$
23. $4 + 9a \geq -23$ $a \geq -3$
24. $10.5 < -4y + 2.5$ $-2 > y$
25. $19 - 3x \geq -2$ $x \leq 7$
26. $-5(a - 3) \leq 45$ $a \geq -6$
27. $\frac{1}{2}(t - 6) \leq 22$ $t \leq 50$
28. $\frac{y}{4} - 6 < -9$ $y < -12$
29. $-31.4 \leq 2x + 1$ $x \geq -16.2$
30. $5.8 > 1 + 0.2m$ $m < 24$

**Solve for the variable indicated in red.** Lesson 7-7

31. $s = p + c$ $p = s - c$
32. $x + y = 180$ $y = 180 - x$
33. $a - b = c$ $a = c + b$
34. $I = prt$ $\frac{I}{rt} = p$

**Find the simple interest.** Lesson 7-8

35. \$450 deposited at an interest rate of 2% for 4 years \$36
36. \$3,000 deposited at an interest rate of 3% for 10 years \$900
37. \$10,000 deposited at an interest rate of 9% for 5 years \$4,500

**Find each balance.**

38. \$9,000 at 6% compounded annually for 5 years \$12,044.03
39. \$25,000 at 7% compounded semiannually for 10 years \$49,744.72
40. \$12,000 at 3% compounded semiannually for 8 years \$15,227.83
41. \$1,000 at 4% compounded annually for 10 years \$1,480.24
42. \$500 at 1.5% compounded annually for 4 years \$530.68
43. \$2,000 at 5% compounded semiannually for 2 years \$2,207.63



## CHAPTER 8

**page 717 Extra Practice**

21.
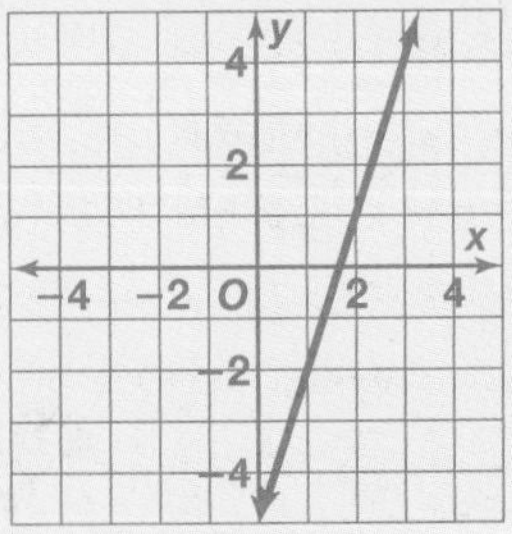


22.
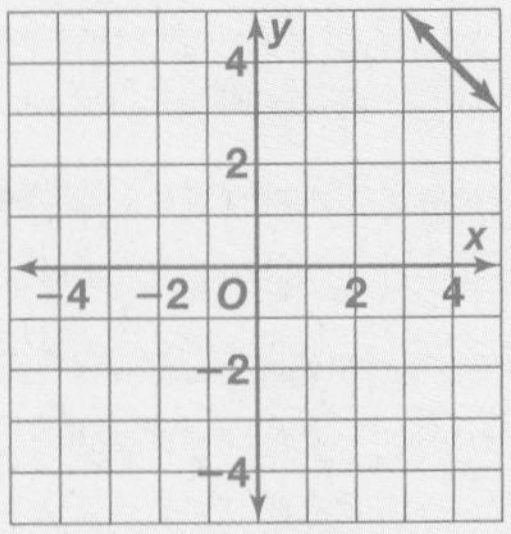


23.
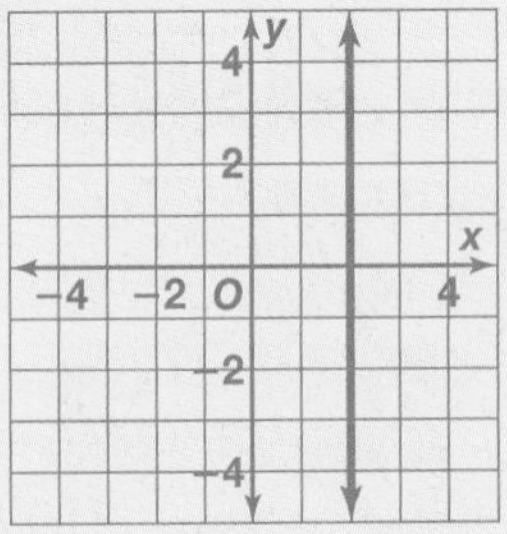


24.
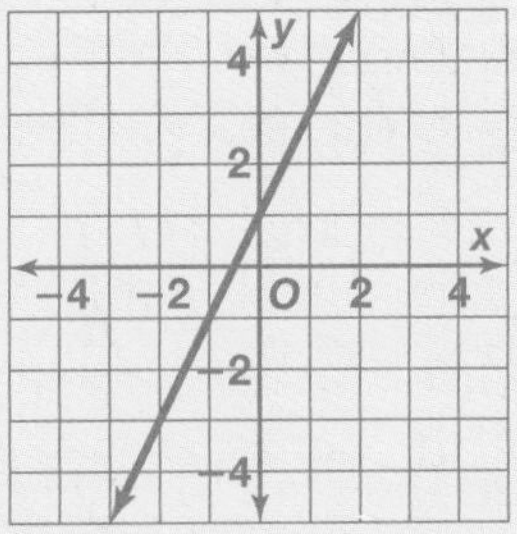

CHAPTER 8 
# Extra Practice

**Is each relation a function? Explain.** Lesson 8-1

1. $\{(3, 5), (4, 7), (4, 8), (6, 10)\}$ No, 7 and 8 are both mapped from 4.
2. $\{(0, -1), (1, 3), (-2, 4), (3, 6)\}$ Yes, each $y$ term is mapped from a different $x$ term.
3. $\{(4, 5), (5, 2), (1, -3), (-2, -3), (0, 2)\}$ Yes, each $y$ term is mapped from a different $x$ term.
4. $\{(1.5, 0.6), (1.5, 1.1), (2, 1.9), (1, 3.2)\}$ No, 1.1 and 0.6 are both mapped from 1.5.

**Find the solution of each equation for $x = -3, 0$, and 2.** Lesson 8-2

5. $y = 3x - 2$ (−3, −11), (0, −2), (2, 4)
6. $y = 2x + 5$ (−3, −1), (0, 5), (2, 9)
7. $y = \frac{1}{2}x + 8$ $(-3, 6\frac{1}{2})$, (0, 8), (2, 9)
8. $x = 3 - y$ (−3, 6), (0, 3), (2, 1)
9. $y = -4$ (−3, −4), (0, −4), (2, −4)
10. $2y = 6x - 10$ (−3, −14), (0, −5), (2, 1)
11. $x - 2y = 3$ (−3, −3), $(0, -\frac{3}{2})$, $(2, -\frac{1}{2})$
12. $y = -x - 1.5$ (−3, 1.5), (0, −1.5), (2, −3.5)

**Find the slope and $y$-intercept of the graph of each equation.** Lesson 8-3

13. $y = 5x - 4$ 5, −4
14. $y = 10 - 3x$ −3, 10
15. $2y = 3x + 12$ $\frac{3}{2}$, 6
16. $4x + y = 16$ −4, 16
17. $y = \frac{3}{5}x - 1$ $\frac{3}{5}$, −1
18. $12x - 6y = 30$ 2, −5
19. $y = x - \frac{1}{2}$ 1, $-\frac{1}{2}$
20. $x - y = -2$ 1, 2

**Graph each line.** 21–26. See margin.

21. slope 3, through (0, −5)
22. slope −1, through (3, 5)
23. no slope, through (2, −1)
24. $y = 2x + 1$
25. $x + y = 4$
26. $y = \frac{1}{2}x - 1$

**Write a rule for each function.** Lesson 8-4

27. $y = 3x - 1$

| $x$ | $y$ |
|---|---|
| 0 | −1 |
| 1 | 2 |
| 2 | 5 |
| 3 | 8 |

28. $y = 2x + 6$

| $x$ | $y$ |
|---|---|
| −1 | 4 |
| 0 | 6 |
| 1 | 8 |
| 2 | 10 |

29. $y = 5x + 4$

| $x$ | $y$ |
|---|---|
| −2 | −6 |
| 0 | 4 |
| 2 | 14 |
| 4 | 24 |

**Use the table to complete Exercises 30 and 31.** Lesson 8-5

30. Make a scatter plot of (time studying, test grade). See margin.
31. Is there a positive correlation, negative correlation, or no correlation between the sets of data? Explain. Positive correlation; as you move to the right, most scores increase.

**Study Time**

| Time Spent Studying (minutes) | 40 | 30 | 20 | 50 | 75 |
|---|---|---|---|---|---|
| Test Grade | 85 | 80 | 60 | 80 | 90 |

**Solve each system by graphing.** 32–35. See margin for graphs. Lessons 8-7 and 8-8

32. $y = x + 3$; $3x - y = 1$ (2, 5)
33. $x + y = -7$; $x - y = 1$ (−3, −4)
34. $y > 2x - 4$; $y < -3x + 6$
35. $x + y < 10$; $x - y < -5$

25.
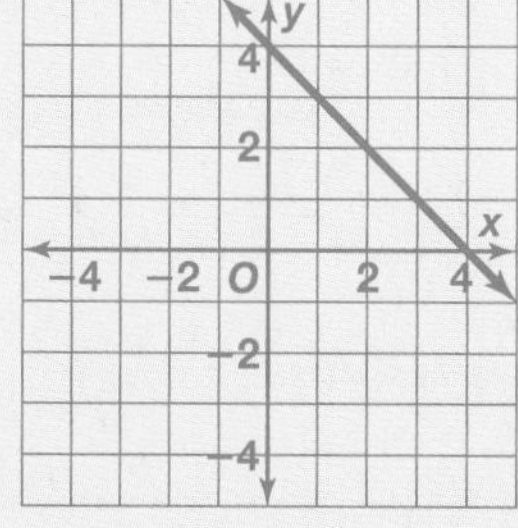

26.
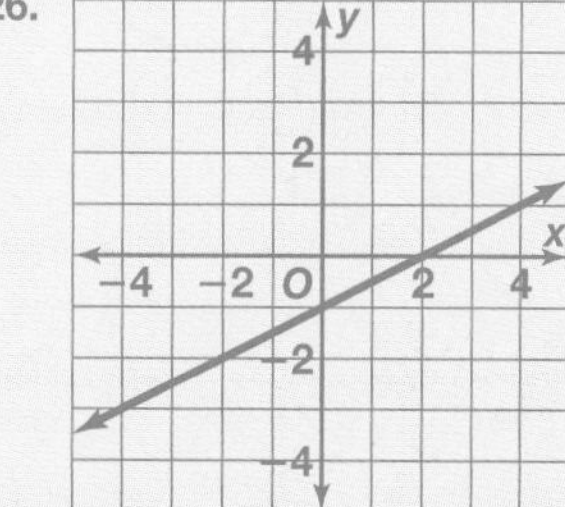

30.
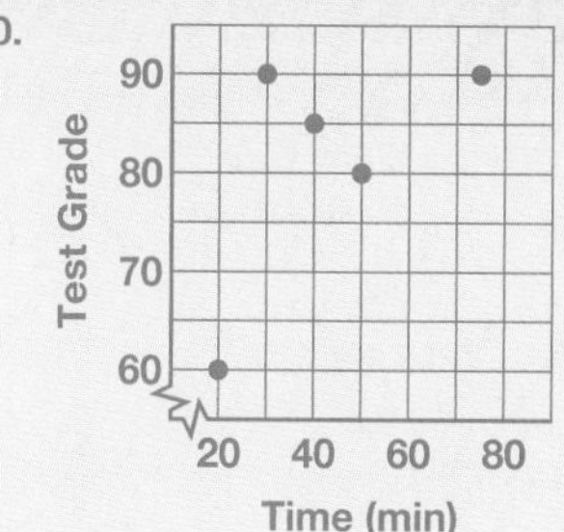

32.
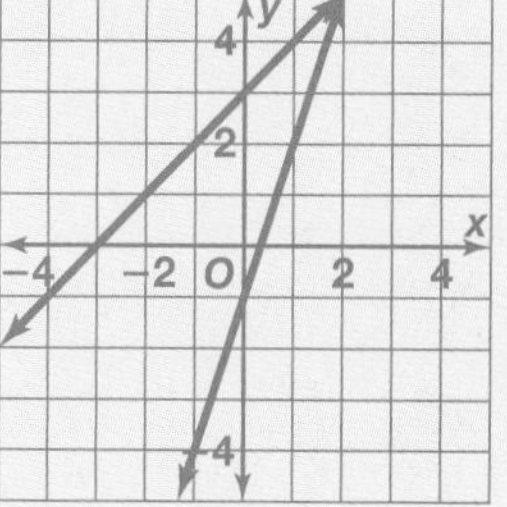
33.
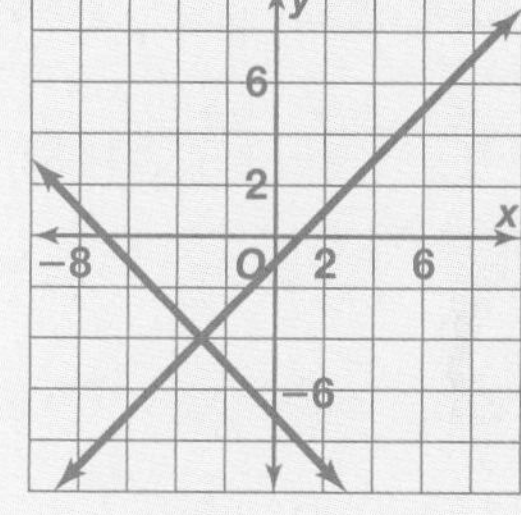
34.
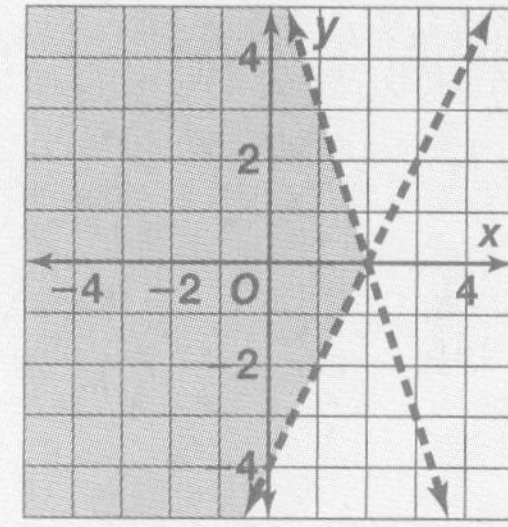
35.
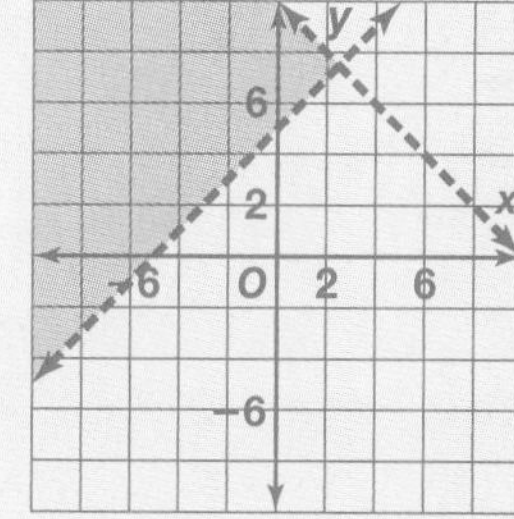

## CHAPTER 9

**page 718 Extra Practice**

16.

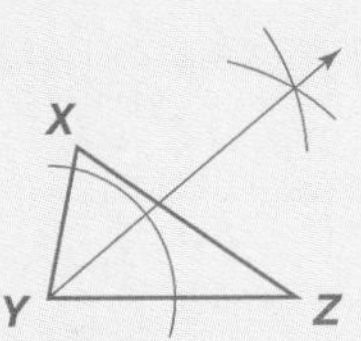


17.

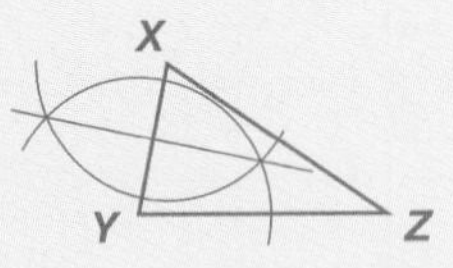


18.

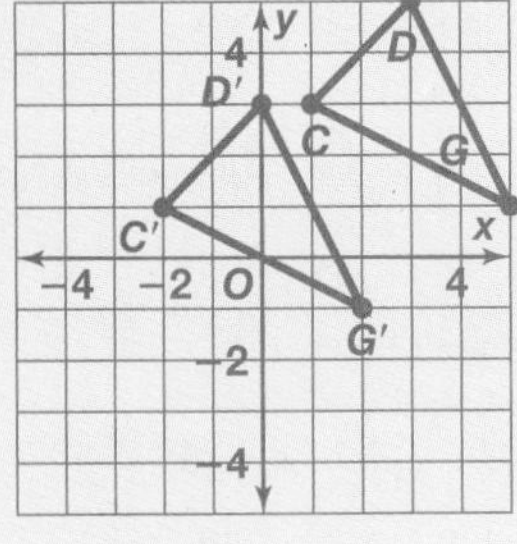


19.

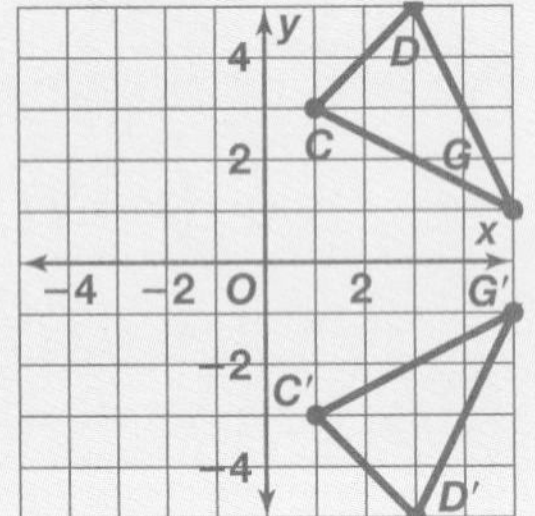


20.

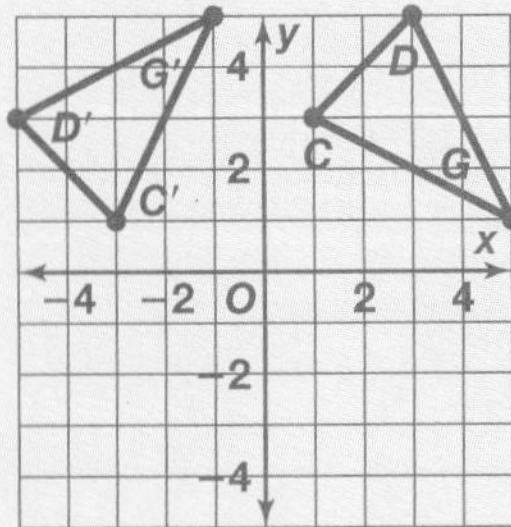


# CHAPTER 9 Extra Practice

**Use the figure at the right.** Lesson 9-1

1. Name the line in three ways.
   $\overleftrightarrow{AB}, \overleftrightarrow{AC}, \overleftrightarrow{BC}$
2. Name four different rays.
   $\overrightarrow{AC}, \overrightarrow{BC}, \overrightarrow{CA}, \overrightarrow{BA}$

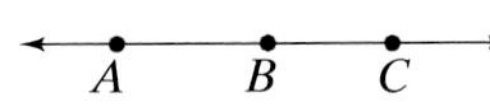


**Use the figure at the right. Name each of the following.** Lesson 9-1

3. four segments that intersect $\overline{MR}$
   $\overline{RS}, \overline{MQ}, \overline{MN}, \overline{UR}$
4. three segments parallel to $\overline{MR}$
   $\overline{NU}, \overline{PT}, \overline{QS}$
5. three segments skew to $\overline{MR}$
   $\overline{UT}, \overline{NP}, \overline{ST}$

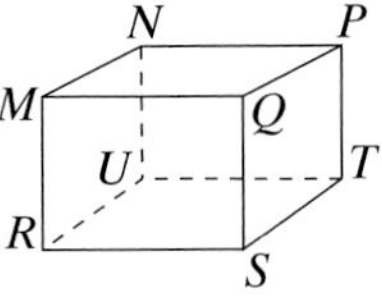


**In the figure at the right, $x \parallel y$.** Lesson 9-2

6. List all angles that are congruent to $\angle 1$.
   $\angle 4, \angle 5, \angle 7$
7. If $m\angle 5 = 67°$, what are the measures of the other angles? $m\angle 7 = 67°$; $m\angle 4 = 67°$;
   $m\angle 1 = 67°$; $m\angle 8 = 113°$; $m\angle 6 = 113°$; $m\angle 2 = 113°$; $m\angle 3 = 113°$

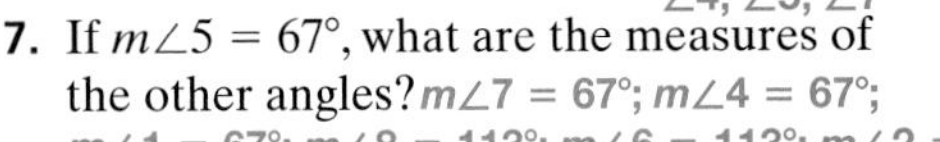

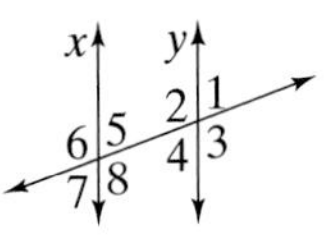


**Judging by appearances, classify each figure.** Lesson 9-3

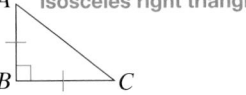

8. isosceles right triangle
   (Figure: triangle $ABC$)
9. rectangle

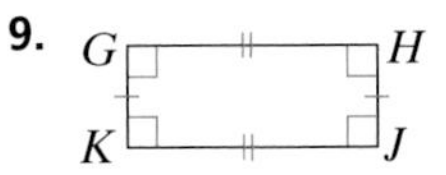

10. isosceles obtuse triangle

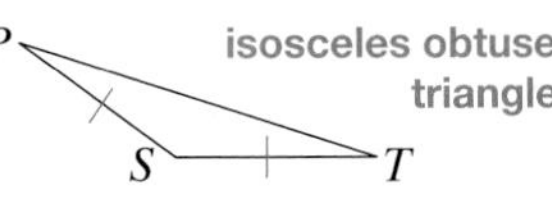


11. $\triangle XYZ \cong \triangle STU$. Which of the following must be true? A Lesson 9-5

   A. $\overline{YZ} \cong \overline{TU}$ B. $\angle X \cong \angle T$ C. $\overline{ZX} \cong \overline{TS}$
   D. $\angle YZX \cong \angle STU$ E. $\triangle YZX \cong \triangle UTS$

**Find the circumference of each circle with the given radius or diameter.** Lesson 9-6

12. radius = 4 in. about 25.12 in.
13. diameter = 25 ft about 78.5 ft
14. radius = 7.8 cm about 48.984 cm
15. diameter = 100 m about 314 m

**Draw $\triangle XYZ$ with acute $\angle Y$.** Lesson 9-7

16. Construct the angle bisector of $\angle Y$. See margin.
17. Construct a bisector of $\overline{XY}$. See margin.

**Graph the image of $\triangle CDG$ with vertices $C(1, 3)$, $D(3, 5)$, and $G(5, 1)$ after each transformation.** 18–20. See margin. Lessons 9-8, 9-9, and 9-10

18. 3 units left, 2 units down
19. reflected over the $x$-axis
20. rotated 90° about the origin

# CHAPTER 10 Extra Practice

**Find the area of each figure.** Lessons 10-1 and 10-2

**1.**

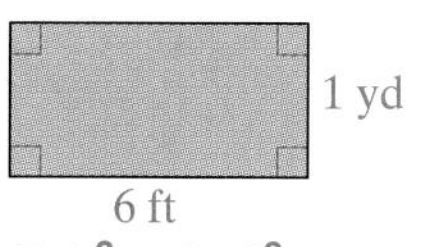


18 ft$^2$ or 2 yd$^2$

**2.**

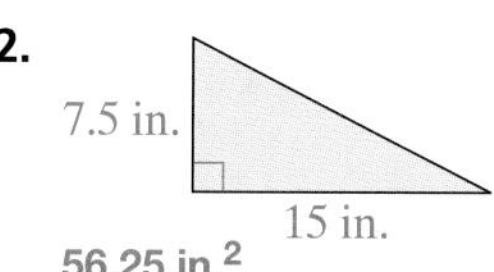


56.25 in.$^2$

**3.**

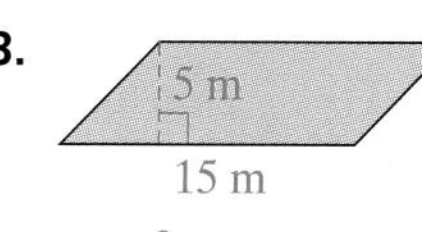


75 m$^2$

**4.**

50 mi
30 mi
80 mi

1,950 mi$^2$

**5.**

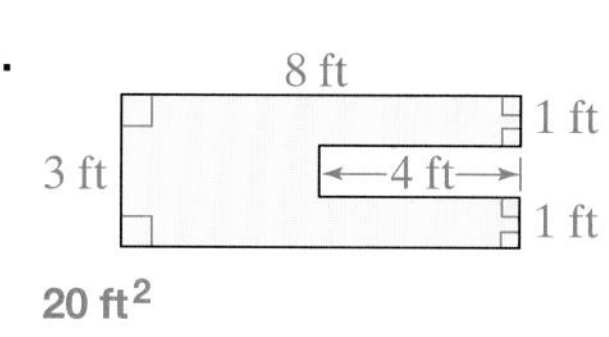


20 ft$^2$

**6.**

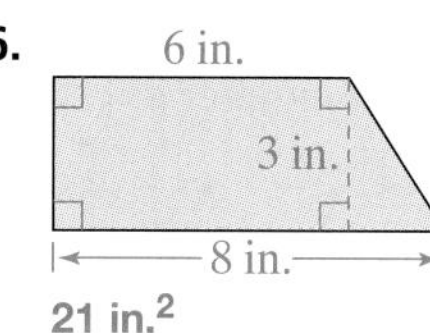


21 in.$^2$

**Find the area of each figure. Give an exact answer and an approximate answer, to the nearest tenth.** Lesson 10-3

**7.**

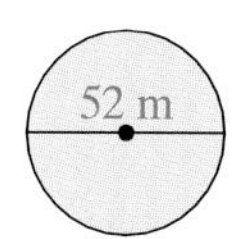


676π m$^2$, 2,122.6 m$^2$

**8.**

5 cm

25π cm$^2$, 78.5 cm$^2$

**9.**

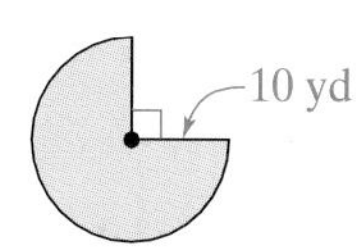


75π yd$^2$, 235.5 yd$^2$

Lesson 10-4

**10.** Draw a net to represent a rectangular box that is 3 ft long, 5 ft wide, and 2 ft high. Label dimensions on the net and find the surface area. 62 ft$^2$

**Find the surface area and volume of each space figure, to the nearest tenth.** Lessons 10-5, 10-6, 10-7, and 10-9

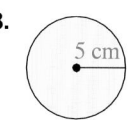

**11.**

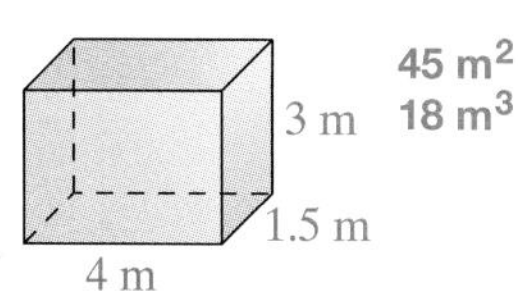


45 m$^2$
18 m$^3$

**12.**

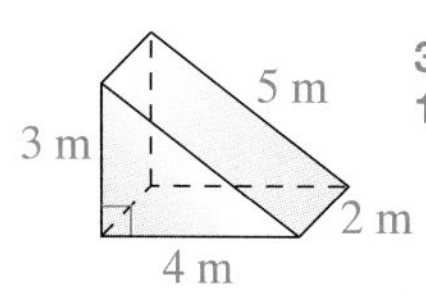


36 m$^2$
12 m$^3$

**13.**

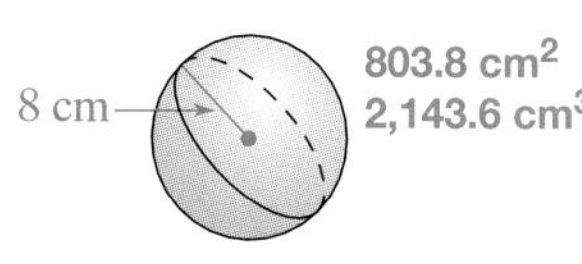


803.8 cm$^2$
2,143.6 cm$^3$

**14.**

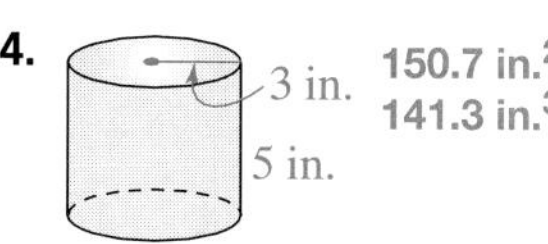


150.7 in.$^2$
141.3 in.$^3$

**15.**

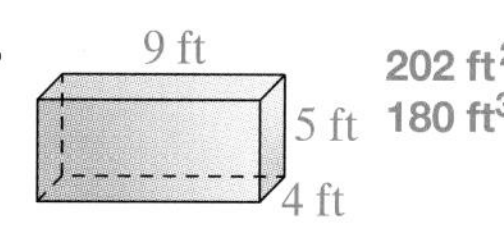


202 ft$^2$
180 ft$^3$

**16.**

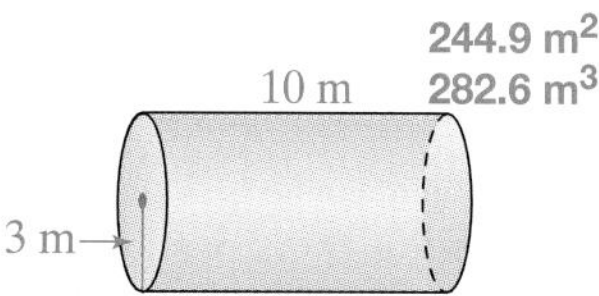


244.9 m$^2$
282.6 m$^3$

**17.**

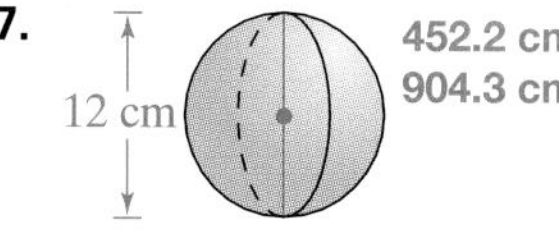


452.2 cm$^2$
904.3 cm$^3$

**18.**

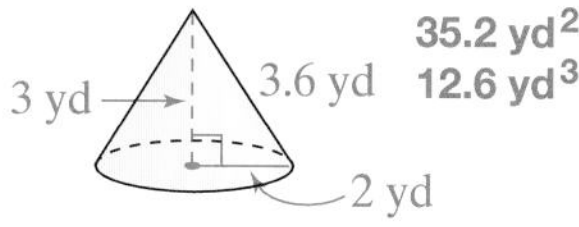


35.2 yd$^2$
12.6 yd$^3$

**19.**

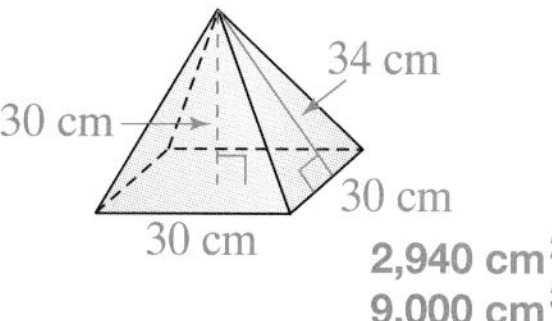


2,940 cm$^2$
9,000 cm$^3$



Extra Practice

## CHAPTER 10

page 719 Extra Practice

10.

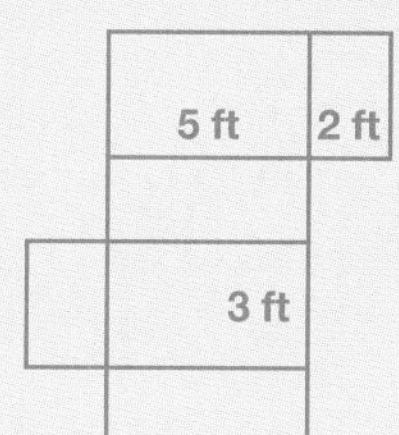

## CHAPTER 11 Extra Practice

**Simplify each square root.** Lesson 11-1

**1.** $\sqrt{4}$ 2 **2.** $\sqrt{100}$ 10 **3.** $-\sqrt{36}$ −6 **4.** $\sqrt{121}$ 11 **5.** $\sqrt{25}$ 5

**Estimate to the nearest integer.**

**6.** $\sqrt{50}$ 7 **7.** $\sqrt{12}$ 3 **8.** $\sqrt{40}$ 6 **9.** $\sqrt{105}$ 10 **10.** $\sqrt{55}$ 7

**Identify each number as rational or irrational.**

**11.** $\sqrt{9}$ rational **12.** 0.6 rational **13.** $\sqrt{5}$ irrational **14.** $0.\overline{6}$ rational **15.** 0.010010001 . . . irrational

**Find each missing length, to the nearest tenth of a unit.** Lesson 11-2

**16.** 50 in.

30 in. $x$ 40 in.

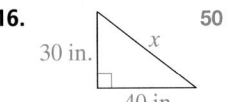

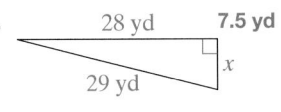

**17.** 7.5 yd

28 yd $x$ 29 yd

**18.** 23.3 m

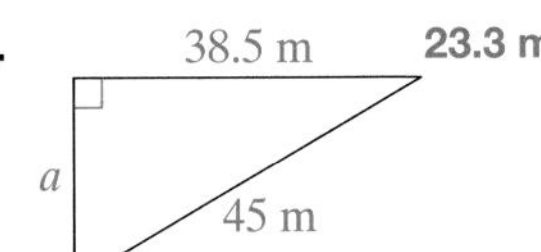


**Find the distance between each pair of points. Round to the nearest tenth.** Lesson 11-3

**19.** (4, 6), (8, 2) 5.7 **20.** (0, −4), (−5, 1) 7.1 **21.** (20, −5), (10, −8) 10.4

**Find the midpoint of each segment with the given endpoints.**

**22.** $A(5, 4)$ and $B(3, 0)$ (4, 2) **23.** $C(-2, -4)$ and $D(3, 1)$ $\left(\frac{1}{2}, -\frac{3}{2}\right)$ **24.** $E(-1, 5)$ and $F(2, -1)$ $\left(\frac{1}{2}, 2\right)$

**Find the missing lengths.** Lesson 11-5

**25.** $x = 32\sqrt{2}$ cm, $y = 32$ cm

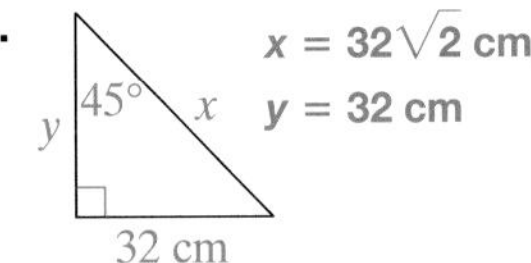


**26.** $y = 72$ mm, $x = 36\sqrt{3}$ mm

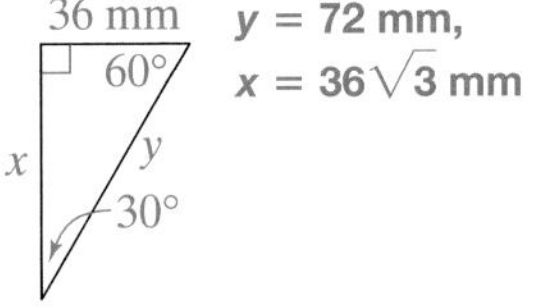

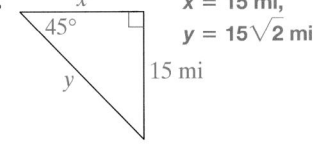

**27.** $x = 15$ mi, $y = 15\sqrt{2}$ mi

$x$ 45° $y$ 15 mi

**Find each value. Round to four decimal places.** Lessons 11-6 and 11-7

**28.** sin 10° 0.1736 **29.** tan 85° 11.4301 **30.** cos 33° 0.8387

**31.** tan 5° 0.0875 **32.** sin 78° 0.9781 **33.** cos 65° 0.4226

**34.** cos 52° 0.6157 **35.** tan 50° 1.1918 **36.** sin 30° 0.5

CHAPTER 12

# Extra Practice

**Display each set of data in a frequency table. Then draw a line plot for each frequency table. Find the range.** 1–2. See margin for tables and line plots. Lesson 12-1

1. 21 22 20 21 21 20 23 22 21 21
   range = 3
2. 95 100 95 95 90 80 85 80 95 100
   range = 20

**Use box-and-whisker plots to compare data sets. Use a single number line.** Lesson 12-2

3. 1st set: 26 60 36 44 62 24 29 50 37 52 40 41 18 39 64 42
   2nd set: 78 22 29 67 10 62 50 72 8 63 35 80 52 60 18 65 61 See margin.

**Use the graph at the right for Exercises 4 and 5.** Lesson 12-3

4. The graph suggests that the number of farms in 1982 was three times the number in 1992. Is this true? Explain. See below.
5. Redraw the graph without a break. See margin.

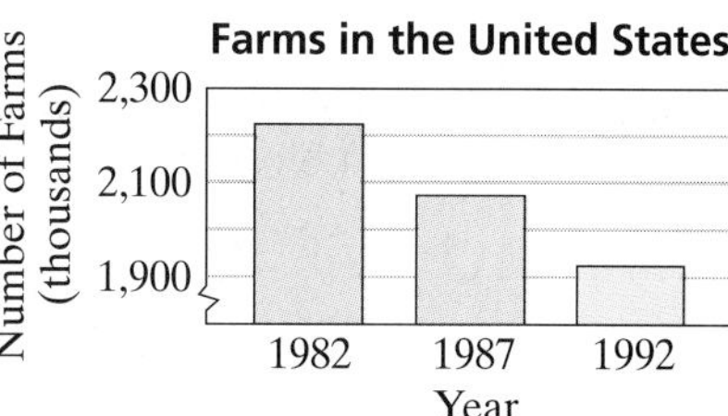


4. No, in 1992 there were about 1,900 thousand farms. Three times 1,900 thousand is 5,700 thousand. In 1982 there were about 2,200 thousand farms.

6. A menu shows that you can pick one vegetable from four choices, one potato dish from five choices, and one main dish from two choices. How many different choices of meals do you have? 40 choices Lesson 12-4

**You select letters at random from the word MATHEMATICS.** Lesson 12-5

7. Find the probability that you select A and, after replacing A, then select T. $\frac{4}{121}$
8. Find the probability that you select A and, without replacing A, then select T. $\frac{2}{55}$

**Simplify each expression.** Lesson 12-6

9. ${}_3C_2$ 3
10. ${}_3P_2$ 6
11. ${}_5P_2$ 20
12. ${}_7C_3$ 35
13. ${}_{10}C_3$ 120
14. ${}_8P_3$ 336

**Some students were surveyed about the number of books in their lockers. The table shows the results.** Lessons 12-7 and 12-8

15. Find the experimental probability that a locker will have 3 books. $\frac{1}{6}$
16. In a school of 600 students, how many lockers would you expect to have one book? 120 lockers

**Number of Books in Students' Lockers**

| Number of Books | 1 | 2 | 3 | 4 | 5 |
|---|---|---|---|---|---|
| Number of Students | 12 | 21 | 10 | 7 | 10 |



Extra Practice

## CHAPTER 12

page 721 Extra Practice

1.

| Number | Frequency |
|---|---|
| 20 | 2 |
| 21 | 5 |
| 22 | 2 |
| 23 | 1 |

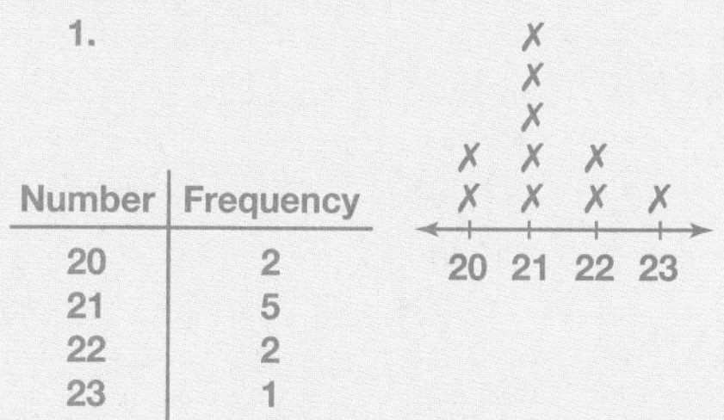


2.

| Number | Frequency |
|---|---|
| 80 | 2 |
| 85 | 1 |
| 90 | 1 |
| 95 | 4 |
| 100 | 2 |

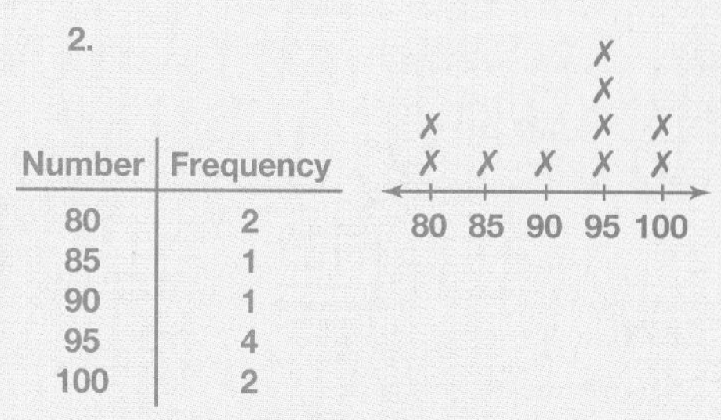


3.

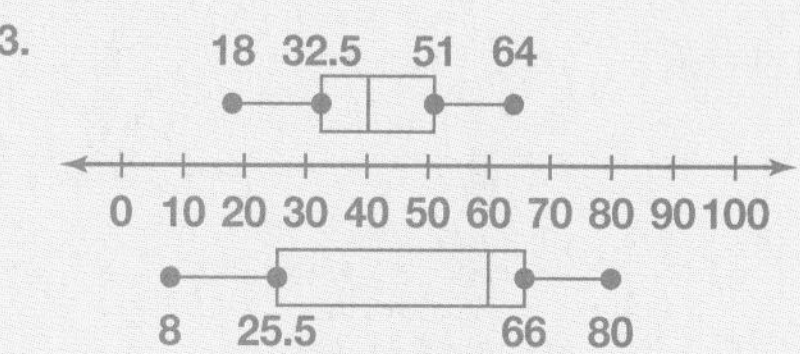


5.

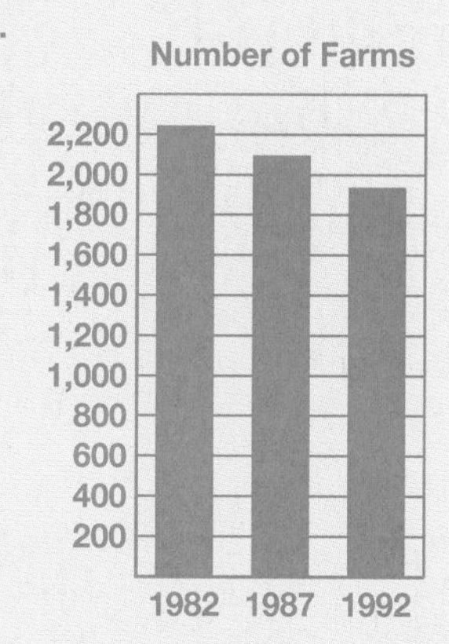


Extra Practice

# CHAPTER 13

## page 722 Extra Practice

3. 40, 48, 56, . . . start with 8 and add 8 to the previous term.

7.

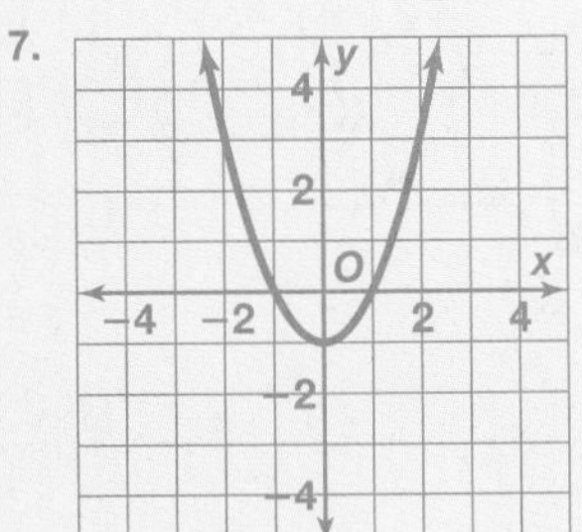

8.

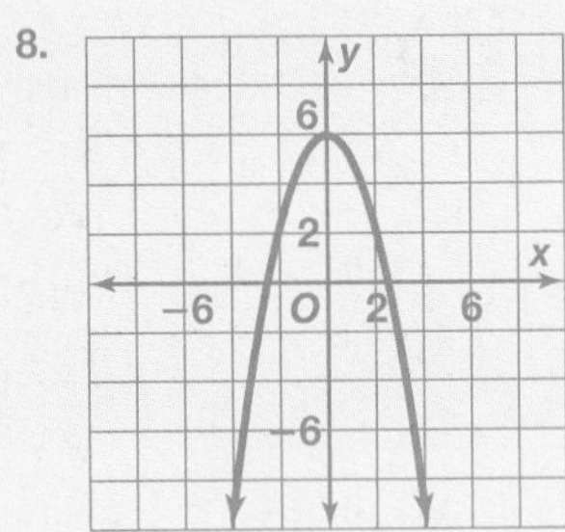

9.

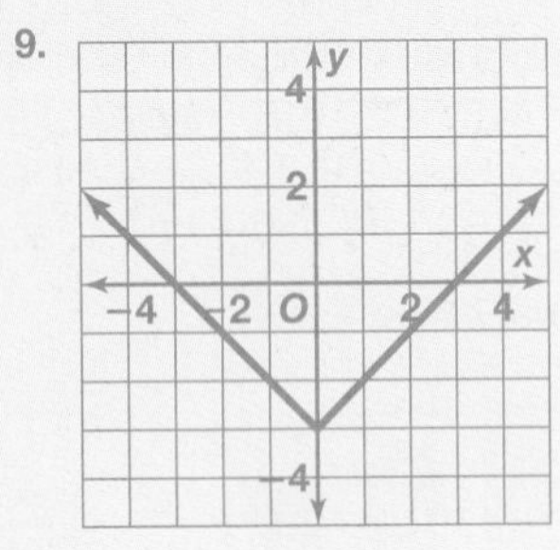

10.

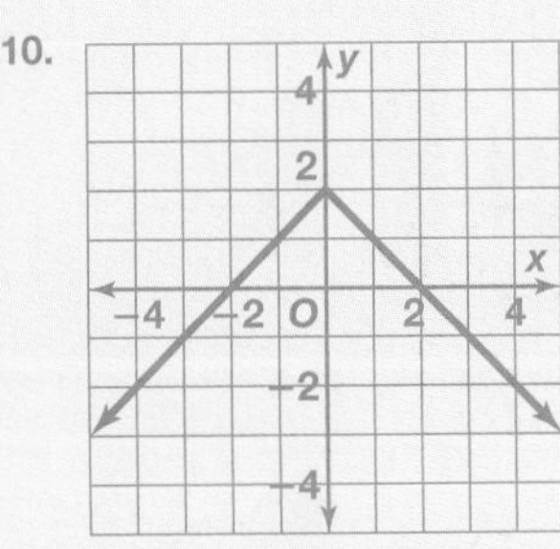

11.

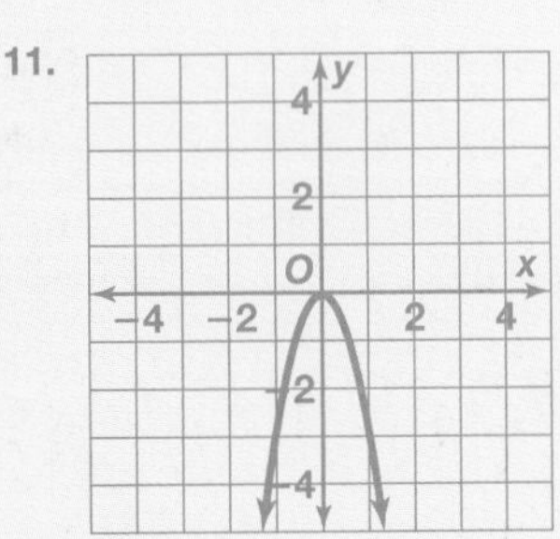

# CHAPTER 13 Extra Practice

**Find the next three terms of each sequence. Then write a rule to describe each sequence.** Lesson 13-1

1. 100, 80, 60, 40, . . . 20, 0, −20, . . . Start with 100 and subtract 20 from the previous term.
2. 6, 12, 18, 24, . . . 30, 36, 42, . . . Start with 6 and add 6 to the previous term.
3. 8, 16, 24, 32, . . . 40, 48, 56, . . . Start with 8 and add 8 to the previous term.
4. 50, 500, 5,000, 50,000, . . . See margin.
5. −5, 25, −125, 625, . . . −3,125, 15,625, −78,125, . . . Start with −5 and multiply the previous term by −5.
6. 50, 10, −30, −70, . . . −110, −150, −190, . . . Start with 50 and subtract 40 from the previous term.

**Graph each function, for $x$ values from −2 to 2.** 7–14. See margin. Lesson 13-2

7. $y = x^2 - 1$
8. $y = -x^2 + 6$
9. $y = |x| - 3$
10. $y = -|x| + 2$
11. $y = -3x^2$
12. $y = -3|x| - 1$
13. $y = 2x^2 - 2$
14. $y = \frac{1}{2}|x|$

**For each function, make a table with integer values of $x$ from 0 to 4. Then graph each function.** 15–18. See margin. Lesson 13-3

15. $y = 4^x$
16. $y = \frac{1}{2} \cdot 10^x$
17. $y = 10(0.5)^x$
18. $y = 2^x$

**Tell whether each polynomial is a *monomial,* a *binomial,* or a *trinomial.*** Lesson 13-4

19. $2x^2 - 3x - 1$ trinomial
20. $3xy$ monomial
21. $5x^3 - 15$ binomial
22. $10 - 2x + 5y$ trinomial
23. $xyz^2$ monomial
24. $56 - y$ binomial
25. $3ab - a^2 - b$ trinomial
26. 80 monomial

**Simplify each sum or difference.** Lesson 13-5

27. $(5y - 12) + (2y + 10)$ $7y - 2$
28. $(x^2 + 3x + 4) + (2x^2 + x + 6)$ $3x^2 + 4x + 10$
29. $(x^2 - 7x + 2) + (-x^2 + 6x - 2)$ $-x$
30. $(4a^2 - 3a - 2) - (2a^2 + 5a + 10)$ $2a^2 - 8a - 12$
31. $(5x - 3) + (6x^2 - 9)$ $6x^2 + 5x - 12$
32. $(15y^2 + 12y) - (12y^2 - 20)$ $3y^2 + 12y + 20$
33. $(3ab + a^2 + b^2) - (a^2 - 3b^2 - 5ab)$ $4b^2 + 8ab$
34. $(10t - t^2 - 15) + (3t^2 + 12)$ $2t^2 + 10t - 3$

**Simplify each product.** Lessons 13-6 and 13-7

35. $2x(5x^2 + 6)$ $10x^3 + 12x$
36. $y^2(x + y)$ $xy^2 + y^3$
37. $6t^2(2t^2 - 3 + 8t)$ $12t^4 - 18t^2 + 48t^3$
38. $(x - 8)(x + 1)$ $x^2 - 7x - 8$
39. $(y + 6)(2y + 4)$ $2y^2 + 16y + 24$
40. $3b(5ab + 2ab^2 + 6b)$ $15ab^2 + 6ab^3 + 18b^2$

**Use the GCF of the terms to write each expression as the product of two factors.** Lesson 13-7

41. $4x^2 - 12$ $4(x^2 - 3)$
42. $5z^2 - 20z + 30$ $5(z^2 - 4z + 6)$
43. $2a^2b - 4a + 6b$ $2(a^2b - 2a + 3b)$
44. $t^2 - 3t$ $t(t - 3)$
45. $6xy + 2x + 3x^2y$ $x(6y + 2 + 3xy)$
46. $5w^3 + 6w^2 - 3w$ $w(5w^2 + 6w - 3)$



12.

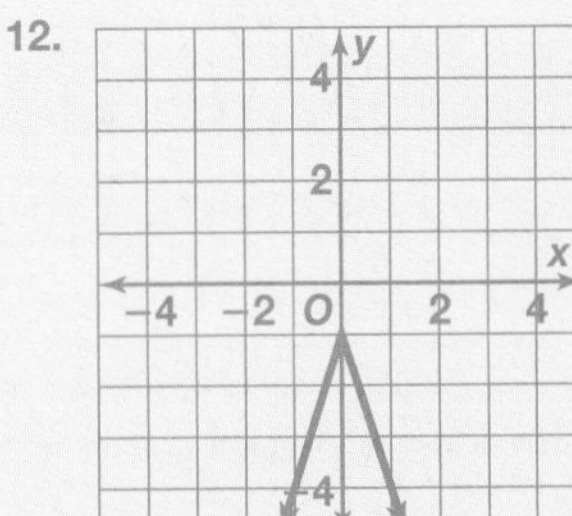

13.

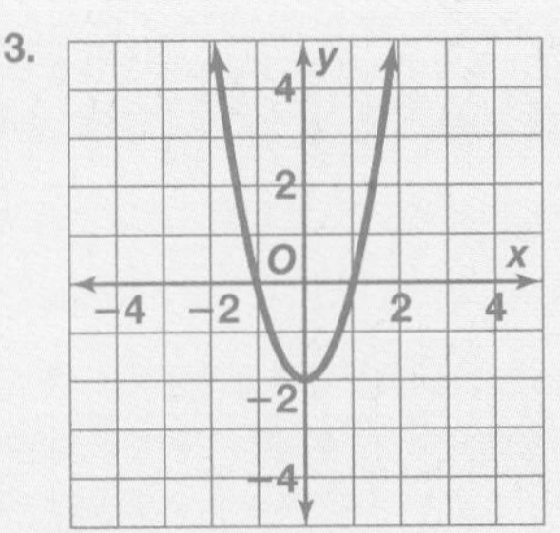

## Comparing and Ordering Whole Numbers

The numbers on a number line are in order from least to greatest.

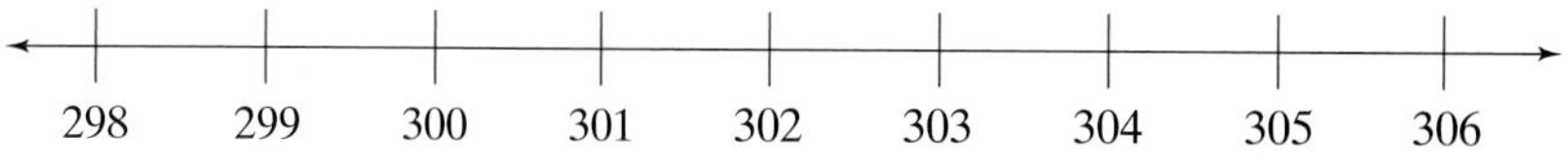

298 299 300 301 302 303 304 305 306

You can use a number line to compare whole numbers. Use the symbols > (is greater than) and < (is less than).

### Example 1

**Use > or < to compare the numbers.**

**a. 303 ■ 299**
303 is to the right of 299.
300 > 299

**b. 301 ■ 305**
301 is to the left of 305.
301 < 305

The value of a digit depends on its place in a number. Compare digits starting from the left.

### Example 2

**Use > or < to compare the numbers.**

**a. 12,060,012,875 ■ 12,060,012,675**
8 hundreds > 6 hundreds, so
12,060,012,875 > 12,060,012,675

**b. 465,320 ■ 4,653,208**
0 millions < 4 millions, so
465,320 < 4,653,208

### Exercises

**Use > or < to compare the numbers.**

1. 3,660 ■ 360 >
2. 74,328 ■ 74,238 >
3. 88,010 ■ 8,101 >
4. 87,524 ■ 9,879 >
5. 295,286 ■ 295,826 <
6. 829,631 ■ 842,832 <
7. 932,401 ■ 932,701 <
8. 60,000 ■ 500,009 <
9. 1,609,372,002 ■ 609,172,002 >
10. 45,248,315,150 ■ 45,283,718,150 <

**Write the numbers from least to greatest.**

11. 3,747; 3,474; 3,774; 3,347; 3,734
3,347; 3,474; 3,734; 3,747; 3,774
12. 70,903; 70,309; 73,909; 73,090
70,309; 70,903; 73,090; 73,909
13. 32,056,403; 302,056,403; 30,265,403; 30,256,403
30,256,403; 30,265,403; 32,056,403; 302,056,403
14. 884,172; 881,472; 887,142; 881,872
881,472; 881,872; 884,172; 887,142



14.

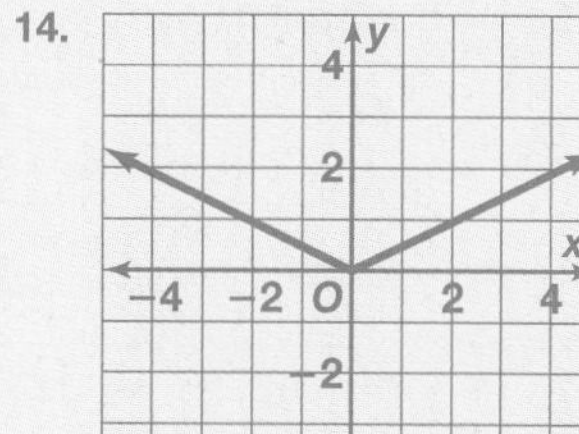


15.

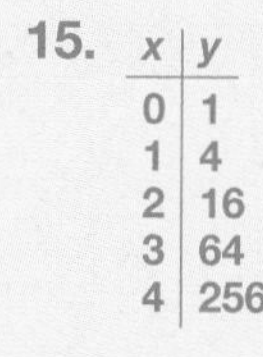

| x | y |
|---|---|
| 0 | 1 |
| 1 | 4 |
| 2 | 16 |
| 3 | 64 |
| 4 | 256 |

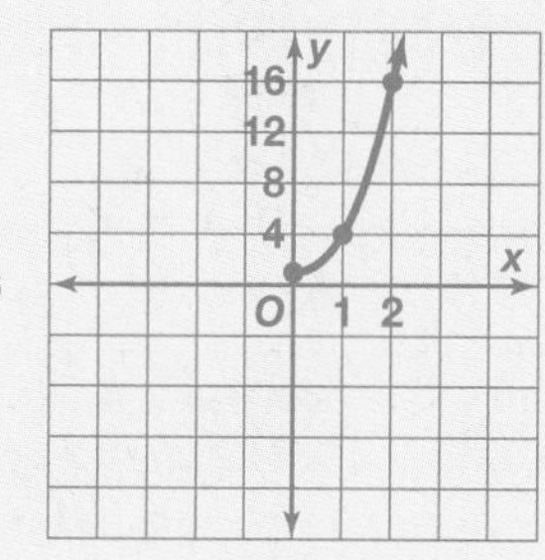


16.

| x | y |
|---|---|
| 0 | 0.5 |
| 1 | 5 |
| 2 | 50 |
| 3 | 500 |
| 4 | 5,000 |

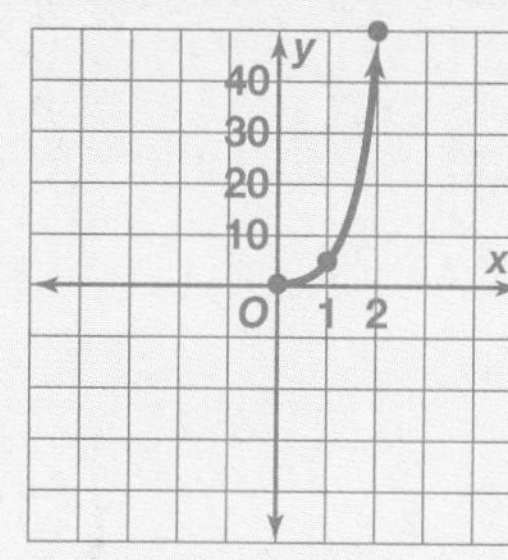


17.

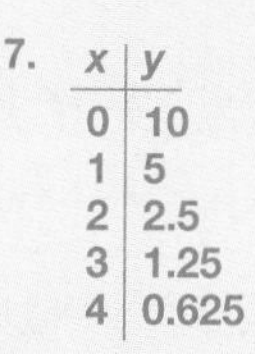

| x | y |
|---|---|
| 0 | 10 |
| 1 | 5 |
| 2 | 2.5 |
| 3 | 1.25 |
| 4 | 0.625 |

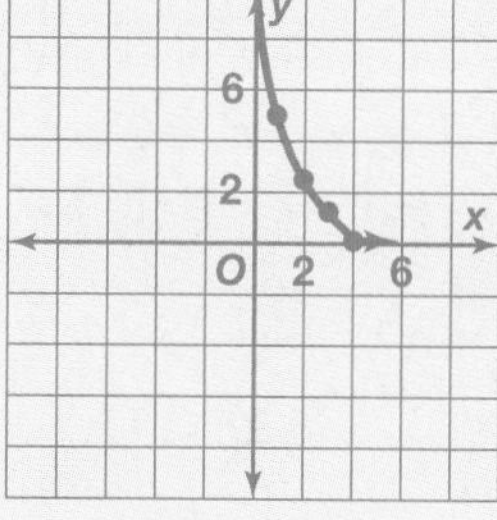


18.

| x | y |
|---|---|
| 0 | 1 |
| 1 | 2 |
| 2 | 4 |
| 3 | 8 |
| 4 | 16 |

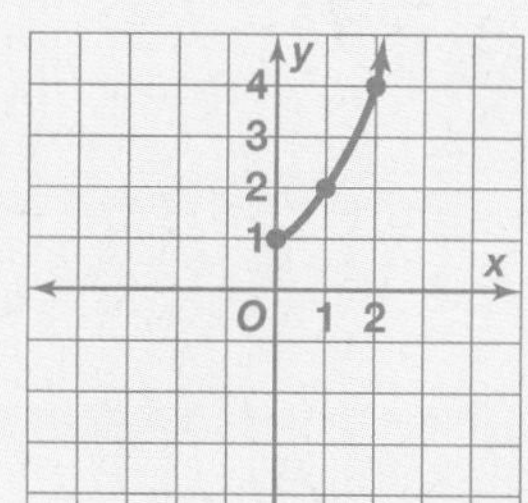

# Rounding Whole Numbers

You can use number lines to help you round numbers.

### Example 1

**a. Round 7,510 to the nearest thousand.**

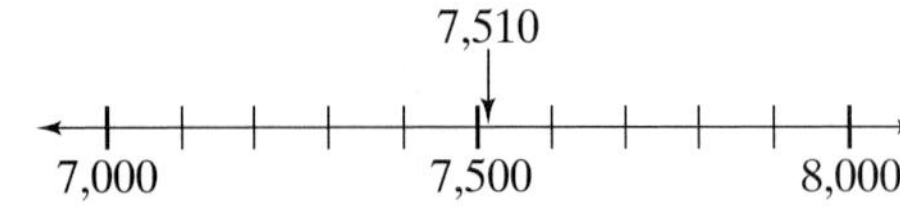


7,510 is between 7,000 and 8,000.
7,510 rounds to 8,000.

**b. Round 237 to the nearest ten.**

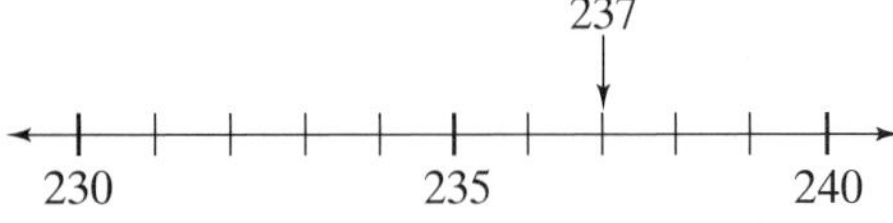


237 is between 230 and 240.
237 rounds to 240.

To round a number to a particular place, look at the digit to the right of that place. If the digit is less than 5, round down. If the digit is 5 or more, round up.

### Example 2

**Round to the place of the underlined digit.**

**a. 3,463,280**
The digit to the right of the 6 is 3, so 3,463,280 rounds down to 3,460,000.

**b. 289,543**
The digit to the right of the 9 is 5, so 289,543 rounds up to 290,000.

## Exercises

**Round to the nearest ten.**

**1.** 42 40 **2.** 89 90 **3.** 671 670 **4.** 3,482 3,480 **5.** 7,029 7,030 **6.** 661,423 661,420

**Round to the nearest thousand.**

**7.** 5,800 6,000 **8.** 3,100 3,000 **9.** 44,280 44,000 **10.** 9,936 10,000 **11.** 987 1,000 **12.** 313,591 314,000

**13.** 5,641 6,000 **14.** 37,896 38,000 **15.** 82,019 82,000 **16.** 808,155 808,000 **17.** 34,501 35,000 **18.** 650,828 651,000

**Round to the place of the underlined digit.**

**19.** 68,852 68,900 **20.** 451,006 500,000 **21.** 3,406,781 3,407,000 **22.** 28,512,030 29,000,000 **23.** 71,225,003 71,230,000

**24.** 96,359 96,400 **25.** 401,223 400,000 **26.** 8,902 9,000 **27.** 3,677 3,680 **28.** 2,551,750 2,551,800

**29.** 68,663 69,000 **30.** 701,803,229 702,000,000 **31.** 565,598 566,000 **32.** 32,810 32,800 **33.** 1,446,300 1,400,000

# Multiplying Whole Numbers

When you multiply by a two-digit number, first multiply by the ones and then multiply by the tens. Add the products.

## Example 1

**Multiply 62 × 704.**

**Step 1**

$$\begin{array}{r} 704 \\ \times\ 62 \\ \hline 1408 \end{array}$$

**Step 2**

$$\begin{array}{r} 704 \\ \times\ 62 \\ \hline 1408 \\ 42240 \end{array}$$

**Step 3**

$$\begin{array}{r} 704 \\ \times\ 62 \\ \hline 1\ 408 \\ +\ 42\ 240 \\ \hline 43{,}648 \end{array}$$

## Example 2

**Find each product.**

**a. 93 × 6**

$$\begin{array}{r} 93 \\ \times\ 6 \\ \hline 558 \end{array}$$

**b. 25 × 48**

$$\begin{array}{r} 48 \\ \times\ 25 \\ \hline 240 \\ +\ 960 \\ \hline 1{,}200 \end{array}$$

**c. 80 × 92**

$$\begin{array}{r} 921 \\ \times\ 80 \\ \hline 73{,}680 \end{array}$$

## Exercises

**Find each product.**

1. 74 × 6 — 444
2. 35 × 9 — 315
3. 53 × 7 — 371
4. 80 × 8 — 640
5. 98 × 4 — 392
6. 65 × 8 — 520
7. 512 × 3 — 1,536
8. 407 × 9 — 3,663
9. 225 × 6 — 1,350
10. 340 × 5 — 1,700
11. 816 × 7 — 5,712
12. 603 × 3 — 1,809
13. 70 × 36 — 2,520
14. 41 × 55 — 2,255
15. 38 × 49 — 1,862
16. 601 × 87 — 52,287
17. 271 × 34 — 9,214
18. 450 × 67 — 30,150
19. 6 × 82 — 492
20. 405 × 5 — 2,025
21. 81 × 9 — 729
22. 3 × 274 — 822
23. 552 × 4 — 2,208
24. 60 × 84 — 5,040
25. 52 × 17 — 884
26. 31 × 90 — 2,790
27. 78 × 52 — 4,056
28. 43 × 66 — 2,838
29. 826 × 3 — 2,478
30. 702 × 4 — 2,808
31. 8 × 180 — 1,440
32. 6 × 339 — 2,034
33. 781 × 7 — 5,467

# Dividing Whole Numbers

First estimate the quotient by rounding the divisor, the dividend, or both. When you divide, after you bring down a digit, you must write a digit in the quotient.

## Example

**Find each quotient.**

**a.** $741 \div 8$

Estimate:

$720 \div 8 \approx 90$

$$\begin{array}{r} 92 \text{ R5} \\ 8\overline{)741} \\ -72 \\ \hline 21 \\ -16 \\ \hline 5 \end{array}$$

**b.** $838 \div 43$

Estimate:

$800 \div 40 \approx 20$

$$\begin{array}{r} 19 \text{ R21} \\ 43\overline{)838} \\ -43 \\ \hline 408 \\ -387 \\ \hline 21 \end{array}$$

**c.** $367 \div 9$

Estimate:

$360 \div 9 \approx 40$

$$\begin{array}{r} 40 \text{ R7} \\ 9\overline{)367} \\ -360 \\ \hline 7 \end{array}$$

## Exercises

**Divide.**

| | | | | |
|---|---|---|---|---|
| **1.** $4\overline{)61}$ 15 R 1 | **2.** $8\overline{)53}$ 6 R 5 | **3.** $7\overline{)90}$ 12 R 6 | **4.** $3\overline{)84}$ 28 | **5.** $6\overline{)81}$ 13 R 3 |
| **6.** $6\overline{)469}$ 78 R 1 | **7.** $3\overline{)653}$ 217 R 2 | **8.** $8\overline{)645}$ 80 R 5 | **9.** $9\overline{)231}$ 25 R 6 | **10.** $4\overline{)415}$ 103 R 3 |
| **11.** $60\overline{)461}$ 7 R 41 | **12.** $40\overline{)213}$ 5 R 13 | **13.** $70\overline{)517}$ 7 R 27 | **14.** $30\overline{)432}$ 14 R 12 | **15.** $80\overline{)276}$ 3 R 36 |
| **16.** $43\overline{)273}$ 6 R 15 | **17.** $52\overline{)281}$ 5 R 21 | **18.** $69\overline{)207}$ 3 | **19.** $38\overline{)121}$ 3 R 7 | **20.** $81\overline{)433}$ 5 R 28 |
| **21.** $94\overline{)1{,}368}$ 14 R 52 | **22.** $62\overline{)1{,}147}$ 18 R 31 | **23.** $55\overline{)2{,}047}$ 37 R 12 | **24.** $85\overline{)1{,}450}$ 17 R 5 | **25.** $46\overline{)996}$ 21 R 30 |
| **26.** $94 \div 4$ 23 R 2 | **27.** $66 \div 9$ 7 R 3 | **28.** $90 \div 5$ 18 | **29.** $69 \div 6$ 11 R 3 | **30.** $58 \div 8$ 7 R 2 |
| **31.** $323 \div 5$ 64 R 3 | **32.** $849 \div 7$ 121 R 2 | **33.** $404 \div 8$ 50 R 4 | **34.** $934 \div 3$ 311 R 1 | **35.** $619 \div 6$ 103 R 1 |
| **36.** $777 \div 50$ 15 R 27 | **37.** $528 \div 20$ 26 R 8 | **38.** $443 \div 70$ 6 R 23 | **39.** $312 \div 40$ 7 R 32 | **40.** $335 \div 60$ 5 R 35 |
| **41.** $382 \div 72$ 5 R 22 | **42.** $580 \div 68$ 8 R 36 | **43.** $279 \div 43$ 6 R 21 | **44.** $232 \div 27$ 8 R 16 | **45.** $331 \div 93$ 3 R 52 |
| **46.** $614 \div 35$ 17 R 19 | **47.** $423 \div 28$ 15 R 3 | **48.** $489 \div 15$ 32 R 9 | **49.** $1{,}134 \div 51$ 22 R 12 | **50.** $1{,}103 \div 26$ 42 R 11 |

# Decimals and Place Value

Each digit in a whole number or a decimal has both a place and a value. The value of any place is one tenth the value of the place to its left. The chart below can help you read and write decimals.

| Billions | Hundred millions | Ten millions | Millions | Hundred thousands | Ten thousands | Thousands | Hundreds | Tens | Ones | . | Tenths | Hundredths | Thousandths | Ten-thousandths | Hundred-thousandths | Millionths |
|---|---|---|---|---|---|---|---|---|---|---|---|---|---|---|---|---|
| 2 | 4 | 0 | 1 | 2 | 6 | 2 | 8 | 3 | 0 | . | 7 | 5 | 0 | 1 | 9 | 1 |

**EXAMPLE**

**a. What is the value of the digit 8 in the number above?**
The digit 8 is in the hundreds place.
So, its value is 8 hundreds.

**b. Write 2.006 in words.**
The digit 6 is in the thousandths place.
So, 2.006 is read two and six thousandths.

**c. Write five and thirty-four ten-thousandths as a decimal.**
Ten-thousandths is 4 places to the right of the decimal point.
So, the decimal will have 4 places after the decimal point.
The answer is 5.0034.

## EXERCISES

**Use the chart above. Write the value of each digit.**

**1.** the digit 9 9 hundred-thousandths
**2.** the digit 7 7 tenths
**3.** the digit 5 5 hundredths
**4.** the digit 6 6 ten thousands
**5.** the digit 4 4 hundred millions
**6.** the digit 3 3 tens

**Write a decimal for the given words.**

**7.** forty-one ten-thousandths 0.0041
**8.** eighteen and five hundred four thousandths 18.504
**9.** eight millionths 0.000008
**10.** seven and sixty-three hundred-thousandths 7.00063
**11.** twelve thousandths 0.012
**12.** sixty-five and two hundred one thousandths 65.201

**Write each decimal in words.**

**13.** 0.06 six hundredths
**14.** 4.7 four and seven tenths
**15.** 0.00011 eleven hundred-thousandths
**16.** 0.9 nine tenths
**17.** 0.012 twelve thousandths
**18.** 0.000059 fifty-nine millionths
**19.** 0.0042 forty-two ten-thousandths
**20.** 6.029186 See above.

20. six and twenty-nine thousand one hundred eighty-six millionths




Skills Handbook

# Comparing and Ordering Decimals

To compare two decimals, use the symbols > (is greater than), < (is less than), or = (is equal to). When you compare, start at the left and compare the digits.

### Example 1

**Use >, <, or = to compare the decimals.**

**a. 0.1 ■ 0.06**
1 tenth > 0 tenths, so 0.1 > 0.06

**b. 2.4583 ■ 2.48**
5 hundredths < 8 hundredths, so 2.4583 < 2.48

**c. 0.30026 ■ 0.03026**
3 tenths > 0 tenths, so 0.30026 > 0.03026

### Example 2

**Draw number lines to compare the decimals.**

**a. 0.1 ■ 0.06**

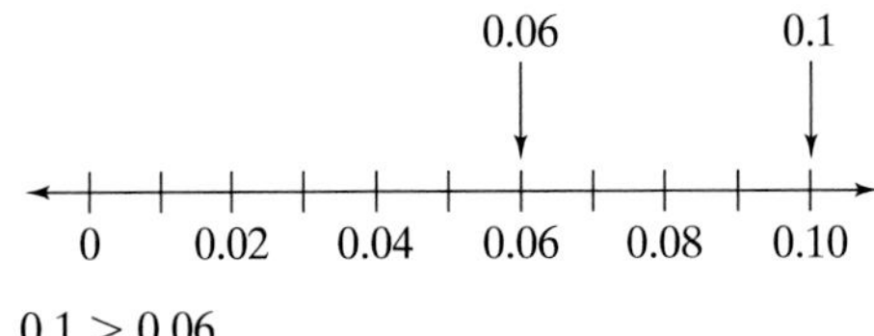


0.1 > 0.06

**b. 2.4583 ■ 2.48**

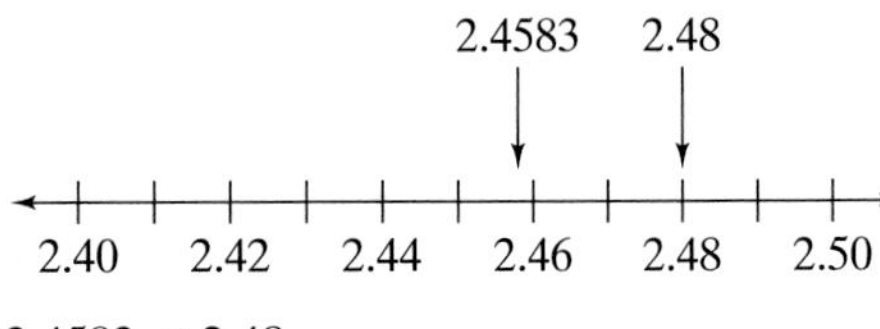


2.4583 < 2.48

## Exercises

**Use >, <, or = to compare the decimals. Draw number lines if you wish.**

1. 0.003 ■ 0.02 <
2. 84.2 ■ 842 <
3. 0.162 ■ 0.106 >
4. 0.0659 ■ 0.6059 <
5. 2.13 ■ 2.99 <
6. 3.53 ■ 3.529 >
7. 02.01 ■ 02.010 =
8. 0.00072 ■ 0.07002 <
9. 0.458 ■ 0.4589 <
10. 8.627 ■ 8.649 <
11. 0.0019 ■ 0.0002 >
12. 0.19321 ■ 0.19231 >

**Write the decimals in order from least to greatest.**

13. 2.31, 0.231, 23.1, 0.23, 3.21
    0.23, 0.231, 2.31, 3.21, 23.1
14. 1.02, 1.002, 1.2, 1.11, 1.021
    1.002, 1.02, 1.021, 1.11, 1.2
15. 0.02, 0.002, 0.22, 0.222, 2.22
    0.002, 0.02, 0.22, 0.222, 2.22
16. 55.5, 555.5, 55.555, 5.5555
    5.5555, 55.5, 55.555, 555.5
17. 0.07, 0.007, 0.7, 0.71, 0.72
    0.007, 0.07, 0.7, 0.71, 0.72
18. 2.78, 2.7001, 2.701, 2.71, 2.7
    2.7, 2.7001, 2.701, 2.71, 2.78
19. 7, 7.3264, 7.3, 7.3246, 7.0324
    7, 7.0324, 7.3, 7.3246, 7.3264
20. 0.0101, 0.0099, 0.011, 0.00019
    0.00019, 0.0099, 0.0101, 0.011

# Rounding

When you round to a particular place, look at the digit to the right of that place. If it is 5 or more, the digit in the place you are rounding to will increase by 1. If it is less than 5, the digit in the place you are rounding to will stay the same.

### Example

**a. Round 1.627 to the nearest whole number.** The digit to the right of the units place is 6, so 1.627 rounds up to 2.

**b. Round 12,034 to the nearest thousand.** The digit to the right of the thousands place is 0, so 12,034 rounds down to 12,000.

**c. Round 2.7195 to the nearest hundredth.** The digit to the right of the hundredths place is 9, so 2.7195 rounds up to 2.72.

**d. Round 0.060521 to the nearest thousandth.** The digit to the right of the thousandths place is 5, so 0.060521 rounds up to 0.061.

### Exercises

**Round to the nearest thousand.**

**1.** 105,099 105,000 **2.** 10,400 10,000 **3.** 79,527,826 79,528,000 **4.** 79,932 80,000 **5.** 4,312,349 4,312,000

**Round to the nearest whole number.**

**6.** 135.91 136 **7.** 3.001095 3 **8.** 96.912 97 **9.** 101.167 101 **10.** 299.9 300

**Round to the nearest tenth.**

**11.** 82.01 82 **12.** 4.67522 4.7 **13.** 20.397 20.4 **14.** 399.95 400.0 **15.** 129.98 130.0

**Round to the nearest hundredth.**

**16.** 13.458 13.46 **17.** 96.4045 96.40 **18.** 0.699 0.70 **19.** 4.234 4.23 **20.** 12.09531 12.10

**Round to the place of the underlined digit.**

**21.** $7.0\underline{6}15$ 7.06 **22.** $\underline{5}.77125$ 6 **23.** $1{,}5\underline{2}2$ 1,520 **24.** $0.919\underline{5}2$ 0.9195 **25.** $4.\underline{2}43$ 4.2

**26.** $2\underline{3}6.001$ 240 **27.** $\underline{3}52$ 400 **28.** $3.4953\underline{6}6$ 3.49537 **29.** $8.\underline{0}7092$ 8.1 **30.** $\underline{0}.6008$ 1

**31.** $4\underline{0}9$ 410 **32.** $23{,}\underline{9}51{,}888$ 24,000,000 **33.** $2.5\underline{7}84$ 2.58 **34.** $8\underline{6}2$ 860 **35.** $1\underline{9}.32$ 19

**36.** $\underline{9}18$ 900 **37.** $7{,}\underline{7}35$ 7,700 **38.** $25.66\underline{0}47$ 25.66 **39.** $9\underline{8}3{,}240{,}631$ 980,000,000 **40.** $\underline{2}7$ 30

**41.** $0.0037\underline{7}1$ 0.00377 **42.** $0.\underline{0}649$ 0.1 **43.** $12.\underline{7}77$ 12.8 **44.** $1{,}75\underline{9}{,}230$ 1,759,000 **45.** $2\underline{0}{,}908$ 21,000


Skills Handbook

# Adding and Subtracting Decimals

You add or subtract decimals just as you do whole numbers. You line up the decimal points and then add or subtract. If you wish, you can use zeros to make the columns even.

## Example

**Find each sum or difference.**

**a. 37.6 + 8.431**

$$\begin{array}{r} 37.6 \\ +\ 8.431 \\ \hline \end{array} \rightarrow \begin{array}{r} 37.600 \\ +\ 8.431 \\ \hline 46.031 \end{array}$$

**b. 8 − 4.593**

$$\begin{array}{r} 8 \\ -\ 4.593 \\ \hline \end{array} \rightarrow \begin{array}{r} 8.000 \\ -\ 4.593 \\ \hline 3.407 \end{array}$$

**c. 8.3 + 2.99 + 17.5**

$$\begin{array}{r} 8.3 \\ 2.99 \\ +\ 17.5 \\ \hline \end{array} \rightarrow \begin{array}{r} 8.30 \\ 2.99 \\ +\ 17.50 \\ \hline 28.79 \end{array}$$

## Exercises

**Find each sum or difference.**

1. $\begin{array}{r} 39.7 \\ -\ 36.03 \\ \hline \end{array}$ 3.67
2. $\begin{array}{r} 1.08 \\ -\ 0.9 \\ \hline \end{array}$ 0.18
3. $\begin{array}{r} 6.784 \\ +\ 0.528 \\ \hline \end{array}$ 7.312
4. $\begin{array}{r} 5.01 \\ -\ 0.87 \\ \hline \end{array}$ 4.14
5. $\begin{array}{r} 13.02 \\ +\ 23.107 \\ \hline \end{array}$ 36.127
6. $\begin{array}{r} 8.634 \\ +\ 1.409 \\ \hline \end{array}$ 10.043
7. $\begin{array}{r} 2.1 \\ -\ 0.5 \\ \hline \end{array}$ 1.6
8. $\begin{array}{r} 8.23 \\ -\ 3.1 \\ \hline \end{array}$ 5.13
9. $\begin{array}{r} 1.05 \\ +\ 12.9 \\ \hline \end{array}$ 13.95
10. $\begin{array}{r} 2.6 \\ +\ 0.003 \\ \hline \end{array}$ 2.603
11. $\begin{array}{r} 0.1 \\ 58.21 \\ +\ 1.9 \\ \hline \end{array}$ 60.21
12. $\begin{array}{r} 12.2 \\ 3.06 \\ +\ 0.5 \\ \hline \end{array}$ 15.76
13. $\begin{array}{r} 9.42 \\ 3.6 \\ +\ 21.003 \\ \hline \end{array}$ 34.023
14. $\begin{array}{r} 15.22 \\ 7.4 \\ +\ 8.125 \\ \hline \end{array}$ 30.745
15. $\begin{array}{r} 3.7 \\ 20.06 \\ +\ 16.19 \\ \hline \end{array}$ 39.95
16. 76.39 − 8.47 67.92
17. 8.7 + 17.03 25.73
18. 32.403 + 12.06 44.463
19. 20.5 + 11.45 31.95
20. 8.9 − 4.45 4.45
21. 1.245 + 5.8 7.045
22. 3.9 + 6.57 10.47
23. 14.81 − 8.6 6.21
24. 11.9 − 2.06 9.84
25. 3.45 + 4.061 7.511
26. 8.29 + 4.3 12.59
27. 7.06 − 4.235 2.825
28. 6.02 + 4.005 10.025
29. 7.05 − 3.5 3.55
30. 1.18 + 3.015 4.195
31. 2.304 − 0.87 1.434
32. 5.002 − 3.45 1.552
33. 6.8 + 3.57 10.37
34. 0.23 + 0.091 0.321
35. 0.5 − 0.18 0.32
36. 8.3 + 2.99 + 17.52 28.81
37. 9.5 + 12.32 + 6.4 28.22
38. 4.521 + 1.8 + 3.07 9.391
39. 3.602 + 9.4 + 24 37.002
40. 11.6 + 8.05 + 5.13 24.78
41. 7.023 + 1.48 + 3.9 12.403
42. 57 + 0.6327 + 189.007 246.6397
43. 741 + 6.08 + 0.0309 747.1109
44. 0.045 + 16.32 + 8.6 24.965
45. 4.27 + 6.18 + 0.91 11.36
46. 3.856 + 14.01 + 1.72 19.586
47. 11.45 + 3.79 + 23.861 39.101

# Multiplying Decimals

Multiply decimals as you would whole numbers. Then place the decimal point in the product. To do this, add the number of decimal places in the factors.

## Example 1

**Multiply 0.068 × 2.3.**

**Step 1** Multiply.

$$\begin{array}{r} 0.068 \\ \times\ 2.3 \\ \hline 204 \\ +\ 1360 \\ \hline 1564 \end{array}$$

**Step 2** Place the decimal point.

$$\begin{array}{rl} 0.068 & \leftarrow \text{three decimal places} \\ \times\ 2.3 & \leftarrow \text{one decimal place} \\ \hline 204 & \\ +\ 1360 & \\ \hline 0.1564 & \leftarrow \text{four decimal places} \end{array}$$

## Example 2

**Find each product.**

**a. 3.12 × 0.9**

$$\begin{array}{r} 3.12 \\ \times\ 0.9 \\ \hline 2.808 \end{array}$$

**b. 5.75 × 42**

$$\begin{array}{r} 5.75 \\ \times\ 42 \\ \hline 11\ 50 \\ +\ 230\ 00 \\ \hline 241.50 \end{array}$$

**c. 0.964 × 0.28**

$$\begin{array}{r} 0.964 \\ \times\ 0.28 \\ \hline 7712 \\ +\ 19280 \\ \hline 0.26992 \end{array}$$

## Exercises

**Multiply.**

**1.** 1.48 × 3.6 5.328
**2.** 191.2 × 3.4 650.08
**3.** 0.05 × 43 2.15
**4.** 0.27 × 5 1.35
**5.** 1.36 × 3.8 5.168
**6.** 6.23 × 0.21 1.3083
**7.** 0.512 × 0.76 0.38912
**8.** 0.04 × 7 0.28
**9.** 0.136 × 8.4 1.1424
**10.** 3 × 0.05 0.15

**11.** 2.07 × 1.004 2.07828
**12.** 0.12 × 6.1 0.732
**13.** 3.2 × 0.15 0.48
**14.** 0.74 × 0.23 0.1702
**15.** 2.6 × 0.14 0.364
**16.** 0.77 × 51 39.27
**17.** 9.3 × 0.706 6.5658
**18.** 71.13 × 0.4 28.452
**19.** 0.42 × 98 41.16
**20.** 6.3 × 85 535.5
**21.** 45 × 0.028 1.26
**22.** 76 × 3.3 250.8
**23.** 9 × 1.35 12.15
**24.** 4.56 × 7 31.92
**25.** 5 × 2.41 12.05
**26.** 704 × 0.3 211.2
**27.** 8.003 × 0.6 4.8018
**28.** 42.2 × 0.9 37.98
**29.** 0.6 × 30.02 18.012
**30.** 0.05 × 11.8 0.59





Skills Handbook

# Zeros in a Product

When you multiply with decimals, you may have to write one or more zeros to the left of a product before you can place the decimal point.

### Example 1

**Multiply 0.06 × 0.015.**

**Step 1** Multiply.

$$\begin{array}{r} 0.015 \\ \times\ 0.06 \\ \hline 90 \end{array}$$

**Step 2** Place the decimal point.

$$\begin{array}{r} 0.015 \\ \times\ 0.06 \\ \hline 0.00090 \end{array}$$

← The product should have 5 decimal places, so you must write three zeros before placing the decimal point.

### Example 2

**a. 0.02 × 1.3**

$$\begin{array}{r} 1.3 \\ \times\ 0.02 \\ \hline 00.026 \end{array}$$

**b. 0.012 × 2.4**

$$\begin{array}{r} 2.4 \\ \times\ 0.012 \\ \hline 48 \\ +\ 240 \\ \hline 0.0288 \end{array}$$

**c. 0.022 × 0.051**

$$\begin{array}{r} 0.051 \\ \times\ 0.022 \\ \hline 102 \\ +\ 1020 \\ \hline 0.001122 \end{array}$$

## Exercises

**Multiply.**

1. 0.03 × 0.9 = 0.027
2. 0.06 × 0.5 = 0.03
3. 2.4 × 0.03 = 0.072
4. 7 × 0.01 = 0.07
5. 0.05 × 0.05 = 0.0025
6. 0.016 × 0.12 = 0.00192
7. 0.031 × 0.08 = 0.00248
8. 0.03 × 0.2 = 0.006
9. 0.27 × 0.033 = 0.00891
10. 0.014 × 0.25 = 0.0035
11. 0.003 × 0.55 0.00165
12. 0.01 × 0.74 0.0074
13. 0.47 × 0.08 0.0376
14. 0.76 × 0.1 0.076
15. 0.3 × 0.27 0.081
16. 0.19 × 0.05 0.0095
17. 0.018 × 0.04 0.00072
18. 0.43 × 0.2 0.086
19. 0.03 × 0.03 0.0009
20. 4.003 × 0.02 0.08006
21. 0.5 × 0.08 0.04
22. 0.06 × 0.7 0.042
23. 0.047 × 0.008 0.000376
24. 0.05 × 0.06 0.003
25. 0.03 × 0.4 0.012
26. 0.05 × 0.036 0.0018
27. 0.4 × 0.23 0.092
28. 0.3 × 0.017 0.0051
29. 0.3 × 0.24 0.072
30. 0.67 × 0.09 0.0603
31. 3.02 × 0.006 0.01812
32. 0.31 × 0.08 0.0248
33. 0.14 × 0.05 0.007
34. 0.07 × 0.85 0.0595

Skills Handbook

# Dividing Decimals by Whole Numbers

When you divide a decimal by a whole number, the decimal point in the quotient goes directly above the decimal point in the dividend. You may need extra zeros to place the decimal point.

## Example 1

**Divide 2.432 ÷ 32.**

**Step 1** Divide.

```
    76
32)2.432
 - 2 24
    192
  - 192
      0
```

**Step 2** Place the decimal point.

```
  0.076   ← Put extra zeros to the left.
32)2.432     Then place the decimal point.
 - 2 24
    192
  - 192
      0
```

## Example 2

**a. 37.6 ÷ 8**

```
   4.7
8)37.6
 - 32
    5 6
  - 5 6
      0
```

**b. 39.33 ÷ 69**

```
    0.57
69)39.33
  - 34 5
     4 83
   - 4 83
        0
```

**c. 4.482 ÷ 54**

```
   0.083
54)4.482
  - 4 32
     162
   - 162
       0
```

## Exercises

**Divide.**

1. $7\overline{)17.92}$ 2.56
2. $5\overline{)16.5}$ 3.3
3. $9\overline{)6.984}$ 0.776
4. $6\overline{)91.44}$ 15.24
5. $4\overline{)35.16}$ 8.79
6. $56\overline{)8.848}$ 0.158
7. $22\overline{)2.42}$ 0.11
8. $26\overline{)1{,}723.8}$ 66.3
9. $83\overline{)15.272}$ 0.184
10. $39\overline{)26.91}$ 0.69
11. 14.49 ÷ 7 2.07
12. 10.53 ÷ 9 1.17
13. 17.52 ÷ 2 8.76
14. 37.14 ÷ 6 6.19
15. 0.1352 ÷ 8 0.0169
16. 0.0324 ÷ 9 0.0036
17. 0.0882 ÷ 6 0.0147
18. 0.8682 ÷ 6 0.1447
19. 12.342 ÷ 22 0.561
20. 29.792 ÷ 32 0.931
21. 22.568 ÷ 26 0.868
22. 11.340 ÷ 36 0.315
23. 45.918 ÷ 18 2.551
24. 79.599 ÷ 13 6.123
25. 58.5 ÷ 15 3.9
26. 74.664 ÷ 12 6.222
27. 2.1 ÷ 84 0.025
28. 89.378 ÷ 67 1.334
29. 0.0672 ÷ 48 0.0014
30. 171.031 ÷ 53 3.227

# Multiplying and Dividing by Powers of Ten

You can use shortcuts to multiply or divide by powers of ten.

| When you multiply by | Move the decimal point |
|---|---|
| 10,000 | 4 places to the right |
| 1,000 | 3 places to the right |
| 100 | 2 places to the right |
| 10 | 1 place to the right |
| 0.1 | 1 place to the left |
| 0.01 | 2 places to the left |
| 0.001 | 3 places to the left |

| When you divide by | Move the decimal point |
|---|---|
| 10,000 | 4 places to the left |
| 1,000 | 3 places to the left |
| 100 | 2 places to the left |
| 10 | 1 place to the left |
| 0.1 | 1 place to the right |
| 0.01 | 2 places to the right |
| 0.001 | 3 places to the right |

## Example

**Multiply or divide.**

**a. 0.7 × 0.001**

Move the decimal point 3 places to the left.

0.000.7

0.7 × 0.001 = 0.0007

**b. 0.605 ÷ 100**

Move the decimal point 2 places to the left.

0.00.605

0.605 ÷ 100 = 0.00605

## Exercises

**Multiply or divide.**

**1.** 10,000 × 0.056 560
**2.** 0.001 × 0.09 0.00009
**3.** 5.2 × 10 52
**4.** 0.03 × 1,000 30
**5.** 236.7 ÷ 0.1 2,367
**6.** 45.28 ÷ 10 4.528
**7.** 0.9 ÷ 1,000 0.0009
**8.** 1.07 ÷ 0.01 107
**9.** 100 × 0.08 8
**10.** 1.03 × 10,000 10,300
**11.** 1.803 × 0.001 0.001803
**12.** 4.1 × 100 410
**13.** 13.7 ÷ 0.001 13,700
**14.** 203.05 ÷ 0.01 20,305
**15.** 4.7 ÷ 10 0.47
**16.** 0.05 ÷ 100 0.0005
**17.** 23.6 × 0.01 0.236
**18.** 1,000 × 0.12 120
**19.** 0.41 × 0.001 0.00041
**20.** 0.01 × 6.2 0.062
**21.** 42.3 ÷ 0.1 423
**22.** 0.4 ÷ 10,000 0.00004
**23.** 5.02 ÷ 0.01 502
**24.** 16.5 ÷ 100 0.165
**25.** 0.27 ÷ 0.01 27
**26.** 1.05 × 0.001 0.00105
**27.** 10 × 0.04 0.4
**28.** 2.09 ÷ 100 0.0209
**29.** 0.65 × 0.1 0.065
**30.** 0.03 ÷ 100 0.0003
**31.** 2.6 ÷ 0.1 26
**32.** 12.6 × 10,000 126,000
**33.** 0.3 ÷ 1,000 0.0003
**34.** 0.01 × 6.7 0.067
**35.** 100 × 0.158 15.8
**36.** 23.1 ÷ 10 2.31

# Dividing Decimals by Decimals

To divide with a decimal divisor, multiply it by the smallest power of ten that will make the divisor a whole number. Then multiply the dividend by that same power of ten.

## Example

**Find each quotient.**

**a. 3.348 ÷ 6.2**

Multiply by 10.

$$\begin{array}{r} 0.54 \\ 6.2.\overline{)3.3.48} \\ -3\ 1\ 0 \\ \hline 2\ 48 \\ -2\ 48 \\ \hline 0 \end{array}$$

**b. 2.4885 ÷ 0.35**

Multiply by 100.

$$\begin{array}{r} 7.11 \\ 0.35.\overline{)2.48.85} \\ -2\ 45 \\ \hline 3\ 8 \\ -3\ 5 \\ \hline 35 \\ -35 \\ \hline 0 \end{array}$$

**c. 0.0576 ÷ 0.012**

Multiply by 1,000.

$$\begin{array}{r} 4.8 \\ 0.012.\overline{)0.057.6} \\ -48 \\ \hline 96 \\ -96 \\ \hline 0 \end{array}$$

## Exercises

**Divide.**

**1.** $3.2\overline{)268.8}$ 84 **2.** $1.9\overline{)123.5}$ 65 **3.** $0.3\overline{)135.6}$ 452 **4.** $2.3\overline{)170.2}$ 74 **5.** $7.9\overline{)252.8}$ 32

**6.** $5.7\overline{)10.26}$ 1.8 **7.** $2.3\overline{)71.53}$ 31.1 **8.** $3.1\overline{)16.12}$ 5.2 **9.** $7.8\overline{)24.18}$ 3.1 **10.** $6.3\overline{)14.49}$ 2.3

**11.** 134.42 ÷ 5.17 26 **12.** 89.96 ÷ 3.46 26 **13.** 160.58 ÷ 5.18 31 **14.** 106.59 ÷ 6.27 17

**15.** 62.4 ÷ 3.9 16 **16.** 260.4 ÷ 8.4 31 **17.** 316.8 ÷ 7.2 44 **18.** 162.4 ÷ 2.9 56

**19.** 1.512 ÷ 0.54 2.8 **20.** 3.225 ÷ 0.43 7.5 **21.** 2.484 ÷ 0.69 3.6 **22.** 511.5 ÷ 5.5 93

**23.** 0.992 ÷ 0.8 1.24 **24.** 4.53 ÷ 0.05 90.6 **25.** 3.498 ÷ 0.06 58.3 **26.** 59.2 ÷ 0.8 74

**27.** 2.198 ÷ 0.07 31.4 **28.** 14.28 ÷ 0.7 20.4 **29.** 1.98 ÷ 0.5 3.96 **30.** 26.36 ÷ 0.04 659

**31.** 3.922 ÷ 7.4 0.53 **32.** 23.52 ÷ 0.98 24 **33.** 71.25 ÷ 7.5 9.5 **34.** 114.7 ÷ 3.7 31

**35.** 0.832 ÷ 0.52 1.6 **36.** 1.125 ÷ 0.09 12.5 **37.** 9.666 ÷ 2.7 3.58 **38.** 1.456 ÷ 9.1 0.16

**39.** 0.4374 ÷ 1.8 0.243 **40.** 2.3414 ÷ 0.46 5.09 **41.** 0.07224 ÷ 0.021 3.44 **42.** 0.1386 ÷ 0.18 0.77

**43.** 0.16926 ÷ 0.091 1.86 **44.** 0.6042 ÷ 5.3 0.114 **45.** 2.3374 ÷ 0.62 3.77 **46.** 1.0062 ÷ 0.078 12.9





Skills Handbook

# Zeros in Decimal Division

When you are dividing by a decimal, sometimes you need to use extra zeros in the dividend or the quotient, or both.

### Example 1

**Divide 0.045 ÷ 3.6.**

**Step 1** Multiply by 10.

$3.6.\overline{)0.0.45}$

**Step 2** Divide.

$$\begin{array}{r} 125 \\ 3.6.\overline{)0.0.4500} \\ -36 \\ \hline 90 \\ -72 \\ \hline 180 \\ -180 \\ \hline 0 \end{array}$$

**Step 3** Place the decimal point.

$$\begin{array}{r} 0.0125 \\ 3.6.\overline{)0.0.4500} \\ -36 \\ \hline 90 \\ -72 \\ \hline 180 \\ -180 \\ \hline 0 \end{array}$$

### Example 2

**Find each quotient.**

**a. 0.4428 ÷ 8.2**
Multiply by 10.

$$\begin{array}{r} 0.054 \\ 8.2.\overline{)0.4.428} \end{array}$$

**b. 0.00434 ÷ 0.07**
Multiply by 100.

$$\begin{array}{r} 0.062 \\ 0.07.\overline{)0.00.434} \end{array}$$

**c. 0.00306 ÷ 0.072**
Multiply by 1,000.

$$\begin{array}{r} 0.0425 \\ 0.072.\overline{)0.003.0600} \end{array}$$

## Exercises

**Divide.**

1. $0.05\overline{)0.0023}$ 0.046
2. $0.02\overline{)0.000162}$ 0.0081
3. $0.12\overline{)0.009}$ 0.075
4. $2.5\overline{)0.021}$ 0.0084
5. 0.0019 ÷ 0.2 0.0095
6. 0.9 ÷ 0.8 1.125
7. 0.000175 ÷ 0.07 0.0025
8. 0.142 ÷ 0.04 3.55
9. 0.0017 ÷ 0.02 0.085
10. 0.003 ÷ 0.6 0.005
11. 0.0105 ÷ 0.7 0.015
12. 0.034 ÷ 0.05 0.68
13. 0.00056 ÷ 0.16 0.0035
14. 0.0612 ÷ 7.2 0.0085
15. 0.217 ÷ 3.1 0.07
16. 0.052 ÷ 0.8 0.065
17. 0.000924 ÷ 0.44 0.0021
18. 0.05796 ÷ 0.63 0.092
19. 0.00123 ÷ 8.2 0.00015
20. 0.0954 ÷ 0.09 1.06
21. 0.0084 ÷ 1.4 0.006
22. 0.259 ÷ 3.5 0.074
23. 0.00468 ÷ 0.52 0.009
24. 0.104 ÷ 0.05 2.08
25. 0.00063 ÷ 0.18 0.0035
26. 0.011 ÷ 0.25 0.044
27. 0.3069 ÷ 9.3 0.033
28. 0.00045 ÷ 0.3 0.0015

# Writing Equivalent Fractions

If you multiply or divide both the numerator and the denominator of a fraction by the same number, you get an equivalent fraction.

## Example 1

**a. Find the missing number in $\frac{5}{6} = \frac{20}{\blacksquare}$.**

$$\frac{5}{6} \xrightarrow{\times 4} \frac{20}{\blacksquare}$$

$$\frac{5}{6} = \frac{20}{24} \quad (\times 4)$$

**b. Find the missing number in $\frac{12}{30} = \frac{\blacksquare}{15}$.**

$$\frac{12}{30} \xrightarrow{\div 2} \frac{\blacksquare}{15}$$

$$\frac{12}{30} = \frac{6}{15} \quad (\div 2)$$

To write a fraction in simplest form, divide both the numerator and the denominator by the greatest common factor.

## Example 2

**a. Write $\frac{6}{15}$ in simplest form.**

3 is the greatest common factor.

$$\frac{6}{15} = \frac{6 \div 3}{15 \div 3} = \frac{2}{5}$$

The simplest form of $\frac{6}{15}$ is $\frac{2}{5}$.

**b. Write $\frac{36}{42}$ in simplest form.**

6 is the greatest common factor.

$$\frac{36}{42} = \frac{36 \div 6}{42 \div 6} = \frac{6}{7}$$

The simplest form of $\frac{36}{42}$ is $\frac{6}{7}$.

## Exercises

**Find each missing number.**

1. $\frac{1}{3} = \frac{\blacksquare}{6}$ **2**
2. $\frac{3}{4} = \frac{\blacksquare}{16}$ **12**
3. $\frac{18}{30} = \frac{6}{\blacksquare}$ **10**
4. $\frac{2}{3} = \frac{\blacksquare}{21}$ **14**
5. $\frac{3}{4} = \frac{9}{\blacksquare}$ **12**
6. $\frac{3}{10} = \frac{9}{\blacksquare}$ **30**
7. $\frac{4}{5} = \frac{\blacksquare}{30}$ **24**
8. $\frac{2}{3} = \frac{8}{\blacksquare}$ **12**
9. $\frac{33}{55} = \frac{\blacksquare}{5}$ **3**
10. $\frac{27}{72} = \frac{9}{\blacksquare}$ **24**
11. $\frac{2}{3} = \frac{\blacksquare}{24}$ **16**
12. $\frac{11}{12} = \frac{55}{\blacksquare}$ **60**
13. $\frac{3}{5} = \frac{18}{\blacksquare}$ **30**
14. $\frac{60}{72} = \frac{10}{\blacksquare}$ **12**
15. $\frac{7}{8} = \frac{\blacksquare}{24}$ **21**

**Write each fraction in simplest form.**

16. $\frac{12}{36}$ **$\frac{1}{3}$**
17. $\frac{25}{30}$ **$\frac{5}{6}$**
18. $\frac{14}{16}$ **$\frac{7}{8}$**
19. $\frac{27}{36}$ **$\frac{3}{4}$**
20. $\frac{21}{35}$ **$\frac{3}{5}$**
21. $\frac{40}{50}$ **$\frac{4}{5}$**
22. $\frac{24}{40}$ **$\frac{3}{5}$**
23. $\frac{32}{64}$ **$\frac{1}{2}$**
24. $\frac{15}{45}$ **$\frac{1}{3}$**
25. $\frac{27}{63}$ **$\frac{3}{7}$**
26. $\frac{44}{77}$ **$\frac{4}{7}$**
27. $\frac{45}{75}$ **$\frac{3}{5}$**
28. $\frac{60}{72}$ **$\frac{5}{6}$**
29. $\frac{77}{84}$ **$\frac{11}{12}$**
30. $\frac{12}{24}$ **$\frac{1}{2}$**
31. $\frac{24}{32}$ **$\frac{3}{4}$**
32. $\frac{7}{21}$ **$\frac{1}{3}$**
33. $\frac{18}{42}$ **$\frac{3}{7}$**

# Mixed Numbers and Improper Fractions

A fraction, such as $\frac{10}{7}$, in which the numerator is greater than or equal to the denominator is an improper fraction. You can write an improper fraction as a mixed number that shows the sum of a whole number and a fraction.

Sometimes it is necessary to do the opposite and write a mixed number as an improper fraction.

## Example

**a. Write $\frac{11}{5}$ as a mixed number.**

$$\frac{11}{5} \rightarrow \begin{array}{r} 2 \\ 5\overline{)11} \\ -\ 10 \\ \hline 1 \end{array}$$

2 ← whole number

1 ← remainder

$\frac{11}{5} = 2\frac{1}{5}$ ← whole number + $\frac{\text{remainder}}{\text{denominator}}$

**b. Write $2\frac{5}{6}$ as an improper fraction.**

$2\frac{5}{6} = 2 + \frac{5}{6}$

$= \frac{12}{6} + \frac{5}{6}$ ← Write 2 as $\frac{12}{6}$.

$= \frac{12 + 5}{6}$ ← Add the numerators.

$2\frac{5}{6} = \frac{17}{6}$

## Exercises

**Write each improper fraction as a mixed number.**

1. $\frac{7}{5}$ $1\frac{2}{5}$
2. $\frac{9}{2}$ $4\frac{1}{2}$
3. $\frac{13}{4}$ $3\frac{1}{4}$
4. $\frac{21}{5}$ $4\frac{1}{5}$
5. $\frac{13}{10}$ $1\frac{3}{10}$
6. $\frac{49}{5}$ $9\frac{4}{5}$
7. $\frac{21}{8}$ $2\frac{5}{8}$
8. $\frac{13}{7}$ $1\frac{6}{7}$
9. $\frac{17}{5}$ $3\frac{2}{5}$
10. $\frac{49}{6}$ $8\frac{1}{6}$
11. $\frac{17}{4}$ $4\frac{1}{4}$
12. $\frac{5}{2}$ $2\frac{1}{2}$
13. $\frac{27}{5}$ $5\frac{2}{5}$
14. $\frac{12}{9}$ $1\frac{1}{3}$
15. $\frac{30}{8}$ $3\frac{3}{4}$
16. $\frac{37}{12}$ $3\frac{1}{12}$
17. $\frac{8}{6}$ $1\frac{1}{3}$
18. $\frac{19}{12}$ $1\frac{7}{12}$
19. $\frac{45}{10}$ $4\frac{1}{2}$
20. $\frac{15}{12}$ $1\frac{1}{4}$
21. $\frac{11}{2}$ $5\frac{1}{2}$
22. $\frac{20}{6}$ $3\frac{1}{3}$
23. $\frac{34}{8}$ $4\frac{1}{4}$
24. $\frac{21}{9}$ $2\frac{1}{3}$

**Write each mixed number as an improper fraction.**

25. $1\frac{1}{2}$ $\frac{3}{2}$
26. $2\frac{2}{3}$ $\frac{8}{3}$
27. $1\frac{1}{12}$ $\frac{13}{12}$
28. $3\frac{1}{5}$ $\frac{16}{5}$
29. $2\frac{2}{7}$ $\frac{16}{7}$
30. $4\frac{1}{2}$ $\frac{9}{2}$
31. $2\frac{7}{8}$ $\frac{23}{8}$
32. $1\frac{2}{9}$ $\frac{11}{9}$
33. $5\frac{1}{5}$ $\frac{26}{5}$
34. $4\frac{7}{9}$ $\frac{43}{9}$
35. $9\frac{1}{4}$ $\frac{37}{4}$
36. $2\frac{3}{8}$ $\frac{19}{8}$
37. $7\frac{7}{8}$ $\frac{63}{8}$
38. $1\frac{5}{12}$ $\frac{17}{12}$
39. $3\frac{3}{7}$ $\frac{24}{7}$
40. $6\frac{1}{2}$ $\frac{13}{2}$
41. $3\frac{1}{10}$ $\frac{31}{10}$
42. $4\frac{6}{7}$ $\frac{34}{7}$

# Adding and Subtracting Fractions with Like Denominators

When you add or subtract fractions with the same denominator, add or subtract the numerators and then write the answer over the denominator.

## Example 1

**Add or subtract. Write each answer in simplest form.**

**a.** $\frac{5}{8} + \frac{7}{8}$

$\frac{5}{8} + \frac{7}{8} = \frac{5 + 7}{8} = \frac{12}{8} = 1\frac{4}{8} = 1\frac{1}{2}$

**b.** $\frac{11}{12} - \frac{2}{12}$

$\frac{11}{12} - \frac{2}{12} = \frac{11 - 2}{12} = \frac{9}{12} = \frac{3}{4}$

To add or subtract mixed numbers, add or subtract the fractions first. Then add or subtract the whole numbers.

## Example 2

**Add or subtract. Write each answer in simplest form.**

**a.** $3\frac{4}{6} + 2\frac{5}{6}$

$$\begin{array}{r} 3\frac{4}{6} \\ +\ 2\frac{5}{6} \\ \hline 5\frac{9}{6} \end{array} = 5 + 1 + \frac{3}{6} = 6\frac{1}{2}$$

**b.** $6\frac{1}{4} - 1\frac{3}{4}$

$$\begin{array}{r} 6\frac{1}{4} \\ -\ 1\frac{3}{4} \\ \hline \end{array} \rightarrow \begin{array}{r} 5\frac{5}{4} \\ -\ 1\frac{3}{4} \\ \hline 4\frac{2}{4} \end{array} = 4\frac{1}{2}$$

← Rewrite 1 unit as as $\frac{4}{4}$ and add it to $\frac{1}{4}$.

## Exercises

**Add or subtract. Write each answer in simplest form.**

1. $\frac{4}{5} + \frac{3}{5}$ $1\frac{2}{5}$
2. $\frac{2}{6} - \frac{1}{6}$ $\frac{1}{6}$
3. $\frac{2}{7} + \frac{2}{7}$ $\frac{4}{7}$
4. $\frac{7}{8} + \frac{2}{8}$ $1\frac{1}{8}$
5. $1\frac{2}{5} - \frac{1}{5}$ $1\frac{1}{5}$
6. $\frac{3}{6} - \frac{1}{6}$ $\frac{1}{3}$
7. $\frac{6}{8} - \frac{3}{8}$ $\frac{3}{8}$
8. $\frac{2}{9} + \frac{1}{9}$ $\frac{1}{3}$
9. $\frac{4}{5} - \frac{1}{5}$ $\frac{3}{5}$
10. $\frac{5}{9} + \frac{7}{9}$ $1\frac{1}{3}$
11. $9\frac{1}{3} - 8\frac{1}{3}$ $1$
12. $8\frac{6}{7} - 4\frac{2}{7}$ $4\frac{4}{7}$
13. $3\frac{1}{10} + 1\frac{3}{10}$ $4\frac{2}{5}$
14. $2\frac{2}{9} + 3\frac{4}{9}$ $5\frac{2}{3}$
15. $4\frac{5}{12} - 3\frac{1}{12}$ $1\frac{1}{3}$
16. $9\frac{5}{9} + 6\frac{7}{9}$ $16\frac{1}{3}$
17. $5\frac{7}{8} + 2\frac{3}{8}$ $8\frac{1}{4}$
18. $4\frac{4}{7} - 2\frac{1}{7}$ $2\frac{3}{7}$
19. $9\frac{3}{4} + 1\frac{3}{4}$ $11\frac{1}{2}$
20. $8\frac{2}{3} - 4\frac{1}{3}$ $4\frac{1}{3}$
21. $8\frac{7}{10} + 2\frac{3}{10}$ $11$
22. $1\frac{4}{5} + 3\frac{3}{5}$ $5\frac{2}{5}$
23. $7\frac{1}{5} - 2\frac{3}{5}$ $4\frac{3}{5}$
24. $4\frac{1}{3} - 1\frac{2}{3}$ $2\frac{2}{3}$
25. $4\frac{3}{8} - 3\frac{5}{8}$ $\frac{3}{4}$
26. $5\frac{1}{12} - 2\frac{7}{12}$ $2\frac{1}{2}$



Skills Handbook

Skills Handbook

739

# Multiplying and Dividing Fractions

To multiply fractions, multiply the numerators and the denominators.
To divide fractions, multiply by the reciprocal of the divisor.

## EXAMPLE

**Multiply. Write each answer in simplest form.**

**a.** $\frac{8}{9} \times \frac{3}{10} = \frac{^{4}\cancel{8}}{_{3}\cancel{9}} \times \frac{^{1}\cancel{3}}{_{5}\cancel{10}} = \frac{4}{15}$

**b.** $3\frac{1}{8} \times 1\frac{3}{4} = \frac{25}{8} \times \frac{7}{4}$

$= \frac{175}{32} = 5\frac{15}{32}$ ← Rewrite as a mixed number.

**Divide. Write each answer in simplest form.**

**c.** $\frac{2}{3} \div \frac{4}{5} = \frac{2}{3} \times \frac{5}{4}$

$= \frac{^{1}\cancel{2}}{3} \times \frac{5}{_{2}\cancel{4}} = \frac{5}{6}$

**d.** $3\frac{1}{8} \div 1\frac{3}{4} = \frac{25}{8} \div \frac{7}{4}$

$= \frac{25}{_{2}\cancel{8}} \times \frac{^{1}\cancel{4}}{7} = \frac{25}{14} = 1\frac{11}{14}$ ← Rewrite as a mixed number.

## EXERCISES

**Multiply. Write each answer in simplest form.**

**1.** $\frac{3}{4} \times \frac{3}{5}$ $\frac{9}{20}$
**2.** $\frac{2}{3} \times \frac{3}{4}$ $\frac{1}{2}$
**3.** $6 \times \frac{2}{3}$ $4$
**4.** $\frac{3}{4} \times \frac{5}{6}$ $\frac{5}{8}$
**5.** $\frac{5}{8} \times \frac{2}{3}$ $\frac{5}{12}$
**6.** $\frac{9}{16} \times \frac{2}{3}$ $\frac{3}{8}$
**7.** $\frac{3}{10} \times \frac{2}{15}$ $\frac{1}{25}$
**8.** $\frac{3}{4} \times \frac{1}{6}$ $\frac{1}{8}$
**9.** $\frac{1}{4} \times \frac{5}{20}$ $\frac{1}{16}$
**10.** $\frac{9}{10} \times \frac{1}{3}$ $\frac{3}{10}$
**11.** $1\frac{1}{3} \times 2\frac{2}{3}$ $3\frac{5}{9}$
**12.** $\frac{3}{5} \times 2\frac{3}{4}$ $1\frac{13}{20}$
**13.** $2\frac{1}{4} \times 3\frac{1}{3}$ $7\frac{1}{2}$
**14.** $\frac{1}{4} \times 3\frac{1}{3}$ $\frac{5}{6}$
**15.** $6\frac{1}{4} \times 7$ $43\frac{3}{4}$
**16.** $1\frac{3}{4} \times 2\frac{1}{5}$ $3\frac{17}{20}$
**17.** $2\frac{3}{4} \times \frac{1}{2}$ $1\frac{3}{8}$
**18.** $3\frac{4}{5} \times 2\frac{1}{3}$ $8\frac{13}{15}$

**Divide. Write each answer in simplest form.**

**19.** $\frac{5}{8} \div \frac{5}{7}$ $\frac{7}{8}$
**20.** $\frac{5}{7} \div \frac{5}{8}$ $1\frac{1}{7}$
**21.** $\frac{3}{4} \div \frac{6}{11}$ $1\frac{3}{8}$
**22.** $\frac{1}{9} \div \frac{1}{9}$ $1$
**23.** $\frac{1}{9} \div 9$ $\frac{1}{81}$
**24.** $\frac{9}{10} \div \frac{3}{5}$ $1\frac{1}{2}$
**25.** $\frac{2}{3} \div \frac{1}{9}$ $6$
**26.** $\frac{4}{5} \div \frac{5}{6}$ $\frac{24}{25}$
**27.** $\frac{1}{5} \div \frac{8}{9}$ $\frac{9}{40}$
**28.** $\frac{7}{8} \div \frac{1}{3}$ $2\frac{5}{8}$
**29.** $4\frac{1}{5} \div 2\frac{2}{5}$ $1\frac{3}{4}$
**30.** $6\frac{1}{4} \div 4\frac{3}{8}$ $1\frac{3}{7}$
**31.** $2\frac{1}{3} \div 5\frac{5}{6}$ $\frac{2}{5}$
**32.** $1\frac{1}{2} \div 4\frac{1}{2}$ $\frac{1}{3}$
**33.** $15\frac{2}{3} \div 1\frac{1}{3}$ $11\frac{3}{4}$
**34.** $10\frac{1}{3} \div 2\frac{1}{5}$ $4\frac{23}{33}$
**35.** $6\frac{1}{4} \div 1\frac{3}{4}$ $3\frac{4}{7}$
**36.** $6\frac{2}{3} \div 3\frac{1}{8}$ $2\frac{2}{15}$

# Working with Integers

Quantities less than zero can be written using negative integers. For example, a temperature of 5 degrees below zero can be written as −5. Positive integers are used for quantities greater than zero.

### Example 1

**Write an integer for each situation.**

**a. 10 degrees above zero**
+10, or 10

**b. a loss of $20**
−20

**c. 15 yards lost**
−15

A number line can be used to compare integers. The integer to the right is greater.

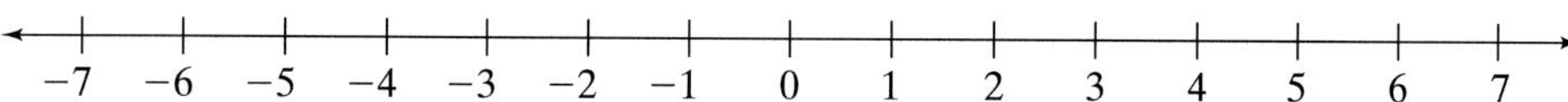


### Example 2

**Compare. Use $>$, $<$, or $=$ to complete each statement.**

**a. $0 \blacksquare -3$**
0 is to the right, so it is greater.
$0 > -3$

**b. $-2 \blacksquare -6$**
−2 is to the right, so it is greater.
$-2 > -6$

**c. $-7 \blacksquare 3$**
−7 is to the left, so it is less.
$-7 < 3$

## Exercises

**Write an integer for each situation.**

1. 6 yards gained 6
2. 10 yards lost −10
3. 5 steps forward 5
4. 4 steps backward −4
5. find $3 3
6. lose $8 −8
7. 12 floors up 12
8. 4 floors down −4

**Compare. Use $>$, $<$, or $=$ to complete each statement.**

| | | | | |
|---|---|---|---|---|
| **9.** $0 \blacksquare -1$ $>$ | **10.** $-9 \blacksquare 0$ $<$ | **11.** $-3 \blacksquare 3$ $<$ | **12.** $7 \blacksquare -3$ $>$ | **13.** $0 \blacksquare 1$ $<$ |
| **14.** $3 \blacksquare 0$ $>$ | **15.** $1 \blacksquare -4$ $>$ | **16.** $-2 \blacksquare -9$ $>$ | **17.** $6 \blacksquare -1$ $>$ | **18.** $3 \blacksquare -10$ $>$ |
| **19.** $-7 \blacksquare 3$ $<$ | **20.** $4 \blacksquare 6$ $<$ | **21.** $-16 \blacksquare -25$ $>$ | **22.** $-15 \blacksquare -12$ $<$ | **23.** $7 \blacksquare -8$ $>$ |
| **24.** $2 \blacksquare 3$ $<$ | **25.** $-7 \blacksquare -8$ $>$ | **26.** $35 \blacksquare -40$ $>$ | **27.** $-30 \blacksquare -20$ $<$ | **28.** $25 \blacksquare -25$ $>$ |
| **29.** $9 \blacksquare -9$ $>$ | **30.** $-6 \blacksquare -5$ $<$ | **31.** $-23 \blacksquare -15$ $<$ | **32.** $-17 \blacksquare -19$ $>$ | **33.** $-15 \blacksquare -25$ $>$ |

# Tables

## Table 1 Measures

### Metric

**Length**
10 millimeters (mm) = 1 centimeter (cm)
100 cm = 1 meter (m)
1,000 m = 1 kilometer (km)

**Area**
100 square millimeters ($mm^2$) = 1 square centimeter ($cm^2$)
10,000 $cm^2$ = 1 square meter ($m^2$)
1,000,000 $m^2$ = 1 square kilometer ($km^2$)

**Volume**
1,000 cubic millimeters ($mm^3$) = 1 cubic centimeter ($cm^3$)
1,000,000 $cm^3$ = 1 cubic meter ($m^3$)

**Mass**
1,000 milligrams (mg) = 1 gram (g)
1,000 g = 1 kilogram (kg)

**Volume**
1,000 milliliters (mL) = 1 liter (L)
1 mL = 1 $cm^3$

### Customary

**Length**
12 inches (in.) = 1 foot (ft)
3 ft = 1 yard (yd)
36 in. = 1 yd
5,280 ft = 1 mile (mi)
1,760 yd = 1 mi

**Area**
144 square inches ($in.^2$) = 1 square foot ($ft^2$)
9 $ft^2$ = 1 square yard ($yd^2$)
4,840 $yd^2$ = 1 acre

**Volume**
1,728 cubic inches ($in.^3$) = 1 cubic foot ($ft^3$)
27 $ft^3$ = 1 cubic yard ($yd^3$)

**Weight**
16 ounces (oz) = 1 pound (lb)
2,000 lb = 1 ton (t)

**Volume**
8 fluid ounces (fl oz) = 1 cup (c)
2 c = 1 pint (pt)
2 pt = 1 quart (qt)
4 qt = 1 gallon (gal)

**Time**
1 minute (min) = 60 seconds (s)
1 hour (h) = 60 min
1 day (d) = 24 h
1 year (yr) = 365 d



## Table 2 Symbols

| Symbol | Meaning |
|---|---|
| $>$ | is greater than |
| $<$ | is less than |
| $\geq$ | is greater than or equal to |
| $\leq$ | is less than or equal to |
| $=$ | is equal to |
| $\neq$ | is not equal to |
| $\approx$ | is approximately equal to |
| $\stackrel{?}{=}$ | is this statement true? |
| $+$ | plus (addition) |
| $-$ | minus (subtraction) |
| $\pm$ | plus or minus |
| $\times, \cdot$ | times (multiplication) |
| $\div, \overline{)\ }$ | divide (division) |
| $\sqrt{x}$ | nonnegative square root of $x$ |
| $^\circ$ | degrees |
| % | percent |
| ( ) | parentheses for grouping |
| $\lvert a \rvert$ | absolute value of $a$ |
| $a:b, \frac{a}{b}$ | ratio of $a$ to $b$ |
| $(a, b)$ | ordered pair with $x$-coordinate $a$ and $y$-coordinate $b$ |
| $\cong$ | is congruent to |
| $\ncong$ | is not congruent to |
| $\sim$ | is similar to |
| $\perp$ | is perpendicular to |
| $\parallel$ | is parallel to |
| $\pi$ | pi, an irrational number approximately equal to 3.14 |
| $f(n)$ | function value at $n$, $f$ of $n$ |
| $b$ | $y$-intercept |
| $m$ | slope of a line |
| $\begin{bmatrix} 1 & 3 \\ 2 & 4 \end{bmatrix}$ | matrix |
| $-a$ | opposite of $a$ |
| $\frac{1}{a}$ | reciprocal of $a$ |
| $a^n$ | $n$th power of $a$ |
| $d$ | distance, diameter |
| $A'$ | image of $A$, $A$ prime |
| $A$ | Area |
| $b_1, b_2$ | base lengths of a trapezoid |
| $b$ | base length |
| $h$ | height |
| $p$ or $P$ | perimeter |
| $\ell$ | slant height, length |
| $w$ | width |
| $C$ | circumference |
| S.A. | surface area |
| $B$ | area of a base |
| $V$ | volume |
| $r$ | rate, radius |
| $\overline{AB}$ | segment AB |
| $\overrightarrow{AB}$ | ray AB |
| $\overleftrightarrow{AB}$ | line AB |
| $\triangle ABC$ | triangle with vertices $A$, $B$, and $C$ |
| $\angle A$ | angle with vertex $A$ |
| $\angle ABC$ | angle with sides $\overrightarrow{BA}$ and $\overrightarrow{BC}$ |
| $m\angle ABC$ | measure of angle $ABC$ |
| $AB$ | length of segment $\overline{AB}$ |
| $\sin A$ | sine of $\angle A$ |
| $\cos A$ | cosine of $\angle A$ |
| $\tan A$ | tangent of $\angle A$ |
| $P(\text{event})$ | probability of an event |
| $n!$ | $n$ factorial |
| ${}_nP_r$ | permutations of $n$ things taken $r$ at a time |
| ${}_nC_r$ | combinations of $n$ things taken $r$ at a time |
| $\wedge$ | raised to a power (in a spreadsheet formula) |
| * | multiply (in a spreadsheet formula) |
| / | divide (in a spreadsheet formula) |

Tables



## Table 3 Properties of Real Numbers

Unless otherwise stated, $a$, $b$, $c$, and $d$ are real numbers.

**Identity Properties**
Addition $a + 0 = a$ and $0 + a = a$
Multiplication $a \cdot 1 = a$ and $1 \cdot a = a$

**Commutative Properties**
Addition $a + b = b + a$
Multiplication $a \cdot b = b \cdot a$

**Associative Properties**
Addition $(a + b) + c = a + (b + c)$
Multiplication $(a \cdot b) \cdot c = a \cdot (b \cdot c)$

**Inverse Properties**
Addition
$a + (-a) = 0$ and $-a + a = 0$
Multiplication
$a \cdot \frac{1}{a} = 1$ and $\frac{1}{a} \cdot a = 1 (a \neq 0)$

**Distributive Properties**
$a(b + c) = ab + ac$ $(b + c)a = ba + ca$
$a(b - c) = ab - ac$ $(b - c)a = ba - ca$

**Properties of Equality**
Addition If $a = b$, then $a + c = b + c$.
Subtraction If $a = b$, then $a - c = b - c$.
Multiplication If $a = b$, then $a \cdot c = b \cdot c$.
Division If $a = b$, and $c \neq 0$, then $\frac{a}{c} = \frac{b}{c}$.
Substitution If $a = b$, then $b$ can replace $a$ in any expression.
Reflexive $a = a$
Symmetric If $a = b$, then $b = a$.
Transitive If $a = b$ and $b = c$, then $a = c$.

**Cross Product Property**
$\frac{a}{b} = \frac{c}{d}$ is equivalent to $ad = bc$.

**Zero-Product Property**
If $ab = 0$ then $a = 0$ or $b = 0$.

**Closure Property**
$a + b$ is a unique real number.
$ab$ is a unique real number.

**Density Property**
Between any two rational numbers, there is at least one other rational number.

**Properties of Inequality**
Addition If $a > b$, then $a + c > b + c$.
If $a < b$, then $a + c < b + c$.
Subtraction If $a > b$, then $a - c > b - c$.
If $a < b$, then $a - c < b - c$.
Multiplication
If $a > b$ and $c > 0$, then $ac > bc$.
If $a < b$ and $c > 0$, then $ac < bc$.
If $a > b$ and $c < 0$, then $ac < bc$.
If $a < b$ and $c < 0$, then $ac > bc$.
Division
If $a > b$ and $c > 0$, then $\frac{a}{c} > \frac{b}{c}$.
If $a < b$ and $c > 0$, then $\frac{a}{c} < \frac{b}{c}$.
If $a > b$ and $c < 0$, then $\frac{a}{c} < \frac{b}{c}$.
If $a < b$ and $c < 0$, then $\frac{a}{c} > \frac{b}{c}$.
Transitive If $a > b$ and $b > c$, then $a > c$.
Comparison If $a = b + c$ and $c > 0$ then $a > b$.

**Properties of Exponents**
For any nonzero number $a$ and any integers $m$ and $n$:
Zero Exponent $a^0 = 1$
Negative Exponent $a^{-n} = \frac{1}{a^n}$
Product of Powers $a^m \cdot a^n = a^{m+n}$
Quotient of Powers $\frac{a^m}{a^n} = a^{m-n}$



## Table 4 Geometric Formulas

### Perimeter and Circumference

**Rectangle**
$P = 2\ell + 2w$

**Circle**
$C = \pi d$ or $C = 2\pi r$

### Area

**Square**
$A = s^2$

**Parallelogram and Rectangle**
$A = bh$

**Triangle**
$A = \frac{1}{2}bh$

**Trapezoid**
$A = \frac{1}{2}h(b_1 + b_2)$

**Circle**
$C = \pi r^2$

### Triangle Formulas

**Pythagorean Theorem**
In a right triangle with legs of lengths $a$ and $b$ and hypotenuse of length $c$, $a^2 + b^2 = c^2$.

**Trigonometric Ratios**
tangent of $\angle A = \frac{\text{length of leg opposite } \angle A}{\text{length of leg adjacent to } \angle A}$
sine of $\angle A = \frac{\text{length of leg opposite } \angle A}{\text{length of hypotenuse}}$
cosine of $\angle A = \frac{\text{length of leg adjacent to } \angle A}{\text{length of hypotenuse}}$

**Triangle Angle Sum**
For any $\triangle ABC$,
$m\angle A + m\angle B + m\angle C = 180^\circ$.

### Surface Area

**Rectangular Prism**
L.A. = $ph$
S.A. = L.A. + $2B$

**Cylinder**
L.A. = $2\pi rh$
S.A. = L.A. + $2B$

**Square Pyramid**
L.A. = $n\left(\frac{1}{2}b\ell\right)$, where $n$ is the number of faces
S.A. = L.A. + $B$

**Cone**
L.A. = $\pi r\ell$
S.A. = L.A. + $B$

**Sphere**
S.A. = $4\pi r^2$

### Volume

**Prism**
$V = Bh$

**Cylinder**
$V = Bh$ or $B = \pi r^2 h$

**Pyramid**
$V = \frac{1}{3}Bh$

**Cone**
$V = \frac{1}{3}Bh$ or $V = \frac{1}{3}\pi r^2 h$

**Sphere**
$V = \frac{4}{3}\pi r^3$

Tables

## Table 5 Squares and Square Roots

| N | $N^2$ | $\sqrt{N}$ | N | $N^2$ | $\sqrt{N}$ |
|---|---|---|---|---|---|
| 1 | 1 | 1 | 51 | 2,601 | 7.141 |
| 2 | 4 | 1.414 | 52 | 2,704 | 7.211 |
| 3 | 9 | 1.732 | 53 | 2,809 | 7.280 |
| 4 | 16 | 2 | 54 | 2,916 | 7.348 |
| 5 | 25 | 2.236 | 55 | 3,025 | 7.416 |
| 6 | 36 | 2.449 | 56 | 3,136 | 7.483 |
| 7 | 49 | 2.646 | 57 | 3,249 | 7.550 |
| 8 | 64 | 2.828 | 58 | 3,364 | 7.616 |
| 9 | 81 | 3 | 59 | 3,481 | 7.681 |
| 10 | 100 | 3.162 | 60 | 3,600 | 7.746 |
| 11 | 121 | 3.317 | 61 | 3,721 | 7.810 |
| 12 | 144 | 3.464 | 62 | 3,844 | 7.874 |
| 13 | 169 | 3.606 | 63 | 3,969 | 7.937 |
| 14 | 196 | 3.742 | 64 | 4,096 | 8 |
| 15 | 225 | 3.873 | 65 | 4,225 | 8.062 |
| 16 | 256 | 4 | 66 | 4,356 | 8.124 |
| 17 | 289 | 4.123 | 67 | 4,489 | 8.185 |
| 18 | 324 | 4.243 | 68 | 4,624 | 8.246 |
| 19 | 361 | 4.359 | 69 | 4,761 | 8.307 |
| 20 | 400 | 4.472 | 70 | 4,900 | 8.367 |
| 21 | 441 | 4.583 | 71 | 5,041 | 8.426 |
| 22 | 484 | 4.690 | 72 | 5,184 | 8.485 |
| 23 | 529 | 4.796 | 73 | 5,329 | 8.544 |
| 24 | 576 | 4.899 | 74 | 5,476 | 8.602 |
| 25 | 625 | 5 | 75 | 5,625 | 8.660 |
| 26 | 676 | 5.099 | 76 | 5,776 | 8.718 |
| 27 | 729 | 5.196 | 77 | 5,929 | 8.775 |
| 28 | 784 | 5.292 | 78 | 6,084 | 8.832 |
| 29 | 841 | 5.385 | 79 | 6,241 | 8.888 |
| 30 | 900 | 5.477 | 80 | 6,400 | 8.944 |
| 31 | 961 | 5.568 | 81 | 6,561 | 9 |
| 32 | 1,024 | 5.657 | 82 | 6,724 | 9.055 |
| 33 | 1,089 | 5.745 | 83 | 6,889 | 9.110 |
| 34 | 1,156 | 5.831 | 84 | 7,056 | 9.165 |
| 35 | 1,225 | 5.916 | 85 | 7,225 | 9.220 |
| 36 | 1,296 | 6 | 86 | 7,396 | 9.274 |
| 37 | 1,369 | 6.083 | 87 | 7,569 | 9.327 |
| 38 | 1,444 | 6.164 | 88 | 7,744 | 9.381 |
| 39 | 1,521 | 6.245 | 89 | 7,921 | 9.434 |
| 40 | 1,600 | 6.325 | 90 | 8,100 | 9.487 |
| 41 | 1,681 | 6.403 | 91 | 8,281 | 9.539 |
| 42 | 1,764 | 6.481 | 92 | 8,464 | 9.592 |
| 43 | 1,849 | 6.557 | 93 | 8,649 | 9.644 |
| 44 | 1,936 | 6.633 | 94 | 8,836 | 9.695 |
| 45 | 2,025 | 6.708 | 95 | 9,025 | 9.747 |
| 46 | 2,116 | 6.782 | 96 | 9,216 | 9.798 |
| 47 | 2,209 | 6.856 | 97 | 9,409 | 9.849 |
| 48 | 2,304 | 6.928 | 98 | 9,604 | 9.899 |
| 49 | 2,401 | 7 | 99 | 9,801 | 9.950 |
| 50 | 2,500 | 7.071 | 100 | 10,000 | 10 |



## Table 6 Trigonometric Ratios

| Angle | Sine | Cosine | Tangent | Angle | Sine | Cosine | Tangent |
|---|---|---|---|---|---|---|---|
| 1° | 0.0175 | 0.9998 | 0.0175 | 46° | 0.7193 | 0.6947 | 1.0355 |
| 2° | 0.0349 | 0.9994 | 0.0349 | 47° | 0.7314 | 0.6820 | 1.0724 |
| 3° | 0.0523 | 0.9986 | 0.0524 | 48° | 0.7431 | 0.6691 | 1.1106 |
| 4° | 0.0698 | 0.9976 | 0.0699 | 49° | 0.7547 | 0.6561 | 1.1504 |
| 5° | 0.0872 | 0.9962 | 0.0875 | 50° | 0.7660 | 0.6428 | 1.1918 |
| 6° | 0.1045 | 0.9945 | 0.1051 | 51° | 0.7771 | 0.6293 | 1.2349 |
| 7° | 0.1219 | 0.9925 | 0.1228 | 52° | 0.7880 | 0.6157 | 1.2799 |
| 8° | 0.1392 | 0.9903 | 0.1405 | 53° | 0.7986 | 0.6018 | 1.3270 |
| 9° | 0.1564 | 0.9877 | 0.1584 | 54° | 0.8090 | 0.5878 | 1.3764 |
| 10° | 0.1736 | 0.9848 | 0.1763 | 55° | 0.8192 | 0.5736 | 1.4281 |
| 11° | 0.1908 | 0.9816 | 0.1944 | 56° | 0.8290 | 0.5592 | 1.4826 |
| 12° | 0.2079 | 0.9781 | 0.2126 | 57° | 0.8387 | 0.5446 | 1.5399 |
| 13° | 0.2250 | 0.9744 | 0.2309 | 58° | 0.8480 | 0.5299 | 1.6003 |
| 14° | 0.2419 | 0.9703 | 0.2493 | 59° | 0.8572 | 0.5150 | 1.6643 |
| 15° | 0.2588 | 0.9659 | 0.2679 | 60° | 0.8660 | 0.5000 | 1.7321 |
| 16° | 0.2756 | 0.9613 | 0.2867 | 61° | 0.8746 | 0.4848 | 1.8040 |
| 17° | 0.2924 | 0.9563 | 0.3057 | 62° | 0.8829 | 0.4695 | 1.8807 |
| 18° | 0.3090 | 0.9511 | 0.3249 | 63° | 0.8910 | 0.4540 | 1.9626 |
| 19° | 0.3256 | 0.9455 | 0.3443 | 64° | 0.8988 | 0.4384 | 2.0503 |
| 20° | 0.3420 | 0.9397 | 0.3640 | 65° | 0.9063 | 0.4226 | 2.1445 |
| 21° | 0.3584 | 0.9336 | 0.3839 | 66° | 0.9135 | 0.4067 | 2.2460 |
| 22° | 0.3746 | 0.9272 | 0.4040 | 67° | 0.9205 | 0.3907 | 2.3559 |
| 23° | 0.3907 | 0.9205 | 0.4245 | 68° | 0.9272 | 0.3746 | 2.4751 |
| 24° | 0.4067 | 0.9135 | 0.4452 | 69° | 0.9336 | 0.3584 | 2.6051 |
| 25° | 0.4226 | 0.9063 | 0.4663 | 70° | 0.9397 | 0.3420 | 2.7475 |
| 26° | 0.4384 | 0.8988 | 0.4877 | 71° | 0.9455 | 0.3256 | 2.9042 |
| 27° | 0.4540 | 0.8910 | 0.5095 | 72° | 0.9511 | 0.3090 | 3.0777 |
| 28° | 0.4695 | 0.8829 | 0.5317 | 73° | 0.9563 | 0.2924 | 3.2709 |
| 29° | 0.4848 | 0.8746 | 0.5543 | 74° | 0.9613 | 0.2756 | 3.4874 |
| 30° | 0.5000 | 0.8660 | 0.5774 | 75° | 0.9659 | 0.2588 | 3.7321 |
| 31° | 0.5150 | 0.8572 | 0.6009 | 76° | 0.9703 | 0.2419 | 4.0108 |
| 32° | 0.5299 | 0.8480 | 0.6249 | 77° | 0.9744 | 0.2250 | 4.3315 |
| 33° | 0.5446 | 0.8387 | 0.6494 | 78° | 0.9781 | 0.2079 | 4.7046 |
| 34° | 0.5592 | 0.8290 | 0.6745 | 79° | 0.9816 | 0.1908 | 5.1446 |
| 35° | 0.5736 | 0.8192 | 0.7002 | 80° | 0.9848 | 0.1736 | 5.6713 |
| 36° | 0.5878 | 0.8090 | 0.7265 | 81° | 0.9877 | 0.1564 | 6.3138 |
| 37° | 0.6018 | 0.7986 | 0.7536 | 82° | 0.9903 | 0.1392 | 7.1154 |
| 38° | 0.6157 | 0.7880 | 0.7813 | 83° | 0.9925 | 0.1219 | 8.1443 |
| 39° | 0.6293 | 0.7771 | 0.8098 | 84° | 0.9945 | 0.1045 | 9.5144 |
| 40° | 0.6428 | 0.7660 | 0.8391 | 85° | 0.9962 | 0.0872 | 11.4301 |
| 41° | 0.6561 | 0.7547 | 0.8693 | 86° | 0.9976 | 0.0698 | 14.3007 |
| 42° | 0.6691 | 0.7431 | 0.9004 | 87° | 0.9986 | 0.0523 | 19.0811 |
| 43° | 0.6820 | 0.7314 | 0.9325 | 88° | 0.9994 | 0.0349 | 28.6363 |
| 44° | 0.6947 | 0.7193 | 0.9657 | 89° | 0.9998 | 0.0175 | 57.2900 |
| 45° | 0.7071 | 0.7071 | 1.0000 | | | | |

# Glossary/Study Guide

## A

EXAMPLES

**Absolute value (p. 18)** Absolute value is the distance of a number from zero on a number line. You write *the absolute value of* $-3$ as $|-3|$.

The absolute value of $-3$ is 3 because $-3$ is 3 units from zero on a number line.

**Absolute value function (p. 670)** An absolute value function is a function with a graph that is V-shaped and opens up or down.

EXAMPLE This absolute value function is the graph of the equation $y = |x| - 3$.

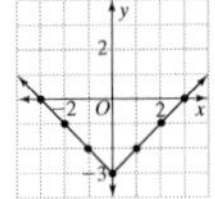

**Acute angle (p. 448)** An acute angle is an angle with a measure less than 90°.

EXAMPLE $0° < m\angle 1 < 90°$

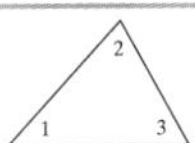

**Acute triangle (p. 454)** An acute triangle is a triangle with three acute angles.

EXAMPLE $\angle 1$, $\angle 2$, and $\angle 3$ are acute.

**Addition Property of Equality (p. 86)** If $a = b$, then $a + c = b + c$.

$8 = 2(4)$, so $8 + 3 = 2(4) + 3$

**Addition Property of Inequality (p. 105)** If $a > b$, then $a + c > b + c$. If $a < b$, then $a + c < b + c$.

$7 > 3$, so $7 + 4 > 3 + 4$
$2 < 5$, so $2 + 6 < 5 + 6$

**Additive inverses (p. 23)** Additive inverses are two numbers with a sum of zero.

23 and $-23$ are additive inverses because $-23 + 23 = 0$.

**Additive identity (p. 65)** The additive identity is zero. When you add a number and 0, the sum equals the original number.

$a + 0 = a$

**Adjacent angles (p. 449)** Adjacent angles are two angles that share a vertex and a side but no points in their interiors.

EXAMPLE $\angle 1$ and $\angle 2$ are adjacent angles.

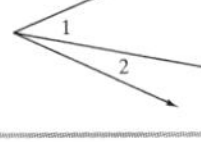

**Alternate interior angles (p. 450)** Alternate interior angles are angles between two lines and on opposite sides of a transversal.

EXAMPLE $\angle 2$ and $\angle 3$ are alternate interior angles. $\angle 1$ and $\angle 4$ are also alternate interior angles.



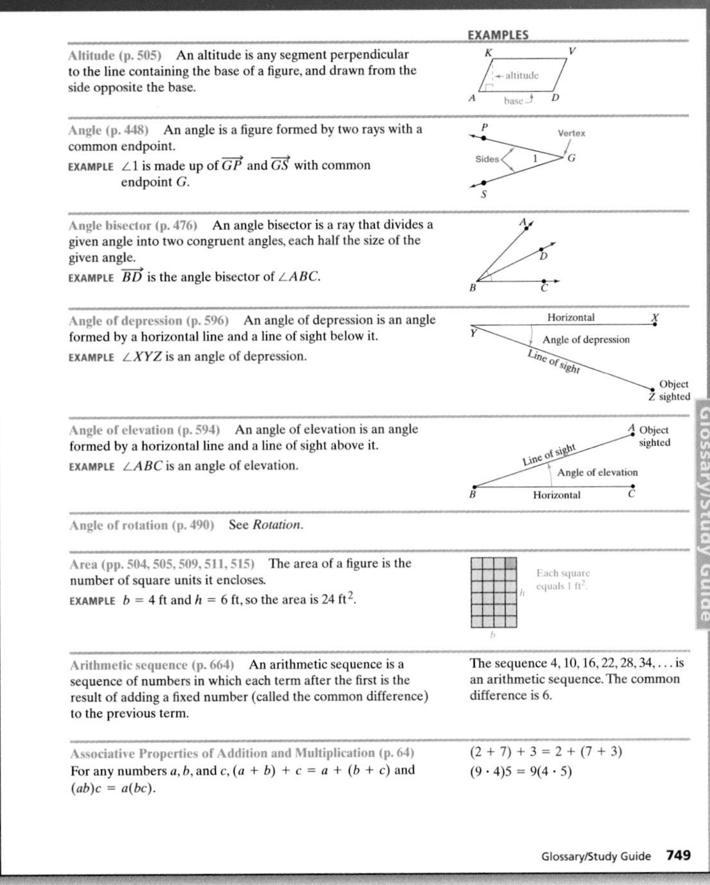

EXAMPLES

**Altitude (p. 505)** An altitude is any segment perpendicular to the line containing the base of a figure, and drawn from the side opposite the base.

**Angle (p. 448)** An angle is a figure formed by two rays with a common endpoint.

EXAMPLE $\angle 1$ is made up of $\overrightarrow{GP}$ and $\overrightarrow{GS}$ with common endpoint $G$.

**Angle bisector (p. 476)** An angle bisector is a ray that divides a given angle into two congruent angles, each half the size of the given angle.

EXAMPLE $\overrightarrow{BD}$ is the angle bisector of $\angle ABC$.

**Angle of depression (p. 596)** An angle of depression is an angle formed by a horizontal line and a line of sight below it.

EXAMPLE $\angle XYZ$ is an angle of depression.

**Angle of elevation (p. 594)** An angle of elevation is an angle formed by a horizontal line and a line of sight above it.

EXAMPLE $\angle ABC$ is an angle of elevation.

**Angle of rotation (p. 490)** See *Rotation.*

**Area (pp. 504, 505, 509, 511, 515)** The area of a figure is the number of square units it encloses.

EXAMPLE $b = 4$ ft and $h = 6$ ft, so the area is 24 ft$^2$.

**Arithmetic sequence (p. 664)** An arithmetic sequence is a sequence of numbers in which each term after the first is the result of adding a fixed number (called the common difference) to the previous term.

The sequence 4, 10, 16, 22, 28, 34, . . . is an arithmetic sequence. The common difference is 6.

**Associative Properties of Addition and Multiplication (p. 64)** For any numbers $a$, $b$, and $c$, $(a + b) + c = a + (b + c)$ and $(ab)c = a(bc)$.

$(2 + 7) + 3 = 2 + (7 + 3)$
$(9 \cdot 4)5 = 9(4 \cdot 5)$



## B

EXAMPLES

**Balance (p. 370)** The balance in an account is the principal plus the earned interest.

See *Compound interest.*

**Bar graph (p. 99)** A bar graph is a graph that compares amounts.

EXAMPLE This bar graph compares the numbers of students in grades 6, 7, and 8.

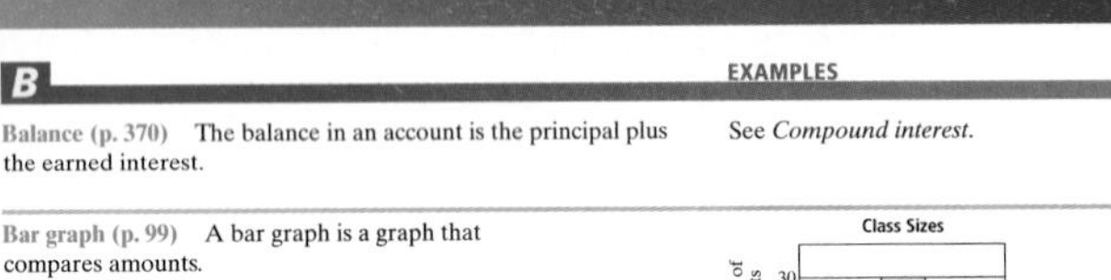

**Base (p. 176)** The base is the repeated factor of a number written in exponential form.

$5^4 = 5 \cdot 5 \cdot 5 \cdot 5$
5 is the base.

**Bases of two-dimensional figures (pp. 504, 509)** See *Parallelogram, Triangle,* and *Trapezoid.*

**Bases of three-dimensional figures (p. 521)** See *Cone, Cylinder, Prism,* and *Pyramid.*

**Binomial (p. 678)** A binomial is a polynomial with two terms.

$3x^2 - 1$ is a binomial.

**Box-and-whisker plot (p. 613)** A box-and-whisker plot is a graph that shows the distribution of data along a number line. Quartiles divide the data into four equal parts.

EXAMPLE The box-and-whisker plot at the right is for the data
16 19 26 27 27 29 30 31 34 35 37 39 40.
The lower quartile is 26.5. The median is 30. The upper quartile is 36.

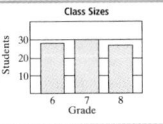

## C

**Center of rotation (p. 490)** See *Rotation.*

**Central angle (p. 470)** A central angle is an angle whose vertex is the center of a circle.

EXAMPLE In circle $O$, $\angle AOB$ is a central angle.

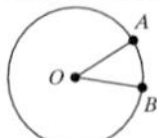

**Chord (p. 469)** A chord of a circle is a segment whose endpoints are on the circle.

EXAMPLE $\overline{AB}$ is a chord of circle $O$.

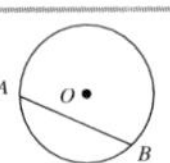



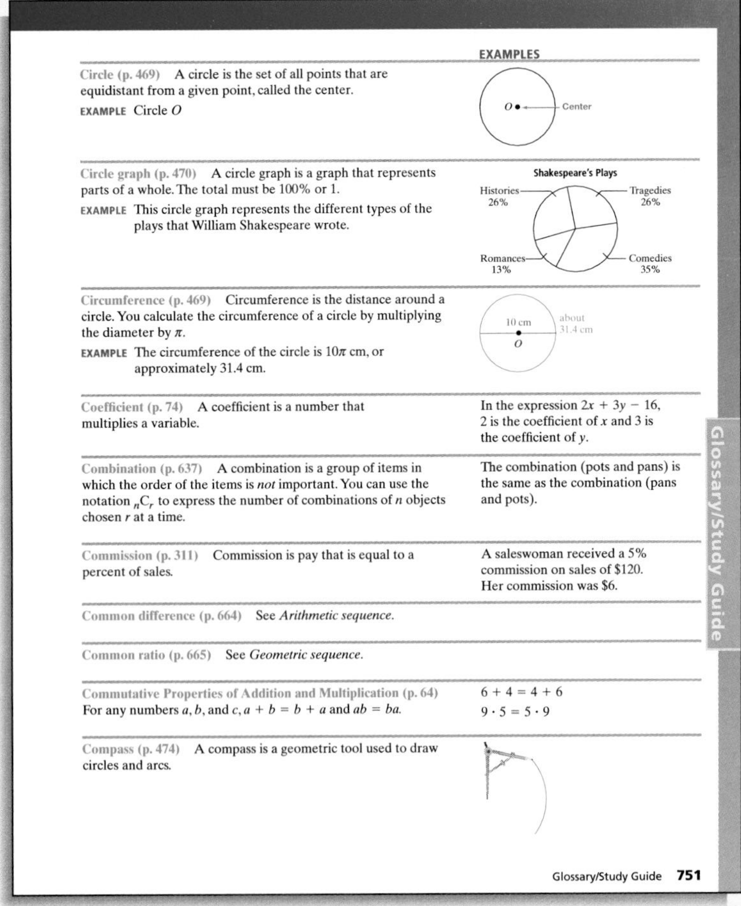

EXAMPLES

**Circle (p. 469)** A circle is the set of all points that are equidistant from a given point, called the center.

EXAMPLE Circle $O$

**Circle graph (p. 470)** A circle graph is a graph that represents parts of a whole. The total must be 100% or 1.

EXAMPLE This circle graph represents the different types of the plays that William Shakespeare wrote.

**Circumference (p. 469)** Circumference is the distance around a circle. You calculate the circumference of a circle by multiplying the diameter by $\pi$.

EXAMPLE The circumference of the circle is $10\pi$ cm, or approximately 31.4 cm.

**Coefficient (p. 74)** A coefficient is a number that multiplies a variable.

In the expression $2x + 3y - 16$, 2 is the coefficient of $x$ and 3 is the coefficient of $y$.

**Combination (p. 637)** A combination is a group of items in which the order of the items is *not* important. You can use the notation ${}_nC_r$ to express the number of combinations of $n$ objects chosen $r$ at a time.

The combination (pots and pans) is the same as the combination (pans and pots).

**Commission (p. 311)** Commission is pay that is equal to a percent of sales.

A saleswoman received a 5% commission on sales of \$120. Her commission was \$6.

**Common difference (p. 664)** See *Arithmetic sequence.*

**Common ratio (p. 665)** See *Geometric sequence.*

**Commutative Properties of Addition and Multiplication (p. 64)** For any numbers $a$, $b$, and $c$, $a + b = b + a$ and $ab = ba$.

$6 + 4 = 4 + 6$
$9 \cdot 5 = 5 \cdot 9$

**Compass (p. 474)** A compass is a geometric tool used to draw circles and arcs.

EXAMPLES

**Compatible numbers (p. 128)** Compatible numbers are numbers that are close in value to the numbers you want to divide, and that are easy to divide mentally. Estimating quotients is easy to do mentally when you use compatible numbers.

Estimate $151 \div 14.6$.
$151 \approx 150$
$14.6 \approx 15$
$150 \div 15 = 10$
$151 \div 14.6 \approx 10$

**Complement of an event (p. 296)** The complement of an event is the opposite of that event. The probability of an event plus the probability of its complement equals 1.

The event *no rain* is the complement of the event *rain*.

**Complementary angles (p. 449)** Complementary angles are two angles whose measures add to 90°.

EXAMPLE $\angle BCA$ and $\angle CAB$ are complementary angles.



**Composite number (p. 180)** A composite number is an integer greater than 1 with more than two factors.

24 is a composite number that has 1, 2, 3, 4, 6, 8, 12, and 24 as factors.

**Compound inequalities (p. 364)** Compound inequalities are two inequalities joined by the word *and* or the word *or*.

$x > 4$ and $x \leq 6$



$x \leq -2$ or $x > 3$



**Compound interest (p. 370)** Compound interest is interest paid on both the principal and the interest earned in previous interest periods. You can use the formula $B = p(1 + r)^n$ where $B$ is the final balance, $p$ is the principal, $r$ is the interest rate for each interest period, and $n$ is the number of interest periods.

You deposit \$500 in an account earning 5% annual compound interest. The balance after six years is $500(1 + 0.05)^6$, or \$670.05. The compound interest is $670.05 - 500$, or \$170.05.

**Cone (p. 521)** A cone is a space figure with one circular base and one vertex.



**Congruent angles (p. 449)** Congruent angles are angles that have the same measure.

EXAMPLE $\angle B \cong \angle C$





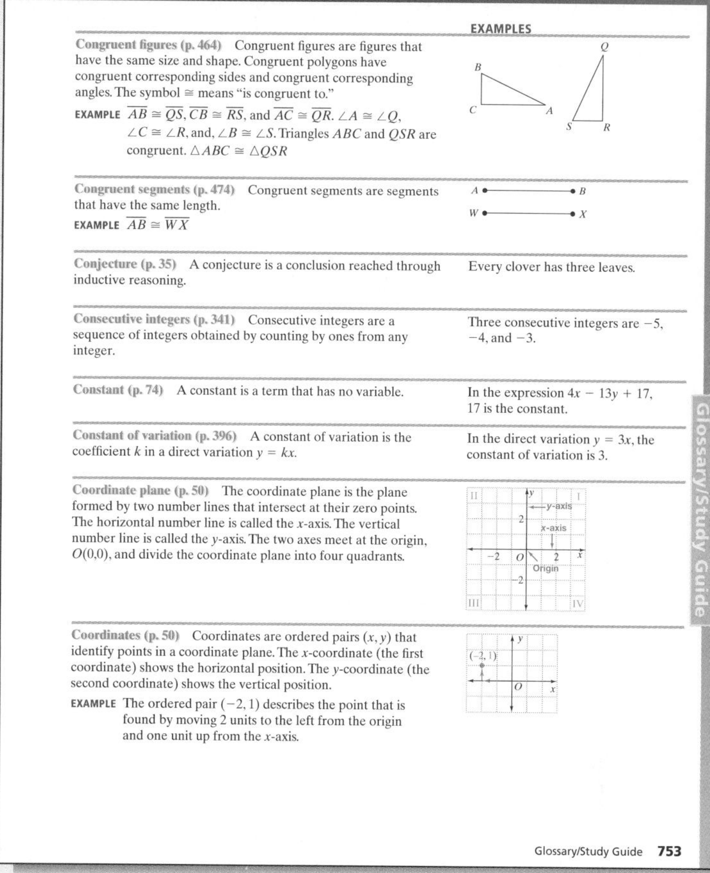

EXAMPLES

**Congruent figures (p. 464)** Congruent figures are figures that have the same size and shape. Congruent polygons have congruent corresponding sides and congruent corresponding angles. The symbol ≅ means "is congruent to."

EXAMPLE $\overline{AB} \cong \overline{QS}$, $\overline{CB} \cong \overline{RS}$, and $\overline{AC} \cong \overline{QR}$. $\angle A \cong \angle Q$, $\angle C \cong \angle R$, and, $\angle B \cong \angle S$. Triangles $ABC$ and $QSR$ are congruent. $\triangle ABC \cong \triangle QSR$



**Congruent segments (p. 474)** Congruent segments are segments that have the same length.

EXAMPLE $\overline{AB} \cong \overline{WX}$



**Conjecture (p. 35)** A conjecture is a conclusion reached through inductive reasoning.

Every clover has three leaves.

**Consecutive integers (p. 341)** Consecutive integers are a sequence of integers obtained by counting by ones from any integer.

Three consecutive integers are −5, −4, and −3.

**Constant (p. 74)** A constant is a term that has no variable.

In the expression $4x - 13y + 17$, 17 is the constant.

**Constant of variation (p. 396)** A constant of variation is the coefficient $k$ in a direct variation $y = kx$.

In the direct variation $y = 3x$, the constant of variation is 3.

**Coordinate plane (p. 50)** The coordinate plane is the plane formed by two number lines that intersect at their zero points. The horizontal number line is called the $x$-axis. The vertical number line is called the $y$-axis. The two axes meet at the origin, $O(0,0)$, and divide the coordinate plane into four quadrants.



**Coordinates (p. 50)** Coordinates are ordered pairs $(x, y)$ that identify points in a coordinate plane. The $x$-coordinate (the first coordinate) shows the horizontal position. The $y$-coordinate (the second coordinate) shows the vertical position.

EXAMPLE The ordered pair $(-2, 1)$ describes the point that is found by moving 2 units to the left from the origin and one unit up from the $x$-axis.







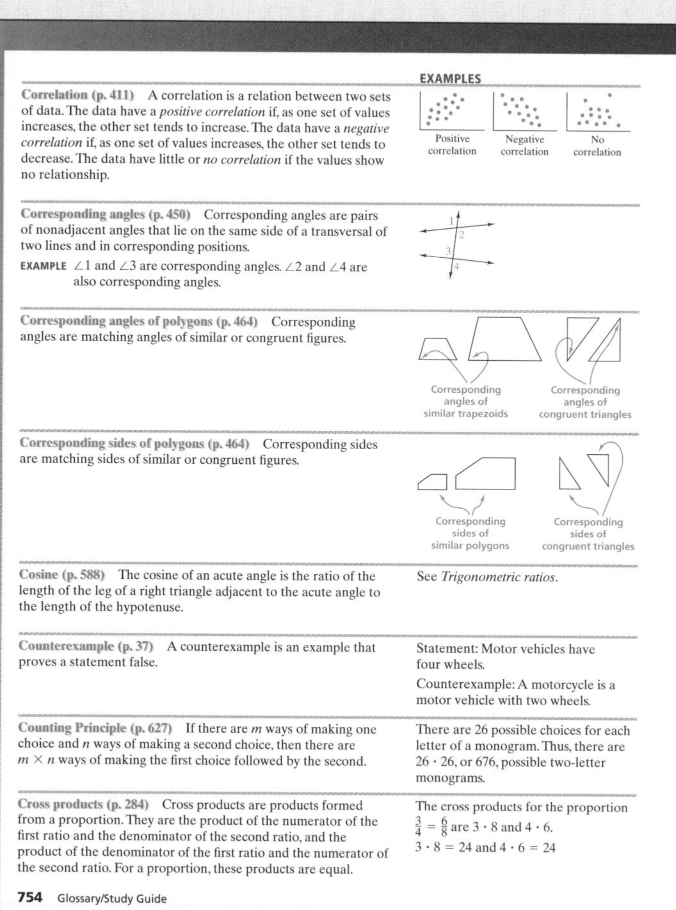

EXAMPLES

**Correlation (p. 411)** A correlation is a relation between two sets of data. The data have a *positive correlation* if, as one set of values increases, the other set tends to increase. The data have a *negative correlation* if, as one set of values increases, the other set tends to decrease. The data have little or *no correlation* if the values show no relationship.



**Corresponding angles (p. 450)** Corresponding angles are pairs of nonadjacent angles that lie on the same side of a transversal of two lines and in corresponding positions.

EXAMPLE $\angle 1$ and $\angle 3$ are corresponding angles. $\angle 2$ and $\angle 4$ are also corresponding angles.



**Corresponding angles of polygons (p. 464)** Corresponding angles are matching angles of similar or congruent figures.



**Corresponding sides of polygons (p. 464)** Corresponding sides are matching sides of similar or congruent figures.



**Cosine (p. 588)** The cosine of an acute angle is the ratio of the length of the leg of a right triangle adjacent to the acute angle to the length of the hypotenuse.

See *Trigonometric ratios.*

**Counterexample (p. 37)** A counterexample is an example that proves a statement false.

Statement: Motor vehicles have four wheels.
Counterexample: A motorcycle is a motor vehicle with two wheels.

**Counting Principle (p. 627)** If there are $m$ ways of making one choice and $n$ ways of making a second choice, then there are $m \times n$ ways of making the first choice followed by the second.

There are 26 possible choices for each letter of a monogram. Thus, there are $26 \cdot 26$, or 676, possible two-letter monograms.

**Cross products (p. 284)** Cross products are products formed from a proportion. They are the product of the numerator of the first ratio and the denominator of the second ratio, and the product of the denominator of the first ratio and the numerator of the second ratio. For a proportion, these products are equal.

The cross products for the proportion $\frac{3}{4} = \frac{6}{8}$ are $3 \cdot 8$ and $4 \cdot 6$.
$3 \cdot 8 = 24$ and $4 \cdot 6 = 24$



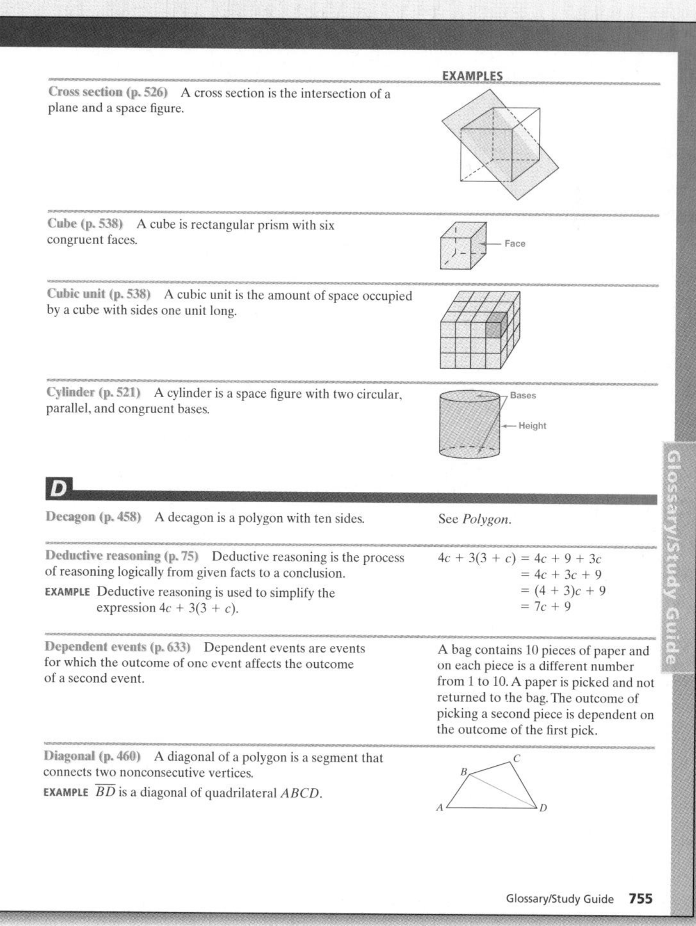

EXAMPLES

**Cross section (p. 526)** A cross section is the intersection of a plane and a space figure.

**Cube (p. 538)** A cube is rectangular prism with six congruent faces.



**Cubic unit (p. 538)** A cubic unit is the amount of space occupied by a cube with sides one unit long.

**Cylinder (p. 521)** A cylinder is a space figure with two circular, parallel, and congruent bases.



## D

**Decagon (p. 458)** A decagon is a polygon with ten sides.

See *Polygon.*

**Deductive reasoning (p. 75)** Deductive reasoning is the process of reasoning logically from given facts to a conclusion.

EXAMPLE Deductive reasoning is used to simplify the expression $4c + 3(3 + c)$.

$$\begin{aligned} 4c + 3(3 + c) &= 4c + 9 + 3c \\ &= 4c + 3c + 9 \\ &= (4 + 3)c + 9 \\ &= 7c + 9 \end{aligned}$$

**Dependent events (p. 633)** Dependent events are events for which the outcome of one event affects the outcome of a second event.

A bag contains 10 pieces of paper and on each piece is a different number from 1 to 10. A paper is picked and not returned to the bag. The outcome of picking a second piece is dependent on the outcome of the first pick.

**Diagonal (p. 460)** A diagonal of a polygon is a segment that connects two nonconsecutive vertices.

EXAMPLE $\overline{BD}$ is a diagonal of quadrilateral $ABCD$.

EXAMPLES

**Diameter** (p. 469) A diameter of a circle is a chord that passes through the center of the circle.
EXAMPLE $\overline{RS}$ is a diameter of circle $O$.

**Dilation** (p. 294) A dilation is a transformation that results in a size change. The scale factor describes the size of the change from the original figure to its image. If $r > 1$, the dilation is an enlargement. If $r < 1$, the dilation is a reduction.
EXAMPLE The blue triangle is an enlargement of the red triangle. The red triangle is a reduction of the blue triangle.

**Dimensional analysis** (p. 246) Dimensional analysis is a process of analyzing units to decide which conversion factors to use.
$0.5 \text{ mi} = \frac{0.5 \text{ mi}}{1} \cdot \frac{5{,}280 \text{ ft}}{1 \text{ mi}} = 2{,}640 \text{ ft}$

**Direct variation** (p. 396) A direct variation is a linear function modeled by the equation $y = kx$, where $k \neq 0$.
$y = 3x$

**Discount** (p. 319) A discount is the amount by which a price is decreased.
The price of a \$10 book is reduced by a discount of \$1.50 to sell for \$8.50.

**Distance Formula** (p. 572) The distance $d$ between any two points $(x_1, y_1)$ and $(x_2, y_2)$ is $d = \sqrt{(x_2 - x_1)^2 + (y_2 - y_1)^2}$.
The distance between (6, 3) and (1, 9) is $d$:
$d = \sqrt{(1 - 6)^2 + (9 - 3)^2}$
$= \sqrt{(-5)^2 + 6^2}$
$= \sqrt{61}$
$\approx 7.8$

**Distributive Property** (p. 69) For any numbers $a$, $b$, and $c$, $a(b + c) = ab + ac$ and $a(b - c) = ab - ac$.
$2\left(3 + \frac{1}{2}\right) = 2 \cdot 3 + 2 \cdot \frac{1}{2}$
$8(5 - 3) = 8(5) - 8(3)$

**Divisible** (p. 172) Divisible means that the remainder is 0 when you divide one integer by another.
15 is divisible by 5 because $15 \div 5 = 3$ with remainder 0.

**Division Property of Equality** (p. 89) If $a = b$ and $c \neq 0$, then $\frac{a}{c} = \frac{b}{c}$.
$6 = 3(2)$, so $\frac{6}{3} = \frac{3(2)}{3}$



EXAMPLES

**Division Properties of Inequality** (p. 108) If $a < b$ and $c$ is positive, then $\frac{a}{c} < \frac{b}{c}$. If $a > b$ and $c$ is positive, then $\frac{a}{c} > \frac{b}{c}$.
$3 < 6$, so $\frac{3}{3} < \frac{6}{3}$
$8 > 2$, so $\frac{8}{2} > \frac{2}{2}$

If you divide each side of an inequality by a negative number, the direction of the inequality symbol is reversed.
If $a < b$ and $c$ is negative, then $\frac{a}{c} > \frac{b}{c}$.
$6 < 12$, so $\frac{6}{-3} > \frac{12}{-3}$
If $a > b$ and $c$ is negative, then $\frac{a}{c} < \frac{b}{c}$.
$16 > 8$, so $\frac{16}{-4} < \frac{8}{-4}$

**Domain** (p. 386) A domain is the set of first coordinates of the ordered pairs of a relation.
In the relation $\{(0, 1), (-3, 2), (0, 2)\}$, the domain is $\{0, -3\}$.

## E

**Edge** (p. 521) An edge is the intersection of two faces of a space figure.
Faces
Edges

**Equation** (p. 78) An equation is a mathematical sentence with an equal sign, =. An equation says that the side to the left of the equal sign has the same value as the side to the right of the equal sign.
$2(6 + 17) = 46$

**Equilateral triangle** (p. 454) An equilateral triangle is a triangle with three congruent sides.
EXAMPLE $\overline{SL} \cong \overline{LW} \cong \overline{WS}$

**Equivalent fractions** (p. 186) Equivalent fractions are fractions that describe the same part of a whole.
$\frac{3}{4}$ and $\frac{6}{8}$

**Evaluate an expression** (p. 13) To evaluate an expression is to replace each variable with a number, and then follow the order of operations.
To evaluate the expression $3x + 2$ for $x = 4$, substitute 4 for $x$.
$3x + 2 = 3(4) + 2 = 12 + 2 = 14$

**Event** (p. 295) An event is any outcome or group of outcomes.
In a game that includes tossing a coin and rolling a number cube, *tossing heads and rolling a 2* is an event.

**Experimental probability** (p. 642) See *Probability*.

**Exponent** (p. 176) An exponent is a number that shows how many times a base is used as a factor.
$3^4 = 3 \cdot 3 \cdot 3 \cdot 3$

Glossary/Study Guide



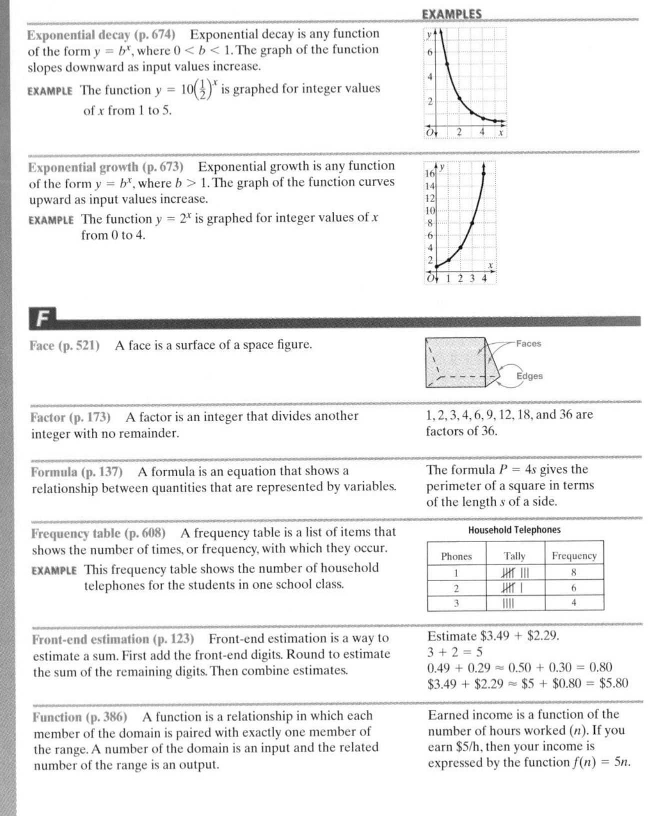

EXAMPLES

**Exponential decay** (p. 674) Exponential decay is any function of the form $y = b^x$, where $0 < b < 1$. The graph of the function slopes downward as input values increase.
EXAMPLE The function $y = 10\left(\frac{1}{2}\right)^x$ is graphed for integer values of $x$ from 1 to 5.

**Exponential growth** (p. 673) Exponential growth is any function of the form $y = b^x$, where $b > 1$. The graph of the function curves upward as input values increase.
EXAMPLE The function $y = 2^x$ is graphed for integer values of $x$ from 0 to 4.

## F

**Face** (p. 521) A face is a surface of a space figure.
Faces
Edges

**Factor** (p. 173) A factor is an integer that divides another integer with no remainder.
1, 2, 3, 4, 6, 9, 12, 18, and 36 are factors of 36.

**Formula** (p. 137) A formula is an equation that shows a relationship between quantities that are represented by variables.
The formula $P = 4s$ gives the perimeter of a square in terms of the length $s$ of a side.

**Frequency table** (p. 608) A frequency table is a list of items that shows the number of times, or frequency, with which they occur.
EXAMPLE This frequency table shows the number of household telephones for the students in one school class.

Household Telephones

| Phones | Tally | Frequency |
|---|---|---|
| 1 | 𝍸 \|\|\| | 8 |
| 2 | 𝍸 \| | 6 |
| 3 | \|\|\|\| | 4 |

**Front-end estimation** (p. 123) Front-end estimation is a way to estimate a sum. First add the front-end digits. Round to estimate the sum of the remaining digits. Then combine estimates.
Estimate \$3.49 + \$2.29.
$3 + 2 = 5$
$0.49 + 0.29 \approx 0.50 + 0.30 = 0.80$
$\$3.49 + \$2.29 \approx \$5 + \$0.80 = \$5.80$

**Function** (p. 386) A function is a relationship in which each member of the domain is paired with exactly one member of the range. A number of the domain is an input and the related number of the range is an output.
Earned income is a function of the number of hours worked ($n$). If you earn \$5/h, then your income is expressed by the function $f(n) = 5n$.



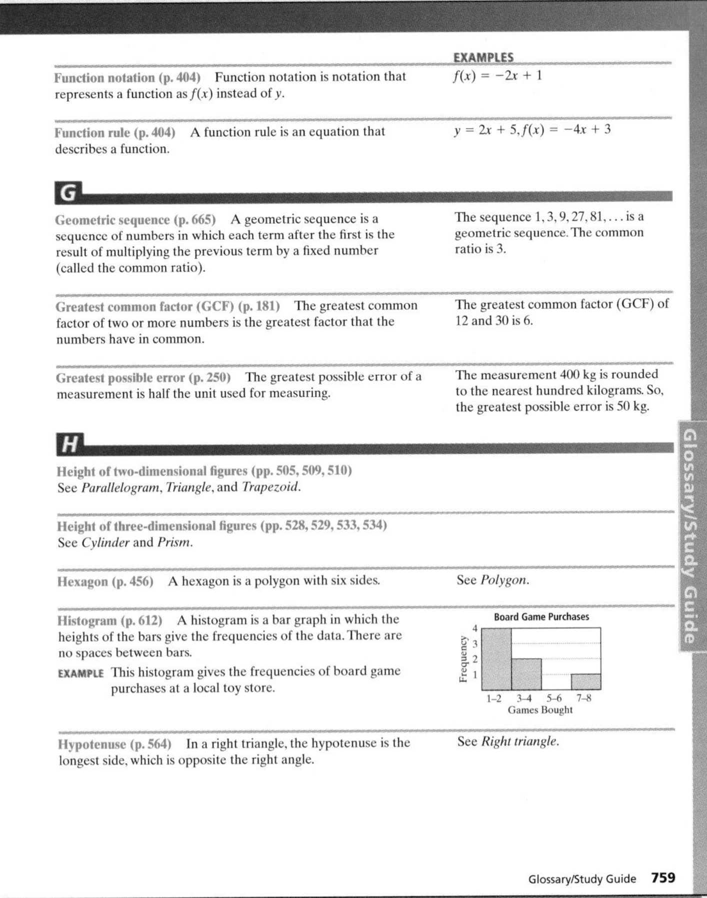

EXAMPLES

**Function notation** (p. 404) Function notation is notation that represents a function as $f(x)$ instead of $y$.
$f(x) = -2x + 1$

**Function rule** (p. 404) A function rule is an equation that describes a function.
$y = 2x + 5, f(x) = -4x + 3$

## G

**Geometric sequence** (p. 665) A geometric sequence is a sequence of numbers in which each term after the first is the result of multiplying the previous term by a fixed number (called the common ratio).
The sequence 1, 3, 9, 27, 81, . . . is a geometric sequence. The common ratio is 3.

**Greatest common factor (GCF)** (p. 181) The greatest common factor of two or more numbers is the greatest factor that the numbers have in common.
The greatest common factor (GCF) of 12 and 30 is 6.

**Greatest possible error** (p. 250) The greatest possible error of a measurement is half the unit used for measuring.
The measurement 400 kg is rounded to the nearest hundred kilograms. So, the greatest possible error is 50 kg.

## H

**Height of two-dimensional figures** (pp. 505, 509, 510) See *Parallelogram*, *Triangle*, and *Trapezoid*.

**Height of three-dimensional figures** (pp. 528, 529, 533, 534) See *Cylinder* and *Prism*.

**Hexagon** (p. 456) A hexagon is a polygon with six sides.
See *Polygon*.

**Histogram** (p. 612) A histogram is a bar graph in which the heights of the bars give the frequencies of the data. There are no spaces between bars.
EXAMPLE This histogram gives the frequencies of board game purchases at a local toy store.



**Hypotenuse** (p. 564) In a right triangle, the hypotenuse is the longest side, which is opposite the right angle.
See *Right triangle*.

Glossary/Study Guide

## I

EXAMPLES

**Identity Properties of Addition and Multiplication (p. 65)** The sum of any number $a$ and 0 is $a$. The product of any number $a$ and 1 is $a$. — $a + 0 = a$; $a \cdot 1 = a$

**Image (p. 479)** An image is the result of the transformation of a point, line, or figure to a new set of coordinates. — See *Transformation.*

**Improper fraction (p. 236)** An improper fraction is a fraction with a numerator that is greater than or equal to the denominator. — $\frac{24}{15}$ and $\frac{16}{16}$ are improper fractions.

**Independent events (p. 631)** Independent events are events for which the outcome of one event does not affect the outcome of a second event. — When a number cube is rolled twice, the events (rolling 6, rolling 3) are independent.

**Indirect measurement (p. 289)** Indirect measurement is a method of determining length or distance without measuring directly.

EXAMPLE By using the distances shown in the diagram and using properties of similar figures, you can find the height of the taller tower.

$\frac{240}{540} = \frac{x}{1,192} \rightarrow x \approx 529.8$ ft



**Inductive reasoning (p. 35)** Inductive reasoning is making conclusions based on patterns you observe. — By inductive reasoning, the next number in the pattern 2, 4, 6, 8, . . . is 10.

**Inequality (p. 100)** An inequality is a sentence that uses one of the symbols $>, <, \geq, \leq$, or $\neq$. — $0 \leq 2, k > -3, 10 < t$

**Integer (p. 18)** The integers are the whole numbers and their opposites. — $-45$, 0, and 289 are integers.

**Interest (p. 369)** See *Compound interest* and *Simple interest.*

**Interest rate (p. 369)** An interest rate is the percentage of the balance that an account or investment earns in a fixed period of time. — A savings account pays $2\frac{1}{4}\%$ per year.

**Inverse operations (p. 84)** Inverse operations are operations that undo each other. — Multiplication and division are inverse operations.



EXAMPLES

**Irrational number (p. 561)** An irrational number is a number that can be represented by a nonrepeating, nonterminating decimal. — The number $\pi$, which is approximately equal to 3.141592654, is an irrational number.

**Isosceles triangle (p. 454)** An isosceles triangle is a triangle with at least two congruent sides.

EXAMPLE $\overline{LM} \cong \overline{LB}$

$\triangle MLB$ is an isosceles triangle.



## L

**Lateral area (p. 528)** The lateral area of a prism is the sum of the areas of the lateral faces.



**Lateral face (p. 534)** See *Prism* and *Pyramid.*

**Least common denominator (LCD) (p. 226)** The least common denominator of two or more fractions is the least common multiple (LCM) of their denominators. — The least common denominator (LCD) of the fractions $\frac{3}{8}$ and $\frac{7}{10}$ is $2 \cdot 2 \cdot 2 \cdot 5$, or 40.

**Least common multiple (LCM) (p. 224)** The least common multiple (LCM) of two or more numbers is the least number that is a common multiple. — The least common multiple (LCM) of 6 and 15 is $2 \cdot 3 \cdot 5$, or 30.

**Legs of a right triangle (p. 564)** The legs of a right triangle are the two shorter sides of the triangle. — See *Right triangle.*

**Like terms (p. 74)** Like terms are terms with the same variable(s), raised to the same power(s).

EXAMPLE $3b$ and $12b$ are like terms. Like terms can be combined by using the Distributive Property. — $3b + 12b = (3 + 12)b = 15b$

**Line (p. 442)** A line is a series of points that extends in two directions without end.

EXAMPLE $\overleftrightarrow{AB}, \overleftrightarrow{BA}$, or $n$ is a line.





EXAMPLES

**Line graph (p. 98)** A line graph is a graph that shows changes over time.

EXAMPLE This line graph shows the change in the number of listeners to station KLZR during the day.



EXAMPLE This multiple line graph represents seasonal air conditioner and snowblower sales (in thousands) for a large chain of stores.



**Line of reflection (p. 486)** A line of reflection is a line across which a figure is reflected. — See *Reflection.*

**Line (of ) symmetry (p. 485)** A line of symmetry is a line that divides a figure with reflectional symmetry into two congruent halves.



**Line plot (p. 609)** A line plot is a graph that displays data by using X's above a number line.

EXAMPLE This line plot shows the heights in inches of the girls on a field hockey team.



**Linear equation (p. 392)** A linear equation is any equation whose graph is a line.

EXAMPLE $y = \frac{1}{2}x + 3$ is linear because its graph is a line.



**Linear inequality (p. 426)** A linear inequality is a number sentence in which the equal sign of a linear equation is replaced with $>, <, \geq$, or $\leq$. — $y \geq 2x + 3$; $y < -4x - 1$

**Lower quartile (p. 613)** The lower quartile is the median of the lower half of a data set. — See *Box-and-whisker plot.*



## M

EXAMPLES

**Matrix (p. 484)** A matrix is a rectangular arrangement of numbers. — $\begin{bmatrix} 0 & -1 & -4 \\ 0 & 4 & 0 \end{bmatrix}$

**Markup (p. 318)** Markup is the amount of increase in price. Markup is added to the cost of merchandise to arrive at the selling price. — A store buys a coat for \$60 and sells it for \$100. The markup is \$40.

**Mean (p. 131)** The mean of a collection of data is the sum of the data items divided by the number of data items. — The mean temperature (°F) for the temperatures 44, 52, 48, 55, 61, 67 and 58 is 55.

**Measures of central tendency (p. 131)** Measures of central tendency in statistics are *mean*, *median*, and *mode*. — See *Mean*, *Median*, and *Mode.*

**Median (p. 131)** The median of a collection of data is the middle number when there are an odd number of data items and they are written in order. For an even number of data items, the median is the mean of the two middle numbers. — The median temperature (°F) for the temperatures 44, 48, 52, 55, 58, 61, and 67 is 55.

**Midpoint Formula (p. 572)** The midpoint of a line segment with endpoints $A(x_1, y_1)$ and $B(x_2, y_2)$ is $\left(\frac{x_1 + x_2}{2}, \frac{y_1 + y_2}{2}\right)$. — The midpoint of $A(-3, 2)$ and $B(7, -2)$ is $\left(\frac{-3 + 7}{2}, \frac{2 + -2}{2}\right)$, or (2, 0).

**Mixed number (p. 229)** A mixed number is the sum of a whole number and a fraction. — $3\frac{11}{16}$ is a mixed number. $3\frac{11}{16} = 3 + \frac{11}{16}$

**Mode (p. 131)** The mode of a collection of data is the data item that occurs most often. There can be no mode, one mode, or more than one mode. — The mode of the collection of numbers 3, 4, 1, 3, 2, 2, 5, 3 is 3.

**Monomial (p. 678)** A monomial is a real number, a variable, or a product of a real number and variables with whole number exponents. — $5x$, $-4$, and $y^3$ are all monomials.

**Multiple (p. 224)** A multiple of a number is the product of that number and any nonzero whole number. — The multiples of 13 are 13, 26, 39, 52, and so on.

**Multiple line graph (p. 98)** A multiple line graph is a graph that shows more than one data set changing over time. — See *Line graph.*

**Multiplication Property of Equality (p. 90)** If $a = b$, then $ac = bc$. — $12 = 3(4)$, so $12 \cdot 2 = 3(4) \cdot 2$

EXAMPLES

**Multiplication Properties of Inequality (p. 109)** If $a < b$, and $c$ is positive, then $ac < bc$. If $a > b$, and $c$ is positive, then $ac > bc$.

$3 < 4$, so $3(5) < 4(5)$
$7 > 2$, so $7(6) > 2(6)$

If you multiply each side of an inequality by a negative number, the direction of the inequality symbol is reversed.

If $a < b$, and $c$ is negative, then $ac > bc$. If $a > b$, and $c$ is negative, then $ac < bc$.

$6 < 9$, so $6(-2) > 9(-2)$
$7 > 5$, so $7(-3) < 5(-3)$

**Multiplicative identity (p. 65)** The multiplicative identity is one.

$a \cdot 1 = a$

**Multiplicative inverse (p. 242)** The reciprocal of a number is its multiplicative inverse.

The multiplicative inverse of $\frac{4}{9}$ is $\frac{9}{4}$.

## N

**Negative correlation (p. 411)** See *Correlation*.

**Net (p. 522)** A net is a pattern that can be folded to form a space figure.

**EXAMPLE** This net can be folded to form a cube.

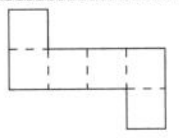

**No correlation (p. 411)** See *Correlation*.

## O

**Obtuse angle (p. 448)** An obtuse angle is an angle with a measure greater than 90° and less than 180°.

**Obtuse triangle (p. 454)** An obtuse triangle is a triangle with one obtuse angle.

**EXAMPLE** $\triangle NJX$ is an obtuse triangle, since $\angle J$ is an obtuse angle.

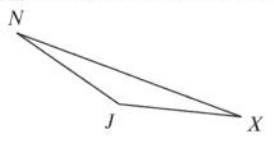

**Octagon (p. 460)** An octagon is a polygon with eight sides.

See *Polygon*.

**Odds (p. 297)** Odds are a ratio that describe the likelihood of an event. Odds in favor of an event $= \frac{\text{number of favorable outcomes}}{\text{number of unfavorable outcomes}}$.

For the toss of a coin, the odds of tossing heads are 1 to 1.

**Open sentence (p. 78)** An open sentence is an equation with one or more variables.

$3a = 5a + 8$

**Opposites (p. 18)** Opposites are numbers that are the same distance from zero on the number line but in opposite directions.

$-17$ and 17 are opposites because they are both 17 units from zero on the number line.



EXAMPLES

**Order of operations (pp. 9, 177)**

1. Work inside grouping symbols.
2. Simplify any terms with exponents.
3. Multiply and divide in order from left to right.
4. Add and subtract in order from left to right.

$2^3(7 - 4) = 2^3(3) = 8 \cdot 3 = 24$

**Ordered pair (p. 50)** An ordered pair is a pair of numbers that gives the location of a point in a coordinate plane. The first number is the $x$-coordinate and the second number is the $y$-coordinate.

See *Coordinates*.

**Origin (p. 50)** The origin is the intersection of the $x$-axis and the $y$-axis in a coordinate plane. The ordered pair $(0, 0)$ describes the origin.

See *Coordinate plane*.

**Outcomes (p. 295)** Outcomes are the possible results of an action.

*Heads* is an outcome of tossing a coin.

**Outlier (p. 132)** An outlier is a data value that is much higher or lower than the other data values in a collection of data.

An outlier in the data 1, 1, 2, 3, 4, 4, 6, 7, 7, 52, is 52.

## P

**Parabola (p. 669)** A parabola is the U-shaped graph of a quadratic function.

**EXAMPLE** This parabola is the graph of the equation $y = x^2 - 2$.

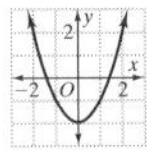

**Parallel lines (p. 443)** Parallel lines are lines that lie in the same plane and do not intersect. The symbol $\parallel$ means "is parallel to."

**EXAMPLE** $\overleftrightarrow{EF} \parallel \overleftrightarrow{HI}$

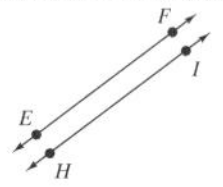

**Parallelogram (p. 455)** A parallelogram is a quadrilateral with both pairs of opposite sides parallel.

**EXAMPLE** $KVDA$ is a parallelogram.

$\overline{KV} \parallel \overline{AD}$ and $\overline{AK} \parallel \overline{DV}$.

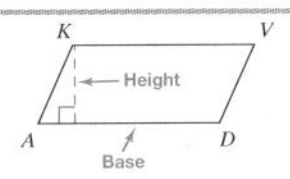

**Pentagon (p. 456)** A pentagon is a polygon with five sides.

See *Polygon*.

**Percent (p. 300)** A percent is a ratio that compares a number to 100. The symbol for percent is %.

$\frac{50}{100} = 50\%$





EXAMPLES

**Percent of change (p. 314)** Percent of change is the percent something increases or decreases from its original amount.

A school's population increases from 500 to 520 students. The percent of change is $\frac{520 - 500}{500} = 4\%$.

**Perfect square (p. 560)** A perfect square is the square of an integer.

$3^2 = 9$, so 9 is a perfect square.

**Perimeter (p. 138)** The perimeter of a figure is the distance around the figure. To find the perimeter of a rectangle, find the sum of the lengths of all its sides, or use the formula $P = 2\ell + 2w$.

**EXAMPLE** The perimeter of $ABCD$ is 12 ft.

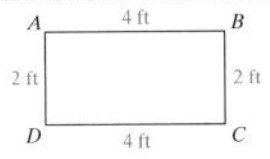

**Permutation (p. 636)** A permutation is an arrangement of objects in a particular order. You can use the notation $_nP_r$ to express the number of permutations of $n$ objects chosen $r$ at a time.

The seating plans (Judith, Ann, Adrian) and (Ann, Judith, Adrian) are two different permutations.

**Perpendicular bisector (p. 475)** A perpendicular bisector is a line, segment, or ray that is perpendicular to a segment.

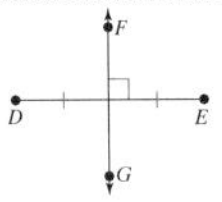

**Perpendicular lines (p. 475)** Perpendicular lines are lines that intersect to form right angles.

**EXAMPLE** $\overleftrightarrow{DE} \perp \overleftrightarrow{RS}$

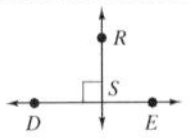

**Pi (p. 470)** Pi ($\pi$) is the name for the ratio of the circumference $C$ to the diameter $d$ of a circle.

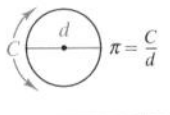

$\pi = \frac{C}{d}$

**Plane (p. 442)** A plane is a flat surface that has no thickness and continues without end in all directions.

**EXAMPLE** $ABCD$ or $M$ is a plane.

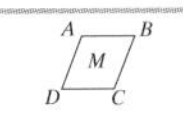

**Point (p. 442)** A point is a location in space that has no size.

**EXAMPLE** $A$ is a point.

$\cdot A$

**Polygon (p. 454)** A polygon is a closed plane figure with at least three sides.

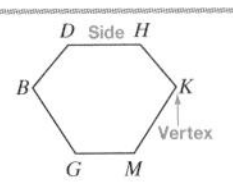

EXAMPLES

**Polynomial (p. 678)** A polynomial is a monomial or a sum or difference of monomials.

$4x^2 - 3x + 7$ is a polynomial.

**Population (p. 646)** A population is a group about which you want information.

See *Sample*.

**Positive correlation (p. 411)** See *Correlation*.

**Power (p. 176)** A power is any expression in the form $a^n$. *Power* is also used to refer to the exponent.

$5^4$ is a power and can be read as "five to the fourth power."

**Precision in measurement (p. 156)** The precision of a measurement is its exactness. A measurement cannot be more precise than the precision of the measuring tool used.

A hundredth of a meter is a smaller unit than a tenth of a meter. So, 2.72 m is more precise than 2.7 m.

**Prime factorization (p. 181)** The prime factorization of a number is the expression of the number as the product of its prime factors.

The prime factorization of 30 is $2 \cdot 3 \cdot 5$.

**Prime number (p. 180)** A prime number is an integer greater than 1 with only two factors, 1 and itself.

13 is a prime number because its only factors are 1 and 13.

**Principal (p. 369)** The principal is the initial amount of an investment or loan.

See *Simple interest*.

**Prism (p. 521)** A prism is a space figure with two parallel and congruent polygonal faces, called bases, and lateral faces that are parallelograms. A prism is named for the shape of its base.

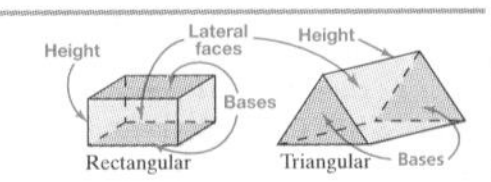

**Probability (pp. 296, 627, 642)** The *theoretical probability* of an event $E$ is $P(E) = \frac{\text{number of favorable outcomes}}{\text{number of possible outcomes}}$ when outcomes are equally likely.

The experimental probability of an event $E$ is $P(E) = \frac{\text{number of times an event occurs}}{\text{number of times experiment is done}}$. Experimental probability is based on experimental data.

The theoretical probability of spinning the number 4 is $\frac{1}{8}$.

In 100 trials, you spin the number 4 ten times. The experimental probability of spinning 4 is $\frac{10}{100}$, or $\frac{1}{10}$.

**Proportion (p. 284)** A proportion is an equality of two ratios.

$\frac{3}{12} = \frac{12}{48}$ is a proportion.

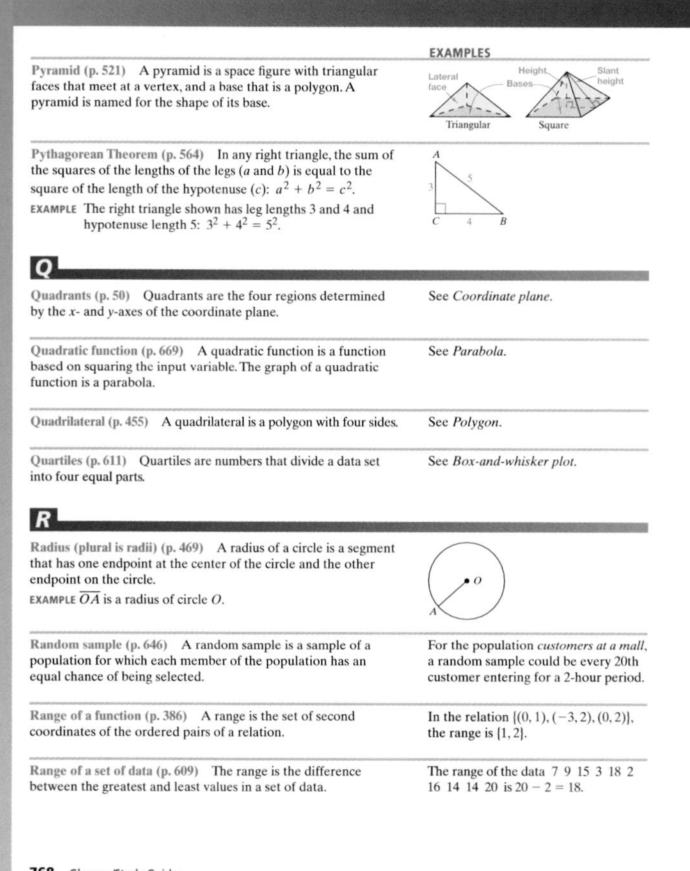

EXAMPLES

**Pyramid (p. 521)** A pyramid is a space figure with triangular faces that meet at a vertex, and a base that is a polygon. A pyramid is named for the shape of its base.

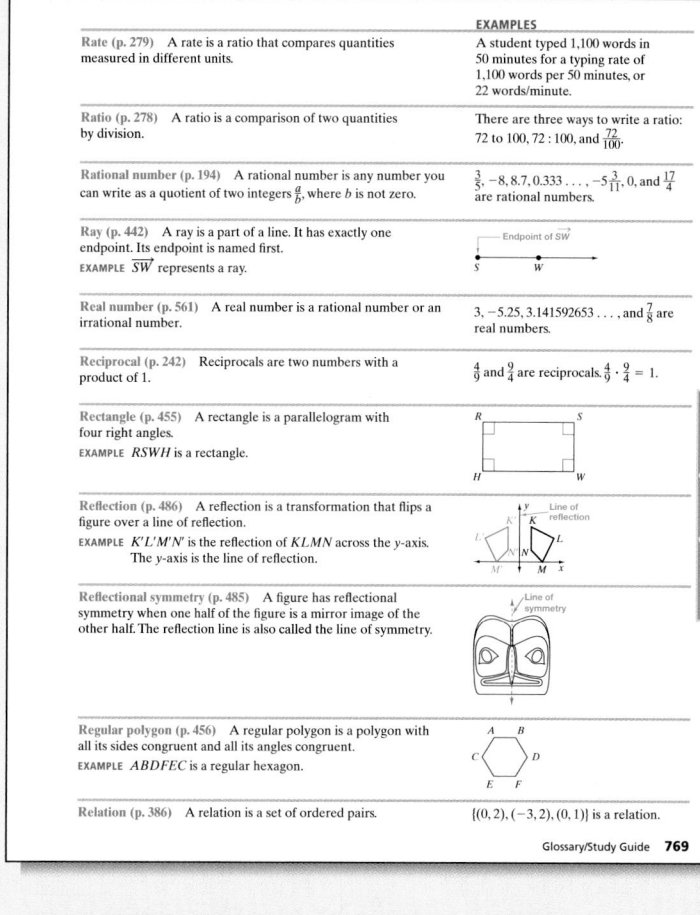

**Pythagorean Theorem (p. 564)** In any right triangle, the sum of the squares of the lengths of the legs ($a$ and $b$) is equal to the square of the length of the hypotenuse ($c$): $a^2 + b^2 = c^2$.

EXAMPLE The right triangle shown has leg lengths 3 and 4 and hypotenuse length 5: $3^2 + 4^2 = 5^2$.

## Q

**Quadrants (p. 50)** Quadrants are the four regions determined by the $x$- and $y$-axes of the coordinate plane. — See *Coordinate plane.*

**Quadratic function (p. 669)** A quadratic function is a function based on squaring the input variable. The graph of a quadratic function is a parabola. — See *Parabola.*

**Quadrilateral (p. 455)** A quadrilateral is a polygon with four sides. — See *Polygon.*

**Quartiles (p. 611)** Quartiles are numbers that divide a data set into four equal parts. — See *Box-and-whisker plot.*

## R

**Radius (plural is radii) (p. 469)** A radius of a circle is a segment that has one endpoint at the center of the circle and the other endpoint on the circle.

EXAMPLE $\overline{OA}$ is a radius of circle $O$.

**Random sample (p. 646)** A random sample is a sample of a population for which each member of the population has an equal chance of being selected. — For the population *customers at a mall*, a random sample could be every 20th customer entering for a 2-hour period.

**Range of a function (p. 386)** A range is the set of second coordinates of the ordered pairs of a relation. — In the relation $\{(0, 1), (-3, 2), (0, 2)\}$, the range is $\{1, 2\}$.

**Range of a set of data (p. 609)** The range is the difference between the greatest and least values in a set of data. — The range of the data 7 9 15 3 18 2 16 14 14 20 is $20 - 2 = 18$.



EXAMPLES

**Rate (p. 279)** A rate is a ratio that compares quantities measured in different units. — A student typed 1,100 words in 50 minutes for a typing rate of 1,100 words per 50 minutes, or 22 words/minute.

**Ratio (p. 278)** A ratio is a comparison of two quantities by division. — There are three ways to write a ratio: 72 to 100, 72 : 100, and $\frac{72}{100}$.

**Rational number (p. 194)** A rational number is any number you can write as a quotient of two integers $\frac{a}{b}$, where $b$ is not zero. — $\frac{3}{5}, -8, 8.7, 0.333\ldots, -5\frac{3}{11}, 0,$ and $\frac{17}{4}$ are rational numbers.

**Ray (p. 442)** A ray is a part of a line. It has exactly one endpoint. Its endpoint is named first.

EXAMPLE $\overrightarrow{SW}$ represents a ray.

**Real number (p. 561)** A real number is a rational number or an irrational number. — $3, -5.25, 3.141592653\ldots,$ and $\frac{7}{8}$ are real numbers.

**Reciprocal (p. 242)** Reciprocals are two numbers with a product of 1. — $\frac{4}{9}$ and $\frac{9}{4}$ are reciprocals. $\frac{4}{9} \cdot \frac{9}{4} = 1$.

**Rectangle (p. 455)** A rectangle is a parallelogram with four right angles.

EXAMPLE $RSWH$ is a rectangle.

**Reflection (p. 486)** A reflection is a transformation that flips a figure over a line of reflection.

EXAMPLE $K'L'M'N'$ is the reflection of $KLMN$ across the $y$-axis. The $y$-axis is the line of reflection.

**Reflectional symmetry (p. 485)** A figure has reflectional symmetry when one half of the figure is a mirror image of the other half. The reflection line is also called the line of symmetry.

**Regular polygon (p. 456)** A regular polygon is a polygon with all its sides congruent and all its angles congruent.

EXAMPLE $ABDFEC$ is a regular hexagon.

**Relation (p. 386)** A relation is a set of ordered pairs. — $\{(0, 2), (-3, 2), (0, 1)\}$ is a relation.





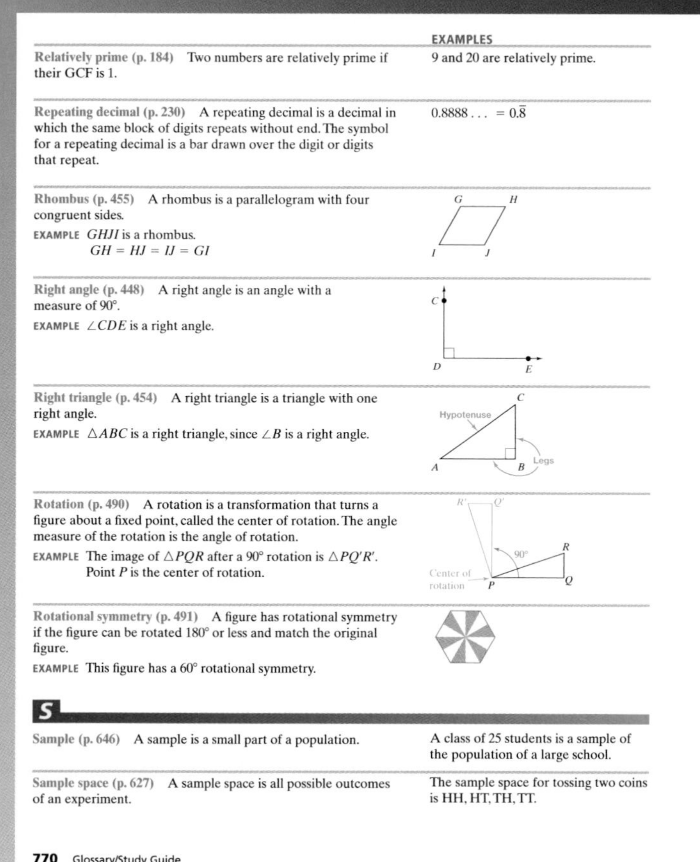

EXAMPLES

**Relatively prime (p. 184)** Two numbers are relatively prime if their GCF is 1. — 9 and 20 are relatively prime.

**Repeating decimal (p. 230)** A repeating decimal is a decimal in which the same block of digits repeats without end. The symbol for a repeating decimal is a bar drawn over the digit or digits that repeat. — $0.8888\ldots = 0.\overline{8}$

**Rhombus (p. 455)** A rhombus is a parallelogram with four congruent sides.

EXAMPLE $GHJI$ is a rhombus. $GH = HJ = IJ = GI$

**Right angle (p. 448)** A right angle is an angle with a measure of 90°.

EXAMPLE $\angle CDE$ is a right angle.

**Right triangle (p. 454)** A right triangle is a triangle with one right angle.

EXAMPLE $\triangle ABC$ is a right triangle, since $\angle B$ is a right angle.



**Rotation (p. 490)** A rotation is a transformation that turns a figure about a fixed point, called the center of rotation. The angle measure of the rotation is the angle of rotation.

EXAMPLE The image of $\triangle PQR$ after a 90° rotation is $\triangle PQ'R'$. Point $P$ is the center of rotation.



**Rotational symmetry (p. 491)** A figure has rotational symmetry if the figure can be rotated 180° or less and match the original figure.

EXAMPLE This figure has a 60° rotational symmetry.

## S

**Sample (p. 646)** A sample is a small part of a population. — A class of 25 students is a sample of the population of a large school.

**Sample space (p. 627)** A sample space is all possible outcomes of an experiment. — The sample space for tossing two coins is HH, HT, TH, TT.



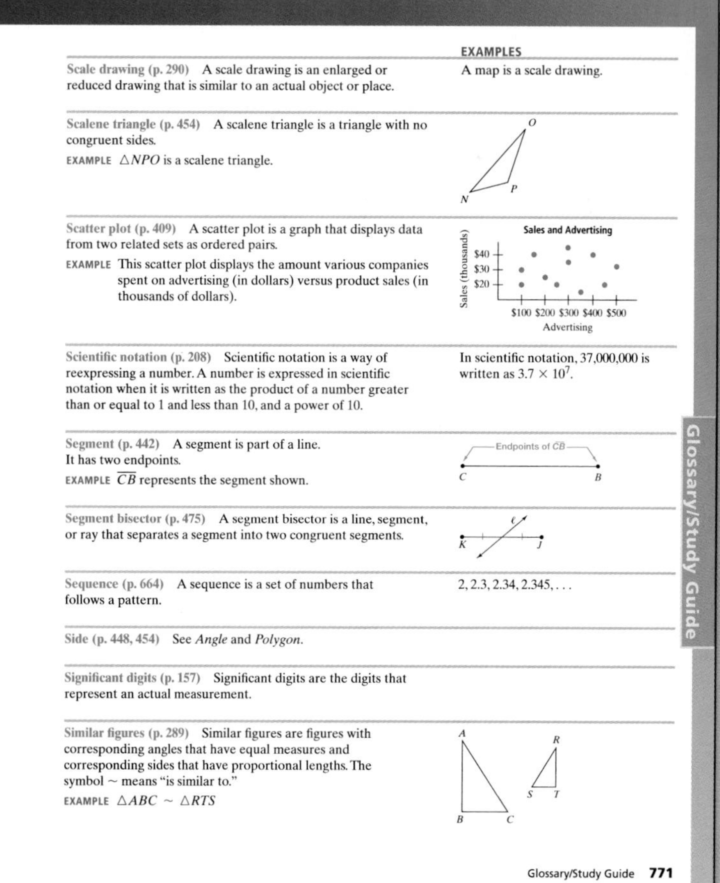

EXAMPLES

**Scale drawing (p. 290)** A scale drawing is an enlarged or reduced drawing that is similar to an actual object or place. — A map is a scale drawing.

**Scalene triangle (p. 454)** A scalene triangle is a triangle with no congruent sides.

EXAMPLE $\triangle NPO$ is a scalene triangle.

**Scatter plot (p. 409)** A scatter plot is a graph that displays data from two related sets as ordered pairs.

EXAMPLE This scatter plot displays the amount various companies spent on advertising (in dollars) versus product sales (in thousands of dollars).



**Scientific notation (p. 208)** Scientific notation is a way of reexpressing a number. A number is expressed in scientific notation when it is written as the product of a number greater than or equal to 1 and less than 10, and a power of 10. — In scientific notation, 37,000,000 is written as $3.7 \times 10^7$.

**Segment (p. 442)** A segment is part of a line. It has two endpoints.

EXAMPLE $\overline{CB}$ represents the segment shown.



**Segment bisector (p. 475)** A segment bisector is a line, segment, or ray that separates a segment into two congruent segments.

**Sequence (p. 664)** A sequence is a set of numbers that follows a pattern. — 2, 2.3, 2.34, 2.345, . . .

**Side (p. 448, 454)** See *Angle* and *Polygon*.

**Significant digits (p. 157)** Significant digits are the digits that represent an actual measurement.

**Similar figures (p. 289)** Similar figures are figures with corresponding angles that have equal measures and corresponding sides that have proportional lengths. The symbol ~ means "is similar to."

EXAMPLE $\triangle ABC \sim \triangle RTS$

EXAMPLES

**Simple interest (p. 369)** Simple interest is interest paid only on the principal, the initial amount of money invested or borrowed. The formula for simple interest is $I = prt$, where $I$ is the interest, $p$ is the principal, $r$ is the interest rate per year, and $t$ is the time in years.

The simple interest on \$1,000 at 5% for 2 years is \$1,000 · 0.05 · 2, or \$100.

**Simplest form of a fraction (p. 186)** The simplest form of a fraction is the form in which the only common factor of the numerator and denominator is 1.

The simplest form of the fraction $\frac{15}{20}$ is $\frac{3}{4}$.

**Simplify a variable expression (p. 74)** To simplify a variable expression is to replace it with an equivalent expression having as few terms as possible.

$2x + 5 + 4x$ simplifies to $6x + 5$.

**Simulation (p. 642)** A simulation is a model used to find experimental probability.

Your baseball team has an equal chance of winning or losing each of its next five games. You can toss a coin to simulate the outcomes of the next five games.

**Sine (p. 588)** The sine of an acute angle is the ratio of the length of the leg of a right triangle opposite the acute angle to the length of the hypotenuse.

See *Trigonometric ratios.*

**Skew lines (p. 443)** Skew lines are lines in space that do not intersect and are not parallel. They do not lie in the same plane. Skew segments must be parts of skew lines.

EXAMPLE $\overleftrightarrow{MT}$ and $\overleftrightarrow{QR}$ are skew lines.

M N Q R T V P S

**Slant height (p. 533)** See *Cone* and *Pyramid*.

**Slope (pp. 397, 398)** Slope is a ratio that describes the tilt of a line.

$$\text{slope} = \frac{\text{vertical change}}{\text{horizontal change}} = \frac{\text{difference in } y\text{-coordinates}}{\text{difference in } x\text{-coordinates}}$$

EXAMPLE The slope of the given line is $\frac{2}{4}$ or $\frac{1}{2}$.

y 2 rise: 2 run: 4 4 x

**Slope-intercept form of an equation (p. 399)** The slope-intercept form of an equation is $y = mx + b$, where $m$ is the slope and $b$ is the $y$-intercept of the line.

The equation $y = 2x + 1$ is in slope-intercept form with $m = 2$ and $b = 1$.

**Solid (p. 520)** A solid is a three-dimensional figure.

See *Space figure.*



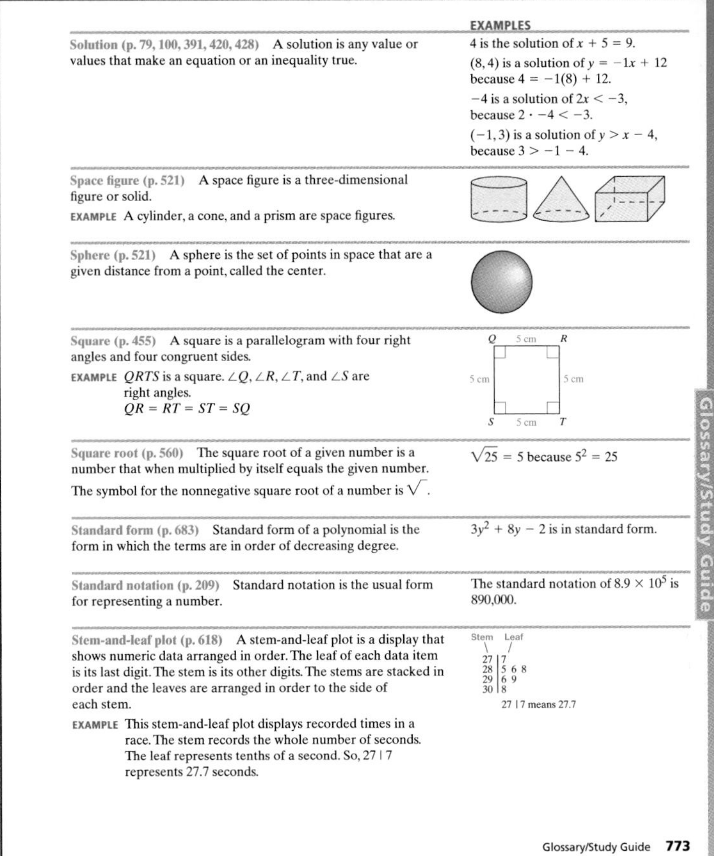

EXAMPLES

**Solution (p. 79, 100, 391, 420, 428)** A solution is any value or values that make an equation or an inequality true.

4 is the solution of $x + 5 = 9$.

$(8, 4)$ is a solution of $y = -1x + 12$ because $4 = -1(8) + 12$.

$-4$ is a solution of $2x < -3$, because $2 \cdot -4 < -3$.

$(-1, 3)$ is a solution of $y > x - 4$, because $3 > -1 - 4$.

**Space figure (p. 521)** A space figure is a three-dimensional figure or solid.

EXAMPLE A cylinder, a cone, and a prism are space figures.

**Sphere (p. 521)** A sphere is the set of points in space that are a given distance from a point, called the center.

**Square (p. 455)** A square is a parallelogram with four right angles and four congruent sides.

EXAMPLE $QRTS$ is a square. $\angle Q, \angle R, \angle T,$ and $\angle S$ are right angles. $QR = RT = ST = SQ$

Q 5 cm R 5 cm 5 cm S 5 cm T

**Square root (p. 560)** The square root of a given number is a number that when multiplied by itself equals the given number. The symbol for the nonnegative square root of a number is $\sqrt{\phantom{x}}$.

$\sqrt{25} = 5$ because $5^2 = 25$

**Standard form (p. 683)** Standard form of a polynomial is the form in which the terms are in order of decreasing degree.

$3y^2 + 8y - 2$ is in standard form.

**Standard notation (p. 209)** Standard notation is the usual form for representing a number.

The standard notation of $8.9 \times 10^5$ is 890,000.

**Stem-and-leaf plot (p. 618)** A stem-and-leaf plot is a display that shows numeric data arranged in order. The leaf of each data item is its last digit. The stem is its other digits. The stems are stacked in order and the leaves are arranged in order to the side of each stem.

EXAMPLE This stem-and-leaf plot displays recorded times in a race. The stem records the whole number of seconds. The leaf represents tenths of a second. So, 27 | 7 represents 27.7 seconds.

| Stem | Leaf |
|---|---|
| 27 | 7 |
| 28 | 5 6 8 |
| 29 | 6 9 |
| 30 | 8 |

27 | 7 means 27.7



EXAMPLES

**Straight angle (p. 448)** A straight angle is an angle with a measure of 180°.

**Subtraction Property of Equality (p. 84)** If $a = b$, then $a - c = b - c$.

$10 = 2(5)$, so $10 - 5 = 2(5) - 5$

**Subtraction Property of Inequality (p. 104)** If $a > b$, then $a - c > b - c$. If $a < b$, then $a - c < b - c$.

$7 > 4$, so $7 - 3 > 4 - 3$
$6 < 9$, so $6 - 2 < 9 - 2$

**Supplementary angles (p. 449)** Supplementary angles are two angles whose measures add to 180°.

EXAMPLE $\angle A$ and $\angle D$ are supplementary.

130° 50° A D

**Surface area (pp. 527–529, 533, 534)** Surface area is the sum of the areas of the base(s) and lateral faces of a space figure.

EXAMPLE The surface area of the prism is the sum of the areas of its faces. $(12 + 12 + 12 + 12 + 12 + 12)\text{ in.}^2 = 72\text{ in.}^2$

Each square = 1 in.$^2$

**System of linear equations (p. 420)** A system of linear equations is two or more linear equations.

$y = 3x + 1$ and $y = -2x - 3$ are a system of linear equations.

**System of linear inequalities (p. 428)** A system of linear inequalities is two or more linear inequalities.

$y \geq 3x + 1$ and $y < -2x - 3$ are a system of linear inequalities.

## T

**Tangent (p. 588)** The tangent of an acute angle is the ratio of the length of the leg of a right triangle opposite the acute angle to the length of the leg adjacent to the angle.

See *Trigonometric ratios.*

**Term of an expression (p. 74)** A term is a number or the product of a number and variable(s).

The expression $7x + 12 + (-9y)$ has three terms: $7x$, 12, and $-9y$.

**Term of a sequence (p. 664)** A term of a sequence is any number in the sequence.

EXAMPLE In this sequence, 1 is the first term, 2 is the second term, 3 is the third term, and 4 is the fourth term.

1, 2, 3, 4, . . .

**Terminating decimal (p. 229)** A terminating decimal is a decimal with a finite number of digits.

Both 0.6 and 0.7265 are terminating decimals.



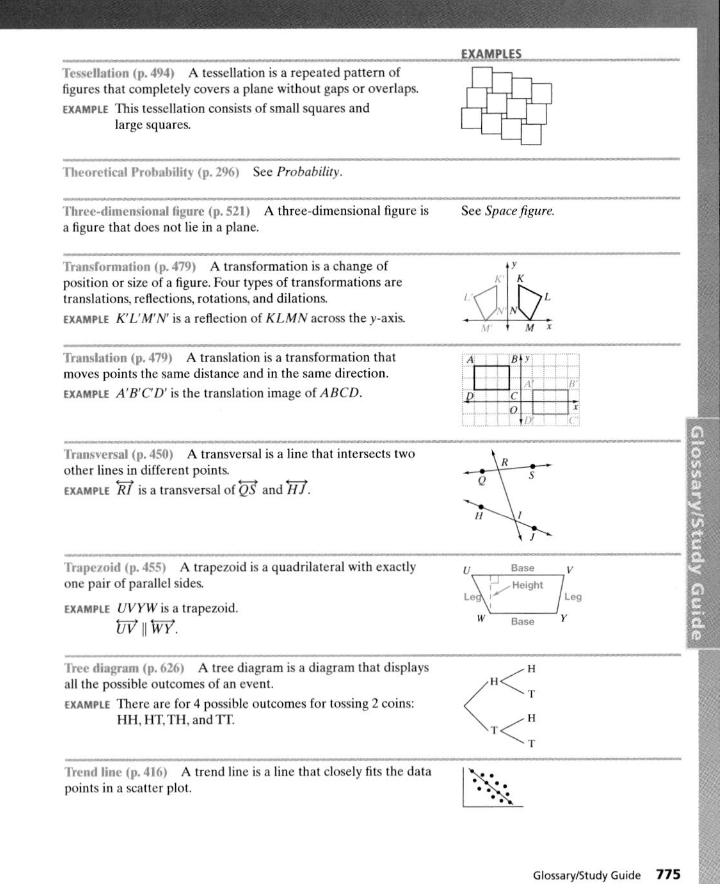

EXAMPLES

**Tessellation (p. 494)** A tessellation is a repeated pattern of figures that completely covers a plane without gaps or overlaps.

EXAMPLE This tessellation consists of small squares and large squares.

**Theoretical Probability (p. 296)** See *Probability.*

**Three-dimensional figure (p. 521)** A three-dimensional figure is a figure that does not lie in a plane.

See *Space figure.*

**Transformation (p. 479)** A transformation is a change of position or size of a figure. Four types of transformations are translations, reflections, rotations, and dilations.

EXAMPLE $K'L'M'N'$ is a reflection of $KLMN$ across the $y$-axis.

y K' K L' L N' N M' M x

**Translation (p. 479)** A translation is a transformation that moves points the same distance and in the same direction.

EXAMPLE $A'B'C'D'$ is the translation image of $ABCD$.

A B y A' B' D C O x D' C'

**Transversal (p. 450)** A transversal is a line that intersects two other lines in different points.

EXAMPLE $\overleftrightarrow{RI}$ is a transversal of $\overleftrightarrow{QS}$ and $\overleftrightarrow{HJ}$.

R S Q H I J

**Trapezoid (p. 455)** A trapezoid is a quadrilateral with exactly one pair of parallel sides.

EXAMPLE $UVYW$ is a trapezoid. $\overline{UV} \parallel \overline{WY}$.

U Base V Height Leg Leg W Base Y

**Tree diagram (p. 626)** A tree diagram is a diagram that displays all the possible outcomes of an event.

EXAMPLE There are for 4 possible outcomes for tossing 2 coins: HH, HT, TH, and TT.

H H T T H T

**Trend line (p. 416)** A trend line is a line that closely fits the data points in a scatter plot.

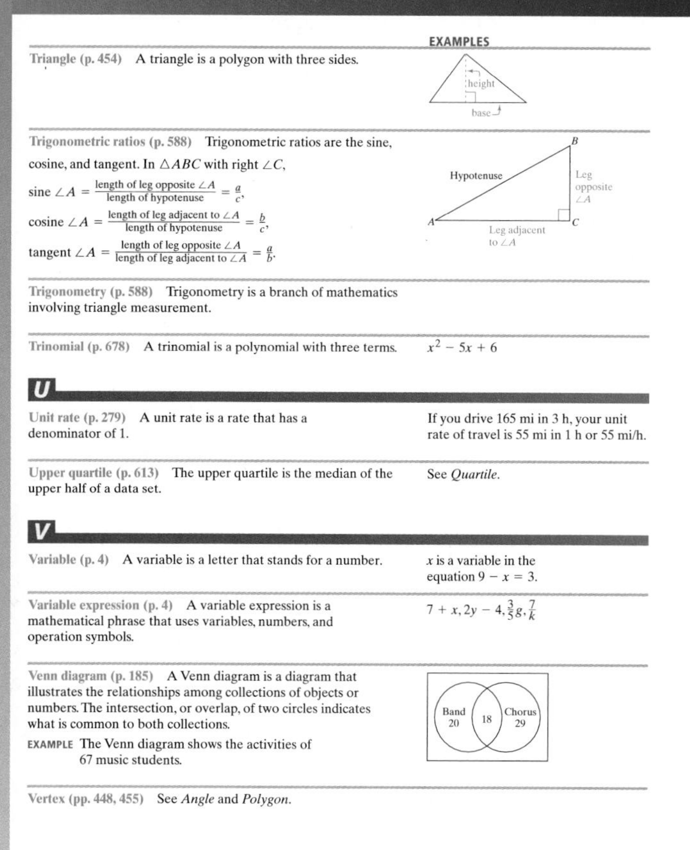

EXAMPLES

**Triangle (p. 454)** A triangle is a polygon with three sides.



**Trigonometric ratios (p. 588)** Trigonometric ratios are the sine, cosine, and tangent. In $\triangle ABC$ with right $\angle C$,

sine $\angle A = \frac{\text{length of leg opposite } \angle A}{\text{length of hypotenuse}} = \frac{a}{c}$,

cosine $\angle A = \frac{\text{length of leg adjacent to } \angle A}{\text{length of hypotenuse}} = \frac{b}{c}$,

tangent $\angle A = \frac{\text{length of leg opposite } \angle A}{\text{length of leg adjacent to } \angle A} = \frac{a}{b}$.



**Trigonometry (p. 588)** Trigonometry is a branch of mathematics involving triangle measurement.

**Trinomial (p. 678)** A trinomial is a polynomial with three terms. $x^2 - 5x + 6$

## U

**Unit rate (p. 279)** A unit rate is a rate that has a denominator of 1. If you drive 165 mi in 3 h, your unit rate of travel is 55 mi in 1 h or 55 mi/h.

**Upper quartile (p. 613)** The upper quartile is the median of the upper half of a data set. See *Quartile*.

## V

**Variable (p. 4)** A variable is a letter that stands for a number. $x$ is a variable in the equation $9 - x = 3$.

**Variable expression (p. 4)** A variable expression is a mathematical phrase that uses variables, numbers, and operation symbols. $7 + x, 2y - 4, \frac{3}{5}g, \frac{7}{k}$

**Venn diagram (p. 185)** A Venn diagram is a diagram that illustrates the relationships among collections of objects or numbers. The intersection, or overlap, of two circles indicates what is common to both collections.

EXAMPLE The Venn diagram shows the activities of 67 music students.



**Vertex (pp. 448, 455)** See *Angle* and *Polygon*.



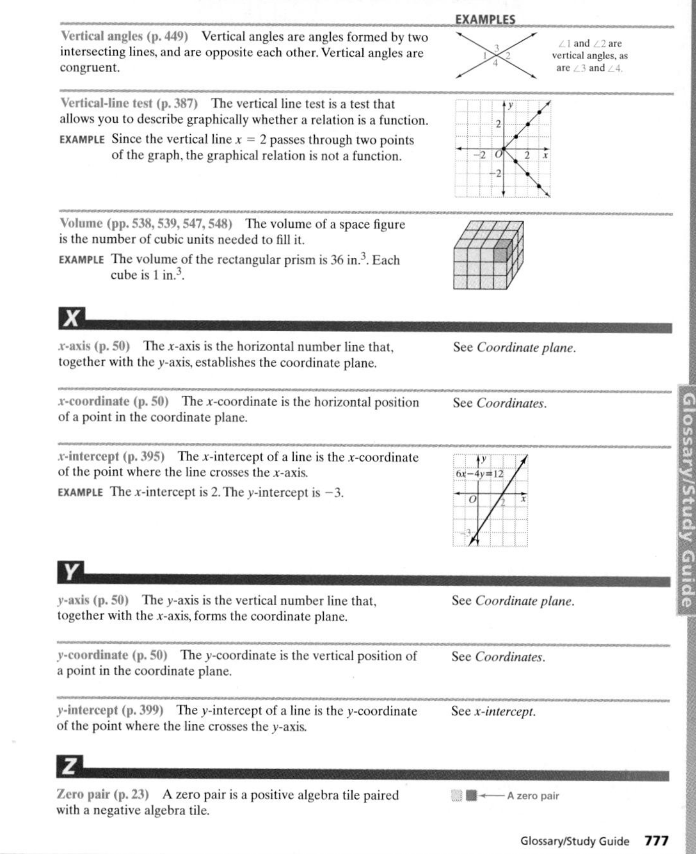

EXAMPLES

**Vertical angles (p. 449)** Vertical angles are angles formed by two intersecting lines, and are opposite each other. Vertical angles are congruent.



**Vertical-line test (p. 387)** The vertical line test is a test that allows you to describe graphically whether a relation is a function.

EXAMPLE Since the vertical line $x = 2$ passes through two points of the graph, the graphical relation is not a function.



**Volume (pp. 538, 539, 547, 548)** The volume of a space figure is the number of cubic units needed to fill it.

EXAMPLE The volume of the rectangular prism is 36 in.$^3$. Each cube is 1 in.$^3$.

## X

**x-axis (p. 50)** The $x$-axis is the horizontal number line that, together with the $y$-axis, establishes the coordinate plane. See *Coordinate plane*.

**x-coordinate (p. 50)** The $x$-coordinate is the horizontal position of a point in the coordinate plane. See *Coordinates*.

**x-intercept (p. 395)** The $x$-intercept of a line is the $x$-coordinate of the point where the line crosses the $x$-axis.

EXAMPLE The $x$-intercept is 2. The $y$-intercept is −3.



## Y

**y-axis (p. 50)** The $y$-axis is the vertical number line that, together with the $x$-axis, forms the coordinate plane. See *Coordinate plane*.

**y-coordinate (p. 50)** The $y$-coordinate is the vertical position of a point in the coordinate plane. See *Coordinates*.

**y-intercept (p. 399)** The $y$-intercept of a line is the $y$-coordinate of the point where the line crosses the $y$-axis. See *x-intercept*.

## Z

**Zero pair (p. 23)** A zero pair is a positive algebra tile paired with a negative algebra tile.

# Selected Answers

## ▶ Tools for Problem Solving

*The Four-Step Approach* — page xxii

**1.** Nikki 18; Jing 30 **3.** 9 **5.** C **7.** cannot be determined

*Using Strategies* — page xxv

**1.** 28 days **3.** 6 wall, 5 desk **5.** in a 6 by 4 array **7.** north

*Standardized Test Prep* — page xxxi

**1.** D **3.** C **5.** B **7.** D

## ▶ Chapter 1

*Skills You Need* — page 1

**1.** 1 **2.** 11 **3.** 11 **4.** 19 **5.** 13 **6.** 40 **7.** 17 **8.** 43 **9.** 176 **10.** 28 **11.** 166 **12.** 75 **13.** > **14.** > **15.** < **16.** < **17.** < **18.** = **19.** 12 **20.** 30 **21.** 28 **22.** 5 **23.** 96 **24.** 5 **25.** 200 **26.** 80 **27.** 31 **28.** 13 **29.** 480 **30.** 12 **31.** 1 **32.** 4 **33.** 7 **34.** 10

*Lesson 1-1* — pages 4–7

**TRY THIS** **1.** Variable expression; $x$ is the variable. **2.** numerical expression **3.** Variable expression; $d$ is the variable. **4.** $0.50b$ **5.** $\frac{m}{60}$

**CHECK UNDERSTANDING** **1.** Variable expression; $b$ is the variable. **2.** numerical expression **3.** Variable expression; $n$ is the variable. **4.** $2 \cdot 12$ **5.** $5 \cdot 12$ **6.** $d \cdot 12$ **7.** $m + 16$ **8.** $\frac{6}{z}$ **9.** $3c$

**PRACTICE AND PROBLEM SOLVING**
**11.** Variable expression; $d$ is the variable.
**13.** Variable expression; $x$ is the variable.
**15.** Variable expression; $p$ is the variable.
**17.** $z - 8$ **19.** $\frac{3}{n}$ **21.** $32g$ **23.** $2 - x$ **25.** $12v$ **27.** $m + 250$ **29.** $\frac{100}{z}$ **31.** $7w$ **33.** $5n$ **35.** $\frac{i}{12}$ **37.** A **39.** C **41.** $d - 20$ **43.** $110e + 55$ **45a.** $2f$ **b.** $\frac{s}{2}$ **47.** The balloon rose 34 m. **49.** The balloon tripled its altitude.

**MIXED REVIEW** **51.** 72 **53.** 75 **55.** 9,563

*Lesson 1-2* — pages 8–12

**TRY THIS** **4.** 17 **5.** 3 **6.** 3 **7.** 4 **8.** 12 **9.** 6 **10.** 3

**CHECK UNDERSTANDING** **1.** Multiplication; multiplication comes before subtraction in the order of operations. **2.** Subtraction; when operations have the same rank in the order of operations, do them from left to right. **3.** Division; work within parentheses first. **4.** 4 **5.** 16 **6.** 13 **7.** 108 **8.** 49 **9.** 8

**PRACTICE AND PROBLEM SOLVING** **11.** 17 **13.** 14 **15.** 17 **17.** 24 **19.** 16 **21.** 3 **23.** 33 **25.** 3 **27.** 3 **29.** 4 **31.** > **33.** > **35.** D **37.** $7 \cdot (8 - 6) + 3 = 17$ **39.** $2 \cdot 3 - (8 - 5) \cdot 2 = 0$, or $2 \cdot [3 - (8 - 5)] \cdot 2 = 0$ **41.** We must agree on an order of operations to ensure that everyone gets the same value for an expression. **43.** $4 \cdot 9 + 5$; 41 **45.** $17 - (25 \div 5)$; 12

**MIXED REVIEW** **53.** $\frac{k}{20}$ **55.** $10d$

*Lesson 1-3* — pages 13–16

**TRY THIS** **1.** 28 **2.** 45 **3.** 90 **4.** 23 **5.** 12 **6.** $29c$; \$145 **7.** \$104

**CHECK UNDERSTANDING** **1.** 7 **2.** 6 **3.** 12 **4.** 4 **5.** 16 **6.** 12 **7.** 18 **8.** 60 **9.** 12 **10.** $55m$; 1,100 words

**PRACTICE AND PROBLEM SOLVING** **11.** 35 **13.** 5 **15.** 1 **17.** 24 **19.** 15 **21.** 11 **23.** 91 **25.** 48 **27.** 2 **29.** 10 **31a.** $153h$ **b.** 306 calories **33.** $8h$; 24 km **35.** $145m$; 870 babies; 208,800 babies

**MIXED REVIEW** **39.** 53 **41.** $19 - t$ **43.** $\frac{d}{20}$

*Lesson 1-4* — pages 17–21

**TRY THIS** **1.** −2
**2.** (number line: −6, −1 0 1 2) 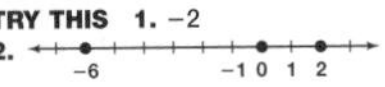 −6, 0, 2

**3.** the absolute value of negative ten; 10

**CHECK UNDERSTANDING** **1.** 250 **2.** −18 **3.** −45 **4.** 2 **5.** 5 **6.** −4 **7.** 18 **8.** 9 **9.** 3 **10a.** spending a dollar **b.** −1



**PRACTICE AND PROBLEM SOLVING** **11.** 110 **13.** −300 **15.** −8
**21.**  (number line: −12 −9 −3 0 2) −12, −9, −3

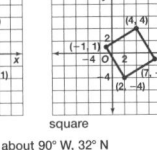

**23.** 6 **25.** 2 **27.** −6 **29.** 0 **31.** 2 **33.** B **35.** $|-90|$; 90 **37.** $-(-8)$; 8
**39.**  (number line: −1 0 1)
**41.** 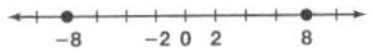 (number line: −8 −2 0 2 8)
**43.** 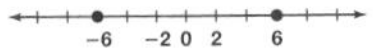 (number line: −6 −2 0 2 6)

**45.** < **47.** < **49.** < **57.** negative **59.** negative

**MIXED REVIEW** **63.** 14 **65.** 440 **67.** <

**CHECKPOINT 1** **1.** $f + 23$ **2.** $\frac{g}{34}$ **3.** $9p$ **4.** 20 **5.** 2 **6.** 19 **7.** 0 **8.** 54 **9.** 15
**10.** 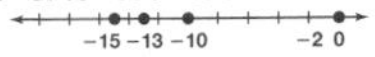 (number line: −15 −13 −10 −2 0)

Tuesday, Wednesday, Monday, Thursday

*Math Toolbox* — page 22

**9.** 2 **11.** −2 **13.** 0 **15.** 4

*Lesson 1-5* — pages 23–28

**TRY THIS** **1.** 3 **2.** 4 **3.** −4 **4.** −4 **5.** 5 **6.** −6 **7.** −38 **8.** 47 **9.** −90 **10.** 1,280 m **11.** −10 **12.** 70

**CHECK UNDERSTANDING** **1.** $-4 + 7$; 3 **2.** $5 + 0$; 5 **3.** $-4 + (-2)$; −6 **4.** $3 + (-8)$; −5 **9.** −65 **10.** 53 **11.** −185 **12.** 0

**PRACTICE AND PROBLEM SOLVING**
**17.** Negative; both numbers are negative.
**19.** Negative; the number with greater absolute value is negative. **21.** 3 **23.** −13 **25.** 100 **27.** 34 **29.** 55 **31.** −48 **33.** 15 **35.** 7 **37.** 16 **39.** −40 **41.** −22 **43.** −30 **45.** > **47.** > **49.** > **53.** $-2 + (-7)$; −9 **55.** $3 + (-8)$; −5 **57.** $-20 + 18$; −2 **59.** $120 + (-25)$; 95 **61.** $-10 + (-2) + 8 + (-5) + (-13) + 1$; −21 **63.** \$158 **65.** positive; 0.4 **67.** negative; −12.19 **69.** negative **71.** negative **73.** B

**MIXED REVIEW** **75.** > **77.** > **79.** < **81.** $25 + 10n$; \$55

*Lesson 1-6* — pages 29–33

**TRY THIS** **1.** −5 **2.** −1 **3.** −3 **4.** −4 **5.** −6 **6.** 5 **7.** 35 **8.** −106 **9.** −46 **10.** about 80°C

**CHECK UNDERSTANDING** **3.** $6 + (-2)$; 4 **4.** $6 + 2$; 8 **5.** $-6 + (-2)$; −8 **6.** $-6 + 2$; −4 **7.** $2 + (-6)$; −4 **8.** $2 + 6$; 8 **9.** $-2 + (-6)$; −8 **10.** $-2 + 6$; 4 **11b.** $5 - 7$; −2

**PRACTICE AND PROBLEM SOLVING**
**13.** $-9 - (-2) = -7$ **21.** −6 **23.** 100 **25.** 96 **27.** 191 **29.** −80 **31.** 19 **33.** −68 **35.** −42 **37.** 850 **39.** −60 **41.** 150 **43.** 66 **51.** 50 **53.** −470 **55.** −500 **57.** $3{,}000 - 600$; 2,400 **59a.** It decreases. **b.** −24°C **c.** −8°C **61.** 27°C
**63a.** $8 - (-4) = 12$ **b.** 28 **c.** 24
$12 - (-4) = 16$
$16 - (-4) = 20$
$20 - (-4) = 24$
$24 - (-4) = 28$
**65.**

| | | |
|---|---|---|
| −2 | −7 | −6 |
| −9 | −5 | −1 |
| −4 | −3 | −8 |

−15

**MIXED REVIEW** **67.** −5 **69.** −6

*Standardized Test Prep* — page 34

**1.** C **3.** B **5.** A **7.** C **9.** B **11.** $\frac{m}{8}$; 5 mi

*Lesson 1-7* — pages 35–39

**TRY THIS** **2.** Start with 1 and add 2 repeatedly; 9, 11 **3.** Start with 4 and add 5 repeatedly.
**4.** Start with 3 and multiply by 3 repeatedly.
**5.** Add the previous two numbers. **6.** No; if the coin toss is fair, the coin can come up tails on any toss. **7.** correct **8.** Incorrect; 8 and $|8|$ are not opposites.

**CHECK UNDERSTANDING**
**1.** a square with four corners shaded **2.** a six-sided figure with a six-sided figure inside it

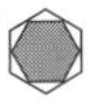

**3.** Start with 100 and subtract 15 repeatedly; 40, 25 **4.** Start with 5 and multiply by 4 repeatedly; 1,280, 5,120. **5.** Start with 1 and alternately add 1 and 3; 10, 13. **6.** Incorrect; an ostrich cannot fly.
**7.** correct **8.** Incorrect; $0.2 \cdot 0.2 = 0.04$, which is less than 0.2.



**PRACTICE AND PROBLEM SOLVING** **9.** an eight-sided figure with bottom right eighth shaded **11.** Start with −10 and add 6 repeatedly; 14, 20, 26 **13.** Start with 1 and add 0.5 repeatedly; 3.5, 4, 4.5

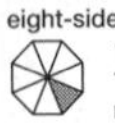

**15.** Start with 1, add 3 initially, and then add the last added number multiplied by 2, repeatedly; 190, 382, 766. **19.** Incorrect; $8 + (-6)$ is 2, and $2 < 8$.
**23b.**
1
1 2 1
1 2 3 2 1
1 2 3 4 3 2 1
1 2 3 4 5 4 3 2 1
1 2 3 4 5 6 5 4 3 2 1
1 2 3 4 5 6 7 6 5 4 3 2 1
1 2 3 4 6 5 7 8 7 6 5 4 3 2 1

**c.** 1, 4, 9, 16, 25, 36, 49, 64 **d.** 81

**MIXED REVIEW** **25.** 9 **27.** 103 **29.** −2 **31a.** $1{,}500n$ **b.** 36,000

*Lesson 1-8* — pages 40–43

**READ** **1.** 2 students **2.** 15 min

**PLAN** **3.** 2 students **4.** 4 periods

**LOOK BACK** **6.** A table; it would be difficult to draw all the branches of the tree. **7.** 9:45 A.M.

**CHECK UNDERSTANDING** **1.** 36 laps/day **2.** 78 students
**3a.**

| | |
|---|---|
| $2 \cdot 2 = 4$ | $3 \cdot 3 = 9$ |
| $1 \cdot 3 = 3$ | $2 \cdot 4 = 8$ |
| Difference = 1 | Difference = 1 |
| $4 \cdot 4 = 16$ | $5 \cdot 5 = 25$ |
| $3 \cdot 5 = 15$ | $4 \cdot 6 = 24$ |
| Difference = 1 | Difference = 1 |

The differences are all 1. **b.** $11 \cdot 11$; 1 greater **c.** 2,208 **d.** 4,225 **4.** \$10.23

**PRACTICE AND PROBLEM SOLVING**
**5.** 6:45 A.M. **7a.** \$59; \$21 **b.** 10 people **9.** 75 4's

**MIXED REVIEW** **11.** a 4 × 4 square; **13.** 0 **15.** −1 **17.** 9°F

*Lesson 1-9* — pages 44–49

**TRY THIS** **4.** −12 **5.** −12 **6.** −14 **7.** 12 **8.** 64 **9.** −90 **10.** 0 **11.** −4 **12.** 8 **13.** 14 **14.** −2

**CHECK UNDERSTANDING** **1.** $4(-9)$; −36 **2.** $5(-5)$; −25 **3.** Positive; the integers have the same sign. **4.** Negative; the integers have opposite signs. **5.** Negative; the integers have opposite signs. **6.** Positive; the first product is negative, so the second product is of integers with the same sign. **7.** −30 **8.** −5 **9.** −44 **10.** 10 **11a.** 6 **b.** They are opposites. **c.** opposite

**PRACTICE AND PROBLEM SOLVING** **13.** −60 **15.** −1 **17.** −10 **19.** −360 **21.** −14 **23.** −21,384 **25.** 19 **27.** 216 **29.** −12 **31.** −3 **33.** 58 **35.** −59 **37.** −87 **39.** $5 \cdot (-2) = -10$ **41.** *D* **43.** *C* **45.** < **47.** < **49.** < **55.** 2 yd **57.** \$143 **59.** −35 **61a.** negative; positive; negative **b.** If there are an even number of negative integers, the sign of the product will be positive; otherwise, the sign will be negative. **63.** 12 **65.** −15, 5

**MIXED REVIEW** **67.** < **69.** < **71.** $50 - n$ **73.** 36

**CHECKPOINT 2** **1.** −8 **2.** 20 **3.** −45 **4.** 8 **5.** 72 **6.** −12 **10.** 13, 18, 23 **11.** 81, 243, 729 **12.** A

*Lesson 1-10* — pages 50–54

**TRY THIS** **1.** (2, −3); (3, 3) **2.** Quadrant IV; Quadrant I
**3a–b.**

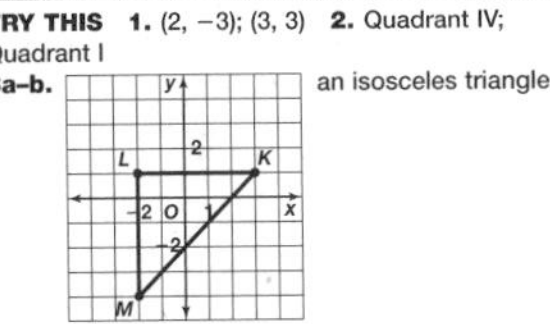

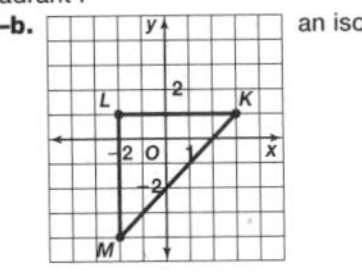


an isosceles triangle

**CHECK UNDERSTANDING** **1.** (0, −7) **2.** (−4, 1) **3.** (1, −4) **4.** (2, 6) **5.** *J* **6.** *G* **7.** *R* **8.** *Q* **9.** (0, 0) **10–15.**

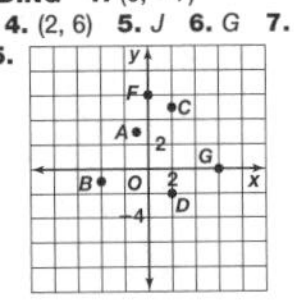


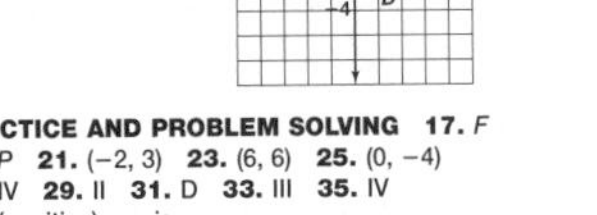

**PRACTICE AND PROBLEM SOLVING** **17.** *F* **19.** *P* **21.** (−2, 3) **23.** (6, 6) **25.** (0, −4) **27.** IV **29.** II **31.** D **33.** III **35.** IV **37.** (positive) $y$-axis



**47.** 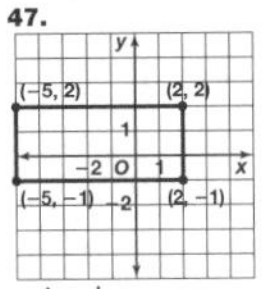 (graph: (−5, 2), (2, 2), (−5, −1), (2, −1)) rectangle

**49.** (graph: (−1, 1), (4, 4), (7, −1), (2, −4)) square

**51.** (0, −5) **53.** about 90° W, 32° N
**55.** Frankfort, KY **59.** 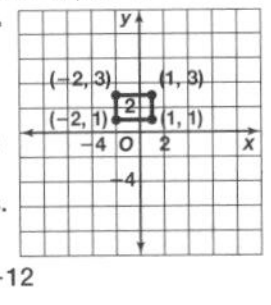 (graph: (−2, 3), (1, 3), (−2, 1), (1, 1))
**61.** 60a shifts the figure right 1 unit; 60b shifts it down 4 units; 60c shifts it right 1 unit and down 4 units; 60d doubles its dimensions.

**MIXED REVIEW** **63.** −9 **65.** 8 **67.** −12

*Wrap Up* — pages 56–58

**1.** $x - 25$ **2.** $3n$ **3.** $y + 2$ **4.** $10 - t$ **5.** $n + 5$ **6.** $\frac{x}{4}$ **7.** 24 **8.** 12 **9.** 37 **10.** 19 **11.** 17 **12.** 20 **13.** 40 **14.** 450 **15.** 16 **16.** −17 **17.** 1,000 **18.** 9 **19.** −12 **20.** > **21.** > **22.** = **23.** < **25.** −7 **26.** 12 **27.** 14 **28.** −11 **29.** −27 **30.** −15 **31.** −1 **32.** Start with 0 and add 6 repeatedly; 24, 30, 36. **33.** Start with −18 and add 9 repeatedly; 18, 27, 36. **34.** Start with $\frac{1}{2}$ and add $\frac{1}{2}$ repeatedly; $2\frac{1}{2}$, 3, $3\frac{1}{2}$. **35.** 8 weeks **36.** \$112 **37.** −42 **38.** −5 **39.** 72 **40.** 7 **41.** −3 **42.** −165 **43.** −8 **44.** 35 **45.** (1, −3) **46.** (−2, 1) **47.** (−3, −3) **48.** (2, 2)

*Cumulative Review* — page 60

**1.** A **3.** C **5.** A **7.** A **9.** D **11.** Start with 1 and multiply by −2 repeatedly; 16, −32. **13.** 2
**15.** 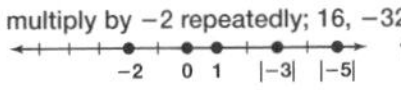 (number line: −2 0 1 |−3| |−5|) **17.** −12

**19.** (−2, 3); (0, 0); (2, −2)

## ▶ Chapter 2

*Skills You Need* — page 61

**1.** 25 **2.** 28 **3.** 15 **4.** −110 **5.** 36 **6.** 16 **7.** −24 **8.** 45 **9.** −20 **10.** −27 **11.** 72 **12.** −72 **13.** −18 **14.** −5 **15.** −45 **16.** 3; 3 **17.** 11; 11 **18.** 5; 5 **19.** 35; 35 **20.** −3; −3 **21.** −19; −19 **22.** 6; 6 **23.** 25; 25 **24.** 6; 6 **25.** 5; 5 **26.** −7; −7 **27.** 6; 6 **28.** 7; 7 **29.** 13; 13 **30.** < **31.** > **32.** > **33.** < **34.** > **35.** < **36.** = **37.** > **38.** > **39.** < **40.** = **41.** < **42.** < **43.** > **44.** <

*Lesson 2-1* — pages 64–68

**TRY THIS** **1.** \$18 **2.** Comm. Prop. of Add. **3.** Ident. Prop. of Mult. **4.** Assoc. Prop. of Mult. **5.** 47 **6.** 3 **7.** 40 **8.** 10 **9.** \$6.30 **10.** 300 **11.** 120 **12.** −240 **13.** −540

**CHECK UNDERSTANDING** **1.** Comm. Prop. of Add. **2.** Ident. Prop. of Add. **3.** Assoc. Prop. of Mult. **4.** Assoc. Prop. of Mult. **5.** Ident. Prop. of Mult. **6.** Comm. Prop. of Mult. **7.** 5 and 95; they are easiest to add. **8.** 5 and 2; they are easiest to multiply. **9.** 50 and (−2); they are easiest to multiply. **10.** −1,300 **11.** 93 **12.** 107 **13.** −6,600 **14.** 97 **15.** 5,400

**PRACTICE AND PROBLEM SOLVING**
**17.** Comm. Prop. of Add. **19.** Comm. Prop. of Add. **21.** Ident. Prop. of Mult. **23.** Ident. Prop. of Add. **25.** Comm. Prop. of Mult. **27.** Comm. Prop. of Mult. **29.** 800 **31.** 3,700 **33.** 100 **35.** −10,000 **37.** 380 **39.** 35 **41.** 240 **43.** −100 **45.** B **47.** \$924; \$720

**MIXED REVIEW** **49.** I **51.** III **53.** II **55.** 60 **57.** 100

*Lesson 2-2* — pages 69–73

**TRY THIS** **4.** 2,650 **5.** 3,120 **6.** 1,791 **7.** \$1,428 **8.** 210 **9.** −120 **10.** 35 **11.** $8x - 12$ **12.** $3x + 12$ **13.** $6x + 2$ **14.** $14 + 6d$ **15.** $18m + 3$ **16.** $-15t + 6$

**CHECK UNDERSTANDING** **1.** 12, 12 **2.** $z$, $z$ **3.** $a$, $a$ **4.** $b$ **5.** 138 **6.** 336 **7.** 90 **8.** 1,313

**PRACTICE AND PROBLEM SOLVING** **9.** 312 **11.** 784 **13.** 832 **15.** 56 **17.** 72 **19.** 8 **21.** 36 **23.** −55 **25.** −18 **27.** $4(x + 2)$; $4x + 8$ **29.** $7t - 35$ **31.** $14z + 6$ **33.** $4b + 20$ **35.** $-6t - 18$ **37.** $-48 + 8c$ **39.** $-28 + 7t$ **41.** Dist. Prop. **43.** Comm. Prop. of Mult. **45.** 3,888 mi

**MIXED REVIEW** **51.** Comm. Prop. of Mult. **53.** Assoc. Prop. of Mult. **55.** 1 **57.** −3

## Lesson 2-3 page 74–77

**TRY THIS** **1.** 2, 4; 2s, 4s; 6 **2.** −4; none; none **3.** 9, 2, −2, 1; 9m and −2m, 2r and r; none **4.** 7a + 1 **5.** 13a **6.** 2b **7.** −13m **8.** −y + 5m **9.** 2x − 7

**CHECK UNDERSTANDING** **1.** 3; 5; none; −3 **2.** 2; none; −7 **3.** 4, −7, 3; 4x, − 7x, 3x; none **4.** 6, −5; 6xy, −5xy; none **5.** a, a; a; a **6.** m; m; m **7.** 8r − 5 **8.** 13a **9.** 7x + 3 **10.** 4 + m

**PRACTICE AND PROBLEM SOLVING** **11.** 5, 8; 5a, 8a; none **13.** −3; none; −8 **15.** −4, 7, −9, −1; −4x and −9x, 7w and −w; 12 **17.** x + 2 + 3x + 5 + x + 3 + 2x; 7x + 10 **19.** 9a −3 **21.** −2y + 5 **23.** 3 **25.** 11z + 8y **27.** 5g + 15 **29.** −24t + 20 **31.** Comm. Prop. of Add.; Dist. Prop.; Add within parentheses.; Simplify. **33.** 6a **35.** 54k − 60 **37.** 3b + 2c + 189 **39.** A

**MIXED REVIEW** **43.** 324 **45.** 369

**CHECKPOINT 1** **1.** Comm. Prop. of Mult. **2.** Assoc. Prop. of Mult. **3.** Ident. Prop. of Mult. **4.** Comm. Prop. of Add. **5.** Comm. Prop. of Mult. **6.** Dist. Prop. **7.** 9a **8.** 18y **9.** 16w − 6 **10.** B

## Lesson 2-4 pages 78–81

**TRY THIS** **1.** false **2.** open **3.** true **4.** 20 − x = 3; open **5.** no **6.** yes **7.** b + 6 = 33; 27 + 6 = 33 ✔; Yes, the backpack weighs 27 lb.

**CHECK UNDERSTANDING** **1.** True; for example, 3 + 2 = 7. **2.** False; 3w − 7 is not an equation. **3.** True; by definition, an open sentence is one that contains a variable. **4.** True; it contains a variable. **5.** true **6.** open **7.** false **8.** true **9.** false **10.** true

**PRACTICE AND PROBLEM SOLVING** **11.** false **13.** open **15.** true **17.** true **19.** open **21.** no **23.** yes **25.** no **27.** yes **29.** 4(−5) = −20; true **31.** 15 + n = 50; open **33.** 25 = v + 15; open **35.** 10 dimes or 100 pennies; both have a value of one dollar. **37.** 140 + d = 192; yes **39.** A

**MIXED REVIEW** **43.** −4t − 19 **45.** 7 **47.** 0 **49.** 25 mi

## Math Toolbox pages 82–83

**1.**

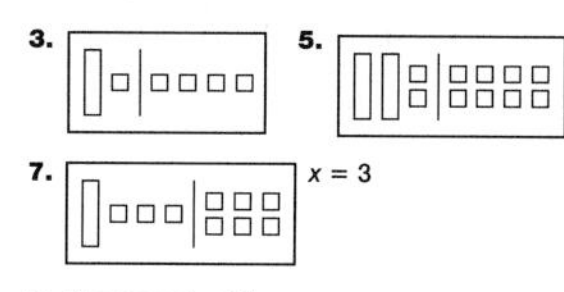

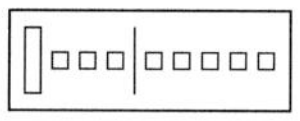

**3.** **5.**

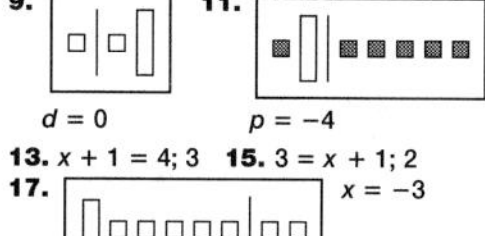

**7.** x = 3

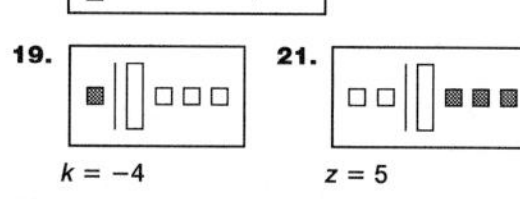

**9.** d = 0 **11.** p = −4

**13.** x + 1 = 4; 3 **15.** 3 = x + 1; 2

**17.** x = −3

**19.** k = −4 **21.** z = 5

**23.** x + 3 = −2; −5

## Lesson 2-5 pages 84–89

**TRY THIS** **1.** −5 **2.** 4 **3.** −1 **4.** 123 = r + 55; 68 beats/min **5.** 13 **6.** 72 **7.** 112 **8.** h − 17 = 5; $22

**CHECK UNDERSTANDING** **1.** 8, 8; 7 **2.** 3, 3; −2 **3.** Subtract 8 from each side. **4.** Subtract 54 from each side. **5.** Add 19 to each side. **6.** 3 **7.** −20 **8.** −1 **9.** −3 **10.** 54 **11.** −15

**PRACTICE AND PROBLEM SOLVING** **13.** 28 **15.** 31 **17.** 125 **19.** 626 **21.** 23 **23.** −1 **25.** −49 **27.** 200 **29.** −75 **31.** 6 **33.** −20 **35.** −300 **37.** −6 + y = 18; 24 **39.** −5 = x − 8; 3 **41.** D **43.** 108 = d − 42; 150 million km **45.** Yes; subtracting a number is the same as adding its opposite. **47.** 5,200 = s + 2,520; 2,680 m/s

**MIXED REVIEW** **49.** true **51.** 48 **53.** −400

## Lesson 2-6 pages 89–92

**TRY THIS** **1.** 21 **2.** 13 **3.** 9 **4.** −8 **5.** −12 **6.** 14 **7.** −50 **8.** −324 **9.** −600



**CHECK UNDERSTANDING** **1.** Divide each side by 6. **2.** Divide each side by 3. **3.** Multiply each side by −5. **4.** −6 **5.** 12 **6.** 5 **7.** 42 **8.** −24 **9.** 40

**PRACTICE AND PROBLEM SOLVING** **11.** yes; −6 = 2(−3) **13.** no; $\frac{-18}{-3} \neq -6$ **15.** 7 **17.** −5 **19.** 19 **21.** −10 **23.** 52 **25.** −16 **27.** 300 **29.** −24 **31.** 100 **33.** −15,000 **35.** 7, −7 **37.** 3, −3 **39.** b + a **41.** $\frac{b}{a}$; a ≠ 0 **43.** −20y = 100; −5 **45.** 13 = $\frac{x}{3}$; 39 **47.** 14 ft

**MIXED REVIEW** **51.** 17 **53.** 2 **55.** 7(w − 9)

## Standardized Test Prep page 93

**1.** D **3.** A **5.** A **7.** 987,654,321

## Lesson 2-7 pages 94–97

**READ** **1.** adult $4; student $3 **2.** 133 tickets **3.** $471

**PLAN** **4.** Subtract the number of adult tickets from 133. **5.** 4

**LOOK BACK** **6.** 53 adult tickets, 80 student tickets

**CHECK UNDERSTANDING** **2.** 1, 10, and 4, or 3, 7, and 5, or 5, 4, and 6, or 7, 1, and 7 **3.** 11 years and 12 years

**PRACTICE AND PROBLEM SOLVING** **5.** 16 ft² **7.** 48 years **9.** 11 nickels, 7 quarters **11.** 122, 123 **13.** 2,750 m, 2,250 m

**MIXED REVIEW** **15.** 2 **17.** −6 **19.** Ident. Prop. of Mult. **21.** Comm. Prop. of Add.

## Math Toolbox pages 98–99

**3.** Use a line graph to show change over time. Use a bar graph to compare quantities.

## Lesson 2-8 pages 100–103

**TRY THIS**

**1.** (number line: −2, 0)

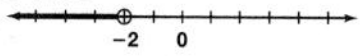

**2.** (number line: 0, 4)

**3.** (number line: −5, 0)

**4.** (number line: 0, 2)

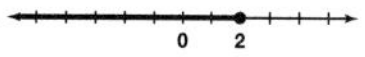

**5.** x ≥ 3 **6.** n < 5

**CHECK UNDERSTANDING** **1.** D **2.** A **3.** B **4.** C **5.** x < 5 **6.** y > −3 **7.** b ≤ 8

**PRACTICE AND PROBLEM SOLVING**

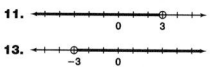

**9.** (number line: 0, 2, 7)

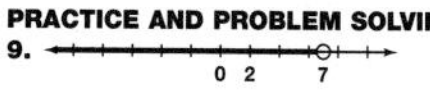

**11.** (number line: 0, 3)

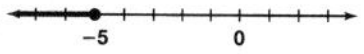

**13.** (number line: −3, 0)

**15.** (number line: −4, 0)

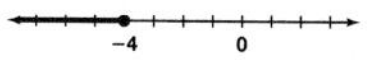

**17.** (number line: 0, 4)

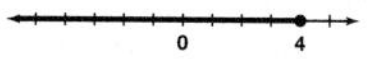

**19.** (number line: −1, 0) **21.** x ≥ 2

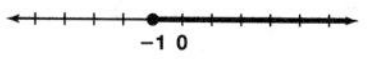

**23.** x > −4 **25.** c ≥ 12 **27.** p ≤ 30 **29.** A **31.** n < 45 **33.** 3t < 20 **35.** s = speed in mi/h; s ≤ 25

**MIXED REVIEW** **41.** 5 **43.** −11 **45.** 3n + 6

## Lesson 2-9 pages 104–107

**TRY THIS**

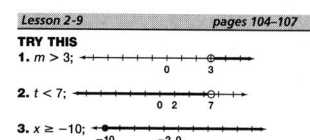

**1.** m > 3; (number line: 0, 3)

**2.** t < 7; (number line: 0, 2, 7)

**3.** x ≥ −10; (number line: −10, −2, 0)

**4.** ≤ 28 lb **5.** m > 42 **6.** v ≤ 11 **7.** t ≥ 16

**CHECK UNDERSTANDING** **1.** Each side had 5 added. **2.** Each side had 8 subtracted.

**3.** n ≤ 15; (number line: 0, 5, 15)

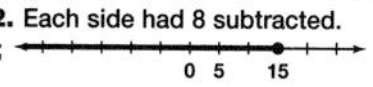

**4.** x > 6; (number line: 0, 2, 6)

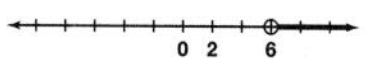

**5.** w < 7; (number line: 0, 2, 7)

**6.** a < −7; (number line: −7, −2, 0)

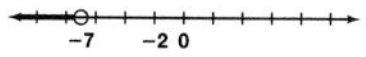

**PRACTICE AND PROBLEM SOLVING**

**9.** m ≤ 0; (number line: 0, 1)

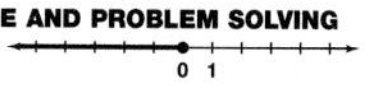

**11.** w ≥ −2; (number line: −2, 0)

**13.** t < 26; (number line: −20, 0, 26)





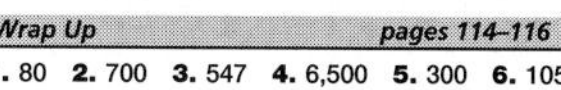

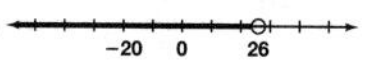

**15.** b > 5.3; (number line: 0, 1, 5.3)

**17.** x < −8; (number line: −8, 0, 2)

**19.** h ≥ 16; (number line: 0, 4, 16)

**21.** y ≥ 8; (number line: 0, 2, 8)

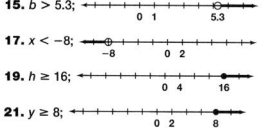

**23.** Comm. Prop. of Add.; Simplify.; Subt. Prop. of Equality; Simplify.

**25.** 13 + n > 15; n > 2 **27.** b − 11 < −12; b < −1 **29.** Yes; solving m + 4 > 2 gives m > −2, which can also be written −2 < m. **31.** 45 + m ≥ 120; at least $75

**MIXED REVIEW**

**33.** (number line: 0, 2)

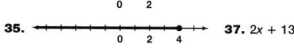

**35.** (number line: 0, 2, 4) **37.** 2x + 13

**39.** −4t − 14

**CHECKPOINT 2** **1.** true **2.** open **3.** false **4.** −4 **5.** 4 **6.** 6 **7.** −32 **8.** −9 **9.** m > −9 **10.** r < 19 **11.** a ≥ 6 **13.** 1 quarter, 5 dimes, 2 pennies

## Lesson 2-10 pages 108–112

**TRY THIS** **3.** x > 10 **4.** m ≤ −7 **5.** t ≥ −4 **6.** m ≥ 8 **7.** t > −21 **8.** r > 35

**CHECK UNDERSTANDING** **1.** unchanged **2.** unchanged **3.** reverses **4.** reverses **5.** Divide each side by 4. **6.** Divide each side by −4. **7.** Multiply each side by 3. **8.** x > −7 **9.** t > 7 **10.** x < −18 **11.** m ≤ −108

**PRACTICE AND PROBLEM SOLVING** **13.** m > 4 **15.** x ≤ 3 **17.** m < −9 **19.** m > 4 **21.** x ≥ −6 **23.** y > 12 **25.** b ≥ −93 **27.** v > 120 **29.** Div. Prop. of Ineq.; Simplify. **31.** My friend reversed the direction of the inequality when dividing each side by a positive number. **33.** −2a > 10; a < −5 **35.** $\frac{b}{4}$ ≥ 3; b ≥ 12

**MIXED REVIEW** **41.** t > 11 **43.** r ≤ −14 **45.** Dist. Prop. **47.** 41°F

## Wrap Up pages 114–116

**1.** 80 **2.** 700 **3.** 547 **4.** 6,500 **5.** 300 **6.** 105 **7.** 864 **8.** 496 **9.** 387 **10.** 4w + 36 **11.** 24 + 48a **12.** −42 + 14m **13.** D **14.** 7 − 3a **15.** 7w + 9 **16.** 9 − 3x **17.** 15 − 24n **18.** k **19.** 31 − 17r **20.** Check whether the variable parts of the terms are identical. **21.** 32 + 5 = 6 · 6; false **22.** $\frac{t}{17}$ = −3; open **23.** 4 · 20 = 80; true **24.** p + 1.75 = 6.50 **25.** 11 **26.** 8 **27.** −5 **28.** 27 **29.** 128 **30.** −8 **31.** $6.50

**32.** (number line: 0, 2, 5)

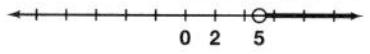

**33.** (number line: −2, 0)

**34.** (number line: 0, 2)

**35.** (number line: 0, 6)

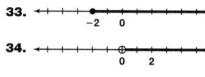

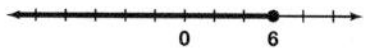

**36.** t < 0 **37.** h > 12 **38.** n > 14 **39.** t ≥ −3 **40.** r > −8 **41.** k ≥ 2 **42.** s ≤ 3 **43.** m < −6 **44.** d < −14 **45.** c ≤ 36

## Cumulative Review page 118

**1.** D **3.** B **5.** C **7.** C **9.** A **11.** 406 **13.** 5,010 **15.** 7t + 42 **17.** −5s **19.** 6b + 2p + 7.59 **21.** false **23.** true **25.** 19 **27.** −12

**29.** (number line: −3, 0) **31.** x < −5 **33.** s ≤ 14

# ▶Chapter 3

## Skills You Need page 119

**1.** 40 **2.** 10 **3.** 10 **4.** 0 **5.** 50 **6.** 110 **7.** 210 **8.** 600 **9.** 830 **10.** 6,010 **11.** 0 **12.** 50 **13.** > **14.** < **15.** < **16.** < **17.** > **18.** < **19.** < **20.** > **21.** > **22.** < **23.** < **24.** < **25.** 3.25, 3.8, 4.19, 4.91 **26.** 8.349, 8.35, 8.351, 9.25 **27.** 12.01, 12.09, 12.1, 12.9 **28.** 0.017, 0.02, 0.0201, 0.201 **29.** −14.1, −1.401, −1.4, −1.04 **30.** −3.2, −3.19, −2.8, −2.3 **31.** 11.49 **32.** 1.67 **33.** 14.9 **34.** 3.07 **35.** 2.47 **36.** 0.88 **37.** 15.217 **38.** 1.206 **39.** 7.14 **40.** 12 **41.** 6.7067 **42.** 6.5 **43.** 53.07 **44.** 6.9 **45.** 55.12 **46.** 10.6 **47.** 98.7 **48.** 532 **49.** 300 **50.** 154,070 **51.** 0.08 **52.** 0.0842 **53.** 0.0161 **54.** 0.001209 **55.** 0.87 **56.** 15,740 **57.** 143 **58.** 0.0189



## Lesson 3-1 pages 122–126

**TRY THIS** **5.** tenths; 38.4 **6.** ones; 1 **7.** tenths; 7,098.6 **8.** thousandths; 274.943 **9.** tenths; 5.0 **10.** hundredths; 9.85 **11.** about 560 **12.** about 220 **13.** about 18.6 **14.** about $11 **15.** about $15 **16.** about 125

**CHECK UNDERSTANDING** **1.** 27.39 **2.** 0.912 **3.** 1,046 **4.** 345.7 **5.** about $11 **6.** about 19 **7.** about 45 **8.** about $13.90 **9.** about $10 **10.** about 20.7 **11.** about $129 **12.** about $27 **13.** about 0.60

**PRACTICE AND PROBLEM SOLVING** **15.** 1.5 **17.** 1 **19.** about $9 **21.** about $28 **23.** about $4 **25.** about 17 **27.** about 93.5 **29.** about 90.4 **31.** about 9.5 **33.** about 10.1 **35.** about $28 **37.** about 3,220 **39.** about $17; rounding **41.** about $40; rounding **43.** about 20; rounding **45.** $37.50; front-end **47.** about 3.4 million **49.** about 44 in.

**MIXED REVIEW** **53.** x ≤ 3 **55.** k < 4 **57.** 4 **59.** −30 **61.** 7 bikes; 3 trucks

## Lesson 3-2 pages 127–130

**TRY THIS** **1.** about 10 **2.** about 68 **3.** about 160 **4.** about $40 **5.** about 19 **6.** about 6 **7.** about 20 **8.** yes **9.** no

**CHECK UNDERSTANDING** **1.** about 35 **2.** about 44 **3.** about 54 **4.** about 100 **5.** about 2 **6.** about 2 **7.** about 20 **8.** about $50

**PRACTICE AND PROBLEM SOLVING** **11.** about 40 **13.** about 144 **15.** about 400 **17.** about 64 **19.** about $5 **21.** about 4 **23.** about $6 **25.** about 4 **27.** not reasonable; 4.56 **29.** not reasonable; 70.23 **31.** not reasonable; about 0.3168 **33.** about $12 **37.** physical therapist: about $18/h in Dallas; about $16/h in Washington, D.C.; pharmacist: about $20/h in Dallas, about $21/h in Washington, D.C.; nurse: about $15/h in Dallas, about $18/h in Washington, D.C. **39.** about $2 **41.** I rounded to 20 ÷ 4. My friend used compatible numbers, 21 ÷ 3.

**MIXED REVIEW** **43.** about $39 **45.** about 1,220 **47.** about $2 **49.** Quadrant III **51.** y-axis **53.** x-axis

## Lesson 3-3 pages 131–135

**TRY THIS** **1.** 18.5, 14, 14 **2.** 2.95, 2.8, 2.3 **3.** 3 modes **4.** 1 mode **5.** 31; raises the mean by 2.6 **6.** 1; lowers the mean by 2.8 **7a.** $25.25, $23.50, $20

**CHECK UNDERSTANDING** **1.** 11.1, 8, none; outlier: 37 **2.** 122.4, 123, 123; outlier: 115 **3.** 112, 61, none; median; there is no mode, and the outlier (367) affects the mean too much. **4.** 49.1, 50, 50; mean (or mode); there are no outliers.

**PRACTICE AND PROBLEM SOLVING** **5.** 58.9, 56, 56; outlier: 89 **7.** 2.7, 3, 3; no outliers **9.** Mean; there likely are no outliers. **11.** Mean; there likely are no outliers. **13.** Mean; there likely are no outliers. **15.** 13.5, 14.5, 13.5 and 15; median; the outlier (7) affects the mean too much. **17.** 15, 18, 18; median (or mode); the outlier (1) affects the mean too much. **19.** D

**MIXED REVIEW** **23.** about 6 **25.** about 6 **27.** 6x + 10 **29.** x − 2t + 5

## Math Toolbox page 136

**1.** 648.5 species; 641.5 species **3.** $5.62; $4.70 **5.** about 159 mi; 127 mi

## Lesson 3-4 pages 137–140

**TRY THIS** **1.** r = 28 mi/h **2.** t = 51.5 yr **3.** 61°F **4.** 59°F **5.** 53.5°F **6.** 88.2 cm **7.** 52 in.

**CHECK UNDERSTANDING** **1.** 67°F **2.** 57°F **3.** 60°F **4.** 53°F **5.** d = 481.25 m **6.** r = 280 mi/h **7.** t = 259.3 s **8.** t = 20.4 h **9.** 5.84 mi

**PRACTICE AND PROBLEM SOLVING** **11.** 57.2°F **13.** 132.8°F **15.** 21 m **17.** 43.2 yd **19a.** 701.32 ft² **b.** 358.66 ft **21.** 0.425 mi

**MIXED REVIEW** **23.** 106 min, 123 min, 125 min; median **25.** 33 **27.** 56

**CHECKPOINT 1** **1.** 15.66 **2.** 0.891 **3.** 7,023 **4.** 345.7 **5.** about 32 **6.** about 24 **7.** about −1 **8.** about 6 **9.** 56, 57, no mode **10.** 2, 2, 1 **11.** $4.05, $2.25, no mode **12.** B

## Math Toolbox page 141

**1.** 27 in. **3.** 3 in. **5.** 28 h **7.** = 0.5*A2*B2 **9.** = A2*B2+C2

### *Lesson 3-5* *pages 142–145*

**TRY THIS** **1.** 13.9 **2.** 38.96 **3.** $35.48 + m = 70$; \$34.52 **4.** 21.1 **5.** −7.4 **6.** $x - 14.95 = 12.48$; \$27.43

**CHECK UNDERSTANDING** **1.** 1.2, 1.2; 13.8 **2.** 3.33, 3.33; 15.75 **3.** Subtract 8.5 from each side, or add −8.5 to each side. **4.** Subtract 54.2 from each side, or add −54.2 to each side. **5.** Add 1.9 to each side. **6.** 3.54 **7.** 0.88 **8.** 10.73 **9.** 23.7 **10.** 43.2 **11.** −0.8 **12.** No; the solution of the first equation is −0.9, while the solution of the second equation is −9.

**PRACTICE AND PROBLEM SOLVING** **13.** 1.2 **15.** 11 **17.** 15.4 **19.** 2.4 **21.** 0 **23.** −23.95 **25.** 1.1 **27.** 9.502 **29.** 5.3 **31.** Simplify; Subtraction Property of Equality; Simplify. **33.** The student should have *added* 1.6 to each side. **35.** Add −1.8 to each side.

**MIXED REVIEW** **37.** 369.72 $in.^2$ **39.** 4 **41.** −9 **43.** \$1.30

### *Lesson 3-6* *pages 146–149*

**TRY THIS** **1.** −2 **2.** 0.5 **3.** 90.9 **4.** $5.5p = 7.7$; \$1.40 **5.** −3 **6.** 12.5 **7.** −360 **8.** 12 hits

**CHECK UNDERSTANDING** **1.** 0.8, 0.8; 1.875 **2.** 4.5, 4.5; −13.5 **3.** Divide each side by 0.9. **4.** Multiply each side by 0.6. **5.** Multiply each side by 15. **6.** Divide each side by −0.4. **7.** 1.46 **8.** 0.56 **9.** −11.04 **10.** −1.94 **11a.** Harry multiplied the right side by 4 instead of dividing each side by 4.

**PRACTICE AND PROBLEM SOLVING** **13.** −25.1 **15.** 2.3 **17.** 30 **19.** 1.3 **21.** 0.0804 **23.** 0.9912 **25.** 3,104.32 **27.** 456 **29.** 13.5 **31.** 0.048308 **33.** $n \div (-4.5) = 200.6$; −902.7 **35a.** $f = 3.28\ell$ **b.** 24.6 ft **c.** about 1.83 m **d.** 16.7 $m^2$ **37a.** 20 hits **b.** You can have only a whole number of hits.

**MIXED REVIEW** **39.** −5.3 **41.** 26.1 **43.** 7.285 **45.** yes **47.** no

### *Lesson 3-7* *pages 150–155*

**TRY THIS** **1.** Centimeter; a meter is too large unless you use fractional parts of a meter; millimeters are too small. **2.** Gram; an energy bar has a mass of several grams, but it is much less than 1 kilogram. **3.** Kilogram; a horse is very heavy, so grams are too small. **4.** Liter; a gas tank holds several liters, so milliliters are too small. **5.** 50 km **6.** 10 mL **7.** 0.035 **8.** 250,000 **9.** 6,800 **10.** 3,800 m **11.** 250 mL

**CHECK UNDERSTANDING** **1.** C **2.** F **3.** B **4.** E **5.** A **6.** D **7.** 5,400 **8.** 0.234 **9.** 0.012 **10.** 3,010 **11.** 5.18 m

**PRACTICE AND PROBLEM SOLVING** **13.** Meter; the depth is less than a kilometer, so kilometers are too large. **15.** Kilogram; a car is very heavy, so grams are too small. **17.** Milliliter; a spoon holds much less than a liter, so a liter is too large. **19.** 2,000 mL; 2,000 L is about 2,000 qt and 2,000 mL ≈ 2 qt. **21.** 150 cm; 150 m is greater than the length of a football field. **23.** 1 g; 1 mg is closer to the mass of a speck of sawdust. **25.** m **27.** 25 **29.** 0.595 **31.** 0.035 **33.** 9.12 **35.** 0.005 **37.** 5.623 **39.** E **41.** C **43.** A **45.** 6,008,835 L **47.** 3.068 kg **49.** Camille multiplied by 1,000, so she changed grams to milligrams. **51.** A kilometer is 1,000 meters, a kilogram is 1,000 grams, a milliliter is 0.001 liter, and a milligram is 0.001 gram. **53a.** 5 to 6 km **b.** 5,000 to 6,000 m

**MIXED REVIEW** **55.** about 80 **57.** $a \geq 21$ **59.** $r \geq -7$

**CHECKPOINT 2** **1.** 0.25 **2.** 130 **3.** 8.55 **4.** 3.05 **5.** 6.5 **6.** 129.6 **7.** 1.5 m; 1.5 cm is a little wider than the width of a thumbnail. **8.** 500 mL; 500 L would have a mass of about 500 kg. **9.** 0.095 **10.** 7,650,000 **11.** 0.675 **12.** 7,100 **13.** 9,100 g

### *Math Toolbox* *pages 156–157*

**1.** 5.2 m **3.** 8.7 cm **7.** 14.6 kg **9.** 7 cm **11.** 4 significant digits **13.** 5 significant digits **15.** 15.9 $ft^2$ **17.** 5,720 $cm^2$

### *Standardized Test Prep* *page 158*

**1.** A **3.** B **5.** B **7.** B **9.** $d - 40.65 = 182.33$; \$222.98

### *Lesson 3-8* *pages 159–162*

**READ** **1.** 1 ft **2.** 3 ft **3.** 2 ft

**SOLVE** **4.** The number of days it takes to get out is 1 less than the depth of the well in feet. **5.** 9 days



**LOOK BACK** **6.**

out of well
Feet Climbed
10 9 8 7 6 5 4 3 2 1
1 2 3 4 5 6 7 8 9
Day

**CHECK UNDERSTANDING** **1.** 107 digits **2.** 66 matches **3.** 13 triangles

**PRACTICE AND PROBLEM SOLVING** **5.** 80 sketches **7.** 3.25 ft **9.** 1,320 pieces **11.** about 3,095 people/$mi^2$

**MIXED REVIEW** **13.** 0.27 **15.** 2 **17.** 300 **19.** about \$46.50 **21.** 91

### *Wrap Up* *pages 164–166*

**1.** about 10; front-end **2.** about 4; rounding **3.** about 24; rounding **4.** about 10; rounding **5.** about 60; clustering **6.** about 7; rounding **7.** about 12; rounding **8.** about 6; rounding **9.** about 18; clustering **11.** C **12.** about 48 **13.** about 4 **14.** about 10 **15.** about 5 **16.** about 12 **17.** about 6 **18.** about −8 **19.** about −6 **20.** about 12 **21.** 5.4, 5, 2 and 5; no outliers **22.** 16.1, 16.2, 16.3; no outliers **23.** 36, 33, none; outlier: 57 **24.** 1.0, 0.2, 0.1; outlier: 7.9 **28.** 70 mi **29.** 384 $mm^2$ **30.** 37.68 in. **31.** 52 cm **32.** 7.1 **33.** 9.25 **34.** −2.01 **35.** −0.8 **36.** −9.1 **37.** 10.6 **38.** 2.5 **39.** 40.817 **40.** 11.3 **41.** 968.75 **42.** −19.4 **43.** −185.0125 **44.** C **45.** Meter; a kilometer is too large unless you use fractional parts of a kilometer; centimeters are too small. **46.** Kilogram; a bicycle is heavy, so grams are too small. **47.** Milliliter; a liter is about the same as a quart, so liters are too large. **48.** 85 **49.** 0.160 **50.** 230 **51.** 1,600 **52.** 620 **53.** 0.080 **54.** D **55.** 1, 4, 9, 16, 25, 36, 49, 64, 81, 100

### *Cumulative Review* *page 168*

**1.** C **3.** C **5.** C **7.** D **9.** B **11.** A **13.** B **15.** C

## ▶CHAPTER 4

### *Skills You Need* *page 169*

**1.** 90 **2.** 900 **3.** 22 **4.** 49 **5.** 21 **6.** 45 **7.** 212 **8.** 27 **9.** 130 **10.** 140 **11.** 91 **12.** 23 **13.** 1,728 **14.** 512 **15.** 6,561 **16.** 15,625 **17.** −64 **18.** 64 **34.** $\frac{6}{8}, \frac{3}{4}$ **35.** $\frac{2}{8}, \frac{1}{4}$ **36.** $\frac{3}{9}, \frac{1}{3}$

### *Lesson 4-1* *pages 172–175*

**TRY THIS** **1.** Yes; 160 ends in 0. **2.** No; 56 does not end in 0. **3.** No; 53 does not end in 0, 2, 4, 6, or 8. **4.** Yes; 1,118 ends in 8. **5.** No; the sum of the digits, 10, is not divisible by 9. **6.** No; the sum of the digits, 13, is not divisible by 3. **7.** Yes; the sum of the digits, 12, is divisible by 3. **8.** Yes; the sum of the digits, 18, is divisible by 9. **9.** 1, 2, 5, 10 **10.** 1, 3, 7, 21 **11.** 1, 2, 3, 4, 6, 8, 12, 24 **12.** 1, 31 **13.** 1 row of 36 students, 2 rows of 18 students, 3 rows of 12 students, 4 rows of 9 students, or 6 rows of 6 students

**CHECK UNDERSTANDING** **1.** 2, 5, 10 **2.** none **3.** 3, 5, 9 **4.** 3, 9 **5.** 2, 3, 5, 10 **6.** 3, 9 **7a.** 66 and 4,710 **b.** 66 and 4,710 **c.** An integer is divisible by 6 if it is divisible by 2 and 3. **8.** 1, 2, 4, 8 **9.** 1, 2, 4, 8, 16 **10.** 1, 23 **11.** 1, 2, 3, 6, 9, 18, 27, 54 **12.** 1, 3, 5, 15, 25, 75 **13.** 1, 2, 4, 17, 34, 68

**PRACTICE AND PROBLEM SOLVING** **15.** none **17.** 2, 3, 5, 9, 10 **19.** none **21.** 2, 3, 5, 10 **23.** 3, 9 **25.** 2 **27.** 7 **29.** 2 **31.** 1, 2, 4 **33.** 1, 2, 3, 6 **35.** 1, 3, 5, 15 **37.** 1, 2, 11, 22 **39.** 1, 2, 4, 7, 14, 28 **41.** 1, 5, 7, 35 **43.** 1, 2, 5, 10, 25, 50 **45.** 1, 2, 3, 4, 6, 8, 9, 12, 18, 24, 36, 72 **47.** 1, 2, 3, 4, 6, 8, 9, 12, 16, 18, 24, 36, 48, 72, 144 **53a.** 2 plates of 21 cookies, 3 plates of 14 cookies, 6 plates of 7 cookies **b.** 2 plates of 28 cookies, 4 plates of 14 cookies, 7 plates of 8 cookies, 8 plates of 7 cookies **c.** 2 plates of 30 cookies, 3 plates of 20 cookies, 4 plates of 15 cookies, 5 plates of 12 cookies, 6 plates of 10 cookies

**MIXED REVIEW** **55.** cm **57.** 27 **59.** 42

### *Lesson 4-2* *pages 176–179*

**TRY THIS** **1.** $6^3$ **2.** $(-3)^4$ **3.** $4xy^2$ **4.** 36 **5.** −16, 16 **6.** −58 **7.** 81

**CHECK UNDERSTANDING** **1.** $8^3$ **2.** $r^4s^2$ **3.** $-21a^2b$ **4.** 64 **5.** 0.25 **6.** −9 **7.** 108 **8.** −15 **9.** 81 **10.** 49 **11.** 22 **12.** No; $-6^2$ is −36 while $(-6)^2$ is 36.



**PRACTICE AND PROBLEM SOLVING** **13.** $25a^2$ **15.** $-15x^2y^2$ **17.** $4b^3c$ **19.** 125 and 243 **21.** −1 and 1 **23.** 31 **25.** −288 **27.** 35 **29.** 9 **31.** 0.36 **33.** 1 **35.** −24 **37.** 7.2 **39.** 48 **41.** 243 **43.** 29 **45.** D **47.** The student didn't use parentheses around *ab*. **49.** An even power of a negative number is positive. An odd power of a negative number is negative. **51.** 216 $in.^3$ **53.** 4 in. **55.** No; $5x^2y$ for $x = 1$ and $y = 2$ is 10, but $5xy^2$ for $x = 1$ and $y = 2$ is 20.

**MIXED REVIEW** **57.** 3, 5, 9 **59.** 2, 5, 10 **61.** $4x - 2y$ **63.** $11a - 7$

### *Lesson 4-3* *pages 180–184*

**TRY THIS** **4.** 11, 13, 17, 19; 10, 12, 14, 15, 16, 18, 20 **5.** $2^3 \cdot 3^2$ **6.** $2 \cdot 3 \cdot 5^2$ **7.** $3^2 \cdot 5^2$ **8.** $2^2 \cdot 59$ **9.** 4 **10.** 3 **11.** $4r$ **12.** $15m$

**CHECK UNDERSTANDING** **1.** composite; $3^3$ **2.** prime **3.** prime **4.** composite; $2 \cdot 19$ **5.** composite; $3^2 \cdot 5$ **6.** prime **7.** composite; $3 \cdot 29$ **8.** composite; $3 \cdot 31$ **9.** composite; $5^3$ **10.** composite; $2^3 \cdot 3^2 \cdot 5$ **11.** 5 **12.** 2 **13.** 1 **14.** $7c$ **15.** $3y^2$

**PRACTICE AND PROBLEM SOLVING** **17.** composite; $2^3$ **19.** prime **21.** neither **23.** composite; $5 \cdot 23$ **25.** composite; $7^2$ **27.** composite; $11 \cdot 23$ **29.** 7 **31.** 3 **33.** 4 **35.** 90 **37.** $z$ **39.** $6c^3$ **41.** $3s$ **43.** $x^2y$ **45.** 50, 52 **47.** B **49.** Yes; the GCF is 1. **51.** No; the GCF is 13. **53.** No; the GCF is 13. **55.** 1, 2, 4, 8, 16; 16 members **57.** 42 chairs

**MIXED REVIEW** **59.** 50 **61.** 11 **63.** −8.7 **65.** 9.3

### *Math Toolbox* *page 185*

**1.** 17 students **3.** 7 **5.** 36

### *Lesson 4-4* *pages 186–189*

**TRY THIS** **4.** $\frac{3}{4}$ **5.** $\frac{3}{4}$ **6.** $\frac{4}{5}$ **7.** $\frac{1}{ac}$ **8.** $\frac{n}{3}$ **9.** $3x$

**CHECK UNDERSTANDING** **6.** $\frac{1}{3}$ **7.** $\frac{2}{5}$ **8.** $\frac{1}{4}$ **9.** $\frac{2}{3}$ **10.** $\frac{m^2}{3}$ **11.** $\frac{2 \cdot 2 \cdot 2 \cdot 3}{2 \cdot 2 \cdot 2 \cdot 2 \cdot 2} = \frac{3}{4}$

**PRACTICE AND PROBLEM SOLVING** **19.** $\frac{1}{3}$ **21.** $\frac{3}{5}$ **23.** $\frac{9}{16}$ **25.** $\frac{3}{4}$ **27.** $\frac{3}{5}$ **29.** $\frac{3x}{2}$ **31.** $\frac{7a}{12}$ **33.** 8 **35.** $\frac{x^2}{3z}$ **37.** 13 **41.** $\frac{1}{3}$ **43.** $\frac{9}{25}$

**MIXED REVIEW** **45.** 2 **47.** $7a$ **49.** 2.62 **51.** −6.33

**CHECKPOINT 1** **1.** 2, 3, 5, 10 **2.** 2, 3, 9 **3.** 2, 3 **4.** none **5.** 3, 9 **6.** 64 **7.** 125 **8.** −18 **9.** $\frac{1}{2}$ **10.** $\frac{2}{3}$ **11.** $\frac{4}{7}$ **12.** $\frac{1}{4}$ **13.** $2y$

### *Lesson 4-5* *pages 190–193*

**READ** **1.** the number of pictures that must be taken **2.** 7 people **3.** 2 people

**SOLVE**

**4.**
Keisha — Darren, Lin, Chris, Jen
Darren — Lin, Chris, Jen
Lin — Chris, Jen
Chris — Jen

**5.** Each successive "tree" has one less "branch." **6.** 21 pictures **7.** 45 pictures

**CHECK UNDERSTANDING** **1.** 15 days **2.** 30, 24, 21, 18, 15, 12, 9, 6, 3 **3.** 28 handshakes **4.** 15 amounts of money

**PRACTICE AND PROBLEM SOLVING** **5.** 15 pizzas **7.** 12 ways **9.** 6 **11a.** 60 person-hours **b.** 3 hours

**MIXED REVIEW** **13.** $\frac{1}{2}$ **15.** $\frac{2a^2}{5}$ **17.** Start with 10; add 10 repeatedly. **19.** Start with 2; multiply by 3 repeatedly.

### *Lesson 4-6* *pages 194–197*

**TRY THIS**

**5–8.** −2, $-\frac{1}{2}$, $-\frac{4}{10}$, 0, 0.9, 2

**9.** $-\frac{1}{3}$ **10.** $\frac{2}{3}$ **11.** −3

**CHECK UNDERSTANDING** **6.** $\frac{2}{3}$ **7.** $-\frac{5}{6}$ **8.** $\frac{5}{6}$ **9.** $-\frac{7}{10}$

**PRACTICE AND PROBLEM SOLVING** **19.** $-\frac{1}{4}$ **21.** $\frac{5}{7}$ **23.** $-\frac{2}{27}$ **25.** $\frac{4}{-5}, \frac{-12}{15}, -\frac{16}{20}$ **27.** No; if equivalent, you could multiply the numerator and denominator of one fraction by the same nonzero number to get the other, meaning that the numerator and the denominator of the other fraction have a common factor. **29.** 64



**31.** $-\frac{2}{3}, \frac{2}{3}$ **33.** $-\frac{1}{4}, \frac{1}{4}$ **35.** always true

**MIXED REVIEW** **39.** 1 **41.** −2 **43.** −95 **45.** −34

### *Lesson 4-7* *pages 198–201*

**TRY THIS** **1.** 32 **2.** $m^{12}$ **3.** $x^5y^5$ **4.** $18a^4$ **5.** $15c^9$ **6.** $12x^6$ **7.** 256 **8.** $c^{20}$ **9.** $m^6$

**CHECK UNDERSTANDING** **1.** 64 **2.** $a^7$ **3.** $x^9y^2$ **4.** $28b^7$ **5.** $18c^{10}$ **6.** 1,000,000 **7.** $x^{12}$ **8.** $m^{24}$ **9.** No; the bases are not the same.

**PRACTICE AND PROBLEM SOLVING** **11.** 128 **13.** $a^{13}$ **15.** $m^{52}$ **17.** $24y^{11}$ **19.** $144b^4$ **21.** 64 **23.** $c^{16}$ **25.** $m^{25}$ **27.** 8 **29.** 3 **31.** 4 **33.** 5 **35.** < **37.** = **39.** > **41.** No; $-(2^3)^2$ is −64 but $(-2^3)^2$ is 64. **43.** Both $x^8 \cdot x^2$ and $x^5 \cdot x^5$ are equivalent to $x^{10}$. **45.** $2^{16}$; $2^{16} = 2^{1+15} = 2 \cdot 2^{15}$ **47.** $15x^3$

**MIXED REVIEW** **49.** $-\frac{1}{2}$ **51.** −4

**53.** −2 0 2

**55.** −2 0 2

### *Standardized Test Prep* *page 202*

**1.** A **3.** B **5.** C **7.** $\frac{7}{12}, \frac{9}{24}$

### *Lesson 4-8* *pages 203–207*

**TRY THIS** **1.** 1,000 **2.** $x^7$ **3.** $4m^4$ **4.** 1 **5.** 5 **6.** $y^3$ **7.** 5 **8.** $\frac{1}{16}$ **9.** $\frac{1}{a^2}$ **10.** $\frac{1}{3y^4}$ **11.** $b^{-6}$ **12.** $m^{-3}n^{-6}$ **13.** $x^{-4}y^2$

**CHECK UNDERSTANDING** **1.** 8 **2.** $h^4$ **3.** $\frac{3y^5}{5}$ **4.** $\frac{n}{m^2}$ **5.** 1 **6.** 5 **7.** $\frac{1}{m^4}$ **8.** $\frac{1}{8}$ **9.** $\frac{1}{5a^3}$ **10.** $\frac{x^3}{y^5}$ **11.** $y^{-3}$ **12.** $a^{-6}b^2$ **13.** $m^{-2}n^{-2}$ **14.** $x^{-3}y^{-7}$ **15.** $b^6c^{-5}$

**PRACTICE AND PROBLEM SOLVING** **17.** 121 **19.** $x^4$ **21.** $a^8$ **23.** $\frac{x^8}{2}$ **25.** $6a^3b^4$ **27.** $\frac{1}{b^3}$ **29.** $\frac{1}{8}$ **31.** $\frac{1}{a^4}$ **33.** 1 **35.** $\frac{1}{a^5}$ **37.** $\frac{1}{4y^4}$ **39.** $\frac{x^7}{2}$ **41.** 8 **43.** 2 **45.** −2 **47.** 5 **49.** $x^{-2}$ **51.** $m^7n^{-7}$ **53.** $b^5c^{-9}$ **55.** The student thought that the base was −5. **57.** 900 times as much

**MIXED REVIEW** **59.** $x^9$ **61.** $16a^{16}$ **63.** about 20.2 **65.** about 51

**CHECKPOINT 2** **6.** $-\frac{1}{3}$ **7.** $-\frac{1}{2}$ **8.** $\frac{2}{3}$ **9.** $-\frac{5}{8}$ **10.** $\frac{1}{4}$ **11–15.** −1, −0.8, $-\frac{2}{10}$, 0, $\frac{1}{2}$, 0.6, $\frac{9}{10}$, 1 **16.** 128 **17.** $x^{50}$ **18.** $6a^2$ **19.** $\frac{1}{x^5}$ **20.** $\frac{1}{a^6}$ **21.** C **22.** $\frac{3}{4}$

### *Lesson 4-9* *pages 208–213*

**TRY THIS** **4.** $5.45 \times 10^7$ **5.** $7.23 \times 10^5$ **6.** $6.02 \times 10^{11}$ **7.** $2.1 \times 10^{-4}$ **8.** $5 \times 10^{-8}$ **9.** $8.03 \times 10^{-11}$ **10.** 32,100,000 **11.** 0.000000059 **12.** 10,060,000,000 **13.** $1.6 \times 10^6$ **14.** $2.03 \times 10^5$ **15.** $7.243 \times 10^{15}$ **16.** $18.3 \times 10^6$, $0.098 \times 10^9$, $526 \times 10^7$ **17.** $0.22 \times 10^{-10}$, $8 \times 10^{-9}$, $14.7 \times 10^{-7}$ **18.** $2.4 \times 10^{11}$ **19.** $5.68 \times 10^{-3}$ **20.** $1.002 \times 10^{-23}$ kg

**CHECK UNDERSTANDING** **1.** $8.9 \times 10^9$ **2.** $6.31 \times 10^{-4}$ **3.** $5.559 \times 10^8$ **4.** $9 \times 10^{10}$ **5.** 59,400,000 **6.** 0.00000002104 **7.** 120,000 **8.** 0.00072 **9.** $0.065 \times 10^{11}$, $16 \times 10^9$, $2.3 \times 10^{12}$ **10.** $3.7 \times 10^{-8}$, $253 \times 10^{-9}$, $12.9 \times 10^{-7}$ **11.** $3 \times 10^9$ **12.** $8.6 \times 10^{11}$ **13.** $6.3 \times 10^{12}$

**PRACTICE AND PROBLEM SOLVING** **15.** $6 \times 10^{-6}$ **17.** $5.28 \times 10^{10}$ **19.** $1 \times 10^{-9}$ m **21.** $4 \times 10^{-3}$ in. **23.** 8,430,000 **25.** 0.000000602 **27.** 0.00714 cm **29.** $10^{-8}, 10^{-6}, 10^0, 10^5, 10^9$ **31.** $782 \times 10^{-8}$, $0.8 \times 10^{-4}$, $9.1 \times 10^{-5}$, $55.8 \times 10^{-5}$, $1{,}009 \times 10^2$ **33.** $6 \times 10^4$ **35.** $2 \times 10^{-4}$ **37.** $2 \times 10^{10}$ lb **39.** about \$$2.18 \times 10^{12}$ **41a.** $3.8 \times 10^8$ m **b.** $7.6 \times 10^8$ footsteps

**MIXED REVIEW** **45.** $x^2$ **47.** $\frac{3m^2}{n}$ **49.** 0.9 ft/h **51.** 78 chimes

### *Math Toolbox* *page 214*

**1.** $1.4976 \times 10^{11}$ **3.** $2.0196 \times 10^{16}$ **5.** $9.338 \times 10^{23}$ **7.** $6.19 \times 10^{-5}$ **9.** $1.1907 \times 10^{-12}$ **11.** $4.2585 \times 10^{-10}$

### Wrap Up — pages 216–218

**1.** 1, 2, 3, 4, 6, 12 **2.** 1, 2, 3, 5, 6, 10, 15, 30 **3.** 1, 2, 3, 6, 7, 14, 21, 42 **4.** 1, 2, 3, 4, 6, 8, 9, 12, 18, 24, 36, 72 **5.** 1, 3, 37, 111 **6.** 1, 2, 3, 4, 6, 7, 9, 12, 14, 18, 21, 28, 36, 42, 63, 84, 126, 252 **7.** 8 **8.** 27 **9.** 172 **10.** −25 **11.** 121 **12.** 58 **13.** 49 **14.** 16 **15.** prime **16.** composite; $2^2 \cdot 5$ **17.** prime **18.** composite; $2 \cdot 5 \cdot 11$ **19.** composite; $3 \cdot 29$ **20.** 4 **21.** 9 **22.** 1 **23.** $3x^2$ **24.** $2ab$ **25.** No factor of a positive integer is greater than the integer. **26.** $\frac{1}{5}$ **27.** $\frac{1}{2}$ **28.** $\frac{4}{13}$ **29.** $\frac{7}{10}$ **30.** $\frac{7}{11}$ **31.** $\frac{1}{6}$ **32.** $x$ **33.** 5 **34.** $\frac{1}{4}$ **35.** $\frac{2}{5}$ **36.** $\frac{x}{3}$ **37.** $4b$ **38.** 24 days

**39–42.** −2, −0.6, $-\frac{5}{10}$, 0, $\frac{2}{10}$, 1, 2 **43.** $\frac{2}{5}$ **44.** $\frac{7}{8}$

**45.** −1 **46.** $-\frac{4}{5}$ **47.** 128 **48.** $21a^6$ **49.** $b^7c^4$ **50.** $x^{15}$ **51.** $y^{20}$ **52.** 4,096 **53.** $\frac{1}{b^2}$ **54.** $\frac{7}{8y^5}$ **55.** $2 \times 10^6$ **56.** $4.58 \times 10^8$ **57.** $7 \times 10^{-7}$ **58.** $5.9 \times 10^{-9}$ **59.** 800,000,000,000 **60.** 0.0000032 **61.** 11,190,000 **62.** 0.000000000005 **63.** $4.3 \times 10^{10}$, $12 \times 10^{11}$, $3{,}644 \times 10^9$ **64.** $8 \times 10^{-10}$, $58 \times 10^{-10}$, $716 \times 10^{-10}$ **65.** $2.4 \times 10^{16}$ **66.** $1.8 \times 10^{11}$

### Cumulative Review — page 220

**1.** B **3.** C **5.** A **7.** D **9.** D **11.** A **13.** B **15.** A **17.** $4a$; 28 **19.** 1, 2, 3, 6, 9, 18, 27, 54

## ▶Chapter 5

### Skills You Need — page 221

**1.** $\frac{1}{2}$; $\frac{3}{6}$ **2.** $\frac{8}{12}$; $\frac{2}{3}$ **3.** $\frac{2}{5}$; $\frac{4}{10}$ **4.** $\frac{3}{4}$; $\frac{6}{8}$ **5.** $\frac{5}{6}$ **6.** $\frac{2}{5}$ **7.** −2 **8.** $\frac{1}{8}$ **9.** $-\frac{24}{25}$ **10.** $\frac{1}{3}$ **11.** $\frac{4}{15}$ **12.** $\frac{4}{31}$ **13.** $-\frac{2}{9}$ **14.** $-\frac{2}{13}$ **15.** $\frac{1}{6}$ **16.** $\frac{5}{7}$ **17.** 5.4 **18.** 0.6 **19.** 0.625 **20.** 0.75 **21.** 0.375 **22.** 1.2 **23.** 60 **24.** 23.7 **25.** −45 **26.** −40 **27.** 1.5 **28.** 74 **29.** 8 **30.** −1.78 **31.** 3 **32.** 4 **33.** 12 **34.** 1 **35.** 10 **36.** 5 **37.** 9 **38.** 11 **39.** 10 **40.** 7

### Lesson 5-1 — pages 224–228

**TRY THIS** **1.** 12 **2.** 20 **3.** 60 **4.** 48 **5.** 45 **6.** 180 **7.** $60xy$ **8.** $56m^4$ **9.** $75xy^2$ **10.** $\frac{2}{9} < \frac{4}{9}$ **11.** $-\frac{4}{9} < -\frac{2}{9}$ **12.** $-\frac{4}{9} < \frac{2}{9}$ **13.** $\frac{6}{7} > \frac{4}{5}$ **14.** $\frac{2}{3} < \frac{3}{4}$ **15.** $\frac{3}{4} > \frac{7}{10}$ **16.** $\frac{1}{6} < \frac{5}{12} < \frac{8}{12}$ **17.** $\frac{1}{5} < \frac{3}{10} < \frac{1}{2} < \frac{7}{12}$

**CHECK UNDERSTANDING** **1.** 90 **2.** 18 **3.** 60 **4.** 45 **5.** < **6.** < **7.** = **8.** > **9.** $\frac{3}{9} < \frac{5}{9} < \frac{7}{9}$ **10.** $\frac{1}{4} < \frac{1}{3} < \frac{1}{2}$ **11.** $\frac{2}{7} < \frac{2}{5} < \frac{2}{3}$ **12.** $\frac{3}{9}$ or $\frac{1}{3} < \frac{2}{5} < \frac{2}{4}$ **13.** Yes; $\frac{2}{3} > \frac{5}{8}$.

**PRACTICE AND PROBLEM SOLVING** **15.** 180 **17.** 30 **19.** 1,800 **21.** 60 **23.** $200xy$ **25.** $1{,}008a^2b$ **27.** = **29.** = **31.** > **33.** > **35.** > **37.** > **39.** > **41.** = **43.** < **45.** > **47.** < **49.** = **51.** wood shingle, siding, plywood, asphalt shingle, stucco, brick **53.** you

### Mixed Review — page 228

**55.** $1.394 \times 10^{-3}$ **57.** $5 \times 10^{-6}$ **59.** −8 **61.** −13

### Lesson 5-2 — pages 229–233

**TRY THIS** **1.** 0.25 **2.** 1.875 **3.** 3.3 **4.** 0.6 **5.** $0.\overline{7}$; repeating; 7 **6.** $0.9\overline{54}$; repeating; 54 **7.** 1.375; terminating **8.** $0.\overline{72}$; repeating; 72 **9.** 0.2, 0.5, $\frac{7}{10}$, $\frac{4}{5}$ **10.** −0.75, −0.375, $-\frac{1}{4}$, $-\frac{1}{8}$ **11.** $1\frac{3}{4}$ **12.** $3\frac{1}{250}$ **13.** $2\frac{8}{25}$ **14.** $\frac{7}{9}$ **15.** $\frac{6}{11}$ **16.** $\frac{71}{333}$

**CHECK UNDERSTANDING** **1.** 0.28 **2.** 0.6 **3.** −0.625 **4.** $-0.1\overline{6}$ **5.** $0.\overline{2}$ **6.** $0.\overline{6}$ **7.** < **8.** = **9.** > **10.** < **11.** $\frac{1}{10}$ **12.** $5\frac{9}{25}$ **13.** $2\frac{11}{20}$ **14.** $\frac{5}{9}$ **15.** $2\frac{5}{33}$ **16.** $\frac{2}{9}$; $0.\overline{2}$

**PRACTICE AND PROBLEM SOLVING** **17.** 0.45 **19.** 2.3125 **21.** 0.04 **23.** −0.31 **25.** $0.\overline{3}$ **27.** 0.65 **29.** $0.\overline{4}$ **31.** 0.06 **33.** 0.3, $\frac{1}{2}$, $\frac{3}{2}$, $\frac{5}{2}$ **35.** $0.0\overline{6}$, $\frac{2}{5}$, $\frac{2}{3}$, $\frac{5}{6}$ **37.** $\frac{22}{11}$, 2.01, 2.1, $\frac{22}{10}$ **39.** $6\frac{4}{5}$ **41.** $-3\frac{9}{10}$ **43.** $\frac{272{,}727}{1{,}000{,}000}$ **45.** $-\frac{1}{3}$ **47.** 2 **49.** $\frac{91}{495}$ **51.** $\frac{149}{234}$; 0.64

**53.**

| Fraction | $\frac{1}{8}$ | $\frac{1}{4}$ | $\frac{3}{8}$ | $\frac{1}{2}$ |
|---|---|---|---|---|
| Decimal | 0.125 | 0.25 | 0.375 | 0.5 |
| | $\frac{5}{8}$ | $\frac{3}{4}$ | $\frac{7}{8}$ | |
| | 0.625 | 0.75 | 0.875 | |
| Fraction | $\frac{1}{5}$ | $\frac{2}{5}$ | $\frac{3}{5}$ | $\frac{4}{5}$ |
| Decimal | 0.2 | 0.4 | 0.6 | 0.8 |

**55.** No; there is no block of digits that repeats.



**MIXED REVIEW** **57.** $-\frac{5}{6}$, $-\frac{1}{3}$, $\frac{1}{6}$, $\frac{2}{3}$ **59.** $-\frac{6}{7}$, $-\frac{4}{7}$, $-\frac{3}{14}$, $-\frac{1}{14}$ **61.** $\frac{11}{6}$ **63.** $\frac{61}{8}$ **65.** $3.485 \times 10^{10}$

### Math Toolbox — page 234

**1–8.** Answers may vary. Sample answers are given. **1.** 2 **3.** 4 **5.** 4 **7.** 2

### Lesson 5-3 — pages 235–239

**TRY THIS** **4.** $\frac{3}{5}$ **5.** $\frac{2}{5}$ **6.** $\frac{6}{y}$ **7.** $\frac{7}{15}$ **8.** $-\frac{1}{8}$ **9.** $\frac{3m + 14}{7m}$ **10.** $6\frac{5}{8}$ **11.** $29\frac{1}{6}$ **12.** $2\frac{13}{16}$ **13.** $3\frac{1}{2}$ qt

**CHECK UNDERSTANDING** **1.** $\frac{5}{8}$ **2.** $\frac{1}{12}$ **3.** $4m$ **4.** $\frac{3x}{7}$ **5.** $3\frac{5}{8}$ **6.** $1\frac{5}{8}$ **7.** $13\frac{7}{8}$ **8.** $\frac{5}{6}$ **9.** $1\frac{7}{8}$ in.

**PRACTICE AND PROBLEM SOLVING** **11.** $\frac{5}{12}$ **13.** $-\frac{2}{5}$ **15.** $\frac{5}{x}$ **17.** $1\frac{3}{10}$ **19.** $\frac{21 + 2d^2}{3d}$ **21.** $\frac{3}{8y}$ **23.** 6 **25.** $6\frac{5}{24}$ **27.** $-1\frac{1}{8}$ **33.** $1\frac{3}{8}$ **35.** $\frac{x}{2}$ **37.** $\frac{1}{8}$ **39.** $\frac{9}{98}$ **43.** $1\frac{1}{2}$ lb **45.** $\frac{2x}{3}$

**MIXED REVIEW** **47.** 0.6, 0.66, $\frac{2}{3}$ **49.** $x^3$ **51.** $x^{12}$

**CHECKPOINT 1** **1.** 150 **2.** 100 **3.** 5 **4.** 60 **5.** 864 **6.** > **7.** < **8.** < **9.** < **10.** = **11.** 0.51 **12.** $\frac{3}{250}$ **13.** 1.25 **14.** $\frac{1}{3}$ **15.** $0.8\overline{3}$ **16.** $\frac{17}{33}$ **17.** B

### Lesson 5-4 — pages 240–244

**TRY THIS** **6.** $\frac{2}{15}$ **7.** $-\frac{5}{9}$ **8.** $\frac{35}{72}$ **9.** $\frac{3}{32}$ **10.** $\frac{4}{7}$ **11.** $-\frac{3}{10}$ **12.** $\frac{x}{6}$ **13.** $1\frac{1}{2}$ **14.** $\frac{6}{7}$ **15.** $-4\frac{8}{15}$ **16.** $\frac{15}{16}$ **17.** $-\frac{1}{2}$ **18.** $1\frac{1}{2}$ **19.** $1\frac{3}{5}$ **20.** $-1\frac{1}{3}$ **21.** $7\frac{1}{2}$

**CHECK UNDERSTANDING** **1.** $\frac{2}{15}$ **2.** $-\frac{3}{16}$ **3.** $5\frac{1}{28}$ **4.** $3\frac{3}{10}$ **5.** $\frac{7}{10}$ **6.** $5\frac{2}{3}$ **7.** $\frac{2y}{5}$ **8.** $\frac{9x}{2}$ **9.** $1\frac{1}{2}$ **10.** $\frac{5}{6}$ **11.** $-2\frac{1}{4}$ **12.** $-1\frac{1}{21}$ **13.** $16\frac{8}{9}$ **14.** $1\frac{7}{9}$ **15.** −2 **16.** $1\frac{1}{2}$ **17.** 9 oz

**PRACTICE AND PROBLEM SOLVING** **19.** $\frac{1}{2}$ **21.** $\frac{2x}{7}$ **23.** $-8\frac{1}{3}$ **25.** $-\frac{3}{5}$ **27.** $\frac{2a}{15}$ **29.** $\frac{35}{72}$ **31.** $1\frac{1}{2}$ **33.** $\frac{1}{3}$ **35.** $1\frac{1}{3}$ **37.** $1\frac{7}{8}$ **39.** $-1\frac{1}{5}$ **41.** $\frac{32}{75}$ **43.** $1\frac{1}{4}$ **45.** 40 **47.** $1\frac{1}{24}$ **49.** $1\frac{1}{6}$ **51.** 6 days **53.** 5 rest stops **57.** D

**MIXED REVIEW** **59.** $1\frac{23}{35}$ **61.** $\frac{3}{10}$ **63.** $\frac{5}{6}$ **65.** $4\frac{1}{2}$ **67.** $\frac{34}{51}$ **69.** \$20

### Lesson 5-5 — pages 245–249

**TRY THIS** **1.** Yard; it is the largest customary unit of length smaller than the length of a pool. **2.** Pound; it is the largest customary unit of weight smaller than the weight of a baby. **3.** Inch; it is the largest customary unit of length smaller than the length of a pencil. **4.** Fluid ounce; it is the smallest customary unit of capacity. An eyedropper may hold a fraction of a fluid ounce. **5.** $\frac{7}{8}$ **6.** $1\frac{1}{6}$ **7.** 7 **8.** 56 **9.** $10\frac{1}{2}$ **10.** 7

**CHECK UNDERSTANDING** **1.** C **2.** B **3.** F **4.** D **5.** E **6.** A **7.** $\frac{1}{2}$ **8.** $1\frac{1}{2}$ **9.** $\frac{3}{4}$ **10.** 1,000 **11.** 2,640 **12.** 12 **13.** 56 fl oz, or $3\frac{1}{2}$ pt

**PRACTICE AND PROBLEM SOLVING** **15.** weight **17.** weight **19.** volume **21.** Fluid ounce; baby bottles are usually marked in fluid ounces. **23.** Yard; it is the largest customary unit of length less than the length of a sports field. **25.** Pound; it is the largest customary unit of weight less than the weight of a medium-sized fish. **27.** no; 10 pt **29.** no; 2 in. **31.** A **33.** F **35.** B **37.** 146 **39.** $2\frac{1}{3}$ **41.** 26,400 **43.** $\frac{1}{2}$ **45.** 168 **47.** 60 **49.** 25 **51.** 6.5 **53.** 21 **55.** $3\frac{1}{8}$ **57.** 24 **59.** 48 **61.** ft **63.** t **65.** B **67.** A quarter pound is $\frac{1}{4}$ of 16 oz, or 4 oz, and 4 oz < 6 oz. **69.** $8\text{ c} \cdot \frac{1\text{ pt}}{2\text{ c}} = 4$ pt; the student's answer is not reasonable.

**MIXED REVIEW** **71.** $3\frac{5}{11}$ **73.** $1\frac{13}{20}$ **75.** $x + 3y$ **77.** $-3y$

### Math Toolbox — page 250

**1.** 0.005 mg **3.** 0.05 cm **5.** $\frac{1}{2}$ ft **7.** 0.05 L **9.** $\frac{1}{4}$ yd **11.** $\frac{1}{16}$ oz **13.** 0.5 cm, 0.05 cm

### Lesson 5-6 — pages 251–254

**READ** **1.** the time you should leave home **2.** 12:30 P.M. **3.** 10 min **4.** $\frac{3}{4}$ h **5.** 10 min

**SOLVE** **6a.** 1:00 P.M. **b.** 12:30 P.M. **c.** 12:20 P.M. **d.** 11:35 A.M. **e.** 11:25 A.M.

**CHECK UNDERSTANDING** **1.** 8:30 A.M. **2.** 9:00 A.M. **3.** the 12:15 P.M. bus

**PRACTICE AND PROBLEM SOLVING** **5.** 22 stakes **7.** Start with $\frac{2}{3}$ and add $\frac{3}{4}$ repeatedly; $3\frac{2}{3}$, $4\frac{5}{12}$, $5\frac{1}{6}$.





**MIXED REVIEW** **11.** $\frac{2}{5}$ **13.** −8 **15.** $\frac{3}{32}$ **17.** −40 **19.** 1 **21.** −50 **23.** about \$48

### Lesson 5-7 — pages 255–258

**TRY THIS** **1.** $-\frac{1}{3}$ **2.** $\frac{1}{15}$ **3.** $\frac{13}{20}$ **4.** $\frac{4}{5}$ **5.** $1\frac{1}{7}$ **6.** $7\frac{5}{12}$ **7.** $4\frac{13}{18}$

**CHECK UNDERSTANDING** **1.** $\frac{3}{4}$ **2.** $1\frac{1}{9}$ **3.** $1\frac{7}{30}$ **4.** $3\frac{1}{2}$ **5.** $2\frac{3}{4}$ **6.** $-2\frac{7}{8}$ **7.** $60\frac{7}{8}$ in.

**PRACTICE AND PROBLEM SOLVING** **9.** 0 **11.** $5\frac{1}{6}$ **13.** $\frac{1}{5}$ **15.** 5 **17.** $1\frac{5}{24}$ **19.** $5\frac{5}{8}$ **21.** $\frac{1}{8}$ **23.** $\frac{23}{24}$ **25.** $-3\frac{5}{8}$ **27.** $5\frac{5}{8}$ **35.** A **37.** $4\frac{1}{4}$ lb **39.** 10 ft $\frac{1}{4}$ in.

**MIXED REVIEW** **43.** C **45.** pt **47.** yd **49.** −152 **51.** 5

### Lesson 5-8 — pages 259–263

**TRY THIS** **1.** $\frac{5}{56}$ **2.** $\frac{7}{18}$ **3.** $\frac{4}{15}$ **4.** $\frac{15}{4}$, or $3\frac{3}{4}$ **5.** $\frac{32}{27}$, or $1\frac{5}{27}$ **6.** 1 **7.** $-\frac{7}{8}$ **8.** $\frac{13}{15}$ **9.** $-\frac{1}{14}$ **10.** 8 **11.** $-\frac{3}{10}$ **12.** $4\frac{6}{11}$

**CHECK UNDERSTANDING** **1.** $\frac{5}{48}$ **2.** $3\frac{1}{3}$ **3.** $1\frac{1}{4}$ **4.** 4 **5.** $-\frac{4}{27}$ **6.** $\frac{1}{4}$ **7.** $\frac{2}{33}$ **8.** $\frac{7}{15}$ **9.** $\frac{3}{4}s = 9$; 12 sheets

**PRACTICE AND PROBLEM SOLVING** **11.** 6 **13.** $\frac{7}{3}$ **15.** $-\frac{1}{7}$ **17.** $\frac{4}{25}$ **19.** $\frac{5}{63}$ **21.** 4 **23.** $\frac{2}{3}$ **25.** $-7\frac{1}{2}$ **27.** $-1\frac{7}{26}$ **29.** $-\frac{2}{9}$ **31.** $3\frac{5}{17}$ **33.** $2\frac{8}{27}$ **35.** $1\frac{1}{6}$ **37.** $-1\frac{19}{81}$ **39.** Positive; product of positive and positive is positive. **41.** Positive; product of negative (−6) and negative $\left(-\frac{4}{3}\right)$ is positive. **43.** Negative; product of negative $\left(-\frac{3}{5}\right)$ and positive $\left(\frac{-7}{-5}\right)$ is negative. **45.** Zero; product involving 0 is 0. **47.** 81.75 tons **49.** 20 weeks **51.** $1\frac{2}{15}$ mi; 68 mi **53.** 10 min **55.** C

**MIXED REVIEW** **57.** $\frac{1}{8}$ **59.** $3\frac{5}{8}$ **61.** $3r^5$ **63.** $100s^5$ **65.** $x^{13}$

**CHECKPOINT 2** **1.** 14 **2.** $\frac{1}{2}$ **3.** $-\frac{4}{27}$ **4.** $1\frac{1}{3}$ **5.** −2 **6.** 34 **7.** $2\frac{1}{4}$ **8.** 90 **9.** $1\frac{1}{2}$ **10.** $\frac{1}{3}$ **11.** $\frac{1}{5}$ **12.** $1\frac{5}{8}$ **13.** $11\frac{1}{4}$ **14.** $-17\frac{1}{3}$ **15.** $\frac{7}{15}$ **16.** $\frac{6}{35}$ **17.** $-\frac{27}{40}$ **18.** $3\frac{3}{5}$ **19.** \$12

### Standardized Test Prep — page 264

**1.** A **3.** C **5.** B **7.** \$9.29

### Lesson 5-9 — pages 265–268

**TRY THIS** **1.** 216 **2.** $16p^4$ **3.** $x^5y^{10}$ **4.** $25x^6$ **5.** $16y^4$ **6.** $-16y^4$ **7.** $-125a^6b^3$ **8.** $\frac{1}{8}$ **9.** $\frac{16}{81}$ **10.** $\frac{8x^6}{27}$

**CHECK UNDERSTANDING** **1.** 225 **2.** $16a^{10}$ **3.** $8c^6$ **4.** $10{,}000x^{12}$ **5.** $\frac{4}{25}$ **6.** $-\frac{8}{125}$ **7.** $\frac{16}{49y^2}$ **8.** $\frac{81x^8}{10{,}000}$ **9.** 2 **10.** 1 **11.** 4 **12.** 3 **13.** 5 **14.** 3 **15.** $16c^2$ units$^2$

**PRACTICE AND PROBLEM SOLVING** **17.** 100 **19.** $8x^6$ **21.** $-9x^2$ **23.** $25c^6$ **25.** $-x^4y^4$ **27.** $m^8n^4$ **29.** $\frac{9}{49}$ **31.** $-\frac{32}{x^{15}}$ **33.** $-\frac{27a^3}{b^6}$ **35.** $\frac{16c^4}{d^8}$ **37.** $-\frac{1}{32y^{15}}$ **39.** $\frac{1}{81x^8}$ **41.** 4 **43.** −8 **45.** $\frac{1}{64}$ **47.** 216 **49.** 1 **51.** $(3x^2)^2$; $9x^4$ **55.** $\frac{343}{1{,}000}$ units$^3$ **57.** $\frac{343a^3}{8c^3}$ units$^3$

**MIXED REVIEW** **59.** $\frac{56}{243}$ **61.** $-1\frac{21}{22}$ **63.** *E* **65.** *H* **67.** *B*

### Wrap Up — pages 270–272

**1.** 36 **2.** $56\ m^2$ **3.** 105 **4.** $30xy$ **5.** > **6.** < **7.** > **8.** = **9.** 0.6 **10.** $0.1\overline{6}$ **11.** 0.625 **12.** 0.3 **13.** 0.07 **14.** $\frac{1}{4}$ **15.** $\frac{5}{6}$ **16.** $5\frac{3}{5}$ **17.** $2\frac{4}{99}$ **18.** $3\frac{1}{12}$ **19.** $7\frac{2}{15}$ **20.** $\frac{30 + 3x}{5x}$ **21.** $\frac{7}{8}$ **22.** $\frac{7}{12}$ ft, or 7 in. **23.** $\frac{7}{40}$ **24.** $-\frac{4}{5}$ **25.** $1\frac{1}{5}$ **26.** $2\frac{1}{52}$ **27.** $\frac{1}{2}$ **28.** $2\frac{1}{2}$ **29.** $3\frac{3}{8}$ **30.** 60 **31.** 24 **32.** 96 **33.** 5,500 **34.** 1:30 P.M. **35.** 15 buses **37.** $2\frac{3}{8}$ **38.** $1\frac{2}{15}$ **39.** $1\frac{1}{3}$ **40.** $\frac{1}{54}$ **41.** $-\frac{8}{21}$ **42.** $\frac{56}{363}$ **43.** $16d^4$ **44.** 36 **45.** $a^{10}b^5$ **46.** $-\frac{1}{8}$ **47.** $\frac{x^2}{9}$ **48.** $\frac{16a^4}{c^8}$

### Cumulative Review — page 274

**1.** A **3.** A **5.** C **7.** 11 **9.** $\frac{3}{4}$ **11.** $\frac{13}{55}$ **13.** $\frac{13}{36}$ **15.** $16\frac{1}{2}$ **17.** $\frac{1}{2}$ **19.** 7,920 **21.** $\frac{14}{25}$ **23.** $\frac{9}{50}$ **25.** 75 **27.** $\frac{4}{7}$ **29.** $-8\frac{5}{8}$ **31.** $9\frac{3}{4}$ **33.** $\frac{16}{25}$ **35.** $\frac{27x^3}{y^3}$ **37.** $16y^2$



## ▶Chapter 6

### Skills You Need — page 275

**1.** $\frac{1}{4}$ **2.** $\frac{1}{4}$ **3.** $\frac{4}{5}$ **4.** $\frac{3}{8}$ **5.** $\frac{3}{7}$ **6.** $\frac{1}{8}$ **7.** $\frac{5}{6}$ **8.** $\frac{1}{25}$ **9.** 16 **10.** 13.5 **11.** $\frac{7}{8}$ **12.** 2.5 **13.** $1\frac{1}{4}$ **14.** 27.5 **15.** 0.35 **16.** $\frac{3}{50}$ **17.** 3.75 **18.** $\frac{7}{20}$ **19.** $\frac{7}{8}$ **20.** 3.6 **21.** $1\frac{7}{100}$ **22.** $0.\overline{6}$ **23.** $11.\overline{1}$ **24.** $\frac{1}{3}$ **25.** 6.25 **26.** $3\frac{49}{50}$ **27.** 5% **28.** 50% **29.** 0.5% **30.** 0.17% **31.** 1.7% **32.** 17%

### Lesson 6-1 — pages 278–281

**TRY THIS** **1.** $\frac{2}{5}$ **2.** $\frac{3}{2}$ **3.** \$.9/L **4.** 34 mi/gal **5.** 52.5 **6.** 432

**CHECK UNDERSTANDING** **1.** $\frac{1}{3}$ **2.** $\frac{3}{2}$ **3.** $\frac{5}{8}$ **4.** $\frac{1}{9}$ **5.** $\frac{3}{25}$ **6.** $\frac{1}{10}$ **7.** 8 m/s **8.** 63 words/min **9.** $\frac{1}{2}$ **10.** 360 **11.** 15

**PRACTICE AND PROBLEM SOLVING** **13.** $\frac{7}{9}$ **15.** $\frac{7}{9}$ **17.** $\frac{3}{4}$ **19.** $\frac{4}{3}$ **21.** $\frac{3}{5}$ **23.** $\frac{14}{25}$ **25.** 6 gal/min **27.** $4\frac{3}{8}$ mi/h **29.** 5 gal/min **31.** 19.2 **33.** $117.\overline{3}$ **35.** 81 **37a.** class A, $\frac{6}{30}$ or $\frac{1}{5}$; class B, $\frac{4}{24}$ or $\frac{1}{6}$ **b.** class A **39.** 19.3 g/cm$^3$ **41.** 300 : 7, 300 to 7, $\frac{300}{7}$

**MIXED REVIEW** **43.** −1,728 **45.** $-\frac{b^6}{a^3}$ **47.** = **49.** 1,239 mi

### Math Toolbox — pages 282–283

**1.** 6.3 **3.** 161 **5.** 426 **7.** 30.8 **9.** 2.8 **11.** 1.1 **13.** 5.3 **15.** 3 packages

### Lesson 6-2 — pages 284–288

**TRY THIS** **1.** 6 **2.** 44 **3.** 77 **4.** yes **5.** no **6.** yes **7.** 87 nautical miles

**CHECK UNDERSTANDING** **1.** 16 **2.** 15 **3.** 6 **4.** no **5.** yes **6.** yes **7.** $\frac{14}{c} = \frac{4}{50}$; 175 calories **8.** $\frac{12}{16} = \frac{h}{60}$; 45 heartbeats **9.** Yes; multiply each side by $\frac{b}{c}$.

**PRACTICE AND PROBLEM SOLVING** **11.** 5 **13.** 8 **15.** 45 **17.** 5 **19.** 28 **21.** 14 **23.** 6.7 **25.** 76.5 **27.** 30.3 **29.** 1.5 **31.** 20 **33.** 3 **35.** 20 **37.** 38 **39.** no **41.** yes **43.** no **45.** no **47.** $\frac{20}{27.50} = \frac{12}{x}$; \$16.50 **49.** $\frac{25}{2.5} = \frac{100}{x}$; 10 s **51.** $\frac{4}{1.85} = \frac{16}{t}$; \$7.40 **53.** 12 tea bags **55.** \$36.67 **57.** 12.6 cm **59.** 156 francs **63.** 15 s **65.** 30 more times

**MIXED REVIEW** **67.** $\frac{1}{100}$ **69.** $\frac{25}{14}$ **71.** false **73.** \$67.97

### Lesson 6-3 — pages 289–293

**TRY THIS** **1.** 15.75 **2.**

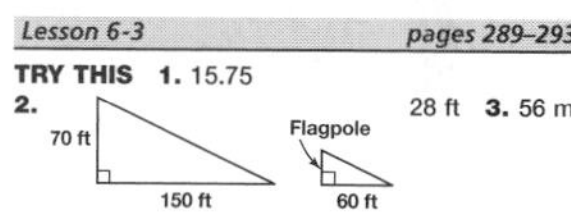


28 ft **3.** 56 mi

**CHECK UNDERSTANDING** **1.** $2\frac{2}{5}$ **2.** $2\frac{1}{2}$ **3.** 2 in.; 4.5 in.

**PRACTICE AND PROBLEM SOLVING** **5.** 5 in. **7.** 5.7 **9.** 45 km **11.** 7.5 km **13.** 2 in. **15.** $1\frac{3}{4}$ in. **17.** 51 cm **21.** 8 in. **23.** N model; HO model **25.** 4.5 in. **27.** N scale **29.** 1 in. : 10 ft **31.** 2.5 ft **33.** Yes; the narrow section in the drawing is $\frac{3}{4}$ in. by $\frac{3}{4}$ in., representing a space 7.5 ft by 7.5 ft.

**MIXED REVIEW** **35.** 2 **37.** $2\frac{2}{5}$ **39.** 9, 9.5, 10 **41.** 0.375 **43.** 0.4375 **45.** 22 mi/gal

### Math Toolbox — page 294

**1b.** No; the dilation could lie outside or it could overlap the original triangle. **c.** $\triangle PQR$ lies inside $\triangle XYZ$. **3.** $\triangle XYZ$ lies inside $\triangle PQR$.

### Lesson 6-4 — pages 295–299

**TRY THIS** **5.** $\frac{1}{2}$ **6.** $\frac{1}{6}$ **7.** $\frac{1}{3}$ **8.** $\frac{5}{6}$ **9.** a certain event **10.** 1 to 4; 4 to 1 **11a.** 2 to 3 **b.** 3 to 2

**CHECK UNDERSTANDING** **1.** $\frac{3}{8}$ **2.** $\frac{5}{8}$ **3.** 0 **4.** $\frac{3}{5}$

**PRACTICE AND PROBLEM SOLVING** **7.** $\frac{1}{3}$ **9.** 0 **11.** $\frac{2}{3}$ **13.** $\frac{1}{3}$ **15.** $\frac{2}{11}$ **17.** 0 **19.** $\frac{3}{2}$ **21.** $\frac{3}{2}$ **23.** $\frac{0}{25}$ **25.** 5 to 4 **27.** 5 to 1 **29.** 25 to 11 **31.** $\frac{3}{14}$ **33a.** 1 to 9 **b.** 9 to 1

**MIXED REVIEW** **37.** $6\frac{2}{3}$ mi **39.** 70 mi **41.** $\frac{2}{3}$ **43.** $5\frac{3}{20}$

**CHECKPOINT 1** **1.** 4 mi/h **2.** 6 gal/min **3.** 48 ft/s **4.** 4.5 **5.** 42 times **6.** D

### Lesson 6-5 pages 300–304

**TRY THIS** **1.** $\frac{29}{50}$ **2.** $\frac{18}{25}$ **3.** $1\frac{11}{25}$ **4.** 0.16 **5.** 0.625 **6.** 1.2 **7.** 0.45, $\frac{9}{20}$ **8.** 40% **9.** 2.3% **10.** 175% **11.** 27%

**CHECK UNDERSTANDING** **1.** $\frac{2}{5}$, 0.4 **2.** $\frac{7}{25}$, 0.28 **3.** $\frac{39}{100}$, 0.39 **4.** $\frac{11}{20}$, 0.55 **5.** 168% **6.** 36% **7.** 70% **8.** 0.2% **9.** 23% **10.** 25% **11.** 55% **12.** $16.\overline{6}$%

**PRACTICE AND PROBLEM SOLVING** **15.** $\frac{3}{50}$ **17.** $\frac{49}{50}$ **19.** $\frac{9}{25}$ **21.** $\frac{1}{250}$ **23.** 0.1925 **25.** 0.063 **27.** 0.797 **29.** 0.045 **31.** 85% **33.** 0.75% **35.** 259% **37.** 52% **39.** 22.2% **41.** 111% **45.** 16.7% **47.** 33.3% **49.** 0.8, 80% **51.** $\frac{1}{2}$, 50% **53.** $\frac{67}{100}$, 0.67 **55.** < **57.** < **59.** < **61.** $\frac{1}{10{,}000}$ **67.** 12.5 **69.** Yes; $\frac{32}{45} \approx 71\%$. **71a.** $\frac{3}{5}$, 60% **b.** $\frac{7}{40}$, 17.5% **c.** $\frac{9}{40}$, 22.5%

**MIXED REVIEW** **73.** $\frac{1}{4}$ **75.** $\frac{1}{8}$ **77.** 47 **79.** 1,320 **81.** 93

### Lesson 6-6 pages 305–309

**TRY THIS**

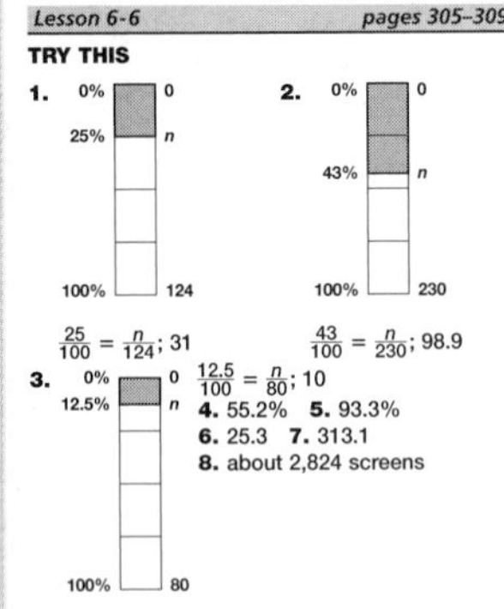

**1.** $\frac{25}{100} = \frac{n}{124}$; 31 **2.** $\frac{43}{100} = \frac{n}{230}$; 98.9 **3.** $\frac{12.5}{100} = \frac{n}{80}$; 10 **4.** 55.2% **5.** 93.3% **6.** 25.3 **7.** 313.1 **8.** about 2,824 screens

**CHECK UNDERSTANDING** **1.** 16 **2.** 150 **3.** 75% **4.** 200% **5.** 24 **6.** 37.1 **7.** 32 **8.** 80 **9.** 20

**PRACTICE AND PROBLEM SOLVING** **11.** $\frac{n}{100} = \frac{16}{20}$; 80 **13.** $\frac{75}{100} = \frac{420}{n}$; 560 **15.** $\frac{18}{100} = \frac{n}{150}$; 27 **17.** $\frac{60}{100} = \frac{n}{15}$; 9 **19.** $\frac{92}{100} = \frac{n}{625}$; 575 **21.** $\frac{n}{100} = \frac{17}{92}$; 18.5% **23.** $\frac{98}{100} = \frac{n}{6.1}$; 6.0 **25.** $\frac{35}{100} = \frac{14}{n}$; 40 **27.** $\frac{35}{100} = \frac{52.5}{n}$; 150 **29.** $\frac{2.5}{100} = \frac{912.5}{n}$; 36,500 **31.** $\frac{116}{100} = \frac{125}{a}$; 107.8 **33.** 21% **35.** Avocados; $\frac{1}{3} = 33.\overline{3}\%$ **37.** A **39.** 50 members

**MIXED REVIEW** **43.** 52.3% **45.** 456% **47.** $2.4 \times 10^3$, $2.03 \times 10^4$, $2.3 \times 10^4$, $2.03 \times 10^5$

### Lesson 6-7 pages 310–313

**TRY THIS** **1.** $n = 0.455 \cdot 20$; 9.1 **2.** $380 = 1.25n$; 304 **3.** $.85 **4.** 1,344 people

**CHECK UNDERSTANDING** **1.** $n = 0.3 \cdot 30$; 9 **2.** $25 = n \cdot 40$; 62.5% **3.** $120 = 0.15n$; 800 **4.** $n = 1.5 \cdot 90$; 135 **5.** 4%

**PRACTICE AND PROBLEM SOLVING** **7.** $n \cdot 20 = 11$; 55% **9.** $1.35t = 63$; 46.7 **11.** $n = 5 \cdot 12$; 60 **13.** $n \cdot 4 = 9$; 225% **15.** $n \cdot 150 = 96$; 64% **17.** $n = 0.15 \cdot 150$; 22.5 **19.** $n = 2.25 \cdot 3.6$; 8.1 **21.** 50% **23.** 100 **25.** 20% **27.** 1.8 **29.** 300 **31.** about $.50 **33.** about $3 **35.** 92% **37a.** 76.9 million households **b.** 66.8 million households **39a.** False; 18 is not less than 10% of 63, or 6.3. **b.** True; 18 is more than 1,000% of 1, or 10. **41.** $0.588x$

**MIXED REVIEW** **43.** $\frac{35}{100} = \frac{21}{60}$; 21 **45.** 1,000,000 **47.** $x^{21}$

### Lesson 6-8 pages 314–317

**TRY THIS** **5.** 14% **6.** 60% **7.** 112.5% **8.** 9% **9.** 50% **10.** 5% **11.** 92.9% **12.** 9%

**CHECK UNDERSTANDING** **1.** 30% increase **2.** 220% increase **3.** 25% increase **4.** 20% decrease **5.** 18.75% decrease **6.** 62.5% decrease **7.** Eva should compare 8 − 7 to 7, not 8.

**PRACTICE AND PROBLEM SOLVING** **9.** 18.8% increase **11.** 133.3% increase **13.** 166.7% increase **15.** 62.5% decrease **17.** 55% decrease **19.** 70% decrease **21.** 12.5% increase **23.** 24.1% increase **25.** 83.1% decrease **27.** 44.4% decrease **29.** 64% **31.** 13% **33a.** Growtown, 30% increase; Slowtown, 20% decrease **b.** 3 years



**MIXED REVIEW** **35.** 75 **37.** 1 **39.** $-1\frac{5}{6}$ **41.** 94%

### Lesson 6-9 pages 318–321

**TRY THIS** **1.** $42 **2.** $8.50

**CHECK UNDERSTANDING** **1.** $1.05 **2.** $22.04 **3.** $55.50 **4.** $27 **5.** $4.90 **6.** $210

**PRACTICE AND PROBLEM SOLVING** **7.** $10.50 **9.** $299.98 **11.** $12.74 **13.** $8.55 **15a.** $9.80 **b.** $39.20 **17a.** $y - x$ **b.** $\frac{y-x}{x}(100)$ **19.** store B; $.11 **21.** The sweater at the first store; its sale price ($17.50) is less (by $.50).

**MIXED REVIEW** **23.** 66.7%

**CHECKPOINT 2** **1.** = **2.** < **3.** > **4.** $0.33 \cdot 120 = n$; 39.6 **5.** $1.25 \cdot 42 = n$; 52.5 **6.** $n \cdot 5.6 = 1.4$; 25% **7.** $0.15q = 9.75$; 65 **8.** $n \cdot 500 = 1{,}375$; 275% **9.** $0.8w = 120$; 150 **10.** $9,600

### Standardized Test Prep page 322

**1.** B **3.** D **5.** A **7.** A **9.** Chan's; 70% of 20 = 14, which is greater than 80% of 15 = 12. **11.** $21.60 **13.** $815.50 **15.** 19%

### Lesson 6-10 pages 323–326

**READ** **1.** the population at the beginning of 2010 **2.** the population in 2000 and the growth rate

**PLAN** **5.** No; each year the increase is the same percent of an increasing amount.

**SOLVE**

**6–7.**

| | | |
|---|---|---|
| | 2.5 | 292.6 |
| 292.6 | 2.5 | 295.1 |
| 295.1 | 2.5 | 297.6 |
| 297.6 | | |

**9.** 297.6 million

**LOOK BACK** **11.** about 299 million

**CHECK UNDERSTANDING** **1.** 64 microbes **2.** 6 orders **3.** 7 ways

**PRACTICE AND PROBLEM SOLVING** **5.** 16 outfits **7.** 1 adult, 5 children; 3 adults, 2 children **9.** 14 cm, 7 cm **11.** 8 qt **13.** 15%

**MIXED REVIEW** **15.** $3.30 **17.** $127.96 **19.** $\frac{2}{13}$ **21.** $\frac{1}{2}$

### Wrap Up pages 328–330

**1.** $\frac{3}{8}$ **2.** $\frac{4}{7}$ **3.** $\frac{3}{4}$ **4.** $\frac{10}{13}$ **5.** 50 mi/h **6.** 90 words/min **7.** $1.89/lb **8.** 35 **9.** 0.7 **10.** 49 **11.** 126 **12.** 45 **13.** 35 **14.** 0.5 cm **15.** $\frac{1}{8}$; 1 to 7 **16.** $\frac{1}{4}$; 1 to 3 **17.** $\frac{3}{8}$; 3 to 5 **18.** $\frac{6}{25}$; 0.24 **19.** $\frac{18}{25}$; 0.72 **20.** $\frac{2}{25}$; 0.08 **21.** $\frac{1}{200}$; 0.005 **22.** 30% **23.** 33% **24.** 33.3% **25.** 35% **26.** 88.9% **27.** 2.1% **28.** 240% **29.** 0.6% **30.** $\frac{15}{100} = \frac{n}{48}$; 7.2 **31.** $\frac{20}{100} = \frac{30}{x}$; 150 **32.** $\frac{n}{100} = \frac{90}{300}$; 30 **33.** $\frac{125}{100} = \frac{100}{y}$; 80 **34.** $0.35a = 70$; 200 **35.** $n = 0.68 \cdot 300$; 204 **36.** $n \cdot 180 = 9$; 5% **37.** $n \cdot 56 = 3.5$; 6.25% **38.** 25% decrease **39.** 75% decrease **40.** 20% increase **41.** 75% decrease **42.** $8.75 **43.** $1.70/lb **44.** 30 mi

**CUMULATIVE REVIEW** **1.** C **3.** B **5.** C **7.** A **9.** C **11.** C **13.** $31.90 **15.** 84% **17.** 60% **19.** 262% **21.** $\frac{1}{3}$ **23.** 27.5 mi **25.** 48.75 mi **27.** 5 **29.** 20 **31.** $\frac{1}{12}$ **33.** $\frac{3}{2}$

## ▶ CHAPTER 7

### Skills You Need page 333

**1.** 11 **2.** −21 **3.** −98 **4.** 5 **5.** 8 **6.** 9.0 **7.** −32 **8.** −8 **9.** −12 **10.** $4n$ **11.** $-3b + 10$ **12.** $8x$ **13.** $19c + 13$ **14.** $-7x - 5y$ **15.** $2a + 6$ **16.** $-36b + 54$ **17.** $9m - 35$ **18.** $2x - 3y$ **19.** $p + 3$ **20.** $q - 6$ **21.** $12y$ **22.** $10d$ **23.** $2b$ **24.** $n - 8$

**25.** $c \geq 1$

**26.** $y < 2$

**27.** $a < 10$

**28.** $b < 4$

**29.** $x > 0$

**30.** $x \geq -6$

**31.** $m < -17$

Selected Answers



**32.** $x \leq 15$

**33.** $b \leq 19$

**34.** $a > -3$

**35.** $m \geq 80$

**36.** $y \geq -1$

### Lesson 7-1 pages 336–339

**TRY THIS** **1.** 3; subtract 3, divide by 15. **2.** 16; add 10, multiply by 4. **3.** −1; subtract 11, divide by 9. **4.** −2 **5.** 21 **6.** −3 **7.** $16

**CHECK UNDERSTANDING** **1.** Subtract 9 from each side. **2.** Add 4 to each side. **3.** Subtract −3 from each side. **4.** 72 **5.** −3 **6.** 15 **7.** $\frac{1}{2}$ **8.** −1 **9.** −3 **10.** 45 muffins

**PRACTICE AND PROBLEM SOLVING** **11.** 6 **13.** −9 **15.** −16 **17.** 20 **19.** −6 **21.** −1 **23.** −75 **25.** 98 **27.** −60 **29.** 18 **31.** $20 **33.** $8 **35a.** 34 pickles **b.** 5 pickles

**MIXED REVIEW** **39.** 50% **41.** 80% **43.** $10a + 3b$ **45.** 3 to 4

### Lesson 7-2 pages 340–344

**TRY THIS** **3.** 92 points **4.** 88, 89, 90, 91 **5.** 32, 34 **6.** $\frac{14}{3}$ **7.** −14

**CHECK UNDERSTANDING** **1.** $12a$ **2.** $3b + 11$ **3.** $-2x + 14$ **4.** −6 **5.** 6 **6.** −3 **7.** 14 **8.** $-\frac{1}{2}$ **9.** −2 **10.** D

**PRACTICE AND PROBLEM SOLVING** **11.** 5 **13.** −5 **15.** −2 **17.** $-\frac{5}{2}$ **19.** 18 **21.** $\frac{17}{8}$ **23.** $\frac{1}{4}$ **25.** 8 **27.** 16, 17 **29.** 22 ft **31.** 7, 16 **33.** 8, 9, and 10 birdhouses **35.** 3

**MIXED REVIEW** **37.** −5 **39.** $\frac{6}{7}$ **41.** 18.6 **43.** $1\frac{5}{6}$ c

### Lesson 7-3 pages 345–349

**TRY THIS** **1.** 50 **2.** $\frac{21}{2}$, or $10\frac{1}{2}$ **3.** −38 **4.** $-\frac{5}{2}$, or $-2\frac{1}{2}$ **5.** $\frac{1}{3}$ **6.** $\frac{11}{2}$, or $5\frac{1}{2}$

**CHECK UNDERSTANDING** **1.** Subtract 3 from each side. **2.** Add 1.5 to each side. **3.** Combine like terms. **4.** 12 **5.** $14\frac{6}{7}$ **6.** 12 **7.** 9 **8.** 5.5 **9.** 6.5 **10.** 99°F

**PRACTICE AND PROBLEM SOLVING** **11.** 8 **13.** 100 **15.** $\frac{5}{2}$ **17.** $\frac{35}{81}$ **19.** $\frac{1}{2}$ **21.** $\frac{2}{5}$ **23.** −7 **25.** 36 **27.** $3.\overline{3}$ or $3\frac{1}{3}$ **29.** 1.2 **31.** $\frac{2}{11}$ **33.** $387.30 **35.** 6 pencils

**MIXED REVIEW** **39.** −7 **41.** 0 **43.** $(-7)^2$ **45.** $18a^2$

### Lesson 7-4 pages 350–353

**READ** **1.** to find how many miles Ms. Smith drove **2.** 2 days **3.** $29.95 per day **4.** $.12/mi

**LOOK BACK** **5a.** 9
100, 12, low **b.** 137 miles

**CHECK UNDERSTANDING** **1.** $60 **2.** 16 lessons **3.** 20 cm, 12 cm

**PRACTICE AND PROBLEM SOLVING** **5.** 8 of each coin **7.** 28 posts **9a.** 48 person-hours **b.** 4 h **11.** Jackson, 24 seashells, Petra and Tyrone, 35 seashells apiece

**MIXED REVIEW** **13.** 60 **15.** $\frac{13}{25}$, 0.52 **17.** $\frac{1}{200}$, 0.005 **19.** $1.80

**CHECKPOINT 1** **1.** 20 **2.** 11 **3.** −18 **4.** 4 **5.** 28 **6.** −42 **7.** 2 **8.** 1.3 **9.** −6 **10.** 0 **11.** 1 **12.** 6 **13.** $84 **14.** 43, 44, 45

### Standardized Test Prep page 354

**1.** A **3.** B **5.** C **7.** A **9.** 35 **11.** 27,300 meals

### Lesson 7-5 pages 355–359

**TRY THIS** **3.** 16 **4.** 2 **5.** 6 h

**CHECK UNDERSTANDING**
**1.** $a$; $-3a$; $-3a$; $-3a$; $\frac{-3a}{-3}$; 5 **2.** 16; $x$, $x$; $3x$; 16, 16; $3x$; $3x$; −7 **3.** −4 **4.** −1 **5.** −8 **6.** $2\frac{1}{4}$ h

**PRACTICE AND PROBLEM SOLVING** **7.** 4 **9.** −2 **11.** 6 **13.** 3 **15.** −3 **17.** 3 **19.** −8 **21.** $\frac{1}{3}$ **23.** 4 **27.** 11 **29.** $1\frac{2}{3}$ h **31.** 84 years **33b.** $\frac{80}{13}$ **35.** The student subtracted $4x$ from the left side of the equation instead of adding $4x$. The correct solution is $-\frac{2}{3}$.

**MIXED REVIEW**

**37.** $a \leq 27$



**39.** $y \leq -6$

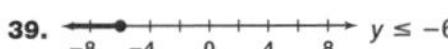

**41.** $28.16 **43.** $82.50

### Lesson 7-6 pages 360–363

**TRY THIS** **1.** $a > 4$

**2.** $x \leq -2$

**3.** $c < -6$

**4.** $m \geq -15$ **5.** $x < 3$ **6.** $b < -22$ **7.** at least $7,500

**CHECK UNDERSTANDING** **1.** Add 2 to each side, simplify, divide each side by 4, and simplify. **2.** Add 1 to each side, simplify, multiply each side by 2, and simplify. **3.** Subtract 2 from each side, simplify, divide each side by −3, reverse the inequality sign, and simplify. **4.** $x > -6$ **5.** $a < -4$ **6.** $b \geq 7$ **7.** $y \leq 2$ **8.** $\frac{x}{-3} - 1 \leq 5$; $x \geq -18$

**PRACTICE AND PROBLEM SOLVING**

**9.** $m > -4$

**11.** $c \leq -2$

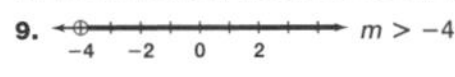

**13.** $a > 9$

**15.** $b < 2$

**17.** $x \leq -2$ **19.** $p > 3$ **21.** $b < 20$ **23.** $m > -7$ **25.** $x > -36$ **27.** $a \geq -2$ **29.** The student simplified $\frac{-36}{-12}$ to −3 instead of 3. **31.** Letter excerpt: First undo addition and subtraction, and then undo division and multiplication. Remember to reverse the inequality sign when multiplying or dividing by a negative number. **33.** 5 mi **35.** at most 9 months

**MIXED REVIEW** **37.** 3 **39.** 146.25 mi **41.** 48 cm/h

### Math Toolbox page 364

**1.**

**3.**

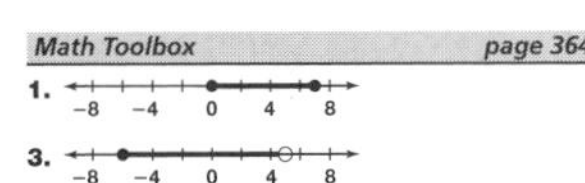

**5.**

**7.**

**9.**

### Lesson 7-7 pages 365–368

**TRY THIS** **1.** $s = p + c$ **2.** $k = hj$ **3.** $p = \frac{I}{rt}$ **4.** $a = \frac{b-7}{5}$ **5.** $w = \frac{P - 2\ell}{2}$ **6.** $x = 3(y - 8)$ **7.** $r = \frac{d}{t}$ **8.** $h = an$; 11 hits

**CHECK UNDERSTANDING** **1.** 3; 3; 6; 6; $c$; **2.** $j$; $h$; $g$; $j$ **3.** A **4.** C **5.** B

**PRACTICE AND PROBLEM SOLVING** **7.** $s = \frac{P}{4}$ **9.** $a = 2m - b$ **11.** $b = \frac{2A}{h}$ **13.** $k = \frac{T - 2h}{3}$ **15a.** $d = \frac{C}{\pi}$ **b.** 5 in. **17a.** $H = \frac{N}{7L}$ **b.** 9 ft

**MIXED REVIEW** **19.** $x > 2$ **21.** $b > 24$ **23.** 75% **25.** 31.3

**CHECKPOINT 2** **1.** −2 **2.** −6 **3.** $\frac{2}{9}$ **4.** 4 **5.** 3 **6.** 5 **7.** $y > -\frac{9}{10}$ **8.** $x > -56$ **9.** $x > 5$ **10.** $h = s - g$ **11.** $r = \frac{k-4}{3}$ **12.** $t = \frac{I}{pr}$ **13.** $h = 0.375M$ **14.** D

### Lesson 7-8 pages 369–373

**TRY THIS** **1.** $30 **2.** $4.38

**3.**

| Bal. at Yr Start | Interest | Bal. at Yr End |
|---|---|---|
| $500.00 | $15.00 | $515.00 |
| $515.00 | $15.45 | $530.45 |

**4.**

| Bal. at Yr Start | Interest | Bal. at Yr End |
|---|---|---|
| $625.00 | $12.50 | $637.50 |
| $637.50 | $12.75 | $650.25 |
| $650.25 | $13.01 | $663.26 |
| $663.26 | $13.27 | $676.53 |

**5.** $955.09 **6.** $955.37

**CHECK UNDERSTANDING** **1.** $28 **2.** $39.15 **3.** $577.37 **4.** $1,846.91 **5.** $2,207.63 **6.** $20,905.49 **7.** $900

**PRACTICE AND PROBLEM SOLVING** **9.** $.88

**11.**

| | | |
|---|---|---|
| | $120.00 | $3,120.00 |
| $3,120.00 | $124.80 | $3,244.80 |
| $3,244.80 | $129.79 | $3,374.59 |

**13.** $5,066.88 **15.** $71,250.06 **17a.** $1,181.96 **b.** $381.96 **21a.** $1,400 and $1,469.33 **b.** 9 **c.** about 11.1%

**MIXED REVIEW** **23.** $m = \frac{E}{c^2}$ **25.** $k = \frac{8}{5}(d - 1)$

Selected Answers

### Math Toolbox — page 374

**1a.** 13 **b.** $27.41 **c.** $57.42 **3a.** $109.96 **b.** $88.51 **c.** If you increase the monthly payments, the interest charges will be less.

### Wrap Up — pages 376–378

**1.** −4 **2.** 2 **3.** 48 **4.** 3 **5.** 21 **6.** $\frac{5}{3}$ **7.** $\frac{4}{5}$ **8.** −2 **9.** $-6\frac{3}{8}$ **10.** 39 **11.** −9 **12.** 8 **13.** −18, −17, −16, −15 **14.** $34.99 **15.** 34 tens, 34 twenties **16.** $1,211.11 **17.** 3 **18.** −4 **19.** $\frac{6}{5}$ **20.** 4 **21.** −7 **22.** $\frac{2}{3}$ **23.** 2 h

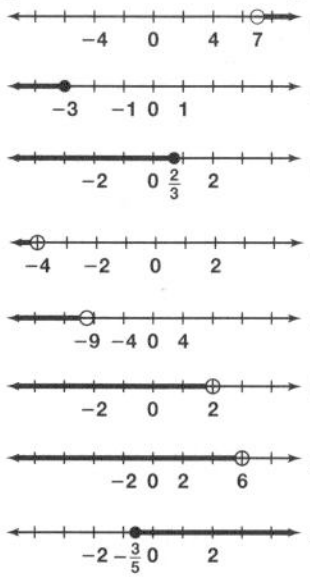

**24.** $a > 7$
**25.** $y \le -3$
**26.** $c \le \frac{2}{3}$
**27.** $x < -4$
**28.** $x < -9$
**29.** $b < 2$
**30.** $x < 6$
**31.** $x \ge -\frac{3}{5}$

**32.** 64 megabytes **33.** $m = \frac{r}{6k}$ **34.** $y = \frac{4}{3}x$ **35.** $g = \frac{Q}{p}$ **36.** $b = a + 2c$ **37.** $a = \frac{w - 5n}{3}$ **38.** $h = 6(e - 11)$ **39.** $27 **40.** $252.50 **41.** $97.50 **42.** $11,239.42 **43.** $44,890.37 **44.** $35,303.54 **45.** $80,016.89

### Cumulative Review — page 380

**1.** A **3.** C **5.** C **7.** D **9.** B **11.** D **13.** $320 **15.** 5 **17.** $-\frac{3}{2}$ **19.** $-\frac{23}{2}$ **21.** −2

## ▶Chapter 8

### Skills You Need — page 381

**1.** $y = -4x + 3$ **2.** $y = -2x + 4$ **3.** $y = 2x - 6$ **4.** $y = -6x - 8$ **5.** $y = -x + 12$ **6.** $y = -\frac{1}{2}x + \frac{5}{2}$

**7.** $y = \frac{1}{5}x + 4$ **8.** $y = -\frac{3}{4}x + 3$ **9.** (5, 2) **10.** (−3, 4) **11.** (4, 0) **12.** (6, −3) **13.** (−4, −3) **14.** (0, 3)

**15–20.**

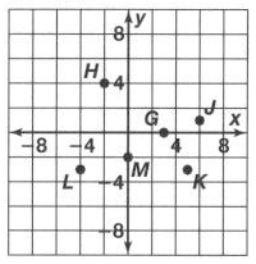


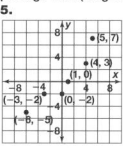

**21.** 2 **22.** $1\frac{1}{2}$ **23.** 1 **24.** −2 **25.** $-\frac{1}{18}$ **26.** 3 **27.** 1 **28.** $\frac{1}{3}$ **29.** −11, −13 **30.** 27, 32 **31.** −4, −7 **32.** 19, 13 **33.** 10.5, 12 **34.** 83, 97

### Math Toolbox — pages 384–385

**3a.** $2 **b.** $6 **c.** 6h

### Lesson 8-1 — pages 386–390

**TRY THIS 1.** No; there are two range values for the domain value 2. **2.** Yes; there is one range value for each domain value. **3.** No; a specific postage cost (domain value) can mail packages of different weights (range values). **4.** Yes; for each package weight (domain value) there is one postage cost (range value) to each zip code.

**5.**

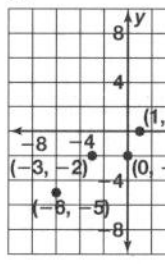


a function

**6.**

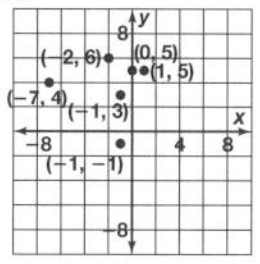


not a function

**7.**

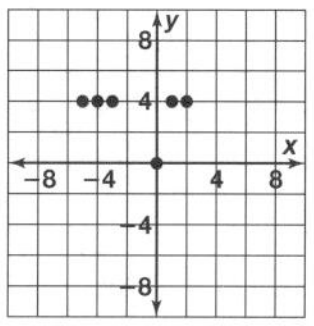

a function

**CHECK UNDERSTANDING 1.** $-\frac{1}{2}$, 0, 2, 3; $\frac{4}{5}$, 1, 2, 5 **2.** −2, −1, 0; 2, 3 **3.** No; there are three range values for the domain value 3. **4.** Yes; there is one range value for each domain value. **5.** Yes; there is one range value for each domain value.



**6.** No; there are, for example, two range values for the domain value −4. **7.** Yes; no vertical line passes through two graphed points (vertical-line test). **8.** Yes; no vertical line passes through two points (vertical-line test). **9.** no **10.** yes **11.** yes

**PRACTICE AND PROBLEM SOLVING 13.** Yes; there is one range value for each domain value. **15.** Yes; there is one range value for each domain value. **17.** Yes; no vertical line passes through two graphed points (vertical-line test). **19.** Yes; no vertical line passes through two graphed points (vertical-line test).

**21.**

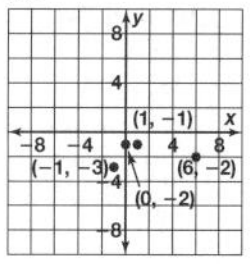


A function; no vertical line passes through two graphed points.

**23.**

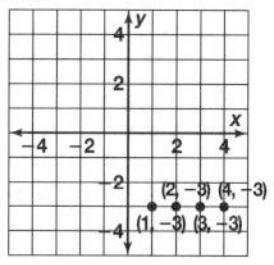


A function; no vertical line passes through two graphed points.

**25.** Each range value is the absolute value of its domain value. **27.** Each range value is the square of its domain value. **29.** Yes; a specific number of students (domain value) requires a particular number of buses (range value). **31.** For each side length, there is one and only one area of the square. **33.** A function can have the same *y*-coordinate with different *x*-coordinates.

**MIXED REVIEW 35.** 3 **37.** 3

### Lesson 8-2 — pages 391–395

**TRY THIS 1.** (−3, −5) **2.** (−3, 15) **3.** (−3, −4) **4.** 14°C

**5.**

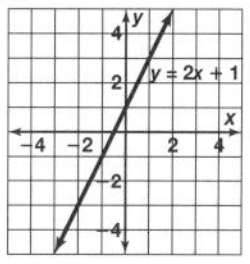


**6.**

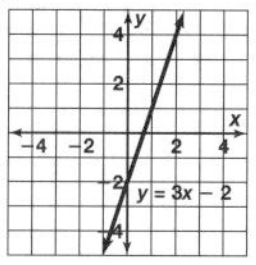


**7.**

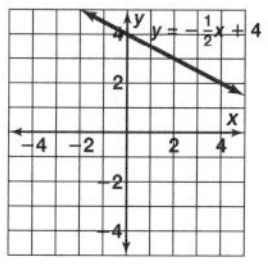


**8.**

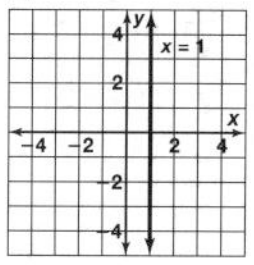


no

**9.**

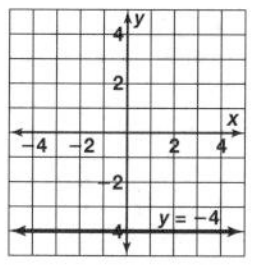


yes

**10.**

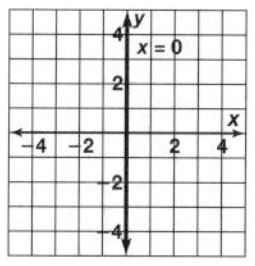


no

**11.** $y = -2x + 3$

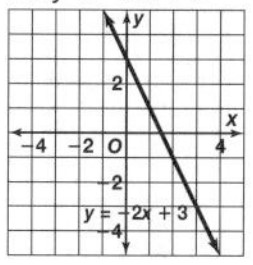


**12.** $y = x + 5$

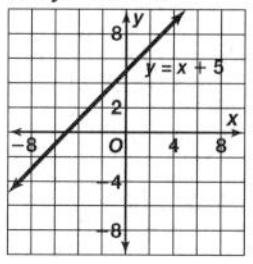


**13.** $y = \frac{3}{2}x + 3$

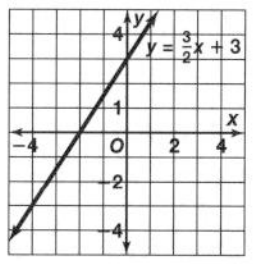


**CHECK UNDERSTANDING 1.** yes **2.** no **3.** no **4.** no **5.** yes **6.** $y = 4x + 16$ **7.** $y = -x + 3$ **8.** $y = \frac{1}{2}x - 3$



**9.**

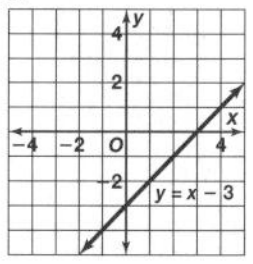


**10.**

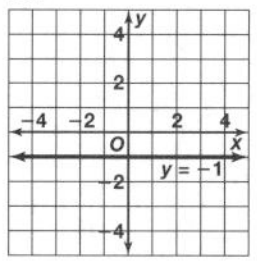


**11.**

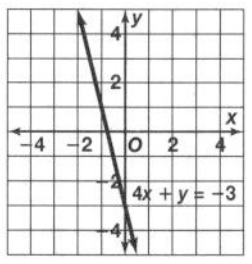


**PRACTICE AND PROBLEM SOLVING**
**13.** (−2, 4), (1, −2), (4, −8) **15.** (−2, 13), (1, 4), (4, −5) **17.** (−2, 34), (1, 31), (4, 28)
**19.** $\left(-2, -7\frac{1}{5}\right)$, $\left(1, -5\frac{2}{5}\right)$, $\left(4, -3\frac{3}{5}\right)$

**21.**

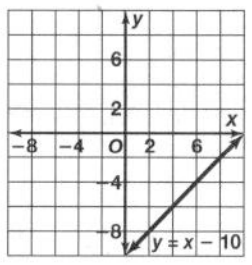


**23.**

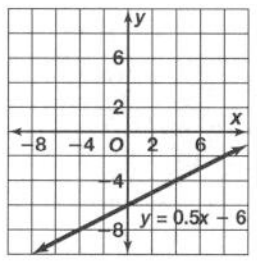


**25.**

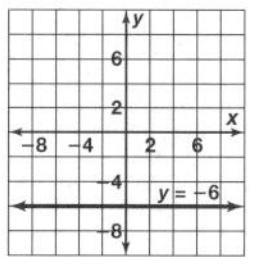


**27.**

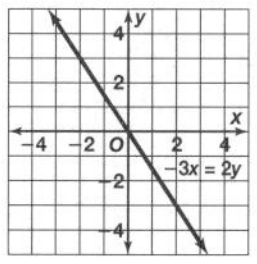


**29.**

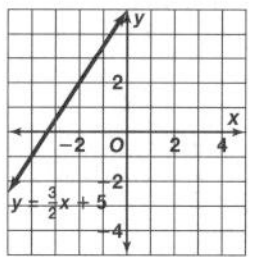


**31.**

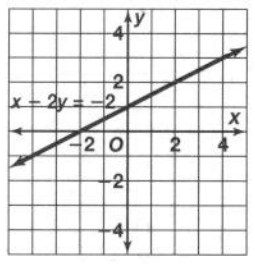


**33a.**

| *x* | (*x*, *y*) |
|---|---|
| 1 | (1, 1) |
| 2 | (2, 4) |
| 3 | (3, 7) |
| 4 | (4, 10) |
| 5 | (5, 13) |

**b.** Begin with 1 and add 3 repeatedly. **37a.** (0, 30) and (40, 0); You burn 360 cal by swimming only the butterfly stroke for 30 min and only the backstroke for 40 min.

**b.**

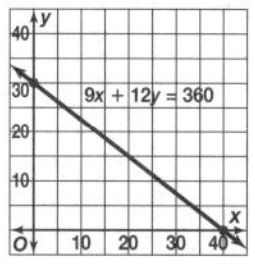


**c.** (0, 30) is the point at which the graph and the *y*-axis intercept each other. (40, 0) is the point at which the graph and the *x*-axis intercept each other.
**d.** about 27 min

**MIXED REVIEW 39.** Yes; there is one range value for each domain value. **41.** 62% **43.** 120% **45.** 85% **47.** about $4.86 \times 10^5$ mi; about $8.16 \times 10^7$ mi

### Math Toolbox — page 396

**1.** $y = \frac{3}{4}x$ **3.** $y = -\frac{3}{4}x$ **5.** $y = 0.945x$ (*y* is the number of liters and *x* is the number of quarts) or $y = 1.058x$ (*y* is the number of quarts and *x* is the number of liters); 7.56 L

### Lesson 8-3 — pages 397–402

**TRY THIS 2.** $-\frac{5}{4}$ **3.** no slope **4.** 0 **5.** $\frac{3}{4}$ **6.** −1

**7.**

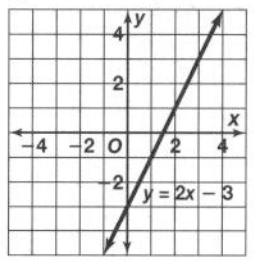


**8.**

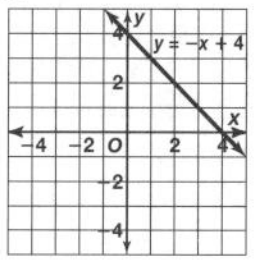




**CHECK UNDERSTANDING 1.** $\frac{3}{4}$ **2.** −1 **3.** no slope **4.** $-\frac{5}{6}$ **5.** 0 **6.** $-\frac{2}{3}$ **7.** 7, 3 **8.** −1, 4 **9.** $\frac{1}{2}$, −8

**PRACTICE AND PROBLEM SOLVING 11.** 0 **13.** $-\frac{1}{3}$ **15.** $-\frac{3}{5}$ **17.** no slope **19.** −1 **21.** $-\frac{5}{2}$ **23.** 5, −3 **25.** $-\frac{2}{3}$, 1 **27.** $-\frac{2}{5}$, −2 **29.** 0, −3

**31.**

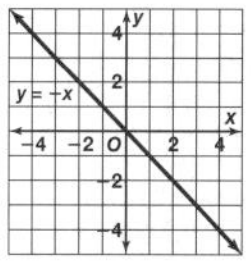


**33.**

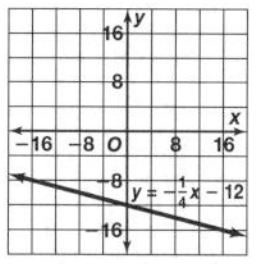


**35.**

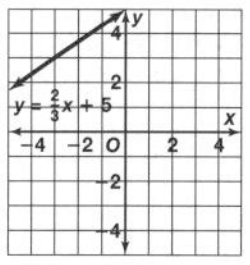


**37.**

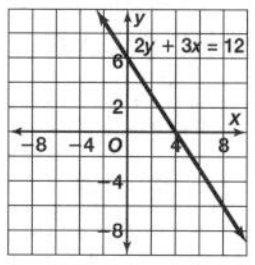


**39.**

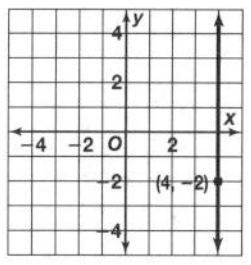


**41.** The upper roof has the steeper pitch because it has the greater slope.

**43a.**

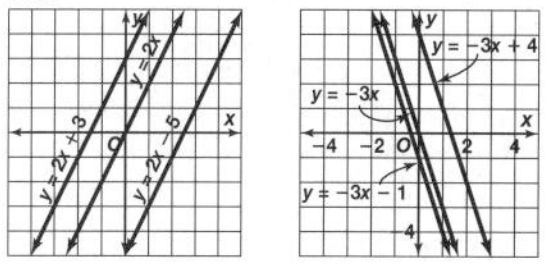


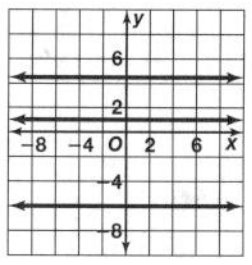

**b.** The lines are parallel. Explanations may vary. Sample: Their slope ratios are the same, so they never meet. **c.** 0 **45.** B

**MIXED REVIEW 49.** 10% decrease **51.** 25% decrease

### Math Toolbox — page 403

**1.**

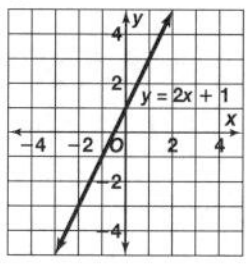


**3.**

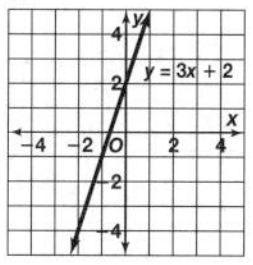


**5.**

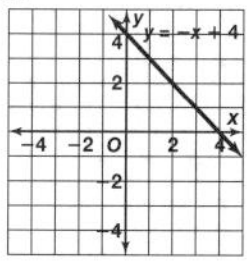


**7.**

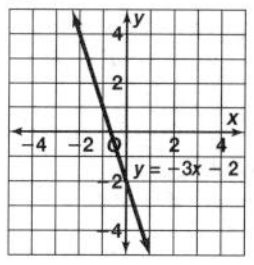


### Lesson 8-4 — pages 404–408

**TRY THIS 1.** $c(p) = 3p + 4$; $19 **2.** $f(x) = 2x$ **3.** $f(x) = -2x$ **4.** $y = 2x + 1$ **5.** $y = -x + 2$

**CHECK UNDERSTANDING 1.** $a(c) = 20 - c$ **2.** $f(x) = x - 9$ **3.** $f(x) = -x$ **4.** $y = -\frac{4}{5}x + 2$

**PRACTICE AND PROBLEM SOLVING 5.** $k(c) = c - 273.15$ **7a.** $q(p) = \frac{1}{2}p$ **b.** $q(f) = \frac{f}{32}$

**9a.** $p(s) = 4s$ **b.** $p(7) = 4(7) = 28$; the perimeter is 28 in. **11.** $f(x) = -1.2x$ **13.** $f(x) = x - 2$
**15.** $f(x) = \frac{2}{5}x + 1$ **17.** $f(x) = \frac{1}{4}x + 1$ **19.** $f(x) = x$
**23a.** $c(k) = 0.04968k + 6.87$ **b.** 315 kWh

**25a.**

| $x$ | $f(x)$ |
|---|---|
| −6 | −9 |
| −4 | −6 |
| −2 | −3 |
| 0 | 0 |
| 2 | 3 |
| 4 | 6 |

**b.** increase by 3 **c.** $\frac{\text{increase in range values}}{\text{increase in domain values}} = \frac{3}{2}$, which is the slope of the line.

**MIXED REVIEW** **27.** $\frac{2}{3}$ **29.** $\frac{3}{8}$ **31.** $\frac{7}{8}$

**CHECKPOINT 1**

**2.**

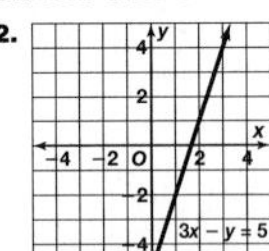


**3.** Yes; there is one range value for each domain value.
**4.** Answers may vary. Sample: If every vertical line passes through at most one graphed point, then the relation is a function. **5.** 5 **6.** −1

**7.** no slope **8.** −2, 5 **9.** $p(t) = 2{,}000t$ **10.** C

*Lesson 8-5* *pages 409–414*

**TRY THIS** **4.** has 14 years of education and annual income of $90,000 **5.** 4 people

**6.**

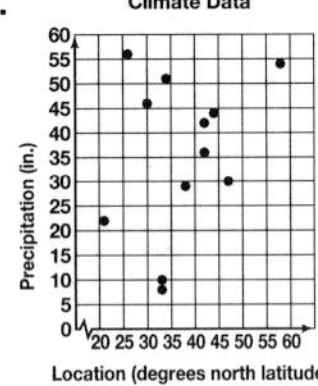


**7.**

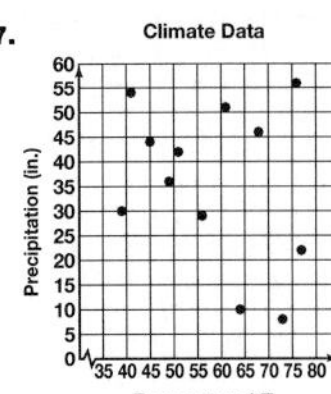


**8.** Positive correlation; as time goes by, the winning distance has tended to increase.

**CHECK UNDERSTANDING** **1.** averaged 4 h watching television and 2 h of physical activity daily **2.** 8 students **3.** 6 students **4.** No correlation; there is no apparent relationship. **5.** Positive correlation; as one set of values increases, the other set tends to increase. **6.** Negative correlation; as one set of values increases, the other set tends to decrease.

**PRACTICE AND PROBLEM SOLVING** **7.** 10 min **9.** 3 students **11.** Positive correlation; as one set of values increases, the other set tends to increase. **13.** No correlation; there is no apparent relationship. **15.** Positive correlation; candles with longer burning times are likely to have greater original heights (assuming equal diameters).

**17.**

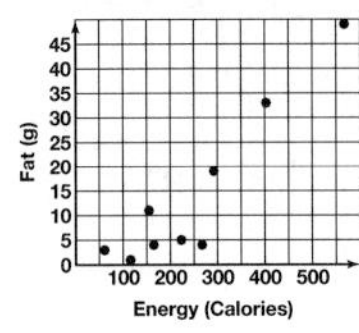




**19.** Nutritional Values (Carbohydrates (g) vs. Energy (Calories)) **21.** A

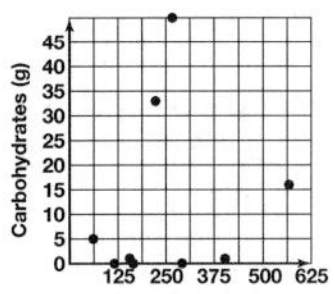

**MIXED REVIEW** **23.** $y = \frac{5}{2}x$ **25.** $f(x) = -x + 7$ **27.** $h = \frac{2A}{b + c}$ **29.** $a = S(1 - r)$ **31.** $41.54

*Standardized Test Prep* *page 415*

**1.** A **3.** D **5.** A **7.** B **9.** 3

*Lesson 8-6* *pages 416–419*

**READ** **1.** the number of wolves and the number of moose **2.** the number of moose when there are 18 wolves

**CHECK UNDERSTANDING** **1a–b.** Trend lines may vary. Sample is given.

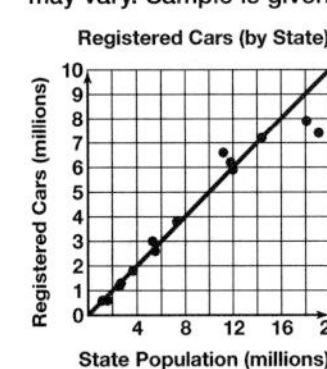


**c.** about 13 million cars **d.** $y = 0.4x + 0.4$; about 3.3 million cars **2.** positive correlation

**PRACTICE AND PROBLEM SOLVING** **3.** 309 mi **5.** 12 ways **7.** 45 ft

**MIXED REVIEW** **11.** (−3, 9), (0, 0), (2, −6) **13.** $\left(-3, -3\frac{1}{2}\right)$, (0, −2), (2, 1) **15.** −3 **17.** about 0.75%

*Lesson 8-7* *pages 420–425*

**TRY THIS**

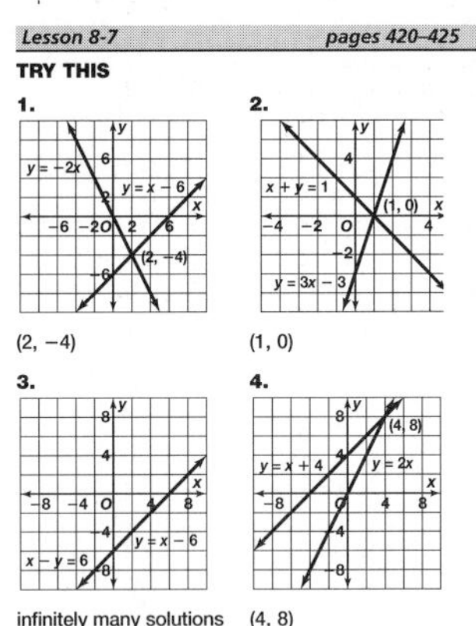


**1.** (2, −4) **2.** (1, 0)

**3.** infinitely many solutions **4.** (4, 8)

**5.** −3, −5

**CHECK UNDERSTANDING** **1.** (4, 5) **2.** (−2, −1) **3.** no solution **4.** no **5.** no **6.** yes

**7.**

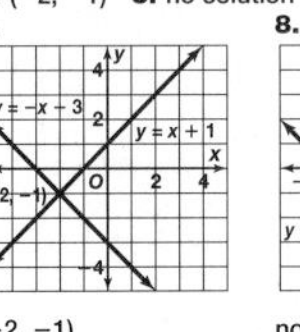


(−2, −1)

**8.** no solution

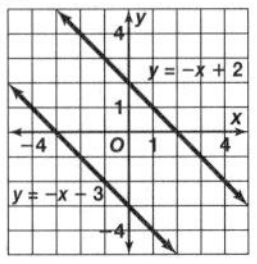

**9.** infinitely many solutions

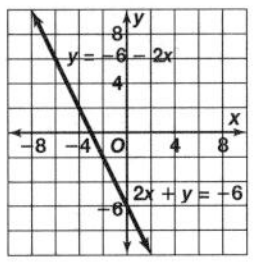

**10a.** $x = y + 6$; $x + 2 = 2(y + 2)$

**b.**

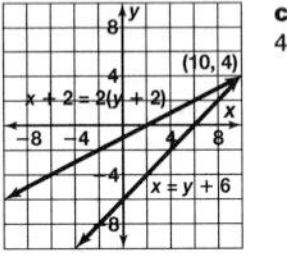


**c.** Cliff, 10 years; Claire, 4 years

**PRACTICE AND PROBLEM SOLVING**

**11.** yes **13.** no

**15.** (−2, −6)

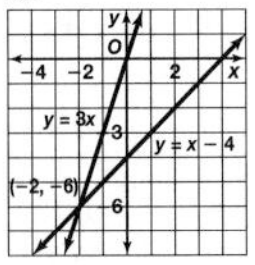

**17.**

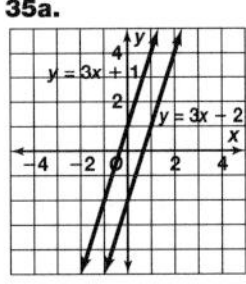

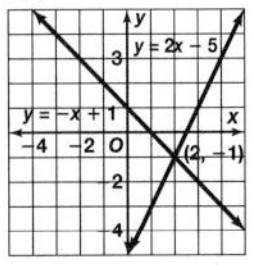

(2, −1)

**19.** (3, 3) **21.** (1, 5)

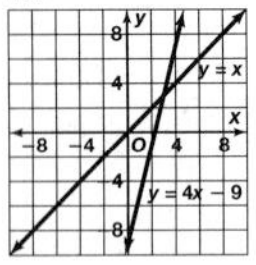

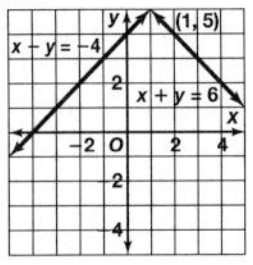

**23.** infinitely many solutions **25.** infinitely many solutions

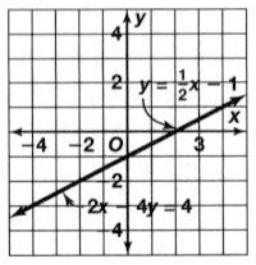

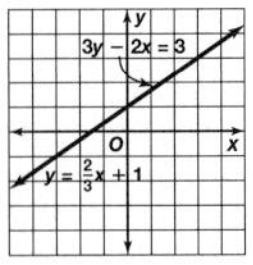

**29a.** $x + y = 16$
$5x + 10y = 100$

**b.** (12, 4) **c.** 12 five-point questions, 4 ten-point questions **31.** −2, −6 **33.** 20 $ft^2$

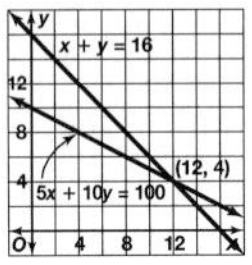

**35a.**

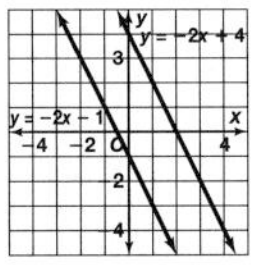

**37.** (−3, −1)

**MIXED REVIEW** **41.** $x < -2$ **43.** $t \le 6$ **45.** $\frac{1}{6}$ **47.** 0

**CHECKPOINT 2**

**1a., 1c.**

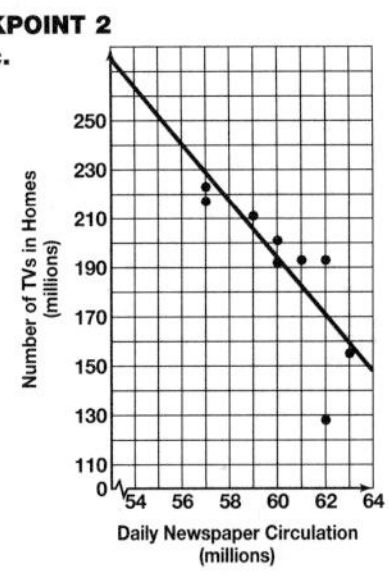


**b.** Negative correlation; as the number of television sets increases, the newspaper circulation decreases.



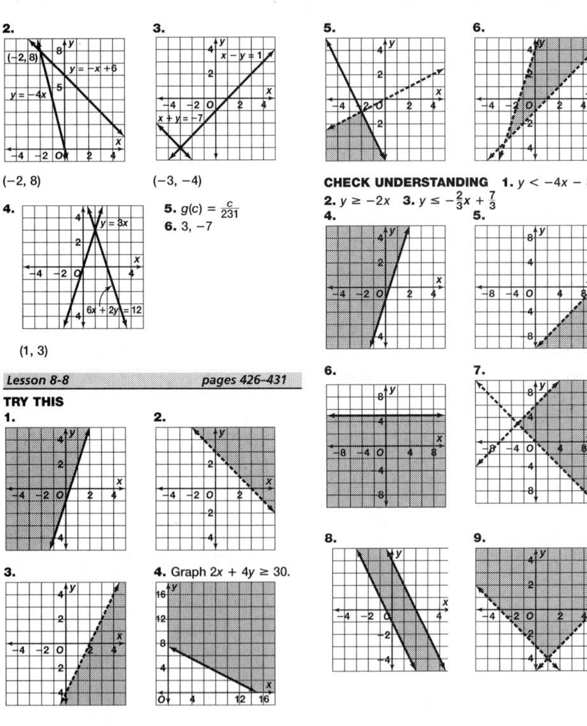

**2.** (−2, 8) **3.** (−3, −4)

**4.** (1, 3)

**5.** $g(c) = \frac{c}{231}$
**6.** 3, −7

*Lesson 8-8* *pages 426–431*

**TRY THIS**

**1.** **2.** **3.**

**4.** Graph $2x + 4y \ge 30$.

**5.** **6.**

**CHECK UNDERSTANDING** **1.** $y < -4x - 3$ **2.** $y \ge -2x$ **3.** $y \le -\frac{2}{3}x + \frac{7}{3}$

**4.** **5.** **6.** **7.** **8.** **9.**

**10a.** $6x + 3y \geq 45$
**b.**

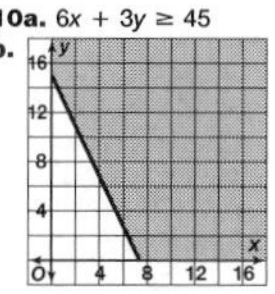

**c.** $4\frac{1}{2}$h

**PRACTICE AND PROBLEM SOLVING** **11.** C **13.** A **15.** $y = 3x + 2$; dashed **17.** $y = \frac{1}{2}x$; solid **19.** $y = x - 7$; solid **21.** $y = 2x - 5$; dashed

**23.** **25.**

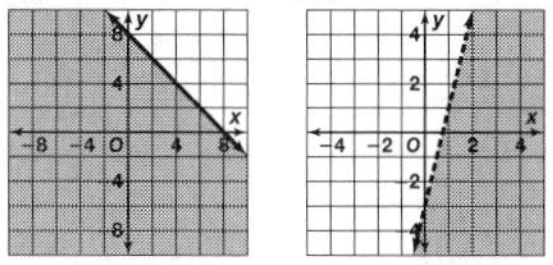

**27.** **29.**

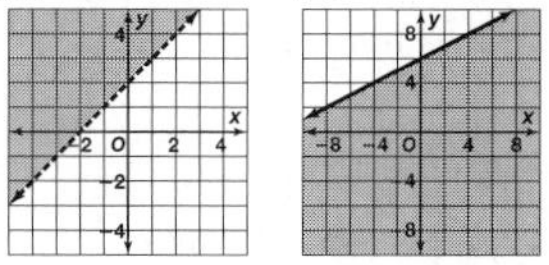

**31.** **33.**

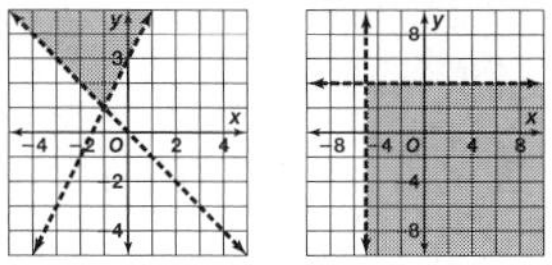

**35.** **37.**

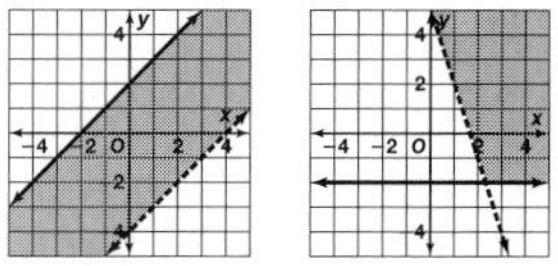

**39.** **41.**

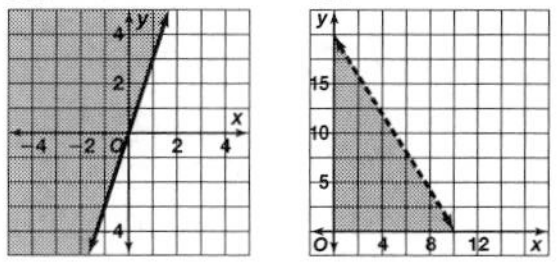

$y \geq 3x$ $\quad$ $10x + 5y < 100$

**43.** B **45a.** $y > -6$; $x < 2$ **b.** $y \leq x - 1$; $y > -2x - 4$

**MIXED REVIEW**
**47.** **49.**

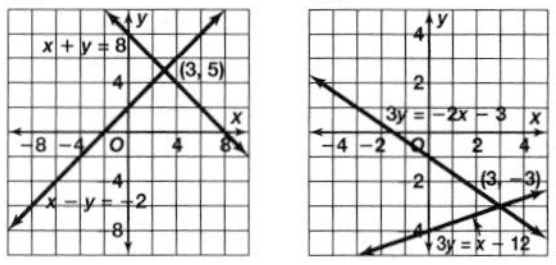


(3, 5) $\quad$ (3, −3)

**51.** $1\frac{1}{5}$ **53.** $\frac{3}{4}$ **55.** $-\frac{7}{2}$ **57.** 6

*Math Toolbox* *page 432*

**1.** **3.**

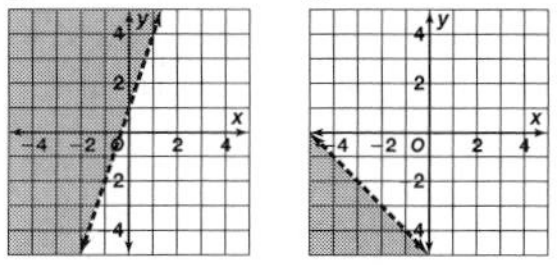



**5.** **7.**

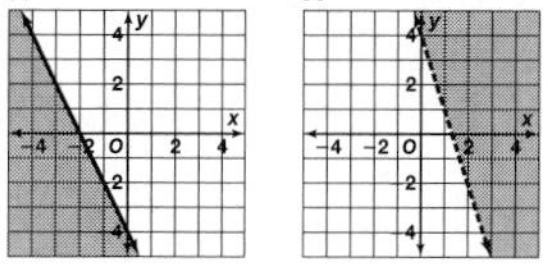

**9.**

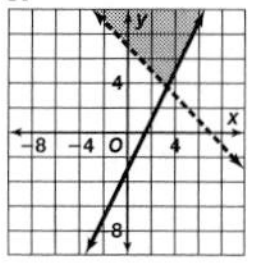

*Wrap Up* *pages 434–436*

**1.** Yes; there is one range value for each domain value. **2.** Yes; there is one range value for each domain value. **3.** No; there are domain values for which there are more than one range value. **4.** No; one length of time (for different distances) could result in different costs. **5.** (−3, 2), (0, 5), (2, 7) **6.** (−3, 12), (0, 0), (2, −8) **7.** $\left(-3, 1\frac{1}{2}\right)$, (0, 3), (2, 4) **8.** (−3, 12), (0, 6), (2, 2)
**9.** −1, 7 **10.** 1, 2

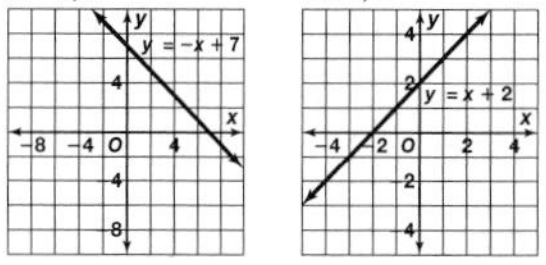


**11.** $-\frac{2}{5}$, 2 **12.** $\frac{3}{2}$, −6

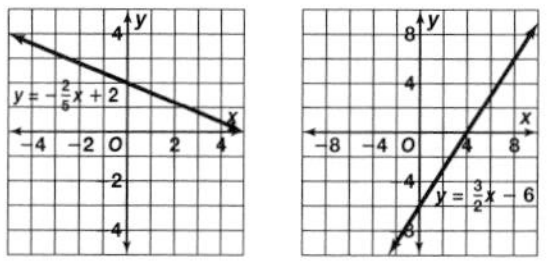


**13.** −2 **14.** 3 **15.** $-\frac{1}{2}$ **16.** $f(x) = -x$ **17.** $y = 2x + 1$ **18.** $y = -x + 4$ **19.** $c(t) = 14t + 2$ **20.** 30 min **21.** about 620 calories **22.** Positive correlation; as the time riding increases, the calories used increases.
**23a.**

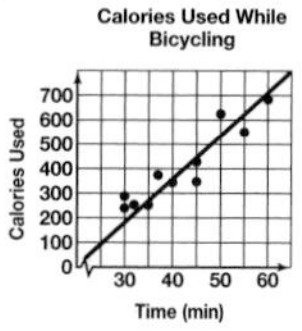


**24.** **25.**

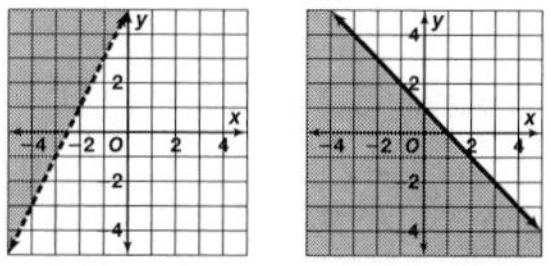

**26.** **27.**

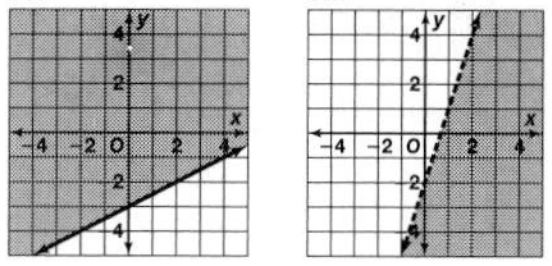

**28.** **29.**

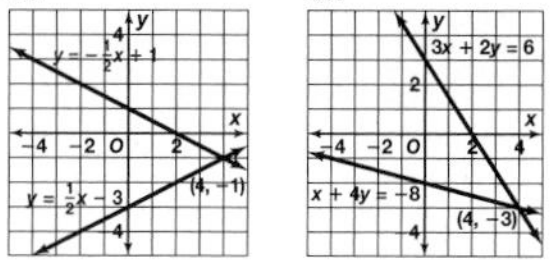


(4, −1) $\quad$ (4, −2)



**30.** **31.**

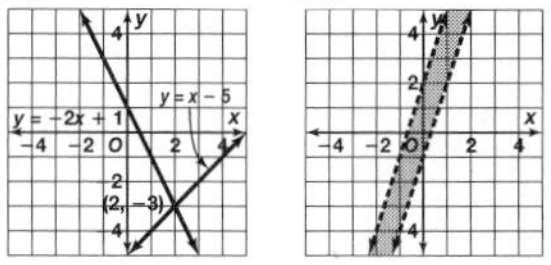


(2, −3)

**32.** The graphs could be parallel lines, so there is no common solution.

*Cumulative Review* *page 438*

**1.** C **3.** D **5.** D **7.** D **9.** B **11.** D **13.** (−3, −5), (0, −2), (2, 0) **15.** $y = 2x - 2$; 2, −2

## ▶CHAPTER 9

*Skills You Need* *page 439*

**1.** D **2.** B **3.** A **4.** C **5.** 6 cm **6.** $\frac{1}{2}$ in. **7.** 2.8 cm **8.** 7.5 ft **9.** 6 in. **10.** 2 in. **11.** 7 m **12.** $3\frac{1}{2}$ ft
**13–22.**

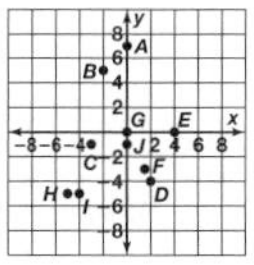

*Lesson 9-1* *pages 443–447*

**TRY THIS** **1.** C, N, V **2.** $\overline{NC}$, $\overline{NV}$ **3.** $\overrightarrow{NC}$, $\overrightarrow{NV}$ **4.** $\overline{EH}$, $\overline{FG}$, $\overline{AE}$, $\overline{BF}$ **5.** $\overline{HG}$, $\overline{DC}$, $\overline{AB}$ **6.** $\overline{DH}$, $\overline{CG}$, $\overline{AD}$, $\overline{BC}$

**CHECK UNDERSTANDING** **2.** $\overline{AB}$, $\overline{BC}$, $\overline{AC}$ **3.** $\overrightarrow{AC}$, $\overrightarrow{BC}$, $\overrightarrow{BA}$, $\overrightarrow{CA}$ **4.** $\overline{KD}$, $\overline{DG}$, $\overline{EH}$, $\overline{EF}$ **5.** $\overline{GF}$, $\overline{JI}$, $\overline{KH}$ **6.** $\overline{GJ}$, $\overline{FI}$, $\overline{KJ}$, $\overline{HI}$

**PRACTICE AND PROBLEM SOLVING** **7.** Z, R, F; $\overline{ZR}$, $\overline{RF}$, $\overline{ZF}$; $\overleftrightarrow{ZR}$ (or $\overleftrightarrow{RF}$ or $\overleftrightarrow{ZF}$); $\overrightarrow{ZR}$, $\overrightarrow{RF}$, $\overrightarrow{RZ}$, $\overrightarrow{FR}$ **9.** A, B, C, D; $\overline{AB}$, $\overline{AD}$, $\overline{BD}$, $\overline{BC}$; $\overleftrightarrow{DA}$; $\overrightarrow{BA}$, $\overrightarrow{BC}$, $\overrightarrow{BD}$, $\overrightarrow{AD}$, $\overrightarrow{DA}$ **11.** R, Q, J, Y, V; $\overline{YQ}$, $\overline{QV}$, $\overline{YV}$, $\overline{RQ}$, $\overline{QJ}$, $\overline{RJ}$; $\overleftrightarrow{QJ}$, $\overrightarrow{QR}$, $\overrightarrow{QJ}$, $\overrightarrow{JR}$, $\overrightarrow{RJ}$
**13.** **15.**

**17.**

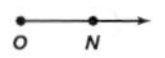

**23.** Parallel; they are in the same plane and do not intersect. **25.** Skew; they are not in the same plane. **27.** $\overline{RS}$, $\overline{QP}$, $\overline{LK}$ **29a.** infinitely many **b.** one **33.** $6 + 5x + 4x + 1 = 12x + 1$; 6, 10, 9, 25 **35.** sometimes **37.** always **39.** sometimes **41.** $\overline{AB}$ is the segment from A to B. AB is a number, the length of $\overline{AB}$. **43a.** intersecting **b.** parallel **c.** parallel **d.** intersecting **e.** intersecting

**MIXED REVIEW** **45.**

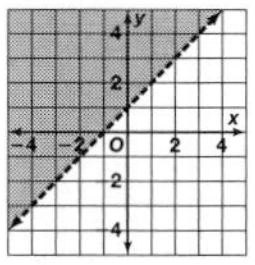

**47.** $\frac{23}{24}$ **49.** $\frac{15}{32}$

*Math Toolbox* *page 448*

**1.** **3.** **5.**

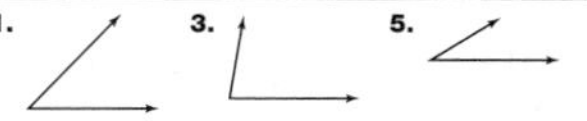

**7.** 90°, right **9.** 120°, obtuse

*Lesson 9-2* *pages 450–453*

**TRY THIS** **1.** 160°, 20°, 160° **2.** $\angle 1 \cong \angle 5$, $\angle 4 \cong \angle 8$, $\angle 2 \cong \angle 6$, $\angle 3 \cong \angle 7$; $\angle 4 \cong \angle 6$, $\angle 3 \cong \angle 5$

**CHECK UNDERSTANDING** **1.** 180° **2.** complementary **3.** ∠3 is vertical to ∠1. ∠2 and the 140° angle are adjacent to ∠1. $m\angle 1 = 40°$ **4.** ∠3 is vertical to ∠1. ∠2 and the 70° angle are adjacent to ∠1. $m\angle 1 = 110°$ **5.** ∠KPL is vertical to ∠1. ∠JPI and ∠HPM are adjacent to ∠1. $m\angle 1 = 34°$ **6.** ∠1 and ∠5, ∠2 and ∠6, ∠3 and ∠7, ∠4 and ∠8. **7.** ∠2 and ∠8, ∠3 and ∠5 **8.** ∠6, ∠2, ∠4

**PRACTICE AND PROBLEM SOLVING** **9a.** $3x = x + 30$, $x = 15$ **b.** 45° **c.** 135° **11.** $m\angle 1 = 80°$, $m\angle 2 = 100°$, $m\angle 3 = 80°$ **13.** $m\angle 1 = 60°$, $m\angle 2 = 60°$ **15.** $m\angle 1 = 55°$, $m\angle 2 = 125°$

**MIXED REVIEW** **19.**

**21.**

**23.**

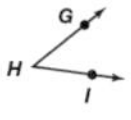

**25.** $52.25 **27.** seven



*Lesson 9-3* *pages 454–458*

**TRY THIS** **1.** scalene right triangle **2.** isosceles obtuse triangle **3.** scalene obtuse triangle **4.** rectangles and squares **5.** $P = 5x$; 80 cm

**CHECK UNDERSTANDING** **4.** 23.1 cm **5.** 108 yd **6.** 20.4 cm **7.** **8.**

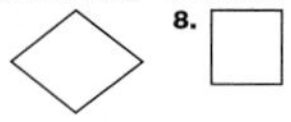

rhombus

**PRACTICE AND PROBLEM SOLVING** **9.** equilateral acute triangle **11.** isosceles right triangle **13.** $P = 4x$; 50 in. **15.** $P = 5x$; $8\frac{1}{3}$ yd **17.** trapezoid, equilateral triangle, rectangle
**19.**

**21.** trapezoid **23.** parallelogram, rhombus, square, rectangle **25.** parallelogram, rectangle, rhombus, square, trapezoid **27.** If the congruent sides are 10 cm long, the perimeter is 10 + 10 + 12, or 32 cm. If the congruent sides are 12 cm long, the perimeter is 12 + 12 + 10, or 34 cm.

**MIXED REVIEW**
**29.**

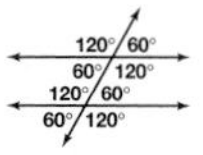


**31.** 10 **33.** 8

*Math Toolbox* *page 459*

**1.** 360° **3.** 1,080° **5.** $s = 180(n - 2)$

*Lesson 9-4* *pages 460–463*

**READ** **1.** a polygon with 8 sides **2.** a line segment that connects two non-consecutive vertices

**PLAN** **3.** 5 **4.** 4

**SOLVE**

| | |
|---|---|
| D | 3 |
| E | 2 |
| F | 1 |
| G | 0 |
| | 0 |
| Total | 20 |

**CHECK UNDERSTANDING** **1.** 4 mi **2.** Jim **3.** 4

**PRACTICE AND PROBLEM SOLVING** **5.** 8 **7.** $\frac{1}{4}$ **11.** the dog **13.** 28, 36, 45; each increase is one greater than the increase before it. **15.** 5 cm

**MIXED REVIEW** **17.** scalene right triangle **19.** scalene obtuse triangle **21.** $\frac{7}{50}$, 14% **23.** $\frac{11}{100}$, 11% **25.** $\frac{1}{8}$, 12.5%

*Lesson 9-5* *pages 464–468*

**TRY THIS** **3.** $\overline{AB} \cong \overline{DE}$, $\overline{BC} \cong \overline{EC}$, $\overline{AC} \cong \overline{DC}$, $\angle A \cong \angle D$, $\angle B \cong \angle E$, $\angle BCA \cong \angle ECD$, $AC = 50$ m **4.** $\overline{FJ} \cong \overline{FG}$, $\overline{FI} \cong \overline{FH}$, $\overline{JI} \cong \overline{GH}$, $\triangle JFI \cong \triangle GFH$ by SSS

**CHECK UNDERSTANDING** **1.** $\overline{AB} \cong \overline{XY}$, $\overline{BC} \cong \overline{YZ}$, $\overline{AC} \cong \overline{XZ}$, $\angle A \cong \angle X$, $\angle B \cong \angle Y$, $\angle C \cong \angle Z$ **2.** $\overline{AB} \cong \overline{KH}$, $\overline{BC} \cong \overline{HG}$, $\angle B \cong \angle H$, $\triangle ABC \cong \triangle KHG$ by SAS **3.** $\overline{BC} \cong \overline{EC}$, $\overline{AC} \cong \overline{DC}$, $\angle BCA \cong \angle ECD$, $\triangle ABC \cong \triangle DEC$ by SAS **4.** $\overline{OM} \cong \overline{RP}$, $\overline{ON} \cong \overline{RQ}$, $\overline{NM} \cong \overline{QP}$, $\triangle ONM \cong \triangle RQP$ by SSS

**PRACTICE AND PROBLEM SOLVING** **5.** ∠D **7.** ∠F **9.** m∠E or 90° **11.** $\overline{DF}$ **13.** $\overline{ED}$ **15.** DF or 5mm **17.** △FED **19.** $\angle D \cong \angle R$, $\angle DCE \cong \angle RCA$, $\overline{CD} \cong \overline{CR}$, $\triangle ACR \cong \triangle ECD$ by ASA **21.** $\overline{RT} \cong \overline{WU}$, $\overline{RS} \cong \overline{WV}$, $\overline{TS} \cong \overline{UV}$, $\triangle RST \cong \triangle WVU$ by SSS **23.** $\overline{AC} \cong \overline{CA}$, $\overline{AB} \cong \overline{CD}$, $\overline{BC} \cong \overline{DA}$, $\triangle ABC \cong \triangle CDA$ by SSS **25.** Congruent by SAS. $\angle D \cong \angle K$, so $x = 53°$. Because the sum of the angle measures in a triangle is 180°, $y = 37°$. **27.** Incorrect; ∠R does not correspond with ∠U. **29.** Correct; these are corresponding sides. **31.** Correct; these are corresponding angles.
**33.**

No; △ABJ and △KWR are both equiangular but the sides are not congruent.

**35.** △AEB, △CDH, △MIL, and △KJF appear to be congruent. △BDE, △HID, △LJI, and △FEJ appear to be congruent. △CDB, △MIH, △JKL, △AEF, △DEG, △IDG, △IJG, and △EJG appear to be congruent.

**MIXED REVIEW** **37.** $\frac{3}{8}, \frac{1}{2}, \frac{2}{3}, \frac{5}{6}$ **39.** $\frac{1}{7}, \frac{1}{6}, \frac{1}{5}, \frac{1}{4}$ **41.** $0.15x = 12$, 80 **43.** 14 students

**CHECKPOINT 1** **1.** ray **2.** line **3.** point **4.** angle **5a.** $6x + 16 + 2x + 12 = 180$, $x = 19$ **b.** 50° **c.** 130° **d.** 130° **6.**

**7.** C

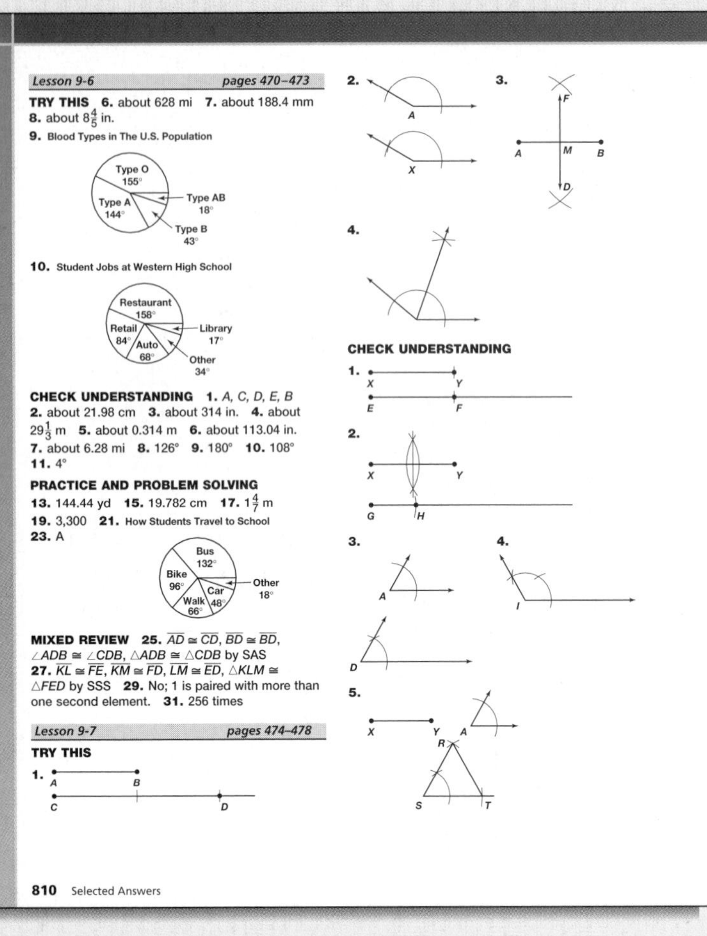

**Lesson 9-6** pages 470–473

**TRY THIS** **6.** about 628 mi **7.** about 188.4 mm **8.** about $8\frac{4}{5}$ in.

**9.** Blood Types in The U.S. Population

Type O 155°, Type A 144°, Type AB 18°, Type B 43°

**10.** Student Jobs at Western High School

Restaurant 158°, Retail 84°, Auto 68°, Library 17°, Other 34°

**CHECK UNDERSTANDING** **1.** *A, C, D, E, B* **2.** about 21.98 cm **3.** about 314 in. **4.** about $29\frac{1}{3}$ m **5.** about 0.314 m **6.** about 113.04 in. **7.** about 6.28 mi **8.** 126° **9.** 180° **10.** 108° **11.** 4°

**PRACTICE AND PROBLEM SOLVING** **13.** 144.44 yd **15.** 19.782 cm **17.** $1\frac{4}{7}$ m **19.** 3,300 **21.** How Students Travel to School

Bus 132°, Bike 96°, Walk 66°, Car 48°, Other 18°

**23.** A

**MIXED REVIEW** **25.** $\overline{AD} \cong \overline{CD}$, $\overline{BD} \cong \overline{BD}$, $\angle ADB \cong \angle CDB$, $\triangle ADB \cong \triangle CDB$ by SAS **27.** $\overline{KL} \cong \overline{FE}$, $\overline{KM} \cong \overline{FD}$, $\overline{LM} \cong \overline{ED}$, $\triangle KLM \cong \triangle FED$ by SSS **29.** No; 1 is paired with more than one second element. **31.** 256 times

**Lesson 9-7** pages 474–478

**TRY THIS** **1.** **2.** **3.** **4.**

**CHECK UNDERSTANDING** **1.** **2.** **3.** **4.** **5.**



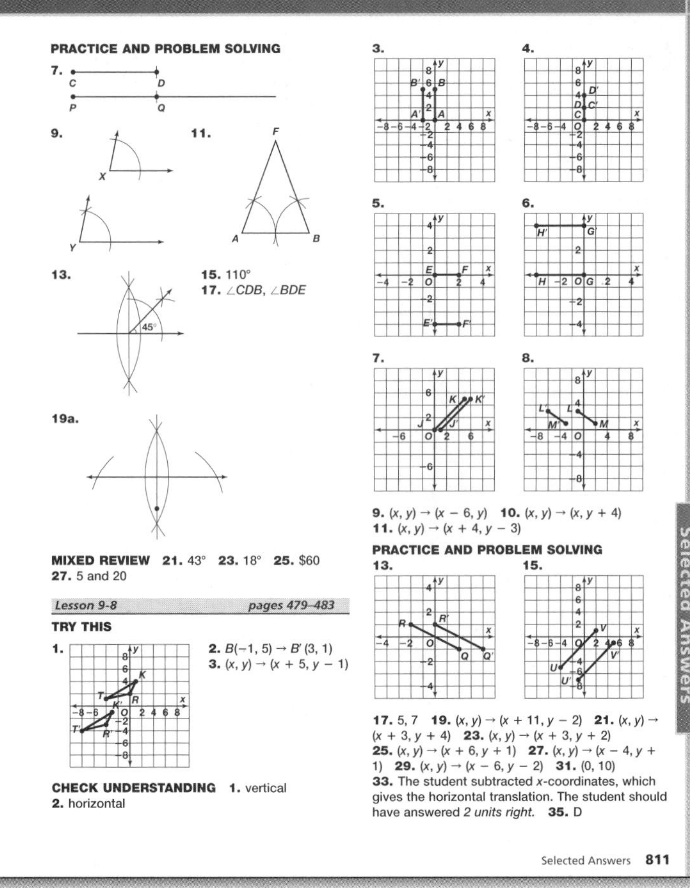

**PRACTICE AND PROBLEM SOLVING** **7.** **9.** **11.** **13.**

**15.** 110° **17.** $\angle CDB$, $\angle BDE$

**19a.**

**MIXED REVIEW** **21.** 43° **23.** 18° **25.** \$60 **27.** 5 and 20

**Lesson 9-8** pages 479–483

**TRY THIS** **1.** **2.** $B(-1, 5) \rightarrow B'(3, 1)$ **3.** $(x, y) \rightarrow (x + 5, y - 1)$

**CHECK UNDERSTANDING** **1.** vertical **2.** horizontal

**3.** **4.** **5.** **6.** **7.** **8.**

**9.** $(x, y) \rightarrow (x - 6, y)$ **10.** $(x, y) \rightarrow (x, y + 4)$ **11.** $(x, y) \rightarrow (x + 4, y - 3)$

**PRACTICE AND PROBLEM SOLVING** **13.** **15.**

**17.** 5, 7 **19.** $(x, y) \rightarrow (x + 11, y - 2)$ **21.** $(x, y) \rightarrow (x + 3, y + 4)$ **23.** $(x, y) \rightarrow (x + 3, y + 2)$ **25.** $(x, y) \rightarrow (x + 6, y + 1)$ **27.** $(x, y) \rightarrow (x - 4, y + 1)$ **29.** $(x, y) \rightarrow (x - 6, y - 2)$ **31.** (0, 10) **33.** The student subtracted *x*-coordinates, which gives the horizontal translation. The student should have answered *2 units right.* **35.** D





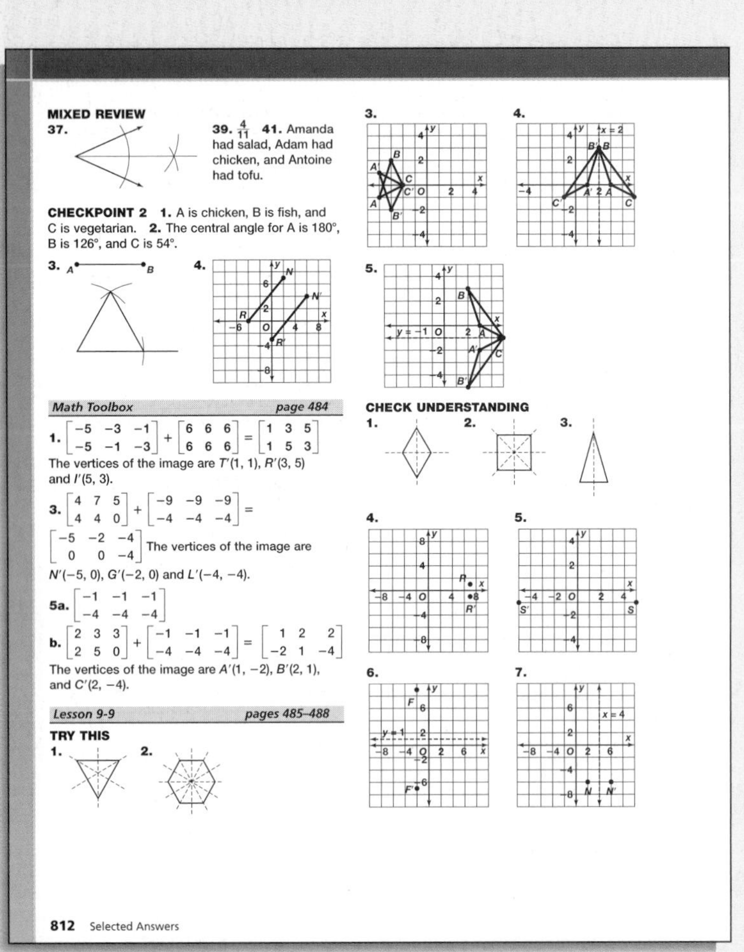

**MIXED REVIEW** **37.** **39.** $\frac{4}{11}$ **41.** Amanda had salad, Adam had chicken, and Antoine had tofu.

**CHECKPOINT 2** **1.** A is chicken, B is fish, and C is vegetarian. **2.** The central angle for A is 180°, B is 126°, and C is 54°. **3.** **4.**

**Math Toolbox** page 484

**1.** $\begin{bmatrix} -5 & -3 & -1 \\ -5 & -1 & -3 \end{bmatrix} + \begin{bmatrix} 6 & 6 & 6 \\ 6 & 6 & 6 \end{bmatrix} = \begin{bmatrix} 1 & 3 & 5 \\ 1 & 5 & 3 \end{bmatrix}$

The vertices of the image are $T'(1, 1)$, $R'(3, 5)$ and $I'(5, 3)$.

**3.** $\begin{bmatrix} 4 & 7 & 5 \\ 4 & 4 & 0 \end{bmatrix} + \begin{bmatrix} -9 & -9 & -9 \\ -4 & -4 & -4 \end{bmatrix} = \begin{bmatrix} -5 & -2 & -4 \\ 0 & 0 & -4 \end{bmatrix}$ The vertices of the image are $N'(-5, 0)$, $G'(-2, 0)$ and $L'(-4, -4)$.

**5a.** $\begin{bmatrix} -1 & -1 & -1 \\ -4 & -4 & -4 \end{bmatrix}$

**b.** $\begin{bmatrix} 2 & 3 & 3 \\ 2 & 5 & 0 \end{bmatrix} + \begin{bmatrix} -1 & -1 & -1 \\ -4 & -4 & -4 \end{bmatrix} = \begin{bmatrix} 1 & 2 & 2 \\ -2 & 1 & -4 \end{bmatrix}$

The vertices of the image are $A'(1, -2)$, $B'(2, 1)$, and $C'(2, -4)$.

**Lesson 9-9** pages 485–488

**TRY THIS** **1.** **2.**

**3.** **4.** **5.**

**CHECK UNDERSTANDING** **1.** **2.** **3.** **4.** **5.** **6.** **7.**



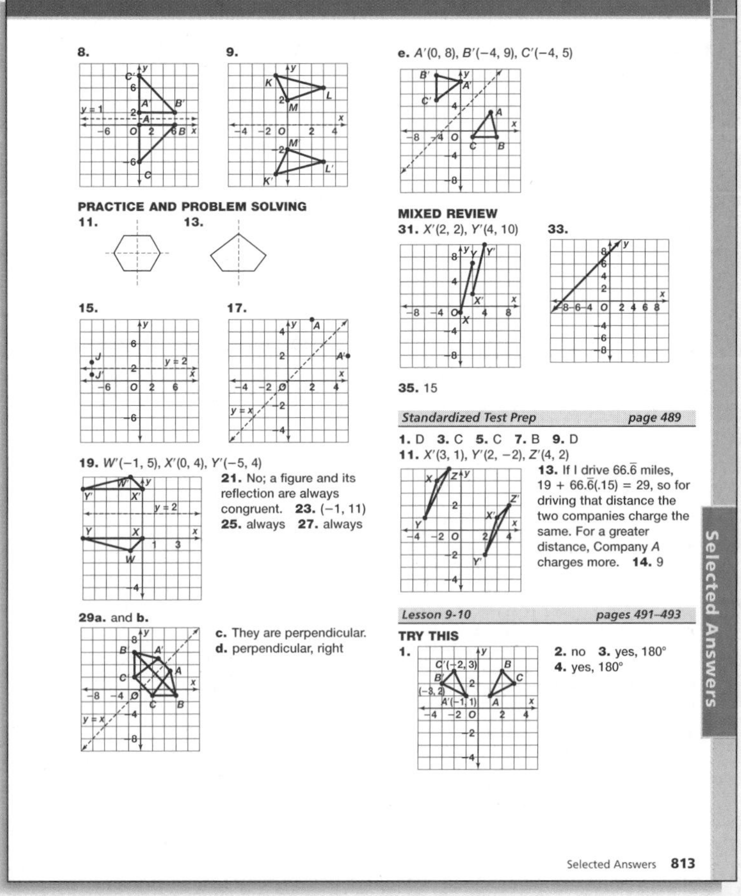

**8.** **9.**

**PRACTICE AND PROBLEM SOLVING** **11.** **13.** **15.** **17.**

**19.** $W'(-1, 5)$, $X'(0, 4)$, $Y'(-5, 4)$

**21.** No; a figure and its reflection are always congruent. **23.** (−1, 11) **25.** always **27.** always

**29a.** and **b.** **c.** They are perpendicular. **d.** perpendicular, right

**e.** $A'(0, 8)$, $B'(-4, 9)$, $C'(-4, 5)$

**MIXED REVIEW** **31.** $X'(2, 2)$, $Y'(4, 10)$ **33.** **35.** 15

**Standardized Test Prep** page 489

**1.** D **3.** C **5.** C **7.** B **9.** D **11.** $X'(3, 1)$, $Y'(2, -2)$, $Z'(4, 2)$ **13.** If I drive $66.\overline{6}$ miles, $19 + 66.\overline{6}(.15) = 29$, so for driving that distance the two companies charge the same. For a greater distance, Company *A* charges more. **14.** 9

**Lesson 9-10** pages 491–493

**TRY THIS** **1.** **2.** no **3.** yes, 180° **4.** yes, 180°

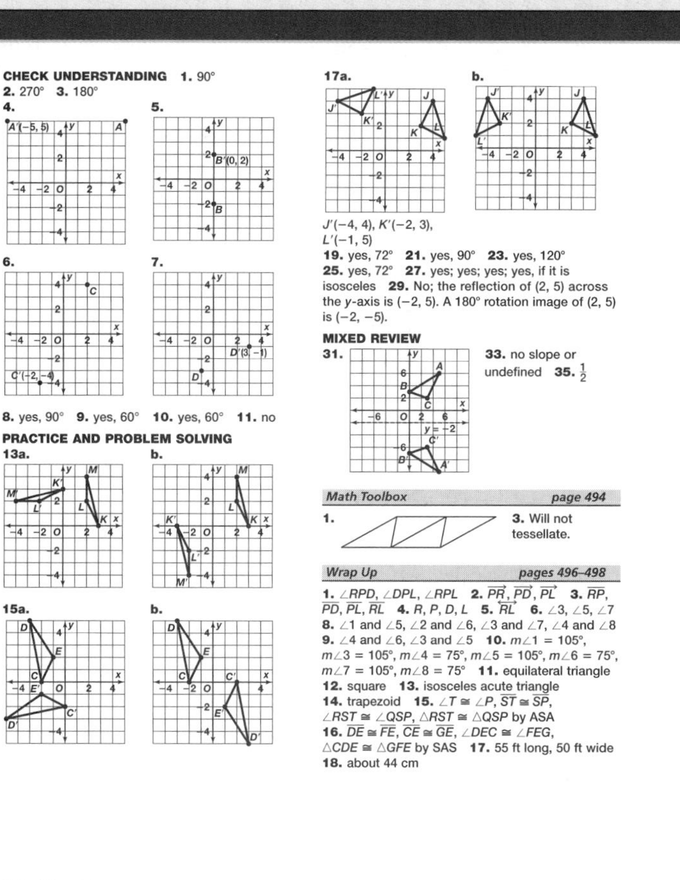

**CHECK UNDERSTANDING** **1.** 90° **2.** 270° **3.** 180°

**4.** **5.** **6.** **7.**

**8.** yes, 90° **9.** yes, 60° **10.** yes, 60° **11.** no

**PRACTICE AND PROBLEM SOLVING**

**13a.** **b.** **15a.** **b.**

**17a.** **b.**

$J'(-4, 4)$, $K'(-2, 3)$, $L'(-1, 5)$

**19.** yes, 72° **21.** yes, 90° **23.** yes, 120° **25.** yes, 72° **27.** yes; yes; yes; yes, if it is isosceles **29.** No; the reflection of (2, 5) across the $y$-axis is (−2, 5). A 180° rotation image of (2, 5) is (−2, −5).

**MIXED REVIEW**

**31.** **33.** no slope or undefined **35.** $\frac{1}{2}$

*Math Toolbox* page 494

**1.** **3.** Will not tessellate.

*Wrap Up* pages 496–498

**1.** $\angle RPD$, $\angle DPL$, $\angle RPL$ **2.** $\overrightarrow{PR}$, $\overrightarrow{PD}$, $\overrightarrow{PL}$ **3.** $\overrightarrow{RP}$, $\overrightarrow{PD}$, $\overrightarrow{PL}$, $\overrightarrow{RL}$ **4.** $R, P, D, L$ **5.** $\overrightarrow{RL}$ **6.** $\angle 3$, $\angle 5$, $\angle 7$ **8.** $\angle 1$ and $\angle 5$, $\angle 2$ and $\angle 6$, $\angle 3$ and $\angle 7$, $\angle 4$ and $\angle 8$ **9.** $\angle 4$ and $\angle 6$, $\angle 3$ and $\angle 5$ **10.** $m\angle 1 = 105°$, $m\angle 3 = 105°$, $m\angle 4 = 75°$, $m\angle 5 = 105°$, $m\angle 6 = 75°$, $m\angle 7 = 105°$, $m\angle 8 = 75°$ **11.** equilateral triangle **12.** square **13.** isosceles acute triangle **14.** trapezoid **15.** $\angle T \cong \angle P$, $\overline{ST} \cong \overline{SP}$, $\angle RST \cong \angle QSP$, $\triangle RST \cong \triangle QSP$ by ASA **16.** $\overline{DE} \cong \overline{FE}$, $\overline{CE} \cong \overline{GE}$, $\angle DEC \cong \angle FEG$, $\triangle CDE \cong \triangle GFE$ by SAS **17.** 55 ft long, 50 ft wide **18.** about 44 cm



**19.** Television Programming (Ch. X 144°, Ch. Y 90°, Ch. Z 126°) **20.** **21.**

**22.** $A'(11, 1)$ **23.** $A'(-7, -2)$ **24.** $A'(2, 7)$ **25.** $A'(7, 0)$ **26.** In each case the image is congruent to the original figure. None of these transformations affect size or shape.

*Cumulative Review* page 500

**1.** C **3.** B **5.** C **7.** A **9.** C **11.** B **13.** B

**15.** **17.**

## ▶Chapter 10

*Skills You Need* page 501

**1.** 36 m$^2$ **2.** 20 in.$^2$ **3.** $45y^2$ cm$^2$ **4.** 6 **5.** $\frac{39}{2}$ **6.** 9 **7.** $10x$ **8.** $5x^2$ **9.** 55 **10.** 1,364 **11.** 500 **12.** 8 **13.** 45 **14.** 78.5 **15.** 864 **16.** 48 **17.** 300 **18.** 452.16 **19.** 157 yd **20.** 628 m **21.** 17.27 in.

*Lesson 10-1* pages 504–508

**TRY THIS** **5.** 1,000 cm$^2$ **6.** 12 ft$^2$ **7.** 6 m$^2$ **8.** 24 in.$^2$

**CHECK UNDERSTANDING** **1.** 135 ft$^2$ or 15 yd$^2$ **2.** 1 m$^2$ or 10,000 cm$^2$ **3.** 1,000 cm$^2$ or 0.1 m$^2$ **4.** 3 yd$^2$ or 27 ft$^2$ **5.** 368 ft$^2$ **6.** 3 m$^2$ **7.** 40 ft$^2$ **8.** 100 in.$^2$ **9.** 15,000 cm$^2$ or 1.5 m$^2$

**PRACTICE AND PROBLEM SOLVING** **11.** 14 yd$^2$ **13.** 10 m$^2$ or 100,000 cm$^2$ **15.** 8 in.$^2$ **17.** 1,400 mm$^2$ or 14 cm$^2$ **19.** 12 **21.** 24 ft$^2$ **23.** 16 yd$^2$ **25.** A

**MIXED REVIEW**

**31.** **33.**

**35.** $\frac{4}{25}$ **37.** $\frac{44}{9}$

*Lesson 10-2* pages 509–513

**TRY THIS** **1.** 7.38 ft$^2$ **2.** 5 m$^2$ **3.** 24 yd$^2$ **4.** 13 ft$^2$ **5.** 342 mm$^2$

**CHECK UNDERSTANDING** **1.** 60 m$^2$ **2.** 47.6 m$^2$ **3.** 36 in.$^2$ **4.** 22 cm$^2$ **5.** 15 in.$^2$ **6.** 63 ft$^2$ **7.** The triangle is two times as high as the parallelogram.

**PRACTICE AND PROBLEM SOLVING** **9.** 37.6 cm$^2$ **11.** 410 in.$^2$ **13.** 1,800 ft$^2$ **15.** 412.5 mm$^2$ **17.** 34 cm$^2$ **19.** 108 in.$^2$ **21.** 50 m$^2$ **25.** A

**MIXED REVIEW** **27.** 0.5 m$^2$ or 5,000 cm$^2$ **29.** −2 **31.** $1.\overline{54}$ **33.** $10

*Lesson 10-3* pages 514–519

**TRY THIS** **7.** $2{,}500\pi$ in.$^2$ **8.** 28.26 mi$^2$ **9.** 40.2 cm$^2$

**CHECK UNDERSTANDING** **1.** $9\pi$ ft$^2$; 28 ft$^2$ **2.** $25\pi$ m$^2$; 79 m$^2$ **3.** $400\pi$ cm$^2$; 1,256 cm$^2$ **4.** $144\pi$ ft$^2$; 452 ft$^2$ **5.** $64\pi$ m$^2$; 201 m$^2$ **6.** $900\pi$ cm$^2$; 2,826 cm$^2$ **7.** 89 in.$^2$ **8.** 2,856 yd$^2$ **9.** The circle has a greater area. A circle with radius 2 m has an area of $4\pi$ m$^2$, but a square of side length 2 m only has an area of 4 m$^2$.

**PRACTICE AND PROBLEM SOLVING** **11.** $\frac{1}{4}\pi$ m$^2$; 0.8 m$^2$ **13.** $30.25\pi$ mi$^2$; 95 mi$^2$





**15.** $17.64\pi$ mm$^2$; 55.4 mm$^2$ **17.** 19 cm$^2$ **19.** 14 ft$^2$ **21.** 357 mi$^2$ **23.** A **25.** C **27a.** 392.5 ft$^2$ **b.** 9 ft$^2$ **c.** 43.6 yd$^2$ **29a.** 3 in. **b.** 226.08 in.$^2$ **c.** 61.92 in.$^2$ **31.** The circle with radius 4 m has greater area because the four circles will have a total area of $4\pi$ m$^2$, but the circle with radius 4 m will have an area of $16\pi$ m$^2$. **33.** 4

**MIXED REVIEW** **35.** 5.25 yd$^2$ **37.** $10\frac{4}{15}$ **39.** $1\frac{17}{24}$ **41.** 32

**CHECKPOINT 1** **1.** 300 yd$^2$ **2.** 2,100 cm$^2$ **3.** 150 m$^2$ **4.** $100\pi$ yd$^2$; 314 yd$^2$ **5.** $625\pi$ ft$^2$; 1,963 ft$^2$ **6.** $(800 + 50\pi)$ cm$^2$; 957 cm$^2$ **7.** D

*Math Toolbox* page 520

**1.** Top **1.** Front **1.** Right Side **3.** Top **3.** Front **3.** Right Side

*Lesson 10-4* pages 521–525

**TRY THIS** **1.** The figure is a cylinder. **2.** The figure is a cone. **3.** With a triangular base and three triangular sides, you can form a triangular pyramid. **4.** With two square bases and 4 square lateral sides, you can form a square prism.

**CHECK UNDERSTANDING** **1.** The base is a hexagon. The figure is a hexagonal pyramid. **2.** The bases are pentagons. The figure is a pentagonal prism. **3.** The bases are triangles. The figure is a triangular prism. **4.** square prism **5.** triangular pyramid **6.** triangular prism **7.**

**PRACTICE AND PROBLEM SOLVING** **9.** The base is a rectangle. The figure is a rectangular pyramid. **11.** square pyramid **13.** square prism **15.** B **17.** A **19.** The student forgot that there need to be bases on both sides of the vertical faces. **21.** triangular prism **23.** The rectangular pyramid's net will have several triangles attached to a rectangular base. The rectangular prism's net will be made entirely of rectangles. **25a.** rectangular prism **b.** cone **c.** sphere

**MIXED REVIEW** **29.** $6.25\pi$ m$^2$; 19.625 m$^2$ **31.** $100\pi$ m$^2$; 314 m$^2$ **33.** $y = x - 5$ **35.** 9

*Math Toolbox* page 526

**1.** square **3.** equilateral triangle **5.** **7.** **9.** They are all circles.

*Lesson 10-5* pages 527–532

**TRY THIS** **1.** 84 yd$^2$ **2.** 108 m$^2$ **3.** 785 cm$^2$

**CHECK UNDERSTANDING** **1.** 1,078 m$^2$ **2.** 603 yd$^2$ **3.** 1,008 m$^2$ **4.** 105.5 m$^2$ **5.** 1,056 mm$^2$ **6.** 96 in.$^2$ **7.** (11 in., 5 in., 3 in.) 206 in.$^2$

**PRACTICE AND PROBLEM SOLVING** **9.** 8,777 cm$^2$ **11.** 408 cm$^2$ **13.** 175.8 cm$^2$ **15.** 518 m$^2$ **17.** 10,800 in.$^2$ **19a.** 5 **b.** 3,600 ft$^2$ **c.** $600 **23.** Doubling the radius has a greater effect on the surface area because the radius appears as a higher power than the height in determining surface area. **25.** The height of the base is the height of the triangular base, but the height of the prism is the shortest distance between the two bases. **27.** 658 ft$^2$



**MIXED REVIEW** **29.** pentagonal pyramid **31.** **33.**

*Lesson 10-6* pages 533–537

**TRY THIS** **1.** 720 ft$^2$ **2.** 1,011.08 ft$^2$

**CHECK UNDERSTANDING** **1.** 1,256 cm$^2$ **2.** 1,017 cm$^2$ **3.** 60 m$^2$ **4.** 104 ft$^2$ **5.** 105 cm$^2$ **6.** Both have the same surface area of $16\pi$ in.$^2$

**PRACTICE AND PROBLEM SOLVING** **7.** 33 yd$^2$ **9.** 540 cm$^2$ **11.** 49 m$^2$ **13.** My friend forgot to add the area of the second base of the prism. **15.** 122 m$^2$ **17a.** 23,766.66 ft$^2$ **b.** 9.6 ft$^2$ **19.** B

**MIXED REVIEW** **21.** 52 ft$^2$ **23.** 848 cm$^2$ **25.** 1, 2, 4, 5, 10, 20, 25, 50, 100 **27.** 1, 2, 4, 8, 16, 32 **29.** 5 months

*Lesson 10-7* pages 538–541

**TRY THIS** **1.** 216 ft$^3$ **2.** 1,900 ft$^3$

**CHECK UNDERSTANDING** **1.** 24 cubic units **2.** 54 cm$^3$ **3.** 480 cm$^3$ **4.** 628 ft$^3$ **5.** 603 cm$^3$ **6.** 5,341 in.$^3$ **7.** 128 ft$^3$

**PRACTICE AND PROBLEM SOLVING** **9.** 166.4 in.$^3$ **11.** 500 m$^3$ **13.** 6,028.8 m$^3$ **15.** 27; $290.37 **17.** The student forgot to square the radius when making this calculation of the area of the base. **19.** 27 in.$^3$

**MIXED REVIEW** **21.** 120 cm$^2$ **23.** $m\angle 4$, $m\angle 5$, $m\angle 8 = x°$; $m\angle 2$, $m\angle 3$, $m\angle 6$, $m\angle 7 = (180 - x)°$

*Lesson 10-8* pages 542–545

**READ** **1.** The goal is to find the dimensions of the box that will hold the most popcorn. **2.** The size of the piece of cardboard is known as well as the size of the square corners.

**PLAN** **3a.** $6\frac{1}{2}$ in. by 9 in. by 1 in. **b.** 58.5 in.$^3$

**4.** The length and width are decreased by 4 in. and the height is increased by 2 in.

**SOLVE** **5.** The box with 2-in. by 2-in. corners. **6.** No, such a box would require more cardboard than is actually available in an $8\frac{1}{2}$-in. by 11-in. piece of cardboard.

**LOOK BACK** **7.** 7, 4.5, 2, 63; 5, 2.5, 3, 37.5; 3, 0.5, 4, 6 **8.** Yes, $5\frac{1}{2}$ in. by 8 in. by $1\frac{1}{2}$ in.

**CHECK UNDERSTANDING** **1.** Use several different lengths of string and a single weight. Record the time it takes the weight to swing back and forth when tied to each of the strings. **3.** The shorter side should be the height because it will yield a volume of 81.8 in.$^3$, and using the longer side as the height yields a volume of only 63.3 in.$^3$

**PRACTICE AND PROBLEM SOLVING** **5.** C **7.** 14 cm, 7 cm

**MIXED REVIEW** **9.** 30 cm$^3$ **11.** 18 ft$^3$ **13.** 15, 10, 20 **15.** about 220 cm

**CHECKPOINT 2** **1.** square prism, 56 cm$^2$ **2.** cylinder, 207 in.$^2$ **3.** square pyramid, 85 cm$^2$ **4.** cone, 377 cm$^2$ **5.** 78.1 cm$^3$ **6.** 169.6 in.$^3$ **7.** 0.2 m$^3$ or 176,625 cm$^3$

*Standardized Test Prep* page 546

**1.** A **3.** D **5.** B **7.** D **9.** The area quadruples and the circumference doubles.

**11a.**

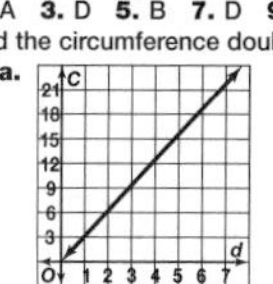

**b.** $\pi$ **c.** The slope is the rate of change of $C$ per unit $d$.

*Lesson 10-9* pages 547–550

**TRY THIS** **1.** 21 cm$^3$ **2.** 167 ft$^3$ **3.** 14,130 m$^3$ **4.** 179,503,333,333 mi$^3$

**CHECK UNDERSTANDING** **1.** 216 in.$^3$ **2.** 25 yd$^3$ **3.** 10,467 in.$^3$ **4.** 523 in.$^3$ **5.** 4 yd$^3$ **6.** 87 m$^3$ **7.** 4

**PRACTICE AND PROBLEM SOLVING** **9.** 819 cm$^3$ **11.** 65 yd$^3$ **13.** 7,235 cm$^3$ **15.** 447 cm$^3$ **17a.** 547.8 ft$^2$ **b.** 1,205.9 ft$^3$ **19.** 33.5 cm$^3$

**MIXED REVIEW** **21.** $27a^3b^6$ **23.** $\frac{9}{64}$ **25.** 18 **27.** 4

| Wrap Up | pages 552–554 |
|---|---|

**1.** 189 $m^2$ **2.** 14 $cm^2$ **3.** 6.25 $yd^2$ **4.** 17 $in.^2$ **5.** 79 $m^2$ **6.** 201 $mm^2$ **7.** 57 $m^2$ **8.** 31 $in.^2$ **9.** triangular prism **10.** square pyramid **11.** cylinder **12.** 164 $cm^2$ **13.** 63 $in.^2$ **14.** 84 $cm^2$ **15.** 251,200 $m^2$ **16.** 84 $cm^2$ **17.** 85 $cm^2$ **18.** 314 $ft^2$ **19.** 27 $ft^2$ **20.** 24 in. by 18 in. **21.** Find the area of the walk and garden and then subtract the area of the garden. **22.** 384 $cm^3$ **23.** 18 $ft^3$ **24.** 311 $in.^3$ **25.** 268 $m^3$

| Cumulative Review | page 556 |
|---|---|

**1.** B **3.** A **5.** B **7.** 28 $yd^2$ **9.** 113 $in.^2$ **11.** 61 $in.^2$ **13.** 132 $cm^2$ **15.** 1,256 $yd^2$ **17.** 240 $m^3$ **19.** 117 $m^3$ **21.** 904 $yd^3$

## ▶Chapter 11

| Skills You Need | page 557 |
|---|---|

**1.** 100 **2.** 36 **3.** 4 **4.** 81 **5.** 121 **6.** 0.04 **7.** 49 **8.** 5.29 **9.** 16 **10.** 25 **11.** *G* **12.** *K* **13.** *H* **14.** *D* **15.** *B* **16.** *F* **17.** *N* **18.** *Q* **19.** (−5, 4) **20.** (−2, −5) **21.** (2, 1) **22.** (7, 0) **23.** (−7, 1) **24.** (4, −2) **25.** (8, 6) **26.** (−6, −3) **27.** 4 **28.** 4 **29.** 1 **30.** 10 **31.** 2 **32.** 60 **33.** 77 **34.** 26 **35.** 10 **36.** 32 **37.** 17 **38.** 8 **39.** 60 **40.** 63 **41.** 3 **42.** 21

| Lesson 11-1 | pages 560–563 |
|---|---|

**TRY THIS** **1.** 10 **2.** −10 **3.** 4 **4.** −4 **5.** 5 **6.** −8 **7.** 7 **8.** −5 **9.** irrational **10.** rational **11.** rational **12.** irrational

**CHECK UNDERSTANDING** **1.** 2 **2.** −6 **3.** 8 **4.** 5 **5.** −7 **6.** 3 **7.** −2 **8.** 8 **9.** 4 **10.** −6 **11.** rational **12.** irrational **13.** irrational **14.** rational **15.** *x*

**PRACTICE AND PROBLEM SOLVING** **17.** −3 **19.** 12 **21.** 3 **23.** 6 **25.** 8 **27.** −10 **29.** −7 **31.** rational **33.** rational **35.** irrational **37a.** In each repetition of the pattern there is one more zero than in the previous one. **39.** 3, −3 **41.** 10, −10 **43.** 9 **45.** 12 **47.** 1 in. **49.** 0.000113 $m^3$ **51.** 1, 2, 3, 6, 9, 18 **53.** 1, 3, 11, 33 **55.** 1, 2, 5, 10, 25, 50 **57.** yes

| Lesson 11-2 | pages 564–569 |
|---|---|

**TRY THIS** **3.** 5 ft **4.** 9 m **5.** 12.7 m **6.** 8.7 ft **7.** No, $7^2 + 8^2 \neq 9^2$. **8.** No, $5^2 + 6^2 \neq 10^2$.

**CHECK UNDERSTANDING** **1.** 7.9 **2.** 3.5 **3.** 5.7 **4.** 9.7 **5.** 7.1 **6.** 2.8 **7.** $\overline{XY}$ and $\overline{XZ}$ are legs, and $\overline{ZY}$ is the hypotenuse. **8.** $\overline{PR}$ and $\overline{QR}$ are legs, and $\overline{PQ}$ is the hypotenuse. **9.** $\overline{AB}$ and $\overline{BC}$ are legs, and $\overline{AC}$ is the hypotenuse. **10.** 15 cm **11.** 9.8 ft **12.** 8 m **13.** yes

**PRACTICE AND PROBLEM SOLVING** **15.** 7.9 in. **17.** 13 cm **19.** 3.5 ft **21.** yes **23.** no **25.** no **27.** yes **29.** 4.5 in. **31.** 4 ft **33.** $\sqrt{32}$ units **35.** $\sqrt{34}$ units **37.** 6, 8, 10; yes, 36 + 64 = 100 **39.** 10, 24, 26; yes, 100 + 576 = 676

**41.**

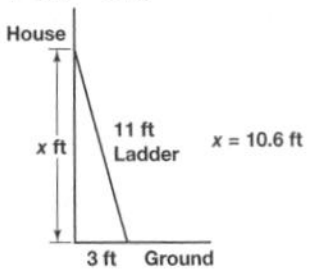
House
x ft
11 ft
Ladder
x = 10.6 ft
3 ft
Ground

**43a.** 10 in. **b.** 10.8 in. **c.** 15.8 in. **45.** C

**MIXED REVIEW** **47.** rational **49.** rational **51.** $b^5c^5$ **53.** $-27b^3$ **55.** $\frac{9m^2}{25}$

| Math Toolbox | pages 570–571 |
|---|---|

**1.** The perpendicular bisector of a chord of a circle passes through the center of the circle. **3.** 5.3 **5.** 11.2 **7.** 8.9 **9.** 5.7 **11.** 25.3

| Lesson 11-3 | pages 572–576 |
|---|---|

**TRY THIS** **1.** 4.1 **2.** 9.5 **3.** 17.5 **4.** (5, 3) **5.** (−1, 0.5)

**CHECK UNDERSTANDING** **1.** 5 units **2.** 8.9 units **3.** 7.1 units **4.** (7, 1) **5.** (3.5, −5) **6.** (−6, 9.5) **7.** No, interchanging $x_1$ and $x_2$ will only affect the sign. Since you will square the difference, the sign is not important.

**PRACTICE AND PROBLEM SOLVING** **9.** 13 **11.** 19.2 **13.** 24.0 **15.** (2.5, −4) **17.** (8.5, −7.5) **19.** (0.65, 4.75) **21.** 17 units **23.** (12, 9) **25a.** (−0.5, 3)
**b.** $\sqrt{[-3-(-0.5)]^2+(5-3)^2} = \sqrt{(-0.5-2)^2+(3-1)^2} = \sqrt{(-2.5)^2+2^2} = \sqrt{(-2.5)^2+2^2}$

**MIXED REVIEW** **27.** no **29.** 9 **31.** 12.5



**33.**

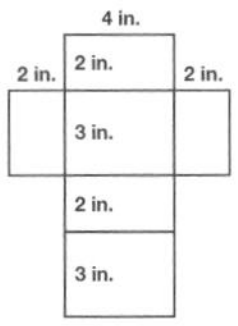
4 in.
2 in.
2 in.
2 in.
3 in.
2 in.
3 in.

| Checkpoint 1 | page 576 |
|---|---|

**1.** −2 **3.** 5 **5.** −7 **7.** 10 ft **9.** 25 yd **11.** 9.2; (−3, −5.5) **13.** 21.5; (−9, 2.5)

| Standardized Test Prep | page 577 |
|---|---|

**1.** B **3.** A **5.** B **7a.** $n(d) = 100d$
**b.**

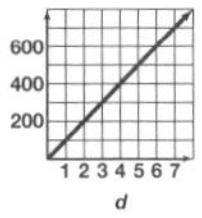
600
n(d) 400
200
1 2 3 4 5 6 7
d

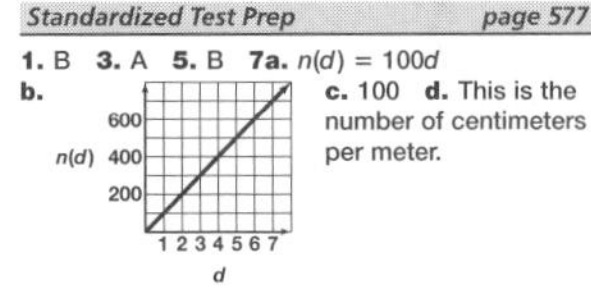

**c.** 100 **d.** This is the number of centimeters per meter.

| Lesson 11-4 | pages 578–581 |
|---|---|

**READ** **1.** $\overline{RS} \perp \overline{RP}$, $\overline{QT} \perp \overline{RP}$, $\triangle PRS \sim \triangle PQT$, *RS*, *RQ*, and *QT* **2.** *QP*

**LOOK BACK** **3.** $\overline{RQ}$ and $\overline{RP}$, $\overline{ST}$ and $\overline{SP}$ **4.** It forces you to draw the entire 40 + *x* side to complete the larger triangle.

**CHECK UNDERSTANDING** **1.** $\frac{90}{x} = \frac{80}{120}$; 135 m **2.** $\frac{x}{10+x} = \frac{39}{48}$; $43\frac{1}{3}$ ft **3.** 1.2 mi

**PRACTICE AND PROBLEM SOLVING**
**5.** $\frac{x}{60} = \frac{15}{25}$; 36 yd **7.** 10.5 yd **9.** 13 **11.** 7:43 A.M. **13.** 6.3 $ft^2$

**MIXED REVIEW** **15.** (3, 5) **17.** (1.5, −6.5)
**19.**

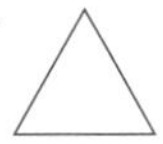

**21.** Keith \$80, Lucy \$40

| Lesson 11-5 | pages 582–586 |
|---|---|

**TRY THIS** **1.** 5.9 cm **2.** 17 m **3.** $a \approx 6.9$ cm $b = 8$ cm **4.** $e = 6$ in. $f \approx 10.4$ in.

**CHECK UNDERSTANDING** **1.** Neither. In a 45°-45°-90° triangle two sides are congruent. In a 30°-60°-90° triangle one leg is twice the hypotenuse. **2.** This is a 45°-45°-90° triangle because two sides are congruent and the hypotenuse is $\sqrt{2}$ times a leg. **3.** This is a 30°-60°-90° triangle because the hypotenuse is twice the shorter leg and the longer leg is $\sqrt{3}$ times the shorter leg. **4.** 4.2 yd **5.** $x = 6$ m, $y \approx 5.2$ m **6.** $x \approx 18.4$ cm, $y = 13$ cm **7.** Yes, because the hypotenuse is twice the shorter leg.

**PRACTICE AND PROBLEM SOLVING** **9.** 9 cm, 12.7 cm **11.** 3.5 ft, 4 ft **13.** 12.1 mm, 14 mm **17a.** 4 in. **b.** $2\sqrt{3}$ in. **c.** $4\sqrt{3}$ $in.^2$ **d.** $24\sqrt{3}$ $in.^2$

**MIXED REVIEW** **19.** Yes, for each domain value there is only one range value. **21.** 25.1 in. **23.** 15.7 ft

| Math Toolbox | page 587 |
|---|---|

**1.** $7y$ **3.** $-5x^3$ **5.** $a^6$ **7.** $9b^4$ **9.** $-x^2y^6$ **11.** $x^{11}\sqrt{x}$ **13.** $3b^5\sqrt{3b}$

| Lesson 11-6 | pages 588–592 |
|---|---|

**TRY THIS** **4.** $\sin Y = \frac{12}{13}$, $\cos Y = \frac{5}{13}$, $\tan Y = \frac{12}{5}$ **5.** 0.1736 **6.** 0.2588 **7.** 1.3270 **8.** 0.9272 **9.** 14.3 ft

**CHECK UNDERSTANDING** **1a.** 4 **b.** 3 **c.** 5 **2.** $\sin A = \frac{4}{5}$, $\cos A = \frac{3}{5}$, $\tan A = \frac{4}{3}$ **3.** 57.2900 **4.** 0.5 **5.** 0.9703 **6.** 0.9205 **7.** 0.5317 **8.** 1 **9.** $\frac{1}{2}$ **10.** $\frac{1}{2}$

**PRACTICE AND PROBLEM SOLVING** **11.** $\frac{3}{5}$, $\frac{12}{15}$, $\frac{9}{12}$ **13.** 0 **15.** 0.8290 **17.** 0.3746 **19.** 0.9925 **21.** 1.7321 **23.** 0.2250 **27.** The two ratios are equal. **29.** 4.8 m

**MIXED REVIEW** **31.** 14 ft **33.** −6, −4, 2 **35.** 21, 20, 17 **37.** $\overline{RE} \cong \overline{EA}$

**CHECKPOINT 2** **1.** 45°-45°-90° **2.** 30°-60°-90° **3.** 30°-60°-90° **4.** 0.4848 **5.** 0.5774 **6.** 0.5299 **7.** 0.9986 **8.** B

| Math Toolbox | page 593 |
|---|---|

**1.** $m\angle X \approx 44°$, $m\angle Y \approx 46°$ **3.** $m\angle C \approx 36°$, $m\angle D \approx 54°$





| Lesson 11-7 | pages 594–598 |
|---|---|

**TRY THIS** **1.** 141 m **2.** 16.1 m **3.** 22.7 m

**CHECK UNDERSTANDING** **1.** angle of elevation = ∠*ADC*, angle of depression = ∠*BAD* **2.** angle of elevation = ∠*QRS*, angle of depression = ∠*PQR* **3.** 32.2 m **4.** 95.3 ft **5.** The angle of depression is between the line of sight and the horizontal.

**PRACTICE AND PROBLEM SOLVING** **7.** 502.4 m **9.** 1,293.8 m **11.** 3.3 km **13.** 17.4 yd

**MIXED REVIEW** **15.** 0.5543 **17.** 0.8290 **19.** 2.4751 **21.** $3.61\pi$ $cm^2 \approx 11.3$ $cm^2$ **23.** $20.25\pi$ $in.^2 \approx 63.6$ $in.^2$

| Wrap Up | pages 600–602 |
|---|---|

**1.** 1 **2.** −4 **3.** 7 **4.** 8 **5.** −6 **6.** 2 **7.** 3 **8.** 6 **9.** 8 **10.** 10 **11.** rational **12.** rational **13.** rational **14.** irrational **15.** rational **16.** It is irrational because there is not a block of identical repeating digits. **17.** No, 1 + 9 ≠ 9. **18.** Yes, 81 + 144 = 225. **19.** Yes, 6 + 10 = 16. **20.** Yes, 900 + 1,600 = 2,500. **21.** 3.6 **22.** 5 **23.** 12.6 **24.** 2.2 **25.** 9.2 **26.** 13.4 **27.** (2, 4) **28.** (3, 4) **29.** (−2, 2) **30.** (4.5, 10) **31.** (−12, −8) **32.** (2.5, −0.5) **33.** 337.5 ft **34.** $a = 6$ in., $b \approx 10.4$ in **35.** $y \approx 9.9$ m **36.** $f = 4$ ft, $c \approx 3.5$ ft **37.** 0.2756 **38.** 7.1154 **39.** 0.9063 **40.** 0.0524 **41.** 0.9986 **42.** 0.2924 **43.** 0.6947 **44.** 1 **45.** 0.9816 **46.** 0.2309 **47.** 8 ft **48.** about 99 ft

| Cumulative Review | page 604 |
|---|---|

**1.** C **3.** B **5.** A **7.** D **9.** 0.5592 **11.** 0.1908 **13.** 0.9877 **15.** 2.1 ft

## ▶Chapter 12

| Skills You Need | page 605 |
|---|---|

**1.** 12 **2.** 52 **3.** 101 **4.** 0.225 **5.** $\frac{1}{6}$ **6.** $\frac{1}{6}$ **7.** $\frac{1}{3}$ **8.** 0 **9.** $\frac{1}{2}$ **10.** $\frac{1}{3}$ **11.** $\frac{5}{6}$ **12.** 0 **13.** $\frac{6}{11}$ **14.** $\frac{5}{11}$ **15.** $\frac{5}{11}$ **16.** $\frac{1}{3}$ **17.** $\frac{3}{4}$ **18.** $\frac{4}{5}$ **19.** $\frac{2}{3}$ **20.** $\frac{1}{2}$ **21.** $\frac{1}{8}$ **22.** $\frac{5}{8}$ **23.** $\frac{1}{10}$ **24.** 0.5 **25.** 0.36 **26.** 0.2 **27.** 0.05 **28.** 20% **29.** 87.5% **30.** 28% **31.** 30%

| Lesson 12-1 | pages 608–611 |
|---|---|

**TRY THIS**

**4.**

| Number | Frequency |
|---|---|
| 10 | 5 |
| 11 | 3 |
| 12 | 2 |
| 13 | 2 |
| 14 | 1 |
| 15 | 2 |

**5.**

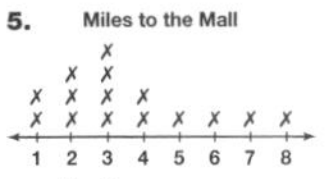
Miles to the Mall
1 2 3 4 5 6 7 8

; 7 miles

**6.** \$0.19

**CHECK UNDERSTANDING**

**1.**

| Number | Frequency |
|---|---|
| 0 | 2 |
| 1 | 2 |
| 2 | 2 |
| 3 | 2 |
| 4 | 2 |

**2.**

| Number | Frequency |
|---|---|
| 1 | 1 |
| 2 | 2 |
| 3 | 1 |
| 4 | 3 |
| 5 | 1 |
| 6 | 2 |
| 7 | 1 |
| 8 | 2 |
| 9 | 1 |

**3.**

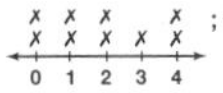
0 1 2 3 4

; 4

**4.**

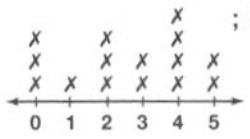
0 1 2 3 4 5

; 5

**PRACTICE AND PROBLEM SOLVING**

**7.**

| Number | Frequency |
|---|---|
| 25 | 2 |
| 26 | 2 |
| 27 | 1 |
| 28 | 3 |
| 29 | 2 |
| 30 | 2 |

**9.** Test Scores

| Score | Frequency |
|---|---|
| 60 | 1 |
| 65 | 1 |
| 70 | 4 |
| 75 | 2 |
| 80 | 1 |
| 85 | 2 |
| 90 | 2 |
| 95 | 1 |
| 100 | 2 |

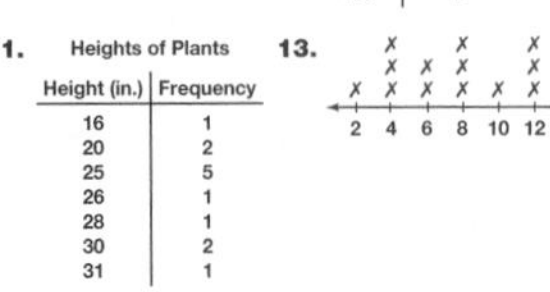

**11.** Heights of Plants

| Height (in.) | Frequency |
|---|---|
| 16 | 1 |
| 20 | 2 |
| 25 | 5 |
| 26 | 1 |
| 28 | 1 |
| 30 | 2 |
| 31 | 1 |

**13.**

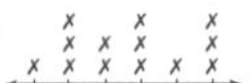
2 4 6 8 10 12



**15.**

16 17 18 19 20

**17.**

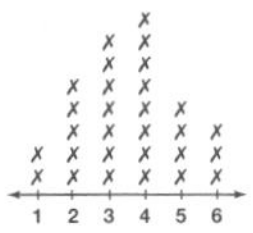
1 2 3 4 5 6

**19.**

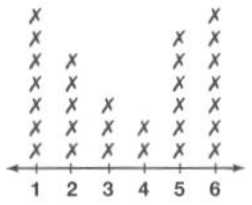
1 2 3 4 5 6

**21.**

| Number | Frequency |
|---|---|
| 1 | 1 |
| 2 | 0 |
| 3 | 2 |
| 4 | 3 |
| 5 | 1 |
| 6 | 2 |

**23.**

| Number | Frequency |
|---|---|
| 70 | 4 |
| 75 | 3 |
| 80 | 4 |
| 85 | 3 |
| 90 | 3 |
| 95 | 4 |

**25.**

Number of Gold Medals
1998 Winter Olympics
1 2 3 4 5 6 7 8 9 10 11 12

**27a.**

Weekly Earnings
300 400 500 600 700 800 900 1000
Earnings ($)

**b.** Weekly Earnings

| Earnings (\$) | Frequency |
|---|---|
| 320 | 3 |
| 400 | 6 |
| 480 | 3 |
| 720 | 3 |
| 1000 | 1 |

**c.** \$680

**MIXED REVIEW** **29.** 15.5, 16, 16 and 18 **31.** ∠*R* **33.** *LM*

| Math Toolbox | page 612 |
|---|---|

**1.**

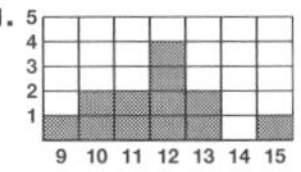
5
4
3
2
1
9 10 11 12 13 14 15

**3.**

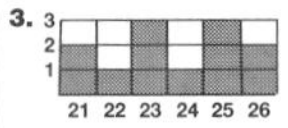
3
2
1
21 22 23 24 25 26

| Lesson 12-2 | pages 613–617 |
|---|---|

**TRY THIS**

**1.**

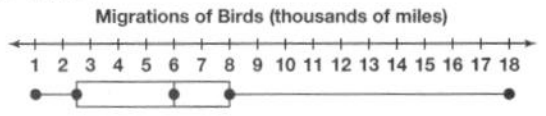
Migrations of Birds (thousands of miles)
1 2 3 4 5 6 7 8 9 10 11 12 13 14 15 16 17 18

**2.**

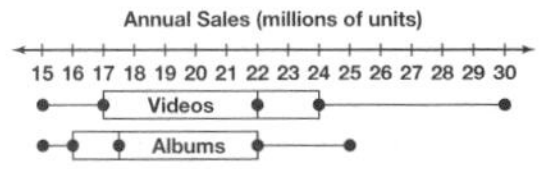
Annual Sales (millions of units)
15 16 17 18 19 20 21 22 23 24 25 26 27 28 29 30
Videos
Albums

**3.** The values range from 10 to 50. The median is 22.5. At least half of the values are within 2.5 units of the median. **4.** The values range from 15 to 45. The median is 35. At least half of the values are within 10 units of the median. **5.** The women's heights have a median of 71 in. and a range of only 10 in. The men's heights have a median of 79 in. and a range of 12 in. Most of the men are taller than the tallest woman.

**CHECK UNDERSTANDING**

**1.**

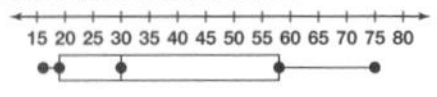
15 20 25 30 35 40 45 50 55 60 65 70 75 80

**2.**

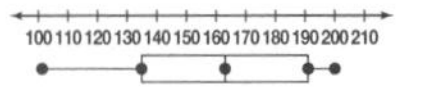
100 110 120 130 140 150 160 170 180 190 200 210

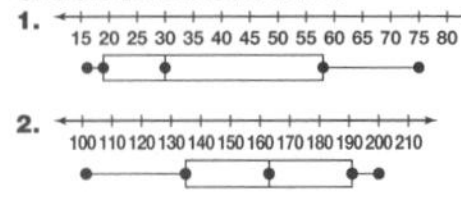

**3.** \$115, \$50 **4.** \$70 **5.** \$60 **6.** \$85 **7.** No; the median is not in the middle of the box.

**PRACTICE AND PROBLEM SOLVING**

**9.** Eagle Wingspans (m)

1.5 1.6 1.7 1.8 1.9 2.0 2.1 2.2 2.3 2.4 2.5 2.6 2.7

**11.** Pages in Books

180 200 220 240 260 280 300 320 340 360 380 400

**13.** 0 5 10 15 20 25 30 35 40 45 50 55 60

1st set

2nd set

**15.** The lower quartile is the median of the lower half of the data; The upper quartile is the median of the upper half of the data. The middle quartile is the median of the data.

**17.** Maximum Speeds of Animals (mi/h)

0 10 20 30 40 50 60 70 80 90 100

**19.** The acreages vary considerably, from about 25 acres to about 650 acres. However, most of the parks are between 50 and 250 acres, with a median of 125 acres. **21.** The median can be determined from the line across the box. The mean and mode are not indicated, and the detailed data to calculate them is not shown in the plot.

**MIXED REVIEW**

**23.**

| Number | Frequency |
|---|---|
| 29 | 1 |
| 30 | 1 |
| 31 | 3 |
| 32 | 4 |
| 33 | 2 |
| 34 | 0 |
| 35 | 1 |

**25.** 11.4 units **27.** 20.2 units

| *Math Toolbox* | *pages 618–619* |
|---|---|

**1a.** 0

**b.** Animal Life Spans

```
0 | 17
1 | 0022555
2 | 05
3 |
4 | 1

1 | 6 means 16
```

**c.** 13.5 **d.** 15 years **e.** 40 years

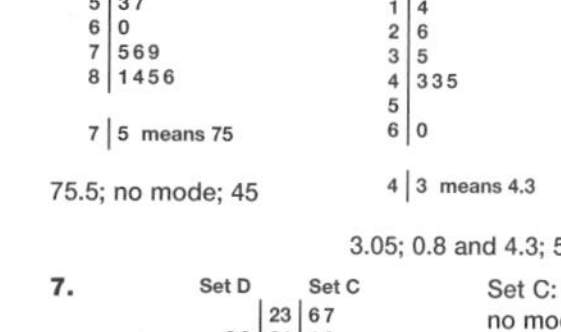

**3.**

```
4 | 17
5 | 37
6 | 0
7 | 569
8 | 1456

7 | 5 means 75
```

75.5; no mode; 45

**5.**

```
0 | 288
1 | 4
2 | 6
3 | 5
4 | 335
5 |
6 | 0

4 | 3 means 4.3
```

3.05; 0.8 and 4.3; 5.8

**7.**

```
Set D       Set C
     | 23 | 67
  83 | 24 | 12
  71 | 25 | 0
   2 | 26 |

means 251 ← 1 | 25 | 0 → means 250
```

Set C: 241, no mode
Set D: 251, no mode

**9.** Class A: 63 min; Class B: 61 min
**11.** Class A: 74, 79, and 96 min; Class B: 99 min

| *Lesson 12-3* | *pages 620–625* |
|---|---|

**TRY THIS**

**1.**

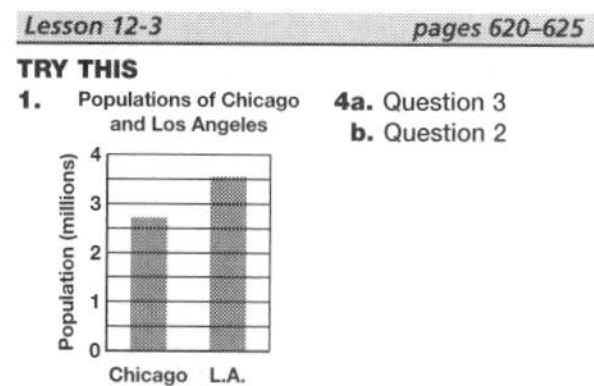


**4a.** Question 3 **b.** Question 2

**CHECK UNDERSTANDING** **1.** *American Ampersand* **2.** *Fossil Week* **3.** One tends to compare the lengths of the bars without noticing the break in the scale.

**4.**

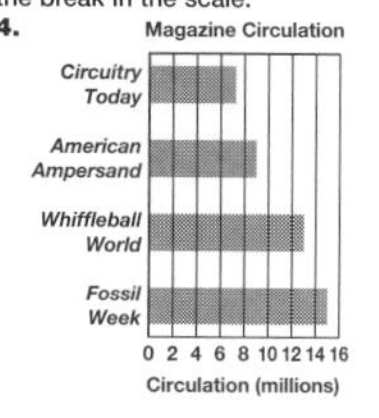




**PRACTICE AND PROBLEM SOLVING** **7.** nearly 2 to 1; about 1.14 to 1 **9.** It suggests that the percent is rising rapidly, by putting 1989 and 1993 very close together. **11.** That sales more than quadrupled. **13.** No. The break in the vertical axis shows that the presenter is intending to be deceptive.

**MIXED REVIEW** **19.** 18 20 22 24 26 28 30 32

**21.** 90 92 94 96 98 100 102 104 106 108 110 112 114 116 118

**23.** $\frac{3}{10}$ **25.** $\frac{1}{5}$

| *Lesson 12-4* | *pages 626–630* |
|---|---|

**TRY THIS**

**3.**

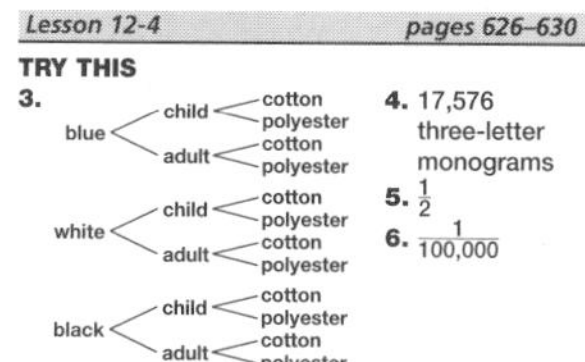


12 choices

**4.** 17,576 three-letter monograms **5.** $\frac{1}{2}$ **6.** $\frac{1}{100{,}000}$

**CHECK UNDERSTANDING**

**1.**

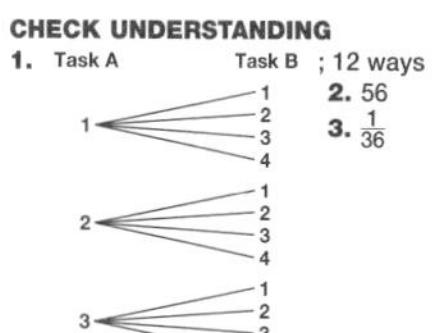


; 12 ways

**2.** 56 **3.** $\frac{1}{36}$

**PRACTICE AND PROBLEM SOLVING**

**5.**

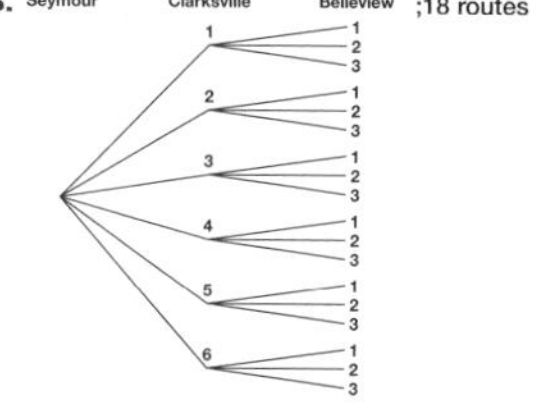


;18 routes

**7.** 440 cars **9.** HHH, HHT, HTH, THH, HTT, THT, TTH, TTT **11.** Mon. A.M., Mon. P.M., Tue. A.M., Tue. P.M., Wed. A.M., Wed. P.M., Thur. A.M., Thur. P.M., Fri. A.M., Fri. P.M. **13.** $\frac{3}{8}$ **15.** blue cardigan, blue crewneck, blue V-neck, pink cardigan, pink crewneck, pink V-neck, red cardigan, red crewneck, red V-neck, brown cardigan, brown crewneck, brown V-neck, black cardigan, black crewneck, black V-neck; 15 sweaters. **17.** $\frac{1}{3}$

**MIXED REVIEW** **19.** 3 4 5 6 7 range = 4

**21.** (0, 2) **23.** While the height of the 1990 bar is $1\frac{2}{3}$ times the height of the 1980 bar, the area is 5 times as great.

**CHECKPOINT 1**

**1.**

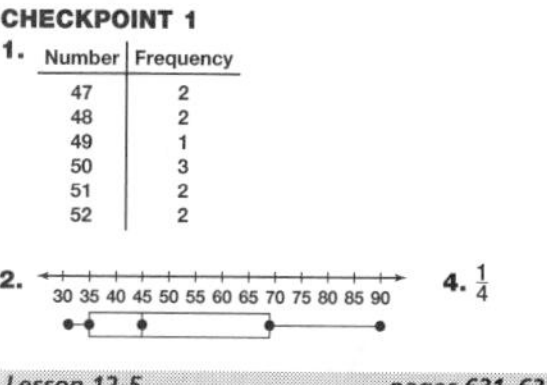

| Number | Frequency |
|---|---|
| 47 | 2 |
| 48 | 2 |
| 49 | 1 |
| 50 | 3 |
| 51 | 2 |
| 52 | 2 |

**2.** 30 35 40 45 50 55 60 65 70 75 80 85 90

**4.** $\frac{1}{4}$

| *Lesson 12-5* | *pages 631–635* |
|---|---|

**TRY THIS** **5.** $\frac{1}{4}$ **6.** 9% **7.** $\frac{3}{10}$

**CHECK UNDERSTANDING** **1.** $\frac{2}{25}$ or 8% **2.** $\frac{9}{100}$ or 9% **3.** $\frac{3}{25}$ or 12% **4.** $\frac{3}{50}$ or 6% **5.** $\frac{5}{18}$ **6.** $\frac{5}{18}$ **7.** $\frac{1}{6}$ **8.** $\frac{5}{18}$ **9.** Dependent. The total number of cards has been reduced by 1.



**10.** Independent. The total number of cards is unchanged. **11.** Independent. The possibilities on the second roll are the same as on the first.

**PRACTICE AND PROBLEM SOLVING** **13.** $\frac{1}{18}$ **15.** $\frac{1}{36}$ **17.** $\frac{1}{4}$ **19.** $\frac{2}{45}$ **21.** $\frac{2}{45}$ **23.** $\frac{4}{15}$ **27a.** $\frac{9}{56}$ **b.** $\frac{3}{28}$ **29.** 83%

**MIXED REVIEW** **31.** $\frac{7}{25}, \frac{24}{25}, \frac{7}{24}$

| *Lesson 12-6* | *pages 636–640* |
|---|---|

**TRY THIS** **1.** 120 **2.** 20 **3.** 60 **4.** 120 **5.** 120 **6.** 20 ways **7.** 28 **8.** 56 **9.** 70 **10.** 56 **11.** combinations **12.** permutations

**CHECK UNDERSTANDING** **1.** 6 **2.** 120 **3.** 5,040 **4.** CA, CT, AT; 3 **5.** MA, MT, MH, AT, AH, TH; 6 **6.** VA, VL, VU, VE, AL, AU, AE, LU, LE, UE; 10 **7.** 12 **8.** 360 **9.** 3,024 **10.** 1,814,400 **11.** 6 **12.** 6 **13.** 15 **14.** 126 **15.** 45 **16.** 3

**PRACTICE AND PROBLEM SOLVING** **17.** 24 **19.** 336 **21.** SIX; 1 combination **23.** 120 **25.** 30,240 **27.** 79,833,600 **29.** 2 **31.** 35 **33a.** 24 **b.** Three: pest, pets, and step **c.** $\frac{1}{8}$ **37.** permutations **39.** C

**MIXED REVIEW** **41.** $\frac{1}{20}$ **43.** $33.\overline{3}\%$

| *Standardized Test Prep* | *page 641* |
|---|---|

**1.** A **3.** C **5.** D **7.** The height is the length of an altitude. The altitude divides the triangle into two right triangles, both with leg 6 and hypotenuse 12. The altitude is the other leg. $h^2 + 6^2 = 12^2$ and $h = 10.4$

| *Lesson 12-7* | *pages 642–645* |
|---|---|

**TRY THIS** **1.** 52%

**CHECK UNDERSTANDING** **1.** $\frac{1}{2}$ **2.** $\frac{1}{8}$ **3.** $\frac{3}{8}$ **4.** $\frac{7}{8}$

**PRACTICE AND PROBLEM SOLVING** **7.** 16.2% **9.** 25% **11.** 0% **13a.** Toss 3 coins repeatedly, perhaps 100 times, and record the results. The percent of the time that you get 3 heads is the experimental probability. **b.** Find the experimental probability as in part (a). Calculate the theoretical probability $\left(\frac{1}{2} \cdot \frac{1}{2} \cdot \frac{1}{2} = \frac{1}{8}\right)$. Compare the probabilities. They will not necessarily be the same. As one performs many experiments, experimental probability will approach theoretical.

**MIXED REVIEW** **19.** 12 **21.** 4 **23.** $(x, y) \rightarrow (x + 7, y + 4)$ **25.** 0.4 $m^3$

| *Lesson 12-8* | *pages 646–649* |
|---|---|

**TRY THIS** **1.** Not a good sample, because these students would be most interested in racing bikes. **2.** Not a good sample, because this sample would not include teens who do not rent videos. **3.** This is a good sample, because there is no built-in bias for or against any cereal. **4.** 200 calculators **5.** Less accurate. A larger sample is likely to be more representative of the population. **6.** The entire population might be too large to be surveyed. Also, the testing might be destructive, as in testing flash bulbs.

**CHECK UNDERSTANDING** **1.** Not a good sample, since tall students are more likely to be basketball players than other students. **2.** This is a good sample, since there is no bias built into the sample. **3.** Not a good sample, since it excludes students not interested in basketball. **4.** 5,760 eggs

**PRACTICE AND PROBLEM SOLVING** **5.** A good sample, since there is no bias built into it. **7.** Not a good sample, because restaurant critics may be looking for things the general public pays little attention to. **11.** Write and solve the equation that states that the ratio of defective chips to the 250 chips in the sample is equal to the ratio of defective chips to the 50,000 chips produced.

**MIXED REVIEW** **13.** $\frac{9}{26}$ **15.** $\frac{5}{26}$ **17.** 576 $\pi$ $cm^2$; 1,809 $cm^2$ **19.** 2,500 $\pi$ $mi^2$; 7,850 $mi^2$

**CHECKPOINT 2** **1.** D **2a.** 380 outcomes **b.** 190 committees **3a.** $\frac{2}{15}$ **b.** 3 **c.** No. The player will have off days, and lucky days, and may improve with experience. **4.** 9,444 premium oranges

| *Lesson 12-9* | *pages 650–653* |
|---|---|

**READ** **1.** $\frac{4}{5}$

**PLAN** **3.** one or two spins **4.** Many—perhaps 100

**SOLVE** **5a.** 69% **b.** 15% **c.** 84%

**PRACTICE AND PROBLEM SOLVING** **5.** \$67.50 **7.** 3 yd × 9 yd **11.** Yes. Since circumference equals $\pi d$, $d = \frac{3 \text{ in.}}{\pi} \approx \frac{3 \text{ in.}}{3.14}$, which is less than 1 in.



**MIXED REVIEW** **13.** 3 **15.** −9 **17.** 57 in.

| *Math Toolbox* | *page 654* |
|---|---|

**1.** 10%; 0 **3.** Let an even digit represent being stopped by a red light. Look for groups with 2 or more even digits.

| *Wrap Up* | *pages 656–658* |
|---|---|

**1.**

| Number | Frequency |
|---|---|
| 9 | 1 |
| 10 | 3 |
| 11 | 3 |
| 12 | 4 |
| 13 | 1 |

**2.**

| Number | Frequency |
|---|---|
| 45 | 1 |
| 46 | 3 |
| 47 | 2 |
| 48 | 3 |
| 49 | 2 |
| 50 | 1 |

**3.** 1 2 3 4 5 6 ; 5

**4.** 1 2 3 4 5 6 ; 5

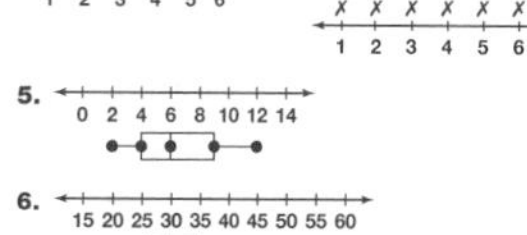

**5.** 0 2 4 6 8 10 12 14

**6.** 15 20 25 30 35 40 45 50 55 60

**7.** Because the vertical axis is short, the bars appear to be nearly the same height. **9a.** 15 **b.** $\frac{4}{15}$ **10.** $\frac{2}{25}$ **11.** $\frac{1}{20}$ **12.** permutation, since order is important; 120 ways **13.** combination, since order does not matter; 220 groups **14.** $\frac{9}{20}$ **15.** $\frac{1}{2}$ **17.** Not a good sample, because it includes students not in the skating population. **18.** Not a good sample, because it includes students not in the skating population. **19.** A good sample. These people are all in the skating population, and there is not built-in bias.

| *Cumulative Review* | *page 660* |
|---|---|

**1.** B **3.** B **5.** A

**7.** 25 30 35 40 45 50 55 60 65 70 75 80

**9a.** $\frac{1}{4}$

**11.** This is not a good sample, since it excludes men, who are part of the total population.

## ▶CHAPTER 13

| *Skills You Need* | *page 661* |
|---|---|

**1.** −10, −4, 2 **2.** 6, 0, −6 **3.** −10, −2, 6 **4.** −1, 0, 1 **5.** $-6\frac{1}{5}, -5, -3\frac{4}{5}$ **6.** 10, 6, 2 **7.** $-7\frac{1}{2}, -8, -8\frac{1}{2}$ **8.** $5\frac{1}{2}, 6, 6\frac{1}{2}$ **9.** 5, −1, −7 **10.** 40 **11.** 11 **12.** 208 **13.** 28 **14.** 17 **15.** 25 **16.** 21 **17.** 0.64 **18.** −32 **19.** 2 **20.** 7 **21.** $11a - 4$ **22.** 5 **23.** $4 - g$ **24.** $10t + 5s$ **25.** $7b + 4d$ **26.** $-45c$ **27.** $7v + 21$ **28.** $3d - 12$ **29.** $15x + 5$ **30.** $15t - 30$ **31.** $3u - 24$ **32.** $9p + 72$ **33.** $8y + 28$ **34.** $-12d + 4$ **35.** $50 - 30s$ **36.** $-21 + 6w$ **37.** $6h + 54$ **38.** $27 - 6b$

| *Lesson 13-1* | *pages 664–668* |
|---|---|

**TRY THIS** **2.** 5 **3.** −3 **4.** 7, 3, −1; start with 23 and add −4 repeatedly. **5.** $-\frac{2}{3}, \frac{2}{3}$, 2; start with −6 and add $1\frac{1}{3}$ repeatedly. **6.** The common ratio is 3. 162, 486, 1,458; start with 2 and multiply by 3 repeatedly. **7.** The common ratio is $\frac{1}{2}$. 0.25, 0.125, 0.0625; start with 4 and multiply by $\frac{1}{2}$ repeatedly. **8.** geometric; 243, 729, 2,187 **9.** neither; 34, 45, 58 **10.** geometric; −12, 12, −12 **11.** arithmetic; 650, 800, 950

**CHECK UNDERSTANDING** **1.** −1 **2.** 7 **3.** $\frac{1}{2}$ **4.** −6 **5.** 2 **6.** 2 **7.** $\frac{1}{5}$ **8.** 5 **9.** 256, 1,024, 4,096; start with 1 and multiply by 4 repeatedly. **10.** −9, −6, −3; start with −21 and add 3 repeatedly. **11.** 7.3, 7.5, 7.7; start with 6.5 and add 0.2 repeatedly.

**PRACTICE AND PROBLEM SOLVING** **13.** 6 **15.** 1.4 **17.** −3 **19.** $\frac{1}{3}$ **21.** 144, 288, 576; start with 9 and multiply by 2 repeatedly. **23.** −3, −9, −15; start with 21 and add −6 repeatedly. **25.** −40, −70, −100; start with 80 and add −30 repeatedly. **27.** 512, 2,048, 8,192; start with 2 and multiply by 4 repeatedly. **29.** arithmetic; −10, −15, −20 **31.** neither; 10, 16, 26 **33.** arithmetic; $1\frac{5}{6}, 2\frac{1}{6}, 2\frac{1}{2}$ **35.** neither; 32, 45, 60 **37.** neither; 3, −2, −8 **39.** geometric; $-\frac{1}{80}, -\frac{1}{160}, -\frac{1}{320}$ **41a.** 12, 11, and 14 million **b.** 1.053, 1.046, 1.056 **c.** geometric **d.** 290 million **43.** 2, 0, 0, 2; neither **45.** −4, −2, 0, 2; arithmetic **47a.** \$2,040, \$2,080.80, \$2,122.42, \$2,164.86 **b.** Geometric; each balance is 1.02 times the previous balance. **49.** B

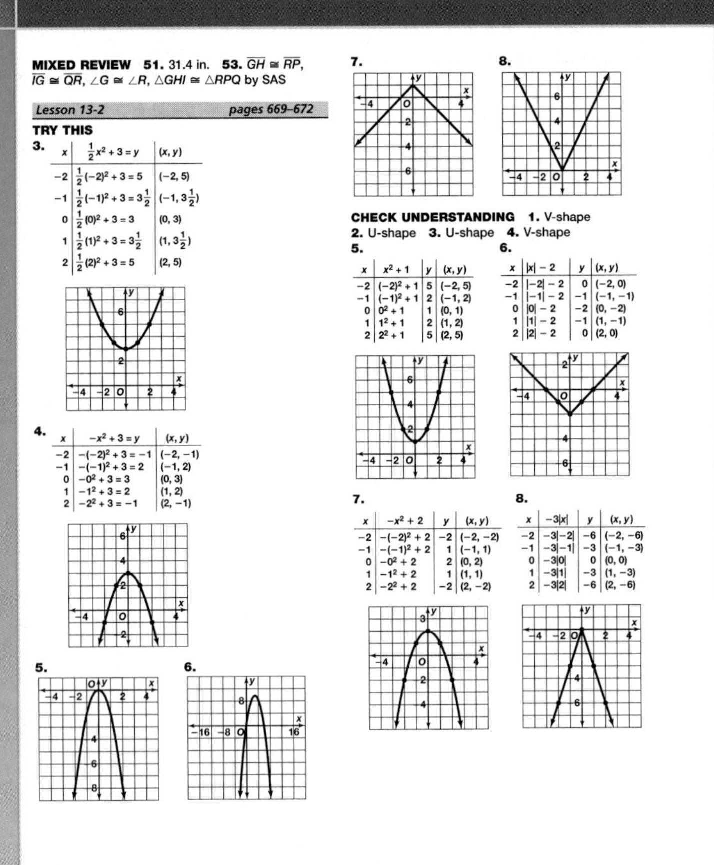

**MIXED REVIEW** **51.** 31.4 in. **53.** $\overline{GH} \cong \overline{RP}$, $\overline{IG} \cong \overline{QR}$, $\angle G \cong \angle R$, $\triangle GHI \cong \triangle RPQ$ by SAS

*Lesson 13-2* *pages 669–672*

**TRY THIS**

**3.**

| $x$ | $\frac{1}{2}x^2 + 3 = y$ | $(x, y)$ |
|---|---|---|
| −2 | $\frac{1}{2}(-2)^2 + 3 = 5$ | (−2, 5) |
| −1 | $\frac{1}{2}(-1)^2 + 3 = 3\frac{1}{2}$ | $(-1, 3\frac{1}{2})$ |
| 0 | $\frac{1}{2}(0)^2 + 3 = 3$ | (0, 3) |
| 1 | $\frac{1}{2}(1)^2 + 3 = 3\frac{1}{2}$ | $(1, 3\frac{1}{2})$ |
| 2 | $\frac{1}{2}(2)^2 + 3 = 5$ | (2, 5) |

**4.**

| $x$ | $-x^2 + 3 = y$ | $(x, y)$ |
|---|---|---|
| −2 | $-(-2)^2 + 3 = -1$ | (−2, −1) |
| −1 | $-(-1)^2 + 3 = 2$ | (−1, 2) |
| 0 | $-0^2 + 3 = 3$ | (0, 3) |
| 1 | $-1^2 + 3 = 2$ | (1, 2) |
| 2 | $-2^2 + 3 = -1$ | (2, −1) |

**5.** **6.** **7.** **8.**

**CHECK UNDERSTANDING** **1.** V-shape **2.** U-shape **3.** U-shape **4.** V-shape

**5.**

| $x$ | $x^2 + 1$ | $y$ | $(x, y)$ |
|---|---|---|---|
| −2 | $(-2)^2 + 1$ | 5 | (−2, 5) |
| −1 | $(-1)^2 + 1$ | 2 | (−1, 2) |
| 0 | $0^2 + 1$ | 1 | (0, 1) |
| 1 | $1^2 + 1$ | 2 | (1, 2) |
| 2 | $2^2 + 1$ | 5 | (2, 5) |

**6.**

| $x$ | $\lvert x\rvert - 2$ | $y$ | $(x, y)$ |
|---|---|---|---|
| −2 | $\lvert -2\rvert - 2$ | 0 | (−2, 0) |
| −1 | $\lvert -1\rvert - 2$ | −1 | (−1, −1) |
| 0 | $\lvert 0\rvert - 2$ | −2 | (0, −2) |
| 1 | $\lvert 1\rvert - 2$ | −1 | (1, −1) |
| 2 | $\lvert 2\rvert - 2$ | 0 | (2, 0) |

**7.**

| $x$ | $-x^2 + 2$ | $y$ | $(x, y)$ |
|---|---|---|---|
| −2 | $-(-2)^2 + 2$ | −2 | (−2, −2) |
| −1 | $-(-1)^2 + 2$ | 1 | (−1, 1) |
| 0 | $-0^2 + 2$ | 2 | (0, 2) |
| 1 | $-1^2 + 2$ | 1 | (1, 1) |
| 2 | $-2^2 + 2$ | −2 | (2, −2) |

**8.**

| $x$ | $-3\lvert x\rvert$ | $y$ | $(x, y)$ |
|---|---|---|---|
| −2 | $-3\lvert -2\rvert$ | −6 | (−2, −6) |
| −1 | $-3\lvert -1\rvert$ | −3 | (−1, −3) |
| 0 | $-3\lvert 0\rvert$ | 0 | (0, 0) |
| 1 | $-3\lvert 1\rvert$ | −3 | (1, −3) |
| 2 | $-3\lvert 2\rvert$ | −6 | (2, −6) |

826 Selected Answers

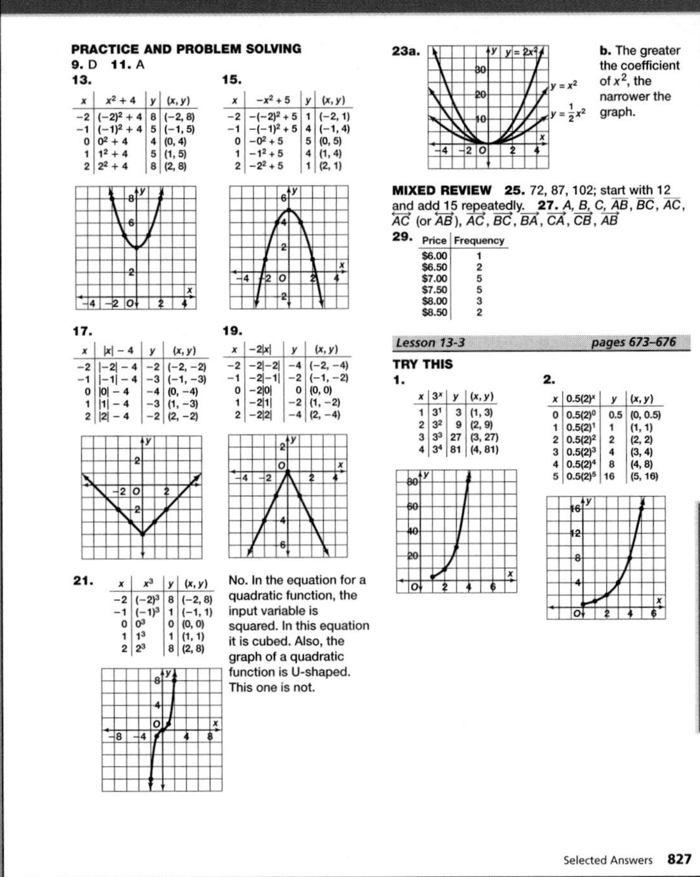

**PRACTICE AND PROBLEM SOLVING**

**9.** D **11.** A

**13.**

| $x$ | $x^2 + 4$ | $y$ | $(x, y)$ |
|---|---|---|---|
| −2 | $(-2)^2 + 4$ | 8 | (−2, 8) |
| −1 | $(-1)^2 + 4$ | 5 | (−1, 5) |
| 0 | $0^2 + 4$ | 4 | (0, 4) |
| 1 | $1^2 + 4$ | 5 | (1, 5) |
| 2 | $2^2 + 4$ | 8 | (2, 8) |

**15.**

| $x$ | $-x^2 + 5$ | $y$ | $(x, y)$ |
|---|---|---|---|
| −2 | $-(-2)^2 + 5$ | 1 | (−2, 1) |
| −1 | $-(-1)^2 + 5$ | 4 | (−1, 4) |
| 0 | $-0^2 + 5$ | 5 | (0, 5) |
| 1 | $-1^2 + 5$ | 4 | (1, 4) |
| 2 | $-2^2 + 5$ | 1 | (2, 1) |

**17.**

| $x$ | $\lvert x\rvert - 4$ | $y$ | $(x, y)$ |
|---|---|---|---|
| −2 | $\lvert -2\rvert - 4$ | −2 | (−2, −2) |
| −1 | $\lvert -1\rvert - 4$ | −3 | (−1, −3) |
| 0 | $\lvert 0\rvert - 4$ | −4 | (0, −4) |
| 1 | $\lvert 1\rvert - 4$ | −3 | (1, −3) |
| 2 | $\lvert 2\rvert - 4$ | −2 | (2, −2) |

**19.**

| $x$ | $-2\lvert x\rvert$ | $y$ | $(x, y)$ |
|---|---|---|---|
| −2 | $-2\lvert -2\rvert$ | −4 | (−2, −4) |
| −1 | $-2\lvert -1\rvert$ | −2 | (−1, −2) |
| 0 | $-2\lvert 0\rvert$ | 0 | (0, 0) |
| 1 | $-2\lvert 1\rvert$ | −2 | (1, −2) |
| 2 | $-2\lvert 2\rvert$ | −4 | (2, −4) |

**21.**

| $x$ | $x^3$ | $y$ | $(x, y)$ |
|---|---|---|---|
| −2 | $(-2)^3$ | 8 | (−2, 8) |
| −1 | $(-1)^3$ | 1 | (−1, 1) |
| 0 | $0^3$ | 0 | (0, 0) |
| 1 | $1^3$ | 1 | (1, 1) |
| 2 | $2^3$ | 8 | (2, 8) |

No. In the equation for a quadratic function, the input variable is squared. In this equation it is cubed. Also, the graph of a quadratic function is U-shaped. This one is not.

**23a.** $y = 2x^2$, $y = x^2$, $y = \frac{1}{2}x^2$ **b.** The greater the coefficient of $x^2$, the narrower the graph.

**MIXED REVIEW** **25.** 72, 87, 102; start with 12 and add 15 repeatedly. **27.** $A$, $B$, $C$, $\overline{AB}$, $\overline{BC}$, $\overline{AC}$, $\overleftrightarrow{AC}$ (or $\overleftrightarrow{AB}$), $\overrightarrow{AC}$, $\overrightarrow{BC}$, $\overrightarrow{BA}$, $\overrightarrow{CA}$, $\overrightarrow{CB}$, $\overrightarrow{AB}$

**29.**

| Price | Frequency |
|---|---|
| \$6.00 | 1 |
| \$6.50 | 2 |
| \$7.00 | 5 |
| \$7.50 | 5 |
| \$8.00 | 3 |
| \$8.50 | 2 |

*Lesson 13-3* *pages 673–676*

**TRY THIS**

**1.**

| $x$ | $3^x$ | $y$ | $(x, y)$ |
|---|---|---|---|
| 1 | $3^1$ | 3 | (1, 3) |
| 2 | $3^2$ | 9 | (2, 9) |
| 3 | $3^3$ | 27 | (3, 27) |
| 4 | $3^4$ | 81 | (4, 81) |

**2.**

| $x$ | $0.5(2)^x$ | $y$ | $(x, y)$ |
|---|---|---|---|
| 0 | $0.5(2)^0$ | 0.5 | (0, 0.5) |
| 1 | $0.5(2)^1$ | 1 | (1, 1) |
| 2 | $0.5(2)^2$ | 2 | (2, 2) |
| 3 | $0.5(2)^3$ | 4 | (3, 4) |
| 4 | $0.5(2)^4$ | 8 | (4, 8) |
| 5 | $0.5(2)^5$ | 16 | (5, 16) |

Selected Answers

Selected Answers 827

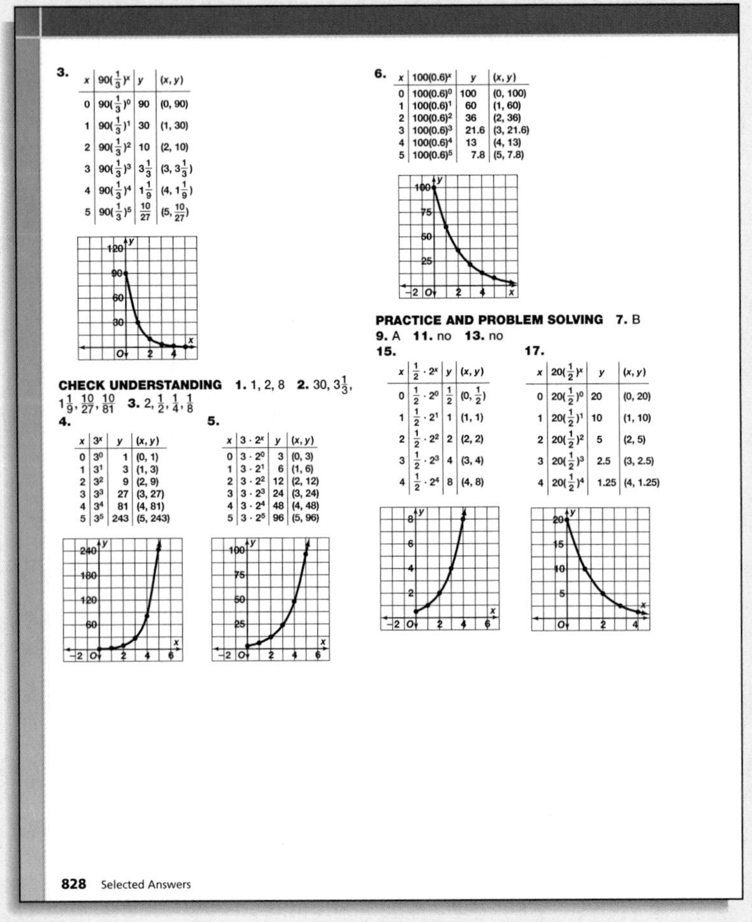

**3.**

| $x$ | $90(\frac{1}{3})^x$ | $y$ | $(x, y)$ |
|---|---|---|---|
| 0 | $90(\frac{1}{3})^0$ | 90 | (0, 90) |
| 1 | $90(\frac{1}{3})^1$ | 30 | (1, 30) |
| 2 | $90(\frac{1}{3})^2$ | 10 | (2, 10) |
| 3 | $90(\frac{1}{3})^3$ | $3\frac{1}{3}$ | $(3, 3\frac{1}{3})$ |
| 4 | $90(\frac{1}{3})^4$ | $1\frac{1}{9}$ | $(4, 1\frac{1}{9})$ |
| 5 | $90(\frac{1}{3})^5$ | $\frac{10}{27}$ | $(5, \frac{10}{27})$ |

**CHECK UNDERSTANDING** **1.** 1, 2, 8 **2.** 30, $3\frac{1}{3}$, $1\frac{1}{9}$, $\frac{10}{27}$, $\frac{10}{81}$ **3.** 2, $\frac{1}{2}$, $\frac{1}{4}$, $\frac{1}{8}$

**4.**

| $x$ | $3^x$ | $y$ | $(x, y)$ |
|---|---|---|---|
| 0 | $3^0$ | 1 | (0, 1) |
| 1 | $3^1$ | 3 | (1, 3) |
| 2 | $3^2$ | 9 | (2, 9) |
| 3 | $3^3$ | 27 | (3, 27) |
| 4 | $3^4$ | 81 | (4, 81) |
| 5 | $3^5$ | 243 | (5, 243) |

**5.**

| $x$ | $3 \cdot 2^x$ | $y$ | $(x, y)$ |
|---|---|---|---|
| 0 | $3 \cdot 2^0$ | 3 | (0, 3) |
| 1 | $3 \cdot 2^1$ | 6 | (1, 6) |
| 2 | $3 \cdot 2^2$ | 12 | (2, 12) |
| 3 | $3 \cdot 2^3$ | 24 | (3, 24) |
| 4 | $3 \cdot 2^4$ | 48 | (4, 48) |
| 5 | $3 \cdot 2^5$ | 96 | (5, 96) |

**6.**

| $x$ | $100(0.6)^x$ | $y$ | $(x, y)$ |
|---|---|---|---|
| 0 | $100(0.6)^0$ | 100 | (0, 100) |
| 1 | $100(0.6)^1$ | 60 | (1, 60) |
| 2 | $100(0.6)^2$ | 36 | (2, 36) |
| 3 | $100(0.6)^3$ | 21.6 | (3, 21.6) |
| 4 | $100(0.6)^4$ | 13 | (4, 13) |
| 5 | $100(0.6)^5$ | 7.8 | (5, 7.8) |

**PRACTICE AND PROBLEM SOLVING** **7.** B **9.** A **11.** no **13.** no

**15.**

| $x$ | $\frac{1}{2} \cdot 2^x$ | $y$ | $(x, y)$ |
|---|---|---|---|
| 0 | $\frac{1}{2} \cdot 2^0$ | $\frac{1}{2}$ | $(0, \frac{1}{2})$ |
| 1 | $\frac{1}{2} \cdot 2^1$ | 1 | (1, 1) |
| 2 | $\frac{1}{2} \cdot 2^2$ | 2 | (2, 2) |
| 3 | $\frac{1}{2} \cdot 2^3$ | 4 | (3, 4) |
| 4 | $\frac{1}{2} \cdot 2^4$ | 8 | (4, 8) |

**17.**

| $x$ | $20(\frac{1}{2})^x$ | $y$ | $(x, y)$ |
|---|---|---|---|
| 0 | $20(\frac{1}{2})^0$ | 20 | (0, 20) |
| 1 | $20(\frac{1}{2})^1$ | 10 | (1, 10) |
| 2 | $20(\frac{1}{2})^2$ | 5 | (2, 5) |
| 3 | $20(\frac{1}{2})^3$ | 2.5 | (3, 2.5) |
| 4 | $20(\frac{1}{2})^4$ | 1.25 | (4, 1.25) |

828 Selected Answers

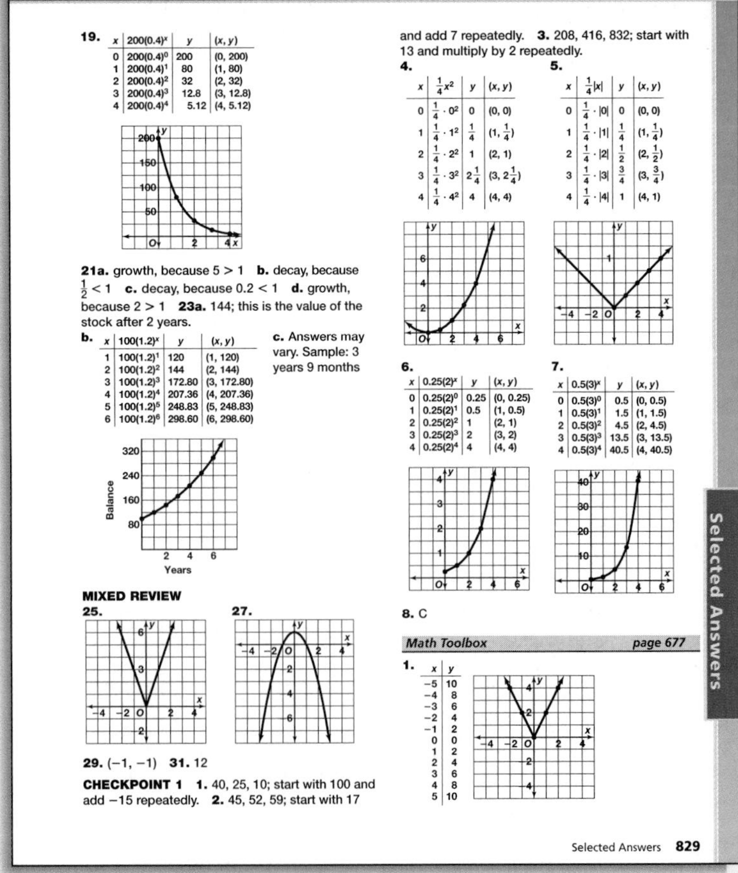

**19.**

| $x$ | $200(0.4)^x$ | $y$ | $(x, y)$ |
|---|---|---|---|
| 0 | $200(0.4)^0$ | 200 | (0, 200) |
| 1 | $200(0.4)^1$ | 80 | (1, 80) |
| 2 | $200(0.4)^2$ | 32 | (2, 32) |
| 3 | $200(0.4)^3$ | 12.8 | (3, 12.8) |
| 4 | $200(0.4)^4$ | 5.12 | (4, 5.12) |

**21a.** growth, because $5 > 1$ **b.** decay, because $\frac{1}{2} < 1$ **c.** decay, because $0.2 < 1$ **d.** growth, because $2 > 1$ **23a.** 144; this is the value of the stock after 2 years.

**b.**

| $x$ | $100(1.2)^x$ | $y$ | $(x, y)$ |
|---|---|---|---|
| 1 | $100(1.2)^1$ | 120 | (1, 120) |
| 2 | $100(1.2)^2$ | 144 | (2, 144) |
| 3 | $100(1.2)^3$ | 172.80 | (3, 172.80) |
| 4 | $100(1.2)^4$ | 207.36 | (4, 207.36) |
| 5 | $100(1.2)^5$ | 248.83 | (5, 248.83) |
| 6 | $100(1.2)^6$ | 298.60 | (6, 298.60) |

Balance

Years

**c.** Answers may vary. Sample: 3 years 9 months

**MIXED REVIEW**

**25.** **27.**

**29.** (−1, −1) **31.** 12

**CHECKPOINT 1** **1.** 40, 25, 10; start with 100 and add −15 repeatedly. **2.** 45, 52, 59; start with 17 and add 7 repeatedly. **3.** 208, 416, 832; start with 13 and multiply by 2 repeatedly.

**4.**

| $x$ | $\frac{1}{4}x^2$ | $y$ | $(x, y)$ |
|---|---|---|---|
| 0 | $\frac{1}{4} \cdot 0^2$ | 0 | (0, 0) |
| 1 | $\frac{1}{4} \cdot 1^2$ | $\frac{1}{4}$ | $(1, \frac{1}{4})$ |
| 2 | $\frac{1}{4} \cdot 2^2$ | 1 | (2, 1) |
| 3 | $\frac{1}{4} \cdot 3^2$ | $2\frac{1}{4}$ | $(3, 2\frac{1}{4})$ |
| 4 | $\frac{1}{4} \cdot 4^2$ | 4 | (4, 4) |

**5.**

| $x$ | $\frac{1}{4}\lvert x\rvert$ | $y$ | $(x, y)$ |
|---|---|---|---|
| 0 | $\frac{1}{4} \cdot \lvert 0\rvert$ | 0 | (0, 0) |
| 1 | $\frac{1}{4} \cdot \lvert 1\rvert$ | $\frac{1}{4}$ | $(1, \frac{1}{4})$ |
| 2 | $\frac{1}{4} \cdot \lvert 2\rvert$ | $\frac{1}{2}$ | $(2, \frac{1}{2})$ |
| 3 | $\frac{1}{4} \cdot \lvert 3\rvert$ | $\frac{3}{4}$ | $(3, \frac{3}{4})$ |
| 4 | $\frac{1}{4} \cdot \lvert 4\rvert$ | 1 | (4, 1) |

**6.**

| $x$ | $0.25(2)^x$ | $y$ | $(x, y)$ |
|---|---|---|---|
| 0 | $0.25(2)^0$ | 0.25 | (0, 0.25) |
| 1 | $0.25(2)^1$ | 0.5 | (1, 0.5) |
| 2 | $0.25(2)^2$ | 1 | (2, 1) |
| 3 | $0.25(2)^3$ | 2 | (3, 2) |
| 4 | $0.25(2)^4$ | 4 | (4, 4) |

**7.**

| $x$ | $0.5(3)^x$ | $y$ | $(x, y)$ |
|---|---|---|---|
| 0 | $0.5(3)^0$ | 0.5 | (0, 0.5) |
| 1 | $0.5(3)^1$ | 1.5 | (1, 1.5) |
| 2 | $0.5(3)^2$ | 4.5 | (2, 4.5) |
| 3 | $0.5(3)^3$ | 13.5 | (3, 13.5) |
| 4 | $0.5(3)^4$ | 40.5 | (4, 40.5) |

**8.** C

*Math Toolbox* *page 677*

**1.**

| $x$ | $y$ |
|---|---|
| −5 | 10 |
| −4 | 8 |
| −3 | 6 |
| −2 | 4 |
| −1 | 2 |
| 0 | 0 |
| 1 | 2 |
| 2 | 4 |
| 3 | 6 |
| 4 | 8 |
| 5 | 10 |

Selected Answers

Selected Answers 829

3.

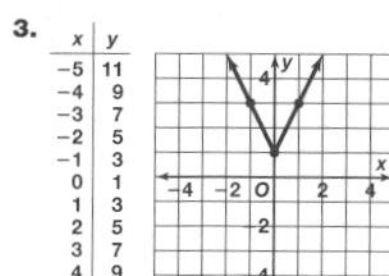

| x | y |
|---|---|
| −5 | 11 |
| −4 | 9 |
| −3 | 7 |
| −2 | 5 |
| −1 | 3 |
| 0 | 1 |
| 1 | 3 |
| 2 | 5 |
| 3 | 7 |
| 4 | 9 |
| 5 | 11 |

5.

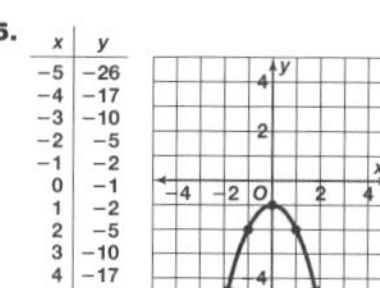

| x | y |
|---|---|
| −5 | −26 |
| −4 | −17 |
| −3 | −10 |
| −2 | −5 |
| −1 | −2 |
| 0 | −1 |
| 1 | −2 |
| 2 | −5 |
| 3 | −10 |
| 4 | −17 |
| 5 | −26 |

7.

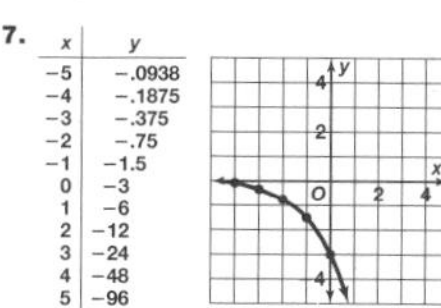

| x | y |
|---|---|
| −5 | −.0938 |
| −4 | −.1875 |
| −3 | −.375 |
| −2 | −.75 |
| −1 | −1.5 |
| 0 | −3 |
| 1 | −6 |
| 2 | −12 |
| 3 | −24 |
| 4 | −48 |
| 5 | −96 |

9.

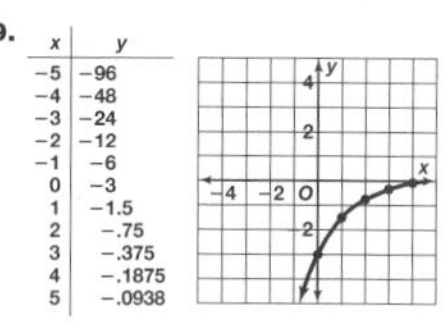

| x | y |
|---|---|
| −5 | −96 |
| −4 | −48 |
| −3 | −24 |
| −2 | −12 |
| −1 | −6 |
| 0 | −3 |
| 1 | −1.5 |
| 2 | −.75 |
| 3 | −.375 |
| 4 | −.1875 |
| 5 | −.0938 |

### Lesson 13-4 — pages 678–681

**TRY THIS**
**1.** No; the denominator contains a variable. **2.** Yes; it is the product of the variable $m$ and the real number $\frac{1}{6}$. **3.** Yes; it is a real number. **4.** No; it is a sum. **5.** monomial **6.** binomial **7.** binomial **8.** trinomial **9.** −50 **10.** 13 **11.** 13 **12.** 264 ft

**CHECK UNDERSTANDING** **1.** No; it is a sum. **2.** Yes; it is a product of the real number 18 and the variables $a$ and $b$. **3.** No; the denominator contains a variable. **4.** Yes; it is a real number. **5.** No; a variable has an exponent that is not a whole number. **6.** Yes; it is a product of the real number 0.82 and the variable $k$. **7.** binomial **8.** trinomial **9.** trinomial **10.** monomial **11.** 14 **12.** −18 **13.** 37 **14.** 16

**PRACTICE AND PROBLEM SOLVING** **17.** Yes; it is a product of the real number −0.3 and the variable $y$. **19.** Yes; it is a real number. **21.** No; it is a sum. **23.** monomial **25.** binomial **27.** binomial **29.** binomial **31.** −4 **33.** 13 **35.** 4 **37.** 0 **39.** The term $\frac{1}{x}$ contains a variable in the denominator. **41.** The expression is a quotient with a variable in the denominator. **43.** binomial **45.** 170

**MIXED REVIEW**
**47.**

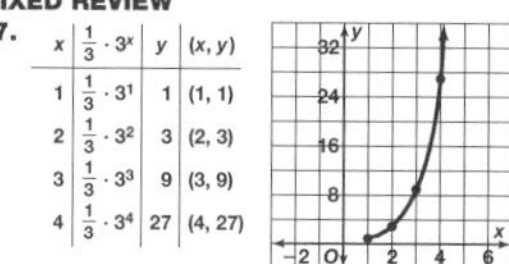

| x | $\frac{1}{3} \cdot 3^x$ | y | (x, y) |
|---|---|---|---|
| 1 | $\frac{1}{3} \cdot 3^1$ | 1 | (1, 1) |
| 2 | $\frac{1}{3} \cdot 3^2$ | 3 | (2, 3) |
| 3 | $\frac{1}{3} \cdot 3^3$ | 9 | (3, 9) |
| 4 | $\frac{1}{3} \cdot 3^4$ | 27 | (4, 27) |

**49.** $4m + 5$ **51.** $3a + 10b - 2$

### Math Toolbox — pages 682–683

**1.** binomial of degree 1 **3.** trinomial of degree 2 **5.** binomial of degree 4 **7.** monomial of degree 5 **9.** $5a + 8$ **11.** $4c^2 + 2c - 7$ **13.** $b^3 + 2b^2 - b - 2$ **15.** $4x^5 + 4x^4 + 2x^3 + x^2$ **17.** $6a^3 - 5a^2 + 9a - 5$ **19.** $5a^2 + 5a + 6$ **21.** $-2p^2 + 10p$ **23.** $x^2 + 2x + 8$ **25.** $5m^3 + 8m^2 + 11m + 14$ **27.** $-y^2 - 6y - 11$ **29.** $18x^2 + 26x + 6$

### Lesson 13-5 — pages 684–688

**TRY THIS** **1.** $9d^2 + 10d$ **2.** $4x^2 + 3x + 17$ **3.** $7x + 4y$ **4.** $9a^2 - 2a - 4$ **5.** $6g^2 - 2g - 1$ **6.** $-2t^2 + 3t + 9$ **7.** $2a^2 - 5a$ **8.** $9z^2 + 14z - 2$ **9.** $-2w^2 + 8v + 11$

**CHECK UNDERSTANDING**
**1.** $(2x^2 + x + 2) + (x^2 + 4) = 3x^2 + x + 6$
**2.** $(x^2 + 2x - 4) + (x^2 + 2x + 2) = 2x^2 + 4x - 2$
**3.** $2x^2 + 4x + 7$ **4.** $4x^2 + 6x + 3$ **5.** $2a + 9b$ **6.** $9x^2 + x + 5$ **7.** $3x + 8$ **8.** $-18a^2 - 2a$



**PRACTICE AND PROBLEM SOLVING**
**9.** $-x + 5$ **11.** $x^4 + 10x^3 - 4x - 11$ **13.** $2x^3 + 5x^2 + x + 4$ **15.** $8x + 2y$ **17.** $-3x^2 + x + 7$ **19.** $15a^2b + 2ab^2$ **21.** $x^2 + x$ **23.** $10j - 3k + 3m$ **25.** $4y - 15$ **27.** commutative and associative properties; distributive property; simplify **29.** $3x + 3x + 3x + 3x = 12x$ **31.** $(m^2 + 1) + (3m - 1) + 2m = m^2 + 5m$ **33.** $(c + 1) + c + (3c - 1) + c + 4c + 2c = 12c$ **37a.** $(3x^3 + 9) - (x^3 - 3) = 2x^3 + 12$ **b.** 28 in.$^3$ **c.** With $x = 2$, the original volume is 33 in.$^3$, so its side is less than 4 in. It will fit into the box. **39.** $4x + 1$ **41.** $2m^2 + 2m$ **43.** $2x^2$

**MIXED REVIEW** **45.** −15 **47.** 3 **49.** 12 in.$^2$ **51.** 4.5 cm$^2$

### Lesson 13-6 — pages 689–692

**TRY THIS** **1.** $3x^2 + 12x$ **2.** $2x^2 - 3x$ **3.** $x^3 + 2x^2 + 4x$ **4.** $4a^5 - 6a^4 + 6a^2$ **5.** $x(2x + 1)$ **6.** $2b(b^2 + 3b - 6)$

**CHECK UNDERSTANDING** **1.** $3x^2 + 3x$ **2.** $x^2 + 5x$ **3.** $2x^2 + 6x$ **4.** $6x^2 + 2x$ **5.** $3x^2 + 15x$ **6.** $-8x^2 + 12x$ **7.** $-15x^3 + 10x^2$ **8.** $5x^3 + x^2 - 4x$ **9.** $3a^3 + 6a^2 + 3a$ **10.** $6b^3 - 3b^2 + 12b$ **11.** $d^2(3d^2 + 1)$ **12.** $5x(2x^4 - x^2 + 2)$ **13.** $4y(y^2 - 2y - 3)$ **14.** $3b(-3b - 1)$

**PRACTICE AND PROBLEM SOLVING**
**15.** $2x^2 + 12x$ **17.** $6x^2 - 2x$ **19.** $2x^2 + 8x$ **21.** $3y^2 + 21y$ **23.** $5x^2 + 15x$ **25.** $12y^2 - 3y$ **27.** $2x^2 - 5x$ **29.** $-16y^2 - 24y$ **31.** $60x^3 + 24x^2$ **33.** $6y^4 - 12y^3 - 2y^2$ **35.** $4x^5 + 4x^4 - 4x^3$ **37.** $-14a^3 - 42a^2 + 56a$ **39.** $-6x^3y^2 - 3x^2y^2 - 3xy^3 + 9xy$ **41.** $4a^2 + a$ **43.** $7x(x - 2)$ **45.** $7(2a^2 + a - 1)$ **47.** $5z(z - 4)$ **49.** $4x^2(-x^3 - x^2 + 2)$ **51.** $4a(3a^2 - 4a - 1)$ **53.** $a(2a + b)$ **57.** $w(4w - 5) = 4w^2 - 5w$ **59.** $\frac{1}{2}b\left(\frac{1}{3}b - 3\right) = \frac{1}{6}b^2 - \frac{3}{2}b$

**MIXED REVIEW** **61.** $-9x^2 - 5x + 13$
**63.** [line plot: 11 12 13 14 15 16 17]

### Standardized Test Prep — page 693

**1.** C **3.** D
**5b.** about 160 ft
**c.** 3.5 sec

**7.** **9.**

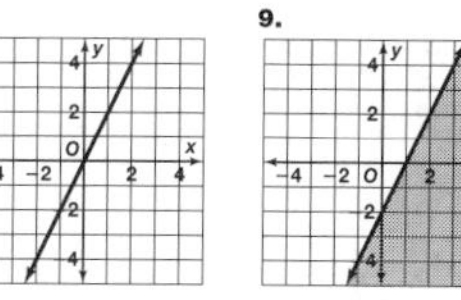

**11.** It is a positive correlation.
**13.**

| x | $2x^3$ | y | (x, y) |
|---|---|---|---|
| 0 | $2 \cdot 0^3$ | 2 | (0, 0) |
| 1 | $2 \cdot 1^3$ | 2 | (1, 2) |
| 2 | $2 \cdot 2^3$ | 16 | (2, 16) |
| 3 | $2 \cdot 3^3$ | 54 | (3, 54) |

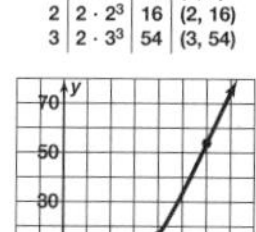

### Lesson 13-7 — pages 694–697

**TRY THIS** **1.** $x^2 + 5x + 6$ **2.** $y^2 + 5y + 4$ **3.** $x^2 - 3x - 10$ **4.** $2m^2 + 7m + 6$

**CHECK UNDERSTANDING** **1.** $x^2 + 3x + 2$ **2.** $x^2 + 4x + 4$ **3.** $x^2 + 4x + 3$ **4.** $x^2 + 7x + 12$ **5.** $x^2 + 9x + 20$ **6.** $x^2 + 12x + 27$ **7.** $x^2 + x - 2$ **8.** $c^2 + 16c + 63$ **9.** $x^2 - 2x - 15$ **10.** $a^2 - 6a + 8$ **11.** $x^2 + 10x + 25$ **12.** $b^2 - 36$ **13.** The student neglected to distribute the 5 to the −3. The third line should read $x^2 - 3x + 5x - 15$.



**PRACTICE AND PROBLEM SOLVING**
**15.** $10c^2 + 26c + 12$ **17.** $x^2 + 9x + 18$ **19.** $m^2 + 7m + 6$ **21.** $x^2 + x - 6$ **23.** $2x^2 + 9x + 4$ **25.** $x^2 + 10x + 16$ **27.** $m^2 - 11m + 24$ **29.** $6c^2 - 10c - 4$ **31.** $2x^2 + 40x + 72$ **33.** $y^2 - 1$; $y^2 - 4$; $y^2 - 25$. The product is a binomial consisting of the square of the first term minus the square of the second term. **35.** $(w^2 + 8w + 15)$ cm$^2$

**MIXED REVIEW** **37.** $7a^2 + 35ab + 14ac$ **39.** $-32m^5 + 8m^3p + 16m^2p^4$ **41.** Combinations, since the order of the colors is not important. There are 56 possible choices.

**CHECKPOINT 2** **1.** monomial **2.** binomial **3.** monomial **4.** trinomial **5.** −8 **6.** 8 **7.** 10 **8.** 9 **9.** $7a + 4b$ **10.** $2x^2 + 7x + 5$ **11.** $10p^2q + 16p^2q^2 + 4pq$ **12.** $g^2 + 10g + 24$ **13.** $-18m^2 - 6m^3p - 30mp$

### Math Toolbox — page 698

**1.** $(x + 1)^2$ **3.** $(x + 2)(x + 5)$ **5.** $(x + 2)^2$ **7.** $(x + 8)(x + 1)$ **9.** $(2x + 5)(x + 2)$ **11a.** 5 and 6 **b.** $(x + 5)(x + 6)$

### Lesson 13-8 — pages 699–702

**READ** **1.** the length of the tail **2.** The tail is 12 ft plus twice the length of the kite. Together, the two lengths total 21 ft.

**LOOK BACK** **3a.** $18 = 12 + 2 \cdot 3$ **b.** $18 + 3 = 21$

**CHECK UNDERSTANDING**
**1a.** 4:30 P.M. **b.** 180 mi **2.** 40 rounds **3.** 30 ft

**PRACTICE AND PROBLEM SOLVING** **5.** 7.5 ft **7.** 51 people **9a.** 31.8 cm$^2$ **b.** 25 cm$^2$ **c.** the circle **11a.** the clerk **b.** after 5 years **13.** $24 **15.** 7

**MIXED REVIEW** **17.** $2d^2 + 9d + 10$ **19.** GO, GA, GT, OA, OT, AT; 6 **21.** HY, HE, HN, HA, YE, YN, YA, EN, EA, NA; 10

### Wrap Up — pages 704–706

**1.** 17, 21, 25; start with 1 and add 4 repeatedly. **2.** −3.75, −1.875, −0.9375; start with −60 and multiply by $\frac{1}{2}$ repeatedly. **3.** 128, 135, 142; start with 100 and add 7 repeatedly. **4.** −20, −25, −30; start with 0 and add −5 repeatedly. **5.** −18, −29, −40; start with 26 and add −11 repeatedly. **6.** 62.5, 312.5, 1,562.5; start with $\frac{1}{10}$ and multiply by 5 repeatedly. **7.** arithmetic; 25, 29, 33

**8.** geometric; $-\frac{1}{2}, -\frac{1}{4}, -\frac{1}{8}$ **9.** arithmetic; 7, 8, 9 **10.** arithmetic; 22, 33, 44 **11.** neither; 30, 3, 40 **12.** geometric; $\frac{2}{25}, \frac{4}{25}, \frac{8}{25}$

**14.**

| x | $\frac{1}{2}x^2$ | y | (x, y) |
|---|---|---|---|
| −2 | $\frac{1}{2} \cdot (-2)^2$ | 2 | (−2, 2) |
| −1 | $\frac{1}{2} \cdot (-1)^2$ | $\frac{1}{2}$ | $(-1, \frac{1}{2})$ |
| 0 | $\frac{1}{2} \cdot (0)^2$ | 0 | (0, 0) |
| 1 | $\frac{1}{2} \cdot (1)^2$ | $\frac{1}{2}$ | $(1, \frac{1}{2})$ |
| 2 | $\frac{1}{2} \cdot (2)^2$ | 2 | (2, 2) |

**15.**

| x | 2\|x\| | y | (x, y) |
|---|---|---|---|
| −2 | 2\|−2\| | 4 | (−2, 4) |
| −1 | 2\|−1\| | 2 | (−1, 2) |
| 0 | 2\|0\| | 0 | (0, 0) |
| 1 | 2\|1\| | 2 | (1, 2) |
| 2 | 2\|2\| | 4 | (2, 4) |

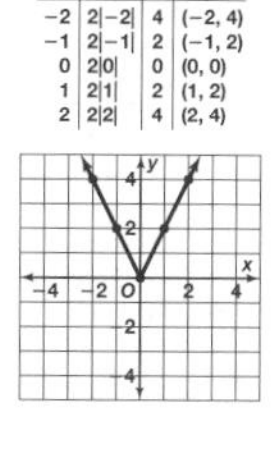

**16.**

| x | \|x\| + 1 | y | (x, y) |
|---|---|---|---|
| −2 | \|−2\| + 1 | 3 | (−2, 3) |
| −1 | \|−1\| + 1 | 2 | (−1, 2) |
| 0 | \|0\| + 1 | 1 | (0, 1) |
| 1 | \|1\| + 1 | 2 | (1, 2) |
| 2 | \|2\| + 1 | 3 | (2, 3) |

**17.**

| x | $x^2 + 5$ | y | (x, y) |
|---|---|---|---|
| −2 | $(-2)^2 + 5$ | 9 | (−2, 9) |
| −1 | $(-1)^2 + 5$ | 6 | (−1, 6) |
| 0 | $0^2 + 5$ | 5 | (0, 5) |
| 1 | $1^2 + 5$ | 6 | (1, 6) |
| 2 | $2^2 + 5$ | 9 | (2, 9) |

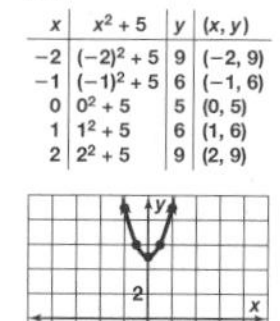



**18.**

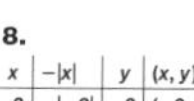

| x | −\|x\| | y | (x, y) |
|---|---|---|---|
| −2 | −\|−2\| | −2 | (−2, −2) |
| −1 | −\|−1\| | −1 | (−1, −1) |
| 0 | −\|0\| | 0 | (0, 0) |
| 1 | −\|1\| | −1 | (1, −1) |
| 2 | −\|2\| | −2 | (2, −2) |

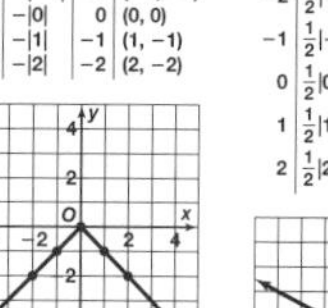

**19.**

| x | $\frac{1}{2}$\|x\| | y | (x, y) |
|---|---|---|---|
| −2 | $\frac{1}{2}$\|−2\| | 1 | (−2, 1) |
| −1 | $\frac{1}{2}$\|−1\| | $\frac{1}{2}$ | $(-1, \frac{1}{2})$ |
| 0 | $\frac{1}{2}$\|0\| | 0 | (0, 0) |
| 1 | $\frac{1}{2}$\|1\| | $\frac{1}{2}$ | $(1, \frac{1}{2})$ |
| 2 | $\frac{1}{2}$\|2\| | 1 | (2, 1) |

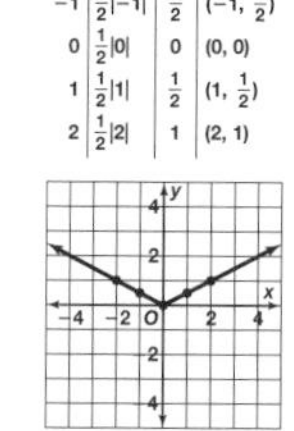

**20.**

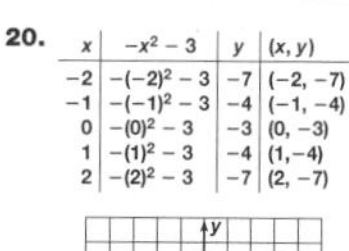

| x | $-x^2 - 3$ | y | (x, y) |
|---|---|---|---|
| −2 | $-(-2)^2 - 3$ | −7 | (−2, −7) |
| −1 | $-(-1)^2 - 3$ | −4 | (−1, −4) |
| 0 | $-(0)^2 - 3$ | −3 | (0, −3) |
| 1 | $-(1)^2 - 3$ | −4 | (1, −4) |
| 2 | $-(2)^2 - 3$ | −7 | (2, −7) |

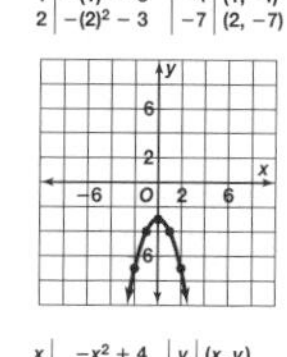

**21.**

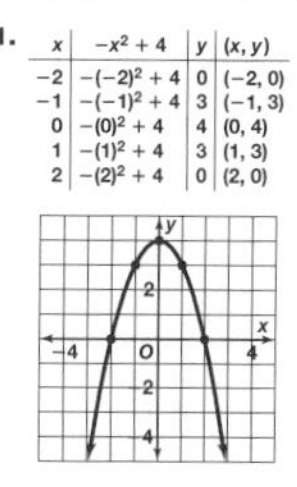

| x | $-x^2 + 4$ | y | (x, y) |
|---|---|---|---|
| −2 | $-(-2)^2 + 4$ | 0 | (−2, 0) |
| −1 | $-(-1)^2 + 4$ | 3 | (−1, 3) |
| 0 | $-(0)^2 + 4$ | 4 | (0, 4) |
| 1 | $-(1)^2 + 4$ | 3 | (1, 3) |
| 2 | $-(2)^2 + 4$ | 0 | (2, 0) |

**22.** **23.**

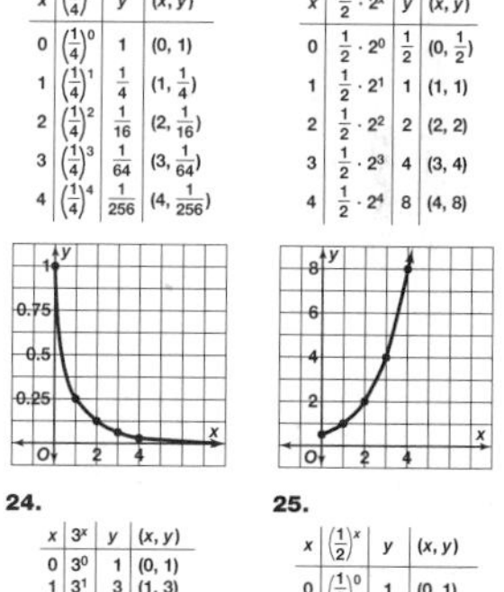

| x | $\left(\frac{1}{4}\right)^x$ | y | (x, y) |
|---|---|---|---|
| 0 | $\left(\frac{1}{4}\right)^0$ | 1 | (0, 1) |
| 1 | $\left(\frac{1}{4}\right)^1$ | $\frac{1}{4}$ | $(1, \frac{1}{4})$ |
| 2 | $\left(\frac{1}{4}\right)^2$ | $\frac{1}{16}$ | $(2, \frac{1}{16})$ |
| 3 | $\left(\frac{1}{4}\right)^3$ | $\frac{1}{64}$ | $(3, \frac{1}{64})$ |
| 4 | $\left(\frac{1}{4}\right)^4$ | $\frac{1}{256}$ | $(4, \frac{1}{256})$ |

| x | $\frac{1}{2} \cdot 2^x$ | y | (x, y) |
|---|---|---|---|
| 0 | $\frac{1}{2} \cdot 2^0$ | $\frac{1}{2}$ | $(0, \frac{1}{2})$ |
| 1 | $\frac{1}{2} \cdot 2^1$ | 1 | (1, 1) |
| 2 | $\frac{1}{2} \cdot 2^2$ | 2 | (2, 2) |
| 3 | $\frac{1}{2} \cdot 2^3$ | 4 | (3, 4) |
| 4 | $\frac{1}{2} \cdot 2^4$ | 8 | (4, 8) |

**24.** **25.**

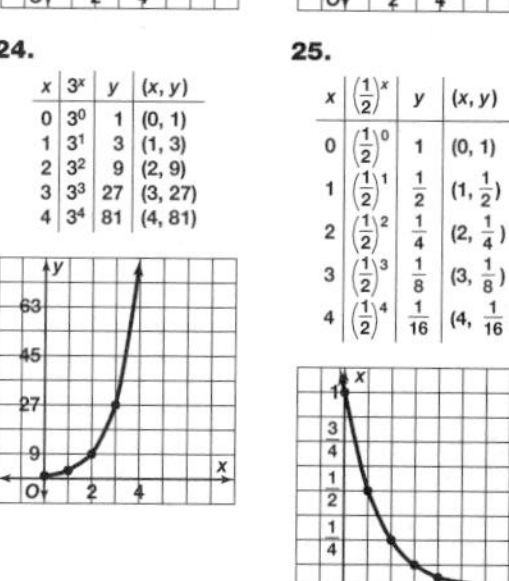

| x | $3^x$ | y | (x, y) |
|---|---|---|---|
| 0 | $3^0$ | 1 | (0, 1) |
| 1 | $3^1$ | 3 | (1, 3) |
| 2 | $3^2$ | 9 | (2, 9) |
| 3 | $3^3$ | 27 | (3, 27) |
| 4 | $3^4$ | 81 | (4, 81) |

| x | $\left(\frac{1}{2}\right)^x$ | y | (x, y) |
|---|---|---|---|
| 0 | $\left(\frac{1}{2}\right)^0$ | 1 | (0, 1) |
| 1 | $\left(\frac{1}{2}\right)^1$ | $\frac{1}{2}$ | $(1, \frac{1}{2})$ |
| 2 | $\left(\frac{1}{2}\right)^2$ | $\frac{1}{4}$ | $(2, \frac{1}{4})$ |
| 3 | $\left(\frac{1}{2}\right)^3$ | $\frac{1}{8}$ | $(3, \frac{1}{8})$ |
| 4 | $\left(\frac{1}{2}\right)^4$ | $\frac{1}{16}$ | $(4, \frac{1}{16})$ |

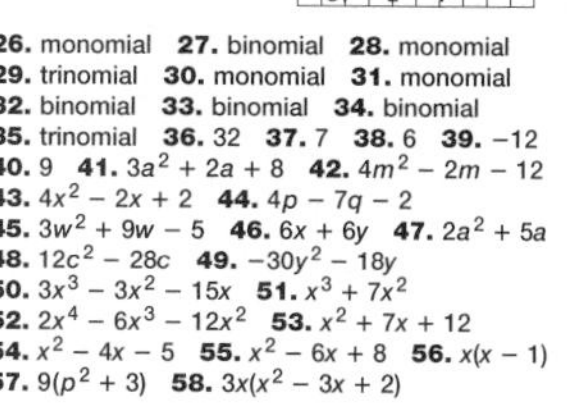

**26.** monomial **27.** binomial **28.** monomial **29.** trinomial **30.** monomial **31.** monomial **32.** binomial **33.** binomial **34.** binomial **35.** trinomial **36.** 32 **37.** 7 **38.** 6 **39.** −12 **40.** 9 **41.** $3a^2 + 2a + 8$ **42.** $4m^2 - 2m - 12$ **43.** $4x^2 - 2x + 2$ **44.** $4p - 7q - 2$ **45.** $3w^2 + 9w - 5$ **46.** $6x + 6y$ **47.** $2a^2 + 5a$ **48.** $12c^2 - 28c$ **49.** $-30y^2 - 18y$ **50.** $3x^3 - 3x^2 - 15x$ **51.** $x^3 + 7x^2$ **52.** $2x^4 - 6x^3 - 12x^2$ **53.** $x^2 + 7x + 12$ **54.** $x^2 - 4x - 5$ **55.** $x^2 - 6x + 8$ **56.** $x(x - 1)$ **57.** $9(p^2 + 3)$ **58.** $3x(x^2 - 3x + 2)$

59. $5(b^5 + 4b^3 - 6)$ **60.** $2x(4x^2 + x + 2)$
**61.** $4a(7a - b)$ **62.** 2,401 $ft^2$

*Cumulative Review* *pages 708–709*

**1.** C **3.** D **5.** C **7.** A **9.** D **11.** D **13.** C **15.** A **17.** D **19.** A **21.** A **23.** D
**25.** $5b + 5b + 5b + 5b = 20b$
**27.**

| $x$ | $3^x$ | $y$ | $(x, y)$ |
|---|---|---|---|
| 0 | $3^0$ | 1 | (0, 1) |
| 1 | $3^1$ | 3 | (1, 3) |
| 2 | $3^2$ | 9 | (2, 9) |
| 3 | $3^3$ | 27 | (3, 27) |
| 4 | $3^4$ | 81 | (4, 81) |

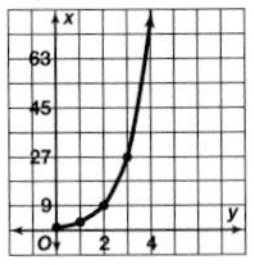

**31.** (number line: −12, 0)
**33.** (number line: 0)
**35.** (number line: 0, 7)

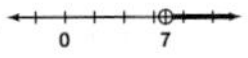

**37.** $a < -4$ **39.** $x > -13$ **41.** $w \le 47$ **43.** $c \le -15$ **45.** $0 < r$ **47.** $a > -242$

## ▶Extra Practice

**CHAPTER 1** **1.** $x - 6$ **3.** $z + 2$ **5.** $8p$ **7.** 75 **9.** 9 **11.** 5 **13.** 42 **15.** 11 **17.** 10 **19.** = **21.** > **23.** −7 **25.** 24 **27.** −32 **29.** −144 **31.** Start with −12, and add 9 to the previous term. 33, 42, 51 . . . **33.** Add the two previous terms. 21, 34, 55, . . . **35.** 120 **37.** 24 **39.** −6 **41.** 9

**CHAPTER 2**
**1.** 99 + (−99) + (−46) + 45 Commutative Property of Addition
0 + (−46) + 45 Additive Inverse
−1 Identity Property of Addition
**3.** 18 + 12 + 13 + (−25) Commutative Property of Addition
18 + −25 + (12 + 13) Associative Property of Addition
18 + −25 + 25 Commutative Property of Addition
18
**5.** 2 · 50 · 58 Commutative Property of Multiplication
100 · 58 Multiply from left to right.
5,800
**7.** 20 **9.** 96 **11.** $3a - 6c$ **13.** $-17y + 38$ **15.** $-x + 2$ **17.** $\frac{-3}{-1} = 3$; true **19.** −15 **21.** −24 **23.** −67 **25.** 24 **27.** −15 **29.** −64

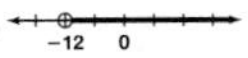

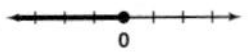

**CHAPTER 3** **7.** about 120 **9.** about 18 **11.** about 18
**13.** mean: 12.9, median: 12, modes: 10 and 12, outlier: 19 **15.** mean: \$27.30, median: \$29, mode: \$30, outlier: \$15
**17.** 130 yd **19.** 175 mi **21.** 12.7 **23.** 93.8 **25.** 63.6 **27.** 40.95 **29.** 0.1 **31.** 184.3 **33.** 3 **35.** 32.75 **37.** 0.25 L **39.** 0.060 kg **41.** 562 cm **43.** 0.564 m **45.** 0.036g **47.** 0.567 g

**CHAPTER 4** **1.** 1, 2, 3, 4, 5, 6, 10, 12, 15, 20, 30, 60 **3.** 1, 2, 4, 8, 16, 32, 64 **5.** 1, 2, 3, 4, 6, 9, 12, 18, 36 **7.** 64 **9.** 76 **11.** 48 **13.** composite; $5^2$ **15.** prime **17.** neither **19.** 10 **21.** $5x$ **23.** $\frac{3}{5}$ **25.** $\frac{7}{16}$ **27.** $\frac{1}{4}$ **29.** $\frac{8}{25}$ **31.** $\frac{x}{15}$ **33.** $\frac{9x}{4}$ **41.** $-\frac{2}{5}$ **43.** $\frac{4}{25}$ **45.** $6y^5$ **47.** $x^8y$ **49.** $3t^{15}$ **51.** 1 **53.** $6.6 \times 10^{16}$

**CHAPTER 5** **1.** 30 **3.** $24xy$ **5.** > **7.** = **9.** 0.875 **11.** $0.\overline{27}$ **13.** −0.7 **15.** $1\frac{3}{10}$ **17.** $\frac{2}{3}$ **19.** $\frac{7}{20}$ **21.** 1 **23.** $-\frac{3}{8}$ **25.** $-\frac{1}{4}$ **27.** $\frac{20 + 3t}{4t}$ **29.** $\frac{2}{5}$ **31.** −1 **33.** $\frac{3}{11}$ **35.** $\frac{x}{7}$ **37.** −2 **39.** 5 ft **41.** 64 oz **43.** $8\frac{1}{2}$ **45.** $\frac{3}{20}$ **47.** $1\frac{13}{24}$ **49.** $x^8y^{12}$ **51.** $a^5b^5c^{15}$ **53.** $8x^3y^3$ **55.** $\frac{4c^2}{d^6}$ **57.** $\frac{1}{64}$

**CHAPTER 6** **1.** $\frac{1}{2}$ **3.** $\frac{1}{4}$ **5.** $58.\overline{6}$ ft/s **7.** 82.5 gal/h **9.** 84 **11.** 24 **13.** 26.7 **15.** 0.4 **17.** 34.4 mi **19.** 18.8 mi **21.** 0; 0 to 6 **23.** $\frac{1}{3}$; 1 to 2 **25.** $\frac{2}{1}$; 2 **27.** $\frac{7}{400}$; 0.0175 **29.** 15% **31.** 41.7% **33.** 34.5% **35.** 40 **37.** 36.3 **39.** 150% increase **41.** 12.5% decrease **43.** \$45

**CHAPTER 7** **1.** −1 **3.** −4 **5.** 15 **7.** −6 **9.** $-\frac{16}{3}$ **11.** 195 **13.** 1 **15.** 3 **17.** −5 **19.** 28 **21.** 3
**23.** $a \ge -3$ (number line: −3, 0)

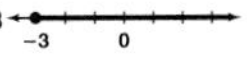

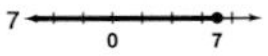

**25.** $x \le 7$ (number line: 0, 7)
**27.** $t \le 50$ (number line: 0, 50) 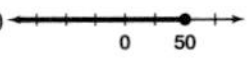
**29.** $x \ge -16.2$ (number line: −16.2, 0)

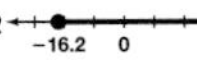

**31.** $p = s - c$ **33.** $a = c + b$ **35.** \$36 **37.** 4,500 **39.** \$49,744.72 **41.** \$1,480.24 **43.** \$2,207.63

**CHAPTER 8** **1.** No, 7 and 8 are both mapped from 4. **3.** Yes, each $y$ term is mapped from a different $x$ term. **5.** (−3, −11), (0, −2), (2, 4) **7.** $(-3, 6\frac{1}{2})$, (0, 8), (2, 9) **9.** (−3, −4), (0, −4), (2, −4) **11.** (−3, −3), $(0, -\frac{3}{2})$, $(2, -\frac{1}{2})$ **13.** 5, −4 **15.** $\frac{3}{2}$, 6 **17.** $\frac{3}{5}$, −1 **19.** 1, $-\frac{1}{2}$
**21.** 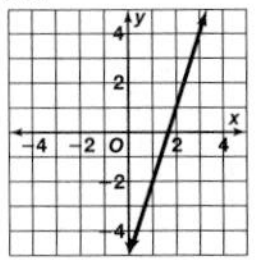 **23.** 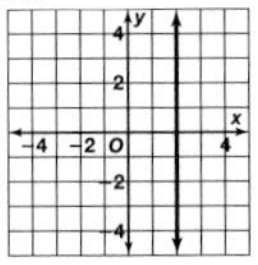
**25.** 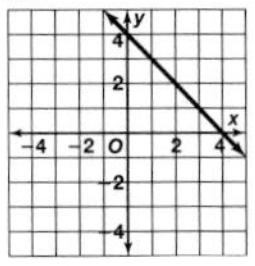
**27.** $y = 3x - 1$
**29.** $y = 5x + 4$
**31.** Positive correlation; as you move to the right, most scores increase.
**33.** 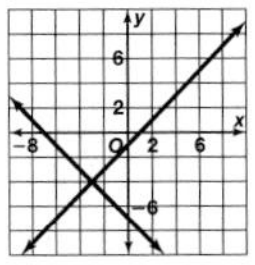 **35.**
(−3, −4)

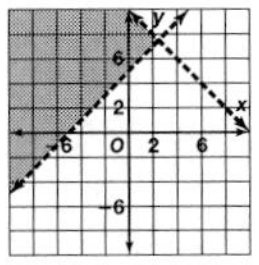

**CHAPTER 9** **1.** $\overleftrightarrow{AB}$, $\overleftrightarrow{AC}$, $\overleftrightarrow{BC}$ **3.** $\overline{RS}$, $\overline{MQ}$, $\overline{MN}$, $\overline{UR}$ **5.** $\overline{UT}$, $\overline{NP}$, $\overline{ST}$ **7.** $m\angle7 = 67°$; $m\angle4 = 67°$; $m\angle1 = 67°$; $m\angle8 = 113°$; $m\angle6 = 113°$; $m\angle2 = 113°$; $m\angle3 = 113°$ **9.** rectangle **11.** A **13.** about 78.5 ft **15.** about 314 m
**17.** 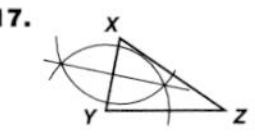 **19.**

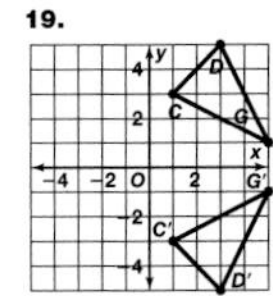

**CHAPTER 10** **1.** 18 $ft^2$ or 2 $yd^2$ **3.** 75 $m^2$ **5.** 20 $ft^2$ **7.** $676\pi$ $m^2$, 2,122.6 $m^2$ **9.** $75\pi$ $yd^2$, 235.5 $yd^2$ **11.** 45 $m^2$, 18 $m^3$ **13.** 803.8 $cm^2$, 2,143.6 $cm^3$ **15.** 202 $ft^2$, 180 $ft^3$ **17.** 452.12 $cm^2$, 904.3 $cm^3$ **19.** 2,940 $cm^2$, 9,000 $cm^3$

**CHAPTER 11** **1.** 2 **3.** −6 **5.** 5 **7.** 3 **9.** 10 **11.** rational **13.** irrational **15.** irrational **17.** 7.5 yd **19.** 5.7 units **21.** 10.4 units **23.** $\left(\frac{1}{2}, -\frac{3}{2}\right)$ **25.** $x = 32\sqrt{2}$ cm, $y = 32$ cm **27.** $x = 15$ mi, $y = 15\sqrt{2}$ mi **29.** 11.4301 **31.** 0.0875 **33.** 0.4226 **35.** 1.1918

**CHAPTER 12**
**1.**

| Number | Frequency |
|---|---|
| 20 | 2 |
| 21 | 5 |
| 22 | 2 |
| 23 | 1 |

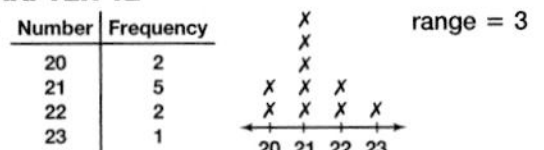

range = 3

**3.**

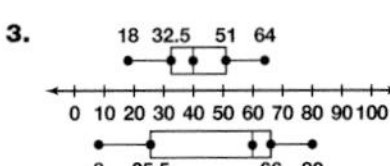



**5.** 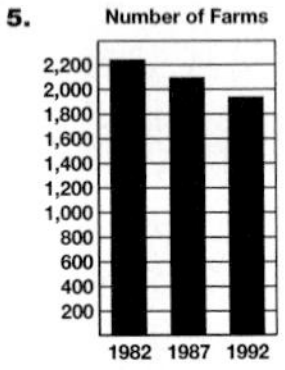 Number of Farms (bar graph: 1982, 1987, 1992)

**7.** $\frac{4}{121}$ **9.** 3 **11.** 20 **13.** 120 **15.** $\frac{1}{6}$

**CHAPTER 13** **1.** 20, 0, −20, . . . Start with 100 and subtract 20 from the previous term. **3.** 40, 48, 56, . . . Start with 8 and add 8 to the previous term. **5.** −3,125, 15,625, −78,125, . . . Start with −5 and multiply the previous term by −5.
**7.** **9.**

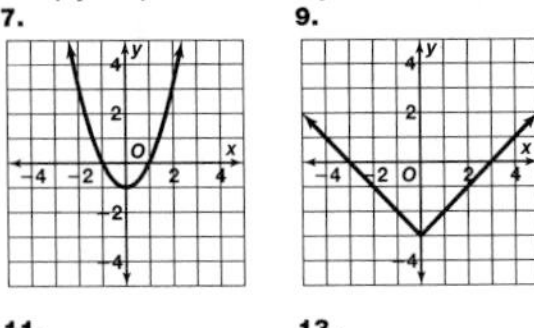

**11.** **13.**

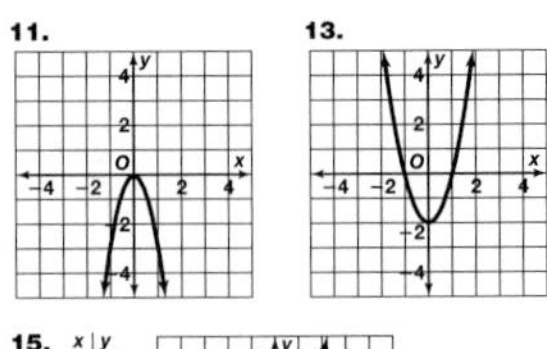

**15.**

| $x$ | $y$ |
|---|---|
| 0 | 1 |
| 1 | 4 |
| 2 | 16 |
| 3 | 64 |
| 4 | 256 |

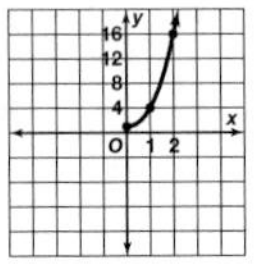

**17.**

| $x$ | $y$ |
|---|---|
| 0 | 10 |
| 1 | 5 |
| 2 | 2.5 |
| 3 | 1.25 |
| 4 | 0.625 |

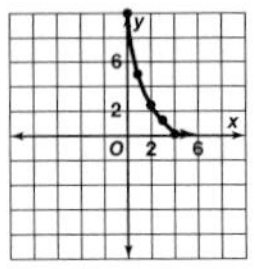

**19.** trinomial **21.** binomial **23.** monomial **25.** trinomial **27.** $7y - 2$ **29.** $-x$ **31.** $6x^2 + 5x - 12$ **33.** $4b^2 + 8ab$ **35.** $10x^3 + 12x$ **37.** $12t^4 + 48t^3 - 18t^2$ **39.** $2y^2 + 16y + 24$ **41.** $4(x^2 - 3)$ **43.** $2(a^2b - 2a + 3b)$ **45.** $x(6y + 2 + 3xy)$

## ▶Skills Handbook

**COMPARING AND ORDERING WHOLE NUMBERS** **1.** > **3.** > **5.** < **7.** < **9.** > **11.** 3,347; 3,474; 3,734; 3,747; 3,774 **13.** 30,256,403; 30,265,403; 32,056,403; 302,056,403

**ROUNDING WHOLE NUMBERS** **1.** 40 **3.** 670 **5.** 7,030 **7.** 6,000 **9.** 44,000 **11.** 1,000 **13.** 6,000 **15.** 82,000 **17.** 35,000 **19.** 68,900 **21.** 3,407,000 **23.** 71,230,000 **25.** 400,000 **27.** 3,680 **29.** 69,000 **31.** 566,000 **33.** 1,400,000

**MULTIPLYING WHOLE NUMBERS** **1.** 444 **3.** 371 **5.** 392 **7.** 1,536 **9.** 1,350 **11.** 5,712 **13.** 2,520 **15.** 1,862 **17.** 9,214 **19.** 492 **21.** 729 **23.** 2,208 **25.** 884 **27.** 4,056 **29.** 2,478 **31.** 1,440 **33.** 5,467

**DIVIDING WHOLE NUMBERS** **1.** 15 R 1 **3.** 12 R 6 **5.** 13 R 3 **7.** 217 R 2 **9.** 25 R 6 **11.** 7 R 41 **13.** 7 R 27 **15.** 3 R 36 **17.** 5 R 21 **19.** 3 R 7 **21.** 14 R 52 **23.** 37 R 12 **25.** 21 R 30 **27.** 7 R 3 **29.** 11 R 3 **31.** 64 R 3 **33.** 50 R 4 **35.** 103 R 1 **37.** 26 R 8 **39.** 7 R 32 **41.** 5 R 22 **43.** 6 R 21 **45.** 3 R 52 **47.** 15 R 3 **49.** 22 R 12

**DECIMALS AND PLACE VALUE** **1.** 9 hundred-thousandths **3.** 5 hundredths **5.** 4 hundred millions **7.** 0.0041 **9.** 0.000008 **11.** 0.012 **13.** six hundredths **15.** eleven hundred-thousandths **17.** twelve thousandths **19.** forty-two ten-thousandths



**COMPARING AND ORDERING DECIMALS** **1.** < **3.** > **5.** < **7.** = **9.** < **11.** > **13.** 0.23, 0.231, 2.31, 3.21, 23.1 **15.** 0.002, 0.02, 0.22, 0.222, 2.22 **17.** 0.007, 0.07, 0.7, 0.71, 0.72 **19.** 7, 7.0324, 7.3, 7.3246, 7.3264

**ROUNDING** **1.** 105,000 **3.** 79,528,000 **5.** 4,312,000 **7.** 3 **9.** 101 **11.** 82 **13.** 20.4 **15.** 130.0 **17.** 96.40 **19.** 4.23 **21.** 7.06 **23.** 1,520 **25.** 4.2 **27.** 400 **29.** 8.1 **31.** 410 **33.** 2.58 **35.** 19 **37.** 7,700 **39.** 980,000,000 **41.** 0.00377 **43.** 12.8 **45.** 21,000

**ADDING AND SUBTRACTING DECIMALS** **1.** 3.67 **3.** 7.312 **5.** 36.127 **7.** 1.6 **9.** 13.95 **11.** 60.21 **13.** 34.023 **15.** 39.95 **17.** 25.73 **19.** 31.95 **21.** 7.045 **23.** 6.21 **25.** 7.511 **27.** 2.825 **29.** 3.55 **31.** 1.434 **33.** 10.37 **35.** 0.32 **37.** 28.22 **39.** 37.002 **41.** 12.403 **43.** 747.1109 **45.** 11.36 **47.** 39.101

**MULTIPLYING DECIMALS** **1.** 5.328 **3.** 2.15 **5.** 5.168 **7.** 0.38912 **9.** 1.1424 **11.** 2.07828 **13.** 0.48 **15.** 0.364 **17.** 6.5658 **19.** 41.16 **21.** 1.26 **23.** 12.15 **25.** 12.05 **27.** 4.8018 **29.** 18.012

**ZEROS IN A PRODUCT** **1.** 0.027 **3.** 0.072 **5.** 0.0025 **7.** 0.00248 **9.** 0.00891 **11.** 0.00165 **13.** 0.0376 **15.** 0.081 **17.** 0.00072 **19.** 0.0009 **21.** 0.04 **23.** 0.000376 **25.** 0.012 **27.** 0.092 **29.** 0.072 **31.** 0.01812 **33.** 0.007

**DIVIDING DECIMALS BY WHOLE NUMBERS** **1.** 2.56 **3.** 0.776 **5.** 8.79 **7.** 0.11 **9.** 0.184 **11.** 2.07 **13.** 8.76 **15.** 0.0169 **17.** 0.0147 **19.** 0.561 **21.** 0.868 **23.** 2.551 **25.** 3.9 **27.** 0.025 **29.** 0.0014

**MULTIPLYING AND DIVIDING BY POWERS OF TEN** **1.** 560 **3.** 52 **5.** 2,367 **7.** 0.0009 **9.** 8 **11.** 0.001803 **13.** 13,700 **15.** 0.47 **17.** 0.236 **19.** 0.00041 **21.** 423 **23.** 502 **25.** 27 **27.** 0.4 **29.** 0.065 **31.** 26 **33.** 0.0003 **35.** 15.8

**DIVIDING DECIMALS BY DECIMALS** **1.** 84 **3.** 452 **5.** 32 **7.** 31.1 **9.** 3.1 **11.** 26 **13.** 31 **15.** 16 **17.** 44 **19.** 2.8 **21.** 3.6 **23.** 1.24 **25.** 58.3 **27.** 31.4 **29.** 3.96 **31.** 0.53 **33.** 9.5 **35.** 1.6 **37.** 3.58 **39.** 0.243 **41.** 3.44 **43.** 1.86 **45.** 3.77

**ZEROS IN DECIMAL DIVISION** **1.** 0.046 **3.** 0.075 **5.** 0.0095 **7.** 0.0025 **9.** 0.085 **11.** 0.015 **13.** 0.0035 **15.** 0.07 **17.** 0.0021 **19.** 0.00015 **21.** 0.006 **23.** 0.009 **25.** 0.0035 **27.** 0.033

**WRITING EQUIVALENT FRACTIONS** **1.** 2 **3.** 10 **5.** 12 **7.** 24 **9.** 3 **11.** 16 **13.** 30 **15.** 21 **17.** $\frac{5}{6}$ **19.** $\frac{3}{4}$ **21.** $\frac{4}{5}$ **23.** $\frac{1}{2}$ **25.** $\frac{3}{7}$ **27.** $\frac{3}{5}$ **29.** $\frac{11}{12}$ **31.** $\frac{3}{4}$ **33.** $\frac{3}{7}$

**MIXED NUMBERS AND IMPROPER FRACTIONS** **1.** $1\frac{2}{5}$ **3.** $3\frac{1}{4}$ **5.** $1\frac{3}{10}$ **7.** $2\frac{5}{8}$ **9.** $3\frac{2}{5}$ **11.** $4\frac{1}{4}$ **13.** $5\frac{2}{5}$ **15.** $3\frac{3}{4}$ **17.** $1\frac{1}{3}$ **19.** $4\frac{1}{2}$ **21.** $5\frac{1}{2}$ **23.** $4\frac{1}{4}$ **25.** $\frac{3}{2}$ **27.** $\frac{13}{12}$ **29.** $\frac{16}{7}$ **31.** $\frac{23}{8}$ **33.** $\frac{26}{5}$ **35.** $\frac{37}{4}$ **37.** $\frac{63}{8}$ **39.** $\frac{24}{7}$ **41.** $\frac{31}{10}$

**ADDING AND SUBTRACTING FRACTIONS WITH LIKE DENOMINATORS** **1.** $1\frac{2}{5}$ **3.** $\frac{4}{7}$ **5.** $1\frac{1}{5}$ **7.** $\frac{3}{8}$ **9.** $\frac{3}{5}$ **11.** 1 **13.** $4\frac{2}{5}$ **15.** $1\frac{1}{3}$ **17.** $8\frac{1}{4}$ **19.** $11\frac{1}{2}$ **21.** 11 **23.** $4\frac{3}{5}$ **25.** $\frac{3}{4}$

**MULTIPLYING AND DIVIDING FRACTIONS** **1.** $\frac{9}{20}$ **3.** 4 **5.** $\frac{5}{12}$ **7.** $\frac{1}{25}$ **9.** $\frac{1}{16}$ **11.** $3\frac{5}{9}$ **13.** $7\frac{1}{2}$ **15.** $43\frac{3}{4}$ **17.** $1\frac{3}{8}$ **19.** $\frac{7}{8}$ **21.** $1\frac{3}{8}$ **23.** $\frac{1}{81}$ **25.** 6 **27.** $\frac{9}{40}$ **29.** $1\frac{3}{4}$ **31.** $\frac{2}{5}$ **33.** $11\frac{3}{4}$ **35.** $3\frac{4}{7}$

**WORKING WITH INTEGERS** **1.** 6 **3.** 5 **5.** 3 **7.** 12 **9.** > **11.** < **13.** < **15.** > **17.** > **19.** < **21.** > **23.** > **25.** > **27.** < **29.** > **31.** < **33.** >

## CHAPTER 1

### LESSON 1-10

TE page 51 **After the Lesson**

1–5.

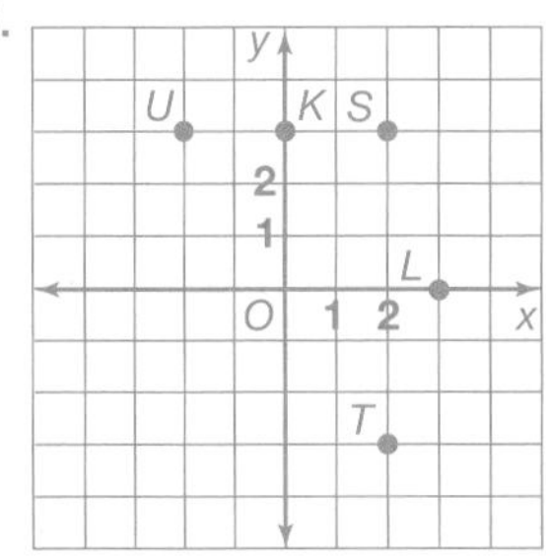


### LESSON 1-10

57.

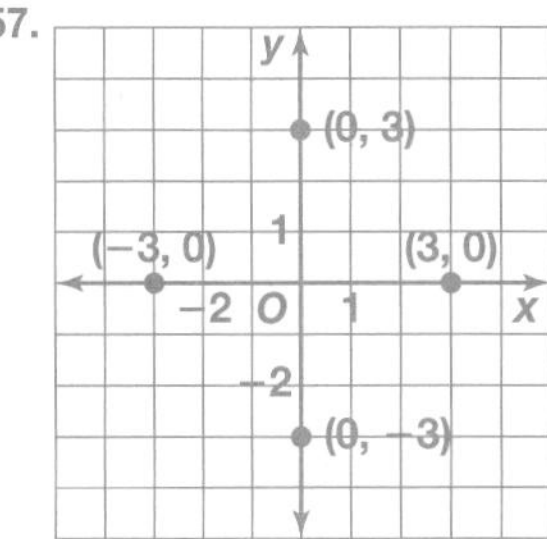


59.

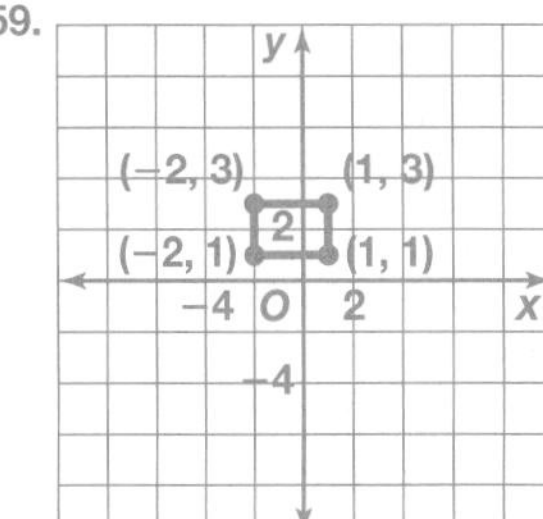


60a.

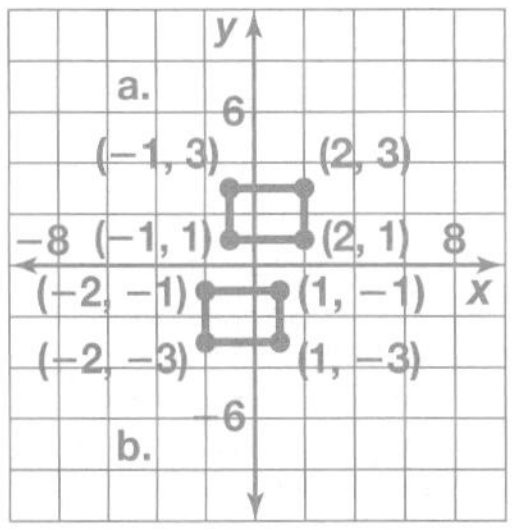

y
a.
6
(−1, 3) (2, 3)
−8 (−1, 1) (2, 1) 8
(−2, −1) (1, −1) x
(−2, −3) (1, −3)
−6
b.

60b.

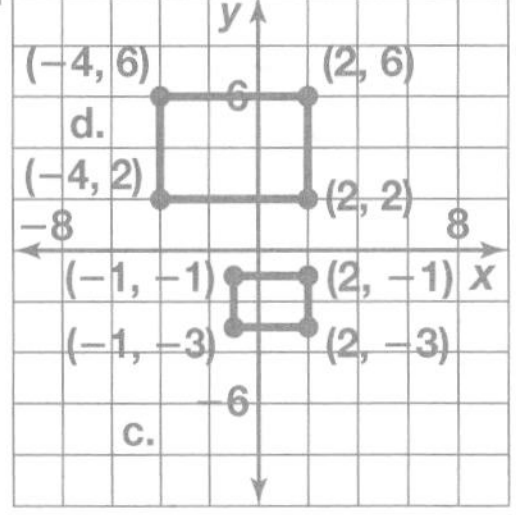


## CHAPTER 2

pages 106–107 **Practice and Problem Solving**

9.

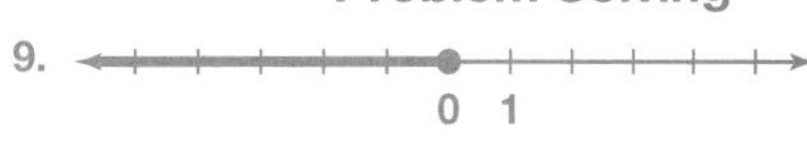


10. −13 0 5

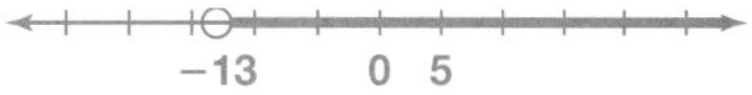

11. −2 0

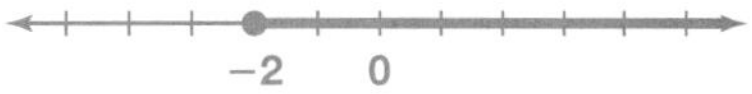

12. −12 0 4

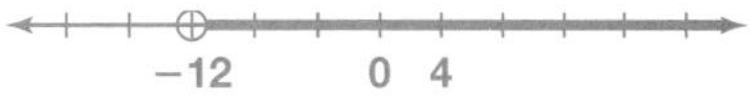

13. −20 0 26

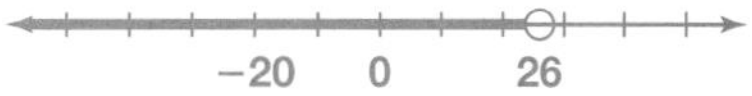

14. 0 1 3.7

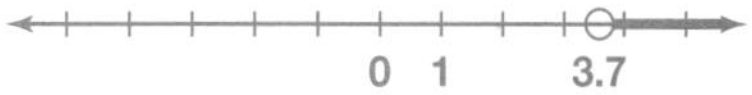

15. 0 1 5.3

16. 0 2 7

17. −8 0 2

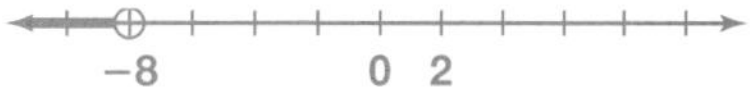

18. 0 1 4

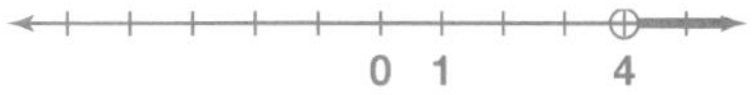

19. 0 4 16

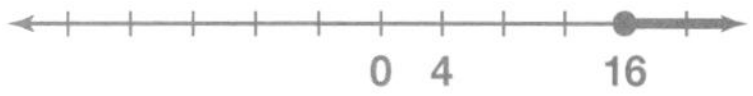

20.

21.

22.

## CHAPTER 4

page 220 **Cumulative Review**

20. Erasers Purchased

| $.05 | $.10 | $.15 |
|---|---|---|
| 0 | 0 | 3 |
| 1 | 1 | 2 |
| 3 | 0 | 2 |
| 0 | 3 | 1 |
| 2 | 2 | 1 |
| 4 | 1 | 1 |
| 6 | 0 | 1 |
| 1 | 4 | 0 |
| 3 | 3 | 0 |
| 5 | 2 | 0 |
| 7 | 1 | 0 |
| 9 | 0 | 0 |

## CHAPTER 7

page 333 **Skills You Need**

25.

26. −2 0 2

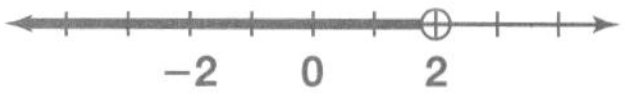

27. −10 0 10

28. −4 −2 0 2 4

29. −1 0 1

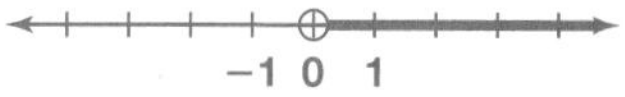

30. −6 −2 0 2

31. −17 −10 0 10

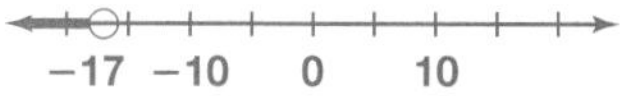

32. −10 0 10 15

33. −10 0 10 19

34. −3 0 3

35. −40 0 40 80

36. −1 0 1

## CHAPTER 8

### LESSON 8-1

pages 389–390 **Practice and Problem Solving**

23.

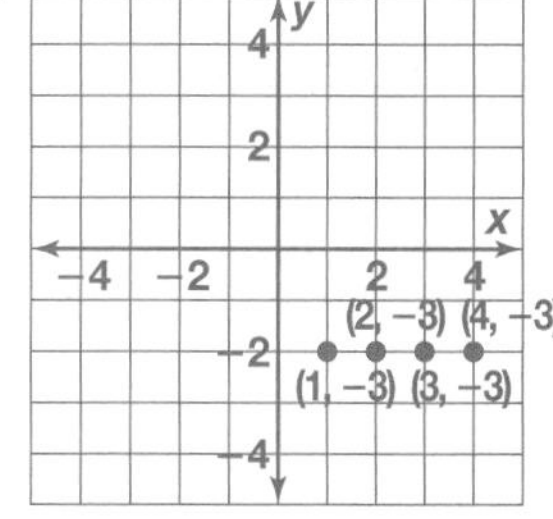


Additional Answers

32b. 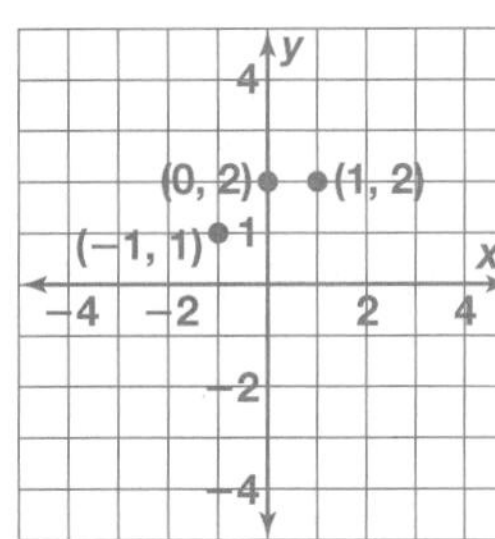


a function

(0, 2) (0, 1)
(−1, 1) (1, 1)

not a function

## LESSON 8-2

### page 394 Check Understanding

9.

$y = x - 3$

10. 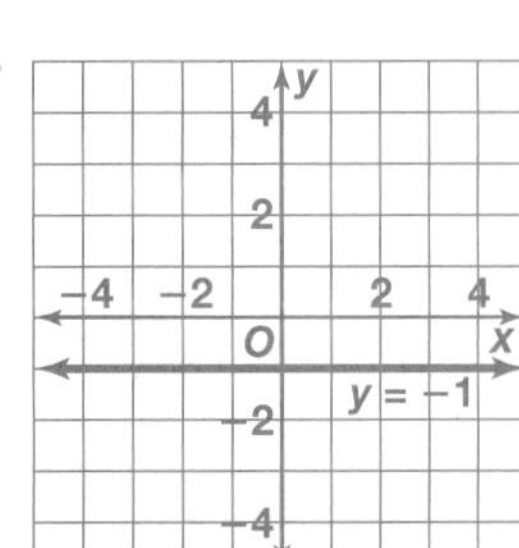


11. 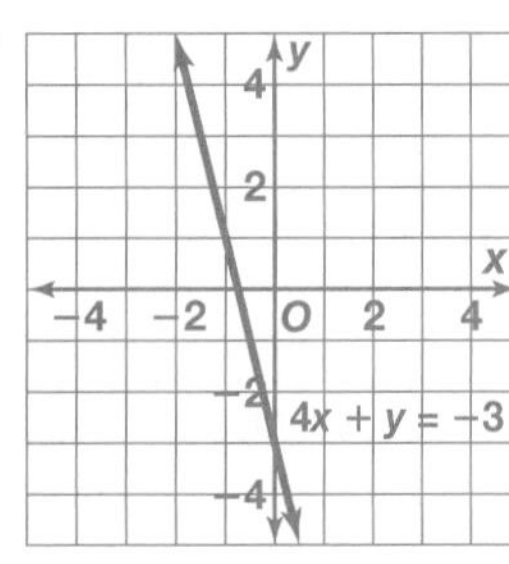


### pages 391–393 Practice and Problem Solving

21. 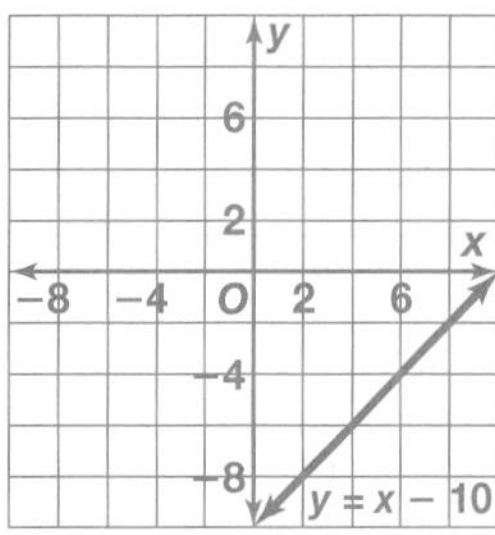


22. 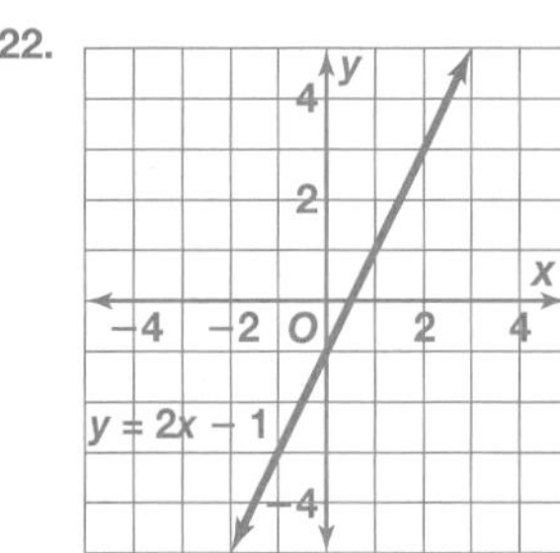


23. 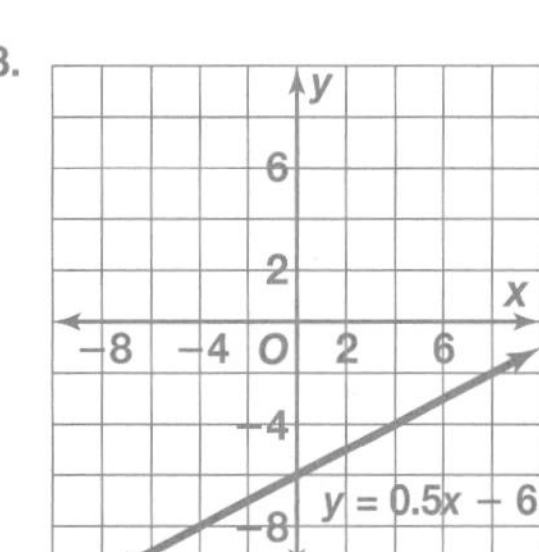


24. 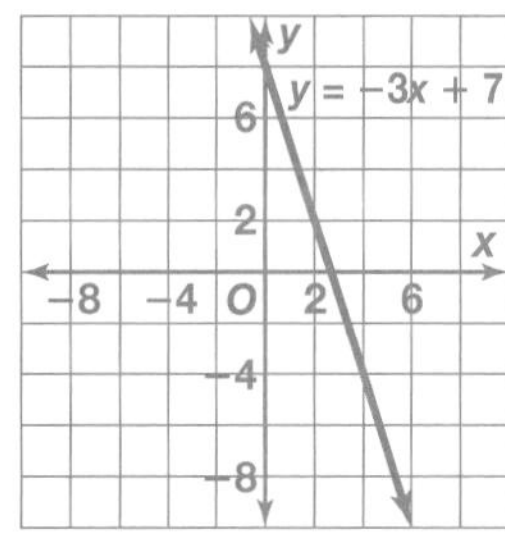


25. 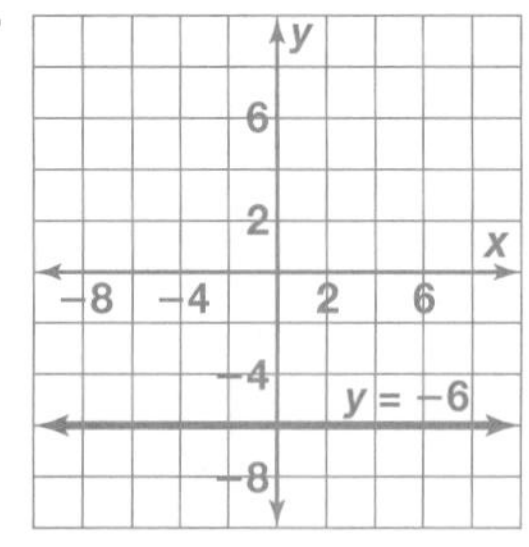


26. 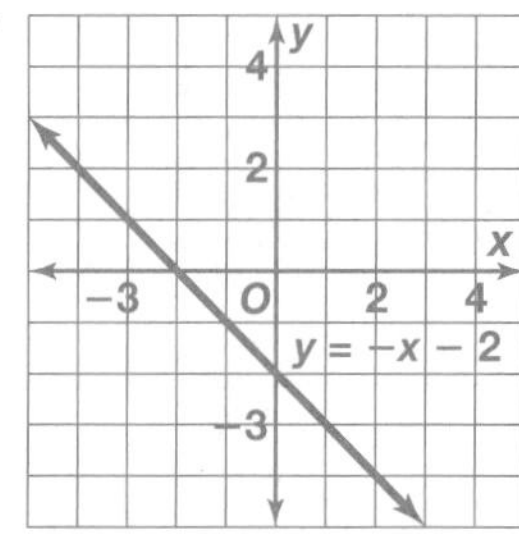


27. 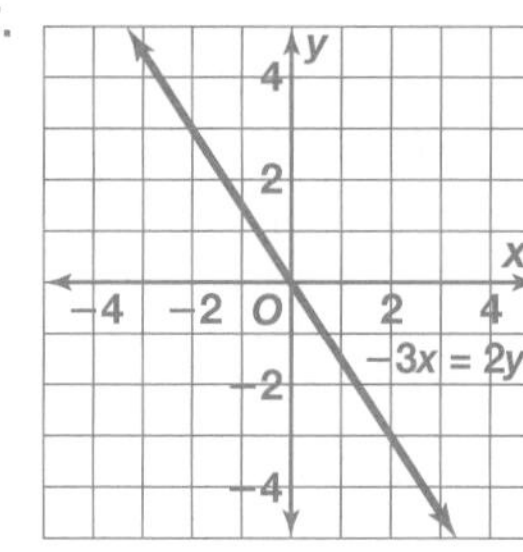


28. 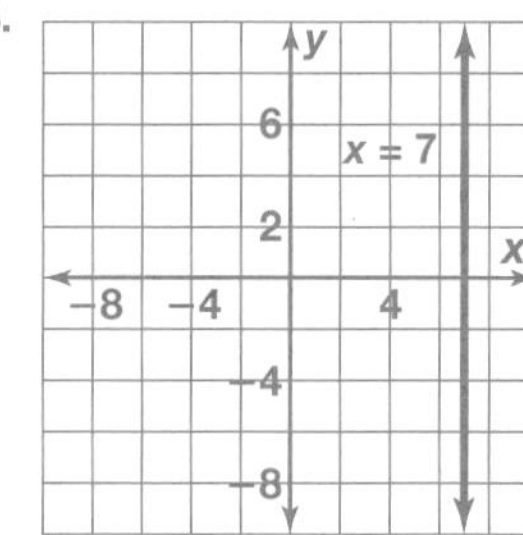


29. 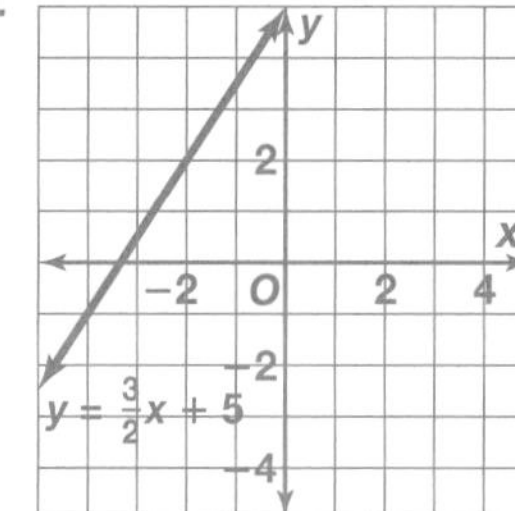


30. 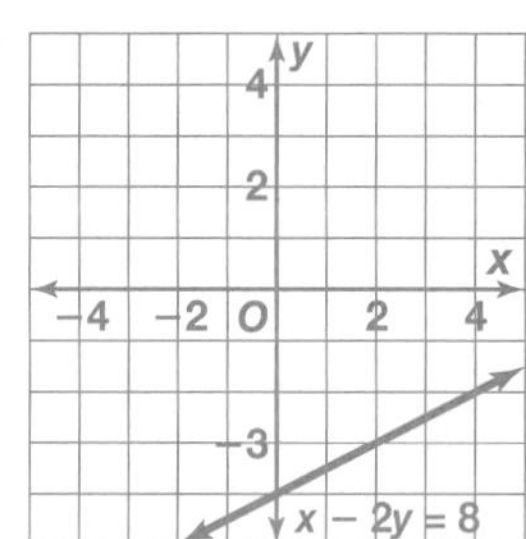

31.

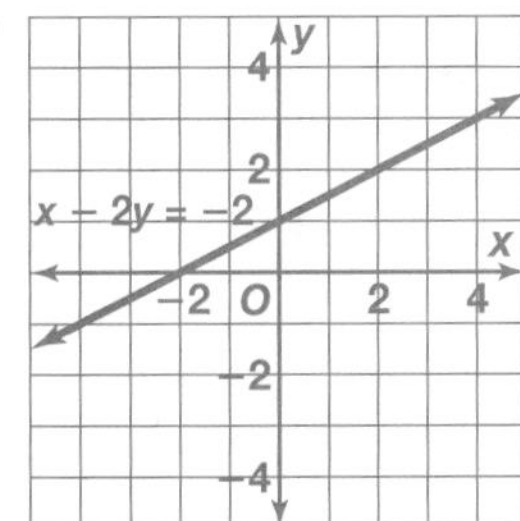


## LESSON 8-3

**pages 400** **Check Understanding**

7.

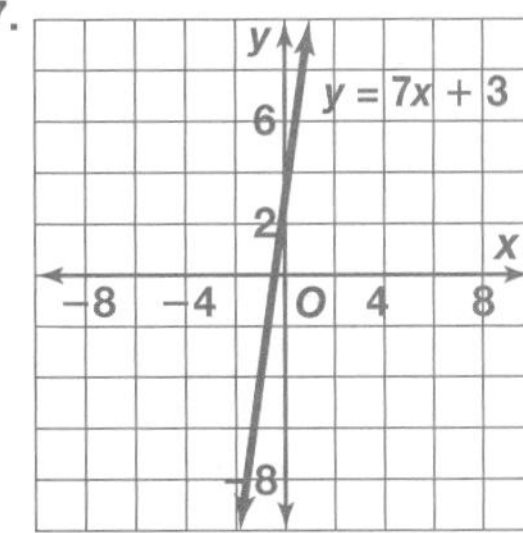


8.

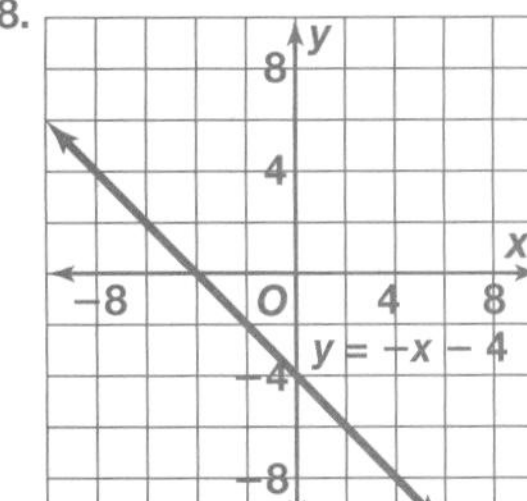


9.

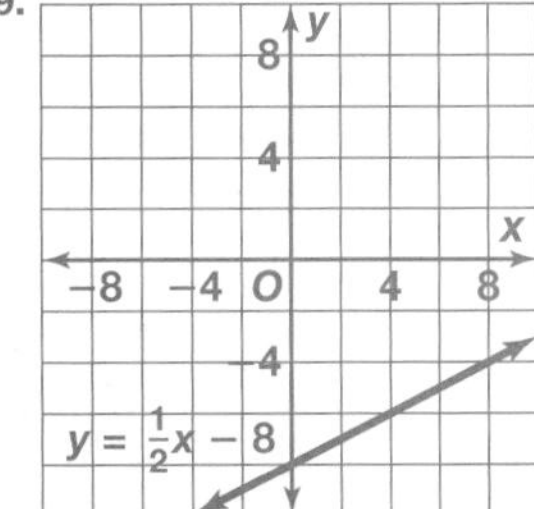


**pages 400–402** **Practice and Problem Solving**

39.

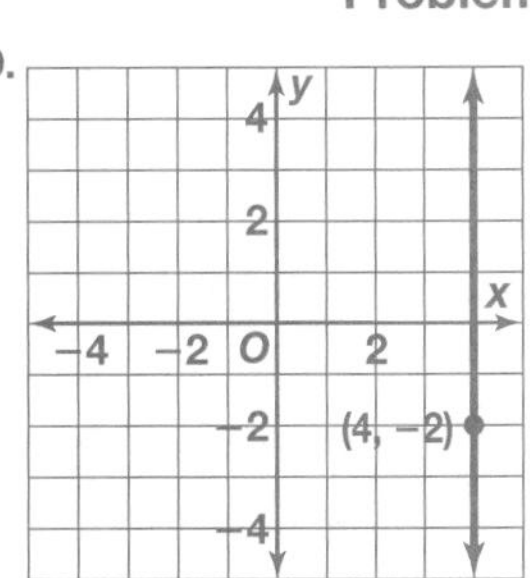


40.

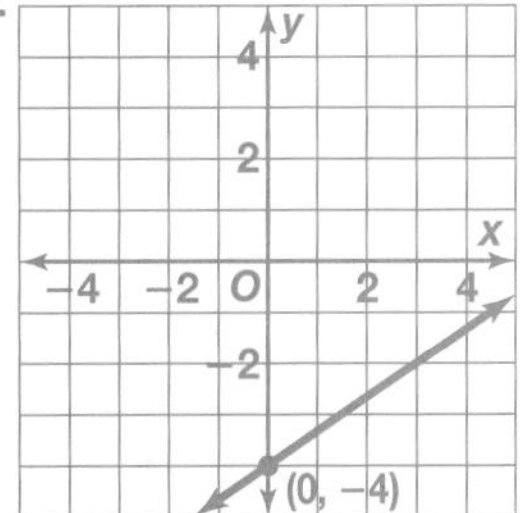


43a.

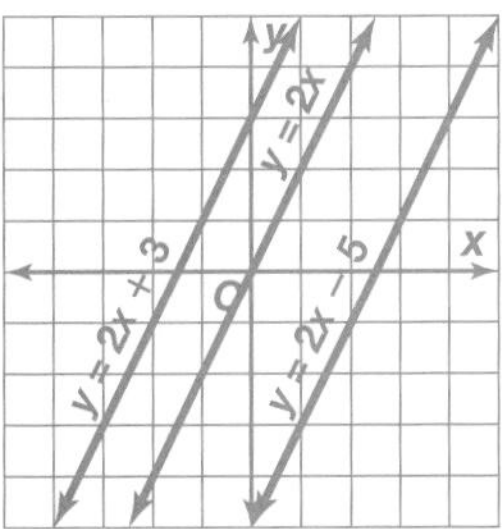


$y = -3x + 4$

$y = -3x$

$y = -3x - 1$

**page 403** **Math Toolbox**

3. $y = 3x + 2$

4. $y = -x$

5.

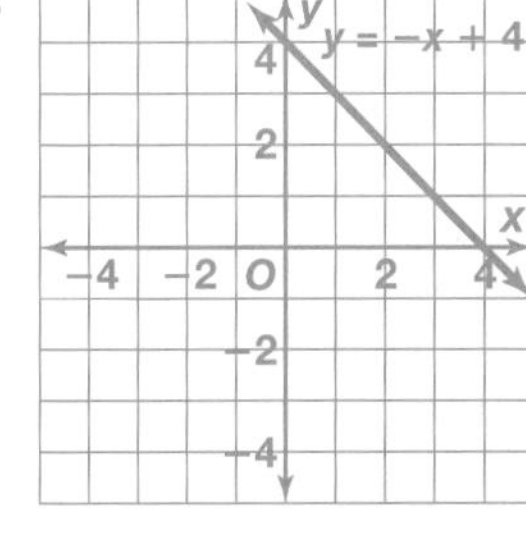


6. $y = 4x - 3$

7.

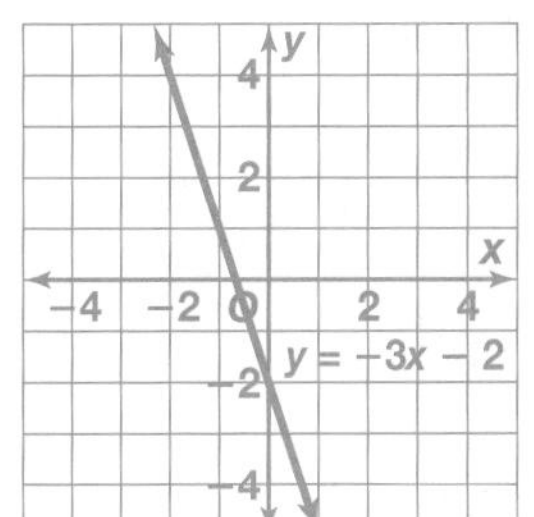


8.

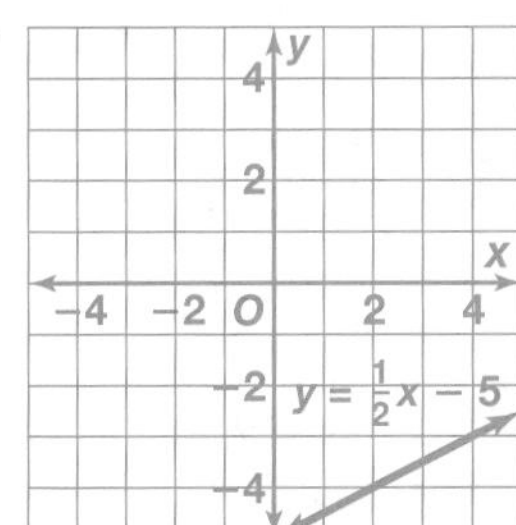


9.

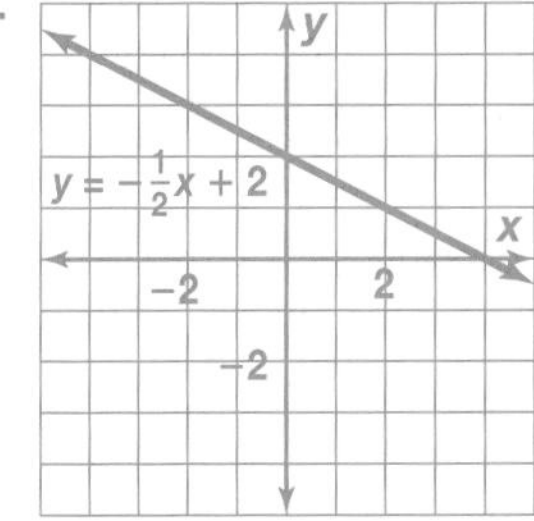

## LESSON 8-7

### page 423 Check Understanding

8.

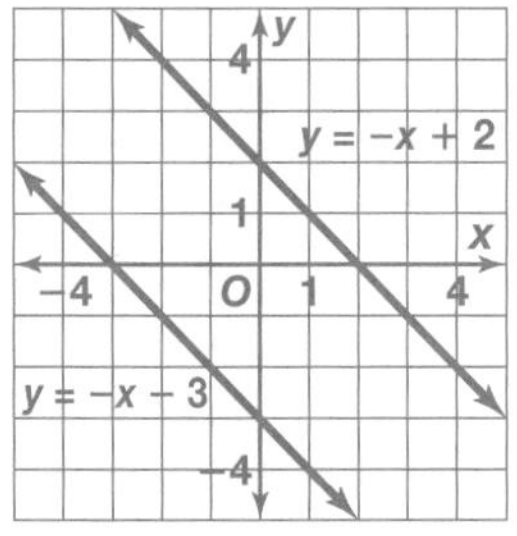


9.

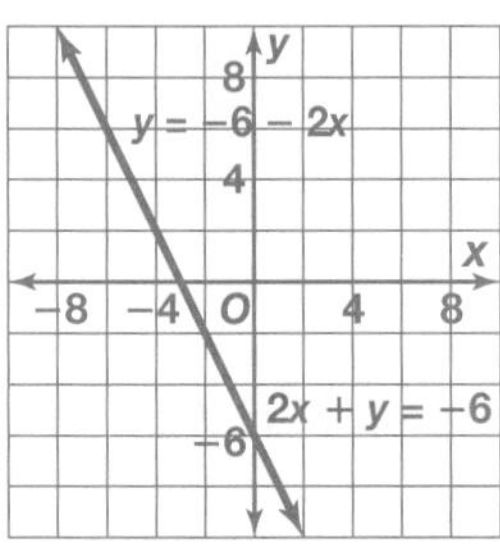


10b.

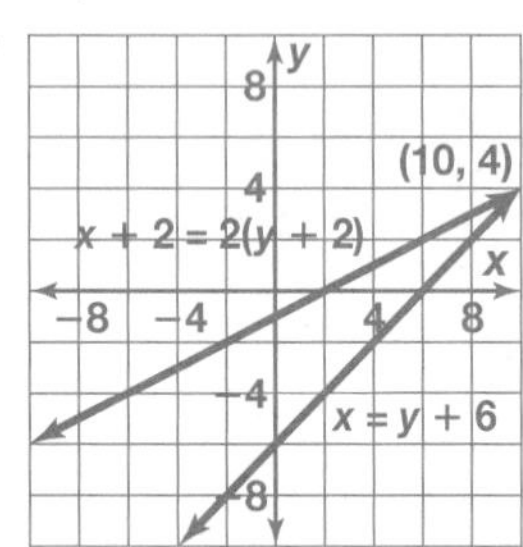


### pages 423–425 Practice and Problem Solving

14.

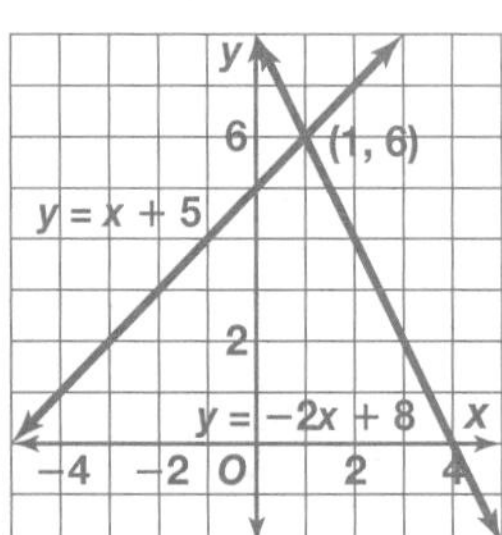


15.

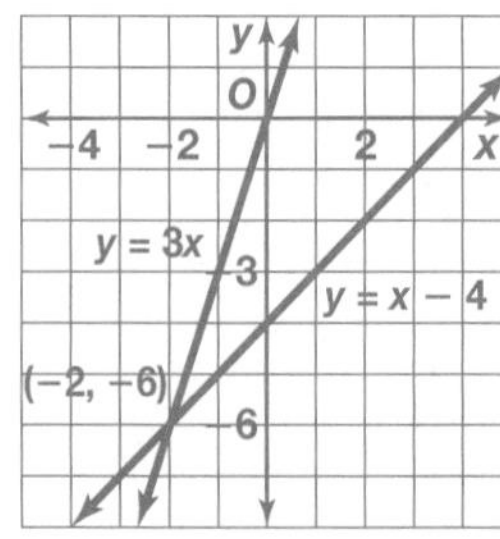


16.

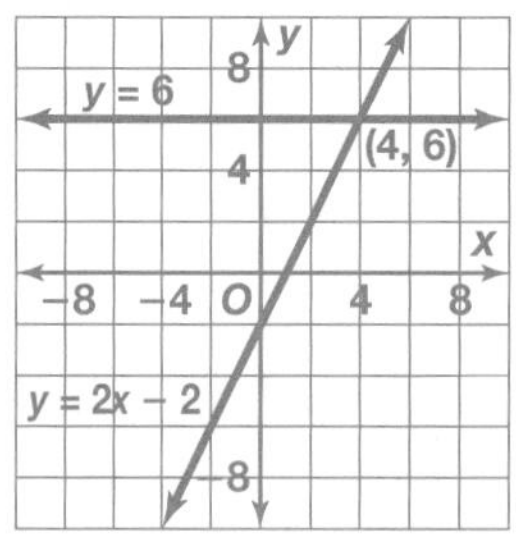


17.

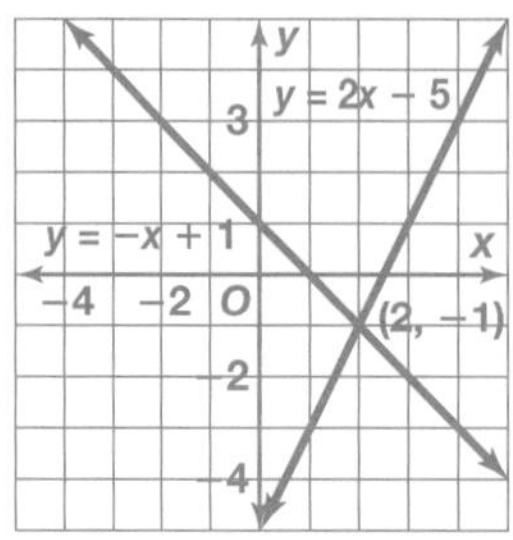


18.

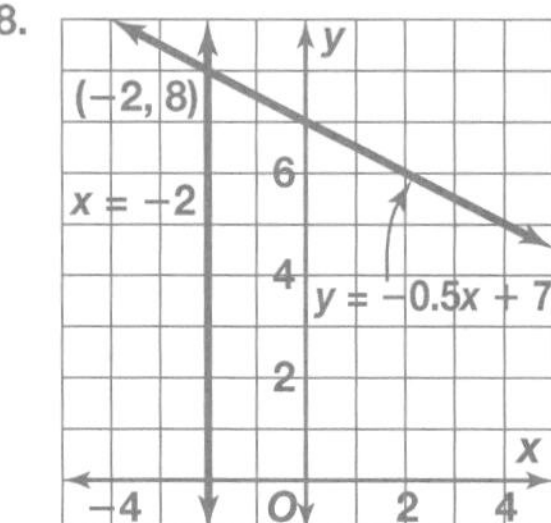


19.

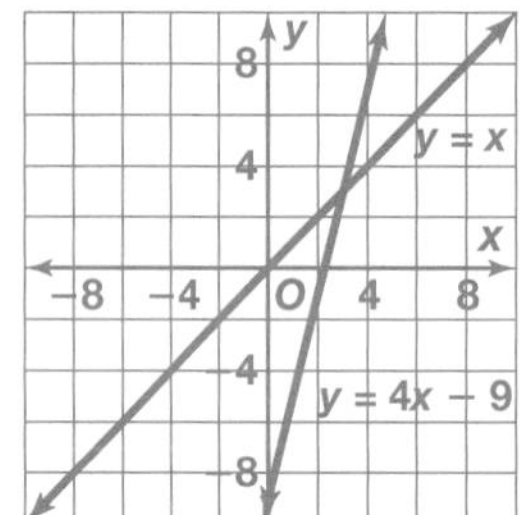


20.

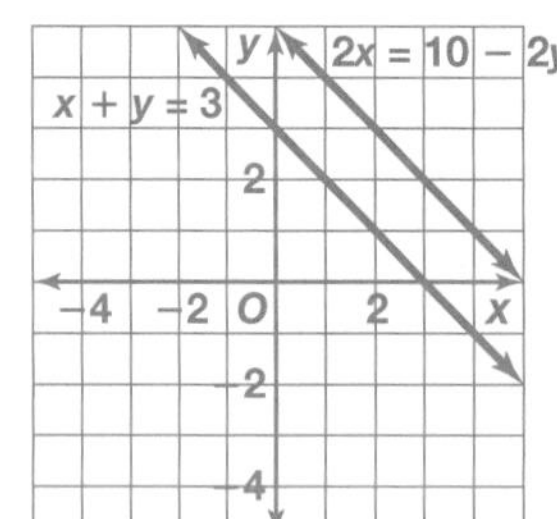


21.

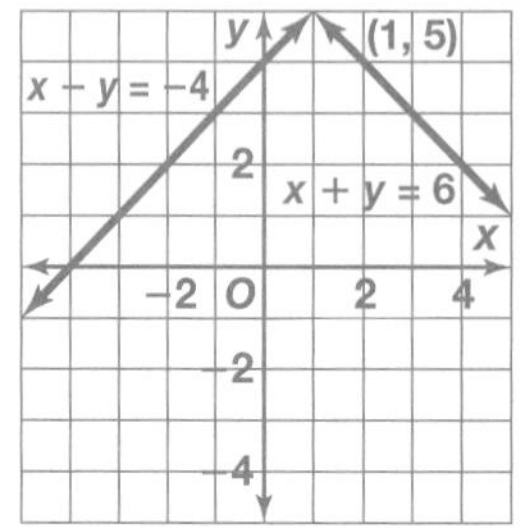


22.

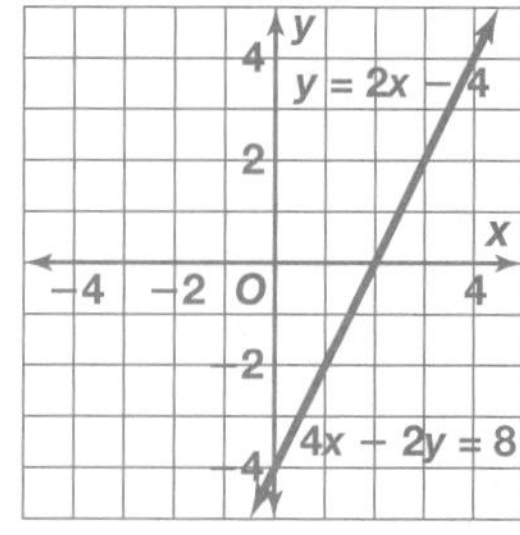


23.

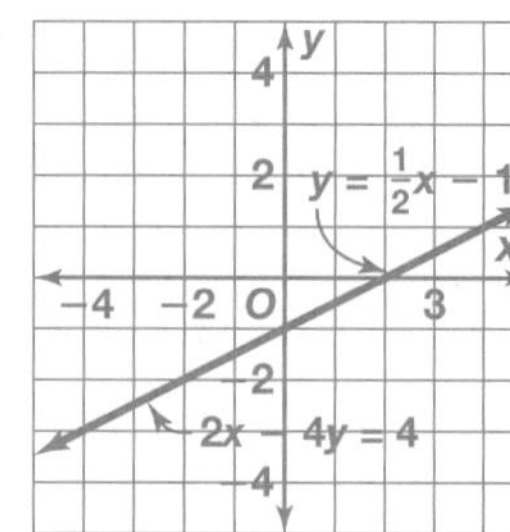


24.

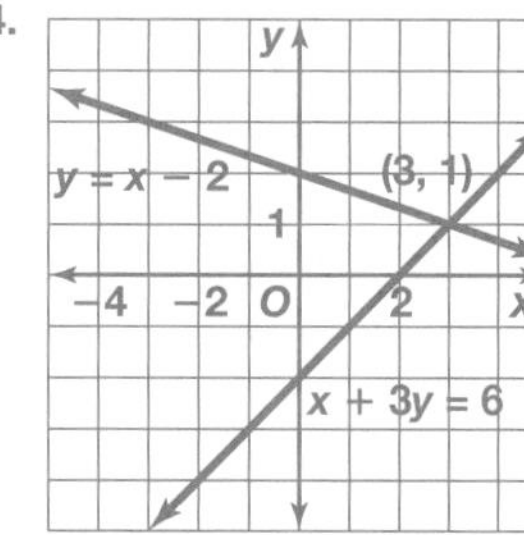


25.

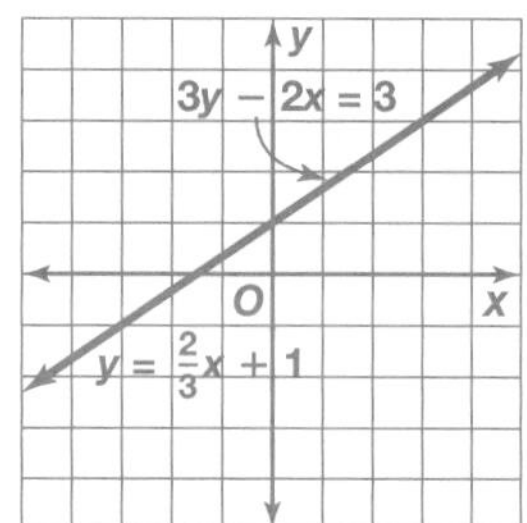

**page 425** **Checkpoint 2**

1a, 1c.

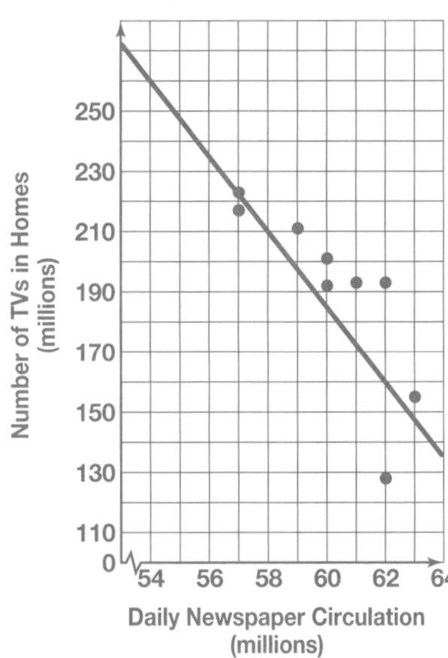


c. Trendlines may vary. Sample: See scatterplot; 250 million television sets

## LESSON 8-8

**page 429** **Check Understanding**

6.

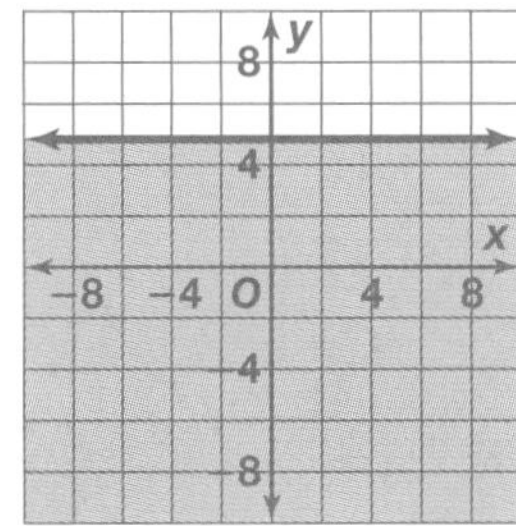

7.

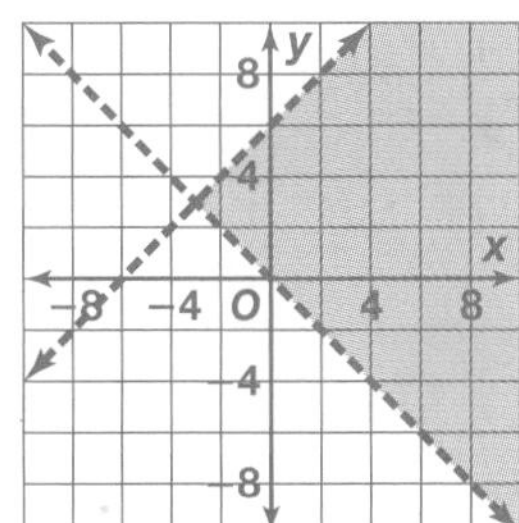

8.

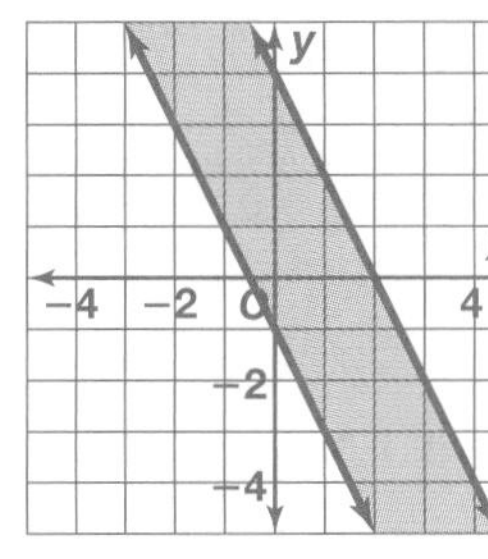

9.

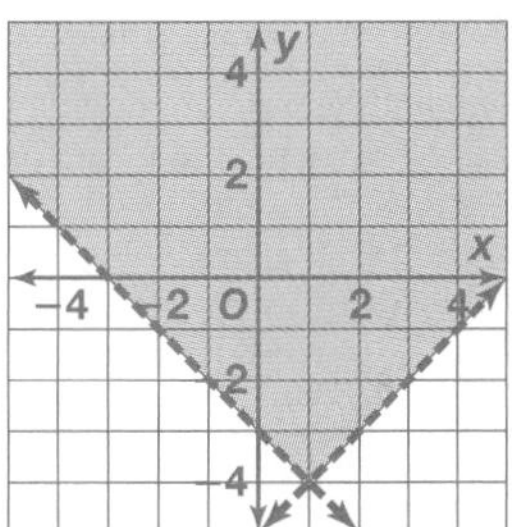

**page 429–431** **Practice and Problem Solving**

30.

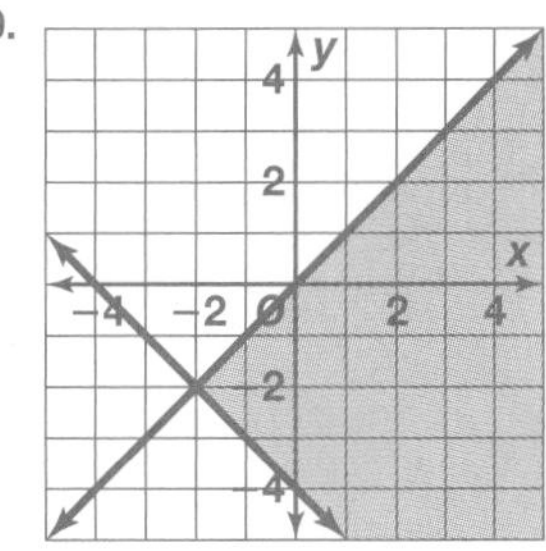

31.

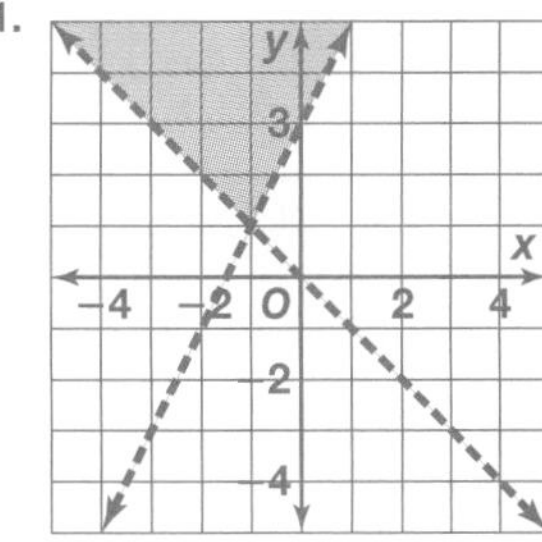

32.

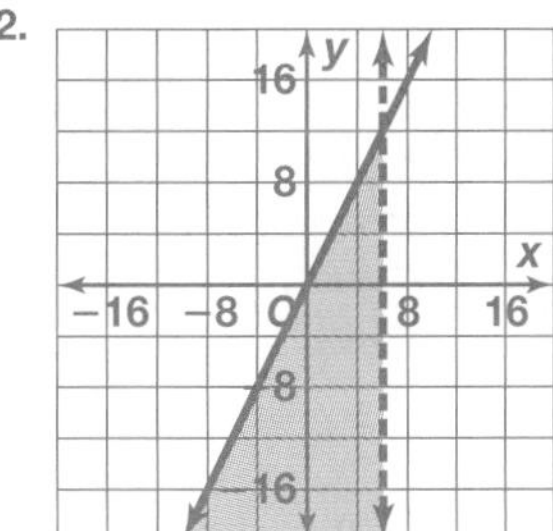

33.

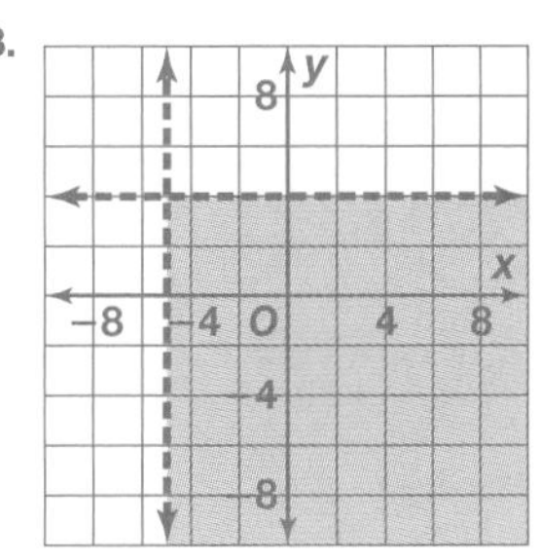

34.

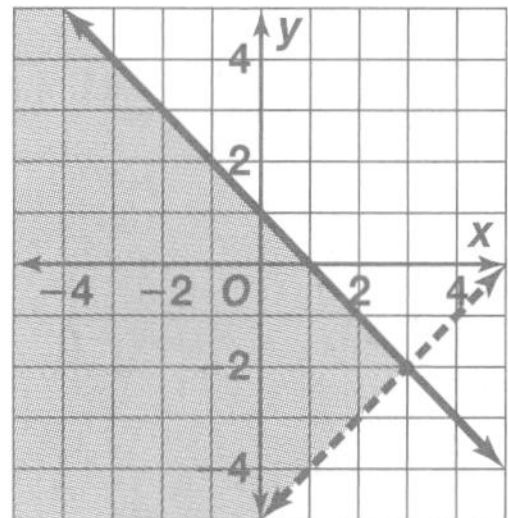

35.

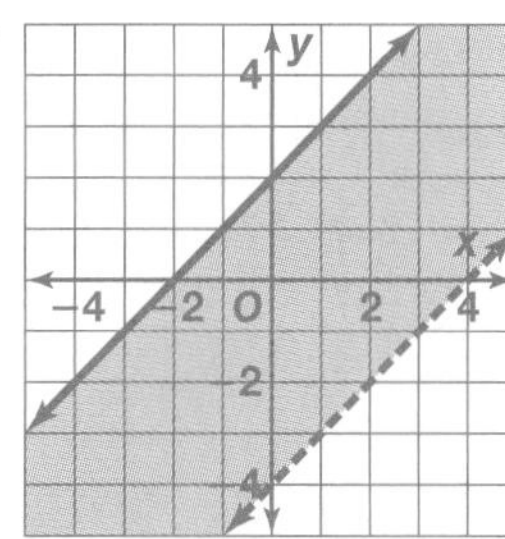

36.

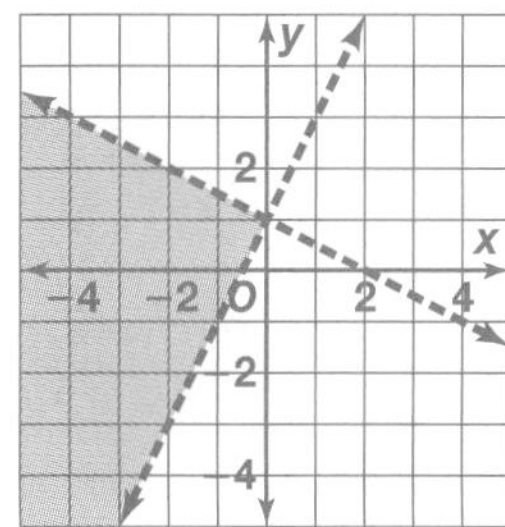

37.

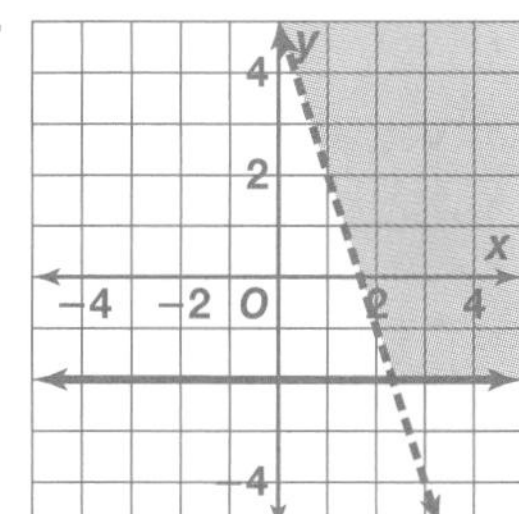

38.

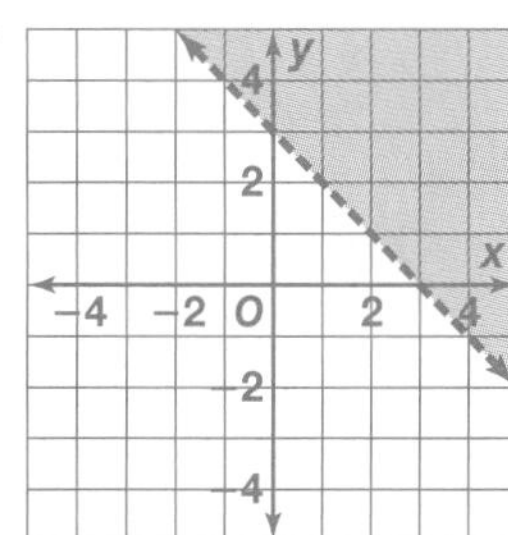

39.

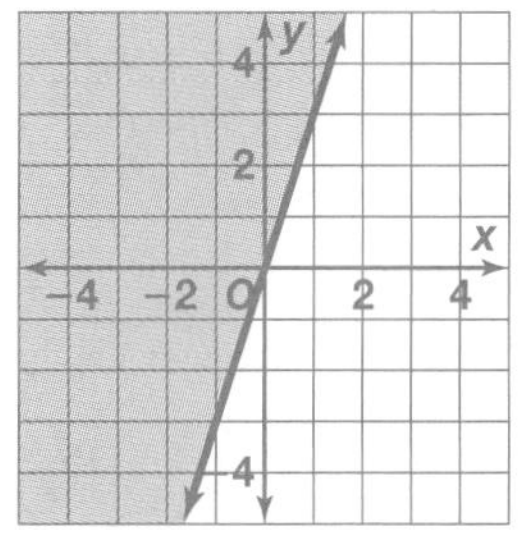

40.
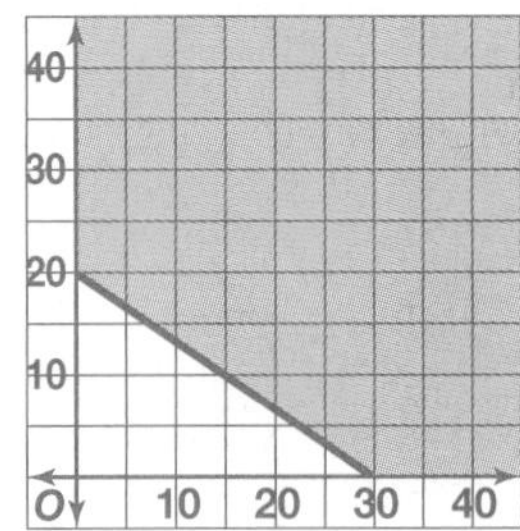

41.
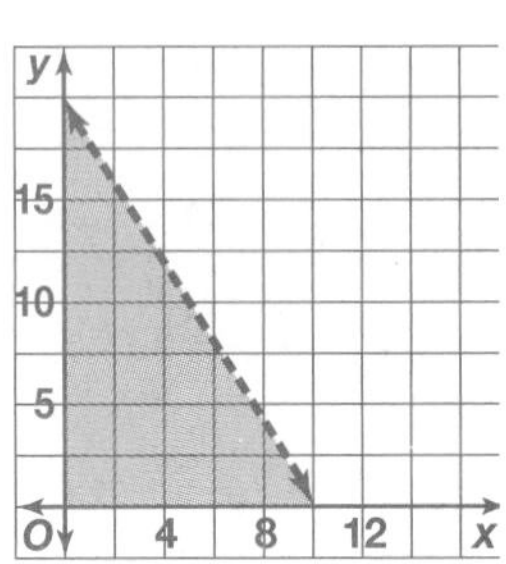

## page 431 Mixed Review

46.
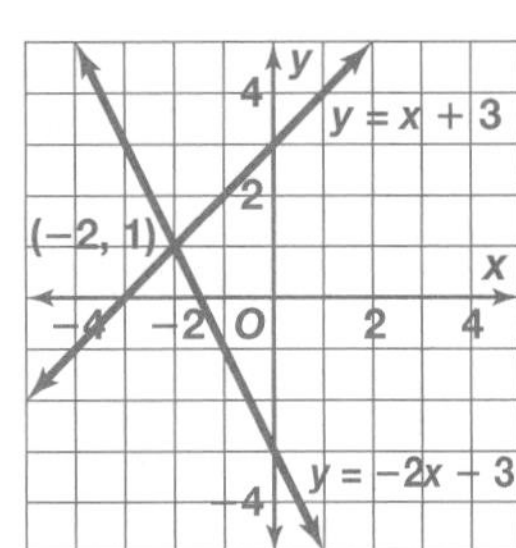


47.
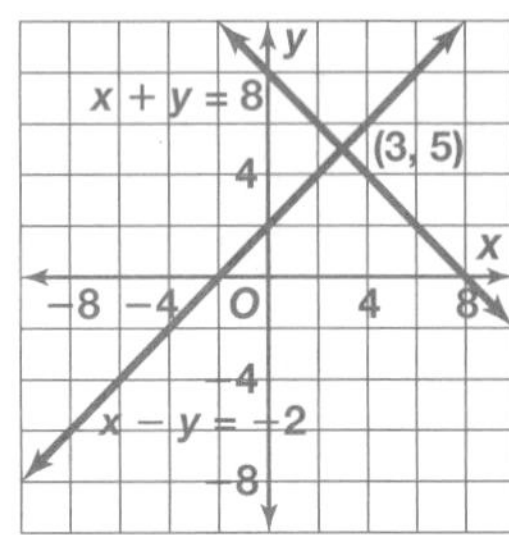


48.
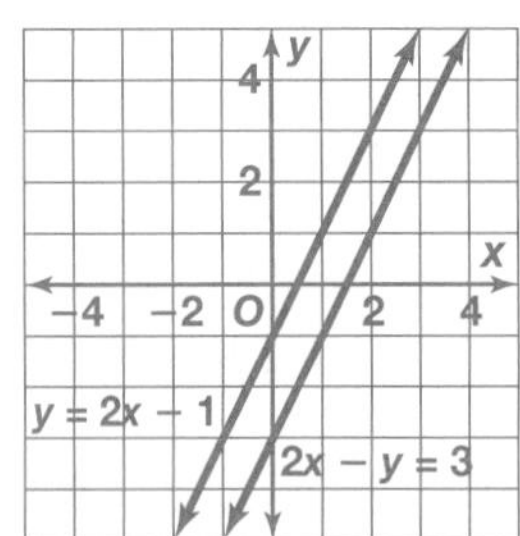


49.
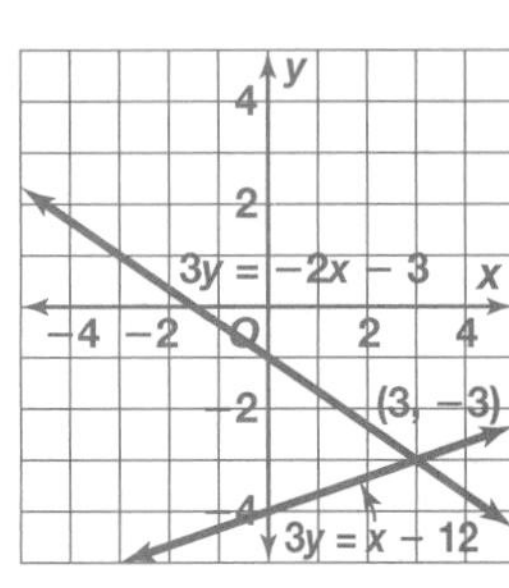


## page 432 Math Toolbox

4.
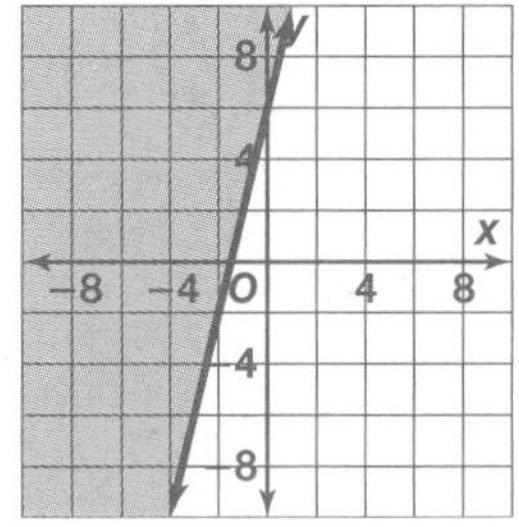

5.
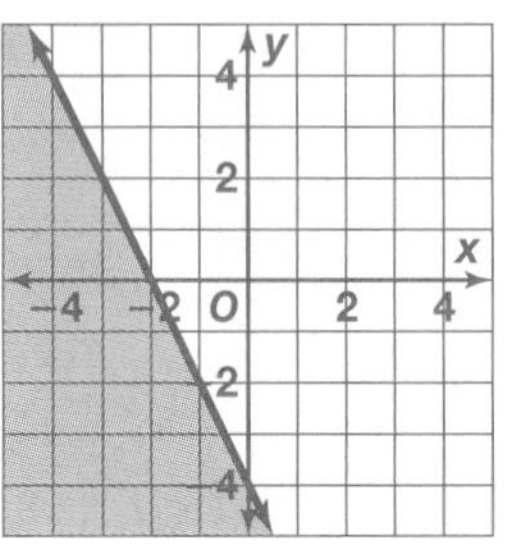

6.
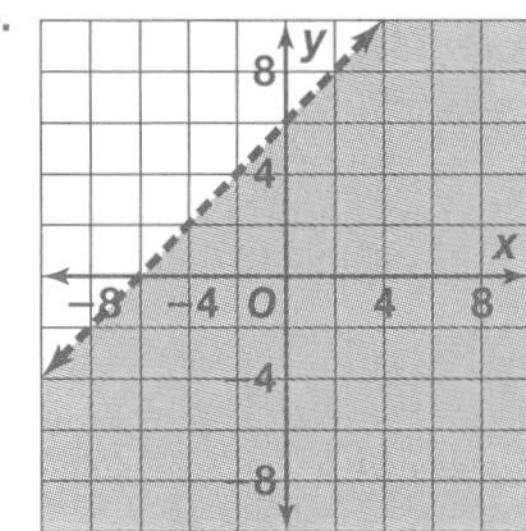

7.
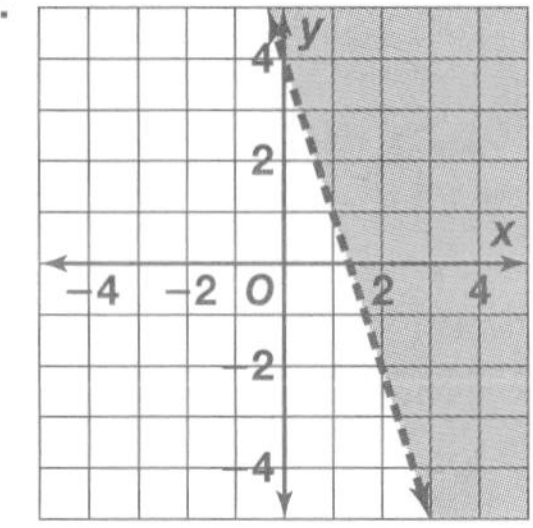

8.
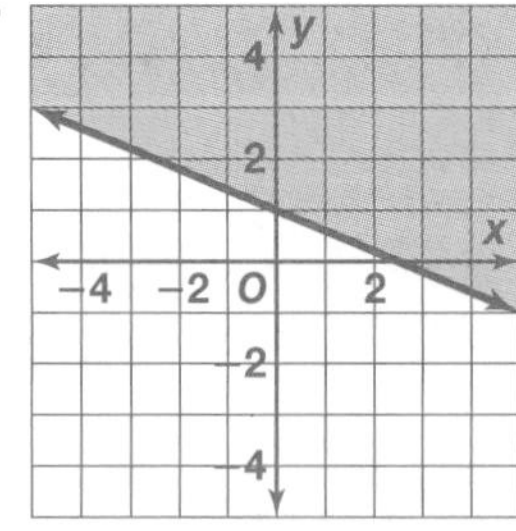

## page 437 Chapter Assessment

17.
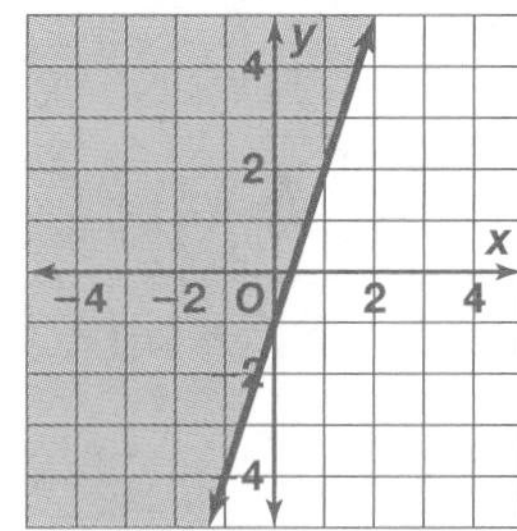

18.
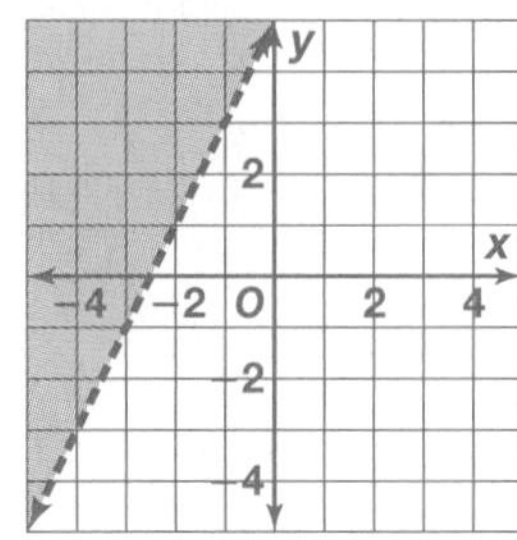

19.
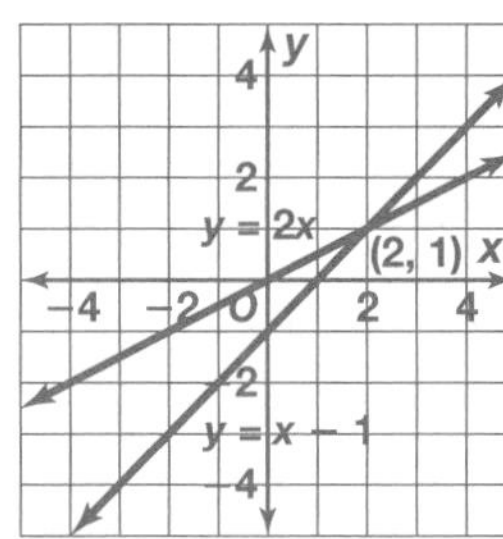


20.
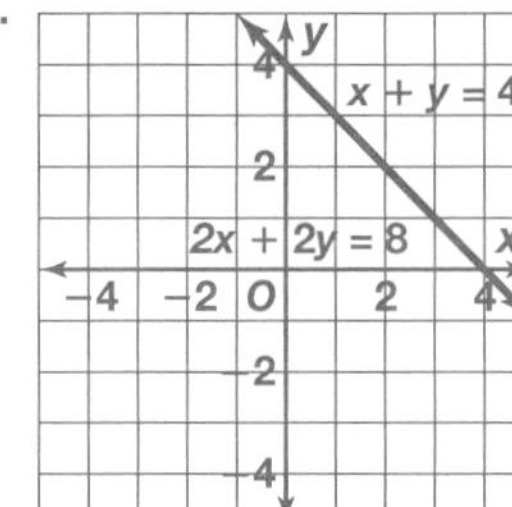


21.
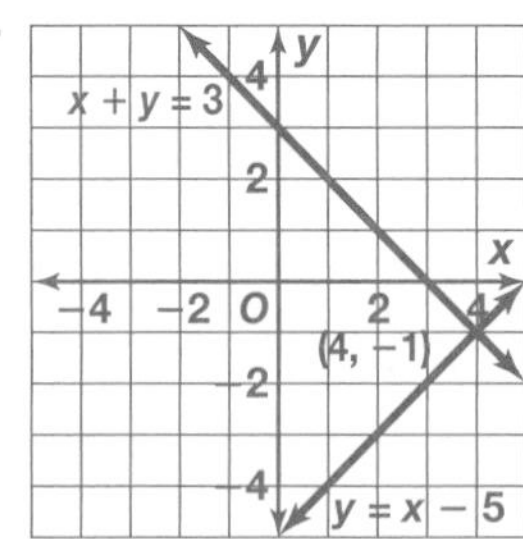

22.

25a.

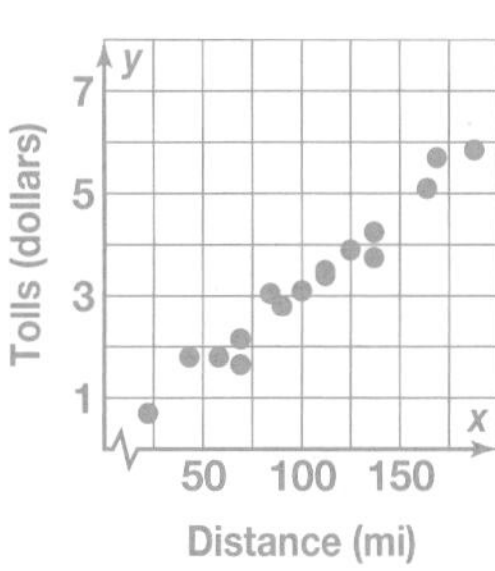


b. Predictions may vary. Sample: $6.00

## CHAPTER 9

### LESSON 9-7

**page 477 Check Understanding**

3.

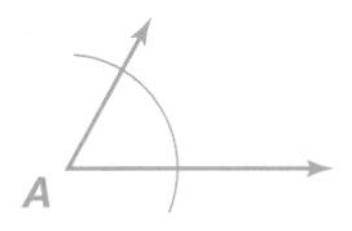


D

4.

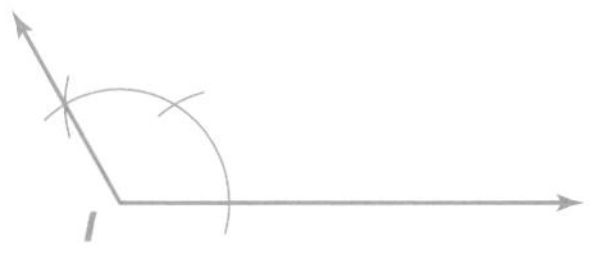


6.

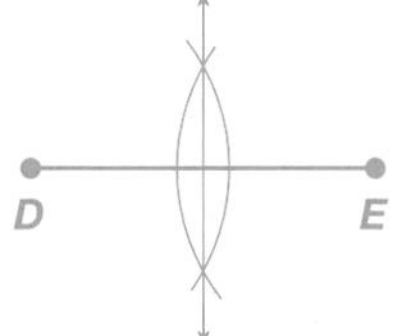


**pages 477–478 Practice and Problem Solving**

9.

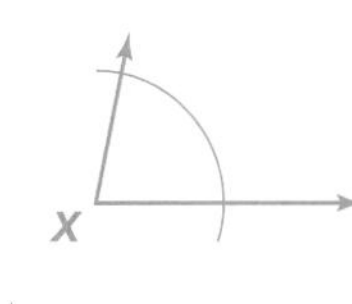


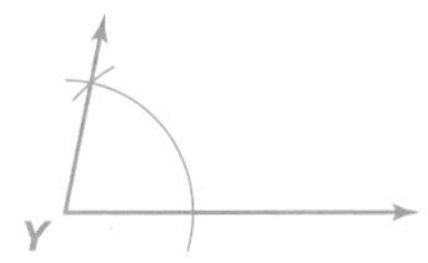


10.

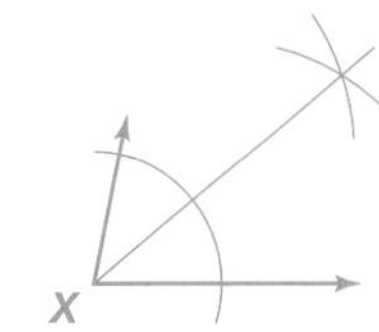


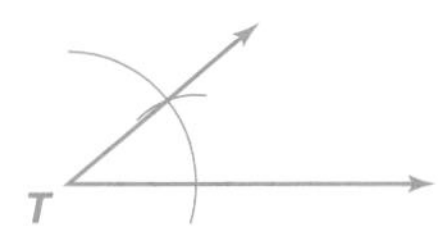


11.

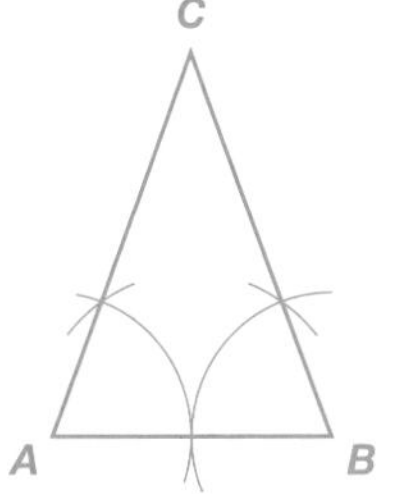


12.

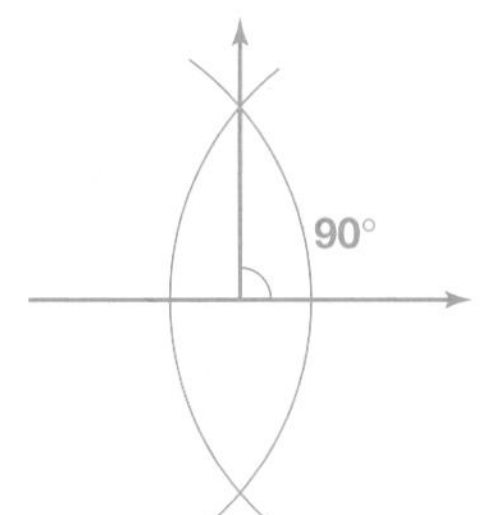


13.

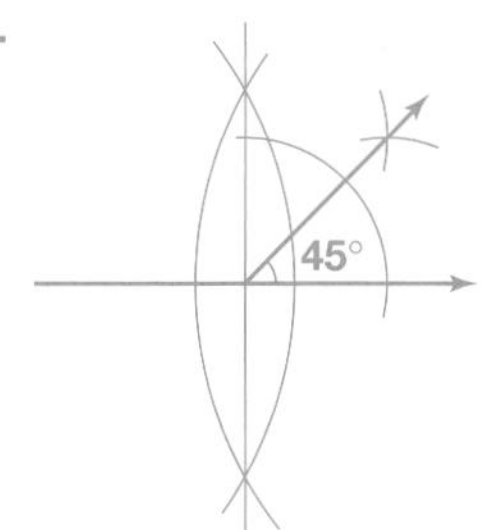


20.

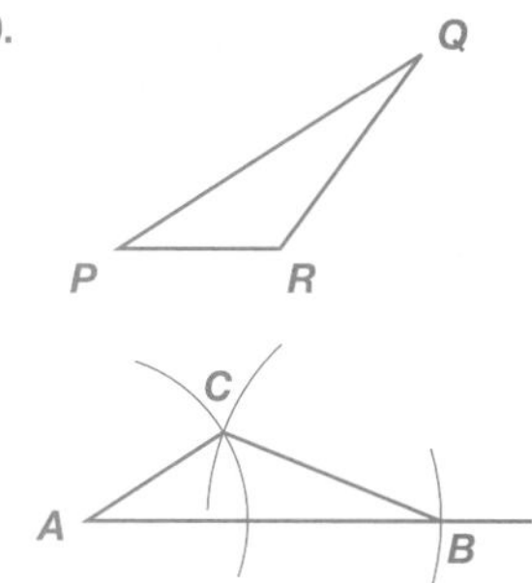


### LESSON 9-8

**page 479 Try This**

1.

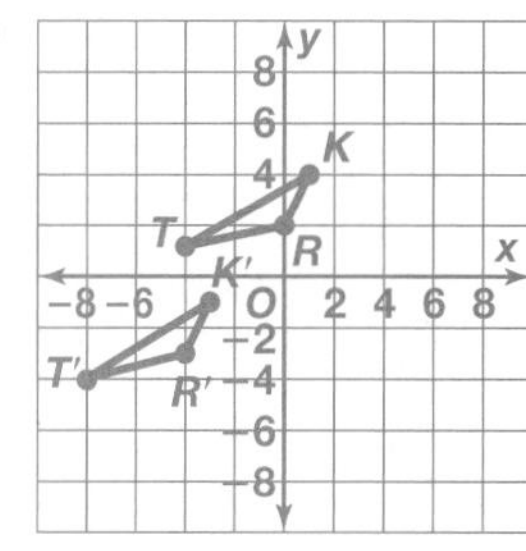


**page 481 Check Understanding**

4.

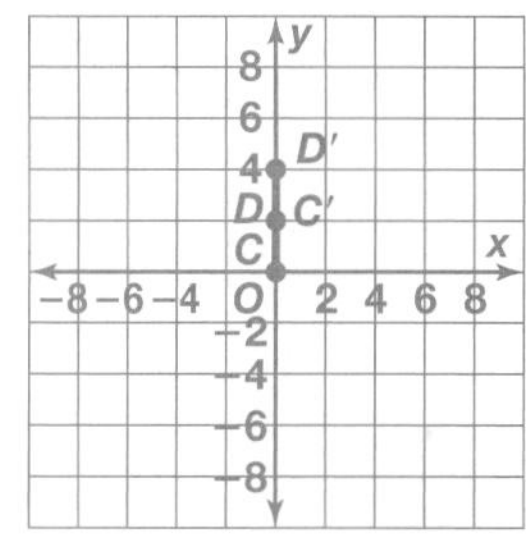


5.

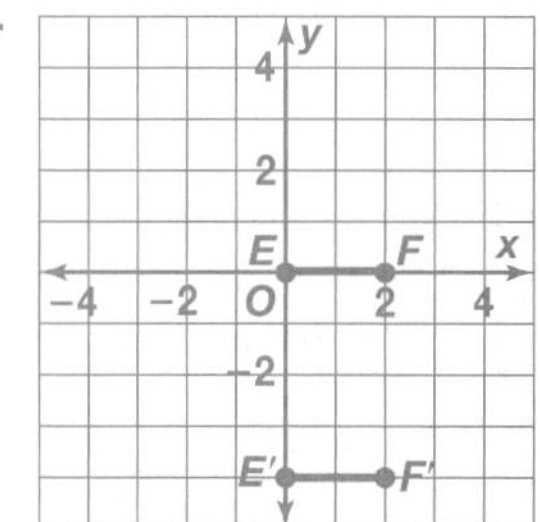


6.

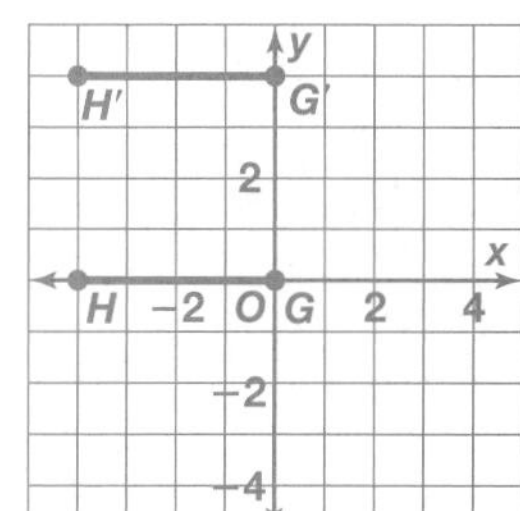


Additional Answers

7.

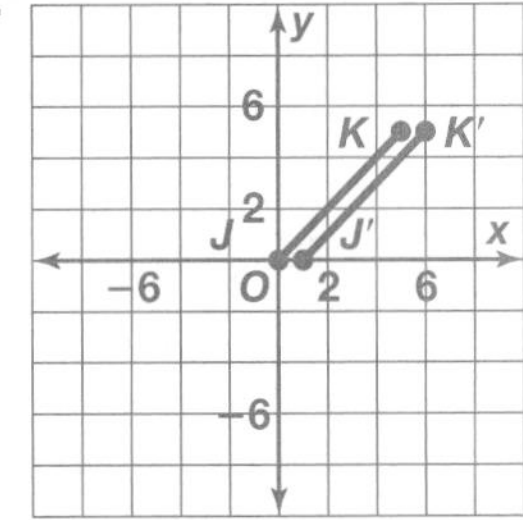


8.

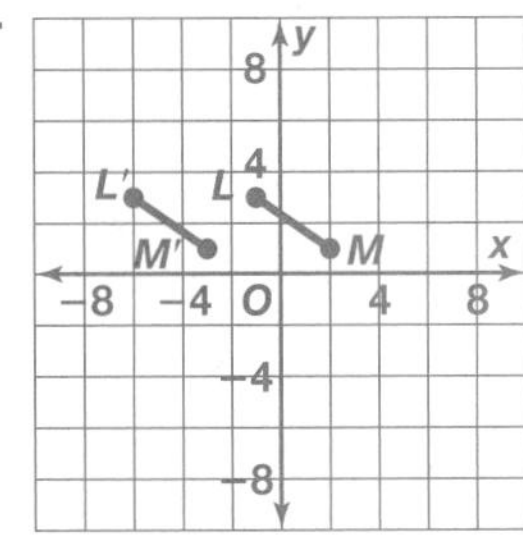


## LESSON 9-9

### page 485–486 Try This

1.

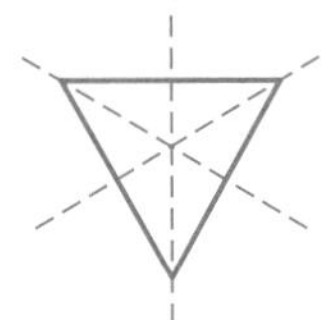

2.

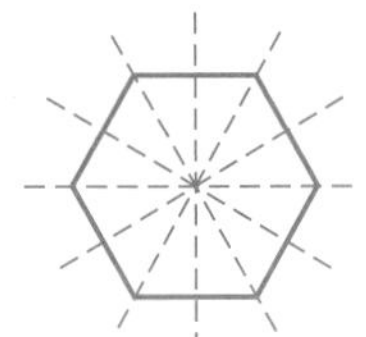

3.

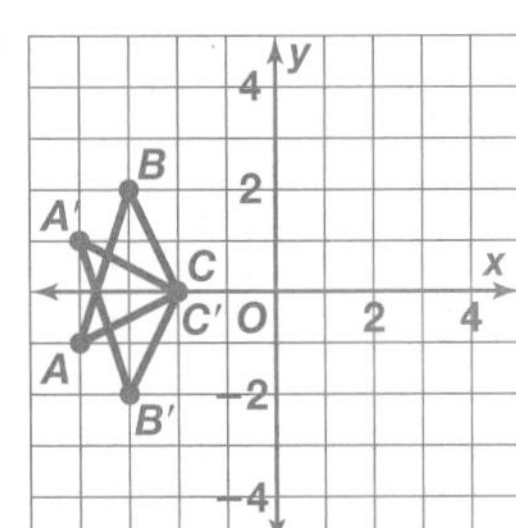


4.

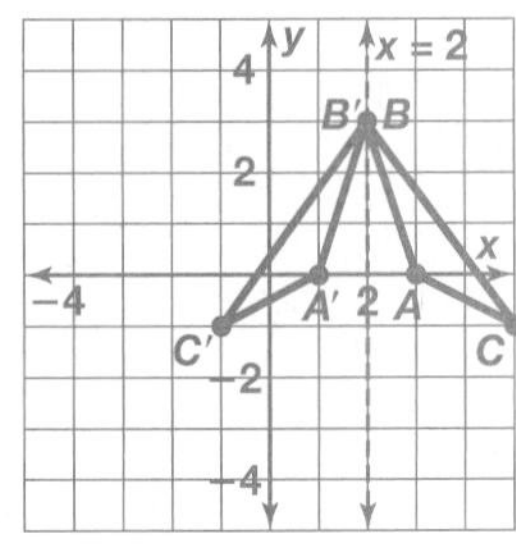


5.

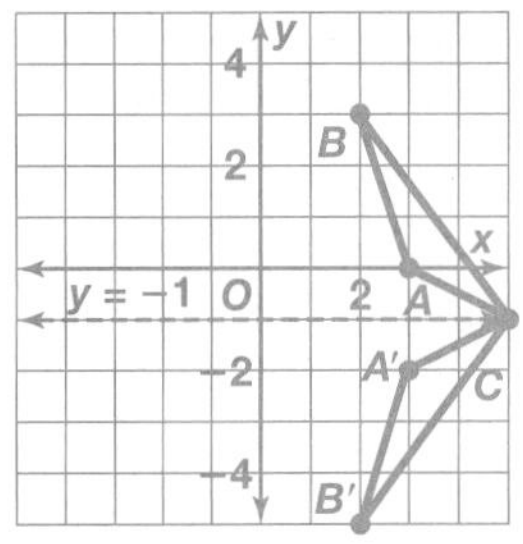


### page 487 Check Understanding

4.

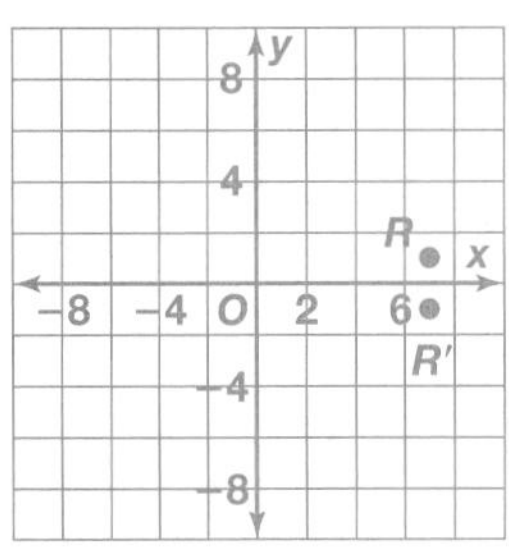


5.

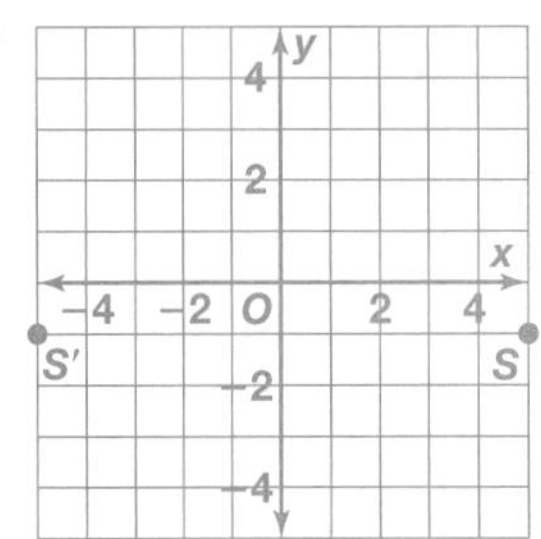


6.

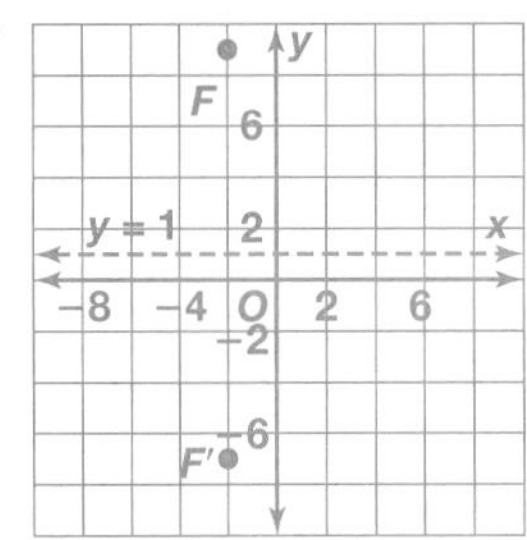


7.

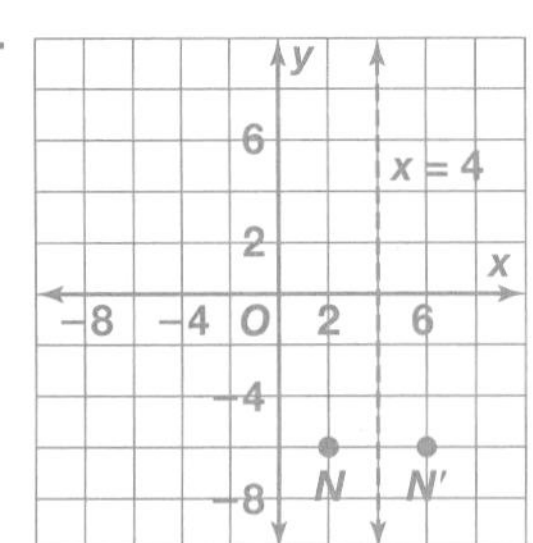


8.

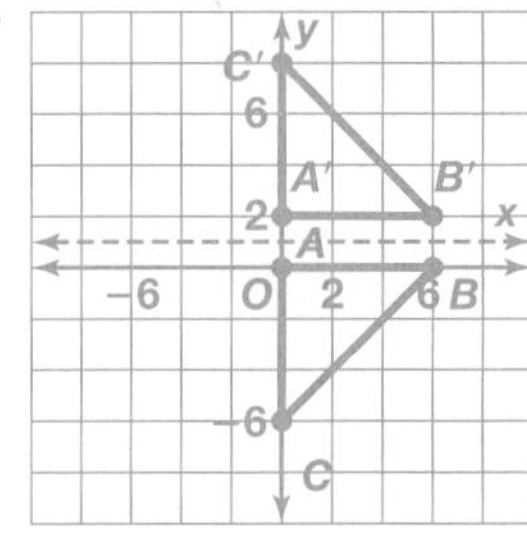


9.

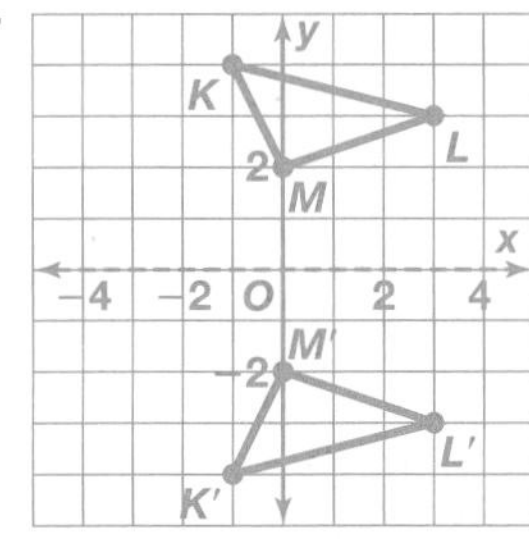


### pages 487–488 Practice and Problem Solving

10.

11.

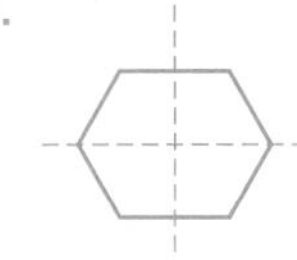

12.

13.

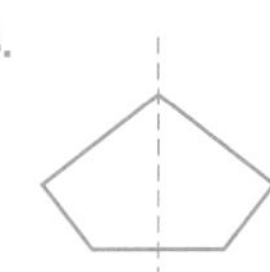

14.

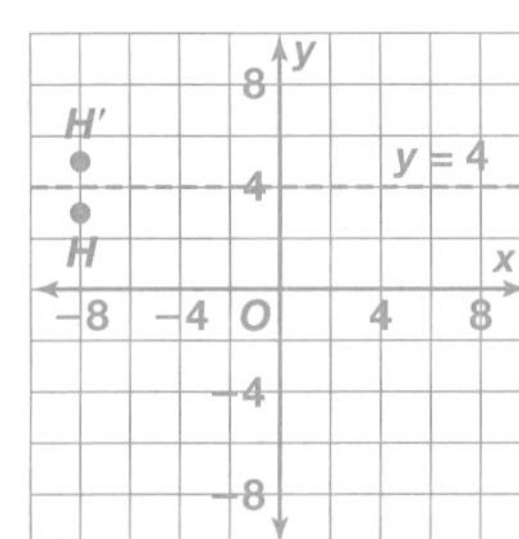

15.

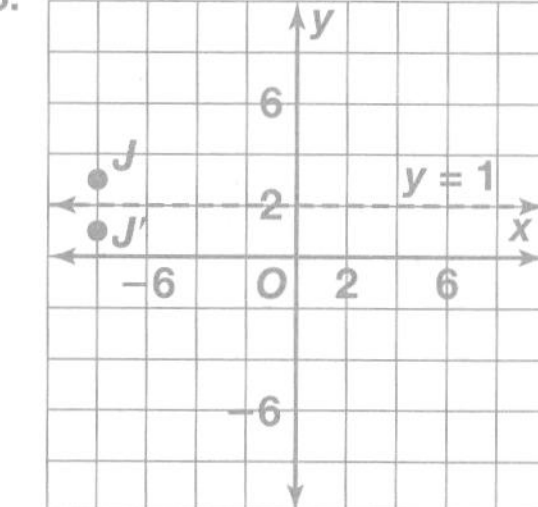


16.

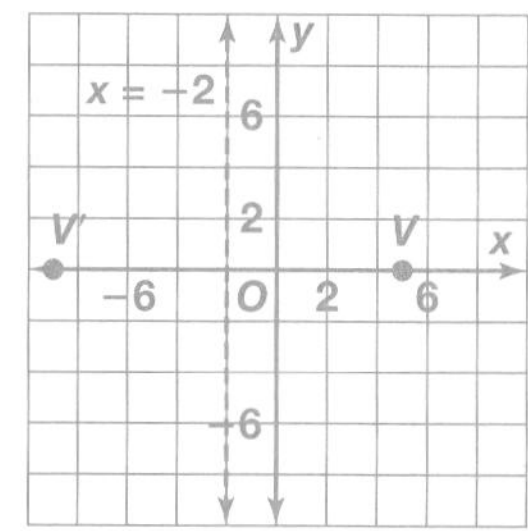


17.

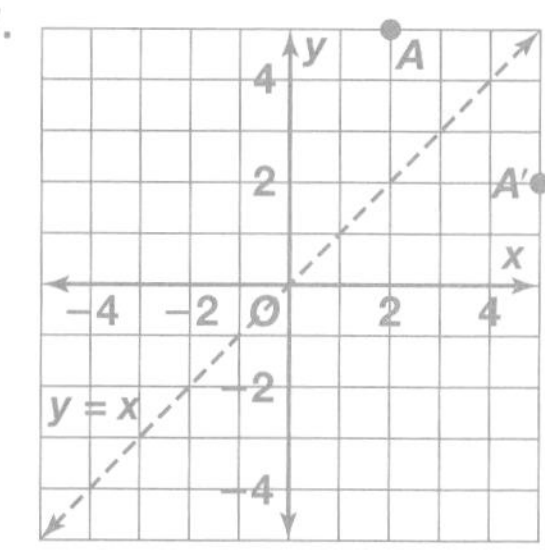


18.

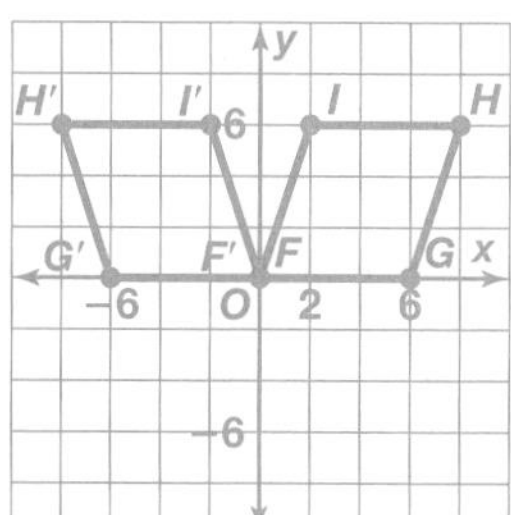


19.

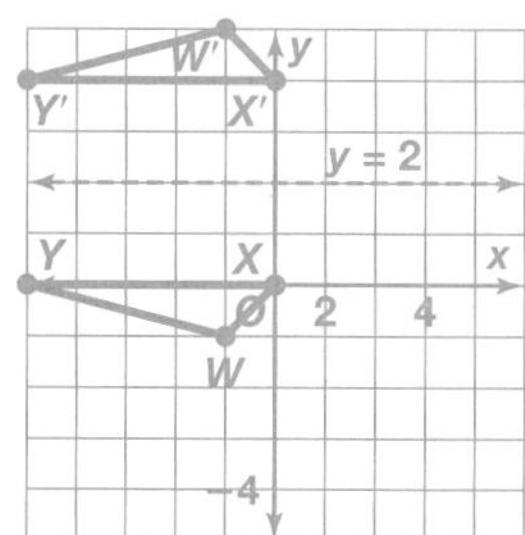


29a.

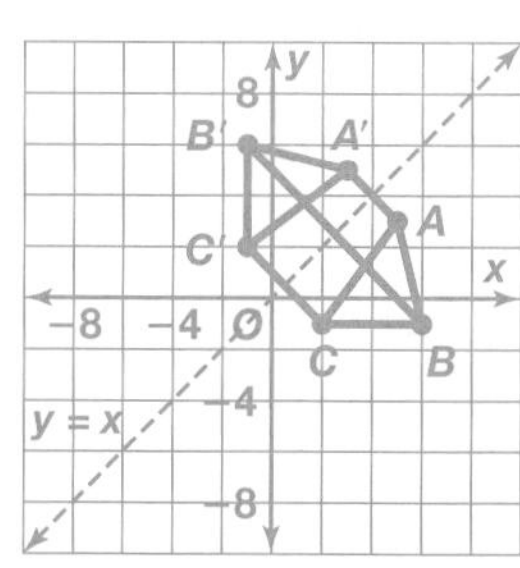


e. $A'(0, 8)$, $B'(-4, 9)$, $C'(-4, 5)$

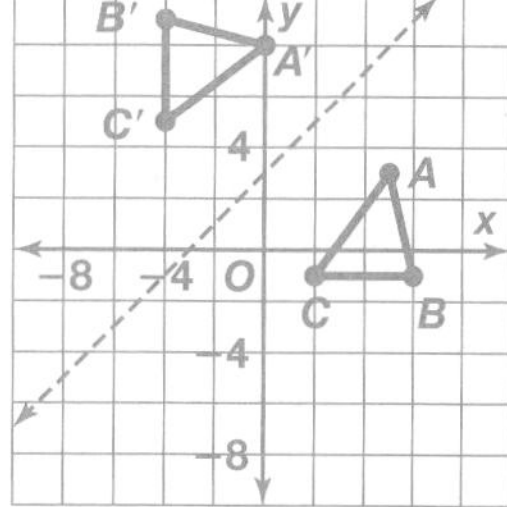

## page 488 Mixed Review

32.

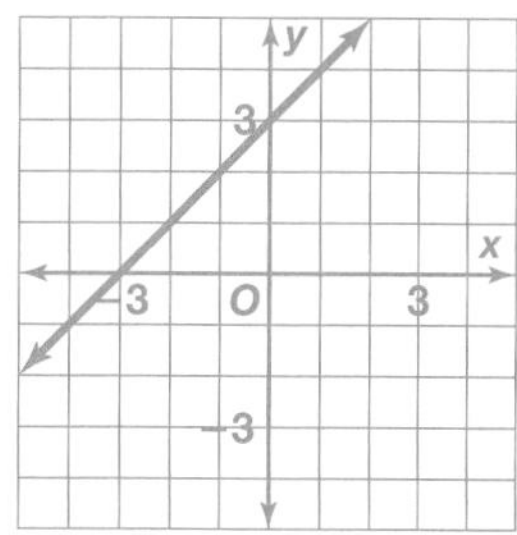


33.

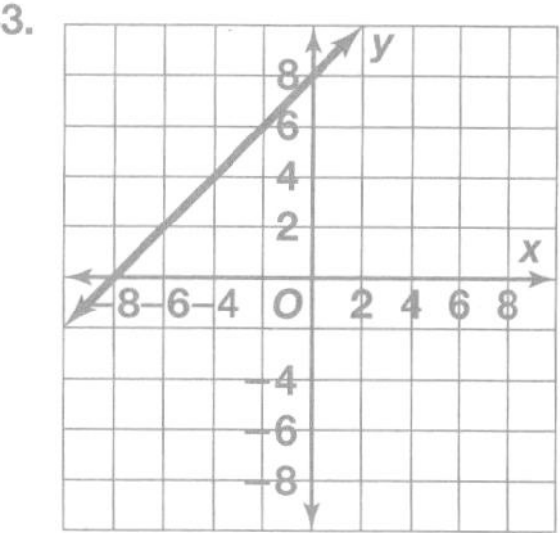


34.

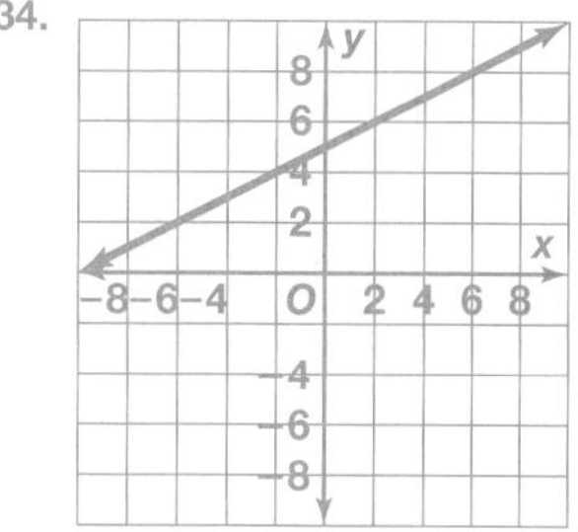


# LESSON 9-10

## page 491 Try This

1.

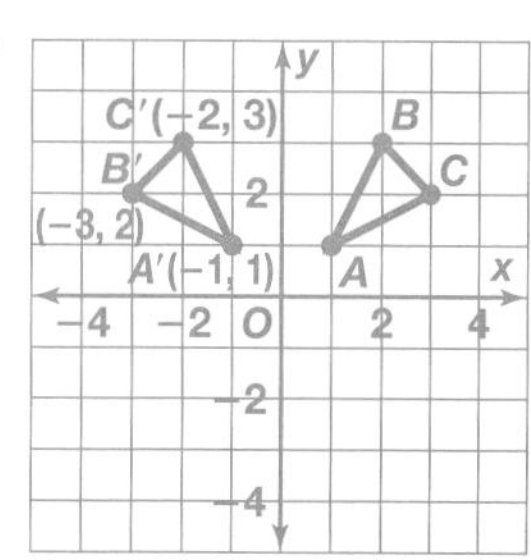


4.

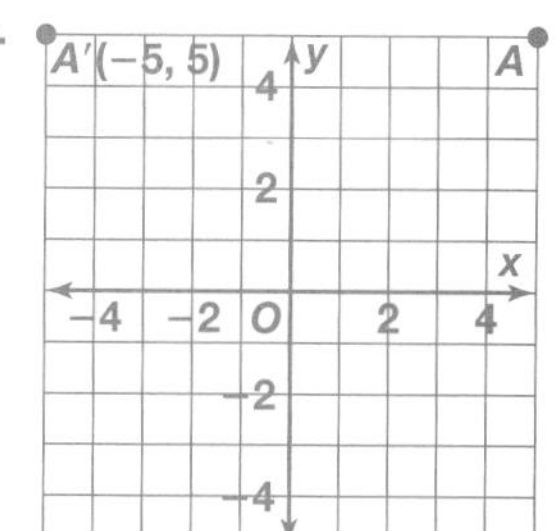


5.

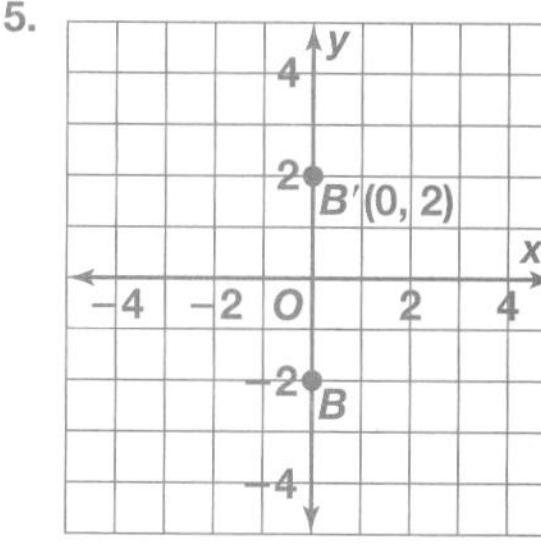


6.

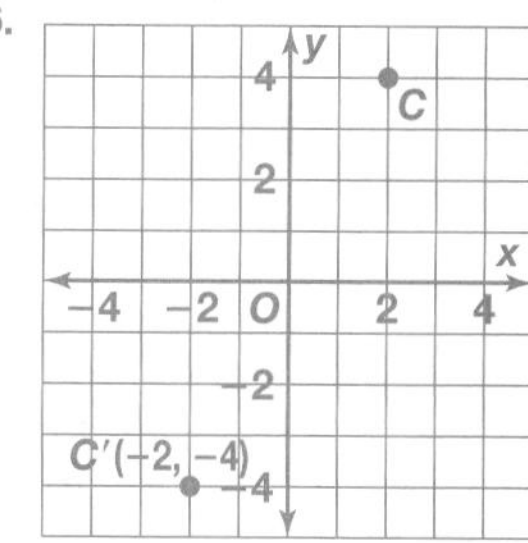


7.

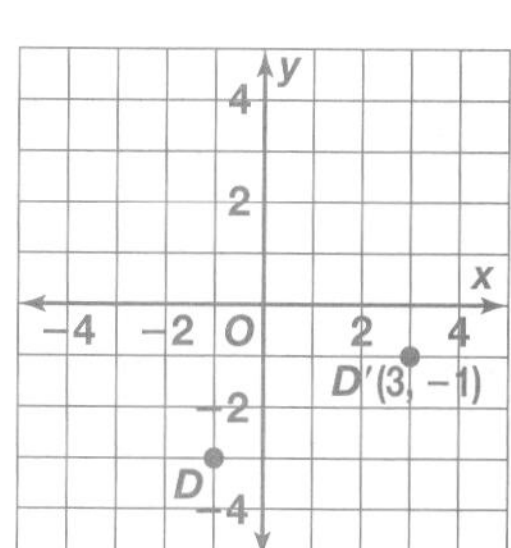


## pages 492–493 Practice and Problem Solving

13a.

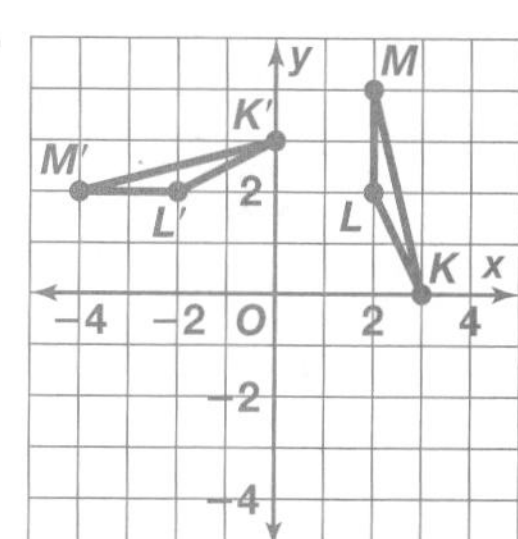


Additional Answers

b.

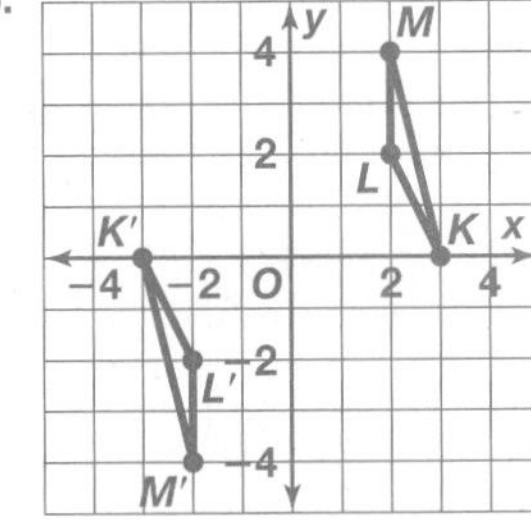


14a.

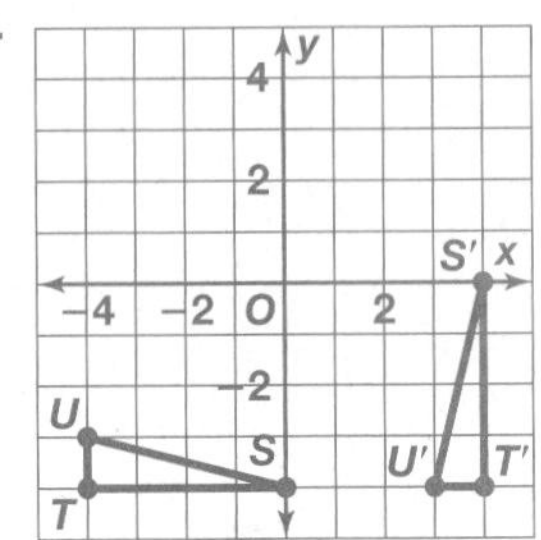


b.

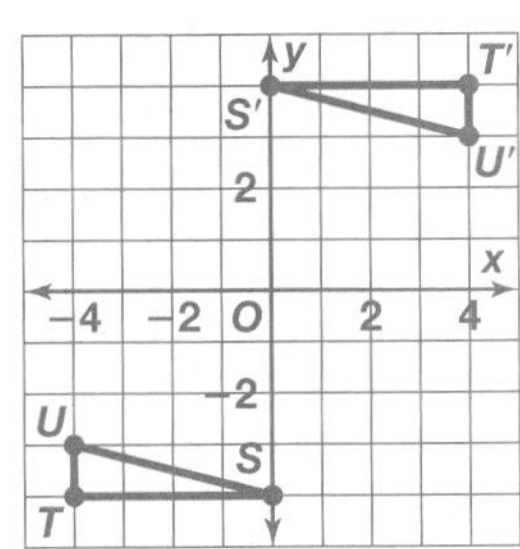


15a.

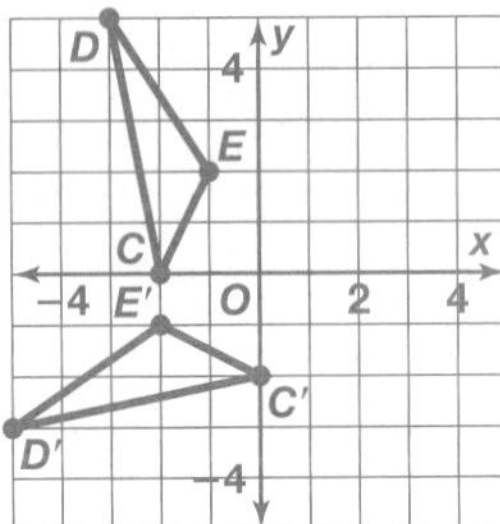


b.

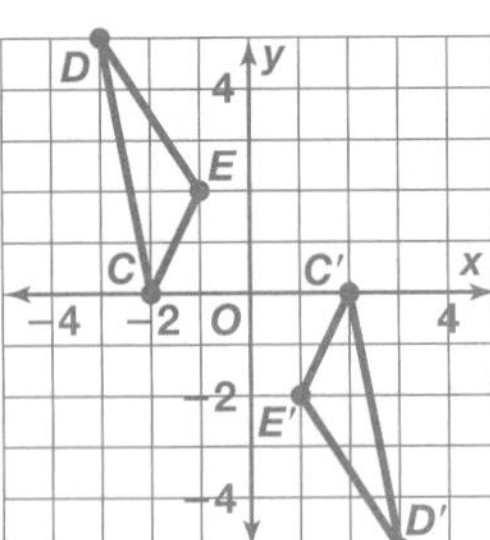


16a.

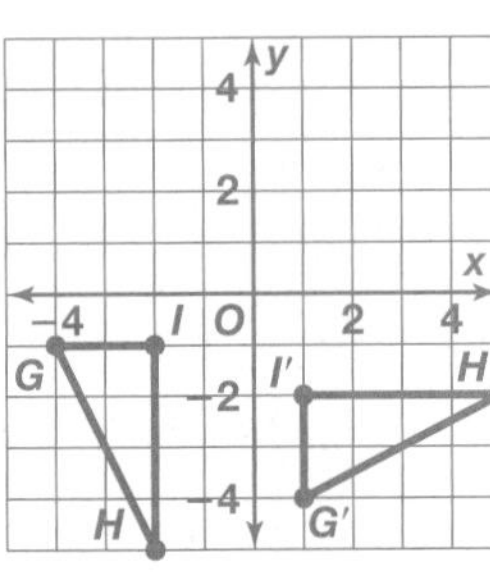


b.

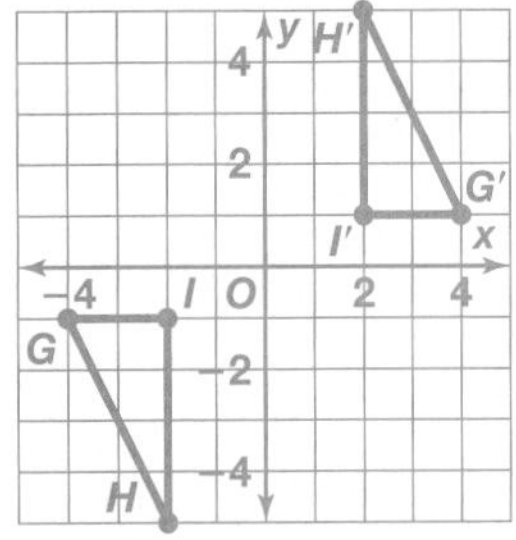


17a.

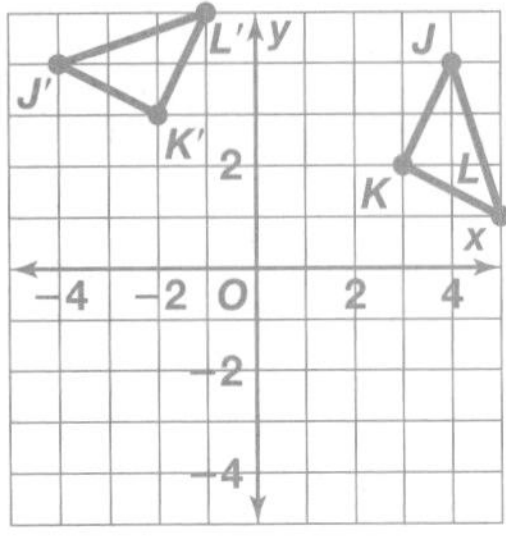


b.

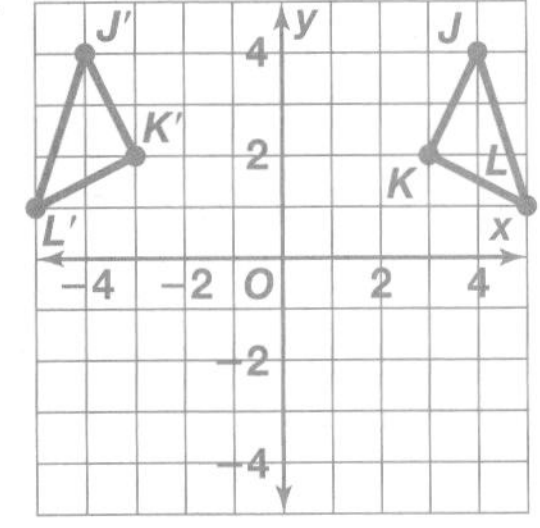


## page 493 Mixed Review

30.

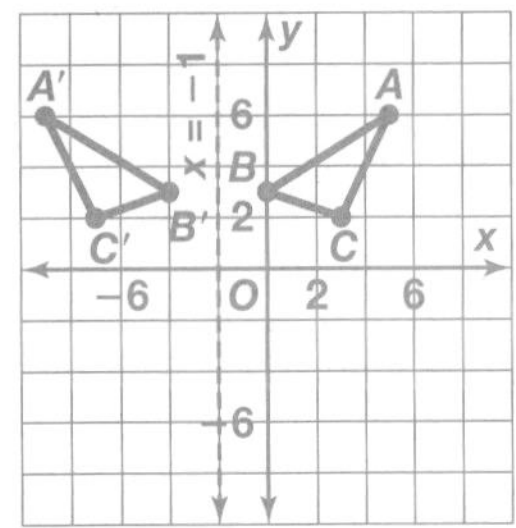


31.

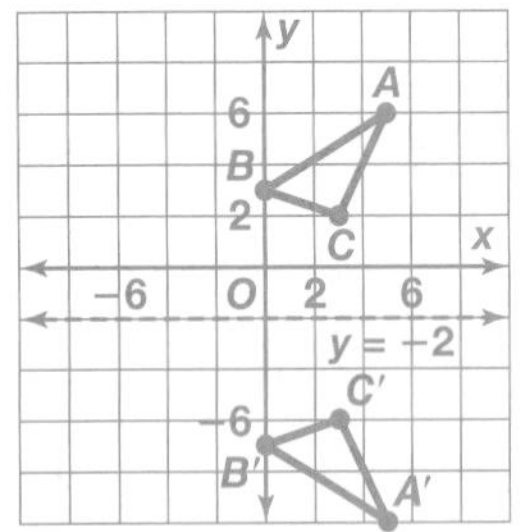


32.

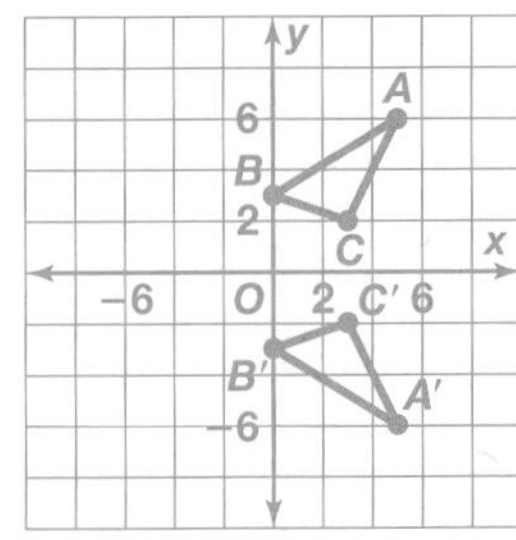


## page 500 Cumulative Review

15.

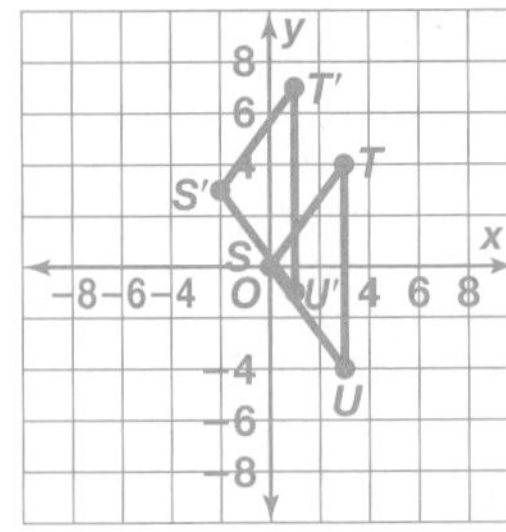


16.

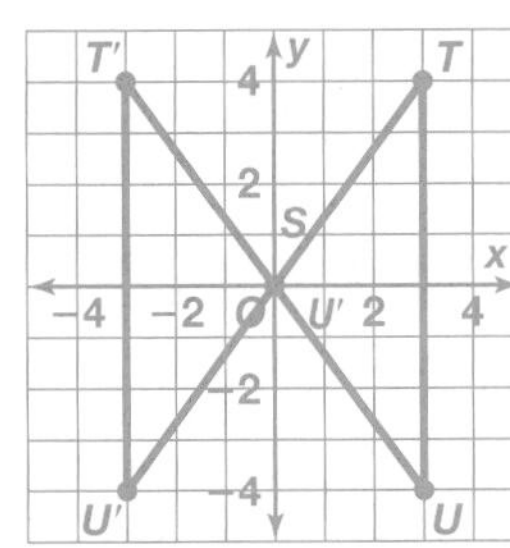


17.

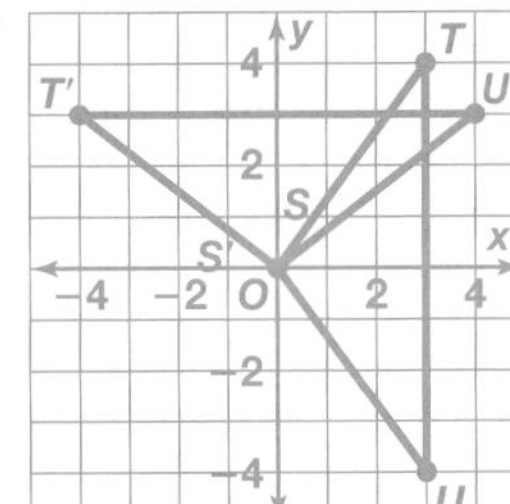


20.

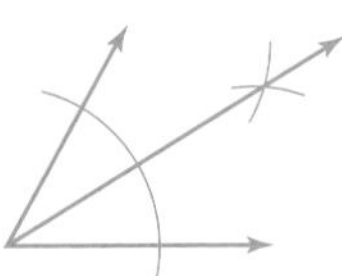

# CHAPTER 10

## LESSON 10-1

### page 508 Mixed Review

32.

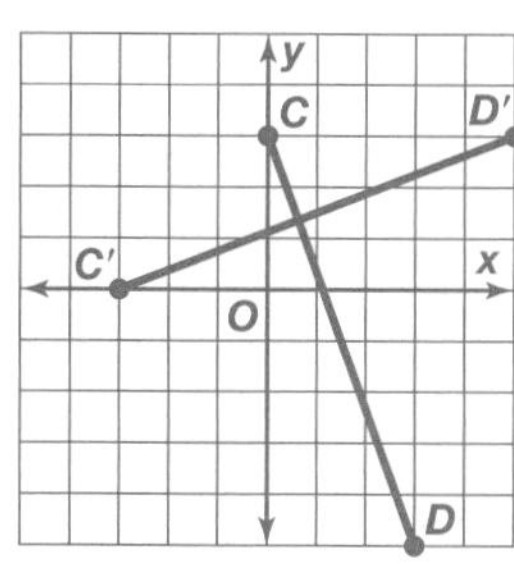


33.

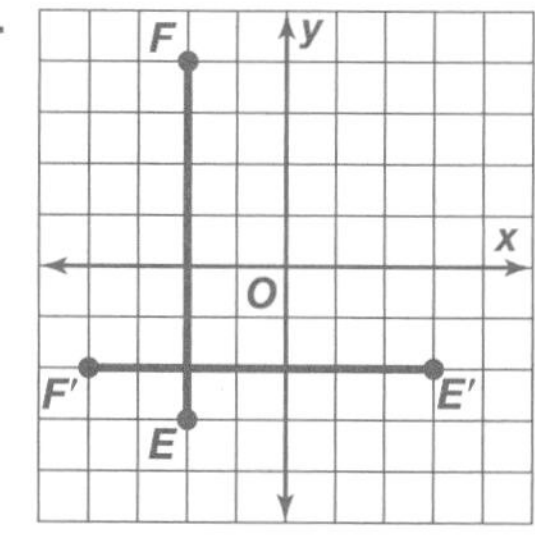


### page 520 Math Toolbox

2.

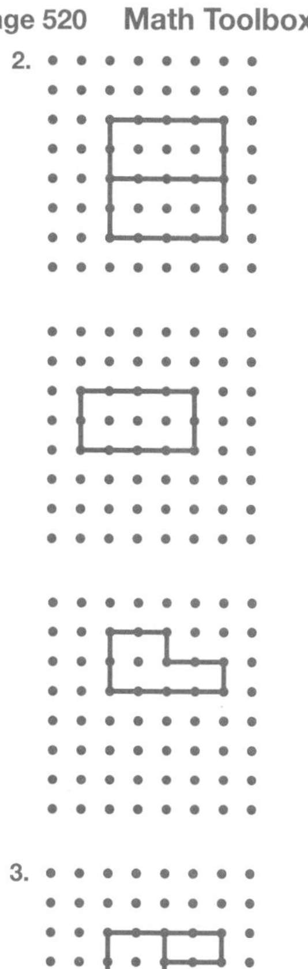

3.

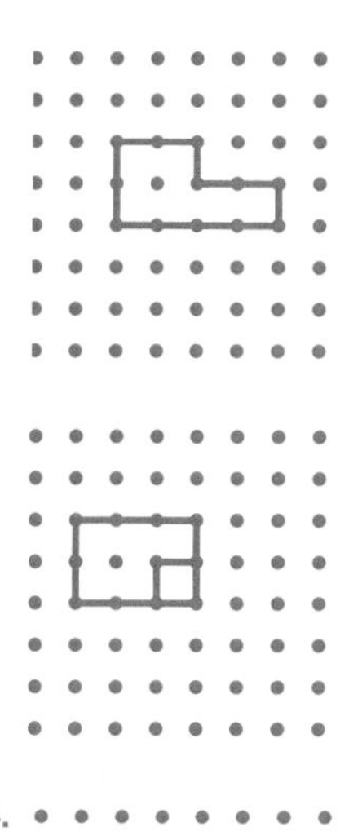

4.

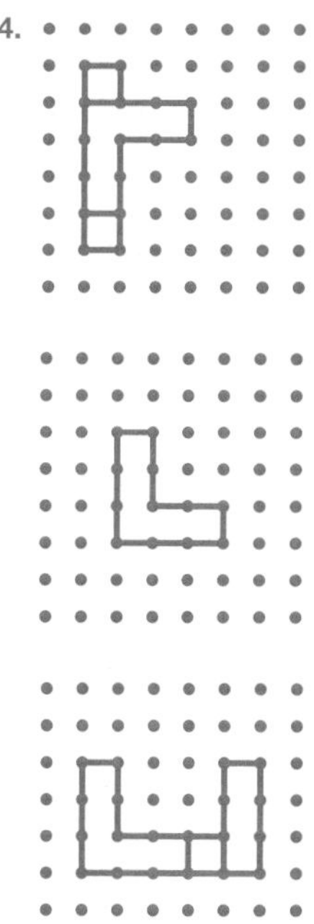

## LESSON 10-5

### page 532 Mixed Review

32.

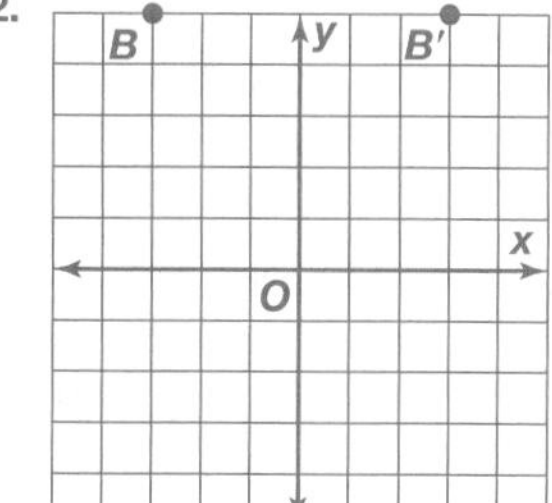


33.

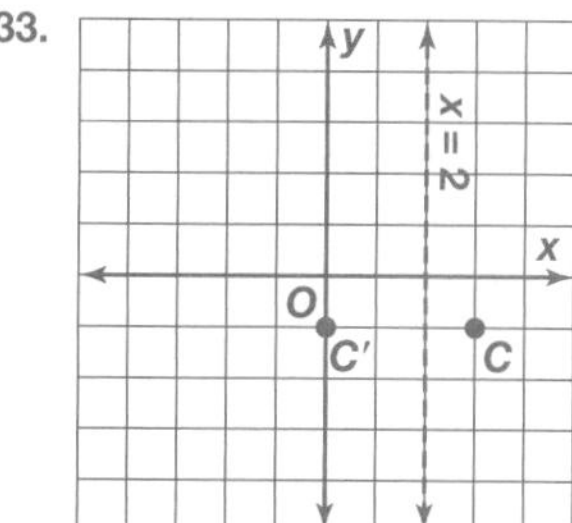


# CHAPTER 12

## LESSON 12-1

### pages 610–612 Practice and Problem Solving

8. Rolls of a Number Cube

| Number | Frequency |
|---|---|
| 1 | 4 |
| 2 | 3 |
| 3 | 3 |
| 4 | 2 |
| 5 | 3 |
| 6 | 2 |

9. Test Scores

| Score | Frequency |
|---|---|
| 60 | 1 |
| 65 | 1 |
| 70 | 4 |
| 75 | 2 |
| 80 | 1 |
| 85 | 2 |
| 90 | 2 |
| 95 | 1 |
| 100 | 2 |

10. Ages of Club Members

| Age | Frequency |
|---|---|
| 12 | 3 |
| 13 | 1 |
| 14 | 4 |
| 15 | 4 |
| 16 | 3 |

11. Heights of Plants

| Height (in.) | Frequency |
|---|---|
| 16 | 1 |
| 20 | 2 |
| 25 | 5 |
| 26 | 1 |
| 28 | 1 |
| 30 | 2 |
| 31 | 1 |

12.

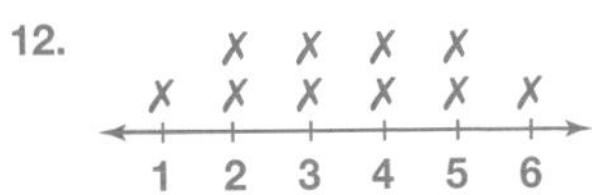

13.

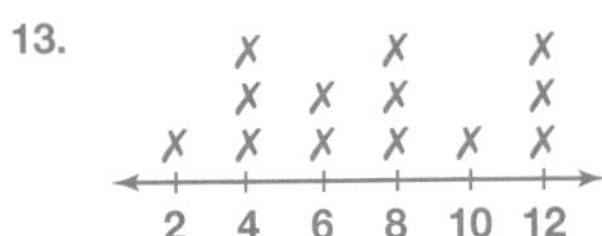

14.

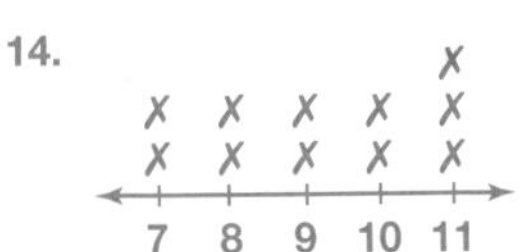

15.

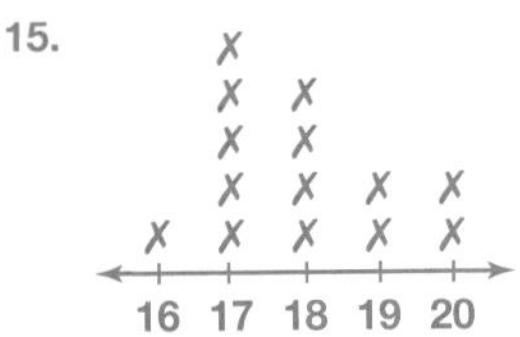

17.

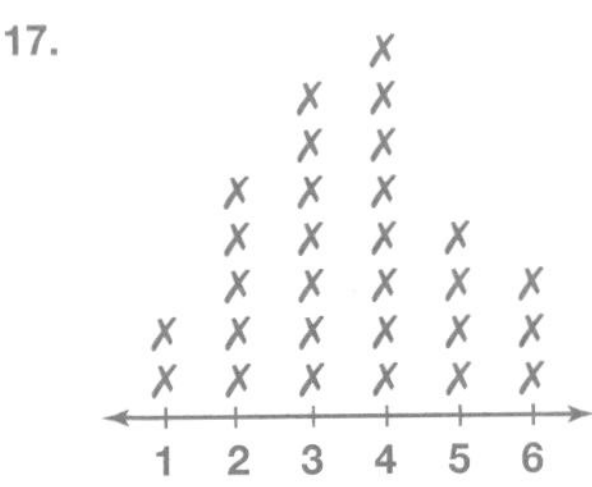

18.

19.

20.

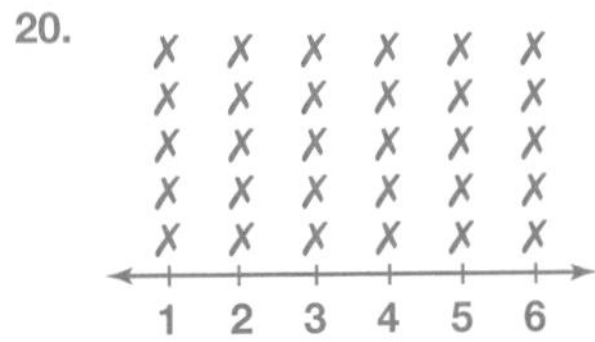

21.

| Number | Frequency |
|---|---|
| 1 | 1 |
| 2 | 0 |
| 3 | 2 |
| 4 | 3 |
| 5 | 1 |
| 6 | 2 |

22.

| Number | Frequency |
|---|---|
| 15 | 4 |
| 16 | 2 |
| 17 | 3 |
| 18 | 2 |
| 19 | 3 |
| 20 | 4 |

23.

| Number | Frequency |
|---|---|
| 70 | 4 |
| 75 | 3 |
| 80 | 4 |
| 85 | 3 |
| 90 | 3 |
| 95 | 4 |

24. Games in the World Series, 1970–1999

| Number of Games | Frequency |
|---|---|
| 0 | 1 |
| 1 | 0 |
| 2 | 0 |
| 3 | 0 |
| 4 | 5 |
| 5 | 5 |
| 6 | 8 |
| 7 | 11 |

25.

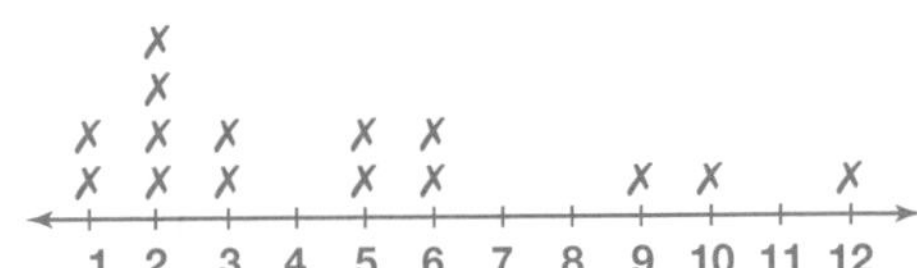

26a. Letters in the First 25 Words of *Alice's Adventures in Wonderland*

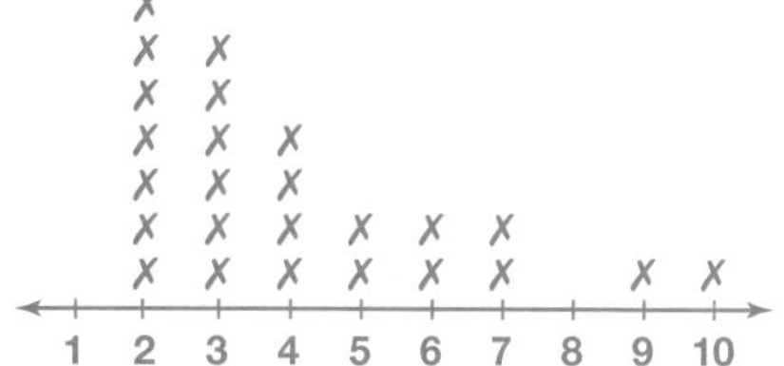


b. Letters in the First 25 Words of *Alice's Adventures in Wonderland*

| Number of Letters | Frequency |
|---|---|
| 1 | 0 |
| 2 | 7 |
| 3 | 6 |
| 4 | 4 |
| 5 | 2 |
| 6 | 2 |
| 7 | 2 |
| 8 | 0 |
| 9 | 1 |
| 10 | 1 |

27a. Weekly Earnings

300 400 500 600 700 800 900 1000

Earnings ($)

b. Weekly Earnings

| Earnings ($) | Frequency |
|---|---|
| 320 | 3 |
| 400 | 6 |
| 480 | 3 |
| 720 | 3 |
| 1000 | 1 |

## LESSON 12-2

**page 659 Chapter Assessment**

6. Answers may vary. Sample:

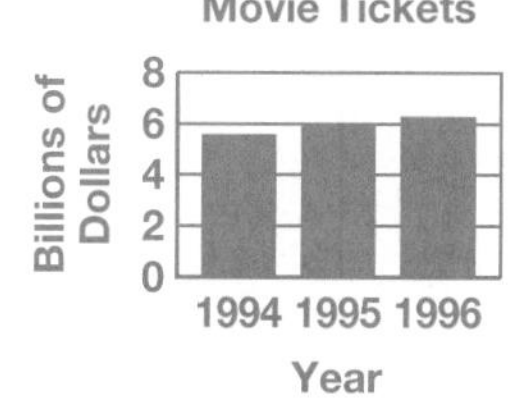


9a.

- H
  - H
    - H
    - T
  - T
    - H
    - T
- T
  - H
    - H
    - T
  - T
    - H
    - T

22a.

| 1,1 | 1,2 | 1,3 | 1,4 | 1,5 | 1,6 |
|---|---|---|---|---|---|
| 2,1 | 2,2 | 2,3 | 2,4 | 2,5 | 2,6 |
| 3,1 | 3,2 | 3,3 | 3,4 | 3,5 | 3,6 |
| 4,1 | 4,2 | 4,3 | 4,4 | 4,5 | 4,6 |
| 5,1 | 5,2 | 5,3 | 5,4 | 5,5 | 5,6 |
| 6,1 | 6,2 | 6,3 | 6,4 | 6,5 | 6,6 |

; $\frac{1}{6}$

# CHAPTER 13

## LESSON 13-2

**pages 669–670 Try This**

4.

| $x$ | $-x^2 + 3 = y$ | $(x, y)$ |
|---|---|---|
| −2 | $-(-2)^2 + 3 = -1$ | (−2, −1) |
| −1 | $-(-1)^2 + 3 = 2$ | (−1, 2) |
| 0 | $-0^2 + 3 = 3$ | (0, 3) |
| 1 | $-1^2 + 3 = 2$ | (1, 2) |
| 2 | $-2^2 + 3 = -1$ | (2, −1) |

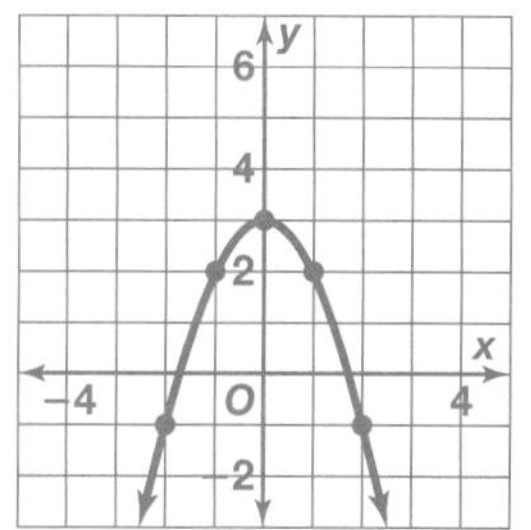


7.

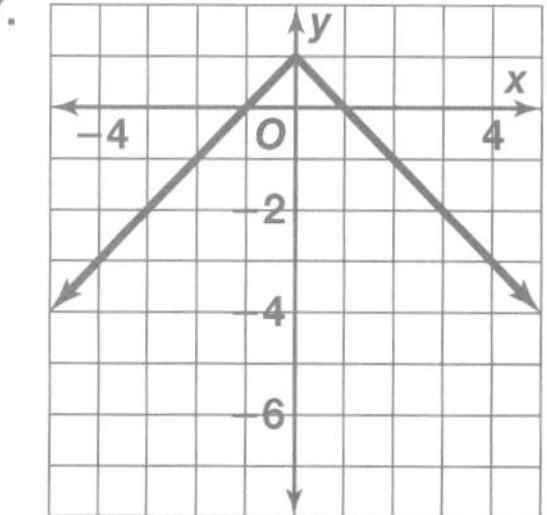


8.

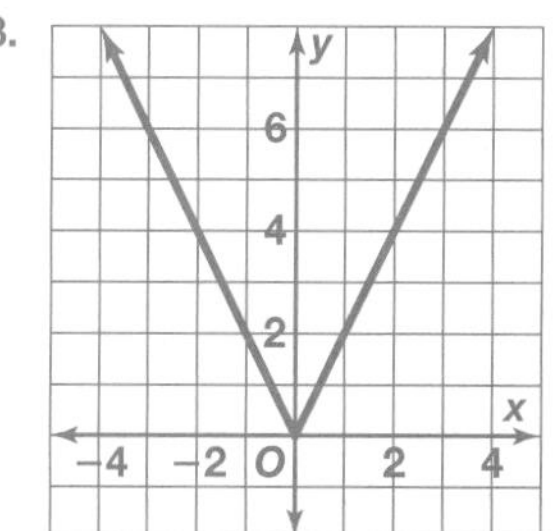

**page 671** **Check Understanding**

6.

| $x$ | $\lvert x\rvert - 2$ | $y$ | $(x, y)$ |
|---|---|---|---|
| −2 | $\lvert -2\rvert - 2$ | 0 | (−2, 0) |
| −1 | $\lvert -1\rvert - 2$ | −1 | (−1, −1) |
| 0 | $\lvert 0\rvert - 2$ | −2 | (0, −2) |
| 1 | $\lvert 1\rvert - 2$ | −1 | (1, −1) |
| 2 | $\lvert 2\rvert - 2$ | 0 | (2, 0) |

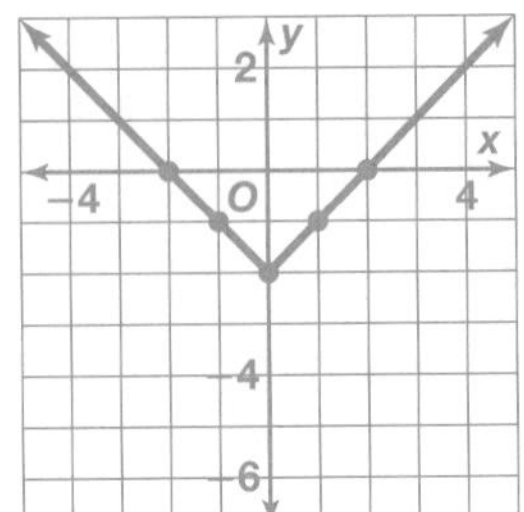

7.

| $x$ | $-x^2 + 2$ | $y$ | $(x, y)$ |
|---|---|---|---|
| −2 | $-(-2)^2 + 2$ | −2 | (−2, −2) |
| −1 | $-(-1)^2 + 2$ | 1 | (−1, 1) |
| 0 | $-0^2 + 2$ | 2 | (0, 2) |
| 1 | $-1^2 + 2$ | 1 | (1, 1) |
| 2 | $-2^2 + 2$ | −2 | (2, −2) |

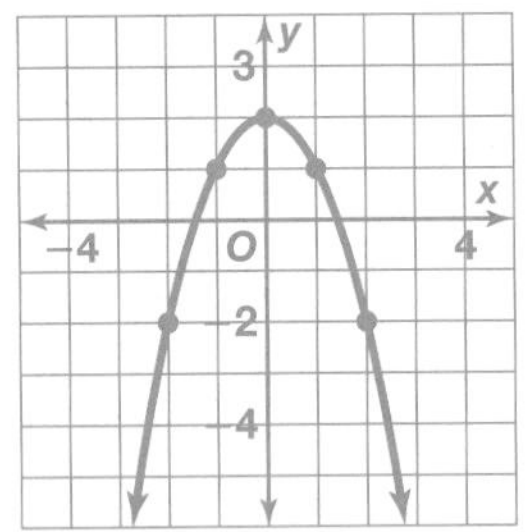

8.

| $x$ | $-3\lvert x\rvert$ | $y$ | $(x, y)$ |
|---|---|---|---|
| −2 | $-3\lvert -2\rvert$ | −6 | (−2, −6) |
| −1 | $-3\lvert -1\rvert$ | −3 | (−1, −3) |
| 0 | $-3\lvert 0\rvert$ | 0 | (0, 0) |
| 1 | $-3\lvert 1\rvert$ | −3 | (1, −3) |
| 2 | $-3\lvert 2\rvert$ | −6 | (2, −6) |

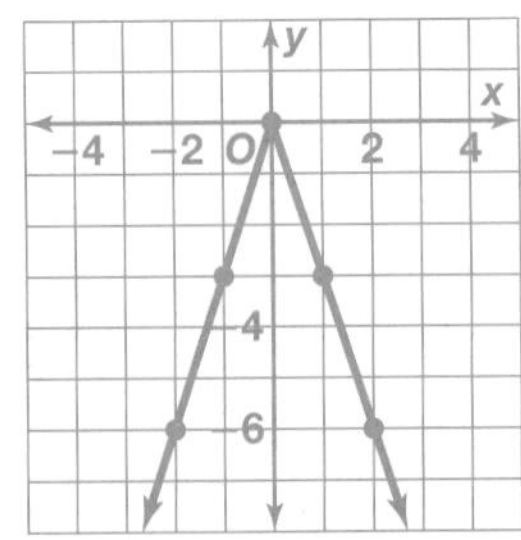

**pages 671–672** **Practice and Problem Solving**

12.

| $x$ | $x^2 - 2$ | $y$ | $(x, y)$ |
|---|---|---|---|
| −2 | $(-2)^2 - 2$ | 2 | (−2, 2) |
| −1 | $(-1)^2 - 2$ | −1 | (−1, −1) |
| 0 | $0^2 - 2$ | −2 | (0, −2) |
| 1 | $1^2 - 2$ | −1 | (1, −1) |
| 2 | $2^2 - 2$ | 2 | (2, 2) |

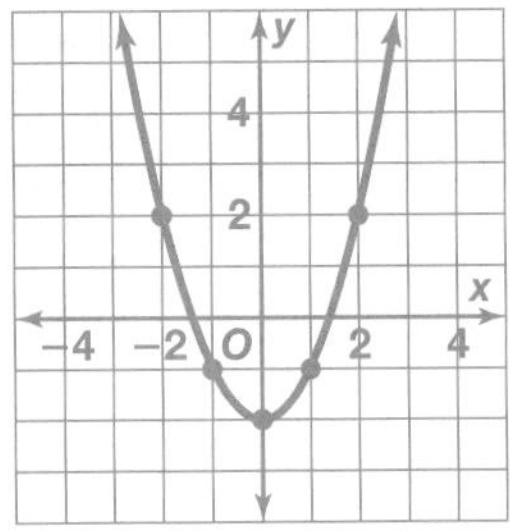

13.

| $x$ | $x^2 + 4$ | $y$ | $(x, y)$ |
|---|---|---|---|
| −2 | $(-2)^2 + 4$ | 8 | (−2, 8) |
| −1 | $(-1)^2 + 4$ | 5 | (−1, 5) |
| 0 | $0^2 + 4$ | 4 | (0, 4) |
| 1 | $1^2 + 4$ | 5 | (1, 5) |
| 2 | $2^2 + 4$ | 8 | (2, 8) |

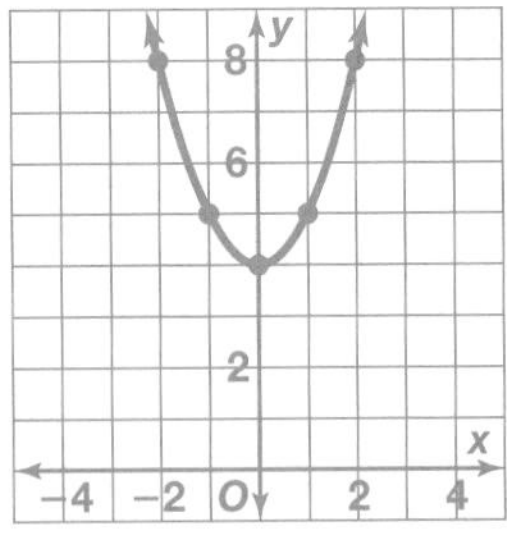

14.

| $x$ | $2x^2$ | $y$ | $(x, y)$ |
|---|---|---|---|
| −2 | $2(-2)^2$ | 8 | (−2, 8) |
| −1 | $2(-1)^2$ | 2 | (−1, 2) |
| 0 | $2(0)^2$ | 0 | (0, 0) |
| 1 | $2(1)^2$ | 2 | (1, 2) |
| 2 | $2(2)^2$ | 8 | (2, 8) |

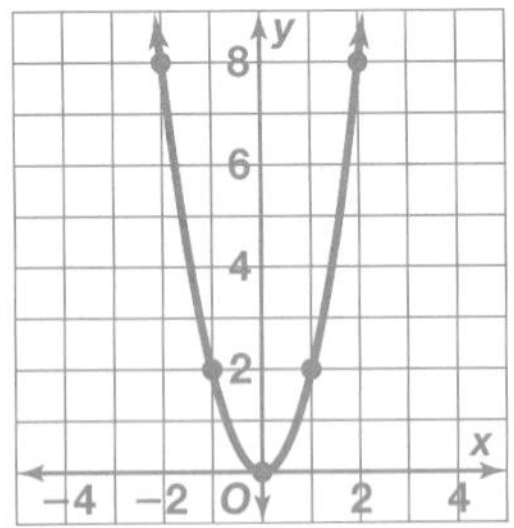

15.

| $x$ | $-x^2 + 5$ | $y$ | $(x, y)$ |
|---|---|---|---|
| −2 | $-(-2)^2 + 5$ | 1 | (−2, 1) |
| −1 | $-(-1)^2 + 5$ | 4 | (−1, 4) |
| 0 | $-0^2 + 5$ | 5 | (0, 5) |
| 1 | $-1^2 + 5$ | 4 | (1, 4) |
| 2 | $-2^2 + 5$ | 1 | (2, 1) |

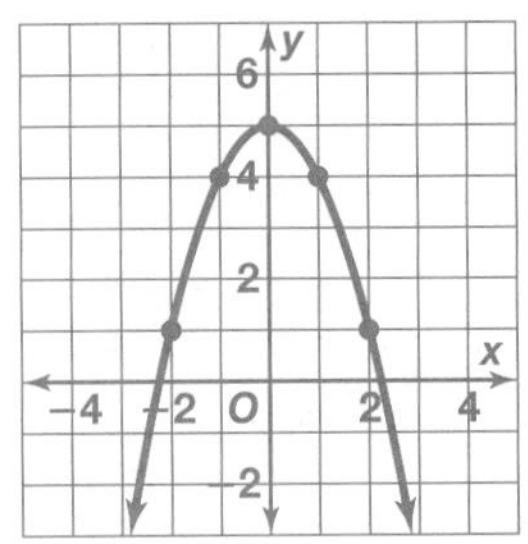

16.

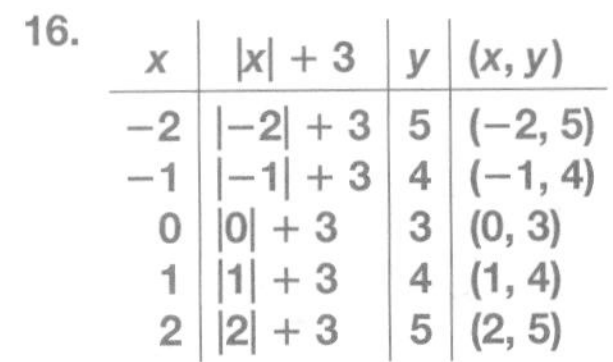

| $x$ | $\lvert x\rvert + 3$ | $y$ | $(x, y)$ |
|---|---|---|---|
| −2 | $\lvert -2\rvert + 3$ | 5 | (−2, 5) |
| −1 | $\lvert -1\rvert + 3$ | 4 | (−1, 4) |
| 0 | $\lvert 0\rvert + 3$ | 3 | (0, 3) |
| 1 | $\lvert 1\rvert + 3$ | 4 | (1, 4) |
| 2 | $\lvert 2\rvert + 3$ | 5 | (2, 5) |

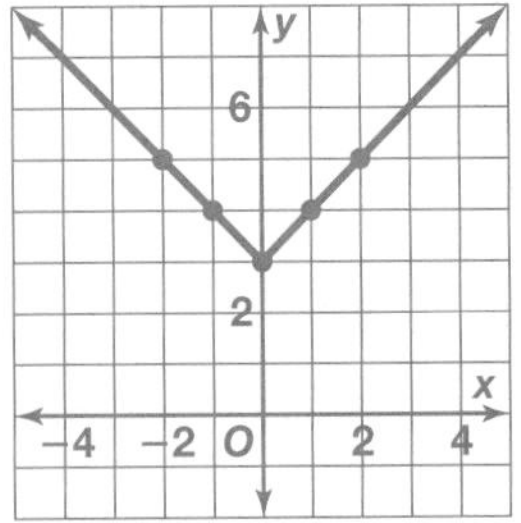

17.

| $x$ | $\lvert x\rvert - 4$ | $y$ | $(x, y)$ |
|---|---|---|---|
| −2 | $\lvert -2\rvert - 4$ | −2 | (−2, −2) |
| −1 | $\lvert -1\rvert - 4$ | −3 | (−1, −3) |
| 0 | $\lvert 0\rvert - 4$ | −4 | (0, −4) |
| 1 | $\lvert 1\rvert - 4$ | −3 | (1, −3) |
| 2 | $\lvert 2\rvert - 4$ | −2 | (2, −2) |

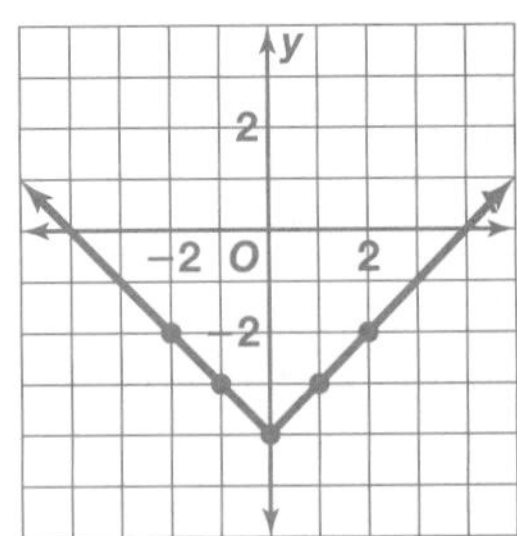

18.

| $x$ | $-\lvert x\rvert - 1$ | $y$ | $(x, y)$ |
|---|---|---|---|
| $-2$ | $-\lvert -2\rvert - 1$ | $-3$ | $(-2, -3)$ |
| $-1$ | $-\lvert -1\rvert - 1$ | $-2$ | $(-1, -2)$ |
| 0 | $-\lvert 0\rvert - 1$ | $-1$ | $(0, -1)$ |
| 1 | $-\lvert 1\rvert - 1$ | $-2$ | $(1, -2)$ |
| 2 | $-\lvert 2\rvert - 1$ | $-3$ | $(2, -3)$ |

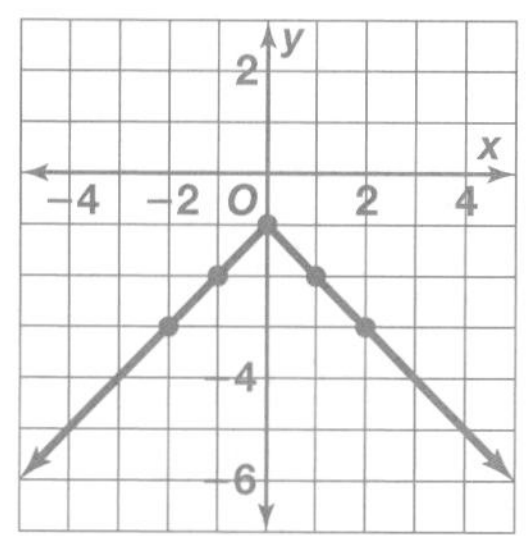

19.

| $x$ | $-2\lvert x\rvert$ | $y$ | $(x, y)$ |
|---|---|---|---|
| $-2$ | $-2\lvert -2\rvert$ | $-4$ | $(-2, -4)$ |
| $-1$ | $-2\lvert -1\rvert$ | $-2$ | $(-1, -2)$ |
| 0 | $-2\lvert 0\rvert$ | 0 | $(0, 0)$ |
| 1 | $-2\lvert 1\rvert$ | $-2$ | $(1, -2)$ |
| 2 | $-2\lvert 2\rvert$ | $-4$ | $(2, -4)$ |

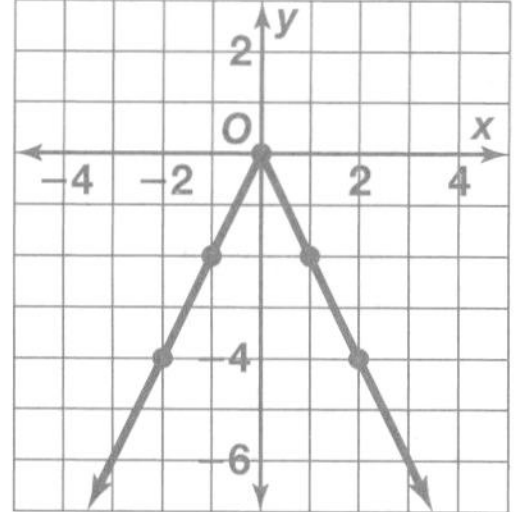

21.

| $x$ | $x^3$ | $y$ | $(x, y)$ |
|---|---|---|---|
| $-2$ | $(-2)^3$ | 8 | $(-2, 8)$ |
| $-1$ | $(-1)^3$ | 1 | $(-1, 1)$ |
| 0 | $0^3$ | 0 | $(0, 0)$ |
| 1 | $1^3$ | 1 | $(1, 1)$ |
| 2 | $2^3$ | 8 | $(2, 8)$ |

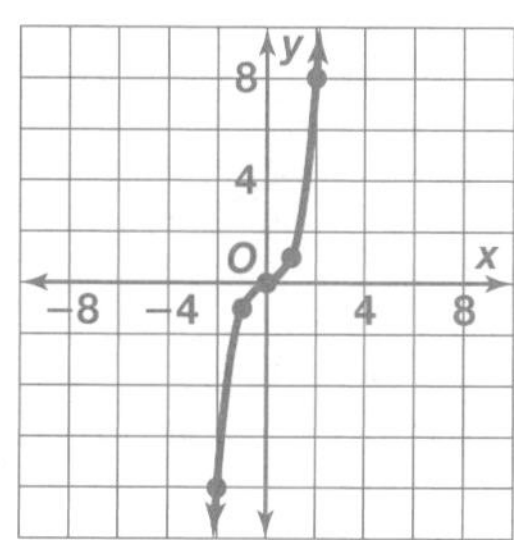

22a.

| Side Length | Volume |
|---|---|
| 1 m | 1 $m^3$ |
| 2 m | 8 $m^3$ |
| 3 m | 27 $m^3$ |
| 4 m | 64 $m^3$ |

b.

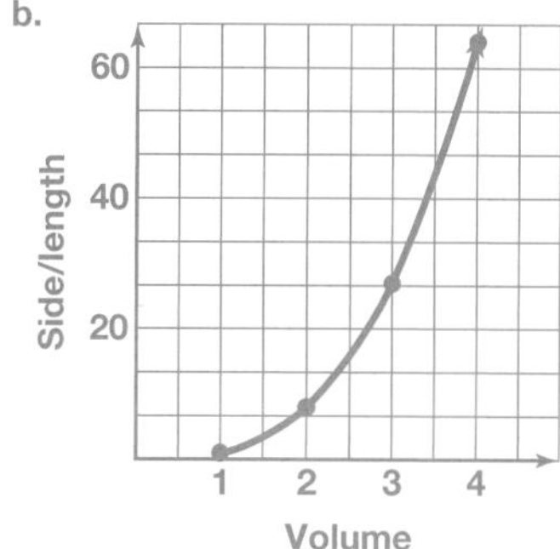


## LESSON 13-3

### pages 673–674 Try This

3.

| $x$ | $90(\frac{1}{3})^x$ | $y$ | $(x, y)$ |
|---|---|---|---|
| 0 | $90(\frac{1}{3})^0$ | 90 | $(0, 90)$ |
| 1 | $90(\frac{1}{3})^1$ | 30 | $(1, 30)$ |
| 2 | $90(\frac{1}{3})^2$ | 10 | $(2, 10)$ |
| 3 | $90(\frac{1}{3})^3$ | $3\frac{1}{3}$ | $(3, 3\frac{1}{3})$ |
| 4 | $90(\frac{1}{3})^4$ | $1\frac{1}{9}$ | $(4, 1\frac{1}{9})$ |
| 5 | $90(\frac{1}{3})^5$ | $\frac{10}{27}$ | $(5, \frac{10}{27})$ |

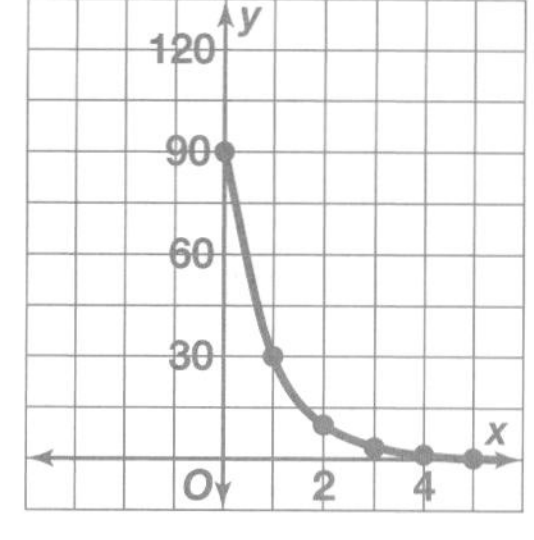

### page 675 Check Understanding

5.

| $x$ | $3 \cdot 2^x$ | $y$ | $(x, y)$ |
|---|---|---|---|
| 0 | $3 \cdot 2^0$ | 3 | $(0, 3)$ |
| 1 | $3 \cdot 2^1$ | 6 | $(1, 6)$ |
| 2 | $3 \cdot 2^2$ | 12 | $(2, 12)$ |
| 3 | $3 \cdot 2^3$ | 24 | $(3, 24)$ |
| 4 | $3 \cdot 2^4$ | 48 | $(4, 48)$ |
| 5 | $3 \cdot 2^5$ | 96 | $(5, 96)$ |

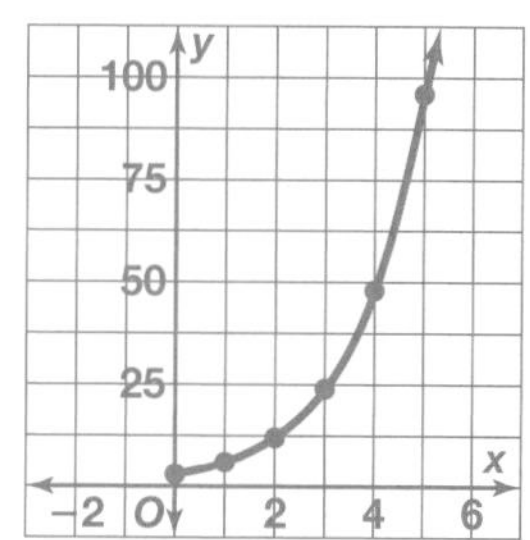

6.

| $x$ | $100(0.6)^x$ | $y$ | $(x, y)$ |
|---|---|---|---|
| 0 | $100(0.6)^0$ | 100 | $(0, 100)$ |
| 1 | $100(0.6)^1$ | 60 | $(1, 60)$ |
| 2 | $100(0.6)^2$ | 36 | $(2, 36)$ |
| 3 | $100(0.6)^3$ | 21.6 | $(3, 21.6)$ |
| 4 | $100(0.6)^4$ | 13 | $(4, 13)$ |
| 5 | $100(0.6)^5$ | 7.8 | $(5, 7.8)$ |

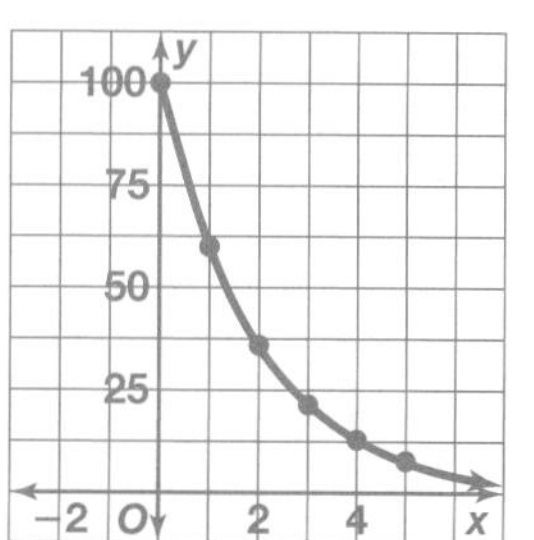

### pages 675–676 Practice and Problem Solving

14.

| $x$ | $2 \cdot 3^x$ | $y$ | $(x, y)$ |
|---|---|---|---|
| 0 | $2 \cdot 3^0$ | 2 | $(0, 2)$ |
| 1 | $2 \cdot 3^1$ | 6 | $(1, 6)$ |
| 2 | $2 \cdot 3^2$ | 18 | $(2, 18)$ |
| 3 | $2 \cdot 3^3$ | 54 | $(3, 54)$ |
| 4 | $2 \cdot 3^4$ | 162 | $(4, 162)$ |

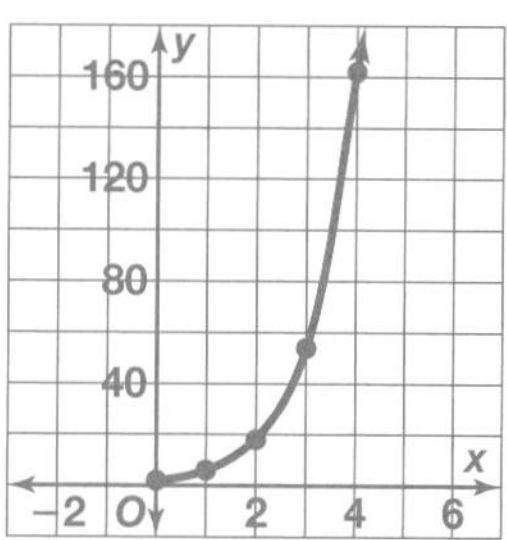

15.

| $x$ | $\frac{1}{2} \cdot 2^x$ | $y$ | $(x, y)$ |
|---|---|---|---|
| 0 | $\frac{1}{2} \cdot 2^0$ | $\frac{1}{2}$ | $(0, \frac{1}{2})$ |
| 1 | $\frac{1}{2} \cdot 2^1$ | 1 | (1, 1) |
| 2 | $\frac{1}{2} \cdot 2^2$ | 2 | (2, 2) |
| 3 | $\frac{1}{2} \cdot 2^3$ | 4 | (3, 4) |
| 4 | $\frac{1}{2} \cdot 2^4$ | 8 | (4, 8) |

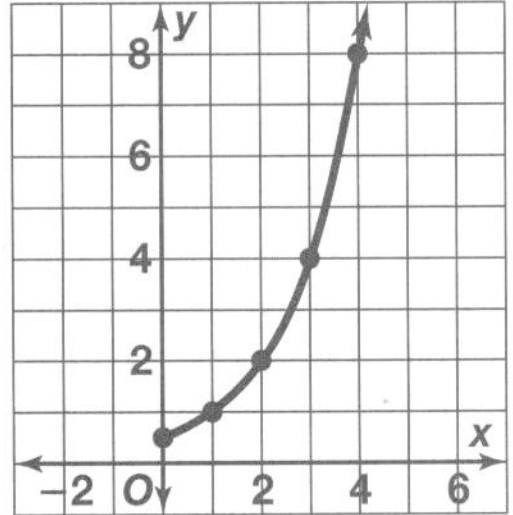

16.

| $x$ | $\frac{1}{5} \cdot 5^x$ | $y$ | $(x, y)$ |
|---|---|---|---|
| 0 | $\frac{1}{5} \cdot 5^0$ | $\frac{1}{5}$ | $(0, \frac{1}{5})$ |
| 1 | $\frac{1}{5} \cdot 5^1$ | 1 | (1, 1) |
| 2 | $\frac{1}{5} \cdot 5^2$ | 5 | (2, 5) |
| 3 | $\frac{1}{5} \cdot 5^3$ | 25 | (3, 25) |
| 4 | $\frac{1}{5} \cdot 5^4$ | 125 | (4, 125) |

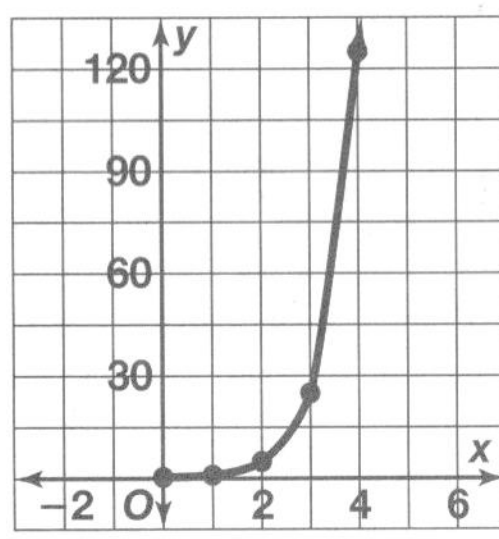

17.

| $x$ | $20(\frac{1}{2})^x$ | $y$ | $(x, y)$ |
|---|---|---|---|
| 0 | $20(\frac{1}{2})^0$ | 20 | (0, 20) |
| 1 | $20(\frac{1}{2})^1$ | 10 | (1, 10) |
| 2 | $20(\frac{1}{2})^2$ | 5 | (2, 5) |
| 3 | $20(\frac{1}{2})^3$ | 2.5 | (3, 2.5) |
| 4 | $20(\frac{1}{2})^4$ | 1.25 | (4, 1.25) |

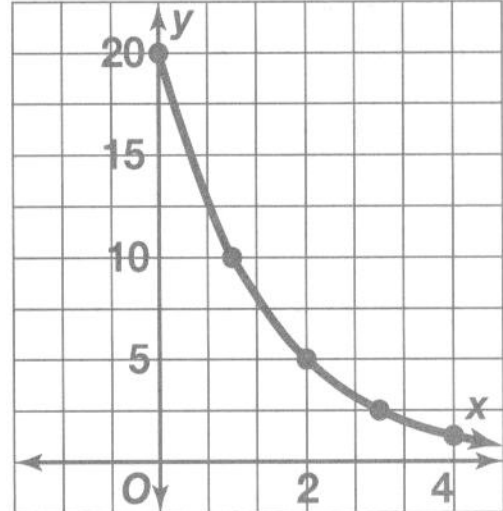

18.

| $x$ | $6(0.5)^x$ | $y$ | $(x, y)$ |
|---|---|---|---|
| 0 | $6(0.5)^0$ | 6 | (0, 6) |
| 1 | $6(0.5)^1$ | 3 | (1, 3) |
| 2 | $6(0.5)^2$ | 1.5 | (2, 1.5) |
| 3 | $6(0.5)^3$ | 0.75 | (3, 0.75) |
| 4 | $6(0.5)^4$ | 0.375 | (4, 0.375) |

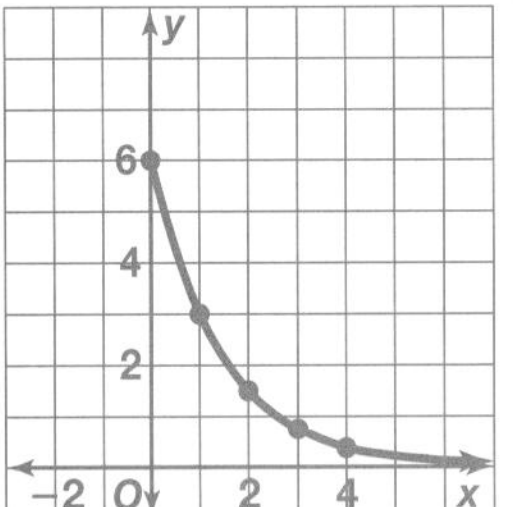

19.

| $x$ | $200(0.4)^x$ | $y$ | $(x, y)$ |
|---|---|---|---|
| 0 | $200(0.4)^0$ | 200 | (0, 200) |
| 1 | $200(0.4)^1$ | 80 | (1, 80) |
| 2 | $200(0.4)^2$ | 32 | (2, 32) |
| 3 | $200(0.4)^3$ | 12.8 | (3, 12.8) |
| 4 | $200(0.4)^4$ | 5.12 | (4, 5.12) |

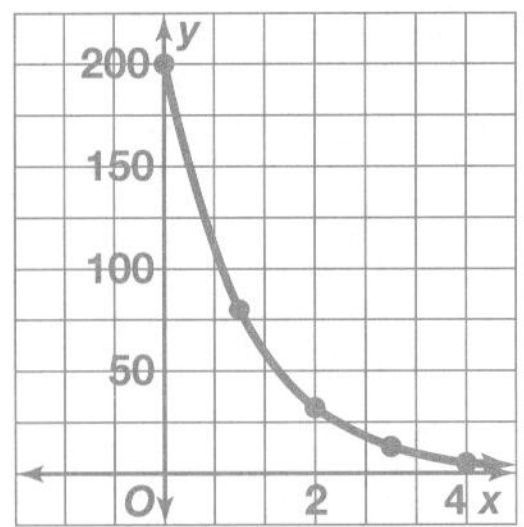

20a.

| $x$ | $2x$ | $y$ | $(x, y)$ |
|---|---|---|---|
| 0 | $2 \cdot 0$ | 0 | (0, 0) |
| 1 | $2 \cdot 1$ | 2 | (1, 2) |
| 2 | $2 \cdot 2$ | 4 | (2, 4) |
| 3 | $2 \cdot 3$ | 6 | (3, 6) |
| 4 | $2 \cdot 4$ | 8 | (4, 8) |
| 5 | $2 \cdot 5$ | 10 | (5, 10) |

| $x$ | $x^2$ | $y$ | $(x, y)$ |
|---|---|---|---|
| 0 | $0^2$ | 0 | (0, 0) |
| 1 | $1^2$ | 1 | (1, 1) |
| 2 | $2^2$ | 4 | (2, 4) |
| 3 | $3^2$ | 9 | (3, 9) |
| 4 | $4^2$ | 16 | (4, 16) |
| 5 | $5^2$ | 25 | (5, 25) |

| $x$ | $2^x$ | $y$ | $(x, y)$ |
|---|---|---|---|
| 0 | $2^0$ | 1 | (0, 1) |
| 1 | $2^1$ | 2 | (1, 2) |
| 2 | $2^2$ | 4 | (2, 4) |
| 3 | $2^3$ | 8 | (3, 8) |
| 4 | $2^4$ | 16 | (4, 16) |
| 5 | $2^5$ | 32 | (5, 32) |

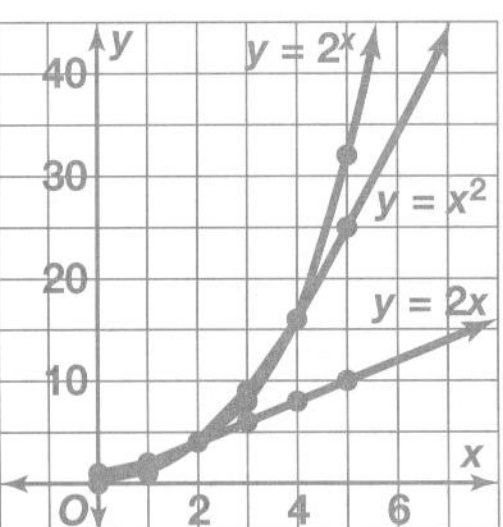


b. They are similar because they all are increasing functions and they all pass through (2, 4). They are different because $y = 2x$ increases at a constant rate while $y = x^2$ and $y = 2^x$ increase at different rates.

**page 676 Mixed Review**

24.

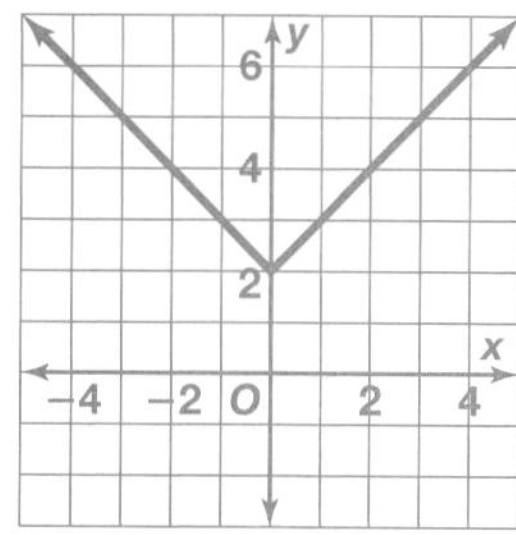

25.

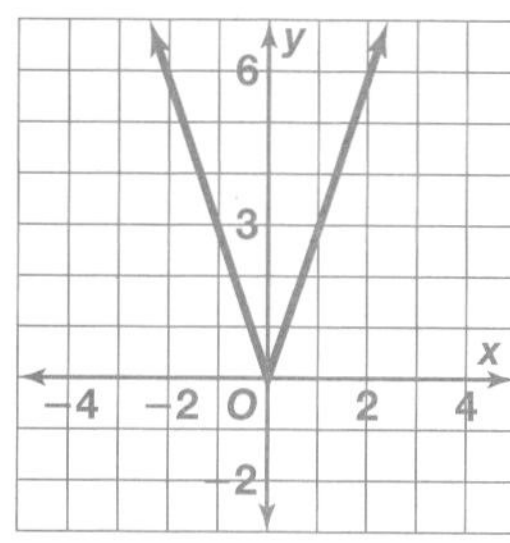

26.

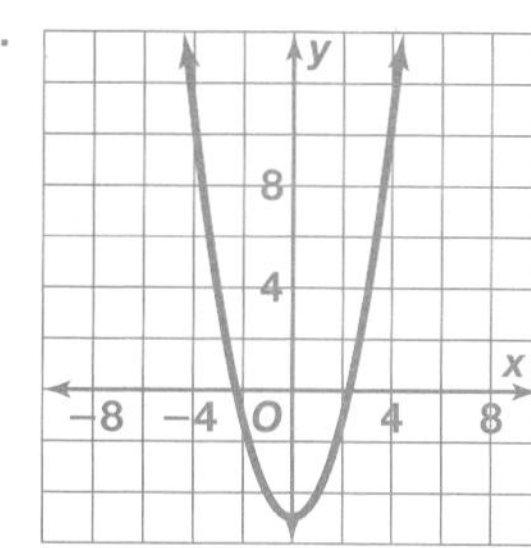

27.

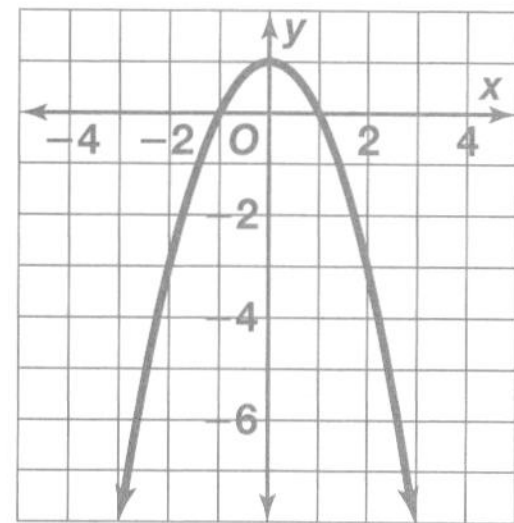

**page 676 Checkpoint 1**

4.

| $x$ | $\frac{1}{4}x^2$ | $y$ | $(x, y)$ |
|---|---|---|---|
| 0 | $\frac{1}{4} \cdot 0^2$ | 0 | (0, 0) |
| 1 | $\frac{1}{4} \cdot 1^2$ | $\frac{1}{4}$ | $(1, \frac{1}{4})$ |
| 2 | $\frac{1}{4} \cdot 2^2$ | 1 | (2, 1) |
| 3 | $\frac{1}{4} \cdot 3^2$ | $2\frac{1}{4}$ | $(3, 2\frac{1}{4})$ |
| 4 | $\frac{1}{4} \cdot 4^2$ | 4 | (4, 4) |

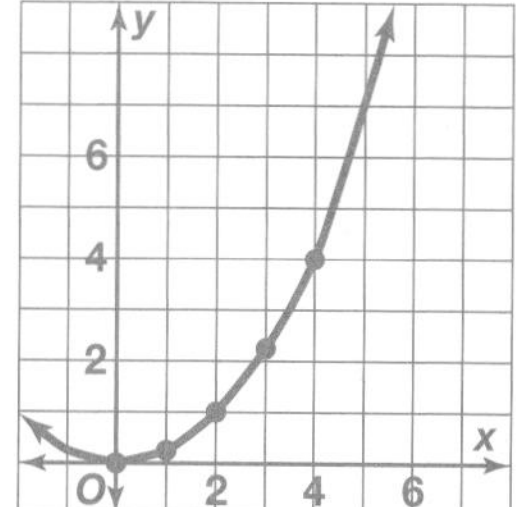

5.

| $x$ | $\frac{1}{4}\lvert x\rvert$ | $y$ | $(x, y)$ |
|---|---|---|---|
| 0 | $\frac{1}{4} \cdot \lvert 0\rvert$ | 0 | (0, 0) |
| 1 | $\frac{1}{4} \cdot \lvert 1\rvert$ | $\frac{1}{4}$ | $(1, \frac{1}{4})$ |
| 2 | $\frac{1}{4} \cdot \lvert 2\rvert$ | $\frac{1}{2}$ | $(2, \frac{1}{2})$ |
| 3 | $\frac{1}{4} \cdot \lvert 3\rvert$ | $\frac{3}{4}$ | $(3, \frac{3}{4})$ |
| 4 | $\frac{1}{4} \cdot \lvert 4\rvert$ | 1 | (4, 1) |

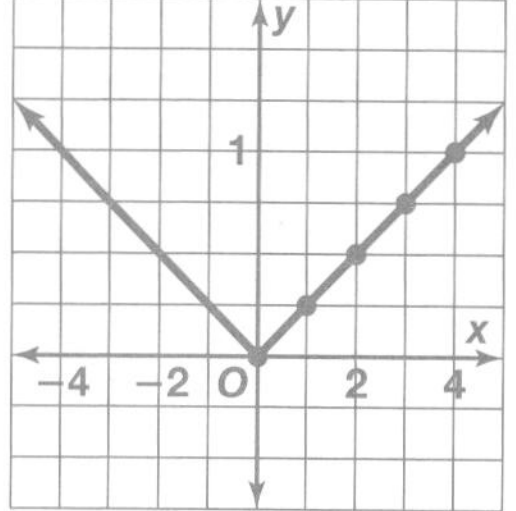

6.

| $x$ | $0.25(2)^x$ | $y$ | $(x, y)$ |
|---|---|---|---|
| 0 | $0.25(2)^0$ | 0.25 | (0, 0.25) |
| 1 | $0.25(2)^1$ | 0.5 | (1, 0.5) |
| 2 | $0.25(2)^2$ | 1 | (2, 1) |
| 3 | $0.25(2)^3$ | 2 | (3, 2) |
| 4 | $0.25(2)^4$ | 4 | (4, 4) |

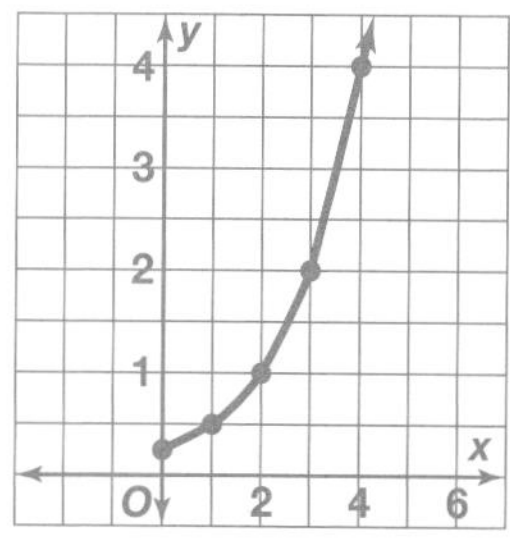

7.

| $x$ | $0.5(3)^x$ | $y$ | $(x, y)$ |
|---|---|---|---|
| 0 | $0.5(3)^0$ | 0.5 | (0, 0.5) |
| 1 | $0.5(3)^1$ | 1.5 | (1, 1.5) |
| 2 | $0.5(3)^2$ | 4.5 | (2, 4.5) |
| 3 | $0.5(3)^3$ | 13.5 | (3, 13.5) |
| 4 | $0.5(3)^4$ | 40.5 | (4, 40.5) |

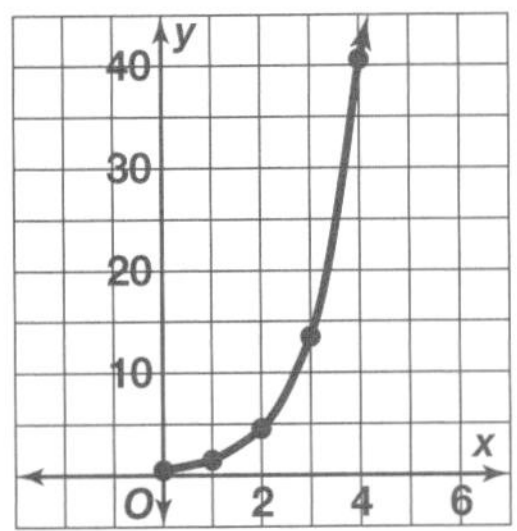


## page 677 Math Toolbox

2.

| $x$ | $y$ |
|---|---|
| −5 | −10 |
| −4 | −8 |
| −3 | −6 |
| −2 | −4 |
| −1 | −2 |
| 0 | 0 |
| 1 | −2 |
| 2 | −4 |
| 3 | −6 |
| 4 | −8 |
| 5 | −10 |

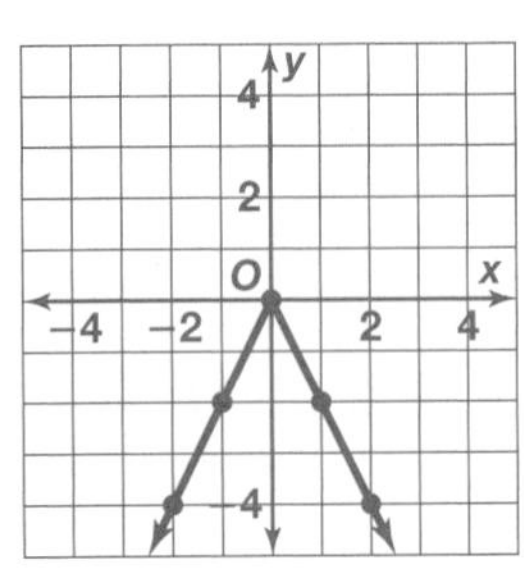

3.

| $x$ | $y$ |
|---|---|
| −5 | 11 |
| −4 | 9 |
| −3 | 7 |
| −2 | 5 |
| −1 | 3 |
| 0 | 1 |
| 1 | 3 |
| 2 | 5 |
| 3 | 7 |
| 4 | 9 |
| 5 | 11 |

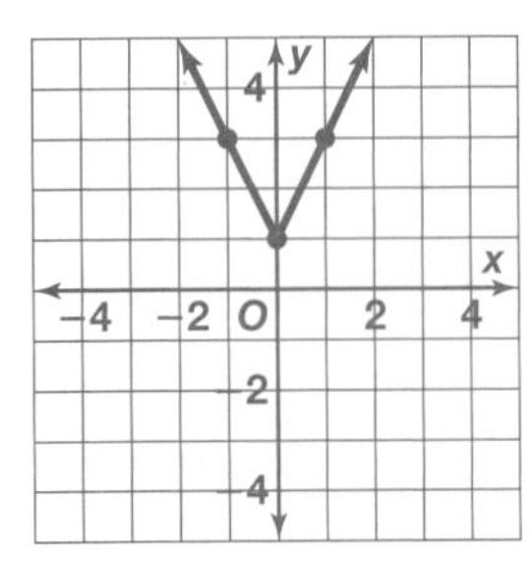

4.

| $x$ | $y$ |
|---|---|
| −5 | 24 |
| −4 | 15 |
| −3 | 8 |
| −2 | 3 |
| −1 | 0 |
| 0 | −1 |
| 1 | 0 |
| 2 | 3 |
| 3 | 8 |
| 4 | 15 |
| 5 | 24 |

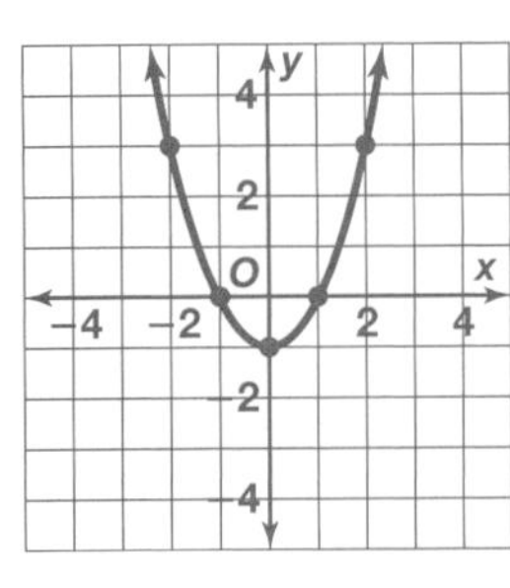

5.

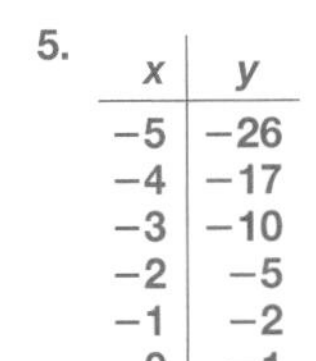

| $x$ | $y$ |
|---|---|
| −5 | −26 |
| −4 | −17 |
| −3 | −10 |
| −2 | −5 |
| −1 | −2 |
| 0 | −1 |
| 1 | −2 |
| 2 | −5 |
| 3 | −10 |
| 4 | −17 |
| 5 | −26 |

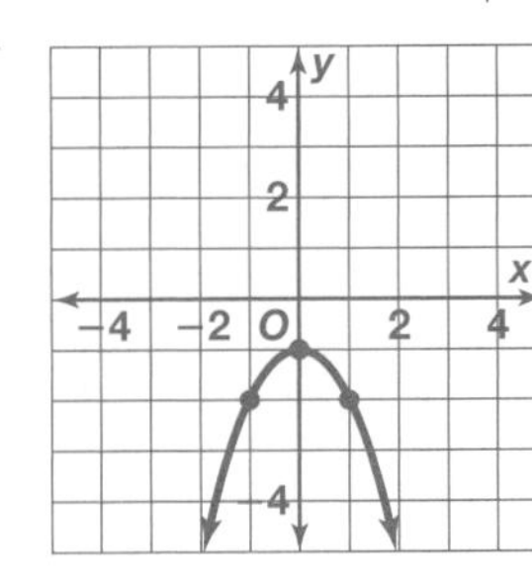

6.

| $x$ | $y$ |
|---|---|
| −5 | .09375 |
| −4 | .1875 |
| −3 | .375 |
| −2 | .75 |
| −1 | 1.5 |
| 0 | 3 |
| 1 | 6 |
| 2 | 12 |
| 3 | 24 |
| 4 | 48 |
| 5 | 96 |

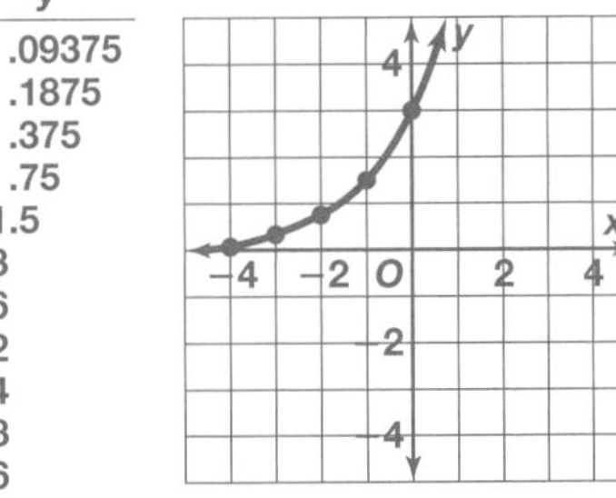

7.

| $x$ | $y$ |
|---|---|
| −5 | −.0938 |
| −4 | −.1875 |
| −3 | −.375 |
| −2 | −.75 |
| −1 | −1.5 |
| 0 | −3 |
| 1 | −6 |
| 2 | −12 |
| 3 | −24 |
| 4 | −48 |
| 5 | −96 |

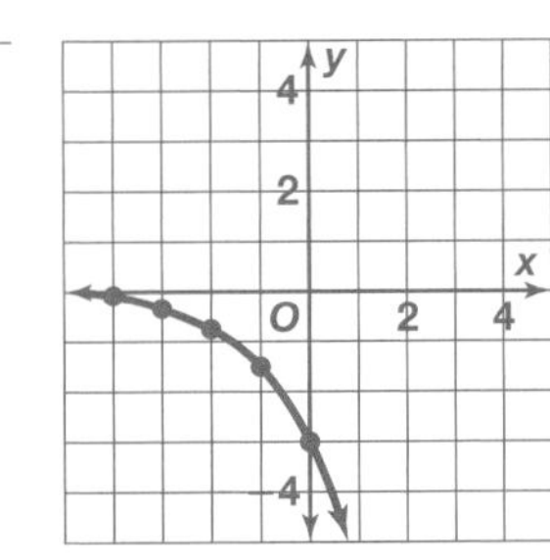

8.

| $x$ | $y$ |
|---|---|
| −5 | 96 |
| −4 | 48 |
| −3 | 24 |
| −2 | 12 |
| −1 | 6 |
| 0 | 3 |
| 1 | 1.5 |
| 2 | .75 |
| 3 | .375 |
| 4 | .1875 |
| 5 | .09375 |

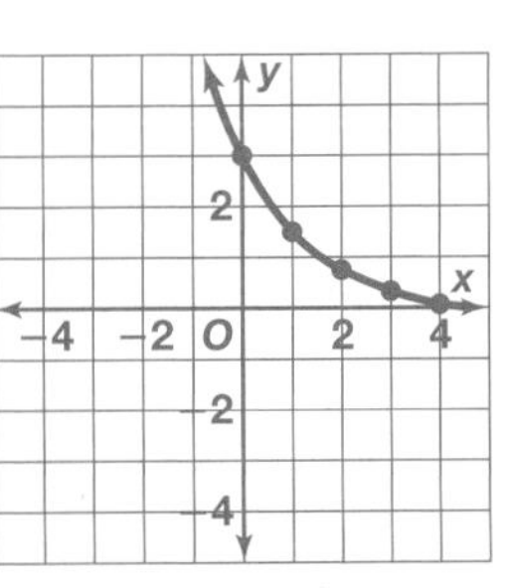

9.

| $x$ | $y$ |
|---|---|
| −5 | −96 |
| −4 | −48 |
| −3 | −24 |
| −2 | −12 |
| −1 | −6 |
| 0 | −3 |
| 1 | −1.5 |
| 2 | −.75 |
| 3 | −.375 |
| 4 | −.1875 |
| 5 | −.0938 |

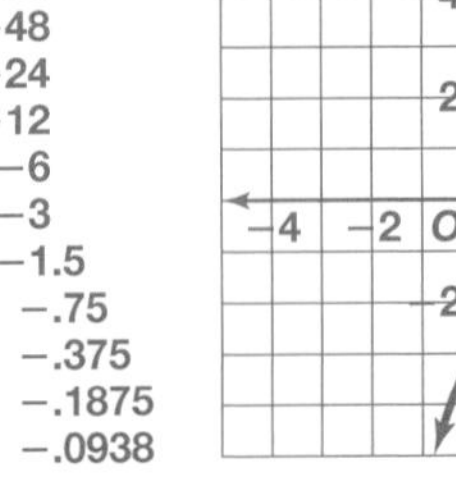

## LESSON 13-4

### page 681 Mixed Review

48.

| $x$ | $18(0.2)^x$ | $y$ | $(x, y)$ |
|---|---|---|---|
| 1 | $18(0.2)^1$ | 3.6 | (1, 3.6) |
| 2 | $18(0.2)^2$ | 0.72 | (2, 0.72) |
| 3 | $18(0.2)^3$ | 0.144 | (3, 0.144) |
| 4 | $18(0.2)^4$ | 0.0288 | (4, 0.0288) |

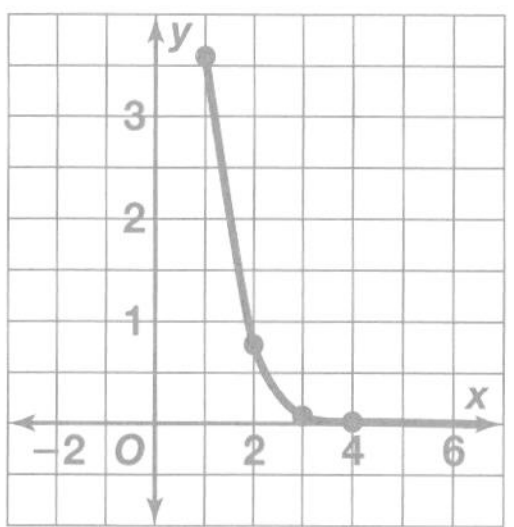

### page 693 Standardized Test Prep

5a.

| $t$ | $200 - 16t^2$ | $d$ | $(t, d)$ |
|---|---|---|---|
| 0 | $200 - 16(0)^2$ | 800 | (0, 200) |
| 1 | $200 - 16(1)^2$ | 184 | (1, 184) |
| 2 | $200 - 16(2)^2$ | 130 | (2, 130) |
| 3 | $200 - 16(3)^2$ | 56 | (3, 56) |
| 4 | $200 - 16(4)^2$ | −56 | (4, −56) |

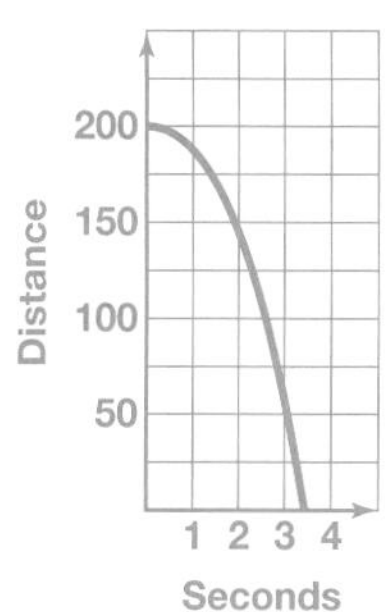


6.

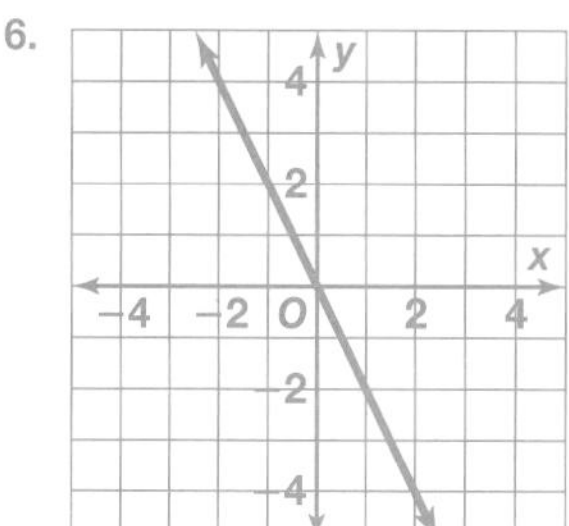

7.

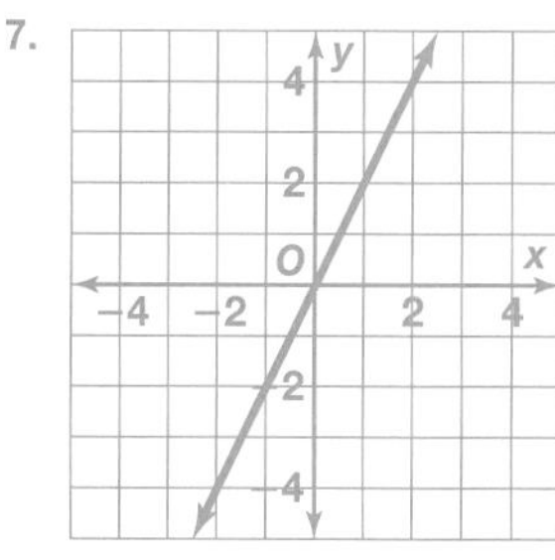

8.

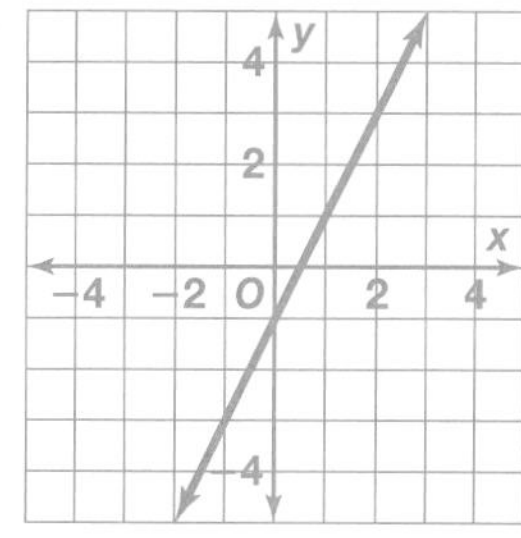

9.

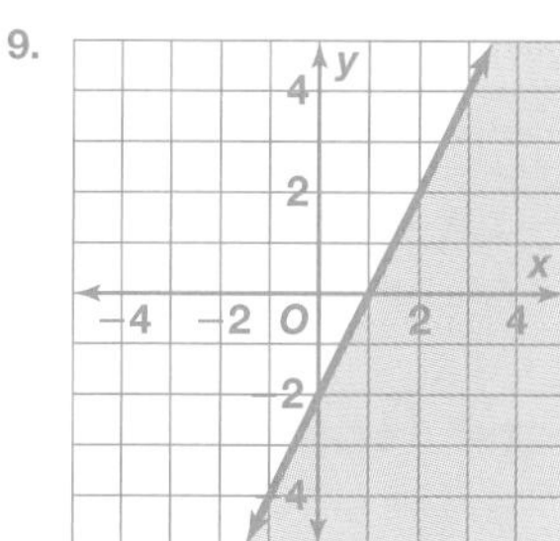

10.

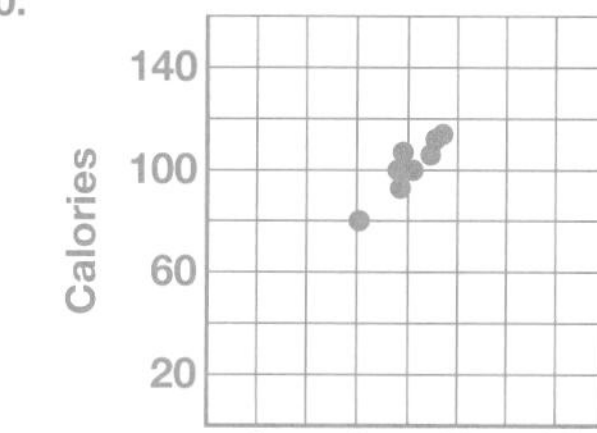


### pages 704–706 Wrap Up

20.

| $x$ | $-x^2 - 3$ | $y$ | $(x, y)$ |
|---|---|---|---|
| −2 | $-(-2)^2 - 3$ | −7 | (−2, −7) |
| −1 | $-(-1)^2 - 3$ | −4 | (−1, −4) |
| 0 | $-(0)^2 - 3$ | −3 | (0, −3) |
| 1 | $-(1)^2 - 3$ | −4 | (1,−4) |
| 2 | $-(2)^2 - 3$ | −7 | (2, −7) |

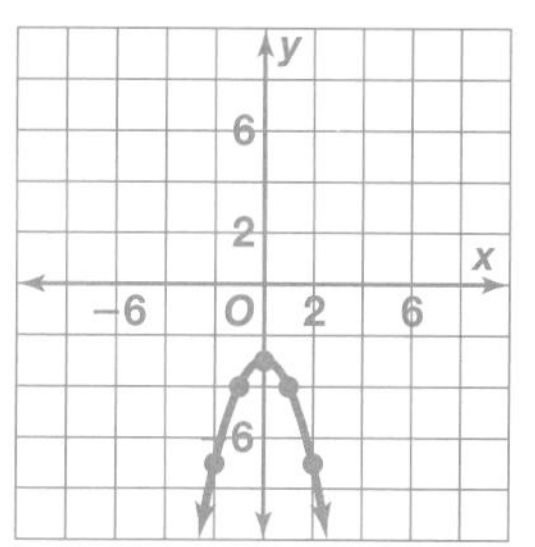

21.

| $x$ | $-x^2 + 4$ | $y$ | $(x, y)$ |
|---|---|---|---|
| −2 | $-(-2)^2 + 4$ | 0 | (−2, 0) |
| −1 | $-(-1)^2 + 4$ | 3 | (−1, 3) |
| 0 | $-(0)^2 + 4$ | 4 | (0, 4) |
| 1 | $-(1)^2 + 4$ | 3 | (1, 3) |
| 2 | $-(2)^2 + 4$ | 0 | (2, 0) |

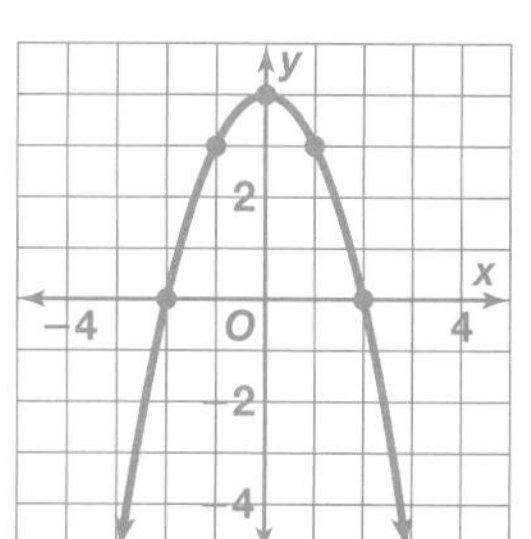

22.

| $x$ | $\left(\frac{1}{4}\right)^x$ | $y$ | $(x, y)$ |
|---|---|---|---|
| 0 | $\left(\frac{1}{4}\right)^0$ | 1 | $(0, 1)$ |
| 1 | $\left(\frac{1}{4}\right)^1$ | $\frac{1}{4}$ | $(1, \frac{1}{4})$ |
| 2 | $\left(\frac{1}{4}\right)^2$ | $\frac{1}{16}$ | $(2, \frac{1}{16})$ |
| 3 | $\left(\frac{1}{4}\right)^3$ | $\frac{1}{64}$ | $(3, \frac{1}{64})$ |
| 4 | $\left(\frac{1}{4}\right)^4$ | $\frac{1}{256}$ | $(4, \frac{1}{256})$ |

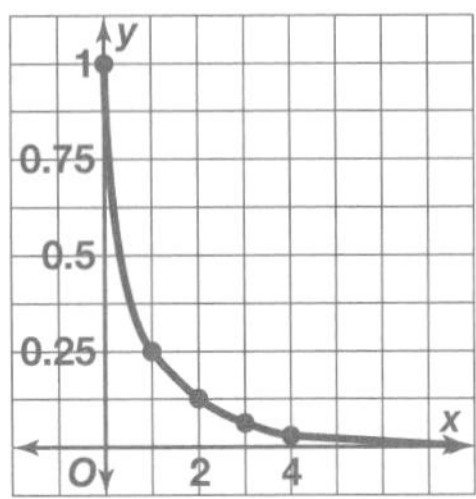


23.

| $x$ | $\frac{1}{2} \cdot 2^x$ | $y$ | $(x, y)$ |
|---|---|---|---|
| 0 | $\frac{1}{2} \cdot 2^0$ | $\frac{1}{2}$ | $(0, \frac{1}{2})$ |
| 1 | $\frac{1}{2} \cdot 2^1$ | 1 | $(1, 1)$ |
| 2 | $\frac{1}{2} \cdot 2^2$ | 2 | $(2, 2)$ |
| 3 | $\frac{1}{2} \cdot 2^3$ | 4 | $(3, 4)$ |
| 4 | $\frac{1}{2} \cdot 2^4$ | 8 | $(4, 8)$ |

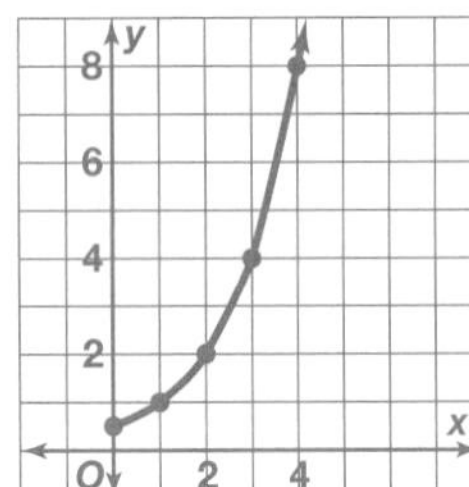


24.

| $x$ | $3^x$ | $y$ | $(x, y)$ |
|---|---|---|---|
| 0 | $3^0$ | 1 | $(0, 1)$ |
| 1 | $3^1$ | 3 | $(1, 3)$ |
| 2 | $3^2$ | 9 | $(2, 9)$ |
| 3 | $3^3$ | 27 | $(3, 27)$ |
| 4 | $3^4$ | 81 | $(4, 81)$ |

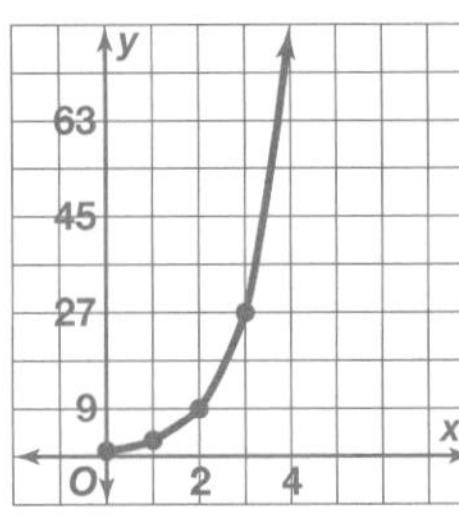


25.

| $x$ | $\left(\frac{1}{2}\right)^x$ | $y$ | $(x, y)$ |
|---|---|---|---|
| 0 | $\left(\frac{1}{2}\right)^0$ | 1 | $(0, 1)$ |
| 1 | $\left(\frac{1}{2}\right)^1$ | $\frac{1}{2}$ | $(1, \frac{1}{2})$ |
| 2 | $\left(\frac{1}{2}\right)^2$ | $\frac{1}{4}$ | $(2, \frac{1}{4})$ |
| 3 | $\left(\frac{1}{2}\right)^3$ | $\frac{1}{8}$ | $(3, \frac{1}{8})$ |
| 4 | $\left(\frac{1}{2}\right)^4$ | $\frac{1}{16}$ | $(4, \frac{1}{16})$ |

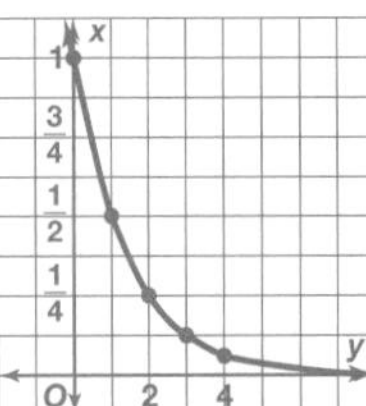


## page 707 Chapter Assessment

11.

| $x$ | $x^2$ | $y$ | $(x, y)$ |
|---|---|---|---|
| $-2$ | $(-2)^2$ | 4 | $(-2, 4)$ |
| $-1$ | $(-1)^2$ | 1 | $(-1, 1)$ |
| 0 | $0^2$ | 0 | $(0, 0)$ |
| 1 | $1^2$ | 1 | $(1, 1)$ |
| 2 | $2^2$ | 4 | $(2, 4)$ |

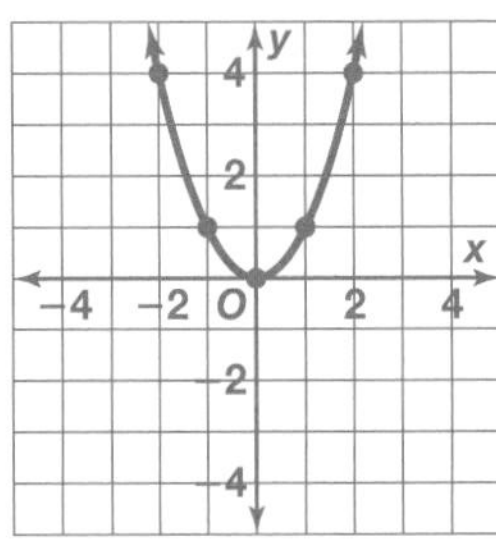


12.

| $x$ | $x^2 - 1$ | $y$ | $(x, y)$ |
|---|---|---|---|
| $-2$ | $(-2)^2 - 1$ | 3 | $(-2, 3)$ |
| $-1$ | $(-1)^2 - 1$ | 0 | $(-1, 0)$ |
| 0 | $0^2 - 1$ | $-1$ | $(0, -1)$ |
| 1 | $1^2 - 1$ | 0 | $(1, 0)$ |
| 2 | $2^2 - 1$ | 3 | $(2, 3)$ |

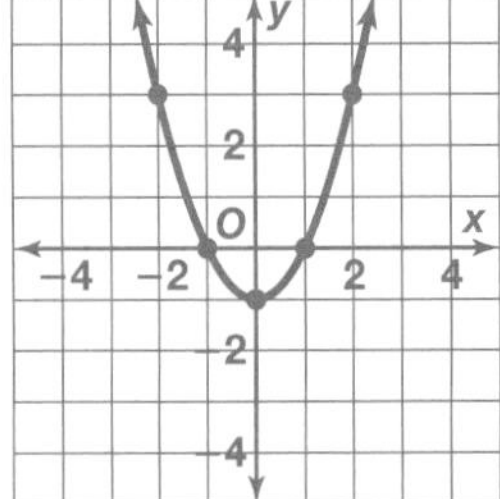


13.

| $x$ | $-x^2 + 1$ | $y$ | $(x, y)$ |
|---|---|---|---|
| $-2$ | $-(-2)^2 + 1$ | $-3$ | $(-2, -3)$ |
| $-1$ | $-(-1)^2 + 1$ | 0 | $(-1, 0)$ |
| 0 | $-(0)^2 + 1$ | 1 | $(0, 1)$ |
| 1 | $-(1)^2 + 1$ | 0 | $(1, 0)$ |
| 2 | $-(2)^2 + 1$ | $-3$ | $(2, -3)$ |

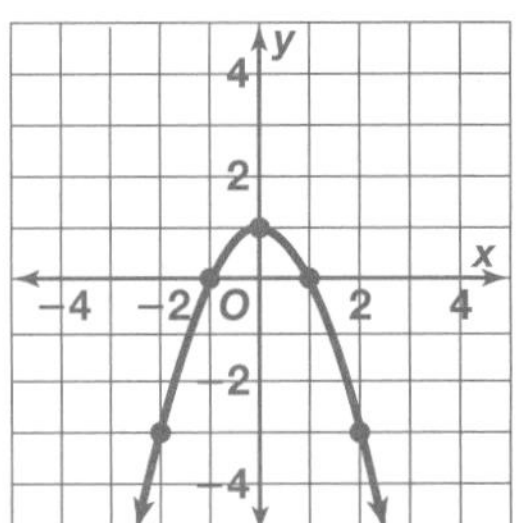


14.

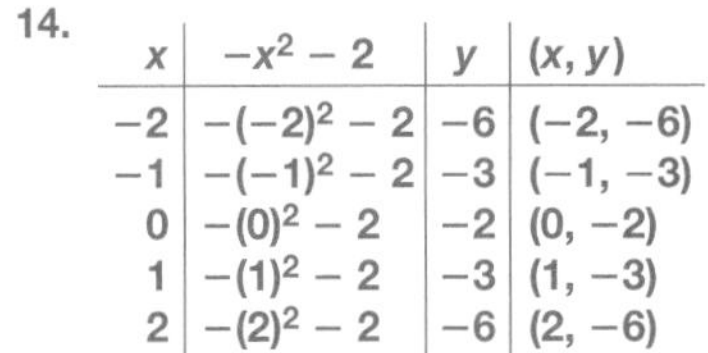

| $x$ | $-x^2 - 2$ | $y$ | $(x, y)$ |
|---|---|---|---|
| $-2$ | $-(-2)^2 - 2$ | $-6$ | $(-2, -6)$ |
| $-1$ | $-(-1)^2 - 2$ | $-3$ | $(-1, -3)$ |
| 0 | $-(0)^2 - 2$ | $-2$ | $(0, -2)$ |
| 1 | $-(1)^2 - 2$ | $-3$ | $(1, -3)$ |
| 2 | $-(2)^2 - 2$ | $-6$ | $(2, -6)$ |

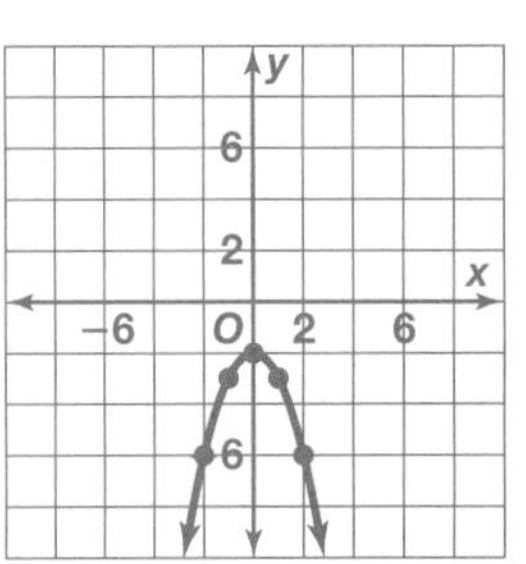


15.

| $x$ | $\lvert x\rvert - 1$ | $y$ | $(x, y)$ |
|---|---|---|---|
| $-2$ | $\lvert -2\rvert - 1$ | 1 | $(-2, 1)$ |
| $-1$ | $\lvert -1\rvert - 1$ | 0 | $(-1, 0)$ |
| 0 | $\lvert 0\rvert - 1$ | $-1$ | $(0, -1)$ |
| 1 | $\lvert 1\rvert - 1$ | 0 | $(1, 0)$ |
| 2 | $\lvert 2\rvert - 1$ | 1 | $(2, 1)$ |

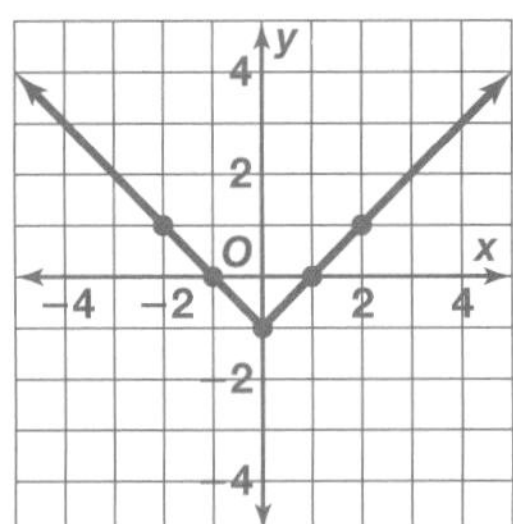

16.

| $x$ | $\frac{1}{2}\lvert x\rvert$ | $y$ | $(x, y)$ |
|---|---|---|---|
| $-2$ | $\frac{1}{2}\lvert -2\rvert$ | 1 | $(-2, 1)$ |
| $-1$ | $\frac{1}{2}\lvert -1\rvert$ | $\frac{1}{2}$ | $(-1, \frac{1}{2})$ |
| 0 | $\frac{1}{2}\lvert 0\rvert$ | 0 | $(0, 0)$ |
| 1 | $\frac{1}{2}\lvert 1\rvert$ | $\frac{1}{2}$ | $(1, \frac{1}{2})$ |
| 2 | $\frac{1}{2}\lvert 2\rvert$ | 1 | $(2, 1)$ |

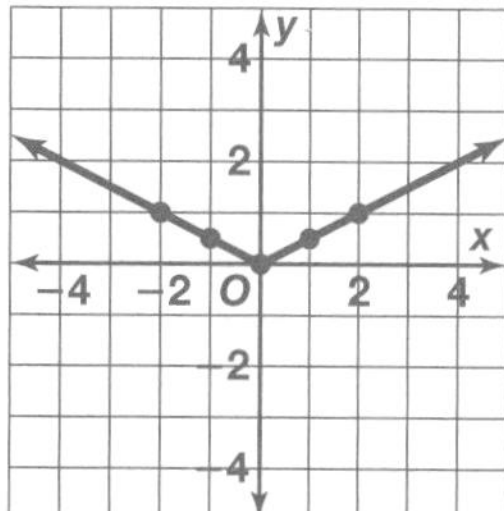


17.

| $x$ | $2^x$ | $y$ | $(x, y)$ |
|---|---|---|---|
| 0 | $2^0$ | 1 | $(0, 1)$ |
| 1 | $2^1$ | 2 | $(1, 2)$ |
| 2 | $2^2$ | 4 | $(2, 4)$ |
| 3 | $2^3$ | 8 | $(3, 8)$ |
| 4 | $2^4$ | 16 | $(4, 16)$ |

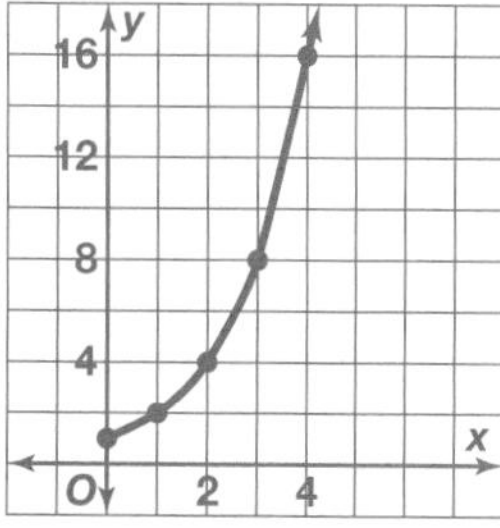


18.

| $x$ | $3^x$ | $y$ | $(x, y)$ |
|---|---|---|---|
| 0 | $3^0$ | 1 | $(0, 1)$ |
| 1 | $3^1$ | 3 | $(1, 3)$ |
| 2 | $3^2$ | 9 | $(2, 9)$ |
| 3 | $3^3$ | 27 | $(3, 27)$ |
| 4 | $3^4$ | 81 | $(4, 81)$ |

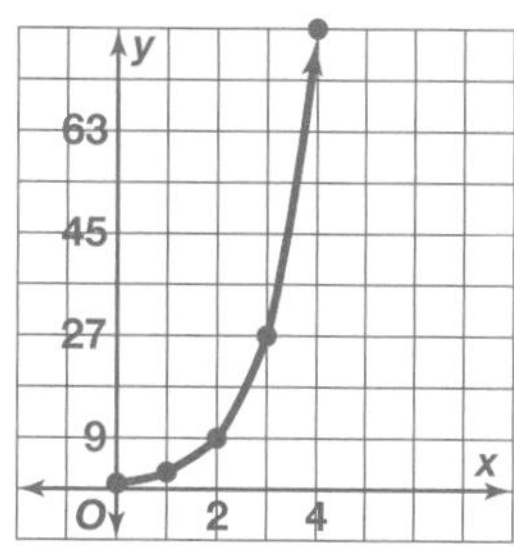


19.

| $x$ | $2(\frac{1}{2})^x$ | $y$ | $(x, y)$ |
|---|---|---|---|
| 0 | $2(\frac{1}{2})^0$ | 2 | $(0, 2)$ |
| 1 | $2(\frac{1}{2})^1$ | 1 | $(1, 1)$ |
| 2 | $2(\frac{1}{2})^2$ | $\frac{1}{2}$ | $(2, \frac{1}{2})$ |
| 3 | $2(\frac{1}{2})^3$ | $\frac{1}{4}$ | $(3, \frac{1}{4})$ |
| 4 | $2(\frac{1}{2})^4$ | $\frac{1}{8}$ | $(4, \frac{1}{8})$ |

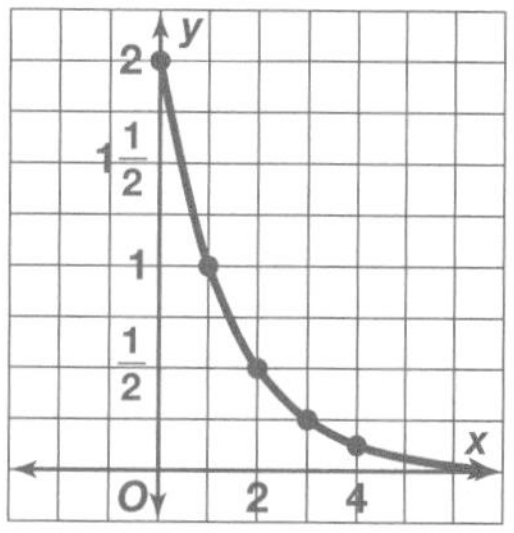

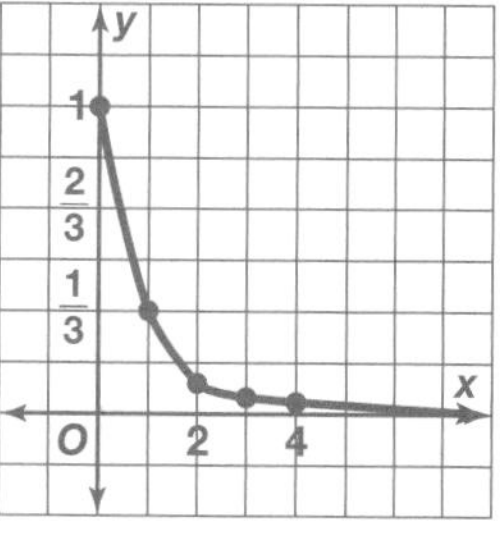


20.

| $x$ | $\left(\frac{1}{3}\right)^x$ | $y$ | $(x, y)$ |
|---|---|---|---|
| 0 | $\left(\frac{1}{3}\right)^0$ | 1 | $(0, 1)$ |
| 1 | $\left(\frac{1}{3}\right)^1$ | $\frac{1}{3}$ | $(1, \frac{1}{3})$ |
| 2 | $\left(\frac{1}{3}\right)^2$ | $\frac{1}{9}$ | $(2, \frac{1}{9})$ |
| 3 | $\left(\frac{1}{3}\right)^3$ | $\frac{1}{27}$ | $(3, \frac{1}{27})$ |
| 4 | $\left(\frac{1}{3}\right)^4$ | $\frac{1}{81}$ | $(4, \frac{1}{81})$ |

Additional Answers

# Index

*Teacher's Edition entries appear in blue type.*

## A

# Index

# Index



## D

# Index



## E

## F

## G

# Index



## H



## I

## J



## K



## L



## M

# Index

# Index

# Index

## Q

# Index

# Index

## T

# Index

# Acknowledgments


**STAFF CREDITS**

The people who made up the *Pre-Algebra* team—representing editorial, editorial services, design services, market research, marketing, marketing services, project office, on-line services/multimedia development, production services, and publishing processes—are listed below. **Bold type** denotes the core team members.

Barbara A. Bertell, **Judith D. Buice,** Bob Craton, **Kathy Carter,** Sheila DeFazio, **Jo DiGiustini, Frederick Fellows,** Linda Ferreira, Maria Green, Kerri Hoar, Russell Lappa, Catherine Maglio, **Eve Melnechuk,** Paul W. Murphy, Suzanne Schineller, **Dennis Slattery,** Deborah Sommer, **Mark Tricca,** Stuart Wallace, **Diane Walsh,** Joe Will

**ADDITIONAL CREDITS**

Carolyn Artin, Suzanne Biron, Susan Clare, Jayne Holman, Jerry H. Hooten, Savitri K. Khalsa, Carolyn Langley, Cheryl Mahan, PoYee Oster, Pat Packer-Williams, Sydney Schuster, Angela Sciaraffa

**Cover Design:** Sweetlight Creative Partners/David Julian

**Cover Image:** John de Visser/Masterfile

**Technical Illustration:** Nesbitt Graphics, Inc.

**ILLUSTRATION**

**Suzanne Biron:** 3, 42, 54, 55, 121, 135, 163, 223, 249, 269, 335, 375, 441, 467, 495, 559, 599, 663, 703; photocompositing—7, 32, 51, 120, 123, 156, 250, 252, 444, 448, 451, 454, 464, 465, 468, 480, 485, 491t, 558

**John Edwards & Associates:** 88

**DLF Group:** 440, 593

**Jared D. Lee:** 624br

**Ortelius Design, Inc.:** 30, 53, 139, 152, 211, 233, 236, 241, 290b, 337, 348, 366, 391, 511, 578t

**Pat Packer-Williams:** 63, 113, 171, 215, 277, 327, 383, 433, 503, 551, 607, 655; photocompositing—85,184, 279, 290b, 397, 413, 424, 531, 613, 620, 621

**Wendy Simpson:** photocompositing—184, 290b, 397, 491b, 531, 611, 613, 617

**J/B Woolsey Associates:** xxiv, 20, 27, 32, 36, 39, 46, 51, 66, 70, 73, 89, 124, 126, 131, 132, 142, 192, 237, 239, 240, 245, 253, 290t, 302, 307, 311, 315, 322, 343, 363, 407, 447, 453, 456, 471, 480, 494, 507, 514, 516, 518, 549, 563, 566, 568, 578b, 580, 581, 586, 590, 594, 596, 597, 603, 618, 620, 622, 624tl, 625, 644, 689

**PHOTOGRAPHY**

**Picture Research:** Toni Michaels

**Front Matter**

**Page v,** OAR/National Undersea Research Program (NURP); **vi,** David R. Frazier Photolibrary; **vii,** Russ Lappa; **viii all,** ©Bruce Iverson; **ix,** Alfred Pasieka/Peter Arnold, Inc.; **x,** Cincinnati Zoo; **xi,** James Frank/Stock Connection/PNI; **xii,** Stone/David Young Wolff; **xiii,** Alfred Pasteka/Science Photo Library/Photo Researchers, Inc.; **xiv,** FPG International; **xv,** Stone/Chad Slattery; **xvi,** Lynn Rogers/Peter Arnold, Inc.; **xvii,** Peter Berndt, M.D., P.A.; **xx,** Stone/David Young-Wolff; **xxi t,** Tony Freeman/PhotoEdit; **xxi b,** David Young-Wolff/PhotoEdit; **xxii,** NASA/John F. Kennedy Space Center; **xxv,** Will Hart/PhotoEdit; **xxviii,** Richard Haynes.

**Chapter One**

**Pages 2–3,** *Kryptos,* James Sanborn, 1990, 11' x 20', courtesy of the artist; **5,** ©Royal Tyrrell Museum of Palaeontology/Alberta Community Development; **7,** PhotoDisc, Inc.; **10,** Minnesota Dept. of Natural Resources; **14,** Russ Lappa; **16,** Stone/Stuart Westmorland; **25,** Albuquerque Seismological Lab, USGS; **28,** Patrick Somelet/DIAF/The Stock Market; **30,** ©Sowers/Penn State University; **32,** Index Stock Imagery; **40,** Michael Simpson/FPG International; **42,** PhotoDisc, Inc.; **43 all,** Russ Lappa; **44,** OAR/National Undersea Research Program (NURP); **51,** Tom Van Sant/The Stock Market; **54,** Prentice Hall; **55,** *Kryptos,* James Sanborn, 1990, 11' x 20', courtesy of the artist.

**Chapter Two**

**Pages 62–63,** Tom Hanson/Liaison Agency; **66,** Russ Lappa; **68,** Mark Kelley/Stock Boston; **70,** Tony Freeman/PhotoEdit; **73,** Russ Lappa; **79,** Stone/Chris Simpson; **81,** Mark Thayer; **82 all,** Ken O'Donoghue; **84 both,** Anthony Neste; **85,** David R. Frazier Photolibrary; **85 inset,** Omni-Photo Communications, Inc.; **94,** Superstock; **97,** Jose L./Palaez; **103 l,** Superstock; **103 m,** Spencer Grant/PhotoEdit; **103 r,** D. & J. Heaton/Stock Boston; **105,** Russ Lappa; **109,** Andrew Yates/Image Bank; **113,** Tom Hanson/Liaison Agency.

**Chapter Three**

**Pages 120–121,** Owen Franken/Stock Boston; **123,** Russ Lappa; **127,** Russ Lappa; **128,** G. Cigolini/Image Bank; **135,** Corel Corp.; **137,** Alvin Staffan/Photo Researchers; **140,** Kevin Schafer/Peter Arnold, Inc.; **142 l,** Lockheed Martin Telecommumications; **42 m, r,** Corel Corp.; **145,** *Dilbert* reprinted by permission of United Features Syndicate, Inc.; **147,** Corbis/Bettmann; **152,** Stone/Ed Simpson; **154,** Stone/Doug Armand; **156 both,** Russ Lappa; **159,** Stone/I. Burgum/P. Boorman; **161,** Russ Lappa; **162,** Bob Daemmrich/Stock Boston; **163,** Owen Franken/Stock Boston.

**Chapter Four**

**Pages 170–171,** Adam Woolfitt/Woodfin Camp & Assoc.; **173,** Russ Lappa; **177 all,** ©Bruce Iverson; **180,** Russ Lappa; **182,** Gary A. Conner/PhotoEdit; **184,** Stone/Michael Rosenfield; **187,** Bob Daemmrich/Stock Boston; **190,** Russ Lappa; **195,** AP/Dusan Vranic/Wide World Photos; **196,** Mehau Kulyk/Science Photo Library/Photo Researchers; **201,** Peggy Yoram Kahana/Peter Arnold, Inc.; **205,** Russell C. Hansen/Peter Arnold, Inc.; **207,** Mark Downey/Liaison Agency; **209,** Tim Barnwell/Stock Boston; **211,** K & G Photo/FPG International; **213,** Stone/Doris De Witt; **215,** Adam Woolfitt/Woodfin Camp & Assoc.

**Chapter Five**

**Pages 222–223,** Arthur Tilley/FPG International; **226,** Monkmeyer/Grant Pix; **228,** Alfred Pasieka/Peter Arnold, Inc.; **229 both,** Ken Karp; **236,** Mark Gibson/Corbis; **241,** Alan Schen; **242,** Russ Lappa; **249,** Photri/The Stock Market; **250,** Russ Lappa; **251,** Stone/Jason Hawkes; **252 all,** Russ Lappa; **255,** Dave Davidson/The Stock Market; **258,** Jim Corwim/Photo Researchers; **262,** Daniel Lyons/Bruce Coleman; **266,** Dirk Weisheit/DDB Stock Photo; **269,** Arthur Tilley/FPG International.

**Chapter Six**

**Pages 276–277,** David-Young Wolfitt/PhotoEdit; **279,** Russ Lappa; **281,** Stone/Kindra Clineff; **285,** NASA; **287,** REAL LIFE ADVENTURES ©1999 GarLanco. Reprinted with permission of Universal Press Syndicate. All rights reserved.; **288,** Russ Lappa; **292,** Richard Haynes; **294, 295,** Russ Lappa; **297 all,** The United States Mint; **301,** Stone/Renee Lynn; **303,** Jay Syverson/Stock Boston; **304,** Bob Daemmrich/Stock Boston/PNI; **317 t,** Cincinnati Zoo; **317 b,** Spencer Grant/Stock Boston; **320,** Robert Brenner/PhotoEdit; **323,** Joseph Sohm/Stock Boston; **325,** Tek Image/Science Photo Library/Photo Researchers; **326,** Spencer Grant/Stock Boston; **327,** David-Young Wolfitt/PhotoEdit.

**Chapter Seven**

**Pages 334–335,** Stone/Hugh Sitton; **337,** Stone/Mark Lewis; **347 t,** Elizabeth Crews/The Image Works; **347 b,** David Young-Wolff/PhotoEdit; **349,** Tim Barnell/Stock Boston; **350,** The Granger Collection, New York; **356,** James Frank/Stock Connection/PNI; **359,** Michael Heron/The Stock Market; **361,** Jose Carrillo/PhotoEdit; **366,** Stone/David Schultz; **375,** Stone/Hugh Sitton.

**Chapter Eight**

**Pages 382–383,** A. Ramey/PhotoEdit; **387,** David Young Wolff; **388,** Corel Corp.; **391,** Lester Lefkowitz/The Stock Market; **397,** Stone/Jess Stock; **401 t,** Bob Daemmrich/The Image Works; **401 b,** Donald Dietz/Stock Boston; **402,** Stone/Don Smetzer; **413,** Russ Lappa; **416,** Erwin & Peggy Bauer/Bruce Coleman Inc.; **427,** Joe Sohm/The Image Works; **430,** Ellen Skye/Monkmeyer; **433,** A. Ramey/PhotoEdit.

**Chapter Nine**

**Pages 440–441,** Stone/Chad Ehlers; **442,** Photo Researchers; **444,** James Marshall/The Stock Market; **447,** AP/Paul Warner/Wide World Photos; **448,** Jon Chomitz; **451,** Courtesy of J.C. Guillois/Santa Fe Stained Glass; **454,** Gianalberto Cigolini/Image Bank; **456,** Peter Gridley/FPG International; **460,** Alfred Pasteka/Science Photo Library/Photo Researchers; **464,** Georg Gerster/Photo Researchers; **465,** John Heiney/Sportschrome; **468,** R. Wahhlstrom/Image Bank; **469, 474 t,** Russ Lappa; **474 b,** Jon Chomitz; **480, 485 tl,** Russ Lappa; **485 bl,** Patti Murray/Animals Animals; **485 tr,** Russ Lappa; **485 br,** C. Zeiss/Bruce Coleman; **491 t,** Russ Lappa; **491 b,** Danilo G. Donadoni/Bruce Coleman; **492 l,** Steve Solum/Bruce Coleman; **492 ml,** Adam Peiperl/The Stock Market; **492 mr,** Larry West/Bruce Coleman; **492 r,** John Gerlach/Tom Stack & Associates; **495,** Stone/Chad Ehlers.

**Chapter Ten**

**Pages 502–503,** Ron Stroud/Masterfile; **504,** Leslye Borden/PhotoEdit; **508,** Ken Chernus/FPG/PNI; **510,** Pascal Quittemelle/Stock Boston; **511,** Corbis-Bettmann; **515,** Alan Carey/Photo Researchers Inc.; **522,** Ellis Herwig/Stock Boston; **524 all, 526, 529,** Russ Lappa; **531,** Keith Gunnar/Bruce Coleman; **533,** FPG International; **535 t,** Russ Lappa; **535 b,** J. Sapinsky/The Stock Market; **537,** Sara Krulwich/NYT Pictures; **539, 541,** Russ Lappa; **542,** Stone/Steven Peters; **548,** Jeff Foott/Bruce Coleman; **550,** Stone/Richard Clintsman; **551,** Ron Stroud/Masterfile.

**Chapter Eleven**

**Pages 558–559, background,** Earth Scenes; **558–559 girl,** Richard Haynes; **561,** Alese/Mort PECHTER/The Stock Market; **563,** Telegraph Colour Library/FPG International; **569,** Stone/Chad Slattery; **578,** Stone/Hideo Kurihara; **581,** H.P. Merten/The Stock Market; **583,** Landslides; **592,** Lance Nelson/The Stock Market; **599,** Earth Scenes.

**Chapter Twelve**

**Pages 606–607,** Russ Lappa/props, courtesy of Winchester High School, Winchester, MA; **613,** Stone; **614 t,** Marilyn Kazmers/Peter Arnold, Inc.; **614 b,** David Madison/Bruce Coleman; **617,** Gerard Lacz/Peter Arnold, Inc.; **620 l,** Brent Jones/Stock Boston; **620 r,** Nik Wheeler/Corbis; **621,** Gerard Lacz/Peter Arnold, Inc.; **627,** Russ Lappa; **632,** John Lemker/Earth Scenes; **637,** Corel Corp.; **639,** Russ Lappa; **640,** Lynn Rogers/Peter Arnold, Inc.; **650,** Stone/Greg Pease; **655,** Russ Lappa/props, courtesy of Winchester High School, Winchester, MA.

**Chapter Thirteen**

**Pages 662–663,** Stone/Ken Biggs; **665,** Marc Romanelli/Image Bank; **670,** Sydney Thompson/Animals Animals; **672,** Bob Daemmrich/Stock Boston; **674,** Peter Berndt, M.D., P.A.; **679,** Bob Burch/Bruce Coleman; **699,** John Davenport/Liaison Agency; **703,** Stone/Ken Biggs.

**TEACHER'S EDITION**

**Editor:** Marian B. De Lollis

**Design Coordinator:** Sue Gerould/Perspectives

**Editorial and Production Services:** Publishers Resource Group